Stanley Gibbons
STAMP CATALOGUE

PART 1
British Commonwealth
1993

Including post-independence issues of
Ireland, Fiji and South Africa

Ninety-sixth edition

VOLUME 2
Countries J to Z

Stanley Gibbons Ltd
London and Ringwood

By Appointment to Her Majesty The Queen
Stanley Gibbons Ltd, London
Philatelists

Published by **Stanley Gibbons Ltd**
Publications Editorial, Sales Offices and Distribution Centre:
5 Parkside, Christchurch Road, Ringwood,
Hants BH24 3SH

ISBN: 0-85259-349-X

Item No. 2812 (93)

Text assembled by Black Bear Press Limited, Cambridge

Made and Printed in Great Britain by William Clowes Limited,
Beccles, Suffolk

Preface to the 1993 Edition

ACROSS THE SPECTRUM

By their very nature stamp catalogues are a collective effort to provide information for individual users. It must be recognised that each reader will open the catalogue for different reasons and will expect to find the information required within it. This can create some difficulty when the readership stretches from dedicated specialists to beginners. It does, however, mean that it is necessary to pay as much attention to the accuracy of the descriptions for the latest Walt Disney commemoration as to a complicated revision of an issue from the classic period.

There is an unfortunate tendency in some quarters to belittle the collecting of "modern" stamps. Such comments have been advanced for many years – my predecessors heard them made with reference to stamps from the reign of King George VI and, no doubt, similar remarks were made in earlier years also. Such a dichotomy is particularly unfortunate in a period when the stamps of the classic period are becoming more difficult, and therefore more expensive, to obtain. Collectors with only a limited amount to spend on their hobby have, in increasing numbers, turned to other fields and it is encouraging to record that the once-despised King George VI issues are becoming increasingly popular and now have their own sought-after varieties to match those of the earlier reigns.

Interest has also revived in the first issues of the present reign and I have heard of several advanced collectors who have found rewarding fields of research in the most unlikely corners of modern Commonwealth philately.

The division of this catalogue into two volumes, viewed with trepidation in some quarters, was successfully accomplished for the last edition. Letters from collectors on this subject have been overwhelmingly in favour and it seems that many of the perceived difficulties were avoided by the policy of listing all issues for a particular country together, under the current name, and by the grouping of forerunner territories before the subsequent national entity. It is, of course, quite possible that much of the welcome has been due to collectors of Australia, Canada and South Africa realising that they could obtain all the listings they required at a considerable saving from the cost of the previous one-volume edition! Another advantage generally welcomed was the ending of the pre-dating of editions. The two volumes of this 1993 edition are published in the summer of the year for which they are dated and this policy will be followed in future.

Further work has been done this year to make each volume more self-contained. More alterations of this nature will certainly be required in the future and I would be grateful if collectors could write and let me know of any between-volume cross-references which they find particularly difficult.

A major advantage of the new two-volume format is that it removes, at a stroke, problems of size and bulk. This will permit the addition of new features and this year sees the introduction of the Philatelic Register, a classified guide which provides the reader with much hobby information alongside the catalogue listings. Next year's edition will see the start of a project to add Commonwealth stamp booklets, listings of which are often requested in letters received from collectors. It is, of course, our intention that the *Part 1* should continue to provide the most up-to-date coverage of prices and reflect the results of recent philatelic research.

PRICES

The revival of the philatelic market has continued over the last twelve months and the position reflected in this year's edition is a far more optimistic one than has been the case in the immediate past. Some classic issues remain quiet, but otherwise rises stretch from the later years of Queen Victoria to the present. Further interest in King George VI stamps has been maintained and now extends into the early years of the present reign. Only issues from the 1960s, 1970s and early 1980s remain generally untouched by this upward trend although, even here, some definitive sets are rising in value. Many commemoratives from the mid-1980s onwards are in very short supply and the merest suggestion of a thematic design is enough to increase demand to a point where the very limited stocks available are unable to cope with it.

Examples of the increasing demand for King George VI issues can be found in the **Leeward Islands, St. Kitts-Nevis, Seychelles** and **South Africa.** In other instances previously-neglected territories show more widespread activity with price rises for **Nigeria** stretching to 1970 and those for both **Sierra Leone** and **Tonga** to the mid-1950s. It is interesting to see a strengthening demand for **Sudan** during the same period where the Officials are increasingly the key area.

Provisionals, and other stamps for which only limited quantities were issued, continue to improve. Many **Mafia Island** (Tanganyika) overprints are up again as are overprints for **Zanzibar.**

Malaysia remains popular with considerable activity in the **Japanese Occupation** issues and for **Labuan. New Zealand** definitives from 1937 to the early years of the present reign continue to improve. The West Indies countries in this second volume show no overall trend with **Montserrat** having useful increases to 1952, but **Trinidad** showing a number of price cuts for the earlier stamps. There are further alterations for a number of key values in **Palestine** which have been reviewed on the advice of Mr. M. Bale.

For those seeking more esoteric fields it should be noted that most prices quoted for Great Britain used in the **Niger Territories** are increased as are those for **Bahawalpur** in used condition. **Papua** "OS" Officials also show many price rises.

REVISIONS IN THIS VOLUME

As mentioned above additional attention has been paid to cross-references between the two volumes and, as a result, the number of Australia illustrations shown for **Papua New Guinea** has been increased. Further plate varieties have been added to the listings including the **Leeward Islands** "broken pearl" and the **South Africa** 1935 Silver Jubilee "cleft skull".

Lesotho. The recently-discovered perforation varieties on the 1991 Butterfly definitives are now listed from information supplied by Prof. David Ambrose.

Malaysia. A number of varieties, provided by Mr. Richard Hale, have been added for **Straits Settlements,** including "S" flaws on Nos. 95/105, and the States. The listing for **Kelantan,** including the Thai Occupation, has been revised following the publication by the Malaya Study Group of *Kelantan* by Mr. W. A. Reeves and Mr. B. E. Dexter. In the **Japanese Occupation** section notes are now provided for the use of these stamps in some former Dutch East Indies post offices and by railway construction camps in Thailand. These notes are based on information very kindly supplied by Mr. Edward Proud.

Morocco Agencies. The King Edward VII issues have been revised following the published research into these stamps by Mr. M. H. Gellatly and Mr. M. K. Wlodarczyk.

New Zealand. The listings of the compound perforations in the period 1882 to 1906 have been improved.

Pakistan (Bahawalpur). Notes concerning the postal history of this state and the abortive attempts, before 1947, to introduce separate stamp issues have been provided by Mr. Wilson Wong.

Pitcairn Islands. Listings are now provided for the "No Stamps Available" cachets used between 1921 and 1927 and for New Zealand stamps used on the island between 1927 and 1940. Illustrations of the cachets and postmark are taken, with permission, from *Pitcairn Islands Postal Markings 1883–1991* by Mr. Cy Kitching and published by the Pitcairn Islands Study Group.

St. Kitts-Nevis. The shades of the 1938–50 3d. definitive have been reviewed as a group and a number of adjustments made.

South Africa – Cape (Vryburg). It has been possible to improve the listing of the Boer Occupation issue with the assistance of Dr. Alan Drysdall and Mr. John Taylor. The listings for **Griqualand West** have been revised to provide clearer information as to the settings used for these complicated overprints and for the **Union of South Africa** itself the two perforations of the 1927–30 definitive series have been listed separately.

Tanzania. It has finally been possible, with the help of Mr. John Hieatt, to list the John Waddington printings of the 1980 Wildlife definitive. Mr. Hieatt has also provided other notes concerning modern Tanzania.

Zambia. The long series of 2 k. provisionals introduced 5 July 1991 is now listed and we are grateful for the information supplied by Dr. Ian Slater of the Rhodesia Study Circle. A number of these provisionals are scarce, even in used condition, and it has not been possible, for this edition, to provide prices.

Zimbabwe. The recently-discovered definitive varieties perforated 14 issued between 1988 and 1992 are now listed.

There are many other alterations and corrections throughout the listings, many of which have been contributed by readers. We do appreciate the assistance provided by collectors, dealers and postal administrations in maintaining and improving the contents of this catalogue.

Finally readers are reminded that editions are now dated for the year in which they appear so that this is the 1993 edition and next year's will be dated 1994.

David J. Aggersberg

Stanley Gibbons Holdings Plc Addresses

STANLEY GIBBONS LIMITED, STANLEY GIBBONS AUCTIONS LIMITED
399 Strand, London WC2R OLX
Auction Room and Specialist Departments. Open Monday–Friday 9.30 a.m. to 5 p.m.
Shop. Open Monday–Friday 8.30 a.m. to 7 p.m. and Saturday 10 a.m. to 4 p.m.
Telephone 071 836 8444 and Fax 071 836 7342 for all departments.

STANLEY GIBBONS PUBLICATIONS
5 Parkside, Christchurch Road, Ringwood, Hants BH24 3SH.
Telephone 0425 472363 (24 hour answer phone service) and Fax 0425 470247
Publications Shop (at above address). Open Monday–Friday 9 a.m. to 3 p.m.
Publications Mail Order. FREEPHONE 0800 611622 Monday–Friday 8.30 a.m. to 5 p.m.

STANLEY GIBBONS PUBLICATIONS OVERSEAS REPRESENTATION

Stanley Gibbons Publications are represented overseas by the following sole distributors (*), distributors (**) or licensees (***).

Australia

Lighthouse Philatelic (Aust.) Pty Ltd*
PO Box 763
Strawberry Hills
New South Wales 2012
Australia

Stanley Gibbons (Australia) Pty Ltd***
PO Box 863J
Melbourne 3001
Australia

Belgium and Luxembourg**

Davo c/o Philac
Rue du Midi 48
Bruxelles 1000
Belgium

Canada*

Lighthouse Publications (Canada) Ltd
255 Duke Street
Montreal
Quebec
Canada H3C 2M2

Denmark**

Davo
c/o Lindner Falzlos
Gl Randersvej 28
8450 Hammel
Denmark

Finland**

Davo
c/o Suomen Postimerkkeily
Ludvingkatu 5
SF-00130 Helsinki
Finland

France*

Davo France
25 Rue Monge
75005 Paris
France

Germany and Austria*

Leuchtturm Albenverlag
Paul Koch KG
Am Spakenberg 45
Postfach 1340
D-2054 Geesthacht
Germany

Hong Kong**

Po-on Stamp Service
GPO Box 2498
Hong Kong

Israel**

Capital Stamps
PO Box 3769
Jerusalem 91036
Israel

Italy*

Secrian Srl
Via Pantelleria 2
1-20156 Milano
Italy

Japan**

Japan Philatelic Co Ltd
PO Box 2
Suginami-Minami
Tokyo
Japan

Netherlands*

Davo Publications
PO Box 411
7400 AK Deventer
Netherlands

New Zealand*

Philatelic Distributors Ltd
PO Box 863
New Plymouth
New Zealand

Norway**

Davo Norge A/S
PO Box 738 Sentrum
N-01 05 Oslo
Norway

Singapore***

Stanley Gibbons (Singapore) Pte Ltd
Raffles City
PO Box 1689
Singapore 9117

South Africa

Philatelic Holdings (Pty) Ltd***
PO Box 930
Parklands
RSA 2121

Republic Coin and Stamp
Accessories (Pty) Ltd**
PO Box 260325
Excom 2023
Johannesburg
RSA

Sweden*

Chr Winther Sorensen AB
Box 43
S-310 Knaered
Sweden

Switzerland**

Phila Service
Burgstrasse 160
CH 4125 Riehen
Switzerland

USA*

Lighthouse Publications Inc
PO Box 705
274 Washington Avenue
Hackensack
New Jersey 07602-0705
USA

West Indies/Caribbean**

Hugh Dunphy
PO Box 413
Kingston 10
Jamaica
West Indies

Stanley Gibbons Stamp Catalogue
Complete List of Parts

1 British Commonwealth
(Annual in two volumes)

2 Austria & Hungary (4th edition, 1988)
Austria, Bosnia & Herzegovina, U.N. (Vienna), Hungary

3 Balkans (3rd edition, 1987)
Albania, Bulgaria, Greece & Islands, Rumania, Yugoslavia

4 Benelux (3rd edition, 1988)
Belgium & Colonies, Netherlands & Colonies, Luxembourg

5 Czechoslovakia & Poland (4th edition, 1991)
Czechoslovakia, Bohemia & Moravia, Slovakia, Poland

6 France (3rd edition, 1987)
France, Colonies, Post Offices, Andorra, Monaco

7 Germany (4th edition, 1992)
Germany, States, Colonies, Post Offices

8 Italy & Switzerland (4th edition, 1993)
Italy & Colonies, Fiume, San Marino, Vatican City, Trieste, Liechtenstein, Switzerland, U.N. (Geneva)

9 Portugal & Spain (3rd edition, 1991)
Andorra, Portugal & Colonies, Spain & Colonies

10 Russia (4th edition, 1991)
Russia, Baltic States, Mongolia, Tuva

11 Scandinavia (3rd edition, 1988)
Aland Island, Denmark, Faroe Islands, Finland, Greenland, Iceland, Norway, Sweden

12 Africa since Independence A-E (2nd edition, 1983)
Algeria, Angola, Benin, Bophuthatswana, Burundi, Cameroun, Cape Verde, Central African Republic, Chad, Comoro Islands, Congo, Djibouti, Equatorial Guinea, Ethiopia

13 Africa since Independence F-M (1st edition, 1981)
Gabon, Guinea, Guinea-Bissau, Ivory Coast, Liberia, Libya, Malagasy Republic, Mali, Mauritania, Morocco, Mozambique

14 Africa since Independence N-Z (1st edition, 1981)
Niger Republic, Rwanda, St. Thomas & Prince, Senegal, Somalia, Sudan, Togo, Transkei, Tunisia, Upper Volta, Venda, Zaire

15 Central America (2nd edition, 1984)
Costa Rica, Cuba, Dominican Republic, El Salvador, Guatemala, Haiti, Honduras, Mexico, Nicaragua, Panama

16 Central Asia (3rd edition, 1992)
Afghanistan, Iran, Turkey

17 China (4th edition, 1989)
China, Taiwan, Tibet, Foreign P.O.s

18 Japan & Korea (3rd edition, 1992)
Japan, Ryukyus, Korean Empire, South Korea, North Korea

19 Middle East (4th edition, 1990)
Bahrain, Egypt, Iraq, Israel, Jordan, Kuwait, Lebanon, Oman, Qatar, Saudi Arabia, Syria, U.A.E., Yemen A.R., Yemen P.D.R.

20 South America (3rd edition, 1989)
Argentina, Bolivia, Brazil, Chile, Colombia, Ecuador, Paraguay, Peru, Surinam, Uruguay, Venezuela

21 South-East Asia (2nd edition, 1985)
Bhutan, Burma, Indonesia, Kampuchea, Laos, Nepal, Philippines, Thailand, Vietnam

22 United States (3rd edition, 1990)
U.S. & Possessions, Canal Zone, Marshall Islands, Micronesia, Palau, U.N. (New York, Geneva, Vienna)

GREAT BRITAIN SPECIALISED CATALOGUES

Volume 1 Queen Victoria (10th edition, 1992)
Volume 2 King Edward VII to King George VI (9th edition, 1993)
Volume 3 Queen Elizabeth II Pre-decimal Issues (8th edition, 1990)
Volume 4 Queen Elizabeth II Decimal Definitive Issues (6th edition, 1991)
Volume 5 Queen Elizabeth II Decimal Special Issues (2nd edition, 1991)

THEMATIC CATALOGUES

Collect Birds on Stamps (3rd edition, 1992)
Collect Mammals on Stamps (1st edition, 1986)
Collect Railways on Stamps (2nd edition, 1990)
Collect Ships on Stamps (2nd edition forthcoming)
Collect Fungi on Stamps (1st edition, 1991)
Collect Butterflies and Other Insects on Stamps (1st edition, 1991)
Collect Chess on Stamps (1st edition, 1992)
Collect Aircraft on Stamps (forthcoming)

Numbers Added or Changed

STAMPS ADDED

Excluding new issues which have appeared in Gibbons *Stamp Monthly* Supplements, the following are the Catalogue numbers of stamps listed in this edition for the first time.

Kenya, Uganda and Tanganyika. 125h, 131ac
Leeward Islands. 87a, 113ca, 114ba
Malawi. 96ca, 283a
Malaysia—Straits Settlements. Z5*a*, 64a, 64ba, 64ca, 89b, 95a, 96a, 97a, 98a, 103a, 104a, 105a
  Malaysia 425a, 426a, 457a, MS461a
  Johore. 6a
  Kelantan. 16ba
  Negri Sembilan (Sungei Ujong). 18a
  Negri Sembilan. 3a
  Selangor. 23a/b, 59a, 60a, 66bd, 67b
  Trengganu. 27*a*, 50*a*, 57*a*
  Japanese Occupation of Malaya. J79a, J274d
  Labuan. 35h, 45a, 55a, 83fa, 85fb, 118b
  Sabah. D54a
Japanese Occupation of Sarawak. J1a

Malta. 246a, 335c/d, 346a
Mauritius. 256a, 256ba, 256ca
Montserrat. 411a, O83a
Morocco Agencies. 35*a*, 36*a*, 112*a*, 113*a*, 114*a*, 115*a*, 116*a*, 117*a*, 118*a*, 119*a*, 120*a*, 121*a*, 122*a*, 124*a*, 200*b*
Namibia. 115a, 135a
New Zealand. 216ba, 216ga, 281b, 282a, 288b, 289b, 290a, 296a, 297a, 304b, 305a, 358a
Nigeria—Niger Coast Protectorate. 54b, 66c
Pakistan. 632a, 833a
  Bahawalpur. O2a
Papua New Guinea—New Guinea. 27a, 55h, 64nb
  Papua New Guinea. 45a, 602a, 640a, 643a
Pitcairn Islands. C1/14, Z1/17
Rhodesia. 78ab, 84ab
St. Kitts-Nevis. 73da, 73f/g, 77ae, 77bd
Seychelles. Z1

Sierra Leone. 322a, 336c
Singapore. 50a
Solomon Islands. 55b
Somaliland Protectorate. O4c
South Africa—Cape of Good Hope (Vryburg). 1a, 2a, 3a, 4a
  Griqualand West. 5g, 11a, 13ea
  Zululand. 13a
  South Africa. 34a, 35a, 35ba, 36a, 37a, 38a, 39b, 65a, 66a, 67a, 68a, 73a, 89a, 112a, 117ab, 426ba, 511ab, 515ab, D22a
Sri Lanka. 1103a, 1104a, 1127a
Swaziland. 580*a*, D2ab
Tanzania. 320*a/f*, MS770a, O64/5, O67/9
Tonga. 21b, 37hi, 825a, 827a
Tristan da Cunha. D2a
Zimbabwe. 65b, 381a, 660a, 661a, 662a, 663a, 666a, 667a, 670a, 672a, 769a/73a

CATALOGUE NUMBERS ALTERED

The table below is a cross-reference for those stamps, the Catalogue numbers of which have altered in this edition.

Old	New
Kenya	
561/5	565/9
566/9	561/4
Kenya, Uganda and Tanganyika	
131*ac*/*ae*	131*ad*/*af*
Malaysia—Straits Settlements	
64*a*/*b*	64*b*/*c*
97*a*	97*b*
103*a*	103*b*
Malta	
335c	335d
346a	346b
Mauritius	
256*a*/*b*	256*b*/*c*

Old	New
Morocco Agencies	
39	38*a*
52	51*b*
114a	114b
120a	120b
200*b*	200*c*
New Zealand	
216ba/bd	216bb/be
226c	227b
226d	228b
226e	234b
305*a*	305*ab*
L9*a*/*b*	L10/11
L10	L10a
L11	L11a

Old	New
Papua New Guinea—New Guinea	
38d	Deleted
Papua New Guinea	
642	640
644/5	645/6
St. Kitts-Nevis	
71bb	71c
73ba/bc	73c/e
74ba/bb	74c/d
St. Vincent	
1115*a*	1115*s*
1187/95	1240/8
1196/248	1187/239
Grenadines of St. Vincent	
791/9	800/8
Seychelles	
Z1/14	Z2/14*a*

Old	New
South Africa—Cape of Good Hope	
28a	Deleted
29a	Deleted
30a	Deleted
Griqualand West	
4/10	4a/g
11/16	5a/f
17/23	6a/g
24/30	7a/g
31/7	8a/g
38/44	9a/g
45/51	10a/g
52/9	11b/i
60/8	12a/i
69/77	13a/i
78/9	14/15
80	20d
81	21d
82	14d
83	15d
84/97	16/29

Old	New
Orange Free State	
P9	P12
P10/12	P9/11
Zululand	
12a	13
South Africa	
35*a*	35*b*
426b	426c
Sri Lanka	
177	Deleted
Tanzania	
46	45a
O61	O66
O62/4	O60/3
O65/73	O70/9
Uganda	
863/974	881/992
Zambia	
656/76	679/99

Contents

General Philatelic Information
and Guidelines to the Scope of the Part 1 (British Commonwealth) Catalogue

The notes which follow seek to reflect current practice in compiling the Part 1 (British Commonwealth) Catalogue.

It scarcely needs emphasising that the *Stanley Gibbons Stamp Catalogue* has a very long history and that the vast quantity of information it contains has been carefully built up by successive generations through the work of countless individuals. Philately itself is never static and the Catalogue has evolved and developed during this long time-span. Thus, while these notes are important for today's criteria, they may be less precise the further back in the listings one travels. They are not intended to inaugurate some unwanted series of piecemeal alterations in a widely respected work, but it does seem to us useful that Catalogue users know as exactly as possible the policies currently in operation.

PRICES

The prices quoted in this Catalogue are the estimated selling prices of Stanley Gibbons Ltd at the time of publication. They are, *unless it is specifically stated otherwise*, for examples in fine condition for the issue concerned. Superb examples are worth more; those of a lower quality considerably less.

All prices are subject to change without prior notice and Stanley Gibbons Ltd may from time to time offer stamps below catalogue price. Individual low value stamps sold at 399, Strand are liable to an additional handling charge.

No guarantee is given to supply all stamps priced, since it is not possible to keep every catalogued item in stock. Commemorative issues may, at times, only be available in complete sets and not as individual values.

Quotation of prices. The prices in the left-hand column are for unused stamps and those in the right-hand column are for used.

A dagger (†) denotes that the item listed does not exist in that condition and a blank, or dash, that it exists, or may exist, but no market price is known.

Prices are expressed in pounds and pence sterling. One pound comprises 100 pence (£1 = 100p).

The method of notation is as follows: pence in numerals (e.g. 10 denotes ten pence); pound and pence, up to £100, in numerals (e.g. 4·25 denotes four pounds and twenty-five pence); prices above £100 expressed in whole pounds with the "£" sign shown.

Unused stamps. Great Britain and Commonwealth: the prices for unused stamps of Queen Victoria to King George V are for lightly hinged examples. Unused prices for King Edward VIII to Queen Elizabeth II issues are for unmounted mint.

Some stamps from the King George VI period are often difficult to find in unmounted mint condition. In such instances we would expect that collectors would need to pay a high proportion of the price quoted to obtain mounted mint examples. Generally speaking lightly mounted mint stamps from this reign, issued before 1945, are in considerable demand.

Mounted mint stamps from the reign of Queen Elizabeth II are frequently available at lower prices than those quoted for the stamps unmounted.

Used stamps. The used prices are normally for stamps postally used but may be for stamps cancelled-to-order where this practice exists.

A pen-cancellation on early issues can sometimes correctly denote postal use. Instances are individually noted in the Catalogue in explanation of the used price given.

Prices quoted for bisects on cover or on large piece are for those dated during the period officially authorised.

Stamps not sold unused to the public (e.g. some official stamps) are priced used only.

The use of "unified" designs, that is stamps inscribed for both postal and fiscal purposes, results in a number of stamps of very high face value. In some instances these may not have been primarily intended for postal purposes, but if they are so inscribed we include them. We only price such items used, however, where there is evidence of normal postal usage.

Cover prices. To assist collectors, cover prices are quoted for issues up to 1945 at the beginning of each country.

The system gives a general guide in the form of a factor by which the corresponding used price of the loose stamp should be multiplied when found in fine average condition on cover.

Care is needed in applying the factors and they relate to a cover which bears a single of the denomination listed; strips and blocks would need individual valuation outside the scope. If more than one denomination is present the most highly priced attracts the multiplier and the remainder are priced at the simple figure for used singles in arriving at a total.

The cover should be of non-philatelic origin, bearing the correct postal rate for the period and distance involved and cancelled with the markings normal to the offices concerned. Purely philatelic items have a cover value only slightly greater than the catalogue value for the corresponding used stamps. This applies generally to those high-value stamps used philatelically rather than in the normal course of commerce. Low-value stamps, e.g. ¼d. and ½d., are desirable when used as a single rate on cover and merit an increase in "multiplier" value.

First-day covers in the period up to 1945 are not within the scope of the system and the multiplier should not be used. As a special category of philatelic usage, with wide variations in valuation according to scarcity, they require separate treatment.

Oversized covers, difficult to accommodate on an album page, should be reckoned as worth little more than the corresponding value of the used stamps. The condition of a cover affects its value. Except for "wreck covers", serious damage or soiling reduce the value where the postal markings and stamps are ordinary ones. Conversely, visual appeal adds to the value and this can include freshness of appearance, important addresses, old-fashioned but legible hand-writing, historic town-names, etc.

The multipliers are a base on which further value would be added to take account of the cover's postal historical importance in demonstrating such things as unusual, scarce or emergency cancels, interesting routes, significant postal markings, combination usage, the development of postal rates, and so on.

For *Great Britain*, rather than multiplication factors, the cover price is shown as a third column, following the prices for unused and used stamps. It will be extended beyond King Edward VII in subsequent editions.

Minimum price. The minimum price quoted is ten pence. This represents a handling charge rather than a basis for valuing common stamps, for which the 10p price should not be reckoned automatically, since it covers a variation in real scarcity.

Set prices. Set prices are generally for one of each value, excluding shades and varieties, but including major colour changes. Where there are alternative shades, etc., the cheapest is usually included. The number of stamps in the set is always stated for clarity. The mint prices for sets containing *se-tenant* pieces are based on the prices quoted for such combinations, and not on those for the individual stamps.

Specimen stamps. The pricing of these items is explained under that heading.

Repricing. Collectors will be aware that the market factors of supply and demand directly influence the prices quoted in this Catalogue. Whatever the scarcity of a particular stamp, if there is no one in the market who wishes to buy it it cannot be expected to achieve a high price. Conversely, the same item actively sought by numerous potential buyers may cause the price to rise.

All the prices in this Catalogue are examined during the preparation of each new edition by expert staff of Stanley Gibbons and repriced as necessary. They take many factors into account, including supply and demand, and are in close touch with the international stamp market and the auction world.

Commonwealth cover prices and advice on postal history material originally provided by Edward B. Proud.

GUARANTEE

All stamps are guaranteed genuine originals in the following terms:

If not as described, and returned by the purchaser, we undertake to refund the price paid to us in the original transaction. If any stamp is certified as genuine by the Expert Committee of the Royal Philatelic Society, London, or by B.P.A. Expertising Ltd, the purchaser shall not be entitled to make any claim against us for any error, omission or mistake in such certificate.

Consumers' statutory rights are not affected by the above guarantee.

The recognised Expert Committees in this country are those of the Royal Philatelic Society, 41 Devonshire Place, London W1N 1PE, and B.P.A. Expertising Ltd, P.O. Box 137, Leatherhead, Surrey KT22 0RG. They do not undertake valuations under any circumstances and fees are payable for their services.

THE CATALOGUE IN GENERAL

Contents. The Catalogue is confined to adhesive postage stamps, including miniature sheets. For particular categories the rules are:

(*a*) Revenue (fiscal) stamps or telegraph stamps are listed only where they have been expressly authorised for postal duty.

(*b*) Stamps issued only precancelled are included, but normally issued stamps available additionally with precancel have no separate precancel listing unless the face value is changed.

(*c*) Stamps prepared for use but not issued, hitherto accorded full listing, are nowadays footnoted with a price (where possible).

(*d*) Bisects (trisects, etc.) are only listed where such usage was officially authorised.

(*e*) Stamps issued only on first day covers or in presentation packs and not available separately are not listed but may be priced in a footnote.

(*f*) New printings are only included in this Catalogue where they show a major philatelic variety, such as a change in shade, watermark or paper. Stamps which exist with or without imprint dates are listed separately; changes in imprint dates are mentioned in footnotes.

(*g*) Official and unofficial reprints are dealt with by footnote.

(*h*) Stamps from imperforate printings of modern issues which also occur perforated are covered by footnotes, but are listed where widely available for postal use.

Exclusions. The following are excluded: (*a*) non-postal revenue or fiscal stamps; (*b*) postage stamps used fiscally; (*c*) local carriage labels and private local issues; (*d*) telegraph stamps; (*e*) bogus or phantom stamps; (*f*) railway or airline letter fee stamps, bus or road transport company labels; (*g*) cut-outs; (*h*) all types of non-postal labels and souvenirs; (*i*) documentary labels for the postal service, e.g. registration, recorded delivery, airmail etiquettes, etc.; (*j*) privately applied embellishments to official issues and privately commissioned items generally; (*k*) stamps for training postal officers.

Full listing. "Full listing" confers our recognition and implies allotting a catalogue number and (wherever possible) a price quotation.

In judging status for inclusion in the catalogue broad considerations are applied to stamps. They must be issued by a legitimate postal authority, recognised by the government concerned, and must be adhesives valid for proper postal use in the class of service for which they are inscribed. Stamps, with the exception of such categories as postage dues and officials, must be available to the general public, at face value, in reasonable quantities without any artificial restrictions being imposed on their distribution.

We record as abbreviated Appendix entries, without catalogue numbers or prices, stamps from countries which either persist in having far more issues than can be justified by postal need or have failed to maintain control over their distribution so that they have not been available to the public in reasonable quantities at face value. Miniature sheets and imperforate stamps are not mentioned in these entries.

The publishers of this catalogue have observed, with concern, the proliferation of "artificial" stamp-issuing territories. On several occasions this has resulted in separately inscribed issues for various component parts of otherwise united states or territories.

Stanley Gibbons Publications Ltd have decided that where such circumstances occur, they will not, in the future, list these items in the SG catalogue without first satisfying themselves that the stamps represent a genuine political, historical or postal division within the country concerned. Any such issues which do not fulfil this stipulation will be recorded in the Catalogue Appendix only.

For errors and varieties the criterion is legitimate (albeit inadvertent) sale through a postal administration in the normal course of business. Details of provenance are always important; printers' waste and deliberately manufactured material are excluded.

Certificates. In assessing unlisted items due weight is given to Certificates from recognised Expert Committees and, where appropriate, we will usually ask to see them.

New issues. New issues are listed regularly in the Catalogue Supplement published in *Gibbons Stamp Monthly*, whence they are consolidated into the next available edition of the Catalogue.

Date of issue. Where local issue dates differ from dates of release by agencies, "date of issue" is the local date. Fortuitous stray usage before the officially intended date is disregarded in listing. For ease of reference, the Catalogue displays in the top corner the date of issue of the first set listed on each page.

Catalogue numbers. Stamps of each country are catalogued chronologically by date of issue. Subsidiary classes are placed at the end of the country, as separate lists, with a distinguishing letter prefix to the catalogue number, e.g. D for postage due, O for official and E for express delivery stamps.

The catalogue number appears in the extreme left column. The boldface Type numbers in the next column are merely cross-references to illustrations. Catalogue numbers in the *Gibbons Stamp Monthly* Supplement are provisional only and may need to be altered when the lists are consolidated. For the numbering of miniature sheets and sheetlets *see* section below.

Once published in the Catalogue, numbers are changed as little as possible; really serious renumbering is reserved for the occasions when a complete country or an entire issue is being rewritten. The edition first affected includes cross-reference tables of old and new numbers.

Our catalogue numbers are universally recognised in specifying stamps and as a hallmark of status.

Illustrations. Stamps are illustrated at three-quarters linear size. Stamps not illustrated are the same size and format as the value shown, unless otherwise indicated. Stamps issued only as miniature sheets have the stamp alone illustrated but sheet size is also quoted. Overprints, surcharges and watermarks are normally actual size. Illustrations of varieties are often enlarged to show the detail.

Designers. Designers' names are quoted where known, though space precludes naming every individual concerned in the production of a set. In particular, photographers supplying material are usually named only where they also make an active contribution in the design stage; posed photographs of reigning monarchs are, however, an exception to this rule.

CONTACTING THE CATALOGUE EDITOR

The editor is always interested in hearing from people who have new information which will improve or correct the Catalogue. As a general rule he must see and examine the actual stamps before they can be considered for listing; photographs or photocopies are insufficient evidence.

Submissions should be made in writing to the Catalogue Editor, Stanley Gibbons Publications Ltd. at the Ringwood office. The cost of return postage for items submitted is appreciated, and this should include the registration fee if required.

Where information is solicited purely for the benefit of the enquirer, the editor cannot undertake to reply if the answer is already contained in these published notes or if return postage is omitted. Written communications are greatly preferred to enquiries by telephone and the editor regrets that he or his staff cannot see personal callers without a prior appointment being made. Correspondence may be subject to delay during the production period of each new edition.

The editor welcomes close contact with study circles and is interested, too, in finding reliable local correspondents who will verify and supplement official information in countries where this is deficient.

> We regret we do not give opinions as to the genuineness of stamps, nor do we identify stamps or number them by our Catalogue.

TECHNICAL MATTERS

The meanings of the technical terms used in the catalogue will be found in our *Philatelic Terms Illustrated* (3rd edition), (*price £7.50 plus postage and packing charge*).

References below to "more specialised" listings are to be taken to indicate, as appropriate, the Stanley Gibbons *Great Britain Specialised Catalogue* in 5 volumes or the *Great Britain, Australia* or *New Zealand Concise Catalogues*.

1. Printing

Printing errors. Errors in printing are of major interest to the Catalogue. Authenticated items meriting consideration would include: background, centre or frame inverted or omitted; centre or subject transposed; error of colour; error or omission of value; double prints and impressions; printed both sides; and so on. Designs *tête-bêche*, whether intentionally or by accident, are listable. *Se-tenant* arrangements of stamps are recognised in the listings or footnotes. Gutter pairs (a pair of stamps separated by blank margin) are not included in this volume. Colours only partially omitted are not listed. Stamps with embossing omitted and (for Commonwealth countries) stamps printed on the gummed side are reserved for our more specialised listings.

Printing varieties. Listing is accorded to major changes in the printing base which lead to completely new types. In recess-printing this could be a design re-engraved; in photogravure or photolithography a screen altered in whole or in part. It can also encompass flat-bed and rotary printing if the results are readily distinguishable.

To be considered at all, varieties must be constant.

Early stamps, produced by primitive methods, were prone to numerous imperfections: the lists reflect this, recognising re-entries, retouches, broken frames, misshapen letters, and so on. Printing technology has, however, radically improved over the years, during which time photogravure and lithography have become predominant. Varieties nowadays are more in the nature of flaws and these, being too specialised for this general catalogue, are almost always outside the scope. The development of our range of specialised catalogues allows us now to list those items which have philatelic significance in their appropriate volume.

In no catalogue, however, do we list such items as: dry prints, kiss prints, doctor-blade flaws, colour shifts or registration flaws (unless they lead to the complete omission of a colour from an individual stamp), lithographic ring flaws, and so on. Neither do we recognise fortuitous happenings like paper creases or confetti flaws.

Overprints (and surcharges). Overprints of different types qualify for separate listing. These include overprints in different colours; overprints from different printing processes such as litho and typo; overprints in totally different typefaces, etc. Major errors in machine-printed overprints are important and listable. They include: overprint inverted or omitted; overprint double (treble, etc.); overprint diagonal; overprint double, one inverted; pairs with one overprint omitted, e.g. from a radical shift to an adjoining stamp; error of colour; error of type fount; letters inverted or omitted, etc. If the overprint is handstamped, few of these would qualify and a distinction is drawn. We continue, however, to list pairs of stamps where one has a handstamped overprint and the other has not.

Varieties occurring in overprints will often take the form of broken letters, slight differences in spacing, rising spaces, etc. Only the most important would be considered for footnote mention.

Sheet positions. If space permits we quote sheet positions of listed varieties and authenticated data is solicited for this purpose.

De La Rue plates. The Catalogue classifies the general plates used by De La Rue for printing British Colonial stamps as follows:

VICTORIAN KEY TYPE

Die I

1. The ball of decoration on the second point of the crown appears as a dark mass of lines.
2. Dark vertical shading separates the front hair from the bun.
3. The vertical line of colour outlining the front of the throat stops at the sixth line of shading on the neck.

4. The white space in the coil of the hair above the curl is roughly the shape of a pin's head.

Die II

1. There are very few lines of colour in the ball and it appears almost white.
2. A white vertical strand of hair appears in place of the dark shading.
3. The line stops at the eighth line of shading.
4. The white space is oblong, with a line of colour partially dividing it at the left end.

Plates numbered 1 and 2 are both Die I. Plates 3 and 4 are Die II.

GEORGIAN KEY TYPE

Die I

A. The second (thick) line below the name of the country is cut slanting, conforming roughly to the shape of the crown on each side.
B. The labels of solid colour bearing the words "POSTAGE" and "& REVENUE" are square at the inner top corners.
C. There is a projecting "bud" on the outer spiral of the ornament in each of the lower corners.

Die II

A. The second line is cut vertically on each side of the crown.
B. The labels curve inwards at the top.
C. There is no "bud" in this position.

Unless otherwise stated in the lists, all stamps with watermark Multiple Crown CA (w **8**) are Die I while those with watermark Multiple Crown Script CA (w **9**) are Die II. The Georgian Die II was introduced in April 1921 and was used for Plates 10 to 22 and 26 to 28. Plates 23 to 25 were made from Die I by mistake.

2. Paper

All stamps listed are deemed to be on "ordinary" paper of the wove type and white in colour; only departures from this are normally mentioned.

Types. Where classification so requires we distinguish such other types of paper as, for example, vertically and horizontally laid; wove and laid bâtonné; card(board); carton; cartridge; glazed; granite; native; pelure; porous; quadrillé; ribbed; rice; and silk thread.

Wove paper   Laid paper

Granite paper   Quadrillé paper

Burelé band

The various makeshifts for normal paper are listed as appropriate. The varieties of double paper and joined paper are recognised. The security device of a printed burelé band on the back of a stamp, as in early Queensland, qualifies for listing.

Descriptive terms. The fact that a paper is handmade (and thus probably of uneven thickness) is mentioned where necessary. Such descriptive terms as "hard" and "soft"; "smooth" and 'rough"; "thick", "medium" and "thin" are applied where there is philatelic merit in classifying papers. We do not, for example, even in more specialised listings, classify paper thicknesses in the Wilding and Machin definitives of Great Britain. Weight standards for the paper apply to complete reels only, so that differences on individual stamps are acceptable to the printer provided the reel conforms overall.

Coloured, very white and toned papers. A coloured paper is one that is coloured right through (front and back of the stamp). In the Catalogue the colour of the paper is given in *italics,* thus:

black/*rose* = black design on rose paper.

Papers have been made specially white in recent years by, for example, a very heavy coating of chalk. We do not classify shades of whiteness of paper as distinct varieties. There does exist, however, a type of paper from early days called toned. This is off-white, often brownish or buffish, but it cannot be assigned any definite colour. A toning effect brought on by climate, incorrect storage or gum staining is disregarded here, as this was not the state of the paper when issued.

Modern developments. Two modern developments also affect the listings: printing on self-adhesive paper and the use of metallic foils. For self-adhesive stamps *see* under "Gum", below.

Care should be taken not to damage the embossing on stamps impressed on metallic foils, such as Sierra Leone 1965–67, by subjecting the album pages to undue pressure. The possibility of faked "missing gold heads" is noted at the appropriate places in the listing of modern Great Britain.

"Ordinary" and "Chalk-surfaced" papers. The availability of many postage stamps for revenue purposes made necessary some safeguard against the illegitimate re-use of stamps with removable cancellations. This was at first secured by using fugitive inks and later by printing on chalk-surfaced paper, both of which made it difficult to remove any form of obliteration without also damaging the stamp design.

This catalogue lists these chalk-surfaced paper varieties from their introduction in 1905. Where no indication is given, the paper is "ordinary".

Our chalk-surfaced paper is specifically one which shows a black mark when touched with a silver wire. The paper used during the Second World War for high values, as in Bermuda, the Leeward Islands, etc., was thinly coated with some kind of surfacing which does not react to silver and is therefore regarded (and listed) as "ordinary". Stamps on chalk-surfaced paper can easily lose this coating through immersion in water.

Another paper introduced during the War as a substitute for chalk-surfaced is rather thick, very white and glossy and shows little or no watermark, nor does it show a black line when touched with silver. In the Bahamas high values this paper might be mistaken for the chalk-surfaced (which is thinner and poorer-looking) but for the silver test.

Glazed paper. In 1969 the Crown Agents introduced a new general-purpose paper for use in conjunction with all current printing processes. It generally has a marked glossy surface but the degree varies according to the process used, being more marked in recess-printing stamps. As it does not respond to the silver test this presents a further test where previous printings were on chalky paper. A change of paper to the glazed variety merits separate listing.

Green and yellow papers. Issues of the First World War and immediate postwar period occur on green and yellow papers and these are given separate Catalogue listing. The original coloured papers (coloured throughout) gave way to surface-coloured papers, the stamps having "white backs"; other stamps show one colour on the front and a different one at the back. Because of the numerous variations a grouping of colours is adopted as follows:

YELLOW PAPERS

(1) The original *yellow* paper (throughout), usually bright in colour. The gum is often sparse, of harsh consistency and dull-looking.

(2) The *white backs.*

(3) A bright *lemon* paper. The colour must have a pronounced greenish tinge, different from the "yellow" in (1). As a rule, the gum on stamps using this lemon paper is plentiful, smooth and shiny, and the watermark shows distinctly. Care is needed with stamps printed in green on yellow paper (1) as it may appear that the paper is this lemon.

(4) An *orange-buff* paper. The colour must have a distinct brownish tinge. It is not to be confused with a muddy yellow (1) nor the misleading appearance (on the surface) of stamps printed in red on yellow paper where an engraved plate has been insufficiently wiped.

(5) A *pale yellow* paper that has a creamy tone to the yellow.

GREEN PAPERS

(6) The original "green" paper, varying considerably through shades of *blue-green* and *yellow-green*, the front and back sometimes differing.

(7) The *white backs.*

(8) A paper blue-green on the surface with *pale olive* back. The back must be markedly paler than the front and this and the pronounced olive tinge to the back distinguish it from (6).

(9) Paper with a vivid green surface, commonly called *emerald-green*; it has the olive back of (8).

(10) Paper with *emerald-green* both back and front.

3. Perforation and Rouletting

Perforation gauge. The gauge of a perforation is the number of holes in a length of 2 cm. For correct classification the size of the holes (large or small) may need to be distinguished; in a few cases the actual number of holes on each edge of the stamp needs to be quoted.

Measurement. The Gibbons *Instanta* gauge is the standard for measuring perforations. The stamp is viewed against a dark background with the transparent gauge put on top of it. Though the gauge measures to decimal accuracy, perforations read from it are generally quoted in the Catalogue to the nearest half. For example:

Just over perf $12\frac{3}{4}$ to just under $13\frac{1}{4}$ = perf 13
Perf $13\frac{1}{4}$ exactly, rounded up = perf $13\frac{1}{2}$
Just over perf $13\frac{1}{4}$ to just under $13\frac{3}{4}$ = perf $13\frac{1}{2}$
Perf $13\frac{3}{4}$ exactly, rounded up = perf 14

However, where classification depends on it, actual quarter-perforations are quoted.

Notation. Where no perforation is quoted for an issue it is imperforate. Perforations are usually abbreviated (and spoken) as follows, though sometimes they may be spelled out for clarity. This notation for rectangular stamps (the majority) applies to diamond shapes if "top" is read as the edge to the top right.

P 14: perforated alike on all sides (read: "perf 14").

P 14 × 15: the first figure refers to top and bottom, the second to left and right sides (read: "perf 14 by 15"). This is a compound perforation. For an upright triangular stamp the first figure refers to the two sloping sides and second to the base. In inverted triangulars the base is first and the second figure refers to the sloping sides.

P 14–15: perforation measuring anything between 14 and 15: the holes are irregularly spaced, thus the gauge may vary along a single line or even along a single edge of the stamp (read: "perf 14 to 15").

P 14 *irregular*: perforated 14 from a worn perforator, giving badly aligned holes irregularly spaced (read: "irregular perf 14").

P comp(ound) 14 × 15: two gauges in use but not necessarily on opposite sides of the stamp. It could be one side in one gauge and three in the other; or two adjacent sides with the same gauge. (Read: "perf compound of 14 and 15".) For three gauges or more, abbreviated as "*P* 14, 14½, 15 *or* compound" for example.

P 14, 14½: perforated approximately $14\frac{1}{4}$ (read: "perf 14 or 14½"). It does *not* mean two stamps, one perf 14 and the other perf 14½. This obsolescent notation is gradually being replaced in the Catalogue.

Imperf: imperforate (not perforated).

Imperf × *P* 14: imperforate at top and bottom and perf 14 at sides.

Perf × imperf

P 14 × *imperf*: perf 14 at top and bottom and imperforate at sides.

Such headings as "*P* 13 × 14 (*vert*) and *P* 14 × 13

(*horiz*)" indicate which perforations apply to which stamp format—vertical or horizontal.

Some stamps are additionally perforated so that a label or tab is detachable; others have been perforated suitably for use as two halves. Listings are normally for whole stamps, unless stated otherwise.

Other terms. Perforation almost always gives circular holes; where other shapes have been used they are specified, e.g. square holes; lozenge perf. Interrupted perfs are brought about by the omission of pins at regular intervals. Perforations merely simulated by being printed as part of the design are of course ignored. With few exceptions, privately applied perforations are not listed.

In the nineteenth century perforations are often described as clean cut (clean, sharply incised holes), intermediate or rough (rough holes, imperfectly cut, often the result of blunt pins).

Perforation errors and varieties. Authenticated errors, where a stamp normally perforated is accidentally issued imperforate, are listed provided no traces of perforation (blind holes or indentations) remain. They must be provided as pairs, both stamps wholly imperforate, and are only priced in that form.

In Great Britain, numerous of these part-perforated stamps have arisen from the introduction of the Jumelle Press. This has a rotary perforator with rows of pins on one drum engaging with holes on another. Engagement is only gradual when the perforating unit is started up or stopped, giving rise to perforations "fading out", a variety mentioned above as not listed.

Stamps imperforate between stamp and sheet margin are not listed in this catalogue, but such errors on Great Britain stamps will be found in the *Great Britain Specialised Catalogue*.

Pairs described as "imperforate between" have the line of perforations between the two stamps omitted.

Imperf between (*horiz pair*): a horizontal pair of stamps with perfs all around the edges but none between the stamps.

Imperf between (*vert pair*): a vertical pair of stamps with perfs all around the edges but none between the stamps.

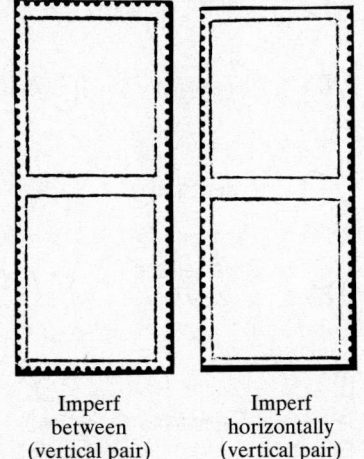

Imperf   Imperf
between   horizontally
(vertical pair) (vertical pair)

Where several of the rows have escaped perforation the resulting varieties are listable. Thus:

Imperf vert (*horiz pair*): a horizontal pair of stamps perforated top and bottom; all three vertical directions are imperf—the two outer edges and between the stamps.

Imperf horiz (*vert pair*): a vertical pair perforated at left and right edges; all three horizontal directions are imperf—the top, bottom and between the stamps.

Straight edges. Large sheets cut up before issue to post offices can cause stamps with straight edges, i.e. imperf on one side or on two sides at right angles. They are not usually listable in this condition and are worth less than corresponding stamps

properly perforated all round. This does not, however, apply to certain stamps, mainly from coils and booklets, where straight edges on various sides are the manufacturing norm affecting every stamp. The listings and notes make clear which sides are correctly imperf.

Malfunction. Varieties of double, misplaced or partial perforation caused by error or machine malfunction are not listable, neither are freaks, such as perforations placed diagonally from paper folds, nor missing holes caused by broken pins.

Centering. Well-centred stamps have designs surrounded by equal opposite margins. Where this condition affects the price the fact is stated.

Types of perforating. Where necessary for classification, perforation types are distinguished. These include:

Line perforation from one line of pins punching single rows of holes at a time.

Comb perforation from pins disposed across the sheet in comb formation, punching out holes at three sides of the stamp a row at a time.

Harrow perforation applied to a whole pane or sheet at one stroke.

Rotary perforation from toothed wheels operating across a sheet, then crosswise.

Sewing-machine perforation. The resultant condition, clean-cut or rough, is distinguished where required.

Pin-perforation is the commonly applied term for pin-roulette in which, instead of being punched out, round holes are pricked by sharp-pointed pins and no paper is removed.

Mixed perforation occurs when stamps with defective perforations are re-perforated in a different gauge.

Punctured stamps. Perforation holes can be punched into the face of the stamp. Patterns of small holes, often in the shape of initial letters, are privately applied devices against pilferage. These "perfins" are outside the scope except for Australia, Papua and Sudan where they were used as official stamps by the national administration. Identification devices, when officially inspired, are listed or noted; they can be shapes, or letters or words formed from holes, sometimes converting one class of stamp into another.

Rouletting. In rouletting the paper is cut, for ease of separation, but none is removed. The gauge is measured, when needed, as for perforations. Traditional French terms descriptive of the type of cut are often used and types include:

Arc roulette (*percé en arc*). Cuts are minute, spaced arcs, each roughly a semicircle.

Cross roulette (*percé en croix*). Cuts are tiny diagonal crosses.

Line roulette (*percé en ligne* or *en ligne droite*). Short straight cuts parallel to the frame of the stamp. The commonest basic roulette. Where not further described, "roulette" means this type.

Rouletted in colour or *coloured roulette* (*percé en lignes colorées* or *en lignes de couleur*). Cuts with coloured edges, arising from notched rule inked simultaneously with the printing plate.

Saw-tooth roulette (*percé en scie*). Cuts applied zigzag fashion to resemble the teeth of a saw.

Serpentine roulette (*percé en serpentin*). Cuts as sharply wavy lines.

Zigzag roulette (*percé en zigzags*). Short straight cuts at angles in alternate directions, producing sharp points on separation. U.S. usage favours "serrate(d) roulette" for this type.

Pin-roulette (originally *percé en points* and now *perforés trous d'epingle*) is commonly called pin-perforation in English.

4. Gum

All stamps listed are assumed to have gum of some kind; if they were issued without gum this is stated. Original gum (o.g.) means that which was present on the stamp as issued to the public. Deleterious climates and the presence of certain chemicals can cause gum to crack and, with early stamps, even make the paper deteriorate. Unscrupulous fakers are adept in removing it and regumming the stamp to meet the unreasoning demand often made for "full o.g." in cases where such a thing is virtually impossible.

The gum normally used on stamps has been gum arabic until the late 1960s when synthetic adhesives were introduced. Harrison and Sons Ltd for instance use *polyvinyl alcohol*, known to philatelists as PVA. This is almost invisible except for a slight yellowish tinge which was incorporated to make it possible to see that the stamps have been gummed. It has advantages in hot countries, as stamps do not curl and sheets are less likely to stick together. Gum arabic and PVA are not distinguished in the lists except that where a stamp exists with both forms this is indicated in footnotes. Our more specialised catalogues provide separate listing of gums for Great Britain.

Self-adhesive stamps are issued on backing paper, from which they are peeled before affixing to mail. Unused examples are priced as for backing paper intact, in which condition they are recommended to be kept. Used examples are best collected on cover or on piece.

5. Watermarks

Stamps are on unwatermarked paper except where the heading to the set says otherwise.

Detection. Watermarks are detected for Catalogue description by one of four methods: (1) holding stamps to the light; (2) laying stamps face down on a dark background; (3) adding a few drops of petroleum ether 40/60 to the stamp laid face down in a watermark tray; (4) by use of the Morley-Bright Detector, or other equipment, which work by revealing the thinning of the paper at the watermark (Note that petroleum ether is highly inflammable in use and can damage photogravure stamps.)

Listable types. Stamps occurring on both watermarked and unwatermarked papers are different types and both receive full listing.

Single watermarks (devices occurring once on every stamp) can be modified in size and shape as between different issues; the types are noted but not usually separately listed. Fortuitous absence of watermark from a single stamp or its gross displacement would not be listable.

To overcome registration difficulties the device may be repeated at close intervals (a *multiple watermark*), single stamps thus showing parts of several devices. Similarly, a large *sheet watermark* (or *all-over watermark*) covering numerous stamps can be used. We give informative notes and illustrations for them. The designs may be such that numbers of stamps in the sheet automatically lack watermark: this is not a listable variety. Multiple and all-over watermarks sometimes undergo modifications, but if the various types are difficult to distinguish from single stamps notes are given but not separate listings.

Papermakers' watermarks are noted where known but not listed separately, since most stamps in the sheet will lack them. Sheet watermarks which are nothing more than officially adopted papermakers' watermarks are, however, given normal listing.

Marginal watermarks, falling outside the pane of stamps, are ignored except where misplacement caused the adjoining row to be affected, in which case they are footnoted.

Watermark errors and varieties. Watermark errors are recognised as of major importance. They comprise stamps intended to be on unwatermarked paper but issued watermarked by mistake, or stamps printed on paper with the wrong watermark. Watermark varieties, on the other hand, such as broken or deformed bits on the dandy roll, are not listable.

Watermark positions. The diagram shows how watermark position is described in the Catalogue. Paper has a side intended for printing and watermarks are usually impressed so that they read

normally when looked through from that printed side. However, since philatelists customarily detect watermarks by looking at the back of the stamp the watermark diagram also makes clear what is actually seen.

Illustrations in the Catalogue are of watermarks in normal positions (from the front of the stamps) and are actual size where possible.

Differences in watermark position are collectable as distinct varieties. In this Catalogue, however, only normal and sideways watermarks are listed (and "sideways inverted" is treated as "sideways"). Inverted and reversed watermarks have always been outside its scope: in the early days of flat-bed printing sheets of watermarked paper were fed indiscriminately through the press and the resulting watermark positions had no particular philatelic significance. Similarly, the special make-up of sheets for booklets can in some cases give equal quantities of normal and inverted watermarks.

Collectors are reminded that inverted and reversed watermarks are listed in the *Great Britain Specialised Catalogue* and the *Great Britain, Australia* or *New Zealand Concise Catalogues.*

Where a watermark comes indiscriminately in various positions our policy is to cover this by a general note: we do not give separate listings because the watermark position in these circumstances has no particular philatelic importance. There is a general note of this sort in modern Cyprus, for example. Issues printed since 1962 by Aspioti-Elka occur with the vertical stamps having the watermark normal or inverted, while horizontal stamps are likewise found with the watermark reading upwards or downwards.

AS DESCRIBED (Read through front of stamp)		AS SEEN DURING WATERMARK DETECTION (Stamp face down and back examined)
GvR	Normal	ᴚvひ
ᴚʌＧ	Inverted	ᗡʌᴚ
ᴚʌＧ	Reversed	GvR
ᗡʌᴚ	Reversed and inverted	GvR
GvR	Sideways	ᴚvＧ
GvR	Sideways inverted	ᴚvＧ

Standard types of watermark. Some watermarks have been used generally for various British possessions rather than exclusively for a single colony. To avoid repetition the Catalogue classifies 17 general types, as under, with references in the headings throughout the listings being given either in words or in the form "*W* w **14**"

(meaning "watermark type w **14**"). In those cases where watermark illustrations appear in the listings themselves, the respective reference reads, for example, *W* 153, thus indicating that the watermark will be found in the normal sequence of illustrations as (type) **153**.

The general types are as follows, with an example of each quoted.

W	Description	Example
w 1	Large Star	St. Helena No. 1
w 2	Small Star	Turks Is. No. 4
w 3	Broad (pointed) Star	Grenada No. 24
w 4	Crown (over) CC, small stamp	Antigua No. 13
w 5	Crown (over) CC, large stamp	Antigua No. 31
w 6	Crown (over) CA, small stamp	Antigua No. 21
w 7	Crown CA (CA over Crown), large stamp	Sierra Leone No. 54
w 8	Multiple Crown CA	Antigua No. 41
w 9	Multiple Crown Script CA	Seychelles No. 158
w 9a	do. Error	Seychelles No. 158a
w 9b	do. Error	Seychelles No. 158b
w 10	V over Crown	N.S.W. No. 327
w 11	Crown over A	N.S.W. No. 347
w 12	Multiple St. Edward's Crown Block CA	Antigua No. 149
w 13	Multiple PTM	Johore No. 166
w 14	Multiple Crown CA Diagonal	Antigua No. 426
w 15	Multiple POST OFFICE	Kiribati No. 141
w 16	Multiple Crown Script CA Diagonal	Ascension No. 376
w 17	Multiple CARTOR	Brunei No. 357

CC in these watermarks is an abbreviation for "Crown Colonies" and CA for "Crown Agents". Watermarks w **1**, w **2** and w **3** are on stamps printed by Perkins, Bacon; w **4** onwards on stamps from De La Rue and other printers.

w 1
Large Star

w 2
Small Star

w 3
Broad (pointed) Star

Watermark w **1**, *Large Star,* measures 15 to 16 mm across the star from point to point and about 27 mm from centre to centre vertically between stars in the sheet. It was made for long stamps like Ceylon 1857 and St. Helena 1856.

Watermark w **2**, *Small Star,* is of similar design but measures 12 to 13½ mm from point to point and 24 mm from centre to centre vertically. It was for use with ordinary-size stamps such as Grenada 1863–71.

When the Large Star watermark was used with the smaller stamps it only occasionally comes in the centre of the paper. It is frequently so misplaced as to show portions of two stars above and below and this eccentricity will very often help in determining the watermark.

Watermark w **3**, *Broad* (*pointed*) *Star*, resembles w **1** but the points are broader.

w **4**   w **5**
Crown (over) CC   Crown (over) CC

Two *Crown* (*over*) *CC* watermarks were used: w **4** was for stamps of ordinary size and w **5** for those of larger size.

w **6**   w **7**
Crown (over) CA   CA over Crown

Two watermarks of *Crown CA* type were used, w **6** being for stamps of ordinary size. The other, w **7**, is properly described as *CA over Crown*. It was specially made for paper on which it was intended to print long fiscal stamps: that some were used postally accounts for the appearance of w **7** in the Catalogue. The watermark occupies twice the space of the ordinary Crown CA watermark, w **6**. Stamps of normal size printed on paper with w **7** watermark show it *sideways*; it takes a horizontal pair of stamps to show the entire watermark.

w **8**   w **9**
Multiple Crown CA   Multiple Crown
                     Script CA

Multiple watermarks began in 1904 with w **8**, *Multiple Crown CA*, changed from 1921 to w **9**, *Multiple Crown Script CA*. On stamps of ordinary size portions of two or three watermarks appear and on the large-sized stamps a greater number can be observed. The change to letters in script character with w **9** was accompanied by a Crown of distinctly different shape.

w **9a**: Error,
Crown missing

w **9b**: Error,
St. Edward's Crown

The *Multiple Crown Script CA* watermark, w **9**, is known with two errors recurring among the 1950–52 printings of several territories. In the first a crown has fallen away from the dandy-roll that impresses the watermark into the paper pulp. It gives w **9a**, *Crown missing*, but this omission has been found in both "Crown only" (*illustrated*) and "Crown CA" rows. The resulting faulty paper was used for Seychelles, Johore and the postage due stamps of nine colonies.

When the omission was noticed a second mishap occurred, which was to insert a wrong crown in the space, giving w **9b**, *St. Edward's Crown*. This produced varieties in Bahamas, St. Kitts-Nevis and Singapore and the incorrect crown likewise occurs in "Crown only" and "Crown CA" rows.

w **10**   w **11**
V over Crown   Crown over A

Resuming the general types, two watermarks found in issues of several Australian States are: w **10**, *V over Crown*, and w **11**, *Crown over A*.

w **12**
Multiple St. Edward's
Crown Block CA

The *Multiple St. Edward's Crown Block CA* watermark, w **12**, was introduced in 1957 and besides the change in the Crown (from that used in *Multiple Crown Script CA*, w **9**) the letters reverted to block capitals. The new watermark began to appear sideways in 1966 and these stamps are generally listed as separate sets.

w **13**
Multiple PTM

The watermark w **13**, *Multiple PTM*, was introduced for new Malayan issues in November 1961.

w **14**
Multiple Crown CA
Diagonal

By 1974 the two dandy-rolls (the "upright" and the "sideways") for w **12** were wearing out; the Crown Agents therefore discontinued using the sideways-watermark one and retained the other only as a stand-by. A new dandy-roll with the pattern of w **14**, *Multiple Crown CA Diagonal*, was introduced and first saw use with some Churchill Centenary issues.

The new watermark has the design arranged in gradually spiralling rows. It is improved in design to allow smooth passage over the paper (the gaps between letters and rows had caused jolts in previous dandy-rolls) and the sharp corners and angles, where fibres used to accumulate, have been eliminated by rounding.

This watermark has no "normal" sideways position amongst the different printers using it. To avoid confusion our more specialised listings do not rely on such terms as "sideways inverted" but describe the direction in which the watermark points.

w **15**
Multiple POST OFFICE

During 1981 w **15**, *Multiple POST OFFICE*, was introduced for certain issues prepared by Philatelists Ltd, acting for various countries in the Indian Ocean, Pacific and West Indies.

w **16**
Multiple Crown Script CA Diagonal

A new Crown Agents watermark was introduced during 1985, w **16**, *Multiple Crown Script CA Diagonal*. This was very similar to the previous w **14**, but showed "CA" in script rather than block letters. It was first used on the omnibus series of stamps commemorating the Life and Times of Queen Elizabeth the Queen Mother.

w 17
Multiple CARTOR

Watermark w **17**, *Multiple CARTOR*, was used from 1985 for issues printed by this French firm for countries which did not normally use the Crown Agents watermark.

In recent years the use of watermarks has, to a small extent, been superseded by fluorescent security markings. These are often more visible from the reverse of the stamp (Cook Islands from 1970 onwards), but have occurred printed over the design (Hong Kong Nos. 415/30). In 1982 the Crown Agents introduced a new stock paper, without watermark, known as "C-Kurity" on which a fluorescent pattern of blue rosettes is visible on the reverse, beneath the gum. This paper was used for issues from Gambia and Norfolk Island.

6. Colours

Stamps in two or three colours have these named in order of appearance, from the centre moving outwards. Four colours or more are usually listed as multicoloured.

In compound colour names the second is the predominant one, thus:

orange-red = a red tending towards orange;

red-orange = an orange containing more red than usual.

Standard colours used. The 200 colours most used for stamp identification are given in the Stanley Gibbons Stamp Colour Key. The Catalogue has used the Stamp Colour Key as standard for describing new issues for some years. The names are also introduced as lists are rewritten, though exceptions are made for those early issues where traditional names have become universally established.

Determining colours. When comparing actual stamps with colour samples in the Stamp Colour Key, view in a good north daylight (or its best substitute: fluorescent "colour-matching" light). Sunshine is not recommended. Choose a solid portion of the stamp design; if available, marginal markings such as solid bars of colour or colour check dots are helpful. Shading lines in the design can be misleading as they appear lighter than solid colour. Postmarked portions of a stamp appear darker than normal. If more than one colour is present, mask off the extraneous ones as the eye tends to mix them.

Errors of colour. Major colour errors in stamps or overprints which qualify for listing are: wrong colours; one colour inverted in relation to the rest; albinos (colourless impressions), where these have Expert Committee certificates; colours completely omitted, but only on unused stamps (if found on used stamps the information is footnoted) and with good credentials, missing colours being frequently faked.

Colours only partially omitted are not recognised. Colour shifts, however spectacular, are not listed.

Shades. Shades in philately refer to variations in the intensity of a colour or the presence of differing amounts of other colours. They are particularly significant when they can be linked to specific printings. In general, shades need to be quite marked to fall within the scope of this Catalogue; it does not favour nowadays listing the often numerous shades of a stamp, but chooses a single applicable colour name which will indicate particular groups of outstanding shades. Furthermore, the listings refer to colours as issued: they may deteriorate into something different through the passage of time.

Modern colour printing by lithography is prone to marked differences of shade, even within a single run, and variations can occur within the same sheet. Such shades are not listed.

Aniline colours. An aniline colour meant originally one derived from coal-tar; it now refers more widely to colour of a particular brightness suffused on the surface of a stamp and showing through clearly on the back.

Colours of overprints and surcharges. All overprints and surcharges are in black unless stated otherwise in the heading or after the description of the stamp.

7. Specimen Stamps

Originally, stamps overprinted SPECIMEN were circulated to postmasters or kept in official records, but after the establishment of the Universal Postal Union supplies were sent to Berne for distribution to the postal administrations of member countries.

During the period 1884 to 1928 most of the stamps of British Crown Colonies required for this purpose were overprinted SPECIMEN in various shapes and sizes by their printers from typeset formes. Some locally produced provisionals were handstamped locally, as were sets prepared for presentation. From 1928 stamps were punched with holes forming the word SPECIMEN, each firm of printers using a different machine or machines. From 1948 the stamps supplied for U.P.U. distribution were no longer punctured.

Stamps of some other Commonwealth territories were overprinted or handstamped locally, while stamps of Great Britain and those overprinted for use in overseas postal agencies (mostly of the higher denominations) bore SPECIMEN overprints and handstamps applied by the Inland Revenue or the Post Office.

SPECIMEN ⋯⋯ SPECIMEN
De La Rue & Co. Ltd.

SPECIMEN. ⋯ SPECIMEN.
Bradbury, Wilkinson & Co. Ltd.

SPECIMEN ⋯ SPECIMEN
Waterlow & Sons Ltd.

SPECIMEN SPECIMEN SPECIMEN
Great Britain overprints

Some of the commoner types of overprints or punctures are illustrated here. Collectors are warned that dangerous forgeries of the punctured type exist.

The *Part 1* (*British Commonwealth*) Catalogue records those Specimen overprints or perforations intended for distribution by the U.P.U. to member countries. In addition the Specimen overprints of Australia and its dependent territories, which were sold to collectors by the Post Office, are also included.

All other Specimens are outside the scope of this volume.

Specimens are not quoted in Great Britain as they are fully listed in the Stanley Gibbons *Great Britain Specialised Catalogue*.

In specifying type of specimen for individual high-value stamps, "H/S" means handstamped, "Optd" is overprinted and "Perf" is punctured. Some sets occur mixed, e.g. "Optd/Perf". If unspecified, the type is apparent from the date or it is the same as for the lower values quoted as a set.

Prices. Prices for stamps up to £1 are quoted in sets; higher values are priced singly after the colours, thus "(S. £20)". Where specimens exist in more than one type the price quoted is for the cheapest. Specimen stamps have rarely survived even as pairs; these and strips of three, four or five are worth considerably more than singles.

8. Luminescence

Machines which sort mail electronically have been introduced in recent years. In consequence some countries have issued stamps on fluorescent or phosphorescent papers, while others have marked their stamps with phosphor bands.

The various papers can only be distinguished by ultraviolet lamps emitting particular wavelengths. They are separately listed only when the stamps have some other means of distinguishing them, visible without the use of these lamps. Where this is not so, the papers are recorded in footnotes or headings.

For this Catalogue we do not consider it appropriate that collectors be compelled to have use of an ultraviolet lamp before being able to identify stamps by our listings. Some experience will also be found necessary in interpreting the results given by ultraviolet. Collectors using the lamps, nevertheless, should exercise great care in their use as exposure to their light is extremely dangerous to the eyes.

Phosphor bands are listable, since they are visible to the naked eye (by holding stamps at an angle to the light and looking along them, the bands appear dark). Stamps existing with and without phosphor bands or with differing numbers of bands are given separate listings. Varieties such as double bands, bands omitted, misplaced or printed on the back are not listed.

Detailed descriptions appear at appropriate places in the listings in explanation of luminescent papers; *see*, for example, Australia above No. 308, Canada above Nos. 472 and 611, Cook Is. above No. 249, etc.

For Great Britain, where since 1959 phosphors have played a prominent and intricate part in stamp issues, the main notes above Nos. 599, 723 and after the Decimal Machin issue (No. X841 onwards) should be studied, as well as the footnotes to individual listings where appropriate. In general the classification is as follows.

Stamps with *phosphor bands* are those where a separate cylinder applies the phosphor after the stamps are printed. Issues with "all-over" phosphor have the "band" covering the entire stamp. Parts of the stamp covered by phosphor bands, or the entire surface for "all-over" phosphor versions, appear matt. Stamps on *phosphorised paper* have the phosphor added to the paper coating before the stamps are printed. Issues on this paper have a completely shiny surface.

Further particularisation of phosphor—their methods of printing and the colours they exhibit under ultraviolet—is outside the scope. The more specialised listings should be consulted for this information.

9. Coil Stamps

Stamps issued only in coil form are given full listing. If stamps are issued in both sheets and coils the coil stamps are listed separately only where there is some feature (e.g. perforation or watermark sideways) by which singles can be distinguished. Coil strips containing different stamps *se-tenant* are also listed.

Coil join pairs are too random and too easily faked to permit of listing; similarly ignored are coil stamps which have accidentally suffered an extra row of perforations from the claw mechanism in a malfunctioning vending machine.

10. Booklet Stamps

Stamp booklets are outside the scope of this Catalogue.

Single stamps from booklets are listed if they are distinguishable in some way (such as watermark or perforation) from similar sheet stamps.

Booklet panes are listed where they contain stamps of different denominations *se-tenant*, where stamp-size labels are included, or where such panes are otherwise identifiable. Booklet panes are placed in the listing under the lowest denomination present.

Particular perforations (straight edges) are covered by appropriate notes.

11. Miniature Sheets and Sheetlets

We distinguish between "miniature sheets" and "sheetlets" and this affects the catalogue numbering. An item in sheet form that is postally valid, containing a single stamp, pair, block or set of stamps, with wide, inscribed and/or decorative margins, is a *miniature sheet* if it is sold at post offices as an indivisible entity. As such the Catalogue allots a single **MS** number and describes what stamps make it up. (*See* Great Britain 1978 Historic Buildings, No. MS1058, as an example.) The *sheetlet* or *small sheet* differs in that the individual stamps are intended to be purchased separately for postal purposes. For sheetlets, all the component postage stamps are numbered individually and the composition explained in a footnote. (The 1978 Christmas Island Christmas sheetlet, Nos. 99/107, is an example.) Note that the definitions refer to post office sale—not how items may be subsequently offered by stamp dealers.

Production as sheetlets is a modern marketing development chosen by postal administrations to interest collectors in purchasing the item complete; if he has done so he should, as with all *se-tenant* arrangements, keep the sheetlet intact in his collection.

The Catalogue will in future no longer give full listing to designs, originally issued in normal sheets, which subsequently appear in sheetlets showing changes of colour, perforation, printing process or face value. Such stamps will be covered by footnotes.

12. Forgeries and Fakes

Forgeries. Where space permits, notes are considered if they can give a concise description that will permit unequivocal detection of a forgery. Generalised warnings, lacking detail, are not nowadays inserted, since their value to the collector is problematic.

Fakes. Unwitting fakes are numerous, particularly "new shades" which are colour changelings brought about by exposure to sunlight, soaking in water contaminated with dyes from adherent paper, contact with oil and dirt from a pocketbook, and so on. Fraudulent operators, in addition, can offer to arrange: removal of hinge marks; repairs of thins on white or coloured papers; replacement of missing margins or perforations; reperforating in true or false gauges; removal of fiscal cancellations; rejoining of severed pairs, strips and blocks; and (a major hazard) regumming. Collectors can only be urged to purchase from reputable sources and to insist upon Expert Committee certification where there is any kind of doubt.

The Catalogue can consider footnotes about fakes where these are specific enough to assist in detection.

1935 SILVER JUBILEE CROWN COLONY ISSUE

The Crown Colony Windsor Castle design by Harold Fleury is, surely, one of the most impressive produced in the 20th-century and its reproduction in the recess process by three of the leading stamp-printing firms of the era has provided a subject for philatelic research which has yet to be exhausted.

Each of the three, Bradbury, Wilkinson & Co. and Waterlow and Sons, who both produced fifteen issues, together with De La Rue & Co. who printed fourteen, used a series of vignette (centre) plates coupled with individual frame plates for each value. All were taken from dies made by Waterlow. Several worthwhile varieties exist on the frame plates, but most interest has been concentrated on the centre plates, each of which was used to print a considerable number of different stamps.

Sheets printed by Bradbury, Wilkinson were without printed plate numbers, but it is believed that there were six centre plates of which a number exist in different states due to rechroming. The centre plates were often used in pairs. Stamps from some of these centre plates have revealed a number of prominent plate flaws, the most famous of which, the extra flagstaff, has been eagerly sought by collectors for many years.

Extra flagstaff (Plate "1" R. 9/1)

Short extra flagstaff (Plate "2" R. 2/1)

Lightning conductor (Plate "3" R. 2/5)

Flagstaff on right-hand turret (Plate "5" R. 7/1)

Double flagstaff (Plate "6" R. 5/2)

De La Rue sheets were initially printed with plate numbers, but in many instances these were subsequently trimmed off. Surviving examples do, however, enable a positive identification of six centre plates, 2A, 2B, (2A), (2B), 4 and 4/ to be made. The evidence of sheet markings and plate flaws clearly demonstrates that there were two different pairs of plates numbered 2A 2B. The second pair is designated (2A) (2B) by specialist collectors to avoid further confusion. The number of major plate flaws is not so great as on the Bradbury, Wilkinson sheets, but four examples are included in the catalogue.

Diagonal line by turret (Plate 2A R. 10/2)

Dot to left of chapel (Plate 2B R. 8/3)

Dot by flagstaff (Plate 4 R. 8/4)

Dash by turret (Plate 4/ R. 3/6)

Much less is known concerning the Waterlow centre plate system as the sheets did not show plate numbers. Ten individual plates have, so far, been identified and it is believed that these were used in pairs. The two versions of the kite and log flaw from plate "2" show that this plate exists in two states.

Kite and vertical log (Plate "2A" R. 10/6)

Kite and horizontal log (Plate "2B" R. 10/6)

Abbreviations

Printers

A.B.N. Co	American Bank Note Co, New York.
A. & M.	Alden & Mowbray Ltd, Oxford.
Ashton-Potter	Ashton-Potter Ltd, Toronto.
Aspioti-Elka (Aspiotis)	Aspioti-Elka, Greece.
B.A.B.N.	British American Bank Note Co, Ottawa.
B.D.T.	B.D.T. International Security Printing Ltd, Dublin, Ireland.
B.W.	Bradbury Wilkinson & Co, Ltd.
Cartor	Cartor S.A., L'Aigle, France
C.B.N.	Canadian Bank Note Co, Ottawa.
Continental B.N. Co	Continental Bank Note Co.
Courvoisier	Imprimerie Courvoisier S.A., La-Chaux-de-Fonds, Switzerland.
D.L.R.	De La Rue & Co, Ltd, London, and (from 1961) Bogota, Colombia.
Edila	Editions de l'Aubetin, S.A.
Enschedé	Joh. Enschedé en Zonen, Haarlem, Netherlands.
Format	Format International Security Printers, Ltd, London.
Harrison	Harrison & Sons, Ltd, London
Heraclio Fournier	Heraclio Fournier S.A., Vitoria, Spain.
J.W.	John Waddington Security Print Ltd., Leeds
P.B.	Perkins Bacon Ltd, London.
Questa	Questa Colour Security Printers, Ltd., London
Ueberreuter	Ueberreuter (incorporating Bruder Rosenbaum), Korneuburg, Austria.
Walsall	Walsall Security Printers, Ltd.
Waterlow	Waterlow & Sons, Ltd, London.

General Abbreviations

Alph	Alphabet
Anniv	Anniversary
Comp	Compound (perforation)
Des	Designer; designed
Diag	Diagonal; diagonally
Eng	Engraver; engraved
F.C.	Fiscal Cancellation
H/S	Handstamped
Horiz	Horizontal; horizontally
Imp, Imperf	Imperforate
Inscr	Inscribed
L	Left
Litho	Lithographed
mm	Millimetres
MS	Miniature sheet
N.Y.	New York
Opt(d)	Overprint(ed)
P or P-c	Pen-cancelled
P, Pf or Perf	Perforated
Photo	Photogravure
Pl	Plate
Pr	Pair
Ptd	Printed
Ptg	Printing
R	Right
R.	Row
Recess	Recess-printed
Roto	Rotogravure
Roul	Rouletted

S	Specimen (overprint)
Surch	Surcharge(d)
T.C.	Telegraph Cancellation
T	Type
Typo	Typographed
Un	Unused
Us	Used
Vert	Vertical; vertically
W or wmk	Watermark
Wmk s	Watermark sideways

(†)=Does not exist.
(—) (or blank price column)=Exists, or may exist, but no market price is known.
/ between colours means "on" and the colour following is that of the paper on which the stamp is printed.

Colours of Stamps

Bl (blue); blk (black); brn (brown); car, carm (carmine); choc (chocolate); clar (claret); emer (emerald); grn (green); ind (indigo); mag (magenta); mar (maroon); mult (multicoloured); mve (mauve); ol (olive); orge (orange); pk (pink); pur (purple); scar (scarlet); sep (sepia); turq (turquoise); ultram (ultramarine); verm (vermilion); vio (violet); yell (yellow).

Colour of Overprints and Surcharges

(B.) = blue, (Blk.) = black, (Br.) = brown, (C.) = carmine, (G.) = green, (Mag.) = magenta, (Mve.) = mauve, (Ol.) = olive, (O.) = orange, (P.) = purple, (Pk.) = pink, (R.)=red, (Sil.) = silver, (V.) = violet, (Vm.) or (Verm.) = vermilion, (W.) = white, (Y.) = yellow.

Arabic Numerals

As in the case of European figures, the details of the Arabic numerals vary in different stamp designs, but they should be readily recognised with the aid of this illustration.

• ١ ٢ ٣ ٤ ٥ ٦ ٧ ٨ ٩
0 1 2 3 4 5 6 7 8 9

Specialist Philatelic Societies

British Decimal Stamps Study Circle
Secretary—Mr. P. R. Daniels
70 Moor Park Close, Rainham, Gillingham,
Kent ME8 8QT

Great Britain Philatelic Society
Membership Secretary—Mr. D. S. Glover
10 Rockwood Park, Saint Hill, East
Grinstead, West Sussex RH19 4JX

Great Britain Decimal Stamp Book Study
Circle
Membership Secretary—Mr. A. J. Wilkins
3 Buttermere Close, Brierley Hill, West
Midlands DY5 3SD

Channel Islands Specialists Society
Membership Secretary—Mr. B. Cropp
17 Westlands Avenue, Huntercombe,
Slough, Berkshire SL1 6AG

Ascension Study Circle
Secretary—Dr. R. C. F. Baker
Greys, Tower Road, Whitstable, Kent
CT5 2ER

Bechuanalands and Botswana Society
Secretary—Mr. M. George
P.O. Box 108, St. Albans, Hertfordshire
AL1 3AD

Belize Philatelic Study Circle
Secretary—Mr. C. R. Gambill
730 Collingswood, Corpus Christi, Texas
78412, U.S.A.

Bermuda Collectors Society
Secretary—Mr. T. J. McMahon
Nash Road, Purdy Station, N.Y. 10578,
U.S.A.

British Caribbean Philatelic Study Group
Overseas Director—Mr. R. V. Swarbrick
The Four Winds, 919 Uppingham Road,
Bushby, Leicestershire LE7 9RR

British Society of Australian Philately
Secretary—Mr. A. J. Griffiths
1 Silvertrees, Bricket Wood, Hertfordshire
AL2 3Q7

British West Indies Study Circle
Secretary—Mr. M. Wilson
Timbers, Chequers Road, Tharston,
Norwich, Norfolk NR15 2YA

Burma Philatelic Study Circle
Secretary—Mr. A. Meech
7208-91 Avenue, Edmonton, Alberta,
Canada T6B 0R8

Canadian Philatelic Society of Great Britain
Secretary—Mr. T. E. Almond
2 Filbert Drive, Tilehurst, Reading,
Berkshire RG3 5DZ

Ceylon Study Circle
Secretary—Mr. R.W.P. Frost
42 Lonsdale Road, Cannington, Bridgwater,
Somerset TA5 2JS

Cyprus Study Circle
Secretary—Dr. R. I. Watson
Hayes Hill Cottage, Slinfold, West Sussex
RH13 7SN

East Africa Study Circle
Secretary—Mr. R. Dunstan
Chantry Court, 1 The Close, Warminster,
Wiltshire BA12 9AL

Falklands Islands Study Group
Membership Secretary—Mr. D. W. A.
Jeffery
38 Bradstock Road, Stoneleigh, Epsom,
Surrey KT17 2LH

Gibraltar Philatelic Society
Honorary Secretary—Mr. H. Busto
P.O. Box 270, Gibraltar

Gibraltar Study Circle
Membership Secretary—Mr. B. M. Walker
21 Orchard Street, Aberdeen AB2 3DA

Great Britain Overprints Society
Membership Secretary—Mr. A. H. Bishop
The Coach House, Ridgemount Road,
Sunningdale, Berkshire SL5 9RL

Greater Southern Africa Philatelic Society
Representative—Mr. A. H. Murray
Erlesdene Garden Cottage, Greenwalk,
Bowdon, Altrincham, Cheshire WA14 2SL

Hong Kong Study Circle
Membership Secretary—Mr. P. V. Ball
37 Hart Court, Newcastle-under-Lyme,
Staffordshire ST5 2AL

Indian Ocean Study Circle (Western
Islands)
Secretary—Mrs. D. J. Hopson
Field Acre, Hoe Benham, Newbury,
Berkshire RG16 8PD

India Study Circle
Secretary—Dr. W. Fincham
10 Vallis Way, London W13 0DD

Irish Philatelic Circle
General Secretary—Mr. P. J. Wood
21 Loftus Road, London W12 7EH

King George V Silver Jubilee Study Circle
Secretary—Mr. N. Levinge
11 Broadway, Northampton NN1 4SF

King George VI Collectors Society
Secretary—Mr. F. R. Lockyer, OBE
24 Stourwood Road, Southbourne,
Bournemouth, Dorset BH6 3QP

Malaya Study Group
Membership Secretary—Mr. D. Moon
Holly Cottage, Barrows Road, Cheddar,
Somerset BS27 3BD

Malta Study Circle
Membership Secretary—Mr. D. Ward
40 Kingsman Road, Stanford-le-Hope,
Essex SS17 0JW

New Zealand Society of Great Britain
General Secretary—Mrs. M. Frankcom
Queens House, 34a Tarrant Street,
Arundel, West Sussex BN18 9DJ

Orange Free State Study Circle
Secretary—Mr. J. R. Stroud
28 Oxford Street, Burnham-on-Sea,
Somerset TA8 1LQ

Pacific Islands Study Circle of Great Britain
Honorary Secretary—Mr. J. D. Ray
24 Woodvale Avenue, London SE25 4AE

Papuan Philatelic Society
Secretary—Mr. G. Amedro
45A Main Street, Gorebridge, Midlothian
EH23 4BX

Pitcairn Islands Study Group (U.K.)
Honorary Secretary—Mr. A. B. Meares
Ragnall Cottage, Ragnall Lane, Walkley
Wood, Nailsworth, Stroud, Gloucestershire
GL6 0RX

Rhodesian Study Circle
Membership Secretary—Miss B. J. R.
Lashbrook
25 Exe View, Exminster, Devon EX6 8AL

St. Helena, Ascension and Tristan da Cunha
Philatelic Society
Secretary—Mrs. V. W. Finne
P.O. Box 366, Calpella, California 95418,
U.S.A.

Sarawak Specialists Society (also Brunei,
North Borneo and Labuan)
Secretary—Dr. J. Higgins
The Stone House, Grimston Road, South
Wootton, Kings Lynn, Norfolk PE30 3NR

South African Collectors' Society
General Secretary—Mr. W. A. Page
138 Chastilian Road, Dartford, Kent
DA1 3LG

Sudan Study Group
Secretary—Mr. J. W. Scott
Bemerton, Lingfield Road, East Grinstead,
West Sussex RH19 2EJ

Tonga and Tin Can Mail Study Circle
Secretary—Mr. T. Jackson
121 Mullingar Ct. 1A, Schaumburg,
IL60193-3258, U.S.A.

Transvaal Study Circle
Secretary—Mr. J. Woolgar
132 Dale Street, Chatham, Kent ME4 6QH

Tuvalu and Kiribati Philatelic Society
Secretary—Mr. C. E. Grey
6 Urlwin Walk, Myatts Fields South,
London SW9 6QG

West Africa Study Circle
Secretary—Mr. J. Powell
7 Pebblemoor, Edlesborough, Dunstable,
Bedfordshire LU6 2HZ

Select Bibliography

The literature on British Commonwealth stamps is vast, but works are often difficult to obtain once they are out of print. The selection of books below has been made on the basis of authority together with availability to the general reader, either as new or secondhand. Very specialised studies, and those covering aspects of postal history to which there are no references in the catalogue, have been excluded.

The following abbreviations are used to denote publishers:
CRL–Christie's Robson Lowe; HH–Harry Hayes; PB–Proud Bailey Co. Ltd.; PC–Philip Cockrill; RPSL–Royal Philatelic Society, London; SG–Stanley Gibbons Ltd.

Where no publisher is quoted, the book is published by its author.

GENERAL. *Encyclopaedia of British Empire Postage Stamps. Vols 1–6.* Edited Robson Lowe. (CRL, 1951–1991)
The Commemorative Stamps of the British Commonwealth. H.D.S. Haverbeck. (Faber, 1955)
Specimen Stamps of the Crown Colonies 1857–1948. Marcus Samuel. (RPSL, 1976 and 1984 Supplement)
U.P.U. Specimen Stamps. J. Bendon. (1988)
Silver Jubilee of King George V Stamps Handbook. A.J. Ainscough. (Ainwheel Developments, 1985)
The Printings of King George VI Colonial Stamps. W.J.W. Potter & Lt-Col R.C.M. Shelton. (1952)
King George VI Large Key Type Stamps of Bermuda, Leeward Islands, Nyasaland. R.W. Dickgiesser and E.P. Yendall. (Triad Publications, 1985)
GREAT BRITAIN. For extensive bibliographies see *G.B. Specialised Catalogues. Vols 1–5.*
Channel Islands. *Stamps and Postal History of the Channel Islands.* W. Newport. (Heineman, 1972)
ADEN. *The Postal History of British Aden 1839–67.* Major R.W. Pratt (PB, 1985)
ASCENSION. *Ascension. The Stamps and Postal History.* J.H. Attwood. (CRL, 1981)
BAHAMAS. *The Postage Stamps and Postal History of the Bahamas.* H.G.D. Gisburn. (SG, 1950)
BARBADOS. *The Stamps of Barbados.* E.A. Bayley. (1989)
BASUTOLAND. *The Cancellations and Postal Markings of Basutoland/Lesotho Post Offices.* A.H. Scott. (Collectors Mail Auctions (Pty) Ltd, 1980)
BATUM. *British Occupation of Batum.* P.T. Ashford. (1989)
BRITISH EAST AFRICA. *British East Africa. The Stamps and Postal Stationery.* J. Minns. (RPSL, 1982 and 1990 Supplement)
BRITISH GUIANA. *The Postage Stamps and Postal History of British Guiana.* W.A. Townsend and F.G. Howe. (RPSL, 1970)
BRITISH OCCUPATION OF GERMAN COLONIES. *G.R.I.* R.M. Gibbs. (CRL, 1989)
BRITISH POSTAL AGENCIES IN EASTERN ARABIA. *The Postal Agencies in Eastern Arabia and the Gulf.* N. Donaldson. (HH, 1975)
BRITISH WEST AFRICA. *The Postal History and Handstamps of British West Africa.* C. McCaig. (CRL, 1978)
BRUNEI. *Brunei. The Definitive Issues and Postal Cancellations to 1974.* E. Thorndike. (PC, 1983)
BURMA. *Burma Postal History.* G. Davis and D. Martin. (CRL, 1971 and 1987 Supplement)

CANADA. *Stamps of British North America.* F. Jarrett. (Quarterman Publications Inc, 1975)
The Postage Stamps and Postal History of Canada. W.S. Boggs. (Quarterman Publications Inc, 1974)
The Edward VII Issue of Canada. G.C. Marler. (National Postal Museum, Canada, 1975)
The Admiral Issue of Canada. G.C. Marler. (American Philatelic Society, 1982)
CAPE OF GOOD HOPE. *Postmarks of the Cape of Good Hope.* R. Goldblatt. (Reijger Publishers (Pty) Ltd, 1984)
CAYMAN ISLANDS. *The Postal History of the Cayman Islands.* T.E. Giraldi and P.P. McCann. (Triad Publications, 1989)
COCOS (KEELING) ISLANDS. *Cocos (Keeling) Islands. A Philatelic and Postal History to 1979.* P. Collas & J. Hill. (B. & K. Philatelic Publishing, 1991)
COOK ISLANDS. *The Early Cook Islands Post Office.* A.R. Burge. (Hawthorn Press, 1978)
CYPRUS. *Cyprus 1353–1986.* W. Castle. (CRL, 3rd edition, 1987)
FALKLAND ISLANDS. *The Postage Stamps of the Falkland Islands and Dependencies.* B.S.H. Grant. (SG, 1952)
The De La Rue Definitives of the Falkland Islands 1901–29. J.P. Bunt. (1986)
The Falkland Islands. Printings of the Pictorial Issue of 1938–49. C.E. Glass. (CRL, 1979)
FIJI. *The Postal History of Fiji 1911–1952.* J.G. Rodger. (Pacific Islands Study Circle, 1991)
GAMBIA. *The Stamps and Postal History of the Gambia.* Edited J.O. Andrew. (CRL, 1985)
GIBRALTAR. *Posted in Gibraltar.* W. Hine-Haycock. (CRL, 1978)
HONG KONG. *The Philatelic History of Hong Kong. Vol 1.* (Hong Kong Study Circle, 1984)
British Post Offices in the Far East. E.B. Proud. (PB, 1991)
Cancellations of the Treaty Ports of Hong Kong. H. Schoenfeld. (1988)
INDIA. *India Used Abroad.* V.S. Dastur. (Mysore Philatelics, 1982)
C.E.F. The China Expeditionary Force 1900–1923. D.S. Virk, J.C. Hume, D. Lang, G. Sattin. (Philatelic Congress of India, 1992)
A Handbook on Gwalior Postal History and Stamps. V.K. Gupta. (1980)
KENYA. *The Postal History of Kenya.* E.B. Proud. (PB, 1992)
LABUAN. *A Concise Guide to the Queen Issues of Labuan.* R. Price. (Sarawak Specialists Society, 1991)
MALAYSIA. *The Postal History of British Malaya. Vols 1–3.* E.B. Proud. (PB, 1982–84)
The Postage Stamps of Federated Malay States. W.A. Reeves. (Malaya Study Group, 1978)
Kelantan. Its Stamps and Postal History. W.A. Reeves and B.E. Dexter. (Malaya Study Group, 1992)
The Postal History of the Occupation of Malaya and British Borneo 1941–1945. E.B. Proud and M.D. Rowell. (PB, 1992)
MALTA. *Malta. The Postal History and Postage Stamps.* Edited R.E. Martin. (CRL, 1980 and 1985 Supplement)
MAURITIUS. *The Postal History and Stamps of Mauritius.* P. Ibbotson. (RPSL, 1991)
MOROCCO AGENCIES. *British Post Offices and Agencies in Morocco 1857–1907 and Local Posts 1891–1914.* R.K. Clough. (Gibraltar Study Circle, 1984).
NEWFOUNDLAND. *The Postage Stamps and Postal History of Newfoundland.* W.S. Boggs. (Quarterman Publications, 1975)

NEW SOUTH WALES. *The Postal History of New South Wales 1788–1901.* Edited J.S. White. (Philatelic Assoc of New South Wales, 1988)
NEW ZEALAND. *The Postage Stamps of New Zealand. Vols I–VII.* (Royal Philatelic Society of New Zealand, 1939–88)
The Postal History and Postage Stamps of the Tokelau/Union Islands. A.H. Burgess. (Pacific Islands Study Circle, 1977)
NIGERIA. *The Postal Services of the British Nigeria Region.* J. Ince and J. Sacher. (RPSL, 1992)
NORTH BORNEO. *The Stamps and Postal History of North Borneo. Parts 1–3.* L.H. Shipman and P.K. Cassells. (Sarawak Specialists Society, 1976–88)
ORANGE FREE STATE. *Stamps of the Orange Free State. Parts 1–3.* G.D. Buckley & W.B. Marriott. (Orange Free State Study Circle, 1967–80)
PAPUA. *The Postal History of British New Guinea and Papua 1885–1942.* R. Lee. (CRL, 1983)
RHODESIA. *Mashonaland. A Postal History 1890–96.* A. Drysdall and D. Collis (CRL, 1990)
Rhodesia. A Postal History. R.C. Smith. (1967 and 1970 Supplement)
ST. HELENA. *St. Helena. Postal History and Stamps.* E. Hibbert. (CRL, 1979)
SAMOA. *A Postal History of the Samoan Islands (Parts I and II).* Edited R. Burge. (Royal Philatelic Society of New Zealand, 1987–89)
SARAWAK. *The Stamps and Postal History of Sarawak.* W.A. Forrester-Wood. (Sarawak Specialists Society, 1959 & 1970 Supplement)
Sarawak: The Issues of 1871 and 1875. W. Batty-Smith & W. Watterson.
SIERRA LEONE. *The Postal Service of Sierra Leone.* P.O. Beale. (RPSL, 1988)
SOLOMON ISLANDS. *British Solomon Islands Protectorate. Its Postage Stamps and Postal History.* H.G.D. Gisburn. (T. Sanders (Philatelist) Ltd., 1956)
SOUTH AUSTRALIA. *The Departmental Stamps of South Australia.* A.R. Butler. (RPSL, 1978)
SOUTH WEST AFRICA. *The Overprinted Stamps of South West Africa to 1930.* N. Becker. (Philatelic Holdings (Pty) Ltd, 1990)
SUDAN. *Sudan. The Stamps and Postal Stationery of 1867 to 1970.* E.C.W. Stagg. (HH, 1977)
TANGANYIKA. *The Postal History of Tanganyika. 1915–1961.* E.B. Proud. (PB, 1989)
TASMANIA. *Stamps and Postal History of Tasmania.* W.E. Tinsley. (RPSL, 1986)
The Pictorial Stamps of Tasmania 1899–1912. K.E. Lancaster. (Royal Philatelic Society of Victoria, 1986)
TRANSVAAL. *Transvaal Philately.* Edited I.B. Mathews. (Reijger Publishers (Pty) Ltd, 1986)
TRISTAN DA CUNHA. *The History and Postal History of Tristan da Cunha.* G. Crabb. (1980)
TURKS AND CAICOS ISLANDS. *Turks Islands and Caicos Islands to 1950.* J.J. Challis. (Roses Caribbean Philatelic Society, 1983)
TUVALU. *Tuvalu. A Philatelic Handbook.* M. Forand. (Tuvalu Philatelic Society, 1982)
VICTORIA. *The Stamps of Victoria.* G. Kellow. (B. & K. Philatelic Publishing, 1990)
WESTERN AUSTRALIA. *Western Australia. The Stamps and Postal History.* Edited M. Hamilton and B. Pope. (Western Australia Study Group, 1979)
Postage Stamps and Postal History of Western Australia. Vols 1–3. M. Juhl. (1981–83)

Jamaica

Records show that the first local Postmaster for Jamaica on a regular basis was appointed as early as 1671, although a reasonably organised service did not evolve until 1687–8. In the early years of the 18th century overseas mail was carried by the British packets, but between 1704 and 1711 this service was run on a commercial basis by Edmund Dummer. Following the collapse of the Dummer scheme Jamaica was virtually without a Post Office until 1720 and it was not until 1755 that overseas mail was again carried by British packets.

The stamps of Great Britain were used on the island from 8 May 1858 to August 1860. Although there had been much friction between the local inhabitants and the British G.P.O. it was not until 1 August 1860 that the Jamaica authorities assumed responsibility for the postal service.

KINGSTON

Z 1

Stamps of GREAT BRITAIN cancelled "A 01" as Type Z 1.

1858 to 1860.

Z1	1d. rose-red (1857), *perf* 16	.. .. ..	£170
Z2	1d. rose-red (1857), *perf* 14	.. .. ..	25·00
Z4	4d. rose (1857)	.. .. ..	35·00
Z5	6d. lilac (1856)	.. .. ..	35·00
Z6	1s. green (1856)	.. .. ..	70·00

Z 2

Stamps of GREAT BRITAIN cancelled "A 01" as Type Z 2.

1859 to 1860.

Z 7	1d. rose-red (1857), *perf* 14	..	£160
Z 9	4d. rose (1857)	..	35·00
Z10	6d. lilac (1856)	..	35·00
Z11	1s. green (1856)	..	£225

Z 3

Stamps of GREAT BRITAIN cancelled "A 01" as Type Z 1.

1859 to 1860.

Z12	1d. rose-red (1857), *perf* 14	.. ..	£200
Z14	4d. rose (1857)	.. ..	£120
	a. Thick glazed paper	..	£400
Z15	6d. lilac (1856)	.. ..	£120
Z16	1s. green (1856)	.. ..	£120

Cancellation "A 01" was later used by the London, Foreign Branch Office.

OTHER JAMAICA POST OFFICES

British stamps were issued to several District post offices between 8 May 1858 and 1 March 1859 (i.e. before the Obliterators A 27–A 78 were issued). These can only be distinguished (off the cover) when they have the Town's date-stamp on them. They are worth about three times the price of those with an obliteration number.

Stamps of GREAT BRITAIN cancelled "A 27" to "A 78" as Type Z 1.

1859 to 1860.

"A 27". ALEXANDRIA

Z17	1d. rose-red (1857), *perf* 14	..	£425
Z17a	2d. blue (1855) Large Crown, *perf* 14 (Plate 6)		£475
Z18	4d. rose (1857)	.. ..	£160
Z19	6d. lilac (1856)	.. ..	£375

"A 28". ANNOTTO BAY

Z20	1d. rose-red (1857), *perf* 14	..	£300
Z21	4d. rose (1857)	..	70·00
Z22	6d. lilac (1856)	..	£225

"A 29". BATH

Z23	1d. rose-red (1857), *perf* 14	..	£120
Z24	4d. rose (1857)	..	85·00
Z25	6d. lilac (1856)	..	£400

"A 30". BLACK RIVER

Z26	1d. rose-red (1857), *perf* 14	..	£120
Z27	4d. rose (1857)	..	50·00
Z28	6d. lilac (1856)	..	£120

"A 31". BROWN'S TOWN

Z29	1d. rose-red (1857), *perf* 14	..	£160
Z30	4d. rose (1857)	..	£160
Z31	6d. lilac (1856)	..	£160

"A 32". BUFF BAY

Z32	1d. rose-red (1857), *perf* 14	..	£120
Z33	4d. rose (1857)	..	£150
Z34	6d. lilac (1856)	..	£120

"A 33". CHAPLETON

Z35	1d. rose-red (1857), *perf* 14	..	£160
Z36	4d. rose (1857)	..	95·00
Z37	6d. lilac (1856)	..	£160

"A 34". CLAREMONT

Z38	1d. rose-red (1857), *perf* 14	..	£300
Z39	4d. rose (1857)	..	£150
Z40	6d. lilac (1856)	..	£300

"A 35". CLARENDON
(Near Four Paths)

Z41	1d. rose-red (1857), *perf* 14	..	£250
Z42	4d. rose (1857)	..	£100
Z43	6d. lilac (1856)	..	£160

"A 36". DRY HARBOUR

Z44	1d. rose-red (1857), *perf* 14	..	£375
Z45	4d. rose (1857)	..	£300
Z46	6d. lilac (1856)	..	£250

"A 37". DUNCANS

Z47	1d. rose-red (1857), *perf* 14	..	£375
Z48	4d. rose (1857)	..	£250
Z49	6d. lilac (1856)	..	£250

"A 38". EWARTON

A 38 was sent out to EWARTON but it is believed that this office was closed towards the end of 1858 before it arrived as no genuine used specimens have been found on British stamps.

"A 39". FALMOUTH

Z53	1d. rose-red (1857), *perf* 14	..	75·00
Z54	4d. rose (1857)	..	35·00
Z55	6d. lilac (1856)	..	55·00
Z56	1s. green (1856)	..	£425

"A 40". FLINT RIVER
(Near Hopewell)

Z57	1d. rose-red (1857), *perf* 14	..	£150
Z58	4d. rose (1857)	..	£100
Z59	6d. lilac (1856)	..	£150
Z60	1s. green (1856)	..	£425

"A 41". GAYLE

Z61	1d. rose-red (1857), *perf* 14	..	£450
Z62	4d. rose (1857)	..	£120
Z63	6d. lilac (1856)	..	£130
Z64	1s. green (1856)	..	£170

"A 42". GOLDEN SPRING
(Near Stony Hill)

Z65	1d. rose-red (1857), *perf* 14	..	£170
Z66	4d. rose (1857)	..	£150
Z67	6d. lilac (1856)	..	£400
Z68	1s. green (1856)	..	£425

"A 43". GORDON TOWN

Z69	1d. rose-red (1857), *perf* 14	..	
Z70	4d. rose (1857)	..	
Z71	6d. lilac (1856)	..	£450

"A 44". GOSHEN
(Near Santa Cruz)

Z72	1d. rose-red (1857), *perf* 14	..	£120
Z73	4d. rose (1857)	..	£110
Z74	6d. lilac (1856)	..	50·00

"A 45". GRANGE HILL

Z75	1d. rose-red (1857), *perf* 14	..	£150
Z76	4d. rose (1857)	..	38·00
Z77	6d. lilac (1856)	..	55·00
Z77a	1s. green (1856)	..	£375

"A 46". GREEN ISLAND

Z78	1d. rose-red (1857), *perf* 14	..	£300
Z79	4d. rose (1857)	..	£150
Z80	6d. lilac (1856)	..	£250
Z81	1s. green (1856)	..	£425

"A 47". HIGHGATE

Z82	1d. rose-red (1857), *perf* 14	..	£170
Z83	4d. rose (1857)	..	£110
Z84	6d. lilac (1856)	..	£170

"A 48". HOPE BAY

Z85	1d. rose-red (1857), *perf* 14	..	£400
Z86	4d. rose (1857)	..	£150
Z87	6d. lilac (1856)	..	£400

"A 49". LILLIPUT
(Near Balaclava)

Z88	1d. rose-red (1857), *perf* 14	..	£150
Z89	4d. rose (1857)	..	£150
Z90	6d. lilac (1856)	..	75·00

"A 50". LITTLE RIVER

A 50 was sent out for use at LITTLE RIVER, but it is believed that this office closed late in 1858, before the obliterator could be issued. No specimen has yet been found used on British stamps.

"A 51". LUCEA

Z91	1d. rose-red (1857), *perf* 14	..	£225
Z92	4d. rose (1857)	..	48·00
Z93	6d. lilac (1856)	..	£150

"A 52". MANCHIONEAL

Z94	1d. rose-red (1857), *perf* 14	..	£300
Z95	4d. rose (1857)	..	£160
Z96	6d. lilac (1856)	..	

"A 53". MANDEVILLE

Z97	1d. rose-red (1857), *perf* 14	..	£160
Z98	4d. rose (1857)	..	50·00
Z99	6d. lilac (1856)	..	£140

"A 54". MAY HILL
(Near Spur Tree)

Z100	1d. rose-red (1857), *perf* 14	..	75·00
Z101	4d. rose (1857)	..	75·00
Z102	6d. lilac (1856)	..	50·00

"A 55". MILE GULLY

Z103	1d. rose-red (1857), *perf* 14	..	£250
Z104	4d. rose (1857)	..	£150
Z105	6d. lilac (1856)	..	£150

"A 56". MONEAGUE

Z106	1d. rose-red (1857), *perf* 14	..	£150
Z107	4d. rose (1857)	..	£190
Z108	6d. lilac (1856)	..	£400

"A 57". MONTEGO BAY

Z109	1d. rose-red (1857), *perf* 14	..	£160
Z110	4d. rose (1857)	..	40·00
Z111	6d. lilac (1856)	..	50·00
Z112	1s. green (1856)	..	£425

"A 58". MONTPELIER

Z113	1d. rose-red (1857), *perf* 14	..	
Z114	4d. rose (1857)	..	
Z115	6d. lilac (1856)	..	£650

"A 59". MORANT BAY

Z116	1d. rose-red (1857), *perf* 14	..	£300
Z117	4d. rose (1857)	..	50·00
Z118	6d. lilac (1856)	..	50·00

"A 60". OCHO RIOS

Z119	1d. rose-red (1857), *perf* 14	..	
Z120	4d. rose (1857)	..	75·00
Z121	6d. lilac (1856)	..	£140

"A 61". OLD HARBOUR

Z122	1d. rose-red (1857), *perf* 14	..	£150
Z123	4d. rose (1857)	..	£110
Z124	6d. lilac (1856)	..	£110

"A 62". PLANTAIN GARDEN RIVER
(Near Golden Grove)

Z125	1d. rose-red (1857), *perf* 14	..	£110
Z126	4d. rose (1857)	..	80·00
Z127	6d. lilac (1856)	..	£110

"A 63". PEAR TREE GROVE

No genuine specimen of A 63 has been found on a British stamp.

"A 64". PORT ANTONIO

Z131	1d. rose-red (1857), *perf* 14	..	£375
Z132	4d. rose (1857)	..	£225
Z133	6d. lilac (1856)	..	£225

"A 65". PORT MORANT

Z134	1d. rose-red (1857), *perf* 14	..	£225
Z135	4d. rose (1857)	..	85·00
Z136	6d. lilac (1856)	..	£225

"A 66". PORT MARIA

Z137	1d. rose-red (1857), *perf* 14	..	£150
Z138	4d. rose (1857)	..	55·00
Z139	6d. lilac (1856)	..	£225

"A 67". PORT ROYAL

Z140	1d. rose-red (1857), *perf* 14			£300
Z140a	2d. blue (1858) (plate 9)			£300
Z141	4d. rose (1857)			£300
Z142	6d. lilac (1856)			£300

"A 68". PORUS

Z143	1d. rose-red (1857), *perf* 14			£150
Z144	4d. rose (1857)			70·00
Z145	6d. lilac (1856)			£300

"A 69". RAMBLE

Z146	1d. rose-red (1857), *perf* 14			£150
Z147	4d. rose (1857)			£150
	a. Thick glazed paper			£400
Z149	6d. lilac (1856)			£225

"A 70". RIO BUENO

Z150	1d. rose-red (1857), *perf* 14			
Z151	4d. rose (1857)			£130
Z152	6d. lilac (1856)			85·00

"A 71". RODNEY HALL
(Now called Linstead)

Z153	1d. rose-red (1857), *perf* 14			£120
Z154	4d. rose (1857)			80·00
Z155	6d. lilac (1856)			£110

"A 72". SAINT DAVID
(Now called Yallahs)

Z156	1d. rose-red (1857), *perf* 14			£150
Z157	4d. rose (1857)			£300
Z158	6d. lilac (1856)			

"A 73". ST. ANN'S BAY

Z159	1d. rose-red (1857), *perf* 14			£150
Z160	4d. rose (1857)			75·00
Z161	6d. lilac (1856)			£150

"A 74". SALT GUT
(Near Oracabessa)

Z162	1d. rose-red (1857), *perf* 14			£140
Z163	4d. rose (1857)			
Z164	6d. lilac (1856)			£150

"A 75". SAVANNA-LA-MAR

Z165	1d. rose-red (1857), *perf* 14			75·00
Z166	4d. rose (1857)			40·00
Z167	6d. lilac (1856)			£150
Z168	1s. green (1856)			£375

"A 76". SPANISH TOWN

Z169	1d. rose-red (1857), *perf* 14			85·00
Z170	4d. rose (1857)			40·00
Z171	6d. lilac (1856)			85·00
Z172	1s. green (1856)			£250

"A 77". STEWART TOWN

Z173	1d. rose-red (1857), *perf* 14			£400
Z174	4d. rose (1857)			£250
Z175	6d. lilac (1856)			£150

"A 78". VERE
(Now called Alley)

Z176	1d. rose-red (1857), *perf* 14			£225
Z177	4d. rose (1857)			75·00
Z178	6d. lilac (1856)			50·00
Z179	1s. green (1856)			£425

The use of British stamps in Jamaica after August 1860 for civilian mail was unauthorised by the P.M.G. of Great Britain.

PRICES FOR STAMPS ON COVER

Nos. 1/6	*from* × 4
Nos. 7/15	*from* × 6
Nos. 16/26	*from* × 8
Nos. 27/9	*from* × 6
No. 30	*from* × 5
Nos. 31/2	*from* × 15
Nos. 33/6	*from* × 5
Nos. 37/56	*from* × 5
No. 57	*from* × 4
Nos. 58/67	*from* × 3
Nos. 68/77	*from* × 6
Nos. 78/89	*from* × 3
Nos. 90/103	*from* × 4
Nos. 104/7	*from* × 5
Nos. 108/17	*from* × 4
Nos. 118/20	*from* × 5
Nos. 121/33a	*from* × 4
Nos. 134/40	*from* × 8
Nos. F1/9	*from* × 3
Nos. O1/5	*from* × 30

CROWN COLONY

PRINTERS. Until 1923, all the stamps of Jamaica were typographed by De La Rue & Co, Ltd, London, *unless otherwise stated.*

The official dates of issue are given, where known, but where definite information is not available the dates are those of earliest known use, etc.

CONDITION. Mint or fine used specimens of stamps with the pineapple watermark are rarely met with and are worth considerably more than our prices which are for stamps in average condition. Inferior specimens can be supplied at much lower prices.

1

2

3

4

5

6

7

A

1860 (23 Nov)–63. W 7. P 14.

1	1	1d. pale blue		60·00	15·00
		a. Pale greenish blue		65·00	19·00
		b. Blue		50·00	12·00
		c. Deep blue		95·00	28·00
		d. Bisected (½d.) (11.61) (on cover)			£650
2	2	2d. rose		£190	45·00
		a. Deep rose		£120	45·00
3	3	3d. green (10.9.63)		£130	25·00
4	4	4d. brown-orange		£200	38·00
		a. Red-orange		£200	22·00
5	5	6d. dull lilac		£180	18·00
		a. Grey-purple		£275	32·00
		b. Deep purple		£800	40·00
6	6	1s. yellow-brown		£450	23·00
		a. Purple-brown		£500	23·00
		b. Dull brown		£180	27·00
		c. "$" for "S" in "SHILLING" (A)		£1600	£600

The diagonal bisection of the 1d. was authorized by a P.O. notice dated 20 November 1861. Specimens are only of value when on original envelope or wrapper. The authority was withdrawn as from 1 December 1872. Fakes are frequently met with. Other bisections were unauthorized.

The so-called "dollar variety" of the 1s. occurs once in each sheet of stamps in all shades and in later colours, etc, on the second stamp in the second row of the left upper pane. The prices quoted above are for the dull brown shade, the prices for the other shades being proportionate to their normal value.

All values except the 3d. are known imperf, mint only.

There are two types of watermark in the 3d. and 1s., one being short and squat and the other elongated.

8

9

10

1870–83. Wmk Crown CC. (a) P 14.

7	8	½d. claret (29.10.72)		12·00	3·50
		a. Deep claret (1883)		13·00	3·50
8	1	1d. blue (4.73)		48·00	75
		a. Deep blue		50·00	1·50
9	2	2d. rose (4.70)		50·00	70
		a. Deep rose		70·00	85
10	3	3d. green (1.70)		90·00	7·50
11	4	4d. brown-orange (1872)		£150	9·00
		a. Red-orange		£350	6·00
12	5	6d. mauve (10.3.71)		50·00	5·50
13	6	1s. dull-brown (*to* deep) (23.2.73)		25·00	8·50
		a. "$" for "S" in "SHILLING" (A)		£1100	£600

(b) P 12½

14	9	2s. Venetian red (27.8.75)		40·00	15·00
15	10	5s. lilac (27.8.75)		90·00	£130
7/15			Set of 9	£450	£150

The ½d., 1d., 4d., 2s. and 5s. are known imperforate.

1883–97. Wmk Crown CA. P 14.

16	8	½d. yellow-green (1885)		2·25	30
		a. Green		80	10
17	1	1d. blue (1884)		£350	4·50
18		1d. rose (*to* deep) (3.3.85)		48·00	75
		a. Carmine		24·00	50
19	2	2d. rose (*to* deep) (17.3.84)		£150	3·75
20		2d. grey (1885)		55·00	1·50
		a. Slate		42·00	50
21	3	3d. sage-green (1886)		4·00	85
		a. Pale olive-green		2·50	1·00
22	4	4d. red-orange* (9.3.83)		£350	20·00
		a. Red-brown (shades)		2·00	35
23	5	6d. deep yellow (4.10.90)		16·00	6·00
		a. Orange-yellow		4·00	3·50
24	6	1s. brown (*to* deep) (3.97)		5·00	4·50
		a. "$" for "S" in "SHILLING" (A)		£850	£450
		b. Chocolate		15·00	11·00
25	9	2s. Venetian red (1897)		27·00	17·00
26	10	5s. lilac (1897)		48·00	48·00
16/26			Set of 11	£550	80·00

16, 18, 20, 21, 22 and 23 Optd "Specimen"   *Set of 6* £450

*No. 22 is the same colour as No. 11a.

The 1d. carmine, 2d. slate, and 2s. are known imperf. All values to the 6d. inclusive are known perf 12. These are proofs.

NEW INFORMATION

The editor is always interested to correspond with people who have new information that will improve or correct the Catalogue.

11

TWO PENCE HALF-PENNY

(12)

1889–91. *Value tablet in second colour. Wmk Crown CA. P* 14.

27	11	1d. purple and mauve (8.3.89)		2·25	10
28		2d. green (8.3.89)		18·00	3·50
		a. Deep green (brown gum)		4·50	6·00
29		2½d. dull purple and blue (25.2.91)		4·75	40
27/9			Set of 3	10·50	3·50
27/9 Optd "Specimen"			Set of 3	£100	

A very wide range of shades may be found in the 1d. The headplate was printed in many shades of purple, and the duty-plate in various shades of mauve and purple and also in carmine, etc. There are fewer shades for the other values and they are not so pronounced.

1890 (4(?) June). *No. 22a surch with T* 12 *by C. Vendyres, Kingston.*

30	4	2½d. on 4d. red-brown		27·00	8·50
		a. Spacing between lines of surch 1½ mm		32·00	17·00
		b. Surch double		£325	£225
		c. "PFNNY" for "PENNY"		75·00	65·00
		ca. Ditto and broken "K" for "Y"		£130	£110

This provisional was issued pending receipt of No. 29 which is listed above for convenience of reference.

Three settings exist. (1) Ten varieties arranged in a single vertical row and repeated six times in the pane. (2) Twelve varieties, in two horizontal rows of six, repeated five times, alternate rows show 1 and 1½ mm spacing between lines of surcharge. (3) Three varieties, arranged horizontally and repeated twenty times. All these settings can be reconstructed by examination of the spacing and relative position of the words of the surcharge and of the broken letters, etc, which are numerous.

A variety reading "PFNNK", with the "K" unbroken, is a forgery. Varieties c. and ca. may be found in the double surcharge.

Surcharges misplaced either horizontally or vertically are met with, the normal position being central at the foot of the stamp with "HALF-PENNY" covering the old value.

13 Llandovery Falls, Jamaica   14 Arms of Jamaica
(photo by Dr. J. Johnston)

(Recess D.L.R.)

1900–1. Wmk Crown CC (sideways). P 14.

31	13	1d. red (1.5.00)		1·00	10
32		1d. slate-black and red (25.9.01)		1·75	10
		a. Blued paper		£110	£100
		b. Imperf between (pair)		£5500	
31/32 Optd "Specimen"			Set of 2	£130	

Many shades exist of both centre and frame of the bi-coloured 1d. which was, of course, printed from two plates and the design shows minor differences from that of the 1d. red which was printed from a single plate.

(Typo D.L.R.)

1903–4. Wmk Crown CA. P 14.

33	14	½d. grey and dull green (16.11.03)		1·50	10
		a. "SER.ET" for "SERVIET"		40·00	45·00
34		1d. grey and carmine (24.2.04)		1·50	10
		a. "SER.ET" for "SERVIET"		32·00	35·00
35		2½d. grey and ultramarine (16.11.03)		2·25	30
		a. "SER.ET" for "SERVIET"		60·00	70·00
36		5d. grey and yellow (1.3.04)		12·00	23·00
		a. "SER.ET" for "SERVIET"		£600	£700
33/6			Set of 4	16·00	23·00
33/6 Optd "Specimen"			Set of 4	£500	

The "SER.ET" variety occurs once in each sheet of stamps on the second stamp in the fourth row of the left upper pane.

The centres of the above and later bi-coloured stamps in the Arms type vary in colour from grey to grey-black.

15 Arms type redrawn   16

1905–11. *Wmk Mult Crown CA. P* 14 *(a) Arms types. Chalk-surfaced paper.*

37	14	½d. grey and dull green (24.11.05)		5·50	20
		a. "SER.ET" for "SERVIET"		32·00	32·00
38	15	½d. yell-grn (ordinary paper) (8.11.06)		6·00	40
		a. Dull green		3·75	20
		b. Deep green		3·75	20
39	14	1d. grey and carmine (20.11.05)		17·00	25
40	16	1d. carmine (ordinary paper) (1.10.06)		1·25	10
41	14	2½d. grey and ultramarine (12.11.07)		2·75	1·00
42		2½d. pale ultramarine (ordinary paper) (21.9.10)		2·50	1·25
		a. Deep ultramarine		2·50	1·25
43		5d. grey and orange-yellow (24.4.07)		32·00	38·00
		a. "SER.ET" for "SERVIET"		£800	£900
44		6d. dull and bright purple (18.8.11)		12·00	12·00
45		5s. grey and violet (11.05)		40·00	30·00
37/45			Set of 9	£100	£130

38, 40, 42, 44, 45 Optd "Specimen"   *Set of 5* £130

See note below No. 36 concerning grey centres.

(b) Queen Victoria types. Ordinary paper

46	3	3d. olive-green (15.5.05)	..	6·00	1·50
		a. Sage-green (1907)	..	5·00	1·25
47		3d. purple/yellow (10.3.10)	..	4·25	2·50
		a. Chalk-surfaced paper. Pale purple yellow (11.7.10)	..	2·00	1·40
48	4	4d. red-brown (6.6.08)	..	70·00	38·00
49		4d. black/yellow (chalk-surfaced paper) (21.9.10)	..	7·00	25·00
50		4d. red/yellow (3.10.11)	..	1·50	5·00
51	5	6d. dull orange (27.6.06)	..	15·00	22·00
		a. Golden yellow (9.09)	..	22·00	32·00
52		6d. lilac (19.11.09)	..	22·00	22·00
		a. Chalk-surfaced paper. Purple (7.10)	..	7·00	11·00
53	6	1s. brown (11.06)	..	17·00	12·00
		a. Deep brown	..	27·00	17·00
		b. "$" for "S" in "SHILLING" (A)	..	£900	£900
54		1s. black/green (chalk-surfaced paper) (21.9.10)	..	3·75	8·50
		a. "$" for "S" in "SHILLING" (A)	..	£800	£1000
55	9	2s. Venetian red (11.08)	..	90·00	£120
56		2s. purple/blue (chalk-surfaced paper) (21.9.10)	..	6·00	3·50
46/56		.. .. ..	Set of 11	£190	£225

47, 49, 50, 52, 54, 56 Optd "Specimen" Set of 6 £170

17   **18**

(T 17/18 typo D.L.R.)

1911 (3 Feb). *Wmk Mult Crown CA. P 14.*

57	17	2d. grey (Optd S. £35)	..	1·75	13·00

1912–20. *Wmk Mult Crown CA. Chalk-surfaced paper (3d. to 5s.). P 14.*

58	18	1d. carmine-red (5.12.12)	..	45	10
		a. Scarlet (1916)	..	30	20
59		1½d. brown-orange (13.7.16)	..	1·00	20
		a. Yellow-orange	..	8·00	1·00
		b. Wmk sideways	..	† £1300	
60		2d. grey (2.8.12)	..	90	1·75
		a. Slate-grey	..	1·00	3·00
61		2½d. blue (13.2.13)	..	40	15
		a. Deep bright blue	..	65	45
62		3d. purple/yellow (6.3.12)	..	40	45
		a. White back (2.4.13)	..	55	40
		b. On lemon (25.9.16) (Optd S. £32)	..	3·50	1·25
63		4d. black and red/yellow (4.4.13)	..	50	1·75
		a. White back (7.5.14)	..	50	3·00
		b. On lemon (1916) (Optd S. £32)	..	18·00	18·00
		c. On pale yellow (1919)	..	22·00	14·00
64		6d. dull and bright purple (14.11.12)	..	4·25	8·50
		a. Dull purple and bright mauve (1915)	..	70	1·00
		b. Dull purple & bright magenta (1920)	..	2·25	2·25
65		1s. black/green (2.8.12)	..	2·25	2·00
		a. White back (4.1.15)	..	70	3·50
		b. On blue-green, olive back (1920)	..	2·25	4·00
66		2s. purple and bright blue/blue (10.1.19)	..	10·00	10·00
67		5s. green and red/yellow (5.9.19)	..	35·00	55·00
		a. On pale yellow	..	45·00	60·00
		b. On orange-buff	..	£100	£130
58/67		.. .. ..	Set of 10	45·00	70·00

58/67 Optd "Specimen" Set of 10 £190

For the ½d. and 6d. with Script wmk see Nos. 89a/90.

The paper of No. 67 is a bright yellow and the gum rough and dull. No. 67a is on practically the normal creamy "pale yellow" paper, and the gum is smooth and shiny. The paper of No. 67b approaches the "coffee" colour of the true "orange-buff", and the colours of both head and frame are paler, the latter being of a carmine tone.

RED CROSS LABELS. A voluntary organization, the Jamaica War Stamp League later the Jamaica Patriotic Stamp League, was founded in November 1915 by Mr. Lewis Ashenheim, a Kingston solicitor. The aims of the League were to support the British Red Cross, collect funds for the purchase of aircraft for the Royal Flying Corps and the relief of Polish Jews.

One fund-raising method used was the sale, from 1 December 1915, of ½d. charity labels. These labels, which were available from post offices, depicted a bi-plane above a cross and were printed in red by Dennison Manufacturing Company, Framingham, U.S.A., the stamps being perforated 12 except for those along the edges of the sheet which have one side imperforate.

From 22 December 1915 supplies of the labels were overprinted "JAMAICA" in red, the colour of this overprint being changed to black from 15 January 1916. Copies sold from 11 March 1916 carried an additional "Half-Penny" surcharge, also in black.

Such labels had no postal validity when used by the general public, but, by special order of the Governor, were accepted for the payment of postage on the League's official mail. To obtain this concession the envelopes were to be inscribed "Red Cross Business" or "Jamaica Patriotic Stamp League" and the labels used endorsed with Mr. Ashenheim's signature. Such covers are rare.

WAR STAMP.	WAR STAMP.	WAR STAMP.
(19)	(20)	(21)

(T 19/21 optd locally)

1916 (1 Apr–Sept). *Optd with T 19.*

68	15	½d. yellow-green	..	10	35
		a. No stop after "STAMP" (R. 18/2)	..	7·50	18·00
		b. Opt double	..	95·00	95·00
		c. Opt inverted	..	80·00	90·00
		d. Space between "W" and "A" (R. 20/1)	..	7·50	18·00
		e. Blue-green	..	10	50
		ea. No stop after "STAMP" (R. 3/11 or 11/1)	..	7·50	18·00
		eb. Space between "W" and "A" (R. 20/1)	..	7·50	18·00

69	18	3d. purple/yellow (white back)	..	4·00	14·00
		a. On lemon (6.16)	..	1·00	13·00
		ab. No stop after "STAMP" (R. 8/6 or 9/6)	22·00	60·00
		b. On pale yellow (9.16)	..	3·75	17·00

Minor varieties: ½d. (i) Small "P"; (ii) "WARISTAMP" (raised quad between words); (iii) Two stops after "STAMP". 3d. "WARISTAMP". There were several settings of the overprint used for each value. Where two positions are quoted for a variety these did not occur on the same sheet.

NOTE. The above and succeeding stamps with "WAR STAMP" overprint were issued for payment of a special war tax on letters and postcards or on parcels. Ordinary unoverprinted stamps could also be used for this purpose.

1916 (Sept–Dec). *Optd with T 20.*

70	15	½d. blue-green (shades) (2.10.16)	..	10	30
		a. No stop after "STAMP" (R. 5/7)	..	9·00	25·00
		b. Opt omitted (in pair with normal)	..	£700	£600
		c. "R" inserted by hand (R. 11/10)	..	£400	£325
71	18	1½d. orange (1.9.16)	..	10	15
		aa. Wmk sideways	..	—	£1200
		a. No stop after "STAMP" (R. 4/12, 8/6, 10/10, 11/1, 18/12, 19/12)	..	5·00	5·50
		b. "S" in "STAMP" omitted (R. 6/12) (Dec)	..	£100	£110
		c. "S" inserted by hand	..	£250	
		d. "R" in "WAR" omitted (R. 1/10)	..	£550	£475
		e. "R" inserted by hand	..	£350	£300
		f. Inverted "d" for "P"	..	£150	£120
72		3d. purple/lemon (2.10.16)	..	25	90
		aa. Opt inverted	..	£325	
		a. No stop after "STAMP" (R. 5/7)	..	20·00	45·00
		b. "S" in "STAMP" omitted (R. 6/12) (Dec)	..	£275	£225
		c. "S" inserted by hand	..	£180	£180
		d. "S" inserted inverted	..	£275	£225
		e. On yellow (12.16)	..	6·00	9·00
		ea. "S" in "STAMP" omitted (R. 6/12)	..	£350	£250
		eb. "S" inserted by hand	..	£275	£180
		ec. "S" inserted inverted	..	£325	£225

Minor varieties, such as raised quads, small stop, double stop, spaced letters and letters of different sizes, also exist in this overprint. The setting was altered several times.

1917 (March). *Optd with T 21.*

73	15	½d. blue-green (shades) (25.3.17)	..	10	20
		a. No stop after "STAMP" (R. 2/5, 8/11, 8/12)	..	7·50	18·00
		b. Stop inserted and "P" impressed a second time (R. 7/6)	..	£140	
		c. Optd on back only	..	95·00	
		d. Opt inverted	..	9·50	25·00
74	18	1½d. orange (3.3.17)	..	10	10
		aa. Wmk sideways	..	—	£1300
		a. No stop after "STAMP" (R. 2/5, 8/11, 8/12)	..	7·50	16·00
		b. Stop inserted and "P" impressed a second time (R. 7/6)	..	£190	
		c. Opt double	..	80·00	85·00
		d. Opt inverted	..	80·00	75·00
75		3d. purple/yellow (3.3.17)	..	15	30
		a. No stop after "STAMP" (R. 2/5, 8/11, 8/12)	..	13·00	23·00
		b. Stop inserted and "P" impressed a second time (R. 7/6)	..	£170	
		c. Opt inverted	..	£140	
		d. Opt sideways (reading up)	..	£300	
		da. Opt omitted (in horiz pair with No. 75d)	..	£1600	

No. 75da shows the left-hand stamp as No. 75d and the right-hand stamp without overprint.

There are numerous minor varieties in this overprint with the setting being altered several times.

WAR STAMP
(22)

1919 (4 Oct). *Optd with T 22 by D.L.R.*

76	15	½d. green (R.)	..	10	15
77	18	3d. purple/yellow (R.)	..	1·40	3·00
		a. Pale purple/buff (R.)	..	75	1·25
		b. Deep purple/buff (R.)	..	4·25	6·00

76/7 Optd "Specimen" Set of 2 70·00

We list the most distinct variations in the 3d. The buff tone of the paper varies considerably in depth.

23 Jamaica Exhibition 1891   **24** Arawak Woman preparing Cassava

25 War Contingent embarking   **26** King's House, Spanish Town

Re-entry. Nos. 80a, 93a

The greater part of the design is re-entered, the hull showing in very solid colour and the people appear very blurred. There are also minor re-entries on stamps above (R. 7/4 and 6/4).

27 Return of War Contingent   A   B

28 Landing of Columbus   **29** Cathedral, Spanish Town

34

(Typo (½d., 1d.), recess (others) D.L.R.)

1919–21. *T 23/29, 34 and similar vert designs. Wmk Mult Crown CA (sideways on 1d., 1½d. and 10s.). Chalk-surfaced paper (½d., 1d.). P 14.*

78	23	½d. green and olive-green (12.11.20)	..	50	40
79	24	1d. carmine and orange (3.10.21)	..	1·75	1·10
80	25	1½d. green (shades) (4.7.19)	..	30	35
		a. Major re-entry (R. 8/4)	..	60·00	
81	26	3d. indigo and green (18.2.21)	..	1·00	2·50
82	27	2½d. deep blue and blue (A) (18.2.21)	..	11·00	3·00
		a. Blue-black and deep blue (A)	..	90	90
83	28	3d. myrtle-green and blue (8.4.21)	..	1·50	90
84	29	4d. brown and deep green (21.2.21)	..	2·50	6·50
85	—	1s. orange-yell & red-orge (10.12.20)	£18000	£13000
		a. Frame inverted			
86	—	2s. light blue and brown (10.12.20)	..	13·00	22·00
87	—	3s. violet-blue and orange (10.12.20)	..	20·00	55·00
88	—	5s. blue and yellow-orange (15.4.21)	..	48·00	50·00
		a. Blue and pale dull orange	..	45·00	48·00
89	34	10s. myrtle-green (6.5.20)	..	75·00	£140
78/89		.. .. ..	Set of 12	£140	£250

78/89 Optd "Specimen" Set of 12 £250

Designs: *Vert*—1s. Statue of Queen Victoria, Kingston; 2s. Admiral Rodney Memorial; 3s. Sir Charles Metcalfe Monument; 5s. Jamaican scenery.

The 2½d. of the above series showed the Union Jack at left, incorrectly, as indicated in illustration A. In the issue on paper with Script wmk the design was corrected (Illustration B).

A 6d. stamp showing the reading of the Declaration of Freedom from Slavery in 1836 was prepared and sent out in April 1921, but for political reasons was not issued and the stock was destroyed. Copies overprinted "Specimen" are known on both the Mult CA and Script CA papers, and are worth £500 each. Price without "Specimen" on Script CA £14000.

"Bow" flaw (R.18/12)

1921 (21 Oct)–**27.** *Wmk Mult Script CA. Chalk-surfaced paper* (6d.). *P* 14.

89a	**18**	½d. green (Optd S. £45) (3.11.27)	..	30	10
		ab. Bow flaw		22·00	
90		6d. dull pur & brt magenta (Optd S. £35)		5·50	3·00

35 "POSTAGE & REVENUE" added   **36** "Port Royal in 1853" (A. Duperly)

(Printing as before; the 6d. recess-printed)

1921–29. *As Nos. 78/89. Wmk Mult Script CA* (sideways on 1d. and 1½d.). *Chalk-surfaced paper* (½d., 1d.). *P* 14.

91	**23**	½d. green and olive-green (5.2.22)	..	50	15
		a. Green and deep olive-green		25	10
92	**35**	1d. carmine and orange (5.12.22)		1·50	10
93	**25**	1½d. green (shades) (2.2.21)		30	15
		a. Major re-entry (R. 8/4)	..	60·00	
94	**26**	2d. indigo and green (4.11.21)	..	3·25	30
		a. Indigo and grey-green (1925)	..	3·75	35
95	**27**	2½d. deep blue and blue (B) (4.11.21)	..	5·50	90
		a. Dull blue and blue (B)		6·00	45
96	**28**	3d. myrtle-green and blue (6.3.22)	..	1·50	30
		a. Green and pale blue		40	15
97	**29**	4d. brown and deep green (5.12.21)	..	50	15
		a. Chocolate and dull green		40	15
98	**36**	6d. black and blue (5.12.22)	..	10·00	85
		a. Grey and dull blue	..	6·50	60
99	—	1s. orange and red-orange (4.11.21)		1·40	65
		a. Orange-yellow and brown-orange	..	75	20
100	—	2s. light blue and brown (5.2.22)	..	2·50	35
101	—	3s. violet-blue and orange (23.8.21)		6·50	9·50
102	—	5s. blue and yellow-brown (8.11.23)		25·00	25·00
		a. Blue and pale dull orange	..	50·00	55·00
		b. Blue and yellow-orange (1927)		22·00	22·00
		c. Blue and pale bistre-brown (1929)		22·00	22·00
103	**34**	10s. myrtle-green (March (?) 1922)		48·00	60·00
91/103			Set of 13	85·00	85·00
91/103 Optd "Specimen"			Set of 13	£250	

The frame of No. 102a is the same colour as that of No. 88a.

The designs of all values of the pictorial series, with the exception of the 5s. and 10s. (which originated with the Governor, Sir Leslie Probyn), were selected by Mr. F. C. Cundall, F.S.A. The 1d. and 5s. were drawn by Miss Cundall, the 3d. by Mrs. Cundall, and the 10s. by De La Rue & Co. The 6d. is from a lithograph. The other designs are from photographs, the frames of all being the work of Miss Cundall and Miss Wood.

37   **38**

39

(Centres from photos by Miss V. F. Taylor. Frames des F. C. Cundall, F.S.A., and drawn by Miss Cundall. Recess B.W.)

1923 (1 Nov). *Child Welfare. Wmk Mult Script CA. P* 12.

104	**37**	½d. +½d. black and green	..	60	3·00
105	**38**	1d. +½d. black and scarlet		1·50	10·00
106	**39**	2½d. +½d. black and blue		7·00	18·00
104/6			Set of 3	8·00	28·00
104/6 Optd "Specimen"			Set of 3	£120	

Sold at a premium of ½d. for the Child Welfare League, these stamps were on sale annually from 1 November to 31 January, until 31 January 1927, when their sale ceased, the remainders being destroyed on 21 February 1927.

40   **41**   **42**

Die I   Die II

(Recess D.L.R.)

1929–32. *Wmk Mult Script CA. P* 14.

108	**40**	1d. scarlet (Die I)	..	50	10
		a. Die II (1932)		70	10
109	**41**	1½d. chocolate	..	50	15
110	**42**	9d. maroon	..	2·50	1·00
108/10			Set of 3	3·25	1·10
108/10 Perf "Specimen"			Set of 3	75·00	

In Die I the shading below JAMAICA is formed of thickened parallel lines, and in Die II of diagonal cross-hatching.

43 Coco Palms at Don Christopher's Cove   **44** Wag Water River, St. Andrew

45 Priestman's River, Portland

(Dies eng and recess Waterlow)

1932. *Wmk Mult Script CA* (sideways on 2d. and 2½d.). *P* 12½.

111	**43**	2d. black and green (late 1932)	..	4·50	1·50
		a. Imperf between (vert pair)	..	£5000	
112	**44**	2½d. turquoise-blue & ultram (5.3.32)	..	80	70
		a. Imperf between (vert pair)	..	£6500	£6500
113	**45**	6d. grey-black and purple (2.32)	..	4·00	1·25
111/13			Set of 3	8·50	3·00
111/13 Perf "Specimen"			Set of 3	75·00	

46 Windsor Castle

(Des H. Fleury. Recess B.W.)

1935 (6 May). *Silver Jubilee. Wmk Mult Script CA. P* 11×12.

114	**46**	1d. deep blue and scarlet	..	20	15
		d. Flagstaff on right-hand turret	..	48·00	
115		1½d. ultramarine and grey-black	..	40	45
		a. Extra flagstaff	..	75·00	£100
		b. Short extra flagstaff		60·00	
		c. Lightning conductor		55·00	
116		6d. green and indigo	..	3·50	5·50
		a. Extra flagstaff		£190	£200
		b. Short extra flagstaff		£150	
		c. Lightning conductor		£130	
117		1s. slate and purple	..	3·50	5·50
		a. Extra flagstaff		£275	£350
		b. Short extra flagstaff		£190	
		c. Lightning conductor		£170	
114/17			Set of 4	7·00	10·50
114/17 Perf "Specimen"			Set of 4	75·00	

For illustrations of plate varieties see Omnibus section following Zimbabwe.

47 King George VI and Queen Elizabeth

(Des and recess D.L.R.)

1937 (12 May). *Coronation. Wmk Mult Script CA. P* 14.

118	**47**	1d. scarlet	..	30	15
119		1½d. grey-black	..	50	30
120		2½d. bright blue	..	1·25	70
118/20			Set of 3	1·90	1·00
118/20 Perf "Specimen"			Set of 3	55·00	

48 King George VI   **49** Coco Palms at Don Christopher's Cove

---

50 Bananas

51 Citrus Grove   **52** Kingston Harbour

53 Sugar Industry   **54** Bamboo Walk

55 King George VI   **56** Tobacco Growing and Cigar Making

Repaired chimney (Plate 1 R. 11/1)

(Recess D.L.R. (T 48, 5s. and 10s.), Waterlow (others))

1938–52. *T* **48/56** *and as Nos.* **88,** 112/13, *but with inset portrait of King George VI, as in T* **49.** *Wmk Mult Script CA. P* 13½×14 (½d., 1d., 1½d.), 14 (5s., 10s.) *or* 12½ (others).

121	**48**	½d. blue-green (10.10.38)	..	30	10
		a. Wmk sideways	..	† £2500	
121b		½d. orange (25.10.51)	..	20	30
122		1d. scarlet (10.10.38)	..	20	10
122a		1d. blue-green (25.10.51)	..	30	10
123		1½d. brown (10.10.38)	..	20	10
124	**49**	2d. grey and green	..	20	40
		a. Perf 13×13½	..	35	30
		b. Perf 12½×13 (1951)	..	50	20
125	**44**	2½d. greenish blue and ultramarine	..	1·50	90
126	**50**	3d. ultramarine and green	..	40	50
126a		3d. greenish blue and ultram (15.8.49)		1·50	85
126b		3d. green and scarlet (1.7.52)	..	90	20
127	**51**	4d. brown and green	..	20	10
128	**45**	6d. grey and purple	..	70	30
		a. Perf 13½×13 (10.10.50)	..	70	10
129	**52**	9d. lake	..	30	20
130	**53**	1s. green and purple-brown	..	1·50	10
		a. Repaired chimney	..	£150	80·00
131	**54**	2s. blue and chocolate	..	8·00	70
132	—	5s. slate-blue and yellow-orange	..	9·00	2·25
		a. Perf 14, line (1941)	..	£2250	£130
		b. Perf 13 (24.10.49)	..	6·00	3·00
		ba. Blue and orange (10.10.50)	..	4·00	2·75
133	**55**	10s. myrtle-green	..	11·00	7·00
		aa. Perf 13 (10.10.50)	..	8·50	5·00
133a	**56**	£1 chocolate and violet (15.8.49)	..	26·00	26·00
121/33a			Set of 18	50·00	32·00
121/33 Perf "Specimen"			Set of 13	£180	

No. 132a shows the emergency use of a line perforation machine, giving an irregular gauge of 14–14.15, after the De La Rue works were damaged in December 1940. The normal comb measures 13.8×13.7.

PRICES OF SETS

Set prices are given for many issues, generally those containing three stamps or more. Definitive sets include one of each value or major colour change, but do not cover different perforations, die types or minor shades. Where a choice is possible the set prices are based on the cheapest versions of the stamps included in the listings.

SELF-GOVERNMENT

57 Courthouse, Falmouth | **58** King Charles II and King George VI

59 Institute of Jamaica

(Recess Waterlow)

1945 (20 Aug)–46. *New Constitution. T 57/9 and similar designs. Wmk Mult Script CA. P 12½.*

134	57	1½d. sepia	..	20	20
		a. Perf 12½×13 (1946)	..	1·50	30
135	58	2d. green	..	3·50	70
		a. Perf 12½×13 (1945)	..	20	30
136	59	3d. ultramarine	..	20	20
		a. Perf 13 (1946)	..	70	1·25
137	–	4½d. slate	..	20	25
		a. Perf 13 (1946)	..	70	90
138	–	2s. red-brown	..	30	40
139	–	5s. indigo	..	70	70
140	59	10s. green	..	70	1·50
134/40			Set of 7	2·25	3·25
134/40 Perf "Specimen"			Set of 7	£140	

Designs: *Vert (as T 57)*—2s. "Labour and Learning". *Horiz (as T 59)*—4½d. House of Assembly; 5s. Scroll, flag and King George VI.

60 Houses of Parliament, London

(Des and recess D.L.R.)

1946 (14 Oct). *Victory. Wmk Mult Script CA. P 13½×14.*

141	60	1½d. purple-brown	..	70	10
		a. Perf 13½	..	30	40
142		3d. blue	..	70	65
		a. Perf 13½	..	30	2·50
141/2 Perf "Specimen"			Set of 2	48·00	

61 | **62**
King George VI and Queen Elizabeth

(Des and photo Waterlow (T 61). Design recess, name typo B.W. (T 62))

1948 (1 Dec). *Royal Silver Wedding. Wmk Mult Script CA.*

143	61	1½d. red-brown (p 14×15)	..	30	10
144	62	£1 scarlet (p 11½×11)	..	23·00	42·00

63 Hermes, Globe and Forms of Transport | **64** Hemispheres, Aeroplane and Steamer

65 Hermes and Globe | **66** U.P.U. Monument

(Recess Waterlow (T **63, 66**). Design recess, name typo B.W. (T **64/5**))

1949 (10 Oct). *75th Anniv of Universal Postal Union. Wmk Mult Script CA.*

145	63	1½d. red-brown (p 13½–14)		25	15
146	64	2d. deep blue-green (p 11×11½)		45	1·00
147	65	3d. deep blue (p 11×11½)		45	70
148	66	6d. purple (p 13½–14)		55	1·50
145/8			Set of 4	1·50	3·00

67 Arms of University | **68** Princess Alice

(Recess Waterlow)

1951 (16 Feb). *Inauguration of B.W.I. University College. Wmk Mult Script CA. P 14×14½.*

149	67	2d. black and red-brown	..	30	25
150	68	6d. grey-black and purple	..	35	30

69 Scout Badge and Map of Caribbean | **70** Scout Badge and Map of Jamaica

(Litho B.W.)

1952 (5 Mar). *First Caribbean Scout Jamboree. Wmk Mult Script CA. P 13½×13 (2d.) or 13×13½ (6d.).*

151	69	2d. blue, apple-green and black	..	15	10
152	70	6d. yellow-green, carmine-red and black		15	30

71 Queen Elizabeth II | **72** Coco Palms at Don Christopher's Cove

(Des and eng B.W. Recess D.L.R.)

1953 (2 June). *Coronation. Wmk Mult Script CA. P 13½×13.*

153	71	2d. black and deep yellow-green	..	10	10

(Recess Waterlow)

1953 (25 Nov). *Royal Visit. Wmk Mult Script CA. P 12½×13.*

154	72	2d. grey-black and green	..	10	10

73 Man-o'-War at Port Royal

(Recess D.L.R.)

1955 (10 May). *Tercentenary Issue. T 73 and similar horiz designs. Wmk Mult Script CA. P 12½.*

155		2d. black and olive-green	..	20	10
156		2½d. black and deep bright blue	..	15	35
157		3d. black and claret	..	15	30
158		6d. black and carmine-red	..	20	20
155/8			Set of 4	65	80

Designs:—2½d. Old Montego Bay; 3d. Old Kingston; 6d. Proclamation of Abolition of Slavery, 1838.

74 Palms | **75** Mahoe

---

76 Blue Mountain Peak

77 Arms of Jamaica | **78** Arms of Jamaica

(Recess B.W. (T **77/8**), D.L.R. (others))

1956 (1 May)–58. *T 74/8 and similar designs. Wmk Mult Script CA. P 13 (½d. to 6d.), 13½ (8d. to 2s.) or 11½ (3s. to £1).*

159	74	½d. black and deep orange-red	..	10	10
160	–	1d. black and emerald		10	10
161	–	2d. black and carmine-red (2.8.56)		10	10
162	–	2½d. black and deep bright blue (2.8.56)	15	40
163	75	3d. emerald and red-brown (17.12.56)	15	10
164	–	4d. bronze-green and blue (17.12.56)	15	10
165	–	5d. scarlet and bronze-green (17.12.56)	20	1·00
166	–	6d. black and deep rose-red (3.9.56)	1·25	10
167	76	8d. ultramarine & red-orge (15.11.56)	15	10
168	–	1s. yellow-green and blue (15.11.56)	30	10
169	–	1s. 6d. ultram & reddish pur (15.11.56)	30	10
170	–	2s. blue and bronze-green (15.11.56)	1·75	85
		a. Grey-blue & bronze-green (24.4.58)	2·75	95
171	77	3s. black and blue (2.8.56)	60	80
172		5s. black and carmine-red (15.8.56)	1·00	1·50
173	78	10s. black and blue-green (15.8.56)	11·00	6·50
174		£1 black and purple (15.8.56)	16·00	6·50
159/74			Set of 16	30·00	16·00

Designs: *Vert as T 74/5*—1d. Sugar Cane; 2d. Pineapples; 2½d. Bananas; 4d. Breadfruit; 5d. Ackee; 6d. Streamertail. *Horiz (as T 76)*—1s. Royal Botanic Gardens, Hope; 1s. 6d. Rafting on the Rio Grande; 2s. Fort Charles.

79 Federation Map

(Recess B.W.)

1958 (22 Apr). *Inauguration of British Caribbean Federation. W w 12. P 11½×11.*

175	79	2d. deep green	..	50	10
176		5d. blue	..	85	1·50
177		6d. scarlet	..	85	40
175/7			Set of 3	2·00	1·75

81 "Britannia" flying over City of Berlin, 1860 | **83** 1s. Stamps of 1860 and 1956

(Recess Waterlow)

1960 (4 Jan). *Stamp Centenary. T 81, 83 and similar design. W w 12. P 13 × 13½ (1s.) or 13½ × 14 (others).*

178		2d. blue and reddish purple	..	45	10
179		6d. carmine and olive-green	..	45	15
180		1s. red-brown, yellow-green and blue		45	20
178/80			Set of 3	1·25	40

Design: *As T 81*—6d. Postal mule-cart and motor-van.

INDEPENDENT

```
1        1
9        9
6        6
2        2
INDEPENDENCE    INDEPENDENCE
                1962
  (84)            (85)
```

86 Military Bugler and Map

(Des V. Whiteley. Photo D.L.R. (2, 4d., 1s. 6d., 5s.))

1962 (8 Aug)–**63.** *Independence.*

(a) Nos. 159/60, 162, 171, 173/4 optd as T **84** and Nos. 163, 165/8, 170 optd with T **85**

181	**74**	½d. black and deep orange-red	..	10	60
182	–	1d. black and emerald	..	10	10
183	–	2½d. black and deep bright blue	..	10	85
184	**75**	3d. emerald and red-brown	..	10	10
185	–	5d. scarlet and bronze-green	..	15	60
186	–	6d. black and deep rose-red	..	75	10
187	**76**	8d. ultram & red-orge (opt at upper left)	15	10
		a. Opt at lower left (17.9.63?)		15	15
188	–	1s. yellow-green and blue	..	15	10
189	–	2s. blue and bronze-green	..	80	90
		a. Dp blue & dp bronze-green (20.8.63)	1·75	1·10
190	**77**	3s. black and blue	..	90	1·50
191	**78**	10s. black and blue-green	..	2·00	4·00
192		£1 black and purple	..	2·75	5·50

(b) Horiz designs as T **86**. W w **12**. P **13**

193		2d. multicoloured	..	20	10
194		4d. multicoloured	..	20	10
195		1s. 6d. black and red	..	65	85
196		5s. multicoloured	..	1·25	2·00
181/96			Set of 16	9·00	15·00

Designs:—2, 4d. Type **86**; 1s. 6d. Gordon House and banner; 5s. Map, factories and fruit.

For these overprints on stamps watermarked w **12** see Nos. 205/13.

89 Kingston Seal, Weightlifting, Boxing, Football and Cycling

93 Farmer and Crops

(Photo Harrison)

1962 (11 Aug). *Ninth Central American and Caribbean Games, Kingston.* T **89** *and similar horiz designs.* W w **12**. P 14½ × 14.

197		1d. sepia and carmine-red	..	10	10
198		6d. sepia and greenish blue	..	10	10
199		8d. sepia and bistre	..	10	10
200		2s. multicoloured	..	25	40
197/200			Set of 4	45	50

Designs:—6d. Kingston seal, diving, sailing, swimming and water polo; 8d. Kingston seal, pole-vaulting, javelin throwing, discus throwing, relay-racing and hurdling; 2s. Kingston coat of arms and athlete.

An imperf miniature sheet exists, but this was never available at face value or at any post office.

(Des M. Goaman. Litho D.L.R.)

1963 (4 June). *Freedom from Hunger.* P 12½.

201	**93**	1d. multicoloured	..	15	10
202		8d. multicoloured	..	50	20

94 Red Cross Emblem

95 Carole Joan Crawford ("Miss World 1963")

(Des V. Whiteley. Litho B.W.)

1963 (4 Sept). *Red Cross Centenary.* W w **12**. P 13½.

203	**94**	2d. red and black	..	15	10
204		1s. 6d. red and blue	..	40	65

1963–64. *As Nos. 181/90, but wmk w **12**.*

205	**74**	½d. black & deep orange-red (3.12.63*)	10	15
206	–	1d. black and emerald (3.4.64)	..	10	20
207	–	2½d. black and deep bright blue (3.4.64)	25	1·10
208	**75**	3d. emerald and red-brown (17.12.63*)	15	15
209	–	5d. scarlet and bronze-green (3.4.64)	30	1·75
210	**76**	8d. ultramarine and red-orange (3.4.64)	20	55
211	–	1s. yellow-green and blue (21.12.63*)	35	75
212	–	2s. dp blue & dp bronze-green (3.4.64)	60	2·75
213	**77**	3s. black and blue (5.2.64)	..	2·00	7·50
205/13			Set of 9	3·50	13·50

The overprint on the 8d., 1s. and 2s. is at lower left, the others are as before.

*These are the earliest known dates recorded in Jamaica.

(Des and photo D.L.R.)

1964 (14 Feb–25 May). *"Miss World 1963" Commemoration.* P 13.

214	**95**	3d. multicoloured	..	10	10
215		1s. multicoloured	..	15	10
216		1s. 6d. multicoloured	..	20	20
214/16			Set of 3	40	30
MS216a		153×101 mm. Nos. 214/16. Imperf		80	1·75
		(25.5.64)			

96 Lignum Vitae

97 Blue Mahoe

103 Gypsum Industry

109 Arms of Jamaica

111 Multiple "J" and Pineapple

(Des V. Whiteley. Photo Harrison)

1964 (4 May)–**68.** T **96/7, 103, 109** *and similar designs.* W **111**. P 14½ (1d., 2d., 2½d., 6d., 8d.), 14×14½ (1½d., 3d., 4d., 10s.), 14½×14 (9d., 1s., 3s., 5s., £1) or 13½×14½ (1s. 6d., 2s.).

217		1d. violet-blue, dp green & lt brn (shades)	10	10
218		1½d. multicoloured	..	15	10
219		2d. red, yellow and grey-green	..	15	10
220		2½d. multicoloured	..	70	60
221		3d. yellow, black and emerald	..	15	10
222		4d. ochre and violet	..	35	10
223		6d. multicoloured	..	2·00	10
		a. Blue omitted	..	38·00	
		b. Value omitted			
224		8d. mult (yellowish green background)	1·25	60
		a. Red (beak) omitted	..	80·00	
		b. Greyish green background (16.7.68)	3·50	2·50
225		9d. blue and yellow-bistre	..	45	10
226		1s. black and light brown	..	20	10
		a. Light brown omitted	..	£160	
		ab. Value only omitted	..	£350	
		b. Black omitted	..	£400	
		ba. "NATIONAL STADIUM" etc omitted	£400	
227		1s. 6d. black, light blue and buff	..	75	15
228		2s. red-brown, black and light blue	1·50	15
229		3s. blue and dull green	..	1·00	80
		a. Perf 13½×14½	..	35	65
230		5s. black, ochre and blue	..	1·10	60
231		10s. multicoloured	..	1·25	1·00
		a. Blue ("JAMAICA", etc) omitted	£170	
232		£1 multicoloured	..	1·50	1·00
217/32			Set of 16	10·50	4·25

Designs: *Horiz.* (As T **96**)—1½d. Ackee; 2½d. Land shells; 3d. National flag over Jamaica; 4d. *Murex antillarum*; 6d. *Papilio homerus*; 8d. Streamertail. As T **103**—1s. National Stadium; 1s. 6d. Palisadoes International Airport; 2s. Bauxite mining; 3s. Blue Marlin (sport fishing); 5s. Exploration of sunken city, Port Royal; £1 Queen Elizabeth II and national flag.

No. 223b. Two left half sheets are known with the black printing shifted downwards to such an extent that the value is omitted from the top row.

Nos. 226a/ab came from a sheet on which the two bottom rows had the colour omitted with the next row showing it missing from the lower third of the stamps.

A similar sheet, but with the colour missing from the top two rows and part of the third produced Nos 226b/ba.

112 Scout Belt

113 Globe, Scout Hat and Scarf

114 Scout Badge and Alligator

(Photo Harrison)

1964 (27 Aug). *Sixth Inter-American Scout Conference, Kingston.* W **111**. P 14 (1s.) or 14½×14 (others).

233	**112**	3d. red, black and pink	..	10	10
234	**113**	8d. bright blue, olive and black	..	10	20
235	**114**	1s. gold, deep blue and light blue	15	20
233/5			Set of 3	30	35

115 Gordon House, Kingston

118 Eleanor Roosevelt

(Des V. Whiteley. Photo Harrison)

1964 (16 Nov). *Tenth Commonwealth Parliamentary Conference, Kingston.* T **115** *and similar horiz designs.* W **111**. P 14½ × 14.

236		3d. black and yellow-green	..	10	10
237		6d. black and carmine-red	..	10	10
238		1s. 6d. black and bright blue	..	15	20
236/8			Set of 3	30	30

Designs:—6d. Headquarters House, Kingston; 1s. 6d. House of Assembly, Spanish Town.

(Des V. Whiteley. Photo Harrison)

1964 (10 Dec). *16th Anniv of Declaration of Human Rights.* W **111**. P 14½ × 14.

239	**118**	1s. black, red and light green	..	10	10

119 Guides' Emblem on Map

120 Guide Emblems

(Photo Harrison)

1965 (17 May). *Golden Jubilee of Jamaica Girl Guides Association.* W **111** *(sideways on 3d.).* P 14 × 14½ (3d.) or 14 (1s.).

240	**119**	3d. yellow, green and light blue	..	10	10
241	**120**	1s. yellow, black and apple-green	..	20	20

121 Uniform Cap

122 Flag-bearer and Drummer

(Photo Harrison)

1965 (23 Aug). *Salvation Army Centenary.* W **111**. P 14 × 14½ (3d.) or 14½ × 14 (1s. 6d.).

242	**121**	3d. multicoloured	..	15	10
243	**122**	1s. 6d. multicoloured	..	35	25

123 Paul Bogle, William Gordon and Morant Bay Court House

124 Abeng-blower, "Telstar", Morse Key and I.T.U. Emblem

(Photo Enschedé)

1965 (29 Dec). *Centenary of Morant Bay Rebellion. No wmk.* P 14 × 13.

244	**123**	3d. light brown, ultramarine and black	10	10
245		1s. 6d. lt brown, yellow-green & black	10	10
246		3s. light brown, rose and black	20	30
244/6			Set of 3	35	40

(Photo Harrison)

1965 (29 Dec). *I.T.U. Centenary.* W **111**. P 14 × 14½.

247	**124**	1s. black, grey-blue and red	..	40	15

ROYAL VISIT
MARCH 1966

(125)   126 Sir Winston Churchill

1966 (3 Mar). *Royal Visit. Nos. 221, 223, 226/7 optd with T* 125.
248   3d. yellow, black and emerald   15   10
249   6d. multicoloured   70   10
250   1s. black and light brown   55   10
251   1s. 6d. black, light blue and buff   ..   70   60
248/51   ..   ..   *Set of* 4   1·75   65

(Des Jennifer Toombs. Photo Harrison)

1966 (18 April). *Churchill Commemoration. W* 111. *P* 14.
252   126   6d. black and olive-green   35   20
253   1s. bistre-brown and deep violet-blue   ..   65   70

127 Statue of Athlete and Flags   131 Bolivar's Statue and
                                        Flags of Jamaica and
                                        Venezuela

(Des V. Whiteley. Photo Harrison)

1966 (4 Aug). *Eighth British Empire and Commonwealth Games.
T* 127 *and similar horiz designs. W* 111. *P* 14½ × 14.
254   3d. multicoloured   10   10
255   6d. multicoloured   10   10
256   1s. multicoloured   10   10
257   3s. bright gold and deep blue   ..   20   35
           a. Dull gold and deep blue
254/7   ..   ..   *Set of* 4   35   45
MS258   128×103 mm. Nos. 254/7. Imperf   ..   4·50   7·50
Designs:—6d. Racing cyclists; 1s. National Stadium, Kingston; 3s. Games emblem.
No. MS258 has been seen with the whole printing inverted except for the brown background.

(Des and photo Harrison)

1966 (5 Dec). *150th Anniv of "Jamaica Letter". W* 111. *P* 14 × 15.
259   131   8d. multicoloured   10   10

132 Jamaican Pavilion   133 Sir Donald Sangster
                             (Prime Minister)

(Des V. Whiteley. Photo Harrison)

1967 (28 Apr). *World Fair, Montreal. W* 111. *P* 14½.
260   132   6d. multicoloured   10   10
261   1s. multicoloured   10   10

(Des and photo Enschedé)

1967 (28 Aug). *Sangster Memorial Issue. P* 13½.
262   133   3d. multicoloured   10   10
263   1s. 6d. multicoloured   10   10

134 Traffic Duty

135 Personnel of the Force

(Des V. Whiteley. Photo Enschedé)

1967 (28 Nov). *Centenary of the Constabulary Force. T* 134/5 *and
similar horiz design. Multicoloured. W* 111. *P* 13½ × 14.
264   3d. Type 134   10   10
           a. Wmk sideways   40   45
265   1s. Type 135   15   10
266   1s. 6d. Badge and Constables of 1867 and
           1967 (*as T* 134)   20   20
264/6   ..   ..   *Set of* 3   40   30

---

136 Wicket-   137 Sir Alexander and Lady Bustamante
    keeping

(Des V. Whiteley. Photo Harrison)

1968 (8 Feb). *M.C.C.'s West Indian Tour. T* 136 *and similar
vert designs. Multicoloured. W* 111 (*sideways*). *P* 14.
267   6d. Type 136   20   30
           a. Horiz strip of 3. Nos. 267/9   ..   1·50
268   6d. Batting   20   30
269   6d. Bowling   20   30
267/9   ..   ..   *Set of* 3   55   80
Nos. 267/9 were issued in small sheets of 9 comprising three *se-tenant* strips as No. 267a.
Nos. 267/9 exist on PVA gum as well as on gum arabic.

(Des and photo Harrison)

1968 (23 May). *Labour Day. W* 111. *P* 14.
270   137   3d. rose and black   10   10
271   1s. olive and black   10   10

138 Human Rights Emblem over
     Map of Jamaica

(Photo Harrison)

1968 (3 Dec). *Human Rights Year. T* 138 *and similar multi-coloured designs. W* 111. *P* 14.
272   3d. Type 138   10   10
           a. Gold (flame) omitted   ..   ..   90·00
273   1s. Hands cupping Human Rights emblem
           (*vert*)   10   10
274   3s. Jamaican holding "Human Rights"   ..   20   30
           a. Gold (flame) omitted £100
272/4   ..   ..   *Set of* 3   35   40
Three designs, showing 3d. Bowls of Grain, 1s. Abacus, 3s. Hands in Prayer, were prepared but not issued (*Price for set of* 3 *mint* £100).

141 ILO Emblem   142 Nurse, and Children
                          being weighed and
                          measured

(Des V. Whiteley. Litho Format)

1969 (23 May). *50th Anniv of International Labour Organization.
P* 14.
275   141   6d. orange-yellow and blackish brown   10   10
276   3s. bright emerald and blackish brown   20   30

(Des and photo Harrison)

1969 (30 May). *20th Anniv of W.H.O. T* 142 *and similar designs.
W* 111. *P* 14.
277   6d. grey, brown and orange   10   10
278   1s. black, sepia and blue-green   ..   10   10
279   3s. grey-black, brown and pale bright blue   20   30
277/9   ..   ..   *Set of* 3   30   35
Designs: *Horiz*—1s. Malaria eradication. *Vert*—3s. Trainee nurse.

(New Currency. 100 cents = 1 dollar)

C-DAY
8th September
1969
1c

(145)   146 "The Adoration of the
                      Kings" (detail, Foppa)

1969 (8 Sept). *Decimal currency. Nos.* 217, 219, 221/3 *and* 225/32
surch as T 145. *Sterling values unobliterated except* 1 c. *to* 4 c. *and*
8 c.
280   1 c. on 1d. violet-blue, dp green & lt brown   10   10
281   2 c. on 2d. red, yellow and grey-green   ..   10   10
282   3 c. on 3d. yellow, black and emerald   ..   10   10
283   4 c. on 4d. ochre and violet   55   10
           a. "8t" of "8th" omitted (R. 10/1)   ..   28·00
284   5 c. on 6d. multicoloured   ..   ..   1·00   10
           a. Blue omitted   ..   ..   ..   38·00
285   8 c. on 9d. blue and yellow-bistre   ..   10   10
286   10 c. on 1s. black and light brown   ..   10   10
287   15 c. on 1s. 6d. black, light blue and buff   ..   30   60
288   20 c. on 2s. red-brown, black and light blue   1·50   55
           a. "8th" omitted
289   30 c. on 3s. blue and dull green   ..   1·50   2·00
290   50 c. on 5s. black, ochre and blue   ..   1·25   2·00
291    $1 on 10s. multicoloured   ..   ..   1·50   3·25
292    $2 on £1 multicoloured   ..   ..   1·50   6·00
280/92   ..   ..   ..   *Set of* 13   8·00   13·00
No. 281 exists with PVA gum as well as gum arabic.
Unlike the positional No. 283a the similar variety on the 20 c.
on 2s. was caused by a paper fold.

(Des J. Cooter. Litho D.L.R.)

1969 (25 Oct). *Christmas. Paintings. T* 146 *and similar vert
designs. Multicoloured. W* 111. *P* 13.
293   2 c. Type 146   10   10
294   5 c. "Madonna, Child and St. John" (Raphael)   10   10
295   8 c. "The Adoration of the Kings" (detail,
           Dosso Dossi)   15   15
293/5   ..   ..   *Set of* 3   30   30

149 Half Penny, 1869   151 George William
                             Gordon

(Des G. Drummond. Litho P.B.)

1969 (27 Oct). *Centenary of First Jamaican Coins. T* 149 *and
similar horiz design. W* 111. *P* 12½.
296   3 c. silver, black and mauve   15   25
           b. Wmk sideways   20   20
297   15 c. silver, black and light emerald   ..   10   10
Design:—15 c. One penny, 1869.

(Des G. Vasarhelyi. Litho Enschedé)

1970 (11 Mar). *National Heroes. T* 151 *and similar vert designs.
Multicoloured. P* 12 × 12½.
298   1 c. Type 151   10   10
           a. Yellow (from flags) omitted   ..   £180
299   3 c. Sir Alexander Bustamante   ..   10   10
300   5 c. Norman Manley   10   10
301   10 c. Marcus Garvey   15   10
302   15 c. Paul Bogle   20   15
298/302   ..   ..   ..   *Set of* 5   40   30

156 "Christ appearing   (159)
     to St. Peter" (Carracci)

(Des G. Drummond. Photo Enschedé)

1970 (23 Mar). *Easter. T* 156 *and similar vert designs. Multi-coloured. W* 111. *P* 12 × 12½.
303   3 c. Type 156   10   10
304   10 c. "Christ Crucified" (Antonello da Messina)   10   10
305   20 c. Easter Lily   20   25
303/5   ..   ..   *Set of* 3   30   30

1970 (16 July). *No.* 219 *surch with T* 159.
306   2 c. on 2d. red, yellow and grey-green   ..   15   20

160 Lignum Vitae   161 Cable Ship Dacia

1970 (7 Sept–2 Nov). *Decimal Currency. Designs as Nos. 217/32 but inscr as T 160 in new currency. W 111 (sideways on 2, 4, 15, 20 c. and $1). P 14½ (1, 5 c.), 14 × 14½ (4 c., $1), 13½ × 14½ (15, 20 c.) or 14½ × 14 (others).*

307	1 c. violet-blue, deep green & lt brown			40	50
308	2 c. red, yellow and grey-green (as 2d.)			15	10
309	3 c. yellow, black and emerald (as 3d.)			15	10
310	4 c. ochre and violet (as 4d.)			80	10
311	5 c. multicoloured (as 6d.)			2·25	10
312	8 c. blue and yellow-bistre (as 9d.)			20	10
	a. Wmk sideways			50	45
313	10 c. black and light brown (as 1s.)			20	10
314	15 c. black, light blue and buff (as 1s. 6d.) (2.11)			80	70
315	20 c. red-brown, black & lt blue (as 2s.) (2.11)			1·00	1·00
316	30 c. blue and dull green (as 3s.) (2.11)			1·25	1·50
317	50 c. black, ochre and blue (as 5s.) (2.11)			1·25	1·25
318	$1 multicoloured (as 10s.) (2.11)			1·25	2·75
319	$2 multicoloured (as £1) (2.11)			1·50	2·75
307/19			*Set of 13*	10·00	11·00

(Des G. Drummond. Litho J.W.)

1970 (12 Oct). *Centenary of Telegraph Service. T 161 and similar horiz designs. W 111 (sideways). P 14½ × 14.*

320	3 c. yellow, red and black			15	10
321	10 c. black and turquoise			20	10
322	50 c. multicoloured			50	1·00
320/2			*Set of 3*	75	1·10

Designs:—10 c. Bright's cable gear aboard *Dacia*; 50 c. Morse key and chart.

164 Bananas, Citrus, Sugar-Cane and Tobacco

165 *The Projector (1845)*

(Des G. Drummond. Litho Questa)

1970 (2 Nov). *75th Anniv of Jamaican Agricultural Society. W 111. P 14.*

323	**164**	2 c. multicoloured		10	30
324		10 c. multicoloured		20	10

(Des V. Whiteley. Litho Format)

1970 (21 Nov). *125th Anniv of Jamaican Railways. T 165 and similar horiz designs. Multicoloured. W 111 (sideways). P 13½.*

325	3 c. Type **165**			25	10
326	15 c. Steam locomotive No. 54 (1944)			70	30
327	50 c. Diesel locomotive No. 102 (1967)			1·75	2·00
325/7			*Set of 3*	2·40	2·25

168 Church of St. Jago de la Vega

169 Henry Morgan and Ships

(Des R. Granger Barrett. Litho J.W.)

1971 (22 Feb). *Centenary of Disestablishment of the Church of England in Jamaica. T 168 and similar vert design. Multicoloured. W 111. P 14½.*

328	3 c. Type **168**			10	10
329	10 c. Type **168**			10	10
330	20 c. Type **168**			15	25
331	30 c. Emblem of Church of England in Jamaica			20	45
328/31			*Set of 4*	35	70

(Des J.W. Litho Questa)

1971 (10 May). *Pirates and Buccaneers. T 169 and similar horiz designs. Multicoloured. W 111 (sideways). P 14.*

332	3 c. Type **169**			35	10
333	15 c. Mary Read, Anne Bonny and trial pamphlet			65	15
334	30 c. Pirate schooner attacking merchantman			1·25	1·25
332/4			*Set of 3*	2·00	1·40

PRICES OF SETS

Set prices are given for many issues, generally those containing three stamps or more. Definitive sets include one of each value or major colour change, but do not cover different perforations, die types or minor shades. Where a choice is possible the set prices are based on the cheapest versions of the stamps included in the listings.

170 1s. Stamp of 1919 with Frame Inverted | **171** Satellite and Dish Aerial

(Des Jennifer Toombs. Litho J.W.)

1971 (30 Oct). *Tercentenary of Post Office Establishment. T 170 and similar designs. W 111 (sideways, except 50 c.). P 13½.*

335	3 c. black and lake			10	10
336	5 c. grey-black and bright green			10	10
337	8 c. black and violet			15	10
338	10 c. brown, black and indigo			15	10
339	20 c. multicoloured			25	35
340	50 c. ochre, black and slate			45	80
335/40			*Set of 6*	1·00	1·25

Designs: *Horiz*—3 c. Dummer packet letter, 1705; 5 c. Pre-stamp inland letter, 1793; 8 c. Harbour St. P.O., Kingston, 1820; 10 c. Modern stamp and cancellation; 20 c. British stamps used in Jamaica, 1859.

(Des Cable & Wireless Ltd. Litho J.W.)

1972 (17 Feb). *Opening of Jamaican Earth Satellite Station. W 111. P 14 × 13½.*

341	**171**	3 c. multicoloured		15	10
342		15 c. multicoloured		20	15
343		50 c. multicoloured		55	1·25
341/3			*Set of 3*	80	1·25

172 Causeway, Kingston Harbour | **173** Air Jamaica Hostess and Aircraft

(Des J.W. Litho Format)

1972 (17 Apr–2 Oct). *Multicoloured designs as T 172 (1 to 6 c.) or 173 (8 c. to $2). W 111 (sideways on horiz designs). P 14½ × 14 (1, 2 c.), 14 × 14½ (3, 4, 5, 6 c.) or 13½ (others).*

344	1 c. Pimento (*vert*) (5.6)			10	10
345	2 c. Red Ginger (*vert*) (5.6)			10	10
346	3 c. Bauxite Industry (5.6)			10	10
347	4 c. Type **172**			10	10
348	5 c. Oil Refinery (5.6)			10	10
349	6 c. Senate Building, University of the West Indies (5.6)			10	10
350	8 c. National Stadium (5.6)			10	10
351	9 c. Devon House (5.6)			10	10
352	10 c. Type **173**			10	10
353	15 c. Old Iron Bridge, Spanish Town (*vert*) (2.10)			65	10
354	20 c. College of Arts, Science and Technology (2.10)			30	15
355	30 c. Dunn's River Falls (*vert*) (2.10)			35	15
356	50 c. River rafting (5.6)			60	40
357	$1 Jamaica House (2.10)			75	65
358	$2 Kings House (2.10)			1·00	1·25
344/58			*Set of 15*	3·50	2·75

TENTH ANNIVERSARY INDEPENDENCE 1962-1972
(**174**) | **175** Arms of Kingston

1972 (8 Aug). *Tenth Anniv of Independence. Nos. 346, 352 and 356 optd as T 174.*

359	3 c. Bauxite Industry			10	10
360	10 c. Type **173**			10	10
361	50 c. River rafting			40	1·25
359/61			*Set of 3*	45	1·25

(Des R. Granger Barrett. Litho J.W.)

1972 (4 Dec). *Centenary of Kingston as Capital. W 111 (sideways on 50 c.). P 13½ × 14 (5 and 30 c.) or 14 × 13½ (50 c.).*

362	**175**	5 c. multicoloured		10	10
363		30 c. multicoloured		20	25
364		50 c. multicoloured		40	75
362/4			*Set of 3*	60	1·00

The 50 c. is as T **175**, but horiz.

176 Small Indian Mongoose on Map

(Des R. Granger Barrett. Litho Questa)

1973 (9 Apr). *Centenary of Introduction of the Mongoose. T 176 and similar horiz designs. W 111 (sideways). P 14 × 14½.*

365	8 c. light apple-green, yellow-green and black			10	10
366	40 c. light cobalt, light blue and black			25	50
367	60 c. salmon-pink, brownish salmon & black			50	60
365/7			*Set of 3*	75	1·40
MS368	165 × 95 mm. Nos. 365/7			1·50	3·00

Designs:—40 c. Mongoose and rat; 60 c. Mongoose and chicken.

177 *Euphorbia punicea*

(Des Sylvia Goaman. Litho Questa)

1973 (9 July). *Flora. T 177 and similar diamond-shaped designs. Multicoloured. W 111. P 14.*

369	1 c. Type **177**			10	10
370	6 c. *Hylocereus triangularis*			15	10
371	9 c. *Columnea argentea*			15	10
372	15 c. *Portlandia grandiflora*			25	15
373	30 c. *Samyda pubescens*			50	60
374	50 c. *Cordia sebestena*			80	1·25
369/74			*Set of 6*	1·75	2·00

178 *Broughtonia sanguinea*

(Des Sylvia Goaman. Litho B.W.)

1973 (8 Oct). *Orchids. T 178 and similar multicoloured designs. W 111 (sideways on 5 c., $1). P 14×13½ (5 c., $1) or 13½×14 (others).*

375	5 c. Type **178**			40	10
376	10 c. *Arpophyllum jamaicense* (*vert*)			50	10
377	20 c. *Oncidium pulchellum* (*vert*)			1·25	25
378	$1 *Brassia maculata*			2·75	2·75
375/8			*Set of 4*	4·50	2·75
MS379	161×95 mm. Nos. 375/8. Wmk sideways. P 12			4·00	4·00

179 *Mary, 1808–15* | **180** "Journeys"

(Des J. Cooter. Litho J.W.)

1974 (8 Apr). *Mail Packet Boats. T 179 and similar horiz designs. Multicoloured. W 111 (sideways on Nos. 380/3, upright on MS384). P 13½ (5 c., 50 c.) or 14½ (others).*

380	5 c. Type **179**			20	10
	a. Perf 14½			2·50	
381	10 c. *Queensbury, 1814–27*			25	10
382	15 c. *Sheldrake, 1829–34*			45	40
383	50 c. *Thames, 1842*			1·75	25
380/3			*Set of 4*	2·40	2·50
MS384	133×159 mm. Nos. 380/3. P 13½ (sold at 90 c.)			3·25	4·50

(Des R. Granger Barrett. Litho Questa)

1974 (1 Aug). *National Dance Theatre Company. T 180 and similar vert designs showing dance-works. Multicoloured. W 111. P 13½.*

385	5 c. Type **180**			10	10
386	10 c. "Jamaican Promenade"			10	10
387	30 c. "Jamaican Promenade"			25	30
388	50 c. "Misa Criolla"			45	80
385/8			*Set of 4*	70	1·10
MS389	161 × 102 mm. Nos. 385/8 (sold at $1)			1·50	2·25

181 U.P.U. Emblem and Globe

(Des V. Whiteley. Litho J.W.)

1974 (9 Oct). *Centenary of Universal Postal Union. W* 111 *(sideways). P* 14.
390	181	5 c. multicoloured		10	10
391		9 c. multicoloured		10	10
392		50 c. multicoloured		35	80
390/2			*Set of 3*	50	80

182 Senate Building and Sir Hugh Wooding   183 Commonwealth Symbol

(Des R. Granger Barrett. Litho Questa)

1975 (13 Jan). *25th Anniv of University of West Indies. T* 182 *and similar horiz design. Multicoloured. W* 111 *(sideways). P* 14.
393		5 c. Type 182		10	10
394		10 c. University Chapel and H.R.H. Princess Alice		10	10
395		30 c. Type 182		15	25
396		As 10 c.		30	60
393/6			*Set of 4*	50	80

(Des C. Abbott. Litho Questa)

1975 (29 Apr). *Heads of Commonwealth Conference. T* 183 *and similar square designs. Multicoloured. W* 111. *P* 13½.
397		5 c. Type 183		10	10
398		10 c. Jamaican coat of arms		10	10
399		30 c. Dove of Peace		15	30
400		50 c. Jamaican flag		30	80
397/400			*Set of 4*	50	1·10

184 *Eurytides marcellinus*   185 Koo Koo or Actor Boy

(Des J. Cooter. Litho Questa)

1975 (25 Aug). *Butterflies (1st series). T* 184 *and similar vert designs showing the family Papilionidae. Multicoloured. W* 111. *P* 14.
401		10 c. Type 184		55	20
402		20 c. *Papilo thoas*		1·10	1·10
403		25 c. *Papilo thersites*		1·25	1·60
404		30 c. *Papilo homerus*		1·40	2·00
401/4			*Set of 4*	4·00	4·50
MS405	134×179 mm. Nos. 401/4 (sold at 95 c.)			5·00	7·00

See also Nos. 429/33 and 443/47.

(Des C. Abbott. Litho J.W.)

1975 (3 Nov). *Christmas. T* 185 *and similar vert designs showing Belisario prints of "John Canoe" (Christmas) Festival (1st series). Multicoloured. W* 111. *P* 14.
406		8 c. Type 185		10	10
407		10 c. Red Set-girls		10	10
408		20 c. French Set-girls		15	15
409		50 c. Jaw-bone or House John Canoe		35	70
406/9			*Set of 4*	55	90
MS410	138 × 141 mm. Nos. 406/9. P 13½ (sold at $1)			1·50	2·75

See also Nos. 421/MS424.

186 Bordone Map, 1528

(Des L. Curtis. Litho Questa)

1976 (12 Mar). *16th Century Maps of Jamaica. T* 186 *and similar horiz designs. W* 111 *(sideways). P* 13½.
411		10 c. brown, light stone and light vermilion	20	10
412		20 c. multicoloured		35	25
413		30 c. multicoloured		60	75
414		50 c. multicoloured		85	1·25
411/14			*Set of 4*	1·75	2·10

Designs—20 c. Porcacchi map, 1576; 30 c. DeBry map, 1594; 50 c. Langenes map, 1598.
See also Nos. 425/8.

187 Olympic Rings

(Des Sir H. McDonald: adapted V. Whiteley Studio. Litho Walsall)

1976 (14 June). *Olympic Games, Montreal. W* 111 *(sideways). P* 13½.
415	187	10 c. multicoloured		10	10
416		20 c. multicoloured		15	15
417		25 c. multicoloured		15	20
418		50 c. multicoloured		30	90
415/18			*Set of 4*	60	1·25

187a Map of the Caribbean

(Des PAD Studio. Litho Questa)

1976 (9 Aug). *West Indian Victory in World Cricket Cup. T* 187a *and similar design. No wmk. P* 14.
419		10 c. multicoloured		40	40
420		25 c. black and magenta		85	1·25

Design: *Vert*—25 c. Prudential Cup.

(Des C. Abbott. Litho J.W.)

1976 (8 Nov). *Christmas. Belisario Prints (2nd series). Multicoloured designs as T* 185. *W* 111. *P* 13½.
421		10 c. Queen of the set-girls		10	10
422		20 c. Band of the Jaw-bone John Canoe	15	10
423		50 c. Koo Koo (actor-boy)		30	60
421/3			*Set of 3*	40	70
MS424	110 × 140 mm. Nos. 421/3. P 14 × 14½ (sold at 90 c.)			70	2·00

(Des L. Curtis. Litho J.W.)

1977 (28 Feb). *17th Century Maps of Jamaica. Designs as T* 186. *W* 111 *(sideways). P* 13.
425		9 c. multicoloured		30	10
426		10 c. multicoloured		30	10
427		25 c. grey-black, pale blue and bright blue	70	60
428		40 c. grey-black, light turquoise and grey-blue	40	35
425/8			*Set of 4*	1·90	1·40

Designs:—9 c. Hickeringill map, 1661; 10 c. Ogilby map, 1671; 25 c. Visscher map, 1680; 40 c. Thornton map, 1689.

(Des J. Cooter. Litho J.W.)

1977 (9 May). *Butterflies (2nd series). Multicoloured designs as T* 184 *showing the families Nymphalidae and Pieridae. W* 111. *P* 13½.
429		10 c. *Eurema elathea*		35	10
430		20 c. *Dynamine egaea*		75	55
431		25 c. *Chlosyne pantoni*		1·00	1·25
432		40 c. *Hypolimnas misippus*		1·50	2·00
429/32			*Set of 4*	3·25	3·50
MS433	139×120 mm. Nos. 429/32. P 14½ (sold at $1.05)			4·50	7·00

188 Map, Scout Emblem and Streamertail   189 Trumpeter

(Des Daphne Padden. Litho Questa)

1977 (5 Aug). *Sixth Caribbean Jamboree, Jamaica. Multicoloured; background colours given. W* 111 *(sideways). P* 13½.
434	188	10 c. new blue		20	10
435		20 c. light yellow-green		40	15
436		25 c. orange		45	20
437		50 c. light magenta		75	1·10
434/7			*Set of 4*	1·60	1·25

(Des C. Abbott. Litho Questa)

1977 (19 Dec). *50th Anniv of Jamaica Military Band. T* 189 *and similar multicoloured designs. W* 111 *(sideways on horiz designs). P* 14.
438		9 c. Type 189		15	10
439		10 c. Clarinet players		15	10
440		20 c. Two kettle drummers (*vert*)	40	35
441		25 c. Cellist and trumpeter (*vert*)	55	65
438/41			*Set of 4*	1·10	1·00
MS442	120 × 137 mm. Nos. 438/41. Wmk sideways (sold at 75 c.)			2·50	3·75

(Des J. Cooter. Litho Walsall)

1978 (17 Apr). *Butterflies (3rd series). Multicoloured designs as T* 184. *W* 111. *P* 14.
443		10 c. *Callophrys crethona*		25	10
444		20 c. *Siproeta stelenes*		50	20
445		25 c. *Urbanus proteus*		65	35
446		50 c. *Anaea troglodyta*		1·40	40
443/6			*Set of 4*	2·50	2·00
MS447	100×125 mm. Nos. 443/6 (sold at $1.15)			2·75	3·50
	a. Error. Imperf			£180	

190 Half-figure with Canopy   191 Norman Manley (statue)

(Des J. Cooter. Litho J.W.)

1978 (10 July). *Arawak Artefacts (1st series). T* 190 *and similar vert designs. W* 111. *P* 13½ × 13.
448		10 c. deep brown, yellow and black	10	10
449		20 c. deep brown, mauve and black	10	10
450		50 c. deep brown, apple-green and black	30	35
448/50			*Set of 3*	40	45
MS451	135 × 90 mm. Nos. 448/50. P 14 (sold at 90 c.)			60	1·00

Designs:—20 c. Standing figure; 50 c. Birdman.
See also Nos. 479/83.

(Des and litho J.W.)

1978 (25 Sept). *24th Commonwealth Parliamentary Conference. T* 191 *and similar vert designs. Multicoloured. W* 111. *P* 13.
452		10 c. Type 191		10	10
453		20 c. Sir Alexander Bustamante (statue)	10	10
454		25 c. City of Kingston Crest		15	15
455		40 c. Gordon House Chamber, House of Representatives		25	35
452/5			*Set of 4*	50	60

192 Band and Banner   193 "Negro Aroused" (sculpture by Edna Manley)

(Des V. Whiteley. Litho J.W.)

1978 (4 Dec). *Christmas. Centenary of Salvation Army. T* 192 *and similar horiz designs. Multicoloured. W* 111 *(sideways). P* 14.
456		10 c. Type 192		20	10
457		20 c. Trumpeter		25	10
458		25 c. Banner		25	20
459		50 c. William Booth (founder)		40	1·00
456/9			*Set of 4*	1·00	1·25

(Des G. Hutchins. Litho J.W.)

1978 (11 Dec). *International Anti-Apartheid Year. W* 111. *P* 13.
460	193	10 c. multicoloured		10	10

194 Tennis, Montego Bay   195 Arms and Map of Jamaica

(Des and litho Harrison ($5). Des Walsall. Litho J.W. (others))

1979 (15 Jan)–**84**. *Vert designs as T 194, and T 195. Multi-coloured. White ordinary paper* (15, 65, 75 c., $5) *or cream chalk-surfaced paper* (others). W **111** (*sideways on $5*). P 14½ × 14 ($5) *or* 13½ (*others*).

461	1 c.	Type **194** (26.11.79)	..	30	30
462	2 c.	Golf, Tryall, Hanover (26.11.79). .		50	50
	a.	White ordinary paper (8.84)	..	1·00	1·00
463	4 c.	Horse riding, Negril Beach (26.11.79)		15	30
	a.	White ordinary paper (8.84)	..	1·00	1·00
464	5 c.	Old waterwheel, Tryall, Hanover (26.11.79). .		15	10
	a.	White ordinary paper (27.8.82)	..	45	40
465	6 c.	Fern Gully, Ocho Rios (26.11.79)	..	15	10
466	7 c.	Dunn's River Falls, Ocho Rios (26.11.79)		15	10
467	8 c.	Jamaican Tody (bird) (28.4.80)	..	40	30
468	10 c.	Jamaican Mango (bird) (28.4.80)	..	40	10
	a.	White ordinary paper (27.8.82) ..		60	30
469	12 c.	Yellow-billed Amazon (28.4.80)	..	40	40
470	15 c.	Streamertail (bird) (28.4.80)	..	55	20
471	35 c.	White-chinned Thrush (28.4.80)	..	55	20
472	50 c.	Jamaican Woodpecker (28.4.80). .		70	20
473	65 c.	Rafting, Martha Brae Trelawny (28.4.80)		30	30
474	75 c.	Blue Marlin Fleet, Port Antonio (28.4.80)		30	30
475	$1	Scuba Diving, Ocho Rios (28.4.80)		30	40
	a.	White ordinary paper (27.8.82) ..		80	90
476	$2	Sailing boats, Montego Bay (28.4.80)		50	35
	a.	White ordinary paper (27.8.82) ..		1·00	1·25
477	$5	Type **195** ..		1·00	1·60
461/77		*Set of 17*		6·00	5·25

TENTH
ANNIVERSARY
AIR JAMAICA
1st APRIL 1979
(**196**)

197 Grinding Stone, *circa 400 BC.*

1979 (2 Apr). *10th Anniv of Air Jamaica. No. 352 optd with T* **196**.

478	10 c.	Type **173** ..	..	15	30

(Des D. Bowen. Litho Questa)

1979 (23 Apr). *Arawak Artefacts* (2nd series). *T* **197** *and similar multicoloured designs. W* **111** (*sideways on 10, 20 and 25 c.*). *P 14*.

479	5 c.	Type **197** ..	..	10	10
480	10 c.	Stone implements, c. 500 AD (*horiz*)		10	10
481	20 c.	Cooking pot, c. 300 AD (*horiz*)	..	10	15
482	25 c.	Serving boat, c. 300 AD (*horiz*) ..		15	20
483	50 c.	Storage jar fragment, c. 300 AD.	..	25	35
479/83			*Set of 5*	55	70

198 1962 1s. 6d. Independence Commemorative Stamp

(Des J.W. from a local design by J. Mahfood. Litho Walsall)

1979 (13 Aug). *Death Centenary of Sir Rowland Hill. T* **198** *and similar horiz designs showing stamps and Sir Rowland Hill. W* **111** (*sideways*). *P 14*.

484	10 c.	black, scarlet-vermilion & brt scarlet	..	10	10
485	20 c.	orange-yellow and yellowish brown	..	15	15
486	25 c.	mauve and blue	..	20	20
487	50 c.	multicoloured	..	30	40
484/7			*Set of 4*	65	70
MS488		146 × 94 mm. No. 485 (*sold at 30 c.*)		30	45

Designs:—20 c. 1920 1s. with frame inverted; 25 c. 1860 6d.; 50 c. 1968 3d. Human Rights Year commemorative.

199 Group of Children

(Des J.W. Litho Harrison)

1979 (1 Oct). *Christmas. International Year of the Child. T* **199** *and similar multicoloured designs. W* **111** (*sideways on 10, 25 and 50 c.*). *P 14*.

489	10 c.	Type **199** ..	..	10	10
490	20 c.	Doll (*vert*)..	..	10	10
491	25 c.	"The Family" (painting by child)	..	15	15
492	50 c.	"House on the Hill" (painting by child) ..		25	40
489/92			*Set of 4*	50	60

NEW INFORMATION

The editor is always interested to correspond with people who have new information that will improve or correct the Catalogue.

---

200 Date Tree Hall, 1886 (original home of Institute)

(Des G. Drummond. Litho Walsall)

1980 (25 Feb). *Centenary of Institute of Jamaica. T* **200** *and similar multicoloured designs. W* **111** (*sideways on 5, 15 and 50 c.*). *P 13½*.

493	5 c.	Type **200** ..		10	10
494	15 c.	Institute building, 1980 ..		15	10
495	35 c.	Microfilm reader (*vert*)	..	20	20
496	50 c.	Hawksbill Turtle and Green Turtle		35	30
497	75 c.	Jamaican Owl (*vert*)	..	1·25	80
493/7			*Set of 5*	1·90	1·40

201 Don Quarrie (200 Metres, 1976)

(Des BG Studio. Litho Walsall)

1980 (21 July). *Olympic Games, Moscow. Jamaican Olympic Athletics Gold Medal Winners. T* **201** *and similar horiz designs. Multicoloured. W* **111** (*sideways*). *P 13*.

498	15 c.	Type **201** ..	..	15	10
499	35 c.	Arthur Wint (4 × 400 Metres Relay, 1952)		25	30
	a.	Horiz strip of 4. Nos. 499/502 ..		90	
500	35 c.	Leslie Laing (4 × 400 Metres Relay, 1952)		25	30
501	35 c.	Herbert McKenley (4 × 400 Metres Relay, 1952)		25	30
502	35 c.	George Rhoden (4 × 400 Metres Relay, 1952)		25	30
498/502			*Set of 5*	90	1·10

Nos. 499/502 were printed together, *se-tenant*, in horizontal strips of 4 throughout the sheet.

202 Parish Church **203** Blood Cup Sponge

(Des J.W. Litho Harrison)

1980 (24 Nov). *Christmas. Churches* (1st series). *T* **202** *and similar horiz designs. Multicoloured. W* **111** (*sideways*). *P 14*.

503	15 c.	Type **202** ..	..	10	10
504	20 c.	Coke Memorial Church ..		10	10
505	25 c.	Church of the Redeemer..		15	10
506	$5	Holy Trinity Cathedral ..	..	1·00	2·00
503/6			*Set of 4*	1·10	2·10
MS507		120 × 139 mm. Nos. 503/6. P 14½ (*sold at $5.70*)		1·75	3·00

See also Nos. 537/40 and 570/2.

(Des J. Mahfood. Litho Walsall)

1981 (27 Feb). *Marine Life* (1st series). *T* **203** *and similar multicoloured designs. W* **111** (*sideways on 45 and 75 c.*). *P 14*.

508	20 c.	Type **203** ..	..	15	10
509	45 c.	Tube Sponge (*horiz*)	..	25	35
510	60 c.	Black Coral	..	35	45
511	75 c.	Tyre Reef (*horiz*) ..		40	75
508/11			*Set of 4*	1·00	1·50

See also Nos. 541/5.

204 Brown's Hutia (or Indian Coney) **205** White Orchid

(Des D. Bowen. Litho Questa)

1981 (25 May). *Brown's Hutia* (or Indian Coney). *T* **204** *and similar horiz designs. Multicoloured. W* **111**. *P 14*.

512	20 c.	Hutia facing right	..	15	20
	a.	Horiz strip of 4. Nos. 512/15 ..		55	
513	20 c.	Type **204**	..	15	20
514	20 c.	Hutia facing left and eating	..	15	20
515	20 c.	Hutia family	..	15	20
512/15			*Set of 4*	55	70

Nos. 512/15 were printed together, *se-tenant*, in horizontal strips of 4 throughout the sheet.

(Des J.W. Litho Format)

1981 (29 July). *Royal Wedding. T* **205** *and similar vert designs. Multicoloured. W w* **14** (*sideways*). *P* 13½ ($5) *or* 15 (*others*).

516	20 c.	Type **205**..	..	20	10
	a.	Perf 15 × 14½	..	25	25
	ab.	Booklet pane. Nos. 516a/19a ..		3·50	
517	45 c.	Royal Coach ..	..	35	20
	a.	Perf 15 × 14½	..	50	50
518	60 c.	Prince Charles and Lady Diana Spencer		50	30
	a.	Perf 15 × 14½	..	60	60
519	$5	St. James' Palace	..	1·00	1·50
	a.	Perf 15 × 14½	..	2·50	3·50
516/19			*Set of 4*	1·75	1·90
MS520		98 × 85 mm. No. 519. Wmk upright. P 13½		1·90	2·40

Nos. 516/18 also exist perforated 13½ (*price for set of 3 £2.25 mint or used*) from additional sheetlets of 5 stamps and one label. No. 519 exists from both normal sheets and sheetlets.

Nos. 516a/19a are from $6.25 stamp booklets.

206 Blind Man at Work **207** W.F.D. Emblem on 1964 1½d. Definitive

(Des G. Vasarhelyi. Litho J.W.)

1981 (14 Sept). *International Year for Disabled Persons. T* **206** *and similar horiz designs. Multicoloured. W* **111** (*sideways*). *P 13*.

521	20 c.	Type **206** ..	..	15	15
522	45 c.	Painting with the mouth	..	40	40
523	60 c.	Deaf student communicating with sign language	..	50	50
524	$1.50	Basketball players	..	1·25	1·25
521/4			*Set of 4*	2·10	2·10

(Des J. Mahfood. Litho J.W.)

1981 (16 Oct). *World Food Day. Stamps on Stamps. T* **207** *and similar designs showing W.F.D. emblems on various definitives. W* **111** (*sideways on 20 c.,* $2 *and* $4). *P 13*.

525	20 c.	multicoloured	..	30	15
526	45 c.	black, rose and orange	..	40	45
527	$2	black, violet-blue and green	..	1·75	1·40
528	$4	black, green and light brown	..	3·00	2·50
525/8			*Set of 4*	5·00	4·00

Designs: *Vert as T* **207**—45 c. 1922 1d. (40 × 26 *mm.*)—$2 As 1938 3d. but with W.F.D. emblem replacing King's head; $4 As 1938 1s. but with W.F.D. emblem replacing King's head.

Nos. 525/8 were so designed that the face values obliterated those on the stamps depicted.

208 "Survival" (song title) **209** Webb Memorial Baptist Church

(Litho Format)

1981 (20 Oct). *Bob Marley* (musician) *Commemoration. T* **208** *and similar vert designs inscribed with song titles. In black and vermilion* ($5.25) *or multicoloured* (*others*). *W w* **14** (*sideways*). *P 15*.

529	1 c.	Type **208** ..	..	10	10
530	2 c.	"Exodus"	..	10	10
531	3 c.	"Is this Love"	..	10	10
532	15 c.	"Coming in from the Cold"*	..	50	15
533	20 c.	"Positive Vibration"†	..	60	20
534	60 c.	"War"	..	1·40	1·25
535	$3	"Could you be Loved"	..	7·00	5·50
529/35			*Set of 7*	8·50	6·50
MS536		134 × 110 mm. $5.25, Bob Marley (wmk upright)		6·50	4·75

*Part of initial "C" of song title inscription does not show on the design.

†Incorrectly inscribed "OSITIVE VIBRATION".

(Des J.W. Litho Questa)

1981 (11 Dec). *Christmas. Churches* (2nd series). *T* **209** *and similar horiz designs. Multicoloured. W* **111** (*sideways*). *P 14*.

537	10 c.	Type **209** ..	..	10	10
538	45 c.	Church of God in Jamaica	..	30	15
539	$5	Bryce United Church	..	2·25	2·50
537/9			*Set of 3*	2·40	2·50
MS540		120 × 168 mm. Nos. 537/9 (wmk upright). P 12		3·50	3·25

210 Gorgonian Coral **211** Cub Scout

(Des J. Mahfood; adapted PAD Studio. Litho Questa)

1982 (22 Feb). *Marine Life* (2nd series). T **210** *and similar multicoloured designs.* W **111** *(sideways on 45, 60, 75 c. and $3).* P 14.
541	20 c. Type 210..	..	25	10
542	45 c. Hard Sponge and diver (*horiz*)	..	45	25
543	60 c. American Manatee (*horiz*)	..	60	40
544	75 c. Plume Worm (*horiz*)	..	70	50
545	$3 Coral Banded Shrimp (*horiz*)	..	2·00	1·60
541/5	.. ..	Set of 5	3·50	2·50

(Des L. Curtis. Litho J.W.)

1982 (12 July). *75th Anniv of Boy Scout Movement.* T **211** *and similar vert designs. Multicoloured.* W **111**. P 13½ × 13.
546	20 c. Type 211	..	40	15
547	45 c. Scout camp	..	75	40
548	60 c. "Out of Many, One People"	..	95	50
549	$2 Lord Baden-Powell	..	1·75	1·75
546/9	.. ..	Set of 4	3·50	2·50
MS550	80 × 130 mm. Nos. 546/9 ..		3·50	4·00

**ROYAL BABY
21.6.82**

212 *Lignum vitae*
(national flower)   (212*a*)

(Des R. Sauer. Litho Questa)

1982 (30 Aug). *21st Birthday of Princess of Wales.* T **212** *and similar vert designs.* W **111**. P 14½ × 14.
551	20 c. Type 212	..	20	20
	a. Booklet pane. Nos. 551/3.	..	1·00	
552	45 c. Carriage ride	..	35	35
553	60 c. Wedding	..	50	50
554	75 c. *Saxifraga longifolia*	..	70	70
	a. Booklet pane. Nos. 554/6.	..	3·00	
555	$2 Princess of Wales	..	1·00	1·50
556	$3 *Viola gracilis major*	..	1·25	2·00
551/6	.. .. ..	Set of 6	3·50	4·75
MS557	106 × 75 mm. $5 Honeymoon photograph		2·00	3·00

Nos. 554 and 556 were printed in small sheets of 6 including one *se-tenant*, stamp-size, label. The other values were printed in sheets of 40.

1982 (13 Sept). *Birth of Prince William of Wales.* Nos. 551/7 *optd with* T 212*a*.
558	20 c. Type 212	..	20	20
	a. Booklet pane. Nos. 558/60	..	1·00	
559	45 c. Carriage ride	..	35	35
560	60 c. Wedding	..	50	50
561	75 c. *Saxifraga longifolia*	..	70	70
	a. Booklet pane. Nos. 561/3.	..	3·00	
562	$2 Princess of Wales	..	1·00	1·50
563	$3 *Viola gracilis major*	..	1·25	2·00
558/63	.. ..	Set of 6	3·50	4·75
MS564	106 × 75 mm. $5 Honeymoon photograph		2·25	3·50

213 Prey Captured   **214** Queen Elizabeth II

(Des N. Arlott. Litho Questa)

1982 (25 Oct). *Jamaican Birds* (1st series). *Jamaican Lizard Cuckoo.* T **213** *and similar vert designs. Multicoloured.* W **111**. P 14½.
565	$1 Type 213	..	80	80
	a. Horiz strip of 5. Nos. 565/9		3·50	
566	$1 Searching for prey	..	80	80
567	$1 Calling prior to prey search	..	80	80
568	$1 Adult landing	..	80	80
569	$1 Adult flying in	..	80	80
565/9	.. .. ..	Set of 5	3·50	3·50

Nos. 565/9 were printed in horizontal *se-tenant* strips of 5 throughout the sheet.

See also Nos. 642/5 and 707/10.

(Des and litho J.W.)

1982 (8 Dec). *Christmas. Churches* (3rd series). *Horiz designs as* T **209**. *Multicoloured.* W **111** *(sideways).* P 13.
570	20 c. United Pentecostal Church	..	15	10
571	45 c. Disciples of Christ Church	..	30	25
572	75 c. Open Bible Church	..	55	70
570/2	.. ..	Set of 3	90	95

(Des D. Miller. Litho Walsall)

1983 (14 Feb). *Royal Visit.* T **214** *and similar vert design. Multicoloured.* W **111**. P 14.
573	$2 Type 214	..	2·75	2·25
574	$3 Coat of Arms	..	3·75	3·25

215 Folk Dancing

(Des Walsall. Litho Format)

1983 (14 Mar). *Commonwealth Day.* T **215** *and similar horiz designs.* W **111** *(sideways).* P 14.
575	20 c. Type 215	..	15	15
576	45 c. Bauxite mining	..	35	35
577	75 c. World map showing position of Jamaica		45	45
578	$2 Coat of arms and family ..		1·25	1·40
575/8	.. .. ..	Set of 4	2·00	2·10

216 General Cargo Ship at Wharf   **217** Norman Manley and Sir Alexander Bustamante

(Des A. Theobald. Litho Format)

1983 (17 Mar). *25th Anniv of International Maritime Organization.* T **216** *and similar horiz designs. Multicoloured.* P 14.
579	15 c. Type 216	..	75	20
580	20 c. *Veendam* (cruise liner) at Kingston	..	1·00	30
581	45 c. Container ship entering port	..	1·75	85
582	$1 Tanker passing International Seabed Headquarters Building	..	2·75	3·25
579/82	.. ..	Set of 4	5·50	4·25

(Des D. Miller. Litho Harrison)

1983 (25 July). *21st Anniv of Independence.* W **111**. P 14.
583	217 15 c. multicoloured	..	15	15
584	20 c. multicoloured	..	15	20
585	45 c. multicoloured	..	30	40
583/5	.. ..	Set of 3	55	70

218 Ship-to-Shore Radio   **219** "Racing at Caymanas"
(Sidney Mclaren)

(Des Walsall. Litho Harrison)

1983 (18 Oct). *World Communications Year.* T **218** *and similar horiz designs. Multicoloured.* W **111** *(sideways).* P 14.
586	20 c. Type 218	..	15	15
587	45 c. Postal services	..	35	40
588	75 c. Telephone communications	..	55	1·00
589	$1 T.V. via satellite	..	75	1·50
586/9	.. .. ..	Set of 4	1·50	2·75

(Des D. Miller. Litho J.W.)

1983 (12 Dec). *Christmas. Paintings.* T **219** *and similar multicoloured designs.* W **111** *(sideways on 15 c., 20 c.).* P 13 × 13½ *(15 c., 20 c.) or 13½ × 13 (others).*
590	15 c. Type 219	..	10	10
591	20 c. "Seated Figures" (Karl Parboosingh)	..	10	10
592	75 c. "The Petitioner" (Henry Daley) (*vert*)	..	30	30
593	$2 "Banana Plantation" (John Dunkley) (*vert*)	..	70	1·25
590/3	.. ..	Set of 4	1·00	1·50

220 Sir Alexander Bustamante   **221** "D.H. 60G Gipsy Moth" Seaplane

(Des D. Miller. Litho Questa)

1984 (24 Feb). *Birth Centenary of Sir Alexander Bustamante.* T **220** *and similar vert design. Multicoloured.* W **111**. P 14.
594	20 c. Type 220	..	40	50
	a. Horiz pair. Nos. 594/5	..	80	1·00
595	20 c. Birthplace, Blenheim	..	40	50

Nos. 594/5 were printed together, *se-tenant*, in horizontal pairs throughout the sheet.

(Des A. Theobald. Litho Questa)

1984 (11 June). *Seaplanes and Flying Boats.* T **221** *and similar horiz designs. Multicoloured.* W **111** *(sideways).* P 14.
596	25 c. Type 221	..	65	15
597	55 c. Consolidated "Commodore" flying boat	..	1·00	55
598	$1.50, Sikorsky "S-38" flying boat	..	1·75	2·00
599	$3 Sikorsky "S-40" flying boat	..	2·50	2·75
596/9	..	Set of 4	5·50	5·00

222 Cycling   **223**

(Des G. Vasarhelyi. Litho J.W.)

1984 (11 July). *Olympic Games, Los Angeles.* T **222** *and similar horiz designs. Multicoloured.* W **111** *(sideways).* P 14.
600	25 c. Type 222	..	10	10
601	55 c. Relay running	..	20	25
602	$1.50, Start of race	..	60	1·00
603	$3 Finish of race	..	1·10	1·75
600/3	..	Set of 4	1·75	2·75
MS604	135 × 105 mm. Nos. 600/3 (*sold at $5.40*). P 13 × 13½	..	1·90	2·75

1984 (7 Aug). *Nos. 465 and 469 surch as* T **223**.
605	5 c. on 6 c. Fern Gully, Ocho Rios	..	10	20
606	10 c. on 12 c. Yellow-billed Amazon	..	40	40

224 Head of Jamaican Boa Snake

(Des I. Loe. Litho Questa)

1984 (22 Oct). *Jamaican Boa Snake.* T **224** *and similar horiz designs. Multicoloured.* W **111** *(sideways).* P 14½.
607	25 c. Type 224	..	45	15
608	55 c. Boa snake on branch over stream	..	75	55
609	70 c. Snake with young	..	90	90
610	$1 Snake on log	..	1·10	1·25
607/10	..	Set of 4	2·75	2·50
MS611	133 × 97 mm. As Nos. 607/10 but without W.W.F. emblem (*sold at $2.60*)		2·75	2·50

225 *Enterprise* (1845)   **226** "Accompong Madonna"
(Namba Roy)

(Des D. Hartley-Marjoram. Litho Enschedé)

1984 (16 Nov). *Railway Locomotives* (1st series). T **225** *and similar horiz designs. Multicoloured.* W **111** *(sideways).* P 13½ × 13.
612	25 c. Type 225	..	50	15
613	55 c. Tank locomotive (1880)	..	70	50
614	$1.50, Kitson-Meyer tank locomotive (1904)		1·00	1·25
615	$3 Super-heated locomotive (1916)	..	1·75	2·25
612/15	.. ..	Set of 4	3·50	3·75

See also Nos. 634/7.

(Des G. Vasarhelyi. Litho Harrison)

1984 (6 Dec). *Christmas. Sculptures.* T **226** *and similar vert designs. Multicoloured.* W **111**. P 14.
616	20 c. Type 226	..	20	10
617	25 c. "Head" (Alvin Marriott)	..	25	10
618	55 c. "Moon" (Edna Manley)	..	50	50
619	$1.50, "All Women are Five Women" (Mallica Reynolds (Kapo))	..	1·00	1·75
616/19	..	Set of 4	1·75	2·25

227 Brown Pelicans flying   **228** The Queen Mother at Belfast University

11

(Des N. Arlott. Litho Walsall)

1985 (15 Apr). *Birth Bicentenary of John J. Audubon (ornithologist). Brown Pelican. T 227 and similar vert designs. Multicoloured. W 111. P 13½×13.*

620	20 c. Type 227		50	10
621	55 c. Diving for fish		65	30
622	$2 Young pelican taking food from adult		1·10	1·25
623	$5 "Brown Pelican" (John J. Audubon)		1·75	2·50
620/3		*Set of 4*	3·50	3·75
MS624	100×100 mm. Nos. 620/3 (*sold at*			
	$7.85)		3·00	3·50

(Des A. Theobald ($5), C. Abbott (others). Litho Questa)

1985 (7 June). *Life and Times of Queen Elizabeth the Queen Mother. T 228 and similar vert designs. Multicoloured. W 111. P 14½×14.*

625	25 c. With photograph album, 1963		10	10
626	55 c. With Prince Charles at Garter Ceremony, Windsor Castle, 1983		15	15
627	$1.50, Type 228		35	45
628	$3 With Prince Henry at his christening (from photo by Lord Snowdon)		65	90
625/8		*Set of 4*	1·10	1·40
MS629	91×74 mm. $5 With the Queen, Prince Philip and Princess Anne at Ascot. Wmk sideways		1·25	1·40

229 Maps and Emblems

(Des D. Miller. Litho Harrison)

1985 (30 July). *International Youth Year and 5th Pan-American Scout Jamboree. W 111 (sideways). P 14.*

630	**229**	25 c. multicoloured	15	10
631		55 c. multicoloured	20	20
632		70 c. multicoloured	30	30
633		$4 multicoloured	1·10	1·40
630/3		*Set of 4*	1·60	1·75

(Des D. Hartley. Litho Harrison)

1985 (30 Sept). *Railway Locomotives (2nd series). Horiz designs as T 225. Multicoloured. W 111 (sideways). P 14.*

634	25 c. Baldwin locomotive No. 16		45	10
635	55 c. Rogers locomotive		70	15
636	$1.50, locomotive *The Projector*		1·00	75
637	$4 Diesel locomotive No. 102		1·75	1·75
634/7		*Set of 4*	3·50	2·50

230 "The Old Settlement"   **230a** Princess Elizabeth
(Ralph Campbell)   and Princess Margaret,
1939

(Litho Format)

1985 (9 Dec). *Christmas. Jamaican Paintings. T 230 and similar multicoloured designs. W 111 (sideways on 20, 75 c.). P 14.*

638	20 c. Type 230		10	10
639	55 c. "The Vendor" (Albert Huie) (*vert*)		15	15
640	75 c. "Road Menders" (Gaston Tabois)		15	20
641	$4 "Woman, must I not be about my Father's business?" (Carl Abrahams) (*vert*)		90	95
638/41		*Set of 4*	1·10	1·25

(Des N. Arlott. Litho B.D.T.)

1986 (10 Feb). *Jamaican Birds (2nd series). Vert designs as T 213. Multicoloured. W 111. P 14.*

642	25 c. Chestnut-bellied Cuckoo		40	10
643	55 c. Jamaican Becard		55	30
644	$1.50, White-eyed Thrush		70	1·00
645	$5 Rufous-tailed Flycatcher		1·60	3·00
642/5		*Set of 4*	3·00	4·00

(Des A. Theobald. Litho Harrison)

1986 (21 Apr). *60th Birthday of Queen Elizabeth II. T 230a and similar designs. Multicoloured. W 111. P 14½×14.*

646	20 c. Type 230a		10	10
647	25 c. With Prince Charles and Prince Andrew, 1962		10	10
648	70 c. Queen visiting War Memorial, Montego Bay, 1983		15	25
649	$3 On state visit to Luxembourg, 1976		65	90
650	$5 At Crown Agents Head Office, London, 1983		1·25	1·75
646/50		*Set of 5*	1·90	2·75

231 Bustamante Children's   **231a** Prince
Hospital   Andrew and Miss
Sarah Ferguson,
Ascot, 1985

(Des D. Miller. Litho Questa)

1986 (19 May). *"Ameripex '86" International Stamp Exhibition, Chicago. T 231 and similar vert designs. Multicoloured. W 111. P 14½×14.*

651	25 c. Type 231		30	10
652	55 c. Air Jamaica jet airliner and map of holiday resorts		35	15
653	$3 Norman Manley Law School		1·00	1·40
654	$5 Bauxite and agricultural exports		4·00	4·00
651/4		*Set of 4*	5·00	5·00
MS655	85×106 mm. Nos. 651/4 (*sold at* $8.90)		5·00	5·00

(Des D. Miller. Litho Walsall)

1986 (23 July). *Royal Wedding. T 231a and similar square design. Multicoloured. W 111. P 14½×14.*

656	20 c. Type 231a		15	10
657	$5 Prince Andrew making speech, Fredericton, Canada, 1985		1·40	1·90

232 Richard   **(233)**
"Shrimpy" Clarke

(Des G. Vasarhelyi. Litho Questa)

1986 (27 Oct). *Jamaican Boxing Champions. T 232 and similar vert designs. Multicoloured. W 111. P 14.*

658	45 c. Type 232		20	15
659	70 c. Michael McCallum		30	20
660	$2 Trevor Berbick		70	55
661	$4 Richard "Shrimpy" Clarke, Michael McCallum and Trevor Berbick		1·25	1·25
658/61		*Set of 4*	2·25	1·90

1986 (3 Nov). *Nos. 472/3 surch as T 233.*

662	5 c. on 50 c. Jamaican Woodpecker		40	50
663	10 c. on 65 c. Rafting, Martha Brae Trelawny		40	50

234 *Heliconia*   **235** Crown Cone
wagneriana

(Des Annette Robinson. Litho B.D.T.)

1986 (1 Dec). *Christmas. Flowers (1st series). T 234 and similar multicoloured designs. W 111 (sideways on 25 c., $5). P 13½.*

664	20 c. Type 234		10	10
665	25 c. *Heliconia psittacorum* (*horiz*)		10	10
666	55 c. *Heliconia rostrata*		20	30
667	$5 *Strelitzia reginae* (*horiz*)		1·60	2·75
664/7		*Set of 4*	1·75	2·75

See also Nos. 703/6 and 739/42.

(Des A. Riley. Litho Format)

1987 (23 Feb). *Sea Shells. T 235 and similar vert designs. Multicoloured. W 111. P 15.*

668	35 c. Type 235		20	10
669	75 c. Measled Cowrie		30	20
670	$1 Trumpet Triton		40	40
671	$5 Rooster Tail Conch		1·40	1·75
668/71		*Set of 4*	2·10	2·25

COVER PRICES

Cover factors are quoted at the beginning of each country for most issues to 1945. An explanation of the system can be found on page x. The factors quoted do not, however, apply to philatelic covers.

236 Norman Manley   **237** Arms of Jamaica

(Des C. Slania (1 c. to 90 c.). Litho Enschedé)

1987 (18 May)–92. *Vert portraits as T 236 and T 237. W 111 (sideways on $1 to $50). Cream paper (2 c. to 9 c. (Nos. 673A/80A)). P 12½×13 (1 to 90 c.) or 13×13½ ($1 to $50). A. Without imprint. B. With imprint date at foot.*

			A		B	
672	**236**	1 c. scarlet and pale pink	10	10	†	
673		2 c. brt carm & pale rose-pk	10	10	†	
674		3 c. yellow-ol & pale stone	10	10	†	
675		4 c. myrtle-grn & pale grn	10	10	†	
676		5 c. slate-blue and pale bluish grey	10	10	10	10
677		6 c. dull ultramarine and pale lavender-grey	10	10	†	
678		7 c. reddish vio & pale mve	10	10	†	
679		8 c. dp mag & pale rose-pk	10	10	†	
680		9 c. olive-sepia & pale brn	10	10	†	
681	—	10 c. dp rose-red & pale pink	10	10	†	
682	—	20 c. reddish orange & flesh	15	10	10	10
683	—	30 c. brt green & pale green	10	10	†	
684	—	40 c. dp turquoise-green & pale turquoise-green	10	10	10	10
685	—	50 c. grey-ol & pale ol-grey	15	10	10	10
686	—	60 c. brt blue & pale azure	10	10	†	
687	—	70 c. bluish violet & pale vio	10	10	†	
688	—	80 c. reddish violet and pale rose-lilac	10	10	†	
689	—	90 c. light reddish brown and pale grey-brown	15	10	10	10
690	**237**	$1 olive-sepia and cream	10	15	10	15
691		$2 bright orange & cream	15	20	†	
692		$5 brown-ol & pale stone	30	35	†	
693		$10 dp turquoise-blue & pale azure	55	60	†	
693c		$25 bluish violet and pale lavender		†	1·40	1·60
693d		$50 deep mauve and pale rose-lilac		†	2·75	3·00
672A/93A		*Set of 22*	2·10	2·25		
676B/93dB		*Set of 8*			4·25	4·25

Designs:—10 c. to 90 c. Sir Alexander Bustamante.
Dates of issue: 18.5.87, Nos. 672A/93A; 6.6.88, Nos. 676B, 682B; 12.2.91, Nos. 684B, 685B; 6.6.91 No. 690B; 9.10.91, Nos. 693cB, 693dB; 5.92, No. 689B.
Nos. 682B, 684B/5B and 690B exist with different imprint dates beneath the design.

238 Jamaican Flag and   **239** Marcus Garvey
Coast at Sunset

(Des D. Miller. Litho Walsall)

1987 (27 July). *25th Anniv of Independence. T 238 and similar multicoloured design. W 111 (sideways on 70 c.). P 14.*

694	55 c. Type 238		60	50
695	70 c. Jamaican flag and inscription (*horiz*)		80	1·00

(Des D. Miller. Litho Walsall)

1987 (17 Aug). *Birth Centenary of Marcus Garvey (founder of Universal Negro Improvement Association). T 239 and similar vert design, both black, emerald and lemon. W 111. P 14.*

696	25 c. Type 239		40	55
	a. Horiz pair. Nos. 696/7		80	1·10
697	25 c. Statue of Marcus Garvey		40	55

Nos. 696/7 were printed together, *se-tenant*, in horizontal pairs throughout the sheet.

240 Salvation Army School   **241** Hibiscus Hybrid
for the Blind

(Des L. Curtis. Litho Walsall)

1987 (8 Oct). *Centenary of Salvation Army in Jamaica. T 240 and similar horiz designs. Multicoloured. W 111 (sideways). P 13×13½.*

698	25 c. Type 240		40	40
699	55 c. Col. Mary Booth and Bramwell Booth Memorial Hall		65	30

700	$3 Welfare Service lorry, 1929 ..	..		1·75	2·00
701	$5 Col. Abram Davey and S.S. *Alene*, 1887		2·50	3·00
698/701			*Set of 4*	4·75	4·75
MS702	100×80 mm. Nos. 698/701 (*sold at* $8.90)		4·75	5·00

(Des Annette Robinson. Litho Harrison)

1987 (30 Nov). *Christmas. Flowers (2nd series). T 241 and similar vert designs. Multicoloured. W 111. P 14½×14.*

703	20 c. Type 241..	..	..		10	10
704	25 c. *Hibiscus elatus* ..	..		10	10
705	$4 *Hibiscus cannabinus*	..		90	95
706	$5 *Hibiscus rosasinensis* ..	..		1·25	1·40
703/6	..	..	*Set of 4*	2·00	2·25

242 Chestnut-bellied Cuckoo, Black-billed Amazon and Jamaican Euphonia

243 Blue Whales

(Des N. Arlott. Litho Walsall)

1988 (22 Jan). *Jamaican Birds (3rd series). T 242 and similar vert designs. Multicoloured. W 111. P 14.*

707	45 c. Type 242	..		50	65
	a. Horiz pair. Nos. 707/8	..		1·00	1·25
708	45 c. Jamaican White-eyed Vireo, Rufous-throated Solitaire and Yellow Elaenia		50	65
709	$5 Snowy Plover, Little Blue Heron and Great Blue Heron (white phase)		2·00	2·25
	a. Horiz pair. Nos. 709/10	..		4·00	4·50
710	$5 Black-necked Stilt, Snowy Egret and Black-crowned Night Heron ..		2·00	2·25
707/10	..	..	*Set of 4*	4·50	5·25

The two designs of each value were printed together, *se-tenant*, in horizontal pairs throughout the sheets, each pair forming a composite design.

(Des A. Riley. Litho Harrison)

1988 (14 Apr). *Marine Mammals. T 243 and similar horiz designs. Multicoloured. W 111 (sideways). P 14.*

711	20 c. Type 243	..		60	20
712	25 c. Gervais's Whales	..		60	20
713	55 c. Killer Whales	..		90	35
714	$5 Common Dolphins	..		3·00	3·50
711/14	..	..	*Set of 4*	4·75	3·75

243a Jackie Hendriks

244 Jamaican Red Cross Workers with Ambulance

(Des D. Hartley. Litho Walsall)

1988 (6 June). *West Indian Cricket. T 243a and similar horiz designs, each showing portrait, cricket equipment and early belt buckle. Multicoloured. W 111 (sideways). P 14.*

715	25 c. Type 243a	..		40	10
716	55 c. George Headley	..		75	20
717	$2 Michael Holding	..		1·50	85
718	$3 R. K. Nunes ..	..		1·75	1·25
719	$4 Allan Rae ..	..		2·00	1·50
715/19	..	..	*Set of 5*	5·75	3·50

(Des S. Noon. Litho Walsall)

1988 (8 Aug). *125th Anniv of International Red Cross. T 244 and similar vert design. Multicoloured. W 111. P 14½ × 14.*

720	55 c. Type 244	..		50	20
721	$5 Henri Dunant (founder) in field hospital	..		2·00	2·40

245 Boxing

(Des P. Broadbent. Litho B.D.T.)

1988 (24 Aug). *Olympic Games, Seoul. T 245 and similar horiz designs. Multicoloured. W 111 (sideways). P 14.*

722	25 c. Type 245	..		10	10
723	45 c. Cycling	..		10	10
724	$4 Athletics	..		85	1·10
725	$5 Hurdling	..		1·00	1·25
722/5	..	..	*Set of 4*	1·75	2·25
MS726	127 × 87 mm. Nos. 722/5 (*sold at* $9.90)		2·10	2·50

246 Bobsled Team Members and Logo

(Des D. Miller. Litho B.D.T.)

1988 (4 Nov). *Jamaican Olympic Bobsled Team. T 246 and similar horiz designs. Multicoloured. W 111 (sideways). P 14.*

727	25 c. Type 246	..		10	30
	a. Horiz pair. Nos. 727/8	..		15	60
728	25 c. Two-man bobsled	..		10	30
729	$5 Bobsled team members (*different*) and logo	..		1·00	1·50
	a. Horiz pair. Nos. 729/30	..		2·00	3·00
730	$5 Four-man bobsled	..		1·00	1·50
727/30	..		*Set of 4*	1·90	3·25

Nos. 727/8 and 729/30 were printed together, *se-tenant*, in horizontal pairs throughout the sheets.

+25c

HURRICANE GILBERT RELIEF FUND

(247)

1988 (11 Nov). *Hurricane Gilbert Relief Fund. Nos. 722/5 surch as T 247 by Format. A. In red. B. In black.*

		A		B	
				A	B
731	25 c. + 25 c. Type 245	..	10	15	10	15
732	45 c. + 45 c. Cycling	..	20	25	20	25
733	$4 + $4 Athletics	..	1·75	1·90	1·75	1·90
734	$5 + $5 Hurdling ..	..	2·10	2·25	2·10	2·25
731/4	..	*Set of 4*	3·75	4·00	3·75	4·00

248 Nurses and Firemen

(Des S. Noon. Litho Format)

1988 (24 Nov). *Year of the Worker. T 248 and similar horiz designs. Multicoloured. W 111 (sideways). P 14.*

735	25 c. Type 248	..		30	10
736	55 c. Woodcarver	..		35	20
737	$3 Textile workers	..		1·10	1·50
738	$5 Workers on fish farm ..	..		1·60	1·90
735/8	..	..	*Set of 4*	3·00	3·25

(Des Annette Robinson. Litho Format)

1988 (15 Dec). *Christmas. Flowers (3rd series). Multicoloured designs as T 241. W 111 (sideways on 55 c., $4). P 14.*

739	25 c. *Euphorbia pulcherrima*	..		10	10
740	55 c. *Spathodea campanulata* (*horiz*)	..		15	15
741	$3 *Hylocereus triangularis*	..		75	80
742	$4 *Broughtonia sanguinea* (*horiz*)	..		85	90
739/42	..	..	*Set of 4*	1·60	1·75

249 Old York Castle School

250 *Syntomidopsis variegata*

(Des A. Theobald. Litho B.D.T.)

1989 (19 Jan). *Bicentenary of Methodist Church in Jamaica. T 249 and similar horiz designs. W 111 (sideways). P 13½.*

743	25 c. black and bright blue ..		10	10
744	45 c. black and rosine	..		15	10
745	$5 black and yellow-green	..		1·25	1·50
743/5	..	*Set of 3*	1·25	1·50

Designs:—45 c. Revd. Thomas Coke and Parade Chapel, Kingston; $5 Father Hugh Sherlock and St. John's Church.

(Des I. Loe. Litho B.D.T.)

1989 (30 Aug). *Jamaican Moths (1st series). T 250 and similar vert designs. Multicoloured. W 111. P 14×13½.*

746	25 c. Type 250	..		45	10
747	55 c. *Himantoides perkinsae*	..		70	25
748	$3 *Arctia nigriplaga*	..		1·40	1·50
749	$5 *Sthenognatha toddi*	..		1·75	2·00
746/9	..	..	*Set of 4*	4·00	3·50

See also Nos. 758/61 and 790/3.

251 Arawak Fisherman with Catch

252 Girl Guide

(Des Josephine Martin. Litho Cartor, France)

1989 (22 Dec). *500th Anniv of Discovery of America by Columbus (1992) (1st issue). T 251 and similar vert designs. Multicoloured. W 111. P 13½.*

750	25 c. Type 251	..	..	20	10
751	70 c. Arawak man smoking	..		40	30
752	$5 King Ferdinand and Queen Isabella inspecting caravels	..		1·75	2·00
753	$10 Columbus with chart	..		3·00	3·25
750/3	..	*Set of 4*	4·75	5·00
MS754	150×200 mm. Nos. 750/3. Wmk sideways. P 12½ (*sold at* $16.15)		5·00	6·00

No. MS754 also exists imperforate from a limited printing used in Presentation Packs.

See also Nos. 774/9 and 802/7.

(Des J. Sayer. Litho B.D.T.)

1990 (28 June). *75th Anniv of Girl Guide Movement in Jamaica. T 252 and similar vert designs. Multicoloured. W 111 (inverted on $5). P 14.*

755	45 c. Type 252	..		45	15
756	55 c. Guide leader	..		45	15
757	$5 Brownie, guide and ranger	..		2·50	2·75
755/7	..	*Set of 3*	3·00	2·75

(Des I. Loe. Litho B.D.T.)

1990 (12 Sept). *Jamaican Moths (2nd series). Vert designs as T 250. Multicoloured. W 111. P 14×13½.*

758	25 c. *Eunomia rubripunctata*	..		30	10
759	55 c. *Perigonia jamaicensis*	..		50	25
760	$4 *Uraga haemorrhoa*	..		1·25	1·50
761	$5 *Empyreuma pugione* ..	..		1·40	1·75
758/61	..	*Set of 4*	3·00	3·25

(253)

254 Teaching English

1990 (12 Sept). *"EXPO 90" International Garden and Greenery Exhibition, Osaka. Nos. 758/61 optd with T 253.*

762	25 c. *Eunomia rubripunctata*	..		30	10
763	55 c. *Perigonia jamaicensis*	..		50	25
764	$4 *Uraga haemorrhoa*	..		1·25	1·50
765	$5 *Empyreuma pugione* ..	..		1·40	1·75
762/5	..	*Set of 4*	3·00	3·25

(Des G. Vasarhelyi. Litho B.D.T.)

1990 (10 Oct). *International Literacy Year. T 254 and similar horiz design. Multicoloured. W 111 (sideways). P 14.*

766	55 c. Type 254	..		30	15
767	$5 Teaching maths	..		2·00	2·25

255 "To the Market"

(Adapted J. Mahfood and D. Miller. Litho Walsall)

1990 (7 Dec). *Christmas. Children's Paintings. T 255 and similar multicoloured designs. W 111 (sideways on horiz designs). P 14×13½ ($5) or 13½×14 (others).*

768	20 c. Type 255	..		15	10
769	25 c. "House and Garden"	..		15	10
770	55 c. "Jack and Jill"	..		20	15
771	70 c. "Market"	..		20	20
772	$1.50, "Lonely"	..		60	70
773	$5 "Market Woman" (*vert*)	..		1·50	2·00
768/73	..	*Set of 6*	2·50	2·75

256 Map of First Voyage, 1492

257 Weather Balloon, Dish Aerial and Map of Jamaica

(Des Josephine Martin. Litho Questa)

1990 (19 Dec). *500th Anniv of Discovery of America by Columbus (1992) (2nd issue). T 256 and similar horiz designs. Multicoloured. W 111 (sideways). P 14.*
774	25 c. Type 256	.. ..	10	10
775	45 c. Map of second voyage, 1493	..	10	10
776	$5 Map of third voyage, 1498	..	1·00	1·10
777	$10 Map of fourth voyage, 1502	..	1·90	2·10
774/7		Set of 4	2·75	3·00
MS778	126×99 mm. 25, 45 c., $5, $10 Composite map of Caribbean showing routes of voyages	..	4·00	4·50
MS779	148×207 mm. Nos. 774/7. Imperf	..	4·00	4·50

Unlike the imperforate version of No. MS754, No. MS779 was freely available at face value.

(Adapted G. Vasarhelyi. Litho B.D.T.)

1991 (20 May). *11th World Meteorological Congress, Kingston. W 111 (sideways). P 14.*
780	257	50 c. multicoloured	25	15
781		$10 multicoloured	1·50	1·75

258 Bust of Mary Seacole   **259** Jamaican Iguana

(Des Jennifer Toombs. Litho B.D.T.)

1991 (24 June). *International Council of Nurses Meeting of National Representatives. T 258 and similar horiz designs. W 111 (sideways). P 13½.*
782	50 c. multicoloured	..	25	15
783	$1.10, multicoloured	..	50	60
MS784	89×60 mm. $8 agate, pale orange-brown and yellow-ochre (sold at $8.20)		1·00	1·40

Designs:—$1.10, Mary Seacole House; $8 Hospital at Scutari, 1854.

(Des I. Loe. Litho Cartor)

1991 (29 July). *50th Anniv of Natural History Society of Jamaica. Jamaican Iguana. T 259 and similar vert designs. Multicoloured. W 111. P 13.*
785	$1.10, Type 259	..	30	30
	a. Horiz strip of 5. Nos. 785/9	..	1·40	
786	$1.10, Head of iguana looking right	30	30
787	$1.10, Iguana climbing	..	30	30
788	$1.10, Iguana on rock looking left	30	30
789	$1.10, Close-up of iguana's head	..	30	30
785/9		Set of 5	1·40	1·40

Nos. 785/9 were printed together, *se-tenant,* in horizontal strips of 5 throughout the sheet.

(Des I. Loe. Litho B.D.T.)

1991 (12 Aug). *Jamaican Moths (3rd series). Multicoloured designs as T 250. W 111. P 14×13½.*
790	50 c. *Urania sloanus*	..	25	10
791	$1.10, *Phoenicoprocta jamaicensis*	..	40	20
792	$1.40, *Horama grotei*	..	45	30
793	$8 *Amplypterus gannascus*	..	1·60	1·75
790/3		Set of 4	2·40	2·00

(260)   **261** "Doctor Bird"

1991 (23 Sept). *"Phila Nippon '91" International Stamp Exhibition, Tokyo. Nos. 790/3 optd with T 260.*
794	50 c. *Urania sloanus*	..	25	10
795	$1.10, *Phoenicoprocta jamaicensis*	..	40	20
796	$1.40, *Horama grotei*	..	45	20
797	$8 *Amplypterus gannascus*	..	1·60	1·75
794/7		Set of 4	2·40	2·00

(Litho Enschedé)

1991 (27 Nov). *Christmas. Children's Paintings. T 261 and similar horiz designs. Multicoloured. W 111 (sideways). P 14×15.*
798	50 c. Type 261	..	20	10
799	$1.10, "Road scene"	..	35	20
800	$5 "Children and house"	..	75	80
801	$10 "Cows grazing"	..	1·40	1·60
798/801		Set of 4	2·40	2·40

262 Indians threatening Ships

263 Compasses and Square Symbol

(Des Josephine Martin. Litho B.D.T.)

1991 (16 Dec). *500th Anniv of Discovery of America by Columbus (1992) (3rd issue). T 262 and similar horiz designs. Multicoloured. W 111 (sideways). P 13½.*
802	50 c. Type 262	..	15	10
803	$1.10, Spaniards setting dog on Indians	..	20	15
804	$1.40, Indian with gift of pineapple	..	20	15
805	$25 Columbus describes Jamaica with crumpled paper	..	2·00	2·50
802/5		Set of 4	2·25	2·50
MS806	125×102 mm. Nos. 802/5 (sold at $28.20)		2·50	2·75
MS807	210×150 mm. Nos. 802/5. Imperf		2·50	2·75

(Litho Cartor)

1992 (1 May). *250th Anniv of First Provincial Grand Master of English Freemasonry in Jamaica. T 263 and similar vert designs. Multicoloured. W 111. P 13½.*
808	50 c. multicoloured	..	15	10
809	$1.10, Symbol in stained glass window	..	20	20
810	$1.40, Compasses and square on book	..	20	20
811	$25 Eye in triangle symbol	..	2·50	2·75
808/11		Set of 4	2·75	3·00
MS812	140×80 mm. Nos. 808/11 (sold at $28.50)		3·00	3·25

264 Ship in Flooded Street

(Des J. Batchelor. Litho Cartor)

1992 (1 June). *300th Anniv of Destruction of Port Royal. T 264 and similar horiz designs. Multicoloured. W 111 (sideways). P 14×13½.*
813	50 c. Type 264	..	10	10
814	$1.10, Church tower falling	..	15	15
815	$1.40, Houses collapsing	..	15	15
816	$25 Inhabitants falling into fissure	..	2·00	2·00
813/16		Set of 4	2·25	2·25
MS817	116×75 mm. $5 Contemporary broadsheet of earthquake. Wmk upright. P 13×12		65	70

No. MS817 has a description of the broadsheet printed on the reverse under the gum.

265 Credit Union Symbol

(Des G. Vasarhelyi. Litho Enschedé)

1992 (24 Aug). *50th Anniv of Credit Union Movement. T 265 and similar horiz design. W 111 (sideways). P 14×15.*
818	50 c. dp dull bl, emer & pale turquoise-green	15	10
819	$1.40, multicoloured	..	20	25

Design:—$1.40, O'Hare Hall.

266 Jamaican Flag and Beach Scene

(Des G. Vasarhelyi. Litho Cartor)

1992 (26 Oct). *30th Anniv of Independence. W 111 (sideways). P 13½.*
820	266	50 c. multicoloured	..	10	10
821		$1.10, multicoloured	..	15	15
822		$25 multicoloured	..	2·00	2·00
820/2			Set of 3	2·00	2·00

POSTAL FISCALS

Revenue stamps were authorised for postal use by Post Office notice of 12 October 1887.

CONDITION. The note at the beginning also applies to Nos. F1/6.

F 1

(Typo D.L.R.)

1865–71 (Issued). *P 14. (a) Wmk Pineapple (T 7).*
F1	F 1	1d. rose (1865)	..	70·00	90·00
		a. Imperf (pair)	..	£400	

(b) *Wmk Crown CC*
F2	F 1	1d. rose (1868)	..	50·00	50·00

(c) *Wmk CA over Crown (Type w 7 sideways, covering two stamps)*
F3	F 1	1d. rose (1870 or 1871)	..	17·00	7·00
		a. Imperf	..		

F 2   F 3

(Typo D.L.R.)

1855–74 (Issued). *Glazed paper. P 14. (a) No wmk.*
F4	F 2	1½d. blue/*blue* (1857)	..	45·00	45·00
		a. Imperf (1855)	..		
		b. Blue on white	..	50·00	55·00
F5		3d. purple/*blue* (1857)	..	42·00	50·00
		a. Imperf (1855)	..		
		b. Purple on lilac (1857)	..	42·00	50·00
		ba. Imperf (1855)	..		
		c. Purple on white (1857)	..	50·00	50·00

(b) *Wmk Crown CC*
F6	F 2	3d. purple/*lilac* (1874)	..	9·00	13·00

All the above stamps *imperf* are exceedingly rare postally used.

1858 (1 Jan). (Issued). *No wmk. P 15½ × 15.*
F7	F 3	1s. rose/*bluish*	..	65·00	70·00
F8		5s. lilac/*bluish*	..	£325	£375
F9		10s. green/*bluish*	..	£375	£425

Telegraph stamps were also used postally, but no authority was given for such use.

OFFICIAL STAMPS

OFFICIAL   **OFFICIAL**
(O 1)   (O 2)

1890 (1 April). *No. 16 optd with Type O 1 by C. Vendryes, Kingston.*
		(a) "OFFICIAL" 17 to 17½ mm long			
O1	8	½d. green	..	5·50	1·00
		a. "O" omitted	..	£450	
		b. One "I" omitted			
		c. Both "I"s omitted	..	£500	£500
		d. "L" omitted	..	—	£550
		e. Opt inverted	..	65·00	70·00
		f. Opt double	..	65·00	70·00
		g. Opt double, one inverted	..	£325	£325
		h. Opt double, one vertical	..	£550	
		j. Pair, overprints *tête-bêche*	..		
		(b) "OFFICIAL" 15 to 16 mm long			
O2	8	½d. green	..	22·00	22·00
		a. Opt double	..	£500	

There were four (or possibly five) settings of this overprint, all but one being of the longer type. There are numerous minor varieties, due to broken type, etc. (e.g. a broken "E" used for "F").

Stamps with the 17–17½ mm opt were reissued in 1894 during a temporary shortage of No. O3.

1890–1. *Optd with Type O 2 by D.L.R. Wmk Crown CA. P 14.*
O3	8	½d. green (1891)	..	3·50	15
O4	11	1d. rose (1.4.90)	..	3·50	40
O5		2d. grey (1.4.90)	..	4·00	1·00
O3/5			Set of 3	10·00	1·40
O3/5	Optd "Specimen"	..	Set of 3	£100	

PRICES OF SETS

Set prices are given for many issues, generally those containing three stamps or more. Definitive sets include one of each value or major colour change, but do not cover different perforations, die types or minor shades. Where a choice is possible the set prices are based on the cheapest versions of the stamps included in the listings.

Jordan
see Transjordan

Kenya

INDEPENDENT

1 Cattle Ranching

2 Wood-carving

3 National Assembly

(Des V. Whiteley. Photo Harrison)

1963 (12 Dec). *Independence. T 1/3 and similar designs. P 14 × 15 (small designs) or 14½ (others).*

1	5 c. brown, deep blue, green and bistre	..	10	40
2	10 c. brown		10	10
3	15 c. magenta	..	60	10
4	20 c. black and yellow-green	..	15	10
5	30 c. black and yellow	..	15	10
6	40 c. brown and light blue	..	15	20
7	50 c. crimson, black and green	..	15	10
8	65 c. deep turquoise-green and yellow	..	55	65
9	1 s. multicoloured	..	20	10
10	1 s. 30, brown, black and yellow-green		2·50	10
11	2 s. multicoloured	..	60	40
12	5 s. brown, ultramarine and yellow-green		1·25	40
13	10 s. brown and deep blue	..	7·00	10·00
14	20 s. black and rose	..	5·50	5·00
1/14		*Set of 14*	17·00	8·50

Designs: As *T 1/2*—15 c. Heavy industry; 20 c. Timber industry; 30 c. Jomo Kenyatta and Mt Kenya; 40 c. Fishing industry; 50 c. Kenya flag; 65 c. Pyrethrum industry. As *T 3*—1 s. 30, Tourism (Treetops Hotel); 2 s. Coffee industry; 5 s. Tea industry; 10 s. Mombasa Port; 20 s. Royal College, Nairobi.

The 10 c. was produced in coils of 1000 in addition to normal sheets.

REPUBLIC

4 Cockerel

(Des M. Goaman. Photo J. Enschedé)

1964 (12 Dec). *Inauguration of Republic T 4 and similar vert designs. Multicoloured. P 13 × 12½.*

15	15 c. Type 4	..	20	15
16	30 c. President Kenyatta	..	25	10
17	50 c. Lion	..	35	10
18	1 s. 30, Hartlaub's Turaco	..	2·75	50
19	2 s. 50, Nandi flame	..	1·75	3·75
15/19	..	*Set of 5*	4·75	4·00

5 Thomson's Gazelle

6 Sable Antelope

7 Greater Kudu

(Des Rena Fennessy. Photo Harrison)

1966 (12 Dec)–**71**. *Various designs as T 5/7. Chalk-surfaced paper. P 14 × 14½ (5 c. to 70 c.) or 14½ (others).*

20	5 c. orange, black and sepia	..	20	20
21	10 c. black and apple-green		10	10
	a. Glazed, ordinary paper (13.7.71)	..	70	1·25
22	15 c. black and orange		10	10
	a. Glazed, ordinary paper (13.7.71)	..	70	1·00
23	20 c. ochre, black and blue		10	15
	a. Glazed, ordinary paper (22.1.71)	..	1·00	1·50
24	30 c. Prussian blue, blue and black	..	10	10
25	40 c. black and yellow-brown		50	30
	a. Glazed, ordinary paper (19.2.71)	..	1·00	1·50
26	50 c. black and red-orange		50	10
	a. Glazed, ordinary paper (19.2.71)	..	11·00	2·50
27	65 c. black and light green	..	1·25	2·00
28	70 c. black and claret (15.9.69)	..	2·25	1·25
	a. Glazed, ordinary paper (19.2.71)	..	12·00	9·00
29	1 s. olive-brown, black and slate-blue		30	10
	a. Glazed, ordinary paper (22.1.71)	..	1·25	70
30	1 s. 30, indigo, light olive-green and black		3·00	20
31	1 s. 50, black, orange-brown and dull sage-green (15.9.69)		2·00	2·00
	a. Glazed, ordinary paper (22.1.71)	..	4·00	6·00
32	2 s. 50, yellow, black and olive-brown		3·00	1·25
	a. Glazed, ordinary paper (22.1.71)	..	4·00	6·50
33	5 s. yellow, black and emerald		1·00	10
	a. Glazed, ordinary paper (22.1.71)	..	4·00	8·00
34	10 s. yellow-ochre, black and red-brown		2·50	2·00
35	20 s. yellow-ochre, yellow-orange, blk & gold		8·00	9·50
20/35	..	*Set of 16*	22·00	17·00
21a/33a		*Set of 10*	35·00	35·00

Designs: As *T 5/6*—15 c. Aardvark ("Ant Bear"); 20 c. Lesser Bushbaby; 30 c. Warthog; 40 c. Common Zebra; 50 c. African Buffalo; 65 c. Black Rhinoceros; 70 c. Ostrich. As *T 7*—1 s. 30, African Elephant; 1 s. 50, Bat-eared Fox; 2 s. 50, Cheetah; 5 s. Savanna Monkey ("Vervet Monkey"); 10 s. Giant Ground Pangolin; 20 s. Lion.

On chalk-surfaced paper, all values except 30 c., 50 c. and 2 s. 50 exist with PVA gum as well as gum arabic but the 70 c. and 1 s. 50 exist with PVA gum only. The stamps on glazed, ordinary paper exist with PVA gum only.

Nos. 21 and 26 exist in coils constructed from normal sheets.

8 Rose Dawn

9 Rock Shell (10)

50 c.	A. Inscr "*Janthina globosa*".		
	B. Inscr "*Janthina janthina*".		
70 c.	C. Inscr "*Nautilus pompileus*".		
	D. Inscr "*Nautilus pompilius*".		

(Des Rena Fennessy. Photo Harrison)

1971 (15 Dec)–**74**. *T 8/9 and similar vert designs showing sea-shells. Multicoloured. (a) Size as T 8. P 14½ × 14.*

36	5 c. Type 8	..	10	30
37	10 c. Bishop's Cap (yellow-green background)		10	10
	a. Olive-green background (21.1.74)		50	10
38	15 c. Strawberry Shell	..	15	10
39	20 c. Black Prince	..	15	10
40	30 c. Mermaid's Ear	..	20	10
41	40 c. Top Shell	..	20	10
42	50 c. Violet Shell (A)	..	30	10
43	50 c. Violet Shell (B) (21.1.74)	..	8·50	1·25
44	60 c. Cameo	..	30	45
45	70 c. Pearly Nautilus (C)	..	45	1·50
46	70 c. Pearly Nautilus (D) (21.1.74)	..	8·50	4·50

(b) Size as T 9. P 14

47	1 s. Type 9 (yellow-buff background)	..	30	10
	a. Buff background (21.1.74)	..	20	10
48	1 s. 50, Triton	..	60	10
49	2 s. 50, Neptune's Trumpet	..	80	10
50	5 s. Turban Shell (pale ol-yell background)		1·25	10
	a. Pale olive-bistre background (13.6.73)		1·00	10
51	10 s. Cloth of Gold	..	3·50	15
52	20 s. Spider Shell (grey background)	..	6·00	75
	a. Bluish slate background (12.9.73)	..	3·75	35
36/52		*Set of 17*	25·00	8·00

1975 (17 Nov). *Nos. 48/9 and 52 surch as T 10.*

53	2 s. on 1 s. 50, Triton	..	3·50	3·00
54	3 s. on 2 s. 50, Neptune's Trumpet	..	9·50	16·00
55	40 s. on 20 s. Spider Shell	..	6·00	11·00
53/5		*Set of 3*	16·00	27·00

The surcharge on No. 55 does not have a dot beneath the stroke following the face value.

For commemorative stamps, issued between 1964 and 1976, inscribed "UGANDA KENYA TANGANYIKA AND ZANZIBAR" (or "TANZANIA UGANDA KENYA") see under KENYA, UGANDA AND TANGANYIKA.

The new-issue supplement to this Catalogue appears each month in

GIBBONS
STAMP MONTHLY

—from your newsagent or by postal subscription—
details on request.

---

11 Microwave Tower

12 Akii Bua, Ugandan Hurdler

(Des H. Nickelsen. Litho Format)

1976 (15 Apr). *Telecommunications Development. T 11 and similar multicoloured designs. P 14.*

56	50 c. Type 11	..	10	10
57	1 s. Cordless switchboard (*horiz*)	..	10	10
58	2 s. Telephones	..	20	30
59	3 s. Message Switching Centre (*horiz*)	..	25	45
56/9		*Set of 4*	55	75
MS60	120×120 mm. Nos. 56/9. Imperf		2·50	2·50

Nos. 56/7 and 59 exist imperforate from stock dispersed by the liquidator of Format International Security Printers Ltd.

(Des Beryl Moore. Litho Format)

1976 (7 July*). *Olympic Games, Montreal. T 12 and similar horiz designs. Multicoloured. P 14½.*

61	50 c. Type 12	..	10	10
62	1 s. Filbert Bayi, Tanzanian runner	..	15	10
63	2 s. Steve Muchoki, Kenyan boxer	..	45	35
64	3 s. Olympic flame and East African flags		60	50
61/4		*Set of 4*	1·10	85
MS65	129 × 154 mm. Nos. 61/4. P 13		7·00	7·00

*This is the local date of issue; the Crown Agents released the stamps two days earlier.

Nos. 61 and 63 exist imperforate from stock dispersed by the liquidator of Format Internationl Security Printers Ltd.

13 Diesel Train, Tanzania–Zambia Railway

14 Nile Perch

(Des H. Moghul. Litho Format)

1976 (4 Oct). *Railway Transport. T 13 and similar horiz designs. Multicoloured. P 14½.*

66	50 c. Type 13	..	35	10
67	1 s. Nile Bridge, Uganda	..	60	15
68	2 s. Nakuru Station, Kenya	..	2·25	1·25
69	3 s. Class "A" steam locomotive, 1896		2·50	1·75
66/9		*Set of 4*	5·00	3·00
MS70	154×103 mm. Nos. 66/9. P 13		8·00	8·00

Nos. 66/8 and MS70 exist imperforate from stock dispersed by the liquidator of Format International Security Printers Ltd.

(Des Adrienne Kennaway. Litho Format)

1977 (10 Jan). *Game Fish of East Africa. T 14 and similar vert designs. Multicoloured. P 14*.*

71	50 c. Type 14	..	25	10
72	1 s. Tilapia	..	35	10
73	3 s. Sailfish	..	1·75	90
74	5 s. Black Marlin	..	2·00	1·25
71/4		*Set of 4*	4·00	2·00
MS75	153×129 mm. Nos. 71/4		9·50	4·00

*On No. MS75 the right-hand side of the 5 s. value is perforated 13½.

15 Maasai Manyatta (village), Kenya

(Des Rena Fennessy. Litho Questa)

1977 (15 Jan). *Second World Black and African Festival of Arts and Culture, Nigeria. T 15 and similar horiz designs. Multicoloured. P 13½.*

76	50 c. Type 15	..	15	10
77	1 s. "Heartbeat of Africa" (Ugandan dancers)		25	10
78	2 s. Makonde sculpture, Tanzania	..	1·25	1·50
79	3 s. "Early Man and Technology" (skinning hippopotamus)		1·50	1·75
76/9		*Set of 4*	2·75	3·00
MS80	132 × 109 mm. Nos. 76/9		4·75	4·75

16 Rally-car and Villagers

(Litho Questa)

1977 (5 Apr). *25th Anniv of Safari Rally. T* **16** *and similar horiz designs. Multicoloured. P* 14.

81	50 c. Type **16**			20	10
82	1 s. President Kenyatta starting rally			30	10
83	2 s. Car fording river			70	1·00
84	5 s. Car and elephants			1·25	1·75
81/4			*Set of* 4	2·25	2·50
MS85	126 × 93 mm. Nos. 81/4			4·00	5·50

17 Canon Kivebulaya

(Des Beryl Moore. Litho Questa)

1977 (30 June). *Centenary of Ugandan Church. T* **17** *and similar horiz designs. Multicoloured. P* 14 × 13½.

86	50 c. Type **17**			10	10
87	1 s. Modern Namirembe Cathedral			10	10
88	2 s. The first Cathedral			30	45
89	5 s. Early congregation, Kigezi			50	85
86/9			*Set of* 4	85	1·25
MS90	126 × 94 mm. Nos. 86/9			1·75	3·00

18 Sagana Royal Lodge, Nyeri, 1952

(Des G. Vasarhelyi (50s.), J. Cooter (others). Litho Questa)

1977 (20 July). *Silver Jubilee. T* **18** *and similar multicoloured designs. P* 13½.

91	2 s. Type **18**			30	30
92	5 s. Treetops Hotel (*vert*)			65	65
93	10 s. Queen Elizabeth and President Kenyatta			90	1·25
94	15 s. Royal visit, 1972			1·25	1·75
91/4			*Set of* 4	2·75	3·50
MS95	Two sheets: (a) 140 × 60 mm, No. 94; (b) 152 × 127 mm, 50 s. Queen and Prince Philip in Treetops Hotel		*Set of* 2	3·50	3·50

19 Pancake Tortoise

(Des Rena Fennessy. Litho Questa)

1977 (26 Sept). *Endangered Species. T* **19** *and similar horiz designs. Multicoloured. P* 14.

96	50 c. Type **19**			30	10
97	1 s. Nile Crocodile			40	10
98	2 s. Hunter's Hartebeest			1·40	75
99	3 s. Red Colobus			1·75	1·00
100	5 s. Dugong			2·00	1·50
96/100			*Set of* 5	5·25	3·00
MS101	127 × 101 mm. Nos. 97/100			7·00	8·00

20 Kenya–Ethiopia Border Point

(Litho Questa)

1977 (10 Nov). *Nairobi–Addis Ababa Highway. T* **20** *and similar horiz designs. Multicoloured. P* 14.

102	50 c. Type **20**			15	10
103	1 s. Archer's Post			20	10
104	2 s. Thika Flyover			75	60
105	5 s. Marsabit Game Lodge			1·75	1·50
102/5			*Set of* 4	2·50	2·00
MS106	144 × 91 mm. Nos. 102/5			3·75	5·00

21 Gypsum

22 Amethyst

(Des Rena Fennessy. Photo Harrison)

1977 (10 Dec*). *Minerals. Multicoloured designs.*

(a) Vert as T **21**. *P* 14½ × 14

107	10 c. Type **21**			90	20
108	20 c. Trona			1·25	20
109	30 c. Kyanite			1·40	20
110	40 c. Amazonite			1·40	10
111	50 c. Galena			1·40	10
112	70 c. Silicified wood			1·75	30
113	80 c. Fluorite			1·75	30

(b) Horiz as T **22**. *P* 14

114	1 s. Type **22**			1·75	10
115	1 s. 50, Agate			1·75	20
	a. Gold (face vaue and inscr) omitted				
116	2 s. Tourmaline			1·75	20
	a. Gold (face value and inscr) omitted				
117	3 s. Aquamarine			1·75	45
118	5 s. Rhodolite Garnet			1·75	80
119	10 s. Sapphire			2·00	1·75
120	20 s. Ruby			5·00	2·75
121	40 s. Green Grossular Garnet			13·00	12·00
107/21			*Set of* 15	35·00	17·00

*This is the local issue date. The stamps were released in London on 9 December.

23 Joe Kadenge (Kenya) and Forwards

(Des H. Moghul. Litho Questa)

1978 (10 Apr). *World Cup Football Championship, Argentina. T* **23** *and similar horiz designs showing footballers. Multicoloured. P* 14 × 13½.

122	50 c. Type **23**			10	10
123	1 s. Mohamed Chuma (Tanzania) and Cup presentation			10	10
124	2 s. Omari Kidevu (Zanzibar) and goalmouth scene			40	60
125	3 s. Polly Ouma (Uganda) and three forwards			50	85
122/5			*Set of* 4	1·00	1·40
MS126	136 × 81 mm. Nos. 122/5			3·00	3·00

24 Boxing

(Des H. Moghul. Photo Heraclio Fournier)

1978 (17 July). *Commonwealth Games, Edmonton. T* **24** *and similar horiz designs. Multicoloured. P* 13 × 14.

127	50 c. Type **24**			15	10
128	1 s. Welcoming Olympic Games Team, 1968			20	10
129	3 s. Javelin throwing			60	80
130	5 s. President Kenyatta admiring boxer's trophy			75	1·25
127/30			*Set of* 4	1·50	2·00

25 "Overloading is Dangerous"

(Litho Walsall)

1978 (18 Sept). *Road Safety. T* **25** *and similar horiz designs. Multicoloured. P* 13½.

131	50 c. Type **25**			35	10
132	1 s. "Speed does not pay"			50	20
133	1 s. 50, "Ignoring Traffic Signs may cause death"			65	40
134	2 s. "Slow down at School Crossing"			90	80
135	3 s. "Never cross a continuous line"			1·10	1·25
136	5 s. "Approach Railway Level Crossing with extreme caution"			1·75	2·25
131/6			*Set of* 6	4·75	4·50

26 President Kenyatta at Mass Rally, 1963

27 Freedom Fighters, Namibia

(Des Beryl Moore. Litho J.W.)

1978 (16 Oct). *Kenyatta Day. T* **26** *and similar horiz designs. Multicoloured. P* 14.

137	50 c. "Harambee Water Project"			15	10
138	1 s. Handing over of Independence Instruments, 1963			25	10
139	2 s. Type **26**			45	30
140	3 s. "Harambee, 15 Great Years"			70	55
141	5 s. "Struggle for Independence, 1952"			90	80
137/41			*Set of* 5	2·25	1·60

(Des L. Curtis. Litho Questa)

1978 (11 Dec*). *International Anti-Apartheid Year. T* **27** *and similar horiz designs. P* 14 × 14½.

142	50 c. multicoloured			20	10
143	1 s. black and cobalt			25	10
144	2 s. multicoloured			60	30
145	3 s. multicoloured			80	55
146	5 s. multicoloured			90	80
142/6			*Set of* 5	2·50	1·60

Designs:—1 s. International seminar on apartheid, racial discrimination and colonialism in South Africa; 2 s. Steve Biko's tombstone; 3 s. Nelson Mandela; 5 s. Bishop Lamont.

*This is the local date of issue; the Crown Agents released the stamps the previous day.

28 Children Playing

(Des Beryl Moore. Litho Walsall)

1979 (5 Feb). *International Year of the Child. T* **28** *and similar horiz designs. Multicoloured. P* 13½ × 14.

147	50 c. Type **28**			15	10
148	2 s. Child fishing			40	40
149	3 s. Children singing and dancing			60	60
150	5 s. Children working with camels			85	85
147/50			*Set of* 4	1·75	1·75

29 "The Lion and the Jewel"   30 Blind Telephone Operator

(Des Beryl Moore. Litho Enschedé)

1979 (6 Apr). *Kenya National Theatre. T* **29** *and similar horiz designs. Multicoloured. P* 13 × 13½.

151	50 c. Type **29**			15	10
152	1 s. Scene from "Utisi"			20	10
153	2 s. "Entertainment past and present" (programmes from past productions)			35	30
154	3 s. Kenya National Theatre			50	45
155	5 s. Nairobi City Players production of "Genesis"			90	75
151/5			*Set of* 5	1·90	1·50

(Litho Harrison)

1979 (29 June*). *50th Anniv of Salvation Army Social Services. T* **30** *and similar multicoloured designs. P* 13½ × 13 (50 c., 1s.) *or* 13 × 13½ (*others*).

156	50 c. Type **30**			30	10
157	1 s. Care for the Aged			30	10
158	3 s. Village polytechnic (*horiz*)			1·00	90
159	5 s. Vocational training (*horiz*)			1·25	1·40
156/9			*Set of* 4	2·50	2·25

*This is the local date of issue; the Crown Agents released the stamps on 4 June.

MINIMUM PRICE

The minimum price quote is 10p which represents a handling charge rather than a basis for valuing common stamps. For further notes about prices see introductory pages.

31 "Father of the Nation" **32** British East Africa
(Kenyatta's funeral   Company 1890 1 a. Stamp
procession)

(Des H. Moghul. Litho Questa)

1979 (21 Aug*). 1st Death Anniv of President Kenyatta. T **31** and
similar vert designs. Multicoloured. P 13½ × 14.
160 50 c. Type **31** 10 10
161 1 s. "First President of Kenya" (Kenyatta
     receiving independence) 15 10
162 3 s. "Kenyatta the politician" (speaking at
     rally) 35 45
163 5 s. "A true son of Kenya" (Kenyatta as a boy
     carpenter) 60 85
160/3 .. .. Set of 4 1·00 1·25
*This is the local date of issue; the Crown Agents did not release
the stamps until 29 August.

(Des J.W. Litho Harrison)

1979 (27 Nov). Death Centenary of Sir Rowland Hill. T **32** and
similar vert designs showing stamps. P 14 × 14½.
164 50 c. multicoloured 15 10
165 1 s. multicoloured 15 10
166 2 s. black, magenta and yellow-ochre .. 30 40
167 5 s. multicoloured .. .. .. 60 1·00
164/7 .. .. Set of 4 1·10 1·40
Designs:—1 s. Kenya, Uganda and Tanganyika 1935 1 s.; 2 s.
Penny Black; 5 s. 1964 Inauguration of Republic 2 s. 50,
commemorative.

33 Roads, Globe and Conference Emblem

(Des H. Moghul. Litho Questa)

1980 (10 Jan). I.R.F. (International Road Federation) African
Highway Conference, Nairobi. T **33** and similar horiz designs.
Multicoloured. P 14 × 13½.
168 50 c. Type **33** 10 10
169 1 s. New weighbridge, Athi River .. 15 10
170 3 s. New Nyali Bridge, Mombasa .. 40 75
171 5 s. Highway to Jomo Kenyatta International
     Airport .. .. 70 1·50
168/71 .. .. Set of 4 1·25 2·25

34 Mobile Unit in action, **35** Statue of Sir Rowland
Masailand   Hill

(Des Beryl Moore. Litho Questa)

1980 (20 Mar). Flying Doctor Service. T **34** and similar multicoloured designs. P 14½.
172 50 c. Type **34** 10 10
173 1 s. Donkey transport to Turkana airstrip
     (vert) 15 10
174 3 s. Surgical team in action at outstation (vert) 50 90
175 5 s. Emergency airlift from North Eastern
     Province .. .. 80 1·40
172/5 .. .. Set of 4 1·40 2·25
MS176 146 × 133 mm. Nos. 172/5 .. .. 1·50 2·50

(Des J.W. Litho Questa)

1980 (6 May). "London 1980" International Stamp Exhibition.
P 14.
177 **35** 25 s. multicoloured .. .. .. 1·50 2·50
MS178 114 × 101 mm. No. 177 .. .. 1·60 2·75

36 Pope John Paul II   **37** Taeniura lymma

(Des Sister Frances Randal. Litho Italian Govt Ptg Works, Rome)

1980 (8 May). Papal Visit. T **36** and similar multicoloured
designs. P 13.
179 50 c. Type **36** 30 10
180 1 s. Pope John Paul II, cathedral and coat of
     arms (vert) 40 10
181 5 s. Pope John Paul II, Papal and Kenyan
     flags on dove symbol (vert) .. 85 70
182 10 s. President Moi, Pope John Paul II and map
     of Africa .. .. 1·40 1·40
179/82 .. .. Set of 4 2·75 2·00

(Des Adrienne Kennaway. Litho Harrison)

1980 (27 June). Marine Life. T **37** and similar vert designs. Multicoloured. P 14.
183 50 c. Type **37** 25 10
184 2 s. Amphiprion allardi 75 60
185 3 s. Chromodoris quadricolor .. 90 1·00
186 5 s. Eretmochelys imbricata .. .. 1·40 1·75
183/6 .. .. Set of 4 3·00 3·00

38 National Archives

(Des A. Odhuno; adapted L. Curtis. Litho Questa)

1980 (9 Oct). Historic Buildings. T **38** and similar horiz designs.
Multicoloured. P 14.
187 50 c. Type **38** 10 10
188 1 s. Provincial Commissioner's Office, Nairobi 15 10
189 1 s. 50, Nairobi House 20 20
190 2 s. Norfolk Hotel 25 50
191 3 s. McMillan Library 35 65
192 5 s. Kipande House .. .. .. 55 1·00
187/92 .. .. Set of 6 1·40 2·25

39 "Disabled Enjoys Affection"

(Des H. Moghul. Litho Enschedé)

1981 (10 Feb). International Year for Disabled Persons. T **39** and
similar horiz designs. Multicoloured. P 14 × 13.
193 50 c. Type **39** 15 10
194 1 s. President Moi presenting Kenyan flag to
     Disabled Olympic Games team captain 20 10
195 3 s. Blind people climbing Mount Kenya,
     1975 .. .. 55 65
196 5 s. Disabled artist at work .. .. 85 1·00
193/6 .. .. Set of 4 1·60 1·60

40 Longonot Complex

(Des H. Moghul. Litho Harrison)

1981 (15 Apr). Satellite Communications. T **40** and similar horiz
designs. Multicoloured. P 14 × 14½.
197 50 c. Type **40** 15 10
198 1 s. "Intelsat V" 50 35
199 3 s. "Longonot I" 60 55
200 5 s. "Longonot II" 85 85
197/200 .. .. Set of 4 1·90 1·60

41 Kenyatta Conference Centre **42** St. Paul's Cathedral

(Des L. Curtis. Litho Questa (MS206) or J.W. (others))

1981 (17 June*). O.A.U. (Organisation of African Unity) Summit
Conference, Nairobi. T **41** and similar horiz designs in black,
bistre-yellow and new blue (1s.) or multicoloured (others). P 13½.
201 50 c. Type **41** 15 10
202 1 s. "Panaftel" earth stations .. 20 10
203 3 s. Parliament Building 40 40
204 5 s. Jomo Kenyatta International Airport .. 65 65
205 10 s. O.A.U. flag .. .. .. 1·00 1·00
201/5 .. .. Set of 5 2·25 2·00
MS206 110 × 110 mm. No. 205. P 14½ × 14 1·10 1·50
*This is the local date of issue; the Crown Agents did not release
the stamps until 24 June.

(Des A. Theobald. Litho Questa)

1981 (29 July). Royal Wedding. T **42** and similar vert designs.
Multicoloured. P 14.
207 50 c. Prince Charles and President Daniel
     Arap Moi 15 10
208 3 s. Type **42** 25 20
209 5 s. Royal Yacht Britannia 40 35
210 10 s. Prince Charles on safari in Kenya .. 55 70
207/10 .. .. Set of 4 1·25 1·25
MS211 85 × 102 mm. 25 s. Prince Charles and
     Lady Diana Spencer .. .. .. 1·40 1·60
Nos. 207/10 also exist perforated 12 (price for set of 4 £1.75
mint or used) from additional sheetlets of five stamps and one
label.
Insufficient supplies of No. MS211 were received by 29 July
for a full distribution, but subsequently the miniature sheet was
freely available.

43 Giraffe   **44** "Technical
               Development"

(Des Rena Fennessy. Litho Questa)

1981 (31 Aug). Rare Animals. T **43** and similar vert designs.
Multicoloured. P 14½.
212 50 c. Type **43** 15 10
213 2 s. Bongo 35 20
214 5 s. Roan Antelope 70 55
215 10 s. Agile Mangabey .. .. .. 1·25 1·40
212/15 .. .. Set of 4 2·25 2·00

(Des H. Moghul, adapted L. Curtis. Litho Questa)

1981 (16 Oct). World Food Day. T **44** and similar vert designs.
Multicoloured. P 14.
216 50 c. Type **44** 10 10
217 1 s. "Mwea rice projects" 15 10
218 2 s. "Irrigation schemes" 30 25
219 5 s. "Breeding livestock" 60 70
216/19 .. .. Set of 4 1·00 90

45 Kamba   **46** Australopithecus boisei

(Des Adrienne Kennaway. Litho Harrison)

1981 (18 Dec). Ceremonial Costumes (1st series). T **45** and similar
vert designs. Multicoloured. P 14½ × 13½.
220 50 c. Type **45** 30 10
221 1 s. Turkana 35 10
222 2 s. Giriama 75 35
223 3 s. Masai .. .. 1·00 65
224 5 s. Luo .. .. 1·40 1·10
220/4 .. .. Set of 5 3·50 2·00
See also Nos. 329/33, 413/17 and 515/19.

(Des Adrienne Kennaway. Litho Format)

1982 (19 Jan). *"Origins of Mankind". Skulls. T 46 and similar horiz designs. Multicoloured. P 13½ × 14.*

225	50 c.	Type 46		75	10
226	2 s.	Homo erectus		1·75	65
227	3 s.	Homo habilis		2·25	1·40
228	5 s.	Proconsul africanus		3·00	2·75
225/8			Set of 4	7·00	4·50

47 Tree-planting

(Des L. Curtis. Litho Harrison)

1982 (9 June). *75th Anniv of Boy Scout Movement (Nos. 229, 231, 233 and 235) and 60th Anniv of Girl Guide Movement (Nos. 230, 232, 234 and 236). T 47 and similar horiz designs. Multicoloured. P 14½.*

229	70 c.	Type 47		50	30
	a.	Horiz pair. Nos. 229/30		1·00	60
230	70 c.	Paying homage		50	30
231	3 s. 50,	"Be Prepared"		1·00	1·00
	a.	Horiz pair. Nos. 231/2		2·00	2·00
232	3 s. 50,	"International Friendship"		1·00	1·00
233	5 s.	Helping disabled		1·40	1·50
	a.	Horiz pair. Nos. 233/4		2·75	3·00
234	5 s.	Community service		1·40	1·50
235	6 s. 50,	Paxtu Cottage (Lord Baden-Powell's home)		1·75	2·00
	a.	Horiz pair. Nos. 235/6		3·50	4·00
236	6 s. 50,	Lady Baden-Powell		1·75	2·00
229/36			Set of 8	8·50	8·75
MS237	112 × 112 mm. Nos. 229, 231, 233 and 235			3·00	3·00

The two designs of each value were printed together, *se-tenant*, in horizontal pairs throughout the sheet.

48 Footballer displaying Shooting Skill

(Des local artist. Litho Harrison)

1982 (5 July). *World Cup Football Championships, Spain. T 48 and similar triangular designs showing footballers silhouetted against world map. Multicoloured. P 12½.*

238	70 c.	Type 48		1·00	40
239	3 s. 50,	Heading		2·00	1·60
240	5 s.	Goalkeeping		2·50	2·50
241	10 s.	Dribbling		4·00	4·50
238/41			Set of 4	8·50	8·00
MS242	101 × 76 mm. 20 s. Tackling. P 13 × 14			4·50	4·00

49 Cattle Judging   **50** Micro-wave Radio System   **(51)**

(Des H. Moghul. Litho Harrison)

1982 (28 Sept). *80th Anniv of Agricultural Society of Kenya. T 49 and similar vert designs. Multicoloured. P 14½.*

243	70 c.	Type 49		65	10
244	2 s.	Farm machinery		1·50	1·25
245	3 s. 50,	Musical ride		1·75	1·75
246	6 s. 50,	Agricultural Society emblem		2·25	2·50
243/6			Set of 4	5·50	5·00

(Des H. Moghul. Photo Courvoisier)

1982 (21 Oct). *I.T.U. Plenipotentiary Conference, Nairobi. T 50 and similar vert designs. Multicoloured. P 11½.*

247	70 c.	Type 50		55	10
248	3 s. 50,	Sea-to-shore service link		1·25	1·50
249	5 s.	Rural telecommunications system		1·75	2·25
250	6 s. 50,	I.T.U. emblem		2·25	2·75
247/50			Set of 4	5·25	6·00

1982 (22 Nov). *No. 113 surch with T 51, in white on a black panel.*

251	70 c. on 80 c. Fluorite			60	60

52 Container Cranes

(Des R. Vigurs. Litho Questa)

1983 (20 Jan). *5th Anniv of Kenya Ports Authority. T 52 and similar horiz designs. P 14.*

252	70 c.	Type 52		70	10
253	2 s.	Port by night		1·50	1·25
254	3 s. 50,	Container cranes (different)		2·00	2·00
255	5 s.	Map of Mombasa Port		2·50	3·00
252/5			Set of 4	6·00	5·75
MS256	125 × 85 mm. Nos. 252/5			6·00	7·00

53 Shada Zambarau   **54** Waridi Kikuba

(Des Rena Fennessy. Photo Harrison)

1983 (15 Feb)–**85**. *Flowers. Multicoloured.*

(a) Vert designs as T 53. P 14½ × 14

257	10 c.	Type 53		30	20
258	20 c.	Kilua Kingulima		45	20
259	30 c.	Mwalika Mwiya		45	20
260	40 c.	Ziyungi Buluu		45	20
261	50 c.	Kilua Habashia		45	20
262	70 c.	Chanuo Kato		50	20
262a	80 c.	As 40 c. (7.8.85)		2·25	45
262b	1 s.	Waridi Kikuba (5.8.85*)		2·25	45

(b) Vert designs as T 54. P 14

263	1 s.	Type 54		45	20
264	1 s. 50,	Mshomoro Mtambazi		80	40
265	2 s.	Papatuo Boti		80	40
266	2 s. 50,	Tumba Mboni		1·25	40
266a	3 s.	Mkuku Mrembo (12.8.85)		3·00	1·75
267	3 s. 50,	Mtongo Mbeja		1·25	90
	a.	Gold (inscr and face value) omitted			
267b	4 s.	Mnukia Muuma (7.8.85)		3·00	3·00
268	5 s.	Nyungu Chepuo		1·25	90
268a	7 s.	Mlua Miba (7.8.85)		3·50	4·00
269	10 s.	Muafunili		1·50	2·00
270	20 s.	Mbake Nyanza		2·25	2·75
271	40 s.	Njuga Pagwa		4·00	6·50
257/71			Set of 20	27·00	23·00

*Earliest known postmark date.

55 Coffee Plucking   **56** Examining Parcels

(Des C. Fernandes. Litho Harrison)

1983 (14 Mar). *Commonwealth Day. T 55 and similar multicoloured designs. P 14 × 14½ (70 c., 2 s.) or 14½ × 14 (others).*

272	70 c.	Type 55		10	10
273	2 s.	President Daniel Arap Moi		15	20
274	5 s.	Satellite view of Earth (horiz)		45	45
275	10 s.	Masai dance (horiz)		90	1·00
272/5			Set of 4	1·40	1·50

(Des H. Moghul. Litho Harrison)

1983 (11 May). *30th Anniv of Customs Co-operation Council. T 56 and similar vert designs. Multicoloured. P 14.*

276	70 c.	Type 56		20	10
277	2 s. 50,	Customs Headquarters, Mombasa		45	30
278	3 s. 50,	Customs Council Headquarters, Brussels		55	40
279	10 s.	Customs patrol boat		1·75	2·00
276/9			Set of 4	2·75	2·50

57 Communications via Satellite   **58** Ships in Kilindini Harbour

(Litho Harrison)

1983 (4 July). *World Communications Year. T 57 and similar multicoloured designs. P 14 × 14½ (70 c., 2 s. 50) or 14½ × 14 (others).*

280	70 c.	Type 57		60	10
281	2 s. 50,	"Telephone and Postal Services"		1·25	1·25
282	3 s. 50,	Communications by sea and air (horiz)		1·60	1·75
283	5 s.	Road and rail communications (horiz)		2·00	2·50
280/3			Set of 4	5·00	5·00

(Litho Harrison)

1983 (22 Sept). *25th Anniv of Intergovernmental Maritime Organization. T 58 and similar horiz designs. Multicoloured. P 14.*

284	70 c.	Type 58		75	10
285	2 s. 50,	Life-saving devices		1·50	1·25
286	3 s. 50,	Mombasa container terminal		2·00	1·75
287	10 s.	Marine park		3·00	3·50
284/7			Set of 4	6·50	6·00

59 President Moi signing Visitors' Book

(Litho Harrison)

1983 (31 Oct). *29th Commonwealth Parliamentary Conference. T 59 and similar multicoloured designs. P 14.*

288	70 c.	Type 59		25	10
289	2 s. 50,	Parliament building, Nairobi (vert)		70	45
290	5 s.	State opening of Parliament (vert)		1·25	80
288/90			Set of 3	2·00	1·25
MS291	122 × 141 mm. Nos. 288/90			2·00	2·75

60 Kenyan and British Flags

(Des A. Theobald. Litho Harrison)

1983 (10 Nov). *Royal Visit. T 60 and similar horiz designs. Multicoloured. P 14.*

292	70 c.	Type 60		50	10
293	3 s. 50,	Sagana State Lodge		1·50	55
294	5 s.	Treetops Hotel		2·00	90
295	10 s.	Queen Elizabeth II and President Moi		3·00	2·75
292/5			Set of 4	6·25	3·75
MS296	126 × 100 mm. 25 s. Designs as Nos. 292/5, but without face values. Imperf			3·25	4·00

61 President Moi   **62** White-backed Night Heron

(Des and litho Harrison)

1983 (9 Dec). *20th Anniv of Independence. T 61 and similar horiz designs. Multicoloured. P 14½.*

297	70 c.	Type 61		10	10
298	2 s.	President Moi planting tree		20	20
299	3 s. 50,	Kenyan flag and emblem		35	35
300	5 s.	School milk scheme		50	50
301	10 s.	People of Kenya		1·00	1·10
297/301			Set of 5	1·90	2·00
MS302	126 × 93 mm. 25 s. Designs as Nos. 297 and 299/301, but without face values. Imperf			1·75	2·75

(Des Agnes Odero. Litho Harrison)

1984 (6 Feb). *Rare Birds of Kenya. T 62 and similar vert designs. Multicoloured. P 14½ × 13½.*

303	70 c.	Type 62		1·00	20
304	2 s. 50,	Quail Plover		1·75	1·75
305	3 s. 50,	Taita Olive Thrush		2·00	2·00
306	5 s.	Mufumbiri Shrike ("Yellow Gonolek")		2·25	2·25
307	10 s.	White-winged Apalis		3·00	3·75
303/7			Set of 5	9·00	9·00

NEW INFORMATION

The editor is always interested to correspond with people who have new information that will improve or correct the Catalogue.

63 Radar Tower   **64** Running

(Des C. Fernandes. Litho Harrison)

1984 (2 Apr). *40th Anniv of International Civil Aviation Organization. T* **63** *and similar multicoloured designs. P* 14.

308	70 c. Type **63**		10	10
309	2 s. 50, Kenya School of Aviation (*horiz*)		30	30
310	3 s. 50, Aircraft taking off from Moi airport (*horiz*)		40	45
311	5 s. Air traffic control centre..		55	60
308/11		*Set of 4*	1·25	1·25

(Des and litho Harrison)

1984 (21 May). *Olympic Games, Los Angeles. T* **64** *and similar horiz designs. P* 14½.

312	70 c. black, bright yellow-green and bronze-green		30	10
313	2 s. 50, black, bright magenta and reddish violet		55	30
314	5 s. black, pale turquoise-blue and steel blue		1·25	80
315	10 s. black, bistre-yellow and brown ..		2·25	2·00
312/15		*Set of 4*	4·00	2·75
MS316	130×121 mm. 25 s. Designs as Nos. 312/15 but without face values. Imperf..		2·50	3·00

Designs:—2 s. 50, Hurdling; 5 s. Boxing; 10 s. Hockey.

65 Conference and Kenya Library   **66** Doves and Cross
Association Logos

(Des and litho Harrison)

1984 (28 June). *50th Conference of the International Federation of Library Associations. T* **65** *and similar horiz designs. Multicoloured. P* 14½.

317	70 c. Type **65**		10	10
318	3 s. 50, Mobile library		40	50
319	5 s. Adult library		55	70
320	10 s. Children's library		1·00	1·50
317/20		*Set of 4*	1·75	2·50

(Des K. Bisley. Litho Harrison)

1984 (23 Aug). *4th World Conference on Religion and Peace. T* **66** *and similar vert designs, each showing a different central symbol. Multicoloured. P* 14½.

321	70 c. Type **66**		30	15
322	2 s. 50, Arabic inscription		1·00	1·25
323	3 s. 50, Peace emblem		1·40	1·60
324	6 s. 50, Star and Crescent		1·75	2·25
321/4		*Set of 4*	4·00	4·75

67 Export Year Logo   **68** Knight and Nyayo National Stadium

(Litho Harrison)

1984 (1 Oct). *Kenya Export Year. T* **67** *and similar multicoloured designs. P* 14½.

325	70 c. Type **67**		30	10
326	3 s. 50, Forklift truck with air cargo (*horiz*)		1·50	1·50
327	5 s. Loading ship's cargo		2·00	2·00
328	10 s. Kenyan products (*horiz*)..		3·00	3·75
325/8		*Set of 4*	6·25	6·50

(Litho Harrison)

1984 (5 Nov). *Ceremonial Costumes (2nd series). Vert designs as T* **45**. *Multicoloured. P* 14½ × 13½.

329	70 c. Luhya		55	15
330	2 s. Kikuyu		1·25	1·25
331	3 s. 50, Pokomo		1·75	1·75
332	5 s. Nandi		2·00	2·00
333	10 s. Rendile		3·00	3·75
329/33		*Set of 5*	7·75	8·00

(Litho Harrison)

1984 (21 Dec). *60th Anniv of International Chess Federation. T* **68** *and similar horiz designs showing Staunton chess pieces. Multicoloured. P* 14½.

334	70 c. Type **68**		90	20
335	2 s. 50, Rook and Fort Jesus		1·50	1·25
336	3 s. 50, Bishop and National Monument		2·00	1·75
337	5 s. Queen and Parliament Building		2·25	2·25
338	10 s. King and Nyayo Fountain		3·25	3·50
334/8		*Set of 5*	9·00	8·00

69 Cooking with Wood-burning Stove and
Charcoal Fire

(Des H. Moghul. Litho J.W.)

1985 (22 Jan). *Energy Conservation. T* **69** *and similar horiz designs. Multicoloured. P* 13½.

339	70 c. Type **69**		20	10
340	2 s. Solar energy panel on roof		50	60
341	3 s. 50, Production of gas from cow dung		70	90
342	10 s. Ploughing with oxen		1·75	2·50
339/42		*Set of 4*	2·75	3·75
MS343	110×85 mm. 20 s. Designs as Nos. 339/42, but without face values ..		2·25	2·50

70 Crippled Girl Guide making Table-mat

(Litho J.W.)

1985 (27 Mar). *75th Anniv of Girl Guide Movement. T* **70** *and similar horiz designs. Multicoloured. P* 13½.

344	1 s. Type **70**		55	15
345	3 s. Girl Guides doing community service		1·25	1·00
346	5 s. Lady Olave Baden-Powell (founder)		2·00	2·00
347	7 s. Girl Guides gardening		2·75	3·00
344/7		*Set of 4*	6·00	5·50

71 Stylised Figures and Globe   **72** Man with Malaria

(Des and litho Harrison)

1985 (8 May). *World Red Cross Day. T* **71** *and similar horiz designs. P* 14½.

348	1 s. black and rosine		55	15
349	4 s. multicoloured		1·75	1·75
350	5 s. multicoloured		1·90	1·90
351	7 s. multicoloured		2·50	2·75
348/51		*Set of 4*	6·00	6·00

Designs:—4 s. First aid team; 5 s. Hearts containing crosses ("Blood Donation"); 7 s. Cornucopia ("Famine Relief").

(Des H. Moghul. Litho Harrison)

1985 (25 June). *7th International Congress of Protozoology, Nairobi. T* **72** *and similar vert designs. Multicoloured. P* 14½.

352	1 s. Type **72**		55	15
353	3 s. Child with Leishmaniasis		1·90	1·60
354	5 s. Cow with Trypanosomiasis		2·50	2·00
355	7 s. Dog with Babesiosis		3·00	3·00
352/5		*Set of 4*	7·25	6·00

73 Repairing Water Pipes   **74** The Last Supper

(Des J. Tobula and Harrison. Litho Harrison)

1985 (15 July). *United Nations Women's Decade Conference. T* **73** *and similar vert designs. Multicoloured. P* 14½.

356	1 s. Type **73**		15	10
357	3 s. Traditional food preparation		50	50
358	5 s. Basket-weaving		70	70
359	7 s. Dressmaking		85	90
356/9		*Set of 4*	2·00	2·00

(Des Eucharistic Congress Secretariat. Litho J.W.)

1985 (17 Aug*). *43rd International Eucharistic Congress, Nairobi. T* **74** *and similar horiz designs. Multicoloured. P* 13½.

360	1 s. Type **74**		45	10
361	3 s. Village family ("The Eucharist and the Christian Family")		1·25	90
362	5 s. Congress altar, Uhuru Park		1·50	1·25
363	7 s. St. Peter Claver's Church, Nairobi		2·00	2·25
360/3		*Set of 4*	4·75	4·00
MS364	117×80 mm. 25 s. Pope John Paul II		3·50	3·50

* This is the local date of issue. The Crown Agents released the stamps on 15 August and this date also appears on first day covers serviced by Kenya Posts and Telecommunications Corporation.

75 Black Rhinoceros

(Des Rena Fennessy. Litho Harrison)

1985 (10 Dec). *Endangered Animals. T* **75** *and similar horiz designs. Multicoloured. P* 14½.

365	1 s. Type **75**		80	20
366	3 s. Cheetah		2·00	1·50
367	5 s. De Brazza's Monkey		2·50	2·25
368	10 s. Grevy's Zebra		3·75	4·00
365/8		*Set of 4*	8·00	7·25
MS369	129×122 mm. 25 s. Endangered species (122×114 mm). Imperf		4·50	4·50

76 Borassus aethiopum   **77** Dove and U.N.
Logo (from poster)

(Des Rena Fennessy. Litho Questa)

1986 (24 Jan). *Indigenous Trees. T* **76** *and similar horiz designs. Multicoloured. P* 14½.

370	1 s. Type **76**		50	15
371	3 s. Acacia xanthophloea		1·50	1·50
372	5 s. Ficus natalensis		2·40	2·40
373	7 s. Spathodea nilotica		3·00	3·50
370/3		*Set of 4*	6·75	6·75
MS374	117×96 mm. 25 s. Landscape with trees (109×90 mm). Imperf		3·25	4·00

(Des Advertising Link. Litho Questa)

1986 (30 Apr*). *International Peace Year. T* **77** *and similar multicoloured designs. P* 14½.

375	1 s. Type **77**		20	10
376	5 s. U.N. General Assembly (*horiz*)		55	50
377	7 s. Nuclear explosion		1·25	1·10
378	10 s. Quotation from Wall of Isaiah, U.N. Building, New York (*horiz*)		1·75	1·75
375/8		*Set of 4*	3·25	3·00

*This is the local date of issue. The Crown Agents released the stamps on 17 April and this date also appears on first day covers serviced by Kenya Posts and Telecommunications Corporation.

78 Dribbling the Ball   **79** Rural Post Office
and Telephone

(Des C. Fernandes. Litho Harrison)

1986 (8 May). *World Cup Football Championship, Mexico. T* **78** *and similar multicoloured designs. P* 14½.

379	1 s. Type **78**		55	15
380	3 s. Scoring from a penalty..		1·25	85
381	5 s. Tackling..		2·00	1·50
382	7 s. Cup winners		2·75	2·50
383	10 s. Heading the ball		3·00	3·50
379/83		*Set of 5*	9·00	7·50
MS384	110×86 mm. 30 s. Harambee Stars football team (102×78 mm). Imperf..		3·25	3·75

(Des H. Moghul. Litho Cartor, France)

1986 (11 June). *"Expo '86" World Fair, Vancouver. T* **79** *and similar horiz designs. Multicoloured. P* 13½ × 13.

385	1 s. Type **79**		50	15
386	3 s. Container depot, Embakasi		1·50	1·10
387	5 s. Aircraft landing at game park airstrip.		2·00	1·50
388	7 s. Container ship		2·75	2·75
389	10 s. Transporting produce to market		3·25	3·50
385/9		*Set of 5*	9·00	8·00

On 15 July 1986 Kenya was scheduled to release a set of five stamps, 1, 3, 4, 7 and 10 s., for the Commonwealth Games at Edinburgh. A political decision was taken at the last moment not to issue the stamps, but this instruction did not reach some of the sub-post offices until the morning of 15 July. About two hundred stamps, mainly the 1 s. value, were sold by these sub-post offices before the instruction arrived. Examples of the 1 s. exist used on commercial mail from Kenyatta College sub-post office from 17 July 1986 onwards.

80 Telephone, Computer and Dish Aerial

(Des H. Moghul. Litho Harrison)

1986 (16 Sept). *African Telecommunications. T 80 and similar horiz designs. Multicoloured. P 14½.*

390	1 s. Type 80	30	10
391	3 s. Telephones of 1876, 1936 and 1986	70	60
392	5 s. Dish aerial, satellite, telephones and map of Africa	90	90
393	7 s. Kenyan manufacture of telecommunications equipment	1·25	1·50
390/3	*Set of 4*	2·75	2·75

81 Mashua   **82** The Nativity

(Des Mukund Arts. Litho Mardon Printers Ltd, Zimbabwe)

1986 (30 Oct). *Dhows of Kenya. T 81 and similar horiz designs. Multicoloured. P 14½.*

394	1 s. Type 81	55	20
395	3 s. Mtepe	1·50	1·25
396	5 s. Dau La Mwao	2·00	1·75
397	10 s. Jahazi	3·25	3·50
394/7	*Set of 4*	6·50	6·00
MS398	118×80 mm. 25 s. Lamu dhow and map of Indian Ocean	4·00	4·50

(Des Mukund Arts. Photo Courvoisier)

1986 (5 Dec), *Christmas. T 82 and similar multicoloured designs. Granite paper. P 11½.*

399	1 s. Type 82	20	10
400	3 s. Shepherd and sheep	60	45
401	5 s. Angel and slogan "LOVE PEACE UNITY" (horiz)	1·00	75
402	7 s. The Magi riding camels (horiz)	1·25	1·40
399/402	*Set of 4*	2·75	2·40

83 Immunization   **84** Akamba Woodcarvers

(Des Judith D'Inca. Litho Harrison)

1987 (6 Jan). *40th Anniv of United Nations Children's Fund. T 83 and similar vert designs. Multicoloured. P 14.*

403	1 s. Type 83	20	10
404	3 s. Food and nutrition	50	35
405	4 s. Oral rehydration therapy	70	45
406	5 s. Family planning	85	60
407	10 s. Female literacy	1·25	1·25
403/7	*Set of 5*	3·25	2·50

(Des C. Fernandes. Litho Questa)

1987 (25 Mar). *Tourism. T 84 and similar horiz designs. Multicoloured. P 14½.*

408	1 s. Type 84	30	10
409	3 s. Tourists on beach	95	85
410	5 s. Tourist and guide at view point	1·50	1·75
411	7 s. Pride of lions	2·25	2·50
408/11	*Set of 4*	4·50	4·75
MS412	118×81 mm. 30 s. Geysers	5·00	6·00

(Des Mukund Arts. Litho Harrison)

1987 (20 May). *Ceremonial Costumes (3rd series). Vert designs as T 45. Multicoloured. P 14½×13½.*

413	1 s. Embu	15	10
414	3 s. Kisii	35	35
415	5 s. Samburu	55	70
416	7 s. Taita	80	1·00
417	10 s. Boran	1·10	1·40
413/17	*Set of 5*	2·75	3·25

85 Telecommunications by Satellite   **86** Volleyball

(Des Mukund Arts. Litho Harrison)

1987 (1 July). *10th Anniv of Kenya Posts and Telecommunications Corporation. T 85 and similar triangular designs. Multicoloured. P 13½.*

418	1 s. Type 85	15	15
419	3 s. Rural post office, Kajiado	30	40
420	4 s. Awarding trophy, Welfare Sports	40	55
421	5 s. Village and telephone box	50	65
422	7 s. Speedpost labels and outline map of Kenya	70	90
418/22	*Set of 5*	1·90	2·40
MS423	110×80 mm. 25 s. Corporation flag	1·75	1·90

Nos. 418/22 were each printed as horizontal *tête-bêche* pairs within the sheet.

(Des C. Fernandes. Litho D.L.R.)

1987 (5 Aug). *4th All-Africa Games, Nairobi. T 86 and similar multicoloured designs. P 14½×14.*

424	1 s. Type 86	10	10
425	3 s. Cycling	20	30
426	4 s. Boxing	30	40
427	5 s. Swimming	35	45
428	7 s. Steeplechasing	50	75
424/8	*Set of 5*	1·25	1·75
MS429	117×80 mm. 30 s. Kasarani Sports Complex (horiz). P 14×14½	2·10	2·25

87 *Aloe volkensii*

(Des Advertising Link. Litho Cartor, France)

1987 (10 Nov). *Medicinal Herbs. T 87 and similar vert designs. Multicoloured. P 13½×14.*

430	1 s. Type 87	20	10
431	3 s. *Cassia didymobotrya*	55	55
432	5 s. *Erythrina abyssinica*	80	80
433	7 s. *Adenium obesum*	1·10	1·25
434	10 s. Herbalist's clinic	1·50	1·75
430/4	*Set of 5*	3·75	4·00

88 *Epamera sidus*   **89** *Papilio rex*

(Des Rena Fennessy. Photo Harrison)

1988 (15 Feb)-**90**. *Butterflies. Multicoloured.*

(a) Vert designs as T 88. P 15×14

434a	10 c. *Cyrestis camillus* (1.9.89)	10	10
435	20 c. Type 88	10	10
436	40 c. *Cynthia cardui*	10	10
437	50 c. *Colotis evippe*	10	10
438	70 c. *Precis westermanni*	10	10
439	80 c. *Colias electo*	10	10
440	1 s. *Eronia leda*	10	10
440a	1 s. 50, *Papilio dardanus* (18.5.90)	10	10

(b) Vert designs as T 89. P 14½

441	2 s. Type 89	10	10
442	2 s. 50, *Colotis phisadia*	10	15
443	3 s. *Papilio desmondi*	10	15
444	3 s. 50, *Papilio demodocus*	15	20
445	4 s. *Papilio phorcas*	15	20
446	5 s. *Charaxes druceanus*	20	25
447	7 s. *Cymothoe teita*	25	30
448	10 s. *Charaxes zoolina*	35	40
449	20 s. *Papilio dardanus*	70	75
450	40 s. *Charaxes cithaeron*	1·40	1·50
434a/50	*Set of 18*	3·50	4·00

Examples of the 1 s. value were used in error at Kisumu from 2 February 1988.

90 Samburu Lodge and Crocodiles

(Des Advertising Link. Litho Questa)

1988 (31 May). *Kenyan Game Lodges. T 90 and similar horiz designs. Multicoloured. P 14½.*

451	1 s. Type 90	25	10
452	3 s. Naro Moru River Lodge and rock climbing	65	55
453	4 s. Mara Serena Lodge and zebra with foal	75	65
454	5 s. Voi Safari Lodge and buffalo	85	80
455	7 s. Kilimanjaro Buffalo Lodge and giraffes	1·10	1·10
456	10 s. Meru Mulika Lodge and rhinoceroses	1·50	1·60
451/6	*Set of 6*	4·75	4·25

91 Athletes and Stadium, Commonwealth Games, Brisbane, 1982

(Des D. Ashby. Litho Harrison)

1988 (10 June). *"Expo '88" World Fair, Brisbane, and Bicentenary of Australian Settlement. T 91 and similar horiz designs. Multicoloured. P 14½.*

457	1 s. Type 91	15	10
458	3 s. Flying Doctor Service aircraft	50	45
459	4 s. H.M.S. *Sirius* (frigate), 1788	55	55
460	5 s. Ostrich and emu	70	70
461	7 s. Queen Elizabeth II, President Arap Moi of Kenya and Prime Minister Hawke of Australia	90	1·00
457/61	*Set of 5*	2·50	2·50
MS462	117×80 mm. 30 s. Entrance to Kenya Pavilion	1·90	2·00

92 W.H.O. Logo and Slogan   **93** Handball

(Des Mukund Arts. Litho National Printing & Packaging, Zimbabwe)

1988 (1 July). *40th Anniv of World Health Organization. T 92 and similar horiz designs. P 14½.*

463	1 s. greenish blue, gold and ultramarine	20	10
464	3 s. multicoloured	60	50
465	5 s. multicoloured	80	75
466	7 s. multicoloured	1·25	1·40
463/6	*Set of 4*	2·50	2·50

Designs:—3 s. Mother with young son and nutritious food; 5 s. Giving oral vaccine to baby; 7 s. Village women drawing clean water from pump.

(Des H. Moghul. Litho D.L.R.)

1988 (1 Aug). *Olympic Games, Seoul. T 93 and similar vert designs. Multicoloured. P 14½×14.*

467	1 s. Type 93	15	10
468	3 s. Judo	30	30
469	5 s. Weightlifting	40	40
470	7 s. Javelin	55	60
471	10 s. Relay racing	65	75
467/71	*Set of 5*	1·90	1·90
MS472	110×78 mm. 30 s. Tennis	1·90	2·00

94 Calabashes   **95** Pres. Arap Moi taking Oath, 1978

(Des Mukund Arts. Litho D.L.R.)

1988 (20 Sept). *Kenyan Material Culture. T 94 and similar multicoloured designs. P 14½×14 (vert) or 14×14½ (horiz).*

473	1 s. Type 94	15	10
474	3 s. Milk gourds	35	35

475	5 s. Cooking pots (horiz)	..	..	..	45	45
476	7 s. Winnowing trays (horiz)		..		65	65
477	10 s. Reed baskets (horiz)		..		80	85
473/7				Set of 5	2·25	2·25

MS478 118×80 mm. 25 s. Gourds, calabash and horn (horiz) .. .. 1·50 1·60

(Des Mukund Arts. Litho Harrison)

1988 (13 Oct). *10th Anniv of "Nyayo" Era. T* **95** *and similar horiz designs. Multicoloured. P* 13½×14½.

479	1 s. Type 95	..	..	..	20	10
480	3 s. Building soil conservation barrier			60	50
481	3 s. 50, Passengers boarding bus			60	50
482	4 s. Metalwork shop		..		70	70
483	5 s. Moi University, Eldoret			80	80
484	7 s. Aerial view of hospital			1·25	1·40
485	10 s. Pres. Arap Moi and Mrs. Thatcher at Kapsabet Telephone Exchange			2·00	2·25
479/85		..	..	Set of 7	5·50	5·75

96 Kenya Flag

(Des Mukund Arts. Photo Courvoisier)

1988 (9 Dec). *25th Anniv of Independence. T* **96** *and similar horiz designs. Multicoloured. Granite paper. P* 11½.

486	1 s. Type 96	..	..	..	15	10
487	3 s. Coffee picking		..		40	40
488	5 s. Proposed Kenya Posts and Telecommunications Headquarters building			70	70
489	7 s. Kenya Airways Harambee Star "A310-300" Airbus			1·25	1·25
490	10 s. New diesel locomotive No. 9401			2·00	2·00
486/90		..	..	Set of 5	4·00	4·00

97 Gedi Ruins, Malindi

(Des Mukund Arts. Litho National Printing & Packaging, Zimbabwe)

1989 (15 Mar). *Historic Monuments. T* **97** *and similar multicoloured designs. P* 14½.

491	1 s. 20, Type 97	..	..	..	20	10
492	3 s. 40, Vasco Da Gama Pillar, Malindi (vert)			35	35
493	4 s. 40, Ishiakani Monument, Kiunga			45	45
494	5 s. 50, Fort Jesus, Mombasa			60	70
495	7 s. 70, She Burnan Omwe, Lamu (vert)			80	1·00
491/5		..	..	Set of 5	2·25	2·25

98 125th Anniversary and Kenya Red Cross Logos

99 Female Giraffe and Calf

(Des H. Moghul. Litho Cartor, France)

1989 (8 May). *125th Anniv of International Red Cross. T* **98** *and similar horiz designs. Multicoloured. P* 14×13½.

496	1 s. 20, Type 98	..	..	..	20	10
497	3 s. 40, Red Cross workers with car crash victim			40	40
498	4 s. 40, Disaster relief team distributing blankets			50	50
499	5 s. 50, Henri Dunant (founder)			65	75
500	7 s. 70, Blood donor		..		80	1·00
496/500			..	Set of 5	2·25	2·50

(Des Doreen McGuinness. Litho Walsall)

1989 (12 July). *Reticulated Giraffe. T* **99** *and similar vert designs. Multicoloured. P* 14½.

501	1 s. 20, Type 99	..	..	..	45	15
502	3 s. 40, Giraffe drinking			1·00	1·00
503	4 s. 40, Two giraffes			1·10	1·10
504	5 s. 50, Giraffe feeding			1·25	1·50
501/4		..	..	Set of 4	3·50	3·25

MS505 80×110 mm. 30 s. Designs as Nos. 501/4, but without face values .. .. 4·50 4·50

Designs from No. MS505 are without the Worldwide Fund for Nature logo.

ALTERED CATALOGUE NUMBERS

Any Catalogue numbers altered from the last edition are shown as a list in the introductory pages.

100 Pleurotus sajor-ceju

101 Independence Monuments

(Des Dvora Bochman. Litho Questa)

1989 (6 Sept). *Mushrooms. T* **100** *and similar vert designs. Multicoloured. P* 14½.

506	1 s. 20, Type 100	..	..	..	40	15
507	3 s. 40, Agaricus bisporus			70	55
508	4 s. 40, Agaricus bisporus (different)			85	75
509	5 s. 50, Termitomyces schimperi			1·25	1·25
510	7 s. 70, Lentinus edodes	..		1·90	2·00
506/10		..	..	Set of 5	4·75	4·25

(Des Conference and Exhibitions Secretariat, Nairobi. Litho Cartor, France)

1989 (9 Nov). *Birth Centenary of Jawaharlal Nehru (Indian statesman). T* **101** *and similar vert designs. Multicoloured. P* 13½×14.

511	1 s. 20, Type 101	..	..	..	40	15
512	3 s. 40, Nehru with graduates and open book			80	65
513	5 s. 50, Jawaharlal Nehru			1·25	1·10
514	7 s. 70, Industrial complex and cogwheels			1·90	1·90
511/14		..	..	Set of 4	4·00	3·50

(Des Mukund Arts. Litho Harrison)

1989 (20 Dec). *Ceremonial Costumes (4th series). Vert designs as T* **45**. *Multicoloured. P* 14½×13½.

515	1 s. 20, Kipsigis	..	..	..	30	15
516	3 s. 40, Rabai		..		70	60
517	5 s. 50, Duruma		..		95	95
518	7 s. 70, Kuria		..		1·40	1·50
519	10 s. Bajuni		..		1·75	2·00
515/19		..	..	Set of 5	4·75	4·75

102 EMS Speedpost Letters and Parcel

(Des Conference & Exhibitions Secretariat Ltd, Nairobi. Litho Cartor, France)

1990 (23 Mar). *10th Anniv of Pan African Postal Union. T* **101** *and similar multicoloured designs. P* 14×13½ *(horiz) or* 13½×14 *(vert).*

520	1 s. 20, Type 102	..	..	..	15	10
521	3 s. 40, Mail runner			35	35
522	5 s. 50, Mandera Post Office			55	60
523	7 s. 70, EMS Speedpost Letters and globe (vert)			80	1·00
524	10 s. P.A.P.U. logo (vert)			90	1·40
520/4		..	..	Set of 5	2·50	3·00

103 "Stamp King" with Tweezers and Magnifying Glass

104 Moi Golden Cup

(Des D. Miller. Photo Courvoisier)

1990 (27 Apr). *"Stamp World London 90" International Stamp Exhibition. T* **103** *and similar horiz designs. Granite paper. P* 11½.

525	1 s. 50, multicoloured	..	..	..	15	10
526	4 s. 50, multicoloured			50	40
527	6 s. 50, black, bright carmine and azure	..		55	70
528	9 s. multicoloured			75	1·25
525/8		..	..	Set of 4	1·75	2·25

MS529 113×77 mm. Nos. 525/8 .. 2·50 3·00

Designs:—4 s. 50, Penny Black and Kenya Stamp Bureau postmark; 6 s. 50, Early British cancellations; 9 s. Ronald Ngala Street Post Office, Nairobi.

(Litho Harrison)

1990 (21 May). *World Cup Football Championship, Italy. Trophies. T* **104** *and similar vert designs. Multicoloured. P* 14½.

| 530 | 1 s. 50, Type 104 | .. | .. | .. | 30 | 10 |
| 531 | 4 s. 50, East and Central Africa Challenge Cup | | | 70 | 70 |

532	6 s. 50, East and Central Africa Club Championship Cup			90	90
533	9 s. World Cup	..	..		1·40	1·60
530/3				Set of 4	3·00	3·00

105 K.A.N.U. Flag

(Des Mukund Arts. Litho Harrison)

1990 (11 June). *50th Anniv of Kenya African National Union. T* **105** *and similar horiz designs. Multicoloured. P* 14½.

534	1 s. 50, Type 105	..	..	..	15	10
535	2 s. 50, Nyayo Monument			15	15
536	4 s. 50, Party Headquarters			35	35
537	5 s. 50, Jomo Kenyatta (founder)			40	40
538	6 s. 50, President Arap Moi			50	60
539	9 s. President Moi addressing rally			70	90
540	10 s. Queue of voters			80	1·10
534/40		..	..	Set of 7	2·75	3·25

106 Desktop Computer

(Litho Questa)

1990 (12 July). *125th Anniv of International Telecommunications Union. T* **106** *and similar horiz designs. Multicoloured. P* 14½.

541	1 s. 50, Type 106	..	..	..	15	10
542	4 s. 50, Telephone switchboard assembly, Gilgil			35	35
543	6 s. 50, "125 YEARS"			45	65
544	9 s. Urban and rural telecommunications			70	1·00
541/4		..	..	Set of 4	1·50	1·90

107 Queen Mother at British Museum, 1988

108 Queen Elizabeth at Hospital Garden Party, 1947

(Des D. Miller. Litho Questa)

1990 (4 Aug). *90th Birthday of Queen Elizabeth the Queen Mother. P* 14×15 *(10 s.) or* 14½ *(40 s.).*

| 545 | 107 | 10 s. multicoloured | .. | .. | 80 | 1·00 |
| 546 | 108 | 40 s. black and brown-olive | .. | | 2·75 | 3·25 |

109 Kenya 1988 2 s. Definitive

110 Adult Literacy Class

(Des D. Miller. Litho D.L.R.)

1990 (5 Sept). *Centenary of Postage Stamps in Kenya. T* **109** *and similar vert designs. Multicoloured. P* 14×14½.

547	1 s. 50, Type 109	..	..	..	20	10
548	4 s. 50, East Africa and Uganda 1903 1 a.			45	45
549	6 s. 50, British East Africa Co 1890 ½ a. optd on G.B. 1d.			70	70
550	9 s. Kenya and Uganda 1922 20 c.			95	1·00
551	20 s. Kenya, Uganda, Tanzania 1971 2 s. 50, Railway commemorative			1·75	2·00
547/51		..	..	Set of 5	3·50	3·75

(Des H. Moghul. Litho Cartor, France)

1990 (30 Nov). *International Literacy Year. T* **110** *and similar vert designs. Multicoloured. P* 13½×14.

552	1 s. 50, Type 110	..	..	..	20	10
553	4 s. 50, Teaching by radio			45	45
554	6 s. 50, Technical training			65	75
555	9 s. International Literacy Year logo			95	1·25
552/5		..	..	Set of 4	2·00	2·25

111 National Flag

112 Symbolic Man and Pointing Finger

(Des H. Moghul. Litho Cartor)

1991 (29 Nov). *Olympic Games, Barcelona (1992) (1st issue).
T 111 and similar horiz designs. Multicoloured. P 14×13½.*

556	2 s. Type 111		..	15	10
557	6 s. Basketball	..		40	40
558	7 s. Hockey		..	50	50
559	8 s. 50, Table tennis		..	70	75
560	11 s. Boxing		..	75	85
556/60			Set of 5	2·25	2·40

See also Nos. 580/4.

(Des H. Mogul. Litho Cartor)

1992 (31 Jan). *AIDS Day. T 112 and similar vert designs.
Multicoloured. P 13½×14.*

561	2 s. Type 112		..	20	15
562	6 s. Victim and drugs		..	40	35
563	8 s. 50, Male and female symbols		60	60
564	11 s. Symbolic figure and hypodermic syringe		..	90	1·10
561/4	..	..	Set of 4	1·90	2·00

113 Queen and Prince Philip with Pres. Moi

114 Leopard

(Des D. Miller. Litho Cartor)

1992 (6 Feb). *40th Anniv of Queen Elizabeth II's Accession.
T 113 and similar horiz designs. Multicoloured. P 14×13½.*

565	3 s. Type 113		..	15	10
566	8 s. Storks in tree			40	35
567	11 s. Treetops Hotel		..	55	55
568	14 s. Three portraits of Queen Elizabeth		75	80
569	40 s. Queen Elizabeth II		..	2·00	2·50
565/9			Set of 5	3·50	3·75

(Des Dvora Bochman. Litho National Printing and Packaging, Zimbabwe)

1992 (8 May). *Kenya Wildlife. T 114 and similar vert designs.
Multicoloured. P 14×14½.*

570	3 s. Type 114		..	20	15
571	8 s. Lion		..	60	60
572	10 s. Elephant		..	75	75
573	11 s. Buffalo		..	75	75
574	14 s. Black Rhinoceros			95	95
570/4	..		Set of 5	3·00	2·75

115 International Harvester Safari Truck, 1926

116 Kenyan Athlete winning Race

(Des Dvora Bochman. Litho National Printing and Packaging, Zimbabwe)

1992 (24 June). *Vintage Cars. T 115 and similar horiz designs.
Multicoloured. P 14½×14.*

575	3 s. Type 115		..	15	10
576	8 s. Fiat "509", 1924		..	50	50
577	10 s. Hupmobile, 1923		..	55	55
578	11 s. Chevrolet "Box Body", 1928		55	55
579	14 s. Bentley/Parkward, 1934		..	70	70
575/9			Set of 5	2·25	2·25

(Des Dvora Bochman. Litho National Printing and Packaging, Zimbabwe)

1992 (24 July). *Olympic Games, Barcelona (2nd issue). T 116
and similar vert designs. Multicoloured. P 14×14½.*

580	3 s. Type 116		..	15	10
581	8 s. Men's judo		..	45	45

582	10 s. Kenyan women's volleyball players	..	55	55
583	11 s. Kenyan men's 4×100 metres relay runners		55	55
584	14 s. Men's 10,000 metres ..		65	65
580/4	..	..	Set of 5	2·10	2·10

117 Holy Child, Joseph and Animals

118 Asembo Bay Lighthouse, Lake Victoria

(Litho Cartor)

1992 (14 Dec). *Christmas. T 117 and similar vert designs.
Multicoloured. P 13½×14.*

585	3 s. Type 117		..	10	10
586	8 s. Mary with Holy Child		..	30	35
587	11 s. Christmas tree		..	35	40
588	14 s. Adoration of the Magi			45	50
585/8			Set of 4	1·10	1·25

(Des H. Moghul. Litho Questa)

1993 (25 Jan). *Lighthouses. T 118 and similar vert designs.
Multicoloured. P 14½.*

589	3 s. Type 118		..	10	10
590	8 s. Old Ras Serani lighthouse, Mombasa		30	35
591	11 s. New Ras Serani lighthouse, Mombasa		35	40
592	14 s. Gingira, Lake Victoria		..	45	50
589/92			Set of 4	1·10	1·25

119 Superb Starling

120 Yellow-billed Hornbill

(Des Dvora Bochman. Photo Courvoisier)

1993 (22 Feb). *Birds. Multicoloured. Granite paper.*

(a) Vert designs as T 119. P 15×14

593	50 c. Type 119			10	10
594	1 s. Red and Yellow Barbet			10	10
595	3 s. Black-throated Honeyguide ("Greater Honeyguide")		10	10
596	7 s. Malachite Kingfisher			25	30
597	8 s. Speckled Pigeon			30	35
598	10 s. Cinnamon-chested Bee Eater		35	40
599	11 s. Scarlet-chested Sunbird		35	40
600	14 s. Bagalafecht Weaver ("Reichenow's Weaver")		55	60

(b) Vert designs as T 120. P 14½

601	50 s. Type 120		..	1·75	1·90
602	80 s. Lesser Flamingo		..	2·75	3·00
603	100 s. Hadada Ibis ..		..	3·50	3·75
593/603	..		Set of 11	9·00	10·00

POSTAGE DUE STAMPS

The Postage Due stamps of Kenya, Uganda and Tanganyika were used in Kenya until 2 January 1967.

D 3

(Litho D.L.R.)

1967 (3 Jan)–**70**. *Chalk-surfaced paper. P 14×13½.*

D13	D 3	5 c. scarlet		15	2·00
		a. Perf 14. Ordinary paper. *Dull scarlet* (16.12.69)	30	3·25
D14		10 c. green		20	2·00
		a. Perf 14. Ordinary paper (16.12.69)	45	3·25
D15		20 c. blue		60	2·25
		a. Perf 14. Ordinary paper. *Deep blue* (16.12.69)	45	3·75
D16		30 c. brown		70	2·75
		a. Perf 14. Ordinary paper. *Light red-brown* (16.12.69)	60	5·50
D17		40 c. bright purple		65	4·50
		a. Perf 14. Ordinary paper. *Pale bright purple* (16.12.69)	55	7·50
D18		1 s. bright orange		1·75	6·00
		a. Perf 14. Ordinary paper. *Dull bright orange* (18.2.70)	1·00	8·50
D13/18			Set of 6	3·50	18·00
D13a/18a ..			Set of 6	3·00	28·00

1971 (13 July)–**73**. *P 14 × 15. (a) Chalk-surfaced paper (13.7.71).*

D19	D 3	10 c. green		5·00	7·00
D20		20 c. deep dull blue	..	6·00	8·00
D21		30 c. red-brown	..	7·00	9·00
D22		1 s. dull bright orange	..	9·50	22·00
D19/22			Set of 4	25·00	42·00

(b) Glazed, ordinary paper (20.2.73)

D23	D 3	5 c. bright scarlet	..	1·25	3·50
D24		10 c. dull yellow-green	..	1·25	3·50
D25		20 c. deep blue	..	1·00	3·75
D27		40 c. bright purple	..	90	5·50
D28		1 s. bright orange	..	1·25	9·00
D23/8			Set of 5	5·00	23·00

1973 (12 Dec). *Glazed, ordinary paper. P 15.*

D29	D 3	5 c. red		30	2·75
D30		10 c. emerald		30	2·75
D31		20 c. deep blue		30	3·25
D32		30 c. red-brown		30	4·00
D33		40 c. bright purple		3·25	6·50
D34		1 s. bright orange		95	8·50
D29/34			Set of 6	4·75	25·00

1979 (27 Mar). *Chalk-surfaced paper. P 14.*

D35	D 3	10 c. bright emerald		65	2·75
D36		20 c. deep dull blue		1·40	3·50
D37		30 c. dull red-brown		80	3·00
D38		40 c. bright reddish purple		1·50	4·50
D39		80 c. dull red		70	2·50
D40		1 s. bright reddish orange		70	2·75
D35/40			Set of 6	5·25	17·00

1983 (Dec). *W w 14. P 14.*

D41	D 3	10 c. yellowish green		10	10
D42		20 c. deep blue		10	10
D43		40 c. bright purple		3·50	4·00
D41/3 ..			Set of 3	3·50	4·00

(Litho Harrison)

1985 (7 Aug)–**87**. *Ordinary paper. P 14½×14.*

D44	D 3	30 c. red-brown (9.1.87)		10	10
D45		40 c. bright magenta (9.1.87)	..	10	10
D46		80 c. dull vermilion (9.1.87)	..	10	10
D47		1 s. bright orange (1986)	..	10	10
D48		2 s. violet		..	10	10
D44/8 ..			Set of 5	25	30

No. D47 was issued by the Crown Agents with Nos. D44/6, but was available in Kenya by November 1986.

OFFICIAL STAMPS

Intended for use on official correspondence of the Kenya Government only but there is no evidence that they were so used.

OFFICIAL

(O 4)

(15 c. 30 c. opt typo; others in photogravure)

1964 (1 Oct). *Nos. 1/5 and 7 optd with Type O 4.*

O21	5 c. brown, deep blue, green and bistre		10
O22	10 c. brown			10
O23	15 c. magenta			50
O24	20 c. black and yellow-green	..	20
O25	30 c. black and yellow	..		30
O26	50 c. crimson, black and green	..	2·00
O21/26			Set of 6	2·75

Kenya, Uganda and Tanganyika (Tanzania)

BRITISH EAST AFRICA

The area which became British East Africa had been part of the domain of the Zanzibari Sultans since 1794. In 1887 the administration of the province was granted to the British East Africa Association, incorporated as the Imperial British East Africa Company the following year.

Company post offices were established at Lamu and Mombasa in May 1890, British mails having been previously sent via the Indian post office on Zanzibar, opened in 1875.

A German postal agency opened at Lamu on 22 November 1888 and continued to operate until 31 March 1891, using German stamps. These can be identified by the "LAMU/OSTAFRIKA" cancellations and are listed under German East Africa in our *Part 7 (Germany)* catalogue.

PRICES FOR STAMPS ON COVER

Nos. 1/3	*from* × 6	
Nos. 4/19	*from* × 25	
Nos. 20/6	*from* × 3	
Nos. 27/8	*from* × 7	
Nos. 29/30	*from* × 15	
Nos. 31/2	*from* × 4	
Nos. 33/47	*from* × 10	
No. 48	*from* × 15	
Nos. 49/64	*from* × 12	
Nos. 65/79	*from* × 15	
Nos. 80/91	*from* × 8	
Nos. 92/6	*from* × 12	
Nos. 97/9	—	

BRITISH EAST AFRICA COMPANY ADMINISTRATION

BRITISH EAST AFRICA COMPANY	BRITISH EAST AFRICA COMPANY
HALF ANNA	1 ANNA
(1)	(2)

(Surch D.L.R.)

1890 (May). *Stamps of Great Britain (Queen Victoria) surch as T 1 or T 2 (1 a. and 4 a.).*

1		½ a. on 1d. deep purple (No. 173)	..	£300	£200
2		1 a. on 2d. grey-green and carmine (No. 200)		£375	£275
3		4 a. on 5d. dull purple and blue (No. 207a)		£425	£275

A copy of the ½ a. with the short crossbar of "F" in "HALF" omitted exists in the Royal Collection but is the only known example.

Stamps of INDIA were used in British East Africa between late July and September 1890 being postmarked "MOMBASA" or "LAMU".

3

4

5 ANNAS.

(5)

(Litho B.W.)

1890 (14 Oct)**–94.** *P* 14.

4	3	½ a. dull brown	..	..	2·00	2·50
		a. Imperf (pair)			£600	£425
		b. Deep brown (9.93)	..		70	2·00
		ba. Imperf (pair)			£550	£350
		bb. Imperf between (horiz pair)		£1500	£750
		bc. Imperf between (vert pair)..		£650	£475
		c. Pale brown (12.94) ..			1·00	2·25
5		1 a. blue-green	..		3·00	3·75
		aa. "ANL" (broken "D") (R.6/3)		£250	£275
		a. Imperf (pair)			£700	£450
		ab. "ANL" (broken "D") (R.6/3)		£4750	
		b. Deep blue-green (12.94)			75	
		ba. Imperf (pair)			£700	£450
6		2 a. vermilion	..		2·75	3·25
		a. Imperf (pair)			£1000	£475
7		2½ a. black/yellow-buff (7.91)	..	48·00	15·00
		a. Black/pale buff (7.92)			45·00	5·00
		b. Black/bright yellow (9.93) ..		3·75	3·75
		bb. Imperf (pair)			£650	£400
		bc. Imperf between (horiz pair)		£550	£400
		bd. Imperf between (vert pair)..		£750	£475
8		3 a. black/dull red (2.91)	..	6·00	9·50
		a. Black/bright red (9.93)..		1·25	2·25
		ab. Imperf (pair)			£600	£400
		ac. Imperf between (horiz pair)		£600	£375
		ad. Imperf between (vert pair)..		£450	£375
9		4 a. yellow-brown	..		2·50	4·50
		a. Imperf (pair)			£1200	£500
10		4 a. grey (imperf)	..	..	£1200	£1400

11	3	4½ a. dull violet (2.91)	..		27·00	13·00
		a. Brown-purple (9.93)	..		2·50	12·00
		ab. Imperf (pair)			£850	£400
		ac. Imperf between (horiz pair)		£1200	£1200
		ad. Imperf between (vert pair)..		£600	£425
12		8 a. blue	..		5·50	7·00
		a. Imperf (pair)			£1600	£550
13		8 a. grey	..		£250	£225
14		1 r. carmine	..		6·00	9·00
		a. Imperf (pair)			£2250	£600
15		1 r. grey	..		£225	£225
16	4	2 r. brick-red	..		11·00	15·00
17		3 r. slate-purple	..		8·00	19·00
18		4 r. ultramarine	..		12·00	25·00
19		5 r. grey-green ..	..		30·00	48·00
4/19			*Set of 15 (perf)*	£500	£500

For the 5 a. and 7½ a. see Nos. 29/30.

The paper of Nos. 7, 7a, 7b, 8 and 8a is coloured on the surface only.

Printings of 1890/92 are on thin paper having the outer margins of the sheets imperf and bearing sheet watermark "PURE LINEN WOVE BANK" and "W. C. S. & Co." in a monogram, the trademark of the makers, Messrs. William Collins, Sons & Co.

1893/94 printings are on thicker coarser paper with outer margins perforated through the selvedge and without watermark. Single specimens cannot always be distinguished by lack of watermark alone. Exceptions are the 1893 printings of the 2½ a. and 3 a. which were on Wiggins Teape paper showing a sheet watermark of "1011" in figures 1 centimetre high.

Nos. 7 (coloured through) and 16/19 on thick unwatermarked paper are from a special printing made for presentation purposes.

The printings of the 4 a., 8 a. and 1 r. values in grey were intended for fiscal purposes, but in the event, were made available for postal use.

Forgeries of the 4 a., 8 a., 1 r., grey and 2 to 5 r. exist. The latter are common and can be distinguished by the scroll above "LIGHT" where there are five vertical lines of shading in the forgeries and seven in the genuine stamps. Forged cancellations exist on the commoner stamps. Beware of "imperf" stamps made by trimming margins of stamps from marginal rows.

1891. *Mombasa Provisionals. (a) New value handstamped in dull violet, and manuscript initials in black.*

20	3	"½ Anna' on 2 a. vermilion ("A.D.") (January)	..	£2750	£750
		a. "½ Anna" double			† £3000
21		"1 Anna' on 4 a. brown ("A.B.") (February)	..	£4750	£1200

		(b) Manuscript value and initials in black			
22	3	"½ Anna" on 2 a. vermilion ("A.D.") (January)	..	—	£950
		a. Error. "½ Annas" ("A.D.") ..			£950
23		"½ Anna" on 2 a. vermilion ("A.B.") (February)	..	£2500	£650
		a. Error. "½ Annas" ("A.B.")		—	£900
24		"½ Anna" on 3 a. black/dull red ("A.B.") (May)	..	£3500	£950
25		"1 Anna" on 3 a. black/dull red ("V.H.M.") (June)	..	£3500	£850
26		"1 Anna" on 4 a. brown ("A.B.") (March)	£2750	£850

A.D. = Andrew Dick, Chief Accountant.
A.B. = Archibald Brown, Cashier of the Company.
V.H.M. = Victor H. Mackenzie, Bank Manager.

(Surch B.W.)

1894 (1 Nov). *Surch as* T 5.

27	3	5 a. on 8 a. blue ..	..	55·00	75·00
28		7½ a. on 1 r. carmine	..	55·00	75·00
27/28		Handstamped "Specimen"	*Set of 2*	90·00	

Forgeries exist.

1894 (Dec). *No wmk. P* 14.

29	3	5 a. black/grey-blue	..	1·25	9·50
30		7½ a. black	..		1·25	9·50
29/30		Handstamped "Specimen"	*Set of 2*	75·00	

These two stamps have "LD" after "COMPANY" in the inscription.

The paper of No. 29 is coloured on the surface only.

1895 (Feb). *Surch with manuscript value and initials ("T.E.C.R.").*

31	3	"½ anna" on 3 a. black/dull red (19.2)	£200	45·00
32		"1 anna" on 3 a. black/dull red (22.2)	£2500	£1200

T.E.C.R. = T. E. C. Remington, Postmaster at Mombasa.

The Company experienced considerable financial problems during 1894 with the result that the British Government agreed to assume the administration of the territory, as a protectorate, on 1 July 1895.

IMPERIAL ADMINISTRATION

BRITISH EAST AFRICA	2½
(6)	(7)

(Handstamped at Mombasa)

1895 (9 July). *Handstamped with* T 6.

33	3	½ a. deep brown	..	55·00	20·00
		a. Pale brown	..	65·00	30·00
		b. Double	..	£300	£300
34		1 a. blue-green	..	65·00	65·00
		a. Double	..	£300	£300
		b. "ANL" (broken "D") (R. 6/3)		£1000	
35		2 a. vermilion	..	£120	90·00
		a. Double	..	£350	£325
36		2½ a. black/bright yellow		95·00	48·00
		a. Double	..	£350	£325
37		3 a. black/dull red	..	45·00	38·00
38		4 a. yellow-brown	..	38·00	35·00
		a. Double	..	£325	£325
39		4½ a. dull violet	..	£110	80·00
		a. Double	..	£425	£400
		b. Brown-purple	..	£700	£600
		ba. Double	..	£1300	£1200

40	3	5 a. black/grey-blue	..	£130	90·00
		a. Double	..	£600	£600
		b. Inverted	..	† £2000	
41		7½ a. black	..	80·00	75·00
		a. Double	..	£400	£400
42		8 a. blue	..	80·00	65·00
		a. Double	..	£425	£425
		b. Inverted	..	£1800	
43		1 r. carmine	..	45·00	42·00
		a. Double	..	£375	£375
44	4	2 r. brick-red	..	£200	£180
45		3 r. slate-purple	..	£120	£100
		a. Double	..	£650	£650
		b. Inverted	..		
46		4 r. ultramarine	..	£120	£110
		a. Double	..	£650	£650
47		5 r. grey-green	..	£275	£250
		a. Double	..	£950	£950
33/47			*Set of 15*	£1400	£1100

Forgeries exist.

1895 (29 Sept). *No. 39 surch with* T 7 *by The Zanzibar Gazette.*

48	3	2½ a. on 4½ a. dull violet (R.)	..	80·00	60·00
		a. Opt (T 6) double	..	£600	£550

British East Africa	British East Africa
(8)	(9)

SETTING OF TYPE 8. This consisted of 120 impressions in 10 horizontal rows of 12 stamps. This matched the size of the pane for all the Indian issues to 1 r. with the exception of the 6 a. The sheets of this value contained four panes, each 8 × 10, which meant that the outer vertical margins also received the overprint.

The setting of Type 9 is not known.

Although only the one setting was used for the low values it is known that some of the overprint errors occurred, or were corrected, during the course of the various printings.

(Overprinted at the offices of *The Zanzibar Gazette*)

1895 (27 Oct)**–96.** *Stamps of India (Queen Victoria) optd with* T 8 *or* 9 *(2 r. to 5 r.).* W 13 *(Elephant Head) (6 a.) or* W 34 *(Large Star) (others) of India.*

49	½ a. blue-green (No. 85) (8.11.95)	..	3·25	3·25
	a. "Britlsh" for "British"	..	£1900	£1700
	b. "Br1tish" for "British" (R. 10/12)	..	£225	
	c. "Afr1ca" for "Africa" (R. 1/11)	..	£225	
	d. Opt double, one albino	..	£250	
50	1 a. plum (No. 89) (8.11.95)	..	3·00	3·25
	a. "Britlsh" for "British"	..	£2500	£1400
	b. "Br1tish" for "British" (R. 10/12)	..	£225	
	c. "Afr1ca" for "Africa" (R. 1/11)	..	£225	
51	1 a. 6 p. sepia (No. 90) (23.11.95)	..	3·75	3·00
	a. "Br1tish" for "British" (R. 10/12)	..	£275	
	b. "Afr1ca" for "Africa" (R. 1/11)	..	£275	
52	2 a. blue (No. 92) (8.11.95)	..	3·50	2·50
	a. "Britlsh" for "British"	..	£1600	
	b. "Br1tish" for "British" (R. 10/12)	..	£225	£200
	c. "Afr1ca" for "Africa" (R. 1/11)	..	£225	£200
53	2½ a. yellow-green (No. 103)	..	5·00	2·50
	a. "Biitish" for "British"	..	£3500	
	b. "Bpitish" for "British"	..	£3500	
	c. "Britlsh" for "British"		† £1500	
	d. "Eas" for "East" (R. 2/12)	..	£750	£950
	e. "Br1tish" for "British" (R. 10/12)	..	£300	£250
	f. "Afr1ca" for "Africa" (R. 1/11)	..	£300	
54	3 a. brown-orange (No. 94) (18.12.95)	..	7·50	8·00
	a. "Br1tish" for "British" (R. 10/12)	..	£325	£325
	b. "Afr1ca" for "Africa" (R. 1/11)	..	£325	
55	4 a. olive-green (No. 95) (18.12.95)	..	22·00	15·00
	a. Slate-green	..	20·00	15·00
	b. "Br1tish" for "British" (R. 10/12)	..	£375	£350
	c. "Afr1ca" for "Africa" (R. 1/11)	..	£375	£350
56	6 a. pale brown (No. 81) (18.12.95)	..	23·00	28·00
	a. "Br1tish" for "British" (R. 10/8)	..	£450	
	b. "Afr1ca" for "Africa" (R. 1/7)	..	£450	
	c. Opt double, one albino	..	£750	
57	8 a. dull mauve (No. 98) (18.12.95)	..	48·00	50·00
	a. "Br1tish" for "British" (R. 10/12)	..	£550	
	b. "Afr1ca" for "Africa" (R. 1/11)	..	£550	
	c. Magenta (1896)	..	28·00	35·00
	ca. "Br1tish" for "British" (R. 10/12)	..	£450	
	cb. "Afr1ca" for "Africa" (R. 1/11)	..	£450	
	cc. Inverted "a" for "t" of "East" (R. 2/12)		† £3000	
58	12 a. purple/red (No. 100) (18.12.95)	..	19·00	26·00
	a. "Br1tish" for "British" (R. 10/12)	..	£450	£450
	b. "Afr1ca" for "Africa" (R. 1/11)	..	£450	
59	1 r. slate (No. 101) (18.12.95)	..	48·00	48·00
	a. "Br1tish" for "British" (R. 10/12)	..	£700	
	b. "Afr1ca" for "Africa" (R. 1/11)	..	£700	
60	1 r. green & aniline carm (No. 106) (1896)	28·00	45·00
	a. Inverted "a" for "t" of "East" (R. 2/12)	£2500	
	b. "Br1tish" for "British" (R. 10/12)	..	£475	
	c. "Afr1ca" for "Africa" (R. 1/11)	..	£475	
	d. Opt double, one sideways	..	£300	£500
61	2 r. carm & yellow-brn (No. 107) (18.12.95)	48·00	80·00
	a. "B" handstamped	..	£450	
62	3 r. brown and green (No. 108) (18.12.95)	60·00	90·00
63	5 r. ultramarine & vio (No. 109) (18.12.95)	75·00	£100
	a. Opt double	..	£1800	
	b. "B" handstamped	..	£1400	£1400
49/63		*Set of 15*	£300	£425

Examples of the 2½ a. are known postmarked from 27 October onwards.

The relative horizontal positions of the three lines of the overprint vary considerably but the distance vertically between the lines of the overprint is constant.

In both the "Br1tish" and "Afr1ca" errors the figure one is in a smaller type size.

There are other varieties, such as inverted "s" in "British", wide and narrow "B", and inverted "V" for "A" in "Africa" (R.1/1 and R.6/7).

During the overprinting of the 2 r. and 5 r. the "B" of "British" sometimes failed to print so that only traces of the letter appeared. It was replaced by a handstamped "B" which is often out of alignment with the rest of the overprint. The handstamp is known double. The variety may also exist on the 3 r.

The 2, 3 and 5 r., normally overprinted in larger type than the lower values, are also known with a smaller overprint, for use as specimen stamps for the U.P.U. These were not issued for postal purposes (*Price £375 un per set*). The lower values were reprinted at the same time using similar type to the original overprint.

Forgeries exist.

$2\frac{1}{2}$
(10)　　　11

1895 (20 Dec). *No. 51 surch locally with T* **10** *in bright red.*

64	$2\frac{1}{2}$ on $1\frac{1}{2}$ a. sepia	..	40·00	32·00
	a. Inverted "1" in fraction (R. 5/7, 10/7)		£600	£600
	b. "Br1tish" for "British" (R. 10/12)		£750	
	c. "Afr1ca" for "Africa" (R. 1/11)		£750	

The setting of Type 10 was in 5 horizontal rows of 12 stamps, repeated twice for each pane.

No. 51 also exists surcharged with T **12**, **13** and **14** in brown-red. These stamps were sent to the Postal Union authorities at Berne, but were never issued to the public (*Price unused:* T **12** £60, T **13** £140, T **14** £95).

(Recess D.L.R.)

1896 (26 May)–**1901.** *Wmk Crown CA. P* 14.

65	11	$\frac{1}{2}$ a. yellow-green	..	85	50
66		1 a. carmine-rose	..	1·75	30
		a. Bright rose-red	..	1·75	30
		b. Rosine (1901)	..	16·00	2·75
67		2 a. chocolate	..	1·50	3·00
68		$2\frac{1}{2}$ a. deep blue	..	4·50	1·10
		a. Violet-blue	..	5·50	1·60
		b. Inverted "S" (R.1/1)	..	65·00	42·00
69		3 a. grey	..	2·50	5·00
70		4 a. deep green	..	5·50	2·50
71		$4\frac{1}{2}$ a. orange-yellow	..	3·75	8·00
72		5 a. yellow-bistre	..	7·50	4·00
73		$7\frac{1}{2}$ a. mauve	..	5·00	18·00
74		8 a. grey-olive	..	2·50	4·50
75		1 r. pale dull blue	..	24·00	18·00
		a. Ultramarine	..	30·00	24·00
76		2 r. orange	..	50·00	25·00
77		3 r. deep violet	..	50·00	27·00
78		4 r. carmine-lake	..	50·00	48·00
79		5 r. sepia	..	50·00	40·00
		a. Thin "U" in "RUPEES" (R.3/2)		£1000	£1000
65/79			*Set of* 15	£225	£150
65/79 Optd "Specimen"			*Set of* 15	£250	

(Overprinted at the offices of *The Zanzibar Gazette*)

1897 (2 Jan). *Nos.* 156/7, 159 *and* 165/7 *of Zanzibar optd with* T **8**. *Wmk Single Rosette.*

80		$\frac{1}{2}$ a. yellow-green and red	..	38·00	38·00
81		1 a. indigo and red	..	65·00	65·00
82		2 a. red-brown and red	..	25·00	20·00
83		$4\frac{1}{2}$ a. orange and red	..	35·00	25·00
84		5 a. bistre and red	..	38·00	30·00
		a. "Bri" for "British"	..	†	£900
85		$7\frac{1}{2}$ a. mauve and red	..	38·00	35·00
		a. "Bri" for "British"	..		£900
80/5			*Set of* 6	£200	£180

Nos. 84a and 85a appear to have occurred when the type was obscured during part of the overprinting.

The above six stamps exist with an overprint similar to T **8** but normally showing a stop after "Africa". These overprints (in red on the 1 a.) were made officially to supply the U.P.U. However, the stop does not always show. Pieces are known showing overprints with and without stop *se-tenant* (including the red overprint on the 1 a.).

Stamps of Zanzibar, wmk. "Multiple Rosettes" and overprinted with T **8** are forgeries.

$2\frac{1}{2}$　$2\frac{1}{2}$　$2\frac{1}{2}$
(12)　　(13)　　(14)

SETTING OF TYPES 12/14. The setting of 60 (6×10) contained 26 examples of Type 12, 10 of Type 13 and 24 of Type 14.

1897 (2 Jan). *Nos.* 157 *and* 162 *of Zanzibar optd with* T **8** *and further surch locally, in red.*

86	12	$2\frac{1}{2}$ on 1 a. indigo and red	..	70·00	50·00
		b. Opt Type 8 double	..	£4000	
87	13	$2\frac{1}{2}$ on 1 a. indigo and red	..	£130	90·00
88	14	$2\frac{1}{2}$ on 1 a. indigo and red	..	80·00	55·00
		a. Opt Type 8 double	..	£4500	
89	12	$2\frac{1}{2}$ on 3 a. grey and red	..	65·00	48·00
90	13	$2\frac{1}{2}$ on 3 a. grey and red	..	£120	85·00
91	14	$2\frac{1}{2}$ on 3 a. grey and red	..	75·00	50·00
86/91			*Set of* 6	£450	£325

Both the notes after No. 85 also apply here.

A special printing for U.P.U. requirements was made with the $2\frac{1}{2}$ surcharge on the 1 a. and 3 a. stamps overprinted as T **8** but *with stop* after "Africa". It also included a "2" over "1" error in T **14**.

15

(Recess D.L.R.)

1897 (Nov)–**1903.** *Wmk Crown CC. P* 14.

92	15	1 r. grey-blue	..	30·00	25·00
		a. Dull blue (1901)	..	26·00	17·00
		b. Bright ultramarine (1903)	..	£110	85·00
93		2 r. orange	..	48·00	48·00
94		3 r. deep violet	..	48·00	70·00
95		4 r. carmine	..	£110	£150
96		5 r. deep sepia	..	£110	£160
97		10 r. yellow-bistre (S. £60)	..	£160	£225
98		20 r. pale green (S. £125)	..	£500	£1000
99		50 r. mauve (S. £250)	..	£1600	£2750
92/96 Optd "Specimen"			*Set of* 5	£180	

On 1 April 1901 the postal administrations of British East Africa and Uganda were merged. Subsequent issues were inscribed "EAST AFRICA AND UGANDA PROTECTORATES".

EAST AFRICA AND UGANDA PROTECTORATES

For earlier issues see BRITISH EAST AFRICA and UGANDA. For the issues of the Mandated Territory of Tanganyika and the war-time issues that preceded them, see TANGANYIKA.

PRICES FOR STAMPS ON COVER TO 1945	
Nos. 1/43	*from* × 3
Nos. 44/75	*from* × 2
Nos. 76/95	*from* × 3
Nos. 96/105	—
Nos. 110/23	*from* × 2
Nos. 124/7	*from* × 3
Nos. 128/30	*from* × 5
Nos. 131/54	*from* × 3
Nos. D1/12	*from* × 8

PRINTERS. All the stamps issued between 1903 and 1927 were typographed by De La Rue & Co. Ltd, London.

USED HIGH VALUES. Beware of cleaned fiscally cancelled copies with faked postmarks.

1　　　　2

1903 (24 July)–04. *P* 14. (*a*) *Wmk Crown CA.*

1	1	$\frac{1}{2}$ a. green (16.2.04)	..	1·60	5·00
2		1 a. grey and red	..	1·75	30
3		2 a. dull and bright purple (24.7.03)	..	6·00	2·50
4		$2\frac{1}{2}$ a. blue	..	12·00	35·00
5		3 a. brown-purple and green	..	16·00	32·00
6		4 a. grey-green and black	..	11·00	14·00
7		5 a. grey and orange-brown	..	18·00	38·00
8		8 a. grey and pale blue	..	20·00	28·00

(*b*) *Wmk Crown CC. Ordinary paper*

9	2	1 r. green	..	13·00	40·00
		a. Chalk-surfaced paper	..	22·00	48·00
10		2 r. dull and bright purple	..	45·00	48·00
11		3 r. grey-green and black	..	65·00	£100
12		4 r. grey and emerald-green	..	75·00	£100
13		5 r. grey and red	..	75·00	£120
14		10 r. grey and ultramarine	..	£120	£170
		a. Chalk-surfaced paper	..	£140	£180
15		20 r. grey and stone (Optd S. £120)	..	£400	£600
16		50 r. grey and red-brown (Optd S. £250)		£1000	£1400
1/13			*Set of* 13	£300	£500
1/14 Optd "Specimen"			*Set of* 14	£250	

1904–07. *Wmk Mult Crown CA. Ordinary paper* ($\frac{1}{2}$ *a. to* 8 *a.*) *or chalk-surfaced paper* (1 *r. to* 50 *r.*).

17	1	$\frac{1}{2}$ a. grey-green	..	3·75	1·00
		a. Chalk-surfaced paper	..	3·25	1·40
18		1 a. grey and red	..	3·00	20
		a. Chalk-surfaced paper	..	2·75	20
19		2 a. dull and bright purple	..	3·00	90
		a. Chalk-surfaced paper	..	2·50	1·00
20		$2\frac{1}{2}$ a. blue	..	13·00	26·00
21		$2\frac{1}{2}$ a. ultramarine and blue	..	7·50	17·00
22		3 a. brown-purple and green	..	3·75	18·00
		a. Chalk-surfaced paper	..	3·75	18·00
23		4 a. grey-green and black	..	7·50	12·00
		a. Chalk-surfaced paper	..	7·50	15·00
24		5 a. grey and orange-brown	..	7·50	14·00
		a. Chalk-surfaced paper	..	6·50	20·00
25		8 a. grey and pale blue	..	7·00	8·00
		a. Chalk-surfaced paper	..	7·00	11·00
26	2	1 r. green (1907)	..	26·00	55·00
27		2 r. dull and bright purple (1906)	..	30·00	48·00
28		3 r. grey-green and black (1907)	..	45·00	85·00
29		4 r. grey and emerald-green (1907)	..	48·00	£110
30		5 r. grey and red (1907)	..	55·00	85·00
31		10 r. grey and ultramarine (1907)	..	£120	£150
32		20 r. grey and stone (1907)	..	£450	£650
33		50 r. grey and red-brown (1907)	..	£1200	£1600
17/30			*Set of* 13	£200	£400

(New Currency. 100 cents = 1 rupee)

1907–08. *Wmk Mult Crown CA. Chalk-surfaced paper* (10, 12, 25, 50, 75 *c.*). *P* 14.

34	1	1 c. brown (1908)	..	30	15
35		3 c. grey-green	..	3·25	25
		a. Blue-green	..	5·00	2·00

36	1	6 c. red	..	2·75	10
37		10 c. lilac and pale olive	..	9·00	8·50
38		12 c. dull and bright purple	..	4·50	2·75
39		15 c. bright blue	..	9·50	8·50
40		25 c. grey-green and black	..	4·00	6·50
41		50 c. grey-green and orange-brown	..	7·00	12·00
42		75 c. grey and pale blue (1908)	..	4·50	22·00
34/42			*Set of* 9	40·00	55·00
34/42 Optd "Specimen"			*Set of* 9	£160	

Original　　　Redrawn

1910. T **1** *redrawn. Printed from a single plate. Wmk Mult Crown CA. P* 14.

43		6 c. red	..	4·00	20

In the redrawn type a fine white line has been cut around the value tablets and above the name tablet separating the latter from the leaves above, EAST AFRICA AND UGANDA is in shorter and thicker letters and PROTECTORATES in taller letters than in No. 36.

3　　　4　　　4 cents
(5)

1912–21. *Wmk Mult Crown CA. Chalk-surfaced paper* (25 *c. to* 500 *r.*). *P* 14.

44	3	1 c. black	..	20	65
45		3 c. green	..	2·00	30
		a. Deep blue-green (1917)	..	3·25	75
46		6 c. red	..	50	20
		a. Scarlet (1917)	..	10·00	1·25
47		10 c. yellow-orange	..	2·00	20
		a. Orange (1921)	..	7·00	1·25
48		12 c. slate-grey	..	2·75	20
49		15 c. bright blue	..	2·75	55
50		25 c. black and red/*yellow*	..	45	90
		a. White back (5.14) (Optd S. £25)		50	2·50
		b. On lemon (1916) (Optd S. £25)		9·00	10·00
		c. On orange-buff (1921)	..	27·00	13·00
		d. On pale yellow (1921)	..	6·50	3·50
51		50 c. black and lilac	..	1·50	40
52		75 c. black/*green*	..	1·50	12·00
		a. White back (5.14) (Optd S. £25)		90	10·00
		b. On blue-grn, ol back (Optd S. £25)		6·00	4·00
		c. On emerald, olive back (1919)	..	38·00	95·00
		d. On emerald back (1921)	..	10·00	26·00
53	4	1 r. black/*green*	..	1·75	3·75
		a. On emerald back (1919)	..	5·00	30·00
54		2 r. red and black/*blue*	..	20·00	20·00
55		3 r. violet and green	..	20·00	45·00
56		4 r. red and green/*yellow*	..	45·00	85·00
		a. On pale yellow	..	70·00	£100
57		5 r. blue and dull purple	..	45·00	90·00
58		10 r. red and green/*green*	..	75·00	£120
59		20 r. black and purple/*red*	..	£250	£250
60		20 r. purple and blue/*blue* (1918)	..	£225	£225
61		50 r. carmine and green (Optd S. £140)		£550	£600
		a. Ordinary paper. Dull rose-red and dull greyish green		£650	£700
62		100 r. purple and black/*red* (Optd S. £250)		£2750	£1800
63		500 r. green and red/*green* (Optd S. £550)		£12000	
44/58			*Set of* 15	£190	£325
44/60 Optd "Specimen"			*Set of* 17	£450	

For values in this series overprinted "G.E.A." (German East Africa) see Tanganyika Nos. 45/62.

1919 (7 Apr). *No.* 46a *surch with* T **5** *by the Swift Press, Nairobi.*

64	3	4 c. on 6 c. scarlet (*shades*)	..	30	15
		a. Bars omitted	..	27·00	42·00
		b. Surch double	..	£100	£120
		c. Surch inverted	..	£160	£190
		d. Pair, one without surch	..	£500	£550
64 H/S "Specimen"			..	55·00	

1921–22. *Wmk Mult Script CA. Chalk-surfaced paper* (50 *c. to* 50 *r.*). *P* 14.

65	3	1 c. black	..	35	80
66		3 c. green	..	1·25	3·75
		a. Blue-green	..	7·50	8·00
67		6 c. carmine-red	..	1·25	4·00
68		10 c. orange (12.21)	..	4·00	30
69		12 c. slate-grey	..	3·25	35·00
70		15 c. bright blue	..	3·25	10·00
71		50 c. black and dull purple	..	9·50	50·00
72	4	2 r. red and black/*blue*	..	48·00	£100
73		3 r. violet and green	..	75·00	£130
74		5 r. blue and dull purple	..	80·00	£150
75		50 r. carmine and green (Optd S. £225)		£1900	£2750
65/74			*Set of* 10	£200	£425
65/74 Optd "Specimen"			*Set of* 10	£225	

For values in this series overprinted "G.E.A." see Tanganyika Nos. 63/73.

MINIMUM PRICE

The minimum price quote is 10p which represents a handling charge rather than a basis for valuing common stamps. For further notes about prices see introductory pages.

KENYA AND UGANDA

(New Currency. 100 cents = 1 shilling)

On 23 July 1920 Kenya became a Crown Colony with the exception of the coastal strip, previously part of the Sultan of Zanzibar's territories, which remained a protectorate.

6   **7**

1922 (1 Nov)–**27.** *Wmk Script CA. P* 14.

(a) Wmk upright. Ordinary paper

76	**6**	1 c. pale brown	70	90
		a. *Deep brown* (1923)	1·50	2·50
77		5 c. dull violet	2·25	30
		a. *Bright violet*	3·00	1·25
78		5 c. green (1927)	2·00	10
79		10 c. green	1·25	10
80		10 c. black (5.27)	2·00	10
81		12 c. jet-black	5·00	28·00
		a. *Grey-black*	1·75	21·00
82		15 c. rose-carmine	1·00	10
83		20 c. dull orange-yellow	2·50	10
		a. *Bright orange*	3·00	10
84		30 c. ultramarine	1·25	20
85		50 c. grey	1·75	10
86		75 c. olive	2·25	7·50

(b) Wmk sideways. Chalk-surfaced paper

87	**7**	1 s. green	2·75	2·00
88		2 s. dull purple	7·50	7·00
89		2 s. 50 c. brown (1.10.25)	18·00	60·00
90		3 s. brownish grey	15·00	6·00
		a. *Jet-black*	28·00	26·00
91		4 s. grey (1.10.25)	18·00	65·00
92		5 s. carmine-red	22·00	18·00
93		7 s. 50 c. orange-yellow (1.10.25)	60·00	£130
94		10 s. bright blue	48·00	48·00
95		£1 black and orange	£140	£190
96		£2 green and purple (1.10.25) (S. £110)	£600	
97		£3 purple and yellow (1.10.25) (S. £120)	£750	
98		£4 black & magenta (1.10.25) (S. £160)	£1200	
99		£5 black and blue (S. £200)	£1500	
100		£10 black and green (S. £250)	£7500	
101		£20 red and green (1.10.25) (S. £375)	£12000	
102		£25 black and red (S. £400)	£13000	
103		£50 black and brown (S. £450)	£17000	
104		£75 purple and grey (1.10.25) (S. £550)	£35000	
105		£100 red and black (1.10.25) (S. £600)	£40000	
		76/95	*Set of 20*	£325 £475
		76/95 Optd "Specimen"	*Set of 20*	£425

Specimen copies of Nos. 96/105 are all overprinted.

KENYA, UGANDA AND TANGANYIKA

The postal administrations of Kenya, Tanganyika and Uganda were amalgamated on 1 January 1933. On the independence of the three territories the combined administration became the East African Posts and Telecommunications Corporation.

8 South African Crowned Cranes   **9** Dhow on Lake Victoria

10 Lion   **11** Kilimanjaro

12 Jinja Railway Bridge by Ripon Falls   **13** Mt. Kenya

14 Lake Naivasha   I   II

(Des 1 c., 20 c., 10 s., R. C. Luck, 10 c., £1, A. Ross, 15 c., 2 s., G. Gill Holmes, 30 c., 5 s., R. N. Ambasana. 65 c., L. R. Cutts. T 10 typo, remainder recess D.L.R.).

1935 (1 May)–**36.** *Wmk Mult Script CA. Chalk-surfaced paper* (10 c., £1). *P* 12×13 (10), 14 (9 *and* 14) *and* 13 (*remainder*).

110	**8**	1 c. black and red-brown	15	60
111	**9**	5 c. black and green (I)	40	20
		a. Rope joined to sail (II) (1937)	14·00	3·50
		b. Perf 13×12 (I) (1936)	£600	£160
		ba. Rope joined to sail (II) (1937)	£375	95·00
112	**10**	10 c. black and yellow	2·25	15
113	**11**	15 c. black and scarlet	75	10
114	**8**	20 c. black and orange	85	10
115	**12**	30 c. black and blue	80	90
116	**9**	50 c. bright purple and black (I)	75	10
117	**13**	65 c. black and brown	90	2·00
118	**14**	1 s. black and green	75	35
		a. Perf 13×12 (1936)	£900	85·00
119	**11**	2 s. lake and purple	4·25	3·50
120	**14**	3 s. blue and black	5·00	13·00
		a. Perf 13×12 (1936)	£1500	
121	**12**	5 s. black and carmine	15·00	23·00
122	**8**	10 s. purple and blue	40·00	48·00
123	**10**	£1 black and red	£120	£130
110/23			*Set of 14*	£170 £200
110/23 Perf "Specimen"			*Set of 14*	£225

Line through "0" of 1910 (R.4/2)

1935 (6 May). *Silver Jubilee. As Nos. 114/17 of Jamaica, but ptd by D.L.R. P* 13½×14.

124		20 c. light blue and olive-green	35	10
		h. Dot by flagstaff	40·00	
		i. Dash by turret	40·00	
125		30 c. brown and deep blue	2·00	1·75
		f. Diagonal line by turret	80·00	
		g. Dot to left of chapel	90·00	
		h. Dot by flagstaff	90·00	
		i. Dash by turret	90·00	
126		65 c. green and indigo	1·75	2·25
		f. Diagonal line by turret	75·00	
		g. Dot to left of chapel	85·00	
127		1 s. slate and purple	2·00	1·40
		f. Diagonal line by turret	80·00	
		l. Line through "0" of 1910	75·00	
124/7			*Set of 4*	5·50 5·00
124/7 Perf "Specimen"			*Set of 4*	95·00

For illustrations of the other plate varieties see Omnibus section following Zimbabwe.

1937 (12 May). *Coronation. As Nos. 118/20 of Jamaica.*

128		5 c. green	25	10
129		20 c. orange	55	15
130		30 c. bright blue	85	95
128/30			*Set of 3*	1·50 1·10
128/30 Perf "Specimen"			*Set of 3*	60·00

15 Dhow on Lake Victoria   Retouch on 1 c. (Pl 2, R. 9/6)

Break in bird's breast (Pl 2-2-4A, R. 2/5)   Retouch on 10 c. and 1s. (Pl 7B, R. 5/10 and 6/7)

With dot   Dot removed

In the 50 c., on Frame-plate 3, the dot was removed by retouching on all but five stamps (R.5/2, 6/1, 7/2, 7/4, and 9/1). In addition, other stamps show traces of the dot where the retouching was not completely effective.

PERFORATIONS. In this issue, to aid identification, the perforations are indicated to the nearest quarter.

(T 10 typo, others recess D.L.R.).

1938 (11 Apr)–**54.** *As T* 8 *to* 14 (*but with portrait of King George VI in place of King George V, as in T* 15). *Wmk Mult Script CA. Chalk-surfaced paper* (£1).

131	**8**	1 c. black & red-brown (p 13¼) (2.5.38)		60	40
		a. Perf 13¼×13¾. *Blk & choc-brn* (1942)		15	40
		ab. Retouched value tablet		45·00	45·00
		ac. Break in bird's breast		25·00	
		ad. *Black & dp chocolate-brown* (1946)		90	75
		ae. Ditto. Retouched tablet		50·00	50·00
		af. *Black and red-brown* (26.9.51)		45	90
132	**15**	5 c. black and green (II) (p 13×11¾)		70	10
133		5 c. reddish brn & orange (p 13×11¾) (1.6.49)		35	1·75
		a. Perf 13×12½ (14.6.50)		70	1·75
134	**14**	10 c. red-brn & orge (p 13×11¾) (2.5.38)		55	10
		a. Perf 14 (22.4.41)		75·00	6·00
135		10 c. black and green (p 13×11¾) (1.6.49)		30	10
		a. Mountain retouch		55·00	19·00
		b. Perf 13×12½ (14.6.50)		60	10
136		10 c. brown and grey (p 13×12½) (1.4.52)		45	30
137	**11**	15 c. black and rose-red (p 13¼) (2.5.38)		3·50	15
		a. Perf 13¾×13¼ (2.43)		1·50	2·25
138		15 c. black & green (p 13¾×13¼) (1.4.52)		80	1·75
139	**8**	20 c. black and orange (p 13¼) (2.5.38)		24·00	15
		a. Perf 14 (19.5.41)		45·00	1·50
		b. Perf 13¼×13¾ (25.2.42)		2·50	10
		ba. *Deep black and deep orange* (8.51)		4·00	30
140	**15**	25 c. blk & carm-red (p 13×12½) (1.4.52)		1·25	90
141	**12**	30 c. black and dull vio-bl (p 13¼) (2.5.38)		42·00	40
		a. Perf 14 (3.7.41)		£120	11·00
		b. Perf 13¼×13¾ (9.42)		50	10
142		30 c. dull purple and brown (p 13¼×13¾) (1.4.52)		55	10
143	**8**	40 c. black & blue (p 13¼×13¾) (1.4.52)		1·50	1·75
144	**15**	50 c. purple & blk (II) (p 13×11¾) (2.5.38)		7·00	40
		a. Rope not joined to sail (I) (R. 2/5)		£180	£160
		b. *Dull claret and black* (29.7.47)		6·00	1·10
		c. *Brown-purple and black* (4.48)		7·50	1·10
		d. *Reddish purple and black* (28.4.49)		7·00	60
		e. Ditto. Perf 13×12½ (10.49)		3·25	45
		ea. Dot removed (14.6.50)		9·00	30
		eb. Ditto. In pair, with normal		£180	75·00
145	**14**	1 s. black & yellowish brn (p 13×11¾) (2.5.38)		2·25	20
		a. *Black and brown* (9.42)		2·75	30
		ab. Mountain retouch (7.49)		£140	60·00
		b. Perf 13×12½ (10.49)		3·00	30
		ba. *Deep black and brown (clearer impression)* (14.6.50)		2·25	50
146	**11**	2 s. lake-brn & brn-pur (p 13¼) (2.5.38)		90·00	1·50
		a. Perf 14 (1941)		55·00	9·00
		b. Perf 13¾×13¼ (24.2.44)		7·00	20
147	**14**	3 s. dull ultramarine & blk (p 13×11¾) (2.5.38)		25·00	1·75
		a. *Deep violet-blue and black* (29.7.47)		26·00	3·50
		b. Ditto. Perf 13×12½ (14.6.50)		13·00	90
148	**12**	5 s. black and carmine (p 13¼) (2.5.38)		£120	8·00
		a. Perf 14 (1941)		20·00	1·25
		b. Perf 13¼×13¾ (24.2.44)		13·00	40
149	**8**	10 s. purple and blue (p 13¼) (2.5.38)		£110	16·00
		a. Perf 14. *Reddish purple & bl* (1941)		42·00	17·00
		b. Perf 13¼×13¾ (24.2.44)		20·00	2·75
150	**10**	£1 black and red (p 11¾×13) (12.10.38)		£225	85·00
		a. Perf 14 (1941)		13·00	13·00
		ab. Ordinary paper (24.2.44)		11·00	13·00
		b. Perf 12½ (21.1.54)		10·00	20·00
131/150ab (*cheapest*)			*Set of 20*	70·00 22·00
131/150 Perf "Specimen"			*Set of 13*	£300

The first printing of the 50 c. utilised the King George V centre plate on which each impression had been individually corrected to show the rope joined to sail. R.2/5 was missed, however, and this continued to show Type I until replaced by a new printing in September 1938.

Stamps perf 14, together with Nos. 131a, 137a, 139b, 141b, 146b, 148b and 149b, are known as "Blitz perfs", the differences in perforation being the result of air raid damage to the De La Rue works in which the perforators normally used were destroyed. Where dates of issue are quoted for these stamps they represent earliest known postmark dates.

10c
KENYA
TANGANYIKA
UGANDA

(16)   A screw head in the surcharging forme appears as a crescent moon (R. 20/4)

1941 (1 July)–**42.** *Pictorial Stamps of South Africa variously surch as T* 16 *by Government Printer, Pretoria. Inscr alternately in English and Afrikaans.*

			Unused	*Used*
			pair	*pair*
151		5 c. on 1d. grey and carmine (No. 56)	60	1·50
152		10 c. on 3d. ultramarine (No. 59)	1·00	3·25
153		20 c. on 6d. green and vermilion (No. 61a)	60	2·00
154		70 c. on 1s. brown and chalky blue (No. 62) (20.4.42)	5·50	4·25
		a. Crescent moon flaw	55·00	
151/4			*Set of 4 pairs*	7·00 10·00
151/4 Handstamped "Specimen"			*Set of 4 pairs*	£180

1946 (11 Nov). *Victory. As Nos. 141/2 of Jamaica.*

				Unused	Used
155	20 c. red-orange	..	..	10	10
156	30 c. blue	..	..	10	10
155/6 Perf "Specimen"			Set of 2	50·00	

Examples of Nos. 155/6 were prereleased at Lindi on 15 October 1946.

1948 (1 Dec). *Royal Silver Wedding. As Nos. 143/4 of Jamaica.*

157	20 c. orange	..	..	15	10
158	£1 scarlet	..	..	30·00	35·00

1949 (10 Oct). *75th Anniv of Universal Postal Union. As Nos. 145/8 of Jamaica.*

159	20 c. red-orange	..	15	10
160	30 c. deep blue	..	40	35
161	50 c. grey	..	40	10
162	1 s. red-brown	..	75	40
159/62	..	..	Set of 4	1·50	80

17 Lake Naivasha

(Recess D.L.R.)

1952 (1 Feb). *Visit of Princess Elizabeth and Duke of Edinburgh. Wmk Mult Script CA. P 13 × 12½.*

163	**17**	10 c. black and green	..	..	10	30
164		1 s. black and brown	..	..	20	1·75

1953 (2 June). *Coronation. As No. 153 of Jamaica.*

165	20 c. black and red-orange	..	..	15	10

1954 (28 Apr). *Royal Visit. As No. 171 but inscr "ROYAL VISIT 1954" below portrait.*

166	30 c. black and deep ultramarine	..	10	15

18 Owen Falls Dam   19 Giraffe

20 Royal Lodge, Sagana   21 Queen Elizabeth II

(Des G. Gill Holmes (10, 50 c.), H. Grieme (15 c., 1 s. 30, 5 s.), R. McLellan Sim (10 s.), De La Rue (65 c., 2 s., £1), O.C. Meronti (others). Recess D.L.R.)

1954 (1 June)–**59**. *Designs as T 18/21. Wmk Mult Script CA. P 13 (£1); others, 12½ × 13 (vert) or 13 × 12½ (horiz).*

167	5 c. black and deep brown	..	10	10
	a. Vignette inverted	..	† £12000	
168	10 c. carmine-red	..	50	10
169	15 c. black and light blue (28.3.58)	..	55	40
	a. Redrawn. Stop below "c" of "15 c" (29.4.59)	..	45	20
170	20 c. black and orange	..	40	10
	a. Imperf (pair)	..	£500	£600
171	30 c. black and deep ultramarine	..	45	10
	a. Vignette inverted	..	† £10000	
172	40 c. bistre-brown (28.3.58)	..	2·75	60
173	50 c. reddish purple	..	30	10
	a. Claret (23.1.57)	..	30	10
174	65 c. bluish green & brown-purple (1.12.55)	2·75	70	
175	1 s. black and claret	..	30	10
176	1 s. 30, orange and deep lilac (1.12.55)	..	4·50	10
177	2 s. black and green	..	1·50	30
	a. Black and bronze-green (19.4.56)	..	2·50	55
178	5 s. black and orange	..	4·50	70
179	10 s. black and deep ultramarine	..	12·00	1·50
180	£1 brown-red and black	..	15·00	8·50
	a. Venetian red and black (19.4.56)	..	27·00	11·00
167/80	..	..	Set of 14	40·00	11·50

Designs: *Vert as T 18/19*—5, 30 c. Type 18; 10, 50 c. Type 19; 20, 40 c., 1 s. Lion. *Horiz as T 20*—15 c., 1 s. 30, 5 s. African Elephants; 65 c., 2 s. Kilimanjaro.

Only one example of No. 167a and two of No. 171a have been found, all being used.

25 Map of E. Africa showing Lakes

(Recess Waterlow)

1958 (30 July). *Centenary of Discovery of Lakes Tanganyika and Victoria by Burton and Speke. W w 12. P 12½.*

181	**25**	40 c. blue and deep green	..	20	15
182		1 s. 30 c. green and violet	..	30	70

26 Sisal   27 Cotton

28 Mt Kenya and Giant Plants   29 Queen Elizabeth II

(Des M. Goaman. Photo (5 c. to 65 c.), recess (others) D.L.R.)

1960 (1 Oct). *Designs as T 26/9. W w 12. P 15 × 14 (5 c. to 65 c.), 13 (20 s.) or 14 (others).*

183	5 c. Prussian blue	..	10	15
184	10 c. yellow-green	..	10	10
185	15 c. dull purple	..	15	10
186	20 c. magenta	..	10	10
187	25 c. bronze-green	..	2·50	75
188	30 c. vermilion	..	10	10
189	40 c. greenish blue	..	15	10
190	50 c. slate-violet	..	15	10
191	65 c. yellow-olive	..	30	45
192	1 s. deep reddish violet and reddish purple	..	50	10
193	1 s. 30, chocolate and brown-red	..	1·25	15
194	2 s. deep grey-blue and greenish blue	..	1·25	20
195	2 s. 50, olive-green and deep bluish green	..	2·50	1·75
196	5 s. rose-red and purple	..	3·50	50
197	10 s. blackish green and olive-green	..	5·00	3·50
	a. Imperf (pair)	..	£180	
198	20 s. violet-blue and lake	..	12·00	10·00
183/198	..	Set of 16	26·00	16·00

Designs: *Vert as T 26/7*—15 c. Coffee; 20 c. Blue Wildebeest; 25 c. Ostrich; 30 c. Thomson's Gazelle; 40 c. Manta Ray; 50 c. Common Zebra; 65 c. Cheetah. *Horiz as T 28*—1 s. 30, Murchison Falls and Hippopotamus; 2 s. Mt Kilimanjaro and Giraffe; 2 s. 50, Candelabra Tree and Black Rhinoceros; 5 s. Crater Lake and Mountains of the Moon; 10 s. Ngorongoro Crater and African Buffalo.

The 10 c. and 50 c. exist in coils with the designs slightly shorter in height, a wider horizontal gutter every eleven stamps and, in the case of the 10 c. only, printed with a coarser 200 screen instead of the normal 250. (*Price for 10 c. 10p. unused.*) Plate 2 of 30 c. shows coarser 200 screen. (*Price 25p. unused.*)

30 Land Tillage

(Des V. Whiteley. Photo Harrison)

1963 (21 Mar). *Freedom from Hunger. T 30 and similar horiz design. P 14½.*

199	**30**	15 c. blue and yellow-olive	..	10	10
200		30 c. red-brown and yellow	..	20	10
201	**30**	50 c. blue and orange-brown	..	30	10
202		1 s. 30, red-brown and light blue	..	55	1·10
199/202		..	..	Set of 4	1·00	1·25

Design:—30 c., 1 s. 30, African with Corncob.

31 Scholars and Open Book

(Photo Harrison)

1963 (28 June). *Founding of East African University. P 14½.*

203	**31**	30 c. lake, violet, black and greenish blue	10	10
204		1 s. 30, lake, blue, red & lt yellow-brown	10	10

32 Red Cross Emblem

(Des V. Whiteley. Photo Harrison)

1963 (2 Sept). *Centenary of Red Cross. P 14½.*

205	**32**	30 c. red and blue	..	75	10
206		50 c. red and yellow-brown	..	1·00	35

PRINTERS. All the following stamps were printed in photogravure by Harrison, *unless otherwise stated.*

33 Chrysanthemum Emblems 34

35 East African "Flags"

(Des V. Whiteley)

1964 (21 Oct). *Olympic Games. Tokyo. P 14½.*

207	**33**	30 c. yellow and reddish violet	..	10	10
208	**34**	50 c. deep reddish violet and yellow	15	10
209	**35**	1 s. 30, orange-yellow, dp green & lt blue	20	10
210		2 s. 50, magenta, deep violet-blue & lt bl	25	75
				55	85

KENYA, UGANDA AND TANZANIA

The following stamps were issued by the East African Postal Administration for use in Uganda, Kenya and Tanzania, excluding Zanzibar.

36 Rally Badge   37 Cars *en route*

1965 (15 Apr*). *13th East African Safari Rally. P 14.*

211	**36**	30 c. black, yellow and turquoise	..	10	10
212		50 c. black, yellow and brown	..	10	10
		a. Imperf (pair)	..		
213	**37**	1 s. 30, dp bluish green, yell-ochre & blue	20	10
214		2 s. 50, dp bluish green, brn-red & lt blue	30	75
211/14		..	..	Set of 4	60	90

*This is the local release date. The Crown Agents in London issued the stamps the previous day.

38 I.T.U. Emblem and Symbols

1965 (17 May). *I.T.U. Centenary. P 14½.*

215	**38**	30 c. gold, chocolate and magenta	..	10	10
216		50 c. gold, chocolate and grey	..	15	10
217		1 s. 30, gold, chocolate and blue	..	30	10
218		2 s. 50, gold, chocolate & turquoise-grn	55	80
215/18		..	..	Set of 4	1·00	1·00

39 I.C.Y. Emblem

1965 (4 Aug). *International Co-operation Year. P 14½ × 14.*

219	**39**	30 c. deep bluish green and gold	..	10	10
220		50 c. black and gold	..	15	10
221		1 s. 30, ultramarine and gold	..	30	10
222		2 s. 50, carmine-red and gold	..	75	1·75
219/22		..	..	Set of 4	1·25	1·75

40 Game Park Lodge, Tanzania

(Des Rena Fennessy)

1966 (4 Apr). *Tourism. T* **40** *and similar horiz designs. Multi-coloured. P* 14½.
223	30 c. Type 40	..	15	10
224	50 c. Murchison Falls, Uganda	..	50	10
	a. Blue omitted		£170	
225	1 s. 30, Lesser Flamingoes, Lake Nakuru, Kenya		1·75	20
226	2 s. 50, Deep Sea Fishing, Tanzania.	..	1·75	1·75
223/6	.. ..	*Set of* 4	3·75	1·90

41 Games Emblem

(Des Harrison)

1966 (2 Aug). *Eighth British Empire and Commonwealth Games Jamaica. P* 14½.
227	**41** 30 c. black, gold, turq-green & grey	..	10	10
228	50 c. black, gold, cobalt and cerise	..	15	10
229	1 s. 30, blk, gold, rosine & dp bluish grn		20	10
230	2 s. 50, black, gold, lake and ultramarine		35	65
227/30	.. .. ..	*Set of* 4	70	75

42 U.N.E.S.C.O. Emblem

(Des Harrison)

1966 (3 Oct). *20th Anniv of U.N.E.S.C.O. P* 14½ × 14.
231	**42** 30 c. black, emerald and red	..	25	10
232	50 c. black, emerald and light brown	..	35	10
233	1 s. 30, black, emerald and grey	..	85	15
234	2 s. 50, black, emerald and yellow	..	1·50	1·50
231/4	.. .. ..	*Set of* 4	2·75	1·50

43 D.H. "Dragon Rapide"

(Des R. Granger Barrett)

1967 (23 Jan). *21st Anniv of East African Airways. T* **43** *and similar horiz designs. P* 14½.
235	30 c. slate-violet, greenish blue & myrtle-grn		30	10
236	50 c. multicoloured	.. ..	40	10
	a. Red omitted	.. ..	£160	
237	1 s. 30, multicoloured	..	85	15
238	2 s. 50, multicoloured	..	1·25	1·75
235/8	.. .. ..	*Set of* 4	2·50	1·90

Designs:—50 c. "Super VC-10"; 1 s. 30, "Comet 4"; 2 s. 50, "F-27 Friendship".

44 Pillar Tomb   45 Rock Painting

(Des Rena Fennessy)

1967 (2 May). *Archaeological Relics. T* **44/5** *and similar designs. P* 14½.
239	30 c. ochre, black and deep reddish purple	..	15	10
240	50 c. orange-red, black and greyish brown	..	50	10
241	1 s. 30, black, greenish, yellow and deep yellow-green		75	10
242	2 s. 50, black, ochre and brown-red ..		1·40	1·50
239/42	.. .. ..	*Set of* 4	2·50	1·60

Designs:—1 s. 30, Clay head; 2 s. 50, Proconsul skull.

48 Unified Symbols of Kenya, Tanzania, and Uganda

(Des Rena Fennessy)

1967 (1 Dec). *Foundation of East African Community. P* 14½ × 14.
243	**48** 5 s. gold, black and grey	..	40	1·00

49 Mountaineering

(Des Rena Fennessy)

1968 (4 Mar). *Mountains of East Africa. T* **49** *and similar horiz designs. Multicoloured. P* 14.
244	30 c. Type 49	.. ..	10	10
245	50 c. Mount Kenya	..	15	10
246	1 s. 30, Mount Kilimanjaro	..	30	10
247	2 s. 50, Ruwenzori Mountains		55	1·00
244/7	.. ..	*Set of* 4	1·00	1·10

50 Family and Rural Hospital

(Des Rena Fennessy. Litho D.L.R.)

1968 (13 May). *20th Anniv of World Health Organization. T* **50** *and similar horiz designs. P* 13½.
248	30 c. deep yellow-green, lilac and chocolate	..	10	10
249	50 c. slate-lilac, lilac and black	..	10	10
250	1 s. 30, yellow-brown, lilac and chocolate	..	15	10
251	2 s. 50, grey, black and reddish lilac.	..	25	60
248/51	.. .. ..	*Set of* 4	50	75

Designs:—50 c. Family and nurse; 1 s. 30, Family and microscope; 2 s. 50, Family and hypodermic syringe.

51 Olympic Stadium, Mexico City

(Des V. Whiteley)

1968 (14 Oct). *Olympic Games, Mexico. T* **51** *and similar designs. P* 14.
252	30 c. light green and black	.. ..	10	10
253	50 c. black and blue-green	..	10	10
254	1 s. 30, carmine-red, black and grey.	..	20	10
255	2 s. 50, blackish brown and yellow-brown	..	30	60
252/5	.. .. ..	*Set of* 4	60	75

Designs: *Horiz*—50 c. High-diving boards; 1 s. 30, Running tracks. *Vert*—2 s. 50, Boxing ring.

52 M.V. *Umoja*

(Des A. Grosart)

1969 (20 Jan). *Water Transport. T* **52** *and similar horiz designs. P* 14.
256	30 c. deep blue, light blue and slate-grey	..	15	10
	a. Slate-grey omitted	.. ..	32·00	
257	50 c. multicoloured	.. ..	20	10
258	1 s. 30, bronze-grn, greenish blue & blue	..	45	15
259	2 s. 50, red-orange, dp blue & pale blue		1·00	1·75
256/9	.. .. ..	*Set of* 4	1·60	1·90

Designs:—50 c. S.S. *Harambee*; 1 s. 30, M.V. *Victoria*; 2 s. 50, *St. Michael*.

53 I.L.O. Emblem and Agriculture   54 Pope Paul VI and Ruwenzori Mountains

(Des Rena Fennessy)

1969 (14 Apr). *50th Anniv of International Labour Organization. T* **53** *and similar horiz designs. P* 14.
260	30 c. black, green and greenish yellow		10	10
261	50 c. black, plum, cerise and rose	..	10	10
262	1 s. 30, black, orange-brown & yellow-orange		10	10
263	2 s. 50, black, ultramarine & turquoise-blue		20	40
260/3	.. ..	*Set of* 4	35	50

Designs:—50 c. I.L.O. emblem and building work; 1 s. 30, I.L.O. emblem and factory workers; 2 s. 50, I.L.O. emblem and shipping.

(Des Harrison)

1969 (31 July). *Visit of Pope Paul VI to Uganda. P* 14.
264	**54** 30 c. black, gold and royal blue	..	15	10
265	70 c. black, gold and claret	..	20	10
266	1 s. 50, black, gold and deep blue		30	20
267	2 s. 50, black, gold and violet	..	45	75
264/7	.. .. ..	*Set of* 4	1·00	95

55 Euphorbia Tree shaped   56 Marimba
as Africa and Emblem

(Des Rena Fennessy. Litho B.W.)

1969 (8 Dec). *Fifth Anniv of African Development Bank. P* 13½.
268	**55** 30 c. dp bluish green, gold & blue-green		10	10
269	70 c. dp bluish green, gold & reddish pur		15	10
270	1 s. 50, dp bluish grn, gold & lt turq-bl		25	10
271	2 s. 50, dp bluish grn, gold & orge-brn		30	45
268/71	.. .. ..	*Set of* 4	65	55

(Des Rena Fennessy. Litho B.W.)

1970 (16 Feb). *Musical Instruments. T* **56** *and similar horiz designs. P* 11 × 12.
272	30 c. buff, yellow-brown and bistre-brown	..	15	10
273	70 c. olive-green, yellow-brown and yellow	..	25	10
274	1 s. 50, chocolate and yellow.	..	50	10
275	2 s. 50, salmon, yellow and chocolate	..	75	80
272/5	.. .. ..	*Set of* 4	1·50	90

Designs:—70 c. Amadinda; 1 s. 50, Nzomari; 2 s. 50, Adeudeu.

57 Satellite Earth Station   58 Athlete

(Des V. Whiteley. Litho J.W.)

1970 (18 May). *Inauguration of East African Satellite Earth Station. T* **57** *and similar horiz designs. P* 14½ × 14.
276	30 c. multicoloured	.. ..	10	10
277	70 c. multicoloured	.. ..	15	10
278	1 s. 50, black, slate-violet and pale orange	..	25	70
279	2 s. 50, multicoloured	..	55	70
276/9	.. .. ..	*Set of* 4	90	80

Designs:—70 c. Transmitter in daytime; 1 s. 50, Transmitter at night; 2 s. 50, Earth and satellite.

(Des Rena Fennessy. Litho Walsall)

1970 (13 July). *Ninth Commonwealth Games. P* 14 × 14½.
280	**58** 30 c. orange-brown and black	..	10	10
281	70 c. olive-green, black and black	..	10	10
282	1 s. 50, slate-lilac and black	..	15	10
283	2 s. 50, turquoise-blue and black	..	20	50
280/3	.. .. ..	*Set of* 4	40	60

59 "25" and U.N. Emblem

(Des Rena Fennessy)

1970 (19 Oct). *25th Anniv of United Nations.* P 14½.
284	59	30 c. multicoloured				10	10
285		70 c. multicoloured				10	10
286		1 s. 50, multicoloured				20	10
287		2 s. 50, multicoloured				45	1·00
284/7					Set of 4	70	1·10

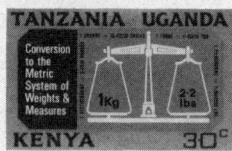

60 Balance and Weight Equivalents

(Des and litho J.W.)

1971 (4 Jan). *Conversion to Metric System.* T 60 *and similar horiz designs. Multicoloured.* P 14½ × 14.
288		30 c. Type 60				10	10
289		70 c. Fahrenheit and Centigrade Thermometers				10	10
290		1 s. 50, Petrol Pump and Liquid Capacities				15	10
291		2 s. 50, Surveyors and Land Measures				35	80
288/91					Set of 4	60	85

61 Class "11" Locomotive

(Des Rena Fennessy)

1971 (5 Apr). *Railway Transport.* T 61 *and similar horiz designs. Multicoloured.* P 14.
292		30 c. Type 61				35	10
293		70 c. Class "90" locomotive				55	10
294		1 s. 50, Class "59" locomotive				1·25	50
295		2 s. 50, Class "30" locomotive				2·25	2·75
292/5					Set of 4	4·00	3·00
MS296	120 × 88 mm. Nos. 292/5					6·50	9·00

62 Syringe and Cow

(Des Rena Fennessy. Litho)

1971 (5 July). *O.A.U. Rinderpest Campaign.* T 62 *and similar horiz design.* P 14.
297	62	30 c. black, pale yell-brn & pale yell-grn		10	10
298	—	70 c. black, pale slate-blue & pale yell-brn		10	10
299	62	1 s. 50, black, plum & pale yellow-brn		15	10
300	—	2 s. 50, black, brown-red & pale yell-brn		25	50
297/300				Set of 4	45	60

Design:—70 c., 2 s. 50, As T 62, but with bull facing right.

63 Livingstone meets Stanley

(Des and litho J.W.)

1971 (28 Oct). *Centenary of Livingstone and Stanley meeting at Ujiji.* P 13½ × 14.
| 301 | 63 | 5 s. multicoloured | | | 30 | 75 |

PRICES OF SETS

Set prices are given for many issues, generally those containing three stamps or more. Definitive sets include one of each value or major colour change, but do not cover different perforations, die types or minor shades. Where a choice is possible the set prices are based on the cheapest versions of the stamps included in the listings.

64 President Nyerere and Supporters

(Des G. Drummond. Litho J.W.)

1971 (9 Dec). *Tenth Anniv of Tanzanian Independence.* T 64 *and similar horiz designs. Multicoloured.* P 13½.
302		30 c. Type 64				10	10
303		70 c. Ujamaa village				10	10
304		1 s. 50, Dar es Salaam University			20	20
305		2 s. 50, Kilimanjaro airport			55	1·60
302/5					Set of 4	80	1·75

65 Flags and Trade Fair Emblem

(Des Trade Fair Publicity Agents. Litho Questa)

1972 (23 Feb). *All-Africa Trade Fair.* P 13½ × 14.
306	65	30 c. multicoloured				10	10
307		70 c. multicoloured				10	10
308		1 s. 50, multicoloured				10	10
309		2 s. 50, multicoloured				25	55
306/9					Set of 4	40	60

66 Child with Cup

(Des Rena Fennessy. Litho Questa)

1972 (24 Apr). *25th Anniv of UNICEF.* T 66 *and similar horiz designs. Multicoloured.* P 14 × 14½.
310		30 c. Type 66				10	10
311		70 c. Children with ball				10	10
312		1 s. 50, Child at blackboard			10	10
313		2 s. 50, Child and tractor			25	60
310/13					Set of 4	35	70

67 Hurdling

(Des G. Vasarhelyi. Litho J.W.)

1972 (28 Aug). *Olympic Games, Munich.* T 67 *and similar horiz designs. Multicoloured.* P 14.
314		40 c. Type 67				10	10
315		70 c. Running				10	10
316		1 s. 50, Boxing				20	10
317		2 s. 50, Hockey				30	1·00
314/17					Set of 4	60	1·10
MS318	131 × 98 mm. Nos. 314/17					3·50	6·00

68 Kobs

(Des G. Drummond. Litho D.L.R.)

1972 (9 Oct). *Tenth Anniv of Ugandan Independence.* T 68 *and similar horiz designs. Multicoloured.* P 14.
319		40 c. Type 68				20	10
320		70 c. Conference Centre				20	10
321		1 s. 50, Makerere University			45	25
322		2 s. 50, Coat of Arms				85	1·75
319/22					Set of 4	1·50	2·00
MS323	132 × 120 mm. Nos. 319/22. P 13 × 14				2·75	3·50

69 Community Flag

(Des Rena Fennessy. Litho)

1972 (1 Dec). *Fifth Anniv of East African Community.* P 14½ × 14.
| 324 | 69 | 5 s. multicoloured | | | | 75 | 1·25 |

70 Run-of-the-wind Anemometer   71 "Learning by Serving"

(Des P. Powell. Litho)

1973 (1 Mar*). *I.M.O./W.M.O. Centenary.* T 70 *and similar multicoloured designs.* P 14½.
325		40 c. Type 70				10	10
326		70 c. Weather balloon (*vert*)			15	10
327		1 s. 50, Meteorological rocket			25	15
328		2 s. 50, Satellite receiving aerial		55	55
325/8					Set of 4	90	1·60

No. 325 exists with country name at foot instead of at top, and also with country name omitted (or with imprint or plate numbers in lieu). These are because of faulty registration of the perforation comb.

*This is the local release date. The Crown Agents in London did not place the stamps on sale until 5 March.

(Des Rena Fennessy. Litho)

1973 (16 July). *24th World Scout Conference, Nairobi.* T 71 *and similar vert designs.* P 14.
329		40 c. multicoloured				15	10
330		70 c. Venetian red, reddish violet and black		20	10
331		1 s. 50, cobalt, reddish violet and black		45	30
332		2 s. 50, multicoloured			1·00	1·75
329/32					Set of 4	1·60	2·00

Designs:—70 c. Baden-Powell's grave, Nyeri; 1 s. 50, World Scout emblem; 2 s. 50, Lord Baden-Powell.

72 Kenyatta Conference Centre

(Des Marketing Communications Ltd, Nairobi; adapted J. Cooter. Litho D.L.R.)

1973 (29 Sept*). *I.M.F./World Bank Conference.* T 72 *and similar designs.* P 13½ × 14 (1 s. 50) or 14 × 13½ (others).
333		40 c. sage-green, light greenish grey & black	10	10
334		70 c. orange-brown, greenish grey and black	10	10
335		1 s. 50, multicoloured			25	35
336		2 s. 50, orange, greenish grey and black	35	1·25
333/6					Set of 4	65	1·50
MS337	166 × 141 mm. Nos. 333/6. Imperf			1·40	2·50

Designs:—Nos. 334/6 show different arrangements of Bank emblems and the Conference Centre, the 1 s. 50 being vertical.

*This is the local release date. The Crown Agents in London issued the stamps on 24 September.

73 Police Dog-handler   74 Tea Factory

(Des C. Abbott. Litho Questa)

1973 (24 Oct)–74. *50th Anniv of Interpol.* T 73 *and similar vert designs.* P 14.
338		40 c. yellow, blue and black			40	10
339		70 c. turquoise-green, orange-yellow & black		70	15
340		1 s. 50, light violet, yellow and black		1·25	90
341		2 s. 50, light yellow-green, red-orange and black (I)		3·50	4·75
342		2 s. 50, light yellow-green, red-orange, and black (II) (25.2.74)		3·50	4·75
338/42					Set of 5	8·50	9·50

Designs:—70 c. East African Policeman; 1 s. 50, Interpol emblem; 2 s. 50, Interpol H.Q.

Nos. 341/2. Type I inscribed "St. Clans"; Type II corrected to "St. Cloud".

(Des G. Drummond. Litho Enschedé)

1973 (12 Dec). *10th Anniv of Kenya's Independence. T **74** and similar horiz designs. Multicoloured.* P 13 × 13½.
343	40 c. Type **74**	.. ..	10	10
344	70 c. Kenyatta Hospital	.. ..	10	10
345	1 s. 50, Nairobi Airport	.. ..	30	20
346	2 s. 50, Kindaruma hydro-electric scheme		65	1·50
343/6	.. ..	*Set of 4*	1·00	1·60

75 Party H.Q.

(Des PAD Studio. Litho D.L.R.)

1974 (12 Jan). *Tenth Anniv of Zanzibar's Revolution. T **75** and similar horiz designs. Multicoloured.* P 13½.
347	40 c. Type **75**	.. .. ..	10	10
348	70 c. Housing scheme	.. ..	10	10
349	1 s. 50, Colour T.V.	.. ..	30	20
350	2 s. 50, Amaan Stadium	.. ..	65	1·60
347/50	.. ..	*Set of 4*	1·00	1·75

76 "Symbol of Union"

(Des Jennifer Toombs. Litho Questa)

1974 (26 Apr). *Tenth Anniv of Tanganyika–Zanzibar Union. T **76** and similar horiz designs. Multicoloured.* P 14½.
351	40 c. Type **76**	.. .. ..	10	10
352	70 c. Handclasp and map	..	20	10
353	1 s. 50, "Communications"	..	45	25
354	2 s. 50, Flags of Tanu, Tanzania and Afro-Shirazi Party		95	1·25
351/4	.. ..	*Set of 4*	1·40	1·40

77 East African Family ("Stability of the Home")

(Des locally; adapted PAD Studio. Litho)

1974 (15 July). *17th Social Welfare Conference, Nairobi. T **77** and similar horiz designs.* P 14½.
355	40 c. greenish yellow, lake-brown and black	..	10	10
356	70 c. multicoloured	.. ..	10	10
357	1 s. 50, olive-green, yellow-green and black		20	30
358	2 s. 50, light rose, reddish violet and black		45	1·50
355/8	.. ..	*Set of 4*	70	1·75

Designs:—70 c. Dawn and drummer (U.N. Second Development Plan); 1 s. 50, Agricultural scene (Rural Development Plan); 2 s. 50, Transport and telephone ("Communications").

78 New Postal H.Q., Kampala

(Des Rena Fennessy. Litho)

1974 (9 Oct). *Centenary of Universal Postal Union. T **78** and similar horiz designs. Multicoloured.* P 14½.
359	40 c. Type **78**	.. .. ..	10	10
360	70 c. Mail-train and post-van	..	15	10
361	1 s. 50, U.P.U. Building, Berne	..	15	20
362	2 s. 50, Loading mail into "VC-10"	..	30	1·00
359/62	.. ..	*Set of 4*	60	1·25

79 Family-planning Clinic

(Des C. Abbott. Litho)

1974 (16 Dec). *World Population Year. T **79** and similar horiz designs.* P 14.
363	40 c. multicoloured	.. ..	10	10
364	70 c. deep reddish violet and scarlet	..	10	10
365	1 s. 50, multicoloured	.. ..	15	20
366	2 s. 50, apple-green, blue-green & bluish blk		30	1·10
363/6	.. ..	*Set of 4*	55	1·25

Designs:—70 c. "Tug of war"; 1 s. 50, Population "scales"; 2 s. 50, W.P.Y. emblem.

80 Seronera Wild-Life Lodge, Tanzania

(Des R. Granger Barrett. Litho)

1975 (26 Feb*). *East Africa Game Lodges. T **80** and similar horiz designs. Multicoloured.* P 14.
367	40 c. Type **80**	.. ..	15	10
368	70 c. Mweya Safari Lodge, Uganda	..	20	10
369	1 s. 50, "Ark"—Aberdare Forest Lodge, Kenya		35	30
370	2 s. 50, Paraa Safari Lodge, Uganda		80	2·00
367/70	..	*Set of 4*	1·40	2·25

*This is the local release date. The Crown Agents in London issued the stamps on 24 February.

81 Kitana (wooden comb), Bajun of Kenya

82 International Airport, Entebbe

(Des Mrs. Gombe of the E.A.P.T.; adapted C. Abbott. Litho Questa)

1975 (5 May). *African Arts. T **81** and similar vert designs. Multicoloured.* P 13½.
371	50 c. Type **81**	.. ..	10	10
372	1 s. Earring, Chaga of Tanzania	..	15	10
373	2 s. Okoco (armlet), Acholi of Uganda		45	45
374	3 s. Kitete (Kamba gourd), Kenya		85	1·10
371/4	.. ..	*Set of 4*	1·40	1·50

(Des PAD Studio. Litho State Ptg Wks, Warsaw)

1975 (28 July). *O.A.U. Summit Conference, Kampala. T **82** and similar multicoloured designs.* P 11.
375	50 c. Type **82**	.. ..	10	10
376	1 s. Map of Africa and flag (*vert*)	..	10	10
377	2 s. Nile Hotel, Kampala	..	30	65
378	3 s. Martyrs' Shrine, Namugongo (*vert*)		40	1·25
375/8	..	*Set of 4*	80	1·90

83 Ahmed ("Presidential" Elephant)

84 Maasai Manyatta (village), Kenya

(Des locally. Litho State Ptg Wks, Warsaw)

1975 (11 Sept). *Rare Animals. T **83** and similar vert designs. Multicoloured.* P 11.
379	50 c. Type **83**	.. ..	50	10
380	1 s. Albino buffalo	.. ..	50	10
381	2 s. Ahmed in grounds of National Museum		1·50	1·50
382	3 s. Abbott's Duiker	.. ..	1·50	2·25
379/82	..	*Set of 4*	3·50	3·50

(Des Rena Fennessy. Litho Questa)

1975 (3 Nov). *Second World Black and African Festival of Arts and Culture, Nigeria (1977). T **84** and similar horiz designs. Multicoloured.* P 13½ × 14.
383	50 c. Type **84**	.. ..	15	10
384	1 s. "Heartbeat of Africa" (Ugandan dancers)		20	10
385	2 s. Makonde sculpture, Tanzania	..	55	75
386	3 s. "Early Man and Technology" (skinning hippopotamus)		85	1·25
383/6	..	*Set of 4*	1·60	2·00

For similar stamps see Nos. 76/80 of Kenya and the corresponding issues of Tanzania and Uganda.

The new-issue supplement to this Catalogue appears each month in

GIBBONS STAMP MONTHLY

—from your newsagent or by postal subscription— sample copy and details on request.

85 Fokker "Friendship" at Nairobi Airport

(Des local artist. Litho State Security Ptg Wks, Warsaw)

1976 (2 Jan). *30th Anniv of East African Airways. T **85** and similar triangular designs. Multicoloured.* P 11½.
387	50 c. Type **85**	.. ..	65	25
	a. Black (aircraft) and blue omitted	†	£550	
388	1 s. "DC 9" at Kilimanjaro Airport	..	75	25
389	2 s. Super "VC 10" at Entebbe Airport		2·25	2·25
390	3 s. East African Airways Crest	..	2·75	2·75
387/90	..	*Set of 4*	5·75	5·00

Two black plates were used for each of Nos. 387/9: one for the frame and the other for the centre. No. 387a, three used copies of which are known, has the printing from the blue and centre black plates omitted.

Further commemorative issues were released during 1976–78, using common designs, but inscribed for one republic only. These are listed under KENYA, TANZANIA, or UGANDA.

Co-operation between the postal services of the three member countries virtually ceased after 30 June 1977, the postal services of Kenya, Tanzania and Uganda then operating independently.

OFFICIAL STAMPS

For use on official correspondence of the Tanganyika Government.

OFFICIAL
(O 1)

1959 (1 July). *Nos. 167/71, 173 and 175/80 optd as Type O 1.*
O 1	5 c. black and deep brown	..	10	10
O 2	10 c. carmine-red	.. ..	10	10
O 3	15 c. black and light blue (No. 169a).		10	10
O 4	20 c. black and orange	.. ..	10	10
	a. Opt double	.. ..	—	£650
O 5	30 c. black and deep ultramarine	..	10	10
O 6	50 c. reddish purple	.. ..	10	10
O 7	1 s. black and claret.	.. ..	15	10
O 8	1 s. 30, orange and deep lilac	..	65	30
O 9	2 s. black and bronze-green.	..	85	50
O10	5 s. black and orange	.. ..	2·00	1·25
O11	10 s. black and deep ultramarine	..	2·00	2·50
O12	£1 brown-red and black	.. ..	6·00	10·00
O1/12	.. ..	*Set of 12*	11·00	13·50

The 30 c., 50 c. and 1 s. exist with overprint double, but with the two impressions almost coincident.

OFFICIAL	**OFFICIAL**
(O 2)	(O 3)

1960 (18 Oct). *Nos. 183/6, 188, 190, 192 and 196 optd with Type O 2 (cents values) or O 3.*
O13	5 c. Prussian blue	.. ..	10	20
O14	10 c. yellow-green	.. ..	10	10
O15	15 c. dull purple	.. ..	10	20
O16	20 c. magenta. .	.. ..	10	10
O17	30 c. vermilion	.. ..	10	10
O18	50 c. slate-violet	.. ..	30	20
O19	1 s. deep reddish violet and reddish purple ..		30	10
O20	5 s. rose-red and purple	.. ..	4·50	65
O13/20	..	*Set of 8*	5·00	1·40

POSTAGE DUE STAMPS

D 1   D 2

(Typo Waterlow)

1928–33. *Wmk Mult Script CA. P 15 × 14.*
D1	D 1	5 c. violet	.. ..	1·50	25
D2		10 c. vermilion	.. ..	1·50	15
D3		20 c. yellow-green	.. ..	1·50	2·50
D4		30 c. brown (1931)	.. ..	8·50	8·50
D5		40 c. dull blue	.. ..	4·75	12·00
D6		1 s. grey-green (1933)	..	32·00	55·00
D1/6		.. ..	*Set of 6*	45·00	70·00
D1/6	Optd/Perf "Specimen"	..	*Set of 6*	£100	

(Typo D.L.R.)

1935 (1 May)–60. *Wmk Mult Script CA. P 14.*
D 7	D 2	5 c. violet	.. ..	1·50	40
D 8		10 c. scarlet	.. ..	30	10
D 9		20 c. green	.. ..	40	15
D10		30 c. brown	.. ..	60	50
		a. Bistre-brown (19.7.60)	..	2·25	3·50
D11		40 c. ultramarine	.. ..	1·50	3·00
D12		1 s. grey	.. ..	11·00	18·00
D7/12		.. ..	*Set of 6*	14·00	20·00
D7/12	Perf "Specimen"	..	*Set of 6*	75·00	

Kiribati

(formerly Gilbert Islands)

GILBERT ISLANDS

On 1 January 1976, the Gilbert Islands and Tuvalu (Ellice Islands) became separate Crown Colonies.

1 Charts of Gilbert Islands and Tuvalu (formerly Ellice) Islands (2)

(Des J. Cooter. Litho Questa)

1976 (2 Jan). *Separation of the Islands. T* **1** *and similar horiz design. Multicoloured. W w* **14** *(sideways). P* 14.

1	4 c. Type **1**	50	75
2	35 c. Maps of Tarawa and Funafuti	1·25	2·00

1976 (2 Jan). *Nos. 173/86 of Gilbert & Ellice Is optd as T* **2**.

(a) W w **12** *(sideways on Nos. 5/7 and 9/10)*

3	1 c. Cutting toddy (R.)	25	20
4	2 c. Lagoon fishing (R.)	50	75
5	2 c. Lagoon fishing (*wmk sideways*) (R.)	50	30
6	3 c. Cleaning pandanus leaves (R.)	17·00	22·00
7	4 c. Casting nets (R.)	30	50
8	20 c. Beating a pandanus leaf (R.)	†	£100
9	20 c. Beating a pandanus leaf (*wmk sideways*) (R.)	5·00	3·25
10	25 c. Loading copra	42·00	50·00
	a. Opt double (Blk. + R.)	£250	
10*b*	50 c. Local handicrafts	£700	£800

(b) W w **14** *(sideways on 3, 5, 20, 25 and 35 c.; inverted on others)*

11	1 c. Cutting toddy (R.)	20	30
12	3 c. Cleaning pandanus leaves (R.)	40	50
13	5 c. Gilbertese canoe (R.)	50	50
14	6 c. De-husking coconuts	50	60
15	8 c. Weaving pandanus fronds (R.)	50	60
16	10 c. Weaving a basket	50	60
17	15 c. Tiger Shark	1·50	1·25
18	20 c. Beating a pandanus leaf (R.)	1·50	90
19	25 c. Loading copra	2·00	1·25
20	35 c. Fishing at night (Gold)	2·00	1·75
21	50 c. Local handicrafts	2·00	2·75
22	$1 Weaving coconut screens (R.)	6·00	9·00
	a. Opt double	£275	
3, 4, 7 *and* 12/22	Set of 14	17·00	19·00

3 M.V. *Teraaka* (training ship)

(Des J. Cooter. Litho Questa)

1976 (1 July). *Horiz designs as T* **3**. *Multicoloured. W w* **14** *(sideways). P* 14.

23	1 c. Type **3**	20	15
24	3 c. M.V. *Tautunu* (inter-island freighter)	30	20
25	4 c. Moorish Idol (fish)	30	20
26	5 c. Hibiscus	30	20
27	6 c. Eastern Reef Heron	35	30
28	7 c. Catholic Cathedral, Tarawa	30	30
29	8 c. Frangipani	30	30
30	10 c. Maneaba, Bikenibeu	30	30
31	12 c. Betio Harbour	45	45
32	15 c. Evening scene	55	45
33	20 c. Marakei Atoll	35	35
34	35 c. G.I.P.C. Chapel, Tangintebu	35	40
35	40 c. Flamboyant Tree	40	45
36	50 c. *Hypolimnas bolina* (butterfly)	2·25	1·75
37	$1 *Tabakea* (Tarawa Lagoon ferry)	2·00	2·50
38	$2 National flag	2·25	2·75
23/38	Set of 16	9·50	10·00

For similar designs inscribed "KIRIBATI" see Nos. 86/99*a* and 121/35.

4 Church

5 Porcupine Fish Helmet

1976 (15 Sept). *Christmas. Children's Drawings. T* **4** *and similar multicoloured designs. W w* **14** *(sideways on 5 and 35 c.). P* 14.

39	5 c. Type **4**	35	15
40	15 c. Feasting (*vert*)	50	15
41	20 c. Maneaba (*vert*)	55	30
42	35 c. Dancing	70	45
39/42	Set of 4	1·90	95

(Des J. Cooter. Litho J.W.)

1976 (6 Dec). *Artefacts. T* **5** *and similar vert designs. Multicoloured. W w* **14**. *P* 13.

43	5 c. Type **5**	35	15
44	15 c. Shark's Teeth Dagger	50	35
45	20 c. Fighting Gauntlet	55	40
46	35 c. Coconut Body Armour	70	55
43/6	Set of 4	1·90	1·25
MS47	140 × 130 mm. Nos. 43/6. P 14	10·00	14·00

6 Queen in Coronation Robes

7 Commodore Byron and H.M.S. *Dolphin*

(Des J. Cooter. Litho Questa)

1977 (7 Feb). *Silver Jubilee. T* **6** *and similar vert designs. Multicoloured. W w* **14**. *P* 14.

48	8 c. Prince Charles' visit, 1970	15	10
49	20 c. Prince Philip's visit, 1959	20	15
50	40 c. Type **6**	30	35
48/50	Set of 3	60	55

(Des J. Cooter. Litho Questa)

1977 (1 June). *Explorers. T* **7** *and similar horiz designs. Multicoloured. W w* **14** *(sideways). P* 14.

51	5 c. Type **7**	1·00	1·50
52	15 c. Capt. Fanning and *Betsey*	1·50	2·75
53	20 c. Admiral Bellingshausen and *Vostok*	2·00	3·25
54	35 c. Capt. Wilkes and *Vincennes*	3·50	5·75
51/4	Set of 4	7·00	12·00

8 H.M.S. *Resolution* and H.M.S. *Discovery*

9 Emblem and Island Scene

(Des J. Cooter. Litho Questa)

1977 (12 Sept). *Christmas and Bicentenary of Capt. Cook's Discovery of Christmas Is. T* **8** *and similar multicoloured designs. W w* **14** *(sideways on 15 and 40 c.). P* 14.

55	8 c. Type **8**	55	10
56	15 c. Logbook entry (*horiz*)	70	15
57	20 c. Capt. Cook	85	20
58	40 c. Landing party (*horiz*)	1·75	60
55/8	Set of 4	3·50	95
MS59	140 × 140 mm. Nos. 55/8. Wmk sideways	10·00	12·00

(Des J. Cooter. Litho J.W.)

1977 (5 Dec). *50th Anniv of Scouting in the Gilbert Is. T* **9** *and similar multicoloured designs. W w* **14** *(sideways on 15 and 20 c.). P* 13.

60	8 c. Type **9**	20	10
61	15 c. Patrol meeting (*horiz*)	30	20
62	20 c. Mat making (*horiz*)	40	20
63	40 c. Canoeing	50	55
60/3	Set of 4	1·25	95

10 Taurus (The Bull)

11 Unicorn of Scotland

(Des J. Cooter. Litho Questa)

1978 (20 Feb). *Night Sky over the Gilbert Is. T* **10** *and similar vert designs. W w* **14**. *P* 14.

64	10 c. black and light new blue	20	15
65	20 c. black and light rose-red	30	30
66	25 c. black and sage-green	35	35
67	45 c. black and orange	50	60
64/7	Set of 4	1·25	1·25

Designs:—20 c. Canis Major (the Great Dog); 25 c. Scorpio (the Scorpion); 45 c. Orion (the Giant Warrior).

(Des C. Abbott. Litho Questa)

1978 (21 Apr). *25th Anniv of Coronation. T* **11** *and similar vert designs. P* 15.

68	45 c. green, bluish violet and silver	30	40
	a. Sheetlet. Nos. 68/70 × 2	1·60	
69	45 c. multicoloured	30	40
70	45 c. green, bluish violet and silver	30	40
68/70	Set of 3	80	1·10

Designs:—No. 68, Type **11**; No. 69, Queen Elizabeth II; No. 70, Great Frigate Bird.

Nos. 68/70 were printed together in small sheets of 6, containing two *se-tenant* strips of 3, with horizontal gutter margin between.

12 Birds in Flight to Tarawa

(Des local artists; adapted G. Hutchins. Litho Enschedé)

1978 (5 June). *25th Anniv of Return of King George V School to Tarawa. T* **12** *and similar horiz designs. Multicoloured. W w* **14** *(sideways). P* 14 × 13.

71	10 c. Type **12**	10	10
72	20 c. Tarawa, Abemama and school badge	20	20
73	25 c. Rejoicing islanders	20	20
74	45 c. King George V School on Tarawa and Abemama	35	35
71/4	Set of 4	75	75

13 "Te Kaue ni Maie"

14 H.M.S. *Endeavour*

(Des W. Walsh. Litho J.W.)

1978 (25 Sept). *Christmas. Kaue (traditional head decorations). T* **13** *and similar horiz designs. Multicoloured. W w* **14** *(sideways). P* 14.

75	10 c. Type **13**	15	10
76	20 c. "Te Itera"	20	15
77	25 c. "Te Bau"	25	20
78	45 c. "Te Tai"	35	30
75/8	Set of 4	85	65
MS79	149 × 99 mm. Nos. 75/8. P 13 × 13½	1·75	4·50

(Des and litho (45 c. also embossed) Walsall)

1979 (22 Feb*). *Bicentenary of Captain Cook's Voyages, 1768–79. T* **14** *and similar vert designs. P* 11.

80	10 c. multicoloured	25	15
81	20 c. multicoloured	40	30
82	25 c. black, light green and pale lilac	50	45
83	45 c. multicoloured	75	80
80/3	Set of 4	1·75	1·50

Designs:—20 c. Green Turtle; 25 c. Quadrant; 45 c. Flaxman/Wedgwood medallion of Captain Cook.

*This was the local issue date; the stamps were released in London on 15 January.

The Gilbert Islands achieved independence on 12 July 1979 and were renamed Ķiribati.

KIRIBATI

INDEPENDENT

15 Kiribati Flag

(Des G. Drummond. Litho Questa)

1979 (12 July). *Independence. T* **15** *and similar horiz design. Multicoloured. W w* **14** *(sideways). P* 14.

84	10 c. Type **15**	10	20
85	45 c. Houses of Parliament and Maneaba ni Maungatabu (House of Assembly)	30	50

16 M.V. *Teraaka* (training ship)   17 Gilbert and Ellice Islands 1911 ½d. Stamp

(Des J. Cooter. Litho Questa)

1979 (12 July)–**80**. *Multicoloured designs as Nos. 23/32 and 34/8, some with values changed, inscr "KIRIBATI" as T 16. W w 14 (sideways). P 14.*

86	1 c. Type 16		10	10
87	3 c. M.V. *Tautunu* (inter-island freighter)		10	10
88	5 c. Hibiscus		10	10
89	7 c. Catholic Cathedral, Tarawa		10	10
90	10 c. Maneaba, Bikenibeu		10	10
91	12 c. Betio Harbour		15	15
92	15 c. Eastern Reef Heron (as No. 27)		35	20
93	20 c. Flamboyant Tree (as No. 35)		20	20
94	25 c. Moorish Idol (fish) (as No. 25)		30	30
95	30 c. Frangipani (as No. 29)		25	25
96	35 c. G.I.P.C. Chapel, Tangintebu		25	25
97	50 c. *Hypolimnas bolina* (butterfly)		75	55
98	$1 *Tabakea* (Tarawa Lagoon ferry)		70	75
99	$2 Evening scene (as No. 32)		80	1·00
99a	$5 National flag (as No. 38) (27.8.80)		5·00	7·50
86/99a		Set of 15	8·00	10·50

See also Nos. 121/35.

(Des J.W. Litho Questa)

1979 (27 Sept). *Death Centenary of Sir Rowland Hill. T 17 and similar vert designs showing stamps. Multicoloured. W w 14. P 14.*

100	10 c. Type 17		10	10
101	20 c. Gilbert and Ellice Islands 1956 2s. 6d. definitive		15	20
102	25 c. Great Britain 1902 2s. 6d.		15	20
103	45 c. Gilbert and Ellice Islands 1924 10s.		25	35
100/3		Set of 4	60	75
MS104	113 × 110 mm. Nos. 100/3		90	1·00

18 Boy with Clam Shell

(Des D. Bowen. Litho Enschedé)

1979 (28 Nov). *International Year of the Child. T 18 and similar multicoloured designs. W w 14 (sideways on 20 c.). P 13 × 13½ (20 c.) or 13½ × 13 (others).*

105	10 c. Type 18		10	10
106	20 c. Child climbing coconut tree (*horiz*)		10	10
107	45 c. Girl reading		15	20
108	$1 Child in costume		30	50
105/8		Set of 4	55	75

19 Downrange Station, Christmas Island

(Des J. Cooter. Litho Format)

1980 (20 Feb). *Satellite Tracking. T 19 and similar multicoloured designs. P 14½.*

109	25 c. Type 19		10	10
110	45 c. Map of South Pacific showing trajectory of Experimental Communications Satellite		15	15
111	$1 Rocket launch, Tanegashima, Japan (*vert*)		30	35
109/11		Set of 3	50	55

20 T.S. *Teraaka*

(Litho Format)

1980 (30 Apr). *"London 1980" International Stamp Exhibition. T 20 and similar horiz designs. Multicoloured. P 14½.*

112	12 c. Type 20		10	10
113	25 c. Loading Air Tungaru aeroplane, Bonriki Airport		10	10
114	30 c. Radio Operator		15	10
115	$1 Bairiki Post Office		30	35
112/15		Set of 4	50	50
MS116	139 × 116 mm. Nos. 112/15. P 14 ×14½		65	75

Nos. 112/15 were each printed in sheets of 12 containing *se-tenant* stamp-size labels in positions 4 and 6.

21 *Achaea janata*

(Des J. Cooter. Litho Questa)

1980 (27 Aug). *Moths. T 21 and similar horiz designs. Multi-coloured. P 14.*

117	12 c. Type 21		15	10
118	25 c. *Ethmia nigroapicella*		20	15
119	30 c. *Utetheisa pulchelloides*		20	15
120	50 c. *Anua coronata*		25	25
117/20		Set of 4	70	60

1980 (27 Aug)–**81**. *As Nos. 86/99a but no wmk.*

121	1 c. Type 16 (4.81)		10	20
122	3 c. M.V. *Tautunu* (inter-island freighter) (6.1.81)		10	20
123	5 c. Hibiscus		10	15
124	7 c. Catholic Cathedral, Tarawa		10	15
125	10 c. Maneaba, Bikenibeu (19.11.80)		10	15
126	12 c. Betio Harbour (11.12.80)		15	20
127	15 c. Eastern Reef Heron (11.12.80)		35	30
128	20 c. Flamboyant Tree (6.1.81)		20	40
129	25 c. Moorish Idol (fish) (19.11.80)		25	30
130	30 c. Frangipani (4.81)		25	50
131	35 c. G.I.P.C. Chapel, Tangintebu (4.81)		25	50
132	50 c. *Hypolimnas bolina* (butterfly) (4.81)		75	1·00
133	$1 *Tabakea* (Tarawa Lagoon ferry) (11.12.80)		90	2·00
134	$2 Evening scene (11.12.80)		1·40	2·75
135	$5 National flag (11.12.80)		3·00	5·50
121/35		Set of 15	7·00	13·00

22 Captain Cook Hotel, Christmas Island

(Des J. Cooter. Litho Format)

1980 (19 Nov). *Development. T 22 and similar horiz designs. Multicoloured. P 13½ × 14.*

136	10 c. Type 22		10	10
137	20 c. Sports Stadium		10	10
138	25 c. International Airport, Bonriki		15	10
139	35 c. National Library and Archives		15	10
140	$1 Otintai Hotel		30	40
136/40		Set of 5	65	65

23 *Acalypha godseffiana*

(Des J. Cooter. Litho Format)

1981 (18 Feb). *Flowers. T 23 and similar vert designs. Multi-coloured. W w 15. P 14 × 13½.*

141	12 c. Type 23		10	10
142	30 c. *Hibiscus schizopetalus*		15	15
143	35 c. *Calotropis gigantea*		15	15
144	50 c. *Euphorbia pulcherrima*		20	20
141/4		Set of 4	55	55

ALTERED CATALOGUE NUMBERS

Any Catalogue numbers altered from the last edition are shown as a list in the introductory pages.

25 Maps of Abaiang and Marakei, and String Figures

(Des J. Cooter. Litho Format)

1981 (6 May). *Island Maps (1st series). T 25 and similar horiz designs. Multicoloured. W w 15 (sideways). P 13½ × 14.*

145	12 c. Type 25		15	10
146	30 c. Maps of Little Makin and Butaritari, and village house		25	10
147	35 c. Map of Maiana, and coral road		30	15
148	$1 Map of Christmas Island, and Captain Cook's H.M.S. *Resolution*		90	75
145/8		Set of 4	1·40	1·00

See also Nos. 201/4, 215/18, 237/40 , 256/60 and 270/3.

26 *Katherine*

27 Prince Charles and Lady Diana Spencer

(Des D. Shults. Litho Questa)

1981 (29 July–26 Nov). *Royal Wedding. Horiz designs as T 26, showing Royal Yachts, and T 27. Multicoloured. (a) W w 15. P 14.*

149	12 c. Type 26		15	15
	a. Sheetlet. No. 149 × 6 and No. 150		1·00	
150	12 c. Type 27		30	30
151	50 c. *Osborne*		45	45
	a. Sheetlet No. 151 × 6 and No. 152		3·00	
152	50 c. Type 27		75	75
153	$2 *Britannia*		75	1·00
	a. Sheetlet. No. 153 × 6 and No. 154		6·00	
154	$2 Type 27		2·00	3·00
149/154		Set of 6	4·00	5·00
MS155	120 × 109 mm. $1.20, Type 27. Wmk sideways. P 12 (26 Nov)		2·00	2·25

(b) Booklet stamps. No wmk. P 12 (26 Nov)

156	12 c. Type 26		15	15
	a. Booklet pane. No. 156 × 4		60	
157	50 c. Type 27		75	80
	a. Booklet pane. No. 157 × 2		1·50	

Nos. 49/54 were printed in sheetlets of seven stamps of the same face value, each containing six of the "Royal Yacht" design and one as Type 27.

Nos. 156/7 come from $1.96 stamp booklets.

28 Tuna Bait Breeding Centre, Bonriki Fish Farm

(Des G. Drummond. Litho Questa)

1981 (19 Nov). *Tuna Fishing Industry. T 28 and similar horiz designs. Multicoloured. W w 15. P 14.*

158	12 c. Type 28		15	10
159	30 c. Tuna fishing		25	20
160	35 c. Cold storage, Betio		25	25
161	50 c. Government Tuna Fishing Vessel *Nei Manganibuka*		50	50
158/61		Set of 4	1·00	95
MS162	134 × 99 mm. Nos. 158/61. Wmk sideways		1·25	1·40

29 Pomarine Skua

(Des G. Drummond. Litho Questa)

1982 (18 Feb)–**85**. *Birds. Multicoloured designs as T 29. P 14.*

163	1 c. Type 29		15	15
164	2 c. Mallard		15	15
165	4 c. Collared Petrel		20	20
166	5 c. Blue-faced Booby		20	20
167	7 c. Friendly Quail Dove		20	20

168	8 c. Common Shoveler	..	20	20
169	12 c. Polynesian Reed Warbler	..	20	20
170	15 c. American Golden Plover	..	25	25
171	20 c. Eastern Reef Heron	..	30	30
171a	25 c. Common Noddy (31.1.83)	..	2·00	1·50
172	30 c. Brown Booby	..	30	30
173	35 c. Audubon's Shearwater	..	30	35
174	40 c. White-throated Storm Petrel (vert)	..	35	40
175	50 c. Bristle-thighed Curlew (vert)	..	40	45
175a	55 c. White Tern (inscr "Fairy Tern") (vert) (19.11.85)	..	6·00	7·00
176	$1 Kuhl's Lory (vert)	..	85	90
177	$2 Long-tailed Koel (vert)	..	1·60	1·75
178	$5 Great Frigate Bird (vert)	..	4·25	4·50
163/78		Set of 18	16·00	17·00

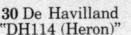

30 De Havilland "DH114 (Heron)"

31 Mary of Teck, Princess of Wales, 1893

(Des G. Drummond. Litho Format)

1982 (18 Feb). *Inauguration of Air Tungaru Airline. T* **30** *and similar horiz designs. Multicoloured. W w* **15** *(sideways). P* 14.

179	12 c. Type **30**	..	10	10
180	30 c. Britten-Norman "Trislander"	..	20	20
181	35 c. Casa "212 (Aviocar)"	..	25	25
182	50 c. Boeing "727"	..	35	35
179/82		Set of 4	75	75

(Des D. Shults and J. Cooter. Litho Format)

1982 (19 May). *21st Birthday of Princess of Wales. T* **31** *and similar vert designs. Multicoloured. W w* **15**. *P* 13½ × 14.

183	12 c. Type **31**	..	10	10
184	50 c. Coat of Arms of Mary of Teck	..	30	30
185	$1 Diana, Princess of Wales	..	50	50
183/5		Set of 3	75	75

The 12 c. design is incorrectly dated; Mary of Teck became Princess of Wales in 1901.

1982 (14 July). *Birth of Prince William of Wales. Nos.* 183/5 *optd with T* **19** *of St. Kitts.*

186	12 c. Type **31**	..	15	15
187	50 c. Coat of arms of Mary of Teck	..	35	35
	a. Opt inverted	..	14·00	
188	$1 Diana, Princess of Wales	..	55	55
186/8		Set of 3	95	95

32 First Aid Practice

(Des J. Cooter. Litho Format)

1982 (12 Aug). *75th Anniv of Boy Scout Movement. T* **32** *and similar horiz designs. Multicoloured. W w* **15** *(sideways). P* 13½ × 14.

189	12 c. Type **32**	..	15	15
190	25 c. Boat repairs	..	30	30
191	30 c. On parade	..	35	35
192	50 c. Gilbert Islands 1977 8 c. Scouting stamp and "75"	..	60	60
189/92		Set of 4	1·25	1·25

33 Queen and Duke of Edinburgh with Local Dancer

(Des PAD Studio. Litho Walsall)

1982 (23 Oct). *Royal Visit. T* **33** *and similar horiz designs. Multicoloured. W w* **15** *(sideways). P* 14.

193	12 c. Type **33**	..	15	15
194	25 c. Queen, Duke of Edinburgh and outrigger canoe	..	20	20
195	35 c. New Philatelic Bureau building	..	30	30
193/5		Set of 3	60	60
MS196	88 × 76 mm. 50 c. Queen Elizabeth II		60	60

On No. **MS**196 the captions on the map for the islands of Teraina and Tabuaeren have been transposed.

34 "Obaia, The Feathered" (Kiribati legend)

(Des J.W. Litho Format)

1983 (14 Mar). *Commonwealth Day. T* **34** *and similar horiz designs. Multicoloured. W w* **15** *(sideways). P* 14.

197	12 c. Type **34**	..	15	10
198	30 c. Robert Louis Stevenson Hotel, Abemama	..	20	20
199	50 c. Container ship off Betio	..	25	25
200	$1 Map of Kiribati	..	45	65
197/200		Set of 4	95	1·10

(Des J. Cooter. Litho Format)

1983 (19 May). *Island Maps (2nd series). Multicoloured designs as T* **25**. *W w* **15** *(sideways on 12 and 25 c.). P* 13½ × 14 *(horiz) or* 14 × 13½ *(vert).*

201	12 c. Beru, Nikunau and canoe	..	20	20
202	25 c. Abemama, Aranuka, Kuria and fish	..	30	30
203	35 c. Nonouti and reef fishing	..	40	40
204	50 c. Tarawa and House of Assembly (vert)	..	60	55
201/4		Set of 4	1·40	1·25

35 Collecting Coconuts

(Des G. Drummond. Litho Questa)

1983 (8 Aug). *Copra Industry. T* **35** *and similar horiz designs. Multicoloured. W w* **15**. *P* 14.

205	12 c. Type **35**	..	25	20
206	25 c. Selecting coconuts for copra	..	45	35
207	30 c. Removing husks	..	50	40
208	35 c. Drying copra	..	55	45
209	50 c. Loading copra at Betio	..	65	55
205/9		Set of 5	2·25	1·75

36 War Memorials

(Des J. Cooter. Litho Format)

1983 (17 Nov). *40th Anniv of Battle of Tarawa. T* **36** *and similar horiz designs. Multicoloured. W w* **15**. *P* 14.

210	12 c. Type **36**	..	20	20
211	30 c. Maps of Tarawa and Pacific Ocean	..	45	40
212	35 c. Gun emplacement	..	50	45
213	50 c. Modern and war-time landscapes	..	75	65
214	$1 Aircraft carrier U.S.S. *Tarawa*	..	1·25	1·10
210/14		Set of 5	2·75	2·50

(Des J. Cooter. Litho Format)

1984 (14 Feb). *Island Maps (3rd series). Multicoloured designs as T* **25**. *W w* **15** *(sideways). P* 13½ × 14.

215	12 c. Teraina and Captain Fanning's ship *Betsey*, 1798	..	50	15
216	30 c. Nikumaroro and Hawksbill Turtle	..	80	35
217	35 c. Kanton and local postmark	..	90	40
218	50 c. Banaba and Flying Fish	..	1·40	55
215/18		Set of 4	3·25	1·25

37 Tug *Riki*

(Des J. Cooter. Litho J.W.)

1984 (9 May). *Kiribati Shipping Corporation. T* **37** *and similar horiz designs. Multicoloured. W w* **15** *(sideways). P* 14.

219	12 c. Type **37**	..	30	15
220	35 c. Ferry *Nei Nimanoa*	..	55	35
221	50 c. Ferry *Nei Tebaa*	..	85	60
222	$1 Cargo ship *Nei Momi*	..	1·40	1·10
219/22		Set of 4	2·75	2·00
MS223	115 × 98 mm. Nos. 219/222. P 13 × 13½		2·75	4·00

NEW INFORMATION

The editor is always interested to correspond with people who have new information that will improve or correct the Catalogue.

38 Water and Sewage Schemes

(Des J. Cooter. Litho Format)

1984 (21 Aug). *"Ausipex" International Stamp Exhibition, Melbourne. T* **38** *and similar horiz designs. Multicoloured. W w* **15** *(sideways). P* 13½ × 14.

224	12 c. Type **38**	..	25	15
225	30 c. *Nouamake* (game fishing boat)	..	50	30
226	35 c. Overseas training schemes	..	60	40
227	50 c. International communications link	..	75	55
224/7		Set of 4	1·90	1·25

39 "Tabakea supporting Banaba"

(Des Jennifer Toombs. Litho Format)

1984 (21 Nov). *Kiribati Legends (1st series). T* **39** *and similar horiz designs. Multicoloured. W w* **15** *(sideways). P* 14.

228	12 c. Type **39**	..	20	20
229	30 c. "Nakaa, Judge of the Dead"	..	35	35
230	35 c. "Naareau and Dragonfly"	..	45	45
231	50 c. "Whistling Ghosts"	..	55	55
228/31		Set of 4	1·40	1·40

See also Nos. 245/8.

40 Tang

(Des G. Drummond. Litho Questa)

1985 (19 Feb). *Reef Fishes. T* **40** *and similar horiz designs. Multicoloured. W w* **15**. *P* 14.

232	12 c. Type **40**	..	60	25
233	25 c. White-barred Triggerfish	..	1·00	55
234	35 c. Surgeon Fish	..	1·25	70
235	80 c. Squirrel Fish	..	2·00	1·75
232/5		Set of 4	4·25	3·00
MS236	140 × 107 mm. Nos. 232/5. Wmk sideways		4·75	4·25

(Des J. Cooter. Litho J.W.)

1985 (9 May). *Island Maps (4th series). Horiz designs as T* **25**. *Multicoloured. W w* **15** *(sideways). P* 13½.

237	12 c. Tabuaeran and Great Frigate Bird	..	55	15
238	35 c. Rawaki and germinating coconuts	..	85	40
239	50 c. Arorae and Xanthid Crab	..	1·10	55
240	$1 Tamana and fish hook	..	1·75	1·00
237/40		Set of 4	3·75	2·00

41 Youths playing Football on Beach

(Des R. Stokes. Litho Cambec Press, Melbourne)

1985 (5 Aug). *International Youth Year. T* **41** *and similar multicoloured designs. P* 13½.

241	15 c. Type **41**	..	60	45
242	35 c. Logos of I.Y.Y. and Kiribati Youth Year	..	1·00	1·00
243	40 c. Girl preparing food (vert)	..	1·10	1·25
244	55 c. Map illustrating Kiribati's youth exchange links	..	1·40	1·60
241/4		Set of 4	3·75	3·75

(Des Jennifer Toombs. Litho Questa)

1985 (19 Nov). *Kiribati Legends (2nd series). Horiz designs as T* **39**. *Multicoloured. P* 14.

245	15 c. "Nang Kineia and the Tickling Ghosts"	..	50	30
246	35 c. "Auriaria and Tituabine"	..	85	75
247	40 c. "The first coming of Babai at Arorae"	..	1·00	1·00
248	55 c. "Riiki and the Milky Way"	..	1·25	1·50
245/8		Set of 4	3·25	3·25

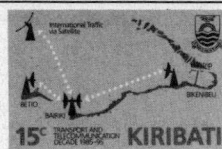

42 Map showing Telecommunications
Satellite Link

(Litho Walsall)

1985 (9 Dec). *Transport and Telecommunications Decade (1st issue). T **42** and similar horiz design. Multicoloured.* P 14.
249	15 c. Type **42**	..	..	1·00	75
250	40 c. M.V. *Moanaraoi* (Tarawa-Suva service)		2·00	2·25

See also Nos. 268/9, 293/4 and 314/15.

(Des A. Theobald. Litho Questa)

1986 (21 Apr). *60th Birthday of Queen Elizabeth II. Vert designs as T **230a** of Jamaica. Multicoloured.* P 14½×14.
251	15 c. Princess Elizabeth in Girl Guide uniform, Windsor Castle, 1938		15	15
252	35 c. At Trooping the Colour, 1980		30	35
253	40 c. With Duke of Edinburgh in Kiribati, 1982		35	40
254	55 c. At banquet, Austrian Embassy, London, 1966		50	60
255	$1 At Crown Agents Head Office, London, 1983		90	1·25
251/5 ..	.. .. .. *Set of 5*		2·00	2·50

(Des J. Cooter. Litho Questa)

1986 (17 June). *Island Maps (5th series). Horiz designs as T **25**. Multicoloured.* P 13½×14.
256	15 c. Manra and Coconut Crab		80	45
257	30 c. Birnie and McKean Islands and cowrie shells		1·50	1·10
258	40 c. Orona and Red-footed Booby		1·75	1·75
259	40 c. Malden Island and whaling ship, 1844.		1·75	1·75
260	55 c. Vostok, Flint and Caroline Islands and Vostok, 1820		2·00	2·50
256/60	.. .. .. *Set of 5*		7·00	6·50

43 *Lepidodactylus lugubris*   **44** Maps of Australia and Kiribati

(Des G. Drummond. Litho Questa)

1986 (26 Aug). *Geckos. T **43** and similar horiz designs. Multicoloured.* P 14.
261	15 c. Type **43**		1·00	45
262	35 c. *Gehyra mutilata*		1·50	1·25
263	40 c. *Hemidactylus frenatus*		1·75	1·75
264	55 c. *Gehyra oceanica.*		2·50	2·75
261/4 ..	.. .. *Set of 4*		6·00	5·75

(Des D. Miller. Litho Format)

1986 (29 Dec). *America's Cup Yachting Championship. T **44** and similar vert designs. Multicoloured.* P 13½×14.
265	15 c. Type **44**		20	30
	a. Horiz strip of 3. Nos. 265/7		1·75	
266	55 c. America's Cup and map of course		50	75
267	$1·50, *Australia II* (1983 winner)		1·25	1·50
265/7 ..	.. .. *Set of 3*		1·75	2·25

Nos. 265/7 were printed together, *se-tenant*, in horizontal strips of 3 throughout the sheet with the $1·50 at left and the 15 c. at centre of each strip.

45 Freighter *Moamoa*   (**45a**)

(Des and litho Questa)

1987 (31 Mar). *Transport and Telecommunications Decade (2nd issue). T **45** and similar horiz design. Multicoloured.* P 13½×14.
268	30 c. Type **45**		1·50	1·50
269	55 c. Telephone switchboard and automatic exchange		2·50	2·50

(Des J. Cooter. Litho Format)

1987 (22 Sept). *Island Maps (6th series). Multicoloured designs as T **25**, but vert.* P 14×13½.
270	15 c. Starbuck and Red-tailed Tropic Bird ..		50	35
271	30 c. Enderbury and White Tern		75	60
272	55 c. Tabiteuea and Pandanus Tree..		1·00	90
273	$1 Onotoa and okai (house)		1·75	2·00
270/3 ..	.. .. *Set of 4*		3·50	3·50

Nos. 271/3 exist imperforate from stock dispersed by the liquidator of Format International Security Printers Ltd.

(Des G. Drummond. Litho Format)

1987 (27 Oct). *Skinks. Horiz designs as T **43**. Multicoloured.* P 15.
274	15 c. *Emoia nigra*	..	40	30
275	35 c. *Cryptoblepharus sp.*		75	60
276	40 c. *Emoia cyanura*		80	70
277	$1 *Lipinia noctua*		1·75	2·00
274/7 ..	.. .. *Set of 4*		3·25	3·25
MS278	130×114 mm. Nos. 274/7		3·50	4·00

Nos. 274/8 exist imperforate from stock dispersed by the liquidator of Format International Security Printers Ltd.

1987 (30 Nov). *Royal Ruby Wedding. Nos. 251/5 optd with T **45a** in silver.*
279	15 c. Princess Elizabeth in Girl Guide uniform, Windsor Castle, 1938		15	15
280	35 c. At Trooping the Colour, 1980		30	35
281	40 c. With Duke of Edinburgh in Kiribati, 1982		35	45
282	55 c. At banquet, Austrian Embassy, London, 1966		50	60
283	$1 At Crown Agents Head Office, London, 1983		90	1·25
279/83	.. .. *Set of 5*		2·00	2·50

46 Henri Dunant   **47** Causeway built by Australia
(founder)

(Des A. Theobald. Litho Questa)

1988 (9 May). *125th Anniv of International Red Cross. T **46** and similar vert designs. Multicoloured.* P 14½×14.
284	15 c. Type **46**		35	30
285	35 c. Red Cross workers in Independence parade, 1979		60	60
286	40 c. Red Cross workers with patient		70	70
287	55 c. Gilbert & Ellice Islands 1970 British Red Cross Centenary 10 c. stamp		90	1·00
284/7 ..	.. .. *Set of 4*		2·25	2·40

(Des CPE Australia Ltd ($2), D. Miller (others). Litho CPE Australia Ltd, Melbourne ($2), Format (others))

1988 (30 July). *Bicentenary of Australian Settlement and "Sydpex '88" National Stamp Exhibition, Sydney. T **47** and similar horiz designs. Multicoloured.* P 14½.
288	15 c. Type **47**		25	20
289	35 c. Capt. Cook and Pacific map		60	50
290	$1 Obverse of Australian $10 Bicentenary banknote		1·25	1·25
	a. Horiz pair. Nos. 290/1		2·50	2·50
291	$1 Reverse of $10 Bicentenary banknote		1·25	1·25
288/91	.. .. *Set of 4*		3·00	3·00
MS292	95 × 76 mm. $2 *Logistic Ace* (container ship) (37 × 26 mm). P 13½ × 14		1·90	2·50

Nos. 290/1 were printed together, *se-tenant*, in horizontal pairs throughout the sheet.
No. MS292 also commemorates the 150th anniversary of the first screw-driven steamship.

48 Manual Telephone
Exchange and Map of
Kiritimati

(Des A. Theobald. Litho Questa)

1988 (28 Dec). *Transport and Communications Decade (3rd issue). T **48** and similar horiz design. Multicoloured. W w **14** (sideways).* P 14.
293	35 c. Type **48**		50	50
294	45 c. Betio–Bairiki Causeway		60	60

49 *Hound* (brigantine), 1835   **50** Eastern Reef Heron

(Des E. Nisbet. Litho Questa)

1989 (26 May). *Nautical History (1st series). T **49** and similar horiz designs. Multicoloured. W w **16** (sideways).* P 14½.
295	15 c. Type **49**		65	40
296	30 c. *Phantom* (brig), 1854		90	70
297	40 c. H.M.S. *Alacrity* (schooner), 1873		1·00	90
298	$1 *Charles W. Morgan* (whaling ship), 1851		2·25	2·50
295/8 ..	.. .. *Set of 4*		4·25	4·00

See also Nos. 343/7.

(Des D. Johnstone. Litho Questa)

1989 (28 June). *Birds with Young. T **50** and similar vert designs. Multicoloured. W w **16**.* P 14½.
299	15 c. Type **50**		35	35
	a. Vert pair. Nos. 299/300		70	70
300	15 c. Eastern Reef Heron chicks in nest		35	35
301	$1 White-tailed Tropic Bird		1·50	1·75
	a. Vert pair. Nos. 301/2		3·00	3·50
302	$1 Young White-tailed Tropic Bird		1·50	1·75
299/302	.. .. *Set of 4*		3·25	3·75

Nos. 299/300 and 301/2 were each printed together, *se-tenant*, in vertical pairs throughout the sheets, each pair forming a composite design.

51 House of Assembly   **51a** "Apollo 10" on Launch Gantry

(Des D. Miller. Litho Cartor, France)

1989 (12 July). *10th Anniv of Independence. T **51** and similar vert design. Multicoloured. W w **16** (inverted).* P 13½×14.
303	15 c. Type **51**		25	25
304	$1 Constitution		1·25	1·25

(Des A. Theobald ($2.50), D. Miller (others). Litho Questa)

1989 (20 July). *20th Anniv of First Manned Landing on Moon. T **51a** and similar multicoloured designs. W w **16** (sideways on 50, 60 c.)* P 14×13½ (20, 75 c.) or 14 (others).
305	20 c. Type **51a**		30	30
306	50 c. Crew of "Apollo 10" (30×30 mm)		70	70
307	60 c. "Apollo 10" emblem (30×30 mm)		80	80
308	75 c. "Apollo 10" splashdown, Hawaii		95	95
305/8 ..	.. .. *Set of 4*		2·50	2·50
MS309	82×100 mm. $2.50, "Apollo 11" command module in lunar orbit. P 14×13½		3·25	3·75

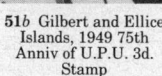

51b Gilbert and Ellice Islands, 1949 75th Anniv of U.P.U. 3d. Stamp   **51c** Examining Fragment of Statue

(Des D. Miller. Litho Walsall)

1989 (7 Aug*). *"Philexfrance 89" International Stamp Exhibition, Paris, and "World Stamp Expo '89", Washington (1st issue). Sheet 104×86 mm. W w **16**.* P 14×13½.
MS310	**51b** $2 multicoloured		2·25	2·75

*This is the local date of issue. The agents, Caphco Ltd, placed stocks on sale in London and Paris from 7 July.

(Des D. Miller, adapted Walsall. Litho Walsall)

1989 (25 Sept). *"Philexfrance 89" International Stamp Exhibition, Paris, and "World Stamp Expo '89", Washington (2nd issue). T **51c** and similar vert designs, showing Statue of Liberty. Multicoloured. W w **14**.* P 14×13½.
311	35 c. Type **51c**		60	75
	a. Sheetlet. Nos. 311/13		1·60	
312	35 c. Workman drilling Statue		60	75
313	35 c. Surveyor with drawing		60	75
311/13	.. .. *Set of 3*		1·60	2·00

Nos. 311/13 were printed, *se-tenant*, in sheetlets of 3.

52 Telecommunications   (**53**)
Centre

(Des L. Curtis. Litho Questa)

1989 (16 Oct). *Transport and Communications Decade (4th issue). T **52** and similar horiz design. Multicoloured. W w **16** (sideways).* P 14.
314	30 c. Type **52**		1·00	1·00
315	75 c. *Mataburo* (inter-island freighter)		2·00	2·25

1989 (21 Oct). *"Melbourne Stampshow '89". Nos. 301/2 optd with T* 53.

316	$1 White-tailed Tropic Bird	..	1·75	2·00
	a. Vert pair. Nos. 316/17	..	3·50	4·00
317	$1 Young White-tailed Tropic Bird	..	1·75	2·00

54 Virgin and Child (detail, "The Adoration of the Holy Child" (Denys Calvert))

55 Gilbert and Ellice Islands 1912 1d. and G.B. Twopence Blue Stamps

(Des D. Miller. Litho Questa)

1989 (1 Dec). *Christmas. T* **54** *and similar vert designs showing paintings. Multicoloured. W w* **16**. *P* 14.

318	15 c. Type **53**	..	30	20
319	15 c. "The Adoration of the Holy Child" (Denys Calvert)	..	45	30
320	55 c. "The Holy Family and St. Elizabeth" (Rubens)	..	1·10	85
321	$1 "Madonna with Child and Maria Magdalena" (School of Correggio)	..	2·00	2·50
318/21		*Set of 4*	3·50	3·50

(Des D. Miller. Litho Questa)

1990 (1 May). *150th Anniv of the Penny Black and "Stamp World London 90" International Stamp Exhibition. T* **55** *and similar horiz designs. Multicoloured. W w* **16** (*sideways*). *P* 14.

322	15 c. Type **55**	..	40	30
323	50 c. Gilbert and Ellice Islands 1911 ½d. and G.B. Penny Black	..	90	80
324	60 c. Kiribati 1982 1 c. bird and G.B. 1870 ½d.	..	1·00	1·00
325	$1 Gilbert Islands 1976 1 c. ship and G.B. 1841 1d. red-brown	..	1·75	2·00
322/5		*Set of 4*	3·50	3·75

56 Blue-barred Orange Parrotfish

(Des G. Drummond. Litho Questa)

1990 (12 July). *Fishes. T* **56** *and similar horiz designs. Multicoloured. W w* **14** (*sideways*). *P* 14.

326	1 c. Type **56**	..	10	10
327	5 c. Honeycomb Rock Cod	..	10	10
328	10 c. Blue-fin Jack	..	10	15
329	15 c. Paddle Tail Snapper	..	15	20
330	20 c. Variegated Emperor	..	15	20
331	25 c. Rainbow Runner	..	25	30
332	30 c. Black-saddled Coral Trout	..	25	30
333	35 c. Great Barracuda	..	30	35
334	40 c. Convict Surgeonfish	..	35	40
335	50 c. Violet Squirrelfish	..	45	50
336	60 c. Freckled Hawkfish	..	55	60
337	75 c. Pennant Coralfish	..	65	70
338	$1 Yellow and Blue Sea Perch	..	85	90
339	$2 Pacific Sailfish	..	1·75	1·90
340	$5 Whitetip Reef Shark	..	4·25	4·50
326/40		*Set of 15*	9·25	10·00

For 23 c. value watermarked w **16** (sideways) see No. 356.

(Des D. Miller. Litho Questa)

1990 (4 Aug). *90th Birthday of Queen Elizabeth the Queen Mother. Vert designs as T* **107** (75 c.) *or* **108** ($2) *of Kenya. W w* **16**. *P* 14×15 (75 c.) *or* 14½ ($2).

341	75 c. multicoloured	..	1·25	1·00
342	$2 brownish black and myrtle-green	..	2·75	3·00

Designs:—75 c. Queen Elizabeth the Queen Mother; $2 King George VI and Queen Elizabeth with air raid victim, London, 1940.

(Des E. Nisbet. Litho Questa)

1990 (5 Nov). *Nautical History (2nd series). Horiz designs as T* **49**. *Multicoloured. W w* **16** (*sideways*). *P* 14½.

343	15 c. *Herald* (whaling ship), 1851	..	30	20
344	50 c. *Belle* (barque), 1849	..	65	60
345	60 c. *Supply* (schooner), 1851	..	75	80
346	75 c. *Triton* (whaling ship), 1848	..	90	1·00
343/6		*Set of 4*	2·40	2·40
MS347	95×75 mm. $2 *Charlotte* (convict transport), 1789		4·00	4·50

MINIMUM PRICE

The minimum price quote is 10p which represents a handling charge rather than a basis for valuing common stamps. For further notes about prices see introductory pages.

---

57 Manta Ray   **58** Queen Elizabeth II

(Des G. Drummond. Litho Questa)

1991 (17 Jan). *Endangered Fishes. T* **57** *and similar horiz designs. Multicoloured. W w* **14** (*sideways*). *P* 14.

348	15 c. Type **57**	..	40	30
349	20 c. Manta Ray (*different*)	..	45	35
350	30 c. Whale Shark	..	75	75
351	35 c. Whale Shark (*different*)	..	80	85
348/51		*Set of 4*	2·25	2·25

1991 (30 Apr). *Horiz design as Nos.* 326/40, *but W w* **16** (*sideways*). *P* 14.

356	23 c. Bennett's Pufferfish	..	15	20

(Des D. Miller. Litho Questa)

1991 (17 June). *65th Birthday of Queen Elizabeth II and 70th Birthday of Prince Philip. T* **58** *and similar vert design. Multicoloured. W w* **16** (*sideways*). *P* 14½×14.

366	65 c. Type **58**	..	1·00	1·00
	a. Horiz pair. Nos. 366/7 separated by label	..	2·00	2·00
367	70 c. Prince Philip in R.A.F. uniform	..	1·00	1·00

Nos. 366/7 were printed together, *se-tenant*, in sheetlets of 10 (2×5) with designs alternating and the vertical rows separated by inscribed labels.

59 Aerial View of Hospital

(Des G. Vasarhelyi. Litho Questa)

1991 (16 Nov). *"Phila Nippon '91" International Stamp Exhibition, Tokyo, and Opening of Tungaru Central Hospital. T* **59** *and similar horiz designs. Multicoloured. W w* **16** (*sideways*). *P* 13½×14.

368	23 c. Type **59**	..	30	30
369	50 c. Traditional dancers	..	60	60
370	60 c. Hospital entrance	..	70	70
371	75 c. Foundation stone and plaques	..	95	95
368/71		*Set of 4*	2·25	2·25
MS372	125×83 mm. $5 Casualty on trolley and ambulance		5·25	5·50

60 Mother and Child   **(61)**

(Des G. Vasarhelyi. Litho Questa)

1991 (2 Dec). *Christmas. T* **60** *and similar horiz designs. Multicoloured. W w* **14** (*sideways*). *P* 14.

373	23 c. Type **60**	..	30	30
374	50 c. The Holy Family in Pacific setting	..	65	65
375	60 c. The Holy Family in traditional setting	..	75	75
376	75 c. Adoration of the Shepherds	..	1·00	1·00
373/6		*Set of 4*	2·40	2·40

(Des D. Miller. Litho Questa)

1992 (6 Feb). *40th Anniv of Queen Elizabeth II's Accession. Horiz designs as T* **113** *of Kenya. W w* **14** (*sideways*). *P* 14.

377	23 c. Kiribati village	..	30	30
378	30 c. Lagoon at sunset	..	40	45
379	50 c. Tarawa waterfront	..	60	65
380	60 c. Three portraits of Queen Elizabeth	..	70	80
381	75 c. Queen Elizabeth II	..	90	1·00
377/81		*Set of 5*	2·50	2·75

1992 (6 June). *"EXPO '92" Worlds Fair, Seville. Nos.* 356, 336/7 *and* 339 *optd with T* **61**.

382	23 c. Bennett's Pufferfish	..	35	35
383	60 c. Freckled Hawkfish	..	80	80
384	75 c. Pennant Coralfish	..	95	95
385	$2 Pacific Sailfish	..	2·25	2·25
382/5		*Set of 4*	4·00	4·00

62 Marine Training Centre Sign

(Des A. Theobald. Litho Questa)

1992 (28 Aug). *25th Anniv of Marine Training Centre. T* **62** *and similar horiz designs. Multicoloured. W w* **16** (*sideways*). *P* 14.

386	23 c. Type **62**	..	35	35
387	50 c. Cadets on parade	..	70	70
388	60 c. Fire school	..	75	75
389	75 c. Lifeboat training	..	90	90
386/9		*Set of 4*	2·40	2·40

63 Healthy Children

(Des O. Ball. Litho Questa)

1992 (1 Dec). *United Nations World Health and Food/Agriculture Organizations. T* **63** *and similar horiz designs. Multicoloured. W w* **14** (*sideways*). *P* 14.

390	23 c. Type **63**	..	35	35
391	50 c. Fishing at night	..	70	70
392	60 c. Fruit	..	75	75
393	75 c. *Papuan Chief* (container ship)	..	90	90
390/3		*Set of 4*	2·40	2·40

POSTAGE DUE STAMPS

D 1 Kiribati Coat of Arms

(Litho Format)

1981 (27 Aug). *P* 14.

D1	**D 1**	1 c. black and magenta	..	..	10	10
D2		2 c. black and greenish blue	..		10	10
D3		5 c. black and bright green	..		10	10
D4		10 c. black and chestnut	..		10	15
D5		20 c. black and bright blue	..		20	25
D6		30 c. black and brown-ochre	..		25	30
D7		40 c. black and purple	..		35	40
D8		50 c. black and deep blue-green	..		45	50
D9		$1 black and orange-red	..		90	95
D1/9			*Set of 9*		2·10	2·40

Nos. D1/9 exist imperforate from stock dispersed by the liquidator of Format International Security Printers Ltd.

OFFICIAL STAMPS

O.K.G.S.   O.K.G.S.
(O 1)   **(O 2)**

1981 (May). *Optd with Type O* 1. A. *On Nos.* 86, 90/3, 95 *and* 97/9a, *W w* **14** (*sideways*). B. *On Nos.* 121/35. *No wmk.*

				A		B	
O 1	1 c. Type **16**	..	2·50	2·75	10	10
O 2	3 c. M.V. *Tautunu* (inter-island freighter)	..	†		10	10
O 3	5 c. Hibiscus	..	†		10	10
O 4	7 c. Catholic Cathedral, Tarawa	..			10	10
O 5	10 c. Maneaba, Bikenibeu	..	15·00	14·00	10	10
	a. Opt double	..	†		15·00	
O 6	12 c. Betio Harbour	..	3·75	3·75	15	15
O 7	15 c. Reef Egret	..	13·00	13·00	15	20
O 8	20 c. Flamboyant Tree	..	10·00	10·00	20	25
O 9	25 c. Moorish Idol	..	†		25	30
O10	30 c. Frangipani	..	7·00	7·00	30	35
	a. Opt double	..	†		20·00	
O11	35 c. G.I.P.C. Chapel, Tangintebu	..	†		35	40
O12	50 c. *Hypolimnas bolina* (butterfly)	..	5·00	5·00	50	55
	a. Opt double	..	†		60·00	
	b. Opt inverted	..	†		60·00	—
O13	$1 *Tabakea* ('Tarawa Lagoon ferry)	..	10·00	10·00	1·00	1·00
O14	$2 Evening scene	..	14·00	14·00	2·00	2·25
	a. Opt double	..	†		£110	
O15	$5 National flag	..	3·75	3·75	4·00	4·25
	a. Opt inverted	..	£150		—	†
O1A/15A		*Set of 10*	75·00	75·00		
O1B/15B		*Set of 15*			8·00	9·00

1983. *Nos.* 86, 90/3, 95, 97/9 *and* 131 *optd with Type O* 2.

O16	1 c. Type **16**	..	3·50	3·50
O17	10 c. Maneaba, Bikenibeu	..	11·00	8·00
O18	12 c. Betio Harbour	..	4·00	4·00
O19	15 c. Eastern Reef Heron	..	13·00	13·00
O20	20 c. Flamboyant Tree	..	6·50	6·50
O21	30 c. Frangipani	..	8·00	
O21a	35 c. G.I.P.C. Chapel, Tangintebu	..	†	
O22	50 c. *Hypolimnas bolina elliciana* (butterfly)	..	5·50	4·00
O23	$1 *Tabakea* (Tarawa Lagoon ferry)	..	10·00	8·00
O24	$2 Evening scene	..	16·00	10·00

1983 (28 June). *Nos.* 169, 172/3, 175 *and* 177 *optd with Type O* 2.

O25	12 c. Polynesian Reed Warbler	..	40	30
O26	30 c. Brown Booby	..	70	50
O27	35 c. Audubon's Shearwater	..	80	60
O28	50 c. Bristle-thighed Curlew	..	1·00	80
O29	$2 Long-tailed Koel	..	3·00	2·75
O25/9		*Set of 5*	5·50	4·50

Kuwait

Kuwait, an independent Arab shaikhdom since 1756, placed itself under British protection in 1899 to counter the spread of Ottoman influence in the Arabian Gulf.

The first, somewhat limited, postal service, via Bushire, commenced with the appointment of a Political Agent to Kuwait in August 1904. Because of diplomatic problems this system continued until 21 January 1915 when a regular Indian post office was established.

Limited supplies of Indian stamps were used by the Political Agency postal service, but these became available to the general public from 21 January 1915. Stamps seen postally used from Kuwait before 1923 are usually ½ a., 1 a., 1 r. or 5 r. values, with the occasional Official issue. Much more common are values to 15 r., both postage and Official, used telegraphically.

Before 1910 the name of the shaikhdom was spelt "KOWEIT" and this spelling appears on various circular postmarks used between 1915 and 1923. The more modern version of the name was first used for a postal cancellation in 1923.

1915 "KOWEIT"

1923 "KUWAIT"

On 1 August 1921 responsibility for the Kuwait postal service passed to the Iraq Post Office, but later it reverted to Indian administration some time before 1929.

PRICES FOR STAMPS ON COVER TO 1945	
Nos. 1/15	from × 5
Nos. 16/29	from × 3
Nos. 31/51	from × 2
Nos. 52/63	from × 4
Nos. O1/27	from × 10

USED HIGH VALUES. It is necessary to emphasize that used prices quoted for high value stamps are for postally used examples.

KUWAIT (1)   KUWAIT (2)

1923 (1 Apr)–**24**. *Stamps of India (King George V), optd with T 1 or 2 (rupee values, 15½ mm). W 34 (Large Star) of India. P 14.*

1	½ a. pale blue-green (No. 156)	..	60	2.50
	a. Opt double	..	£180	
	b. Vert pair, one without opt	..	£400	
2	1 a. chocolate (No. 197)	..	1.25	1.25
	a. Opt double	..	£200	
	b. Opt omitted (lower stamp of vert pair)		£650	
3	1½ a. chocolate (A) (No. 163)	..	1.00	4.00
4	2 a. violet (No. 168)	..	1.50	60
	a. Bright purple	..	..	
5	2½ a. ultramarine (No. 171)	..	1.75	7.50
6	3 a. orange-brown (No. 173)	..	3.75	15.00
7	3 a. ultramarine (No. 200) (1924)	..	9.00	1.50
8	4 a. deep olive (No. 174)	..	7.00	22.00
	a. Olive-green	..	..	
9	6 a. yellow-bistre (No. 177)	..	8.50	13.00
10	8 a. purple (No. 179)	..	8.00	24.00
	a. Mauve	..	..	
11	12 a. claret (No. 184)	..	14.00	26.00
12	1 r. brown and green (No. 185)	..	14.00	13.00
	a. Red-brown and blue-green	..	18.00	17.00
13	2 r. carmine and brown (No. 187)	..	40.00	90.00
14	5 r. ultramarine and violet (No. 188)	..	80.00	£200
15	10 r. green and scarlet (No. 189)	..	£120	£450
1/15		*Set of 15*	£275	£750

Essays of the overprint using the obsolete spelling "KOWEIT" were prepared in 1923 and can be found on the original 14 values of the postage stamps and on the 13 stamps of the Official series. (*Price per set of 27 unused* £19000).

Nos. 1/4 and 6/7 are all known with inverted overprint. It is doubtful if such errors were actually sold at the Kuwait Post Office, although some are known on registered or ordinary covers.

From 22 April 1929 the post office in Kuwait was again placed under the control of the Iraq Mandate postal administration.

KUWAIT (3)   KUWAIT (4)

1929–37. *Stamps of India (King George V, Nasik printing), optd with T 3 or 4 (rupee values). W 69 (Mult Stars) of India. P 14.*

16	½ a. green (No. 202)	..	1.00	1.25
16a	½ a. green (No. 232) (1934)	..	4.50	60
17	1 a. chocolate (No. 203)	..	7.00	1.25
17a	1 a. chocolate (No. 234) (1934)	..	4.50	50
18	2 a. purple (No. 206)	..	1.50	50
19	2 a. vermilion (No. 236)	..	23.00	60.00
19a	2 a. vermilion (No. 236a) (1934)	..	16.00	5.00
19b	2 a. vermilion (*small die*) (No. 236b) (1937)	3.00	1.60
20	3 a. blue (No. 209)	..	2.75	1.50
21	3 a. carmine (No. 237)	..	5.50	4.50
22	4 a. sage-green (No. 211)	..	25.00	60.00
22a	4 a. pale sage-green (No. 210) (1934)	..	5.00	8.50
22b	6 a. bistre (No. 239) (1937)	..	18.00	35.00
23	8 a. reddish purple (No. 212)	..	9.00	13.00
24	12 a. claret (No. 213) (1933)	..	18.00	35.00
25	1 r. chocolate and green (No. 214)	..	10.00	23.00
	a. Extended "T"	..	£180	
26	2 r. carmine and orange (No. 215)	..	10.00	50.00
	a. Extended "T"	..	£200	
27	5 r. ultramarine & purple (No. 216) (1937)	70.00	£180
	a. Extended "T"	..	£325	
28	10 r. green and scarlet (No. 217) (1934)	£160	£350
	a. Extended "T"	..	£650	
29	15 r. blue and olive (No. 218) (1937)	£450	£700
	a. Extended "T"	..	£900	
16/29		*Set of 20*	£750	£1300

The "T" of "KUWAIT" shows a ¾ mm downward extension on R. 3/2, lower left pane.

Nos. 16, 17, 18/19 and 22 are inscribed "INDIA POSTAGE & REVENUE". The remainder are inscribed "INDIA POSTAGE". No. 19a measures 19×22.6 mm and No. 19b 18.4×21.8 mm.

1933 (Feb)–**34.** *Air. Nos. 220/3 of India optd as T 2 (16½ mm).*

31	2 a. deep blue-green	..	11.00	20.00
32	3 a. blue	..	1.25	2.00
	a. Stamp doubly printed	..	£850	£650
33	4 a. olive-green	..	85.00	£170
34	6 a. bistre (2.34)	..	1.25	4.00
31/4		*Set of 4*	90.00	£180

1939. *Nos. 248, 250/1, 253, 255/63 of India (King George VI) optd with T 3 or 4 (rupee values). P 14.*

36	½ a. red-brown	..	7.00	90
38	1 a. carmine	..	7.00	90
39	2 a. vermilion	..	7.00	1.75
41	3 a. yellow-green	..	6.50	1.50
43	4 a. brown	..	25.00	90.00
44	6 a. turquoise-green	..	22.00	6.50
45	8 a. slate-violet	..	26.00	26.00
46	12 a. lake	..	22.00	26.00
47	1 r. grey and red-brown	..	4.00	2.00
	a. Extended "T"	..	£190	
48	2 r. purple and brown	..	3.75	7.50
	a. Extended "T"	..	£190	
49	5 r. green and blue	..	12.00	15.00
	a. Extended "T"	..	£300	
50	10 r. purple and claret	..	60.00	60.00
	a. Opt double	..	£300	
	b. Extended "T"	..	£425	
51	15 r. brown and green	..	85.00	£140
	a. Extended "T"	..	£600	
36/51		*Set of 13*	£250	£275

On later printings the extended "T" variety was corrected in two stages.

Following the rebellion in Iraq control of the Kuwait postal service was assumed by the Indian authorities.

Unoverprinted stamps of INDIA were used in Kuwait between 1941 and 1945.

1945. *Nos. 265/8 and 269a of India (King George VI, on white background) optd with T 3.*

52	3 p. slate	..	1.00	1.25
53	½ a. purple	..	1.00	1.25
54	9 p. green	..	1.00	4.75
55	1 a. carmine	..	1.00	85
56	1½ a. dull violet	..	1.00	3.50
57	2 a. vermilion	..	1.10	1.25
58	3 a. bright violet	..	1.00	1.75
59	3½ a. bright blue	..	2.75	2.75
60	4 a. brown	..	1.00	1.25
60a	6 a. turquoise-green	..	12.00	8.50
61	8 a. slate-violet	..	3.00	1.25
62	12 a. lake	..	4.50	1.75
63	14 a. purple	..	7.00	12.00
52/63		*Set of 13*	35.00	38.00

Following a short period of Pakistani control, from August 1947 the Kuwait postal service passed to British administration on 1 April 1948.

KUWAIT (5) ≡ ≡ KUWAIT (6)

KUWAIT

1 ANNA (5)

5 RUPEES (6)

NOTE. From 1948 onwards, for stamps with similar surcharges, but without name of country, see British Postal Agencies in Eastern Arabia.

1948 (1 Apr)–**49.** *Nos. 470, 475, 476a/7, 478a and 485/90 of Great Britain (King George VI), surch as T 5 or 6 (rupee values).*

64	½ a. on ½d. pale green	..	30	40
65	1 a. on 1d. pale scarlet	..	30	40
66	1½ a. on 1½d. pale red-brown	..	30	40
67	2 a. on 2d. pale orange	..	30	40
68	2½ a. on 2½d. light ultramarine	..	30	50
69	3 a. on 3d. pale violet	..	30	10
	a. Pair, one surch albino			
70	6 a. on 6d. purple	..	30	10
71	1 r. on 1s. bistre-brown	..	40	50
72	2 r. on 2s. 6d. yellow-green	..	1.00	2.50
73	5 r. on 5s. red	..	1.75	4.25
73a	10 r. on 10s. ultramarine (4.7.49)	..	35.00	6.00
64/73a		*Set of 11*	35.00	14.00

KUWAIT 2½ ANNAS (7)   KUWAIT 15 RUPEES ≡ (8)

1948 (26 Apr). *Royal Silver Wedding. Nos. 493/4 of Great Britain surch with T 7 or 8.*

74	2½ a. on 2½d. ultramarine	..	50	30
75	15 r. on £1 blue	..	30.00	27.00
	a. Short bars (R. 3/4)	..	£120	

No. 75a has the bars cancelling the original face value 3 mm long instead of the 3½ mm of the normal surcharge.

1948 (29 July). *Olympic Games. Nos. 495/8 of Great Britain surch as T 7, but in one line (6 a.) or two lines (others).*

76	2½ a. on 2½d. ultramarine	..	1.00	1.00
77	3 a. on 3d. violet	..	1.00	1.00
78	6 a. on 6d. bright purple	..	1.25	1.25
79	1 r. on 1s. brown	..	1.25	1.25
76/9		*Set of 4*	4.00	4.00

1949 (10 Oct). *75th Anniv of U.P.U. Nos. 499/502 of Great Britain surch "KUWAIT" and new values.*

80	2½ a. on 2½d. ultramarine	..	60	70
81	3 a. on 3d. violet	..	85	1.00
82	6 a. on 6d. bright purple	..	1.10	1.10
83	1 r. on 1s. brown	..	1.50	1.00
80/3		*Set of 4*	3.50	3.50

≡ KUWAIT   ≡ KUWAIT

2 RUPEES   2 RUPEES
Type I   Type II
              (8a)

KUWAIT

Type I

10 RUPEES ≡

KUWAIT

Type II

10 RUPEES ≡
(8b)

2 r. Type I   Type-set surcharge. "2" level with "RUPEES". Surcharge sharp.
    Type II   Plate-printed surcharge. "2" raised. Surcharge worn.
10 r. Type I   Type-set surcharge. "1" and "0" spaced. Surcharge sharp and clean.
    Type II   Plate-printed surcharge. "1" and "0" closer together. Surcharge appears heavy and worn, see especially "A", "R" and "P".

≡ KUWAIT   ≡ KUWAIT

Extra bar in centre   Extra bar at top
(R. 7/2)   (R. 2/2)

1950 (2 Oct)–**54.** *Nos. 503/11 of Great Britain (King George VI) surch as T 5 or 8a/b (rupee values).*

84	½ a. on ½d. pale orange (3.5.51)	..	30	1.50
85	1 a. on 1d. light ultramarine (3.5.51)	..	30	50
86	1½ a. on 1½d. pale green (3.5.51)	..	30	2.25
87	2 a. on 2d. pale red-brown (3.5.51)	..	30	35
88	2½ a. on 2½d. pale scarlet (3.5.51)	..	40	1.00
89	4 a. on 4d. light ultramarine	..	30	35
90	2 r. on 2s. 6d. yellow-green (I) (3.5.51)	12.00	4.25
	a. Extra bar in centre	..	£250	£250
	b. Type II surch (1954)	..	£160	42.00
91	5 r. on 5s. red (3.5.51)	..	15.00	5.00
	a. Extra bar at top	..	£190	£180
92	10 r. on 10s. ultramarine (I) (3.5.51)	26.00	5.50
	a. Type II surch (1953)	..	£200	50.00
84/92		*Set of 9*	50.00	18.00

No. 92a is known with surch spaced 10 mm apart instead of 9 mm.

W **153** of Great
Britain

W **165** of Great
Britain

1952 (10 Dec)–**54.** *Nos. 515/21, 523 and 530/1 of Great Britain (Queen Elizabeth II. W* **153***), surch as T* **5** *(in two lines only on 2½ and 6 a.).*

93	½ a. on ½d. orange-red (31.8.53) ..	15	10
94	1 a. on 1d. ultramarine (31.8.53) ..	15	10
95	1½ a. on 1½d. green	15	10
96	2 a. on 2d. red-brown (31.8.53)	35	10
97	2½ a. on 2½d. carmine-red	15	10
98	3 a. on 3d. deep lilac (B.) (18.1.54)	40	10
99	4 a. on 4d. ultramarine (2.11.53) ..	1·25	55
100	6 a. on 6d. reddish purple (18.1.54)	85	10
101	12 a. on 1s. 3d. green (2.11.53) ..	4·50	2·00
102	1 r. on 1s. 6d. grey-blue (2.11.53)	4·50	10
93/102	.. .. *Set of* 10	11·00	2·50

1953 (3 June). *Coronation. Nos. 532/5 of Great Britain surch* "KUWAIT" *and new values.*

103	2½ a. on 2½d. carmine-red ..	2·25	75
104	4 a. on 4d. ultramarine	3·00	80
105	12 a. on 1s. 3d. deep yellow-green ..	4·00	2·00
106	1 r. on 1s. 6d. deep grey-blue	4·00	80
103/6	.. .. .. *Set of* 4	12·00	4·00

KUWAIT 2 RUPEES
═══
I

KUWAIT 2 RUPEES
═══
II

(9)

KUWAIT 5 RUPEES
═══
I

KUWAIT 5 RUPEES
═══
II

(10)

KUWAIT 10 RUPEES
═══
I

KUWAIT 10 RUPEES
═══
II

(11)

Type I (9/11). Type-set overprints. Bold (generally thicker) letters with sharp corners and straight edges. Bars close together and usually slightly longer than in Type II.
Type II (9/11). Plate-printed overprints. Thinner letters, rounder corners and rough edges. Bars wider apart.

1955 (23 Sept)–**57.** *Nos. 536/8 of Great Britain ("Castles" high values) surch with T* **9/11.**

		I		II	
107	2 r. on 2s. 6d. black-brown ..	5·00	1·25	55·00	7·00
108	5 r. on 5s. rose-carmine ..	7·00	3·50	85·00	26·00
109	10 r. on 10s. ultramarine ..	8·00	4·00	£140	90·00
107/9	.. .. *Set of* 3	18·00	8·00	£250	£110

Nos. 107II/9II were issued on 10 October 1957.

1956. *Nos. 540/6, 548 and 555/6 of Great Britain (Queen Elizabeth II. W* **165***) surch as T* **5** *(in two lines only on 2½ and 6 a.).*

110	½ a. on ½d. orange-red ..	15	20
111	1 a. on 1d. ultramarine ..	40	30
112	1½ a. on 1½d. green ..	20	20
113	2 a. on 2d. red-brown ..	20	20
114	2½ a. on 2½d. carmine-red ..	40	40
116	4 a. on 4d. ultramarine ..	4·75	1·75
117	6 a. on 6d. reddish purple ..	2·00	30
118	12 a. on 1s. 3d. green ..	9·50	5·50
119	1 r. on 1s. 6d. grey-blue ..	2·50	10
110/19	.. .. *Set of* 9	18·00	8·00

(New Currency. 100 naye paise = 1 rupee)

KUWAIT   **KUWAIT**   **KUWAIT**

NP **1** NP   NP **3** NP   NP **75** NP

(12)   (13)   (14)

1957 (1 June)–**58.** *Nos. 540/2, 543a/8, 551 and 555 of Great Britain (Queen Elizabeth II. W* **165***) surch as T* **12** *(1, 15, 25, 40, 50 n.p.), 14 (75 n.p.) or 13 (others).*

120	1 n.p. on 5d. brown	10	50
121	3 n.p. on ½d. orange-red ..	40	75
122	6 n.p. on 1d. ultramarine ..	40	75
123	9 n.p. on 1½d. green ..	40	60
124	12 n.p. on 2d. light red-brown ..	40	70
125	15 n.p. on 2½d. carmine-red (Type I) ..	40	10
	a. Type II (11.58) ..	28·00	48·00
126	20 n.p. on 3d. deep lilac (B.) ..	40	10
127	25 n.p. on 4d. ultramarine ..	1·75	2·50
128	40 n.p. on 6d. reddish purple ..	80	10
129	50 n.p. on 9d. bronze-green ..	4·50	3·25
130	75 n.p. on 1s. 3d. green ..	4·50	3·75
120/30	.. .. *Set of* 11	12·50	11·50

15 Shaikh Abdullah
as-Salim as-Sabah

(Recess D.L.R.)

1958 (1 Feb). *P* 12½.

131	**15**	5 n.p. bluish green ..	30	10
132		10 n.p. rose-red ..	35	10
136		40 n.p. maroon	1·00	30
131/6		.. .. *Set of* 3	1·50	40

Nos. 131/6 were only valid for internal use in Kuwait prior to 1 February 1959. Further values were added to this series following the closure of the British Agency Post Offices on 31 January 1959. Responsibility of the postal service then passed to the Kuwait Government and later issues are listed in Part 19 (*Middle East*) of this catalogue.

OFFICIAL STAMPS

KUWAIT   **KUWAIT**

KUWAIT

SERVICE   **SERVICE**
(O **1**)   (O **2**)

1923–24. *Stamps of India (King George V), optd with Type O* **1** *or O* **2** *(rupee values, 15½–16 mm). W* **34** *(Large Star) of India. P* 14.

O **1**	½ a. pale blue-green (No. 156) ..	50	13·00
	a. Opt double, one albino ..	75·00	
O **2**	1 a. chocolate (No. 197) ..	55	7·00
	a. Opt double, one albino ..	75·00	
O 3	1½ a. chocolate (A) (No. 163) ..	1·25	18·00
O 4	2 a. violet (No. 168) ..	3·25	15·00
	a. Bright purple ..		
O 5	2½ a. ultramarine (No. 171) ..	2·75	29·00
O 6	3 a. orange-brown (No. 173) ..	3·25	42·00
O 7	3 a. ultramarine (No. 200) (1924) ..	3·50	29·00
O 8	4 a. olive-green (No. 175) ..	3·00	40·00
O 9	8 a. purple (No. 179) ..	4·50	42·00
	a. Mauve ..		
O10	1 r. brown and green (No. 185) ..	10·00	75·00
	a. Opt double, one albino ..	75·00	
O11	2 r. carmine and brown (No. 187) ..	16·00	£110
O12	5 r. ultramarine and violet (No. 188) ..	48·00	£225
	a. Opt double, one albino ..	£120	
O13	10 r. green and scarlet (No. 189) ..	90·00	£350
O14	15 r. blue and olive (No. 190) ..	£150	£475
O1/14	.. .. .. *Set of* 14	£300	£1300

1929–33. *Nos. 203, 206, 209 and 211/18 of India (King George V, Nasik printing) optd as Types O* **1** *(spaced 10 mm) or O* **2** *(14½ mm × 19–20 mm wide). W* **69** *(Mult Stars) of India. P* 14.

O16	1 a. chocolate ..	1·75	18·00
O17	2 a. purple ..	48·00	£110
O19	3 a. blue ..	1·90	25·00
O20	4 a. sage-green ..	4·25	60·00
O21	8 a. reddish purple ..	3·25	65·00
O22	12 a. claret ..	18·00	£100
O23	1 r. chocolate and green ..	4·00	£120
O24	2 r. carmine and orange ..	7·00	£180
O25	5 r. ultramarine and purple ..	25·00	£375
O26	10 r. green and scarlet ..	50·00	£550
O27	15 r. blue and olive ..	£110	£950
O16/27	.. .. .. *Set of* 11	£225	£2250

Labuan
see Malaysia

Lagos
see Nigeria

Leeward Islands

The Federal Colony of the Leeward Islands was constituted in 1871 formalising links between Antigua, British Virgin Islands, Dominica, Montserrat and St. Kitts-Nevis which stretched back to the 1670s. Issues for the individual islands were superseded by those inscribed "LEEWARD ISLANDS", but were in concurrent use with them from 1903. Dominica was transferred to the Windward Islands on 31 December 1939.

PRICES FOR STAMPS ON COVER TO 1945	
Nos. 1/8	*from* × 10
Nos. 9/16	*from* × 12
Nos. 17/19	*from* × 8
Nos. 20/8	*from* × 5
Nos. 29/35	*from* × 4
Nos. 36/45	*from* × 5
Nos. 46/57	*from* × 4
Nos. 58/87	*from* × 5
Nos. 88/91	*from* × 6
Nos. 92/4	*from* × 10
Nos. 95/114	*from* × 5

PRINTERS. All the stamps of Leeward Islands were typographed by De La Rue & Co, Ltd, London, *except where otherwise stated.*

1   2

1890 (31 Oct). *Name and value in second colour. Wmk Crown CA. P* 14.

1	1	½d. dull mauve and green ..	1·25	40
2		1d. dull mauve and rose ..	1·25	10
3		2½d. dull mauve and blue ..	2·75	15
4		4d. dull mauve and orange ..	2·75	7·00
5		6d. dull mauve and brown ..	6·00	7·00
6		7d. dull mauve and slate ..	1·75	9·00
7	2	1s. green and carmine ..	11·00	28·00
8		5s. green and blue ..	£130	£250
1/8		*Set of* 8	£140	£250
1/8	Optd "Specimen"..	*Set of* 8	£200	

The colours of this issue are fugitive.

          One
                       Penny   **One Penny**

(3)   (4)   (5)

1897 (22 July). *Queen Victoria's Diamond Jubilee. Hand-stamped with T* **3.**

9	1	½d. dull mauve and green ..	2·50	8·00
		a. Opt double ..	£1200	
10		1d. dull mauve and rose ..	3·25	8·50
		a. Opt double ..	£1000	
		b. Opt triple..	£3250	
11		2½d. dull mauve and blue ..	3·50	8·50
		a. Opt double ..	£1200	
12		4d. dull mauve and orange ..	24·00	55·00
		a. Opt double ..	£1200	
13		6d. dull mauve and brown ..	40·00	80·00
		a. Opt double ..	£1400	
14		7d. dull mauve and slate ..	45·00	80·00
		a. Opt double ..	£1400	
15	2	1s. green and carmine ..	£120	£190
		a. Opt double ..	£1800	
16		5s. green and blue ..	£650	£950
		a. Opt double ..	£5000	
9/16		*Set of* 8	£800	£1200

Beware of forgeries.

1902 (11 Aug.) *Nos. 4/6 surch.*

17	4	1d. on 4d. dull mauve and orange ..	80	3·75
		a. Pair, one with tall narrow "O" in "One" ..	27·00	60·00
		b. Surch double ..		
18		1d. on 6d. dull mauve and brown ..	90	5·00
		a. Pair, one with tall narrow "O" in "One"	40·00	65·00
19	5	1d. on 7d. dull mauve and slate ..	90	3·25
17/19		*Set of* 3	2·40	11·00

The tall narrow "O" variety occurred on R. 1/1, 5/3, 5/5 and 7/4.

6   7   8

Wide "A" (R. 6/1 of both panes)

Dropped "R" (R. 1/1 of both panes)

1902 (1 Sept–Oct). *Wmk Crown CA. P* 14.

20	6	½d. dull purple and green	..	1·50	40
21		1d. dull purple and carmine	..	2·75	10
22	7	2d. dull purple and ochre (Oct)		2·25	4·00
23	6	2½d. dull purple and ultramarine		1·25	1·25
		a. Wide "A" in "LEEWARD"	..	£140	£140
24	7	3d. dull purple and black (Oct)		1·00	5·00
25	6	6d. dull purple and brown	..	1·00	6·50
26	8	1s. green and carmine	..	1·75	13·00
		a. Dropped "R" in "LEEWARD"		£130	
27	7	2s. 6d. green and black (Oct)		20·00	45·00
28	8	5s. green and blue (Oct)		35·00	50·00
20/8				*Set of* 9	60·00 £110
20/8 Optd "Specimen"				*Set of* 9	£130

1905 (Apr)–08. *Wmk Mult Crown CA. Ordinary paper* (½d., 3d.) *or chalk-surfaced paper* (*others*).

29	6	½d. dull purple and green (2.06)		80	1·75
		a. Chalk-surfaced paper (25.7.08)		2·50	3·50
30		1d. dull purple and carmine (29.8.06)		2·75	70
31	7	2d. dull purple and ochre (25.7.08)		2·75	8·50
32	6	2½d. dull purple and ultramarine (23.7.06)		26·00	26·00
		a. Wide "A" in "LEEWARD"	..	£300	£300
33	7	3d. dull purple and black		6·00	24·00
		a. Chalk-surfaced paper (18.4.08)		15·00	35·00
34	6	6d. dull purple and brown (15.7.08)		23·00	48·00
35	8	1s. green and carmine (15.7.08)		28·00	60·00
29/35			..	*Set of* 7	80·00 £150

1907 (14 Apr)–**11**. *Wmk Mult Crown CA. Chalk-surfaced paper* (3d. *to* 5s.). *P* 14.

36	7	¼d. brown ((7.8.09)	..	45	75
37	6	½d. dull green	..	95	65
38		1d. bright red (7.07)	..	1·75	40
		a. Rose-carmine		16·00	80
39	7	2d. grey (3.8.11)	..	1·00	7·50
40	6	2½d. bright blue (5.07)	..	1·40	2·50
		a. Wide "A" in "LEEWARD"		£140	£140
41	7	3d. purple/yellow (28.10.10)		1·00	4·25
42	6	6d. dull and bright purple (3.8.11)		3·00	5·50
43	8	1s. black/green (3.8.11)		2·75	14·00
44	7	2s. 6d. black and red/blue (15.9.11)		28·00	42·00
45	8	5s. green and red/yellow (21.11.10)		28·00	48·00
36/45				*Set of* 10	60·00 £110
36/45 Optd "Specimen"				*Set of* 10	£170

10   11

12   13

1912 (23 Oct)–**22**. *Wmk Mult Crown CA. Chalk-surfaced paper* (3d. *to* 5s.). *P* 14.

46	10	¼d. brown	..	50	20
		a. Pale brown (1916)	..	60	50
47	11	½d. yellow-green (12.12)		1·50	60
		a. Deep green (1916)	..	1·25	50
48		1d. carmine-red	..	1·00	20
		a. Bright scarlet (1915)		1·50	30
49	10	2d. slate-grey (9.1.13)	..	90	1·75
50	11	2½d. bright blue	..	2·75	7·00
		a. Deep bright blue	..	3·50	4·00
51	10	3d. purple/yellow (9.1.13)		1·00	6·00
		a. White back (Optd S. £35) (11.13)		35·00	60·00
		b. On lemon (1916)	..	1·25	12·00
		c. On pale yellow (Optd S. £30) (1920)	25·00	42·00
		d. On orange-buff (1920)		1·25	5·50
52		4d. black and red/pale yellow (Die II) (12.5.22)		80	13·00
53	11	6d. dull and bright purple (9.1.13)		1·00	6·00
54	12	1s. black/green (9.1.13)		1·00	4·50
		a. White back (Optd S. £35) (11.13)		24·00	35·00
		b. On blue-green, olive back (Optd S. £35) (1914)		1·25	5·50
55	10	2s. purple and blue/blue (Die II) (12.5.22)	3·50	23·00
56		2s. 6d. black and red/blue (11.13)		11·00	26·00

57	12	5s. green and red/yellow (9.14)	..	23·00	60·00
		a. White back (Optd S. £40) (11.13)		30·00	48·00
		b. On lemon (1916)	..	10·00	40·00
		c. On orange-buff (1920)		65·00	£110
46/57b			*Set of* 12	30·00 £110
46/57 Optd "Specimen"	..	*Set of* 12	£225

HIGH VALUE KEY TYPES. The reign of King Edward VII saw the appearance of the first in a new series of "key type" designs, initially on the issues of Malaya—Straits Settlements and Nyasaland, to be used for high value denominations where a smaller design was felt to be inappropriate. The system was extended during the reign of King George V, using the portrait as Leeward Islands Type **13**, to cover Bermuda, Ceylon, Leeward Islands, Malaya—Straits Settlements, Malta and Nyasaland. A number of these territories continued to use the key type concept for high value King George VI stamps and one, Leeward Islands, for stamps of Queen Elizabeth II.

In each instance the King George V issues were printed in sheets of 60 (12×5) on various coloured papers. The system utilised a common "head" plate used with individual "duty" plates which printed the territory name and face value.

Two major plate flaws occur on the King George V head plate: the break on scroll on R. 1/12 and the broken crown and scroll on R. 2/12. Both of these occur in different states, having been repaired and then damaged once again, perhaps on several occasions. The prices quoted in the listings are for examples approximately as illustrated.

Break in scroll (R. 1/12)

Broken crown and scroll (R. 2/12)

"D I" shaved at foot 1d. R. 7/3 of left pane (all ptgs between Sept 1947 and July 1949. 1s. R. 9/6 of right pane (all ptgs between 1932 and 1938)

1921 (Oct)–**32**. *Wmk Mult Script CA or Mult Crown CA* (£1). *Chalk-surfaced paper* (3d. *to* £1). *P* 14.

(a) Die II (1921–29)

58	10	¼d. brown (1.4.22)	..	45	1·00
59	11	½d. blue-green	..	30	30
60		1d. carmine-red	..	30	15
61		1d. bright violet (21.8.22)		30	40
62		1d. bright scarlet (1929)		75	60
63	10	1½d. carmine-red (10.9.26)		30	55
64		1½d. red-brown (1929)	..	30	10
65		2d. slate-grey (6.22)	..	50	30
66	11	2½d. orange-yellow (22.9.23)		3·75	29·00
67		2½d. bright blue (1.3.27)		75	30
68	10	3d. light ultramarine (22.9.23)		2·00	16·00
		a. Deep ultramarine		25·00	45·00
69		3d. purple/yellow (1.7.27)		40	4·00
70		4d. black and red/pale yellow (2.24)		1·25	12·00
71		5d. dull purple and olive-green (12.5.22)		50	4·25
72	11	6d. dull and bright purple (17.7.23)		7·00	23·00
73	12	1s. black/emerald (17.7.23)		1·50	6·00
74	10	2s. purple and blue/blue (12.5.22)		16·00	35·00
		a. Red-purple and blue/blue (1926)		7·00	32·00
75		2s. 6d. black and red/blue (17.7.23)		6·50	22·00
76		3s. bright green and violet (12.5.22)		8·00	22·00
77		4s. black and red (12.5.22)		8·00	32·00
78	12	5s. green and red/pale yellow (17.7.23)		28·00	48·00
79	13	10s. green and red/green (1928)		48·00	70·00
		a. Break in scroll	..	£150	
		b. Broken crown and scroll	..	£150	

80	13	£1 purple and black/red (1928)	..	£225	£250
		a. Break in scroll	..	£375	
		b. Broken crown and scroll		£375	
58/80			*Set of* 22	£300 £450
58/80 Optd/Perf "Specimen"		*Set of* 23	£550

(b) Reversion to Die I (*Plate* 23) (1931–32)

81	10	¼d. brown	..	60	6·50
82	11	½d. blue-green (1931)	..	6·00	17·00
83		1d. bright scarlet	..	3·00	10
84	10	1½d. red-brown	..	1·50	1·75
85	11	2½d. bright blue	..	3·50	3·50
86		6d. dull and bright purple		11·00	45·00
87	12	1s. black/emerald	..	24·00	38·00
		a. "D I" flaw	..	£150	
81/7			*Set of* 7	45·00 £100

1935 (6 May). *Silver Jubilee. As Nos.* 114/17 *of Jamaica, but printed by Waterlow. P* 11×12.

88		1d. deep blue and scarlet	..	90	40
89		1½d. ultramarine and grey	..	1·00	60
90		2½d. brown and deep blue	..	1·50	2·50
91		1s. slate and purple	..	5·50	9·00
		j. Kite and vertical log	..	95·00	
		k. Kite and horizontal log	..	£100	
88/91			*Set of* 4	8·00 11·00
88/91 Perf "Specimen"		*Set of* 4	75·00

For illustrations of plate varieties see Omnibus section following Zimbabwe.

1937 (12 May). *Coronation. As Nos.* 118/20 *of Jamaica*.

92		1d. scarlet	..	30	15
93		1½d. buff	..	40	35
94		2½d. bright blue	..	40	45
92/4			*Set of* 3	1·00	85
92/4 Perf "Specimen"		*Set of* 3	55·00

14   15

(Die A)   (Die B)

In Die B the figure "1" has a broader top and more projecting serif.

Broken second "E" in "LEEWARD" (R. 4/1 of right pane) (Pl. 3 ptgs from December 1943 until corrected in June 1949)

Broken lower right scroll (R. 5/12. 1942 ptgs only)

Missing pearl (R. 5/1. 1944 ptgs only)

Gash in chin (R. 2/5. 1942 ptgs only)

1938 (25 Nov)–**51**. *T* 14 (*and similar type, but shaded value tablet,* ½d., 1d., 2½d., 6d.) *and* 15 (10s., £1). *Chalk-surfaced paper* (3d. *to* £1). *P* 14.

(a) Wmk Mult Script CA

95		¼d. brown	..	10	30
		a. Chalk-surfaced paper. Dp brn (13.6.49)	10	20
96		½d. emerald	..	20	20
97		½d. slate-grey (chalk-surfaced paper) (1.7.49)	30	30
98		1d. scarlet (Die A)	..	6·50	90

99		1d. scarlet (*shades*) (Die B) (1940)	..	80	50
	a.	"D I" flaw (9.47)	..	70·00	
	b.	*Carmine* (9.42)	..	60	2·75
	c.	*Red* (13.9.48)..	..	2·50	1·50
	ca.	"D I" flaw	..	80·00	
100		1d. blue-green (*chalk-surfaced paper*) (1.7.49)	..	55	15
	a.	"D I" flaw	..	70·00	
101		1½d. chestnut	..	30	30
102		1½d. yellow-orange and black (*chalk-surfaced paper*) (1.7.49)	..	50	15
103		2d. olive-grey	..	30	30
	a.	*Slate-grey* (11.42)	..	60	2·75
104		2d. scarlet (*chalk-surfaced paper*) (1.7.49)		1·40	30
	a.	*Vermilion* (24.10.51)..	..	10·00	8·00
105		2½d. bright blue	..	4·00	1·10
	a.	*Light bright blue* (11.42)	..	50	40
106		2½d. black and purple (*chalk-surfaced paper*) (1.7.49)		55	15
107		3d. orange	..	30·00	2·00
	a.	Ordinary paper. *Pale orange* (11.42)		40	55
108		3d. bright blue (1.7.49)	..	65	15
109		6d. deep dull purple and bright purple	..	13·00	3·50
	a.	Ordinary paper (8.42)	..	2·75	1·75
	ab.	*Broken "E"*	..	90·00	
	b.	*Purple and deep magenta* (9.47)	..	2·50	1·75
	ba.	*Broken "E"*	..	80·00	
110		1s. black/*emerald*	..	7·50	1·50
	a.	"D I" flaw	..	£150	
	b.	Ordinary paper (3.42)	..	1·50	60
	ba.	*Grey and black/emerald* (8.42)	..	20·00	2·00
	bb.	*Black and grey/emerald* (11.42)	..	£100	11·00
111		2s. reddish purple and blue/*blue*	..	14·00	1·25
	a.	Ordinary paper (3.42)	..	8·50	70
	ab.	*Deep purple and blue/blue* (29.9.47)	..	6·50	1·00
112		5s. green and red/*yellow*	..	32·00	14·00
	a.	Ordinary paper (12.43)	..	23·00	12·00
	ab.	*Broken "E"*	..	£225	
	b.	*Bright green and red/yellow* (24.10.51)	..	32·00	15·00
113		10s. bluish green and deep red/*green*	..	£140	95·00
	a.	Ordinary paper. *Pale green and dull red/green* (26.6.44*)	..	£225	£160
	ae.	Broken lower right scroll	..	£1300	
	b.	Ordinary paper. *Green and red/green* (22.2.45*)	..	90·00	42·00
	c.	Ordinary paper. *Deep green and deep vermilion/green* (17.7.48*)	..	85·00	55·00
	ca.	Missing pearl..	..	£650	

(b) Wmk Mult Crown CA

114		£1 brown-purple and black/*red*	..	£225	£160
	a.	*Purple and black/carmine* (3.42)	..	65·00	35·00
	ae.	Broken lower right scroll	..	£650	£375
	af.	*Gash in chin* ..	..	£500	
	b.	*Brown-purple & blk/salmon* (3.12.43)	..	26·00	22·00
	ba.	Missing pearl	..	£450	
	c.	Perf 13. *Violet & black/scar* (13.12.51)	27·00	30·00	
	ca.	Wmk sideways	..	£2500	
95/114*b*			*Set of 19*	£140	75·00
95/114		Perf "Specimen" ..	*Set of 13*	£400	

* Dates quoted for Nos. 113a/c are earliest known postmark dates. No. 113a was despatched to the Leeward Islands in March 1942, No. 113b in December 1943 and No. 113c in June 1944.

For illustration of Nos. 99a, 99ca, 100a and 110a see above No. 58.

Nos. 96, 98/9 and 99b exist in coils constructed from normal sheets.

1946 (1 Nov). *Victory. As Nos. 141/2 of Jamaica.*

115		1½d. brown	..	15	10
116		3d. red-orange	..	15	10
115/16	Perf "Specimen" ..	*Set of 2*	50·00		

1949 (2 Jan). *Royal Silver Wedding. As Nos. 143/4 of Jamaica.*

117		2½d. ultramarine	..	10	10
118		5s. green	..	3·75	2·75

1949 (10 Oct). *75th Anniv of Universal Postal Union. As Nos. 145/8 of Jamaica.*

119		2½d. blue-black	..	15	10
120		3d. deep blue	..	40	40
121		6d. magenta ..	..	40	30
122		1s. blue-green	..	45	30
119/22		..	*Set of 4*	1·25	1·00

1951 (16 Feb). *Inauguration of B.W.I. University College. As Nos. 149/50 of Jamaica.*

123		3 c. orange and black..	..	20	20
124		12 c. rose-carmine and reddish violet..	..	50	20

1953 (2 June). *Coronation. As No. 153 of Jamaica.*

125		3 c. black and green ..	..	10	35

16 Queen Elizabeth II **17**

1954. (22 Feb). *Chalk-surfaced paper. Wmk Mult Script CA. P 14 (T 16) or 13 (T 17)*

126	16	½ c. brown	..	10	10
127		1 c. grey ..	..	10	10
128		2 c. green	..	10	10
129		3 c. yellow-orange and black	..	10	10
130		4 c. rose-red	..	10	10
131		5 c. black and brown-purple	..	40	10
132		6 c. yellow-orange	..	40	10
133		8 c. ultramarine	..	80	10
134		12 c. dull and reddish purple	..	80	10
135		24 c. black and green	..	80	10
136		48 c. dull purple and ultramarine	..	5·00	2·75
137		60 c. brown and green	..	5·00	2·00

Column 2 (middle):

138	16	$1.20, yellow-green and rose-red	..	4·00	2·75
139	17	$2.40, bluish green and red ..	..	4·25	5·00
140		$4.80, brown-purple and black	..	5·00	6·50
126/40			*Set of 15*	24·00	17·00

The 3 c., 4 c. 6 c., 8 c., 24 c., 48 c., 60 c. and $1.20 have their value tablets unshaded.

The stamps of Leeward Islands were withdrawn and invalidated on 1 July 1956 when the federal colony was dissolved.

Lesotho

(formerly Basutoland)

BASUTOLAND

Stamps of CAPE OF GOOD HOPE were used in Basutoland from about 1876, initially cancelled by upright oval with framed number type postmarks of that colony. Cancellation numbers known to have been used in Basutoland are 133 (Quthing), 156 (Mafeteng), 210 (Mohaleshoek), 277 (Morija), 281 (Maseru), 317 (Thlotse Heights) and 688 (Teyateyaneng).

From 1910 until 1933 the stamps of SOUTH AFRICA were in use. Stamps of the Union provinces are also known used in Basutoland during the early years of this period and can also be found cancelled-to-order during 1932–33.

The following post offices and postal agencies existed in Basutoland before December 1933. Stamps of Cape of Good Hope or South Africa with recognisable postmarks from them are worth a premium. For a few of the smaller offices or agencies there are, as yet, no actual examples recorded. Dates given are those generally accepted as the year in which the office was first opened.

Bokong (1931)	Motsekuoa (1915)
Butha Buthe (1907)	Mount Morosi (1918)
Jonathan's (1927)	Mphotos (1914)
Khabos (1927)	Peka (1908)
Khetisas (1930)	Phamong (1932)
Khukhune (1933)	Pitseng (1921)
Kolonyama (1914)	Qachasnek (1895)
Kueneng (1914)	Qalo (1923?)
Leribe (1890)	Quthing (1882)
Mafeteng (1874)	Rankakalas (1933)
Majara (1912)	Roma Mission (1913)
Makhoa (1932)	Sebapala (1930)
Makoalis (1927)	Seforong (1924)
Mamathes (1919)	Sehlabathebe (1921)
Mapoteng (1925)	Sekake (1931)
Marakabeis (1932)	Teyateyaneng (1886)
Maseru (1872)	Thaba Bosigo (1913)
Maseru Rail (1915?)	Thabana Morena (1922)
Mashai (1929)	Thabaneng (1914)
Matsaile (1930)	Thaba Tseka (1929)
Mekading (1914)	Thlotse Heights (1872)
Mofokas (1915)	Tsepo (1923)
Mohaleshoek (1873)	Tsoelike (1927)
Mokhotlong (1921)	Tsoloane (1918)
Morija (1884)	

For further details of the postal history of Basutoland see *The Cancellations and Postal Markings of Basutoland/Lesotho* by A. H. Scott, published by Collectors Mail Auctions (Pty) Ltd, Cape Town, from which the above has been, with permission, extracted.

PRICES FOR STAMPS ON COVER TO 1945

Nos. 1/19	*from* × 5
Nos. 11/14	*from* × 6
Nos. 15/17	*from* × 10
Nos. 18/28	*from* × 6
Nos. 29/31	*from* × 10
Nos. O1/4	*from* × 4
Nos. D1/2	*from* × 25

CROWN COLONY

1 King George V, Nile Crocodile and Mountains	2 King George VI, Nile Crocodile and Mountains

(Recess Waterlow)

1933 (1 Dec). *Wmk Mult Script CA. P 12½.*

1	1	½d. emerald	..	60	85
2		1d. scarlet	..	60	35
3		2d. bright purple	..	70	35
4		3d. bright blue ..	..	70	60
5		4d. grey ..	..	2·50	6·50
6		6d. orange-yellow	..	3·00	1·50
7		1s. red-orange	..	3·75	4·50
8		2s. 6d. sepia	..	20·00	42·00
9		5s. violet	..	42·00	60·00
10		10s. olive-green ..	..	£100	£110
1/10			*Set of 10*	£150	£190
1/10	Perf "Specimen"	*Set of 10*	£250		

1935 (4 May). *Silver Jubilee. As Nos. 114/17 of Jamaica, but ptd by D.L.R. P 13½×14.*

11		1d. deep blue and carmine	..	45	25
12		2d. ultramarine and grey	..	55	75
	f.	Diagonal line by turret	..	45·00	
	g.	Dot to left of chapel	..	50·00	
13		3d. brown and deep blue	..	3·50	1·00
	g.	Dot to left of chapel	..	75·00	
	h.	Dot by flagstaff	..	75·00	
14		6d. slate and purple	..	3·75	1·25
	g.	Dot to left of chapel	..	85·00	
	h.	Dot by flagstaff	..	85·00	
	i.	Dash by turret	..	85·00	
11/14			*Set of 4*	7·50	3·00
11/14	Perf "Specimen"	*Set of 4*	75·00		

For illustrations of plate varieties see Omnibus section following Zimbabwe.

1937 (12 May). *Coronation. As Nos. 118/20 of Jamaica. P 14.*

15		1d. scarlet	..	35	10
16		2d. bright purple	..	50	70
17		3d. bright blue	..	80	75
15/17			*Set of 3*	1·50	1·40
15/17	Perf "Specimen"	*Set of 3*	55·00		

Tower flaw (R. 2/4)

(Recess Waterlow)

1938 (1 Apr). *Wmk Mult Script CA. P 12½.*

18	2	½d. green	..	30	40
19		1d. scarlet	..	40	15
	a.	Tower flaw ..	..	50·00	
20		1½d. light blue	..	40	40
21		2d. bright purple	..	30	30
22		3d. bright blue ..	..	30	50
23		4d. grey..	..	1·50	2·25
24		6d. orange-yellow	..	50	50
25		1s. red-orange	..	50	60
26		2s. 6d. sepia	..	8·00	5·50
27		5s. violet	..	19·00	8·50
28		10s. olive-green	..	19·00	15·00
18/28			*Set of 11*	45·00	30·00
18/28	Perf "Specimen"	*Set of 11*	£180		

Basutoland

(3)

1945 (3 Dec). *Victory. Stamps of South Africa, optd with T 3, inscr alternately in English and Afrikaans.*

					Un. pair	Used pair
29	55	1d. brown and carmine..	..		20	25
30	56	2d. slate-blue and violet	..		20	30
31	57	3d. deep blue and blue ..	..		20	50
29/31			*Set of 3 pairs*		55	95

4 King George VI	5 King George VI and Queen Elizabeth

6 Queen Elizabeth II as Princess, and Princess Margaret

7 The Royal Family

(Recess Waterlow)

1947 (17 Feb). *Royal Visit. Wmk Mult Script CA. P 12½.*

32	4	1d. scarlet	..	10	10
33	5	2d. green	..	10	10
34	6	3d. ultramarine	..	10	10
35	7	1s. mauve	..	15	10
32/5			*Set of 4*	40	30
32/5	Perf "Specimen"	*Set of 4*	80·00		

1948 (1 Dec). *Royal Silver Wedding. As Nos. 143/4 of Jamaica.*

36		1½d. ultramarine	..	20	10
37		10s. grey-olive	..	28·00	24·00

1949 (10 Oct). *75th Anniv of Universal Postal Union. As Nos. 145/8 of Jamaica.*

38	1½d. blue	..	30	25
39	3d. deep blue	..	1·40	60
40	6d. orange	..	1·50	80
41	1s. red-brown	..	1·25	80
38/41		*Set of 4*	4·00	2·25

1953 (3 June). *Coronation. As No. 153 of Jamaica.*

42	2d. black and reddish purple..	..	15	40

8 Qiloane

9 Mohair (Shearing Angora Goats)

(Recess D.L.R.)

1954 (18 Oct)–58. *Designs as T 8/9. Wmk Mult Script CA. P 11½ (10s.) or 13½ (others).*

43	½d. grey-black and sepia	..	10	10
44	1d. grey-black and bluish green	..	10	10
45	3d. deep bright blue and orange	..	60	10
46	3d. yellow-green and deep rose-red	..	80	20
	a. Yellow-green and rose (27.11.58)		1·75	35
47	4½d. indigo and deep ultramarine	..	70	10
48	6d. chestnut and deep grey-green	..	1·25	15
49	1s. bronze-green and purple	..	1·25	20
50	1s. 3d. brown and turquoise-green	..	8·00	4·00
51	2s. 6d. deep ultramarine and crimson	..	6·00	5·50
	a. Brt ultram & crimson-lake (27.11.58)		17·00	11·00
52	5s. black and carmine-red	..	4·75	8·50
53	10s. black and maroon	..	17·00	22·00
43/53		*Set of 11*	35·00	35·00

Designs: Horiz as T 8—1d. Orange River; 2d Mosuto horseman; 3d. Basuto household; 4½d. Maletsunyane Falls; 6d. Herd-boy with Lesiba. 1s. Pastoral scene; 1s. 3d. Aeroplane over Lancers' Gap; 2s. 6d. Old Fort Centre; 5s. Mission Cave House.

½d. ▬

(19)

20 "Chief Moshoeshoe I"
(engraving by Delangle)

1959 (1 Aug). *No. 45 surch with T 19, by South African Govt Ptr, Pretoria.*

54	½d. on 2d. deep bright blue and orange	..	10	10

(Des from drawings by James Walton. Recess Waterlow)

1959 (15 Dec). *Basutoland National Council. T 20 and similar vert designs. W w 12. P 13 × 13½.*

55	3d. black and yellow-olive	..	20	10
56	1s. carmine and yellow-green	..	25	10
57	1s. ultramarine and red-orange..	..	45	35
55/7		*Set of 3*	80	45

Designs:—1s. Council house; 1s. 3d. Mosuto horseman.

(New Currency. 100 cents = 1 rand)

½c. (23) **1c.** (24) **2c** (25)

2½c (I) **2½c** (II) **3½c** (I) **3½c** (II)

5c (I) **5c** (II) **10c** (I) **10c** (II)

12½c (I) **12½c** (II) **50c** (I) **50c** (II)

25c (I) **25c** (II) **25c** (III)

R1 (I) **R1** (II) **R1** (III)

1961 (14 Feb). *Nos. 43/53 surch with T 23 (½ c.), 24 (1 c.) or as T 25 (others) by South African Govt Printer, Pretoria.*

58	½ c. on ½d. grey-black and sepia		10	10
	a. Surch double		£250	
59	1 c. on 1d. grey-black and bluish green		10	10
60	2 c. on 2d. deep bright blue and orange		10	10
	a. Surch inverted		90·00	
61	2½ c. on 3d. yellow-green and rose (Type I)		10	10
	a. Type II		10	10
	b. Type II inverted		—	£900
62	3½ c. on 4½d. indigo & deep ultram (Type I)		10	10
	a. Type II		2·00	2·50
63	5 c. on 6d. chestnut & dp grey-green (Type I)		10	10
	a. Type II		15	10
64	10 c. on 1s. bronze-green and purple (Type I)		10	10
	a. Type II		60·00	60·00
65	12½ c. on 1s. 3d. brown & turq-green (Type I) ..		15	20
	a. Type II		20	10
66	25 c. on 2s. 6d. bright ultramarine and crimson-lake (Type I)		15	30
	a. Type II		18·00	7·00
	b. Type III		25	50
67	50 c. on 5s. black and carmine-red (Type I)		1·75	2·00
	a. Type II		90	1·25
68	1 r. on 10s. black and maroon (Type I)		18·00	3·75
	a. Type II		8·50	18·00
	b. Type III		3·00	3·50
58/68b		*Set of 11*	4·50	4·50

There were two printings of the 2½ c. Type II, differing in the position of the surcharge on the stamps.
Examples of the 2 c. surcharge are known in a fount similar to Type 24.

26 Basuto Household

27 Protein Foods

(Recess D.L.R.)

1961–63. *As Nos. 43/53 but values in cents as in T 26. Wmk Mult Script CA. P 13½ or 11½ (1 r.).*

69	½ c. grey-black and sepia (as ½d.) (25.9.62)		10	15
	a. Imperf (pair)		£180	
70	1 c. grey-blk & bluish grn (as 1d.) (25.9.62)		10	30
71	2 c. dp brt blue & orange (as 2d.) (25.9.62)		50	85
72	2½ c. yellow-green & deep rose-red (14.2.61)		80	10
	a. Pale yellow-green & rose-red (22.5.62)		1·50	20
73	3½ c. indigo & dp ultram (as 4½d.) (25.9.62)		30	1·00
74	5 c. chestnut and deep grey-green (as 6d.) (10.8.62)		30	45
75	10 c. bronze-green & pur (as 1s.) (22.10.62)		20	20
76	12½ c. brown and turquoise-green (as 1s. 3d.) (17.12.62)		7·50	6·00
77	25 c. deep ultramarine and crimson (as 2s. 6d.) (25.9.62)		2·50	6·00
78	50 c. black & carmine-red (as 5s.) (22.10.62)		4·50	8·00
79	1 r. black and maroon (as 10s.) (4.2.63)		13·00	8·50
	a. Black and light maroon (16.12.63) ..		15·00	12·00
69/79		*Set of 11*	27·00	28·00

(Des M. Goaman. Photo Harrison)

1963 (4 June). *Freedom from Hunger. W w 12. P 14×14½.*

80	27	12½ c. reddish violet	40	15

1963 (2 Sept). *Red Cross Centenary. As Nos. 203/4 of Jamaica.*

81	2½ c. red and black	..	20	10
82	12½ c. red and blue	..	60	50

1964. *As Nos. 70, 72, 74, 76 and 78, but W w 12.*

84	1 c. grey-black and bluish green (11.8.64)		10	20
86	2½ c. pale yellow-green and rose-red (10.3.64)		15	15
88	5 c. chestnut and deep grey-green (10.11.64)		30	40
90	12½ c. brown and turquoise-green (10.11.64)		2·25	1·50
92	50 c. black and carmine-red (29.9.64)..		6·75	10·00
84/92	..	*Set of 5*	8·50	11·00

SELF-GOVERNMENT

28 Mosotho Woman and Child

29 Maseru Border Post

1965 (10 May). *New Constitution. T 28/9 and similar horiz designs. Multicoloured. W w 12. P 14×13½.*

94	2½ c. Type 28	..	15	10
95	3½ c. Type 29	..	20	15
96	5 c. Mountain scene	..	20	15
97	12½ c. Legislative Buildings	..	35	60
94/7		*Set of 4*	80	80

30 I.T.U. Emblem

31 I.C.Y. Emblem

(Des M. Goaman. Litho Enschedé)

1965 (17 May). *I.T.U. Centenary. W w 12. P 11×11½.*

98	30	1 c. orange-red and bright purple	15	10
99		20 c. light blue and orange-brown ..	35	30

(Des V. Whiteley. Litho Harrison)

1965 (25 Oct). *International Co-operation Year. W w 12. P 14½.*

100	31	½ c. reddish purple & turquoise-green	10	10
101		12½ c. deep bluish green and lavender	45	35

32 Sir Winston Churchill and St. Paul's Cathedral in Wartime

(Des Jennifer Toombs. Photo Harrison)

1966 (24 Jan). *Churchill Commemoration. Printed in black, cerise, gold and background in colours stated. W w 12. P 14.*

102	32	1 c. new blue	15	25
103		2½ c. deep green	40	10
104		10 c. brown	60	25
105		22½ c. bluish violet	80	50
102/5		*Set of 4*	1·75	1·00

Basutoland attained independence on 4 October 1966 as the Kingdom of Lesotho.

LESOTHO

INDEPENDENT KINGDOM

33 Moshoeshoe I and Moshoeshoe II

(Des and photo Harrison)

1966 (4 Oct). *Independence. P 12½×13.*

106	33	2½ c. light brown, black and red	..	10	10
107		5 c. light brown, black and new blue ..	10	10
108		10 c. light brown, black and emerald	15	10
109		20 c. light brown, black & bright purple	20	15
106/9		*Set of 4*	45	30

(34)

35 "Education Culture and Science"

1966 (1 Nov). *Stamps of Basutoland optd as T 34. A. Nos. 69/71 and 73/9 (Script CA wmk). B. Nos. 84/92 and unissued 1 r. (wmk 12).*

			A		B	
110		½ c. grey-black and sepia	10	10	†	
111		1 c. grey-blk and bluish grn	10	10	10	10
112		2 c. deep bright blue & orange	60	10	†	
113		2½ c. pale yell-grn & rose-red ..	†		20	10
114		3½ c. ind & dp ultram	30	10	†	
115		5 c. chestnut & dp grey-grn	20	10	20	10
116		10 c. bronze-green and purple	20	10	†	
117		12½ c. brown & turq-green	2·75	35	30	20
118		25 c. deep ultram & crimson ..	40	20	†	
119		50 c. black and carmine-red ..	1·00	65	80	50
120		1 r. black and maroon	1·00	1·75	1·00	75
		a. "LSEOTHO"	—	60·00	—	40·00
		b. Opt double	80·00	—	†	
		ba. Ditto. "LSEOTHO"	—	—	†	
110A/120A	..	*Set of 10*	6·00	3·00		
111B/120B		*Set of 6*			2·25	1·40

(Des V. Whiteley. Litho D.L.R.)

1966 (1 Dec). *20th Anniv of U.N.E.S.C.O. P 14½ × 14.*

121	35	2½ c. orange-yellow and emerald-green	10	10
122		5 c. light green and olive	15	10
123		12½ c. light blue and red..	35	10
124		25 c. red-orange and deep greenish blue	60	25
121/4	..	*Set of 4*	1·10	40

36 Maize

37 Moshoeshoe II

(Des and photo Harrison)

1967 (1 Apr). *Designs as T* **36/7**. *No wmk. P* 14½×13½ (2 r.) or 13½×14½ (*others*).

125	½ c. bluish green and light bluish violet	..	10	10
126	1 c. sepia and rose-red		10	10
127	2 c. orange-yellow and light green		10	10
128	2½ c. black and ochre		10	10
129	3½ c. chalky blue and yellow		10	10
130	5 c. bistre and new blue		10	10
131	10 c. yellow-brown and bluish grey		10	10
132	12½ c. black and red-orange ..		20	10
133	25 c. black and bright blue		75	20
134	50 c. black, new blue and turquoise		4·50	45
135	1 r. multicoloured		1·25	75
136	2 r. black, gold and magenta		1·50	1·75
125/36		*Set of* 12	7·50	3·00

Designs: *Horiz as T* **36**—1 c. Cattle; 2 c. Agaves (wrongly inscr "Aloes"); 2½ c. Basotho Hat; 3½ c. Merino Sheep ("Wool"); 5 c. Basotho Pony; 10 c. Wheat; 12½ c. Angora Goat ("Mohair"); 25 c. Maletsunyane Falls; 50 c. Diamonds; 1 r. Arms of Lesotho. See also Nos. 147/59 and 191/203.

46 Students and University

(Des V. Whiteley. Photo Harrison)

1967 (7 Apr). *First Conferment of University Degrees. P* 14 × 14½.

137	**46**	1 c. sepia, ultram & light yellow-orange	10	10
138		2½ c. sepia, ultram & light greenish blue	10	10
139		12½ c. sepia, ultramarine and rose	10	10
140		25 c. sepia, ultramarine and light violet	15	10
137/40		*Set of* 4	30	15

47 Statue of Moshoeshoe I

(Des and photo Harrison)

1967 (4 Oct). *First Anniv of Independence. T* **47** *and similar triangular designs. P* 14½ × 14.

141	2½ c. black and light yellow-green ..		10	10
142	12½ c. multicoloured		25	10
143	25 c. black, green and light ochre ..		35	15
141/3		*Set of* 3	65	25

Designs:—12½ c. Lesotho flag; 25 c. Crocodile (national emblem).

50 Lord Baden-Powell and Scout Saluting

(Des V. Whiteley. Photo Harrison)

1967 (1 Nov). *60th Anniv of Scout Movement. P* 14 × 14½.

144	**50**	15 c. multicoloured	15	10

51 W.H.O. Emblem and World Map

(Des G. Vasarhelyi. Photo Harrison)

1968 (7 Apr). *20th Anniv of World Health Organization. T* **51** *and similar horiz design. P* 14 × 14½.

145	2½ c. blue, gold and carmine-red ..		15	10
	a. Gold (emblem) omitted			
146	25 c. multicoloured		35	10

Design:—25 c. Nurse and child.

ALTERED CATALOGUE NUMBERS

Any Catalogue numbers altered from the last edition are shown as a list in the introductory pages.

---

53 Basotho Hat

54 Sorghum

1968–69. *As Nos.* 125/36 *and T* **54**, *but wmk* **53** (*sideways on 2 r.*).

147	½ c. bluish green & lt bluish vio (26.11.68)		10	10
	a. *Blue-green and violet* (30.9.69)	..	60	60
148	1 c. sepia and rose-red (26.11.68)		10	10
149	2 c. orange-yellow & lt green (26.11.68)		10	10
	a. *Orange-yellow & yell-grn* (30.9.69)		40	40
150	2½ c. black and ochre (21.10.68)		15	10
	a. *Black and yellow-ochre* (30.9.69)		40	40
151	3 c. chocolate, green & yell-brn (1.8.68)		15	15
152	3½ c. chalky blue and yellow (26.11.68)		15	10
153	5 c. bistre and new blue (22.7.68)		30	10
154	10 c. yell-brn & pale bluish grey (26.11.68)		15	10
155	12½ c. black and red-orange (30.9.69)		60	35
156	25 c. black and bright blue (30.9.69)		1·50	1·00
157	50 c. black, new blue & turquoise (30.9.69)		9·00	1·50
158	1 r. multicoloured (26.11.68) ..		3·50	3·00
159	2 r. black, gold and magenta (30.9.69)		16·00	14·00
147/59	.. ..		28·00	18·00

55 Running Hunters

(Des Jennifer Toombs. Photo Harrison)

1968 (1 Nov). *Rock Paintings. T* **55** *and similar designs. W* **53** (*sideways on 5 c., 15 c.*). *P* 14 × 14½ (5 c., 15 c.) *or* 14½ × 14 (*others*).

160	3 c. yellow-brown. lt blue-green & blackish green		20	10
161	3½ c. greenish yellow, yellow-olive and sepia		25	10
162	5 c. Venetian red, yell-ochre & blackish brn		30	10
163	10 c. yellow, rose and deep maroon.		40	10
164	15 c. light buff, pale olive-yell & blackish brn		70	30
165	20 c. yellow-grn, greenish yellow & blackish brown		85	45
166	25 c. yellow, orange-brown and black		1·00	65
160/6		*Set of* 7	3·25	1·50

Designs: *Horiz*—3½ c. Baboons; 10 c. Archers; 20 c. Eland; 25 c. Hunting scene. *Vert*—5 c. Javelin throwing; 15 c. Blue Cranes.

62 Queen Elizabeth II Hospital

(Des C. R. Househam and G. Drummond. Litho P.B.)

1969 (11 Mar). *Centenary of Maseru (capital). T* **62** *and similar horiz designs. Multicoloured. W* **53** (*sideways*). *P* 14 × 13½.

167	2½ c. Type **62**		10	10
168	10 c. Lesotho Radio Station. . ..		10	10
169	12½ c. Leabua Jonathan Airport ..		10	10
170	25 c. Royal Palace		15	15
167/70		*Set of* 4	30	30

66 Rally Car passing Mosotho Horseman

(Des P. Wheeler. Photo Harrison)

1969 (26 Sept). *Roof of Africa Car Rally. T* **66** *and similar horiz designs. W* **53**. *P* 14.

171	2½ c. yellow, mauve and plum ..		10	10
172	12½ c. cobalt, greenish yellow and olive-grey		15	10
173	15 c. blue, black and mauve ..		15	10
174	20 c. black, red and yellow ..		15	10
171/4		*Set of* 4	45	30

Designs:—12½ c. Rally car on mountain road; 15 c. Chequered flags and mountain scenery; 20 c. Map of rally route and Rally Trophy.

---

71 Gryponyx and Footprints   75 Moshoeshoe I, when a Young Man

(Des Jennifer Toombs. Photo Harrison)

1970 (5 Jan). *Prehistoric Footprints (1st series.) T* **71** *and similar designs. W* **53** (*sideways*). *P* 14 × 14½ (3 c.) *or* 14½ × 14 (*others*).

175	3 c. pale brown, yellow-brown and sepia		30	20
176	5 c. dull purple, pink and sepia		45	30
177	10 c. pale yellow, black, and sepia		60	35
178	15 c. olive-yellow, black and sepia		90	1·00
179	25 c. cobalt and black ..		1·90	2·00
175/9		*Set of* 5	3·75	3·50

Designs: (60 × 23 *mm*)—3 c. Dinosaur footprints at Moyeni. (40 × 24 *mm*)—10 c. Plateosauravus and footprints; 15 c. Tritylodon and footprints; 25 c. Massospondylus and footprints. See also Nos. 596/8.

(Des G. Vasarhelyi. Litho D.L.R.)

1970 (11 Mar). *Death Centenary of King Moshoeshoe I. T* **75** *and similar vert design. W* **53**. *P* 13½.

180	2½ c. pale green and magenta ..		10	10
181	25 c. pale blue and chesnut..		20	20

Design:—25 c. Moshoeshoe I as an old man.

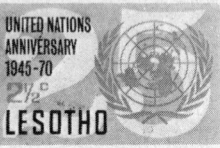
77 U.N. Emblem and "25"

1970 (26 June). *25th Anniv of United Nations. T* **77** *and similar horiz designs. W* **53** (*sideways*). *P* 14½ × 14.

182	2½ c. light pink, light blue and maroon		10	10
183	10 c. multicoloured ..		10	10
184	12½ c. brown-red, cobalt and drab ..		10	10
185	25 c. multicoloured ..		15	15
182/5		*Set of* 4	30	30

Designs:—10 c. U.N. Building; 12½ c. "People of the World"; 25 c. Symbolic dove.

78 Basotho Hat Gift Shop, Maseru

(Des G. Drummond. Litho Questa)

1970 (27 Oct). *Tourism. T* **78** *and similar horiz designs. Multicoloured. W* **53** (*sideways*). *P* 14.

186	2½ c. Type **78**		10	10
187	5 c. Trout fishing		25	10
188	10 c. Pony trekking.. ..		35	10
189	12½ c. Skiing		60	10
190	20 c. Holiday Inn, Maseru ..		60	50
186/90		*Set of* 5	1·60	70

79 Maize   80 Lammergeier

(Des Harrison. Litho Questa)

1971 (4 Jan–1 Apr). *As Nos.* 147/58 *but in new format omitting portrait of Moshoeshoe II, as in T* **79**. 4 *c. and* 2 r. *in new designs. W* **53** (*sideways except 2 r.*). *P* 14.

191	½ c. blue-green and light bluish violet		10	10
192	1 c. brown and orange-red..		10	10
193	2 c. yellow and green		10	10
194	2½ c. black, olive-green and yellow-ochre		10	10
195	3 c. brown, green and yellow-ochre		10	10
196	3½ c. indigo and yellow		10	10
196a	4 c. multicoloured (1.4.71)		20	10
197	5 c. yellow-brown and pale blue		15	10
198	10 c. orange-brown and grey-blue		15	10
199	12½ c. chocolate and yellow-orange		25	30
200	25 c. slate and pale bright blue		60	40
201	50 c. black, pale blue and turquoise-green ..		6·00	3·50
202	1 r. multicoloured ..		2·75	2·25
203	2 r. yellow-brown and ultramarine		2·75	3·00
191/203		*Set of* 14	12·00	9·00

Designs: *Horiz*—4 c. National flag. *Vert*—2 r. Statue of Moshoeshoe I.

For 2 r. value without watermark see No. 401.

(Des R. Granger Barrett. Litho J.W.)

1971 (1 Mar). *Birds. T* **80** *and similar vert designs. Multicoloured.* W **53**. P 14.

204	2½ c. Type 80	..	1·25	10
205	5 c. Bald Ibis	..	2·00	90
206	10 c. Rufous Rockjumper	..	2·75	1·25
207	12½ c. Blue Bustard	..	3·25	1·40
208	15 c. Painted Snipe	..	4·00	2·50
209	20 c. Golden-breasted Bunting	..	4·00	2·50
210	25 c. Ground Woodpecker	..	4·25	2·75
204/10		*Set of* 7	19·00	10·00

81 Lionel Collett Dam

(Des G. Drummond. Litho J.W.)

1971 (15 July). *Soil Conservation. T* **81** *and similar horiz designs. Multicoloured.* W **53** (*sideways*). P 14.

211	4 c. Type 81	..	10	10
212	10 c. Contour ridges	..	10	10
213	15 c. Earth dams	..	25	10
214	25 c. Beaver dams	..	35	35
211/14		*Set of* 4	70	50

82 Diamond Mining

(Des J.W. Litho Questa)

1971 (4 Oct). *Development. T* **82** *and similar horiz designs. Multicoloured.* W **53** (*sideways*). P 14.

215	4 c. Type 82	..	75	20
216	10 c. Pottery	..	30	10
217	15 c. Weaving	..	45	30
218	20 c. Construction	..	55	55
215/18		*Set of* 4	1·90	1·10

83 Mail Cart   84 Sprinting

(Des D. B. Picton-Phillips. Litho Questa)

1972 (3 Jan). *Post Office Centenary. T* **83** *and similar designs.* W **53** (*sideways on* 5, 10 *and* 20 c.). P 14 × 13½ (15 c.) *or* 13½ × 14 (*others*).

219	5 c. pale pink and black	..	15	10
220	10 c. multicoloured	..	15	10
221	15 c. pale drab, light blue and black	..	30	15
222	20 c. multicoloured	..	45	70
219/22		*Set of* 4	95	80

Designs: *Horiz*—10 c. Postal bus; 20 c. Maseru P.O. *Vert*—15 c. Cape of Good Hope 4d. stamp of 1876.

(Des J. W. Litho Questa)

1972 (1 Sept). *Olympic Games. Munich. T* **84** *and similar vert designs. Multicoloured.* W **53**. P 14.

223	4 c. Type 84	..	10	10
224	10 c. Shot putting	..	15	10
225	15 c. Hurdling	..	20	10
226	25 c. Long-jumping	..	30	20
223/6		*Set of* 4	60	35

85 "Adoration of the Shepherds" (Matthias Stomer)

(Des and litho J.W.)

1972 (1 Dec). *Christmas.* W **53** (*sideways*). P 14.

227	**85** 4 c. multicoloured	..	10	10
228	10 c. multicoloured	..	10	10
229	25 c. multicoloured	..	15	20
227/9		*Set of* 3	30	30

86 W.H.O. Emblem	O.A.U. 10th Anniversary Freedom in Unity (87)

(Des. J. Cooter. Litho Questa)

1973 (7 Apr). *25th Anniv of W.H.O.* W **53** (*sideways*). P 13½.

230	**86** 20 c. greenish blue and yellow	30	20

1973 (25 May). *Tenth Anniv of O.A.U. Nos.* 194 *and* 196a/8 *optd with T* **87** *by Govt Printer, Maseru.*

231	2½ c. black, olive-green and yellow-ochre		10	10
232	4 c. multicoloured		10	10
	a. Horiz pair, one without opt	..	£150	
233	5 c. yellow-brown and pale blue		10	10
234	10 c. orange-brown and grey-blue		15	15
231/4		*Set of* 4	35	35

88 Basotho Hat and W.F.P. Emblem

(Des locally; adapted J. Cooter. Litho Format)

1973 (1 June). *Tenth Anniv of World Food Programme. T* **88** *and similar horiz designs. Multicoloured.* W **53** (*sideways*). P 13½.

235	4 c. Type 88	..	10	10
236	15 c. School feeding	..	20	15
237	20 c. Infant feeding	..	20	20
	a. Imperf (pair)			
238	25 c. "Food for Work"	..	25	25
235/8		*Set of* 4	65	60

89 *Aeropetes tulbaghia*	90 Kimberlite Volcano

(Des A. McLeod; artwork G. Drummond. Litho Questa)

1973 (3 Sept). *Butterflies. T* **89** *and similar horiz designs. Multicoloured.* W **53** (*sideways*). P 14.

239	4 c. Type 89	..	30	10
240	5 c. Papilio demodocus	..	40	25
241	10 c. Cynthia cardui	..	80	50
242	15 c. Precis hierta	..	1·10	1·00
243	20 c. Precis oenone	..	1·10	1·00
244	25 c. Danaus chrysippus	..	1·60	1·75
245	30 c. Colotis evenina	..	1·90	2·00
239/45		*Set of* 7	6·50	6·00

(Des PAD Studio. Litho Questa)

1973 (1 Oct). *International Kimberlite Conference. T* **90** *and similar multicoloured designs.* W **53** (*sideways on* 10 *and* 15 c.). P 13½.

246	10 c. Map of diamond mines (*horiz*)		1·00	50
247	15 c. Kimberlite-diamond rock (*horiz*)		1·25	1·00
248	20 c. Type 90	..	1·60	1·50
249	30 c. Diamond prospecting	..	2·50	3·00
246/9		*Set of* 4	5·75	5·50

Type **90** is incorrectly inscribed "KIMERLITE VOLCANO".

91 "Health"	92 Open Book and Wreath

(Des R. Granger Barrett. Litho Questa)

1974 (18 Feb). *Youth and Development. T* **91** *and similar horiz designs. Multicoloured.* W **53** (*sideways*). P 13½.

250	4 c. Type 91	..	10	10
251	10 c. "Education"	..	10	10
252	20 c. "Agriculture"	..	15	10
253	25 c. "Industry"	..	25	20
254	30 c. "Service"	..	30	25
250/4		*Set of* 5	75	55

(Des PAD Studio. Litho Questa)

1974 (7 Apr). *Tenth Anniv of U.B.L.S. T* **92** *and similar vert designs. Multicoloured.* W **53**. P 14.

255	10 c. Type 92	..	10	10
256	15 c. Flags, mortar-board and scroll	..	10	10
257	20 c. Map of Africa	..	10	10
258	25 c. King Moshoeshoe II capping a graduate		15	15
255/8		*Set of* 4	40	30

93 Senqunyane River Bridge, Marakabei

(Des J. Cooter. Litho Questa)

1974 (26 June). *Rivers and Bridges. T* **93** *and similar horiz designs. Multicoloured.* W **53** (*sideways*). P 14½.

259	4 c. Type 93	..	10	10
260	5 c. Tsoelike River and bridge	..	10	10
261	10 c. Makhaleng River Bridge	..	20	10
262	15 c. Seaka Bridge, Orange/Senqu River	..	35	35
263	20 c. Masianokeng Bridge, Phuthiatsana River		40	40
264	25 c. Mahobong Bridge, Hlotse River	..	45	45
259/64		*Set of* 6	1·50	1·25

94 U.P.U. Emblem

(Des R. Granger Barrett. Litho Enschedé)

1974 (6 Sept). *Centenary of Universal Postal Union. T* **94** *and similar horiz designs.* W **53** (*sideways*). P 13½ × 13.

265	4 c. light emerald and black	..	10	10
266	5 c. orange, greenish yellow and black	..	10	10
267	15 c. multicoloured	..	15	15
268	20 c. multicoloured	..	20	20
265/8		*Set of* 4	45	40

Designs:—10 c. Map of air-mail routes; 15 c. Post Office H.Q., Maseru; 20 c. Horseman taking rural mail.
On No. 266 the inscriptions for the airstrips at Makhotlong and Mohlanapeng were transposed in error.

95 Siege of Thaba-Bosiu

(Des Jennifer Toombs. Litho Enschedé)

1974 (25 Nov). *150th Anniv of Establishment of Thaba-Bosiu as Capital. T* **95** *and similar multicoloured designs.* W **53** (*sideways on* 4 *and* 5 c.). P 12½ × 12 (4 *and* 5 c.) *or* 12 × 12½ (*others*).

269	4 c. Type 95	..	10	10
270	5 c. The wreath-laying	..	10	10
271	10 c. Moshoeshoe I (*vert*)	..	25	10
272	20 c. Makoanyane, the warrior (*vert*)	..	65	30
269/72		*Set of* 4	1·00	40

96 Mamokhorong

(Des PAD Studio. Litho Questa)

1975 (25 Jan). *Basotho Musical Instruments. T* **96** *and similar horiz designs. Multicoloured.* W **53** (*sideways*). P 14.

273	4 c. Type 96	..	10	10
274	10 c. Lesiba	..	10	10
275	15 c. Setolotolo	..	15	20
276	20 c. Meropa	..	15	20
273/6		*Set of* 4	40	45
MS277	108 × 92 mm. Nos. 273/6	..	1·25	2·00

97 Horseman in Rock Archway	98 Morena Moshoeshoe I

(Des J. Cooter. Litho Questa)

1975 (15 Apr). *Sehlabathebe National Park. T* **97** *and similar horiz designs. Multicoloured. W* **53** (*sideways*). *P* 14.

278	4 c. Type **97**				15	10
279	5 c. Mountain view through arch				15	10
280	15 c. Antelope by stream				35	30
281	20 c. Mountains and lake				40	35
282	25 c. Tourists by frozen waterfall				50	50
278/82				*Set of* 5	1·40	1·10

(Des G. Vasarhelyi. Litho Questa)

1975 (10 Sept). *Leaders of Lesotho. T* **98** *and similar vert designs. W* **53**. *P* 14.

283	3 c. black and light blue			10	10
284	4 c. black and light mauve			10	10
285	5 c. black and pink			10	10
286	6 c. black and light grey-brown			10	10
287	10 c. black and light claret			20	20
288	15 c. black and light orange-red			25	30
289	20 c. black and dull green			25	25
290	25 c. black and azure			25	40
283/90			*Set of* 8	1·00	1·10

Designs:—4 c. King Moshoeshoe II; 5 c. Morena Letsie I; 6 c. Morena Lerotholi; 10 c. Morena Letsie II; 15 c. Morena Griffith; 20 c. Morena Seeiso Griffith Lerotholi; 25 c. Mofumahali Mantsebo Seeiso, O.B.E.

The 25 c. also commemorates International Women's Year.

99 Mokhibo Dance

(Des PAD Studio. Litho Questa)

1975 (17 Dec). *Traditional Dances. T* **99** *and similar horiz designs. Multicoloured. W* **53** (*sideways*). *P* 14 × 14½.

291	4 c. Type **99**				10	10
292	10 c. Ndlamo				10	10
293	15 c. Baleseli				25	40
294	20 c. Mohobelo				30	45
291/4				*Set of* 4	60	85
MS295	111 × 100 mm. Nos. 291/94				2·75	2·75

100 Enrolment

(Des L. Curtis. Litho Questa)

1976 (20 Feb). *25th Anniv of the Lesotho Red Cross. T* **100** *and similar horiz designs. Multicoloured. W* **53** (*sideways*). *P* 14.

296	4 c. Type **100**			35	10
297	10 c. Medical aid			50	10
298	15 c. Rural service			95	55
299	25 c. Relief supplies			1·25	70
296/9			*Set of* 4	2·75	1·25

101 Tapestry   **102** Football

(Des V. Whiteley Studio. Litho Format)

1976 (2 June). *Multicoloured designs as T* **101**. *W* **53** (*sideways on 2 to 50 c.*). *P* 14.

300	2 c. Type **101**			10	10
301	3 c. Mosotho horseman			20	10
302	4 c. Map of Lesotho			35	10
303	5 c. Lesotho Brown diamond			55	10
304	10 c. Lesotho Bank			30	10
305	15 c. Lesotho and O.A.U. flags			65	20
306	25 c. Sehlabathebe National Park			80	35
307	40 c. Pottery			80	50
308	50 c. Prehistoric rock art			1·50	90
309	1 r. King Moshoeshoe II (*vert*)			1·40	1·75
300/309			*Set of* 10	6·00	3·50

For 25 c., 40 c. and 50 c. values on unwatermarked paper, see Nos. 398/400.

(Des P. Powell. Litho Questa)

1976 (9 Aug). *Olympic Games, Montreal. T* **102** *and similar vert designs. Multicoloured. W* **53**. *P* 14.

310	4 c. Type **102**			10	10
311	10 c. Weightlifting			10	10
312	15 c. Boxing			15	10
313	25 c. Throwing the discus			30	25
310/13			*Set of* 4	55	40

103 "Rising Sun"   **104** Telephones, 1876 and 1976

(Des L. Curtis. Litho Questa)

1976 (4 Oct). *Tenth Anniv of Independence. T* **103** *and similar vert designs. Multicoloured. W* **53**. *P* 14.

314	4 c. Type **103**				10	10
315	10 c. Open gates				10	10
316	15 c. Broken chains				40	20
317	25 c. Aeroplane over hotel				50	35
314/17				*Set of* 4	1·00	55

(Des and litho J.W.)

1976 (6 Dec). *Telephone Centenary. T* **104** *and similar horiz designs. Multicoloured. W* **53** (*sideways*). *P* 13.

318	4 c. Type **104**				10	10
319	10 c. Early handset and telephone-user, 1976				10	10
320	15 c. Wall telephone and telephone exchange				15	15
321	25 c. Stick telephone and Alexander Graham Bell				30	40
318/21				*Set of* 4	55	55

105 *Aloe striatula*   **106** Large-toothed Rock Hyrax

(Des D. Findlay. Litho Walsall)

1977 (14 Feb). *Aloes and Succulents. T* **105** *and similar vert designs. Multicoloured. W* **53** (*inverted*). *P* 14.

322	3 c. Type **105**				20	10
323	4 c. *Aloe aristata*				25	10
324	5 c. *Kniphofia caulescens*				30	10
325	10 c. *Euphorbia pulvinata*				45	10
326	15 c. *Aloe saponaria*				80	40
327	20 c. *Caralluma lutea*				1·10	65
328	25 c. *Aloe polyphylla*				1·60	90
322/8				*Set of* 7	4·25	2·00

(Des D. Findlay. Litho Questa)

1977 (25 Apr). *Animals. T* **106** *and similar horiz designs. Multicoloured. W* **53** (*sideways*). *P* 14.

329	4 c. Type **106**				20	10
330	5 c. Cape Porcupine				25	10
331	10 c. Zorilla (polecat)				40	10
332	15 c. Klipspringer				90	70
333	25 c. Chacma Baboon				1·40	1·10
329/33				*Set of* 5	2·75	1·75

107 "Rheumatic Man"   **108** *Barbus holubi*

(Des C. Abbott. Litho Questa)

1977 (4 July). *World Rheumatism Year. T* **107** *and similar vert designs showing the "Rheumatic Man". W* **53**. *P* 14.

334	4 c. yellow and red				10	10
335	10 c. new blue and deep blue				10	10
336	15 c. yellow and blue-green				10	10
337	25 c. orange-red and black				40	45
334/7				*Set of* 4	75	55

Designs:—10 c. Man surrounded by "pain"; 15 c. Man surrounded by "chain"; 25 c. Man supporting globe.

(Des D. Findlay. Litho Questa)

1977 (28 Sept). *Fish. T* **108** *and similar horiz designs. Multicoloured. W* **53** (*sideways*). *P* 14.

338	4 c. Type **108**				15	10
339	10 c. *Labeo capensis*				30	10
340	15 c. *Salmo gairdneri*				60	35
341	25 c. *Oreodaimon quathlambae*				85	60
338/41				*Set of* 4	1·75	1·00

(109)   **110** Black and White Heads

1977 (7 Dec*). *No.* 198 *surch with T* **109** *by Govt Printer, Maseru.*

342	3 c. on 10 c. yellow-brown and pale bluish grey	1·25	90

*Earliest known date of use.

(Des Jennifer Toombs. Litho Walsall)

1977 (12 Dec). *Decade for Action to Combat Racism. T* **110** *and similar vert designs. W* **53**. *P* 14.

343	4 c. chocolate and mauve			10	10
344	10 c. chocolate and light new blue			10	10
345	15 c. chocolate and light orange			15	15
346	25 c. chocolate and light turquoise-green			25	25
343/6			*Set of* 4	55	45

Designs:—10 c. Jigsaw pieces; 15 c. Cogwheels; 25 c. Handshake.

(Des D. Findlay. Litho Questa)

1978 (13 Feb). *Flowers. Vert designs similar to T* **105**. *Multicoloured. W* **53**. *P* 14.

347	2 c. *Papaver aculeatum*			10	20
348	3 c. *Diascia integerrima*			10	20
349	4 c. *Helichrysum trilineatum*			10	10
350	5 c. *Zaluzianskya maritima*			10	10
351	10 c. *Gladiolus natalensis*			20	20
352	15 c. *Chironia krebsii*			30	40
353	25 c. *Wahlenbergia undulata*			50	1·00
354	40 c. *Brunsvigia radulosa*			85	1·75
347/54			*Set of* 8	2·00	3·50

111 Edward Jenner performing Vaccination   **112** Tsoloane Falls

(Des G. Hutchins. Litho J.W.)

1978 (8 May). *Global Eradication of Smallpox. T* **111** *and similar vert design. Multicoloured. W* **53**. *P* 13.

355	5 c. Type **111**			10	10
356	25 c. Head of child and W.H.O. emblem			30	25

(Des Kobus De Beer Art Studio. Litho Questa)

1978 (28 July). *Waterfalls. T* **112** *and similar vert designs. Multicoloured. W* **53**. *P* 14.

357	4 c. Type **112**			15	10
358	10 c. Qiloane Falls			25	10
359	15 c. Tsoelikana Falls			45	30
360	25 c. Maletsunyane Falls			75	75
357/60			*Set of* 4	1·40	1·10

113 Wright *Flyer*, 1903   **114** *Orthetrum farinosum*

(Des L. Curtis. Litho Harrison)

1978 (9 Oct). *75th Anniv of Powered Flight. T* **113** *and similar horiz design. W* **53** (*sideways*). *P* 14½ × 14.

361	5 c. black, brown-ochre and new blue			10	10
362	25 c. multicoloured			30	20

Design:—25 c. Wilbur and Orville Wright.

(Des D. Findlay. Litho Questa)

1978 (18 Dec). *Insects. T* **114** *and similar vert designs. Multicoloured. W* **53**. *P* 14.

363	4 c. Type **114**			10	10
364	10 c. *Phymateus viridipes*			20	10
365	15 c. *Belonogaster lateritis*			30	30
366	25 c. *Sphodromantis gastrica*			50	65
363/6			*Set of* 4	1·00	1·00

115 Oudehout Branch   116 Mampharoane
in flower

(Des D. Findlay. Litho Questa)

1979 (26 Mar).   *Trees. T* **115** *and similar vert designs showing branches in flower. Multicoloured.* W **53**. P 14.

367	4 c. Type **115**	..	15	10
368	10 c. Wild Olive	..	20	10
369	15 c. Blinkblaar	..	35	70
370	25 c. Cape Holly	..	70	1·40
367/70		*Set of* 4	1·25	2·00

(New Currency. 100 lisente = 1(ma)loti)

(Des D. Findlay. Litho Questa)

1979 (1 June).   *Reptiles. T* **116** *and similar horiz designs. Multicoloured.* P 14. A. *No wmk.* B. W **53** (*sideways*).

			A		B	
371	4 s. Type **116**	..	10	10	10	10
372	10 s. Qoaane	..	20	10	20	10
373	15 s. Leupa	..	30	35	30	60
374	25 s. Masumu	..	60	65	60	1·25
371/4		*Set of* 4	1·10	1·00	1·10	1·75

117 Basutoland 1933 1d.   118 Detail of Painting
Stamp   "Children's Games" by
Brueghel

(Des J.W. Litho Format)

1979 (22 Oct).   *Death Centenary of Sir Rowland Hill. T* **117** *and similar vert designs showing stamps.* P 14.

375	4 s. multicoloured	..	10	10
376	15 s. multicoloured	..	30	20
377	25 s. black, yellow-orange and olive-bistre	..	40	30
375/7		*Set of* 3	70	50
MS378	118 × 95 mm. 50 s. multicoloured		60	80

Designs:—15 s. Basutoland 1962 ½ c. definitive; 25 s. Penny Black; 50 s. 1972 15 c. Post Office Centenary commemorative.

(Des C. Abbott. Litho Questa)

1979 (10 Dec).   *International Year of the Child. T* **118** *and similar vert designs showing details of the painting "Children's Games" by Brueghel.* W **53**. P 14.

379	4 s. multicoloured	..	10	10
380	10 s. multicoloured	..	10	10
381	15 s. multicoloured	..	15	15
379/81		*Set of* 3	30	30
MS382	113 × 88 mm. 25 s. multicoloured (*horiz*) (wmk sideways)		40	45

119 Beer Strainer, Broom and Mat

(Des Kobus de Beer Art Studio. Litho Walsall)

1980 (18 Feb).   *Grasswork. T* **119** *and similar horiz designs. Multicoloured.* W **53** (*sideways*). P 14.

383	4 s. Type **119**	..	10	10
384	10 s. Winnowing Basket	..	10	10
385	15 s. Basotho Hat	..	20	15
386	25 s. Grain storage	..	35	25
383/6		*Set of* 4	60	45

120 Praise Poet

(Des BG Studio. Litho Walsall)

1980 (6 May).   *Centenary of Gun War. T* **120** *and similar horiz designs. Multicoloured.* P 14.

387	4 s. Type **120**	..	15	10
388	5 s. Lerotholi (commander of Basotho Army)		15	10
389	10 s. Ambush at Qalabane	..	20	10
390	15 s. Snider and Martini-Henry rifles	..	40	35
391	25 s. Map showing main areas of action		50	45
387/91		*Set of* 5	1·25	90

121 Olympic Flame, Flags and Kremlin   (**122**)

(Des G. Vasarhelyi. Litho Format)

1980 (20 Sept).   *Olympic Games, Moscow. T* **121** *and similar horiz designs. Multicoloured.* P 14½.

392	25 s. Type **121**	..	25	25
	a. Horiz strip of 5. Nos. 392/6	..	1·10	
393	25 s. Doves, flame and flags	..	25	25
394	25 s. Football	..	25	25
395	25 s. Running	..	25	25
396	25 s. Opening ceremony	..	25	25
392/6		*Set of* 5	1·10	1·10
MS397	110 × 85 mm. 1 m. 40, Ancient and modern athletes carrying Olympic torch		1·10	1·25

Nos. 392/6 were printed together, *se-tenant*, in horizontal strips of 5 throughout the sheet.

1980.   *As Nos. 203 and 306/8, but without wmk.*

398	25 c. Sehlabathebe National Park	..	1·50	
399	40 c. Pottery	..	6·00	
400	50 c. Prehistoric rock art	..	6·00	6·00
401	2 r. Statue of Moshoeshoe I (yellow-brown and ultramarine)		2·50	4·50
398/401		*Set of* 4	14·50	

Two opt types of No. 409:

Type I .   Cancelling bars centred on depth of "M1" (stamps surcharged in individual panes of 25 and from the righthand panes of those surcharged in sheets of 50 (2 panes 5 × 5)).

Type II.   Lower cancelling bar aligns with foot of "M1" (stamps from lefthand panes of those surcharged in sheets of 50).

1980 (20 Oct)–81.   *As Nos. 300/5, 309 and 398/401 surch as T* **122** *or with new figures of value (5 s. (No. 410A), 6, 75 s., 1 and 2 m.).* A. *By typo (locally).* B. *By litho (London).*

(a) W **53** (*sideways on* 2, 3, 6, 10, 40, 50 *and* 75 *s.*)

			A		B	
402	2 s. on 2 c. Type **101**	..	10	10	10	10
403	3 s. on 3 c. Mosotho horseman		10	10	10	10
404	6 s. on 4 c. Map of Lesotho		10	10	10	10
	a. Surch double		†	—	†	
	b. Albino surch		†	—	†	
405	10 s. on 10 c. Lesotho Bank	..	80	10	5·00	5·50
405a	25 s. on 25 c. Sehlabathebe National Park		5·00	5·00	†	
406	40 s. on 40 c. Pottery	..	45	50	45	50
407	50 s. on 50 c. Prehistoric rock art		1·25	—	50	55
408	75 s. on 15 c. Lesotho and O.A.U. flags		70	75	†	
409	1 m. on 1 r. King Moshoeshoe II (I) (Sil.)		95	1·00	†	
	a. Surch double, one inverted		55·00	—	†	
	b. Opt Type II	..	3·75	4·00	†	

(b) No wmk

			A		B	
410	5 s. on 5 c. Lesotho Brown diamond		10	10	10	10
	a. Third surch (Basotho hat and "5 s.") double		—	—	†	
	b. Basotho hat and "5 s." surch albino				†	
	c. Basotho hat and "5 s." omitted		25·00	—	†	
	d. Second surch ("6 s." and bars) albino		28·00		†	
411	10 s. on 10 c. Lesotho Bank		†		10	10
412	25 s. on 25 c. Sehlabathebe National Park		25	30	25	30
	a. Surch double	..	20·00	—	†	
413	40 s. on 40 c. Pottery	..	5·00	5·00	†	
414	50 s. on 50 c. Prehistoric rock art		50	55	†	
415	75 s. on 15 c. Lesotho and O.A.U. flags				70	75
416	1 m. on 1 r. King Moshoeshoe II (Blk. and Sil.)		†		95	1·00
417	2 m. on 2 r. Statue of Moshoeshoe I		1·90	2·00	1·90	2·00
402/17		*Set of* 12	4·50		4·75	

No. 410A is a further surcharge on No. 410B. Initially sheets of No. 410B were locally surcharged "6 s.", but this was later obliterated by a Basotho hat emblem and a further "5 s." surcharge added, both in typography.

The surcharge on No. 416 is similar to that on No. 409 but has the cancelling bars printed in black and the new face value in silver.

On each value except the 5 s. and 1 m. stamps, the design of the surcharge on the local printing is identical to that on the London printing. Stamps from the local printing can easily be identified from those of the London printing as indentations are clearly visible on the reverse of stamps with the typographed surcharge.

It is believed that the local surcharges were not placed on general sale before 1 December 1980. No. 410A did not appear until 20 January 1981.

---

123 Beer Mug   124 Queen Elizabeth
the Queen Mother
and Prince Charles

(Des G. Vasarhelyi (No. MS422), Kobus de Beer Art Studio (others). Litho Format (No. MS422), Questa (others)).

1980 (20 Nov).   *Pottery. T* **123** *and similar horiz designs. Multicoloured.* W **53** (*sideways*). P 14.

418	4 s. Type **123**	..	10	10
419	10 s. Beer brewing pot	..	10	10
420	15 s. Water pot	..	15	15
421	25 s. Pot shapes	..	25	30
418/21		*Set of* 4	50	50
MS422	150 × 110 mm. 40 s. × 4 Wedgwood plaques of Prince Philip; Queen Elizabeth II; Prince Charles; Princess Anne (*each* 22 × 35 *mm*). P 14 × 14½		1·00	1·40

No. MS422 was issued to commemorate the 250th birth anniversary of Josiah Wedgwood.

(Des G. Vasarhelyi. Litho Format)

1980 (1 Dec).   80*th Birthday of Queen Elizabeth the Queen Mother. T* **124** *and similar multicoloured designs.* P 14½.

423	5 s. Type **124**	..	25	25
	a. Horiz strip of 3. Nos. 423/5		1·60	
424	10 s. Queen Elizabeth the Queen Mother		30	30
425	1 m. Basutoland 1947 Royal Visit 2d. commemorative and flags (54 × 44 *mm*)		1·25	1·25
423/5		*Set of* 3	1·60	1·60

Nos. 423/5 were printed together, *se-tenant*, in horizontal strips of 3 throughout small sheets of nine stamps.

125 Lesotho Evangelical Church, Morija

(Des G. Vasarhelyi. Litho Format (75 s., 1 m. 50), Harrison (others))

1980 (8 Dec).   *Christmas. T* **125** *and similar horiz designs. Multicoloured. No wmk* (75 s.) *or* W **53** (*others*). P 14 × 14½.

426	4 s. Type **125**	..	10	10
427	15 s. St. Agnes' Anglican Church, Teyateyaneng		10	10
428	25 s. Cathedral of Our Lady of Victories, Maseru		15	15
429	75 s. University Chapel, Roma	..	45	50
426/9		*Set of* 4	65	60
MS430	110 × 85 mm. 1 m. 50, Nativity scene (43 × 29 *mm*). No wmk. P 14½		1·00	1·25

126 "Voyager" Satellite and Jupiter   127 Greater Kestrel

(Des G. Vasarhelyi. Litho Format)

1981 (15 Mar).   *Space Exploration. T* **126** *and similar horiz designs. Multicoloured.* P 13½ × 14.

431	25 s. Type **126**	..	40	30
	a. Horiz strip of 5. Nos. 431/5		1·75	
432	25 s. "Voyager" and Saturn	..	40	30
433	25 s. "Voyager" passing Saturn	..	40	30
434	25 s. "Space Shuttle" releasing satellite		40	30
435	25 s. "Space Shuttle" launch	..	40	30
431/5		*Set of* 5	1·75	1·40
MS436	111 × 85 mm. 1 m. 40, Saturn		1·75	1·50

Nos. 431/5 were printed together, *se-tenant*, in horizontal strips of 5 throughout the sheet.

(Des G. Vasarhelyi. Litho Format)

1981 (20 Apr–Dec).   *Birds. Multicoloured designs as T* **127**. P 14½.

437	1 s. Type **127**	..	15	10
	a. Perf 13 (12.81)	..	40	10
438	2 s. Speckled Pigeon (*horiz*)	..	15	10
	a. Perf 13 (12.81)	..	55	30
439	3 s. South African Crowned Crane	..	20	10
440	5 s. Bokmakierie Shrike	..	20	10
	a. Perf 13 (12.81)	..	75	30
441	6 s. Cape Robin Chat	..	30	10
442	7 s. Yellow Canary	..	30	10

443	10 s.	Red-billed Pintail (horiz)			40	10
	a.	Perf 13 (12.81)			80	30
444	25 s.	Malachite Kingfisher			1·00	15
445	40 s.	Yellow-tufted Malachite Sunbird (horiz)			1·25	30
446	60 s.	Cape Longclaw (horiz)			1·50	45
447	75 s.	Hoopoe (horiz)			2·25	50
448	1 m.	Red Bishop (horiz)			2·50	1·00
449	2 m.	Egyptian Goose (horiz)			3·50	3·00
450	5 m.	Lilac-breasted Roller (horiz)			6·00	7·00
437/50				Set of 14	18·00	11·50

Nos. 437/41 and 443 exist with different imprint dates below the designs.

Nos. 437/50 exist imperforate and as progressive proofs from stock dispersed by the liquidator of Format International Security Printers Ltd.

For these stamps watermarked w 14 see Nos. 500/13.

128 Wedding Bouquet from Lesotho

(Des J.W. Litho Format)

1981 (22 July). *Royal Wedding.* T **128** *and similar vert designs. Multicoloured.* P 14.

451	25 s.	Type 128			30	40
	a.	Booklet pane. No. 451 × 3 plus printed label			90	
	b.	Booklet pane. Nos. 451/3 plus printed label			1·40	
452	50 s.	Prince Charles riding			55	75
	a.	Booklet pane. No. 452 × 3 plus printed label			1·60	
453	75 s.	Prince Charles and Lady Diana Spencer			75	1·00
	a.	Booklet pane. No. 453 × 3 plus printed label			2·25	
451/3				Set of 3	1·40	1·90

Nos. 451/3 also exist imperforate from a restricted printing (price for set of 3 £6 mint).

Booklet panes Nos. 451a/3a exist part-perforated from stock dispersed by the liquidator of Format International Security Printers Ltd.

129 Prince Charles and Lady Diana Spencer

(Des G. Vasarhelyi. Litho Format)

1981 (5 Sept). *Royal Wedding (2nd issue). Sheet* 115 × 90 mm. P 14½.

MS454	129	1 m. 50, multicoloured			2·75	2·40

No. MS454 also exists imperforate from a restricted printing (price £5 mint).

130 "Santa planning his Annual Visit"

131 Duke of Edinburgh, Award Scheme Emblem and Flags

(Des G. Vasarhelyi. Litho Format)

1981 (5 Oct). *Christmas. Paintings by Norman Rockwell (6 to 60 s.) or Botticelli (1 m. 25).* T **130** *and similar multicoloured designs.* P 13½.

455	6 s.	Type 130			20	10
456	10 s.	"Santa reading his Mail"			30	10
457	15 s.	"The Little Spooners"			35	15
458	20 s.	"Raleigh Rockwell Travels"			45	20
459	25 s.	"Ride 'em Cowboy"			55	25
460	60 s.	"The Discovery"			1·00	75
455/60				Set of 6	2·50	1·40
MS461		111 × 85 mm. 1 m. 25, "Mystic Nativity" (48 × 31 mm). P 13½ × 14			2·00	1·90

(Des G. Vasarhelyi. Litho Format)

1981 (5 Nov). *25th Anniv of Duke of Edinburgh Award Scheme.* T **131** *and similar multicoloured designs.* P 14½.

462	6 s.	Type 131			10	10
463	7 s.	Tree planting			10	10
464	25 s.	Gardening			30	30
465	40 s.	Mountain climbing			50	50
466	75 s.	Award Scheme emblem			85	85
462/6				Set of 5	1·75	1·75
MS467		111 × 85 mm. 1 m. 40, Duke of Edinburgh (45 × 30 mm)			1·60	1·60

132 Wild Cat

(Des G. Vasarhelyi. Litho Format)

1981 (16 Nov). *Wildlife.* T **132** *and similar multicoloured designs.* P 13½ (6, 25 s.) or 14½ (others).

468	6 s.	Type 132			15	10
469	20 s.	Chacma Baboon (44 × 31 mm)			30	30
470	25 s.	Eland			35	35
471	40 s.	Cape Porcupine (44 × 31 mm)			60	60
472	50 s.	Oribi (44 × 31 mm)			75	75
468/72				Set of 5	1·90	1·90
MS473		111 × 85 mm. 1 m. 50, Black-backed Jackal (47 × 31 mm). P 13½ × 14			1·60	1·90

133 Scout Bugler

(Des G. Vasarhelyi. Litho Format)

1982 (5 Mar). *75th Anniv of Boy Scout Movement.* T **133** *and similar horiz designs. Multicoloured.* P 13½.

474	6 s.	Type 133			45	25
	a.	Booklet pane. Nos. 474/8 × 2 and MS479			8·50	
475	30 s.	Scouts hiking			70	50
476	40 s.	Scout sketching			75	60
477	50 s.	Scout with flag			80	65
478	75 s.	Scouts saluting			90	80
474/8				Set of 5	3·25	2·50
MS479		117 × 92 mm. 1 m. 50, Lord Baden-Powell			2·00	2·50

134 Jules Rimet Trophy with Footballers and Flags of 1930 Finalists (Argentina and Uruguay)

(Des G. Vasarhelyi. Litho Format)

1982 (14 Apr). *World Cup Football Championship, Spain.* T **134** *and similar horiz designs showing World Football Cup with players and flags of countries in past finals (Nos. 480/90). Multicoloured.* P 14½.

480	15 s.	Type 134			20	20
	a.	Sheetlet. Nos. 480/91			2·10	
481	15 s.	Jules Rimet Trophy with Czechoslovakia and Italy, 1934			20	20
482	15 s.	Jules Rimet Trophy with Hungary and Italy, 1938			20	20
483	15 s.	Jules Rimet Trophy with Brazil and Uruguay, 1950			20	20
484	15 s.	Jules Rimet Trophy with Hungary and West Germany, 1954			20	20
485	15 s.	Jules Rimet Trophy with Sweden and Brazil, 1958			20	20
486	15 s.	Jules Rimet Trophy with Czechoslovakia and Brazil, 1962			20	20
487	15 s.	Jules Rimet Trophy with West Germany and England, 1966			20	20
488	15 s.	Jules Rimet Trophy with Italy and Brazil, 1970			20	20
489	15 s.	World Cup with Holland and West Germany, 1974			20	20
490	15 s.	World Cup with Holland and Argentina, 1978			20	20
491	15 s.	World Cup and map of World on footballs			20	20
480/91				Set of 12	2·10	2·10
MS492		118 × 93 mm. 1 m. 25, Bernabeu Stadium, Madrid (47 × 35 mm). P 13½			2·00	2·25

Nos. 480/91 were printed together, *se-tenant,* in a sheetlet of 12.

135 Portrait of George Washington

136 Lady Diana Spencer in Tetbury, May 1981

(Des G. Vasarhelyi. Litho Format)

1982 (7 June). *250th Birth Anniv of George Washington.* T **135** *and similar horiz designs. Multicoloured.* P 14 × 13½.

493	6 s.	Type 135			10	10
494	7 s.	Washington with step-children and dog			10	10
495	10 s.	Washington with Indian chief			15	10
496	25 s.	Washington with troops			35	35
497	40 s.	Washington arriving in New York			50	50
498	1 m.	Washington on parade			1·25	1·25
493/8				Set of 6	2·25	2·25
MS499		117 × 92 mm. 1 m. 25, Washington crossing the Delaware			2·00	1·50

1982 (14 June). *As Nos. 437/50 but W* w 14 *(sideways on Nos. 500, 502/5 and 507).*

500	1 s.	Type 127			10	30
501	2 s.	Speckled Pigeon (horiz)			10	30
502	3 s.	South African Crowned Crane			10	30
503	5 s.	Bokmakierie Shrike			10	10
504	6 s.	Cape Robin Chat			10	10
505	7 s.	Yellow Canary			10	10
506	10 s.	Red-billed Pintail (horiz)			15	10
507	25 s.	Malachite Kingfisher			35	30
508	40 s.	Yellow-tufted Malachite Sunbird (horiz)			55	35
509	60 s.	Cape Longclaw (horiz)			80	50
510	75 s.	Hoopoe (horiz)			1·25	85
511	1 m.	Red Bishop (horiz)			1·60	2·00
512	2 m.	Egyptian Goose (horiz)			2·75	4·00
513	5 m.	Lilac-breasted Roller (horiz)			5·50	10·00
500/13				Set of 14	12·00	18·00

(Des Jennifer Toombs. Litho Format)

1982 (1 July). *21st Birthday of Princess of Wales.* T **136** *and similar vert designs. Multicoloured.* W w 14. A. P 13½. B. P 13½ × 14.

				A		B	
514	30 s.	Lesotho coat of arms		50	50	30	30
515	50 s.	Type 136		45	50	75	80
516	75 s.	Wedding picture at Buckingham Palace		75	80	70	70
517	1 m.	Formal portrait		1·00	1·25	1·00	80
514/17			Set of 4	2·40	2·75	2·40	2·75

137 Mosotho reading Sesotho Bible

138 Birthday Greetings

(Des G. Vasarhelyi. Litho Format)

1982 (20 Aug). *Centenary of Sesotho Bible,* T **137** *and similar multicoloured designs.* P 14½.

518	6 s.	Type 137			10	10
	a.	Horiz strip of 3. Nos. 518/20			90	
519	15 s.	Sesotho Bible and Virgin Mary holding infant Jesus			20	20
520	1 m.	Sesotho Bible and Cathedral (62 × 42 mm)			70	80
518/20				Set of 3	90	1·00

Nos. 518/20 were printed together, *se-tenant,* in horizontal strips of 3 throughout the sheet.

(Des G. Vasarhelyi. Litho Questa)

1982 (30 Sept). *Birth of Prince William of Wales.* T **138** *and similar vert design. Multicoloured.* P 14 × 13½.

521	6 s.	Type 138			15	15
	a.	Sheetlet. No. 521 and 522 × 5			4·00	
522	60 s.	Princess Diana and Prince William of Wales			80	80

Nos. 521/2 come from sheetlets of 6 containing one 6 s. and five 60 s. stamps.

139 "A Partridge in a Pear Tree"

(Litho Format)

1982 (1 Dec). *Christmas. "The Twelve Days of Christmas".* T **139** *and similar horiz designs depicting Walt Disney cartoon characters. Multicoloured.* P 11.

523	2 s.	Type 139			10	10
	a.	Horiz pair. Nos. 523/4			10	10
524	2 s.	"Two turtle doves"			10	10
525	3 s.	"Three French hens"			10	10
	a.	Horiz pair. Nos. 525/6			10	10
526	3 s.	"Four calling birds"			10	10
527	4 s.	"Five golden rings"			15	15
	a.	Horiz pair. Nos. 527/8			15	15
528	4 s.	"Six geese a-laying"			10	10

529 75 s. "Seven swans a-swimming" .. .. 1·25 1·25
    a. Horiz pair. Nos. 529/30 .. .. 2·50 2·50
530 75 s. "Eight maids a-milking".. .. 1·25 1·25
523/30 .. .. Set of 8 2·50 2·50
MS531 126 × 101 mm. 1 m. 50, "Nine ladies dancing, ten lords a-leaping, eleven pipers piping, twelve drummers drumming". P 13½ .. 2·25 2·25
  Nos. 523/4, 525/6, 527/8 and 529/30 were each printed in horizontal *se-tenant* pairs throughout the sheet.

140 *Lepista caffrorum*

(Des G. Vasarhelyi. Litho Format)

1983 (11 Jan). *Fungi. T* **140** *and similar horiz designs. Multicoloured. P* 14½.
532 10 s. Type **140** 15 10
    a. Tête-bêche (vert pair) 30 30
    b. Booklet pane. Nos. 532/5 .. 2·50
    c. Booklet pane. Nos. 532/3 .. 55
533 30 s. *Broomeia congregata* 40 40
    a. Tête-bêche (vert pair) 80 80
534 50 s. *Afroboletus luteolus* 85 85
    a. Tête-bêche (vert pair) .. .. 1·60 1·60
535 75 s. *Lentinus tuber-regium* .. .. 1·40 1·40
    a. Tête-bêche (vert pair) .. .. 2·75 2·75
532/5 .. .. Set of 4 2·50 2·50
  Nos. 532/5 were each printed in sheets of 36 stamps plus 4 labels as the fourth horizontal row. The stamps in horizontal rows two, six, eight and ten were inverted, forming vertical *tête-bêche* pairs.

141 Ba-Leseli Dance

(Des J.W. Litho Format)

1983 (14 Mar). *Commonwealth Day. T* **141** *and similar multicoloured designs. P* 14½.
536 5 s. Type **141** 10 10
537 30 s. Tapestry weaving 35 40
538 60 s. Queen Elizabeth II (*vert*).. .. 70 85
539 75 s. King Moshoeshoe II (*vert*) .. 90 1·10
536/9 .. .. Set of 4 1·75 2·25

142 "Dancers in a Trance"
(rock painting from Ntloana Tsoana)

(Des G. Drummond. Litho Format)

1983 (20 May). *Rock Paintings. T* **142** *and similar multicoloured designs. P* 14½.
540 6 s. Type **142** 15 10
541 25 s. "Baboons", Sehonghong 40 35
542 60 s. "Hunters attacking Mountain Reedbuck", Makhetha .. .. 90 1·10
543 75 s. "Eland", Lehaha la Likhomo .. 1·25 1·60
540/3 .. .. Set of 4 2·40 2·75
MS544 166 × 84 mm. Nos. 540/3 and 10 s. "Cattle herding", Sehonghong (52 × 52 *mm*) .. 2·40 3·00

143 Montgolfier Balloon, 1783

(Des J.W. Litho Format)

1983 (11 July). *Bicentenary of Manned Flight. T* **143** *and similar multicoloured designs. P* 14½.
545 7 s. Type **143** 15 10
    a. Booklet pane. Nos. 545/8 .. 3·50
546 30 s. Wright brothers and *Flyer* .. 45 40
547 60 s. First airmail flight 80 75
548 1 m. "Concorde" .. .. .. 2·50 1·60
545/8 .. .. Set of 4 3·50 2·50
MS549 180 × 92 mm. Nos. 545/8 and 6 s. Dornier "228" of Lesotho Airways (60 × 60 *mm*) .. 3·25 2·75

144 Rev. Eugene Casalis

(Des G. Vasarhelyi. Litho Questa)

1983 (5 Sept). *150th Anniv of Arrival of the French Missionaries. T* **144** *and similar horiz designs. Multicoloured. P* 13½ × 14.
550 6 s. Type **144** 10 10
    a. Tête-bêche (vert pair) 10 15
551 25 s. The founding of Morija 30 40
    a. Tête-bêche (vert pair) 60 80
552 40 s. Baptism of Libe 50 70
    a. Tête-bêche (vert pair) .. .. 1·00 1·40
553 75 s. Map of Lesotho .. .. .. 90 1·25
    a. Tête-bêche (vert pair) .. .. 1·75 2·50
550/3 .. .. Set of 4 1·60 2·25
  Nos. 550/3 were each issued in sheets of 20 containing two panes (2 × 5) separated by a vertical gutter. Within these sheets horizontal rows two and four are inverted forming *tête-bêche* vertical pairs.

145 Mickey Mouse and Pluto
Greeted by Friends

(Litho Questa)

1983 (18 Oct). *Christmas. T* **145** *and similar horiz designs showing Disney cartoon characters in scenes from "Old Christmas" (Washington Irving's sketchbook). Multicoloured. P* 14 × 13½.
554 1 s. Type **145** 10 10
555 2 s. Donald Duck and Pluto 10 10
556 3 s. Donald Duck with Huey, Dewey and Louie 10 10
557 4 s. Goofy, Donald Duck and Mickey Mouse 10 10
558 5 s. Goofy holding turkey, Donald Duck and Mickey Mouse 10 10
559 6 s. Goofy and Mickey Mouse 10 10
560 75 s. Donald and Daisy Duck .. .. 1·75 1·00
561 1 m. Goofy and Clarabell .. .. 2·25 1·50
554/61 .. .. Set of 8 4·00 2·50
MS562 132 × 113 mm. 1 m. 75, Scrooge McDuck, Pluto and Donald Duck .. .. .. 3·00 2·50

14 *Danaus chrysippus*

(Des and litho Format)

1984 (20 Jan). *Butterflies. T* **146** *and similar horiz designs. Multicoloured. P* 14.
563 1 s. Type **146** 15 10
564 2 s. *Aeropetes tulbaghia* 15 10
565 3 s. *Colotis evenina* 20 10
566 4 s. *Precis oenone* 20 10
567 5 s. *Precis hierta* 20 10
568 6 s. *Catopsilia florella* 20 10
569 7 s. *Phalanta phalantha* 20 10
570 10 s. *Acraea stenobea* 30 10
571 15 s. *Cynthia cardui* 50 10
572 20 s. *Colotis subfasciatus* 60 10
573 30 s. *Charaxes jasius* 65 20
574 50 s. *Terias brigitta* 85 30
575 60 s. *Pontia helice* 95 35
576 75 s. *Colotis regina* .. .. 1·25 40
577 1 m. *Hypolimnas misippus* .. .. 1·50 70
578 5 m. *Papilio demodocus* .. .. 4·50 4·00
563/78 .. .. Set of 16 11·00 6·00
  Nos. 563/73 and 576 exist imperforate and as progressive proofs from stock dispersed by the liquidator of Format International Security Printers Ltd.

STANLEY GIBBONS STAMP COLLECTING SERIES

Introductory booklets on *How to Start, How to Identify Stamps* and *Collecting by Theme.* A series of well illustrated guides at a low price. Write for details.

147 "Thou Shalt not have Strange
Gods before Me"

(Des G. Vasarhelyi. Litho Format)

1984 (30 Mar). *Easter. The Ten Commandments. T* **147** *and similar vert designs. Multicoloured. P* 13½ × 14.
579 20 s. Type **147** 30 25
    a. Sheetlet. Nos. 579/88 .. 2·75
580 20 s. "Thou shalt not take the name of the Lord thy God in vain" 30 25
581 20 s. "Remember thou keep holy the Lord's Day" 30 25
582 20 s. "Honour thy father and mother" .. 30 25
583 20 s. "Thou shalt not kill" 30 25
584 20 s. "Thou shalt not commit adultery" .. 30 25
585 20 s. "Thou shalt not steal" 30 25
586 20 s. "Thou shalt not bear false witness against thy neighbour" 30 25
587 20 s. "Thou shalt not covet thy neighbour's wife" 30 25
588 20 s. "Thou shalt not covet thy neighbour's goods" 30 25
579/88 .. .. Set of 10 2·75 2·25
MS589 102 × 73 mm. 1 m. 50, Moses with Tablets (45 × 28 *mm*). P 14. .. .. .. 1·50 2·00
  Nos. 579/88 were printed together in small sheets of 12 including 2 *se-tenant* stamp-size labels.

148 Torch Bearer

(Des G. Vasarhelyi. Litho Format)

1984 (3 May). *Olympic Games, Los Angeles. T* **148** *and similar horiz designs. Multicoloured. P* 13½ × 14.
590 10 s. Type **148** 10 10
591 30 s. Horse-riding 30 35
592 50 s. Swimming 50 55
593 75 s. Basketball 70 75
594 1 m. Running .. .. .. 95 1·10
590/4 .. .. Set of 5 2·25 2·50
MS595 101 × 72 mm. 1 m. 50, Olympic Flame and flags .. .. 1·50 2·00

149 Sauropodomorph Footprints

(Des G. Drummond. Litho Format)

1984 (2 July). *Prehistoric Footprints (2nd series). T* **149** *and similar horiz designs. Multicoloured. P* 13½ × 14.
596 10 s. Type **149** 55 20
597 30 s. Lesothosaurus footprints .. .. 1·50 1·50
598 50 s. Footprint of carnivorous dinosaur .. 1·75 1·50
596/8 .. .. Set of 3 3·50 2·75

150 Wells Fargo Coach, 1852

(Des G. Vasarhelyi. Litho Format)

1984 (5 Sept). *"Ausipex" International Stamp Exhibition, Melbourne, and Bicentenary of First Mail Coach Run. T* **150** *and similar horiz designs. Multicoloured. P* 14.
599 6 s. Type **150** 10 10
    a. Sheetlet. Nos. 599 × 4 and No. 603 70
600 7 s. Basotho mail cart, *circa* 1900 .. 10 10
    a. Sheetlet. No. 600 × 4 and No. 603 80
601 10 s. Bath mail coach, 1784 .. .. 10 10
    a. Sheetlet. No. 601 × 4 and No. 603 90
602 30 s. Cobb coach, 1853.. .. .. 30 35
    a. Sheetlet. No. 602 × 4 and No. 603 1·60

603 50 s. Exhibition logo and Royal Exhibition Buildings, Melbourne (82 × 25 mm) .. | 50 | 55
599/603 .. .. Set of 5 | 95 | 1·10
MS604 147 × 98 mm. 1 m. 75, G.B. Penny Black, Basutoland 1934 "OFFICIAL" optd 6d. and Western Australia 1854 4d. with frame inverted (82 × 25 mm) .. .. | 1·60 | 1·75

In addition to the listed sheetlets, Nos. 599/602 also exist in separate sheets of 50. No. 603 only comes from the sheetlets.

151 "The Orient Express" (1900)

(Des Walsall. Litho Format)

1984 (5 Nov). *Railways of the World. T 151 and similar horiz designs. Multicoloured. P 14 × 13½.*
605 6 s. Type 151.. | 40 | 10
606 15 s. German State Railways Class "05" No. 05001 (1935) .. | 45 | 20
607 30 s. Caledonian Railway *Cardean* (1906) | 70 | 45
608 60 s. Santa Fe "Super Chief" (1940) .. | 1·25 | 90
609 1 m. L.N.E.R. "Flying Scotsman" (1934) .. | 1·75 | 1·25
605/9 .. .. Set of 5 | 4·00 | 2·50
MS610 108 × 82 mm. 2 m. South African Railways "The Blue Train" (1972) .. .. | 2·75 | 2·50

152 Eland Calf   **153 Crown of Lesotho**

(Des G. Drummond. Litho Format)

1984 (20 Dec). *Baby Animals. T 152 and similar horiz designs. Multicoloured. P 14 × 13½ (1 m.) or 15 (others).*
611 15 s. Type 152.. | 35 | 20
612 20 s. Young Chacma Baboons | 40 | 25
613 30 s. Oribi calf | 55 | 30
614 75 s. Young Natal Red Hares | 1·25 | 75
615 1 m. Black-backed Jackal pups (46 × 27 mm) | 1·50 | 1·25
611/15 .. .. Set of 5 | 3·50 | 2·50

(Des G. Vasarhelyi. Litho Format)

1985 (30 Jan). *Silver Jubilee of King Moshoeshoe II. T 153 and similar vert designs. Multicoloured. P 15.*
616 6 s. Type 153.. | 10 | 10
617 30 s. King Moshoeshoe in 1960 | 20 | 30
618 75 s. King Moshoeshoe in traditional dress, 1985 | 50 | 65
619 1 m. King Moshoeshoe in uniform, 1985 | 70 | 90
616/19 .. .. Set of 4 | 1·25 | 1·75

154 Christ condemned to Death

(Des G. Vasarhelyi. Litho Format)

1985 (8 Mar). *Easter. The Stations of the Cross. T 154 and similar vert designs. Multicoloured. P 11.*
620 20 s. Type 154.. | 15 | 15
a. Sheetlet. Nos. 620/33 .. | 1·75 |
621 20 s. Christ carrying the Cross | 15 | 15
622 20 s. Falling for the first time | 15 | 15
623 20 s. Christ meets Mary | 15 | 15
624 20 s. Simon of Cyrene helping to carry the Cross | 15 | 15
625 20 s. Veronica wiping the face of Christ | 15 | 15
626 20 s. Christ falling a second time | 15 | 15
627 20 s. Consoling the women of Jerusalem | 15 | 15
628 20 s. Falling for the third time | 15 | 15
629 20 s. Christ being stripped | 15 | 15
630 20 s. Christ nailed to the Cross | 15 | 15
631 20 s. Dying on the Cross | 15 | 15
632 20 s. Christ taken down from the Cross | 15 | 15
633 20 s. Christ being laid in the sepulchre | 15 | 15
620/33 .. .. Set of 14 | 1·75 | 1·75
MS634 138 × 98 mm. 2 m. "The Crucifixion" (Mathias Grünewald). P 13½×14 .. | 2·50 | 3·00
Nos. 620/33 were printed together, *se-tenant*, in a sheetlet of 14 stamps with one stamp-sized label which appears in the central position.

155 Duchess of York with Princess Elizabeth, 1931

(Des G. Vasarhelyi. Litho Format)

1985 (30 May). *Life and Times of Queen Elizabeth the Queen Mother. T 155 and similar multicoloured designs. P 13½ × 14.*
635 10 s. Type 155.. | 15 | 10
636 30 s. The Queen Mother in 1975 | 50 | 50
637 60 s. Queen Mother with Queen Elizabeth and Princess Margaret, 1980 | 80 | 80
638 2 m. Four generations of Royal Family at Prince Henry's christening, 1984 | 3·00 | 3·00
635/8 .. .. Set of 4 | 4·00 | 4·00
MS639 139 × 98 mm. 2 m. Queen Elizabeth with the Princess of Wales and her children at Prince Henry's christening (37 × 50 mm) .. | 2·75 | 2·75

156 B.M.W. "732i"   **157 American Cliff Swallow**

(Litho Format)

1985 (10 June). *Century of Motoring. T 156 and similar multicoloured designs. P 14 × 13½.*
640 6 s. Type 156.. | 25 | 15
641 10 s. Ford "Crown Victoria" .. | 35 | 15
642 30 s. Mercedes-Benz "500SE" | 75 | 50
643 90 s. Cadillac "Eldorado Biarritz" | 2·00 | 2·00
644 2 m. Rolls-Royce "Silver Spirit" | 3·00 | 3·25
640/4 .. .. Set of 5 | 5·75 | 5·50
MS645 139 × 98 mm. 2 m. Rolls-Royce "Silver Ghost Tourer", 1907 (37 × 50 mm). P 13½×14 .. | 4·25 | 4·25
Nos. 640/5 exist imperforate from stock dispersed by the liquidator of Format International Security Printers Ltd.

(Litho Format)

1985 (5 Aug). *Birth Bicentenary of John J. Audubon (ornithologist). T 157 and similar multicoloured designs showing original paintings. P 15.*
646 5 s. Type 157.. | 30 | 15
647 6 s. Great Crested Grebe (horiz) | 30 | 15
648 10 s. Vesper Sparrow (horiz) .. | 45 | 15
649 30 s. Greenshank (horiz) | 1·00 | 55
650 60 s. Stilt Sandpiper (horiz) | 1·75 | 1·75
651 2 m. Glossy Ibis (horiz) | 3·25 | 3·50
646/51 .. .. Set of 6 | 6·50 | 5·75
Nos. 646/51 were reissued in February 1986 in sheetlets containing five stamps and one label.

158 Two Youths Rock-climbing   **159 U.N. (New York) 1951 1 c. Definitive and U.N. Flag**

(Des Walsall. Litho Format)

1985 (26 Sept). *International Youth Year and 75th Anniv of Girl Guide Movement. T 158 and similar vert designs. Multicoloured. P 15.*
652 10 s. Type 158.. | 20 | 10
653 30 s. Young technician in hospital laboratory | 50 | 40
654 75 s. Three guides on parade.. | 1·00 | 1·00
655 2 m. Guide saluting .. | 2·40 | 2·75
652/5 .. .. Set of 4 | 3·75 | 3·75
MS656 138 × 98 mm. 2 m. "Olave, Lady Baden-Powell" (Grace Wheatley) (37 × 50 mm). P 13½×14 | 2·40 | 2·75

(Des G. Vasarhelyi. Litho Format)

1985 (15 Oct). *40th Anniv of United Nations Organization. T 159 and similar designs. P 15.*
657 10 s. multicoloured | 25 | 10
658 30 s. multicoloured | 60 | 35
659 50 s. multicoloured | 95 | 65
660 2 m. black and bronze-green.. | 5·00 | 3·25
657/60 .. .. Set of 4 | 5·75 | 3·75
Designs: Vert—30 s. Ha Sofonia Earth Satellite Station; 2 m. Maimonides (physician, philosopher and scholar). Horiz—50 s. Lesotho Airways aircraft at Maseru Airport.

160 Cosmos   **160a Mrs. Jumbo and Baby Dumbo**

(Des G. Drummond. Litho Format)

1985 (11 Nov). *Wild Flowers. T 160 and similar vert designs. Multicoloured. P 15.*
661 6 s. Type 160.. | 40 | 15
662 10 s. Small Agapanthus | 55 | 15
663 30 s. Pink Witchweed.. | 1·10 | 50
664 60 s. Small Iris | 1·75 | 1·25
665 90 s. Wild Geranium or Cranesbill | 2·40 | 2·00
666 1 m. Large Spotted Orchid | 3·75 | 3·75
661/6 .. .. Set of 6 | 9·00 | 7·00

(Des Walt Disney Productions. Litho Questa)

1985 (2 Dec). *150th Birth Anniv of Mark Twain. T 160a and similar vert designs showing Walt Disney cartoon characters illustrating various Mark Twain quotations. Multicoloured. P 11.*
667 6 s. Type 160a .. | 40 | 15
668 50 s. Uncle Scrooge and Goofy reading newspaper | 1·25 | 80
669 90 s. Winnie the Pooh, Tigger, Piglet and Owl | 1·75 | 1·40
670 1 m. 50, Goofy at ship's wheel | 2·75 | 2·25
667/70 .. .. Set of 4 | 5·50 | 4·25
MS671 127 × 102 mm. 1 m. 25, Mickey Mouse as astronaut. P 13½×14 | 4·00 | 2·75
No. 669 was printed in sheetlets of 8 stamps.

160b Donald Duck as the Tailor   **161 Male Lammergeier on Watch**

(Des Walt Disney Productions. Litho Format)

1985 (2 Dec). *Birth Bicentenaries of Grimm Brothers (folklorists). T 160b and similar vert designs showing Walt Disney cartoon characters in scenes from "The Wishing Table". Multicoloured. P 11.*
672 10 s. Type 160b .. | 35 | 15
673 60 s. The second son (Dewey) with magic donkey and gold coins .. | 1·25 | 75
674 75 s. The eldest son (Huey) with wishing table laden with food | 1·50 | 90
675 1 m. The innkeeper stealing the third son's (Louie) magic cudgel | 2·00 | 1·50
672/5 .. .. Set of 4 | 4·50 | 3·00
MS676 127 × 102 mm. 1 m. 50, The tailor and eldest son with wishing table. P 13½×14 | 3·00 | 3·50
No. 673 was printed in sheetlets of 8 stamps.

(Des G. Drummond. Litho Format)

1986 (20 Jan). *Flora and Fauna of Lesotho. T 161 and similar vert designs. Multicoloured. P 15.*
677 7 s. Type 161.. | 60 | 15
678 9 s. Prickly Pear | 60 | 15
679 12 s. Stapelia | 60 | 15
680 15 s. Pair of Lammergeiers | 1·50 | 35
681 35 s. Pig's Ears | 1·10 | 50
682 50 s. Male Lammergeier in flight | 2·50 | 1·60
683 1 m. Adult and juvenile Lammergeiers | 3·50 | 3·50
684 2 m. Columnar cereus | 3·75 | 4·00
677/84 .. .. Set of 8 | 13·00 | 9·25
MS685 125 × 106 mm. 2 m. Verreaux's Eagle | 6·00 | 7·00

162 Two Players chasing Ball   **162a Galileo and 200-inch Hale Telescope at Mt Palomar Observatory, California**

(Des Lori Anzalone. Litho Questa)

1986 (17 Mar). *World Cup Football Championship, Mexico. T* **162** *and similar vert designs. Multicoloured. P* 14.
686	35 s. Type **162**..	1·00	50
687	50 s. Goalkeeper saving goal.	1·50	1·25
688	1 m. Three players chasing ball	2·75	2·50
689	2 m. Two players competing for ball	4·50	4·50
686/9	*Set of* 4	8·75	8·00
MS690	104×74 mm. 3 m. Player heading ball..	8·50	8·50

(Des W. Hanson. Litho Questa)

1986 (5 Apr). *Appearance of Halley's Comet. T* **162***a and similar horiz designs. Multicoloured. P* 14.
691	9 s. Type **162***a*	50	15
692	15 s. Halley's Comet and "Pioneer Venus 2" spacecraft	75	20
693	70 s. Halley's Comet of 684 A.D. (from Nuremberg Chronicle, 1493)..	1·60	1·25
694	3 m. Comet and landing of William the Conqueror, 1066	4·00	4·50
691/4	*Set of* 4	6·25	5·50
MS695	101×70 mm. 4 m. Halley's Comet over Lesotho	6·00	6·50

Nos. 691/3 show the face value followed by "S". Examples of these stamps without this currency abbreviation were prepared, but not issued.

163 International Year of the Child Gold Coin

163a Princess Elizabeth in Pantomime

(Litho Format)

1986 (Apr). *First Anniv of New Currency* (1980). *T* **163** *and similar horiz designs. Multicoloured. P* 13½×14.
696	30 s. Type **163**..	6·50	5·50
	a. Horiz strip of 5. Nos. 696/700..	30·00	
697	30 s. Five maloti banknote	6·50	5·50
698	30 s. Fifty lisente coin	6·50	5·50
699	30 s. Ten maloti banknote	6·50	5·50
700	30 s. One sente coin	6·50	5·50
696/700	*Set of* 5	30·00	25·00

Nos. 696/700 were printed together, *se-tenant*, in horizontal strips of 5 throughout the sheet.

These stamps were prepared in 1980, but were not issued at that time. Due to increased postal rates a severe shortage of 30 s. stamps occurred in 1986 and Nos. 696/700 were sold for postal purposes from mid-April until early August.

(Des L. Nardo. Litho Questa)

1986 (21 Apr). *60th Birthday of Queen Elizabeth II. T* **163***a and similar vert designs. P* 14.
701	90 s. black and yellow..	60	60
702	1 m. multicoloured	65	65
703	2 m. multicoloured	1·40	1·40
701/3	*Set of* 3	2·40	2·40
MS704	119×85 mm. 4 m. black and grey-brown	3·00	3·50

Designs:— 1 m. Queen at Windsor Horse Show, 1971; 2 m. At Royal Festival Hall, 1971; 4 m. Princess Elizabeth in 1934.

163b Statue of Liberty and Bela Bartok (composer)

(Des J. Iskowitz. Litho Questa)

1986 (5 May). *Centenary of Statue of Liberty. T* **163***b and similar horiz designs showing the Statue of Liberty and immigrants to the U.S.A. Multicoloured. P* 14.
705	15 s. Type **163***b*..	75	20
706	35 s. Felix Adler (philosopher)..	75	30
707	1 m. Victor Herbert (composer)	2·50	1·50
708	3 m. David Niven (actor)..	3·50	3·50
705/8	*Set of* 4	6·75	5·00
MS709	103×74 mm. 3 m. Statue of Liberty (*vert*)	5·00	5·50

163c Mickey Mouse and Goofy as Japanese Mail Runners

(Des Walt Disney Productions. Litho Format)

1986 (25 May). *"Ameripex" International Stamp Exhibition, Chicago. T* **163***c and similar horiz designs showing Walt Disney cartoon characters delivering mail. Multicoloured. P* 11.
710	15 s. Type **163***c*	40	20
711	35 s. Mickey Mouse and Pluto with mail sledge	70	30
712	1 m. Goofy as postman riding Harley-Davidson motorcycle..	1·50	1·25
713	2 m. Donald Duck operating railway mail-bag apparatus..	2·25	2·00
710/13	*Set of* 4	4·25	3·25
MS714	127×101 mm. 4 m. Goofy driving mail to aircraft. P 14×13½	6·00	6·00

9s (164) **9**s (165) **15**s (166) **35**s (167) **35s** (167a)

35s
Small "s"

Nos. 720a, 720ba, 721a, 721ca. Occurs eleven times in the sheet of 40 on R. 1/5, 1/6, 1/8, 1/9, 2/6, 2/7, 2/8, 3/5, 4/4, 4/6 and 4/8 for Nos. 720a and 720ba or R. 1/4, 2/4, 4/4, 5/4, 6/4, 7/1, 7/4, 9/1, 9/3, 10/1 and 10/2 for Nos. 721a and 721ca.
No. 728a. Occurs thirteen times in the sheet of 49 on R. 6/2 to 7 and on all positions in Row 7.

9s (168) **35**s (169) **20**s (170)

1986 (6 June)–88. *Various stamps surch* (*a*) *As T* **164***/7a by Lesotho Ads, Maseru.* (i) *On Nos.* 440, 447, 500/1, 506/7 *and* 509.
715	9 s. on 10 s. Red-billed Pintail (*horiz*) (No. 506) (Type 164)	1·25	1·25
	a. Surch on No. 443 ("1982" imprint date)	2·25	2·25
	b. Surch double..	†	—
	c. Surch double, one inverted..	†	—
716	15 s. on 1 s. Type 127 (No. 500) (22.8.86)	4·00	3·00
	a. Surch on No. 437 ("1982" imprint date)	£110	
	b. Surch on No. 437a	5·00	6·00
717	15 s. on 2 s. Speckled Pigeon (*horiz*) (22.8.86)	4·00	4·50
	a. Surch double	60·00	
718	15 s. on 5 s. Bokmakierie Shrike ("1982" imprint date)	40	35
719	15 s. on 60 s. Cape Longclaw (*horiz*) (No. 509) (22.8.86)	20	10
	a. Surch on No. 446	60	30
720	35 s. on 25 s. Malachite Kingfisher (No. 507) (9.87)	15·00	20·00
	a. Small "s"	32·00	35·00
	b. Surch on No. 444	50·00	50·00
	ba. Small "s"	£100	£100
721	35 s. on 75 s. Hoopoe (*horiz*) (No. 447) (Type 167) (9.87)	16·00	16·00
	a. Small "s"	32·00	32·00
	b. Surch double	55·00	
	c. Surch on No. 510	£110	95·00
	ca. Small "s"	£200	
721*d*	35 s. on 75 s. Hoopoe (*horiz*) (No. 447) (Type 167*a*) (1.88)	75·00	

(ii) *On Nos.* 563/5, 567, 573 *and* 575/6
722	9 s. on 30 s. *Charaxes jasius* (Type 164) (1.7.86)	15	10
	a. Surch with Type 165	6·50	4·50
	ab. Surch double	†	—
723	9 s. on 60 s. *Pontia helice* (Type 165) (1.7.86)	4·00	4·00
	a. Surch double	50·00	
	b. Surch double, one inverted..	50·00	
724	15 s. on 1 s. Type 146 (25.6.86)	2·75	2·75
725	15 s. on 2 s. *Aeropetes tulbaghia* (25.6.86)	20	20
726	15 s. on 3 s. *Colotis evenina* (25.6.86)	20	20
727	15 s. on 5 s. *Precis hierta* (14.8.87)	20	20
	a. Surch double	32·00	
728	35 s. on 75 s. *Colotis regina* (15.8.86)	35	35
	a. Small "s"	1·50	1·50

(*b*) *As T* **168***/70 by Epic Printers, Maseru.* (i) *On Nos.* 440 *and* 444
729	9 s. on 5 s. Bokmakierie Shrike ("1982" imprint date) (30.12.87)	15	20
730	16 s. on 25 s. Malachite Kingfisher (No. 444) (3.88)	1·00	1·00
	a. Surch on No. 507	£225	
731	35 s. on 25 s. Malachite Kingfisher (No. 444) (15.12.87)	60	60
	a. Surch on No. 507	13·00	10·00

(ii) *On Nos.* 566 *and* 569
732	20 s. on 4 s. *Precis oenone* (30.12.87)	10	10
	a. Surch double, one inverted	12·00	90·00
733	40 s. on 7 s. *Phalanta phalantha* (30.12.87)	15	20

(iii) *On No.* 722
734	3 s. on 9 s. on 30 s. *Charaxes jasius* (2.2.88)	15	15
	a. Surch Type 164 double..	†	—
735	7 s. on 9 s. on 30 s. *Charaxes jasius* (2.2.88)	25	25
715/35	*Set of* 21	45·00	50·00

NEW INFORMATION
The editor is always interested to correspond with people who have new information that will improve or correct the Catalogue.

170a Prince Andrew and Miss Sarah Ferguson

171 Basotho Pony and Rider

(Des D. Miller. Litho Questa)

1986 (23 July). *Royal Wedding. T* **170***a and similar vert designs. Multicoloured. P* 14.
736	50 s. Type **170***a*..	40	40
737	1 m. Prince Andrew	70	70
738	3 m. Prince Andrew piloting helicopter	2·00	2·00
736/8	*Set of* 3	2·75	2·75
MS739	88×88 mm. 4 m. Prince Andrew and Miss Sarah Ferguson (*different*)	5·00	5·00

(Des B. Bundock. Litho Format)

1986 (3 Oct). *20th Anniv of Independence. T* **171** *and similar horiz designs. Multicoloured. P* 15.
740	9 s. Type **171**..	30	10
741	15 s. Basotho woman spinning mohair	40	15
742	35 s. Crossing river by rowing boat..	55	30
743	3 m. Thaba Tseka Post Office	2·75	3·00
740/3	*Set of* 4	3·50	3·25
MS744	109×78 mm. 4 m. King Moshoeshoe I..	6·50	7·00

171a Chip n'Dale pulling Christmas Cracker

172 Rally Car

(Des Walt Disney Co. Litho Format)

1986 (4 Nov). *Christmas. T* **171***a and similar vert designs showing Walt Disney cartoon characters. Multicoloured. P* 11.
745	15 s. Type **171***a*	30	15
746	35 s. Mickey and Minnie Mouse..	55	30
747	1 m. Pluto pulling Christmas taffy..	1·25	1·25
748	2 m. Aunt Matilda baking	2·00	2·00
745/8	*Set of* 4	3·75	3·25
MS749	126×102 mm. 5 m. Huey and Dewey with gingerbread house. P 13½×14	5·00	5·50

(Litho Questa)

1987 (28 Apr). *Roof of Africa Motor Rally. T* **172** *and similar vert designs. Multicoloured. P* 14.
750	9 s. Type **172**..	20	10
751	15 s. Motorcyclist	25	15
752	35 s. Motorcyclist (*different*)..	45	30
753	4 m. Rally car (*different*)..	3·00	3·00
750/3	*Set of* 4	3·50	3·25

173 Lawn Tennis

174 Isaac Newton and Reflecting Telescope

(Des Y. Berry. Litho Questa)

1987 (29 May). *Olympic Games, Seoul* (1988) (*1st issue*). *T* **173** *and similar vert designs. Multicoloured. P* 14.
754	9 s. Type **173**..	20	10
755	15 s. Judo	20	15
756	20 s. Athletics..	25	20
757	35 s. Boxing	40	30
758	1 m. Diving	1·10	1·25
759	3 m. Ten-pin bowling	2·50	3·00
754/9	*Set of* 6	4·25	4·50
MS760	Two sheets, each 75×105 mm. (*a*) 2 m. Lawn tennis (*different*). (*b*) 4 m. Football		
	Set of 2 sheets	3·25	3·75

Nos. 754/60 incorrectly show the Lesotho flag with white field and emblem at top right.
Similar stamps, with face values of 5, 10, 25, 40, 50 s., 3 m. 50 and a 4 m. miniature sheet showing the correct flag with white field and emblem at top left, were placed on philatelic sale from 30 November 1987. They were not, however, according to the Lesotho Philatelic Bureau, sold through post offices and agencies for postal purposes (*Price for set of 6 £2.40, mint; miniature sheet £2.75 mint*).
See also Nos. 838/42.

(Des Mary Walters. Litho Format)

1987 (30 June). *Great Scientific Discoveries. T* **174** *and similar horiz designs. Multicoloured. P* 15.

761	5 s. Type **174**..	15	10
762	9 s. Alexander Graham Bell and first telephone	15	15
763	75 s. Robert Goddard and liquid fuel rocket..	55	60
764	4 m. Chuck Yeager and "X-1" rocket plane ..	2·50	3·00
761/4	*Set of 4*	3·00	3·50
MS765	98×68 mm. 4 m. "Mariner 10" spacecraft	2·25	2·75

175 Grey Rhebuck

176 Scouts hiking

(Des G. Drummond. Litho Format)

1987 (14 Aug). *Flora and Fauna. T* **175** *and similar multicoloured designs. P* 15.

766	5 s. Type **175**..	..	..	30	15
767	9 s. Cape Clawless Otter	..	..	30	15
768	15 s. Cape Grey Mongoose	..	..	40	20
769	20 s. Free State Daisy (*vert*) ..		..	45	20
770	35 s. River Bells (*vert*)	..		60	30
771	1 m. Turkey Flower (*vert*)	..	..	1·50	1·50
772	2 m. Sweet Briar (*vert*)	..	..	2·25	2·50
773	3 m. Mountain Reedbuck	..	..	2·75	3·00
766/73		*Set of 8*		7·75	7·25
MS774	114×98 mm. (a) 2 m. Pig-Lily (*vert*). (b) 4 m. Cape Wildebeest	*Set of 2 sheets*		3·75	4·25

(Des Mary Walters. Litho Questa)

1987 (10 Sept). *World Scout Jamboree, Australia. T* **176** *and similar vert designs. Multicoloured. P* 14.

775	9 s. Type **176**..		..	40	20
776	15 s. Scouts playing football ..	..	..	45	20
777	35 s. Kangaroos	..	..	60	30
778	75 s. Scout saluting ..	..	..	1·25	75
779	4 m. Australian scout windsurfing ..	..		3·50	3·75
775/9		*Set of 5*		5·75	4·75
MS780	96×66 mm. 4 m. Outline map and flag of Australia ..	..		3·00	3·50

177 Spotted Trunkfish and Columbus' Fleet

178 "Madonna and Child" (detail)

(Des I. MacLaury. Litho Questa)

1987 (14 Dec). *500th Anniv of Discovery of America by Columbus (1992). T* **177** *and similar horiz designs. Multicoloured. P* 14.

781	9 s. Type **177**..	..	..	20	15
782	15 s. Green Turtle and ships..	..	..	25	15
783	35 s. Columbus watching Common Dolphins from ship			40	30
784	5 m. White-tailed Tropic Bird and fleet at sea			3·50	4·00
781/4		*Set of 4*		4·00	4·25
MS785	105×76 mm. 4 m. *Santa Maria* and Cuban Amazon in flight ..	..		3·25	3·50

No. 782 is inscribed "Carribbean" in error.

(Litho Questa)

1987 (21 Dec). *Christmas. T* **178** *and similar vert designs showing religious paintings by Raphael. Multicoloured. P* 14.

786	9 s. Type **178**..		..	25	10
787	15 s. "Marriage of the Virgin"	..		35	15
788	35 s. "Coronation of the Virgin" (detail)		70	35
789	90 s. "Madonna of the Chair"	..		1·75	1·75
786/9	..	..	*Set of 4*		2·75	2·10
MS790	75×100 mm. 3 m. "Madonna and Child enthroned with Five Saints" (detail)			2·50	3·00

179 Lesser Pied Kingfisher   (180)

(Des G. Drummond. Litho Format)

1988 (5 Apr). *Birds. T* **179** *and similar horiz designs. Multicoloured. Without printer's imprint. P* 15.

791	2 s. Type **179**	10	10
792	3 s. Three-banded Plover	10	10
793	5 s. Spur-winged Goose	10	10
794	10 s. Clapper Lark	10	10
795	12 s. Red-eyed Bulbul	10	10
796	16 s. Cape Weaver	10	10
797	20 s. Paradise Sparrow ("Red-headed Finch")	10	10
798	30 s. Mountain Chat	15	20
799	40 s. Stonechat	20	25
800	55 s. Pied Barbet	25	30
801	60 s. Red-shouldered Glossy Starling	25	30
802	70 s. Cape Sparrow	35	40
803	1 m. Cattle Egret	45	50
804	3 m. Giant Kingfisher	1·25	1·40
805	10 m. Helmet Guineafowl ..	4·50	4·75
791/805	*Set of 15*	7·00	7·50

For these stamps showing Questa imprint at bottom left see Nos. 887/99.

1988 (3 May)* *Royal Ruby Wedding. Nos.* 701/4 *optd with T* **180** *in silver.*

806	90 s. black and yellow	45	45
807	1 m. multicoloured	55	55
808	2 m. multicoloured	1·00	1·00
806/8	*Set of 3*	1·75	1·75
MS809	119×85 mm. 4 m. black and grey-brown	2·00	2·00

*Nos. 806/9 were not available in Lesotho until the middle of 1990.

181 Mickey Mouse and Goofy outside Presidential Palace, Helsinki

(Des Walt Disney Co. Litho Questa)

1988 (2 June). *"Finlandia '88" International Stamp Exhibition, Helsinki. T* **181** *and similar horiz designs showing Walt Disney cartoon characters in Finland. Multicoloured. P* 14×13½.

810	1 s. Type **181**	10	10
811	2 s. Goofy and Mickey Mouse in sauna	10	10
812	3 s. Goofy and Mickey Mouse fishing in lake	10	10
813	4 s. Mickey and Minnie Mouse and Finlandia Hall, Helsinki	10	10
814	5 s. Mickey Mouse photographing Goofy at Sibelius Monument, Helsinki ..	10	10
815	10 s. Mickey Mouse and Goofy pony trekking	10	10
816	3 m. Goofy, Mickey and Minnie Mouse at Helsinki Olympic Stadium ..	1·75	1·75
817	5 m. Mickey Mouse and Goofy meeting Santa at Arctic Circle	2·50	2·50
810/17	*Set of 8*	4·25	4·25
MS818	Two sheets, each 127×102 mm. (a) 4 m. Mickey Mouse and nephew as Lapps. (b) 4 m. Daisy Duck, Goofy, Mickey and Minnie Mouse by fountain, Helsinki .. *Set of 2 sheets*	3·75	4·00

182 Pope John Paul II giving Communion

183 Large-toothed Rock Hyrax

(Litho Questa)

1988 (1 Sept). *Visit of Pope John Paul II. T* **182** *and similar multicoloured designs. P* 14.

819	55 s. Type **182**	30	25
820	2 m. Pope leading procession	1·00	1·00
821	3 m. Pope at airport	1·50	1·50
822	4 m. Pope John Paul II	2·00	2·00
819/22	*Set of 4*	4·25	4·25
MS823	98×79 mm. 5 m. Archbishop Morapeli (*horiz*) ..	3·00	3·25

(Des L. Watkins. Litho B.D.T.)

1988 (13 Oct). *Small Mammals of Lesotho. T* **183** *and similar vert designs. Multicoloured. P* 14.

824	16 s. Type **183**	15	10
825	40 s. Ratel and Black-throated Honey Guide (bird)	25	25
826	75 s. Small-spotted Genet	45	45
827	3 m. Yellow Mongoose	1·75	2·00
824/7	*Set of 4*	2·40	2·50
MS828	110×78 mm. 4 m. Meerkat ..	2·25	2·50

184 "Birth of Venus" (detail) (Botticelli)

(Litho Questa)

1988 (17 Oct). *Famous Paintings. T* **184** *and similar vert designs. Multicoloured. P* 13½ × 14.

829	15 s. Type **184**	15	15
830	25 s. "View of Toledo" (El Greco)	20	20
831	40 s. "Maids of Honour" (detail) (Velasquez)	25	25
832	50 s. "The Fifer" (Manet)	30	30
833	55 s. "Starry Night" (detail) (Van Gogh)	30	30
834	75 s. "Prima Ballerina" (Degas)	45	45
835	2 m. "Bridge over Water Lilies" (Monet)	1·00	1·00
836	3 m. "Guernica" (detail) (Picasso)	1·50	1·50
829/36	*Set of 8*	3·75	3·75
MS837	Two sheets, each 110×95 mm. (a) 4 m. "The Presentation of the Virgin in the Temple" (Titian). (b) 4 m. "The Miracle of the Newborn Infant" (Titian) .. *Set of 2 sheets*	4·00	4·00

185 Wrestling

(Des J. Martin. Litho B.D.T.)

1988 (11 Nov). *Olympic Games, Seoul (2nd issue). T* **185** *and similar multicoloured designs. P* 14.

838	12 s. Type **185**	10	10
839	16 s. Show jumping (*vert*)	10	10
840	55 s. Shooting	20	30
841	3 m. 50, As 16 s. (*vert*)	1·40	1·75
838/41	*Set of 4*	1·50	2·00
MS842	108×77 mm. 4 m. Olympic flame (*vert*) ..	1·90	2·00

186 Yannick Noah and Eiffel Tower, Paris

186a "The Averoldi Polyptych" (detail) (Titian)

(Des J. McDaniels. Litho Questa)

1988 (18 Nov). *75th Anniv of International Tennis Federation. T* **186** *and similar multicoloured designs. P* 14.

843	12 s. Type **186**	15	15
844	20 s. Rod Laver and Sydney Harbour Bridge and Opera House	20	20
845	30 s. Ivan Lendl and Prague	25	25
846	65 s. Jimmy Connors and Tokyo (*vert*) ..	40	40
847	1 m. Arthur Ashe and Barcelona (*vert*)	60	60
848	1 m. 55, Althea Gibson and New York (*vert*)	80	80
849	2 m. Chris Evert and Vienna (*vert*)	1·00	1·00
850	2 m. 40, Boris Becker and Houses of Parliament, London (*vert*)	1·40	1·40
851	3 m. Martina Navratilova and Golden Gate Bridge, San Francisco	1·60	1·60
843/51	*Set of 9*	5·75	5·75
MS852	98×72 mm. 4 m. Steffi Graf and Berlin	2·75	3·00

No. 844 is inscribed "SIDNEY" in error.

(Litho Questa)

1988 (1 Dec). *Christmas. 500th Birth Anniv of Titian (artist). T* **186a** *and similar multicoloured designs. P* 13½×14.

853	12 s. Type **186a**	15	10
854	20 s. "Christ and the Adulteress" (detail) ..	15	10
855	35 s. "Christ and the Adulteress" (different detail)	20	20
856	45 s. "Angel of the Annunciation"	30	30
857	65 s. "Saint Dominic"	40	40
858	1 m. "The Vendramin Family" (detail)	60	60
859	2 m. "Mary Magdalen"	1·00	1·00
860	3 m. "The Tribute Money"	1·50	1·75
853/60	*Set of 8*	3·75	4·00
MS861	(a) 94 × 110 mm. 5 m. "Mater Dolorosa". P 13½ × 14. (b) 110 × 94 mm. 5 m. "Christ and the Woman taken in Adultery" (*horiz*). P 14 × 13½ .. .. .. *Set of 2 sheets*	4·50	4·75

187 Pilatus "PC-6 Turbo Porter"

(Des K. Gromell. Litho Questa)

1989 (30 Jan). *125th Anniv of International Red Cross. Aircraft.* T **187** *and similar multicoloured designs.* P 14.
862	12 s. Type **187**		15	10
863	20 s. Unloading medical supplies from Cessna "Caravan"		20	15
864	55 s. De Havilland "DHC-6 Otter"		40	40
865	3 m. Douglas "DC-3"		2·00	2·25
862/5		Set of 4	2·50	2·50
MS866	109×80 mm. 4 m. Red Cross logo and Douglas "DC-3" (vert)		2·50	2·75

187a "Dawn Mist at Mishima" (Hiroshige)

(Litho Questa)

1989 (19 June). *Japanese Art. Paintings by Hiroshige.* T **187a** *and similar horiz designs. Multicoloured.* P 14×13½.
867	12 s. Type **187a**		10	10
868	16 s. "Night Snow at Kambara"		10	10
869	20 s. "Wayside Inn at Mariko Station"		10	10
870	35 s. "Shower at Shono"		15	20
871	55 s. "Snowfall on the Kisokaido near Oi"		20	25
872	1 m. "Autumn Moon at Seba"		40	45
873	3 m. 20, "Evening Moon at Ryogoku Bridge"		1·25	1·40
874	5 m. "Cherry Blossoms at Arashiyama"		2·00	2·10
867/74		Set of 8	3·75	4·25
MS875	Two sheets, each 102×76 mm. (a) 4 m. "Listening to the Singing Insects at Dokanyama". (b) 4 m. "Moonlight, Nagakubo". Set of 2 sheets		3·25	3·50

Nos. 867/74 were each printed in sheetlets of 10 containing two horizontal strips of 5 stamps separated by printed labels commemorating Emperor Hirohito.

188 Mickey Mouse as General   **189** *Paxillus involutus*

(Des Walt Disney Company. Litho Questa)

1989 (10 July). *"Philexfrance 89" International Stamp Exhibition, Paris.* T **188** *and similar multicoloured designs showing Walt Disney cartoon characters in French military uniforms of the Revolutionary period.* P 13½×14.
876	1 s. Type **188**		10	10
877	2 s. Ludwig von Drake as infantryman		10	10
878	3 s. Goofy as grenadier		10	10
879	4 s. Horace Horsecollar as cavalryman		10	10
880	5 s. Pete as hussar		10	10
881	10 s. Donald Duck as marine		10	10
882	3 m. Gyro Gearloose as National Guard		1·75	1·75
883	5 m. Scrooge McDuck as admiral		2·50	2·50
876/83		Set of 8	4·25	4·25
MS884	Two sheets, each 127×102 mm. (a) 4 m. Mickey and Minnie Mouse as King Louis XVI and Marie Antoinette with Goofy as a National Guard (horiz). P 14×13½. (b) 4 m. Mickey Mouse as drummer. P 13½×14. Set of 2 sheets		4·25	4·25

No. 879 is inscribed "CALVARYMAN" in error.

(Litho Questa)

1989 (31 Aug)–91. *As Nos. 793, 795/7 and 803/5, but with printer's imprint at bottom left.* P 14.
887	5 s. Spur-winged Goose (18.1.90)		10	10
889	12 s. Red-eyed Bulbul		10	10
890	16 s. Cape Weaver (11.11.89)		10	10
891	20 s. Paradise Sparrow ("Red-headed Finch") (2.12.89)		10	10
897	1 m. Cattle Egret (1991)		45	50
898	3 m. Giant Kingfisher (1991)		1·25	1·40
899	10 m. Helmet Guineafowl (1991)		4·50	4·75
887/99		Set of 7	5·75	6·25

(Des S. Wood. Litho Questa)

1989 (8 Sept). *Fungi.* T **189** *and similar vert designs. Multicoloured.* P 14.
900	12 s. Type **189**		15	10
901	16 s. Ganoderma applanatum		15	15
902	55 s. Suillus granulatus		35	35
903	5 m. Stereum hirsutum		2·75	3·00
900/3		Set of 4	3·00	3·25
MS904	96×69 mm. 4 m. Scleroderma flavidum		2·50	2·75

190 Sesotho Huts   **191** Marsh Sandpiper

(Des S. Wood. Litho Questa)

1989 (18 Sept). *Maloti Mountains.* T **190** *and similar vert designs. Multicoloured.* P 14.
905	1 m. Type **190**		60	60
	a. Horiz strip of 4. Nos. 905/8		2·25	
906	1 m. American Aloe and mountains		60	60
907	1 m. River valley with waterfall		60	60
908	1 m. Sesotho tribesman on ledge		60	60
905/8		Set of 4	2·25	2·25
MS909	86×117 mm. 4 m. Spiral Aloe		2·75	2·75

Nos. 905/8 were printed together, *se-tenant*, in horizontal strips of 4 throughout the sheet forming a composite design.

(Des Tracy Pedersen. Litho Questa)

1989 (18 Sept). *Migrant Birds.* T **191** *and similar multicoloured designs.* P 14.
910	12 s. Type **191**		15	10
911	65 s. Little Stint		40	40
912	1 m. Ringed Plover		60	60
913	4 m. Curlew Sandpiper		2·25	2·75
910/13		Set of 4	3·00	3·50
MS914	97×69 mm. 5 m. Ruff (vert)		3·25	3·25

192 Launch of "Apollo 11"   **193** English Penny Post Paid Mark, 1680

(Des G. Welker. Litho Questa)

1989 (6 Nov). *20th Anniv of First Manned Landing on Moon.* T **192** *and similar multicoloured designs.* P 14.
915	12 s. Type **192**		15	10
916	16 s. Lunar module Eagle landing on Moon (horiz)		15	15
917	40 s. Neil Armstrong leaving Eagle		25	25
918	55 s. Edwin Aldrin on Moon (horiz)		30	30
919	1 m. Aldrin performing scientific experiment (horiz)		60	60
920	2 m. Eagle leaving Moon (horiz)		1·00	1·00
921	3 m. Command module Columbia in Moon orbit (horiz)		1·50	1·50
922	4 m. Command module on parachutes		1·90	1·90
915/22		Set of 8	5·25	5·25
MS923	81×111 mm. 5 m. Astronaut on Moon		3·00	3·25

(Des U. Purins. Litho B.D.T.)

1989 (17 Nov). *"World Stamp Expo '89" International Stamp Exhibition, Washington (1st issue). Stamps and Postmarks.* T **193** *and similar horiz designs.* P 14.
924	75 s. brown-lake, black and stone		40	40
	a. Sheetlet. Nos. 924/32		3·25	
925	75 s. black, grey and rosine		40	40
926	75 s. dull violet, black and cinnamon		40	40
927	75 s. red-brown, black and cinnamon		40	40
928	75 s. black and olive-yellow		40	40
929	75 s. multicoloured		40	40
930	75 s. black and bright brown-lilac		40	40
931	75 s. black, bright carmine and pale brown		40	40
932	75 s. brt carmine, black & greenish yellow		40	40
924/32		Set of 9	3·25	3·25

Designs:— No. 925, German postal seal and feather, 1807; 926, British Post Offices in Crete 1898 20 pa. stamp; 927, Bermuda 1848 Perot 1d. provisional; 928, U.S.A. Pony Express cancellation, 1860; 929, Finland 1856 5 k. stamp; 930, Fiji 1870 *Fiji Times* 1d. stamp, 1870; 931, Sweden newspaper wrapper handstamp, 1823; 932, Bhor 1879 ½ a. stamp.

Nos. 924/32 were printed together, *se-tenant*, in sheetlets of 9.

193a Cathedral Church of St. Peter and St. Paul, Washington **193b** "The Immaculate Conception" (Velasquez)

(Des Design Element. Litho Questa)

1989 (17 Nov). *"World Stamp Expo '89" International Stamp Exhibition, Washington (2nd issue). Sheet 78×61 mm.* P 14.
MS933	**193a** 4 m. multicoloured		2·25	2·50

(Litho Questa)

1989 (18 Dec). *Christmas. Paintings by Velasquez.* T **193b** *and similar vert designs. Multicoloured.* P 14.
934	12 s. Type **193b**		10	10
935	20 s. "St. Anthony Abbot and St. Paul the Hermit"		15	10
936	35 s. "St. Thomas the Apostle"		25	25
937	55 s. "Christ in the House of Martha and Mary"		35	35
938	1 m. "St. John writing The Apocalypse on Patmos"		60	60
939	3 m. "The Virgin presenting the Chasuble to St. Ildephonsus"		1·60	1·75
940	4 m. "The Adoration of the Magi"		2·00	2·25
934/40		Set of 7	4·50	4·75
MS941	71×96 mm. 5 m. "The Coronation of the Virgin"		3·00	3·25

194 Scene from 1966 World Cup Final, England

(Des G. Vasarhelyi. Litho Questa)

1989 (27 Dec). *World Cup Football Championship, Italy.* T **194** *and similar horiz designs showing scenes from past finals. Multicoloured.* P 14.
942	12 s. Type **194**		15	10
943	16 s. 1970 final, Mexico		15	15
944	55 s. 1974 final, West Germany		40	40
945	5 m. 1982 final, Spain		2·75	3·00
942/5		Set of 4	3·00	3·25
MS946	106×85 mm. 4 m. Player's legs and symbolic football		2·25	2·50

16s **16**s **16**s **16**s
(195) (196) Long bars (R. 6/3) (196a)

1990 (22 Feb)–91. *Nos. 795, 798/9 and 889 surch with* T **195/6a** *by Lesotho Ads.*
947	16 s. on 12 s. Red-eyed Bulbul (No. 795) (T **195**)		40	30
948	16 s. on 12 s. Red-eyed Bulbul (No. 889) (T **196**)		10	10
	a. Surch inverted		40·00	
	b. Surch double		60·00	
	c. Long bars			
	d. Surch with Type **195**			
948e	16 s. on 30 s. Mountain Chat (No. 798) (T **196a**) (18.1.91)		10	10
	ea. Surch inverted			
	eb. Lower bar omitted			
948f	16 s. on 40 s. Stonechat (No. 799) (T **196a**) (18.1.91)		10	10
	fa. Lower bar omitted			
947/8f		Set of 4	60	55

The lower cancelling bar is frequently completely omitted from Type **196a** on R. 4/4, although on occasions traces of it do remain.

197 *Byblia anvatara*   **198** *Satyrium princeps*

(Des L. Nelson. Litho Questa)

1990 (26 Feb). *Butterflies. T* **197** *and similar vert designs. Multicoloured. P* 14.

949	12 s. Type **197**	..	10	10
950	16 s. *Cynthia cardui*	..	10	10
951	55 s. *Precis oenone* ..	..	25	30
952	65 s. *Pseudacraea boisduvali*	..	30	35
953	1 m. *Precis orithya*	..	45	50
954	2 m. *Precis sophia* ..	..	85	90
955	3 m. *Danaus chrysippus*	..	1·25	1·40
956	4 m. *Druryia antimachus*	..	1·75	1·90
949/56		*Set of 8*	4·50	5·00
MS957	105×70 mm. 5 m. *Papilio democus*		2·25	2·40

(Des B. Tear. Litho Questa)

1990 (12 Mar). *"EXPO 90" International Garden and Greenery Exhibition, Osaka. Local Orchids. T* **198** *and similar horiz designs. Multicoloured. P* 14.

958	12 s. Type **198**	..	10	10
959	16 s. *Huttonaea pulchra*	..	10	10
960	55 s. *Herschelia graminifolia*	..	25	30
961	1 m. *Ansellia gigantea*	..	45	50
962	1 m. 55, *Polystachya pubescens*	..	65	70
963	2 m. 40, *Penthea filicornis* ..	..	1·10	1·25
964	3 m. *Disperis capensis*	..	1·25	1·40
965	4 m. *Disa uniflora* ..	..	1·75	1·90
958/65		*Set of 8*	5·00	5·75
MS966	95×68 mm. 5 m. *Stenoglottis longifolia*		2·25	2·40

198a Lady Elizabeth Bowes-Lyon and Brother in Fancy Dress

199 King Moshoeshoe II and Prince Mohato wearing Seana-Marena Blankets

(Des Young Phillips Studio. Litho Questa)

1990 (5 July). *90th Birthday of Queen Elizabeth the Queen Mother. T* **198a** *and similar vert portraits, 1910–1919. P* 14.

967	1 m. 50, brownish black and bright magenta		65	70
	a. Strip of 3. Nos. 967/9 ..		1·75	
968	1 m. 50, brownish black and bright magenta		65	70
969	1 m. 50, brownish black and bright magenta		65	70
967/9		*Set of 3*	1·75	1·90
MS970	90×75 mm. 5 m. dull orange-brown, brownish black and bright magenta		2·25	2·40

Designs:—No. 967, Type **198a**; No. 968, Lady Elizabeth Bowes-Lyon in evening dress; No. 969, Lady Elizabeth Bowes-Lyon wearing hat; No. **MS**970, Lady Elizabeth Bowes-Lyon as a child.

Nos. 967/9 were printed together, horizontally and vertically se-tenant, in sheetlets of 9 (3×3).

(Litho B.D.T.)

1990 (17 Aug). *Traditional Blankets. T* **199** *and similar multicoloured designs. P* 14.

971	12 s. Type **199**	..	10	10
972	16 s. Prince Mohato wearing Seana-Marena blanket		10	10
973	1 m. Pope John Paul II wearing Seana-Marena blanket		45	50
974	3 m. Basotho horsemen wearing Matlama blankets		1·25	1·40
971/4		*Set of 4*	1·75	1·90
MS975	85×104 mm. 5 m. Pope John Paul II wearing hat and Seana-Marena blanket (*horiz*)		2·25	2·40

200 Filling Truck at No. 1 Quarry

201 Mother breastfeeding Baby

(Litho B.D.T.)

1990 (24 Aug). *Lesotho Highlands Water Project. T* **200** *and similar vert designs. Multicoloured. P* 14.

976	16 s. Type **200**	..	10	10
977	20 s. Tanker lorry on Pitseng–Malibamatso road		10	10
978	55 s. Piers for Malibamatso Bridge		25	30
979	2 m. Excavating Mphosong section of Pitseng–Malibamatso road		85	90
976/9		*Set of 4*	1·10	1·25
MS980	104×85 mm. 5 m. Sinking blasting boreholes on Pitseng–Malibamatso road		2·25	2·40

(Litho Questa)

1990 (26 Oct). *U.N.I.C.E.F. Child Survival Campaign. T* **201** *and similar vert designs. Multicoloured. P* 14.

981	12 s. Type **201**	..	10	10
982	55 s. Baby receiving oral rehydration therapy		25	30
983	1 m. Weight monitoring	..	45	50
981/3		*Set of 3*	70	80

202 Men's Triple Jump

203 "Virgin and Child" (detail, Rubens)

(Des B. Grout. Litho Questa)

1990 (5 Nov). *Olympic Games, Barcelona* (1992). *T* **202** *and similar multicoloured designs. P* 14.

984	16 s. Type **202**	..	10	10
985	55 s. Men's 200 metres race		25	30
986	1 m. Men's 5000 metres race		45	50
987	4 m. Show jumping	..	1·75	1·90
984/7		*Set of 4*	2·25	2·50
MS988	100×70 mm. 5 m. Olympic flame (*horiz*)		2·25	2·40

(Litho Questa)

1990 (5 Dec). *Christmas. Paintings by Rubens. T* **203** *and similar vert designs. Multicoloured. P* 13½×14.

989	12 s. Type **203**	..	10	10
990	16 s. "Adoration of the Magi" (detail)		10	10
991	55 s. "Head of One of the Three Kings"		25	30
992	80 s. "Adoration of the Magi" (different detail)		35	40
993	1 m. "Virgin and Child" (different detail) ..		45	50
994	2 m. "Adoration of the Magi" (different detail)		85	90
995	3 m. "Virgin and Child" (different detail) ..		1·25	1·40
996	4 m. "Adoration of the Magi" (different detail)		1·75	1·90
989/96		*Set of 8*	4·50	5·00
MS997	71×100 mm. 5 m. "Assumption of the Virgin" (detail) ..		2·25	2·40

204 Mickey Mouse at Nagasaki Peace Park

(Des Walt Disney Company. Litho Questa)

1991 (10 June). *"Phila Nippon '91" International Stamp Exhibition, Tokyo. T* **204** *and similar horiz designs showing Walt Disney cartoon characters in Japan. Multicoloured. P* 14×13½.

998	20 s. Type **204**	..	10	10
999	30 s. Mickey Mouse on Kamakura Beach		15	20
1000	40 s. Mickey and Donald Duck with Bunraku puppet		20	25
1001	50 s. Mickey and Donald eating soba		20	25
1002	75 s. Mickey and Minnie Mouse at tea house		35	40
1003	1 m. Mickey running after bullet train		45	50
1004	3 m. Mickey Mouse with deer at Todaiji Temple, Nara		1·25	1·40
1005	4 m. Mickey and Minnie outside Imperial Palace		1·75	1·90
998/1005		*Set of 8*	4·00	4·50
MS1006	Two sheets, each 127×112 mm. (a) 5 m. Mickey Mouse skiing; (b) 5 m. Mickey and Minnie having a picnic ..	*Set of 2 sheets*	5·50	5·75

205 Stewart Granger (*King Solomon's Mines*)

206 *Satyrus aello*

(Des R. Jung. Litho Questa)

1991 (20 June). *Famous Films with African Themes. T* **205** *and similar vert designs. Multicoloured. P* 14.

1007	12 s. Type **205**	..	10	10
1008	16 s. Johnny Weissmuller (*Tarzan the Ape Man*)		10	10
1009	30 s. Clark Gable with Grace Kelly (*Mogambo*)		15	20
1010	55 s. Sigourney Weaver and male gorilla (*Gorillas in the Mist*)		25	30
1011	70 s. Humphrey Bogart and Katharine Hepburn (*The African Queen*)		30	35
1012	1 m. John Wayne and capture of rhinoceros (*Hatari!*)		45	50
1013	2 m. Meryl Streep and light aircraft (*Out of Africa*)		85	90
1014	4 m. Arsenio Hall and Eddie Murphy (*Coming to America*)		1·75	1·90
1007/14		*Set of 8*	3·50	3·75
MS1015	108×77mm. 5 m. Elsa the lioness (*Born Free*) ..		2·25	2·40

(Des S. Heimann. Litho Cartor)

1991 (1 Aug)–**92**. *Butterflies. T* **206** *and similar horiz designs. Multicoloured. P* 14×13½. A. *Without imprint date.* B. *With imprint date* ("1992") *at foot* (4.92).

			A		B	
1016	2 s. Type **206**		†		10	10
1017	3 s. *Erebia medusa*	..	†		10	10
	a. Perf 13½	..	10	10	†	
1018	5 s. *Melanargia galathea*	..	10	10	10	10
1019	10 s. *Erebia aethiops*	..	10	10	10	10
1020	20 s. *Coenonympha pamphilus*	..	10	10	10	10
	a. Perf 13½	..	10	10	10	10
1021	25 s. *Pyrameis atalanta*	..	10	10	10	10
1022	30 s. *Charaxes jasius*	..	15	20	15	20
	a. Perf 13½	..	15	20	15	20
1023	40 s. *Colias palaeno*	..	20	25	20	25
1024	50 s. *Colias cliopatra*	..	20	25	20	25
1025	60 s. *Colias philodice*	..	25	30	25	30
1026	70 s. *Rhumni gonepterix*	..	30	35	30	35
1027	1 m. *Colias caesonia* ..		†		45	50
1028	2 m. *Pyrameis cardui*	..	85	90	85	90
	a. Perf 13½	..	85	90	†	
1029	3 m. *Danaus chrysippus*		†		1·25	1·50
	a. Perf 13½	..	1·25	1·50		
1030	10 m. *Apatura iris*		†		5·50	5·75
	a. Perf 13½	..	5·50	5·75	†	
1016/30		*Set of 15*	8·50	9·25	8·50	9·25

207 Victim of Drug Abuse

208 Wattled Cranes

(Litho Cartor)

1991 (23 Sept). *"Say No To Drugs" Campaign. P* 13½×14.

1031	**207** 16 s. multicoloured ..	..	10	10

(Litho Cartor)

1991 (10 Oct). *Southern Africa Development Co-ordination Conference Tourism Promotion. T* **208** *and similar horiz designs. Multicoloured. P* 14×13½.

1032	12 s. Type **208**	..	10	10
1033	16 s. Butterfly on flowers..		10	10
1034	25 s. Zebra and tourist bus at Mukurub (former rock formation), Namibia		10	10
1032/4		*Set of 3*	30	30
MS1035	75×117 mm. 3 m. Basotho women in ceremonial dress. P 13×12 ..		1·25	1·50

209 De Gaulle in 1939

210 Prince and Princess of Wales

(Des D. Miller. Litho B.D.T.)

1991 (6 Dec). *Birth Centenary of Charles de Gaulle (French statesman). T* **209** *and similar vert designs. P* 14.

1036	20 s. black and lake-brown	..	10	10
1037	40 s. black and purple	..	20	25
1038	50 s. black and yellow-olive	..	20	25
1039	60 s. black and greenish blue	..	25	30
1040	4 m. black and dull vermilion	..	1·75	1·90
1036/40		*Set of 5*	2·25	2·50

Designs:—40 s. General De Gaulle as Free French leader; 50 s. De Gaulle as provisional President of France 1944–46; 60 s. Charles de Gaulle in 1958; 4 m. Pres. De Gaulle, 1969.

(Des D. Miller. Litho B.D.T.)

1991 (9 Dec). *10th Wedding Anniv of Prince and Princess of Wales. T 210 and similar horiz designs. Multicoloured.* P 14.
1041	50 s. Type **210**		20	25
1042	70 s. Prince Charles at polo and Princess Diana holding Prince Henry		30	35
1043	1 m. Prince Charles with Prince Henry and Princess Diana in evening dress		45	50
1044	3 m. Prince William and Prince Henry in school uniform		1·25	1·50
1041/4		*Set of 4*	2·10	2·50
MS1045	68×91 mm. 4 m. Portraits of Prince with Princess and sons		1·75	1·90

211 "St. Anne with Mary and the Child Jesus" (Dürer)

212 Mickey Mouse and Pluto pinning the Tail on the Donkey

(Litho Walsall)

1991 (13 Dec). *Christmas. Drawings by Albrecht Dürer. T 211 and similar vert designs.* P 12.
1046	20 s. black and bright magenta		10	10
1047	30 s. black and new blue		15	20
1048	50 s. black and yellowish green		20	25
1049	60 s. black and vermilion		25	30
1050	70 s. black and lemon		30	35
1051	1 m. black and orange		45	50
1052	2 m. black and bright purple		85	90
1053	4 m. black and ultramarine		1·75	1·90
1046/53		*Set of 8*	3·75	4·00
MS1054	Two sheets, each 102×127 mm. (a) 5 m. black and carmine-rose. (b) 5 m. black and cobalt. P 14	*Set of 2 sheets*	5·50	5·75

Designs:—30 s. "Mary on Grass Bench"; 50 s. "Mary with Crown of Stars"; 60 s. "Mary with Child beside Tree"; 70 s. "Mary with Child beside Wall"; 1 m. "Mary in Halo on Crescent Moon"; 2 m. "Mary breastfeeding Child"; 4 m. "Mary with Infant in Swaddling Clothes"; 5 m. (No. **MS**1054a) "The Birth of Christ"; 5 m. (No. **MS**1054b) "The Holy Family with Dragonfly".

(Des Walt Disney Co. Litho Questa)

1991 (16 Dec). *Children's Games. T 212 and similar vert designs showing Walt Disney cartoon characters. Multicoloured.* P 13½×14.
1055	20 s. Type **212**		10	10
1056	30 s. Mickey playing mancala		15	20
1057	40 s. Mickey rolling hoop		20	25
1058	50 s. Minnie Mouse hula-hooping		20	25
1059	70 s. Mickey and Pluto throwing a frisbee		30	35
1060	1 m. Donald Duck with a diabolo		45	50
1061	2 m. Donald's nephews playing marbles		85	90
1062	3 m. Donald with Rubik's cube		1·25	1·50
1055/62		*Set of 8*	3·25	3·75
MS1063	Two sheets, each 127×112 mm. (a) 5 m. Donald's and Mickey's nephews playing tug-of-war; (b) 5 m. Mickey and Donald mock fighting	*Set of 2 sheets*	5·50	5·75

213 Lanner Falcon

214 Queen Elizabeth II and Cooking at a Mountain Homestead

(Des Tracy Pedersen. Litho Questa)

1992 (10 Feb). *Birds. T 213 and similar vert designs. Multicoloured.* P 14½×14.
1064	30 s. Type **213**		15	20
	a. Sheetlet. Nos. 1064/83		2·75	
1065	30 s. Bateleur		15	20
1066	30 s. Paradise Sparrow ("Red-headed Finch")		15	20
1067	30 s. Lesser Striped Swallow		15	20
1068	30 s. Alpine Swift		15	20
1069	30 s. Didric Cuckoo		15	20
1070	30 s. Yellow-tufted Malachite Sunbird		15	20
1071	30 s. Burchell's Gonolek ("Crimson-breasted Shrike")		15	20
1072	30 s. Pin-tailed Whydah		15	20
1073	30 s. Lilac-breasted Roller		15	20
1074	30 s. Little Black Bustard ("Korhaan")		15	20
1075	30 s. Black-collared Barbet		15	20
1076	30 s. Secretary Bird		15	20
1077	30 s. Red-billed Quelea		15	20
1078	30 s. Red Bishop		15	20
1079	30 s. Ring-necked Dove		15	20
1080	30 s. Yellow Canary		15	20

1081	30 s. Cape Longclaw		15	20
1082	30 s. Cordon-bleu ("Blue Waxbill")		15	20
1083	30 s. Golden Bishop		15	20
1064/83		*Set of 20*	2·75	3·50

Nos. 1064/83 were printed together, *se-tenant*, as a sheetlet of 20 with the backgrounds forming a composite design.

(Des D. Miller. Litho Questa)

1992 (2 Mar). *40th Anniv of Queen Elizabeth II's Accession. T 214 and similar horiz designs. Multicoloured.* P 14.
1084	20 s. Type **214**		10	10
1085	30 s. View of the Lowlands		15	20
1086	1 m. Agaves and escarpment		45	50
1087	4 m. Thaba-Bosiu		1·75	1·90
1084/7		*Set of 4*	2·25	2·40
MS1088	75×97 mm. 5 m. Mountains at sunset		2·25	2·40

215 Minnie Mouse as Spanish Lady, 1540–1660

216 Men's Discus

(Des Walt Disney Co. Litho Questa)

1992 (13 Apr). *International Stamp Exhibitions. T 215 and similar vert designs showing Walt Disney cartoon characters. Multicoloured.* P 13½×14.

(a) *"Granada 92", Spain. Traditional Spanish Costumes.*
1089	20 s. Type **215**		10	10
1090	50 s. Mickey Mouse as Don Juan at Lepanto, 1571		20	25
1091	70 s. Donald in Galician costume, 1880		30	35
1092	2 m. Daisy Duck in Aragonese costume, 1880		85	90
1089/92		*Set of 4*	1·10	1·40
MS1093	127×112 mm. 5 m. Goofy the Bullfighter		2·25	2·40

(b) *"World Columbian Stamp Expo '92". Red Indian Life.*
1094	30 s. Donald Duck making arrowheads		15	20
1095	40 s. Goofy playing lacrosse		20	25
1096	1 m. Mickey Mouse and Donald Duck planting corn		45	50
1097	3 m. Minnie Mouse doing bead work		1·25	1·40
1094/7		*Set of 4*	1·90	2·10
MS1098	127×112 mm. 5 m. Mickey paddling canoe		2·25	2·40

(Litho Questa)

1992 (5 Aug). *Olympic Games, Albertville and Barcelona. T 216 and similar multicoloured designs.* P 14.
1099	20 s. Type **216**		10	10
1100	30 s. Men's long jump		15	20
1101	40 s. Women's 4×100 metres relay		20	25
1102	70 s. Women's 100 metres		30	35
1103	1 m. Men's parallel bars		45	50
1104	2 m. Men's double luge (*horiz*)		85	90
1105	3 m. Women's 30k cross-country skiing (*horiz*)		1·25	1·40
1106	4 m. Men's biathlon		1·75	1·90
1099/106		*Set of 8*	4·50	5·00
MS1107	Two sheets, each 100×70 mm. (a) 5 m. Women's figure skating. (b) 5 m. Ice hockey (*horiz*)	*Set of 2 sheets*	4·50	5·00

217 Stegosaurus

218 "Virgin and Child" (Sassetta)

(Des D. Burkhart. Litho Questa)

1992 (9 June). *Prehistoric Animals. T 217 and similar horiz designs. Multicoloured.* P 14.
1108	20 s. Type **217**		10	10
1109	30 s. Ceratosaurus		15	20
1110	40 s. Procompsognathus		20	25
1111	50 s. Lesothosaurus		20	25
1112	70 s. Plateosaurus		30	35
1113	1 m. Gasosaurus		45	50
1114	2 m. Massospondylus		85	90
1115	3 m. Archaeopteryx		1·25	1·40
1108/15		*Set of 8*	3·25	3·50
MS1116	Two sheets, each 105×77 mm. (a) 5 m. As 50 s. (b) 5 m. As 3 m.	*Set of 2 sheets*	4·50	4·75

(Litho Questa)

1992 (2 Nov). *Christmas. Religious Paintings. T 218 and similar vert designs. Multicoloured.* P 13½×14.
1117	20 s. Type **218**		10	10
1118	30 s. "Coronation of the Virgin" (Master of Bonastre)		15	20
1119	40 s. "Virgin and Child" (Master of SS. Cosmas and Damian)		20	25
1120	70 s. "The Virgin of Great Panagia" (detail) (12th-century Russian school)		30	35
1121	1 m. "Madonna and Child" (Vincenzo Foppa)		45	50
1122	2 m. "Madonna and Child" (School of Lippo Memmi)		85	90
1123	3 m. "Virgin and Child" (Barnaba da Modena)		1·25	1·40
1124	4 m. "Virgin and Child with Saints" (triptych) (Simone dei Crocifissi)		1·75	1·90
1117/24		*Set of 8*	4·50	5·00
MS1125	Two sheets, each 76×102 mm. (a) 5 m. "Virgin and Child with Saints" (different detail) (Simone dei Crocifissi). (b) 5 m. "Virgin and Child enthroned and surrounded by Angels" (Cimabue)	*Set of 2 sheets*	4·50	4·75

OFFICIAL STAMPS

OFFICIAL

(O 1)

1934 (4 May). *Nos. 1/3 and 6 optd with Type* O 1.
O1	1	½d. emerald	..	..	£2000 £2000
O2		1d. scarlet	..	..	£1300 £1000
O3		2d. bright purple	..	..	£750 £550
O4		6d. orange-yellow	..	..	£10000 £4500
O1/4				*Set of* 4	£13000 £7000

Collectors are advised to buy these stamps only from reliable sources. They were not sold to the public.

POSTAGE DUE STAMPS

D 1	Normal	Large "d." (R. 9/6, 10/6)

(Typo D.L.R.)

1933 (1 Dec)–52. *Wmk Mult Script CA. Ordinary paper. P* 14.
D1	D 1	1d. carmine	..		1·75	4·00
		a. *Scarlet* (1938)	..	..	24·00	27·00
		b. Chalk-surfaced paper. *Deep carmine*				
		(24.10.51)	..	..	30	50
		ba. Error. Crown missing, W9a	..	85·00	
		bb. Error. St. Edward's Crown, W9b	..	48·00	
D2		2d. violet	..	..	4·50	7·50
		a. Chalk-surfaced paper (6.11.52)	..	30	1·25
		ab. Error. Crown missing, W9a	..	90·00	
		ac. Error. St. Edward's Crown, W9a	..	48·00	
		ad. Large "d"	..	..	4·50	
D1/2 Perf "Specimen"		..	*Set of* 2	42·00	

D 2

(Typo D.L.R.)

1956 (1 Dec). *Wmk Mult Script CA. P* 14.
D3	D 2	1d. carmine	..	..	20	1·50
D4		2d. deep reddish violet	..	..	20	2·25

5c **5c**

(I)   (II)

1961 (14 Feb). *Surch as T* 24, *but without stop.*
D5	D 2	1 c. on 1d. carmine	..	..	10	30
D6		1 c. on 2d. deep reddish violet	..	10	30
D7		5 c. on 2d. deep reddish violet (Type I)	15	30
		a. Type II	..	..	15·00	40·00
D5/7	..	..	..	*Set of* 3	30	80

1961 (June). *No. D2a surch as T* 24 (*without stop*).
D8	D 1	5 c. on 2d. violet	..	..	1·50	6·00
		a. Error. Missing Crown, W9a	..	£950	
		b. Error. St. Edward's Crown, W9b	..	£225	
		c. Large "d"	..	..	15·00	

1964. *As No. D3/4 but values in cents and W w* 12 (*sideways on* 1 c.).
D9	D 2	1 c. carmine	..	..	1·50	6·50
D10		5 c. deep reddish violet	..	..	1·50	6·50

1966 (1 Nov). *Nos. D9/10 optd as T* 32 *but smaller.*
D11	D 2	1 c. carmine	..	..	20	60
		a. "LSEOTHO" (R.4/7)	..	25·00	
D12		5 c. deep reddish violet	..	20	90
		a. "LSEOTHO" (R.4/7)	..	45·00	

No. D11 exists with the overprint centred near the foot of the stamp (just above "POSTAGE DUE") (*price* £50 *mint*). It is believed that this comes from a proof sheet which was issued in the normal way. It contains the "LSEOTHO" error, which only occurred in the first printing.

D 1	D 2

(Litho B.W.)

1967 (18 Apr). *No wmk. P* 13½.
D13	D 1	1 c. blue	..	..	15	2·00
D14		2 c. brown-rose	..	..	15	2·50
D15		5 c. emerald	..	..	20	2·75
D13/15	..	..	..	*Set of* 3	45	6·50

1976 (30 Nov). *W* 53 (*sideways*). *P* 13½.
D17	D 1	2 c. rose-red	..	..	1·25	3·00
D18		5 c. emerald	..	..	1·50	3·50

(Des G. Vasarhelyi. Litho Format)

1986. *No wmk. P* 13 × 13½.
D19	D 2	2 s. light green	..	..	10	10
D20		5 s. new blue	..	..	10	10
D21		25 s. violet	..	*Set of* 3	10	10
D19/21	..	..	..	*Set of* 3	20	20

POSTAL FISCAL

In July 1961 the 10s. stamp, T **9**, surcharged "R1 Revenue", was used for postage at one post office at least, but such usage was officially unauthorised.

Appendix

The following stamps have either been issued in excess of postal needs, or have not been made available to the public in reasonable quantities at face value. Miniature sheets, imperforate stamps etc., are excluded from this section.

1981–83

15*th Anniv of Independence. Classic Stamps of the World.*
10 m. × 40, each embossed on gold foil.

Long Island

The Turkish island of Chustan (or Keustan) in the Gulf of Smyrna was occupied by the Royal Navy during April 1916 and renamed Long Island.

The following stamps were provided by the Civil Administrator, Lieut-Cmdr H. Pirie-Gordon, for the postal service inaugurated on 7 May 1916.

USED STAMPS. Stamps of Long Island were cancelled by hand-drawn circular date stamps in blue crayon for the Northend post office ("N") or in red crayon for Nikola post office ("S").

(1) 2

1916 (7 May). *Turkish fiscal stamps surch by typewriter as in T 1. No wmk. P 12.*

1	½d. on 20 pa. green and buff (new value in red, remainder of surch in black)	£2250	£4000
2	1d. on 10 pa. carmine and buff	£2500	£4000
3	2½d. on 1 pi. violet and buff (R.)	£2500	£4000

Quantities issued: ½d. 25; 1d. 20; 2½d. 25.

1916 (7 May). *Typewritten as T 2 in various colours of ribbon and carbon. Each stamp initialled by the Civil Administrator. No gum. Imperf.*

(a) On pale green paper with horizontal grey lines. No wmk. Sheets of 16 or 12 with stamps initialled in red ink.

4	½d. black	£500	£550
	a. "G.R.I." double	£1600	
	b. "7" for "&"	£1600	
5	½d. blue	£500	
	a. "G.R.I." double	£1600	
	b. "7" for "&"	£1600	
6	½d. mauve	£475	£550
	a. "G.R.I." double	£1200	
	b. "7" for "&"	£1500	

Quantity issued: 140 in all.

(b) On thin horiz laid paper with sheet wmk of "SILVER LINEN" in double-lined capitals. Sheets of 20 with stamps initialled in red ink.

7	½d. black	£250	£300
	a. "postage" for "Postage"	£650	
8	½d. blue	£300	
	b. "7" for "&"	£650	
9	½d. mauve	£160	£200
	a. "postage" for "Postage"	£550	
	b. "7" for "&"	£550	
10	1d. black	£110	£200
	a. "7" for "&"	£475	
	b. "Rvenue" for "Revenue"	£475	
	g. "Postegg" for "Postage"	£475	
11	1d. blue	£140	£200
	a. "7" for "&"	£550	
	c. "postage" for "Postage"	£550	
	e. "G.R?I?" for "G.R.I."	£800	
	f. "ONR" for "ONE"	£550	
12	1d. mauve	£110	£200
	a. "7" for "&"	£550	
	b. "Rvenue" for "Revenue"	£550	
	c. "postage" for "Postage"	£550	
	e. "G.R?I?" for "G.R.I."	†	£800
	f. "ONR" for "ONE"	£550	£600
	g. "Postegg" for "Postage"	£550	
13	1d. red	£120	£180
	a. "7" for "&"	£475	
	c. "postage" for "Postage"	£475	
	f. "ONR" for "ONE"	£475	£650
14	2½d. black	£475	
15	2½d. blue	£475	£550
16	2½d. mauve	£425	£500
17	6d. black (inscr "SIX PENCE")	£600	£600
	b. Without red ink initials	—	£950
19	6d. mauve (inscr "SIX PENCE")	£225	£400
	a. "SIXPENCE" (one word)	£600	
20	1s. black	£100	£200
	a. "ISLANA" for "ISLAND"	£425	
	b. "Postge" for "Postage"	£550	£650
	c. "Rebenue" for "Revenue"	£550	
21	1s. black	£375	
22	1s. mauve	£100	£200
	a. "ISLANA" for "ISLAND"	£450	
	b. "Postge" for "Postage"	£450	
	c. "Rebenue" for "Revenue"	£600	

Quantities issued (all colours); ½d. 280; 1d. 1068; 2½d. 80; 6d. 100; 1s. 532.

(c) On thin wove paper. No wmk. Sheets of 24 with stamps initialled in indelible pencil.

23	½d. black	£160	£250
25	½d. mauve	£425	
26	1d. black	£170	£200
27	1d. red	£900	£500

30	2d. black		£140	£200
	a. "ISTAD" for "ISLAND"		£1200	
	b. Error. 1d. and 2d. *se-tenant*		£1600	
	c. Initialled in red ink		—	£400
31	2d. mauve		£140	£200
	a. Error. 1d. and 2d. *se-tenant*		£2000	
32	2½d. black		£250	£300
33	2½d. blue		£700	
34	2½d. mauve		£425	£475
35	6d. black		£140	£200
	a. "Rvenne&" for "Revenue"		£475	
	b. Error. 2d. and 6d. *se-tenant*, also "ISLND" for "ISLAND"		£1800	£1800
36	6d. blue		£475	
	a. "Rvenne&" for "Revenue"		£475	
	b. Error. 2d. and 6d. *se-tenant*, also "ISLND" for "ISLAND"		£1300	

Quantities issued (all colours); ½d. 144; 1d. 144; 2d. 288; 2½d. 144; 6d. 240.

TOP COPIES AND CARBONS. It is believed that the production sequence of the typewritten stamps was as follows:

Nos. 4/6   Three sheets of black top copies, two of 12 and one of 16
        Three sheets of blue carbons, two of 12 and one of 16
        Five sheets of mauve carbons, all of 12

Nos. 7/9   *Sheets of 20*
        Three sheets of black top copies
        Three sheets of blue carbons
        Eight sheets of mauve carbons

Nos. 10/13 *Sheets of 20*
        Eleven sheets of red top copies
        Fifteen sheets of black carbons
        Six sheets of blue carbons
        Twenty-two sheets of mauve carbons

Nos. 14/16 *Sheets of 20*
        One sheet of black top copies
        One sheet of blue carbons
        Two sheets of mauve carbons

Nos. 17/19 *Sheets of 20*
        One sheet of black top copies
        One sheet of blue carbons*
        Three sheets of mauve carbons

Nos. 20/22 *Sheets of 20*
        Five sheets of black top copies
        Nine sheets of black carbons
        Two sheets of blue carbons
        Twelve sheets of mauve carbons

Nos. 23/5 *Sheets of 24*
        One sheet of black top copies
        Three sheets of black carbons
        One sheet of blue carbons*
        One sheet of mauve carbons

Nos. 26/9 *Sheets of 24*
        One sheet of red top copies
        Three sheets of black carbons
        One sheet of blue carbons*
        One sheet of mauve carbons*

Nos. 30/1 *Sheets of 24*
        Two sheets of black top copies
        Six sheets of black carbons (inc one as No. 30c)
        Four sheets of mauve carbons

Nos. 32/4 *Sheets of 24*
        One sheet of black top copies
        Three sheets of black carbons
        One sheet of blue carbons
        One sheet of mauve carbons

Nos. 35/6 *Sheets of 24*
        Two sheets of black top copies
        Six sheets of black carbons
        Two sheets of blue carbons

*These carbons are described in written records, but their existence has yet to be confirmed by actual examples.

Madagascar

BRITISH CONSULAR MAIL

After May 1883 mail from the British community at Antananarivo, the capital, was sent by runner to the British Consulate at Tamatave for forwarding via the French Post Office.

In March of the following year the British Vice-Consul at Antananarivo, Mr. W. C. Pickersgill, reorganised this service and issued stamps for use on both local and overseas mail. Such stamps were only gummed at one of the top corners. This was to facilitate their removal from overseas mail where they were replaced by Mauritius stamps (at Port Louis) or by French issues (at the Vice-Consulate) for transmission via Tamatave and Reunion. Local mail usually had the stamps removed also, being marked by a "PAID" or a Vice-Consular handstamp, although a few covers have survived intact.

CONDITION. Due to the type of paper used, stamps of the British Consular Mail are usually found with slight faults, especially thins. Our prices are for average examples, really fine stamps being worth a premium.

USED STAMPS. Postmarks are not usually found on these issues. Cancellations usually take the form of a manuscript line or cross in crayon, ink or pencil or as five parallel horizontal bars in black or red, approximately 15 mm long.

1   2

1884 (Mar). *Typo locally. Rouletted vertically in colour. No gum, except on one upper corner. With circular consular handstamp reading "BRITISH VICE-CONSULATE ANTANANARIVO" around Royal arms in black.*

(a) Inscr "LETTER".

1	1	6d. (½ oz) magenta	£400	£425
		a. Violet handstamp	£1300	
2		1s. (1 oz) magenta	£375	
3		1s. 6d. (1½ oz) magenta	£375	
4		2s. (2 oz) magenta	£550	

(b) Inscr "POSTAL PACKET"

5	1	1d. (1 oz) magenta	£400	£350
		a. Without handstamp	£2250	£2250
6		2d. (2 oz) magenta	£250	£250
7		3d. (3 oz) magenta	£250	£225
8		4d. (1 oz amended in ms to "4 oz") magenta	£600	£600
		a. Without manuscript amendment	£1700	£1700
		ab. Violet handstamp	£1000	
		ac. Without handstamp	£2250	£2250

Nos. 1/8 were printed in horizontal strips of four, each strip containing two impressions of the setting. Each strip contained two stamps with normal stops after "B.C.M." and two with a hollow stop after "B" (1d., 2d., 3d., 4d., 6d. and 2s.) or after "M" (1s. and 1s. 6d.).

Several values are known with the handstamp either inverted or double.

1886. *Manuscript provisionals.*

(a) No. 2 with "SHILLING" erased and "PENNY" written above in red ink

9	1	1d. on 1s. (1 oz) magenta	

(b) No. 2 surch "4½d." and "W.C.P." in red ink with a line through the original value

10	1	4½d. on 1s. (1 oz) magenta	

1886. *As No. 1, but colour changed. Handstamped with circular "BRITISH VICE-CONSULATE ANTANANARIVO" in black.*

11	1	6d. (½ oz) rose-red	£500	£450

1886. *As No. 8, but handstamped "BRITISH CONSULAR MAIL ANTANANARIVO" in black (B) or violet (V)*

			B	V
12	1	4d. (1 oz) magenta	£1600	—	£2500	—

1886. *Typo locally. "POSTAGE" and value in words printed in black. Rouletted vertically in colour. No gum, except on one upper corner.*

I. "POSTAGE" 29½ mm long. Stops after "POSTAGE" and value

(a) Handstamped "BRITISH VICE-CONSULATE ANTANANARIVO" in black (B) or violet (V)

			B		V	
14	2	1d. rose	£100	£120	£250	—
15		1½d. rose	£900	£900	£650	—
16		2d. rose	£110	—	£275	—
17		3d. rose	£800	£800	£275	£275
18		4½d. rose	£750	£500	£325	£300
19		8d. rose	£1300	£1300	£1000	£1000
20		9d. rose	£2250	£2250	£900	—

(b) Handstamped "BRITISH CONSULAR MAIL ANTANANARIVO" in black

21	2	1d. rose	65·00
22		1½d. rose	65·00
23		2d. rose	75·00
24		3d. rose	80·00	85·00
		a. Handstamp in red	† £2750
25		4½d. rose	80·00	85·00
		a. Handstamp in red	† £2000
26		8d. rose	90·00
		a. Handstamp in violet	£1200
27		9d. rose	£100	£110
		a. Without handstamp	£1700
		b. Handstamp in violet	£225

II. "POSTAGE" 29½ mm long. No stops after "POSTAGE" or value

(a) Handstamped "BRITISH VICE-CONSULATE ANTANANARIVO" in violet

28	2	1d. rose	£850
29		1½d. rose	£1100
30		3d. rose	£1000
31		4½d. rose	£1000
32		6d. rose	£850

(b) Handstamped "BRITISH CONSULAR MAIL ANTANANARIVO" in black (B) or violet (V)

			B		V	
33		1d. rose	70·00	75·00	85·00	—
		a. Without handstamp	£1100			
34		1½d. rose	65·00	70·00	95·00	—
		a. Without handstamp	£1100			
35		2d. rose	65·00	70·00	£120	—

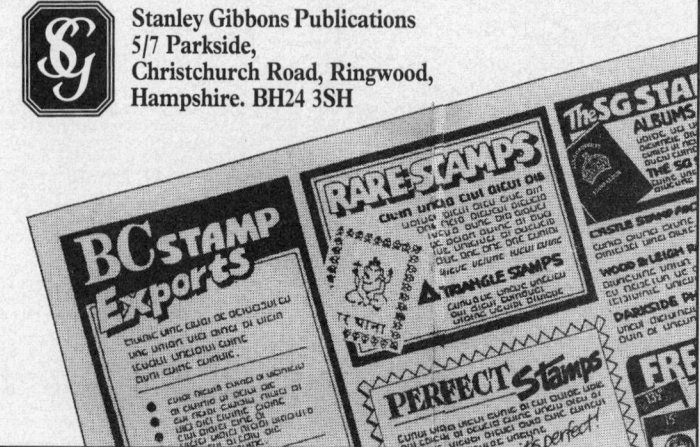

36	3d. rose	..	65·00	70·00	£120	—
	a. Without handstamp	..	£1300			
37	4½d. rose	..	70·00	75·00	£120	—
	a. Without handstamp	..	£1400			
38	6d. rose	..	70·00	75·00	£225	—
	a. Without handstamp	..	£1500			

III. "POSTAGE" 24½ mm long. No stop after "POSTAGE", but stop after value.

(a) Handstamped "BRITISH VICE-CONSULATE ANTANANARIVO" in violet

39	2	4d. rose	..	..	£400
40		8d. rose	..	..	£500
41		1s. 6d. rose	..	..	£2000
42		2s. rose	..	..	£1400
		a. Handstamp in black			

(b) Handstamped "BRITISH CONSULAR MAIL ANTANANARIVO" in black (B) or violet (V)

			B	V
43	4d. rose	..	£180	— £275
	a. Without handstamp	..	£1300	
44	8d. rose	..	£400	— £450
	a. Without handstamp	..	£1400	
45	1s. rose	..	£350	—£1000
	a. Without handstamp	..	£1400	
46	1s. 6d. rose	..	£350	—£1200
	a. Without handstamp	..	£2000	
47	2s. rose	..	£450	—£1300
	a. Without handstamp	..	£2000	—

The above were also printed in horizontal strips of four.

The stamps of the British Consular Mail were suppressed in 1887, but the postal service continued with the charges paid in cash.

BRITISH INLAND MAIL

In January 1895 the Malagasy government agreed that a syndicate of British merchants at Antananarivo, including the Vice-Consul, should operate an inland postal service during the war with France. Mail was sent by runner to the port of Vatomandry and forwarded via Durban where Natal stamps were added.

Nos. 50/62 were cancelled with dated circular postmarks inscribed "BRITISH MAIL".

4	5 Malagasy Runners

(Typeset London Missionary Society Press, Antananarivo)

1895 (Jan). Rouletted in black. (a) Thick laid paper.
| 50 | 4 | 4d. black | .. | 22·00 | 12·00 |
| | | a. "FUOR" for "FOUR" | .. | — | £650 |

(b) In black on coloured wove paper
51	4	1d. blue-grey	..	22·00	12·00
52		6d. pale yellow	..	22·00	12·00
53		8d. salmon	..	22·00	12·00
54		1s. fawn	..	35·00	12·00
55		2s. bright rose	..	35·00	14·00
		a. Italic "2" at left	..	£120	60·00
56		4s. grey	..	50·00	12·00
50/6			Set of 7	£180	75·00

There are six types of each value, printed in blocks of 6 (2×3) separated by gutters, four times on each sheet; the upper and lower blocks being *tête-bêche*.

Nos. 50a and 55a occur in the sixth position in their respective blocks. No. 50a was soon corrected.

(Typo John Haddon & Co, London)
1895 (Mar). The inscription in the lower label varies for each value. P 12.
57	5	2d. blue	..	5·00	20·00
		a. Imperf between (pair)	..	£400	
58		4d. rose	..	5·00	20·00
		a. Imperf between (pair)	..	£250	
59		6d. green	..	5·00	20·00
		a. Imperf between (pair)	..	£400	
60		1s. slate-blue	..	6·50	26·00
		a. Imperf between (pair)	..	£400	
61		2s. chocolate	..	7·00	30·00
		a. Imperf between (pair)	..	£400	
62		4s. bright purple	..	10·00	40·00
		a. Imperf between (pair)	..	£400	
57/62		..	Set of 6	35·00	£140

This post was suppressed when the French entered Antananarivo on 30 September 1895.

PRICES OF SETS

Set prices are given for many issues, generally those containing three stamps or more. Definitive sets include one of each value or major colour change, but do not cover different perforations, die types or minor shades. Where a choice is possible the set prices are based on the cheapest versions of the stamps included in the listings.

Malawi
(formerly Nyasaland)

PRICES FOR STAMPS ON COVER TO 1945	
Nos. 1/9a	from × 15
Nos. 10/19	
No. 20	from × 10
Nos. 21/6	from × 5
Nos. 27/31	
Nos. 32/7	from × 6
Nos. 38/42	
Nos. 43/7	from × 12
Nos. 48/52	
No. 53	from × 15
No. 54	from × 2
No. 55	from × 4
Nos. 55b/7a	from × 7
Nos. 57d/63	from × 6
Nos. 64/71	
Nos. 72/9	from × 5
Nos. 80/2	
Nos. 83/95	from × 4
Nos. 96/9	
Nos. 100/57	from × 2

By 1891 the territory west of Lake Nyasa was recognised as being under British protection and the southern, eastern and northern borders had been delineated with the Portuguese and German governments.

BRITISH CENTRAL AFRICA

A protectorate under the name "Nyassaland Districts" was declared on 14 May 1891, the title being changed to the "British Central Africa Protectorate" on 22 February 1893. Such a description had been in use for some time previously and the handwritten notice of 20 July 1891, announcing the introduction of postal services, described the area as "British Central Africa".

Until 1895 the British South Africa Company contributed to the revenues of the protectorate administration which, in return governed North-eastern Rhodesia. Stamps of the British South Africa Company overprinted "B.C.A.", in addition to use in British Central Africa, were issued to post offices at Fife, Fort Rosebery, Katwe, Johnston Falls, Rhodesia (later Kalungwisi) and Tanganyika (later Abercorn) in North-eastern Rhodesia from 1893 until 1899.

B.C.A.
(1)

FOUR SHILLINGS.
(2)

ONE PENNY.
(3)

1891 (April)–1895. Stamps of Rhodesia optd as T 1. P 14. 14½.
1	1	1d. black	..	2·00	2·25
2	4	2d. sea-green and vermilion	..	2·00	2·50
		a. Bisected (1d.) (on cover) (1895)	..	† £1800	
3		4d. reddish chestnut and black	..	1·75	3·75
4	1	6d. ultramarine	..	42·00	20·00
5		6d. deep blue	..	5·00	8·00
6	4	8d. rose-lake and ultramarine	..	12·00	28·00
6a		8d. red and ultramarine	..	23·00	45·00
7	1	1s. grey-brown	..	9·50	11·00
8		2s. vermilion	..	20·00	40·00
9		2s. 6d. grey-purple	..	45·00	65·00
9a		2s. 6d. lilac	..	50·00	65·00
10	4	3s. brown and green (1895)	..	45·00	50·00
11		4s. grey-black and vermilion (2.93)	..	45·00	75·00
12	1	5s. orange-yellow	..	45·00	65·00
13		10s. deep green	..	85·00	£120
14	2	£1 deep blue	..	£450	£450
15		£2 rose-red	..		£650
16		£5 sage-green	..		£1200
17		£10 brown	..		£2750
1/14			Set of 13	£600	£750

The overprint varies on values up to 10s. Sets may be made with thin or thick letters.

The bisected 2d, No. 2a, was authorised for use at Blantyre, Chiromo and Zomba in July and October 1895.

1892 (Aug)–93. Stamps of Rhodesia surch as T 2.
| 18 | 4 | 3s. on 4s. grey-black and vermilion (10.93) | .. | £300 | £300 |
| 19 | 1 | 4s. on 5s. orange-yellow | .. | 70·00 | 80·00 |

1895. No. 2 surch at Cape Town with T 3.
| 20 | 4 | 1d. on 2d. sea-green and vermilion | .. | 6·00 | 25·00 |
| | | a. Surch double | .. | £2750 | £2000 |

Specimens are known with double surcharge, without stop after "PENNY". These are from a trial printing made at Blantyre, but it is believed that they were not issued to the public (Price £600 un.).

| 5 | Arms of the Protectorate | 6 |

(Des Sir Harry Johnston. Litho D.L.R.)

1895. No wmk. P 14.
21	5	1d. black	..	6·50	5·00
22		2d. black and green	..	13·00	11·00
23		4d. black and reddish buff	..	25·00	26·00
24		6d. black and blue	..	35·00	6·00
25		1s. black and rose	..	45·00	20·00
26	6	2s. 6d. black and bright magenta	..	£110	£140
27		3s. black and yellow	..	70·00	32·00
28		5s. black and olive	..	90·00	£100
29		£1 black and yellow-orange	..	£650	£350
30		£10 black and orange-vermilion	..	£3000	£2750
31		£25 black and blue-green	..	£5500	
21/8			Set of 8	£350	£300
21/9	Optd "Specimen"		Set of 9	£375	

Cancellations inscribed "BRITISH CENTRAL AFRICA" within a double-circle and with the name of a town across the centre or at foot were intended for use on stamps presented for the payment of the hut tax. Such marks can be found in black, violet or blue and are without date.

1896 (Feb). Wmk Crown CA (T 5) or CC (sideways) (T 6). P 14.
32	5	1d. black	..	3·00	4·50
33		2d. black and green	..	13·00	5·00
34		4d. black and orange-brown	..	15·00	17·00
35		6d. black and blue	..	12·00	9·00
36		1s. black and rose	..	17·00	10·00
37	6	2s. 6d. black and magenta	..	80·00	80·00
38		3s. black and yellow	..	60·00	35·00
39		5s. black and olive	..	80·00	95·00
40		£1 black and blue	..	£650	£375
41		£10 black and orange (Optd S. £175)	..	£3500	£2500
42		£25 black and green (Optd S. £325)	..	£7500	
32/9			Set of 8	£250	£200
32/40	Optd "Specimen"		Set of 9	£375	

| 7 | 8 |

(Typo D.L.R.)

1897 (Aug). T 7 (wmk Crown CA) and 8 (wmk Crown CC). P 14.
43	7	1d. black and ultramarine	..	1·00	60
44		2d. black and yellow	..	1·40	80
45		4d. black and carmine	..	5·00	1·50
46		6d. black and green	..	27·00	24·00
47		1s. black and dull purple	..	6·50	7·00
48	8	2s. 6d. black and ultramarine	..	35·00	38·00
49		3s. black and sea-green	..	£160	£200
50		4s. black and carmine	..	50·00	70·00
50a		10s. black and olive-green	..	80·00	90·00
51		£1 black and dull purple	..	£200	£140
52		£10 black and yellow (Optd S. £175)	..	£2750	£1500
43/51			Set of 10	£500	£500
43/51	Optd "Specimen"		Set of 10	£225	

ONE PENNY
(9)

| 10 |

1897 (31 Dec). No. 49 surch with T 9, in red.
53	8	1d. on 3s. black and sea-green	..	5·00	8·50
		a. "PNNEY" (R. 4/2)		£1400	£1400
		b. "PENN"		£800	£750
		c. Surch double		£450	

No. 53b shows an albino impression of the "Y".

1898 (11 Mar). Imperf.

(a) Setting I. The vertical frame lines of the stamps cross the space between the two rows of the sheet.
(i) With the initials "J.G." or "J.T.G." on the back in black ink
54	10	1d. vermilion and grey-blue	..	—	£450
		a. Without the initials	..	..	£1500
		b. Without the initials and centre inverted	..	..	£6500

(ii) With a control number and letter or letters, printed in plain relief at the back
| 55 | 10 | 1d. vermilion and grey-blue | .. | — | £225 |

(b) Setting II. The vertical frame lines do not cross the space between the rows except at the extreme ends of the sheet. Control as No. 55.
55b	10	1d. vermilion and pale ultramarine	..	—	42·00
		c. Control on face	..		— £3000
		d. Centre omitted (vert pair with normal)	..		£7000
56		1d. vermilion and deep ultramarine	..	—	42·00
		a. Without Control at back	..	£1300	80·00
		b. Control doubly impressed	..	—	£225

1898 (June). *Setting II. Control as No. 55. P 12.*
57	10	1d. vermilion and pale ultramarine		£1400	14·00
57a		1d. vermilion and deep ultramarine		—	14·00
		ab. Without Control at back		£1400	48·00
		ac. Two different Controls on back		—	£400
		ad. Control printed in black			£1500

The two different settings of these stamps are each in 30 types, issued without gum.

1901. *Wmk Crown CA. P 14.*
57d	7	1d. dull purple and carmine-rose		1·00	40
57e		4d. dull purple and olive-green		4·25	5·50
58		6d. dull purple and brown		3·50	3·00
57d/8			*Set of 3*	8·00	8·00
57d/58 Optd "Specimen"			*Set of 3*	60·00	

11 12

(Typo D.L.R.)

1903–4. *T 11 (Wmk Crown CA) and 12 (Wmk Crown CC). P 14.*
59	11	1d. grey and carmine		3·25	40
60		2d. dull and bright purple		3·25	1·00
61		4d. grey-green and black		2·50	5·50
62		6d. grey and reddish buff		2·50	2·00
62a		1s. grey and blue		2·50	7·00
63	12	2s. 6d. grey-green and green		27·00	38·00
64		4s. dull and bright purple		48·00	75·00
65		10s. grey-green and black		65·00	£120
66		£1 grey and carmine		£180	£150
67		£10 grey and blue (Optd S. £200)		£3500	£3250
59/66			*Set of 9*	£275	£350
59/66 Optd "Specimen"			*Set of 9*	£275	

1907. *Wmk Mult Crown CA. Chalk-surfaced paper. P 14.*
68	11	1d. grey and carmine		1·75	90
69		2d. dull and bright purple		£8000	
70		4d. grey-green and black		£8000	
71		6d. grey and reddish buff		26·00	35·00

Nos. 69/70 were not issued in Nyasaland.

NYASALAND PROTECTORATE

The title of the Protectorate was changed again from 6 July 1907.

13 14

(Typo D.L.R.)

1908 (22 July). *P 14. (a) Wmk Crown CA. Chalk-surfaced paper.*
72	13	1s. black/green		1·40	6·00

(b) Wmk Mult Crown CA. Ordinary paper (¹/₂d., 1d.) or chalk-surfaced paper (others).
73	13	¹/₂d. green		1·00	75
74		1d. carmine		1·50	30
75		3d. purple/yellow		1·00	2·25
76		4d. black and red/yellow		1·00	1·50
77		6d. dull purple and bright purple		3·75	6·50
78	14	2s. 6d. black and red/blue		32·00	55·00
79		4s. carmine and black		60·00	75·00
80		10s. green and red/green		75·00	£120
81		£1 purple and black/red		£375	£425
82		£10 purple & ultramarine (Optd S. £450)		£7000	£4250
72/81			*Set of 10*	£475	£600
72/81 Optd "Specimen"			*Set of 10*	£400	

15 16

1913 (1 Apr)–19. *Wmk Mult Crown CA. Ordinary paper (¹/₂d. to 2¹/₂d.) or chalk-surfaced paper (others). P 14.*
83	15	¹/₂d. green		50	70
84		¹/₂d. blue-green (1918)		50	70
85		1d. carmine-red		75	75
86		1d. scarlet (1916)		55	45
87		2d. grey (1916)		1·25	70
88		2d. slate		2·75	1·25
89		2¹/₂d. bright blue		70	2·25
90		3d. purple/yellow (1914)		2·00	2·50
		a. On pale yellow		2·50	7·00
91		4d. black and red/yellow (shades)		2·00	2·00
		a. On pale yellow		3·75	7·00
92		6d. dull and bright purple		2·50	5·00
92a		6d. dull purple and bright violet		6·50	10·00

93	15	1s. black/green		1·75	5·00
		a. On blue-green, olive back		2·25	1·50
		b. On emerald back (Optd S. £35)		1·00	4·25
94	16	2s. 6d. black and red/blue		9·50	10·00
		a. Break in scroll		65·00	
		b. Broken crown and scroll		65·00	
95		4s. carmine and black		10·00	32·00
		a. Break in scroll		85·00	
		b. Broken crown and scroll		85·00	
96		10s. pale green and deep scarlet/green		48·00	70·00
		a. Break in scroll		£160	
		b. Broken crown and scroll		£160	
		c. Green and deep scarlet/green (1919)		48·00	70·00
		ca. Break in scroll		£180	
98		£1 purple and black/red		£150	£140
		a. Break in scroll		£350	
		b. Broken crown and scroll		£350	
99		£10 purple & dull ultram (Optd S. £300)		£3500	
		a. Purple and royal blue (1919)		£2500	£1500
		ab. Break in scroll			
		ac. Broken crown and scroll			
83/98			*Set of 12*	£180	£200
83/98 Optd "Specimen"			*Set of 12*	£350	

For illustrations of the varieties on Nos. 94/9 see above Leeward Islands No. 58.

For stamps overprinted "N.F." see TANZANIA.

1921–30. *Wmk Mult Script CA. Ordinary paper (¹/₂d. to 2d.) or chalk-surfaced paper (others). P 14.*
100	15	¹/₂d. green		60	30
101		1d. carmine		50	30
102		1¹/₂d. orange		3·25	16·00
103		2d. grey		55	30
105		3d. purple/pale yellow		5·00	2·50
106		4d. black and red/yellow		2·50	4·75
107		6d. dull and bright purple		3·00	3·25
108		1s. black/emerald (1930)		5·50	6·50
109		2s. purple and blue/blue		9·00	10·00
		a. Break in scroll		60·00	
		b. Broken crown and scroll		60·00	
110	16	2s. 6d. black and red/blue (1924)		12·00	15·00
		a. Break in scroll		70·00	
		b. Broken crown and scroll		70·00	
111		4s. carmine and black		10·00	12·00
		a. Break in scroll		75·00	
		b. Broken crown and scroll		75·00	
112		5s. green and red/yellow (1929)		27·00	45·00
		a. Break in scroll		£110	
		b. Broken crown and scroll		£110	
113		10s. green and red/pale emerald (1926)		65·00	85·00
		a. Break in scroll		£190	
		b. Broken crown and scroll		£190	
		c. Green and scarlet/emerald (1927)		£225	£400
		ca. Break in scroll		£550	
		cb. Broken crown and scroll		£550	
100/13			*Set of 13*	£130	£160
100/13 Optd "Specimen"			*Set of 13*	£325	

For illustrations of the varieties on Nos. 109/13 see above Leeward Islands No. 58.

17 King George V and Symbol of the Protectorate

(Des Major H. E. Green. Recess Waterlow)

1934 (June)–35. *Wmk Mult Script CA. P 12¹/₂.*
114	17	¹/₂d. green		75	55
115		1d. brown		75	50
116		1¹/₂d. carmine		75	1·25
117		2d. pale grey		80	1·00
118		3d. blue		1·50	1·50
119		4d. bright magenta (20.5.35)		2·25	2·00
120		6d. violet		1·50	40
121		9d. olive-bistre (20.5.35)		3·00	9·00
122		1s. black and orange		3·00	6·00
114/22			*Set of 9*	13·00	20·00
114/22 Perf "Specimen"			*Set of 9*	£120	

1935 (6 May). *Silver Jubilee. As Nos. 114/17 of Jamaica, but ptd by Waterlow. P 11×12.*
123		1d. ultramarine and grey		90	60
		j. Kite and vertical log		38·00	
124		2d. green and indigo		90	45
125		3d. brown and deep blue		7·00	9·50
		j. Kite and vertical log		90·00	
126		1s. slate and purple		15·00	20·00
		j. Kite and vertical log		£130	
123/6			*Set of 4*	21·00	27·00
123/6 Perf "Specimen"			*Set of 4*	75·00	

For illustration of plate variety see Omnibus section following Zimbabwe.

1937 (12 May). *Coronation. As Nos. 118/20 of Jamaica, but ptd by B.W. P 11×11¹/₂.*
127		¹/₂d. green		30	30
128		1d. brown		70	30
129		2d. grey-black		70	50
127/9			*Set of 3*	1·50	1·00
127/9 Perf "Specimen"			*Set of 3*	55·00	

18 Symbol of the Protectorate 19

(T 18 recess Waterlow; T 19 typo D.L.R.)

1938 (1 Jan)–44. *Chalk-surfaced paper (2s. to £1). P 12¹/₂ (T 18) or 14 (T 19). (a) Wmk Mult Script CA.*
130	18	¹/₂d. green		30	30
130a		¹/₂d. brown (12.12.42)		10	50
131		1d. brown		30	15
131a		1d. green (12.12.42)		15	30
132		1¹/₂d. carmine		75	2·50
132a		1¹/₂d. grey (12.12.42)		20	1·50
133		2d. grey		1·25	40
133a		2d. carmine (12.12.42)		20	35
134		3d. blue		20	15
135		4d. bright magenta		1·00	30
136		6d. violet		1·10	30
137		9d. olive-bistre		1·75	2·00
138		1s. black and orange		1·75	65
139	19	2s. purple and blue/blue		10·00	6·50
140		2s. 6d. black and red/blue		11·00	6·50
141		5s. pale green and red/yellow		40·00	14·00
		a. Ordinary paper. Green and red/ pale yellow (3.44)		80·00	48·00
142		10s. emerald and deep red/pale green		48·00	20·00
		a. Ordinary paper. Bluish green and brown-red/pale green (1.38)		£250	95·00

(b) Wmk Mult Crown CA
143	19	£1 purple and black/red		28·00	22·00
130/43			*Set of 18*	£130	70·00
130/43 Perf "Specimen"			*Set of 18*	£600	

No. 141a has a yellow surfacing often applied in horizontal lines giving the appearance of laid paper.

The printer's archives record the despatch of No. 142a to Nyasaland in January 1938, but no used examples have been reported before 1945.

20 Lake Nyasa 21 King's African Rifles

(Recess B.W.)

1945 (1 Sept). *T 20/1 and similar designs. Wmk Mult Script CA (sideways on horiz designs). P 12.*
144		¹/₂d. black and chocolate		10	10
145		1d. black and emerald		10	10
146		1¹/₂d. black and grey-green		15	50
147		2d. black and scarlet		15	15
148		3d. black and light blue		15	30
149		4d. black and claret		75	45
150		6d. black and violet		1·00	40
151		9d. black and olive		75	2·25
152		1s. indigo and deep green		90	20
153		2s. emerald and maroon		3·50	3·50
154		2s. 6d. emerald and blue		5·00	2·50
155		5s. purple and blue		4·50	3·50
156		10s. claret and emerald		8·00	7·50
157		20s. scarlet and black		15·00	15·00
144/57			*Set of 14*	35·00	32·00
144/57 Perf "Specimen"			*Set of 14*	£250	

Designs: *Horiz*—1¹/₂d., 6d. Tea estate; 2d., 1s., 10s. Map of Nyasaland; 4d., 2s. 6d. Tobacco; 9d. Type 20 ; 5s., 20s. Badge of Nyasaland. *Vert*—3d., 2s. Fishing Village.

1946 (16 Dec). *Victory. As Nos. 141/2 of Jamaica.*
158		1d. green		10	10
159		2d. red-orange		10	10
158/9 Perf "Specimen"			*Set of 2*	50·00	

26 Symbol of the 27 Arms in 1891 and 1951
Protectorate

(Recess B.W.)

1947 (20 Oct). *Wmk Mult Script CA. P 12.*
160	26	1d. red-brown and yellow-green		30	10
160 Perf "Specimen"				45·00	

1948 (15 Dec). *Royal Silver Wedding. As Nos. 143/4 of Jamaica.*
161		1d. green		15	10
162		10s. mauve		12·00	16·00

1949 (21 Nov). *75th Anniv of U.P.U. As Nos. 145/8 of Jamaica.*
163		1d. blue-green		30	15
164		3d. greenish blue		1·00	50
165		6d. purple		1·00	50
166		1s. ultramarine		1·00	50
163/6			*Set of 4*	3·00	1·50

(Des C. Twynam. Recess B.W.)

1951 (15 May). *Diamond Jubilee of Protectorate. Wmk Mult Script CA. P 11 × 12.*
167	27	2d. black and scarlet		60	30
168		3d. black and turquoise-blue		60	75
169		6d. black and violet		60	90
170		5s. black and indigo		1·40	6·00
167/70			*Set of 4*	2·75	7·25

28 Arms of Rhodesia and Nyasland

29 Grading Cotton

(Recess Waterlow)

1953 (30 May). *Rhodes Centenary Exhibition. Wmk Mult Script CA. P 14×13½.*
171 **28** 6d. violet 15 20

1953 (2 June). *Coronation. As No. 153 of Jamaica, but ptd by B.W.*
172 2d. black and brown-orange 30 20

(Recess B.W.)

1953 (1 Sept)–**54**. *Designs previously used for King George VI issue, but with portrait of Queen Elizabeth II as in T* **29**. *Wmk Mult Script CA. P 12.*
173 ½d. black and chocolate 10 65
  a. Perf 12 × 12½ (8.3.54) 10 55
174 1d. brown and bright green.. .. .. 40 15
175 1½d. black and deep grey-green .. 20 1·60
176 2d. black and yellow-orange .. 60 15
  a. Perf 12 × 12½ (8.3.54) 20 10
177 2½d. green and black 15 30
178 3d. black and scarlet 30 10
179 4½d. black and light blue 30 40
180 6d. black and violet 70 60
  a. Perf 12 × 12½ (8.3.54) 30 10
181 9d. black and deep olive .. .. 70 2·25
182 1s. deep blue and slate-green .. 60 15
183 2s. deep green and brown-red .. 2·00 3·00
184 2s. 6d. deep emerald and deep blue 3·00 4·25
185 5s. purple and Prussian blue .. 5·50 4·50
186 10s. carmine and deep emerald .. 4·25 8·00
187 20s. red and black .. .. 11·00 10·00
173a/87 *Set of 15* 26·00 32·00
Designs: *Horiz*—½d., 9d. Lake Nyasa; 1½d., 6d. Tea estate; 2d., 1s., 10s. Map of Nyasaland; 3d., 2s. 6d. Tobacco; 5s., 20s. Badge of Nyasaland. *Vert*—1d. Symbol of the protectorate; 4½d., 2s. Fishing village.
Stamps perf 12 × 12½ come from sheets comb-perforated 11.8 × 12.25. They were also issued in coils of 480 stamps made up from sheets.

For issues between 1954 and 1963, see RHODESIA AND NYASALAND.

30

(31)

(Recess B.W.)

1963 (1 Nov). *Revenue stamps optd "POSTAGE", as in T* **30**, *or additionally surch as T* **31**. *P 12.*
188 ½d. on 1d. greenish blue 30 30
189 1d. green 30 10
190 2d. scarlet 30 30
191 3d. blue 30 10
192 6d. brown-purple 30 10
193 9d. on 1s. cerise 40 25
194 1s. purple 45 10
195 2s. 6d. black .. .. .. 50 1·75
196 5s. chocolate .. .. .. 75 1·25
197 10s. yellow-olive .. .. .. 1·50 3·75
  a. Greenish olive .. .. .. 7·00 10·00
198 £1 deep violet .. .. .. 3·50 3·75
188/98 *Set of 11* 7·50 10·00

32 Mother and Child

33 Chambo (fish)

34 Tea Industry

35 Nyala

(Des V. Whiteley. Photo Harrison)

1964 (1 Jan). *Designs as T* **32/5**. *P 14½.*
199 ½d. reddish violet 10 20
200 1d. black and green 10 10

201 2d. light red-brown 10 10
202 3d. red-brown, yellow-green & bistre-brown 10 10
203 4d. indigo and orange-yellow .. 20 20
204 6d. purple, yellow-green and light blue .. 30 20
205 1s. brown, turquoise-blue and pale yellow 15 10
206 1s. 3d. bronze-green and chestnut .. 1·25 10
207 2s. 6d. brown and blue .. .. 1·25 50
208 5s. blue, green, yellow and black .. 1·25 1·25
209 10s. green, orange-brown and black .. 1·50 3·00
210 £1 deep reddish purple and yellow .. 5·50 4·00
199/210 *Set of 12* 10·50 8·50
Designs: *As T* **32/3**—2d. Zebu Bull; 3d. Groundnuts; 4d. Fishing. *As T* **34**—1s. Timber; 1s. 3d. Turkish tobacco industry; 2s. 6d. Cotton industry; 5s. Monkey Bay, Lake Nyasa; 10s. Forestry, Afzelia.

Nyasaland attained independence on 5 July 1964 when the country was renamed Malawi.

MALAWI
INDEPENDENT

44 Dr. H. Banda (Prime Minister) and Independence Monument

(Des M. Goaman. Photo Harrison)

1964 (6 July). *Independence. T* **44** *and similar horiz designs. P 14½.*
211 3d. yellow-olive and deep sepia .. 10 10
212 6d. red, gold, blue, carmine and lake .. 10 10
213 1s. 3d. red, green, black and bluish violet 20 10
214 2s. 6d. multicoloured 30 35
  a. Blue omitted £200
211/14 *Set of 4* 50 45
Designs:—6d. Banda and rising sun. 1s. 3d. Banda and Malawi flag; 2s. 6d. Banda and Malawi coat of arms.
Six examples of No. 214a are known from the top horizontal row of an otherwise normal sheet.

48 Tung Tree

49 Christmas Star and Globe

(Des V. Whiteley. Photo Harrison)

1964 (6 July)–**65**. *As Nos. 199/210, but inscr "MALAWI" and T* **48** (9d.). *No wmk. P 14½.*
215 ½d. reddish violet 10 35
216 1d. black and green 10 10
217 2d. light red-brown 10 10
218 3d. red-brown, yellow-green & bistre-brown 15 10
219 4d. black and orange-yellow.. .. 25 15
220 6d. bluish violet, yellow-green and light blue 50 10
221 9d. bistre-brown, green and yellow .. 30 15
222 1s. brown, turquoise-blue and pale yellow 25 10
223 1s. 3d. bronze-green and chestnut .. 50 40
224 2s. 6d. brown and blue .. .. 1·10 1·00
225 5s. blue, green, yellow and sepia .. 65 2·00
225a 5s. blue, green, yellow and sepia (1.6.65) 3·50 90
226 10s. green, orange-brown and black .. 1·50 2·00
227 £1 deep reddish purple and yellow .. 6·00 5·50
215/27 *Set of 14* 13·50 11·00
No. 225a is inscribed "LAKE MALAWI" instead of "LAKE NYASA".
See also Nos. 252/62.

(Des V. Whiteley. Photo Harrison)

1964 (1 Dec). *Christmas. P 14½.*
228 **49** 3d. blue-green and gold 10 10
  a. Gold (star) omitted .. .. 90·00
229 6d. magenta and gold 10 10
230 1s. 3d. reddish violet and gold .. 10 10
231 2s. 6d. blue and gold 20 25
228/31 *Set of 4* 30 30
MS231a 83 × 126 mm. Nos. 228/31. Imperf 1·00 1·75
No. 228a comes from a sheet on which 41 examples had the gold colour omitted due to a paper fold.

50 Coins

(51)

(Des V. Whiteley. Photo Enschedé)

1965 (1 Mar). *Malawi's First Coinage. Coins in black and silver. P 13½.*
232 **50** 3d. green 10 10
233 9d. magenta 15 10
  a. Silver omitted .. .. † —
234 1s. 6d. purple 20 10
235 3s. blue 30 30
232/5 *Set of 4* 65 40
MS235a 126 × 104 mm. Nos. 232/5. Imperf 1·25 1·10

1965 (14 June). *Nos. 223/4 surch as T* **51**.
236 1s. 6d. on 1s. 3d. bronze-green and chestnut 10 10
237 3s. on 2s. 6d. brown and blue .. 20 20
On No. 237 "3/–" occurs below the bars.

52 Chilembwe leading Rebels

(Des M. Goaman. Photo Harrison)

1965 (20 Aug). *50th Anniv of 1915 Rising. P 14 × 14½.*
238 **52** 3d. violet and light olive-green .. 10 10
239 9d. olive-brown and red-orange .. 10 10
240 1s. 6d. red-brown and grey-blue .. 10 10
241 3s. turquoise-green and slate-blue .. 15 15
238/41 *Set of 4* 30 30
MS241a 127 × 83 mm. Nos. 238/41 .. 6·50 7·00

53 "Learning and Scholarship"

(Des H. E. Baxter. Photo Harrison)

1965 (6 Oct). *Opening of Malawi University. P 14½.*
242 **53** 3d. black and emerald 10 10
243 9d. black and magenta 10 10
244 1s. 6d. black and reddish violet .. 10 10
245 3s. black and blue 15 30
242/5 *Set of 4* 30 40
MS246 127 × 84 mm. Nos. 242/5 .. .. 3·50 3·50

54 *Papilio ophidicephalus*

(Des V. Whiteley. Photo Enschedé)

1966 (15 Feb). *Malawi Butterflies. T* **54** *and similar horiz designs. Multicoloured. P 13½.*
247 4d. Type **54** 60 10
248 9d. *Papilio desmondi* (*magdae*) .. 85 10
249 1s. 6d. *Epamera handmani* .. .. 1·25 30
250 3s. *Amauris crawshayi* .. .. 2·50 3·50
247/50 *Set of 4* 4·75 3·50
MS251 130×100 mm. Nos. 247/50 .. .. 15·00 11·00

55 Cockerels

56 Burley Tobacco

57 *Cyrestis camillus* (butterfly)

(New values des V. Whiteley (1s. 6d.), M. Goaman (£2). Photo Harrison)

1966–67. *As Nos. 215 etc. but W 55 (sideways on ½d., 2d.), and new values and designs (1s. 6d., £2). P 14½.*

252	–	½d. reddish violet (1.4.66)	..	10	10
253		1d. black and green (1.4.66)	..	15	10
254		2d. light red-brown (4.6.66)*	..	15	10
255		3d. red-brn, yell-grn & bis-brn (4.3.67)*	20	10
256		6d. bluish violet, yell-grn & lt bl (2.7.66)*	25	10
257	48	9d. bistre-brown, green & yell (5.12.66)*	35	10
258		1s. brown, turquoise-bl & pale yell (1.4.66)	25	10
259	56	1s. 6d. chocolate & yellow-grn (15.11.66)	30	10
260		5s. blue, green, yellow & sepia (6.10.66)*	7·50	2·00
261		10s. green, orange-brown & blk (6.10.66)*	17·00	14·00
262	57	£2 black, orange-yellow, pale yellow and slate-violet (7.9.66)*	25·00	24·00
252/62			Set of 11	45·00	35·00

*These are local dates of issue. The Crown Agents, in London, did not distribute these printings until some time later.

No. 260 is inscribed "LAKE MALAWI".

The 2d. exists with both PVA gum and gum arabic.

58 British Central Africa 6d. Stamp of 1891   **59** President Banda

(Des V. Whiteley. Photo Harrison)

1966 (4 May–10 June). *75th Anniv of Postal Services. W 55. P 14½.*

263	58	4d. grey-blue and yellow-green	..	10	10
264		9d. grey-blue and claret	..	10	10
265		1s. 6d. grey-blue and reddish lilac	..	15	10
266		3s. grey-blue and new blue	..	25	30
263/6			Set of 4	45	35
MS267		83 × 127 mm. Nos. 263/6 (10 June)		4·50	3·25

REPUBLIC

(Des M. Goaman. Photo Harrison)

1966 (6 July). *Republic Day. W 55. P 14 × 14½.*

268	59	4d. brown, silver and emerald	..	10	10
269		9d. brown, silver and magenta	..	10	10
270		1s. 6d. brown, silver and violet	..	10	10
271		3s. brown, silver and blue	..	15	15
268/71			Set of 4	30	30
MS272		83 × 127 mm. Nos. 268/71	..	2·00	2·25

60 Bethlehem

(Des and photo Harrison)

1966 (12 Oct). *Christmas. W 55. P 14½.*

273	60	4d. myrtle-green and gold	..	10	10
274		9d. brown-purple and gold	..	10	10
275		1s. 6d. orange-red and gold	..	15	10
276		3s. blue and gold	..	40	50
273/6			Set of 4	65	55

61 *Ilala I*

(Des Mrs. H. Breggar. Photo Harrison)

1967 (4 Jan). *Lake Malawi Steamers. T 61 and similar horiz designs. W 55. P 14½.*

277		4d. black, yellow and bright green	..	30	10
		a. Yellow omitted	..		
278		9d. black, yellow and magenta	..	35	10
279		1s. 6d., black, red and violet	..	55	15
280		3s. black, red and bright blue	..	1·25	1·25
277/80			Set of 4	2·25	1·40

Designs:—9d. *Dove*; 1s. 6d. *Chauncy Maples I* (wrongly inscr "Chauncey"); 3s. *Gwendolen*.

62 Turquoise-gold Chichlid

(Des R. Granger Barrett. Photo Enschedé)

1967 (3 May). *Lake Malawi Chichlids. T 62 and similar horiz designs. Multicoloured. W 55 (sideways). P 12½ × 12.*

281		4d. Type 62	..	15	10
282		9d. Red Finned chichlid	..	20	10
283		1s. 6d. Zebra chichlid	..	30	10
		a. Imperf (pair)	..	£100	
284		3s. Golden chichlid	..	1·00	1·00
		a. Imperf (pair)	..	£140	
281/4			Set of 4	1·50	1·10

63 Rising Sun and Gearwheel

(Des Jennifer Toombs. Litho D.L.R.)

1967 (5 July). *Industrial Development. P 13½ × 13.*

285	63	4d. black and emerald	..	10	10
286		9d. black and carmine	..	10	10
287		1s. 6d. black and reddish violet	..	10	10
288		3s. black and bright blue	..	15	15
285/8			Set of 4	30	30
MS289		134 × 108 mm. Nos. 285/8	..	75	1·40

64 Mary and Joseph beside Crib

(Des Jennifer Toombs. Photo Harrison)

1967 (21 Nov–1 Dec). *Christmas. W 55. P 14 × 14½.*

290	64	4d. royal blue and turquoise-green	..	10	10
291		9d. royal blue and light red	..	10	10
292		1s. 6d. royal blue and yellow	..	10	10
293		3s. royal blue and new blue	..	15	15
290/3			Set of 4	30	30
MS294		114 × 100 mm. Nos. 290/3. Wmk sideways. P 14 × 13½ (1 Dec)	..	1·00	2·50

65 *Calotropis procera*

(Des G. Drummond. Litho D.L.R.)

1968 (24 Apr). *Wild Flowers. T 65 and similar horiz designs. Multicoloured. W 55 (sideways). P 13½ × 13.*

295		4d. Type 65	..	15	10
296		9d. *Borreria dibrachiata*	..	15	10
297		1s. 6d. *Hibiscus rhodanthus*	..	15	10
298		3s. *Bidens pinnatipartita*	..	20	20
295/8			Set of 4	60	30
MS299		135 × 91 mm. Nos. 295/8	..	1·25	2·50

66 Saddleback Steam Locomotive, *Thistle* No. 1

(Des R. Granger Barrett. Photo Harrison)

1968 (24 July). *Malawi Locomotives. T 66 and similar horiz designs. W 55. P 14 × 14½.*

300		4d. grey-green, slate-blue and red	..	30	10
301		9d. red, slate-blue and myrtle-green	..	40	10
302		1s. 6d. multicoloured	..	65	10
303		3s. multicoloured	..	1·25	1·50
300/3			Set of 4	2·40	1·60
MS304		120 × 88 mm. Nos. 300/3. P 14½	..	3·00	5·50

Designs:—9d. Class "G" steam locomotive; 1s. 6d. Diesel locomotive *Zambesi*; 3s. Diesel railcar.

67 "The Nativity" (Piero della Francesca)

(Des and photo Harrison)

1968 (6 Nov). *Christmas. Paintings. T 67 and similar horiz designs. Multicoloured. W 55 (sideways on 4d.). P 14 × 14½.*

305		4d. Type 67	..	10	10
306		9d. "The Adoration of the Shepherds" (Murillo)	..	10	10
307		1s. 6d. "The Adoration of the Shepherds" (Reni)	..	10	10
308		3s. "Nativity with God the Father and Holy Ghost" (Pittoni)	..	15	10
305/8			Set of 4	30	20
MS309		115 × 101 mm. Nos. 305/8. P 14 × 13½	..	35	1·40

68 Scarlet-chested Sunbird   **69** Nyasa Lovebird

70 Carmine Bee Eater

(Des V. Whiteley. Photo Harrison)

1968 (13 Nov). *Birds. T 68/70 and similar designs. Multicoloured. W 55 (sideways on 1d. to 4d. and 3s. to £1). P 14½.*

310		1d. Type 68	..	15	15
311		2d. Violet Starling	..	15	10
312		3d. White-browed Robin Chat	..	20	10
313		4d. Red-billed Fire Finch	..	35	40
		a. Red omitted	..		
314		6d. Type 69	..	45	15
315		9d. Yellow-rumped Bishop	..	50	60
316		1s. Type 70	..	60	15
317		1s. 6d. Grey-headed Bush Shrike	..	5·00	6·00
318		2s. Paradise Whydah	..	5·00	7·00
319		3s. African Paradise Flycatcher	..	4·50	3·75
320		5s. Bateleur	..	6·50	4·00
321		10s. Saddle-bill Stork	..	5·50	7·50
322		£1 Purple Heron	..	12·00	17·00
323		£2 Knysna Turaco	..	35·00	48·00
310/323			Set of 14	65·00	85·00

Sizes:—2d. to 4d. as T 68; 9d. as T 69; 1s. 6d., 2s., £2 as T 70; 3s. to £1 as T 70 but vertical.

No. 310 exists in coils, constructed from normal sheets.

71 I.L.O. Emblem

(Des G. Drummond. Photo, emblem die-stamped Harrison)

1969 (5 Feb). *50th Anniv of the International Labour Organization. W 55 (sideways on No. MS328). P 14.*

324	71	4d. gold and myrtle-green	..	10	10
325		9d. gold and chocolate	..	10	10
326		1s. 6d. gold and blackish brown	..	10	10
327		3s. gold and indigo	..	15	15
324/7			Set of 4	30	30
MS328		127 × 89 mm. Nos. 324/7	..	2·25	6·50

72 White-fringed Ground Orchid   **73** African Development Bank Emblem

(Des J.W. Litho B.W.)

1969 (9 July). *Orchids of Malawi. T 72 and similar horiz designs. Multicoloured. W 55. P 13½ × 13.*

329		4d. Type 72	..	15	10
330		9d. Red Ground orchid	..	20	10
331		1s. 6d. Leopard Tree orchid	..	30	10
332		3s. Blue Ground orchid	..	60	1·75
329/32			Set of 4	1·10	1·75
MS333		118 × 86 mm. Nos. 329/32	..	1·10	3·50

(Des G. Vasarhelyi. Litho D.L.R.)

1969 (10 Sept). *Fifth Anniv of African Development Bank. W 55. P 14.*

334	73	4d. yellow, yellow-ochre and chocolate	10	10
335		9d. yellow, yellow-ochre & myrtle-green	10	10
336		1s. 6d. yellow, yell-ochre & blackish brn	10	10
337		3s. yellow, yellow-ochre and indigo	15	15
334/7			Set of 4	30	30
MS338		102 × 137 mm. Nos. 334/7	..	50	90

74 Dove over Bethlehem

75 *Zonocerus elegans* (grasshopper)

(Des Jennifer Toombs. Photo Harrison)

1969 (5 Nov). *Christmas. W 55. P 14½ × 14.*
339	74	2d. black and olive-yellow	..	10	10
340		4d. black and deep turquoise	..	10	10
341		9d. black and scarlet	..	10	10
342		1s. 6d. black & deep bluish violet		10	10
343		3s. black and ultramarine	..	15	15
339/43			Set of 5	30	30
MS344		130 × 71 mm. Nos. 339/43		1·00	1·75
		a. Ultramarine (background of 3s.) omitted	..	£400	

(Des V. Whiteley. Litho Format)

1970 (4 Feb). *Insects of Malawi. T 75 and similar vert designs. Multicoloured. W 55. P 14.*
345		4d. Type 75	..	15	10
346		9d. *Mylabris dicincta* (beetle)	..	15	10
347		1s. 6d. *Henosepilachna elaterii* (ladybird)		20	10
348		3s. *Sphodromantis speculabunda* (mantid)		35	45
345/8			Set of 4	75	55
MS349		86×137 mm. Nos. 345/8	..	1·25	2·25

Rand Easter Show 1970
(76)

1970 (18 Mar). *Rand Easter Show. No. 317 optd with T 76.*
350		1s. 6d. multicoloured	..	20	90

77 Runner

(Des J. Cooter. Litho B.W.)

1970 (3 June). *Ninth British Commonwealth Games, Edinburgh. W 55. P 13.*
351	77	4d. royal blue and blue-green	..	10	10
352		9d. royal blue and carmine	..	10	10
353		1s. 6d. royal blue and dull yellow		10	10
354		3s. royal blue and new blue	..	15	15
351/4			Set of 4	30	30
MS355		146 × 96 mm. Nos. 351/4	..	55	90

(New Currency, 100 tambalas = 1 kwacha)

10t
(78)

79 *Aegocera trimeni*

1970 (2 Sept). *Decimal Currency. Nos. 316 and 318 surch as T 78.*
356		10 t. on 1s. multicoloured	..	60	25
		a. Surch double	..	†	—
357		20 t. on 2s. multicoloured	..	1·40	1·00

(Des R. Granger Barrett. Litho B.W.)

1970 (30 Sept). *Moths. T 79 and similar horiz designs. Multicoloured. W 55. P 11 × 11½.*
358		4d. Type 79	..	20	10
359		9d. *Faidherbia bauhiniae*		30	10
360		1s. 6d. *Parasa karschi*		50	10
361		3s. *Teracotona euprepia*		1·25	2·00
358/61			Set of 4	2·00	2·00
MS362		112×92 mm. Nos. 358/61	..	4·00	4·50

30t

Special United Kingdom Delivery Service

80 Mother and Child   (81)

(Des Brother W. Meyer. Litho J.W.)

1970 (4 Nov). *Christmas. W 55 (sideways). P 14.*
363	80	2d. black and light yellow	..	10	10
364		4d. black and emerald	..	10	10
365		9d. black and orange-red	..	10	10
366		1s. 6d. black and light purple	..	10	10
367		3s. black and blue	..	15	15
363/7			Set of 5	30	30
MS368		166 × 100 mm. Nos. 363/7		75	1·75

1971 (8 Feb). *No. 319 surch with T 81.*
369		30 t. on 3s. multicoloured	..	20	1·75

No. 369 was issued for use on letters carried by an emergency airmail service from Malawi to Great Britain during the British postal strike. The fee of 30 t. was to cover the charge for delivery by a private service, and ordinary stamps to pay the normal airmail fee had to be affixed as well.

The strike ended on 8 March, when private delivery services were withdrawn.

82 Decimal Coinage and Cockerel

(Des V. Whiteley. Litho Format)

1971 (15 Feb). *Decimal Coinage. W 55 (sideways). P 14.*
370	82	3 t. multicoloured	..	10	10
371		8 t. multicoloured	..	15	10
372		15 t. multicoloured	..	20	10
373		30 t. multicoloured	..	35	45
370/3			Set of 4	65	55
MS374		140 × 101 mm. Nos. 370/73		1·00	1·75

83 Greater Kudu   **84** Eland

(Des and litho J.W.)

1971 (15 Feb)–74. *Decimal Currency. Antelopes. Vert designs as T 83 (1 t. to 8 t.), or T 84 (others). Multicoloured. W 55 (sideways on 1 t. to 8 t.). P 13½ × 14 (1 t. to 8 t.) or 14½ (others).*
375		1 t. Type 83	..	10	10
		a. Coil stamp. P 14½×14	..	15	30
		b. Perf 14† (12.11.74)	..	45	45
376		2 t. Nyala	..	15	10
377		3 t. Mountain Reedbuck	..	20	20
		a. Perf 14† (12.11.74)	..	65	65
378		5 t. Puku	..	40	20
		a. Perf 14† (12.11.74)	..	65	80
379		8 t. Impala	..	45	20
380		10 t. Type 84	..	60	10
381		15 t. Klipspringer	..	1·00	20
382		20 t. Suni	..	1·50	50
383		30 t. Roan Antelope	..	4·50	70
384		50 t. Waterbuck	..	90	65
385		1 k. Bushbuck	..	2·00	85
386		2 k. Red Forest Duiker	..	3·50	1·50
387		4 k. Common Duiker	..	20·00	17·00
375/87			Set of 13	32·00	19·00

No. 387 is incorrectly inscr "Gray Duiker".

† These actually gauge 14·2 × 14 instead of 13·7 × 14 and are line-perforated; in blocks they can easily be distinguished as in alternate rows across the sheet the horizontal perfs have two holes where they cross the vertical perfs; the watermark is also sideways inverted.

85 Christ on the Cross   **87** *Holarrhena febrifuga*

(Des G. Drummond. Litho Questa)

1971 (7 Apr). *Easter. Details from Painting "The Small Passion" by Dürer. T 85 and similar vert design. W 55. P 13½.*
388		3 t. black and green	..	10	10
		a. Pair. Nos. 388/9	..	10	10
389		3 t. black and green	..	10	10
		a. Pair. Nos. 390/1	..	20	20
390		8 t. black and orange-red	..	10	10
		a. Pair. Nos. 390/1	..	20	20
391		8 t. black and orange-red	..	10	10
392		15 t. black and violet	..	15	15
		a. Pair. Nos. 392/3	..	30	30
393		15 t. black and violet	..	15	15

394		30 t. black and bright blue	..	25	25
		a. Pair. Nos. 394/5	..	50	50
395		30 t. black and bright blue	..	25	25
388/95			Set of 8	1·00	60
MS396		Two sheets each 95 × 145 mm (a) Nos. 388, 390, 392 and 394; (b) Nos. 389, 391, 393 and 395		3·00	3·00

Designs:—Nos. 388, 390, 392 and 394, Type 85; Nos. 389, 391, 393 and 395, The Resurrection.

Nos. 388/9, 390/1, 392/3 and 394/5 were each printed together, *se-tenant*, in pairs throughout the sheet.

(Des G. Drummond. Litho J.W.)

1971 (14 July). *Flowering Shrubs and Trees. T 87 and similar vert designs. Multicoloured. W 55. P 14.*
397		3 t. Type 87	..	10	10
398		8 t. *Brachystegia spiciformis*		15	10
399		15 t. *Securidaca longepedunculata*		25	10
400		30 t. *Pterocarpus rotundifolius*		40	50
397/400			Set of 4	80	55
MS401		102 × 135 mm. Nos. 397/400		1·25	2·00

88 Drum Major   **89** "Madonna and Child" (William Dyce)

(Des J.W. Litho Questa)

1971 (5 Oct). *50th Anniv of Malawi Police Force. W 55. P 14 × 14½.*
402	88	30 t. multicoloured	..	65	1·00

(Des J. Cooter. Litho Format)

1971 (10 Nov). *Christmas. T 89 and similar vert designs. Multicoloured. W 55. P 14½.*
403		3 t. Type 89	..	10	10
404		8 t. "The Holy Family" (M. Schöngauer)		15	10
405		15 t. "The Holy Family with St. John" (Raphael)		30	20
406		30 t. "The Holy Family" (Bronzino)		65	80
403/6			Set of 4	1·10	1·00
MS407		101 × 139 mm. Nos. 403/6		1·40	2·50

90 Vickers "Viscount"

(Des R. Granger Barrett. Litho Questa)

1972 (9 Feb). *Air. Malawi Aircraft. T 90 and similar horiz designs. Multicoloured. W 55 (sideways). P 13½.*
408		3 t. Type 90	..	25	10
409		8 t. Hawker Siddeley "748"	..	40	10
410		15 t. Britten-Norman "Islander"	..	65	30
411		30 t. B.A.C. "One-Eleven"	..	1·10	1·75
408/11			Set of 4	2·25	2·00
MS412		143 × 94 mm. Nos. 408/11	..	7·50	5·50

91 Figures (Chencherere Hill)   **92** Boxing

(Des R. Granger Barrett. Litho Format)

1972 (10 May). *Rock Paintings. T 91 and similar horiz designs. W 55 (sideways). P 13½.*
413		3 t. apple-green, grey-green and black	..	35	10
414		8 t. red, grey and black	..	45	10
415		15 t. multicoloured	..	70	30
416		30 t. multicoloured	..	1·00	1·00
413/16			Set of 4	2·25	1·25
MS417		121 × 97 mm. Nos. 413/16. P 15	..	3·50	2·75

Designs:—8 t. Lizard and cat (Chencherere Hill); 15 t. Schematics (Diwa Hill); 30 t. Sun through rain (Mikolongwe Hill).

(Des local artist. Litho Harrison)

1972 (9 Aug). *Olympic Games, Munich. W 55 (sideways). P 14 × 14½.*
418	92	3 t. multicoloured	..	10	10
419		8 t. multicoloured	..	10	10
420		15 t. multicoloured	..	15	10
421		30 t. multicoloured	..	35	45
418/21			Set of 4	60	55
MS422		110 × 92 mm. Nos. 418/21. P 14 × 13½		1·25	1·75

93 Arms of Malawi

94 "Adoration of the Kings" (Orcagna)

(Des G. Drummond. Litho Questa)

1972 (20 Oct). *Commonwealth Parliamentary Conference. W 55. P 13½.*
423	93	15 t. multicoloured	..	30	35

(Des V. Whiteley. Litho Questa)

1972 (8 Nov). *Christmas. T 94 and similar vert designs. Multicoloured. W 55. P 14½ × 14.*
424		3 t. Type 94	..	10	10
425		8 t. "Madonna and Child Enthroned" (Florentine School)	..	10	10
426		15 t. "Virgin and Child" (Crivelli)	..	20	10
427		30 t. "Virgin and Child with St. Anne" (Flemish School)	..	45	70
424/7..			*Set of* 4	70	80
MS428		95 × 121 mm. Nos. 424/7 ..		1·10	2·00

"MALAŴI". All issues from No. 429 onwards have a circumflex accent over the "W", to give the correct pronunciation of "Malavi".

95 *Charaxes bohemani*

(Des PAD Studio. Litho Questa)

1973 (7 Feb–5 Apr). *Butterflies. T 95 and similar horiz designs. Multicoloured. W 55 (sideways). P 13½ × 14.*
429		3 t. Type 95	..	20	10
430		8 t. *Uranothauma crawshayi*	..	45	10
431		15 t. *Charaxes acuminatus*	..	65	30
432		30 t. *Amauris ansorgei* (inscr in error "EUPHAEDRA ZADDACHI")		3·00	7·00
433		30 t. *Amauris ansorgei* (inscr corrected) (5 Apr)		3·00	7·00
429/33			*Set of* 5	6·50	13·00
MS434		145 × 95 mm. Nos. 429/32	..	7·00	11·50

96 Livingstone and Map

(Des J.W. Litho Format)

1973 (1 May). *Death Centenary of David Livingstone (1st issue). W 55 (sideways). P 13½ × 14.*
435	96	3 t. multicoloured	..	10	10
436		8 t. multicoloured	..	15	10
437		15 t. multicoloured	..	30	10
438		30 t. multicoloured	..	45	60
435/8 ..			*Set of* 4	90	70
MS439		144 × 95 mm. Nos. 435/8 ..	..	90	1·50

See also Nos. 450/MS451.

97 Thumb Dulcitone

(Des Jennifer Toombs. Litho Questa)

1973 (8 Aug). *Musical Instruments. T 97 and similar multicoloured designs. W 55 (sideways on 8, 15 t. and MS444). P 14.*
440		3 t. Type 97	..	10	10
441		8 t. Hand zither (*vert*)	..	15	10
442		15 t. Hand drum (*vert*).	..	20	10
443		30 t. One-stringed fiddle	..	40	60
440/3 ..			*Set of* 4	70	65
MS444		120 × 103 mm. Nos. 440/3	..	2·50	2·00

98 The Magi

(Des J.W. Litho Format)

1973 (7 Nov). *Christmas. W 55 (sideways). P 13½.*
445	98	3 t. greenish blue, dp lilac & dull ultram		10	10
446		8 t. salmon-red, bluish lilac & red-brn		10	10
447		15 t. reddish mve, greenish bl & dp mve		15	10
448		30 t. orange-yell, bluish lilac & lt lake-brn		30	55
445/8			*Set of* 4	50	60
MS449		165 × 114 mm. Nos. 445/8	..	75	1·40

99 Stained-glass Window, Livingstonia Mission

(Des PAD Studio. Litho Questa)

1973 (12 Dec). *Death Centenary of David Livingstone (2nd issue). W 55 (sideways). P 13½.*
450	99	50 t. multicoloured	..	45	1·00
MS451		71 × 77 mm. No. 450	..	80	1·60

100 Largemouth Black Bass

(Des Sylvia Goaman. Litho Questa)

1974 (20 Feb). *35th Anniv of Malawi Angling Society. T 100 and similar horiz designs. Multicoloured. W 55 (sideways). P 14.*
452		3 t. Type 100	..	20	10
453		8 t. Rainbow Trout	..	25	10
454		15 t. Lake Salmon	..	45	20
455		30 t. Tiger Fish	..	75	75
452/5 ..			*Set of* 4	1·50	95
MS456		169 × 93 mm. Nos. 452/5	..	1·50	1·60

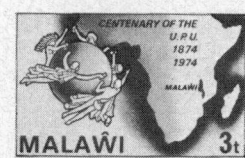

101 U.P.U. Monument and Map of Africa

(Des J. Cooter. Litho J.W.)

1974 (24 Apr). *Centenary of Universal Postal Union. W 55 (sideways). P 13½ (Nos. 460/MS461) or 14½ × 14 (others).*
457	101	3 t. green and ochre	..	10	10
		a. Perf 13½ (pair)			
458		8 t. red and ochre	..	10	10
459		15 t. violet and ochre	..	15	10
460		30 t. indigo and ochre	..	30	70
457/60			*Set of* 4	60	80
MS461		115 × 146 mm. Nos. 457/60	..	65	1·75
		a. Perf 14½ × 14			†

No. 457a comes from normal sheets and not No. MS461. It can also be identified as a marginal single.

102 Capital Hill, Lilongwe

(Des PAD Studio. Litho Questa)

1974 (3 July). *Tenth Anniv of Independence. W 55 (sideways). P 14.*
462	102	3 t. multicoloured	..	10	10
463		8 t. multicoloured	..	10	10
464		15 t. multicoloured	..	10	10
465		30 t. multicoloured	..	25	35
462/5 ..			*Set of* 4	40	40
MS466		120 × 86 mm. Nos. 462/5	..	45	1·00

103 "Madonna of the Meadow" (Bellini)   104 Arms of Malawi

(Des Jennifer Toombs. Litho Enschedé)

1974 (4 Dec). *Christmas. T 103 and similar horiz designs. Multicoloured. W 55 (sideways). P 13 × 13½.*
467		3 t. Type 103	..	10	10
468		8 t. "The Holy Family with Sts. John and Elizabeth" (Jordaens)		10	10
469		15 t. "The Nativity" (Pieter de Grebber)		15	10
470		30 t. "Adoration of the Shepherds" (Lorenzo di Credi)		30	50
467/70			*Set of* 4	50	50
MS471		163 × 107 mm. Nos. 467/70	..	60	1·25

(Des and litho Harrison)

1975 (1 Feb)–84. *Coil stamps. W 55 (sideways). P 14½ × 14.*
472	104	1 t. deep blue	..	10	30
472a		5 t. bright carmine (20.9.84)	..	30	30

105 African Snipe   106 Spur-winged Goose

(Des J.W. Litho Questa)

1975 (19 Feb). *Birds. T 105/6 and similar multicoloured designs. W 55 (sideways on 2, 3, 8, 50 t., 1 k., 4 k.). White, ordinary paper.*

(a) Size as T 105. P 13½ × 14 (1, 5 t.) or 14 × 13½ (others)
473		1 t. Type 105	..	30	90
474		2 t. Double-banded Sandgrouse	..	50	80
475		3 t. Blue Quail	..	1·50	50
476		5 t. Bare-throated Francolin..		3·00	50
477		8 t. Harlequin Quail ..		4·25	55

(b) Size as T 106. P 14
478		10 t. Type 106	..	7·50	50
479		15 t. Barrow's Bustard	..	3·50	2·25
480		20 t. Comb Duck	..	1·00	1·50
481		30 t. Helmet Guineafowl	..	1·25	70
482		50 t. African Pigmy Goose ..		2·00	1·60
483		1 k. Garganey	..	3·00	4·50
484		2 k. White-faced Whistling Duck		12·00	9·50
485		4 k. African Green Pigeon	..	13·00	16·00
473/85			*Set of* 13	48·00	35·00

See also Nos. 501/4.

107 M.V. *Mpasa*   108 *Habenaria splendens*

(Des R. Granger Barrett. Litho J.W.)

1975 (12 Mar). *Ships of Lake Malawi (1st series). T 107 and similar horiz designs. Multicoloured. W 55 (sideways). P 13½.*
486		3 t. Type 107 ..		15	10
487		8 t. M.V. *Ilala II*	..	25	10
488		15 t. M.V. *Chauncy Maples II*	..	40	40
489		30 t. M.V. *Nkwazi*	..	65	80
486/9 ..			*Set of* 4	1·25	1·00
MS490		105 × 142 mm. Nos. 486/9. P 14 ..	..	1·75	2·75

See also Nos. 728/32.

(Des Sylvia Goaman. Litho Questa)

1975 (6 June). *Malawi Orchids. T 108 and similar vert designs. Multicoloured. W 55. P 14.*
491		3 t. Type 108	..	15	10
492		10 t. *Eulophia cucullata*	..	25	10
493		20 t. *Disa welwitschii*	..	40	20
494		40 t. *Angraecum conchiferum*	..	65	80
491/4 ..			*Set of* 4	1·40	1·00
MS495		127 × 111 mm. Nos. 491/4 ..	..	4·50	4·50

10th ACP Ministerial Conference 1975

109 Thick-tailed Bushbaby   **(110)**

(Des R. Granger Barrett. Litho Walsall)

1975 (3 Sept). *Malawi Animals. T* **109** *and similar vert designs. Multicoloured. W* 55 *(inverted). P* 14.

496	3 t. Type 109..			10	10
497	10 t. Leopard ..	..	..	35	10
498	20 t. Roan Antelope	..	..	55	30
499	40 t. Common Zebra ..	..	..	1·00	1·75
496/9			*Set of 4*	1·75	2·00
MS500	88 × 130 mm. Nos. 496/9. W 55 *(sideways)*			2·50	3·00

1975 (1 Oct). *As Nos. 473 etc, but no wmk. Toned, chalk-surfaced paper.*

501	3 t. Blue Quail	..	..	2·50	1·25
502	10 t. Type 106 ..	..	..	2·00	1·25
503	15 t. Barrow's Bustard	..	..	2·00	1·75
504	2 k. White-faced Whistling Duck	..	..	9·50	9·50
501/4 ..			*Set of 4*	14·50	12·50

Nos. 505/13 vacant.

1975 (9 Dec). *Tenth Africa, Caribbean and Pacific Ministerial Conference. No. 482 optd with T* **110**.

514	50 t. African Pigmy Goose	..	..	75	1·10

111 "A Castle with the Adoration of the Magi"   **112** Alexander Graham Bell

(Des PAD Studio. Litho J.W.)

1975 (12 Dec). *Christmas. T* **111** *and similar horiz designs showing religious medallions. Multicoloured. W* 55 *(sideways). P* 13 × 13½.

515	3 t. Type 111	..	..	10	10
516	10 t. "The Nativity"	..	..	15	10
517	20 t. "The Adoration of the Magi"	..	..	20	10
518	40 t. "The Angel appearing to the Shepherds"			50	1·00
515/18			*Set of 4*	80	1·10
MS519	98 × 168 mm. Nos. 515/18. P 14 ..			1·50	2·75

(Des C. Abbott. Litho Questa)

1976 (24 Mar). *Centenary of the Telephone. W* 55. *P* 14.

520	112	3 t. black and dull green	..	10	10
521		10 t. black and magenta	..	10	10
522		20 t. black and light reddish violet		20	10
523		40 t. black and bright blue	..	50	70
520/3 ..			*Set of 4*	80	80
MS524	137 × 114 mm. Nos. 520/3.			1·10	1·75

113 President Banda   **114** Bagnall Diesel Shunter

(Des PAD Studio. Litho J.W.)

1976 (2 July). *Tenth Anniv of the Republic. Multicoloured; frame colour given. W* 55. *P* 13.

525	113	3 t. green	..	10	10
526		10 t. magenta	..	10	10
527		20 t. new blue	..	20	10
528		40 t. dull ultramarine	..	50	70
525/8 ..			*Set of 4*	80	80
MS529	102 × 112 mm. Nos. 524/8. P 13½			95	1·50

(Des G. Drummond. Litho Questa)

1976 (1 Oct). *Malawi Locomotives. T* **114** *and similar horiz designs. Multicoloured. W* 55 *(sideways). P* 14½ × 14.

530	3 t. Type 114..			20	10
531	10 t. "Shire" Class diesel locomotive	..	50	10
532	20 t. Nippon Sharyo diesel locomotive	..	90	45
533	40 t. Hunslet diesel locomotive	..	1·90	2·50
530/3 ..			*Set of 4*	3·25	2·75
MS534	130 × 118 mm. Nos. 530/3			3·25	3·50

Blantyre Mission Centenary 1876-1976

(115)   **116** Child on Bed of Straw

1976 (22 Oct). *Centenary of Blantyre Mission. Nos. 503 and 481 optd with T* **115**.

535	15 t. Barrow's Bustard	..	..	55	70
536	30 t. Helmet Guineafowl	..	..	85	1·40

(Des Jennifer Toombs. Litho Walsall)

1976 (6 Dec). *Christmas. W* 55. *P* 14.

537	116	3 t. multicoloured	..	10	10
538		10 t. multicoloured	..	10	10
539		20 t. multicoloured	..	20	10
540		40 t. multicoloured	..	40	60
537/40			*Set of 4*	70	70
MS541	135 × 95 mm. Nos. 537/40			1·25	1·75

117 Man and Woman   **118** Chileka Airport

(Des G. Hutchins. Litho Questa)

1977 (1 Apr). *Handicrafts. T* **117** *and similar multicoloured designs showing wood-carvings. W* 55 *(sideways on 10 and 20 t.). P* 14.

542	4 t. Type 117 ..	..	..	10	10
543	10 t. Elephant (*horiz*) ..	..	..	15	10
544	20 t. Rhino (*horiz*)	..	..	20	10
545	40 t. Deer	..	..	50	70
542/5 ..			*Set of 4*	80	80
MS546	153 × 112 mm. Nos. 542/5. Wmk sideways		1·50	2·25

(Des Harrison. Litho Walsall)

1977 (12 July). *Transport. T* **118** *and similar horiz designs. Multicoloured. W* 55 *(sideways). P* 14½ × 14.

547	4 t. Type 118 ..	..	..	20	10
548	10 t. Blantyre-Lilongwe Road	..	30	10
549	20 t. M.V. Ilala II	..	90	30
550	40 t. Blantyre-Nacala rail line	..	1·60	1·40
547/50			*Set of 4*	2·75	1·60
MS551	127 × 83 mm. Nos. 547/50			2·75	3·00

119 *Pseudotropheus johanni*   **120** "Madonna and Child with St. Catherine and the Blessed Stefano Maconi" (Borgognone)

(Des R. Granger Barrett. Litho J.W.)

1977 (4 Oct). *Fish of Lake Malawi. T* **119** *and similar horiz designs. Multicoloured. P* 13½. A. *No wmk.* B. *W* 55 *(sideways).*

			A		B	
552	4 t. Type 119 ..		30	10	15	10
553	10 t. *Pseudotropheus livingstoni*	40	10	25	20
554	20 t. *Pseudotropheus zebra*	85	25	—	1·50
555	40 t. *Genyochromis mento*	95	95	95	95
552/5 ..		*Set of 4*	2·25	1·25		†
MS556	147 × 99 mm. Nos. 552/5. P 13	2·50	3·00	4·00	4·50

(Des G. Hutchins. Litho Enschedé)

1977 (21 Nov). *Christmas. T* **120** *and similar vert designs. Multicoloured; frame colours given. No wmk. P* 14 × 13½.

557	4 t. deep blue-green ..	..	..	10	10
558	10 t. light vermilion ..	..	..	10	10
559	20 t. dull violet	..	..	20	10
560	40 t. blue	..	..	50	70
557/60			*Set of 4*	70	70
MS561	150 × 116 mm. Nos. 557/60			2·25	2·50

Designs:—10 t. "Madonna and Child with the Eternal Father and Angels" (Borgognone); 20 t. Bottigella altarpiece (detail, Foppa); 40 t. "Madonna of the Fountain" (van Eyck).

121 "Entry of Christ into Jerusalem" (Giotto)   **122** Nyala

(Des G. Hutchins. Litho Cartor S.A., France)

1978 (1 Mar). *Easter T* **121** *and similar vert designs showing paintings by Giotto. Multicoloured. P* 12 × 12½.

562	4 t. Type 121 ..	..	..	10	10
563	10 t. "The Crucifixion"	..	..	10	10
564	20 t. "Descent from the Cross"	..	20	10
565	40 t. "Jesus appears before Mary"	..	40	55
562/5 ..			*Set of 4*	70	70
MS566	150 × 99 mm. Nos. 562/5 ..			1·00	1·60

(Des G. Hutchins. Litho Enschedé)

1978 (1 June). *Wildlife. T* **122** *and similar multicoloured designs. P* 13½ × 13 (4, 40 *t.*) *or* 13 × 13½ (*others*).

567	4 t. Type 122..			25	10
568	10 t. Lion (*horiz*)	..	..	60	15
569	20 t. Common Zebra (*horiz*)	..	85	60
570	40 t. Mountain Reedbuck	..	1·40	2·00
567/70			*Set of 4*	2·75	2·50
MS571	173 × 113 mm. Nos. 567/70	..	4·50	5·00

123 Malamulo Seventh Day Adventist Church   **124** *Vanilla polylepis*

(Des and litho Walsall)

1978 (15 Nov). *Christmas. Churches. T* **123** *and similar horiz designs. Multicoloured. W* 55 *(sideways). P* 13½.

572	4 t. Type 123 ..	..	..	10	10
573	10 t. Likoma Cathedral	..	..	10	10
574	20 t. St. Michael's and All Angels', Blantyre	20	10
575	40 t. Zomba Catholic Cathedral	..	40	60
572/5 ..			*Set of 4*	70	70
MS576	190 × 105 mm. Nos. 572/5			70	1·50

(Des G. Drummond. Litho J.W.)

1979 (2 Jan). *Orchids. Vert designs as T* **124**. *Multicoloured. W* 55. *P* 13½.

577	1 t. Type 124 ..	..	..	30	10
578	2 t. *Cirrhopetalum umbellatum*	..	30	10
579	5 t. *Calanthe natalensis*	..	30	10
580	7 t. *Ansellia gigantea*	..	30	10
581	8 t. *Tridactyle bicaudata*	..	30	10
582	10 t. *Acampe pachyglossa*	..	30	10
583	15 t. *Eulophia quartiniana*	..	40	15
584	20 t. *Cyrtorchis arcuata (variabilis)*	..	45	30
585	30 t. *Eulophia tricristata*	..	65	30
586	50 t. *Disa hamatopetala*	..	80	50
587	75 t. *Cynorchis glandulosa*	..	1·00	1·00
588	1 k. *Aerangis kotschyana*	..	1·40	80
589	1 k. 50, *Polystachya dendrobiiflora*	..	1·50	1·40
590	2 k. *Disa ornithantha* ..	..	1·75	1·60
591	4 k. *Cyrtorchis praetermissa* ..	..	3·00	3·50
577/91			*Set of 15*	11·50	9·00

125 Tsamba   **126** Train crossing Viaduct

(Des L. Curtis. Litho Questa)

1979 (21 Jan). *National Tree Planting Day. T* **125** *and similar vert designs. Multicoloured. W* 55. *P* 13½.

592	5 t. Type 125 ..	..	..	15	10
593	10 t. Mulanje Cedar	..	..	20	10
594	20 t. Mlombwa	..	..	30	20
595	40 t. Mbawa	..	..	60	75
592/5 ..			*Set of 4*	1·10	1·10
MS596	118 × 153 mm. Nos. 592/5	..	..	1·10	1·75

(Des J.W. Litho Questa)

1979 (17 Feb). *Opening of Salima-Lilongwe Railway. T* **126** *and similar horiz designs. Multicoloured. W* **55** *(sideways)* (5 t.) *or no wmk* (others). P 14½.

597	5 t. Type **126**			25	10
598	10 t. Diesel railcar at station			40	10
599	20 t. Train rounding bend			60	30
600	40 t. Diesel train passing through cutting			85	1·25
597/600			Set of 4	1·90	1·50
MS601	153×103 mm. Nos. 597/600. W **55** (sideways)			4·00	4·25

Examples of an unissued 4 t. value as Type **126** and of a miniature sheet containing this 4 t. value exist from supplies sent to Malawi before it was decided to increase the internal postage rate to 5 t.

127 Young Child

(Des BG Studio. Litho Questa)

1979 (10 July). *International Year of the Child. T* **127** *and similar horiz designs showing young children. Multicoloured; background colours given. W* **55** *(sideways). P* 13½.

602	5 t. green			10	10
603	10 t. red			10	10
604	20 t. mauve			20	10
605	40 t. blue			40	60
602/5			Set of 4	65	70

128 1964 3d. Independence Commemorative Stamp

(Des J.W. Litho Enschedé)

1979 (17 Sept). *Death Centenary of Sir Rowland Hill. T* **128** *and similar horiz designs showing 1964 Independence commemorative stamps. Multicoloured. W* **55** *(sideways). P* 13 × 13½.

606	5 t. Type **128**			10	10
607	10 t. 6d. value			10	10
608	20 t. 1s. 3d. value			20	10
609	40 t. 2s. 6d. value			35	60
606/9			Set of 4	65	70
MS610	163×108 mm. Nos. 606/9			65	1·10

129 River Landscape   130 Limbe Rotary Club Emblem

(Des BG Studio. Litho Format)

1979 (15 Nov). *Christmas. T* **129** *and similar horiz designs showing landscapes. Multicoloured. W* **55** *(sideways). P* 13½ × 14.

611	5 t. Type **129**			10	10
612	10 t. Sunset			10	10
613	20 t. Forest and hill			25	10
614	40 t. Plain and mountain			50	50
611/14			Set of 4	85	65

(Des L. Curtis. Litho J.W.)

1980 (23 Feb). *75th Anniv of Rotary International. T* **130** *and similar vert designs. W* **55**. *P* 13½.

615	5 t. multicoloured			10	10
616	10 t. multicoloured			10	10
617	20 t. multicoloured			30	15
618	40 t. ultramarine and gold			75	1·60
615/18			Set of 4	1·10	1·75
MS619	105 × 144 mm. Nos. 615/18. P 14 × 14½.			1·75	2·00

Designs:—10 t. Blantyre Rotary Club pennant; 20 t. Lilongwe Rotary Club pennant; 40 t. Rotary International emblem.

---

131 Mangochi District Post Office   132 Agate Nodule

(Des C. Abbott. Litho Walsall)

1980 (6 May). *"London 1980" International Stamp Exhibition. T* **131** *and similar horiz designs. W* **55** *(sideways)* P 14½ × 14.

620	5 t. black and blue-green			10	10
621	10 t. black and vermilion			10	10
622	20 t. black and violet			15	10
623	1 k. black and deep blue			65	1·00
620/3			Set of 4	80	1·10
MS624	114 × 89 mm. Nos. 620/3.			2·25	2·25

Designs:–10 t. New Blantyre Sorting Office; 20 t. Mail Transfer Hut, Walala; 1 k. First Nyasaland Post Office, Chiromo.

(Des G. Drummond. Litho J.W.)

1980 (20 Aug). *Gemstones. T* **132** *and similar vert designs. Multicoloured. W* **55**. *P* 13.

625	5 t. Type **132**			50	10
626	10 t. Sunstone			70	10
627	20 t. Smoky Quartz			1·25	30
628	1 k. Kyanite crystal			3·00	4·00
625/8			Set of 4	5·00	4·00

133 Elephants   134 Suni

(Des C. Abbott. Litho J.W.)

1980 (10 Nov). *Christmas. Children's Paintings. T* **133** *and similar horiz designs. Multicoloured. W* **55** *(sideways). P* 13.

629	5 t. Type **133**			15	10
630	10 t. Flowers			15	10
631	20 t. "Shire" class diesel train			30	10
632	1 k. Malachite Kingfisher			95	1·10
629/32			Set of 4	1·40	1·10

(Des G. Drummond. Litho Questa)

1981 (4 Feb). *Wildlife. T* **134** *and similar horiz designs. Multicoloured. W* **55** *(sideways). P* 14.

633	7 t. Type **134**			15	10
634	10 t. Blue Duiker			20	10
635	20 t. African Buffalo			30	15
636	1 k. Lichtenstein's Hartebeest			1·25	1·60
633/6			Set of 4	1·75	1·75

135 "Kanjedza II" Standard "A" Earth Station

(Des L. Curtis. Litho Harrison)

1981 (24 Apr). *International Communications. T* **135** *and similar horiz designs. Multicoloured. W* **55** *(sideways). P* 14½.

637	7 t. Type **135**			10	10
638	10 t. Blantyre International Gateway Exchange			15	10
639	20 t. "Kanjedza I" standard "B" earth station			25	15
640	1 k. "Satellite communications"			1·50	1·50
637/40			Set of 4	1·75	1·60
MS641	101 × 151 mm. Nos. 637/40.			2·00	2·75

136 Maize   137 "The Adoration of the Shepherds" (Murillo)

(Des Jennifer Toombs. Litho Harrison)

1981 (11 Sept). *World Food Day. Agricultural Produce. T* **136** *and similar horiz designs. Multicoloured. W* **55** *(sideways). P* 14.

642	7 t. Type **136**			15	10
643	10 t. Rice			20	10
644	20 t. Finger-millet			30	20
645	1 k. Wheat			1·00	1·40
642/5			Set of 4	1·50	1·50

(Des BG Studio. Litho J.W.)

1981 (26 Nov). *Christmas. Paintings. T* **137** *and similar multicoloured designs. W* **55** *(sideways on 10 and 20 t.). P* 13½ × 13 (7 t., 1 k.) *or* 13 × 13½ (others).

646	7 t. Type **137**			15	10
647	10 t. "The Holy Family" (Lippi) (horiz)			20	10
648	20 t. "The Adoration of the Shepherds" (Louis le Nain) (horiz)			35	10
649	1 k. "The Virgin and Child, St. John the Baptist and an Angel" (Paolo Morando)			90	1·25
646/9			Set of 4	1·40	1·40

138 Impala Herd

(Des A. Theobald. Litho Harrison)

1982 (15 Mar). *National Parks. Wildlife. T* **138** *and similar horiz designs. Multicoloured. P* 14½ × 14.

650	7 t. Type **138**			20	10
651	10 t. Lions			35	10
652	20 t. Greater Kudu			50	15
653	1 k. Greater Flamingoes			2·25	2·25
650/3			Set of 4	3·00	3·00

139 Kamuzu Academy   140 Attacker challenging Goalkeeper

(Des PAD Studio. Litho Questa)

1982 (1 July). *Kamuzu Academy. T* **139** *and similar horiz designs showing buildings. W* **55** *(sideways). P* 14½.

654	7 t. multicoloured			10	10
655	20 t. multicoloured			20	10
656	30 t. multicoloured			30	40
657	1 k. multicoloured			75	1·50
654/7			Set of 4	1·25	1·90

(Des and litho Harrison)

1982 (8 Sept). *World Cup Football Championship, Spain. T* **140** *and similar vert designs. Multicoloured. W* **55**. *P* 14 × 15.

658	7 t. Type **140**			40	10
659	20 t. FIFA World Cup trophy			80	50
660	30 t. Football stadium			1·25	1·40
658/60			Set of 3	2·25	1·50
MS661	80 × 59 mm. 1 k. Football			1·50	1·60

141 Blantyre War Memorial, St. Paul's Church

(Des W. Fenton. Litho Format)

1982 (5 Nov). *Remembrance Day. T* **141** *and similar horiz designs. Multicoloured. W* **55** *(sideways). P* 14½ × 14.

662	7 t. Type **141**			10	10
663	20 t. Zomba war memorial			15	10
664	30 t. Chichiri war memorial			20	30
665	1 k. Lilongwe war memorial			65	2·00
662/5			Set of 4	1·00	2·25

142 Kwacha International Conference Centre   143 "Christ and St. Peter"

(Des Walsall. Litho Format)

1983 (14 Mar). *Commonwealth Day. T* **142** *and similar horiz designs. Multicoloured.* W **55** (*sideways*). *P* 14.
666	7 t. Type 142 ..		10	10
667	20 t. Tea-picking, Mulanje		20	10
668	30 t. World map showing position of Malawi	30	30
669	1 k. President Dr. H. Kamuzu Banda		80	1·25
666/9	..		1·25	1·50

(Des C. Abbott. Litho Format)

1983 (4 Apr). *500th Birth Anniv of Raphael. Details from the cartoon for "The Miraculous Draught of Fishes" Tapestry. T* **143** *and similar multicoloured designs.* W **55** (*sideways on* 30 *t.*). *P* 14.
670	7 t. Type 143 ..		25	10
671	20 t. "Hauling in the Catch"		50	30
672	30 t. "Fishing Village" (*horiz*)..		75	1·00
670/2	..	*Set of* 3	1·40	1·25
MS673	110 × 90 mm. 1 k. "Apostle"	..	1·10	1·25

144 Pair by Lake   **145** Kamuzu International Airport

(Des N. Arlott. Litho Questa)

1983 (11 July). *African Fish Eagle. T* **144** *and similar vert designs.* W **55**. *P* 14.
674	30 t. Type 144 ..	..	80	90
	a. Horiz strip of 5. Nos. 674/8		3·50	
675	30 t. Making gull-like call	..	80	90
676	30 t. Diving on prey ..	..	80	90
677	30 t. Carrying fish	..	80	90
678	30 t. Feeding on catch..	..	80	90
674/8	..	*Set of* 5	3·50	4·00

Nos. 674/8 were printed together, *se-tenant*, in horizontal strips of 5 throughout the sheet, the backgrounds of each design forming a composite picture of Lake Malawi.

(Des A. Theobald. Litho Questa)

1983 (31 Aug). *Bicentenary of Manned Flight. T* **145** *and similar horiz designs. Multicoloured.* W **55** (*sideways*). *P* 14.
679	7 t. Type 145 ..	..	10	10
680	20 t. Kamuzu International Airport (*different*)	25	15
681	30 t. BAC "One Eleven"	..	40	45
682	1 k. Flying boat at Cape Maclear	..	1·10	2·25
679/82	..	*Set of* 4	1·75	2·75
MS683	100 × 121 mm. Nos. 679/82	..	2·00	3·50

146 *Clerodendrum myricoides*   **147** *Melanochromis auratus*

(Des R. Reader. Litho J.W.)

1983 (1 Nov). *Christmas. Flowers. T* **146** *and similar vert designs. Multicoloured. P* 13 (20 *t.*) *or* 14 (*others*).
684	7 t. Type 146 ..	..	40	10
	a. Perf 13		15·00	
685	20 t. *Gloriosa superba* ..	..	90	15
686	30 t. *Gladiolus laxiflorus*	..	1·25	40
687	1 k. *Aframomum angustifolium*	..	2·50	3·00
684/7	..	*Set of* 4	4·50	3·25

(Des L. Curtis. Litho Harrison)

1984 (2 Jan). *Fishes. T* **147** *and similar horiz designs. Multicoloured.* W **55** (*sideways*). *P* 14½ × 14.
688	1 t. Type 147 ..	..	10	15
689	2 t. *Haplochromis compressiceps*	..	15	20
690	5 t. *Labeotropheus fuelleborni*	..	20	20
691	7 t. *Pseudotropheus lombardoi*	..	20	10
692	8 t. Gold *Pseudotropheus zebra*	..	20	10
693	10 t. *Trematocranus jacobfreibergi*	..	20	10
694	15 t. *Melanochromis crabro*	..	30	10
695	20 t. Marbled *Pseudotropheus zebra*	..	30	10
696	30 t. *Labidochromis caeruleus*	..	40	20
697	40 t. *Haplochromis venustus*	..	60	30
698	50 t. *Aulonacara* of Thumbi ..	..	70	50
699	75 t. *Melanochromis vermivorus*	..	90	75
700	1 k. *Pseudotropheus zebra*	..	1·25	1·25
701	2 k. *Trematocranus* spp.	..	2·00	2·50
702	4 k. *Aulonacara* of Mbenje ..	..	2·75	4·50
688/702	..	*Set of* 15	9·25	10·00

Nos. 688 and 691/7 exist with different imprint dates at foot.

NEW INFORMATION

The editor is always interested to correspond with people who have new information that will improve or correct the Catalogue.

148 Smith's Red Hare   **149** Running

(Des Garden Studios. Litho Format)

1984 (2 Feb). *Small Mammals. T* **148** *and similar horiz designs. Multicoloured.* W **55** (*sideways*). *P* 14.
703	7 t. Type 148..	..	30	10
704	20 t. Gambian Sun Squirrel ..	..	70	20
705	30 t. South African Hedgehog	..	1·00	60
706	1 k. Large-spotted Genet	..	2·25	3·50
703/6	..	*Set of* 4	3·75	4·00

(Des C. Collins. Litho Harrison)

1984 (1 June). *Olympic Games, Los Angeles. T* **149** *and similar vert designs. Multicoloured.* W **55** (*sideways*). *P* 14.
707	7 t. Type 149 ..	..	10	10
708	20 t. Boxing	..	25	15
709	30 t. Cycling	..	35	25
710	1 k. Long jumping	..	1·00	1·25
707/10	..	*Set of* 4	1·50	1·50
MS711	90 × 128 mm. Nos. 707/10. Wmk upright	1·50	2·75

150 *Euphaedra neophron*   **151** "The Virgin and Child" (Duccio)

(Des and photo Courvoisier)

1984 (1 Aug). *Butterflies. T* **150** *and similar vert designs. Granite paper. P* 11½.
712	7 t. multicoloured	..	75	10
713	20 t. lemon, blackish brown and red	..	1·25	20
714	30 t. multicoloured	..	1·75	70
715	1 k. multicoloured	..	3·25	3·75
712/15	..	*Set of* 4	6·25	4·25

Designs:—20 t. *Papilio dardanus*; 30 t. *Antanartia schaeneia*; 1 k. *Spindasis nyassae*.

(Des C. Abbott. Litho Harrison)

1984 (22 Oct). *Christmas. Religious Paintings. T* **151** *and similar vert designs. Multicoloured.* W **55**. *P* 14½.
716	7 t. Type 151 ..	..	40	10
717	20 t. "Madonna and Child" (Raphael)	..	90	20
718	30 t. "The Virgin and Child" (ascr to Lippi)	1·40	55
719	1 k. "The Wilton Diptych"	..	2·75	3·25
716/19	..	*Set of* 4	5·00	3·75

152 *Leucopaxillus gracillimus*

(Des A. Jardine. Litho Harrison)

1985 (23 Jan). *Fungi. T* **152** *and similar horiz designs. Multicoloured.* W **55** (*sideways*). *P* 14½ × 14.
720	7 t. Type 152 ..	..	75	10
721	20 t. *Limacella guttata*	..	1·50	30
722	30 t. *Termitomyces eurrhizus*	..	2·00	70
723	1 k. *Xerulina asprata*	..	3·25	3·75
720/3	..	*Set of* 4	6·75	4·25

153 Map showing Member States, and Lumberjack (Forestry)

(Des A. Theobald. Litho Harrison)

1985 (1 Apr). *5th Anniv of Southern African Development Co-ordination Conference. T* **153** *and similar horiz designs showing map and aspects of development.* W **55** (*sideways*). *P* 14.
724	7 t. black, yellowish green and pale green	50	10
725	15 t. black, scarlet-vermilion & salmon pink	80	20
726	20 t. blk, bright bluish violet & bright mauve	2·00	70
727	1 k. black, bright blue and cobalt	..	3·00	3·25
724/7	..	*Set of* 4	5·75	3·75

Designs:—15 t. Radio mast (Communications); 20 t. Diesel locomotive (Transport); 1 k. Trawler and net (Fishing).

154 M.V. *Ufulu*   **155** Stierling's Woodpecker

(Des L. Curtis. Litho Cartor S.A., France)

1985 (3 June). *Ships of Lake Malawi (2nd series). T* **154** *and similar horiz designs. Multicoloured.* W **55** (*sideways*). *P* 13½ × 13.
728	7 t. Type 154..	..	70	10
729	15 t. M.V. *Chauncy Maples II*	..	1·25	20
730	20 t. M.V. *Mtendere*	..	1·75	50
731	1 k. M.V. *Ilala II*	..	3·50	4·00
728/31	..	*Set of* 4	6·50	4·25
MS732	120 × 84 mm. Nos. 728/31. P 13 × 12	6·50	4·75

(Des M. Stringer. Litho Harrison)

1985 (1 Aug). *Birth Bicentenary of John J. Audubon (ornithologist). T* **155** *and similar vert designs. Multicoloured.* W **55**. *P* 14.
733	7 t. Type 155..	..	65	10
734	15 t. Lesser Seedcracker	..	1·25	20
735	20 t. East Coast Akelat	..	1·50	40
736	1 k. Boehm's Bee Eater	..	3·00	3·50
733/6	..	*Set of* 4	5·75	3·75
MS737	130 × 90 mm. Nos. 733/6. Wmk sideways	..	5·75	4·00

156 "The Virgin of Humility" (Jaime Serra)   **157** Halley's Comet and Path of *Giotto* Spacecraft

(Photo Courvoisier)

1985 (14 Oct). *Christmas. Nativity Paintings. T* **156** *and similar vert designs. Multicoloured. Granite paper. P* 11½.
738	7 t. Type 156..	..	25	10
739	15 t. "The Adoration of the Magi" (Stefano da Zevio)	..	50	15
740	20 t. "Madonna and Child" (Gerard van Honthorst)	..	55	20
741	1 k. "Virgin of Zbraslav" (Master of Vissy Brod)	..	2·00	2·00
738/41	..	*Set of* 4	3·00	2·25

(Des N. Shewring. Litho Walsall)

1986 (10 Feb). *Appearance of Halley's Comet. T* **157** *and similar vert designs. Multicoloured.* W **55**. *P* 14½ × 14.
742	8 t. Type 157..	..	20	10
743	15 t. Halley's Comet above Earth	..	30	15
744	20 t. Comet and dish aerial, Malawi	..	40	20
745	1 k. *Giotto* spacecraft	..	1·60	1·60
742/5	..	*Set of* 4	2·25	1·75

158 Two Players competing for Ball   **159** President Banda

(Des and photo Courvoisier)

1986 (26 May). *World Cup Football Championship, Mexico. T* **158** *and similar horiz designs. Multicoloured. Granite paper. P* 11½.
746	8 t. Type 158..	..	40	10
747	15 t. Goalkeeper saving goal	..	65	15
748	20 t. Two players competing for ball (*different*)	..	75	25
749	1 k. Player kicking ball	..	2·75	2·00
746/9	..	*Set of* 4	4·00	2·25
MS750	108 × 77 mm. Nos. 746/9 ..	..	7·50	7·50

(Des and litho Harrison)

1986 (30 June). *20th Anniv of the Republic. T* **159** *and similar vert designs. Multicoloured. P* 14.
751	8 t. Type 159..	..	40	40
752	15 t. National flag	..	50	15
753	20 t. Malawi coat of arms	..	55	25
754	1 k. Kamuzu Airport and emblem of national airline..	..	2·00	1·50
751/4	..	*Set of* 4	3·00	2·10

It is reported that No. 751 was withdrawn locally five days after issue.

160 "Virgin and Child" (Botticelli)

161 Wattled Crane

(Des and photo Courvoisier)

1986 (15 Dec). *Christmas. T* **160** *and similar vert designs showing paintings. Multicoloured. Granite paper. P* 11½.

755	8 t. Type **160**..		30	10
756	15 t. "Adoration of the Shepherds" (Guido Reni)		55	15
757	20 t. "Madonna of the Veil" (Carlo Dolci) ..		70	30
758	1 k. "Adoration of the Magi" (Jean Bourdichon)		3·25	2·00
755/8 ..		*Set of 4*	4·25	2·25

(Des W. Oliver. Litho Walsall)

1987 (16 Feb)–**88**. *Wattled Crane. T* **161** *and similar horiz designs. Multicoloured. P* 14×14½. *(a)* W **55** *(sideways).*

759	8 t. Type **161**..		50	10
760	15 t. Two cranes		90	20
761	20 t. Cranes at nest		1·10	40
762	75 t. Crane in lake		2·50	3·00
759/62		*Set of 4*	4·50	3·25

(b) W w **14** *(sideways).* (10.88).

763	8 t. Type **161**		50	10
764	15 t. Two cranes		90	20
765	20 t. Cranes at nest		1·10	30
766	75 t. Cranes in lake		2·50	3·00
763/6		*Set of 4*	4·50	3·25

162 Locomotive *Shamrock* No. 2, 1902

163 Hippopotamus grazing

(Des and litho Cartor S.A., France)

1987 (25 May). *Steam Locomotives. T* **162** *and similar horiz designs. Multicoloured. P* 14 × 13½.

767	10 t. Type **162**..		65	10
768	25 t. "D" class, No. 8, 1914 ..		1·10	20
769	30 t. *Thistle* No. 1, 1902		1·25	30
770	1 k. "Kitson" class, No. 6, 1903		2·75	2·00
767/70		*Set of 4*	5·25	2·40

(Des and photo Courvoisier)

1987 (24 Aug). *Hippopotamus. T* **163** *and similar vert designs. Multicoloured. Granite paper. P* 12½.

771	10 t. Type **163**		40	10
772	25 t. Hippopotami in water		1·00	20
773	30 t. Female and calf in water		1·10	40
774	1 k. Hippopotami and Cattle Egret		2·50	2·50
771/4		*Set of 4*	4·50	2·75
MS775	78×101 mm. Nos. 771/4		4·50	4·50

164 *Stathmostelma spectabile*

165 African and Staunton Knights

(Des and litho Harrison)

1987 (19 Oct). *Christmas. Wild Flowers. T* **164** *and similar vert designs. Multicoloured. P* 14.

776	10 t. Type **164**..		40	10
777	25 t. *Pentanisia schweinfurthii*		80	20
778	30 t. *Chironia krebsii*..		90	30
779	1 k. *Ochna macrocalyx*		2·25	1·50
776/9		*Set of 4*	4·00	1·90

(Des Jennifer Toombs. Litho Walsall)

1988 (8 Feb). *Chess. T* **165** *and similar vert designs showing local and Staunton chess pieces. Multicoloured. W w* **16**. *P* 14½ × 14.

780	15 t. Type **165**		70	15
781	35 t. Bishops ..		1·25	50
782	50 t. Rooks		1·50	1·25
783	2 k. Queens		4·75	5·00
780/3		*Set of 4*	7·50	6·25

166 High Jumping

167 Scrub Warbler

(Des and litho Harrison)

1988 (13 June). *Olympic Games, Seoul. T* **166** *and similar vert designs. Multicoloured. P* 14.

784	15 t. Type **166**		30	10
785	35 t. Javelin throwing		50	20
786	50 t. Tennis		75	40
787	2 k. Shot-putting ..		1·60	1·75
784/7		*Set of 4*	2·75	2·25
MS788	91×121 mm. Nos. 784/7		2·75	2·50

(Des N. Arlott (10 k.), Courvoisier (others). Litho Questa (10 k.) or photo Courvoisier (others))

1988 (25 July–3 Oct). *Birds. T* **167** *and similar vert designs. Multicoloured. W w* **14** *(sideways) (10 k.) or no wmk (others). Granite paper (1 t. to 4 k.). P* 15×14½ (10 k.) *or* 11½ *(others).*

789	1 t. Type **167**		10	10
790	2 t. Yellow-throated Woodland Warbler		10	10
791	5 t. Moustached Green Tinkerbird		10	10
792	7 t. Waller's Red-winged Starling		10	10
793	8 t. Oriole-Finch		10	10
794	10 t. Starred Robin		10	10
795	15 t. Bar-tailed Trogon		10	10
796	20 t. Green-backed Twin-spot		10	10
797	30 t. African Grey Cuckoo Shrike ..		10	15
798	40 t. Black-fronted Bush Shrike		15	20
799	50 t. White-tailed Crested Flycatcher		15	20
800	75 t. Green Barbet		20	25
801	1 k. Lemon Dove ("Cinnamon Dove")		30	35
802	2 k. Silvery-cheeked Hornbill		60	65
803	4 k. Crowned Eagle		1·25	1·40
804	10 k. Anchieta's Sunbird (3 Oct)		3·00	3·25
789/804		*Set of 16*	5·50	5·75

167a Rebuilt Royal Exchange, 1844

168 "Madonna in the Church" (Jan van Eyck)

(Des D. Miller (15 t.), L. Curtis and D. Miller (35 t.), A. Theobald and D. Miller (50 t.), E. Nisbet and D. Miller (2 k.). Litho B.D.T.)

1988 (24 Oct). *300th Anniv of Lloyd's of London. T* **167a** *and similar multicoloured designs. W w* **14** *(sideways on 35, 50 t.). P* 14.

805	15 t. Type **167a**		30	10
806	35 t. Opening ceremony, Nkula Falls Hydro-electric Power Station		60	20
807	50 t. Air Malawi "1-11" airliner (*horiz*) ..		85	40
808	2 k. *Seawise University* (formerly *Queen Elizabeth*) on fire, Hong Kong, 1972		2·75	2·25
805/8		*Set of 4*	4·00	2·75

(Des and litho Harrison)

1988 (28 Nov). *Christmas. T* **168** *and similar vert designs showing paintings. Multicoloured. P* 14.

809	15 t. Type **168**		20	10
810	35 t. "Virgin, Infant Jesus and St. Anna" (da Vinci)..		35	20
811	50 t. "Virgin and Angels" (Cimabue) ..		45	40
812	2 k. "Virgin and Child" (Baldovinetti Apenio)		1·75	1·60
809/12		*Set of 4*	2·50	2·00

169 *Serranochromis robustus*

(Des and litho Harrison)

1989 (10 Apr). *50th Anniv of Malawi Angling Society. T* **169** *and similar horiz designs. Multicoloured. P* 14.

813	15 t. Type **169**		50	10
814	35 t. Lake Salmon		95	30
815	50 t. Yellow Fish		1·40	80
816	2 k. Tiger Fish		3·75	4·00
813/16		*Set of 4*	6·00	4·75

170 Independence Arch, Blantyre

(Des and litho Harrison)

1989 (26 June). *25th Anniv of Independence. T* **170** *and similar horiz designs. Multicoloured. P* 14.

817	15 t. Type **170**		30	10
818	35 t. Grain silos		55	30
819	50 t. Capital Hill, Lilongwe		75	65
820	2 k. Reserve Bank Headquarters		2·25	2·75
817/20		*Set of 4*	3·50	3·50

171 Blantyre Digital Telex Exchange

(Des and litho Harrison)

1989 (30 Oct). *25th Anniv of African Development Bank. T* **171** *and similar horiz designs. Multicoloured. P* 14.

821	15 t. Type **171**		30	10
822	40 t. Dzalanyama steer		55	30
823	50 t. Mikolongwe heifer		75	65
824	2 k. Zebu bull		2·25	2·75
821/4		*Set of 4*	3·50	3·50

172 Rural House with Verandah

(Des and litho Harrison)

1989 (1 Dec). *25th Anniv of Malawi–United Nations Co-operation. T* **172** *and similar horiz designs. Multicoloured. P* 14.

825	15 t. Type **172**		30	10
826	40 t. Rural house		55	30
827	50 t. Traditional hut and modern houses		75	65
828	2 k. Tea plantation		2·25	2·75
825/8		*Set of 4*	3·50	3·50

173 St. Michael and All Angels Church

(Des and litho Harrison)

1989 (15 Dec). *Christmas. Churches of Malawi. T* **173** *and similar horiz designs. Multicoloured. P* 14.

829	15 t. Type **173**		30	10
830	40 t. Catholic Cathedral, Limbe		55	30
831	50 t. C.C.A.P. Church, Nkhoma		75	65
832	2 k. Cathedral, Likoma Island		2·25	2·75
829/32		*Set of 4*	3·50	3·50

174 Ford "Sedan", 1915

175 Player heading Ball into Net

(Des and litho Cartor, France)

1990 (2 Apr). *Vintage Vehicles. T* **174** *and similar horiz designs. Multicoloured. P* 14×13½.

833	15 t. Type **174**		30	10
834	40 t. Two-seater Ford, 1915		55	30
835	50 t. Ford pick-up, 1915		75	65
836	2 k. Chevrolet bus, 1930		2·25	2·75
833/6		*Set of 4*	3·50	3·50
MS837	120×85 mm. Nos. 833/6. P 13×12		3·75	4·00

(Des and litho Questa)

1990 (14 June). *World Cup Football Championship, Italy. T* **175** *and similar vert designs. Multicoloured. P* 14.
838	15 t. Type **175**	30	10
839	40 t. Player tackling	60	30
840	50 t. Player scoring goal	80	55
841	2 k. World Cup	2·25	2·50
838/41	*Set of* 4	3·50	3·00
MS842	88×118 mm. Nos. 838/41	3·75	4·00

176 Anniversary Emblem on Map

177 *Aerangis kotschyana*

(Des and litho Questa)

1990 (24 Aug). *Tenth Anniv of Southern Africa Development Co-ordination Conference. T* **176** *and similar horiz designs. Multicoloured. P* 14.
843	15 t. Type **176**	20	10
844	40 t. Chambo Fish	35	30
845	50 t. Cedar plantation	45	40
846	2 k. Male Nyala (antelope)	2·00	2·25
843/6	*Set of* 4	2·75	2·75
MS847	174×116 mm. Nos. 843/6	3·25	3·50

(Litho Cartor, France)

1990 (26 Nov). *Orchids. T* **177** *and similar vert designs. Multicoloured. P* 13¹/₂×14.
848	15 t. Type **177**	30	10
849	40 t. Angraecum eburneum	60	30
850	50 t. Aerangis luteo-alba rhodostica	80	50
851	2 k. Cyrtorchis arcuata whytei	2·50	2·50
848/51	*Set of* 4	3·75	3·00
MS852	85×120 mm. Nos. 848/51. P 12×13	4·00	4·00

178 "The Virgin and the Child Jesus" (Raphael)

179 Buffalo

(Litho Cartor, France)

1990 (7 Dec). *Christmas. Paintings by Raphael. T* **178** *and similar vert designs. Multicoloured. P* 13¹/₂×14.
853	15 t. Type **178**	20	10
854	40 t. "Transfiguration" (detail)	40	25
855	50 t. "St. Catherine of Alexandrie" (detail)	50	40
856	2 k. "Transfiguration"	2·00	2·50
853/6	*Set of* 4	2·75	3·00
MS857	85×120 mm. Nos. 853/6. P 12×13	3·25	3·50

(Litho Cartor)

1991 (23 Apr). *Wildlife. T* **179** *and similar horiz designs. Multicoloured. P* 14×13¹/₂.
858	20 t. Type **179**	25	10
859	60 t. Cheetah	65	45
860	75 t. Greater Kudu	75	60
861	2 k. Black Rhinoceros	2·25	2·50
858/61	*Set of* 4	3·50	3·25
MS862	120×85 mm. Nos. 858/61. P 13×12	3·50	3·50

180 Chiromo Post Office, 1891

181 Red Locust

(Litho Cartor)

1991 (2 July). *Centenary of Postal Services. T* **180** *and similar horiz designs. Multicoloured. P* 14×13¹/₂.
863	20 t. Type **180**	25	10
864	60 t. Re-constructed mail exchange hut at Walala	60	45
865	75 t. Mangochi post office	75	60
866	2 k. Satellite Earth station	2·00	2·25
863/6	*Set of* 4	3·25	3·00
MS867	119×83 mm. Nos. 863/6. P 13×12	3·25	3·25

(Litho Cartor)

1991 (26 Sept). *Insects. T* **181** *and similar vert designs. Multicoloured. P* 13¹/₂×14.
868	20 t. Type **181**	25	10
869	60 t. Weevil	60	45
870	75 t. Cotton Stainer Bug	75	60
871	2 k. Pollen Beetle	2·25	2·50
868/71	*Set of* 4	3·50	3·25

182 Child in Manger

183 Red Bishop

(Litho Cartor)

1991 (26 Nov). *Christmas. T* **182** *and similar vert designs. Multicoloured. P* 13¹/₂×14.
872	20 t. Type **182**	20	10
873	60 t. Adoration of the Kings and Shepherds	50	40
874	75 t. Nativity	60	50
875	2 k. Virgin and Child	1·60	1·75
872/5	*Set of* 4	2·75	2·50

(Des Jennifer Toombs. Litho Questa)

1992 (7 July). *Birds. T* **183** *and similar horiz designs. Multicoloured. P* 14.
876	75 t. Type **183**	40	45
	a. Sheetlet. Nos. 876/95	7·25	
877	75 t. Lesser Striped Swallow	40	45
878	75 t. Long-crested Eagle	40	45
879	75 t. Lilac-breasted Roller	40	45
880	75 t. African Paradise Flycatcher	40	45
881	75 t. White-fronted Bee Eater	40	45
882	75 t. White-winged Black Tern	40	45
883	75 t. African Fire Finch	40	45
884	75 t. White-browed Robin Chat	40	45
885	75 t. African Fish Eagle	40	45
886	75 t. Malachite Kingfisher	40	45
887	75 t. Lesser Masked Weaver	40	45
888	75 t. Barn Owl	40	45
889	75 t. Variable Sunbird	40	45
890	75 t. Lesser Flamingo	40	45
891	75 t. Crowned Crane	40	45
892	75 t. African Pitta	40	45
893	75 t. African Darter	40	45
894	75 t. White-faced Whistling Duck	40	45
895	75 t. African Pied Wagtail	40	45
876/95	*Set of* 20	7·25	8·00

Nos. 876/95 were printed together, *se-tenant*, as a sheetlet of 20, forming a composite design.

184 Long Jumping

185 "The Angel Gabriel" (detail, "The Annunciation") (Philippe de Champaigne)

(Des G. Vasarhelyi. Litho B.D.T.)

1992 (28 July). *Olympic Games, Barcelona. T* **184** *and similar horiz designs. Multicoloured. P* 13¹/₂.
896	20 t. Type **184**	15	10
897	60 t. High Jumping	25	25
898	75 t. Javelin	30	30
899	2 k. Running	85	90
896/9	*Set of* 4	1·50	1·50
MS900	110×100 mm. Nos. 896/9	1·50	1·75

(Des D. Miller. Litho Walsall)

1992 (9 Nov). *Christmas. Religious Paintings. T* **185** *and similar vert designs. Multicoloured. P* 14.
901	20 t. Type **185**	15	10
902	75 t. "Virgin and Child" (Bernardino Luini)	35	35
903	95 t. "Virgin and Child" (Sassoferrato)	45	45
904	2 k. "Virgin Mary" (detail, "The Annunciation") (De Champaigne)	1·10	1·25
901/4	*Set of* 4	1·90	1·90

186 "Voyager 2" passing Saturn

187 *Strychnos spinosa*

(Des A. Theobald. Litho Cartor)

1992 (7 Dec). *International Space Year. T* **186** *and similar horiz designs. Multicoloured. P* 13¹/₂.
905	20 t. Type **186**	15	10
906	75 t. Centre of galaxy	35	35
907	95 t. Kanjedza II Standard A Earth Station	45	45
908	2 k. Communications satellite	1·10	1·25
905/8	*Set of* 4	1·90	1·90

(Des Jennifer Toombs. Litho Cartor)

1993 (21 Mar). *Indigenous Fruits. T* **187** *and similar vert designs. Multicoloured. P* 13¹/₂×14.
909	20 t. Type **187**	10	10
910	75 t. Adansonia digitata	20	25
911	95 t. Ximenia caffra	25	30
912	2 k. Uapaca kirkiana	60	65
909/12	*Set of* 4	1·00	1·25

POSTAGE DUE STAMPS

D 1

D 2

(Typo D.L.R.)

1950 (1 July). *Wmk Mult Script CA. P* 14.
D1	D 1	1d. scarlet	2·00	8·00
D2		2d. ultramarine	5·00	15·00
D3		3d. green	7·50	4·75
D4		4d. purple	12·00	30·00
D5		6d. yellow-orange	20·00	60·00
D1/5		*Set of* 5	42·00	£110

1967 (1 Sept). *W* **55**. *P* 11¹/₂.
D 6	D 2	1d. carmine	15	2·00
D 7		2d. sepia	20	2·00
D 8		4d. reddish violet	25	2·25
D 9		6d. blue	25	2·50
D10		8d. emerald	35	2·75
D11		1s. black	45	3·00
D6/11		*Set of* 6	1·50	13·00

1971 (5 Feb). *As Nos. D6/11, but values in tambalas. W* **55**. *P* 11¹/₂.
D12	D 2	2 t. greenish drab	30	2·00
D13		4 t. bright mauve	60	2·00
D14		6 t. royal blue	45	2·25
D15		8 t. dull green	50	2·25
D16		10 t. blackish brown	75	2·25
D12/16		*Set of* 5	2·40	9·75

(Litho Walsall)

1975–84. *Design redrawn, with circumflex accent over "W" of "MALAWI". P* 14. (*a*) *W* **55** (*sideways*).
D17	D 2	2 t. chestnut (15.9.75)	1·25	6·00
D18		2 t. brown (14.6.82)	10	10
D19		4 t. deep mauve (14.6.82)	10	10
D20		6 t. royal blue (9.84)	10	10
D21		8 t. green (9.84)	10	10
D22		10 t. black (14.6.82)	10	10
D17/22		*Set of* 6	1·40	6·00

(*b*) *No wmk*
D23	D 2	2 t. brown (19.10.77)	2·75	3·00
D24		4 t. mauve (19.10.77)	2·75	3·00
D25		8 t. green (15.12.78)	1·75	3·00
D26		10 t. brownish grey (19.10.77)	3·00	3·25
D23/6		*Set of* 4	9·00	11·00

1989. *As Nos. D17/26, but design redrawn smaller, 17×20¹/₂ mm instead of 17¹/₂×21 mm. No wmk. P* 15×14.
D27	D 2	2 t. light brown	10	10
D28		4 t. bright purple	10	10
D29		6 t. bright blue	10	10
D31		10 t. brownish black	10	10
D27/31		*Set of* 4	10	10

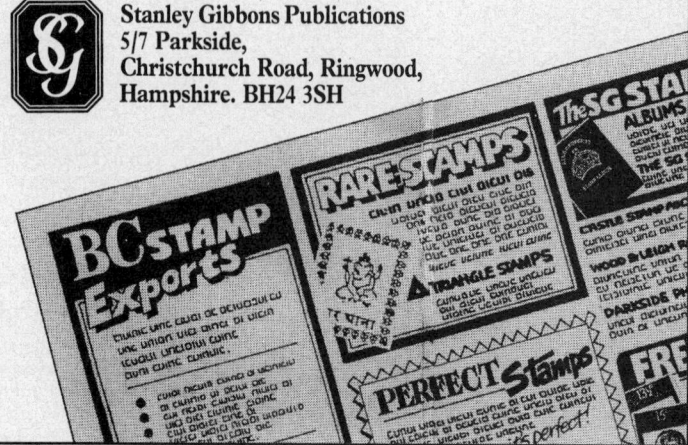

Malaysia

The Federation of Malaysia was set up on 16 September 1963, and consisted of the former Malayan Federation, the State of Singapore and the two former Crown Colonies in Borneo, Sabah (North Borneo) and Sarawak. Singapore left the federation to become an independent republic on 9 August 1965.

Malaysia now consists of thirteen States (11 in Peninsular Malaysia and two in Borneo), together with the Federal Territories of Kuala Lumpur and Labuan.

The philatelic history of the component parts of the federation is most complex. Under this heading are now listed previous issues made by the present States of the Federation.

The method adopted is to show the general issues for the area first, before dealing with the issues for the individual States. The section is divided as follows:

   I. STRAITS SETTLEMENTS
  II. FEDERATED MALAY STATES
 III. MALAYAN POSTAL UNION
 IV. MALAYA (BRITISH MILITARY ADMINISTRATION)
  V. MALAYAN FEDERATION
 VI. MALAYSIA
VII. MALAYAN STATES—Johore, Kedah, Kelantan, Malacca, Negri Sembilan (with Sungei Ujong), Pahang, Penang, Perak, Perlis, Selangor, Trengganu
VIII. JAPANESE OCCUPATION OF MALAYA
 IX. THAI OCCUPATION OF MALAYA
  X. LABUAN
 XI. SABAH (NORTH BORNEO)
XII. JAPANESE OCCUPATION OF NORTH BORNEO
XIII. SARAWAK
XIV. JAPANESE OCCUPATION OF SARAWAK

I. STRAITS SETTLEMENTS

The three original Settlements, Malacca, Penang (with Province Wellesley) and Singapore (including Christmas Island and Cocos (Keeling) Islands) were formed into a Crown Colony during 1867. Labuan was attached to the colony in 1896, becoming the fourth Settlement in 1906.

The first known prestamp cover with postal markings from Penang (Prince of Wales Island) is dated March 1806 and from Malacca, under British civil administration, February 1841. The civil post office at Singapore opened on 1 February 1823.

The stamps of India were used at all three post offices from late in 1854 until the Straits Settlements became a separate colony on 1 September 1867.

The Indian stamps were initially cancelled by dumb obliterators and their use in the Straits Settlements can only be identified from complete covers. In 1856 cancellations of the standard Indian octagonal type were issued, numbered "B 109" for Malacca, "B 147" for Penang and "B 172" for Singapore.

A   B

C

The Penang and Singapore octagonals were replaced by a duplex type, consisting of a double-ringed datestamp and a diamond-shaped obliterator containing the office number, in 1863 and 1865 respectively.

D

E

PRICES. Catalogue prices in this section are for stamps with clearly legible, if partial, examples of the postmarks.

MALACCA

Stamps of INDIA *cancelled with Type* A.

1854. (*Nos.* 2/34).
Z1	½ a. blue (Die I)	..	..	..	..	£550
Z2	1 a. red (Die I)	..	..	..	..	£450
Z3	1 a. dull red (Die II)	..	..	..	..	£500
Z4	2 a. green	..	..	..	..	£750
Z5	4 a. blue and red (Head Die II) (*cut-to-shape*)					£850
Z5a	4 a. blue and red (Head Die III) (*cut-to-shape*)					£850

1855. (*Nos.* 35/6).
Z6	8 a. carmine (Die I)/*blue glazed*	..				£140

1856–64. (*Nos.* 37/49).
Z7	½ a. pale blue (Die I)	..	..	..	..	75·00
Z8	1 a. brown	..	..	..	..	65·00
Z9	2 a. yellow-buff	..	..	..	..	65·00
Z10	2 a. yellow	..	..	..	..	75·00
Z11	4 a. green	..	..	..	..	£120
Z12	8 a. carmine (Die I)	..	..	..	..	90·00

1860. (*Nos.* 51/3).
Z13	8 p. purple/*bluish*	..	..	..	..	£180
Z14	8 p. purple/*white*	..	..	..	..	90·00

1865. (*Nos.* 54/65).
Z15	4 a. green	..	..	..	..	£110

PENANG

Stamps of INDIA *cancelled with Type* B.

1854. (*Nos.* 2/34).
Z20	½ a. blue (Die I)	..	..	..	..	£120
Z21	1 a. red (Die I)	..	..	..	..	85·00
Z22	2 a. green	..	..	..	..	£120
Z23	4 a. blue and pale red (Head Die I)	..	..		£650
Z24	4 a. blue and red (Head Die II)	..	..		£700
Z25	4 a. blue and red (Head Die III)	..	..		£550

1855. (*Nos.* 35/6).
Z26	4 a. black/*blue glazed*	..	..	..		32·00
Z27	8 a. carmine (Die I)/*blue glazed*	..	..		32·00
	a. Bisected (4 a.) (1860) (on cover)	..		£17000

1856–64. (*Nos.* 37/49).
Z28	½ a. pale blue (Die I)	..	..	..	..	32·00
Z29	1 a. brown	..	..	..	..	20·00
Z30	2 a. dull pink	..	..	..	..	28·00
Z31	2 a. yellow-buff	..	..	..	..	25·00
Z32	2 a. yellow	..	..	..	..	25·00
Z33	2 a. orange	..	..	..	..	28·00
Z34	4 a. black	..	..	..	..	18·00
Z35	8 a. carmine (Die I)	..	..	..	..	24·00

1860. (*Nos.* 51/3).
Z36	8 p. purple/*white*	..	..	..	..	55·00

Stamps of INDIA *cancelled with Type* D.

1856–64. (*Nos.* 37/49).
Z40	1 a. brown	..	..	..	..	18·00
Z41	2 a. yellow	..	..	..	..	23·00
Z42	4 a. black	..	..	..	..	20·00
Z43	4 a. green	..	..	..	..	55·00
Z44	8 a. carmine (Die I)	..	..	..		22·00

1860. (*Nos.* 51/3).
Z45	8 p. purple/*white*	..	..	..	..	35·00
Z46	8 p. mauve	..	..	..	..	35·00

1865. (*Nos.* 54/65).
Z47	8 p. purple	..				
Z48	1 a. deep brown	..	..	..		17·00
Z49	2 a. yellow	..	..	..		20·00
Z50	4 a. green	..	..	..		55·00
Z51	8 a. carmine (Die I)	..	..			

1866–67. (*Nos.* 69/72).
Z52	4 a. green (Die I)	..	..	..	..	55·00

SINGAPORE

Stamps of INDIA *cancelled with Type* C.

1854. (*Nos.* 2/34).
Z60	½ a. blue (Die I)	..	..	..	..	80·00
Z61	1 a. red (Die I)	..	..	..	..	65·00
Z62	1 a. dull red (Die II)	..	..	..	..	85·00
Z63	1 a. red (Die III)	..	..	..	..	£450
Z64	2 a. green	..	..	..	..	65·00
	a. Bisected (1 a.) (1857) (on cover)	..			
Z65	4 a. blue and pale red (Head Die I)	..			£550
Z66	4 a. blue and red (Head Die II)	..	..		£600
Z67	4 a. blue and red (Head Die III)	..	..		£450

1855. (*Nos.* 35/6).
Z68	4 a. black/*blue glazed*	..	..	..		18·00
	a. Bisected (2 a.) (1859) (on cover)	..		£4250
Z69	8 a. carmine/*blue glazed*	..	..		20·00
	a. Bisected (4 a.) (1859) (on cover)	..		£19000

1856–64. (*Nos.* 37/49).
Z70	½ a. pale blue (Die I)	..	..	..		13·00
Z71	1 a. brown	..	..	..	..	14·00
	a. Bisected (½ a.) (1859) (on cover)	..		£18000
Z72	2 a. dull pink	..	..	..	..	20·00
Z73	2 a. yellow-buff	..	..	..		15·00
Z74	2 a. yellow	..	..	..	..	15·00
Z75	2 a. orange	..	..	..	..	17·00
Z76	4 a. black	..	..	..	..	13·00
	a. Bisected diagonally (2 a.) (1859) (on cover)	..		£6500
Z77	4 a. green	..	..	..	..	48·00
Z78	8 a. carmine (Die I)	..	..	..		16·00
	a. Bisected (4 a.) (1859) (on cover)	..		£18000

1860. (*Nos.* 51/3).
Z79	8 p. purple/*bluish*	..	..	..		£160
Z80	8 p. purple/*white*	..	..	..		27·00
	a. Bisected diagonally (4 p.) (1862) (on cover)		£19000
Z81	8 p. mauve	..	..	..	..	27·00

1865. (*Nos.* 54/65).
Z82	½ a. blue (Die I)	..	..	..		14·00
Z83	8 p. purple	..	..	..	..	45·00
Z84	1 a. deep brown	..	..	..		13·00
Z85	2 a. yellow	..	..	..	..	15·00
Z86	2 a. orange	..	..	..	..	15·00
Z87	4 a. green	..	..	..	..	48·00
Z88	8 a. carmine (Die I)	..	..	..		£170

1866–67. (*Nos.* 69/72).
Z89	4 a. green (Die I)	..	..	..		45·00
Z90	6 a. 8 p. slate	..	..	..		65·00

OFFICIAL STAMPS

1866–67. (*Nos.* O6/14).
Z91	½ a. pale blue	..	..	..	..	£110
Z92	2 a. yellow	..	..	..	..	£200

Stamps of INDIA *cancelled with Type* E.

1856–64. (*Nos.* 37/49).
Z100	1 a. brown	..	..	..		£140
Z101	2 a. yellow	..	..	..		£170
Z102	4 a. black	..	..	..		£170
Z103	8 a. carmine (Die I)	..	..			£170

1860. (*Nos.* 51/3).
Z104	8 p. purple/*white*	..	..	..		£170

1865. (*Nos.* 54/65).
Z105	2 a. yellow	..	..	..		£140
Z106	2 a. orange	..	..	..		£140
Z107	4 a. green	..	..	..		£180

PRICES FOR STAMPS ON COVER	
Nos. 1/9	*from* × 10
Nos. 11/19	*from* × 8
Nos. 20/47	*from* × 7
Nos. 48/9	*from* × 10
Nos. 50/71	*from* × 5
No. 72	—
Nos. 73/8	*from* × 6
No. 80	*from* × 10
Nos. 82/5	*from* × 5
Nos. 86/7	*from* × 10
Nos. 88/94	*from* × 5
Nos. 95/105	*from* × 6
Nos. 106/9	*from* × 10
Nos. 110/21	*from* × 5
No. 122	—
Nos. 123/6	*from* × 4
Nos. 127/38	*from* × 3
Nos. 139/40	—
Nos. 141/51	*from* × 12
Nos. 152/67	*from* × 3
Nos. 168/9	—
Nos. 193/212	*from* × 3
Nos. 213/15	—
Nos. 216/17	*from* × 10
Nos. 218/40a	*from* × 3
Nos. 240b/d	—
Nos. 241/55	*from* × 15
Nos. 256/9	*from* × 4
Nos. 260/98	*from* × 3
Nos. D1/6	*from* × 20

PRINTERS. All Straits Settlements issues were printed in typography by De La Rue & Co, Ltd, London, *unless otherwise stated.*

THREE HALF CENTS   **32 CENTS**
      (1)

1867 (1 Sept). *Nos.* 54, 59, 61, 64 *and* 73 *of India surch as* T 1 *or* 2 (24 *c.*, 32 *c.*) *by De La Rue. W* 13 (*Elephant's head*) *of India. P* 14.
1	1½ c. on ½ a. blue (Die I) (R.)	..	55·00	£150
2	2 c. on 1 a. deep brown (R.)	..	55·00	50·00
3	3 c. on 1 a. deep brown (B.)	..	60·00	55·00
4	4 c. on 1 a. deep brown (Bk.)	..	£120	£150
5	6 c. on 2 a. yellow (P.)	..	£250	£150
6	8 c. on 2 a. yellow (G.)	..	80·00	30·00

7		12 c. on 4 a. green (R.)	.. ..	£375 £180
	a.	Surch double		£650
8		24 c. on 8 a. rose (Die II) (B.)		£170 60·00
9		32 c. on 2 a. yellow (Bk.)		£180 65·00

The 32 c. was re-issued for postal use in 1884.
No. 7a. is only known unused.

1869 (?). *No. 1 with "THREE HALF" deleted and "2" written above, in black manuscript.*

10		2 on 1½ c. on ½ a. blue		£4000 £2500

This stamp has been known from very early days and was apparently used at Penang, but nothing is known of its history.

5   6   7

8   9

1867 (Dec)–72. *Wmk Crown CC. P 14. Ornaments in corners differ for each value.*

11	5	2 c. brown (6.68)	.. ..	13·00 1·75
	a.	Yellow-brown		14·00 1·75
	b.	Deep brown		45·00 7·50
12		4 c. rose (7.68)		20·00 4·00
	a.	Deep rose		26·00 4·75
13		6 c. dull lilac (1.68)		48·00 10·00
	a.	Bright lilac		48·00 10·00
14	6	8 c. orange-yellow		70·00 5·50
	a.	Orange		70·00 7·00
15		12 c. blue		60·00 4·50
	a.	Ultramarine		60·00 6·50
16	7	24 c. blue-green		65·00 3·50
	a.	Yellow-green		£110 18·00
17	8	30 c. claret (12.72)		85·00 7·00
18	9	32 c. pale red		£225 55·00
19		96 c. grey		£150 28·00
	a.	Perf 12½ (6.71)		£1100 £225

Five Cents. (10)   **Seven Cents.** (11)

1879 (May). *Nos. 14a and 18 surch with T 10 and 11.*

20	6	5 c. on 8 c. orange	.. ..	55·00 80·00
	a.	No stop after "Cents"		£400 £425
	b.	"F i" spaced		£425 £450
21	9	7 c. on 32 c. pale red		60·00 70·00
	a.	No stop after "Cents"		£500 £550

The no stop error occured once in the setting.

10 cents. (12)

10 (a)   **10** (b)   **10** (c)   **10** (d)

10 (e)   **10** (f)   **10** (g)   **10** (h)

10 (i)   **10** (j)   **10** (jj)   **10** (k)   **10** (l)

(a) "1" thin curved serif and thin foot, "0" narrow.
(b) "1" thick curved serif and thick foot; "0" broad. Both numerals heavy.
(c) "1" as (a); "0" as (b)
(d) "1" as (a) but thicker; "0" as (a)
(e) As (a) but sides of "0" thicker.
(f) "1" as (d); "0" as (e)
(g) As (a) but "0" narrower.
(h) "1" thin, curved serif and thick foot; "0" as (g)
(i) "1" as (b); "0" as (a)
(j) "1" as (d); "0" as (g) but raised.
(jj) "1" as (a) but shorter, and with shorter serif and thicker foot; "0" as (g) but level with "1".
(k) "1" as (jj); "0" as (d)
(l) "1" straight serif; "0" as (d).

1880 (Mar). *No. 17 surch with T 12 (showing numerals (a) to (jj)).*

22		10 c. on 30 c. claret (a)	.. ..	£110 45·00
23		10 c. on 30 c. claret (b)		£100 40·00
24		10 c. on 30 c. claret (c)		£1000 £250
25		10 c. on 30 c. claret (d)		£450 95·00
26		10 c. on 30 c. claret (e)		£1700 £425
27		10 c. on 30 c. claret (f)		£1700 £425
28		10 c. on 30 c. claret (g)		£600 £180
29		10 c. on 30 c. claret (h)		£1700 £425
30		10 c. on 30 c. claret (i)		£1700 £425
31		10 c. on 30 c. claret (j)		£1700 £425
32		10 c. on 30 c. claret (jj)		£1700 £425

Nos. 22/32 come from the same setting of 60 (6 × 10)

containing twenty examples of No. 22 (R.1/1-2, 1/4, 1/6, 2/1-6, 3/1, 3/3, 3/5, 4/1, 4/3-4, 10/1, 10/3-5), twenty-two of No. 23 (R.4/1, 5/1-6, 6/1-6, 7/1, 8/2-4, 9/1-5), six of No. 25 (R.1/5, 3/2, 3/4, 4/2, 4/5, 10/2), four of No. 28 (R.7/2-5), two of No. 24 (R.9/6, 10/6) and one each of Nos. 26 (R.3/2), 27 (R.1/3), 29 (R.7/6), 30 (R.8/1), 31 (R.8/6) and 32 (R.8/5).

No. 23 is known with large stop after "cents" and also with stop low.

1880 (April). *No. 17 surch as T 12, but without "cents.", showing numerals (a) to (c), (g), (j), (k) and (l).*

33		10 on 30 c. claret (a)	.. ..	70·00 35·00
34		10 on 30 c. claret (b)		80·00 40·00
35		10 on 30 c. claret (c)		£250 £100
36		10 on 30 c. claret (g)		£550 £225
37		10 on 30 c. claret (i)		£1200 £550
38		10 on 30 c. claret (k)		£1200 £550
39		10 on 30 c. claret (l)		£1200 £550

Nos. 33/9 were surcharged from an amended setting of 60 (6×10) of which only 58 positions have been identified. Of those known No. 33 occurs on twenty-four (R. 6/1-6, 7/1-6, 8/1-6, 9/1-2, 9/6, 10/1-3), No. 34 on twenty (R. 1/2-6, 2/2-6, 3/1-6, 4/3-5, 5/6), No. 35 on eight (R. 2/1, 4/2, 4/6, 5/1-5). No. 36 on three (R. 9/3-5) and Nos. 37 (R. 10/6), 38 (R. 10/4) and 39 (R. 10/5) on one each.

The first and fourth positions in the first vertical column have not been identified. A single example in the Royal Collection shows the "1" as (b) and "0" as (g) which may come from one of these positions, but this has not been confirmed.

5 cents. (13)   **5 cents.** (14)   **5 cents.** (15)

1880 (Aug). *No. 14a surch with T 13 to 15.*

41	13	5 c. on 8 c. orange	.. ..	65·00 80·00
42	14	5 c. on 8 c. orange		55·00 70·00
43	15	5 c. on 8 c. orange		£180 £225

Surcharged in a setting of 60 (6 × 10) with T 13 on rows one to four, T 14 on rows five to nine and T 15 on row ten.

10 cents. (16)   **5 cents.** (17)

1880–81. *Nos. 13, 15/a and 17 surch with T 16.*

44		10 c. on 6 c. lilac (11.81)	..	32·00 6·00
	a.	Surch double		— £1300
45		10 c. on 12 c. ultramarine (1.81)		38·00 16·00
	a.	Blue		26·00 9·00
46		10 c. on 30 c. claret (12.80)		£160 65·00

A second printing of the 10 c. on 6 c. has the surcharge heavier and the "10" usually more to the left or right of "cents".

1882 (Jan). *No. 12 surch with T 17.*

47		5 c. on 4 c. rose	.. ..	£160 £180

18   19

1882 (Jan). *Wmk Crown CC. P 14.*

48	18	5 c. purple-brown	..	65·00 65·00
49	19	10 c. slate (Optd S. £170)		£180 55·00

1882. *Wmk Crown CA. P 14.*

50	5	2 c. brown (Aug)	..	£180 25·00
51		4 c. rose (April)		85·00 4·00
52	6	8 c. orange (Sept)		2·00 35
53	19	10 c. slate (Oct)		2·25 50

For the 4 c. in deep carmine see No. 98.

1884 (Sept). *No. 75 additionally surch with large numeral as T 24 in red.*

TWO CENTS 20a "S" wide   **TWO CENTS** 20b "E" and "S" wide   **TWO CENTS** 20c "N" wide

TWO CENTS 20d All letters narrow   **TWO CENTS** 20e "EN" and "S" wide   **TWO CENTS** 20f "E" wide

1883 (Apr). *Nos. 52 and 18 surch with T 20a/f.*

54	20a	2 c. on 8 c. orange	..	85·00 65·00
55	20b	2 c. on 8 c. orange		85·00 65·00
56	20c	2 c. on 8 c. orange		85·00 65·00
57	20d	2 c. on 8 c. orange		60·00 45·00
	a.	Surch double		£1400 £850
58	20e	2 c. on 8 c. orange		£200 £160
59	20a	2 c. on 32 c. pale red		£325 £100
60	20f	2 c. on 32 c. pale red		£375 £110
	a.	Surch double		

The 8 c. was surcharged using one of two triplet settings, either 54 + 55 + 56 or 57 + 57 + 57, applied to rows 2 to 10. A single handstamp, either No. 57 or No. 58, was then used to complete row 1. The 32 c. was surcharged in the same way with a triplet of 59 + 60 + 59 and a single handstamp as No. 60.

2 Cents. (21)   **4 Cents** (22)   **8 Cents** (23)

1883 (June–July). *Nos. 51 and 15 surch with T 21.*

61		2 c. on 4 c. rose	..	50·00 55·00
	a.	"s" of "Cents" inverted		£850 £1000
62		2 c. on 12 c. blue (July)		£120 65·00
	a.	"s" of "Cents" inverted		£1700 £1400

The inverted "S" error occurred once in the setting of 60.

Broken oval above "O" of "POSTAGE" (Lower right pane R. 10/5)

1883 (July)–91. *Wmk Crown CA. P 14.*

63	5	2 c. pale rose	..	20·00 1·75
	a.	Bright rose (1889)		1·75 15
64		4 c. pale brown		15·00 1·25
	a.	Broken oval		£100 25·00
	b.	Deep brown		22·00 2·75
	ba.	Broken oval		£150 35·00
	c.	Olive-bistre		£350 £275
	ca.	Broken oval		
65	18	5 c. blue (8.83)		5·50 30
66	5	6 c. lilac (11.84)		16·00 8·00
	a.	Violet		1·60 1·75
67	6	12 c. brown-purple		40·00 6·50
68	7	24 c. yellow-green (2.84)		55·00 3·75
	a.	Blue-green		2·75 3·00
69	8	30 c. claret (9.91)		7·00 4·50
70	9	32 c. orange-vermilion (1.87)		5·50 1·50
71		96 c. olive-grey (8.88)		75·00 35·00
63a/71			Set of 9	£140 48·00
63/65, 67		Optd "Specimen"	Set of 4	£450

For the 4 c. in deep carmine and 12 c. in claret see Nos. 98 and 102.

1884 (Feb–Aug). *Nos. 65, 15 and 67 surch with T 22 or 23.*

72	18	4 c. on 5 c. blue (Aug)		£2000 £2500
73		4 c. on 5 c. blue (R.) (Aug)		75·00 65·00
74	6	8 c. on 12 c. blue		£150 80·00
75		8 c. on 12 c. brown-purple (Aug)		£130 90·00
	a.	Inverted "8"		†
	b.	"s" of "Cents" low (R. 5/1)		£650

1884 (Aug). *No. 65 surch with T 20d/f.*

76	20d	2 c. on 5 c. blue	..	65·00 80·00
77	20e	2 c. on 5 c. blue	..	65·00 80·00
	a.	Pair with and without surch		
	b.	Surch double		
78	20f	2 c. on 5 c. blue	..	65·00 80·00

Surcharged as a triplet, 77 + 76 + 78. On No. 76 "TS" are dropped below the line.

8 (24)   **3 CENTS** (25)   **THREE CENTS** (26)

1884 (Sept). *No. 75 additionally surch with large numeral as T 24 in red.*

80	6	8 on 8 c. on 12 c. dull purple	..	£140 £150
	a.	Surch T 24 double		£2500
	b.	Surch T 23 in blue		£3500
	c.	"s" of "Cents" low		£700

Examples as No. 75, but with Type 23 in blue, were further surcharged in error.

A similar "4" surcharge in red on No. 73 exists from a trial printing from which seven examples are known, all used on an official's correspondence (*Price £8000 used*).

1885. *No. 65 and T 9 in new colour, wmk Crown CA, surch with T 25 or 26.*

82	25	3 c. on 5 c. blue (Sept)	..	75·00 £180
	a.	Surch double		£1400
83	26	3 c. on 32 c. pl mag (Dec) (Optd S. £100)		1·60 2·50
	a.	Deep magenta		1·00 90

The surcharge on No. 82 was applied locally by a triplet setting. No. 83 was surcharged by De La Rue in complete panes.

3 cents (27)   **2 Cents** (28)

1886 (Apr). *No. 48 surch with T 27.*

84	18	3 c. on 5 c. purple-brown		£100 £110

The surcharge on No. 84 was applied by a triplet setting.

1887 (July). *No. 65 surch with T 28.*

85	18	2 c. on 5 c. blue	..	14·00 30·00
	a.	"C" of "Cents" omitted		— £1600
	b.	Surch double		£400 £325

The surcharge on No. 85 was applied by a triplet setting.

10 CENTS   **THIRTY CENTS**

(29)   (30)

1891 (Nov). *Nos. 68 and 70 surch with T 29 and 30.*
86 **7** 10 c. on 24 c. yellow-green .. .. 1·50 1·25
        a. Narrow "0" in "10" (R. 4/6) .. 25·00 28·00
87 **9** 30 c. on 32 c. orange-vermilion .. .. 4·75 3·50
The "R" of "THIRTY" and "N" of "CENTS" are found wide or narrow and in all possible combinations.

ONE CENT

ONE CENT

(31)   (32)

1892. *Stamps of 1882–91 (wmk Crown CA) surch with T 31.*
88 1 c. on 2 c. rose (Mar) .. .. 1·25 1·50
89 1 c. on 4 c. brown (Apr) .. .. 3·75 4·00
        a. Surch double £600
        b. Broken oval .. .. .. 40·00 40·00
90 1 c. on 6 c. lilac (Feb) .. .. 1·00 2·50
        a. Surch double, one inverted .. £650 £550
91 1 c. on 8 c. orange (Jan) .. .. 1·00 60
92 1 c. on 12 c. brown-purple (Mar) .. 4·00 9·00
88/92 .. .. *Set of 5* 10·00 16·00
The three settings used for Nos. 88/92 contained various combinations of the following varieties: "ON" of "ONE" and "N" of "CENT" wide; "O" wide, "O" of "ONE" narrow and "N" of "CENT" wide; "O" narrow and both letters "N" wide; "ON" narrow, and "N" of "CENT" wide; "O" wide and both letters "N" narrow; "ON" wide and "N" of "CENT" narrow; "ON" and "N" of "CENT" narrow; "O" narrow "N" of "ONE" wide and "N" of "CENT" narrow. Antique "N" and "E" letters also occur.

1892–94. *Colours changed. Wmk Crown CA. P 14. Surch with T 32 and 26 by De la Rue.*
93 **6** 1 c. on 8 c. green (3.92) 40 75
94 **9** 3 c. on 32 c. carmine-rose (6.94) .. 2·00 70
        a. Surch omitted £2250
93/94 Optd "Specimen" .. .. *Set of 2* 85·00
No. 94a comes from a sheet found at Singapore on which all stamps in the upper left pane had the surcharge omitted. Five of the vertical inter-panneau pairs still exist with the surcharge omitted on the upper stamp (*Price £12000 unused*). The only used example of the error is on cover.

33   34   (35)

4 cents.

1892 (Mar)–**99.** *Wmk Crown CA. P 14.*
95 **33** 1 c. green (9.92) 40 20
        a. Repaired "S" .. .. 60·00 30·00
96 3 c. carmine-rose (2.95) .. .. 6·50 30
        a. Malformed "S" .. .. £100 50·00
97 3 c. brown (3.99) .. .. 2·50 50
        a. Repaired "S" .. .. £100 50·00
        b. Yellow-brown .. .. 2·50 55
98 **5** 4 c. deep carmine (7.99) .. 2·75 1·25
        a. Broken oval .. .. 35·00 30·00
99 **18** 5 c. brown (6.94) .. .. 2·50 90
100 5 c. magenta (7.99) .. .. 1·75 2·00
101 **6** 8 c. ultramarine (6.94) .. 3·75 30
        a. Bright blue .. .. 5·00 35
102 12 c. claret (3.94) .. .. 7·50 8·50
103 **33** 25 c. purple-brown and green .. 13·00 4·50
        a. Repaired "S" .. .. £140 75·00
        b. Dull purple and green .. 13·00 4·25
104 50 c. olive-green and carmine .. 17·00 2·50
        a. Repaired "S" .. .. £180 75·00
105 **34** $5 orange and carmine (10.98) .. £275 £275
        a. Repaired "S" £1200
99/105 .. .. *Set of 11* £300 £275
99/101, 103/5 Optd "Specimen" .. *Set of 10* £250
For illustrations of the Repaired and Malformed "S" varieties see above No. 28 of Seychelles.

1898 (26 Dec). *T 18 and 6 surch with T 35 at Singapore.*
106 4 c. on 5 c. brown (No. 99) .. .. 75 4·25
107 4 c. on 5 c. blue (No. 65) .. .. 1·25 5·50
        a. Surch double .. .. — £700
108 4 c. on 8 c. ultramarine (No. 101) .. 80 2·50
        a. Surch double £600 £500
        b. Bright blue (No. 101a) 50 70
106/8b .. .. .. *Set of 3* 2·25 9·50
Nos. 107 and 108b exist with stop spaced 1½ mm from the "S" (R. 10/6).

FOUR CENTS

(36)   37   38

1899 (Mar). *T 18 (wmk Crown CA. P 14), surch with T 36 by De La Rue.*
109 4 c. on 5 c. carmine (Optd S. £30) .. 30 30
        a. Surch omitted £9000
No. 109a is only known unused.

1902 (Apr)–**03.** *Wmk Crown CA. P 14.*
110 **37** 1 c. grey-green (7.02) .. .. 55 1·10
        a. Pale green .. .. 2·50 2·00
111 3 c. dull purple and orange .. .. 1·00 15
112 4 c. purple/*red* (9.02) .. .. 2·25 30
113 **38** 5 c. dull purple (8.02) .. .. 1·75 65
114 8 c. purple/*blue* .. .. 3·00 20
115 10 c. purple and black/*yellow* (9.02) .. 13·00 85
116 **37** 25 c. dull purple and green (8.02) .. 7·50 3·75
117 **38** 30 c. grey and carmine (7.02) .. 12·00 8·00
118 **37** 50 c. deep green and carmine (9.02) .. 14·00 15·00
        a. Dull green and carmine .. 17·00 16·00
119 **38** $1 dull purple and black (9.02) .. 20·00 45·00
120 **37** $2 dull purple and black (9.02) .. 45·00 45·00
121 **38** $5 dull green and brown-orange (10.02) £130 95·00
122 **37** $100 pur & grn/*yell* (3.03) (Optd S. £225) £5000
110/21 .. .. *Set of 12* £225 £190
110/21 Optd "Specimen" .. .. *Set of 12* £200

39   40

41   42

(Des N. Trotter and W. Egerton)

1903 (Dec)–**04.** *Wmk Crown CA. P 14.*
123 **39** 1 c. grey-green .. .. 50 3·75
124 **40** 3 c. dull purple (1.04) .. .. 5·00 2·50
125 **41** 4 c. purple/*red* (4.04) .. .. 1·50 30
126 **42** 8 c. purple/*blue* (7.04) .. .. 24·00 1·25
123/6 .. .. *Set of 4* 28·00 7·00
123/6 Optd "Specimen" .. .. *Set of 4* £100

1904 (Aug)–**10.** *Wmk Multiple Crown CA. Ordinary paper (1 c. to $1 and $5) or chalk-surfaced paper ($2, $25, $100). P 14.*
127 **39** 1 c. deep green (9.04) .. .. 1·50 10
        a. Chalk-surfaced paper (12.05) .. 3·00 90
128 **40** 3 c. dull purple 75 30
        a. Chalk-surfaced paper (8.06) .. 2·75 45
        b. Plum (2.08) .. .. 3·75 70
129 **41** 4 c. purple/*red* (6.05) .. .. 2·50 30
        a. Chalk-surfaced paper (10.05) .. 3·00 30
130 **38** 5 c. dull purple (12.06) .. .. 3·00 2·00
        a. Chalk-surfaced paper (12.06) .. 4·50 3·00
131 **42** 8 c. purple/*blue* (8.05) .. .. 6·50 60
        a. Chalk-surfaced paper (12.05) .. 6·50 1·25
132 **38** 10 c. purple and black/*yellow* (8.05) .. 3·00 40
        a. Chalk-surfaced paper (11.05) .. 4·75 1·00
133 **37** 25 c. dull purple and green (1.05) .. 10·00 11·00
        a. Chalk-surfaced paper (11.05) .. 12·00 11·00
134 **38** 30 c. grey and carmine (3.05) .. 22·00 2·50
        a. Chalk-surfaced paper (3.06) .. 24·00 2·50
135 **37** 50 c. dull green and carmine (10.05) .. 20·00 8·50
        a. Chalk-surfaced paper (11.06) .. 13·00 8·00
136 **38** $1 dull green and black (10.05) .. 27·00 11·00
        a. Chalk-surfaced paper (3.06) .. 18·00 8·50
137 **37** $2 dull purple and black (10.05) .. 70·00 70·00
138 **38** $5 dull green and brown-orange (10.05) 95·00 95·00
        a. Chalk-surfaced paper (1.08) .. 95·00 95·00
139 **37** $25 grey-grn & blk (7.06) (Optd S. £120) £800 £800
140 $100 purple and green/*yellow* (6.10) .. £6500
127/38 .. .. *Set of 12* £225 £180

STRAITS SETTLEMENTS.   **Straits Settlements.**

(43)   (44)

STRAITS SETTLEMENTS.

FOUR CENTS.

(45)

1906 (Dec)–**07.** *T 18 of Labuan (Nos. 116c etc.) optd with T 43 or 44 (10 c.), or additionally surch with T 45, in black (No. 145), claret (No. 151) or brown-red (others) at Singapore. P 13½–14.*
141 1 c. black and purple (p 14½–15) .. 38·00 75·00
142 2 c. black and green £140 £160
        a. Perf 14½–15 .. .. £130
143 3 c. black and sepia (1.07) .. .. 14·00 70·00
144 4 c. on 12 c. black and yellow .. 1·75 6·00
        a. No stop after "CENTS" (R. 1/8, 6/8) .. £100
145 4 c. on 16 c. green and brown (Blk.) .. 1·75 5·00
        a. "STRAITS SETTLEMENTS" in both brown-red and black .. £450 £450
        b. Ditto. In vert pair with normal .. £1900

146 4 c. on 18 c. black and pale brown .. 1·25 4·50
        a. No stop after "CENTS" (R. 1/8, 6/8) .. 90·00
        b. "FOUR CENTS" and bar double .. £3500
        c. "FOUR CENTS" and bar 1½ mm below normal position (pair with normal) .. £275
147 8 c. black and vermilion .. .. 1·25 6·50
148 10 c. brown and slate .. .. 3·25 4·25
        a. No stop after "SETTLEMENTS" (R. 1/4, 6/4) .. £120
149 25 c. green and greenish blue (1.07) .. 4·50 22·00
        a. Perf 14½–15 .. .. 60·00 75·00
        b. Perf 13½–14 comp 14½–15 .. £150
150 50 c. dull purple and lilac (1.07) .. 9·50 48·00
151 $1 claret and orange (Claret) (1.07) .. 40·00 75·00
        a. Perf 14½–15 .. .. £150
141/51 .. .. .. *Set of 11* £200 £425
Nos. 141/51 were overprinted by a setting of 50 (10×5) applied twice to the sheets of 100. The "FOUR CENTS" surcharges were applied separately by a similar setting.
No. 145a shows impressions of Type 43 in both brown-red and black. It is known from one complete sheet and the top half of another.
No. 146b occurred on row 5 from one sheet only. No. 146c occurred on R. 4/10 and 9/10 of the first printing.
The 1 c. and 2 c. also exist perf 14 all round and are rare.

46   47

1906 (Sept)–**12.** *Wmk Mult Crown CA. Ordinary paper (1 c. to 10 c.) or chalk-surfaced paper (21 c. to $500). P 14.*
152 **39** 1 c. blue-green (3.10) .. .. 7·50 70
153 **40** 3 c. red (6.08) .. .. 1·25 10
154 **41** 4 c. red (7.07) .. .. 5·50 1·25
155 4 c. dull purple (2.08) .. .. 2·25 10
        a. Chalk-surfaced paper (1.12) .. 3·25 40
156 4 c. claret (9.11) 75 80
157 **38** 5 c. orange (4.09) .. .. 2·75 50
158 **42** 8 c. blue .. .. 1·75 30
159 **38** 10 c. purple/*yellow* (7.08) .. 1·50 20
        a. Chalk-surfaced paper (5.12) .. 4·50 1·00
160 **46** 21 c. dull purple and claret (11.10) .. 6·00 26·00
161 **37** 25 c. dull and bright purple (7.09) .. 6·50 2·75
162 **38** 30 c. purple and orange-yellow (11.09) .. 24·00 1·50
163 **46** 45 c. black/*green* (11.10) .. 2·50 3·50
164 **37** 50 c. black/*green* (4.10) .. 4·00 2·00
165 **38** $1 black and red/*blue* (10.10) .. 10·00 3·50
166 **37** $2 green and red/*yellow* (12.09) .. 17·00 17·00
167 **38** $5 green and red/*green* (11.09) .. 70·00 48·00
168 **47** $25 pur & blue/*bl* (5.11) (Optd S. £150) £700 £500
169 $500 purple & orge (5.10) (Optd S. £750) £50000
152/67 .. .. .. *Set of 16* £140 95·00
153/67 Optd "Specimen" .. *Set of 15* £200
Beware of dangerous forgeries of No. 169.

48   49   50

51   52   53

54

1912–23. *$25, $100 and $500 as T 47, but with head of King George V. Wmk Mult Crown CA. Ordinary paper (Nos. 193/6, 198/201, 203) or chalk-surfaced paper (others). P 14.*
193 **48** 1 c. green (9.12) .. .. 3·25 50
        a. Pale green (1.14) .. .. 3·50 40
        b. Blue-green (1917) .. .. 4·50 90
194 1 c. black (2.19) 30 30
195 **52** 2 c. green (10.19) 35 30
196 **49** 3 c. red (2.13) .. .. 1·50 40
        a. Scarlet (2.17) 40 10
197 **50** 4 c. dull purple (3.13) 80 30
        a. Wmk sideways .. .. † £1100
198 4 c. rose-scarlet (2.19) .. .. 1·00 15
        a. Carmine .. .. 1·25 20
199 **51** 5 c. orange (8.12) .. .. 1·50 45
        a. Yellow-orange .. .. 2·00 45
200 **52** 6 c. dull claret (3.20) .. .. 1·75 50
        a. Deep claret .. .. 4·50 2·50
201 8 c. ultramarine (3.13) 70 30
202 **51** 10 c. purple/*yellow* (8.12) .. 1·00 30
        a. White back (9.13) (Optd S. £27) .. 75 50
        b. On lemon (1916) (Optd S. £42) .. 10·00 90

203	51	10 c. deep bright blue (2.19)		5·50	30
		a. *Bright blue*		4·00	30
204	53	21 c. dull and bright purple (11.13)		4·00	7·00
205	54	25 c. dull purple and mauve (7.14)		6·00	4·25
206		25 c. dull purple and violet (1919)		24·00	5·00
207	51	30 c. dull purple and orange (12.14)		4·00	1·50
208	53	45 c. black/*green* (*white back*) (12.14)		6·50	14·00
		a. *On blue-green, olive back* (7.18) (Optd S. £27)		3·00	10·00
		b. *On emerald back* (6.22)		2·75	13·00
209	54	50 c. black/*green* (7.14)		5·50	2·00
		a. *On blue-green, olive back* (1918)		9·00	3·00
		b. *On emerald back* (10.21)		9·00	3·50
		c. *On emerald back (Die II)* (3.23) (Optd S. £27)		2·75	3·00
210	51	$1 black and red/*blue* (10.14)		8·50	6·50
211	54	$2 grn & red/*yell* (7.15) (Optd S. £28)		9·50	22·00
		a. *White back* (7.14)		6·50	23·00
		b. *On orange-buff* (1920)		45·00	55·00
		c. *On pale yellow* (1921)		48·00	60·00
212	51	$5 grn & red/*grn* (4.15) (Optd S. £28)		60·00	32·00
		a. *White back* (11.13)		50·00	25·00
		b. *On blue-green, olive back* (1918)		80·00	42·00
		c. *On emerald back* (6.21)		£110	65·00
		d. *Die II* (1923) (Optd S. £55)		70·00	45·00
213	–	$25 purple and blue/*blue* (Optd S. £100)		£600	£225
		a. Break in scroll		£1000	
		b. Broken crown and scroll		£1000	
214	–	$100 blk & carm/*bl* (8.12) (Optd S. £225)		£3000	
		a. Break in scroll		£3750	
		b. Broken crown and scroll		£3750	
215	–	$500 purple and orange-brown (8.12) (Optd S. £500)		£27000	
		a. Break in scroll		£32000	
		b. Broken crown and scroll		£32000	

193/212 .. .. *Set of 20* £110 70·00
193/210, 211a, 212a Optd "Specimen" *Set of 19* £375

The 6 c. is similar to T **52**, but the head is in a beaded oval as in T **53**. The 2 c., 6 c. (and 12 c. below) have figures of value on a circular ground while in the 8 c. this is of oval shape.

For illustrations of the varieties on Nos. 213/15 see above No. 58 of Leeward Islands.

RED CROSS

2^{C.}

(55)

MALAYA-
BORNEO
EXHIBITION.

(56)

1917 (1 May). *Surch with T* **55**.

216	49	2 c. on 3 c. scarlet		1·50	22·00
		a. No stop (R. 2/3)		£150	£300
217	50	2 c. on 4 c. dull purple		1·50	22·00
		a. No stop (R. 2/3)		£150	£300

Nos. 216a and 217a occur in the first setting only.

Type I   Type II

Two types of duty plate in the 25 c. In Type II the solid shading forming the back of the figure 2 extends to the top of the curve; the upturned end of the foot of the 2 is short; two background lines above figure 5; c close to 5; STRAITS SETTLEMENTS in taller letters.

1921–33. *Wmk Mult Script CA. Ordinary paper* (1 c. to 6 c., 10 c. (No. 230), 12 c.) *or chalk-surfaced paper* (*others*). *P* 14.

218	48	1 c. black (3.22)		30	10
219	52	2 c. green (5.21)		30	10
220		2 c. brown (12.25)		6·00	2·25
221	49	3 c. green (9.23)		1·25	70
222	50	4 c. carmine-red (10.21)		2·00	3·25
223		4 c. bright violet (8.24)		30	10
224		4 c. orange (8.29)		85	10
225	51	5 c. orange (Die II) (5.21)		1·25	40
		a. Die I (7.22)		85	15
		ab. Wmk sideways			†£1200
226		5 c. brown (Die II) (2.32)		1·00	10
		a. Die I (1933)		3·50	10
227	52	6 c. dull claret (10.22)		2·00	15
228		6 c. rose-pink (2.25)		12·00	5·50
229		6 c. scarlet (1.27)		2·25	10
230	51	10 c. bright blue (Die I) (3.21)		1·75	40
231		10 c. purple/*yellow* (Die I) (6.25)		2·25	3·75
		a. Die II. *On pale yellow* (11.26)		1·50	10
		b. Die I. *On pale yellow* (1933)		2·00	15
232	52	12 c. bright blue (1.22)		70	10
233	53	21 c. dull and bright purple (2.23)		4·75	28·00
234	54	25 c. dull purple and mauve (Die I, Type I) (5.23)		24·00	55·00
		a. Die II, Type I (9.23)		15·00	2·50
		b. Die II. Type II (1927)		3·25	1·60
235	51	30 c. dull purple & orange (Die I) (5.21)		13·00	22·00
		a. Die II (1923)		2·00	50
236	53	35 c. dull purple & orange-yellow (8.22)		9·50	5·00
		a. *Dull purple and orange*		3·50	5·00
237		35 c. scarlet and purple (4.31)		8·00	7·00
238	54	50 c. black/*emerald* (9.25)		1·25	40
239	51	$1 black and red/*blue* (6.22)		5·00	45
240	54	$2 green and red/*pale yellow* (5.25)		9·50	8·00
240a	51	$5 green and red/*green* (8.26)		55·00	30·00
240b	–	$25 pur & blue/*bl* (5.23) (Optd S. £100)		£300	75·00
		ba. Break in scroll		£550	
		bb. Broken crown and scroll		£550	
240c	–	$100 black and carmine/*blue* (5.23) (Optd S. £180)		£1500	£700
		ca. Break in scroll		£2000	
		cb. Broken crown and scroll		£2000	

240d	–	$500 purple and orange-brown (4.23) (Optd S. £325)		£15000	
		da. Break in scroll		£18000	
		db. Broken crown and scroll		£18000	

218/40a .. .. .. *Set of 24* £110 85·00
218/40a Optd/Perf "Specimen" .. *Set of 24* £350
Nos. 240b/d are as Type **47**, but with portrait of George V.
An 8 c. in carmine was prepared but not issued (Optd "Specimen" £130).

The paper of No. 231b is the normal *pale yellow* at the back, but with a bright yellow surface. No. 231 is on paper of a *pale lemon* tint and the impression is smudgy.

For illustrations of the varieties on Nos. 240b/d see above No. 58 of Leeward Islands.

1922 (31 Mar). *T* **48** *and* **50** *to* **54**, *overprinted with T* **56**.

(a) Wmk Mult Crown CA

241		2 c. green		19·00	60·00
242		4 c. scarlet		3·75	16·00
243		5 c. orange		3·50	12·00
244		8 c. ultramarine		1·75	6·00
245		25 c. dull purple and mauve (No. 202)		3·00	19·00
246		45 c. black/*blue-green* (olive back)		3·00	16·00
		a. *On green (white back)*		75·00	
247		$1 black and red/*blue*		£100	£350
248		$2 green and red/*orange-buff*		22·00	85·00
		a. *On pale yellow*		50·00	£130
249		$5 green and red/*blue-green* (olive back)		£190	£275

(b) Wmk Mult Script CA

250		1 c. black		60	6·50
251		2 c. green		1·40	11·00
252		4 c. carmine-red		1·75	16·00
253		5 c. orange (Die II)		2·50	30·00
254		10 c. bright blue (Die I)		2·25	18·00
255		$1 black and red/*blue* (Die II)		15·00	75·00

241/55 .. .. *Set of 11* £225 £475

Nos. 241/55 were overprinted by stereo which repeated a setting of 12 (6×2). The following varieties therefore occur ten times on each sheet of 120: (a) Small second "A" in "MALAYA." (b) No stop. (c) No hyphen. (d) Oval last "O" in "BORNEO," (e) "EXH.BITION".

1935 (6 May). *Silver Jubilee. As Nos.* 114/17 *of Jamaica, but ptd by Waterlow & Sons. P* 11×12.

256		5 c. ultramarine and grey		65	20
257		8 c. green and indigo		1·50	1·25
258		12 c. brown and deep blue		2·75	1·50
259		25 c. slate and purple		2·75	3·25

256/9 .. .. *Set of 4* 7·00 5·75
256/9 Perf "Specimen" .. *Set of 4* 85·00

57

58

1936 (1 Jan)–**37**. *Chalk-surfaced paper. Wmk Mult Script CA. P* 14.

260	57	1 c. black (1.1.37)		30	20
261		2 c. green (1.2.36)		30	20
262		4 c. orange (15.6.36)		60	30
263		5 c. brown (1.8.36)		30	10
264		6 c. scarlet (1.2.36)		70	50
265		8 c. grey		50	30
266		10 c. dull purple (1.7.36)		1·25	30
267		12 c. bright ultramarine (1.9.36)		2·00	20
268		25 c. dull purple and scarlet (1.2.36)		1·00	30
269		30 c. dull purple and orange		1·25	2·00
270		40 c. scarlet and dull purple		1·25	2·25
271		50 c. black/*emerald* (1.9.36)		1·75	70
272		$1 black and red/*blue* (1.7.36)		10·00	70
273		$2 green and scarlet (1.4.36)		15·00	10·00
274		$5 green and red/*emerald* (1.1.37)		32·00	10·00

260/74 .. .. *Set of 15* 60·00 27·00
260/74 Perf "Specimen" .. *Set of 15* £150

1937 (12 May). *Coronation. As Nos.* 118/20 *of Jamaica.*

275		4 c. orange		30	10
276		8 c. grey-black		65	10
277		12 c. bright blue		90	60

275/7 .. .. *Set of 3* 1·75 65
275/7 Perf "Specimen" .. *Set of 3* 55·00

1937–41. *Chalk-surfaced paper. Wmk Mult Script CA. P* 14 *or* 15×14 (15 c.). (a) *Die I* (*printed at two operations*).

278	58	1 c. black (1.1.38)		2·50	10
279		2 c. green (6.12.37)		12·00	10
280		4 c. orange (1.1.38)		10·00	10
281		5 c. brown (19.11.37)		16·00	20
282		6 c. scarlet (10.1.38)		7·50	20
283		8 c. grey (26.1.38)		38·00	10
284		10 c. dull purple (8.11.37)		5·50	10
285		12 c. ultramarine (10.1.38)		5·50	10
286		25 c. dull purple and scarlet (11.12.37)		38·00	85
287		30 c. dull purple and orange (1.12.37)		38·00	1·50
288		40 c. scarlet and dull purple (20.12.37)		9·50	2·00
289		50 c. black/*emerald* (26.1.38)		7·00	10
290		$1 black and red/*blue* (26.1.38)		8·00	15
291		$2 green and scarlet (26.1.38)		20·00	3·75
292		$5 green and red/*emerald* (26.1.38)		24·00	3·00

(b) Die II (*printed at one operation*)

293	58	2 c. green (28.12.38)		25·00	10
294		2 c. orange (6.10.41)		1·25	4·50
295		3 c. green (*ordinary paper*) (5.9.41)		2·75	2·25
296		4 c. orange (29.10.38)		48·00	10
297		5 c. brown (18.2.39)		23·00	10
298		15 c. ultram (*ordinary paper*) (6.10.41)		3·50	6·50

278/98 .. .. *Set of 18* £225 23·00
278/92, 294/5, 298 Perf "Specimen" .. *Set of 18* £225

Die I. Lines of background outside central oval touch the oval and the foliage of the palm tree is usually joined to the oval frame. The downward-pointing palm frond, opposite the King's eye, has two points.
Die II. Lines of background are separated from the oval by a

white line and the foliage of the palm trees does not touch the outer frame. The palm frond has only one point.

The 6 c., 8 c. scarlet and $5 purple and orange were issued only with the BMA overprint, but the 8 c. without opt is known although in this state it was never issued (*Price* £11).

POSTAGE DUE STAMPS

D 1

1924 (1 Jan)–**26.** *Wmk Mult Script CA. P* 14.

D1	D 1	1 c. violet		3·75	5·00
D2		2 c. black		3·00	1·25
D3		4 c. green (5.26)		2·00	4·75
D4		8 c. scarlet		4·50	55
D5		10 c. orange		5·00	85
D6		12 c. bright blue		7·00	65

D1/6 .. .. *Set of 6* 23·00 11·50
D1/6 Optd "Specimen" .. *Set of 6* £200
For later issues of Postage Due stamps, see MALAYAN POSTAL UNION.

The Straits Settlements were occupied by the Japanese in 1942. After the Second World War the stamps of MALAYA (BRITISH MILITARY ADMINISTRATION) were used. In 1946 Singapore became a separate Crown Colony and Labuan was transferred to North Borneo. Separate stamps were issued for Malacca and Penang, which both joined the Malayan Federation on 1 February 1948.

II. FEDERATED MALAY STATES

On 1 July 1896, the States of Negri Sembilan, Pahang, Perak and Selangor were organised on a federal basis to be known as the Federated Malay States. For the time being each State continued with individual issues, but stamps for the use of the Federation replaced these in 1900.

PRICES FOR STAMPS ON COVER	
Nos. 1/13	*from* × 12
No. 14	—
Nos. 15/22	*from* × 10
Nos. 23/5	*from* × 3
No. 26	—
Nos. 27/50	*from* × 6
No. 51	—
Nos. 52/81	*from* × 5
No. 82	—
Nos. D1/6	*from* × 10

PRINTERS. All issues of the Federated Malay States were printed in typography by De La Rue & Co, Ltd, London, *unless otherwise stated.*

FEDERATED
MALAY STATES

(1)

FEDERATED
MALAY STATES

(2)

1900. *Optd with T* 1 (*cent values*) *or* 2 (*dollar values*).

(a) Stamps of Negri Sembilan (T 3)

1	1 c. dull purple and green		1·40	3·00
2	2 c. dull purple and brown		22·00	48·00
3	3 c. dull purple and black		1·90	3·25
4	5 c. dull purple and olive-yellow		65·00	£120
5	10 c. dull purple and orange		2·00	13·00
6	20 c. green and olive		50·00	70·00
7	25 c. green and carmine		£150	£180
8	50 c. green and black		60·00	85·00

1/8 .. .. *Set of 8* £325 £475
1/8 Optd "Specimen" .. *Set of 8* £160

(b) Stamps of Perak (T 44 *and* 45)

9	5 c. dull purple and olive-yellow		10·00	48·00
10	10 c. dull purple and orange		55·00	60·00
11	$1 green and pale green		£110	£140
12	$2 green and carmine		90·00	£130
13	$5 green and ultramarine		£200	£300
14	$25 green and orange (Optd S. £250)		£3750	

11/13 Optd "Specimen" .. *Set of 3* £110

The stamps of STRAITS SETTLEMENTS were used in Federated Malay States from 16 July 1900 until replaced by the 1900–1 issue.

3

4

1900–1. *P* 14. (*a*) *T* **3**. *Wmk Crown CA, sideways* (1901).
15 1 c. black and green .. .. .. 1·50 1·75
  a. Grey and green 40 30
  b. Grey-brown and green .. 3·25 25
16 3 c. black and brown .. .. 3·25 90
  a. Grey and brown .. .. 1·25 35
  b. Grey-brown and brown .. 1·25 20
17 4 c. black and carmine .. .. 9·00 1·60
  a. Grey and carmine .. .. 4·25 1·60
  b. Grey-brown and carmine .. 9·00 30
18 5 c. green and carmine/yellow .. 1·50 2·00
19 8 c. black and ultramarine .. 28·00 7·00
  a. Grey and ultramarine .. 20·00 3·50
  b. Grey-brown and ultramarine .. 22·00 2·75
20 10 c. black and claret .. .. 55·00 7·50
  a. Grey and claret .. .. 38·00 3·50
  b. Black and purple .. .. 60·00 7·00
  c. Grey and purple .. .. 45·00 4·75
  d. Grey-brown and purple .. 60·00 2·75
21 20 c. mauve and black .. .. 17·00 6·00
22 50 c. black and orange-brown .. 85·00 55·00
  a. Grey and orange-brown .. 65·00 28·00
  b. Grey-brown and orange-brown .. 65·00 26·00
15/22 .. .. .. *Set of 8* £130 35·00
15/22 Optd "Specimen" .. *Set of 8* £160

Later printings in 1903–4 show the two upper lines of shading in the background at the corner nearest to the "S" of "STATE" blurred and running into one another, whereas in earlier printings these lines are distinct. Two plates were used for printing the central design of *T* **3**. In Plate 1 the lines of background are regular throughout, but in Plate 2 they are lighter around the head and back of the tiger. The 5 c. was the only value with single wmk to be printed from Plate 2. Stamps with multiple wmk were printed for a short time from Plate 1, and show the two blurred lines of background near "S" of "STATE," but the majority of these stamps were printed from Plate 2 and later plates.

(*b*) *T* **4**. *Wmk Crown CC* (1900)
23 $1 green and pale green .. .. 65·00 70·00
24 $2 green and carmine .. .. 70·00 75·00
25 $5 green and bright ultramarine .. £130 £140
  a. Green and pale ultramarine .. £130 £140
26 $25 green and orange (Optd S. £180) .. £950 £650
23/5 Optd "Specimen" .. .. *Set of 3* £110

Two dies for 1 c. green and 4 c. scarlet

Die I. "Head" and duty plates. Thick frame line below "MALAY" and in the 1 c. the "c" is thin whilst in the 4 c. it is thick.

Die II. Single working plate. Thin frame line below "MALAY" and in the 1 c. the "c" is thicker whilst in the 4 c. it is thinner.

1904 (10 Oct)–**22.** *T* **3** *and T* **4** (*dollar values*). *Wmk Mult Crown CA (sideways on T* **3**). *Ordinary paper* (1 c. *to* 50 c.) *or chalk-surfaced paper* ($1 *to* $25).
27 1 c. grey and green .. .. 40·00 5·00
  a. Grey-brown and green .. 14·00 70
28 1 c. green (Die I) (8.7.06) .. 6·00 30
29 1 c. green (Die II) .. .. 1·25 20
  a. Yellow-green .. .. 8·00 40
  b. Blue-green .. .. 12·00 45
30 1 c. deep brown (21.1.19) .. 2·25 90
31 2 c. green (18.2.19) 60 30
32 3 c. grey and brown (10.04) .. 19·00 1·00
  a. Grey-brown and brown (12.05) .. 12·00 30
  ab. Chalk-surfaced paper .. 13·00 40
33 3 c. brown (11.7.06) .. .. 5·00 15
34 3 c. carmine (2.2.09) .. .. 2·00 10
  a. Scarlet (1.17) .. .. 7·00 25
35 3 c. grey (29.10.18) .. .. 1·00 20
36 4 c. grey and scarlet .. .. 22·00 1·50
  a. Chalk-surfaced paper. Grey and rose .. 8·00 85
  b. Grey-brown and scarlet .. 19·00 1·50
  c. Black and scarlet .. 18·00 1·50
  d. Black and rose .. .. 3·75 25
  e. Black and deep rose (aniline) (1909) .. 38·00 4·50
  f. Jet-black and rose (1914) .. 11·00 75
37 4 c. scarlet (Die I) (11.2.19) .. 2·00 2·25
38 4 c. scarlet (Die II) (15.4.19) .. 80 15
  a. Wmk upright (2.22) .. † £325
39 5 c. green and carmine/yellow (5.06) .. 4·00 1·50
  a. Chalk-surfaced paper .. 8·50 2·75
  b. Deep green and carmine/yellow .. 3·50 1·50
  c. On orange-buff (1921) .. 8·00 3·75
  d. On pale yellow (4.22) .. 3·00 1·75
40 6 c. orange (11.2.19) .. .. 2·00 1·50
41 8 c. grey and ultramarine (2.05) .. 30·00 10·00
  a. Grey-brown and ultramarine (12.05) .. 14·00 3·50
  ab. Chalk-surfaced paper .. 20·00 7·50
  b. Wmk upright (3.07) .. 5·00 3·50
42 8 c. ultramarine (8.3.10) .. 13·00 90
  a. Deep blue (1918) .. .. 13·00 1·25
43 10 c. grey-brown and claret .. 25·00 1·50
  a. Chalk-surfaced paper (1905) .. 32·00 2·00
  b. Black and claret .. 8·00 25
  c. Grey-brown and purple (1905) .. 29·00 1·75
  d. Black and purple .. 12·00 1·10
  e. Jet-black and bright purple (1914) .. 40·00 2·50
44 10 c. deep blue (3.6.19) .. 6·00 80
  a. Bright blue .. .. 6·50 85
  b. Wmk upright (inverted) .. †
45 20 c. mauve and black (3.05) .. 2·00 35
  a. Chalk-surfaced paper .. 4·50 90
46 35 c. scarlet/pale yellow (25.8.22) .. 7·50 12·00

47 50 c. grey and orange (3.05) .. 45·00 3·50
  a. Grey-brown and orange-brown (1906) 20·00 3·50
  b. Chalk-surfaced paper. Grey-brown and orange-brown .. 24·00 3·25
  ba. Grey and orange-brown .. 38·00 3·25
  bb. Black and orange-brown .. 48·00 6·00
  bc. Jet-black and orange-brown (1914) 65·00 7·00
  e. Wmk upright (inverted) .. †
48 $1 grey-green and green (11.07) .. 40·00 28·00
  a. Green and pale green .. 40·00 28·00
49 $2 green and carmine (4.12.07) .. 65·00 90·00
50 $5 green and blue (1.08) .. 90·00 95·00
51 $25 green and orange (8.10) .. £750 £400
27/50 .. .. *Set of 22* £275 £200
28, 30/1, 33/5, 37, 40, 42, 44, 46 Optd "Specimen" *Set of 11* £350

Nos. 29/*b*, 30, 31, 33, 34/*a* and 35 were printed from single working plates and all the rest from double plates.
Most examples of No. 47e have fiscal cancellations, but at least one is known postally used.

1922–34. *Wmk Mult Script CA (sideways in T* **3**). *Ordinary paper* (1 c. *to* 10 c. (No. 66), 12 c., 35 c. (No. 72)) *or chalk-surfaced paper (others).*
52 3 1 c. deep brown (1.8.22) .. 2·50 2·25
53 1 c. black (12.6.23) 50 20
54 2 c. brown (5.8.25) .. .. 4·00 2·25
55 2 c. green (15.6.26) 45 10
56 3 c. grey (27.12.22) .. .. 1·75 4·25
57 3 c. green (22.1.24) .. .. 1·50 1·75
58 3 c. brown (31.5.27) 60 40
59 4 c. carmine-red (Die II) (27.11.23) .. 2·75 45
60 4 c. orange (9.11.26) 55 10
  a. No watermark £200 £100
61 5 c. mauve/pale yellow (17.3.22) .. 75 20
62 5 c. brown (1.3.32) .. .. 1·75 10
63 6 c. orange (2.5.22) 55 45
64 6 c. scarlet (9.11.26) 80 10
65 10 c. bright blue (23.10.23) .. 1·25 6·00
66 10 c. black and blue (18.1.24*) .. 2·00 75
67 10 c. purple/pale yellow (14.7.31) .. 3·50 40
68 12 c. ultramarine (12.9.22) .. 1·25 10
69 20 c. dull purple and black (*chalk-surfaced paper*) (3.4.23) .. 4·00 35
  a. Ordinary paper (29.12.26) .. 9·50 50
70 25 c. purple and bright magenta (3.9.29) .. 2·50 75
71 30 c. purple and orange-yellow (3.9.29) .. 3·25 1·25
72 35 c. scarlet/yellow (6.11.28) .. 3·75 13·00
73 35 c. scarlet and purple (29.9.31) .. 12·00 12·00
74 50 c. black and orange (24.4.24) .. 13·00 4·50
  a. Black and orange-brown .. 15·00 4·50
75 50 c. black/green (16.6.31) .. 4·00 1·50
76 4 $1 pale green and green (2.2.26) .. 17·00 50·00
  a. Grey-green and emerald (5.10.26) .. 11·00 24·00
77 3 $1 black and red/blue (10.3.31) .. 10·00 2·50
78 4 $2 green and carmine (17.8.26) .. 10·00 50·00
79 3 $2 green and red/yellow (6.2.34) .. 27·00 26·00
80 4 $5 green and blue (24.2.25) .. 60·00 85·00
81 3 $5 green and red/green (7.34) .. £120 £130
82 4 $25 green & orange (14.2.28) (Optd S. £90) £650 £325
52/81 .. .. *Set of 30* £275 £325
52/81 Optd/Perf "Specimen" .. *Set of 30* £550

Nos. 52, 56 and 59 were printed from single working plates and the rest from double plates.
*No. 66 was released in London by the Crown Agents some months earlier but this is the official date of issue in the States.
The 5 c. in mauve on white Script paper is the result of soaking early printings of No. 61 in water.

POSTAGE DUE STAMPS

D 1

(Typo Waterlow)

1924 (1 Dec)–**26.** *Wmk Mult Script CA (sideways). P* 15 × 14.
D1 D 1 1 c. violet .. .. .. 3·50 8·50
D2 2 c. black .. .. .. 1·75 2·00
D3 4 c. green (27.4.26) .. .. 2·25 4·25
D4 8 c. red .. .. .. 4·25 14·00
D5 10 c. orange .. .. .. 7·50 11·00
D6 12 c. blue .. .. .. 8·50 18·00
D1/6 .. .. *Set of 6* 25·00 50·00
D1/6 Optd "Specimen" .. .. *Set of 6* £150

The issues of the Federated Malay States were replaced by stamps for the individual States from 1935 onwards.

III. MALAYAN POSTAL UNION

The Malayan Postal Union was organised in 1934 and, initially, covered the Straits Settlements and the Federated Malay States. Stamps of the Straits Settlements together with issues for the individual States continued to be used, but Malayan Postal Union postage due stamps were introduced in 1936.
Following the end of the Second World War the use of these postage dues spread throughout Malaya and to Singapore.

PRICES FOR STAMPS ON COVER TO 1945	
Nos. D1/6	*from* × 10
Nos. D7/13	*from* × 4

POSTAGE DUE STAMPS

D 1   (D 2)

(Typo Waterlow until 1961, then D.L.R.)

1936 (June)–**38.** *Wmk Mult Script CA. P* 15 × 14.
D1 D 1 1 c. slate-purple (4.38) .. 3·50 70
D2 4 c. green (9.36) .. .. 6·50 1·00
D3 8 c. scarlet .. .. .. 2·50 3·50
D4 10 c. yellow-orange .. .. 2·25 25
D5 12 c. pale ultramarine (9.36) .. 4·75 7·00
D6 50 c. black (1.38) .. .. 18·00 5·00
D1/6 .. .. *Set of 6* 32·00 16·00
D1/6 Perf "Specimen" .. *Set of 6* £100
For use in Negri Sembilan, Pahang, Perak, Selangor and Straits Settlements including Singapore.

1945–49. *New values and colours. Wmk Mult Script CA. P* 15 × 14.
D 7 D 1 1 c. purple .. .. .. 2·75 1·75
D 8 3 c. green .. .. .. 9·00 11·00
D 9 5 c. scarlet .. .. .. 7·50 7·50
D10 8 c. yell-orange (1949) (Perf S. £75) .. 24·00 16·00
D11 9 c. yellow-orange .. .. 60·00 45·00
D12 15 c. pale ultramarine .. 90·00 35·00
D13 20 c. blue (1948) (Perf S. £75) .. 14·00 7·00
D7/13 .. .. *Set of 7* £190 £110

1951 (8 Aug)–**63.** *Wmk Mult Script CA. P* 14.
D14 D 1 1 c. violet (21.8.52) .. 30 60
D15 2 c. deep slate-blue (16.11.53) .. 30 75
  a. Perf 12½ (15.11.60) .. 40 7·50
  b. Perf 12½. *Chalk-surfaced paper* (10.7.62) .. 35 5·00
  ba. Ditto. Imperf between (vert pair)
D16 3 c. deep green (21.8.52) .. 12·00 10·00
D17 4 c. sepia (16.11.53) .. 45 3·25
  a. Perf 12½ (15.11.60) .. 60 11·00
  ab. Chalk-surfaced paper. Bistre-brown (10.7.62) .. 70 9·50
D18 5 c. vermilion .. .. 32·00 12·00
D19 8 c. yellow-orange .. .. 1·75 3·50
D20 12 c. bright purple (1.2.54) .. 1·00 3·75
  a. Perf 12½. *Chalk-surfaced paper* (10.7.62) .. 1·50 18·00
D21 20 c. blue .. .. .. 4·00 6·00
  a. Perf 12½. *Deep blue* (10.12.57) .. 3·25 24·00
  ab. Chalk-surfaced paper (15.10.63) .. 3·00 27·00
D14/21 .. .. *Set of 8* 45·00 35·00
Nos. D7 to D21b were for use in the Federation and Singapore, and from 1963 throughout Malaysia.

1964 (14 Apr)–**65.** *Chalk-surfaced paper. Wmk* w **12** (*sideways on* 1 c.). *P* 12½.
D22 D 1 1 c. maroon .. .. 30 9·50
  a. Perf 12. *Wmk upright* (4.5.65) .. 30 9·50
D23 2 c. deep slate-blue .. 45 10·00
  a. Perf 12 (9.3.65) .. 35 17·00
D24 4 c. bistre-brown .. .. 75 10·00
  a. Perf 12 (9.3.65) .. 40 12·00
D25 8 c. yellow-orange (*p* 12) (4.5.65) .. 2·00 13·00
D27 12 c. bright purple .. 1·50 16·00
  a. Perf 12 (4.5.65) .. 2·75 28·00
D28 20 c. deep blue .. .. 2·50 35·00
  a. Perf 12 (4.5.65) .. 40·00 6·00
D22/8 .. .. *Set of 6* 6·25 85·00

1964 (Dec). *As No. D19 surch locally with Type* D **2**.
D29 D 1 10 c. on 8 c. yellow-orange .. 30 1·75
First supplies of this stamp differed from No. D19 in that they had been climatically affected but later a fresh printing of No. D19 was surcharged.

1967? *Unsurfaced paper. Wmk* w **12**. *P* 15 × 14.
D30 D 1 50 c. black £475 £400
Nos. D22/9 were for use throughout Malaysia and Singapore. They were superseded on 15 August 1966 by the postage dues inscribed "MALAYSIA", but continued in use, together with No. D30, for Singapore until 31 January 1968 when they were replaced by Singapore Postage Dues.

IV. MALAYA (BRITISH MILITARY ADMINISTRATION)

For use throughout all Malay States and in Singapore. From 1948 this general issue was gradually replaced by individual issues for each state. The last usage was in Kelantan where B M A overprints were not withdrawn until 10 July 1951.

B M A
MALAYA
(1)

1945 (19 Oct)–**48.** *T* **58** *of Straits Settlements from Die I (double-plate printing) or Die II (single-plate printing) optd with T* **1**. *Wmk Mult Script CA. Chalk-surfaced paper. P* 14 *or* 15 × 14 (No. 11).
1 1 c. black (I) (R.) 20 10
  a. Ordinary paper 10 10
2 2 c. orange (II) (8.7.47) .. 1·25 30
  a. Ordinary paper (19.10.45) .. 10 10
3 2 c. orange (I) (*ordinary paper*) (9.46) .. 6·50 2·50
4 3 c. yellow-green (II) (*ordinary paper*) .. 10 10
  a. Blue-green (27.1.47) .. 1·75 40
  b. Chalk-surfaced paper. Blue-grn (8.7.47) .. 2·50 30
5 5 c. brown (II) (11.45) .. 45 10
6 6 c. grey (II) (22.3.48) .. 1·75 55
  a. Ordinary paper (19.10.45) .. 10 10
7 8 c. scarlet (II) (*ordinary paper*) .. 10 10
8 10 c. purple (I) (12.45) .. 1·00 10
  a. Ordinary paper (19.10.45) .. 30 10
  b. Slate-purple (12.45) .. 75 10
  c. Magenta (22.3.48) .. 1·75 30
9 10 c. purple (II) (28.7.48) .. 10·00 1·25
10 12 c. bright ultramarine (I) (11.45) .. 1·75 3·00
11 15 c. brt ultram (II) (*ordinary paper*) (11.45) .. 2·25 5·50
12 15 c. bright ultramarine (II) (R.) (22.3.48) .. 6·50 75
  a. Ordinary paper (12.45) .. 40 20
  b. Blue (27.11.47) .. .. 16·00 75
  ba. Ordinary paper (8.7.47) .. 50·00 10·00

13	25 c. dull purple and scarlet (I) (22.3.48)	..	2·00	30
	a. Ordinary paper (12.45)	..	90	20
	ab. Opt double	..	£2000	
14	50 c. black/*emerald* (I) (R.) (12.45)	..	2·75	30
	a. Ordinary paper	..	40	10
15	$1 black and red (I) (*ordinary paper*) (12.45)	1·50	10
16	$2 green & scar (I) (*ordinary paper*) (12.45)	2·00	55
17	$5 green and red/*emerald* (I) (11.45)	50·00	55·00
18	$5 pur & orge (I) (*ordinary paper*) (12.45)	3·00	1·75
1/18		*Set of 15*	55·00	55·00
1/11, 13/16, 18 Perf "Specimen"	..	*Set of 14*	£375

The 8 c. grey with "B.M.A." opt was prepared but not officially issued (*Price £120 unused*).

Nos. 3 and 9 do not exist without the overprint.

Nos. 1, 2, 6, 7, 8 and 13 exist also on thin, rough ordinary paper.

No. 8 with reddish purple medallion and dull purple frame is from a 1947 printing with the head in fugitive ink which discolours with moisture.

Postal forgeries of the 50 c. value exist made by dyeing examples of the 1 c. and then altering the face value to 50 c.

Stamps in the Crown Colony Victory design were prepared for the Malayan Union in 1946, but not issued. Examples of the 8 c. carmine from this issue were stolen from stock awaiting destruction.

V. MALAYAN FEDERATION

The Malayan Federation, formed on 1 February 1948 by Malacca, Penang, the four Federated Malay States and the five Unfederated States, became an independent member of the British Commonwealth on 31 August 1957.

Commemoratives and a limited series of definitives were issued by the Federation and were used concurrently with the stamps from the individual States.

1 Tapping Rubber **4** Map of the Federation

(Centre recess, frame litho (6 c., 25 c.); centre litho, frame recess (12 c.); recess (30 c.), D.L.R.)

1957 (5 May)–**63**. T **1**, **4** *and similar designs. W* w **12**. *P* 13×12½ (*No. 4*) *or* 13 (*others*).

1	1	6 c. deep blue, red, yellow and grey-blue	40	10
		a. Indigo, red, yellow and grey-blue (20.6.61)	1·00	30
		b. Indigo, red, yellow & slate-blue (12.2.63)	1·00	30
		c. Yellow (star and crescent) omitted	45·00	
2		12 c. red, yellow, blue, black and yellow	50	10
3		25 c. maroon, red, yellow & dull greenish blue	55	10
4		30 c. orange-red and lake	50	20
		a. Perf 13. Orange-red & deep lake (20.6.61)	50	30
		ab. Orange-red and lake (10.7.62)	50	10
1/4		*Set of 4*	1·75	30

Designs: *Horiz*—12 c. Federation coat of arms; 25 c. Tin dredger.

5 Prime Minister Tunku Abdul Rahman and Populace greeting Independence

(Des A. B. Saman. Recess Waterlow)

1957 (31 Aug). *Independence Day. Wmk Mult Script CA. P* 12½.
5	5	10 c. bistre-brown	..	10	10

6 United Nations Emblem **7** United Nations Emblem

(Recess D.L.R.)

1958 (5 Mar). *U.N. Economic Commission for Asia and Far East Conference, Kuala Lumpur. W* w **12**. *P* 13½ (12 c.) *or* 12½ (30 c.).
6	6	12 c. carmine-red	..	30	40
7	7	30 c. maroon	..	40	20

8 Merdeka Stadium, Kuala Lumpur **9** The Yang di-Pertuan Agong (Tuanku Abdul Rahman)

(Photo Harrison)

1958 (31 Aug). *First Anniv of Independence. W* w **12**. *P* 13½ × 14½ (10 c.) *or* 14½ × 13½ (30 c.).
8	8	10 c. green, yellow, red and blue	15	10
9	9	30 c. red, yellow, violet-blue and green	40	10

10 "Human Rights" **11** Malayan with Torch of Freedom

(Des J. P. Hendroff. Litho (10 c.), photo (30 c.) D.L.R.)

1958 (10 Dec). *Tenth Anniv of Declaration of Human Rights.*
(a) W w **12**. *P* 12½ × 13
10	10	10 c. blue, black, carmine and orange	..	10	10
(b) Wmk Mult Script CA. P 13 × 12½
11	11	30 c. deep green	..	..	30	20

12 Mace and Malayan Peoples

(Photo Enschedé)

1959 (12 Sept). *Inauguration of Parliament. No wmk. P* 13 × 14.
12	12	4 c. rose-red	..	10	10
13		10 c. violet	..	10	10
14		25 c. yellow-green	..	35	20
12/14	..	..	*Set of 3*	50	30

13 **14**

(Recess D.L.R.)

1960 (7 Apr). *World Refugee Year. W* w **12**. *P* 13½ (12 c.) *or* 12½ × 13 (30 c.).
15	13	12 c. purple	..	10	30
16	14	30 c. deep green	..	10	10

15 Seedling Rubber Tree and Map **16** The Yang di-Pertuan Agong (Tuanku Syed Putra)

(Photo Japanese Govt Ptg Wks)

1960 (19 Sept). *Natural Rubber Research Conference and 15th International Rubber Study Group Meeting, Kuala Lumpur. T* **15** *and similar vert design. No wmk. P* 13.
17		6 c. yellow-green, black, orange & red-brown	20	30
18		30 c. yellow-green, black, orange & bright blue	50	15

No. 18 is inscribed "INTERNATIONAL RUBBER STUDY GROUP 15th MEETING KUALA LUMPUR" at foot.

(Photo Harrison)

1961 (4 Jan). *Installation of Yang di-Pertuan Agong, Tuanku Syed Putra. W* w **12**. *P* 14 × 14½.
19	16	10 c. black and blue	..	10	10

17 Colombo Plan Emblem **18** Malaria Eradication Emblem

(Photo Japanese Govt Ptg Works)

1961 (30 Oct). *Colombo Plan Conference, Kuala Lumpur. P* 13.
20	17	12 c. black and magenta	..	35	1·75
21		25 c. black and apple-green	..	80	1·50
22		30 c. black and turquoise-blue	70	30
20/2	..	..	..	*Set of 3*	1·75	3·00

(Photo Harrison)

1962 (7 Apr). *Malaria Eradication. W* w **13**. *P* 14 × 14½.
23	18	25 c. orange-brown	..	20	30
24		30 c. deep lilac	..	20	10
25		50 c. ultramarine	..	40	15
23/5	..	..	..	*Set of 3*	70	50

19 Palmyra Palm Leaf **20** "Shadows of the Future"

(Photo Harrison)

1962 (21 July). *National Language Month. W* w **13** (*upright or inverted*). *P* 13½.
26	19	10 c. light brown and deep reddish violet	15	10
27		20 c. light brown and deep bluish green	25	25
28		50 c. light brown and magenta	..	45	60
26/8	..	..	..	*Set of 3*	75	80

(Photo Enschedé)

1962 (1 Oct). *Introduction of Free Primary Education. W* w **13**. *P* 13½.
29	20	10 c. bright purple	..	10	10
30		25 c. ochre	..	30	30
31		30 c. emerald	..	80	10
29/31	..	..	..	*Set of 3*	1·10	10

21 Harvester and Fisherman **22** Dam and Pylon

(Photo Courvoisier)

1963 (21 Mar). *Freedom from Hunger. P* 11½.
32	21	25 c. carmine and apple-green	..	85	1·00
33		30 c. carmine and crimson	..	1·50	40
34		50 c. carmine and bright blue	..	1·50	1·10
32/4	..	..	..	*Set of 3*	3·50	2·25

(Photo Harrison)

1963 (26 June). *Cameron Highlands Hydro-Electric Scheme. W* w **13**. *P* 14.
35	22	20 c. green and reddish violet	..	35	10
36		30 c. blue-green and ultramarine	..	45	40

The definitive general issue for Malaysia and the low value sets for the individual states superseded the stamps of the Malayan Federation by 15 November 1965.

VI. MALAYSIA

On 16 September 1963, the Malayan Federation, Sabah (North Borneo), Sarawak and Singapore formed the Federation of Malaysia. Singapore left the Federation on 9 August 1965, and became an independent republic.

Individual issues for the component States continued, but were restricted to low value definitives and the occasional "State" commemorative. The higher value definitives and the vast majority of commemoratives were issued on a "National" basis.

A. NATIONAL ISSUES

General issues for use throughout the Malaysian Federation.

1 Federation Map **2** Bouquet of Orchids

(Photo Harrison)

1963 (16 Sept). *Inauguration of Federation. W* w **13**. *P* 14½.
1	1	10 c. yellow and bluish violet	..	15	10
		a. Yellow omitted	..	85·00	
2		12 c. yellow and deep green	..	60	60
3		50 c. yellow and chocolate	..	1·00	10
1/3	..	..	..	*Set of 3*	1·60	65

(Photo Enschedé)

1963 (3 Oct). *Fourth World Orchid Conference, Singapore. No wmk. P* 13 × 14.

4	**2**	6 c. multicoloured	..	..	1·00	1·00
5		25 c. multicoloured	..	..	1·25	25

4 Parliament House, Kuala Lumpur

(Des V. Whiteley. Photo Harrison)

1963 (4 Nov). *Ninth Commonwealth Parliamentary Conference, Kuala Lumpur. W* w **13** (*inverted*). *P* 13½.

7	**4**	20 c. deep magenta and gold	..	..	30	40
8		30 c. deep green and gold	..	..	30	15

5 "Flame of Freedom" and Emblems of Goodwill, Health and Charity

6 Microwave Tower and I.T.U. Emblem

(Photo Harrison)

1964 (10 Oct). *Eleanor Roosevelt Commemoration. W* w **13**. *P* 14½ × 13½.

9	**5**	25 c. black, red and greenish blue	..	15	10
10		30 c. black, red and deep lilac	..	15	10
11		50 c. black, red and ochre-yellow	..	15	10
9/11	..	..	*Set of* 3	40	15

(Photo Courvoisier)

1965 (17 May). *I.T.U. Centenary. P* 11½.

12	**6**	2 c. multicoloured	..	..	15	80
13		25 c. multicoloured	..	..	60	40
14		50 c. multicoloured	..	..	1·25	10
12/14	..	..	*Set of* 3	1·75	1·10

7 National Mosque   **8** Air Terminal

(Photo Harrison)

1965 (27 Aug). *Opening of National Mosque, Kuala Lumpur. W* w **13**. *P* 14 × 14½.

15	**7**	6 c. carmine	..	..	10	10
16		15 c. red-brown	..	..	10	10
17		20 c. deep bluish green	..	..	15	15
15/17	..	..	*Set of* 3	30	30

(Photo Harrison)

1965 (30 Aug). *Opening of International Airport, Kuala Lumpur. W* w **13**. *P* 14½ × 14.

18	**8**	15 c. black, yellow-green and new blue	..	15	10
		a. Yellow-green omitted	..	..	20·00	
19		30 c. black, yellow-green and magenta	..	25	20

9 Crested Wood Partridge

17 Sepak Raga (ball game) and Football

(Des A. Fraser-Brunner. Photo Harrison)

1965 (9 Sept). *T* **9** *and similar vert designs. Multicoloured. W* w **13**. *P* 14½.

20	**9**	25 c. Type 9	..	..	50	10
21		30 c. Blue-backed Fairy Bluebird	..	60	10
		a. Blue omitted	..	..	95·00	
22		50 c. Black-eyed Oriole	..	..	70	10
		a. Yellow omitted	..	..	60·00	
		b. Imperf (pair)	..	..	£200	
		c. Scarlet (inscr and berries) omitted	..	35·00	
23		75 c. Rhinoceros Hornbill	..	..	1·25	10
		a. Scarlet omitted*	..	..	50·00	
24		$1 Zebra Dove	..	..	1·75	10
25		$2 Great Argus Pheasant	..	..	4·00	30
		a. Imperf (pair)	..	..	£200	
26		$5 Asiatic Paradise Flycatcher	..	13·00	1·50
27		$10 Blue-tailed Pitta	..	..	40·00	6·50
		a. Imperf (pair)	..	..	£275	
20/7	..	..	*Set of* 8	55·00	8·00

*The inscription at foot is omitted and the background appears paler.

All values except the 75 c. and $10 exist with PVA gum as well as gum arabic.

(Des E. A. F. Anthony. Litho Japanese Govt Ptg Wks)

1965 (14 Dec). *Third South East Asian Peninsular Games. T* **17** *and similar vert designs. P* 13 × 13½.

28		25 c. black and olive-green	..	..	40	90
29		30 c. black and bright purple	..	..	40	20
30		50 c. black and light blue	..	..	70	30
28/30	..	..	*Set of* 3	1·40	1·25

Designs:—30 c. Running; 50 c. Diving.

20 National Monument

21 The Yang di-Pertuan Agong (Tuanku Ismail Nasiruddin Shah)

(Photo Harrison)

1966 (8 Feb). *National Monument, Kuala Lumpur. W* w **13**. *P* 13½.

31	**20**	10 c. multicoloured	..	..	15	10
		a. Blue omitted	..	..	35·00	
32		20 c. multicoloured	..	..	25	20

(Photo Japanese Govt Ptg Wks)

1966 (11 Apr). *Installation of Yang di-Pertuan Agong, Tuanku Ismail Nasiruddin Shah. P* 13½.

33	**21**	15 c. black and light yellow	..	..	10	10
34		50 c. black and greenish blue	..	..	20	20

22 School Building   **23** "Agriculture"

(Photo D.L.R.)

1966 (21 Oct). *150th Anniv of Penang Free School. W* w **13** (*sideways*). *P* 13.

35	**22**	20 c. multicoloured	..	..	30	10
36		50 c. multicoloured	..	..	60	10

The 50 c. is also inscr "ULANG TAHUN KE-150" at foot and bears a shield at bottom left corner.

(Des Enche Ng Peng Nam. Photo Japanese Govt Ptg Wks)

1966 (1 Dec). *First Malaysia Plan. T* **23** *and similar horiz designs. Multicoloured. P* 13½.

37	**23**	15 c. Type 23	..	..	20	10
38		15 c. "Rural Health"	..	..	20	10
39		15 c. "Communications"	..	..	75	15
40		15 c. "Education"	..	..	20	10
41		15 c. "Irrigation"	..	..	20	10
37/41	..	..	*Set of* 5	1·40	50

28 Cable Route Maps

(Des Enche Ng Peng Nam. Photo Japanese Govt Ptg Wks)

1967 (30 Mar). *Completion of Malaysia–Hong Kong Link of SEACOM Telephone Cable. P* 13½.

42	**28**	30 c. multicoloured	..	..	80	30
43		75 c. multicoloured	..	..	2·50	2·50

29 Hibiscus and Paramount Rulers

(Photo Harrison)

1967 (31 Aug). *Tenth Anniv of Independence. W* w **13**. *P* 14½.

44	**29**	15 c. multicoloured	..	..	20	10
45		50 c. multicoloured	..	..	50	35

30 Mace and Shield   **31** Straits Settlements 1867 8 c. and Malaysia 1965 25 c. Definitive

(Des Enche Ng Peng Nam. Photo Harrison)

1967 (8 Sept). *Centenary of Sarawak Council. W* w **13**. *P* 14½.

46	**30**	15 c. multicoloured	..	..	10	10
47		50 c. multicoloured	..	..	20	30

(Des Enche Ng Peng Nam. Photo Japanese Govt Ptg Works)

1967 (2 Dec). *Stamp Centenary. T* **31** *and similar shaped designs. Multicoloured. P* 11½.

48	**31**	25 c. Type 31	..	..	1·00	1·50
		a. Tête-bêche (horiz pair)	..	2·00	3·00
49		30 c. Straits Settlements 1867 24 c. and Malaysia 1965 30 c. definitive	..	1·00	85
		a. Tête-bêche (horiz pair)	..	2·00	1·60
50		50 c. Straits Settlements 1867 32 c. and Malaysia 1965 50 c. definitive	..	1·40	1·25
		a. Tête-bêche (horiz pair)	..	2·75	2·50
48/50	..	..	*Set of* 3	3·00	3·25

Nos. 48/50 were each printed in sheets with the stamps arranged horizontally *tête-bêche*.

34 Tapping Rubber, and Molecular Unit

37 Mexican Sombrero and Blanket with Olympic Rings

(Litho B.W.)

1968 (29 Aug). *Natural Rubber Conference, Kuala Lumpur. T* **34** *and similar horiz designs. Multicoloured. W* w **13**. *P* 12.

51		25 c. Type 34	..	..	25	10
52		30 c. Tapping rubber, and export consignment	..	40	20
53		50 c. Tapping rubber, and aircraft tyres	..	40	10
51/3	..	..	*Set of* 3	95	35

(Litho B.W.)

1968 (12 Oct). *Olympic Games, Mexico. T* **37** *and similar vert design. Multicoloured. W* w **13**. *P* 12 × 11½.

54		30 c. Type 37	..	..	20	10
55		75 c. Olympic rings and Mexican embroidery	..	40	20

39 Tunku Abdul Rahman   **40** against background of Pandanus Weave

(Photo Japanese Govt Ptg Wks)

1969 (8 Feb). *Solidarity Week. T* **39/40** *and similar multicoloured design. P* 13½.

56		15 c. Type 39	..	..	15	10
57		20 c. Type 40	..	..	20	50
58		50 c. Tunku Abdul Rahman with pandanus pattern (*horiz*)	..	20	20
56/8	..	..	*Set of* 3	50	65

42 Peasant Girl with Sheaves of Paddy

(Des Enche Hoessein Anas. Photo Harrison)

1969 (8 Dec). *National Rice Year. W* w **13**. *P* 13½.

59	**42**	15 c. multicoloured	..	..	15	10
60		75 c. multicoloured	..	..	45	65

43 Satellite tracking Aerial

44 "Intelsat III" in Orbit

(Photo Enschedé)

1970 (6 Apr). *Satellite Earth Station.* W w 13. P 14 × 13 (15 c.) or 13½ × 13 (30 c.).

61	43	15 c. multicoloured	..	..	75	15
		a. *Tête-bêche* (horiz pair)	..	..	1·50	1·75
62	44	30 c. multicoloured*	..	..	75	1·40
63		30 c. multicoloured*	..	..	75	1·40
61/3				Set of 3	2·00	2·75

No. 61 was issued horizontally *tête-bêche* in the sheets.
*Nos. 62/3 are of the same design, differing only in the lettering colours (No. 62 white; No. 63 gold).

45 *Euploea*	46 Emblem
leucostictus	

(Des V. Whiteley. Litho B.W. (to 1976) or Harrison)

1970 (31 Aug–16 Nov). *Butterflies.* T 45 *and similar vert designs.* Multicoloured. P 13 × 13½.

64	25 c. Type 45	..	..	1·00	10
65	30 c. *Zeuxidia amethystus*	..	..	1·50	10
66	50 c. *Polyura athamas*	..	..	1·75	10
67	75 c. *Papilio memnon*	..	..	2·00	10
68	$1 *Appias nero* (16.11)	..	..	2·00	10
69	$2 *Trogonoptera brookiana* (16.11)	..	3·25	10
70	$5 *Narathura centaurus* (16.11)	..	4·50	1·25
71	$10 *Terinos terpander* (16.11)	..	10·00	5·00
64/71			Set of 8	23·00	6·00

See also Nos. 144/5.

(Litho Harrison)

1970 (7 Sept). *50th Anniv of International Labour Organization.* P 14 × 13½.

72	46	30 c. grey and new blue ..		10	20
73		75 c. pink and new blue ..		20	30

47 U.N. Emblem encircled	50 The Yang di-Pertuan
by Doves	Agong (Tuanku Abdul
	Halim Shah)

(Des Enche Ng Peng Nam. Litho D.L.R.)

1970 (24 Oct). *25th Anniv of United Nations.* T 47 *and similar horiz designs.* P 13 × 12½.

74	25 c. gold, black and brown	..	35	40
75	30 c. multicoloured	..	45	35
76	50 c. black and dull yellow-green	..	75	75
74/6		Set of 3	1·40	1·40

Designs:—30 c. Line of doves and U.N. emblem; 50 c. Doves looping U.N. emblem.

(Des Union Art Corp. Photo Harrison)

1971 (20 Feb). *Installation of Yang di-Pertuan Agong (Paramount Ruler of Malaysia).* P 14½ × 14.

77	50	10 c. black, gold and lemon	..	20	30
		a. Gold (value and inscr) omitted	..	£160	
78		15 c. black, gold and bright mauve	..	20	30
79		50 c. black, gold and new blue ..	..	60	1·60
77/9		..	Set of 3	90	2·00

51 Bank Negara Complex

(Photo Harrison)

1971 (15 May). *Opening of Bank Negara Building.* P 13½ (and around design).

80	51	25 c. black and silver	..	..	70	90
81		50 c. black and gold	..	..	70	1·10

52 Aerial view of Parliament Buildings

(Des Union Art Corp. Litho Harrison)

1971 (13 Sept). *17th Commonwealth Parliamentary Association Conference, Kuala Lumpur.* T 52 *and similar multicoloured design.* P 13½ (25 c.) or 12½ × 13 (75c.).

82	52	25 c. Type 52	..	90	50
83		75 c. Ground view of Parliament Buildings			
		(73 × 23½ mm) ..	..	1·60	1·75

53	54	55

Malaysian Carnival

(Des locally. Litho Harrison)

1971 (18 Sept). *Visit A.S.E.A.N.* Year.* P 14½.

84	53	30 c. multicoloured	..	1·25	35
		a. Horiz strip of 3. Nos. 84/6 ..		3·25	
85	54	30 c. multicoloured	..	1·25	35
86	55	30 c. multicoloured	..	1·25	35
84/6			Set of 3	3·25	95

*A.S.E.A.N. = Association of South East Asian Nations.
Nos. 84/6 were printed together, *se-tenant*, in horizontal strips of 3 throughout the sheet, forming a composite design.

56 Trees, Elephant and Tiger	57 Athletics

(Des from children's drawings. Litho Harrison)

1971 (2 Oct). *25th Anniv of U.N.I.C.E.F.* T 56 *and similar multicoloured designs.* P 12½.

87	15 c. Type 56	..	..	1·25	35
	a. Horiz strip of 5. Nos. 87/91	..	5·75	
88	15 c. Cat and kittens	..	1·25	35
89	15 c. Sun, flower and bird (22 × 29 mm)	..	1·25	35
90	15 c. Monkey, elephant and lion in jungle	1·25	35
91	15 c. Spider and butterflies	..	1·25	35
87/91	..	..	Set of 5	5·75	1·60

Nos. 87/91 were issued in horizontal *se-tenant* strips of 5 throughout the sheet.

(Des Union Art Corp. Litho B.W.)

1971 (11 Dec). *Sixth S.E.A.P.* Games, Kuala Lumpur.* T 57 *and similar horiz designs.* Multicoloured. P 14½ × 14.

92	57	25 c. Type 57 ..	..	35	40
93		30 c. Sepak Raga players	..	50	50
94		50 c. Hockey	..	80	95
92/4			Set of 3	1·50	1·75

*S.E.A.P. = South East Asian Peninsula.

58	59	60

Map and Tourist Attractions

(Des locally. Litho Harrison)

1972 (31 Jan). *Pacific Area Tourist Association Conference.* P 14 × 14½.

95	58	30 c. multicoloured	..	1·50	50
		a. Horiz strip of 3. Nos. 95/7 ..		4·00	
96	59	30 c. multicoloured	..	1·50	50
97	60	30 c. multicoloured	..	1·50	50
95/7		..	Set of 3	4·00	1·40

Nos. 95/7 were printed together, *se-tenant*, in horizontal strips of 3 throughout the sheet forming a composite design.

61 Kuala Lumpur City Hall

(Des from colour transparencies. Litho Harrison)

1972 (1 Feb). *City Status for Kuala Lumpur.* T 61 *and similar horiz design.* Multicoloured. P 14½ × 14.

98	25 c. Type 61	..	..	1·25	1·25
99	50 c. City Hall in floodlights ..	..	1·75	1·25

62 SOCSO Emblem	63 W.H.O. Emblem

(Des B.W. Litho Harrison)

1973 (2 July). *Social Security Organisation.* P 13½.

100	62	10 c. multicoloured	..	..	15	15
101		15 c. multicoloured	..	..	25	10
102		50 c. multicoloured	..	..	60	1·40
100/2	..			Set of 3	90	1·50

(Des Union Advertising. Litho B.W.)

1973 (1 Aug). *25th Anniv of W.H.O.* T 63 *and similar vert design.* P 13.

103	30 c. multicoloured	..	..	45	25
104	75 c. multicoloured	..	..	1·25	1·75

64 Fireworks, National	65 Emblems of Interpol and Royal
Flag and Flower	Malaysian Police

(Des Clover Associates. Litho Harrison)

1973 (31 Aug). *Tenth Anniv of Malaysia.* P 13½.

105	64	10 c. multicoloured	..	..	25	25
106		15 c. multicoloured	..	..	30	15
107		50 c. multicoloured	..	..	1·25	1·60
105/7	..			Set of 3	1·60	1·75

(Des Union Advertising. Litho Harrison)

1973 (15 Sept). *50th Anniv of Interpol.* T 65 *and similar vert design.* P 13½.

108	25 c. Type 65	..	..	1·00	50
109	75 c. Emblems within "50" ..	..	1·75	2·00

66 Aeroplane and M.A.S. Emblem

(Des Art Dept, Malaysia Airline System. Litho Harrison)

1973 (1 Oct). *Foundation of Malaysia Airline System.* P 14½.

110	66	15 c. multicoloured	..	..	25	10
111		30 c. multicoloured	..	..	45	60
112		50 c. multicoloured	..	..	75	1·60
110/12			Set of 3	1·25	2·10

67 Kuala Lumpur

(Des Malaysian Advertising Services. Litho B.W.)

1974 (1 Feb). *Establishment of Kuala Lumpur as Federal Territory.* P 12½ × 13.

113	67	25 c. multicoloured	..	..	50	85
114		50 c. multicoloured	..	..	1·00	1·75

68 Development Projects	69 Scout Badge and Map

(Des Malaysian Advertising Services. Litho Rosenbaum Bros, Vienna)

1974 (25 Apr). *Seventh Annual Meeting of Asian Development Bank's Board of Governors, Kuala Lumpur.* P 13½.
115	68	30 c. multicoloured	.. ..	25	50
116		75 c. multicoloured	.. .. ..	80	1·75

(Des Malaysian Advertising Services. Litho Harrison)

1974 (1 Aug). *Malaysian Scout Jamboree.* T **69** *and similar multicoloured designs.* P 13 × 13½ (15 c.) or 14 × 13½ (others).
117		10 c. Type 69	..	30	30
118		15 c. Scouts saluting and flags (46 × 24 mm)		35	30
119		50 c. Scout badge	.. ..	1·25	2·25
117/19			Set of 3	1·75	2·50

70 Coat of Arms and Power Installations

(Des Malaysian Advertising Services. Litho Harrison)

1974 (1 Sept). *25th Anniv of National Electricity Board.* T **70** *and similar multicoloured design.* P 14 (30 c.) or 14 × 14½ (75 c.).
120		30 c. Type 70	..	30	50
121		75 c. National Electricity Board Building (37 × 27 mm)	.. ..	1·00	2·00

71 U.P.U. and Post Office Emblems within "100"

(Des Clover Associates. Litho Harrison)

1974 (9 Oct). *Centenary of Universal Postal Union.* P 14½ × 14.
122	71	25 c. dull yell-grn, brt yell & lt rose-carm		20	35
123		30 c. lt new blue, brt yell & lt rose-carm		25	35
124		75 c. brownish orange, bright yellow and light rose-carmine	..	65	1·75
122/4	..		Set of 3	1·00	2·25

72 Gravel Pump in Tin Mine   **73** Hockey-players, World Cup and Federation Emblem

(Des Malaysian Advertising Service. Litho D.L.R.)

1974 (31 Oct). *Fourth World Tin Conference, Kuala Lumpur.* T **72** *and similar horiz designs. Multicoloured.* P 13½.
125		15 c. Type 72	..	1·00	15
126		20 c. Open-cast mine	..	1·25	70
127		50 c. Dredger within "ingot"	..	2·75	3·00
125/7	..		Set of 3	4·50	3·50

(Des Malaysian Advertising Services. Litho Harrison)

1975 (1 Mar). *Third World Cup Hockey Championships.* P 13½ × 13.
128	73	30 c. multicoloured	..	90	60
129		75 c. multicoloured	..	2·10	2·25

74 Congress Emblem   **75** Emblem of M.K.P.W. (Malayan Women's Organisation)

(Des Malaysian Advertising Services. Litho Harrison)

1975 (1 May). *25th Anniv of Malaysian Trade Union Congress.* P 14 × 14½.
130	74	20 c. multicoloured	..	20	25
131		25 c. multicoloured	..	30	30
132		30 c. multicoloured	..	45	60
130/2	..		Set of 3	85	1·00

(Des Malaysian Advertising Services. Litho Harrison)

1975 (25 Aug). *International Women's Year.* P 14.
133	75	10 c. multicoloured	..	15	25
134		15 c. multicoloured	..	30	25
135		50 c. multicoloured	..	1·25	2·25
133/5	..		Set of 3	1·50	2·50

76 Ubudiah Mosque, Kuala Kangsar   **77** Plantation and Emblem

(Des Malaysian Advertising Services. Litho Harrison)

1975 (22 Sept). *Koran Reading Competition.* T **76** *and similar horiz designs. Multicoloured.* P 14.
136		15 c. Type 76	..	1·25	30
		a. Horiz strip of 5. Nos. 136/40		5·75	
137		15 c. Zahir Mosque, Alor Star..		1·25	30
138		15 c. National Mosque, Kuala Lumpur		1·25	30
139		15 c. Sultan Abu Bakar Mosque, Johore Bahru		1·25	30
140		15 c. Kuching State Mosque, Sarawak		1·25	30
136/40			Set of 5	5·75	1·40

The above were printed together, horizontally *se-tenant* throughout the sheet.

(Des E. Sulaiman bin Haji Hassan and E. Hoh Lian Yong. Litho Harrison)

1975 (22 Oct). *50th Anniv of Malaysian Rubber Research Institute.* T **77** *and similar horiz designs. Multicoloured.* P 14 × 14½.
141		10 c. Type 77	..	35	15
142		30 c. Latex cup and emblem	..	1·00	70
143		75 c. Natural rubber in test-tubes		1·60	2·25
141/3	..		Set of 3	2·75	2·75

77a *Hebomoia glaucippe*   **78** Scrub Typhus

(Photo Harrison)

1976 (19 Jan). *Coil Stamps.* T **77a** *and similar horiz design. Multicoloured.* P 13½.
144		10 c. Type 77a	..	60	3·50
145		15 c. *Precis orithya*..	..	65	3·50

(Des Lap Loy Fong (25 c.), Lee Eng Kee (others). Litho Harrison)

1976 (6 Feb). *75th Anniv of the Institute of Medical Research.* T **78** *and similar vert designs. Multicoloured.* P 14.
146		20 c. Type 78	..	25	15
147		25 c. Malaria diagnosis	..	40	20
148		$1 Beri-beri	..	1·60	2·50
146/8	..		Set of 3	2·00	2·50

79 The Yang di-Pertuan Agong (Tuanku Yahya Petra)   **80** State Council Complex

(Des Union Advertising. Photo Harrison)

1976 (28 Feb). *Installation of Yang di-Pertuan Agong.* P 14½ × 13½.
149	79	10 c. black, bistre and yellow	..	25	10
150		15 c. black, bistre and bright mauve		40	10
151		50 c. black, bistre and ultramarine		2·25	2·50
149/51	..		Set of 3	2·75	2·50

(Des Aini bin Abdul Rahman. Litho Harrison)

1976 (17 Aug). *Opening of the State Council Complex and Administrative Building, Sarawak.* P 12½.
152	80	15 c. grey-green and light yellow		35	10
153		20 c. grey-green and light bright mauve		45	40
154		50 c. grey-green and pale blue	..	1·00	1·40
152/4	..		Set of 3	1·60	1·75

81 E.P.F. Building   **82** Blind People at Work

(Litho Harrison)

1976 (18 Oct). *25th Anniv of Employees' Provident Fund.* T **81** *and similar multicoloured designs.* P 14½ (25 c.) or 13½ × 14½ (others).
155		10 c. Type 81	..	15	10
156		25 c. E.P.F. emblems (27 × 27 mm)		25	35
157		50 c. E.P.F. Building at night..		60	1·00
155/7	..		Set of 3	90	1·40

(Des Malayan Association for the Blind, Messrs Advertising Sales Promotion and Hexxon Grafic. Litho Harrison)

1976 (20 Nov). *25th Anniv of Malayan Association for the Blind.* T **82** *and similar horiz design. Multicoloured.* P 13½ × 14½.
158		10 c. Type 82	..	15	15
159		75 c. Blind man and shadow	..	1·25	2·10

83 Independence Celebrations, 1957   **84** F.E.L.D.A. Village Scheme

(Des Hexxon Grafic. Photo Harrison)

1977 (14 Jan). *First Death Anniversary of Tun Abdul Razak (Prime Minister).* T **83** *and similar horiz designs, each sepia and gold.* P 14.
160		15 c. Type 83	..	1·00	30
		a. Horiz strip of 5. Nos. 160/4		4·50	
161		15 c. "Education"	..	1·00	30
162		15 c. Tun Razak and map ("Development")		1·00	30
163		15 c. "Rukunegara" (National Philosophy)		1·00	30
164		15 c. A.S.E.A.N. meeting	..	1·00	30
160/4	..		Set of 5	4·50	1·40

The above were printed together, horizontally *se-tenant* throughout the sheet.

(Des Halim Teh and Basyuni Sumrah. Litho Harrison)

1977 (7 July). *21st Anniv of Federal Land Development Authority (F.E.L.D.A.).* T **84** *and similar horiz design. Multicoloured.* P 13½ × 14.
165		15 c. Type 84	..	25	10
166		30 c. Oil Palm settlement	..	60	80

85 Figure "10"   **86** Games Logos

(Des Hexxon Grafic. Litho Harrison)

1977 (8 Aug). *Tenth Anniv of A.S.E.A.N. (Association of South East Asian Nations).* T **85** *and similar horiz design. Multicoloured.* P 13½ × 14½.
167		10 c. Type 85	..	10	10
168		75 c. Flags of members	..	60	65

(Des PTM Communications & Co. Litho Harrison)

1977 (19 Nov). *9th South East Asia Games, Kuala Lumpur.* T **86** *and similar horiz designs. Multicoloured.* P 13½ × 14½.
169		10 c. Type 86	..	15	15
170		20 c. "Ball"	..	20	15
171		75 c. Symbolic athletes	..	75	1·50
169/71	..		Set of 3	1·00	1·60

87 Islamic Development Bank Emblem   **88** Mobile Post Office

(Des Queen's Advertising. Litho J.W.)

1978 (15 Mar). *Islamic Development Bank Board of Governors Meeting, Kuala Lumpur.* P 14.
172	87	30 c. multicoloured	..	15	15
173		75 c. multicoloured	..	50	55

(Des Hexxon Grafic. Litho J.W.)

1978 (10 July). *4th Commonwealth Postal Administrations Conference, Kuala Lumpur.* T **88** *and similar horiz designs. Multicoloured.* P 13½ × 13.
174		10 c. Type 88	..	20	10
175		25 c. G.P.O., Kuala Lumpur	..	65	85
176		50 c. Postal delivery by motor-cycle	..	95	1·25
174/6	..		Set of 3	1·60	2·00

89 Boy Scout Emblem   **90** Dome of the Rock, Jerusalem

(Des Aini bin Abdul Rahman. Litho J.W.)

1978 (26 July). *4th Malaysian Boy Scout Jamboree, Sarawak.* T **89** *and similar horiz design. Multicoloured.* P 13½ × 13.
177		15 c. Type 89	..	40	10
178		$1 Bees and honeycomb	..	2·00	1·25

(Des Union Advertising. Litho Harrison)

1978 (21 Aug). *"Freedom for Palestine". P 12½.*
179 **90** 15 c. multicoloured 35 10
180 30 c. multicoloured 60 40

91 Globe and Emblems

92 "Seratus Tahun Getah Asli" and Tapping Knives Symbol

(Litho Harrison)

1978 (30 Sept). *Global Eradication of Smallpox. P 13½ × 14½.*
181 **91** 15 c. black, rosine and new blue .. 15 20
182 30 c. black, rosine and yellowish green 20 10
183 50 c. black, rosine and rose-pink .. 35 45
181/3 .. .. .. *Set of 3* 60 65

(Des Azmi bin Anuar. Litho J.W.)

1978 (28 Nov). *Centenary of Rubber Industry. T* **92** *and similar horiz designs. P 13½ × 13.*
184 10 c. gold and blue-green 10 10
185 20 c. ultramarine, brown & brt yellow-green 10 10
186 75 c. gold and blue-green 45 65
184/6 .. .. .. *Set of 3* 55 75
Designs:—20 c. Rubber tree seedling and part of "maxi stump"; 75 c. Graphic design of rubber tree, latex cup and globe arranged to form "100".

93 Sultan of Selangor's New Palace

(Des Queen's Advertising. Litho Harrison)

1978 (7 Dec). *Inauguration of Shah Alam New Town as State Capital of Selangor. T* **93** *and similar horiz designs. Multicoloured. P 13½ × 14½.*
187 10 c. Type **93** 10 10
188 30 c. Shah Alam (aerial view).. .. 15 10
189 75 c. Shah Alam 45 60
187/9 .. .. .. *Set of 3* 65 70

94 Tiger

95 Multiple "POS" in Octagon

(Des Ong Soo Keat; adapted Malaysian Advertising Services. Litho Asher and Co, Melbourne)

1979 (4 Jan). *Wildlife. Multicoloured designs as T* **94**. *W* **95** *(inverted on $10 or sideways on others). P 14½.*
190 30 c. Type **94** 70 10
191 40 c. Malayan Flying Lemur 70 10
192 50 c. Lesser Malay Chevrotain .. 80 10
193 75 c. Leathery Pangolin 90 10
194 $1 Malayan Turtle .. .. .. 1·50 10
195 $2 Malayan Tapir .. .. .. 1·50 10
196 $5 Gaur .. .. 4·25 1·00
197 $10 Orang-Utan (*vert*) .. .. 7·00 3·25
190/7 .. .. .. *Set of 8* 16·00 4·25
For these stamps without watermark, see Nos. 272/9.

96 View of Central Bank of Malaysia

97 I.Y.C. Emblem

(Des Union Advertising. Litho J.W.)

1979 (26 Jan). *20th Anniv of Central Bank of Malaysia. T* **96** *and similar vert design showing view of bank building. P 13.*
198 10 c. multicoloured 10 10
199 75 c. multicoloured 40 45

(Des Queen's Advertising. Litho Harrison)

1979 (24 Feb). *International Year of the Child. T* **97** *and similar vert designs. P 14½ × 14.*
200 10 c. gold, blue and salmon 30 10
201 15 c. multicoloured 40 10
202 $1 multicoloured .. .. .. 1·75 2·25
200/2 .. .. .. *Set of 3* 2·25 2·25
Designs:—15 c. Children of different races holding hands in front of globe; $1 Children taking part in various activities.

98 Dam and Power Station

99 Exhibition Emblem

(Des National Electricity Board. Litho Harrison)

1979 (19 Sept). *Opening of Hydro-Electric Power Station, Temengor. T* **98** *and similar horiz designs showing views of power station and dam. P 13½ × 14½.*
203 15 c. multicoloured 15 15
204 25 c. multicoloured 25 50
205 50 c. multicoloured 45 85
203/5 .. .. .. *Set of 3* 75 1·40

(Des Malaysian Advertising Services. Litho J.W.)

1979 (20 Sept). *World Telecommunications Exhibition, Geneva. T* **99** *and similar designs. P 14 (50 c.) or 13 (others).*
206 10 c. orange, ultramarine and silver .. 10 15
207 15 c. multicoloured 15 10
208 50 c. multicoloured .. .. .. 40 1·25
206/8 .. .. .. *Set of 3* 60 1·40
Designs: (34 × 24 *mm*)—15 c. Telephone receiver joining one half of World to the other. (39 × 28 *mm*)—50 c. Communications equipment.

100 Tuanku Haji Ahmad Shah

101 Pahang and Sarawak Maps within Telephone Dials

(Des Malaysian Advertising Services. Litho Harrison)

1980 (10 July). *Installation of Yang di-Pertuan Agong (Tuanku Haji Ahmad Shah). P 14.*
209 **100** 10 c. black, gold and yellow .. 10 10
210 15 c. black, gold and bright purple .. 15 10
211 50 c. black, gold and new blue .. 40 90
209/11 .. .. .. *Set of 3* 60 1·00

(Des Malaysian Advertising Services. Litho J.W.)

1980 (31 Aug). *Kuantan-Kuching Submarine Cable Project. T* **101** *and similar horiz designs. Multicoloured. P 13.*
212 10 c. Type **101** 10 10
213 15 c. Kuantan and Kuching views within telephone dials 15 10
214 50 c. Pahang and Sarawak Maps within telephone receiver 35 80
212/14 .. .. .. *Set of 3* 50 90

102 Bangi Campus

103 Mecca

(Des Malaysian Advertising Services. Litho J.W.)

1980 (2 Sept). *10th Anniv of National University of Malaysia. T* **102** *and similar horiz designs. Multicoloured. P 13.*
215 10 c. Type **102** 15 15
216 15 c. Jalan Pantai Baru campus .. 20 10
217 75 c. Great Hall .. .. .. 65 1·75
215/17 .. .. .. *Set of 3* 90 1·75

(Des Malaysian Advertising Services. Litho J.W.)

1980 (9 Nov). *Moslem Year 1400 A.H. Commemoration. P 13.*
218 **103** 15 c. multicoloured 10 10
219 50 c. multicoloured 30 90
The 50 c. value is as T **103** but the inscriptions are in Roman lettering and the country name is to the left of the design.

NEW INFORMATION
The editor is always interested to correspond with people who have new information that will improve or correct the Catalogue.

104 Disabled Child learning to Walk

105 Industrial Scene

(Des Malaysian Advertising Services. Litho J.W.)

1981 (14 Feb). *International Year for Disabled Persons. T* **104** *and similar vert designs. Multicoloured. P 13½ × 13.*
220 10 c. Type **104** 30 20
221 15 c. Disabled woman sewing.. .. 55 10
222 75 c. Disabled athlete throwing javelin .. 1·50 2·00
220/2 .. .. .. *Set of 3* 2·10 2·10

(Des Malaysian Advertising Services. Litho J.W.)

1981 (2 May). *"Expo '81" Industrial Training Exposition, Kuala Lumpur and Seminar, Genting Highlands. T* **105** *and similar horiz designs. Multicoloured. P 13½ × 13.*
223 10 c. Type **105** 10 10
224 15 c. Worker and bulldozer 15 10
225 30 c. Workers at ship-building yard .. 25 35
226 75 c. Agriculture and fishing produce, workers and machinery .. .. 65 1·50
223/6 .. .. .. *Set of 4* 1·00 1·75

106 "25"

(Des A. Yusof and Malaysian Advertising Services. Litho J.W.)

1981 (17 June). *25th Anniv of Malaysian National Committee for World Energy Conferences. T* **106** *and similar horiz designs. Multicoloured. P 13½ × 13.*
227 10 c. Type **106** 15 15
228 15 c. Drawings showing importance of energy sources in industry 20 10
229 75 c. Symbols of various energy sources .. 1·00 2·00
227/9 .. .. .. *Set of 3* 1·25 2·00

107 Drawing showing development of Sabah from Village to Urbanised Area

(Des Creative Concepts. Litho J.W.)

1981 (31 Aug). *Centenary of Sabah. T* **107** *and similar horiz design. Multicoloured. P 12.*
230 15 c. Type **107** 50 15
231 80 c. Drawing showing traditional and modern methods of agriculture .. .. 2·00 3·25

108 *Samanea saman*

109 Jamboree Emblem

(Des Yusof bin Hadji Saman. Litho J.W.)

1981 (16 Dec). *Trees. T* **108** *and similar multicoloured designs. P 14.*
232 15 c. Type **108** 55 10
233 50 c. *Dyera costulata* (*vert*) .. .. 1·50 1·50
234 80 c. *Dryobalanops aromatica* (*vert*) .. 1·75 2·75
232/4 .. .. .. *Set of 3* 3·50 3·75

(Des P. Lim (15 c.), Datuk Syed Hashim bin Abdullah (others). Litho J.W.)

1982 (10 Apr). *5th Malaysian/7th Asia–Pacific Boy Scout Jamboree. T* **109** *and similar horiz designs. Multicoloured. P 13½ × 13.*
235 15 c. Type **109** 30 10
236 50 c. Malaysian flag and scout emblem .. 70 80
237 80 c. Malaysian and Asia–Pacific scout emblems .. .. .. 1·10 2·75
235/7 .. .. .. *Set of 3* 1·90 3·25

110 A.S.E.A.N. Building and Emblem　　111 Dome of the Rock, Jerusalem

(Litho J.W.)

1982 (8 Aug). *15th Anniv Ministerial Meeting of A.S.E.A.N. (Association of South East Asian Nations).* T **110** *and similar horiz design. Multicoloured.* P 14.
238　15 c. Type 110 .. .. 15　10
239　$1 Flags of member nations .. 60　1·50

(Litho J.W.)

1982 (21 Aug). *"Freedom for Palestine".* P 13½.
240　111　15 c. gold, blue-green and black .. 75　15
241　　$1 silver, pale turquoise-green & blk .. 2·75　2·75

112 Views of Kuala Lumpur in 1957 and 1982

(Des Ministry of Information. Litho Rosenbaum Bros, Vienna)

1982 (31 Aug). *25th Anniv of Independence.* T **112** *and similar horiz designs. Multicoloured.* P 14 × 13½.
242　10 c. Type 112 .. .. 10　10
243　15 c. Malaysian industries .. .. 15　15
244　50 c. Soldiers on parade .. .. 40　55
245　80 c. Independence ceremony .. .. 70　1·75
242/5 .. .. *Set of* 4　1·25　2·25
MS246　120 × 190 mm. Nos. 242/5 .. 4·00　4·75

113 Shadow Play

(Des N. Ajib. Litho J.W.)

1982 (30 Oct). *Traditional Games.* T **113** *and similar horiz designs. Multicoloured.* P 13.
247　10 c. Type 113 .. .. 30　30
248　15 c. Cross Top .. .. 40　15
249　75 c. Kite flying .. .. .. 1·50　2·50
247/9 .. .. *Set of* 3　2·00　2·75

114 Sabah Hats

(Litho Harrison)

1982 (26 Nov). *Malaysian Handicrafts.* T **114** *and similar horiz designs. Multicoloured.* P 13 × 13½.
250　10 c. Type 114 .. .. 15　30
251　15 c. Gold-threaded cloth .. .. 15　20
252　75 c. Sarawak pottery .. .. 65　2·00
250/2 .. .. *Set of* 3　85　2·25

115 Gas Exploitation Logo　　116 Flag of Malaysia

(Litho Security Printers (M), Malaysia)

1983 (22 Jan). *Export of Liquefied Natural Gas from Bintulu Field, Sarawak.* T **115** *and similar horiz designs. Multicoloured.* P 12.
253　15 c. Type 115 .. .. 55　10
　　　a. Perf 13½ .. ..
254　20 c. *Tenaga Satu* (liquid gas tanker) .. 80　50
　　　a. Perf 13½ .. ..
255　　$1 Gas drilling equipment .. 2·50　3·25
　　　a. Perf 13½ .. ..
253/5 .. .. *Set of* 3　3·50　3·50

(Litho J.W.)

1983 (14 Mar). *Commonwealth Day.* T **116** *and similar horiz designs. Multicoloured.* P 13½ × 14.
256　15 c. Type 116 .. .. 10　10
257　20 c. The King of Malaysia .. .. 15　15
258　40 c. Oil palm tree and refinery .. 25　30
259　　$1 Satellite view of Earth .. .. 60　1·50
256/9 .. .. *Set of* 4　1·00　1·90

117 Tilapia nilotica

(Des and litho Security Printers (M), Malaysia)

1983 (15 June). *Freshwater Fishes.* T **117** *and similar horiz designs. Multicoloured.* P 12.
260　20 c. Type 117 .. .. 30　45
　　　a. Horiz pair. Nos. 260/1 .. .. 60　90
　　　b. Perf 13½ × 14 .. .. 1·75　1·25
　　　ba. Horiz pair. Nos. 260b/1b .. 3·50　2·50
261　20 c. *Cyprinus carpie* .. .. .. 30　45
　　　b. Perf 13½ × 14 .. .. 1·75　1·25
262　40 c. *Puntius gonionotus* .. .. 60　90
　　　a. Horiz pair. Nos. 262/3 .. .. 1·10　1·75
　　　b. Perf 13½ × 14 .. .. 3·00　3·00
　　　ba. Horiz pair. Nos. 262b/3b .. 6·00　6·00
263　40 c. *Ctenopharyngodon idellus* .. 60　90
　　　b. Perf 13½ × 14 .. .. 3·00　3·00
260/3 .. .. *Set of* 4　1·60　2·40
　Nos. 260/1 and 262/3 were each printed together, *se-tenant,* in horizontal pairs throughout the sheet.

118 Lower Pergau River Bridge

(Des Malaysian Public Works Dept. Litho Security Printers (M), Malaysia)

1983 (11 July). *Opening of East–West Highway.* T **118** *and similar horiz designs. Multicoloured.* P 13½.
264　15 c. Type 118 .. .. 60　15
265　20 c. Perak river reservoir bridge .. 70　45
266　　$1 Map showing East–West highway .. 2·25　3·25
264/6 .. .. *Set of* 3　3·25　3·50

119 Northrop "RF-5E" Fighter　　120 Helmeted Hornbill

(Des and litho J.W.)

1983 (16 Sept). *50th Anniv of Malaysian Armed Forces.* T **119** *and similar horiz designs. Multicoloured.* P 13.
267　15 c. Type 119 .. .. 45　15
268　20 c. Missile boat .. .. .. 75　45
269　40 c. Battle of Pasir Panjang .. 1·25　1·25
270　80 c. Trooping the Colour .. .. 1·75　2·50
267/70 .. .. *Set of* 4　3·75　4·00
MS271　130×85 mm. Nos. 267/70. P 13½ .. 4·50　5·00

1983 (3 Oct)–**85**.* *As Nos.* 190/7 *but without wmk.*
272　30 c. Type 94 (1984) .. .. 90　20
273　40 c. Malayan Flying Lemur (6.10.83) 1·00　20
274　50 c. Lesser Malay Chevrotain (10.4.84) 1·25　20
275　75 c. Leathery Pangolin (19.10.85) .. 4·00　6·00
276　　$1 Malayan Turtle (5.10.83) .. 2·50　20
277　　$2 Malayan Tapir .. .. .. 3·25　70
278　　$5 Gaur (1985) .. .. .. 11·00　9·00
279　$10 Orang-Utan (*vert*) (3.84) .. 13·00　11·00
272/9 .. .. *Set of* 8　32·00　25·00
　*There was no official release date for these stamps. Dates shown are the earliest recorded from postmarks and may be revised should earlier examples be reported.

(Des P. Ket. Litho Security Printers (M), Malaysia)

1983 (26 Oct). *Hornbills of Malaysia.* T **120** *and similar vert designs. Multicoloured.* P 13½.
280　15 c. Type 120 .. .. 40　10
281　20 c. Wrinkled Hornbill .. .. 55　40
282　50 c. Long-crested Hornbill .. 85　1·00
283　　$1 Rhinoceros Hornbill .. .. 1·60　2·75
280/3 .. .. *Set of* 4　3·00　3·75

OMNIBUS ISSUES

Details, together with prices for complete sets, of the various Omnibus issues from the 1935 Silver Jubilee series to date are included in a special section following Zimbabwe at the end of Volume 2.

121 Bank Building, Ipoh　　122 Sky-scraper and Mosque, Kuala Lumpur

(Des P. Hoong. Litho Security Printers (M), Malaysia)

1984 (26 Jan). *25th Anniv of Bank Negara.* T **121** *and similar horiz design. Multicoloured.* P 13½ × 14.
284　20 c. Type 121 .. .. 40　30
285　　$1 Bank building, Alor Setar .. 1·40　2·50

(Des Mara Institute of Technology. Litho Security Printers (M), Malaysia)

1984 (1 Feb). *10th Anniv of Federal Territory of Kuala Lumpur.* T **122** *and similar multicoloured designs.* P 13½ × 14 (80 c.) or 14 × 13½ (*others*).
286　20 c. Type 122 .. .. 50　20
287　40 c. Aerial view .. .. .. 1·00　1·00
288　80 c. Gardens and clock-tower (*horiz*).. 1·75　2·75
286/8 .. .. *Set of* 3　3·00　3·50

123 Map showing Industries　　124 Semenanjung Keris

(Litho Security Printers (M), Malaysia)

1984 (16 Apr). *Formation of Labuan Federal Territory.* T **123** *and similar vert design. Multicoloured.* P 13½×14.
289　20 c. Type 123 .. .. 50　25
290　　$1 Flag and map of Labuan .. .. 2·00　2·75

(Des P. Ket. Litho Harrison)

1984 (30 May). *Traditional Malay Weapons.* T **124** *and similar vert designs. Multicoloured.* P 13½ × 14.
291　40 c. Type 124 .. .. 70　90
　　　a. Block of 4. Nos. 291/4 .. 2·50
292　40 c. Pekakak keris .. .. .. 70　90
293　40 c. Jawa keris .. .. .. 70　90
294　40 c. Lada tumbuk .. .. .. 70　90
291/4 .. .. *Set of* 4　2·50　3·25
　Nos. 291/4 were printed in *se-tenant* blocks of four throughout the sheet.

125 Map of World and Transmitter　　126 Facsimile Service

(Des Dept of Broadcasting. Litho Harrison)

1984 (23 June). *20th Anniv of Asia–Pacific Broadcasting Union.* T **125** *and similar horiz design. Multicoloured.* P 13½ × 14½.
295　20 c. Type 125 .. .. 40　25
296　　$1 Clasped hands within "20" .. 2·00　3·00

(Des Mark Johan and Associates. Litho Security Printers (M), Malaysia)

1984 (29 Oct). *Opening of New General Post Office, Kuala Lumpur.* T **126** *and similar horiz designs. Multicoloured.* P 12.
297　15 c. Type 126 .. .. 30　20
298　20 c. New G.P.O. building .. .. 40　30
299　　$1 Mailbag conveyor .. .. 1·75　2·75
297/9 .. .. *Set of* 3　2·25　3·00

127 Yang di Pertuan Agong (Tuanku Mahmood)　　128 White Hibiscus

(Des P. Ket. Litho Security Printers (M), Malaysia)

1984 (15 Nov). *Installation of Yang di Pertuan Agong (Tuanku Mahmood).* T **127** *and similar design.* P 12.

300	**127**	15 c. multicoloured	..	..	40	20
301		20 c. multicoloured	..	..	40	20
302	–	40 c. multicoloured	..	..	75	1·00
303	–	80 c. multicoloured	..	..	1·40	2·25
300/3				*Set of 4*	2·75	3·25

Design: *Horiz* — 40 c., 80 c. Yang di Pertuan Agong and Federal Crest.

(Litho Security Printers (M), Malaysia)

1984 (12 Dec). *Hibiscus.* T **128** *and similar vert designs. Multicoloured.* P 13½.

304	10 c. Type **128**	..			35	15
305	20 c. Red Hibiscus	..	..		70	20
306	40 c. Pink Hibiscus	..	..		1·25	1·00
307	$1 Orange Hibiscus	..			2·25	3·25
304/7	..	..		*Set of 4*	4·00	4·25

129 Parliament Building   **130** Banded Linsang

(Des P. Ket. Litho Security Printers (M), Malaysia)

1985 (30 Mar). *25th Anniv of Federal Parliament.* T **129** *and similar multicoloured design.* P 13½ × 14 (20 c.) or 14 × 13½ ($1).

308	20 c. Type **129**	..	..		30	15
309	$1 Parliament Building (*different*) (*horiz*)		1·75	1·50

(Des P. Ket. Litho J.W.)

1985 (25 Apr). *Protected Animals of Malaysia (1st series).* T **130** *and similar multicoloured designs.* P 14.

310	10 c. Type **130**	..	..		30	10
311	40 c. Slow Loris (*vert*)	..	..		80	80
312	$1 Spotted Giant Flying Squirrel (*vert*)		1·75	2·75
310/12				*Set of 3*	2·50	3·25

See also Nos. 383/6.

131 Stylised Figures   **132** F.M.S.R. "No. 1" Steam Locomotive, 1885

(Des Amir bin Osman. Litho Security Printers (M), Malaysia)

1985 (15 May). *International Youth Year.* T **131** *and similar horiz design. Multicoloured.* P 13.

313	20 c. Type **131**	..	..		30	15
314	$1 Young workers	..	..		1·75	2·75

(Des AMW Communications Management. Litho Security Printers (M), Malaysia).

1985 (1 June). *Centenary of Malayan Railways.* T **132** *and similar horiz designs.* P 13.

315	15 c. black, carmine-verm & pale orange	..	60	15
316	20 c. multicoloured	..	..		70	30
317	$1 multicoloured	..	..		1·75	2·50
315/17				*Set of 3*	2·75	2·75
MS318	119×59 mm. 80 c. multicoloured				
	P 13½×13				1·75	2·75

Designs: *Horiz* (*as* T **132**)—20 c. Class "20" diesel locomotive, 1957; $1 Class "23" diesel locomotive, 1983. (48×31 *mm*)—80 c. Class "56" steam locomotive, 1938.

133 Blue Proton "Saga 1.3s"   **134** Penang Bridge

(Des and litho J.W.)

1985 (9 July). *Production of Proton "Saga" (Malaysian national car).* T **133** *and similar horiz designs. Multicoloured.* P 13½×13.

319	20 c. Type **133**	..	..		30	15
320	40 c. White Proton "Saga 1.3s"	..		45	60
321	$1 Red Proton "Saga 1.5s"	..		80	2·00
319/21	..	..		*Set of 3*	1·40	2·50

(Des Kathy's Design. Litho Security Printers (M), Malaysia)

1985 (14 Sept). *Opening of Penang Bridge.* T **134** *and similar horiz designs. Multicoloured.* P 12 ($1) or 13 (*others*).

322	20 c. Type **134**	..	..		40	15
323	40 c. Penang Bridge and location map		65	50
324	$1 Symbolic bridge linking Penang to mainland (40×24 *mm*)	..	1·50	1·50
322/4				*Set of 3*	2·25	1·90

---

135 Offshore Oil Rig   **136** Sultan Azlan Shah and Perak Royal Crest

(Des Andamaz Enterprise. Litho Security Printers (M), Malaysia)

1985 (4 Nov). *Malaysian Petroleum Production.* T **135** *and similar multicoloured designs.* P 12.

325	15 c. Type **135**	..	..		20	10
326	20 c. Malaysia's first oil refinery (*horiz*)	..	30	30
327	$1 Map of Malaysian offshore oil and gas fields (*horiz*)	..	1·25	1·75
325/7				*Set of 3*	1·60	1·90

(Des Kathy's Design. Litho J.W.)

1985 (9 Dec). *Installation of the Sultan of Perak.* P 14.

328	**136**	15 c. multicoloured	..	..	15	10
329		20 c. multicoloured	..	..	25	25
330		$1 multicoloured	..	..	1·25	2·25
328/30				*Set of 3*	1·50	2·25

137 Crested Fireback Pheasant   **139** Two Indonesian Dancers

138

(Des P. Ket. Litho Security Printers (M), Malaysia)

1986 (11 Mar). *Protected Birds of Malaysia (1st series).* T **137** *and similar multicoloured designs.* W **138** (*sideways on* 40 c.). *Phosphorised paper.* P 13½.

331	20 c. Type **137**	..	..		70	90
	a. Horiz pair. Nos. 331/2	..		1·40	1·75
332	20 c. Malaya Peacock-pheasant	..		70	90
333	40 c. Bulwer's Pheasant (*horiz*)	..		1·00	1·25
	a. Horiz pair. Nos. 333/4	..		2·00	2·50
	b. Perf 12	..	..		1·75	2·50
	ba. Horiz pair. Nos. 333b/4b	..		3·50	5·00
334	40 c. Great Argus Pheasant (*horiz*)	..		1·00	1·25
	b. Perf 12	..	..		1·75	2·50
331/4	..	..		*Set of 4*	3·00	3·75

Nos. 331/2 and 333/4 were each printed together, *se-tenant*, in horizontal pairs throughout the sheets.
See also Nos. 394/7.

(Des AMC Advertising Agencies. Litho Questa)

1986 (14 Apr). *Pacific Area Travel Association Conference, Malaysia.* T **139** *and similar vert designs. Multicoloured.* P 15×14.

335	20 c. Type **139**	..	..		30	40
	a. Horiz strip of 3. Nos. 335/7	..		80	
336	20 c. Dyak dancer and longhouse, Malaysia	..	30	40
337	20 c. Dancers and church, Philippines	..	30	40
338	40 c. Thai dancer and temple	..		50	70
	a. Horiz strip of 3. Nos. 338/40	..		1·40	
339	40 c. Chinese dancer, Singapore	..		50	70
340	40 c. Indian dancer and Hindu temple stairway	..	50	70
335/40				*Set of 6*	2·25	3·00

Nos. 335/7 and 338/40 were each printed together, *se-tenant*, in horizontal strips of 3 throughout the sheets.

COVER PRICES

Cover factors are quoted at the beginning of each country for most issues to 1945. An explanation of the system can be found on page x. The factors quoted do not, however, apply to philatelic covers.

---

140 Stylized Competitors   **141** Rambutan

141a

(Des Design Excelsior. Litho Security Printers (M), Malaysia)

1986 (19 Apr). *Malaysia Games.* T **140** *and similar multicoloured designs.* W **138** (*sideways on* 20 c.). *Phosphorised paper.* P 12.

341	20 c. Type **140**	..	..		75	20
342	40 c. Games emblems (*vert*)	..		1·40	1·40
343	$1 National and state flags (*vert*)	..	3·00	3·50
341/3	..	..		*Set of 3*	4·75	4·75

(Des P. Ket)

1986 (5 June). *Fruits of Malaysia.* T **141** *and similar vert designs. Multicoloured.*

(a) Litho Security Printers (M), Malaysia. W **138**. *Phosphorised paper.* P 12.

344	40 c. Type **141**	..	..		20	25
345	50 c. Pineapple	..	..		25	30
346	80 c. Durian	..	..		40	45
347	$1 Mangostene	..	..		50	55

(b) Photo Harrison. W **141a**. P 13½.

348	$2 Star Fruit	..	..		1·00	1·10
349	$5 Banana	..	..		2·50	2·75
350	$10 Mango	..	..		5·25	5·50
351	$20 Papaya	..	..		10·50	11·00
344/51				*Set of 8*	19·00	20·00

PHOSPHORISED PAPER. From No. 352 onwards all stamps were on phosphorised paper, *unless otherwise stated.*

142 Skull and Slogan "Drugs Can Kill"   **143** MAS Logo and Map showing Routes

(Des Kathy's Design. Litho Security Printers (M), Malaysia)

1986 (26 June). *10th Anniv of National Association for Prevention of Drug Addiction.* T **142** *and similar multicoloured designs.* W **138** (*sideways on* $1). P 13.

352	20 c. Type **142**	..	..		35	20
353	40 c. Bird and slogan "Stay Free From Drugs"	..	55	55
354	$1 Addict and slogan "Drugs Can Destroy" (*vert*)	..	1·10	2·00
352/4	..	..		*Set of 3*	1·75	2·50

(Des PTM Thompson Advertising. Litho Security Printers (M), Malaysia)

1986 (31 July). *Inaugural Flight of Malaysian Airlines Kuala Lumpur–Los Angeles Service.* T **143** *and similar horiz designs. Multicoloured.* W **138** (*sideways*). P 14×13½.

355	20 c. Type **143**	..	..		30	15
356	40 c. Logo, stylized aircraft and route diagram	..	50	60
357	$1 Logo and stylized aircraft	..		1·00	1·75
355/7	..	..		*Set of 3*	1·60	2·25

144 Building Construction   **145** Old Seri Menanti Palace, Negri Sembilan

(Des M. Chin. Litho Security Printers (M), Malaysia)

1986 (3 Nov). *20th Anniv of National Productivity Council and 25th Anniv of Asian Productivity Organization (40 c., $1).* T **144** *and similar multicoloured designs.* W **138** (*sideways on* 40 c., $1). P 13½×14 (20 c.) or 14×13½ (*others*).

358	20 c. Type **144**	..	..		60	25
359	40 c. Planning and design (*horiz*)	..	1·00	85
360	$1 Computer-controlled car assembly line (*horiz*)	..	2·00	2·50
358/60				*Set of 3*	3·25	3·25

(Des P. Ket. Litho Security Printers (M), Malaysia)

1986 (20 Dec). *Historic Buildings of Malaysia (1st series).*
T **145** *and similar horiz designs. Multicoloured. W* **138**
(*sideways*). *P* 13.

361	15 c. Type **145**..	15	15
362	20 c. Old Kenangan Palace, Perak ..	20	15
363	40 c. Old Town Hall, Malacca	35	40
364	$1 Astana, Kuching, Sarawak ..	75	1·40
361/4	.. .. *Set of* 4	1·25	1·90

See also Nos. 465/8.

146 Sompotan (bamboo pipes)

(Des Kathy Wong. Litho Security Printers (M), Malaysia)

1987 (7 Mar). *Malaysian Musical Instruments. T* **146** *and*
similar multicoloured designs. W **138** (*sideways on* 50, 80 *c.*).
P 12.

365	15 c. Type **146**..	15	10
366	20 c. Sapih (four-stringed chordophone) ..	20	15
367	50 c. Serunai (pipes) (*vert*)	35	30
368	80 c. Rebab (three-stringed fiddle) (*vert*)	50	45
365/8	.. .. .. *Set of* 4	1·10	90

147 Modern Housing Estate

(Litho Security Printers (M), Malaysia)

1987 (6 Apr). *International Year of Shelter for the Homeless.*
T **147** *and similar horiz design. Multicoloured. W* **138**. *P* 12.

369	20 c. Type **147**..	20	15
370	$1 Stylised families and houses ..	80	65

148 Drug Addict and Family

(Des Kathy's Design. Litho Security Printers (M), Malaysia)

1987 (8 June). *International Conference on Drug Abuse,*
Vienna. T **148** *and similar horiz designs. Multicoloured. W* **138**
(*sideways*). *P* 13.

371	20 c. Type **148**..	35	30
	a. Vert pair. Nos. 371/2 ..	70	60
372	20 c. Hands holding drugs and damaged internal organs ..	35	30
373	40 c. Healthy boy and broken drug capsule ..	65	50
	a. Vert pair. Nos. 373/4 ..	1·25	1·00
374	40 c. Drugs and healthy internal organs ..	65	50
371/4	.. .. .. *Set of* 4	1·75	1·40

Nos. 371/2 and 373/4 were printed together, *se-tenant*, in
vertical pairs throughout the sheet, each pair forming a
composite design.

149 Spillway and Power Station

(Des Kathy's Design. Litho Security Printers (M), Malaysia)

1987 (13 July). *Opening of Sultan Mahmud Hydro-electric*
Scheme, Kenyir, Trengganu. T **149** *and similar horiz design.*
Multicoloured. W **138**. *P* 12.

375	20 c. Type **149**..	30	10
376	$1 Dam, spillway and reservoir ..	1·10	75

150 Crossed Maces and Parliament Building, Kuala Lumpur	**151** Dish Aerial, Satellite and Globe

(Des R. Zahabuddin. Litho Security Printers (M), Malaysia)

1987 (1 Sept). *33rd Commonwealth Parliamentary Conference.*
T **150** *and similar horiz design. Multicoloured. W* **138**. *P* 12.

377	20 c. Type **150**..	15	10
378	$1 Parliament building and crossed maces emblem ..	60	75

(Des Mark Design. Litho Security Printers (M), Malaysia)

1987 (26 Oct). *Asia/Pacific Transport and Communications*
Decade. T **151** *and similar horiz designs. Multicoloured. W* **138**
(*sideways*). *P* 13.

379	15 c. Type **151**..	20	10
380	20 c. Diesel train and car ..	30	20
381	40 c. Container ships and lorry ..	45	45
382	$1 Malaysian Airlines jumbo jet, Kuala Lumpur Airport..	85	1·25
379/82	.. .. .. *Set of* 4	1·60	1·75

152 Temminck's Golden Cat	**153** Flags of Member Nations and "20"

(Des Ong Soo Keat. Litho Security Printers (M), Malaysia)

1987 (14 Nov). *Protected Animals of Malaysia (2nd series).*
T **152** *and similar horiz designs. Multicoloured. W* **138**
(*sideways on* 15, 20, 40 *c.*). *P* 13.

383	15 c. Type **152**..	40	20
384	20 c. Flatheaded Cat..	40	20
385	40 c. Marbled Cat	75	75
386	$1 Clouded Leopard	1·50	2·00
383/6	.. .. .. *Set of* 4	2·75	2·75

(Des P. Ket. Litho Security Printers (M), Malaysia)

1987 (14 Dec). *20th Anniv of Association of South East Asian*
Nations. T **153** *and similar horiz design. Multicoloured.*
W **138**. *P* 13.

387	20 c. Type **153**..	15	10
388	$1 Flags of member nations and globe	65	1·00

154 Mosque and Portico	**155** Aerial View

(Des R. Zahabuddin. Litho Security Printers (M), Malaysia)

1988 (11 Mar). *Opening of Sultan Salahuddin Abdul Aziz*
Shah Mosque. T **154** *and similar multicoloured designs. W* **138**
(*sideways on* 15, 20 *c.*). *P* 12.

389	15 c. Type **154**..	10	10
390	20 c. Dome, minarets and Sultan of Selangor	15	15
391	$1 Interior and dome (*vert*)	60	1·00
389/91	.. .. .. *Set of* 3	75	1·10

(Des Azmi bin Kassim. Litho Security Printers (M), Malaysia)

1988 (4 Apr). *Sultan Ismail Hydro-electric Power Station,*
Paka, Trengganu. T **155** *and similar horiz design. Multi-*
coloured. W **138** (*sideways*). *P* 13.

392	20 c. Type **155**..	15	10
393	$1 Power station and pylons ..	65	70

156 Black-naped Blue Monarch	**157** Outline Map and Products of Sabah

(Des Ong Soo Keat. Litho Security Printers (M), Malaysia)

1988 (30 June). *Protected Birds of Malaysia (2nd series). T* **156**
and similar vert designs. Multicoloured. W **138**. *P* 13.

394	20 c. Type **156**	20	20
	a. Horiz pair. Nos. 394/5 ..	40	40
395	20 c. Scarlet-backed Flowerpecker ..	20	20
396	50 c. Yellow-backed Sunbird ..	45	45
	a. Horiz pair. Nos. 396/7 ..	90	90
397	50 c. Black and Red Broadbill ..	45	45
394/7	.. .. .. *Set of* 4	1·10	1·10

The two designs of each value were printed together, *se-*
tenant, in horizontal pairs throughout the sheets.

(Des P. Ket. Litho Security Printers (M), Malaysia)

1988 (31 Aug). *25th Anniv of Sabah and Sarawak as States of*
Malaysia. T **157** *and similar vert designs. Multicoloured.*
W **138**. *P* 13.

398	20 c. Type **157**	15	15
	a. Horiz pair. Nos. 398/9 ..	30	30

399	20 c. Outline map and products of Sarawak	15	15
400	$1 Flags of Malaysia, Sabah and Sarawak (30×40 *mm*) ..	60	60
398/400	.. .. .. *Set of* 3	80	80

Nos. 398/9 were printed together, *se-tenant*, in horizontal
pairs throughout the sheet.

158 *Glossodoris atromarginata*	**159** Sultan's Palace, Malacca

(Litho Security Printers (M), Malaysia)

1988 (17 Dec). *Marine Life (1st series). T* **158** *and similar vert*
designs. Multicoloured. W **138**. *P* 12.

401	20 c. Type **158**	25	25
	a. Horiz strip of 5. Nos. 401/5	1·10	
402	20 c. *Phyllidia ocellata* ..	25	25
403	20 c. *Chromodoris annae* ..	25	25
404	20 c. *Flabellina macassarana*	25	25
405	20 c. *Fryeria ruppelli*	25	25
401/5	.. .. .. *Set of* 5	1·10	1·10
MS406	100×75 mm. $1 *Pomacanthus annularis* (50×40 *mm*). P 14	90	1·10

Nos. 401/5 were printed together, *se-tenant*, in horizontal
strips of 5 throughout the sheet, forming a composite
background design.

See also Nos. 410/13, 450/3 and 492/7.

(Des P. Ket. Litho Security Printers (M), Malaysia)

1989 (15 Apr). *Declaration of Malacca as Historic City. T* **159**
and similar multicoloured designs. W **138** (*sideways on* 20 *c.*).
P 13.

407	20 c. Type **159**	15	15
408	20 c. Independence Memorial Building ..	15	15
409	$1 Porta De Santiago Fortress (*vert*)	75	1·40
407/9	.. .. .. *Set of* 3	95	1·50

160 *Tetralia nigrolineata*	**161** Map of Malaysia and Scout Badge

(Des P. Ket. Litho Security Printers (M), Malaysia)

1989 (29 June). *Marine Life (2nd series). Crustaceans. T* **160**
and similar horiz designs. Multicoloured. W **138** (*sideways*).
P 12.

410	20 c. Type **160** ..	20	25
	a. Horiz pair. Nos. 410/11 ..	40	50
	b. Wmk upright..		
	ba. Horiz pair. Nos. 410b/11b		
411	20 c. *Neopetrolisthes maculatus* (crab) ..	20	25
	b. Wmk upright		
412	40 c. *Periclimenes holthuisi* (shrimp) ..	30	40
	a. Horiz pair. Nos. 412/13 ..	60	80
413	40 c. *Synalpheus neomeris* (shrimp) ..	30	40
410/13	.. .. .. *Set of* 4	90	1·10

Nos. 410/11 and 412/13 were each printed together, *se-tenant*,
in horizontal pairs throughout the sheets.

(Des T. Teh. Litho Security Printers (M), Malaysia)

1989 (26 July). *7th National Scout Jamboree. T* **161** *and*
similar multicoloured designs. W **138** (*sideways on* 10, 20 *c.*).
P 13.

414	10 c. Type **161**	20	10
415	20 c. Saluting national flag ..	30	25
416	80 c. Scouts around camp fire (*horiz*) ..	1·10	1·25
414/16	.. .. .. *Set of* 3	1·40	1·40

162 Cycling	**163** Sultan Azlan Shah

(Litho Security Printers (M), Malaysia)

1989 (20 Aug). *15th South East Asian Games, Kuala Lumpur.*
T **162** *and similar multicoloured designs. W* **138** (*sideways on*
50 *c.*, $1). *P* 13.

417	10 c. Type **162**	15	15
418	20 c. Athletics ..	25	20
419	50 c. Swimming (*vert*)	50	60
420	$1 Torch bearer (*vert*)	85	1·40
417/20	.. .. .. *Set of* 4	1·60	2·10

(Des R. Zahabuddin. Litho Security Printers (M), Malaysia)

1989 (18 Sept). *Installation of Sultan Azlan Shah as Yang di Pertuan Agong.* W **138** *(sideways).* P 13.

421	163	20 c. multicoloured	15	15
422		40 c. multicoloured	25	35
423		$1 multicoloured	60	1·00
421/3		*Set of 3*	90	1·40

164 Putra World Trade Centre and Pan-Pacific Hotel

165 Clock Tower, Kuala Lumpur City Hall and Big Ben

(Litho Security Printers (M), Malaysia)

1989 (18 Oct). *Commonwealth Heads of Government Meeting, Kuala Lumpur.* T **164** *and similar multicoloured designs.* W **138** *(sideways on 50 c.).* P 13.

424	20 c. Type **164**		15	10
	a. Wmk sideways			
425	50 c. Traditional dancers *(vert)*		35	55
	a. Wmk upright			
426	$1 National flag and map showing Commonwealth countries		60	1·25
	a. Wmk sideways			
424/6	*Set of 3*		1·00	1·75

(Des AMC-Melewar Zecha Communications. Litho Security Printers (M), Malaysia)

1989 (2 Dec). *Inaugural Malaysia Airlines "747" Non-stop Flight to London.* T **165** *and similar horiz designs, each showing Malaysia Airlines Boeing "747-400". Multicoloured.* W **138**. P 13.

427	20 c. Type **165**		20	25
	a. Horiz pair. Nos. 427/9		40	50
428	20 c. Parliament Buildings, Kuala Lumpur, and Palace of Westminster		20	25
429	$1 World map showing route		80	1·10
427/9	*Set of 3*		1·10	1·40

Nos. 427/8 were printed together, *se-tenant,* in horizontal pairs throughout the sheet.

166 Sloth and Map of Park

167 Outline Map of South-east Asia and Logo

(Des Jermaine. Litho Security Printers (M), Malaysia)

1989 (28 Dec). *50th Anniv of National Park.* T **166** *and similar vert design. Multicoloured.* W **138**. P 12 (20 c.) or 13 ($1).

430	20 c. Type **166**		25	15
	a. Perf 14½			
431	$1 Pair of Malay Ocellated Pheasants		1·00	1·50
	a. Perf 14½			

(Des A. Kassim. Litho Security Printers (M), Malaysia)

1990 (1 Jan). *"Visit Malaysia Year".* T **167** *and similar horiz designs. Multicoloured.* W **138** *(sideways).* P 12.

432	20 c. Type **167**		15	15
433	50 c. Traditional drums		35	55
434	$1 Scuba diving, windsurfing and yachting		65	1·25
432/4	*Set of 3*		1·10	1·75

168 *Dillenia suffruticosa*

169 Monument and Rainbow

(Litho Security Printers (M), Malaysia)

1990 (12 Mar). *Wildflowers.* T **168** *and similar vert designs. Multicoloured.* W **138**. P 12.

435	15 c. Type **168**		15	15
436	20 c. *Mimosa pudica*		20	20
437	50 c. *Ipmoea carnea*		40	60
438	$1 *Nymphaea pubescens*		65	1·25
435/8	*Set of 4*		1·25	2·00

(Des CD Advertising. Litho Security Printers (M), Malaysia)

1990 (14 May). *Kuala Lumpur, Garden City of Lights.* T **169** *and similar multicoloured designs.* W **138** *(sideways on 40 c., $1).* P 12.

439	20 c. Type **169**		15	20
440	40 c. Mosque and skyscrapers at night *(horiz)*		25	40
441	$1 Kuala Lumpur skyline *(horiz)*		60	1·25
439/41	*Set of 3*		90	1·60

170 Seri Negara Building

171 Alor Setar

(Des T. Teh Chin Seng. Litho Security Printers (M), Malaysia)

1990 (1 June). *1st Summit Meeting of South–South Consultation and Co-operation Group, Kuala Lumpur.* T **170** *and similar horiz design. Multicoloured.* W **138** *(sideways).* P 13.

442	20 c. Type **170**		15	15
443	80 c. Summit logo		60	1·10

(Des Penerbit Hidayah. Litho Security Printers (M), Malaysia)

1990 (2 June). *250th Anniv of Alor Setar.* T **171** *and similar multicoloured designs.* W **138** *(sideways on 40 c., $1).* P 12.

444	20 c. Type **171**		15	20
445	40 c. Musicians and monument *(vert)*		25	35
446	$1 Zahir Mosque *(vert)*		70	1·25
444/6	*Set of 3*		1·00	1·60

172 Sign Language Letters

173 Leatherback Turtle

(Des S. Senika. Litho Security Printers (M), Malaysia)

1990 (8 Sept). *International Literacy Year.* T **172** *and similar multicoloured designs.* W **138** *(sideways on 20, 40 c.).* P 13 (40 c.) or 12 (others).

447	20 c. Type **172**		10	10
	a. Perf 13			
448	40 c. People reading		25	35
449	$1 Symbolic person reading *(vert)*		65	1·25
447/9	*Set of 3*		90	1·50

(Des Ong Soo Keat. Litho Security Printers (M), Malaysia)

1990 (17 Nov). *Marine Life (3rd series). Sea Turtles.* T **173** *and similar horiz designs. Multicoloured.* W **138** *(sideways).* P 12.

450	15 c. Type **173**		20	10
451	20 c. Common Green Turtle		20	15
452	40 c. Olive Ridley Turtle		35	40
453	$1 Hawksbill Turtle		75	1·00
450/3	*Set of 4*		1·40	1·50

174 Safety Helmet, Dividers and Industrial Skyline

175 *Eustenogaster calyptodoma*

(Litho Security Printers (M), Malaysia)

1991 (25 Apr). *25th Anniv of MARA (Council of the Indigenous People).* T **174** *and similar horiz designs. Multicoloured.* W **138** *(sideways).* P 12.

454	20 c. Type **174**		15	10
455	80 c. Documents and graph		25	30
456	$1 25th Anniversary logo		65	90
454/6	*Set of 3*		95	1·10

(Des Loh Wen Kong. Litho Security Printers (M), Malaysia)

1991 (29 July). *Insects. Wasps.* T **175** *and similar vert designs. Multicoloured.* W **138** *(sideways).* P 12.

457	15 c. Type **175**		20	30
	a. Wmk upright			
458	20 c. *Vespa affinis indonensis*		20	20
459	50 c. *Sceliphron javanum*		40	50
460	$1 *Ampulex compressa*		90	1·00
457/60	*Set of 4*		1·50	1·75
MS461	130×85 mm. Nos. 457/60. Wmk sideways. P 14½×14		1·50	1·75
	a. Wmk upright. P 12			

15 c. stamps from normal sheets (Nos. 457/a) show the wasp's left-hand feeler touching the edge of the design. On stamps of this value from the miniature sheet the feeler stops short of the edge.

ALTERED CATALOGUE NUMBERS

Any Catalogue numbers altered from the last edition are shown as a list in the introductory pages.

176 Tunku Abdul Rahman Putra and Independence Rally

(Des Design Dimension. Litho Security Printers (M), Malaysia)

1991 (30 Aug). *Former Prime Ministers of Malaysia.* T **176** *and similar horiz designs. Multicoloured.* W **138**. P 12.

462	$1 Type **176**		70	85
463	$1 Tun Abdul Razak Hussein and jungle village		70	85
464	$1 Tun Hussein Onn and standard-bearers		70	85
462/4	*Set of 3*		1·90	2·25

177 Maziah Palace, Trengganu

178 Museum Building in 1891, Brass Lamp and Fabric

(Des A. Kassim. Litho Security Printers (M), Malaysia)

1991 (7 Nov). *Historic Buildings of Malaysia (2nd series).* T **177** *and similar horiz designs. Multicoloured.* W **138**. P 12.

465	15 c. Type **177**		20	10
466	20 c. Grand Palace, Johore		20	15
467	40 c. Town Palace, Kuala Langat, Selangor		35	40
468	$1 Jahar Palace, Kelantan		65	75
465/8	*Set of 4*		1·25	1·25

(Des T. Seng. Litho Security Printers (M), Malaysia)

1991 (21 Dec). *Centenary of Sarawak Museum.* T **178** *and similar horiz design. Multicoloured.* W **138**. P 12.

469	30 c. Type **178**		20	15
470	$1 Museum building in 1991, vase and fabric		65	75

179 Rural Postman on Cycle

180 Hill Forest and Jelutong Tree

(Des Ismail & Associates Sdn Bhd. Litho Security Printers (M), Malaysia)

1992 (1 Jan). *Inauguration of Post Office Corporation.* T **179** *and similar vert designs. Multicoloured.* W **138** *(sideways).* P 12.

471	30 c. Type **179**		25	30
	a. Horiz strip of 5. Nos. 471/5		1·10	
472	30 c. Urban postman on motorcycle		25	30
473	30 c. Inner city post van		25	30
474	30 c. Industrial post van		25	30
475	30 c. Malaysian Airlines Boeing 747 and globe		25	30
471/5	*Set of 5*		1·10	1·40

Nos. 471/5 were printed together, *se-tenant,* in horizontal strips of 5 throughout the sheet.

(Des T. Seng. Litho Security Printers (M), Malaysia)

1992 (23 Mar). *Tropical Forests.* T **180** *and similar horiz designs. Multicoloured.* W **138** *(sideways).* P 12.

476	20 c. Type **180**		15	10
477	50 c. Mangrove swamp and Bakau Minyak tree		35	40
478	$1 Lowland forest and Chengal tree		75	85
476/8	*Set of 3*		1·10	1·25

181 Tuanku Ja'afar and Coat of Arms

182 Badminton Players

(Des TIARA CDP Sdn Bhd. Litho Security Printers (M), Malaysia)

1992 (18 Apr). *25th Anniv of Installation of Tuanku Ja'afar as Yang di-Pertuan Besar of Negri Sembilan. T 181 and similar horiz design.* W 138 *(sideways).* P 12.
479	30 c. Type 181	..	20	20
480	$1 Palace, Negri Sembilan	.. ..	80	90

(Des T. Seng. Litho Security Printers (M), Malaysia)

1992 (25 July). *Malaysian Victory in Thomas Cup Badminton Championship. T 182 and similar multicoloured designs.* W 138. P 12.
481	$1 Type 182	.. ..	55	65
482	$1 Thomas Cup and Malaysian flag	..	55	65
MS483	105×80 mm. $2 Winning team (76×28 mm). Wmk sideways	..	1·50	1·50

183 Women in National Costumes	**184** Straits Settlements 1867 3½ c. and Malaysian Federation 1957 10 c. Stamps

(Des Image Productions Sdn Bhd. Litho Security Printers (M), Malaysia)

1992 (8 Aug). *25th Anniv of A.S.E.A.N. (Association of South East Asian Nations). T 183 and similar horiz designs. Multicoloured.* W 138 *(sideways).* P 12.
484	30 c. Type 183	.. ..	20	30
485	50 c. Regional flowers	..	35	35
486	$1 Traditional architecture	..	80	90
484/6	.. .. ..	Set of 3	1·25	1·40

(Litho Security Printers (M), Malaysia)

1992 (1 Sept). *125th Anniv of Postage Stamps and "Kuala Lumpur '92", International Stamp Exhibition. T 184 and similar horiz designs. Multicoloured.* W 138 *(sideways).* P 12.
487	30 c. Type 184	.. ..	15	20
	a. Horiz pair. Nos. 487/8		30	40
488	30 c. Straits Settlements 1867 2 c. and Malaysia 1963 Federation Inauguration 12 c.		15	20
489	50 c. Straits Settlements 1868 4 c. and Malaysia 1990 Kuala Lumpur 40 c.	..	25	30
	a. Horiz pair. Nos. 489/90	..	50	60
490	50 c. Straits Settlements 1867 12 c. and Malaysia "Kuala Lumpur '92" $2	..	25	30
487/90		Set of 4	70	90
MS491	120×92 mm. $2 "Kuala Lumpur '92" logo on Malaysian flag. P 13×13½	.. ..	1·00	1·10

Nos. 487/8 and 489/90 were printed together, *se-tenant,* in horizontal pairs throughout the sheets.

185 *Acropora*

(Litho Security Printers (M), Malaysia)

1992 (21 Dec). *Marine Life (4th series). Corals. T 185 and similar multicoloured designs.* W 138. P 12.
492	30 c. Type 185	.. ..	15	20
	a. Horiz strip of 5. Nos. 492/6	..	70	
493	30 c. *Dendronephthya*	..	15	20
494	30 c. *Dendrophyllia*	..	15	20
495	30 c. *Sinularia*	..	15	20
496	30 c. *Melithaea*	..	15	20
492/6	.. ..	Set of 5	70	90
MS497	100×70 mm. $2 *Subergorgia* (38×28 mm). Wmk sideways	..	1·00	1·10

Nos. 492/6 were printed together, *se-tenant,* in horizontal strips of 5 throughout the sheet.

POSTAGE DUE STAMPS

Until 15 August 1966 the postage due stamps of MALAYAN POSTAL UNION were in use throughout MALAYSIA.

D 1   D 2

(Litho Harrison)

1966 (15 Aug)–**71.** *Ordinary paper. W* w **13** *(upright). P* 14½ × 14.

D1	D 1	1 c. rose	..	..	20	1·25
D2		2 c. indigo	..	..	25	2·00
D3		4 c. apple-green	..	..	85	2·25
D4		8 c. blue-green	..	..	1·25	6·50
		a. Chalk-surfaced paper. *Bright blue-green* (1.6.71)	..	..	2·75	6·50
D5		10 c. bright blue	..	..	60	2·25
		a. Chalk-surfaced paper (1.6.71)	..		2·75	7·00
D6		12 c. reddish violet	..	..	60	2·50
D7		20 c. red-brown	..	..	60	4·50
		a. Chalk-surfaced paper. *Brown-purple* (22.4.69)	..		2·75	9·00
D8		50 c. brownish bistre	..	..	1·25	7·50
		a. Chalk-surfaced paper. *Olive-bistre* (1.6.71)	..	..	3·00	11·00
D1/8				*Set of 8*	5·00	26·00

1972 (23 May). *Glazed paper. W* w **13** *(sideways). P* 14½ × 14.

D12	D 1	8 c. turquoise-green	..	..	4·00	11·00
D13		10 c. dull ultramarine	..	..	4·00	11·00
D15		20 c. pale chocolate	..	..	5·00	13·00
D16		50 c. pale olive-bistre	..	..	6·00	15·00
D12/16			..	*Set of 4*	17·00	45·00

1980–86. *No wmk. P* 14½ × 14.

D17	D 1	2 c. indigo	..	..	20	1·25
D18		8 c. blue-green	..	..	30	1·50
D19		10 c. dull ultramarine	..	..	40	1·75
D19*a*		12 c. reddish lilac (1986)	..	..	11·00	
D20		20 c. pale chocolate	..	..	50	2·00
D21		50 c. pale olive-bistre	..	..	90	3·00

(Des Kathy Wong. Litho Security Printers (M), Malaysia)

1986 (15 Sept). *P* 12 × 11½.

D22	D 2	5 c. cerise and rose-lilac	..	..	10	10
D23		10 c. brownish black & pale olive-grey			10	10
D24		20 c. dull vermilion and cinnamon	..		10	10
D25		50 c. dp turquoise-green & turq-bl			25	30
D26		$1 ultramarine and cobalt	..		50	55
D22/6	..	..	..	*Set of 5*	95	1·00

B. FEDERAL TERRITORY ISSUES

Kuala Lumpur, previously part of Selangor state, was established as a Federal Territory on 1 February 1974.

The following stamps were produced for use there, corresponding to the low value definitives provided for the states of the federation.

The island of Labuan, formerly part of Sabah, became the second Federal Territory on 16 April 1984, when Nos. K1/14 replaced the low value definitives of Sabah previously used there.

K 1 *Rafflesia hasseltii*   K 2 Coffee

(Des M. Yusof bin Mohammed; adapted Malaysian Advertising Services. Litho Asher and Co., Melbourne)

1979 (30 Apr). *Flowers. Horiz designs as Type* K **1.** *Multicoloured. W* **95** *(sideways). P* 15 × 14½.

K1	1 c. Type K **1**	..	..	10	20
K2	2 c. *Pterocarpus indicus*		..	10	20
K3	5 c. *Lagerstroemia speciosa* (Type I)	..	10	10
K4	10 c. *Durio zibethinus*	..		10	10
K5	15 c. *Hibiscus rosa-sinensis*		..	15	10
K6	20 c. *Rhododendron scortechinii*		..	15	10
K7	25 c. *Etlingera elatior* (inscr "Phaeomeria speciosa")			15	10
K1/7			*Set of 7*	65	50

For higher values used in conjunction with this series see Nos. 190/7.

PRICES OF SETS

Set prices are given for many issues, generally those containing three stamps or more. Definitive sets include one of each value or major colour change, but do not cover different perforations, die types or minor shades. Where a choice is possible the set prices are based on the cheapest versions of the stamps included in the listings.

I   II

Two types of 5 c.:

Type I. "5" over "i" and "c" to right of "a" in "Malaysia" (Nos. K3 and K10).

Type II. "5" over "s" and "c" aligns on "a" of "Malaysia" (No. K10a).

1983–85.* *As Nos.* K3/7 *but without wmk.*

K10	5 c. *Lagerstroemia speciosa* (I) (turquoise-green background) (12.12.84)		6·50	4·00
K10a	5 c. *Lagerstroemia speciosa* (II) (turquoise-blue background) (1.85)		1·50	90
K11	10 c. *Durio zibethinus* (9.84)	..		35	30
K12	15 c. *Hibiscus rosa-sinensis* (5.11.83)	..		45	15
K13	20 c. *Rhododendron scortechinii* (blackish brown background) (1983)		9·00	1·25
K13a	20 c. *Rhododendron scortechinii* (bronze-green background) (13.11.83)		55	35
K14	25 c. *Etlingera elatior* (inscr "Phaeomeria speciosa") (1.85)		5·50	3·00

*There was no official release date for these stamps. Dates shown are the earliest recorded from postmarks and may be revised if earlier examples are reported.

The 10 c., 15 c. and 20 c. (No. K13a) are also from redrawn plates and show the inscriptions or the face value in slightly different positions.

(Des Kathy Wong. Litho Security Printers (M), Malaysia)

1986 (25 Oct). *Agricultural Products of Malaysia. Vert designs as Type* K **2.** *Multicoloured. W* **138.** *P* 12.

K15	1 c. Type K **2**	..	..	..	10	10
K16	2 c. Coconuts	..	..	..	10	10
K17	5 c. Cocoa	..	..	..	10	10
K18	10 c. Black pepper	..	..	..	10	10
K19	15 c. Rubber	..	..	..	10	10
K20	20 c. Oil palm	..	..	..	10	10
K21	30 c. Rice	..	..	..	15	20
K15/21		..	..	*Set of 7*	40	45

VII. MALAYSIAN STATES

PRINTERS. All Malaysian States stamps were printed in typography by De La Rue and Co, Ltd, London, *unless otherwise stated.*

JOHORE

A British adviser was appointed to Johore in 1914. The state joined the Federation of Malaya on 1 February 1948.

> Until 1 January 1899 mail for addresses outside Malaya had the external postage paid by stamps of the STRAITS SETTLEMENTS.

PRICES FOR STAMPS ON COVER TO 1945	
Nos. 1/2	
Nos. 3/5	*from* × 15
No. 6	*from* × 20
Nos. 7/8	
Nos. 9/15	*from* × 25
No. 16	
Nos. 17/20	*from* × 15
Nos. 21/31	*from* × 10
Nos. 32/8	*from* × 15
Nos. 39/53	*from* × 8
Nos. 54/60	*from* × 6
Nos. 61/74	*from* × 8
Nos. 75/7	
Nos. 78/87	*from* × 8
No. 88	*from* × 10
Nos. 89/102	*from* × 6
Nos. 103/25	*from* × 5
Nos. 126/8	
Nos. 129/30	*from* × 6
Nos. D1/5	*from* × 10

(1)

1876 (July). *No. 11 of Straits Settlements handstamped with* T **1.**

1	2 c. brown	..	£6500	£3000

No. 1 is known with the handstamp double.

From September 1878 to August 1884 no overprinted stamps were supplied by Singapore to Johore.

JOHORE
(2)

JOHORE   **JOHORE**   **JOHORE**

(3) ("H" and "E"   (4) ("H" wide, "E"   (5) ("H" and "E"
wide. "J" raised.   narrow. Opt   wide. Opt
Opt 16 mm long)   16 mm long)   16³/₄mm long)

JOHORE.   JOHORE   JOHORE

(6)   (7)   (8)

1884 (June)–**86.** *No. 63 of Straits Settlements optd with* T **2/8.**

2	2	2 c. pale rose		..	..	£1800
3	3	2 c. pale rose (8.84)		..	£400	£170
		a. Opt double				£1100
4	4	2 c. pale rose (8.84)		..	£500	£200
		a. Opt double				
5	5	2 c. pale rose (8.84)		..	£400	£170
		a. Opt double			—	£750
6	6	2 c. pale rose (3.85)		..	75·00	85·00
		a. Opt double				
7	7	2 c. pale rose (1885)		..		£1300
8	8	2 c. pale rose (4.86)		..	38·00	50·00

Nos. 3 to 7 were from triplet settings, either 3+4+5 or three examples of the same overprint. Nos. 2 and 8 are probably single unit handstamps.

JOHOR   JOHOR   JOHOR

(9) (All letters   (10)   (11) ("H" wide)
narrow)

JOHOR   JOHOR   **JOHOR.**

(12)   (13)   (14)

JOHOR   **JOHOR**

(15)   (16)

1884 (Aug)–**91.** *Nos. 63/a of Straits Settlements optd with* T **9/16.**

9	9	2 c. pale rose	..		6·50	9·00
10	10	2 c. pale rose (10.84)	..	..	4·25	4·25
		a. Thin, narrow "J" (R. 6/6)	..	55·00	55·00
		b. Bright rose (1890)	..	..	17·00	23·00
		ba. Thin, narrow "J" (R. 6/6)	..	£110	£120
11	11	2 c. pale rose (2.85)	..	..	38·00	38·00

12	12	2 c. pale rose (1886)			26·00	26·00
		a. Opt double				£650
13	13	2 c. pale rose (1886)			24·00	24·00
14	14	2 c. pale rose (1888)			45·00	30·00
		a. Thin, narrow "J"			£225	£200
		b. Opt double				£475
15	15	2 c. bright rose (9.90)			7·50	6·00
16	16	2 c. bright rose (1891)			£5000	

Settings:
No. 9 — various triplets with the length of the overprint varying from 12 to 15 mm
No. 10 — triplet or 60 (6×10)
No. 11 — triplet 11 + 9 + 9
No. 12 — triplet
No. 13 — triplet
No. 14 — 30 (3×10)
No. 15 — 60 (6×10)
No. 16 — not known. As no used examples are known it is possible that this stamp was not issued.

JOHOR
Two
CENTS
(17)

JOHOR
Two
CENTS
(18)

JOHOR
Two
CENTS
(19)

JOHOR
Two
CENTS
(20)

1891 (May).   *No. 68 of Straits Settlements surch as T* **17/20**.

17	17	2 c. on 24 c. green			22·00	35·00
		a. "CENST" (R. 5/4)			£375	£250
18	18	2 c. on 24 c. green			75·00	75·00
		a. Thin, narrow "J" (R. 6/6)			£170	£170
19	19	2 c. on 24 c. green			28·00	45·00
20	20	2 c. on 24 c. green			70·00	70·00

Nos. 17/20 come from the same setting of 60. Type **17** occurs on horizontal rows 1 to 5, Type **18** on row 6, Type **19** on rows 7, 8 and 9 and Type **20** on row 10.

3 cents.

KEMAHKOTAAN

21 Sultan   (22)   (23)
Aboubakar

1891 (16 Nov)–**94**.   *No wmk. P* 14.

21	21	1 c. dull purple and mauve (7.94)			30	50
22		2 c. dull purple and mauve			30	1·50
23		3 c. dull purple and carmine (7.94)			55	50
24		4 c. dull purple and black			2·75	6·00
25		5 c. dull purple and green			7·00	20·00
26		6 c. dull purple and blue			8·00	20·00
27		$1 green and carmine			45·00	90·00
21/7				*Set of* 7	60·00	£120

1894 (Mar).   *Surch with T* **22**.

28	21	3 c. on 4 c. dull purple and black			75	50
		a. No stop (R. 5/11)			35·00	35·00
29		3 c. on 5 c. dull purple and green			80	2·00
		a. No stop (R. 5/11)			45·00	50·00
30		3 c. on 6 c. dull purple and blue			1·00	2·00
		a. No stop (R. 5/11)			50·00	48·00
31		3 c. on $1 green and carmine			10·00	35·00
		a. No stop (R. 5/11)			£160	£300
28/31				*Set of* 4	11·50	35·00

1896 (Mar).   *Coronation of Sultan Ibrahim. Optd with T* **23**.

32	21	1 c. dull purple and mauve			45	85
		a. "KETAHKOTAAN"			3·00	5·00
33		2 c. dull purple and yellow			45	1·00
		a. "KETAHKOTAAN"			2·75	5·00
34		3 c. dull purple and carmine			55	1·00
		a. "KETAHKOTAAN"			3·50	7·50
35		4 c. dull purple and black			80	2·25
		a. "KETAHKOTAAN"			2·75	6·50
36		5 c. dull purple and green			5·50	7·50
		a. "KETAHKOTAAN"			3·00	7·50
37		6 c. dull purple and blue			3·00	6·00
		a. "KETAHKOTAAN"			3·00	6·00
38		$1 green and carmine			32·00	65·00
		a. "KETAHKOTAAN"			27·00	85·00
32/8				*Set of* 7	40·00	£110
32a/8a				*Set of* 7		

The two spellings of the overprint occur in separate sheets.

24   Sultan Ibrahim   25

26   27

1896 (26 Aug)–**99**. *W* **27**. *P* 14.

39	24	1 c. green			70	45
40		2 c. green and blue			40	20
41		3 c. green and purple			1·25	40
		a. Green and dull claret				
42		4 c. green and carmine			50	35
43		4 c. yellow and red (1899)			75	50
44		5 c. green and brown			75	1·00
45		6 c. green and yellow			80	1·60
46	25	10 c. green and black (1898)			7·00	38·00
47		25 c. green and mauve (1898)			9·00	32·00
48		50 c. green and carmine (1898)			12·00	35·00
49	24	$1 dull purple and green (1898)			22·00	55·00
50	26	$2 dull purple and carmine (1898)			22·00	55·00
51		$3 dull purple and blue (1898)			28·00	80·00
52		$4 dull purple and brown (1898)			28·00	65·00
53		$5 dull purple and yellow (1898)			60·00	90·00
39/53				*Set of* 15	£170	£400

3 cents.   **10 cents.**

(28)   (29)

1903 (Apr).   *Surch with T* **28** *or* **29**.

54	24	3 c. on 4 c. yellow and red			50	1·10
		a. Original value uncancelled			3·00	12·00
55		10 c. on 4 c. green and carmine			2·50	4·50
		a. Tall "1" in "10" (R. 9/12)			50·00	70·00
		b. Original value uncancelled			20·00	50·00
		ba. As b, with tall "1" in "10" (R. 9/12)			£600	£700

The bars on these stamps were ruled by hand with pen and ink.

50 Cents.   **One Dollar**

(30)   (31)

1903 (Oct).   *Surch with T* **30** *or* **31**.

56	26	50 c. on $3 dull purple and blue			20·00	60·00
57		$1 on $2 dull purple and carmine			48·00	85·00
		a. "e" of "One" inverted (R. 7/9)			£1100	

10 CENTS.

(32)

1904.   *Surch as T* **32**.

58	24	10 c. on 4 c. yellow and red (Apr)			22·00	35·00
		a. Surcharge double			£5500	
59		10 c. on 4 c. green and carmine (Aug)			9·00	30·00
60	26	50 c. on $5 dull purple and yellow (May)			50·00	£110
58/60				*Set of* 3	75·00	£160

33   34   35 Sultan Sir Ibrahim

1904 (Sept)–**10**. *W* **27**. *Ordinary paper. P* 14.

61	33	1 c. dull purple and green			40	30
		a. Chalk-surfaced paper (10.10)			1·00	1·25
62		2 c. dull purple and orange			85	1·75
		a. Chalk-surfaced paper (10.10)			2·50	3·25
63		3 c. dull purple and olive-black			80	40
64		4 c. dull purple and carmine			5·50	1·75
65		5 c. dull purple and sage-green			60	2·75
66	35	8 c. dull purple and blue			2·50	4·50
67	34	10 c. dull purple and black			25·00	8·00
		a. Chalk-surfaced paper (1910)			30·00	16·00
68		25 c. dull purple and green			3·50	18·00
69		50 c. dull purple and red			28·00	14·00
70	33	$1 green and mauve			12·00	48·00
71	35	$2 green and carmine			17·00	45·00
72		$3 green and blue			23·00	65·00
73		$4 green and brown			24·00	85·00
74		$5 green and orange			32·00	75·00
75	34	$10 green and black			48·00	£120
76		$50 green and ultramarine			£130	£190
77		$100 green and scarlet			£250	£400
61/75				*Set of* 15	£200	£450

1910–19.   *Wmk Mult Rosettes (vertical). Chalk-surfaced paper. P* 14.

78	33	1 c. dull purple and green (1912)			15	15
79		2 c. dull purple and orange (1912)			3·00	65
80		3 c. dull purple and olive-black (1912)			2·75	65
		a. Wmk horizontal (1910)			10·00	11·00
81		4 c. dull purple and carmine (1912)			2·00	65
		a. Wmk horizontal (1910)			20·00	23·00
82		5 c. dull purple and sage-green (1912)			1·50	50
83	35	8 c. dull purple and blue (1912)			3·75	4·25
84	34	10 c. dull purple and black (1912)			18·00	2·50
		a. Wmk horizontal (1911)			22·00	35·00
85		25 c. dull purple and green (1912)			3·75	16·00
86		50 c. dull purple and red (1919)			40·00	70·00
87	33	$1 green and mauve (1918)			50·00	60·00
78/87				*Set of* 10	£110	£140

3 CENTS.

(36)   37 Sultan Sin Ibrahim and Sultana

1912 (Mar).   *No. 66 surch with T* **36**.

88		3 c. on 8 c. dull purple and blue			1·75	3·25
		a. "T" of "CENTS" omitted			£600	
		b. Bars double				

No. 88b shows the bars printed twice with the upper pair partly erased.

1918–21.   *Wmk Mult Crown CA. Chalk-surfaced paper. P* 14.

89	33	2 c. dull purple and green (1919)			40	80
90		2 c. purple and orange (1921)			50	1·25
91		4 c. dull purple and red			55	30
92		5 c. dull purple and sage-green (1920)			2·00	3·25
93	34	10 c. dull purple and blue			1·50	1·40
94		21 c. dull purple and orange (1919)			2·75	3·00
95		25 c. dull purple and green (1920)			8·00	13·00
96		50 c. dull purple and red (1920)			13·00	23·00
97	33	$1 green and mauve			9·00	40·00
98	35	$2 green and carmine			18·00	38·00
99		$3 green and blue			28·00	65·00
100		$4 green and brown			35·00	80·00
101		$5 green and orange			48·00	95·00
102	34	$10 green and black			£100	£170
89/102				*Set of* 14	£225	£475
89/102		Optd "Specimen"		*Set of* 14	£300	

1922–40.   *Wmk Mult Script CA. Chalk-surfaced paper. P* 14.

103	33	1 c. dull purple and black			30	20
104		2 c. purple and sepia (1924)			75	1·40
105		2 c. green (1928)			30	30
106		3 c. green (1925)			1·50	3·25
107		3 c. purple and sepia (1928)			95	1·50
108		4 c. purple and carmine (1924)			2·25	15
109		5 c. dull purple and sage-green			30	30
110		6 c. dull purple and claret			40	40
111	34	10 c. dull purple and blue			15·00	24·00
112		10 c. dull purple and yellow			30	25
113	33	12 c. dull purple and blue			1·00	1·25
114		12 c. ultramarine (1940)			22·00	7·50
115	34	21 c. dull purple and orange (1928)			2·50	3·00
116		25 c. dull purple and myrtle			1·40	1·00
117	35	30 c. dull purple and orange (1936)			2·50	3·00
118		40 c. dull purple and brown (1936)			3·00	3·50
119	34	50 c. dull purple and red			2·25	1·25
120	33	$1 green and mauve			2·00	85
121	35	$2 green and carmine (1923)			4·75	3·50
122		$3 green and blue (1925)			28·00	60·00
123		$4 green and brown (1926)			50·00	90·00
124		$5 green and orange			32·00	48·00
125	34	$10 green and black (1924)			£110	£170
126		$50 green and ultram (Optd S. £150)			£450	
127		$100 green and scarlet (Optd S. £250)			£1100	
128	35	$500 blue and red (1926) (Optd S. £700)			£16000	
103/25				*Set of* 23	£250	£375
103/25		Optd/Perf "Specimen"		*Set of* 23	£400	

(Recess Waterlow)

1935 (15 May).   *Wmk Mult Script CA (sideways). P* 12½.

129	37	8 c. bright violet and slate			1·25	40
129		Perf "Specimen"			35·00	

38 Sultan Sir Ibrahim   39

(Recess D.L.R.)

1940 (Feb).   *Wmk Mult Script CA. P* 13½.

130	38	8 c. black and pale blue			7·50	15
130		Perf "Specimen"			35·00	

1948 (1 Dec).   *Royal Silver Wedding. As Nos.* 143/4 *of Jamaica.*

131		10 c. violet			20	15
132		$5 green			24·00	30·00

1949 (2 May)–**55**.   *Wmk Mult Script CA. Chalk-surfaced paper. P* 17½ × 18.

133	39	1 c. black			10	10
134		2 c. orange			10	10
		a. Orange-yellow (22.1.52)			10	40
135		3 c. green			35	30
		a. Yellow-green (22.1.52)			2·50	90
136		4 c. brown			10	10
136a		5 c. bright purple (1.9.52)			30	20
137		6 c. grey			20	10
		a. Pale grey (22.1.52)			30	20
		ac. Error. St. Edward's Crown W 9b			£600	
138		8 c. scarlet			75	90
138a		8 c. green (1.9.52)			75	1·25
139		10 c. magenta			20	10
		aa. Imperf (pair)			£950	
139a		12 c. scarlet (1.9.52)			1·25	2·25
140		15 c. ultramarine			1·50	10
141		20 c. black and green			45	1·00
141a		20 c. bright blue (1.9.52)			80	10
142		25 c. purple and orange			30	10
142a		30 c. scarlet and purple (5.9.55)			1·25	2·00
142b		35 c. scarlet and purple (1.9.52)			1·25	1·00
143		40 c. red and purple			1·75	4·75
144		50 c. black and blue			50	10
145		$1 blue and purple			2·00	90
146		$2 green and scarlet			11·00	3·50
147		$5 green and brown			32·00	9·00
133/47				*Set of* 21	50·00	24·00

1949 (10 Oct). *75th Anniv of U.P.U. As Nos. 145/8 of Jamaica.*
148	10 c. purple	..	..	20	15
149	15 c. deep blue	..	..	50	1·00
150	25 c. orange	..	..	65	1·50
151	50 c. blue-black	..	..	1·10	1·75
148/51			Set of 4	2·25	4·00

1953 (2 June). *Coronation. As No. 153 of Jamaica.*
152	10 c. black and reddish purple			30	10

40 Sultan Sir Ibrahim   41 Sultan Sir Ismail and Johore Coat of Arms

(Recess D.L.R.)

1955 (1 Nov). *Diamond Jubilee of Sultan. Wmk Mult Script CA. P 14.*
153	40	10 c. carmine-red	..	10	10

(Photo Courvoisier)

1960 (10 Feb). *Coronation of Sultan. No wmk. P 11½.*
154	41	10 c. multicoloured	..	15	15

1960. *As T 9/19 of Kedah, but with portrait of Sultan Ismail. P 13½ ($1); others 12½ × 13 (vert) or 13 × 12½ (horiz).*
155	1 c. black (7.10.60)	..	10	20
156	2 c. orange-red (7.10.60)	..	10	20
157	4 c. sepia (19.8.60)	..	10	20
158	5 c. carmine-lake (7.10.60)	..	10	10
159	8 c. myrtle-green (9.12.60)	..	1·25	1·75
160	10 c. deep maroon (10.6.60)	..	15	10
161	20 c. blue (9.12.60)	..	15	10
162	50 c. black and bright blue (19.8.60)	..	20	10
163	$1 ultramarine and reddish purple (9.12.60)	1·25	1·50
164	$2 bronze-green and scarlet (9.12.60)	..	3·75	6·00
165	$5 brown and bronze-green (7.10.60)	..	17·00	18·00
155/65		Set of 11	22·00	25·00

In No. 161 there are only two figures in the boat, the steersman being missing. In the 20 c. value for all the other States there are three figures.

The 6, 12, 25 and 30 c. values used with this issue were Nos. 1/4 of Malayan Federation.

42 *Vanda hookeriana*
(Inset portrait of Sultan Ismail)

(Des A. Fraser-Brunner. Photo Harrison)

1965 (15 Nov). *T 42 and similar horiz designs. W w 13 (upright). P 14½.*
166	1 c. Type 42	..	10	30
	a. Black (orchid's name and part of flower) omitted		55·00	
167	2 c. *Arundina graminifolia*	..	10	35
168	5 c. *Paphiopedilum niveum*	..	10	10
	b. Yellow (flower) omitted		18·00	
169	6 c. *Spathoglottis plicata*	..	20	10
170	10 c. *Arachnis flos-aeris*	..	20	10
171	15 c. *Rhyncostylis retusa*	..	85	10
	b. Green (face value and leaves) omitted		85·00	
172	20 c. *Phalaenopsis violacea*	..	1·25	30
	a. Bright purple (blooms) omitted		38·00	
166/72		Set of 7	2·40	1·10

The 2 c. to 15 c. exist with both PVA gum and gum arabic.

The 2 c. with black (name of state, arms and head) omitted is listed under Sarawak No. 213a as there is some evidence that a sheet was issued there; if it also exists from any of the other states it would, of course, be identical.

The higher values used with this issue were Nos. 20/27 of Malaysia (National Issues).

1970. *As No. 166 and 170 but W w 13 (sideways).*
173	1 c. multicoloured (20.11)	..	40	2·00
174	10 c. multicoloured (27.5)	..	40	1·50

44 *Delias ninus*   45 *Rafflesia hasseltii*
(Inset portrait of Sultan Ismail)   (Inset portrait of Sultan Ismail)

(Des V. Whiteley)

1971 (1 Feb)–**78**. *Butterflies. T 44 and similar horiz designs. Multicoloured. No wmk. P 13½ × 13.*

(a) Litho by Bradbury, Wilkinson
175	1 c. Type 44	..	15	50
176	2 c. *Danaus melanippus*	..	40	50
177	5 c. *Parthenos sylvia*	..	55	10
178	6 c. *Papilio demoleus*	..	55	50
179	10 c. *Hebomoia glaucippe*	..	55	10
180	15 c. *Precis orithya*	..	55	10
181	20 c. *Valeria valeria*	..	80	20
175/81		Set of 7	3·25	1·75

(b) Photo Harrison (1977–78)
182	1 c. Type 44	..	80	1·50
183	2 c. *Danaus melanippus*	..	70	2·00
184	5 c. *Parthenos sylvia*	..	2·25	50
185	10 c. *Hebomoia glaucippe*	..	1·25	20
186	15 c. *Precis orithya*	..	2·50	25
187	20 c. *Valeria valeria*	..	3·25	1·00
182/7		Set of 6	9·75	5·00

The higher values used with this issue were Nos. 64/71 of Malaysia (National Issues).

DIFFERENCES BETWEEN LITHO AND PHOTO PRINT-INGS. Stamps from the photogravure printings can be easily identified by the appearance of certain features. The differences are most easily observed on the face values and inscriptions. Stamps printed by lithography show straight edges to letters and figures, but when those produced by photogravure are examined under a magnifying glass it will be seen that these edges are broken by the photogravure screen.

In addition the backgrounds and portraits of those stamps of this series printed by lithography show a regular screen of dots, a feature not visible on those printed by the photogravure process.

A number of instances have come to light of photogravure stamps which have had the top colour "removed" by means of an eraser.

(Des M. Yusof bin Mohammed; adapted Malaysian Advertising Services. Litho Asher and Co., Melbourne)

1979 (30 Apr). *Flowers. Horiz designs as T 45. Multicoloured. W 95 of Malaysia (sideways). P 15 × 14½.*
188	1 c. Type 45	..	10	10
189	2 c. *Pterocarpus indicus*	..	10	10
190	5 c. *Lagerstroemia speciosa*	..	10	10
191	10 c. *Durio zibethinus*	..	10	10
192	15 c. *Hibiscus rosa-sinensis*	..	15	10
193	20 c. *Rhododendron scortechinii*	..	15	10
194	25 c. *Etlingera elatior* (inscr "Phaeomeria speciosa")	..	15	10
188/94		Set of 7	65	30

For higher values used in conjunction with this series see Nos. 190/7 of Malaysia.

1983 (July)–**85**.* *As Nos. 190/3 but without wmk.*
197	5 c. *Lagerstroemia speciosa* (20.11.83)	..	45	50
198	10 c. *Durio zibethinus* (11.7.85)	..	50	60
199	15 c. *Hibiscus rosa-sinensis* (12.83)	..	55	20
200	20 c. *Rhododendron scortechinii* (blackish brown background)		5·50	1·00
200a	20 c. *Rhododendron scortechinii* (bronze-green background) (13.11.83)	..	65	55

*There was no official release date for these stamps. Dates shown are the earliest recorded from postmarks and may be revised if earlier examples are reported.

On Nos. 197/9 and 200a the "Johor" inscription is in rounded instead of square-ended letters.

WATERMARKED AND UNWATERMARKED PRINT-INGS. The first printing of the 20 c, value on unwatermarked paper was from the same plates and in the same shades as the original watermarked issue.

Subsequent no watermark printings of the 20 c. and all no watermark printings of the other values were in changed shades and can be readily identified as follows:

5 c. No watermark printing has the frame in turquoise-blue instead of the dull blue of the watermarked version.

10 c. No watermark printing shows a purple-brown background instead of the sepia of the watermarked.

15 c. No watermark printing shows stronger highlights in the design and more detail on the flowers and leaves.

20 c. Later no watermark printings have a bronze-green background instead of the blackish brown shown on the watermarked and first no watermark stamps.

25 c. No watermark printing has a deep background with more detail on the flower. The latin inscription has also been moved downwards to a more central position up the side of the vignette.

Differences also occur in the plates used to apply the state names, rulers' portraits or crests. Notes on these are provided under the individual issues.

46 Coconuts
(Inset portrait of Sultan Mahmood)

(Des Kathy Wong. Litho Security Printers (M), Malaysia)

1986 (25 Oct). *Agricultural Products of Malaysia. Vert designs as T 46. Multicoloured. W 138. Phosphorised paper. P 12.*
202	1 c. Coffee	..	10	10
203	2 c. Type 46	..	10	10
204	5 c. Cocoa	..	10	10
205	10 c. Black pepper	..	10	10
206	15 c. Rubber	..	10	10
207	20 c. Oil palm	..	10	10
208	30 c. Rice	..	15	20
202/8	..	Set of 7	40	45

ALTERED CATALOGUE NUMBERS

Any Catalogue numbers altered from the last edition are shown as a list in the introductory pages.

KEDAH

Suzerainty over Kedah was transferred by Thailand to Great Britain on 15 July 1909. A British adviser was appointed in 1923.

The state joined the Federation of Malaya on 1 February 1948.

Stamps of THAILAND were used in Kedah at Alor Star (from 1883), Kuala Muda (from 1907), Kulim (from 1907) and Langkawi (from 1908) until 1909. Issues of the FEDERATED MALAY STATES were used in Kedah from 16 July 1909 until 1912.

PRICES FOR STAMPS ON COVER TO 1945	
Nos. 1/14	*from* × 15
Nos. 15/23	*from* × 10
Nos. 24/40	*from* × 8
Nos. 41/8	*from* × 12
Nos. 49/51	—
Nos. 52/9	*from* × 4
Nos. 60/8	*from* × 3
Nos. 68*a*/9*a*	*from* × 4

1 Sheaf of Rice   2 Malay ploughing

3 Council Chamber, Alor Star

1912 (16 June). *Wmk Mult Crown CA (sideways on 10 c. to $5). P 14.*

1	1	1 c. black and green			30	25
2		3 c. black and red			2·25	30
3		4 c. rose and grey			9·00	25
4		5 c. green and chestnut			2·00	3·00
5		8 c. black and ultramarine			1·00	2·00
6	2	10 c. blue and sepia			1·75	90
7		20 c. black and green			2·75	4·00
8		30 c. black and rose			2·25	9·50
9		40 c. black and purple			3·50	14·00
10		50 c. brown and blue			8·00	13·00
11	3	$1 black and red/*yellow*			11·00	18·00
12		$2 green and brown			11·00	55·00
13		$3 black and blue/*blue*			48·00	£110
14		$5 black and red			48·00	95·00
1/14				*Set of 14*	£130	£300
1/14 Optd "Specimen"				*Set of 14*	£275	

Due to an increase in postal rates 1 c. and 4 c. stamps of STRAITS SETTLEMENTS were used in Kedah for some months from March 1919.

(i)   (ii)

DOUBLE AND SINGLE PLATES. (i) Printed from separate plates for frame and centre, with dotted shading extending close to the central sheaf. Soft impression of centre with little clear detail.

(ii) Printed from single plate, with white space around sheaf. Centre more deeply etched with sharp image.

1919 (June)–**21**. *New colours and values. Wmk Mult Crown CA (sideways on 21 c., 25 c.). P 14.*

15	1	1 c. brown (i) (8.19)			55	45
18		2 c. green (ii)			50	20
19		3 c. deep purple (i) (1920)			65	70
20		4 c. rose (i)			1·50	20
21		4 c. red (ii) (1920)			2·25	20
22	2	21 c. purple (8.19)			5·50	38·00
23		25 c. blue and purple (1921)			1·75	20·00
15/23				*Set of 6*	9·50	55·00
15/23 Optd "Specimen"				*Set of 6*	£130	

ONE

DOLLAR   ■   ■

(4)

MALAYA-
BORNEO
EXHIBITION.

(5)

(Surch by Ribeiro & Co, Penang)

1919 (Mar). *Surch as T 4.*

24	3	50 c. on $2 green and brown			40·00	48·00
		a. "C" of "CENTS" inserted by hand-stamp (R. 6/4)			£950	£1000
25		$1 on $3 black and blue/*blue*			20·00	70·00

Two types of centre plate for Type 2 wmkd Mult Script CA:

Type I (Plate 1)

Type II (Plate 2)

A new common centre plate, 2, was prepared from the orginal die in 1926. Stamps from plate 2 show considerably more detail of the ground and have the oxen, ploughman's hat and his clothing much more deeply cut as illustrated in Type II above.

1921–27. *Wmk Mult Script CA (sideways on 10 c. to $5). P 14.*

26	1	1 c. brown (ii)			40	20
27		2 c. dull green (ii) (Die I)*			25	20
28		3 c. deep purple (ii)			80	70
29		4 c. deep carmine (ii)			5·00	20
30	2	10 c. blue and sepia (I)			1·00	75
		a. Type II (1927)			9·00	2·50
31		20 c. black and yellow-green (I)			1·75	2·00
32		21 c. mauve and purple (I)			2·00	11·00
33		25 c. blue and purple (I)			2·25	5·50
		a. Type II (1927)			23·00	3·50
34		30 c. black and rose (I) (1922)			2·50	4·00
		a. Type II (1927)			20·00	3·00
35		40 c. black and purple (I)			2·50	20·00
		a. Type II (1927)			28·00	17·00
36		50 c. brown and grey-blue (I)			1·75	6·50
		a. Type II (1927)			25·00	4·25
37	3	$1 black and red/*yellow* (1924)			6·50	7·50
38		$2 myrtle and brown			13·00	60·00
39		$3 black and blue/*blue*			30·00	50·00
40		$5 black and deep carmine			45·00	95·00
26/40				*Set of 15*	95·00	£225
26/40 Optd "Specimen"				*Set of 15*	£250	

* For 2 c. Die II, see No. 69.

1922 (31 Mar). *Optd as T 5 at Singapore.*

I. "BORNEO" 14 *mm. long.*

(*a*) *Wmk Mult Crown CA*

41	1	2 c. green (ii)			3·50	16·00
42	2	21 c. mauve and purple (I)			18·00	70·00
43		25 c. blue and purple (I)			19·00	70·00
		a. Overprint inverted			£750	
44		50 c. brown and grey-blue (I)			19·00	85·00

(*b*) *Wmk Mult Script CA*

45	1	1 c. brown (ii)			2·25	13·00
46		3 c. purple (ii)			3·00	28·00
47		4 c. deep carmine (ii)			3·00	25·00
48	2	10 c. blue and sepia (I)			4·50	32·00
41/8				*Set of 8*	60·00	£300

There are setting variations in the size and shape of the letters, stop raised, stop omitted, etc.

II. "BORNEO" 15–15½ mm long. Wmk Mult Crown CA

49	2	21 c. mauve and purple (I)			17·00	85·00
50		25 c. blue and purple (I)			22·00	95·00
51		50 c. brown and grey-blue (I)			45·00	£140
49/51				*Set of 3*	75·00	£275

1922–36. *New colours, etc. Wmk Mult Script CA (sideways on 12, 35 c.). P 14.*

52	1	1 c. black (ii) (Die I)*			15	10
53		3 c. green (ii) (1924)			1·50	10
54		4 c. violet (ii) (1926)			90	10
55		5 c. yellow (ii)			1·50	10
56		6 c. carmine (ii) (Die I) (1926)*			70	65
57		8 c. grey-black (10.36)			8·50	10
58	2	12 c. black and indigo (II) (1926)			2·25	4·00
59		35 c. purple (II) (1926)			5·00	25·00
52/9				*Set of 8*	18·00	27·00
52/9 Optd/Perf "Specimen"				*Set of 8*	£130	

*For 1 c. and 6 c. Die II, see Nos. 68*a* and 69*a*.

MINIMUM PRICE

The minimum price quote is 10p which represents a handling charge rather than a basis for valuing common stamps. For further notes about prices see introductory pages.

---

6 Sultan Abdul Hamid Halimshah

(Recess Waterlow)

1937 (30 June). *Wmk Mult Script CA. P 12½.*

60	6	10 c. ultramarine and sepia			1·75	40
61		12 c. black and violet			16·00	12·00
62		25 c. ultramarine and purple			5·50	4·50
63		30 c. green and scarlet			7·50	9·50
64		40 c. black and purple			2·00	12·00
65		50 c. brown and blue			3·00	4·50
66		$1 black and green			2·50	9·00
67		$2 green and brown			85·00	70·00
68		$5 black and scarlet			32·00	70·00
60/8				*Set of 9*	£140	£170
60/8 Perf "Specimen"				*Set of 9*	£170	

I   II   I   II

1938–40. *As Nos. 52, 27 and 56, but redrawn as Dies II.*

68*a*	1	1 c. black			55·00	4·00
69		2 c. bright green (1940)			£110	8·00
69*a*		6 c. carmine-red (1940)			28·00	48·00
68*a*/9*a*				*Set of 3*	£170	55·00

1 c. Die II. Figures "1" have square-cut corners instead of rounded, and larger top serif. Larger "C". Line perf.

2 c. Die II. Figures "2" have circular instead of oval drops and the letters "c" are thin and tall instead of thick and rounded. Size of design: 19½ × 23 mm instead of about 18½ × 22½ mm. Line perf.

6 c. Die II. Design measures 19¼ × 22¼ mm instead of 18¾ × 22½ mm (No. 56). Note also shade of Die II. Line perf.

1948 (1 Dec). *Royal Silver Wedding. As Nos. 143/4 of Jamaica.*

70		10 c. violet			20	20
71		$5 carmine			22·00	32·00

1949 (10 Oct). *75th Anniv of U.P.U. As Nos. 145/8 of Jamaica.*

72		10 c. purple			25	20
73		15 c. deep blue			50	1·25
74		25 c. orange			65	1·25
75		50 c. blue-black			1·25	2·25
72/5				*Set of 4*	2·40	4·50

7 Sheaf of Rice   8 Sultan Badlishah

1950 (1 June)–**55**. *Wmk Mult Script CA. Chalk-surfaced paper. P 17½ × 18.*

76	7	1 c. black			10	30
77		2 c. orange			10	15
78		3 c. green			30	1·00
79		4 c. brown			20	10
79*a*		5 c. bright purple (1.9.52)			35	40
		ab. Bright mauve (24.9.53)			35	30
80		6 c. grey			20	15
81		8 c. scarlet			30	1·75
81*a*		8 c. green (1.9.52)			75	1·75
		ab. Deep green (24.9.53)			3·00	4·50
82		10 c. magenta			15	10
82*a*		12 c. scarlet (1.9.52)			85	2·50
83		15 c. ultramarine			55	35
84		20 c. black and green			40	2·50
84*a*		20 c. bright blue (1.9.52)			85	10
85	8	25 c. purple and orange			30	30
85*a*		30 c. scarlet and purple (5.9.55)			1·25	1·25
85*b*		35 c. scarlet and purple (1.9.52)			85	1·50
86		40 c. red and purple			1·00	6·00
87		50 c. black and blue			50	10
88		$1 blue and purple			2·25	1·75
89		$2 green and scarlet			18·00	22·00
90		$5 green and brown			32·00	32·00
76/90				*Set of 21*	55·00	65·00

1953 (2 June). *Coronation. As No. 153 of Jamaica.*

91		10 c. black and reddish purple			30	10

9 Copra   10 Pineapples

11 Ricefield   12 Masjid Alwi Mosque, Kangar

13 East Coast Railway

14 Tiger

15 Fishing Prau   16 Aborigines with Blowpipes

17 Government Offices   18 Bersilat

19 Weaving

(Recess D.L.R.)

1957. *Inset portrait of Sultan Badlishah. W w 12. P 13 × 12½ (1 c. to 8 c.), 12½ × 13 (10 c., 20 c.), 12½ (50 c., $2, $5) or 13½ ($1).*

92	9	1 c. black (21.8) ..	..	10	35
93	10	2 c. orange-red (25.7)	..	10	40
94	11	4 c. sepia (21.8)..	..	10	10
95	12	5 c. carmine-lake (21.8)..	..	10	20
96	13	8 c. myrtle-green (21.8)..	..	2·00	3·75
97	14	10 c. deep brown (4.8)	..	15	10
98	15	20 c. blue (26.6)	..	30	45
99	16	50 c. black and blue (25.7)	..	60	1·25
100	17	$1 ultramarine & reddish purple (25.7)		2·75	5·50
101	18	$2 bronze-green and scarlet (21.8)	..	12·00	12·00
102	19	$5 brown and bronze-green (26.6)	..	20·00	23·00
92/102			*Set of 11*	35·00	42·00

The 6, 12, 25 and 30 c. values used with this issue were Nos. 1/4 of Malayan Federation.

20 Sultan Abdul Halim   21 Sultan Abdul Halim Shah
Mu'Adzam Shah

(Photo Harrison)

1959 (20 Feb). *Installation of the Sultan. W w 12. P 14 × 14½.*

103	20	10 c. multicoloured	..	10	10

1959 (1 July)–**62.** *As Nos. 92/102 but with inset portrait of Sultan Abdul Halim Shah as in T 21.*

104	21	1 c. black	..	10	30
105	10	2 c. orange-red	..	10	30
106	11	4 c. sepia	..	10	10
107	12	5 c. carmine-lake	..	10	20
108	13	8 c. myrtle-green	..	3·25	1·25
109	14	10 c. deep brown ..	..	30	10
109a		10 c. deep maroon (19.12.61)	..	2·25	30
110	15	20 c. blue ..	..	20	10
111	16	50 c. black and blue (p 12½)	..	30	35
		a. Perf 12½ × 13 (14.6.60)	..	30	10
112	17	$1 ultramarine and reddish purple	..	1·50	2·25
113	18	$2 bronze-green and scarlet	..	6·00	8·50
114	19	$5 brown and bronze-green (p 12½)	..	11·00	11·00
		a. Perf 13 × 12½ (26.11.62)	..	11·00	11·00
104/14			*Set of 12*	22·00	21·00

22 Vanda hookeriana

23 Danaus melanippus

1965 (15 Nov). *As Nos. 166/72 of Johore but with inset portrait of Sultan Abdul Halim Shah as in T 22. W w 13 (upright).*

115		1 c. multicoloured	..	10	30
		a. Black omitted (orchid's name and part of flower)	..	45·00	
116		2 c. multicoloured	..	10	30
		b. Yellow (flower) omitted	..	40·00	
117		5 c. multicoloured	..	10	10
		a. Black (country name and head) omitted	..	60·00	
118		6 c. multicoloured	..	15	30
119		10 c. multicoloured	..	20	10
		a. Red omitted	..	£130	
		b. Green (leaves) omitted ..	..	£130	
120		15 c. multicoloured	..	85	10
121		20 c. multicoloured	..	1·25	50
		a. Bright purple (blooms) omitted	..	85·00	
		b. Yellow (leaves) omitted	..	15·00	
115/21			*Set of 7*	2·40	1·40

The 1 c. to 15 c. exist with PVA gum as well as gum arabic.
The 6 c. value exists with black (country name, arms and head) omitted and is listed under Sarawak where it was issued.
The higher values used with this issue were Nos. 20/27 of Malaysia (National Issues).

1970 (27 May). *As Nos. 115 and 119 but W w 13 (sideways).*

122	22	1 c. multicoloured	..	1·00	3·00
123	–	10 c. multicoloured	..	65	2·50

1971 (1 Feb)–**78.** *As Nos. 175/87 of Johore but with portrait of Sultan Abdul Halim Shah as in T 23. (a) Litho by Bradbury, Wilkinson.*

124		1 c. multicoloured	..	15	55
125		2 c. multicoloured	..	35	55
126		5 c. multicoloured	..	45	10
127		6 c. multicoloured	..	45	55
128		10 c. multicoloured	..	45	10
129		15 c. multicoloured	..	60	10
130		20 c. multicoloured	..	95	45
124/30			*Set of 7*	3·00	2·00

(b) Photo by Harrison (1977–78)

130a		2 c. multicoloured	..	8·50	10·00
131		5 c. multicoloured	..	1·50	40
132		10 c. multicoloured	..	3·00	15
133		15 c. multicoloured	..	1·50	30
134		20 c. multicoloured	..	2·25	1·25
130a/4			*Set of 5*	15·00	11·00

The higher values used with this issue were Nos. 64/71 of Malaysia (National Issues).
For differences between litho and photo printings, see after Johore No. 187.

24 Pterocarpus indicus

25 Sultan Abdul Halim Shah

1979 (30 Apr). *As Nos. 188/94 of Johore but with portrait of Sultan Abdul Halim Shah as in T 24.*

135		1 c. *Rafflesia hasseltii*	..	10	10
136		2 c. Type 24	..	10	10
137		5 c. *Lagerstroemia speciosa*	..	10	10
138		10 c. *Durio zibethinus*	..	10	10
139		15 c. *Hibiscus rosa-sinensis*	..	15	10
140		20 c. *Rhododendron scortechinii*	..	15	10
141		25 c. *Etlingera elatior* (inscr "*Phaeomeria speciosa*")	..	15	10
135/41			*Set of 7*	65	30

For higher values used in conjunction with this series see Nos. 190/7 of Malaysia (National Issues).

(Des and litho Security Printers (M), Malaysia)

1983 (15 July). *Silver Jubilee of Sultan. T 25 and similar multicoloured designs. P 13 × 13½ (20 c.) or 13½ × 13 (others).*

142		20 c. Type 25	..	55	30
143		40 c. Paddy fields (*horiz*)	..	75	50
144		60 c. Paddy fields and Mount Jerai (*horiz*)	1·00	1·50
142/4			*Set of 3*	2·10	2·10

1983 (22 Feb)–**85.*** *As Nos. 138/40 but without wmk.*

148		10 c. *Durio zibethinus* (27.6.85)	..	9·50	1·40
149		15 c. *Hibiscus rosa-sinensis* (12.84) ..	1·75	50
150		20 c. *Rhododendron scortechinii* (blackish brown background)	..	6·00	90
150a		20 c. *Rhododendron scortechinii* (bronze-green background) (16.12.83)	..	30	20

*There was no official release date for these stamps. Dates shown are the earliest recorded from postmarks and may be revised if earlier examples are reported.

For details of the shade differences between watermarked and unwatermarked printings see after Johore No. 200a.

Nos. 148/9 and 150a show "kedah" nearer to "malaysia" than on Nos. 135/41 and 150.

OMNIBUS ISSUES

Details, together with prices for complete sets, of the various Omnibus issues from the 1935 Silver Jubilee series to date are included in a special section following Zululand at the end of the catalogue.

KEDAH
Malaysia 5c

26 Cocoa

1986 (25 Oct). *As Nos. 202/8 of Johore but with portrait of Sultan Abdul Halim Shah as in T 26.*

152		1 c. Coffee	..	10	10
153		2 c. Coconuts..	..	10	10
154		5 c. Type 26	..	10	10
155		10 c. Black pepper	..	10	10
156		15 c. Rubber	..	10	10
157		20 c. Oil palm..	..	10	10
158		30 c. Rice	..	15	20
152/8			*Set of 7*	40	45

KELANTAN

Suzerainty over Kelantan was transferred by Thailand to Great Britain on 15 July 1909. A British adviser was appointed in 1923.

The state joined the Federation of Malaya on 1 February 1948.

From 1903 until 1909 the stamps of THAILAND were used by the post offices at Kota Bharu and Batu Mengkebang. Initially such stamps were postmarked "KALANTAN", but in 1908 cancellations inscribed with the office name were introduced. From 1909 until the introduction of Kelantan stamps in 1911 the issues of the FEDERATED MALAY STATES to $2 were in use.

PRICES FOR STAMPS ON COVER TO 1945

Nos. 1/11	from × 30
No. 12	—
Nos. 13/23	from × 30
Nos. 30/8	from × 15
Nos. 39/a	from × 8
Nos. 40/52	from × 20
No. 53	from × 3
No. 54	—

MALAYA
BORNEO
EXHIBITION

1   (2)

1911 (Jan)–**15.** *Wmk Mult Crown CA. Ordinary paper (1 c. to 10 c.) or chalk-surfaced paper (30 c. to $25). P 14.*

1	1	1 c. yellow-green ..	..	..	1·25	80
		a. *Blue-green*	..	..	1·25	30
2		3 c. red	..	..	1·50	15
3		4 c. black and red	..	..	1·00	15
4		5 c. green and red/*yellow*	..	..	4·50	20
5		8 c. ultramarine	..	..	5·00	1·00
6		10 c. black and mauve	..	..	16·00	90
7		30 c. dull purple and red	..	..	10·00	2·50
		a. *Purple and carmine*	..	..	26·00	13·00
8		50 c. black and orange	..	..	5·50	2·50
9		$1 green and emerald	..	..	45·00	48·00
9a		$1 green and brown (5.15) (Optd S. £45)	..		27·00	2·00
10		$2 green and carmine	..	..	1·00	4·00
11		$5 green and blue	..	..	4·00	7·50
12		$25 green and orange	..	..	38·00	75·00
1/12			..	*Set of 12*	£120	£130
1/12 Optd "Specimen"		..	..	*Set of 12*	£200	

1921 (5 May)–**28.** *Wmk Mult Script CA. Ordinary paper (1 c. to 10 c.) or chalk-surfaced paper (30 c. to $1). P 14.*

14	1	1 c. dull green (7.21)	..	..	4·00	60
15		1 c. black (24.2.23)	..	..	40	50
16		2 c. brown (29.7.22)	..	..	3·25	3·50
16a		2 c. green (24.7.26)	..	..	90	40
16b		3 c. brown (5.3.27)	..	..	2·50	1·50
		ba. "C" of "CA" missing from wmk				
17		4 c. black and red (15.7.22)	..	..	60	10
18		5 c. green and red/*pale yellow* (12.22)	..		60	10
19		6 c. claret (29.7.22)	..	..	2·50	2·00
19a		6 c. scarlet (26.5.28)	..	..	4·00	5·50
20		10 c. black and mauve	..	..	2·00	10
21		30 c. purple and carmine (24.7.26)	..	..	4·00	5·50
22		50 c. black and orange (21.3.25)	..		5·00	28·00
23		$1 green and brown (9.2.24)	..	..	26·00	48·00
14/23			..	*Set of 13*	48·00	85·00
14/23 Optd "Specimen"		..	..	*Set of 13*	£225	

For the 4 c., 5 c. and 6 c. surcharged, see issues under "Japanese Occupation".

1922 (31 Mar). *Optd with T 2 by Govt Survey Office, Khota Bharu.*

(a) *Wmk Mult Crown CA*

30	1	4 c. black and red	..	..	2·75	35·00
31		a. Opt double	..	..	£1500	
31		5 c. green and red/*pale yellow*	..		4·50	35·00
32		30 c. dull purple and red	..	..	4·50	55·00
33		50 c. black and orange	..	..	7·50	60·00
34		$1 green and brown	..	..	20·00	80·00
35		$2 green and carmine	..	..	45·00	£150
36		$5 green and blue	..	..	£130	£300

(b) *Wmk Mult Script CA*

37	1	1 c. green	..	..	2·50	28·00
		a. Opt double	..	..	£1800	
38		10 c. black and mauve	..	..	4·75	48·00
30/8			..	*Set of 9*	£200	£700

3   Sultan Ismail   4

(Recess Harrison (No. 39) or D.L.R. (No. 39a))

1928–**35.** *Wmk Mult Script CA. P 12.*

39	3	$1 blue (Perf S. £40)	..	..	7·50	55·00
		a. Perf 14 (1935)	..	..	30·00	40·00

(Recess B.W.)

1937 (July)–**40.** *Wmk Mult Script CA. P 12.*

40	4	1 c. grey-olive and yellow	..	..	30	40
41		2 c. green	..	..	1·50	10
42		4 c. scarlet	..	..	4·00	45
43		5 c. red-brown	..	..	4·25	10
44		6 c. lake (10.37)	..	..	7·50	1·50
45		8 c. grey-olive	..	..	4·25	10
46		10 c. purple (10.37)	..	..	16·00	2·75
47		12 c. blue	..	..	2·00	3·00
48		25 c. vermilion and violet ..	..		4·00	3·50
49		30 c. violet and scarlet (10.37)	..		28·00	16·00
50		40 c. orange and blue-green	..		7·00	18·00
51		50 c. grey-olive and orange (10.37)	..		45·00	7·50
52		$1 violet and blue-green (10.37)	..		27·00	12·00
53		$2 red-brown and scarlet (3.40)	..		£150	£180
54		$5 vermilion and lake (3.40)	..		£250	£425
40/54			..	*Set of 15*	£450	£600
40/54 Perf "Specimen"		..	*Set of 15*	£375	

For above issue surcharged see issues under "Japanese Occupation".

1948 (1 Dec). *Royal Silver Wedding. As Nos. 143/4 of Jamaica.*

55		10 c. violet	..	..	60	1·25
56		$5 carmine	..	..	23·00	48·00

1949 (10 Oct). *75th Anniv of U.P.U. As Nos. 145/8 of Jamaica.*

57		10 c. purple	..	..	25	30
58		15 c. deep blue ..	..	..	50	90
59		25 c. orange	..	..	60	2·25
60		50 c. blue-black	..	..	1·25	2·25
57/60 ..			..	*Set of 4*	2·40	5·00

5   Sultan Ibrahim   6   Sultan Yahya Petra and Crest of Kelantan

Normal   No. 62a
Tiny stop (R. 1/2)

1951 (11 July)–**55.** *Chalk-surfaced paper. Wmk Mult Script CA. P 17½ × 18.*

61	5	1 c. black	..	..	10	30
62		2 c. orange	..	..	15	35
		a. Tiny stop	..	..	15·00	
		b. *Orange-yellow* (11.5.55)	..		15	30
63		3 c. green	..	..	1·75	1·25
64		4 c. brown	..	..	10	15
65		5 c. bright purple (1.9.52)	..	..	35	40
		a. *Bright mauve* (9.12.53)	..		30	40
66		6 c. grey	..	..	10	20
67		8 c. scarlet	..	..	30	3·00
68		8 c. green (1.9.52)	..	..	75	1·75
69		10 c. magenta	..	..	15	10
70		12 c. scarlet (1.9.52)	..	..	75	2·25
71		15 c. ultramarine	..	..	1·75	60
72		20 c. black and green	..	..	45	4·75
73		20 c. bright blue (1.9.52)	..	..	80	25
74		25 c. purple and orange	..	..	40	55
75		30 c. scarlet and purple (5.9.55)	..		1·25	1·75
76		35 c. scarlet and purple (1.9.52)	..		90	1·50
77		40 c. red and purple	..	..	2·00	8·00
78		50 c. black and blue	..	..	60	40
79		$1 blue and purple	..	..	3·25	3·00
80		$2 green and scarlet	..	..	14·00	20·00
81		$5 green and brown	..	..	40·00	40·00
		a. *Green and sepia* (8.12.53)	..		60·00	65·00
61/81			..	*Set of 21*	60·00	80·00

1953 (2 June). *Coronation. As No. 153 of Jamaica.*

82		10 c. black and reddish purple	..	..	30	20

1957 (26 June)–**63.** *As Nos. 92/102 of Kedah but with inset portrait of Sultan Ibrahim.*

83	9	1 c. black (21.8.57)	..	..	10	30
84	10	2 c. orange-red (25.7.57)	..	..	40	40
		a. *Red-orange* (17.11.59)	..		2·25	4·50
85	11	4 c. sepia (21.8.57)	..	..	10	10
86	12	5 c. carmine-lake (21.8.57)	..		10	10
87	13	8 c. myrtle-green (21.8.57)	..		80	1·75
88	14	10 c. deep brown (4.8.57)..	..		15	10
89		10 c. deep maroon (19.4.61)	..		3·75	3·75
90	15	20 c. blue ..	..	..	30	30
91	16	50 c. black and blue (p 12½) (25.7.57)	..		30	35
		a. Perf 12½ × 13 (28.6.60)	..		65	30
92	17	$1 ultramarine & reddish pur (25.7.57)		2·25	1·50
93	18	$2 bronze-grn & scar (p 12½) (21.8.57)		5·50	6·00
		a. Perf 13 × 12½ (9.4.63)	..		6·00	13·00
94	19	$5 brown and bronze-grn (p 12½)	..		11·00	12·00
		a. Perf 13 × 12½ (13.8.63)	..		15·00	19·00
83/94			..	*Set of 12*	22·00	24·00

The 6, 12, 25 and 30 c. values used with this issue were Nos. 1/4 of Malayan Federation.

(Photo Harrison)

1961 (17 July). *Coronation of the Sultan. W w 12. P 15 × 14.*

95	6	10 c. multicoloured	..	..	40	30

---

7   Sultan Yahya Petra   8   *Vanda hookeriana*

(Recess D.L.R.)

1961–**63.** *As Nos. 92/8 of Kedah but with inset portrait of Sultan Yahya Petra as in T 7. W w 13. P 12½×13 (vert) or 13×12½ (horiz).*

96		1 c. black (1.3.62) ..	..	..	10	55
97		2 c. orange-red (1.3.62)	..	..	10	55
98		4 c. sepia (1.3.62)	..	..	10	10
99		5 c. carmine-lake (1.3.62)	..	..	10	10
100		8 c. myrtle-green (1.3.62) ..	..		3·25	3·50
		a. *Deep green* (15.1.63)	..		4·25	5·00
101		10 c. deep maroon (2.12.61)	..	..	30	10
102		20 c. blue (1.3.62)	..	..	60	30
96/102			..	*Set of 7*	4·00	4·50

1965 (15 Nov). *As Nos. 166/72 of Johore but with inset portrait of Sultan Yahya Petra as in T 8. W w 13 (upright).*

103		1 c. multicoloured	..	..	10	30
		b. Magenta omitted	..		55·00	
104		2 c. multicoloured	..	..	10	30
105		5 c. multicoloured	..	..	15	10
106		6 c. multicoloured	..	..	55	55
107		10 c. multicoloured	..	..	20	10
		a. Red omitted	..		28·00	
108		15 c. multicoloured	..	..	1·25	20
109		20 c. multicoloured	..	..	1·50	1·00
		a. Bright purple (blooms) omitted ..		42·00	
		b. Yellow (leaves) omitted	..		22·00	
103/9			..	*Set of 7*	3·25	2·25

The 5 c. and 10 c. exist with PVA gum as well as gum arabic.

The higher values used with this issue were Nos. 20/27 of Malaysia (National Issues).

1970 (20 Nov). *As Nos. 103 and 107 but W w 13 (sideways).*

110	8	1 c. multicoloured	..	..	40	3·00
111	–	10 c. multicoloured	..	..	1·40	2·50

9   *Parthenos sylvia*   10   *Lagerstroemia speciosa*

1971 (1 Feb)–**78.** *As Nos. 175/87 of Johore but with portrait of Sultan Yahya Petra and arms, as in T 9. (a) Litho by Bradbury, Wilkinson.*

112		1 c. multicoloured	..	..	15	75
113		2 c. multicoloured	..	..	35	75
114		5 c. multicoloured	..	..	60	20
115		6 c. multicoloured	..	..	60	70
116		10 c. multicoloured	..	..	60	10
117		15 c. multicoloured	..	..	85	10
		a. Black (state inscription, portrait and arms) omitted		75·00	
118		20 c. multicoloured	..	..	1·00	60
112/18			..	*Set of 7*	3·75	2·75

(b) *Photo by Harrison (1977–78)*

119		1 c. multicoloured	..	..	50	2·25
120		5 c. multicoloured	..	..	3·00	90
121		10 c. multicoloured	..	..	3·50	80
122		15 c. multicoloured	..	..	5·50	75
119/22			..	*Set of 4*	11·50	4·25

The higher values used with this issue were Nos. 64/71 of Malaysia (National Issues).

For differences between litho and photo printings, see after Johore No. 187.

On No. 117a only the country inscription, portrait and arms are omitted, the remainder of the black printing being as normal. The design was produced using two black plates, one for the main design, value and inscription and the other to apply the state name, head and arms. It is this plate which is omitted from No. 117a.

1979 (30 Apr). *As Nos. 188/94 of Johore but with portrait of Sultan Yahya Petra as in T 10.*

123		1 c. *Rafflesia hasseltii*	..	..	10	30
124		2 c. *Pterocarpus indicus*	..	..	10	30
125		5 c. Type 10	..	..	10	10
126		10 c. *Durio zibethinus*	..	..	10	10
127		15 c. *Hibiscus rosa-sinensis*	..		15	10
128		20 c. *Rhododendron scortechinii*	..		15	10
129		25 c. *Etlingera elatior* (inscr "*Phaeomeria speciosa*")	..		15	30
123/9			..	*Set of 7*	65	1·10

For higher values used in conjunction with this series see Nos. 190/7 of Malaysia (National Issues).

11   Sultan Tengku Ismail Petra   12   Black Pepper

(Des M. A. B. bin Saman. Litho Harrison)

1980 (30 Mar). *Coronation of Sultan Tengku Ismail Petra. P* 14.
130	**11**	10 c. multicoloured	..	..	..	20	30
131		15 c. multicoloured	..	..	..	20	15
132		50 c. multicoloured	..	..	..	70	1·40
130/2	..	..	..	..	*Set of* 3	1·00	1·75

1983–86.* *As Nos.* 125/6 *and* 128 *but without wmk.*
135	5 c. Type **10** (1986)	..	..	2·00	1·25
136	10 c. *Durio zibethinus* (18.9.84)	..		25	15
138	20 c. *Rhododendron scortechinii* (blackish brown background) (1983)	..	5·50	1·25
138a	20 c. *Rhododendron scortechinii* (bronze-green background) (5.10.83)	..	50	15

*There was no official release date for these stamps. Dates shown are the earliest recorded from postmarks and may be revised if earlier examples are reported.

For details of the shade differences between watermarked and unwatermarked printings see after Johore No. 200a.

On Nos. 135/6 and 138a the portrait and state arms have been redrawn smaller.

1986 (25 Oct). *As Nos.* 202/8 *of Johore but with portrait of Sultan Ismail Petra as in T* **12.**
140		1 c. Coffee	..	..	..	10	10
141		2 c. Coconuts..	..	..	..	10	10
142		5 c. Cocoa	..	..	..	10	10
143		10 c. Type **12**	..	..	..	10	10
144		15 c. Rubber	..	..	..	10	10
145		20 c. Oil palm..	..	..	..	10	10
146		30 c. Rice	..	..	..	15	20
140/6	..	..	..	..	*Set of* 7	40	45

MALACCA

One of the Straits Settlements.
Issues from 1965 are inscribed "MELAKA".

1948 (1 Dec). *Royal Silver Wedding. As Nos.* 143/4 *of Jamaica.*
1	10 c. violet	..		25	30
2	$5 brown	..		24·00	35·00

1949 (1 Mar)–52. *As T* **58** *of Straits Settlements, but inscr* "MALACCA" *at foot. Wmk Mult Script CA. Chalk-surfaced paper. P* 17½ × 18.
3	1 c. black	..	..	10	70
4	2 c. orange	..	..	30	45
5	3 c. green	..	..	30	1·50
6	4 c. brown	..	..	15	10
6a	5 c. bright purple (1.9.52)	..	45	85
7	6 c. grey	..	..	30	60
8	8 c. scarlet	..	..	30	3·00
8a	8 c. green (1.9.52)	..		85	3·50
9	10 c. purple	..	..	15	10
9a	12 c. scarlet (1.9.52)	..	95	2·00
10	15 c. ultramarine	..	..	30	60
11	20 c. black and green	..	30	3·50
11a	20 c. bright blue (1.9.52)	..	1·25	1·75
12	25 c. purple and orange	..	30	50
12a	35 c. scarlet and purple (1.9.52)	1·00	1·75
13	40 c. red and purple	..	1·25	8·50
14	50 c. black and blue	..	50	1·00
15	$1 blue and purple	..	4·00	9·50
16	$2 green and scarlet..	..	12·00	17·00
17	$5 green and brown..	..	32·00	35·00
3/17	..	..	*Set of* 20	50·00	80·00

1949 (10 Oct). *75th Anniv of U.P.U. As Nos.* 145/8 *of Jamaica.*
18	10 c. purple	..	..	15	45
19	15 c. deep blue..	..	45	1·75
20	25 c. orange	..	..	45	3·00
21	50 c. blue-black	..	1·00	3·75
18/21	..	..	*Set of* 4	1·90	8·00

1953 (2 June). *Coronation. As No.* 153 *of Jamaica.*
22	10 c. black and reddish purple		20	10

1 Queen Elizabeth II   2 Copra

1954 (9 June)–57. *Chalk-surfaced paper. Wmk Mult Script CA. P* 17½ × 18.
23	**1**	1 c. black (27.4.55)	..	..	10	40
24		2 c. yellow-orange (27.4.55)	..	30	45
25		4 c. brown	..	..	30	10
		a. Pale brown (24.4.57)	..	2·00	1·25
26		5 c. bright purple (12.7.54)	..	30	60
27		6 c. grey	..	..	10	15
28		8 c. green (5.1.55)	..	30	50
29		10 c. brown-purple (1.7.54)	..	30	10
		a. Reddish purple (27.3.57)	..	40	15
30		12 c. rose-red (5.1.55)	..	20	1·00
31		20 c. bright blue (5.1.55)	..	20	30
32		25 c. brown-purple & yellow-orge (27.4.55)	20	30
33		30 c. rose-red and brown-purple (5.9.55)	20	20
34		35 c. rose-red and brown-purple (8.9.54)	20	35
35		50 c. black and bright blue (5.1.55)	30	50
36		$1 bright blue and brown-purple (8.9.54)	2·25	4·75
37		$2 emerald and scarlet (27.4.55)	15·00	20·00
38		$5 emerald and brown (27.4.55)	16·00	22·00
23/38		..	*Set of* 16	32·00	45·00

1957. *As Nos.* 92/102 *of Kedah but with inset portrait of Queen Elizabeth II.*
39	**9**	1 c. black (21.8)	..	..	10	40
40	**10**	2 c. orange-red (25.7)	..	10	40
41	**11**	4 c. sepia (21.8)	..	..	10	10
42	**12**	5 c. carmine-lake (21.8)..	..	10	10
43	**13**	8 c. myrtle-green (21.8)..	..	1·25	2·25
44	**14**	10 c. deep brown (4.8)	..	20	10
45	**15**	20 c. blue (26.6)	..	..	30	40
46	**16**	50 c. black and blue (25.7)	..	30	50
47	**17**	$1 ultramarine and reddish purple (25.7)	..	2·00	2·50
48	**18**	$2 bronze-green and scarlet (21.8)	7·50	13·00
49	**19**	$5 brown and bronze-green (26.6)	10·00	14·00
39/49		..	..	*Set of* 11	20·00	30·00

The 6, 12, 25 and 30 c. values used with this issue were Nos. 1/4 of Malayan Federation.

(Recess D.L.R.)

1960 (15 Mar)–62. *As Nos.* 39/49, *but with inset picture of Melaka tree and Pelandok (mouse deer) as in T* **2.** W w **12.** P 13 × 12½ (1 c. to 8 c., $2, $5), 12½ × 13 (10 c. to 50 c.) or 13½ ($1).
50	1 c. black	..	..	10	30
51	2 c. orange-red	..	..	10	30
52	4 c. sepia	..	..	10	10
53	5 c. carmine-lake	..	..	10	10
54	8 c. myrtle-green	..	1·25	1·25
55	10 c. deep maroon	..	20	10
56	20 c. blue	..	..	20	20
57	50 c. black and blue	..	30	30
	a. Black and ultramarine (9.1.62)	..	55	30
58	$1 ultramarine and reddish purple	..	1·50	2·25
59	$2 bronze-green and scarlet..	..	3·75	4·75
60	$5 brown and bronze-green..	..	8·00	6·00
50/60	..	..	*Set of* 11	14·00	14·00

3 *Vanda hookeriana*   4 *Papilio demoleus*

1965 (15 Nov)–68. *As Nos.* 166/72 *of Johore but with Arms of Malacca inset and inscr* "MELAKA" *as in T* **3.** W w **13** (*upright*).
61		1 c. multicoloured	..	..	10	50
62		2 c. multicoloured	..	..	10	50
63		5 c. multicoloured	..	..	10	10
		b. Yellow (flower) omitted	..	20·00	
		c. Red omitted	..	28·00	
64		6 c. multicoloured	..	..	20	30
65		10 c. multicoloured	..	..	15	10
66		15 c. multicoloured	..	..	1·50	40
67		20 c. multicoloured (purple-brn background)	2·00	65
		a. Red-brown background (2.4.68)	2·00	85
61/7		..	..	*Set of* 7	3·50	2·25

The 5 c., 6 c., 10 c. and 20 c. exist with PVA gum as well as gum arabic.

The higher values used with this issue were Nos. 20/27 of Malaysia (National Issues).

1970. *As Nos.* 61 *and* 65 *but* W w **13** (*sideways*).
68	**3**	1 c. multicoloured (27.5.70)	..	75	3·75
69		10 c. multicoloured (20.11.70)	..	3·25	3·75

1971 (1 Feb)–78. *As Nos.* 175/87 *of Johore but with arms of Malacca and inscr* "melaka", *as in T* **4.** (a) *Litho by Bradbury, Wilkinson.*
70	1 c. multicoloured	..	..	15	60
71	2 c. multicoloured	..	..	40	60
72	5 c. multicoloured	..	..	55	10
73	6 c. multicoloured	..	..	55	60
74	10 c. multicoloured	..	..	55	10
75	15 c. multicoloured	..	..	80	10
76	20 c. multicoloured	..	..	90	90
70/6	..	..	..	*Set of* 7	3·50	2·75

(b) *Photo by Harrison* (1977–78)
77	1 c. multicoloured	..	..	2·25	3·75
78	5 c. multicoloured	..	..	1·50	70
79	10 c. multicoloured	..	..	3·00	70
80	15 c. multicoloured	..	..	4·25	50
81	20 c. multicoloured	..	..	4·25	2·75
77/81	..	..	..	*Set of* 5	14·00	7·50

The higher values used with this issue were Nos. 64/71 of Malaysia (National Issues).

For differences between litho and photo printings, see after Johore No. 187.

5 *Durio zibethinus*   6 Rubber

1979 (30 Apr). *As Nos.* 188/94 *of Johore but with Arms of Malacca and inscr* "melaka" *as in T* **5.**
82		1 c. *Rafflesia hasseltii*	..	..	10	30
83		2 c. *Pterocarpus indicus*	..	..	10	30
84		5 c. *Lagerstroemia speciosa*	..	10	10
85		10 c. Type **5**	..	..	10	10
86		15 c. *Hibiscus rosa-sinensis*	..	15	10
87		20 c. *Rhododendron scortechinii*	..	15	10
88		25 c. *Etlingera elatior* (inscr "Phaeomeria speciosa")	15	30
82/8		..	..	*Set of* 7	65	1·00

For higher values used in conjunction with this series see Nos. 190/7 of Malaysia (National Issues).

1983 (26 Oct)–86.* *As Nos.* 85/7 *but without wmk.*
92	10 c. Type **5** (19.4.85)	..	3·50	3·00
93	15 c. *Hibiscus rosa-sinensis* (9.86)	1·50	55
94	20 c. *Rhododendron scortechinii* (blackish brown background)	6·00	1·75
94a	20 c. *Rhododendron scortechinii* (bronze-green background) (13.6.84)	1·50	70

*There was no official release date for these stamps. Dates shown are the earliest recorded from postmarks and may be revised if earlier examples are reported.

For details of the shade differences between watermarked and unwatermarked printings see after Johore No. 200a.

On Nos. 92/3 and 94a the distance between the coat of arms and the value is greater than on Nos. 85, 87 and 94.

1986 (25 Oct). *As Nos.* 202/8 *of Johore but with Arms of Malacca and inscr* "MELAKA" *as in T* **6.**
96		1 c. Coffee	..	..	10	10
97		2 c. Coconuts..	..	..	10	10
98		5 c. Cocoa	..	..	10	10
99		10 c. Black pepper	..	..	10	10
100		15 c. Type **6**	..	..	10	10
101		20 c. Oil palm..	..	..	10	10
102		30 c. Rice	..	..	15	20
96/102		..	..	*Set of* 7	40	45

NEGRI SEMBILAN

A federation of smaller states reconstituted in 1886. Sungei Ujong, taken under British protection in 1874, was absorbed into Negri Sembilan by Treaty of 8 August 1895. The Negri Sembilan federation joined the Federated Malay States in 1896.

A. SUNGEI UJONG

Until 1 January 1899, when the Federated Malay States joined the U.P.U., mail for addresses outside Malaya was franked with the stamps of the STRAITS SETTLEMENTS.

PRICES FOR STAMPS ON COVER

Nos. 1/14	—
Nos. 15/27	*from* × 25
Nos. 28/36	*from* × 8
Nos. 37/49	*from* × 10
Nos. 50/5	*from* × 25

(1)

1878. No. 11 *of Straits Settlements handstamped with* T 1.
1   2 c. brown £1600 £1400
This overprint on India No. 54 is bogus.

SUNGEI   **SUNGEI**   **SUNGEI**
(2) (Narrow   (3) ("N"   (4) ("S" wide)
letters)   wide)

UJONG   **UJONG**   **UJONG**
(5) ("N" wide)   (6) (Narrow   (7) Narrow
letters, "UJ"   letters, evenly
close together)   spaced)

1881. No. 11 *of Straits Settlements optd with* T 2/7.
2   2+5   2 c. brown £2500 £2250
3   3+5   2 c. brown £1700 £1600
4   2+6   2 c. brown £120
  a. Opt Type 6 double £1000
5   4+6   2 c. brown £400
6   2+7   2 c. brown £200
The two lines of this surcharge were applied as separate operations. On Nos. 2/3 "SUNGEI" was printed as a triplet, probably 2+3+3, "UJONG" being added by a single unit handstamp. Nos. 4 and 5 come from a similar triplet, 4+4+5, completed by another single unit handstamp. No. 6 comes from a single type triplet with the second line added as a triplet instead of by a single unit handstamp.
The 10 c. slate overprinted Types 2 + 7 is bogus.

SUNGEI   **SUNGEI**   **SUNGEI**
(8) ("N" and "E"   (9) ("SUN" and "E"   (10) ("SUN" wide)
wide)   wide)

SUNGEI   **SUNGEI**
(11) ("S" wide)   (12) (Narrow
letters)

UJONG   **UJONG**
(13) ("U" and "NG"   (14) (Narrow
wide)   letters)

1881. No. 11 *of Straits Settlements optd with* T 8/14.
7   8+13   2 c. brown £100
8   9+13   2 c. brown £100
9   10+13   2 c. brown £100
10   11+14   2 c. brown £160
  a. "S" inverted £1800
11   12+14   2 c. brown £100
Nos. 7/11 also had the two lines of the overprint applied at separate operations. "SUNGEI" as a triplet, either 7+8+9 or 10+11+11, and "UJONG" as a single unit.

S.U.
(15)

1882. Nos. 50/1 *of Straits Settlements optd as* T 15.
12   2 c. brown (with stops)..   .. .. £150
13   2 c. brown (without stops) £180 £225
14   4 c. rose (with stops) £1600 £1600
Each of the above was applied by a triplet setting.
Examples of Straits Settlements No. 11 with a similar overprint, including stops, are trials which were not issued.

SUNGEI   **SUNGEI**   **UJONG**
(16) ("S" and "E"   (17) ("E" wide)   (18) ("N" wide)
wide)

1882 (Dec)–84. Nos. 12, 50, 52/3 and 63 of Straits Settlements optd with T 11/12, 14 and 16/18.
15   12+14   2 c. brown £250 £160
16   11+14   2 c. brown £350 £250
17   12+14   2 c. rose (1884)   .. .. 95·00 £110
18   11+14   2 c. rose (1884)   .. .. 95·00 £110
  a. Opt Type 14 double   ..
19   16+14   2 c. rose (1884)   .. .. 70·00 80·00
20   17+14   2 c. rose (1884)   .. .. 80·00 90·00
21   12+18   2 c. rose (1884)   .. .. 80·00 90·00
  a. Opt Type 18 double   ..
22   12+14   4 c. rose £700 £750
23   11+14   4 c. rose £1100 £1200
24   12+14   8 c. orange £900 £750
25   11+14   8 c. orange £1500 £1200
26   12+14   10 c. slate £300 £300
27   11+14   10 c. slate £450 £450
Nos. 15/27 had the two lines of the overprint applied by separate triplets. Settings so far identified are Nos. 15+16+15, 17+18+19, 19+20+21, 22+23+22, 24+25+24 and 26+27+26.
The 4 c. rose overprinted Types 16+14 is now believed to be a trial.

UJONG.   **UJONG.**   **UJONG**
(19) (With   (20) (With   (21) (Without
stop. Narrow   stop "N"   stop. Narrow
letters)   wide)   letters)

1883–84. Nos. 50 and 63/4 of Straits Settlements optd with T 12. 16/17 and 19/21.
28   12+19   2 c. brown   .. .. 30·00 75·00
29   16+19   2 c. brown   .. .. 30·00 75·00
30   12+20   2 c. brown   .. .. 30·00 75·00
31   16+21   2 c. rose (1884)   .. .. 50·00 65·00
32   17+21   2 c. rose (1884)   .. .. 50·00 65·00
33   12+21   2 c. rose (1884)   .. .. 50·00 65·00
34   16+21   4 c. brown (1884) £120 £150
35   17+21   4 c. brown (1884) £120 £150
36   12+21   4 c. brown (1884) £120 £150
  a. Opt Type 21 double £1700
Nos. 28/36 had the two lines of the overprint applied by separate triplets. Settings were Nos. 28+29+30, 31+32+33 and 34+35+36.
The 8 c. orange overprinted Types 12+19 is now believed to be a trial (Price £550 unused).

Sungei   ***SUNGEI***   **SUNGEI**
Ujong   ***UJONG***   **UJONG**
(22)   (23)   (24)

SUNGEI   **SUNGEI**   **SUNGEI**
UJONG   **UJONG**   **UJONG**
(25)   (26)   (27)

SUNGEI   ***SUNGEI***   **SUNGEI**
UJONG   ***UJONG.***   **UJONG**
(28)   (29)   (30)

1885–90. No. 63 of Straits Settlements optd with T 22/30.
37   22   2 c. rose   .. .. 35·00 45·00
  a. Opt double £325 £325
38   23   2 c. rose..   .. .. 16·00 38·00
  a. Opt double £475
39   24   2 c. rose (1886)   .. .. 90·00 £100
40   25   2 c. rose (1886)   .. .. 95·00 £110
  a. Opt double   ..
41   26   2 c. rose (1886)   .. .. 70·00 80·00
  a. Opt double   ..
42   27   2 c. rose (1887)   .. .. 7·50 23·00
43   28   2 c. rose (1889)   .. .. 4·50 6·50
  a. Narrow "E" (2 mm wide) (R. 3/4 and
  4/3)   .. .. 40·00
  b. Antique "N" in "UJONG" (R. 10/6)   .. 75·00
  c. Opt double £1200
44   29   2 c. rose (1889)   .. .. 48·00 48·00
  a. "UNJOG" (R. 7/3) £2250 £1900
45   30   2 c. rose (1890)   .. .. 13·00 13·00
  a. Antique "G" in "SUNGEI" (R. 6/1) .. 95·00
  b. Antique "G" in "UJONG" (R. 8/3) .. 95·00
All the above overprints had both lines applied at the same operation. Nos. 37/42 were from different triplet settings. The first printing of No. 43 was from a triplet, but this was followed by further settings of 60 (6×10), the first containing No. 43a and the second Nos. 43a/b. Nos. 44/5 were both from settings of 60.

SUNGEI   **SUNGEI**   **SUNGEI**
UJONG   **UJONG**   **UJONG**
Two   **Two**   *Two*
CENTS   **CENTS**   **CENTS**

(31)   (32)   (33)

SUNGEI
UJONG
Two
CENTS

(34)

1891. No. 68 of Straits Settlements surch with T 31/4.
46   31   2 c. on 24 c. green £300 £350
47   32   2 c. on 24 c. green £120 £150
48   33   2 c. on 24 c. green £300 £350
49   34   2 c. on 24 c. green   .. .. 75·00 £100
  a. Antique "G" in "SUNGEI" (R. 6/1) .. £375
  b. Antique "G" in "UJONG" (R. 8/3) .. £375
Nos. 46/9 come from the same setting of 60 on which "SUNGEI UJONG" was from the same type as No. 45. No. 46 occurs in row 1. No. 47 from rows 2 to 4, No. 48 from row 5 and No. 49 from rows 6 to 10.

---

   3 CENTS

35   (36)   37

1891–94. Wmk Crown CA. P 14.
50   35   2 c. rose   .. .. 22·00 26·00
51   2 c. orange (1894)..   .. .. 1·40 4·25
52   5 c. blue (1893)   .. .. 4·50 5·50
50/2   Set of 3 25·00 32·00
50/2 Optd "Specimen"   Set of 3 60·00

1894. Surch as T 36 by De La Rue.
53   35   1 c. on 5 c. green 65   70
54   3 c. on 5 c. rose   .. .. 1·75 4·50

1895. Wmk Crown CA. P 14.
55   37   3 c. dull purple and carmine   .. 5·50   75
53/5 Optd "Specimen"   Set of 3 60·00

B. NEGRI SEMBILAN

Stamps of the STRAITS SETTLEMENTS were used in Negri Sembilan during 1891, until replaced by the stamps listed below. Until the Federated Malay States joined the U.P.U. On 1 January 1899 Straits Settlements stamps continued to be used for mail to addresses outside Malaya.

PRICES FOR STAMPS ON COVER TO 1945

No. 1	*from* × 200
Nos. 2/4	*from* × 8
Nos. 5/14	*from* × 5
Nos. 15/20	*from* × 6
Nos. 21/49	*from* × 4

Negri
Sembilan
(1)   2   3

1891 (Aug?). No. 63 of Straits Settlements optd with T 1.
1   2 c. rose   .. .. .. 2·25 4·00

N.SEMBILAN

Short "N" in "SEMBILAN" (Top left pane R. 8/3)

1891–94. Wmk Crown CA. P 14.
2   2   1 c. green (1893)   .. .. 2·50 1·00
3   2 c. rose   .. .. 3·25 4·00
  a. Short "N"
4   5 c. blue (1894)   .. .. 23·00 27·00
2/4   Set of 3 26·00 29·00
2/4 Optd "Specimen"   Set of 3 70·00

1895–99. Wmk Crown CA. P 14.
5   3   1 c. dull purple and green (1899)   .. 4·50 2·50
6   2 c. dull purple and brown (1898)   .. 24·00 75·00
7   3 c. dull purple and carmine   .. 2·50 60
8   5 c. dull purple and orange-yellow (1897)   5·00 5·50
9   8 c. dull purple and ultramarine (1898) .. 23·00 13·00
10   10 c. dull purple and orange (1897)   .. 26·00 12·00
11   15 c. green and violet (1896)   .. 28·00 55·00
12   20 c. green and olive (1897)   .. 32·00 35·00
13   25 c. green and carmine (1896)   .. 60·00 75·00
14   50 c. green and black (1896)   .. 48·00 55·00
5/14   Set of 10 £225 £300
5/14 Optd "Specimen"   Set of 10 £160

Four cents.

Four cents.

(4)   (5)

1898 (Dec)–1900. (a) Surch as T 4.
15   3   1 c. on 15 c. green and violet (1900)   .. 75·00 £150
  a. Raised stop (R. 5/1 and R. 10/1 of each
  pane) £225 £400
16   2   4 c. on 1 c. green ..   .. 1·00 10·00
17   3   4 c. on 3 c. dull purple and carmine   .. 3·00 12·00
  a. Horiz pair, one without surch   ..£2000 £2250
  b. Surch double £850 £650
  ba. Ditto. "Four cents" albino   ..
  c. Surch inverted £600 £600
  d. "cents" repeated at left   .. £600 £650
  e. "Four" repeated at right   .. £600 £650
  f. Without bar £475 £375
  g. Bar double   .. .. †£500
18   2   4 c. on 5 c. blue   .. .. 1·00 9·00
On Nos. 15 and 17 the bar is at the top of the stamp.
The surcharges were applied as a setting of 30 (6×5).

(b) Surch as T 5

19	**3**	4 c. on 8 c. dull purple & ultram (G.) (12.98)		2·00	3·50
		a. Vert pair, one without surch		£2500	£2000
		b. Surch double		£1200	
		c. Surch double (G.+R.)		£700	£700
20		4 c. on 8 c. dull purple and ultramarine (Bk.)		£600	£650

Pending the arrival of the permanent Federated Malay States issue the stamps of SELANGOR, FEDERATED MALAY STATES provisional overprints, STRAITS SETTLEMENTS and PERAK were used at various times between October 1899 and April 1901.

The general issues for FEDERATED MALAY STATES were used in Negri Sembilan from 29 April 1901 until 1935.

6 Arms of Negri Sembilan **7**

1935 (2 Dec)–**41**. *Wmk Mult Script CA. Ordinary paper (6 c. grey, 15 c.) or chalk-surfaced paper (others). P* 14.

21	**6**	1 c. black (1.1.36)		50	10
22		2 c. green (1.1.36)		70	20
23		2 c. orange (11.12.41)		70	28·00
24		3 c. green (21.8.41)		1·50	5·00
		a. Ordinary paper		10·00	5·00
25		4 c. orange		30	10
26		5 c. brown (5.12.35)		50	10
27		6 c. scarlet (1.1.37)		5·50	1·75
		a. Stop omitted at right (R. 10/4)		£130	80·00
28		6 c. grey (18.12.41)		2·25	50·00
		a. Stop omitted at right (R. 10/4)		55·00	£190
29		8 c. grey		1·75	10
30		10 c. dull purple (1.1.36)		30	10
31		12 c. bright ultramarine (1.1.36)		1·00	25
32		15 c. ultramarine (1.10.41)		3·25	35·00
33		25 c. dull purple and scarlet (1.4.36)		75	70
34		30 c. dull purple and orange (1.1.36)		4·25	2·00
35		40 c. scarlet and dull purple		85	2·00
36		50 c. black/*emerald* (1.2.36)		3·75	1·25
37		$1 black and red/*blue* (1.4.36)		2·00	2·00
38		$2 green and scarlet (16.5.36)		18·00	15·00
39		$5 green and red/*emerald* (16.5.36)		13·00	38·00
21/39			*Set of* 19	55·00	£160
21/39 Perf "Specimen"			*Set of* 19	£200	

An 8 c. scarlet was issued but only with opt during Japanese Occupation of Malaya. Unoverprinted specimens result from leakages.

During shortages in 1941 stamps of STRAITS SETTLEMENTS (2 c.), SELANGOR (2 c., 8 c.), PERAK (2 c., 25 c., 50 c.) and PAHANG (8 c.) were issued in Negri Sembilan.

1948 (1 Dec). *Royal Silver Wedding. As Nos.* 143/4 *of Jamaica.*

40		10 c. violet		15	30
41		$5 green		17·00	28·00

1949 (1 Apr)–**55**. *Chalk-surfaced paper. Wmk Mult Script CA. P* 17½ × 18.

42	**7**	1 c. black		10	10
43		2 c. orange		10	10
44		3 c. green		10	30
45		4 c. brown		1200	
46		5 c. bright purple (1.9.52)		30	50
		a. Bright mauve (25.8.53)		30	30
47		6 c. grey		15	10
		a. Pale grey (25.8.53)		50	10
48		8 c. scarlet		20	75
49		8 c. green (1.9.52)		1·50	1·40
50		10 c. purple		15	10
51		12 c. scarlet (1.9.52)		1·50	1·75
52		15 c. ultramarine		1·40	10
53		20 c. black and green		25	75
54		20 c. bright blue (1.9.52)		80	10
55		25 c. purple and orange		25	10
56		30 c. scarlet and purple (5.9.55)		1·25	2·00
57		35 c. scarlet and purple (1.9.52)		70	1·00
58		40 c. red and purple		80	2·75
59		50 c. black and blue		40	10
60		$1 blue and purple		2·25	85
61		$2 green and scarlet		10·00	7·00
62		$5 green and brown		38·00	32·00
42/62			*Set of* 21	55·00	45·00

1949 (10 Oct). *75th Anniv of U.P.U. As Nos.* 145/8 *of Jamaica.*

63		10 c. purple		20	10
64		15 c. deep blue		45	70
65		25 c. orange		50	1·50
66		50 c. blue-black		80	2·50
63/6			*Set of* 4	1·75	4·25

1953 (2 June). *Coronation. As No.* 153 *of Jamaica.*

67		10 c. black and reddish purple		30	30

1957 (26 June)–**63**. *As Nos.* 92/102 *of Kedah but with inset Arms of Negri Sembilan.*

68	**9**	1 c. black (21.8.57)		10	10
69	**10**	2 c. orange-red (25.7.57)		10	10
70	**11**	4 c. sepia (21.8.57)		10	10
71	**12**	5 c. carmine-lake (21.8.57)		10	10
72	**13**	8 c. myrtle-green (21.8.57)		85	90
73	**14**	10 c. deep brown (4.8.57)		15	10
74		10 c. deep maroon (10.1.61)		1·25	10
75	**15**	20 c. blue		20	10
76	**16**	50 c. black and blue (p 12½) (25.7.57)		20	30
		a. Perf 12½ × 13 (19.7.60)		20	20
77	**17**	$1 ultramarine & reddish pur (25.7.57)		1·25	70
78	**18**	$2 bronze-green & scarlet (p 12½) (21.8.57)		3·75	7·50
		a. Perf 13 × 12½ (15.1.63)		7·00	12·00

8 Tuanku Munawir   **9** *Vanda hookeriana*

(Photo Enschedé)

1961 (17 Apr). *Installation of Tuanku Munawir as Yang di-Pertuan Besar of Negri Sembilan. No wmk. P* 14 × 13.

80	**8**	10 c. multicoloured		15	15

1965 (15 Nov)–**69**. *As Nos.* 166/72 *of Johore but with Arms of Negri Sembilan inset and inscr "NEGERI SEMBILAN" as in T* 9. *W w* 13 *(upright).*

81		1 c. multicoloured		10	40
82		2 c. multicoloured		10	40
83		5 c. multicoloured		15	10
		b. Yellow omitted		20·00	
84		6 c. multicoloured		15	40
85		10 c. multicoloured		15	10
86		15 c. multicoloured		80	10
87		20 c. jet-black and multicoloured		1·25	75
		a. Blackish brown & mult (19.12.69)		2·00	20
81/7			*Set of* 7	2·25	1·40

The 2 c., 6 c., 15 c. and 20 c. exist with PVA gum as well as gum arabic.

The higher values used with this issue were Nos. 20/27 of Malaysia (National Issues).

See also No. 90.

10 Negri Sembilan Crest and Tuanku Ja'afar   **11** *Hebomoia glaucippe*

(Des Z. Noor. Photo Japanese Govt Ptg Wks)

1968 (8 Apr). *Installation of Tuanku Ja'afar as Yang di-Pertuan Besar of Negri Sembilan. P* 13.

88	**10**	15 c. multicoloured		15	40
89		50 c. multicoloured		30	1·10

1970 (27 May). *As No.* 81 *but with W w* 13 *(sideways).*

90	**9**	1 c. multicoloured		1·25	3·50

1971 (1 Feb)–**78**. *As Nos.* 175/87 *of Johore but with Arms of Negri Sembilan and inscr "negeri sembilan", as in T* 11.

(a) Litho by Bradbury, Wilkinson

91		1 c. multicoloured		15	50
92		2 c. multicoloured		40	50
93		5 c. multicoloured		50	10
94		6 c. multicoloured		50	50
95		10 c. multicoloured		50	10
96		15 c. multicoloured		70	10
97		20 c. multicoloured		80	20
91/7			*Set of* 7	3·25	1·75

(b) Photo by Harrison (1977–78)

98		2 c. multicoloured		85	2·00
99		5 c. multicoloured		75	65
100		10 c. multicoloured		4·50	50
101		15 c. multicoloured		6·50	30
102		20 c. multicoloured		2·50	1·50
98/102			*Set of* 5	13·50	4·50

The higher values used with issue were Nos. 64/71 of Malaysia (National Issues).

For differences between litho and photo printings, see after Johore No. 187.

12 *Hibiscus rosa-sinensis*   **13** Oil Palm

1979 (30 Apr). *As Nos.* 188/94 *of Johore but with Arms of Negri Sembilan and inscr "negeri sembilan" as in T* 12.

103		1 c. *Rafflesia hasseltii*		10	30
104		2 c. *Pterocarpus indicus*		10	30
105		5 c. *Lagerstroemia speciosa*		10	10
106		10 c. *Durio zibethinus*		10	10
107		15 c. Type 12		15	10
108		20 c. *Rhododendron scortechinii*		15	10
109		25 c. *Etlingera elatior* (inscr "*Phaeomeria speciosa*")		15	10
103/9			*Set of* 7	65	80

For higher values used in conjunction with this series see Nos. 190/7 of Malaysia (National Issues).

1983 (Oct)–**84**.* *As Nos.* 105/8 *but without wmk.*

112		5 c. *Lagerstroemia speciosa* (25.5.84)		2·50	1·75
113		10 c. *Durio zibethinus* (24.10.84)		30	30
114		15 c. Type 12 (11.8.84)		1·75	45
115		20 c. *Rhododendron scortechinii* (blackish brown background)		5·50	1·10

1979

79	**19**	$5 brown and bronze-green (p 12½)		9·00	13·00
		a. Perf 13 × 12½ (6.3.62)		11·00	12·00
		ab. Perf 13 × 12½. Brown and yellow-olive (13.11.62)		£120	55·00
68/79			*Set of* 12	15·00	19·00

The 6, 12, 25 and 30 c. values used with this issue were Nos. 1/4 of Malayan Federation.

115a | 20 c. *Rhododendron scortechinii* (bronze-green background) (1983) | | 30 | 30 |

*There was no official release date for these stamps. Dates shown are the earliest recorded from postmarks and may be revised if earlier examples are reported.

For details of the shade differences between watermarked and unwatermarked printings see after Johore No. 200*a*.

Nos. 112/14 and 115*a* show a larger crest, further from the face value than on Nos. 105/8 and 115.

1986 (25 Oct). *As Nos.* 202/8 *of Johore but with Arms of Negri Sembilan and inscr "NEGERI SEMBILAN" as in T* 13.

117		1 c. Coffee		10	10
118		2 c. Coconuts		10	10
119		5 c. Cocoa		10	10
120		10 c. Black pepper		10	10
121		15 c. Rubber		10	10
122		20 c. Type 13		10	10
123		30 c. Rice		15	20
117/23			*Set of* 7	40	45

PAHANG

The first British Resident was appointed in 1888. Pahang joined the Federated Malay States in 1896.

Until 1 January 1899, when the Federated Malay States joined the U.P.U., mail for addresses outside Malaya was franked with stamps of the STRAITS SETTLEMENTS.

PRICES FOR STAMPS ON COVER TO 1945

Nos. 1/3	from × 12
Nos. 4/6	from × 20
Nos. 7/10	from × 8
Nos. 11/13	from × 20
Nos. 14/16	from × 10
Nos. 17/18	from × 5
Nos. 19/24	from × 4
No. 25	from × 12
Nos. 26/7	—
No. 28	from × 10
Nos. 29/46	from × 6

PAHANG   PAHANG   PAHANG
(1)   (2)   (2a) (Antique letters)

1889 (Jan). *Nos. 52/3 and 63 of Straits Settlements optd with T 1.*

1	2 c. rose	65·00	38·00
2	8 c. orange	£1600	£1300
3	10 c. slate	£225	£250

All three values were overprinted from a triplet setting, but the 2 c. also exists from a similar setting of 30 or 60.

1889. *No. 63 of Straits Settlements optd with T 2.*

4	2 c. rose	3·75	6·50
	a. Opt Type 2a. Antique letters	£400	

No. 4 was overprinted from a setting of 60. No. 4a usually occurs on R. 10/1, but has also been found on R. 8/1 as the result of revision to the setting.

PAHANG   PAHANG
(3)   (4)

1890. *No. 63 of Straits Settlements optd.*

5	3	2 c. rose	£1900	£800
6	4	2 c. rose	55·00	14·00

No. 5 may have been overprinted from a triplet setting. No. 6 was from a setting of 60.

(5)   (6)
(7)   (8)

1891. *No. 68 of Straits Settlements surch with T 5/8.*

7	5	2 c. on 24 c. green	60·00	80·00
8	6	2 c. on 24 c. green	£275	£375
9	7	2 c. on 24 c. green	80·00	£110
10	8	2 c. on 24 c. green	£275	£375

Nos. 7/10 come from one setting used to surcharge the panes of sixty. No. 7 occurs in rows 1 to 5, No. 8 on row 6, No. 9 on rows 7 to 9 and No. 10 on row 10.

9   10

1891–95. *Wmk Crown CA. P 14.*

11	9	1 c. green (1895)	3·75	2·50
12		2 c. rose	2·50	90
13		5 c. blue (1893)	7·00	22·00
11/13			Set of 3	12·00	23·00
11/13 Optd "Specimen"			Set of 3	60·00	

OMNIBUS ISSUES

Details, together with prices for complete sets, of the various Omnibus issues from the 1935 Silver Jubilee series to date are included in a special section following Zululand at the end of the catalogue.

Following an increase of postage rates on 1 March 1894 1 cent stamps of STRAITS SETTLEMENTS were used in Pahang until the autumn of the following year.

1895–99. *Wmk Crown CA. P 14.*

14	10	3 c. dull purple and carmine	2·50	1·25
15		4 c. dull purple and carmine (1899)	9·50	5·50
16		5 c. dull purple and olive-yellow (1897)	17·00	12·00
14/16			Set of 3	26·00	16·00
14/16 Optd "Specimen"			Set of 3	60·00	

1897 (2 Aug). *No. 13 bisected, surch in red manuscript at Kuala Lipis and initialled "JFO".* (a) *Bisected horizontally.*

17	2 c. on half 5 c. blue (surch "2" and bar across "5")	—	£750
17a	3 c. on half of 5 c. blue (surch "3")	—	£750

(b) Bisected diagonally.

18	2 c. on half of 5 c. blue (surch "2" and bar across "5")	£750	£250
	a. Unsevered pair. Nos. 18 and 18d	£4750	£1800
	b. Se-tenant pair. Nos. 18 and 18d	£2250	£650
	c. Surch in black manuscript	£5000	£2250
18d	3 c. on half of 5 c. blue (surch "3")	£750	£250
	dc. Surch in black manuscript	£5000	£2250

The initials are those of John Fortescue Owen, the District Treasurer at Kuala Lipis.
Nos. 17 and 18 only occur on the bottom half of the 5 c. and Nos. 17a and 18d on the top half. No. 18a is a complete example of No. 13 showing the two surcharges. No. 18b is a se-tenant pair of bisects from adjoining stamps.

Pahang.   Pahang.
(11)   (12)

1898–99. (a) *Nos. 72/5 of Perak optd with T 11.*

19	10 c. dull purple and orange	15·00	24·00
20	25 c. green and carmine	65·00	95·00
21	50 c. dull purple and greenish black	£140	£150
22	50 c. green and black (1899)	£100	£110

(b) *Nos. 76 and 79 of Perak optd with T 12.*

23	$1 green and pale green	£150	£160
24	$5 green and ultramarine	£475	£600

Pahang
Four cents
(13)

Four cents.
(14)

1898. (a) *T 44 of Perak surch with T 13.*

25	4 c. on 8 c. dull purple and ultramarine	2·50	5·50
	a. Surch inverted	£1500	£750
	b. Surch double	£475	

(b) *T 13 on plain paper (no stamp), but issued for postage. Imperf.*

26	4 c. black	—	£1000
27	5 c. black	£700	

No. 26 also exists pin-perforated.

1899. *No. 16 surch with T 14.*

28	10	4 c. on 5 c. dull purple and olive-yellow	7·00	32·00

Pending the arrival of the permanent Federated Malay States issue the stamps of SELANGOR, FEDERATED MALAY STATES provisional overprints and PERAK were used at various times between November 1899 and July 1902.
The general issues for the FEDERATED MALAY STATES were used in Pahang from July 1902 until 1935.

15 Sultan Sir Abu Bakar   16 Sultan Sir Abu Bakar

1935 (2 Dec)–41. *Chalk-surfaced paper. Wmk Mult Script CA. P 14.*

29	15	1 c. black (1.1.36)	10	30
30		2 c. green (1.1.36)	50	20
31		3 c. green (21.8.41)	2·00	6·50
		a. Ordinary paper	4·75	4·25
32		4 c. orange	30	10
33		5 c. brown (5.12.35)	50	10
34		6 c. scarlet (1.1.37)	5·50	2·25
35		8 c. grey	50	10
36		8 c. scarlet (11.12.41)	70	30·00
37		10 c. dull purple (1.1.36)	10	10
38		12 c. bright ultramarine (1.1.36)	1·50	1·75
39		15 c. ultram (ordinary paper) (1.10.41)	2·75	35·00
40		25 c. dull purple and scarlet (1.4.36)	80	1·00
41		30 c. dull purple and orange (1.1.36)	70	80
42		40 c. scarlet and dull purple	75	1·40
43		50 c. black/emerald (1.2.36)	3·25	1·75
44		$1 black and red/blue (1.4.36)	2·25	5·00
45		$2 green and scarlet (16.5.36)	18·00	26·00
46		$5 green and red/emerald (16.5.36)	8·00	48·00
29/46			Set of 18	42·00	£140
29/46 Perf "Specimen"			Set of 18	£180	

A 2 c. orange and a 6 c. grey were prepared but not officially issued. (*Price mint £4 each*).

During shortages in 1941 stamps of STRAITS SETTLEMENTS (2 c.), SELANGOR (2 c., 8 c.) and PERAK (2 c.) were issued in Pahang.

1948 (1 Dec). *Royal Silver Wedding. As Nos. 143/4 of Jamaica.*

47	10 c. violet	15	60
48	$5 green	20·00	40·00

1949 (10 Oct). *75th Anniv of U.P.U. As Nos. 145/8 of Jamaica.*

49	10 c. purple	20	20
50	15 c. deep blue	35	70
51	25 c. orange	35	1·10
52	50 c. blue-black	70	2·00
49/52		Set of 4	1·40	3·50

1950 (1 June)–56. *Wmk Mult Script CA. Chalk-surfaced paper. P 17½×18.*

53	16	1 c. black	10	10
54		2 c. orange	10	10
55		3 c. green	20	25
56		4 c. brown	15	10
		a. Chocolate (24.3.54)	2·00	1·00
57		5 c. bright purple (1.9.52)	25	30
		a. Bright mauve (10.9.53)	25	15
58		6 c. grey	15	10
59		8 c. scarlet	20	1·00
60		8 c. green (1.9.52)	85	75
61		10 c. magenta	15	10
62		12 c. scarlet (1.9.52)	85	1·25
63		15 c. ultramarine	30	10
64		20 c. black and green	25	1·75
65		20 c. bright blue (1.9.52)	75	10
		a. Ultramarine (8.3.56)	2·25	1·50
66		25 c. purple and orange	20	10
67		30 c. scarlet and brown-purple (5.9.55)	1·25	35
		a. Scarlet and purple (8.3.56)	4·75	1·90
68		35 c. scarlet and purple (1.9.52)	60	25
69		40 c. red and purple	90	6·00
70		50 c. black and blue	40	10
71		$1 blue and purple	2·00	1·10
72		$2 green and scarlet	10·00	17·00
73		$5 green and brown	42·00	38·00
		a. Green and sepia (24.3.54)	50·00	60·00
53/73			Set of 21	55·00	60·00

1953 (2 June). *Coronation. As No. 153 of Jamaica.*

74	10 c. black and reddish purple	20	10

1957 (26 June)–62. *As Nos. 92/102 of Kedah but with inset portrait of Sultan Sir Abu Bakar.*

75	9	1 c. black (21.8.57)	10	10
76	10	2 c. orange-red (25.7.57)	10	10
77	11	4 c. sepia (21.8.57)	10	10
78	12	5 c. carmine-lake (21.8.57)	10	10
79	13	8 c. myrtle-green (21.8.57)	80	80
80	14	10 c. deep brown (4.8.57)	15	10
81		10 c. deep maroon (21.2.61)	1·40	10
82	15	20 c. blue	20	10
83	16	50 c. black and blue (p 12½) (25.7.57)	20	10
		a. Perf 12½ × 13 (17.5.60)	40	10
84	17	$1 ultramarine & reddish pur (25.7.57)	1·50	1·00
85	18	$2 bronze-grn & scar (p 12½) (21.8.57)	3·00	5·50
		a. Perf 13 × 12½ (13.11.62)	4·50	9·00
86	19	$5 brown and bronze-green (p 12½)	6·00	8·50
		a. Perf 13 × 12½ (17.5.60)	9·00	9·00
		b. Perf 13 × 12½. Brown and yellow-olive (23.10.62)	20·00	25·00
75/86			Set of 12	12·00	14·00

The 6, 12, 25 and 30 c. values used with this issue were Nos. 1/4 of Malayan Federation.

17 *Vanda hookeriana*   18 *Precis orithya*

1965 (15 Nov). *As Nos. 166/72 of Johore but with inset portrait of Sultan Sir Abu Bakar as in T 17. W w 13 (upright).*

87		1 c. multicoloured	10	20
		c. Grey (flower name, etc) omitted	20·00	
88		2 c. multicoloured	10	20
89		5 c. multicoloured	10	10
		c. Red (leaves, etc) omitted	22·00	
90		6 c. multicoloured	15	10
91		10 c. multicoloured	15	10
		a. Red omitted	22·00	
92		15 c. multicoloured	80	10
93		20 c. multicoloured	1·40	30
87/93			Set of 7	2·50	90

The 2 c., 5 c. and 6 c. exist with PVA gum as well as gum arabic.
The higher values used with this issue were Nos. 20/27 of Malaysia (National Issues).

1970 (27 May). *As Nos. 87 and 91 but W w 13 (sideways).*

94	17	1 c. multicoloured	30	3·50
95	–	10 c. multicoloured	70	2·50

(*Litho B.W.*)

1971 (1 Feb). *As Nos. 175/81 of Johore but with portrait of Sultan Sir Abu Bakar and arms, as in T 18.*

96	1 c. multicoloured	15	40
97	2 c. multicoloured	40	40
98	5 c. multicoloured	50	10
99	6 c. multicoloured	50	30
100	10 c. multicoloured	50	10
101	15 c. multicoloured	70	10
102	20 c. multicoloured	85	30
96/102		Set of 7	3·25	1·40

The higher values used with this issue were Nos. 64/71 of Malaysia (National Issues).

19 Sultan Haji
Ahmad Shah

20 *Rhododendron scortechinii*

(Des Union Advertising. Litho Harrison)

1975 (8 May). *Installation of the Sultan.* P 14 × 14½.
103	**19**	10 c. slate-green, light lilac and gold			50	40
104		15 c. greenish black, yellow & dp green			60	10
105		50 c. black, light violet-bl & greenish blk			1·75	2·50
103/5				*Set of 3*	2·50	2·75

(Photo Harrison)

1977 (5 Sept)–**78**. *As Nos. 97/8, 100/2 but with portraits of Sultan Haji Ahmad Shah.*
106	2 c. multicoloured (1978)			25·00	25·00
107	5 c. multicoloured			60	40
108	10 c. multicoloured (10.2.78)			80	20
109	15 c. multicoloured (13.1.78)			80	30
	a. Black (face value, etc.)* omitted			60·00	
110	20 c. multicoloured (1978)			3·50	1·75
106/10			*Set of 5*	28·00	25·00

*There were two black cylinders used for No. 109, one to apply the portrait and state details, the other the face value and parts of the main design.

The higher values used with this issue were Nos. 64/71 of Malaysia (National Issues).

1979 (30 Apr). *As Nos. 188/94 of Johore but with portrait of Sultan Haji Ahmad Shah as in T* **20**.
111	1 c. *Rafflesia hasseltii*			10	20
112	2 c. *Pterocarpus indicus*			10	20
113	5 c. *Lagerstroemia speciosa*			10	10
114	10 c. *Durio zibethinus*			10	10
115	15 c. *Hibiscus rosa-sinensis*			15	10
116	20 c. Type **20**			15	10
117	25 c. *Etlingera elatior* (inscr "*Phaeomeria speciosa*")			15	20
111/17			*Set of 7*	65	70

For higher values used in conjunction with this series see Nos. 190/7 of Malaysia (National Issues).

1983 (5 Oct)–**85**.* *As Nos. 113/16 but without wmk.*
120	5 c. *Lagerstroemia speciosa* (17.11.83)			30	30
121	10 c. *Durio zibethinus* (8.1.85)			3·00	1·75
123	20 c. Type **20** (blackish brown background)			6·00	1·25
123a	20 c. Type **20** (bronze-green background) (20.8.84)			30	30

*There was no official release date for these stamps. Dates shown are the earliest recorded from postmarks and may be revised if earlier examples are reported.

On Nos. 120/1 and 123a "pahang" is one millimetre nearer "malaysia" than on Nos. 113/16 and 123.

21 Rice

1986 (25 Oct). *As Nos. 202/8 of Johore but with portrait of Sultan Ahmad Shah as in T* **21**.
125	1 c. Coffee			10	10
126	2 c. Coconuts			10	10
127	5 c. Cocoa			10	10
128	10 c. Black pepper			10	10
129	15 c. Rubber			10	10
130	20 c. Oil Palm			15	20
131	30 c. Type **21**			15	20
125/31			*Set of 7*	40	45

PENANG

One of the Straits Settlements.
Issues from 1965 are inscribed "PULAU PINANG".

1948 (1 Dec). *Royal Silver Wedding. As Nos. 143/4 of Jamaica.*
1	10 c. violet			25	20
2	$5 brown			24·00	24·00

1949 (21 Feb)–**52**. *As T* **58** *of Straits Settlements, but inscr "PENANG" at foot. Wmk Mult Script CA. Chalk-surfaced paper.* P 17½ × 18.
3	1 c. black			10	10
4	2 c. orange			10	10
5	3 c. green			10	15
6	4 c. brown			10	10
7	5 c. bright purple (1.9.52)			40	80
8	6 c. grey			15	10
9	8 c. scarlet			30	2·50
10	8 c. green (1.9.52)			65	1·00
11	10 c. purple			15	10
12	12 c. scarlet (1.9.52)			65	2·25
13	15 c. ultramarine			20	30
14	20 c. black and green			20	1·00
15	20 c. bright blue (1.9.52)			55	15
16	25 c. purple and orange			30	10
17	35 c. scarlet and purple (1.9.52)			60	70
18	40 c. red and purple			55	5·00
19	50 c. black and blue			40	15
20	$1 blue and purple			4·00	30
21	$2 green and scarlet			6·00	60
22	$5 green and brown			32·00	80
3/22			*Set of 20*	42·00	14·00

1949 (10 Oct). *75th Anniv of U.P.U. As Nos. 145/8 of Jamaica.*
23	10 c. purple			15	10
24	15 c. deep blue			35	40
25	25 c. orange			35	50
26	50 c. blue-black			1·00	1·40
23/6			*Set of 4*	1·75	2·10

1953 (2 June). *Coronation. As No. 153 of Jamaica.*
27	10 c. black and reddish purple			30	10

1954 (9 June)–**57**. *As T* **1** *of Malacca (Queen Elizabeth II) but inscr "PENANG" at foot. Chalk-surfaced paper. Wmk Mult Script CA.* P 17½ × 18.
28	1 c. black (5.1.55)			10	20
29	2 c. yellow-orange (8.9.54)			30	30
30	4 c. brown (1.9.54)			20	10
	a. Yellow-brown (17.7.57)			1·50	2·00
31	5 c. bright purple (1.10.54)			1·50	1·00
	a. Bright mauve (17.7.57)			1·50	1·75
32	6 c. grey			15	10
33	8 c. green (5.1.55)			20	1·75
34	10 c. brown-purple (1.9.54)			15	10
35	12 c. rose-red (5.1.55)			30	2·25
36	20 c. bright blue (1.9.54)			40	10
37	25 c. brown-purple & yellow-orange (1.12.54)			30	10
38	30 c. rose-red and brown-purple (5.9.55)			30	10
39	35 c. rose-red and brown-purple (8.9.54)			40	15
40	50 c. black and bright blue (1.12.54)			40	10
41	$1 bright blue and brown-purple (1.10.54)			2·00	10
42	$2 emerald and scarlet (1.10.54)			4·50	2·75
43	$5 emerald and brown (5.1.55)			21·00	3·00
28/43			*Set of 16*	29·00	10·50

1957. *As Nos. 92/102 of Kedah, but with inset portrait of Queen Elizabeth II.*
44	**9**	1 c. black (21.8)			10	20
45	**10**	2 c. orange-red (25.7)			10	30
46	**11**	4 c. sepia (21.8)			10	10
47	**12**	5 c. carmine-lake (21.8)			10	10
48	**13**	8 c. myrtle-green (21.8)			80	70
49	**14**	10 c. deep blue (4.8)			15	10
50	**15**	20 c. blue (26.6)			20	30
51	**16**	50 c. black and blue (25.7)			25	10
52	**17**	$1 ultramarine and reddish purple (25.7)			2·75	25
53	**18**	$2 bronze-green and scarlet (21.8)			3·75	4·50
54	**19**	$5 brown and bronze-green (26.6)			8·50	4·50
44/54				*Set of 11*	15·00	10·00

The note after No. 86 of Pahang also applies here.

1 Copra

2 *Vanda hookeriana*

(Recess D.L.R.)

1960 (15 Mar). *As Nos. 44/54, but with inset Arms of Penang as in T* **1**. W w **12**. P 13 × 12½ (1 c. to 8 c., $2, $5), 12½ × 13 (10 c. to 50 c.) or 13½ ($1).
55	1 c. black			10	15
56	2 c. orange-red			10	20
57	4 c. sepia			10	10
58	5 c. carmine-lake			10	10
59	8 c. myrtle-green			1·50	1·75
60	10 c. deep maroon			15	10
61	20 c. blue			20	10
62	50 c. black and blue			20	10
	a. Imperf (pair)			£275	
63	$1 ultramarine and reddish purple			1·25	20
64	$2 bronze-green and scarlet			2·25	1·50
65	$5 brown and bronze-green			7·00	3·00
55/65			*Set of 11*	11·50	6·50

No. 62a comes from a sheet purchased at the Penang Post Office which had the upper five horizontal rows imperforate.

1965 (15 Nov)–**68**. *As Nos. 166/72 of Johore but with Arms of Penang inset and inscr "PULAU PINANG" as in T* **2**. W w **13** (upright).
66	1 c. multicoloured			10	40
67	2 c. multicoloured			10	40
68	5 c. multicoloured			20	10
	b. Yellow (flower) omitted			15·00	
	c. Red omitted			25·00	
	d. Blue (background and inscr) omitted			30·00	
	da. Blue and yellow omitted			40·00	
69	6 c. multicoloured			20	30
	b. Yellow omitted			18·00	
70	10 c. grey and multicoloured			15	10
	a. Jet-black and multicoloured (12.11.68)			15	10
71	15 c. multicoloured			90	10
	b. Green (value and leaves) omitted			75·00	
72	20 c. multicoloured			1·40	30
	a. Bright purple (blooms) omitted			£100	
	b. Yellow (leaves) omitted			£100	
66/72			*Set of 7*	2·75	1·40

The 2 c., 5 c., 6 c., 10 c. and 20 c. exist with PVA gum as well as gum arabic.

The higher values used with this issue were Nos. 20/27 of Malaysia (National Issues).

1970. *As Nos. 66 and 70 but W w* **13** *(sideways).*
73	**2**	1 c. multicoloured (27.5.70)		30	3·00
74	–	10 c. multicoloured (20.11.70)		4·00	3·50

3 *Valeria valeria*

4 *Etlingera elatior* (inscr "*Phaeomeria speciosa*")

1971 (1 Feb)–**78**. *As Nos. 175/87 of Johore, but with Arms of Penang and inscr "pulau pinang", as in T* **3**.

(a) *Litho by Bradbury Wilkinson*
75	1 c. multicoloured			15	40
76	2 c. multicoloured			40	40
77	5 c. multicoloured			55	10
78	6 c. multicoloured			55	40
79	10 c. multicoloured			55	10
80	15 c. multicoloured			55	10
81	20 c. multicoloured			65	40
75/81			*Set of 7*	3·00	1·60

(b) *Photo by Harrison* (1977–78)
81a	1 c. multicoloured			5·50	5·00
82	5 c. multicoloured			1·25	60
83	10 c. multicoloured			2·25	60
84	15 c. multicoloured			3·75	30
85	20 c. multicoloured			4·00	95
81a/5			*Set of 5*	15·00	6·75

The higher values used with this issue were Nos. 64/71 of Malaysia (National Issues).

For differences between litho and photo printings, see after Johore No. 187.

1979 (30 Apr). *As Nos. 188/94 of Johore but with Arms of Penang and inscr "pulau pinang" as in T* **4**.
86	1 c. *Rafflesia hasseltii*			10	20
87	2 c. *Pterocarpus indicus*			10	20
88	5 c. *Lagerstroemia speciosa*			10	10
89	10 c. *Durio zibethinus*			10	10
90	15 c. *Hibiscus rosa-sinensis*			15	10
91	20 c. *Rhododendron scortechinii*			15	10
92	25 c. Type **4**			15	20
86/92			*Set of 7*	65	50

For higher values used in conjunction with this series see Nos. 190/7 of Malaysia (National Issues).

1983–85.* *As Nos. 88/91 but without wmk.*
95	5 c. *Lagerstroemia speciosa* (1.84)			30	40
96	10 c. *Durio zibethinus* (2.7.85)			6·00	2·00
97	15 c. *Hibiscus rosa-sinensis* (27.12.83)			2·25	60
98	20 c. *Rhododendron scortechinii* (blackish brown background) (21.10.85)			15·00	80
98a	20 c. *Rhododendron scortechinii* (bronze-green background) (3.84)			30	40

*There was no official release date for these stamps. Dates shown are the earliest recorded from postmarks and may be revised if earlier examples are reported.

For details of the shade differences between watermarked and unwatermarked printings see after Johore No. 200a.

On Nos. 95/7 and 98a the state arms are larger than on the watermarked printing and No. 98.

5 Cocoa

1986 (25 Oct). *As Nos. 202/8 of Johore but with Arms of Penang and inscr "PULAU PINANG" as in T* **5**.
100	1 c. Coffee			10	10
101	2 c. Coconuts			10	10
102	5 c. Type **5**			10	10
103	10 c. Black pepper			10	10
104	15 c. Rubber			10	10
105	20 c. Oil palm			10	10
106	30 c. Rice			15	20
100/6			*Set of 7*	40	45

NEW INFORMATION

The editor is always interested to correspond with people who have new information that will improve or correct the Catalogue.

PERAK

Perak accepted a British Resident in 1874, although he was later murdered.
The state joined the Federated Malay States in 1896.

The stamps of the STRAITS SETTLEMENTS were used in Perak during 1877/8.
Until 1 January 1899, when the Federated Malay States joined the U.P.U., mail for addresses outside Malaya was franked with stamps of the STRAITS SETTLEMENTS.

PRICES FOR STAMPS ON COVER TO 1945

No. 1	—
Nos. 2/9	*from* × 60
Nos. 10/13	*from* × 30
Nos. 14/16	*from* × 8
Nos. 17/22	*from* × 20
No. 23	—
Nos. 24/5	—
Nos. 26/8	*from* × 15
No. 29	*from* × 75
No. 30	*from* × 20
Nos. 31/2	—
Nos. 33/40	*from* × 15
Nos. 43/60	*from* × 6
Nos. 61/5	*from* × 20
Nos. 66/79	*from* × 12
No. 80	—
Nos. 81/7	*from* × 8
Nos. 88/102	*from* × 4
Nos. 103/21	*from* × 3

The Official stamps of Perak are rare used on cover.

(1)

1878. *No.* 11 *of Straits Settlements handstamped with T* 1.
1   2 c. brown £950 £850

PERAK **PERAK** **PERAK**
(2)   (3)   (4)
(14½ mm long) (11 mm long) (10¼ mm long)

PERAK PERAK   PERAK
(5)   (6)   (7)
(17 mm long) ("RA" narrow) ("R" narrow)

PERAK   **PERAK**
(8) ("P" and "K"   (9) (12 to 13½ mm
wide)   long)

1880–81. *No.* 11 (*wmk Crown CC*) *of Straits Settlements optd
with T* 2/9.
2	2	2 c. brown	..	..	£450	£250
3	3	2 c. brown	..	..	£425	£225
4	4	2 c. brown	..	..	£225	£180
5	5	2 c. brown (1881)	..	..	25·00	38·00
6	6	2 c. brown (1881)	..	..	80·00	95·00
7	7	2 c. brown (1881)	..	..	70·00	85·00
8	8	2 c. brown (1881)	..	..	£170	£160
9	9	2 c. brown (1881)	..	..	70·00	80·00

Of the above No. 2 is from a single unit overprint, No. 5 from a setting of sixty and the remainder from settings applied as horizontal strips of three. Nos. 6/8 come from mixed triplets, either 6 + 7 + 7 or 7 + 7 + 8. No. 4 is believed to come from a single unit overprint in addition to a triplet.

PERAK   **PERAK**
(10) ("A" wide)   (11) ("E" wide)

1882–83. *Nos.* 50 (*wmk Crown CA*) *and* 63 *of Straits Settlements optd with T* 9/11.
10	9	2 c. brown	..	..	16·00	22·00
		a. Opt double	..	..	£400	
11		2 c. rose (1883)	..	..	9·00	17·00
12	10	2 c. rose (1883)	..	..	13·00	23·00
13	11	2 c. rose (1883)	..	..	13·00	23·00
		a. Opt double	..	..	£450	

The above were all overprinted as triplet settings. Those for the 2 c. rose were 11 + 12 + 13, 13 + 11 + 11 and 13 + 11 + 12.

2 CENTS PERAK   **2 OENTS**
(12)   (13)

1883 (July). *No.* 51 (*wmk Crown CA*) *of Straits Settlements surch.*

(a) *Surch with T* 12

14	2 c. on 4 c. rose	..			£1400
	a. On Straits Settlements No. 12 (wmk Crown CC)	..	..		£7000

(b) *Optd as T* 9 *or* 11 *and surch with T* 13

15	11	2 c. on 4 c. rose	..	..	£500	£350
16	9	2 c. on 4 c. rose	..	..	£350	£225

It is believed that No. 14 occurred on the top row of the sheet with the remaining nine rows surcharged with a triplet containing 15 + 16 + 16.

PERAK   **PERAK**   **PERAK**
(14)   (15)   (16) (12½–
("E" wide)   ("E" narrow)   13 mm long)

PERAK   **PERAK**   **PERAK**
(17) (12–   (18)   (19)
12½ mm long) (10½ mm long) (10 mm long)

PERAK
(20) (13 mm long)

1884–91. *No.* 63 *of Straits Settlements optd with T* 14/20.
17	14	2 c. rose	..	..	80	80
		a. Opt double	..	..	—	£500
		b. Opt inverted	..	..	£275	£400
18	15	2 c. rose	..	..	30·00	32·00
		b. Opt inverted	..	..	£550	£650
19	16	2 c. rose (1886)	..	..	1·00	4·50
		a. Optd "FERAK"	..	..	£160	£225
20	17	2 c. rose (1886)	..	..	3·25	9·50
		a. Opt double	..	..	£1100	
21	18	2 c. rose (1886)	..	..	55·00	70·00
22	19	2 c. rose (1890)	..	..	7·50	21·00
23	20	2 c. rose (1891)	..	..	£1400	

Settings:
Nos. 17/18 – triplets (either 17 + 17 + 17 or 18 + 17 + 17)
– 30 (3 × 10) (containing twenty-eight as No. 17 and two as No. 18)
– 60 (6 × 10) (containing either fifty-seven as No. 17 and three as No. 18 or all as No. 17)
No. 19 – 60 (6 × 10) (No. 19a occurs on one position of the setting, it is often found amended in manuscript)
No. 20 – triplet
No. 21 – triplet
No. 22 – 60 (6 × 10)
No. 23 – not known

1 CENT
(21)

1886. *No.* 17 *surch with T* 21.
24   14   1 c. on 2 c. rose £1300 £1300

ONE CENT PERAK   **ONE CENT PERAK.**   **ONE CENT PERAK.**
(22)   (23)   (24) ("N" wide in "ONE" and "CENT")

1886. *No.* 63 *of Straits Settlements surch with T* 22/4.
25	22	1 c. on 2 c. rose	..	..		£275
26	23	1 c. on 2 c. rose	..	..	30·00	45·00
		a. Surch double	..	..		£500
27	24	1 c. on 2 c. rose	..	..	48·00	65·00

Nos. 26/7 are from a triplet setting, 26 + 27 + 26, used on the top nine rows of the sheet. No. 25 may have been used on the bottom row.

1 CENT PERAK   **One CENT PERAK**   **ONE CENT PERAK**
(25)   (26)   (27)

1886. *No.* 63 *of Straits Settlements surch with T* 25.
28		1 c. on 2 c. rose	..	..	55·00	65·00
		a. Surch double	..	..		£1500

No. 28 comes from a triplet setting.

1886. *No.* 63 *of Straits Settlements surch with T* 26.
29		1 c. on 2 c. rose	..	..	85	4·25
		a. "One" inverted	..	..		£1400
		b. Surch double	..	..		£850

No. 29 comes from a triplet setting. It is believed that No. 29a occurred when the type was dropped and "One" replaced upside down.

1887. *No.* 63 *of Straits Settlements surch with T* 27 *in blue.*
30		1 c. on 2 c. rose	..	..	20·00	26·00
		a. Optd in black	..	..	£1000	£750

No. 30 was printed from a setting of 60.

I   **1**
CENT   **CENT**
PERAK   **PERAK**
(28)   (29)

1887. *No.* 63 *of Straits Settlements surch with T* 28.
31   1 c. on 2 c. rose £250 £275
No. 31 comes from a triplet setting.

1887. *No.* 63 *of Straits Settlements surch with T* 29.
32   1 c. on 2 c. rose £800 £1000
The size of setting used for No. 32 is not known.

One CENT PERAK   **One CENT PERAK**   **One CENT PERAK**   **One CENT PERAK**
(30)   (31)   (32)   (33)

One CENT PERAK   **One CENT PERAK**   **One CENT PERAK**   **One CENT PERAK**
(34)   (35)   (36)   (37)

1887–89. *No.* 63 *of Straits Settlements surch with T* 30/7.
33	30	1 c. on 2 c. rose	..	..	60	1·50
		a. Surch double	..	..		
34	31	1 c. on 2 c. rose (1889)	..	..	70·00	90·00
35	32	1 c. on 2 c. rose (1889)	..	..	7·00	15·00
		a. "PREAK" (R. 6/1)	..	..	£250	£350
36	33	1 c. on 2 c. rose (1889)	..	..	3·50	5·00
37	34	1 c. on 2 c. rose (1889)	..	..	3·50	8·00
38	35	1 c. on 2 c. rose (1889)	..	..	£300	£375
39	36	1 c. on 2 c. rose (1889)	..	..	£130	£160
40	37	1 c. on 2 c. rose (1889)	..	..	9·00	19·00

Settings. No. 33 originally appeared as a triplet, then as a block of 30 (3 × 10) and, finally, as part of a series of composite settings of 60. Specialists recognise four such composite settings:
Setting I contained No. 33 in Rows 1 to 4, R. 5/1 to 5/5 and Row 7; No. 34 on R. 5/6, 6/1 and 6/2; No. 35 on R. 6/3–6; No. 36 on Row 8; No. 37 on Rows 9 and 10.
Setting II was similar, but had the example of No. 33 on R. 3/5 replaced by No. 38 and those on R. 7/4 and R. 7/6 by No. 39.
Setting III contained No. 33 in Rows 1 to 5; No. 35 in Row 6 with the "PREAK" error on the first position; No. 36 in Row 7; No. 37 in Rows 8 and 9; No. 40 in Row 10.
Setting IV was similar, but showed the "PREAK" error on R. 6/1 corrected.

ONE CENT.   **ONE CENT**
(38)   (39)

1889–90. *No.* 17 *surch with T* 38/9.
41	38	1 c. on 2 c. rose	..	..	90·00	90·00
42	39	1 c. on 2 c. rose (1890)	..	..	—	£140

PERAK Two CENTS   **PERAK One CENT**
(40)   (41)

1891. *Nos.* 63, 66 *and* 68 *of Straits Settlements surch.*

(a) *As T* 30, 32/4 *and* 37, *but with* "PERAK" *at top and a bar through the original value*
43	30	1 c. on 6 c. lilac	..	..	30·00	24·00
44	32	1 c. on 6 c. lilac	..	..	85·00	90·00
45	33	1 c. on 6 c. lilac	..	..	85·00	90·00
46	34	1 c. on 6 c. lilac	..	..	50·00	55·00
47	37	1 c. on 6 c. lilac	..	..	85·00	90·00

(b) *With T* 40 *and as T* 32/4 *and* 37 *but with* "PERAK" *at top, all with a bar through the original value*
48	40	2 c. on 24 c. green	..	..	8·50	8·50
49	32	2 c. on 24 c. green	..	..	55·00	50·00
50	33	2 c. on 24 c. green	..	..	55·00	50·00
51	34	2 c. on 24 c. green	..	..	26·00	22·00
52	37	2 c. on 24 c. green	..	..	55·00	50·00

(c) *With T* 41 *and as T* 30, 34 *and* 37, *but with* "PERAK" *at top.*
(i) *Without bar over original value*
53	30	1 c. on 2 c. rose	..	..		£130
		a. Narrow "O" in "One" (R. 3/3)	..		£1200	
54	41	1 c. on 2 c. rose	..	..		£500
55	34	1 c. on 2 c. rose	..	..		£200
56	37	1 c. on 2 c. rose	..	..		£500

(ii) *With bar through original value*
57	30	1 c. on 2 c. rose	..	..	55	2·25
		a. Narrow "O" in "One" (R. 3/3)	..		15·00	32·00
58	41	1 c. on 2 c. rose	..	..	4·00	10·00
59	34	1 c. on 2 c. rose	..	..	85	2·75
60	37	1 c. on 2 c. rose	..	..	4·00	10·00

Settings. Nos. 43/7 were arranged as Setting IV described under Nos. 33/40.
Nos. 48/52 were similar except that Type 40 replaced Type 30 on the first five rows.
The first printing of the 1 c. on 2 c. was without a bar through the original face value. Both printings, Nos. 53/60, were from the same setting with Type 30 on Rows 1 to 5, 41 on Row 6, 34 on Rows 7 to 9 and 37 on Row 10.

3 CENTS

42   (43)

1892 (1 Jan)–**95.** *Wmk Crown CA. P* 14.
61	42	1 c. green	..	..	2·25	15
62		2 c. rose	..	..	1·50	30
63		2 c. orange (9.9.95)	..	..	35	3·25
64		5 c. blue	..	..	2·75	6·50
61/4				*Set of* 4	6·25	9·00
61/4		Optd "Specimen"		*Set of* 4	75·00	

1895 (18 Apr). *Surch with T* 43.
65	42	3 c. on 5 c. rose (Optd S. £25)		60	1·60

44   45

1895 (2 Sept)–**99.** *P* 14. (*a*) *Wmk Crown CA.*
66	44	1 c. dull purple and green	..	..	90	40
67		2 c. dull purple and brown	..	..	75	40
68		3 c. dull purple and carmine	..	..	1·50	20
69		4 c. dull purple and carmine (1899)	..	6·50	4·75
70		5 c. dull purple and olive-yellow	..	2·75	55
71		8 c. dull purple and ultramarine	..	28·00	65
72		10 c. dull purple and orange	..	..	7·00	45
73		25 c. green and carmine (1897)	..	£100	11·00
74		50 c. dull purple and greenish black	..	26·00	27·00
75		50 c. green and black (2.99)	..	£120	£120

(*b*) *Wmk Crown CC*
76	45	$1 green and pale green (1896)	..	65·00	75·00
77		$2 green and carmine (1896)	..	£130	£140
78		$3 green and ochre (1898)	..	£120	£140
79		$5 green and ultramarine (1896)	..	£325	£300
80		$25 green and orange (1899?) (S. £130)	..	£4000	£1200
66/76				*Set of* 11	£325	£200
66/79		Optd "Specimen"	..	*Set of* 14	£225	

Pending the arrival of the permanent Federated Malay States issue the stamps of FEDERATED MALAY STATES provisional overprints, SELANGOR and STRAITS SETTLEMENTS were used at various times between June 1900 and February 1901.

The general issues for the FEDERATED MALAY STATES were used in Perak from 1901 until 1935.

One Cent.	ONE CENT.
(46)	(47)

Three Cent.	Three Cent.
(48)	(49)

1900. *Stamps of 1895–99 surch.*
81	46	1 c. on 2 c. dull purple and brown (13 July*)	40	1·50
		a. Antique "e" in "One" (R. 5/2)	..	42·00	65·00
		b. Antique "e" in "Cent" (R. 9/4)	..	42·00	65·00
82	47	1 c. on 4 c. dull purple and carmine	55	4·00
		a. Surch double			£600
83	46	1 c. on 5 c. dull purple & ol-yell (30 June*)	70	6·00
		a. Antique "e" in "One" (R. 5/2)	..	45·00	£100
		b. Antique "e" in "Cent" (R. 9/4)	..	45·00	£100
84	48	3 c. on 8 c. dull purple & ultram (26 Sept*)	2·50	3·50
		a. Antique "e" in "Cent" (R. 9/4)	..	75·00	85·00
		b. No stop after "Cent" (R. 9/5)	..	75·00	85·00
		c. Surch double		£225	£225
85		3 c. on 50 c. green and black (31 Aug*)	1·00	4·00
		a. Antique "e" in "Cent" (R. 9/4)	..	60·00	90·00
		b. No stop after "Cent" (R. 9/5)	..	60·00	90·00
86	49	3 c. on $1 green and pale green (21 Oct*)	50·00	£110
		a. Small "t" in "Cent"	..	£250	£375
		b. Surch double			
87		3 c. on $2 green and carmine (24 Oct*)	26·00	70·00
81/7				*Set of* 7	70·00	£180

*Earliest known postmark date.

With the exception of No. 86a, whose sheet position is not known, the remaining surcharge varieties all occur in the left-hand pane.

50   Sultan Iskandar   51

1935 (2 Dec)–**37.** *Chalk-surfaced paper. Wmk Mult Script CA.*
P 14.
88	50	1 c. black (1.1.36)	..	..	15	10
89		2 c. green (1.1.36)	..	..	30	10
90		4 c. orange	..	..	30	10
91		5 c. brown (5.12.35)	..	..	30	10
92		6 c. scarlet (1.1.37)	..	6·00	2·50
93		8 c. grey	..	..	40	10
94		10 c. dull purple (1.1.36)	..	..	30	15
95		12 c. bright ultramarine (1.1.36)	..	60	90
96		25 c. dull purple and scarlet (1.4.36)	..	75	85
97		30 c. dull purple and orange (1.1.36)	..	80	1·50
98		40 c. scarlet and dull purple	..	2·25	4·25
99		50 c. black/*emerald* (1.2.36)	..	3·25	80
100		$1 black and red/*blue* (1.4.36)	..	2·00	80
101		$2 green and scarlet (16.5.36)	..	8·50	8·50
102		$5 green and red/*emerald* (16.5.36)	..	40·00	24·00
88/102				*Set of* 15	60·00	40·00
88/102		Perf "Specimen"		*Set of* 15	£150	

No. 91 exists in coils constructed from normal sheets in 1936.

1938 (2 May)–**41.** *Wmk Mult Script CA. Chalk-surfaced paper.*
P 14.
103	51	1 c. black (4.39)	..	..	3·00	10
104		2 c. green (13.1.39)	..	..	2·25	10
105		2 c. orange (30.10.41)	..	..	50	4·75
		a. Ordinary paper	..	..	1·00	9·00
106		3 c. green (21.8.41)	..	..	1·00	85
107		4 c. orange (5.39)	..	..	27·00	10
108		5 c. brown (1.2.39)	..	..	2·00	10
109		6 c. scarlet (12.39)	..	..	18·00	10
110		8 c. grey (1.12.38)	..	..	20·00	10
111		8 c. scarlet (18.12.41)	..	..	1·00	35·00
112		10 c. dull purple (17.10.38)	..	20·00	10
113		12 c. bright ultramarine (17.10.38)	..	14·00	2·00
114		15 c. brt ultram (*ordinary paper*) (8.41)	1·75	13·00
115		25 c. dull purple and scarlet (12.39)	..	70·00	4·25
116		30 c. dull purple and orange (17.10.38)	9·00	3·00
117		40 c. scarlet and dull purple	..	45·00	2·00
118		50 c. black/*emerald* (17.10.38)	..	22·00	75
119		$1 black and red/*blue* (7.40)	..	90·00	14·00
120		$2 green and scarlet (9.40)	..	95·00	50·00
121		$5 green and red/*emerald* (1.41)	..	£170	£190
103/21				*Set of* 19	£550	£275
103/21		Perf "Specimen"	..	*Set of* 19	£250	

No. 108 exists in coils constructed from normal sheets.

During shortages in 1941 stamps of STRAITS SETTLEMENTS (2 c.), SELANGOR (2 c., 3 c.) and PAHANG (8 c.) were issued in Perak.

1948 (1 Dec). *Royal Silver Wedding. As Nos.* 143/4 *of Jamaica.*
122		10 c. violet	..	..	15	10
123		$5 green	..	..	20·00	20·00

1949 (10 Oct). *75th Anniv of U.P.U. As Nos.* 145/8 *of Jamaica.*
124		10 c. purple	..	..	15	10
125		15 c. deep blue	..	..	45	35
126		25 c. orange	..	..	45	45
127		50 c. blue-black	..	..	1·25	1·50
124/7			..	*Set of* 4	2·10	2·10

52 Sultan Yussuf   53 Sultan Idris Shah
'Izzuddin Shah

1950 (17 Aug)–**56.** *Chalk-surfaced paper. Wmk Mult Script*
CA. P 17½×18.
128	52	1 c. black	..	..	10	10
129		2 c. orange	..	..	10	10
130		3 c. green	..	..	85	10
		a. Yellowish green (15.11.51)	..	1·50	2·00
131		4 c. brown	..	..	10	10
		a. Yellow-brown (20.6.56)	..	65	10
132		5 c. bright purple (1.9.52)	..	50	40
		a. Bright mauve (10.11.54)	..	60	30
133		6 c. grey	..	..	10	10
134		8 c. scarlet	..	..	30	75
135		8 c. green (1.9.52)	..	..	1·00	60
136		10 c. purple	..	..	10	10
		a. Brown-purple (20.6.56)	..	90	30
137		12 c. scarlet (1.9.52)	..	..	1·00	80
138		15 c. ultramarine	..	..	30	10
139		20 c. black and green	..	..	30	20
140		20 c. bright blue (1.9.52)	..	75	10
141		25 c. purple and orange	..	..	30	10
142		30 c. scarlet and purple (5.9.55)	..	1·25	20
143		35 c. scarlet and purple (1.9.52)	..	70	25
144		40 c. red and purple	..	..	85	3·00
145		50 c. black and blue	..	..	40	10
146		$1 blue and purple	..	..	4·00	15
147		$2 green and scarlet	..	..	8·00	70
148		$5 green and brown	..	..	30·00	7·50
128/48				*Set of* 21	45·00	13·50

1953 (2 June). *Coronation. As No.* 153 *of Jamaica.*
149		10 c. black and reddish purple	..	30	10

1957 (26 June)–**61.** *As Nos.* 92/102 *of Kedah but with inset portrait of Sultan Yussuf 'Izzuddin Shah.*
150		1 c. black (21.8.57)	..	..	15	10
151		2 c. orange-red (25.7.57)	..	..	20	10
		a. Red-orange (15.12.59)	..	..	30	60
152		4 c. sepia (21.8.57)	..	..	10	10
153		5 c. carmine-lake (21.8.57)	..	10	10
154		8 c. myrtle-green (21.8.57)	..	1·40	60
155		10 c. deep brown (4.8.57)	..	20	10
156		10 c. deep maroon (21.2.61)	..	45	10
157		20 c. blue	..	..	20	10
158		50 c. black and blue (*p* 12½) (25.7.57)	30	10
		a. Perf 12½ × 13 (24.5.60)	..	40	10
159		$1 ultramarine and reddish purple (25.7.57)	2·00	10

160		$2 bronze-green & scar (*p* 12½) (21.8.57)	2·50	1·50
		a. Perf 13 × 12½ (21.2.61)	..	2·50	1·25
161		$5 brown and bronze-green (*p* 12½)	6·50	4·50
		a. Perf 13 × 12½ (24.5.60)	..	6·50	3·00
150/61				*Set of* 12	12·00	4·50

The 6, 12, 25 and 30 c. values used with this issue were Nos. 1/4 of Malayan Federation.

(Photo Harrison)

1963 (26 Oct). *Installation of the Sultan of Perak. W w* 13. *P* 14½.
162	53	10 c. red, black, blue and yellow	..	10	10

54 *Vanda hookeriana*   55 *Delias ninus*

1965 (15 Nov)–**68.** *As Nos.* 166/72 *of Johore but with inset portrait of Sultan Idris as in T* 54. *W w* 13 (*upright*).
163		1 c. multicoloured	..	..	10	30
164		2 c. multicoloured	..	..	10	30
165		5 c. pale black and multicoloured	..	10	10
		a. Grey-black and multicoloured (2.4.68)	10	10
		b. Yellow (flower) omitted	..	18·00	
166		6 c. multicoloured	..	..	15	10
167		10 c. multicoloured	..	..	15	10
168		15 c. multicoloured	..	..	65	10
		a. Black (country name and head) omitted	£110	
		c. Magenta (background) omitted	..	90·00	
169		20 c. multicoloured	..	..	1·00	10
		a. Bright purple (blooms) omitted	..	25·00	
163/9				*Set of* 7	2·00	80

No. 168a comes from a horizontal strip of three, the centre stamp having the black completely omitted. The two outer stamps show the colour partly omitted.

The 2 c. to 15 c. exist with PVA gum as well as gum arabic.

The higher values used with this issue were Nos. 20/27 of Malaysia (National Issues).

1970. *As Nos.* 163 *and* 167, *but W w* 13 (*sideways*).
170	54	1 c. multicoloured (27.5.70)	..	75	3·50
171		10 c. multicoloured (20.11.70)	..	3·25	2·25

1971 (1 Feb)–**78.** *As Nos.* 175/87 *of Johore, but with portrait of Sultan Idris and arms, as in T* 55.

(*a*) *Litho by Bradbury, Wilkinson*
172		1 c. multicoloured	..	..	15	45
173		2 c. multicoloured	..	..	40	50
174		5 c. multicoloured	..	..	50	10
175		6 c. multicoloured	..	..	50	30
176		10 c. multicoloured	..	..	50	10
177		15 c. multicoloured	..	..	70	10
178		20 c. multicoloured	..	..	85	10
172/8				*Set of* 7	3·25	1·50

(*b*) *Photo by Harrison* (1977–78)
179		1 c. multicoloured	..	..	60	2·50
180		5 c. multicoloured	..	..	2·75	65
181		10 c. multicoloured	..	..	2·25	60
182		15 c. multicoloured	..	..	4·50	30
183		20 c. multicoloured	..	..	2·25	10
179/83				*Set of* 5	11·00	4·25

The higher values used with this issue were Nos. 64/71 of Malaysia (National Issues).

For differences between litho and photo printings, see after Johore, No. 187.

56 *Rafflesia hasseltii*   57 Coffee

1979 (30 Apr). *As Nos.* 188/94 *of Johore but with portrait of Sultan Idris as in T* 56.
184		1 c. Type 56	..	..	10	20
185		2 c. *Pterocarpus indicus*	..	..	10	20
186		5 c. *Lagerstroemia speciosa*	..	..	10	10
187		10 c. *Durio zibethinus*	..	..	10	10
188		15 c. *Hibiscus rosa-sinensis*	..	15	10
189		20 c. *Rhododendron scortechinii*	..	15	10
190		25 c. *Etlingera elatior* (inscr "*Phaeomeria speciosa*")	..	..	15	10
184/90				*Set of* 7	65	50

For higher values used in conjunction with this series see Nos. 190/7 of Malaysia (National Issues).

1983 (15 Oct)–**84.*** *As Nos.* 186/9 *but without wmk.*
193		5 c. *Lagerstroemia speciosa* (9.9.83)	..	30	40
194		10 c. *Durio zibenthinus* (1984)	..	30	40
195		15 c. *Hibiscus rosa-sinensis* (9.9.83)	..	3·00	65
196		20 c. *Rhododendron scortechinii* (blackish brown background)	..	5·50	65
196a		20 c. *Rhododendron scortechinii* (bronze-green background) (20.3.84)	..	30	30

*There was no official release date for these stamps. Dates shown are the earliest recorded from postmarks and may be revised if earlier examples are reported.

For details of the shade differences between watermarked and unwatermarked printings see after Johore No. 200a.

On Nos. 193/5 and 196a the portrait and arms are redrawn smaller.

1986 (25 Oct). *As Nos. 202/8 of Johore but with portrait of Sultan Azlan Shah as in T 57.*

198	1 c. Type 57	..	..	..	10	10
199	2 c. Coconuts..		..	..	10	10
200	5 c. Cocoa	..	..	..	10	10
201	10 c. Black pepper	..	..	..	10	10
202	15 c. Rubber	..	..	..	10	10
203	20 c. Oil palm..		..	..	10	10
204	30 c. Rice	..	..	..	15	20
198/204				*Set of* 7	40	45

OFFICIAL STAMPS

P.G.S.   **Service.**
(O 1)   (O 2)

1889 (1 Nov). *Stamps of Straits Settlements optd with Type O 1. Wmk Crown CC (Nos. O6 and O8) or Crown CA (others).*

O1	2 c. rose	..	2·00	2·75
	a. Overprint double..		£750	£750
	b. Wide space between "G" and "S"		35·00	45·00
	c. No stop after "S"..		35·00	45·00
O2	4 c. brown	..	6·50	13·00
	a. Wide space between "G" and "S"		55·00	75·00
	b. No stop after "S"..		80·00	£100
O3	6 c. lilac	..	18·00	28·00
	a. Wide space between "G" and "S"		85·00	£110
O4	8 c. orange	..	22·00	55·00
	a. Wide space between "G" and "S"		£100	£150
O5	10 c. slate	..	65·00	65·00
	a. Wide space between "G" and "S"		£180	£190
O6	12 c. blue (CC)..		£110	£120
	a. Wide space between "G" and "S"		£400	
O7	12 c. brown-purple (CA)		£160	£190
	a. Wide space between "G" and "S"		£550	
O8	24 c. green (CC)	..	£425	£475
	a. Wide space between "G" and "S"		£1400	
O9	24 c. green (CA)	..	£100	£120
	a. Wide space between "G" and "S"		£400	

Nos. O1/9 were overprinted from a setting of 30 (3 × 10). The variety "wide space between G and S" occurs on R. 10/3 and R. 10/6 of the original printing. A later printing of the 2 c. and 4 c. values had this variety corrected, but was without a stop after "S" on R. 10/1 and R. 10/4.

1894 (1 June). *No. 64 optd with Type O 2.*

O10	5 c. blue	..	..	27·00	80
	a. Overprint inverted	..	..	£475	£375

1897. *No. 70 optd with Type O 2.*

O11	5 c. dull purple and olive-yellow	..	..	1·40	35
	a. Overprint double..	..	..	£350	£375

PERLIS

Suzerainty over Perlis was transferred by Thailand to Great Britain in 1909. A British adviser was appointed in 1930. The State joined the Federation of Malaya on 1 February 1948.

> The stamps of THAILAND were used in Perlis at Kangar (Muang Perlis) until 1909. Issues of the FEDERATED MALAY STATES were in use from 10 July 1909 until 1912 and these were replaced by the stamps of KEDAH between 1912 and 1951.

1948 (1 Dec). *Royal Silver Wedding. As Nos. 143/4 of Jamaica.*

1	10 c. violet	..	..	30	1·50
2	$5 brown	..	..	25·00	42·00

1949 (10 Oct). *75th Anniv of U.P.U. As Nos. 145/8 of Jamaica.*

3	10 c. purple	..	..	25	60
4	15 c. deep blue..		..	50	2·00
5	25 c. orange	..	..	55	1·75
6	50 c. blue-black	..	..	90	3·50
3/6			*Set of* 4	2·00	7·00

1 Raja Syed Putra   2 *Vanda hookeriana*

1951 (26 Mar)–**55**. *Chalk-surfaced paper. Wmk Mult Script CA. P 17½ × 18.*

7	1	1 c. black ..		..	10	40
8		2 c. orange	..	..	10	40
9		3 c. green ..		..	40	1·50
10		4 c. brown..		..	30	20
11		5 c. bright purple (1.9.52)	..	30	75
12		6 c. grey	..	..	30	50
13		8 c. scarlet	..	..	45	2·25
14		8 c. green (1.9.52)..		..	75	1·50
15		10 c. purple	..	..	15	20
16		12 c. scarlet (1.9.52)	..	..	75	2·00
17		15 c. ultramarine	..	..	90	1·75
18		20 c. black and green	..	..	70	2·75
19		20 c. bright blue (1.9.52)	..	85	65
20		25 c. purple and orange	..	70	1·00
21		30 c. scarlet and purple (5.9.55)	..	1·75	5·00
22		35 c. scarlet and purple (1.9.52)	..	75	2·50
23		40 c. red and purple	..	1·25	9·50
24		50 c. black and blue	..	1·50	2·25
25		$1 blue and purple	..	3·25	8·00
26		$2 green and scarlet	..	9·50	17·00
27		$5 green and brown	..	45·00	48·00
7/27			*Set of* 21	65·00	95·00

1953 (2 June). *Coronation. As No. 153 of Jamaica.*

28	10 c. black and reddish purple	..	30	2·00

1957 (26 June)–**62**. *As Nos. 92/102 of Kedah but with inset portrait of Raja Syed Putra.*

29	9	1 c. black (21.8.57)	..	10	30
30	10	2 c. orange-red (25.7.57)	..	10	30
31	11	4 c. sepia (21.8.57)	..	10	10
32	12	5 c. carmine-lake (21.8.57)	..	10	10
33	13	8 c. myrtle-green (21.8.57)	..	1·50	80
34	14	10 c. deep brown (4.8.57)..		20	40
35		10 c. deep maroon (14.3.61)	..	1·50	50
36	15	20 c. blue ..		20	60
37	16	50 c. black and blue (p 12½) (25.7.57)		20	75
		a. Perf 12½ × 13 (8.5.62)	..	85	1·00
38	17	$1 ultram & reddish purple (25.7.57)		3·00	3·50
39	18	$2 bronze-green and scarlet (25.7.57)..		3·75	5·00
40	19	$5 brown and bronze-green (21.8.57)	..	6·50	7·50
29/40			*Set of* 12	15·00	17·00

The 6, 12, 25 and 30 c. values used with this issue were Nos. 1/4 of Malayan Federation.

1965 (15 Nov). *As Nos. 166/72 of Johore but with inset portrait of Tunku Bendahara Abu Bakar as in T 2.*

41	1 c. multicoloured	..	..	10	60
42	2 c. multicoloured	..	..	10	70
43	5 c. multicoloured	..	..	15	15
44	6 c. multicoloured	..	..	40	30
45	10 c. multicoloured	..	..	45	15
46	15 c. multicoloured	..	..	75	35
47	20 c. multicoloured	..	..	1·00	85
41/7			*Set of* 7	2·75	2·75

The 6 c. exists with PVA gum as well as gum arabic.
The higher values used with this issue were Nos. 20/27 of Malaysia (National Issues).

3 *Danaus melanippus*   4 Raja Syed Putra

1971 (1 Feb)–**78**. *As Nos. 175/87 of Johore but with portrait of Raja Syed Putra and Arms, as in T 3.*

(a) Litho by Bradbury, Wilkinson

48	1 c. multicoloured	..	..	15	70
49	2 c. multicoloured	..	..	20	80
50	5 c. multicoloured	..	..	55	20
51	6 c. multicoloured	..	..	55	60
52	10 c. multicoloured	..	..	55	20
53	15 c. multicoloured	..	..	55	25
54	20 c. multicoloured	..	..	65	90
48/54			*Set of* 7	3·00	3·25

(b) Photo by Harrison (1977–78)

54a	10 c. multicoloured				
55	15 c. multicoloured	..	..	4·00	1·50
55a	20 c. multicoloured	..	..	13·00	15·00

The higher values used with this issue were Nos. 64/71 of Malaysia (National Issues).
For differences between litho and photo printings, see after Johore No. 187.

(Des Citizen Studio and Engravers. Litho Enschedé)

1971 (28 Mar). *25th Anniv of Installation of Raja Syed Putra. P 13½ × 13.*

56	4	10 c. multicoloured	..	20	60
57		15 c. multicoloured	..	20	35
58		50 c. multicoloured	..	70	2·00
56/8			*Set of* 3	1·00	2·75

5 *Pterocarpus indicus*   6 Coconuts

1979 (30 Apr). *As Nos. 188/94 of Johore but with portrait of Raja Syed Putra as in T 5.*

59	1 c. *Rafflesia hasseltii*	..	..	10	30
60	2 c. Type 5	..	..	10	30
61	5 c. *Lagerstroemia speciosa*	..	10	10
62	10 c. *Durio zibethinus*	..	..	10	10
63	15 c. *Hibiscus rosa-sinensis*	..	15	10
64	20 c. *Rhododendron scortechinii*	..	15	10
65	25 c. *Etlingera elatior* (inscr "Phaeomeria speciosa")	..	..	15	30
59/65			*Set of* 7	65	1·10

For higher values used in conjunction with this series see Nos. 190/7 of Malaysia (National Issues).

1983–84*. *As No. 64 but without wmk.*

71	20 c. *Rhododendron scortechinii* (blackish brown background)	..	7·50	4·25
71a	20 c. *Rhododendron scortechinii* (bronze-green background) (4.12.84)	..	1·75	1·75

*There was no official release date for these stamps. Dates shown are the earliest recorded from postmarks and may be revised if earlier examples are reported.
For details of the shade differences between watermarked and unwatermarked printings see after Johore No. 200a.
No. 71a shows the Sultan's head larger than on Nos. 64 and 71 and has "perlis" in rounded, instead of square-ended, letters.

1986 (25 Oct). *As Nos. 202/8 of Johore but with portrait of Raja Syed Putra as in T 6.*

73	1 c. Coffee	..	..	10	10
74	2 c. Type 6	..	..	10	10
75	5 c. Cocoa	..	..	10	10
76	10 c. Black pepper	..	..	10	10
77	15 c. Rubber	..	..	10	10
78	20 c. Oil palm	..	..	10	10
79	30 c. Rice	..	..	15	20
73/9			*Set of* 7	40	45

SELANGOR

The first British Resident was appointed in 1874. Selangor joined the Federated Malay States in 1896.

> The stamps of the STRAITS SETTLEMENTS were used in Selangor from 1879 until 1881.
> Until 1 January 1899, when the Federated Malay States joined the U.P.U., mail for addresses outside Malaya was franked with stamps of the STRAITS SETTLEMENTS.

PRICES FOR STAMPS ON COVER TO 1945

Nos. 1/8	—
Nos. 9/19	from × 10
Nos. 20/30	from × 12
Nos. 31/3	from × 25
Nos. 34/6	from × 20
Nos. 37/8	from × 15
Nos. 38a/40	
Nos. 41/2	from × 8
No. 43	—
Nos. 44/8	from × 8
Nos. 49/53	from × 30
Nos. 54/66	from × 10
Nos. 66a/7	from × 4
Nos. 68/85	from × 3
Nos. 86/7	from × 4

The Straits Settlements 1867 2 c. brown with Crown CC watermark (No. 11) has been known since 1881 overprinted in black with a crescent and star over a capital S, all within an oval, similar in style to the overprints listed for Perak and Sungei Ujong.

The status of this item remains unclear, but it may well represent the first issue of distinctive stamps for Selangor. This overprint should not be confused with a somewhat similar cancellation used on Selangor stamps of the same period. This cancellation differs in having a circular frame with the capital S shown above the crescent and star. It is usually struck in red.

A similar overprint in red on the Straits Settlements 2 c. brown with Crown CA watermark is known to be bogus.

SELANGOR (1) ("S" inverted and narrow letters)
SELANGOR (2) ("S" wide)
SELANGOR (3) (narrow letters)

SELANGOR (4) ("N" wide)
SELANGOR (5) ("SE" and "AN" wide)
SELANGOR (6) ("SEL" and "N" wide)

SELANGOR (7) ("SELAN" wide)

1881–82. *No. 11 (wmk Crown CC) of Straits Settlements optd with T 1/7.*

1	1	2 c. brown				£180	£200
2	2	2 c. brown				75·00	85·00
3	3	2 c. brown				55·00	60·00
4	4	2 c. brown				—	£1800
5	5	2 c. brown (1882)				90·00	£100
6	6	2 c. brown (1882)				90·00	£100
7	7	2 c. brown (1882)				90·00	£100

Nos. 1/3 and 5/7 have been identified as coming from triplet settings, either Nos. 1 + 2 + 3, 2 + 3 + 3 or 5 + 6 + 7. The setting for No. 4 is unknown.

S.

(8)

1882. *No. 50 (wmk Crown CA) of Straits Settlements optd with T 8.*

8	8	2 c. brown				—	£1300

SELANGOR (9) ("SEL" and "NG" wide)
SELANGOR (10) ("E" and "ANG" wide)
SELANGOR (11) ("ELANG" wide)

SELANGOR (12) ("S" and "L" wide)
SELANGOR (13) ("S" and "A" wide)
SELANGOR (14) ("E" wide)

SELANGOR (15) ("EL" wide)
SELANGOR (16) ("SE" and "N" wide)
SELANGOR (17) ("S" and "N" wide)

1882–83. *No. 50 (wmk Crown CA) of Straits Settlements optd with T 2/3 and 9/17.*

9	9	2 c. brown				85·00	85·00
10	10	2 c. brown				85·00	85·00
11	11	2 c. brown				85·00	85·00
12	2	2 c. brown (1883)				65·00	60·00
13	3	2 c. brown (1883)				£100	60·00
14	12	2 c. brown (1883)				—	£1400
15	13	2 c. brown (1883)				£200	£170
16	14	2 c. brown (1883)				£110	£100
17	15	2 c. brown (1883)				£110	£100
18	16	2 c. brown (1883)				65·00	65·00
19	17	2 c. brown (1883)				65·00	65·00

The above were all printed from triplet settings. Those so far identified are Nos. 9 + 10 + 11, 12 (with defective "G") + 13 + 13, 15 + 16 + 17 and 18 + 12 + 19. No. 14 occurs as the first position of a triplet, but the second and third units are not yet known.

SELANGOR (18) ("E" and "A" wide)
SELANGOR (19) ("A" wide)
SELANGOR (20) ("L" wide)

SELANGOR (21) ("L" narrow)
SELANGOR (22) ("A" narrow)
SELANGOR (23) (wide letters)

1883–85. *No. 63 of Straits Settlements optd with T 2, 4, 12, 14/15 and 18/23.*

20	12	2 c. rose				80·00	80·00
21	14	2 c. rose				60·00	60·00
		a. Opt double					
22	4	2 c. rose (1884)				95·00	95·00
23	15	2 c. rose (1884)				60·00	60·00
		a. Opt double					
		b. Opt triple					
24	2	2 c. rose (1884)				65·00	65·00
25	18	2 c. rose (1884)				65·00	65·00
26	19	2 c. rose (1884)				£130	£100
27	20	2 c. rose (1884)				£180	£130
28	21	2 c. rose (1885)				55·00	60·00
29	22	2 c. rose (1885)				75·00	85·00
30	23	2 c. rose (1885)				£130	£110

The above come from triplet settings with Nos. 20 + 21 + 21, 22 + 22 + 23, 23 + 26 (with defective "A") + 26, 24 + 25 + 23 and 28 + 29 + 28 so far identified. The triplets for Nos. 27 and 30 are not known.

SELANGOR (24)
Selangor (25)
SELANGOR (26)

SELANGOR (27)
SELANGOR (28)
SELANGOR (29)
SELANGOR (30)

SELANGOR (31)
SELANGOR (32)
SELANGOR (33)
SELANGOR (34)

1885–91. *No. 63 of Straits Settlements optd with T 24/34.*

31	24	2 c. rose				4·50	8·50
		a. Opt double				—	£650
32	25	2 c. rose				£650	£700
33	26	2 c. rose				14·00	20·00
34	27	2 c. rose (1886)				32·00	32·00
		a. Opt double				†	£600
35	28	2 c. rose (horiz opt without stop) (1887)			3·25	2·25
36		2 c. rose (horiz opt with stop) (1887)			25·00	25·00
37	29	2 c. rose (1889)				£120	70·00
38	30	2 c. rose (vert opt) (1889)				38·00	6·00
38a		2 c. rose (horiz opt) (1889)				£3000	
39	31	2 c. rose (diagonal opt) (1889)				£1000	
40	32	2 c. rose (1889)				£200	22·00
41	28	2 c. rose (vert opt without stop) (1890)		10·00	15·00
42	33	2 c. rose (1890)				75·00	2·50
43	34	2 c. rose (1891)				£225	£160

Settings:
Nos. 31/4 – each in triplet containing three examples of the same stamp
No. 35 – triplet or 60 (6 × 10)
No. 36 – 60 (6 × 10)
Nos. 37/8 – 60 (6 × 10) containing both overprints in an unknown combination, but with No. 38 predominating
No. 38a/9 – not known
Nos. 40/3 – each in 60 (6 × 10)

SELANGOR Two CENTS (35)
SELANGOR Two CENTS (36)
SELANGOR Two CENTS (37)

SELANGOR Two CENTS (38)
SELANGOR Two CENTS (39)

1891. *No. 68 of Straits Settlements, surch with T 35/9, each with bar obliterating old value.*

44	35	2 c. on 24 c. green				13·00	35·00
45	36	2 c. on 24 c. green				90·00	£140
46	37	2 c. on 24 c. green				90·00	£140
47	38	2 c. on 24 c. green				55·00	90·00
		a. "SELANGCR"					
48	39	2 c. on 24 c. green				90·00	£140

Nos. 44/8 come from the one setting used to surcharge the panes of sixty. No. 44 occurs in rows 1 to 5, No. 45 on row 6, No. 46 on row 7, No. 47 on rows 8 and 9, and No. 48 on row 10.
The error, No. 47a, occurs in the first printing only and is No. 45 (R.8/3) on the pane.

3 CENTS

40 (41)

1891 (Nov)–95. *Wmk Crown CA. P 14.*

49	40	1 c. green (1893)				70	25
50		2 c. rose				2·75	55
51		2 c. orange (1895)				1·00	50
52		5 c. blue (1892)				11·00	4·00
49/52				Set of 4	14·00	4·75
49/52	Optd "Specimen"			Set of 4	70·00	

1894. *Surch with T 41.*

53	40	3 c. on 5 c. rose (Optd S. £30)			1·00	30

42 43

SELANGOR

Dented frame above "A" of "SELANGOR" (left pane R. 4/5)

1895–99. *Wmk Crown CA or Crown CC (dollar values). P 14.*

54	42	3 c. dull purple and carmine			4·75	20
55		5 c. dull purple and olive-yellow		1·25	30
56		8 c. dull purple and ultramarine (1898)	55·00	7·00
57		10 c. dull purple and orange		6·50	60
58		25 c. green and carmine (1896)		65·00	38·00
59		50 c. dull purple and greenish black (1896)	23·00	16·00
		a. Dented frame				£200	
60		50 c. green and black (1898)		£160	85·00
		a. Dented frame				£200	
61	43	$1 green and yellow-green		35·00	55·00
62		$2 green and carmine (1897)		£100	£100
63		$3 green and ochre (1897)		£225	£100
64		$5 green and blue			£100	£140
65		$10 green and purple (1899) (S. £90)	£275	£300
66		$25 green and orange (1899?) (S. £170)	£1300	
54/62				Set of 9	£400	£275
54/64	Optd "Specimen"			Set of 11	£190	

> Pending the arrival of the permanent Federated Malay States issue the stamps of STRAITS SETTLEMENTS and PERAK were used at various times between July 1900 and March 1901.
> The general issues for the FEDERATED MALAY STATES were used in Selangor from 1901 until 1935.

One cent. (44)
Three cents. (45)

1900 (Oct). *Nos. 55 and 59 surch with T 44 or 45.*

66a	42	1 c. on 5 c. dull purple & ol-yell (31 Oct*)	55·00	75·00
66b		1 c. on 50 c. green and black (22 Oct*)	90	15·00
		bc. "cent" repeated at left		£1200	
		bd. Dented frame			50·00	
67		5 c. on 50 c. green and black (30 Oct*)	6·00	16·00
		a. Antique "t" in "cents"		£110	£180
		b. Dented frame			£150	

*Earliest known postmark date.

It is believed that these stamps were surcharged from settings of 30, repeated four times to complete the sheet of 120.
No. 66bc occurred on two separate vertical strips of five stamps where two impressions of the setting overlapped.
The position in the setting of No. 67a is not known.

46 Mosque at Palace, Klang   47 Sultan Suleiman

(Des E. J. McNaughton)

1935 (2 Dec)–41. *Wmk Mult Script CA (sideways on T 46). Chalk-surfaced paper. P 14 or 14×14½ (No. 70).*

68	46	1 c. black (1.1.36)			20	10
69		2 c. green (1.1.36)			40	10
70		2 c. orange (ordinary paper) (p 14×14½) (21.8.41)	60	1·10
		a. Perf 14. Ordinary paper (9.41)	14·00	4·00
		ab. Chalk-surfaced paper		14·00	4·00
71		3 c. green (21.8.41)			5·00	2·75
		a. Ordinary paper			50	4·50
72		4 c. orange			30	10
73		5 c. brown (5.12.35)			40	10
74		6 c. scarlet (1.1.37)			3·75	10

75	46	8 c. grey	40	10
76		10 c. dull purple (1.1.36) ..	40	10
77		12 c. bright ultramarine (1.1.36)	1·50	10
78		15 c. brt ultram (*ordinary paper*) (1.10.41)	4·50	24·00
79		25 c. dull purple and scarlet (1.4.36)	1·50	60
80		30 c. dull purple and orange (1.1.36)	1·25	85
81		40 c. scarlet and dull purple ..	1·75	1·25
82		50 c. black/*emerald* (1.2.36) ..	1·50	15
83	47	$1 black and rose/*blue* (1.4.36) ..	4·00	40
84		$2 green and scarlet (16.5.36) ..	16·00	7·00
85		$5 green and red/*emerald* (16.5.36)	48·00	23·00
68/85		*Set of 18*	80·00	55·00
68/85		Perf "Specimen" *Set of 18*	£250	

Supplies of an unissued 8 c. scarlet were diverted to Australia in 1941. Examples circulating result from leakages of this supply.

48 Sultan Hisamud-din Alam Shah **49**

1941. *Wmk Mult Script CA. Chalk-surfaced paper.* P 14.

86	48	$1 black and red/*blue* (15.4.41) ..	8·00	5·00
87		$2 green and scarlet (7.7.41) (Perf S. £70)	45·00	27·00

A $5 green and red on emerald, T **48**, was issued overprinted during the Japanese occupation of Malaya. Unoverprinted examples are known, but were not issued (*Price £75*).

During shortages in 1941 stamps of STRAITS SETTLE-MENTS (2 c.) and PERAK (25 c.) were issued in Selangor.

1948 (1 Dec). *Royal Silver Wedding. As Nos. 143/4 of Jamaica.*

88		10 c. violet	20	10
89		$5 green	23·00	14·00

1949 (12 Sept)–**55.** *Wmk Mult Script CA. Chalk-surfaced paper.* P 17½×18.

90	49	1 c. black	10	10
91		2 c. orange	10	10
92		3 c. green	20	65
93		4 c. brown	10	10
94		5 c. bright purple (1.9.52) ..	30	50
		a. Bright mauve (17.9.53)	30	10
95		6 c. grey	10	10
96		8 c. scarlet	25	65
97		8 c. green (1.9.52)	65	50
98		10 c. purple	10	10
99		12 c. scarlet (1.9.52)	80	1·25
100		15 c. ultramarine	35	10
101		20 c. black and green ..	30	10
102		20 c. bright blue (1.9.52) ..	80	10
103		25 c. purple and orange ..	30	10
104		30 c. scarlet and purple (5.9.55)	1·25	50
105		35 c. scarlet and purple (1.9.52)	70	80
106		40 c. scarlet and purple ..	1·50	2·00
107		50 c. black and blue	50	10
108		$1 blue and purple	2·00	10
109		$2 green and scarlet	5·00	15
110		$5 green and brown	35·00	80
90/110		*Set of 21*	45·00	7·00

1949 (10 Oct). *75th Anniv of U.P.U. As Nos. 145/8 of Jamaica.*

111		10 c. purple	15	10
112		15 c. deep blue	45	45
113		25 c. orange	50	90
114		50 c. blue-black	1·10	80
111/14		*Set of 4*	2·00	2·00

1953 (2 June). *Coronation. As No. 153 of Jamaica.*

115		10 c. black and reddish purple ..	30	10

1957 (26 June)–**61.** *As Nos. 92/102 of Kedah but with inset portrait of Sultan Hisamud-din Alam Shah.*

116		1 c. black (21.8.57) ..	10	40
117		2 c. orange-red (25.7.57) ..	10	30
		a. Red-orange (10.11.59) ..	1·25	2·00
118		4 c. sepia (21.8.57) ..	10	10
119		5 c. carmine-lake (21.8.57) ..	10	10
120		8 c. myrtle-green (21.8.57) ..	1·10	25
121		10 c. deep brown (4.8.57) ..	15	10
122		10 c. deep maroon (9.5.61) ..	1·75	10
123		20 c. blue	25	10
124		50 c. black and blue (p 12½) (25.7.57)	25	10
		a. Perf 12½ × 13 (10.5.60) ..	25	10
125		$1 ultramarine and reddish purple (25.7.57)	1·25	10
126		$2 bronze-green & scarlet (p 12½) (21.8.57)	2·25	85
		a. Perf 13 × 12½ (6.12.60) ..	2·00	1·60
127		$5 brown and bronze-green (p 12½)	6·50	1·50
		a. Perf 13 × 12½ (10.5.60) ..	4·25	1·00
116/27a		*Set of 12*	9·00	2·50

The 6, 12, 25 and 30 c. values used with this issue were Nos. 1/4 of Malayan Federation.

50 Sultan Salahuddin Abdul Aziz Shah **51**

(*Photo Harrison*)

1961 (28 June). *Coronation of the Sultan.* W w **12.** P 15×14.

128	50	10 c. multicoloured	10	10
		a. Black ptg misplaced ..	£130	

No. 128a is "The Double-headed Sultan" error, from one sheet where the majority of the stamps showed considerable black printing misplacement.

1961–62. *As Nos. 92/8 of Kedah but with inset portrait of Sultan Salahuddin Abdul Aziz as in T* **51**. W w **13.** *P 12½×13 (vert) or 13×12½ (horiz).*

129		1 c. black (1.3.62)	10	30
130		2 c. orange-red (1.3.62) ..	10	10
131		4 c. sepia (1.3.62)	10	10
132		5 c. carmine-lake (1.3.62) ..	10	10
133		8 c. myrtle-green (1.3.62) ..	1·00	1·25
134		10 c. deep maroon (1.11.61) ..	20	10
135		20 c. blue (1.3.62)	60	10
129/35		*Set of 7*	1·75	2·00

52 *Vanda hookeriana* **53** *Parthenos sylvia*

1965 (15 Nov). *As Nos. 166/72 of Johore but with inset portrait of Sultan Salahuddin Abdul Aziz Shah as in T* **52.**

136		1 c. multicoloured	10	10
		b. Magenta omitted ..	30·00	
137		2 c. multicoloured	10	30
		b. Yellow (flower) omitted ..	18·00	
138		5 c. multicoloured	15	10
		b. Yellow (flower) omitted ..	16·00	
		c. Red (leaves, etc) omitted ..	25·00	
139		6 c. multicoloured	15	10
140		10 c. multicoloured	15	10
		a. Red omitted	28·00	
141		15 c. multicoloured	1·00	10
		b. Green (value and leaves) omitted	£100	
142		20 c. multicoloured	1·40	15
		a. Bright purple (blooms) omitted	30·00	
		b. Yellow (leaves) omitted ..	18·00	
136/42		*Set of 7*	2·75	60

The 2 c. to 20 c. values exist with PVA gum as well as gum arabic. The higher values used with this issue were Nos. 20/27 of Malaysia (National Issues).

1970 (20 Nov). *As Nos. 136 etc. but W w* **13** *(sideways).*

143	52	1 c. multicoloured	70	2·75
144		10 c. multicoloured	2·50	40
145		20 c. multicoloured	4·00	3·00
143/5		*Set of 3*	6·50	5·50

1971 (1 Feb)–**78.** *As Nos. 175/87 of Johore but with portrait of Sultan Salahuddin Abdul Aziz Shah and Arms, as in T* **53.**

(*a*) *Litho by Bradbury, Wilkinson*

146		1 c. multicoloured	15	40
147		2 c. multicoloured	40	50
148		5 c. multicoloured	50	50
149		6 c. multicoloured	50	30
150		10 c. multicoloured	50	10
		a. Black (state inscr, portrait and arms) omitted	60·00	
151		15 c. multicoloured	55	10
152		20 c. multicoloured	90	30
146/52		*Set of 7*	3·25	1·50

(*b*) *Photo by Harrison* (1977–78)

153		1 c. multicoloured	60	2·50
154		5 c. multicoloured	3·00	50
155		10 c. multicoloured	3·75	70
156		15 c. multicoloured	3·75	30
157		20 c. multicoloured	3·25	10
153/7		*Set of 5*	13·00	4·25

The higher values used with this issue were Nos. 64/71 of Malaysia (National Issues).

For differences between litho and photo printings see after Johore No. 187.

A used example of No. 150 has been seen with the magenta apparently missing.

For explanation of No. 150a, see note below No. 122 of Kelantan.

54 *Lagerstroemia speciosa* **55** Sultan Salahuddin Abdul Aziz Shah and Royal Crest

1979 (30 Apr). *As Nos. 188/94 of Johore but with portrait of Sultan Salahuddin Abdul Aziz Shah as in T* **54.**

158		1 c. *Rafflesia hasseltii* ..	10	20
159		2 c. *Pterocarpus indicus* ..	10	20
160		5 c. Type 54	10	10
161		10 c. *Durio zibethinus* ..	10	10
162		15 c. *Hibiscus rosa-sinensis* ..	15	10
163		20 c. *Rhododendron scortechinii* ..	15	10
164		25 c. *Etlingera elatior* (inscr "*Phaeomeria speciosa*")	15	10
158/64		*Set of 7*	65	50

For higher values used in conjunction with this series see Nos. 190/7 of Malaysia (National Issues).

1983 (6 Oct)–**85.*** *As Nos. 160/3 but without wmk.*

166		5 c. Type 54 (20.11.83) ..	30	40
167		10 c. *Durio zibethinus* (3.85) ..	2·50	1·40
168		15 c. *Hibiscus rosa-sinensis* (20.11.83)	2·50	60
169		20 c. *Rhododendron scortechinii* (blackish brown background)	5·50	90
169a		20 c. *Rhododendron scortechinii* (bronze-green background) (12.12.83) ..	60	55

*There was no official release date for these stamps. Dates shown are the earliest recorded from postmarks and may be revised if earlier examples are reported.

For details of the shade differences between watermarked and unwatermarked printings see after Johore No. 200a.

On Nos. 166/8 and 169a the ruler's headdress is bolder than on Nos. 160/3 and 169.

(Des P. Ket. Litho Security Printers (M), Malaysia)

1985 (5 Sept). *Silver Jubilee of Sultan.* P 13.

173	55	15 c. multicoloured	70	10
174		20 c. multicoloured	85	15
175		$1 multicoloured	2·50	3·00
173/5		*Set of 3*	3·50	3·00

56 Black Pepper

1986 (25 Oct). *As Nos. 202/8 of Johore but with portrait of Sultan Salahuddin Abdul Aziz Shah as in T* **56.**

176		1 c. Coffee	10	10
177		2 c. Coconuts	10	10
178		5 c. Cocoa	10	10
179		10 c. Type 56	10	10
180		15 c. Rubber	10	10
181		20 c. Oil palm	10	10
182		30 c. Rice	15	20
176/82		*Set of 7*	40	45

TRENGGANU

Suzerainty over Trengganu was transferred by Thailand to Great Britain in 1909. A British adviser was appointed in 1919. The state joined the Federation of Malaya on 1 February 1948.

PRICES FOR STAMPS ON COVER TO 1945

Nos. 1/17	from × 12
No. 18	—
Nos. 19/22	from × 10
Nos. 23/33	from × 12
Nos. 34/6	—
Nos. 37/47	from × 15
Nos. 48/60	from × 6
Nos. D1/4	—

RED CROSS

2c.

1	Sultan Zain ul ab din	2	(3)

1910 (14 Dec)–**19**. *Wmk Mult Crown CA. Ordinary paper (1 c. to 10 c.) or chalk-surfaced paper (20 c. to $25). P 14.*
1	1	1 c. blue-green	..	..	50	1·00
		a. Green	..	..	95	1·00
2		2 c. brown and purple (1915)	..	40	90
3		3 c. carmine-red	..	..	1·75	1·50
4		4 c. orange	..	..	3·00	5·00
5		4 c. red-brown and green (1915)	..	2·00	3·75
5a		4 c. carmine-red (1919)	..	60	1·75
6		5 c. grey	..	..	1·25	2·25
7		5 c. grey and brown (1915)	..	2·25	2·00
8		8 c. ultramarine	..	..	1·25	6·00
9		10 c. purple/yellow	..	5·00	8·00
		a. On pale yellow	..	3·00	1·75
10		10 c. green and red/yellow (1915)	..	1·00	2·25
11		20 c. dull and bright purple	..	2·50	3·25
12		25 c. green and dull purple (1915)	5·00	20·00
13		30 c. dull purple and black (1915)	6·50	30·00
14		50 c. black/green	..	4·50	5·50
15		$1 black and carmine/blue	..	9·50	16·00
16		$3 green and red/green (1915)	70·00	£140
17	2	$5 green and dull purple (1912)	90·00	£275
18		$25 rose-carmine and green (1912) (Optd S. £150)		£650
1/17			..	Set of 18	£180	£450
1/17 Optd "Specimen"			Set of 18	£375

The 8 c. is known used bisected at Kretai in December 1918. Such use was not officially authorised.

1917 (June)–**18**. *Surch with T 3.*
19	1	2 c. on 3 c. carmine-red	..	30	2·50
		a. Comma after "2 c."	..	5·00	20·00
		b. "SS" in "CROSS" inverted	..	£200	£225
		c. "CSOSS" for "CROSS"	..	60·00	£100
		d. "2" in thick block type	..	17·00	42·00
		e. Surch inverted	..	£600	£650
		f. Pair, one without surch	£2000	£1800
		g. "RED CROSS" omitted	..	£120
		h. "RED CROSS" twice	..	£200
		i. "2 c." omitted	..	£120
		j. "2 c." twice	..	£180
20		2 c. on 4 c. orange	..	70	11·00
		a. Comma after "2 c."	..	15·00	50·00
		b. "SS" in "CROSS" inverted	£1000	£650
		c. "CSOSS" for "CROSS"	..	£130	£200
		d. Surch double	..	£500
		e. "RED CROSS" omitted	..	£190
		f. "RED CROSS" twice	..	£325
		g. "2 c." omitted	..	£190
		h. "2 c." twice	..	£275
21		2 c. on 4 c. red-brown and green (1918)	1·10	22·00
		a. Pair, one without surch	..	£1300
22		2 c. on 8 c. ultramarine (1917)	..	50	2·00
		a. Comma after "2 c."	..	11·00	70·00
		b. "SS" in "CROSS" inverted	..	£600
		c. "CSOSS" for "CROSS"	..	£100	£200
		d. "RED CROSS" omitted	..	£180
		e. "RED CROSS" twice	..	£300
		f. "2 c." omitted	..	£180
		g. "2 c." twice	..	£275

The surcharges on Nos. 19/22 were arranged in settings of 18 (6×3) applied three times to cover the top nine rows of the sheet with the tenth row completed by a further impression so that "RED CROSS" from the centre row of the setting appears on the bottom sheet margin. Specialists recognise six different settings:
Setting I — Shows comma after "2" on both R.1/3 and 1/5, "SS" inverted on R.1/6 and "CSOSS" for "CROSS" on R.2/1. Used for 4 c. orange and 8 c.
Setting Ia — Inverted "SS" on R.1/6 corrected. Other varieties as Setting I. Used for 3 c., 4 c. orange and 8 c.
Setting II — "CSOSS" on R.2/1 corrected. Comma varieties as Setting I. Used for 3 c., 4 c. orange and 8 c.
Setting III — Both comma varieties now corrected. Used for 3 c., both 4 c. and 8 c.
Setting IIIa — "SS" inverted on R.2/5. Used for 3 c. only.
Setting IV — Thick block "2" on R. 2/2. Inverted "SS" on R. 2/5 corrected. Used for 3 c. only.
Nos. 19g/j, 20e/h and 22d/g result from the misplacement of the surcharge.

MINIMUM PRICE

The minimum price quote is 10p which represents a handling charge rather than a basis for valuing common stamps. For further notes about prices see introductory pages.

During a temporary shortage between March and August 1921 2 c., 4 c. and 6 c. stamps of the STRAITS SETTLEMENTS were authorised for use in Trengganu.

2 CENTS

4	Sultan Suleiman	5	(6)

1921. *Chalk-surfaced paper. P 14. (a) Wmk Mult Crown CA.*
23	4	$1 purple and blue/blue	..	11·00	15·00
24		$3 green and red/emerald	..	60·00	£120
25	5	$5 green and red/pale yellow	..	65·00	£150

(b) Wmk Mult Script CA
26	4	2 c. green	..	..	1·00	40
27		4 c. rose-red	..	..	1·00	20
		a. Scarlet-vermilion	..		
28		5 c. grey and deep brown	..	2·00	2·50
29		10 c. bright blue	..	2·00	20
30		20 c. dull orange	..	2·00	1·50
31		25 c. green and deep purple	..	2·25	2·00
32		30 c. dull purple and black	..	3·25	1·00
33		50 c. green and bright carmine	..	4·75	1·00
34	5	$25 purple and blue (S. £70)	..	£450	£600
35		$50 green and yellow (S. £150)	£1000	£1400
36		$100 green and scarlet (S. £300)	..	£3500
23/33			..	Set of 11	£130	£250
23/33 Optd "Specimen"			Set of 11	£250

1922 (31 Mar). *Optd "MALAYA–BORNEO EXHIBITION" as T 56 of Straits Settlements at Singapore.*
37	4	2 c. green	..	75	24·00
38		4 c. rose-red	..	3·50	24·00
39	1	5 c. grey and brown	..	2·50	25·00
40		10 c. green and red/yellow	..	2·50	30·00
41		20 c. dull and bright purple	..	2·00	35·00
42		25 c. green and dull purple	..	2·00	35·00
43		30 c. dull purple and black	..	2·25	35·00
44		50 c. black/green	..	2·50	35·00
45		$1 black and carmine/blue	..	10·00	65·00
46		$3 green and red/green	..	£110	£350
47	2	$5 green and dull purple	..	£190	£600
37/47			Set of 11	£300	£1100

Minor varieties of this overprint exist as in Straits Settlements.

1924–38. *New values, etc. Wmk Mult Script CA. Chalk-surfaced paper. P 14.*
48	4	1 c. black (1926)	..	..	70	45
49		3 c. green (1926)	..	..	75	75
50		3 c. reddish brown (1938)	..	13·00	5·50
		a. Chestnut	..		
51		5 c. purple/yellow (1926)	..	1·25	55
52		6 c. orange	..	..	2·25	30
53		8 c. grey (1938)	..	..	13·00	1·50
54		12 c. bright ultramarine (1926)	..	3·50	3·25
55		35 c. carmine/yellow (1926)	..	3·50	8·00
56		$1 purple and black/blue (1929)	..	9·00	3·50
57		$3 green and lake/green (1926)	..	32·00	70·00
		a. Green and brown-red/green	..		
58	5	$5 green and red/yellow (1938)	..	£225	£850
48/58			Set of 11	£275	£850
48/58 Optd/Perf "Specimen"			Set of 11	£300

The 2 c. yellow, 6 c. grey, 8 c. red and 15 c. blue were prepared, but not officially issued (Price £75 each, unused).

1941 (1 May). *Nos. 51 and 29 surch as T 6.*
59	4	2 c. on 5 c. purple/yellow	..	6·00	4·50
60		8 c. on 10 c. bright blue	..	7·00	4·50

1948 (2 Dec). *Royal Silver Wedding. As Nos. 143/4 of Jamaica.*
61		10 c. violet	..	..	15	50
62		$5 carmine	..	..	20·00	32·00

1949 (10 Oct). *75th Anniv of U.P.U. As Nos. 145/8 of Jamaica.*
63		10 c. purple	..	..	20	35
64		15 c. deep blue	..	..	55	1·60
65		25 c. orange	..	..	55	2·25
66		50 c. blue-black	..	..	90	2·50
63/6			..	..	Set of 4	2·00	6·00

7	Sultan Ismail	8	Vanda hookeriana

1949 (27 Dec)–**55**. *Wmk Mult Script CA. Chalk-surfaced paper. P 17½×18.*
67	7	1 c. black	..	..	10	20
68		2 c. orange	..	..	10	20
69		3 c. green	..	..	20	80
70		4 c. brown	..	..	10	15
71		5 c. bright purple (1.9.52)	..	30	50
72		6 c. grey	..	..	15	15
73		8 c. scarlet	..	..	20	1·25
74		8 c. green (1.9.52)	..	65	1·00
		a. Deep green (11.8.53)	..	1·50	3·00
75		10 c. purple	..	..	15	10
76		12 c. scarlet (1.9.52)	..	65	1·75
77		15 c. ultramarine	..	..	30	25
78		20 c. black and green	..	30	1·25
79		20 c. bright blue (1.9.52)	..	80	25
80		25 c. purple and orange	..	30	55
81		30 c. scarlet and purple (5.9.55)	1·25	1·25
82		35 c. scarlet and purple (1.9.52)	70	1·00

83	7	40 c. red and purple	..	1·25	8·00
84		50 c. black and blue	..	40	60
85		$1 blue and purple	..	2·00	2·75
86		$2 green and scarlet	..	10·00	13·00
87		$5 green and brown	..	42·00	38·00
67/87			..	..	Set of 21	55·00	65·00

1953 (2 June). *Coronation. As No. 153 of Jamaica.*
88		10 c. black and reddish purple	..	..	30	30

1957 (26 June)–**63**. *As Nos. 92/102 of Kedah, but with inset portrait of Sultan Ismail.*
89		1 c. black (21.8.57)	..	..	10	20
90		2 c. orange-red (25.7.57)	..	50	30
		a. Red-orange (21.2.61)	..	7·00	8·00
91		4 c. sepia (21.8.57)	..	10	10
92		5 c. carmine-lake (21.8.57)	..	10	10
93		8 c. myrtle-green (21.8.57)	..	3·50	60
94		10 c. deep brown (4.8.57)	..	15	10
94a		10 c. deep maroon (21.2.61)	..	2·00	10
95		20 c. blue	..	..	20	30
96		50 c. black and blue (p 12½) (25.7.57)	30	50
		a. Perf 12½ × 13 (17.5.60)	..	30	60
		ab. Black and ultramarine (20.3.62)	..	30	60
97		$1 ultramarine and reddish purple (25.7.57)	3·25	3·25
98		$2 bronze-green and scarlet (21.8.57)	5·50	6·00
99		$5 brown and bronze-green (21.8.57)	7·00	10·00
		a. Perf 13 × 12½ (13.8.63)	..	10·00	9·00
89/99			..	Set of 12	20·00	17·00

The 6, 12, 25 and 30 c. values used with this issue were Nos. 1/4 of Malayan Federation.

1965 (15 Nov). *As Nos. 166/72 of Johore but with inset portrait of Sultan Ismail Nasiruddin Shah as in T 8.*
100		1 c. multicoloured	..	..	10	40
101		2 c. multicoloured	..	..	10	40
102		5 c. multicoloured	..	..	10	10
103		6 c. multicoloured	..	..	15	40
104		10 c. multicoloured	..	..	20	10
105		15 c. multicoloured	..	..	85	10
106		20 c. multicoloured	..	..	1·25	40
		a. Bright purple (blooms) omitted	..	30·00	
100/6			..	Set of 7	2·40	1·50

The 5 c. value exists with PVA gum as well as gum arabic.
No. 101a, formerly listed here, is now listed as Sarawak No. 213a.
The higher values used with this issue were Nos. 20/27 of Malaysia (National Issues).

9	Sultan of Trengganu	10	Papilio demoleus

(Des Enche Nik Zainal Abidin. Photo Harrison)

1970 (16 Dec). *25th Anniv of Installation of H.R.H. Tuanku Ismail Nasiruddin Shah as Sultan of Trengganu. P 14½×13½.*
107	9	10 c. multicoloured	..	25	50
108		15 c. multicoloured	..	30	60
109		50 c. multicoloured	..	65	1·60
107/9			..	Set of 3	1·10	2·40

1971 (1 Feb)–**78**. *As Nos. 175/87 of Johore but with portrait of Sultan Ismail Nasiruddin Shah and Arms, as in T 10.*

(a) Litho by Bradbury, Wilkinson
110		1 c. multicoloured	..	..	15	40
111		2 c. multicoloured	..	..	30	70
112		5 c. multicoloured	..	..	40	10
113		6 c. multicoloured	..	..	40	40
114		10 c. multicoloured	..	..	40	10
115		15 c. multicoloured	..	..	55	10
116		20 c. multicoloured	..	..	75	50
110/16			..	Set of 7	2·75	2·25

(b) Photo by Harrison (1977–78)
116a		5 c. multicoloured	..	13·00	5·00
117		10 c. multicoloured	..	3·00	1·25
117a		15 c. multicoloured	..	4·00	1·25

The higher values used with this issue were Nos. 64/71 of Malaysia (National Issues).
For differences between litho and photo printings, see after Johore No. 187.

11	Durio zibethinus	12	Sultan Mahmud

1979 (30 Apr). *As Nos. 188/94 of Johore but with portrait of Sultan Ismail Nasiruddin Shah as in T 11.*
118		1 c. Rafflesia hasseltii	..	10	30
119		2 c. Pterocarpus indicus	..	10	30
120		5 c. Lagerstroemia speciosa	..	10	10
121		10 c. Type 11	..	10	10
122		15 c. Hibiscus rosa-sinensis	..	15	10
123		20 c. Rhododendron scortechinii	..	15	10
124		25 c. Etlingera elatior (inscr "Phaeomeria speciosa")	..	15	10
118/24			Set of 7	65	80

For higher values used in conjunction with this series see Nos. 190/7 of Malaysia (National Issues).

(Des Malaysian Advertising Services. Litho Harrison)

1981 (21 Mar). *Installation of Sultan Mahmud. P* 14.

125	**12**	10 c. black, gold and new blue	..	20	55
126		15 c. black, gold and yellow	..	25	30
127		50 c. black, gold and bright purple		55	1·75
125/7		.. .. .. *Set of* 3		90	2·40

1983 (Oct)–**86.*** *As Nos.* 121/4 *but without wmk.*

131	10 c. Type **11** (5.2.86)	13·00	3·75
132	15 c. *Hibiscus rosa-sinensis* (24.1.85) ..	2·50	1·00
133	20 c. *Rhododendron scortechinii* (blackish brown background) ..	14·00	5·00
133*a*	20 c. *Rhododendron scortechinii* (bronze-green background) (2.3.84) ..	4·50	3·00
134	25 c. *Etlingera elatior* (inscr "*Phaeomeria speciosa*") (13.11.83)..	40	30

*There was no official release date for these stamps. Dates shown are the earliest recorded from postmarks and may be revised if earlier examples are reported.

For details of the shade differences between watermarked and unwatermarked printings see after Johore No. 200*a*.

On Nos. 131/2, 133*a* and 134 the portrait and state arms have been redrawn smaller.

13 Rubber

1986 (25 Oct). *As Nos.* 202/8 *of Johore but with portrait of Sultan Mahmud and inscr* "TERENGGANU" *as in T* **13**.

135	1 c. Coffee	..	..	..	10	10
136	2 c. Coconuts..		..	..	10	10
137	5 c. Cocoa	..	..	..	10	10
138	10 c. Black pepper		..	..	10	10
139	15 c. Type **13** ..		..	..	10	10
140	20 c. Oil palm..		..	..	10	10
141	30 c. Rice	..	..	..	15	20
135/41	..	..	..	*Set of* 7	40	45

POSTAGE DUE STAMPS

D 1

1937 (10 Aug). *Wmk Mult Script CA. P* 14.

D1	**D 1**	1 c. scarlet	..	..	..	6·50	50·00
D2		4 c. green	..	..	..	6·50	50·00
D3		8 c. yellow	..	..	..	48·00	£250
D4		10 c. brown	..	..		90·00	90·00
D1/4		..	..		*Set of* 4	£140	£400
D1/4 Perf "Specimen"			..	..	*Set of* 4	£130	

VIII. JAPANESE OCCUPATION OF MALAYA

PRICES FOR STAMPS ON COVER

Nos. J1/55	*from* × 10
Nos. J56/76	*from* × 12
Nos. J77/89	*from* × 20
Nos. J90/1	*from* × 15
Nos. J92/115	*from* × 6
Nos. J116/18	—
Nos. J119/32	*from* × 12
Nos. J133/45	*from* × 10
Nos. J146/223	*from* × 6
Nos. J224/58	*from* × 12
No. J259	*from* × 15
Nos. J260/96	*from* × 12
Nos. J297/310	*from* × 20
Nos. J311/17	—
Nos. JD1/10	*from* × 30
Nos. JD11/16	*from* × 12
Nos. JD17/20	*from* × 30
Nos. JD21/7	*from* × 20
Nos. JD28/33	*from* × 12
Nos. JD34/41	*from* × 30

Japanese forces invaded Malaya on 8 December 1941 with the initial landings taking place at Kota Bharu on the east coast. Penang fell, to a force which crossed the border from Thailand, on 19 December, Kuala Lumpur on 11 January 1942 and the conquest of the Malay penisula was completed by the capture of Singapore on 15 February.

During the Japanese Occupation various small Dutch East Indies islands near Singapore were administered as part of Malaya. Stamps of the Japanese Occupation of Malaya were issued to the post offices of Dabo Singkep, Puloe Samboe, Tanjong Balei, Tanjong Batu, Tanjong Pinang and Terempa between 1942 and 1945. The overprinted issues were also used by a number of districts in Northern Sumatra whose postal services were administered from Singapore until the end of March 1943.

Malayan post offices were also opened in October 1943 to serve camps of civilians working on railway construction and maintenance in Thailand. Overprinted stamps of the Japanese Occupation of Malaya were used at these offices between October 1943 and the end of the year after which mail from the camps was carried free. Their postmarks were inscribed in Japanese Katakana characters, and, uniquely, showed the Japanese postal symbol.

JOHORE

The postal service in Johore was reconstituted in mid-April 1942 using Nos. J146/60 and subsequently other general issues. Stamps of Johore overprinted "DAI NIPPON 2602" were, however, only used for fiscal purposes. Overprinted Johore postage due stamps were not issued for use elsewhere in Malaya.

POSTAGE DUE STAMPS

郵政局 **馬来軍政部** **大日本郵便** **大口本郵便** ←

(1) (Upright)   (2)   Second character sideways (R.6/3)

1942 (Apr). *Nos. D1/5 of Johore optd as* T 1. *A. In red. B. In black.*

				A		B	
JD1	D 1	1 c. carmine		65·00	—	45·00	70·00
JD2		4 c. green		65·00	—	55·00	70·00
JD3		8 c. orange		80·00	—	55·00	75·00
JD4		10 c. brown		28·00	—	15·00	40·00
JD5		12 c. purple		35·00	—	24·00	40·00

1943. *Nos. D1/5 of Johore optd with* T 2.

JD 6	D 1	1 c. carmine		2·00	9·00
		a. Second character sideways		75·00	£130
JD 7		4 c. green		2·00	9·00
		a. Second character sideways		75·00	£130
JD 8		8 c. orange		3·75	11·00
		a. Second character sideways		£100	£180
JD 9		10 c. brown		3·25	15·00
		a. Second character sideways		£100	£180
JD10		12 c. purple		4·25	20·00
		a. Second character sideways		£100	£180

KEDAH

Postal services resumed on 10 February 1942 using unoverprinted Kedah values from 1 c. to 8 c.

During the Japanese occupation Perlis was administered as part of Kedah.

DAI NIPPON   **DAI NIPPON**

2602   **2602**

(3)   (4)

1942 (13 May)**–43.** *Stamps of Kedah (Script wmk) optd with* T 3 (1 c. *to* 8 c.) *or* 4 (10 c. *to* $5), *both in red.*

J 1	1	1 c. black		2·00	3·50
J 2		2 c. bright green		23·00	30·00
J 3		4 c. violet		3·00	4·00

J 4	1	5 c. yellow		1·60	3·25
		a. Black opt (1943)		£200	£225
J 5		6 c. carmine-red (Blk.)		1·50	4·75
J 6		8 c. grey-black		2·25	1·75
J 7	6	10 c. ultramarine and sepia		6·00	6·50
J 8		12 c. black and violet		11·00	17·00
J 9		25 c. ultramarine and purple		4·25	8·00
		a. Black opt (1943)		£190	£225
J10		30 c. green and scarlet		65·00	75·00
J11		40 c. black and purple		16·00	25·00
J12		50 c. brown and blue		18·00	28·00
J13		$1 black and green		£130	£150
		a. Opt inverted		£450	£475
J14		$2 green and brown		£130	£140
J15		$5 black and scarlet		50·00	55·00
		a. Black opt (1943)		£475	£500

Nos. J1/15 were gradually replaced by issues intended for use throughout Malaya. Kedah and Perlis were ceded to Thailand by the Japanese on 19 October 1943.

KELANTAN

Postal services resumed on 1 June 1942. Stamps used in Kelantan were overprinted with the personal seals of Sunagawa, the Japanese Governor, and of Handa, the Assistant Governor.

(5) Sunagawa Seal   (6) Handa Seal

40 CENTS   **$1.00**

(7)   (8)

1 Cents

(9)

1942 (June). *Stamps of Kelantan surch*

(a) As T 7 *or* 8 *(dollar values). Optd with* T 5 *in red.*

J16	4	1 c. on 50 c. grey-olive and orange		£140	£140
J17		2 c. on 40 c. orange and blue-green		£200	£200
J18		4 c. on 30 c. violet and scarlet		£800	£850
J19		5 c. on 12 c. blue (R.)		£130	£150
J20		6 c. on 25 c. vermilion and violet		£130	£150
J21		8 c. on 5 c. red-brown (R.)		£180	£140
J22		10 c. on 6 c. lake		75·00	90·00
J23		12 c. on 8 c. grey-olive (R.)		45·00	75·00
J24		25 c. on 10 c. purple (R.)		£800	£900
J25		30 c. on 4 c. scarlet		£1200	£1400
J26		40 c. on 2 c. green (R.)		48·00	70·00
J27		50 c. on 1 c. grey-olive and yellow		£850	£900
J28	1	$1 on 4 c. black & red (R., bars Blk.)		48·00	65·00
J29		$2 on 5 c. green and red/*yellow*		48·00	65·00
J30		$5 on 6 c. scarlet		50·00	65·00

(b) As T 7. *Optd with* T 6 *in red.*

J31	4	12 c. on 8 c. grey-olive		95·00	£120

(c) As T 9. *Optd with* T 5 *in red.*

J32	4	1 c. on 50 c. grey-olive and orange		80·00	70·00
		a. "Cente" for "Cents" (R. 5/1)		£550	£500
J33		2 c. on 40 c. orange and blue-green		75·00	75·00
		a. "Cente" for "Cents" (R. 5/1)		£500	
J34		5 c. on 12 c. blue (R.)		65·00	65·00
		a. "Cente" for "Cents" (R. 5/1)		£450	
J35		8 c. on 5 c. red-brown (R.)		75·00	60·00
		a. "Cente" for "Cents" (R. 5/1)		£500	
J36		10 c. on 6 c. lake		65·00	75·00
		a. "Cente" for "Cents" (R. 5/1)		£450	
J37		12 c. on 8 c. grey-olive (R.)		£110	£120
		a. "Cente" for "Cents" (R. 5/1)		£700	
J38		30 c. on 4 c. scarlet		£900	£950
		a. "Cente" for "Cents" (R. 5/1)			
J39		40 c. on 2 c. green (R.)		£120	£130
		a. "Cente" for "Cents" (R. 5/1)		£800	
J40		50 c. on 1 c. grey-olive and yellow		£450	£475
		a. "Cente" for "Cents" (R. 5/1)			

(d) As T 9. *Optd with* T 6 *in red.*

J41	4	1 c. on 50 c. grey-olive and orange		75·00	90·00
		a. "Cente" for "Cents" (R. 5/1)		£500	
J42		2 c. on 40 c. orange and blue-green		70·00	£100
		a. "Cente" for "Cents" (R. 5/1)		£475	
J43		8 c. on 5 c. red-brown (R.)		60·00	90·00
		a. "Cente" for "Cents" (R. 5/1)		£450	
J44		10 c. on 6 c. lake		75·00	£100
		a. "Cente" for "Cents" (R. 5/1)		£500	

As stamps of the above series became exhausted the equivalent values from the series intended for use throughout Malaya were introduced. Stamps as Nos. J28/30, J32/3 and J36/40, but without Type 5 or 6, are from remainders sent to Singapore or Kuala Lumpur after the state had been ceded to Thailand (*Price from* £12 *each unused*).

Kelantan was ceded to Thailand by the Japanese on 19 October 1943.

MALACCA

Postal services from Malacca resumed on 21 April 1942, but there were no stamps available for two days.

PRICES. Those quoted are for single stamps. Blocks of four showing the complete handstamp are worth from six times the price of a single stamp.

(10) Seal of the Government Office of the Malacca Military Dept

1942 (23 Apr). *Stamps of Straits Settlemamts handstamped as* T 10, *in red, each impression covering four stamps.*

					Single	
					Un.	Used
J45	58	1 c. black			60·00	55·00
J46		2 c. orange			55·00	55·00
J47		3 c. green			55·00	55·00
J48		5 c. brown			85·00	95·00
J49		8 c. grey			£110	90·00
J50		10 c. dull purple			65·00	60·00
J51		12 c. ultramarine			80·00	85·00
J52		15 c. ultramarine			60·00	60·00
J53		40 c. scarlet and dull purple			£475	£450
J54		50 c. black/*emerald*			£650	£650
J55		$1 black and red/*blue*			£700	£700

The 30c., $2 and $5 also exist with this overprint, but these values were not available to the public.

POSTAGE DUE STAMPS

1942 (23 Apr). *Postage Due stamps of Malayan Postal Union handstamped as* T 10, *in red, each impression covering four stamps.*

JD11	D 1	1 c. slate-purple			£130	£130
JD12		4 c. green			£190	£190
JD13		8 c. scarlet			£1000	£1000
JD14		10 c. yellow-orange			£200	£200
JD15		12 c. ultramarine			£275	£300
JD16		50 c. black			£1000	£1000

Nos. J45/55 and JD11/16 were replaced during May 1942 by the overprinted issues intended for use throughout Malaya.

PENANG

Postal services on Penang Island resumed on 30 March 1942 using Straits Settlements stamps overprinted by Japanese seals.

(11) Okugawa Seal   (12) Ochiburi Seal   **DAI NIPPON** **2602** **PENANG** (13)

1942 (30 Mar). *Straits Settlements stamps optd.*

(a) As T 11 *(three forms of the seal)*.

J56	58	1 c. black			7·50	9·00
J57		2 c. orange			20·00	18·00
J58		3 c. green			16·00	18·00
J59		5 c. brown			20·00	20·00
J60		8 c. grey			22·00	22·00
J61		10 c. dull purple			35·00	35·00
J62		12 c. ultramarine			20·00	24·00
J63		15 c. ultramarine			22·00	27·00
J64		40 c. scarlet and dull purple			70·00	75·00
J65		50 c. black/*emerald*			£120	£130
J66		$1 black and red/*blue*			£160	£170
J67		$2 green and scarlet			£325	£350
J68		$5 green and red/*emerald*			£900	£1000

(b) With T 12

J69	58	1 c. black			40·00	50·00
J70		2 c. orange			40·00	50·00
J71		3 c. green			40·00	50·00
J72		5 c. brown			£475	£475
J73		8 c. grey			30·00	35·00
J74		10 c. dull purple			30·00	35·00
J75		12 c. ultramarine			30·00	35·00
J76		15 c. ultramarine			30·00	35·00

Straits Settlements stamps overprinted with a similar seal impression, but circular and containing four characters, are believed to be fiscal issues.

1942 (15 Apr) *Straits Settlements stamps optd with* T 13.

J77	58	1 c. black (R.)			1·00	1·00
		a. Opt inverted			£120	£120
J78		2 c. orange			3·50	2·75
		a. "PE" for "PENANG"			60·00	65·00
		b. Opt inverted			£120	
		c. Opt double				
J79		3 c. green (R.)			1·40	1·75
		a. Opt double, one inverted			£150	
J80		5 c. brown (R.)			1·00	2·25
		a. "N PPON"			95·00	
		b. Opt double			£140	
J81		8 c. grey (R.)			2·25	1·40
		a. "N PPON"			40·00	48·00
		b. Opt double, one inverted			£150	
J82		10 c. dull purple (R.)			1·50	2·00
		a. Opt double			£200	
		b. Opt double, one inverted			£350	
J83		12 c. ultramarine (R.)			2·00	5·00
		a. "N PPON"			£225	
		b. Opt double			£225	
		c. Opt double, one inverted			£325	£350

J84	58	15 c. ultramarine (R.)	1·75	2·00
		a. "N PPON"	95·00	£100
		b. Opt inverted	£300	£300
		c. Opt double	£300	
J85		40 c. scarlet and dull purple	2·50	6·00
J86		50 c. black/*emerald* (R.)	3·50	11·00
J87		$1 black and red/*blue*	6·00	16·00
J88		$2 green and scarlet	24·00	50·00
J89		$5 green and red/*emerald*	£300	£400

Nos. J77/89 were replaced by the overprinted issues intended for use throughout Malaya.

SELANGOR

Postal services resumed in the Kuala Lumpur area on 3 April 1942 and gradually extended to the remainder of the state. Stamps of the general overprinted issue were used, but the following commemorative set was only available in Selangor.

SELANGOR EXHIBITION DAI NIPPON 2602 MALAYA

(14)

1942 (3 Nov). *Agri-horticultural Exhibition. Nos. 294 and 283 of Straits Settlements optd with T 14.*

J90	58	2 c. orange	12·00	20·00
		a. "C" for "G" in "SELANGOR" (R.1/2)	£180	£225
		b. Opt inverted	£300	£375
J91		8 c. grey	12·00	20·00
		a. "C" for "G" in "SELANGOR" (R.1/2)	£180	£225
		b. Opt inverted	£300	£375

SINGAPORE

The first post offices re-opened in Singapore on 16 March 1942.

(15) Seal of Post Office of Malayan Military Dept

(Handstamped at Singapore)

1942 (16 Mar). *Stamps of Straits Settlements optd with T 15 in red.*

J92	58	1 c. black	9·50	14·00
J93		2 c. orange	9·50	13·00
J94		3 c. green	45·00	65·00
J95		8 c. grey	18·00	18·00
J96		15 c. ultramarine	14·00	15·00

The overprint Type 15 has a double-lined frame, although the two lines are not always apparent, as in the illustration. Three chops were used, differing slightly in the shape of the characters, but forgeries also exist. It is distinguishable from Type 1, used for the general issues, by its extra width, measuring approximately 14 mm against 12½ mm.

The 6, 10, 30, 40, 50 c., $2 and $5 also exist with this overprint, but were not sold to the public.

Nos. J92/6 were replaced on the 3 May 1942 by the stamps overprinted with Type 1 which were intended for use throughout Malaya.

TRENGGANU

Postal services resumed in Trengganu during March 1942 using unoverprinted stamps up to the 35 c. value.

1942 (Sept). *Stamps of Trengganu (Script wmk) optd as T 1 at Kuala Lumpur.*

J 97	4	1 c. black	95·00	85·00
		a. Red opt	£140	£140
		b. Brown opt	£225	£200
J 98		2 c. green	£140	£140
		a. Red opt	£150	£160
		b. Brown opt	£225	£225
J 99		2 c. on 5 c. purple/*yellow* (No. 59)	70·00	70·00
		a. Red opt	45·00	60·00
J100		3 c. chestnut	80·00	80·00
		a. Brown opt	£275	£275
J101		4 c. scarlet-vermilion	£140	£140
J102		5 c. purple/*yellow*	9·50	13·00
		a. Red opt	16·00	
J103		6 c. orange	7·50	18·00
		a. Red opt	25·00	
		b. Brown opt	£140	£140
J104		8 c. grey	9·00	13·00
		a. Brown to red opt	38·00	50·00
J105		8 c. on 10 c. bright blue (No. 60)	13·00	22·00
		a. Red opt	21·00	
J106		10 c. bright blue	9·00	18·00
		a. Red opt	32·00	
		b. Brown opt	£150	£150
J107		12 c. bright ultramarine	8·00	17·00
		a. Red opt	26·00	
J108		20 c. dull purple and orange	8·50	17·00
		a. Red opt	17·00	

J109	4	25 c. green and deep purple	7·50	18·00
		a. Red opt	21·00	
		b. Brown opt	£140	£140
J110		30 c. dull purple and black	7·00	17·00
		a. Red opt	17·00	
J111		35 c. carmine/*yellow*	12·00	19·00
		a. Red opt	18·00	
J112		50 c. green and bright carmine	55·00	65·00
J113		$1 purple and blue/*blue*	£1200	£1200
J114		$3 green and brown-red/*green*	42·00	70·00
		a. Red opt	50·00	
J115	5	$5 green and red/*yellow*	£120	£170
J116		$25 purple and blue	£700	
		a. Red opt	£1700	
J117		$50 green and yellow	£4500	
J118		$100 green and scarlet	£800	

DAI NIPPON

2602

MALAYA

(16)

1942 (Sept). *Stamps of Trengganu (Script wmk) optd with T 16.*

J119	4	1 c. black	7·00	9·00
J120		2 c. green	£140	£180
J121		2 c. on 5 c. purple/*yellow* (No. 59)	6·00	8·00
J122		3 c. chestnut	9·00	14·00
J123		4 c. scarlet-vermilion	7·50	11·00
J124		5 c. purple/*yellow*	5·00	8·50
J125		6 c. orange	5·00	11·00
J126		8 c. grey	60·00	16·00
J127		8 c. on 10 c. bright blue (No. 60)	5·50	11·00
J128		12 c. bright ultramarine	5·00	11·00
J129		20 c. dull purple and orange	7·00	13·00
J130		25 c. green and deep purple	7·00	17·00
J131		30 c. dull purple and black	7·00	17·00
J132		$3 green and brown-red/*green*	50·00	£100

1943. *Stamps of Trengganu (Script wmk) optd with T 2.*

J133	4	1 c. black	6·50	15·00
J134		2 c. green	6·50	18·00
J135		2 c. on 5 c. purple/*yellow* (No. 59)	5·50	18·00
J136		5 c. purple/*yellow*	5·50	18·00
J137		6 c. orange	7·50	22·00
J138		8 c. grey	45·00	50·00
J139		8 c. on 10 c. bright blue (No. 60)	14·00	35·00
J140		10 c. bright blue	75·00	£120
J141		12 c. bright ultramarine	9·50	28·00
J142		20 c. dull purple and orange	10·00	28·00
J143		25 c. green and deep purple	9·50	32·00
J144		30 c. dull purple and black	9·50	32·00
J145		35 c. carmine/*yellow*	9·50	32·00

POSTAGE DUE STAMPS

1942 (Sept). *Nos. D1/4 of Trengganu optd with T 1 sideways.*

JD17	D 1	1 c. scarlet	45·00	75·00
JD18		4 c. green	55·00	75·00
		a. Red opt	50·00	70·00
JD19		8 c. yellow	14·00	40·00
JD20		10 c. brown	14·00	42·00

The Trengganu 8 c. postage due also exists overprinted with Type 16, but this was not issued (*Price £225 unused*).

Trengganu was ceded to Thailand by the Japanese on 19 October 1943.

GENERAL ISSUES

The following stamps were produced for use throughout Malaya, except for Trengganu.

1942 (3 Apr). *Stamps optd as T 1. (a) On Straits Settlements.*

J146	58	1 c. black (R.)	3·25	3·25
		a. Black opt	£160	£180
		b. Violet opt	£190	£190
J147		2 c. green (V.)	£950	£950
J148		2 c. orange (R.)	2·75	2·25
		a. Black opt	65·00	70·00
		b. Violet opt	70·00	65·00
		c. Brown opt	£225	£250
J149		3 c. green (R.)	2·75	2·25
		a. Black opt	£160	£170
		b. Violet opt	£190	£200
J150		5 c. brown (R.)	18·00	21·00
		a. Black opt	£200	£200
J151		8 c. grey (R.)	3·00	2·25
		a. Black opt	£170	£190
J152		10 c. dull purple (R.)	30·00	32·00
		a. Brown opt	£325	£325
J153		12 c. ultramarine (R.)	70·00	85·00
J154		15 c. ultramarine (R.)	3·50	2·75
		a. Violet opt	£225	£250
J155		30 c. dull purple and orange (R.)	£850	£900
J156		40 c. scarlet and dull purple (R.)	70·00	85·00
		a. Brown opt	£190	£190
J157		50 c. black/*emerald* (R.)	42·00	42·00
J158		$1 black and red/*blue* (R.)	70·00	75·00
J159		$2 green and scarlet (R.)	£120	£130
J160		$5 green and red/*emerald* (R.)	£160	£170

(b) On Negri Sembilan

J161	6	1 c. black (R.)	18·00	13·00
		a. Violet opt	18·00	18·00
		b. Brown opt	14·00	14·00
		c. Black opt	26·00	28·00
J162		2 c. orange (R.)	11·00	12·00
		a. Violet opt	30·00	26·00
		b. Black opt	30·00	28·00
		c. Brown opt	32·00	35·00
J163		3 c. green (R.)	16·00	18·00
		a. Violet opt	23·00	29·00
		b. Violet opt (sideways)	£150	£150
		c. Brown opt	40·00	40·00

J164	6	5 c. brown	20·00	20·00
		a. Brown opt	15·00	14·00
		b. Red opt	12·00	11·00
		c. Violet opt	32·00	32·00
J165		6 c. grey	£120	£120
		a. Brown opt	£325	£325
J166		8 c. scarlet	30·00	35·00
J167		10 c. dull purple	55·00	55·00
		a. Red opt	55·00	50·00
		b. Brown opt	£140	£140
J168		12 c. bright ultramarine (Br.)	£650	£650
J169		15 c. ultramarine (R.)	15·00	8·00
		a. Violet opt	30·00	28·00
J170		25 c. dull purple and scarlet	27·00	32·00
		a. Red opt	60·00	70·00
		b. Brown opt	£150	£160
J171		30 c. dull purple and orange	£120	£130
		a. Brown opt	£425	£425
J172		40 c. scarlet and dull purple	£550	£550
		a. Brown opt	£650	£650
J173		50 c. black/*emerald*	£170	£170
J174		$1 black and red/*blue*	95·00	£110
		a. Red opt	£110	£120
		b. Brown opt	£350	£350
J175		$5 green and red/*emerald*	£350	£375
		a. Red opt	£425	£450

(c) On Pahang

J176	15	1 c. black	25·00	30·00
		a. Red opt	27·00	28·00
		b. Violet opt	£140	£150
		c. Brown opt	£100	£100
J177		3 c. green	75·00	80·00
		a. Red opt	£225	£275
		b. Violet opt	£400	£400
J178		5 c. brown	9·50	6·50
		a. Red opt	80·00	80·00
		b. Brown opt	£110	£100
		c. Violet opt	£250	£225
J179		8 c. grey	£130	£130
J180		8 c. scarlet	17·00	10·00
		a. Red opt	60·00	60·00
		b. Violet opt	65·00	65·00
		c. Brown opt	70·00	75·00
J181		10 c. dull purple	38·00	42·00
		a. Red opt	60·00	65·00
		b. Brown opt	£160	£160
J182		12 c. bright ultramarine	£1000	£1100
		a. Red opt	£1200	£1200
J183		15 c. ultramarine	55·00	55·00
		a. Red opt	80·00	80·00
		b. Violet opt	£375	£375
		c. Brown opt	£200	£225
J184		25 c. dull purple and scarlet	18·00	27·00
J185		30 c. dull purple and orange	12·00	24·00
		a. Red opt	£140	£170
J186		40 c. scarlet and dull purple	15·00	26·00
		a. Brown opt	£140	£150
		b. Red opt	38·00	40·00
J187		50 c. black/*emerald*	£190	£200
		a. Red opt	£300	£325
J188		$1 black and red/*blue* (R.)	80·00	90·00
		a. Black opt	£160	£160
		b. Brown opt	£425	£425
J189		$5 green and red/*emerald*	£550	£650
		a. Red opt	£700	£800

(d) On Perak

J190	51	1 c. black	28·00	28·00
		a. Violet opt	65·00	65·00
		b. Brown opt	75·00	75·00
J191		2 c. orange	18·00	17·00
		a. Violet opt	60·00	65·00
		b. Red opt	28·00	25·00
		c. Brown opt	50·00	55·00
J192		3 c. green	22·00	25·00
		a. Violet opt	£160	£170
		b. Brown opt	£120	£130
		c. Red opt	£140	£140
J193		5 c. brown	6·50	5·50
		a. Brown opt	20·00	20·00
		b. Violet opt	90·00	95·00
		c. Red opt	90·00	95·00
J194		8 c. grey	27·00	27·00
		a. Red opt	£180	£180
		b. Brown opt	£160	£160
J195		8 c. scarlet	13·00	32·00
		a. Violet opt	£180	
J196		10 c. dull purple	12·00	20·00
		a. Red opt	£100	£100
J197		12 c. bright ultramarine	£100	£110
J198		15 c. ultramarine	16·00	23·00
		a. Red opt	55·00	55·00
		b. Violet opt	£120	£120
		c. Brown opt	£120	£120
J199		25 c. dull purple and scarlet	14·00	20·00
J200		30 c. dull purple and orange	17·00	32·00
		a. Brown opt	£130	£130
		b. Red opt	32·00	45·00
J201		40 c. scarlet and dull purple	£150	£160
		a. Red opt	£300	£300
J202		50 c. black/*emerald*	28·00	38·00
		a. Red opt	32·00	45·00
		b. Brown opt	£120	£120
J203		$1 black and red/*blue*	£225	£250
		a. Brown opt	£700	
J204		$2 green and scarlet	£1200	£1200
J205		$5 green and red/*emerald*	£425	
		a. Brown opt	£900	

(e) On Selangor

J206	46	1 c. black, S	10·00	14·00
		a. Red opt, SU	15·00	20·00
		b. Violet opt, SU	26·00	32·00
J207		2 c. green, U	£450	£475
		a. Violet opt, U	£600	£650
J208		2 c. orange (p 14×14½), S	40·00	42·00
		a. Red opt, U	90·00	95·00
		b. Violet opt, U	£120	95·00
		c. Brown opt, S	45·00	48·00
J209		2 c. orange (p 14), S	42·00	48·00
		a. Red opt, U	95·00	95·00
		b. Violet opt, U	£180	£180

J210	46	3 c. green, SU	..	15·00	14·00
		a. Red opt, SU	..	16·00	16·00
		b. Violet opt, S	..	48·00	48·00
		c. Brown opt, SU	..	16·00	16·00
J211		5 c. brown, S	..	5·00	5·00
		a. Red opt, S	..	10·00	14·00
		b. Violet opt, SU	..	21·00	23·00
		c. Brown opt, SU	..	42·00	45·00
J212		6 c. scarlet, S	..	£160	£160
		a. Red opt, S	..	£190	£190
		b. Brown opt, S	..	£300	
J213		8 c. grey, S	..	16·00	17·00
		a. Red opt, SU	..	26·00	24·00
		b. Violet opt, U	..	28·00	30·00
		c. Brown opt, S	..	48·00	32·00
J214		10 c. dull purple, S	..	10·00	19·00
		a. Red opt, S	..	35·00	35·00
		b. Brown opt, S	..	38·00	
J215		12 c. bright ultramarine, S	..	32·00	29·00
		a. Red opt, S	..	75·00	75·00
		b. Brown opt, S	..	80·00	80·00
J216		15 c. ultramarine, S	..	14·00	17·00
		a. Red opt, SU	..	35·00	35·00
		b. Violet opt, U	..	£100	90·00
		c. Brown opt, S	..	35·00	32·00
J217		25 c. dull purple and scarlet, S	..	65·00	75·00
		a. Red opt, S	..	55·00	70·00
J218		30 c. dull purple and orange, S	..	11·00	22·00
		a. Brown opt, S	..	£120	£110
J219		40 c. scarlet and dull purple, S	..	55·00	60·00
		a. Brown opt, S	..	£130	£120
J220		50 c. black/*emerald*, S	..	35·00	35·00
		a. Red opt, S	..	48·00	55·00
		b. Brown opt, S	..	95·00	£100
J221	47	$1 black and red/*blue*	..	30·00	40·00
		a. Red opt	..	95·00	£100
J222		$2 green and scarlet	..	35·00	55·00
		a. Red opt	..	£180	£200
J223		$5 green and red/*emerald*	..	55·00	70·00

On T **46** the overprint is normally sideways (with "top" to either right or left), but on T **47** it is always upright.
S=Sideways
U=Upright
SU=Sideways or upright (our prices being for the cheaper).
Specialists recognise nine slightly different chops as Type **1**. Initial supplies with the overprint in red were produced at Singapore. Later overprintings took place at Kuala Lumpur in violet, red or brown and, finally, black. No. J155 was from the Kuala Lumpur printing only. Except where noted these overprints were used widely in Malaya and, in some instances, Sumatra.
The following stamps also exist with this overprint, but were not available to the public:
Straits Settlements 6, 25 c.
Kelantan (in black) 10 c.
Negri Sembilan 2 c. green (Blk. or Brn.), 4 c. (Blk.), 6 c. scarlet (Blk.), 8 c. grey (Blk.), 12 c. (Blk.), $2 (Blk. or Brn.)
Pahang (in black, 2 c. also in brown) 2, 4, 6 c., $2
Perak 2 c. green (R.), 6 c. (Blk.)
Selangor 4 c. (Blk.)

1942 (May). *Optd with T* **16**. (a) *On Straits Settlements*.

J224	58	2 c. orange	..	50	50
		a. Opt inverted	..	7·00	13·00
		b. Opt double, one inverted	..	38·00	50·00
J225		3 c. green	..	42·00	50·00
J226		8 c. grey	..	2·25	1·75
		a. Opt inverted	..	13·00	25·00
J227		15 c. blue	..	6·50	5·00

(b) *On Negri Sembilan*

J228	6	1 c. black	..	90	60
		a. Opt inverted	..	9·00	18·00
		b. Opt double, one inverted	..	32·00	42·00
J229		2 c. orange	..	1·75	50
J230		3 c. green	..	1·00	45
J231		5 c. brown	..	45	55
J232		6 c. grey	..	1·40	1·00
		a. Opt inverted	..	—	£650
		b. Stop omitted at right (R. 10/4)	..	42·00	45·00
J233		8 c. scarlet	..	1·90	1·25
J234		10 c. dull purple	..	3·00	3·00
J235		15 c. ultramarine	..	5·50	3·00
J236		25 c. dull purple and scarlet	..	2·00	4·75
J237		30 c. dull purple and orange	..	3·50	3·00
J238		$1 black and red/*blue*	..	£100	£110

(c) *On Pahang*

J239	15	1 c. black	..	90	70
J240		5 c. brown	..	65	70
J241		8 c. scarlet	..	22·00	2·50
J242		10 c. dull purple	..	8·50	6·00
J243		12 c. bright ultramarine	..	1·00	3·00
J244		25 c. dull purple and scarlet	..	3·75	7·00
J245		30 c. dull purple and orange	..	80	3·25

(d) *On Perak*

J246	51	2 c. orange	..	85	70
		a. Opt inverted	..	14·00	20·00
J247		3 c. green	..	50	60
		a. Opt inverted	..	10·00	19·00
J248		8 c. scarlet	..	60	40
		a. Opt inverted	..	4·50	7·00
		b. Opt double, one inverted	..	£150	£170
		c. Opt omitted (in pair with normal)	..	£325	
J249		10 c. dull purple	..	5·00	5·00
J250		15 c. ultramarine	..	3·25	2·00
J251		50 c. black/*emerald*	..	1·75	2·75
J252		$1 black and red/*blue*	..	£275	£325
J253		$5 green and red/*emerald*	..	28·00	45·00
		a. Opt inverted	..	£275	£325

(e) *On Selangor*

J254	46	3 c. green	..	40	60
J255		12 c. bright ultramarine	..	1·10	4·25
J256		15 c. ultramarine	..	2·75	2·00
J257		40 c. scarlet and dull purple	..	2·00	2·50
J258	48	$2 green and scarlet	..	11·00	19·00

On T **46** the overprint is sideways, with "top" to left or right.
The following stamps also exist with this overprint, but were not available to the public.
Perak 1, 5, 30 c. (*Price for set of 3 £180 unused*)
Selangor 1, 5, 10, 30 c., $1, $5 (*Price for set of 6 £350 unused*)

DAI NIPPON
2602
MALAYA
2 Cents
(17)

DAI NIPPON
YUBIN
2 Cents
(18)
"Japanese
Postal Service"

1942. *No. 108 of Perak surch with T* **17**.
J259 **51** 2 c. on 5 c. brown .. 1·25 1·00

1942 (7 Dec). *Perak stamps surch or optd only, as in T* **18**.

J260	51	1 c. black	..	2·00	3·50
		a. Opt inverted	..	19·00	28·00
J261		2 c. on 5 c. brown	..	2·00	5·00
		a. "DAI NIPPON YUBIN" inverted	17·00	26·00
		b. Ditto and "2 Cents" omitted	35·00	50·00
J262		8 c. scarlet	..	2·75	1·25
		a. Opt inverted	..	11·00	18·00

A similar overprint exists on the Selangor 3 c., but this was not available to the public (*Price £225 unused*).

On 8 December 1942 contemporary Japanese 3, 5, 8 and 25 s. stamps were issued without overprint in Malaya and the 1, 2, 4, 6, 7, 10, 30 and 50 s. and 1 y. values followed on 15 February 1943.

大日本郵便
(19)

6 cts. **6 cts.** **2 Cents**
(20) (21) (22)

6 cts. **$1·00**
(23) (24)

1943 (Feb)–**45**. *Stamps of various Malayan territories optd "Japanese Postal Service" in Kanji characters as T* **2** *or* **19**, *some additionally surch as T* **20** *to* **24**.

(a) *Stamps of Straits Settlements optd with T* **2**

J263	58	8 c. grey (Blk.)	..	1·10	50
		a. Opt inverted	..	28·00	35·00
		b. Red opt	..	90	90
J264		12 c. ultramarine	..	55	3·00
J265		40 c. scarlet and dull purple	..	65	1·75

(b) *Stamps of Negri Sembilan optd with T* **2** *or surch also*

J266	6	1 c. black	..	30	40
		a. Opt inverted	..	8·00	14·00
		b. Sideways second character	18·00	19·00
		ba. Opt inverted with sideways second character	£400	
J267		2 c. on 5 c. brown (surch as T **20**)	40	45
J268		6 c. on 5 c. brown (surch T **21**)	40	60
J269		25 c. dull purple and scarlet	..	1·10	5·50

(c) *Stamp of Pahang optd with T* **2** *and surch also*

J270	15	6 c. on 5 c. brown (surch T **20**)	50	75
J271		6 c. on 5 c. brown (surch T **21**)	1·00	1·50

(d) *Stamps of Perak optd with T* **2** *or surch also*

J272	51	1 c. black	..	80	60
		a. Sideways second character	£110	£120
J273		2 c. on 5 c. brown (surch as T **20**)	50	50
		a. Opt Type **2** and surch Type **20** both inverted	18·00	29·00
		b. Opt Type **2** inverted	18·00	29·00
		c. Sideways second character	38·00	38·00
J274		2 c. on 5 c. brown (surch T **22**)	45	45
		a. Opt Type **2** and surch Type **22** both inverted	18·00	29·00
		b. Surch Type **22** inverted	18·00	29·00
		c. Sideways second character	25·00	27·00
		ca. Opt Type **2** with sideways second character and surch T **22** both inverted	£700	
		cb. Surch Type **22** inverted	£650	
		d. Inverted "s" in Type **22** (R.3/5)	£400	
J275		5 c. brown	..	45	40
		a. Opt inverted	..	26·00	30·00
		b. Sideways second character	£200	£300
J276		8 c. scarlet	..	55	50
		a. Opt inverted	..	15·00	24·00
		b. Sideways second character	48·00	55·00
		ba. Opt inverted with sideways second character	£600	
J277		10 c. dull purple	..	60	50
J278		30 c. dull purple and orange	1·25	2·50
J279		50 c. black/*emerald*	..	3·00	8·00
J280		$5 green and red/*emerald*	..	40·00	60·00

(e) *Stamps of Selangor optd with T* **2** (*sideways on T* **46**)

J281	46	1 c. black	..	90	90
J282		3 c. green	..	40	45
		a. Sideways second character	15·00	21·00
J283		12 c. bright ultramarine	45	1·25
		a. Sideways second character	20·00	30·00
J284		15 c. ultramarine	..	2·75	3·00
		a. Sideways second character	35·00	40·00
J285	48	$1 black and red/*blue*	..	3·00	9·00
		a. Opt inverted	..	£225	£225
		b. Sideways second character	£225	£225
J286		$2 green and scarlet	..	10·00	24·00
J287		$5 green and red/*emerald*	22·00	50·00
		a. Opt inverted	..	£225	£225

(f) *Stamps of Selangor optd with T* **19** *or surch also*

J288	46	1 c. black (R.)	..	35	50
J289		2 c. on 5 c. brown (surch as T **21**) (R.)	30	50
J290		3 c. on 5 c. brown (surch as T **21**)	30	1·50
		a. "s" in "cts." inverted (R.4/3)	25·00	40·00
		b. Comma after "cts" (R.9/3)	25·00	40·00
J291		5 c. brown (R.)	..	30	1·50

J292	46	6 c. on 5 c. brown (surch T **21**)	30	80
J293		6 c. on 5 c. brown (surch T **23**)	20	70
		a. "6" inverted (R.7/8)	£400	
J294		15 c. ultramarine	..	4·00	4·00
J295		$1 on 10 c. dull purple (surch T **24**)	30	1·00
J296		$1.50 on 30 c. dull purple and orange (surch T **24**)	30	1·00

The error showing the second character in Type **2** sideways occurred on R.6/3 in the first of four settings only.
The 2 c. orange, 3 c. and 5 c. grey of Perak also exist overprinted with Type **2**, but these stamps were not available to the public (*Price for set of 3 £90 unused*).

25 Tapping Rubber   26 Fruit   27 Japanese Shrine, Singapore

(Litho Kolff & Co, Batavia)

1943 (29 Apr–1 Oct). *T* **25/7** *and similar designs. P* 12½.

J297	25	1 c. grey-green (1 Oct)	..	15	35
J298	26	2 c. pale emerald (1 June)	..	15	15
J299	25	3 c. drab (1 Oct)	..	15	15
J300	—	4 c. carmine-rose	..	15	15
J301	—	8 c. dull blue	..	15	15
J302	—	10 c. brown-purple (1 Oct)	..	15	15
J303	27	15 c. violet (1 Oct)	..	35	75
J304	—	30 c. olive-green (1 Oct)	..	35	45
J305	—	50 c. blue (1 Oct)	..	75	75
J306	—	70 c. blue (1 Oct)	..	12·00	10·00
J297/306			*Set of 10*	13·00	11·50

Designs: *Vert*—4 c. Tin dredger; 8 c. War Memorial, Bukit Timah, Singapore; 10 c. Fishing village; 30 c. Sago palms; 50 c. Straits of Johore. *Horiz*—70 c. Malay Mosque, Kuala Lumpur.

28 Ploughman   29 Rice-planting

1943 (1 Sept). *Savings Campaign. Litho. P* 12½.

J307	28	8 c. violet	..	7·00	2·75
J308		15 c. scarlet	..	6·00	2·75

(Des Hon Chin. Litho)

1944 (15 Feb). *"Re-birth" of Malaya. P* 12½.

J309	29	8 c. rose-red	..	8·00	2·75
J310		15 c. magenta	..	4·00	3·00

大日本
マライ郵便
50 セント
(30)

大日本
マライ郵便
1 ドル
(31)

大日本
マライ郵便
1½ ドル
(32)

1944 (16 Dec). *Stamps intended for use on Red Cross letters. Surch with T* **30/2** *in red*. (a) *On Straits Settlements*

J311	58	50 c. on 50 c. black/*emerald*	8·50	18·00
J312		$1 on $1 black and red/*blue*	13·00	24·00
J313		$1.50 on $2 green and scarlet	21·00	55·00

(b) *On Johore*

J314	29	50 c. on 50 c. dull purple and red	7·00	15·00
J315		$1.50 on $2 green and carmine	5·50	11·00

(c) *On Selangor*

J316	48	$1 on $1 black and red/*blue*	4·00	11·00
J317		$1.50 on $2 green and scarlet	6·00	14·00

Nos. J311/17 were issued in Singapore but were withdrawn after one day, probably because supplies of Nos. J295/6 were received and issued on the 18 December.

POSTAGE DUE STAMPS

Postage Due stamps of the Malayan Postal Union overprinted.

1942 (3 Apr). *Handstamped as T* **1** *in black*.

JD21	D **1**	1 c. slate-purple	..	11·00	14·00
		a. Red opt	..	28·00	30·00
		b. Brown opt	..	48·00	55·00
JD22		3 c. green	..	21·00	23·00
		a. Red opt	..	50·00	55·00
JD23		4 c. green	..	15·00	15·00
		a. Red opt	..	22·00	32·00
		b. Brown opt	..	60·00	70·00
JD24		8 c. scarlet	..	22·00	25·00
		a. Red opt	..	48·00	48·00
		b. Brown opt	..	70·00	70·00
JD25		10 c. yellow-orange	..	15·00	19·00
		a. Red opt	..	32·00	32·00
		b. Brown opt	..	28·00	35·00
JD26		12 c. ultramarine	..	17·00	24·00
		a. Red opt	..	60·00	60·00
JD27		50 c. black	..	42·00	50·00
		a. Red opt	..	£130	£140

1942. *Optd with T* 16.			
JD28 D 1	1 c. slate-purple	1·00	3·50
JD29	3 c. green	5·00	8·00
JD30	4 c. green	5·00	8·00
JD31	8 c. scarlet	6·00	9·00
JD32	10 c. yellow-orange	1·60	6·00
JD33	12 c. ultramarine	1·60	9·00

The 9 c. and 15 c. also exist with this overprint, but these were not issued (*Price £200 each unused*).

1943–45. *Optd with T* 2.
JD34 D 1	1 c. slate-purple	30	1·75
JD35	3 c. green	30	1·90
JD36	4 c. green	24·00	28·00
JD37	5 c. scarlet	50	2·50
JD38	9 c. yellow-orange	60	3·25
	a. Opt inverted	24·00	32·00
JD39	10 c. yellow-orange	60	3·25
	a. Opt inverted	40·00	45·00
JD40	12 c. ultramarine	60	4·25
JD41	15 c. ultramarine	60	4·25

IX. THAI OCCUPATION OF MALAYA

Stamps issued for use in the four Malay States of Kedah, Kelantan, Perlis and Trengganu, ceded by Japan to Thailand on 19 October 1943 and restored to British rule on the defeat of the Japanese.
Before the appearance of Nos. TM1/6 Japanese Occupation issues continued in use.

PRICES FOR STAMPS ON COVER
Nos. TK1/5	from × 30
Nos. TM1/6	from × 40
Nos. TT1/29	from × 12

KELANTAN

TK 1

(Typo Kelantan Ptg Dept, Khota Baru)

1943 (15 Nov). *Handstamped with State arms in violet. No gum. P* 11.
TK1 TK 1	1 c. black		75·00	90·00
TK2	2 c. black		80·00	95·00
	a. Handstamp omitted		£325	
TK3	4 c. black		80·00	95·00
	a. Handstamp omitted		£325	
TK4	8 c. black		80·00	95·00
	a. Handstamp omitted		£325	
TK5	10 c. black		85·00	£110

Nos. TK1/5 were printed in sheets of 84 (12×7) and have sheet watermarks in the form of "STANDARD" in block capitals with curved "CROWN" above and "AGENTS" below in double-lined capitals. This watermark occurs four times in the sheet.
Sheets were imperforate at top and left so that stamps exist imperforate at top, left or at top and left.
Similar stamps, but with red handstamps, were for fiscal use.

GENERAL ISSUE

TM 1 War Memorial

(Litho Defence Ministry, Bangkok)

1944 (15 Jan–4 Mar). *Thick opaque, or thin semi-transparent paper. Gummed or ungummed. P* 12½.
TM1 TM 1	1 c. yellow (4 Mar)		15·00	17·00
TM2	2 c. red-brown		6·00	11·00
	a. Imperf (pair)		£350	
	b. Perf 12½×11		—	
TM3	3 c. green (4 Mar)		10·00	20·00
	a. Perf 12½×11		—	
TM4	4 c. purple (4 Mar)		7·00	14·00
	a. Perf 12½×11		—	
TM5	8 c. carmine (4 Mar)		5·00	12·00
	a. Perf 12½×11		—	20·00
TM6	15 c. blue (4 Mar)		15·00	24·00
	a. Perf 12½×11		—	

5 c. and 10 c. stamps in this design were prepared, but never issued.

TRENGGANU

TRENGGANU
(TT 1)

(Overprinted at Trengganu Survey Office)
1944 (1 Oct). *Various stamps optd with Type* TT 1.
(i) *On Trengganu stamp optd as T* 1
TT 1	4	8 c. carmine (J104)		£150 85·00

(ii) *On stamps optd with T* 16. (a) *Pahang*
TT 2	15	12 c. bright ultramarine (J243)		£140 85·00

(b) *Trengganu*
TT 3	4	2 c. on 5 c. purple/*yellow* (J121)*	£150	£150
TT 4		8 c. on 10 c. brt blue (J127) (inverted)	85·00	85·00
TT 5		12 c. brt ultramarine (J128) (inverted)	85·00	85·00

"This is spelt "TRENGANU" with one "G"."

(iii) *On stamps optd with T* 2. (a) *Straits Settlements*
TT 6	58	12 c. ultramarine (J264)	£150	£150
TT 7		40 c. scarlet and dull purple (J265)	£150	£150

(b) *Perak*
TT 8	51	30 c. dull purple and orange (J278)	£300	£150

(c) *Selangor*
TT 9	46	3 c. green (J282)	85·00	80·00
TT10		12 c. brt ultramarine (J283) (L. to R.)	75·00	70·00
TT11		12 c. brt ultramarine (J283) (R. to L.)	70·00	70·00
		a. Sideways second character	£850	£850

(iv) *On Selangor stamps optd with T* 19
TT12	46	2 c. on 5 c. brown (J289)	£150	£150
TT13		3 c. on 5 c. brown (J290)	£150	£150

(v) *On pictorials of* 1943 (*Nos.* J297/306)
TT14	25	1 c. grey-green	£140	£160
TT15	26	2 c. pale emerald	£140	90·00
TT16	25	3 c. drab	£150	£150
TT17		4 c. carmine-rose	£150	£150
TT18		8 c. dull blue	£275	£275
TT19		10 c. brown-purple	£500	£500
TT20	27	15 c. violet	£180	£140
TT21		30 c. olive-green	£170	£110
TT22		50 c. blue	£275	£275
TT23		70 c. blue	£450	£450

(vi) *On Savings Campaign stamps* (*Nos.* J307/8)
TT24	28	8 c. violet	£250	£250
TT25		15 c. scarlet	£225	£225

(vii) *On stamps of Japan*
TT26		5 s. claret (No. 396)	£190	£200
TT27		25 s. brown and chocolate (No. 329)	£100	80·00
TT28		30 s. blue-green (No. 330)	£190	£140

(viii) *On Trengganu Postage Due stamp optd with T* 1
TT29	D 1	1 c. scarlet (JD17)	£750	£750

X. LABUAN

CROWN COLONY

The island of Labuan, off the northern coast of Borneo, was ceded to Great Britain by the Sultan of Brunei in December 1846.

Stamps of STRAITS SETTLEMENTS were used from 1867 until 1879. Covers of 1864 and 1865 are known from Labuan franked with stamps of INDIA or HONG KONG.

PRICES FOR STAMPS ON COVER
Nos. 1/4	—
Nos. 5/10	from × 20
Nos. 11/13	—
Nos. 14/21	from × 15
Nos. 22/5	—
Nos. 26/35	from × 20
Nos. 36/8	—
Nos. 39/47	from × 100
Nos. 49/50	from × 12
Nos. 51/7	from × 60
Nos. 62/74	from × 15
Nos. 75/9	from × 30
Nos. 80/8	from × 20
Nos. 89/97	from × 15
Nos. 98/110	from × 10
Nos. 111/35	from × 30
Nos. 136/40	—
Nos. D1/9	from × 20

1   (2)   (3)

(Recess D.L.R.)

1879 (May). *Wmk CA over Crown, sideways. P* 14.
1	1	2 c. blue-green	£550	£450
2		6 c. orange-brown	£140	£130
3		12 c. carmine	£850	£425
		a. No right foot to second Chinese character (R. 2/3)	£1200	£600
4		16 c. blue	40·00	65·00

This watermark is always found sideways, and extends over two stamps, a single specimen showing only a portion of the Crown or the letters CA, these being tall and far apart. This paper was chiefly used for long fiscal stamps.

1880 (Jan)–82. *Wmk Crown CC. P* 14.
5	1	2 c. yellow-green	9·50	13·00
6		6 c. orange-brown	65·00	75·00
7		8 c. carmine (4.82)	65·00	70·00
8		10 c. brown	60·00	70·00
9		12 c. carmine	£170	£190
		a. No right foot to second Chinese character	£300	£325
10		16 c. blue (1881)	55·00	50·00
5/10			Set of 6 £375	£425

1880 (Aug). (a) *No.* 9 *surch with T* 2 *in black and with the original value obliterated by manuscript bar in red or black.*
11		8 c. on 12 c. carmine	£550	£450
		a. Type 2 inverted	£550	£450
		b. "12" not obliterated	£750	£600
		c. As b. with Type 2 inverted		
		d. No right foot to second Chinese character	£750	£650

(b) *No.* 4 *surch with two upright figures and No.* 9 *surch with two at right angles as T* 3.
12		6 c. on 16 c. blue (R.)	£1000	£550
		a. With one "6" only		
13		8 c. on 12 c. carmine	£700	£500
		a. Both "8's" upright		
		b. Upright "8" inverted	£750	£550
		c. No right foot to second Chinese character	£900	£700

Eight Cents	Eight Cents	
(4)	(5)	(6)

1881 (Mar). *No.* 9 *handstamped with T* 4.
14		8 c. on 12 c. carmine	£160	£200
		a. No right foot to second Chinese character	£300	£350

1881 (June). *No.* 9 *surch with T* 5.
15		8 c. on 12 c. carmine	70·00	80·00
		a. Surch double	£600	£600
		b. Surch inverted	£4500	
		c. "Eighr"	£6500	
		d. No right foot to second Chinese character	£130	£150

The error "Eighr" occurred on R. 2/1 of the first printing, but was soon corrected.

1883. *Wmk Crown CA. P* 14.
17	1	2 c. yellow-green	10·00	13·00
		a. Imperf between (horiz pair)	£4000	
18		8 c. carmine	£120	65·00
19		10 c. yellow-brown	19·00	28·00
20		16 c. blue	65·00	85·00
21		40 c. amber	8·50	27·00
17/21			Set of 5 £190	£190

1883 (May). *No.* 10 *surch "One Dollar A.S.H." by hand, as T* 6.
22	1	$1 on 16 c. blue (R.)		£1900

The initials are those of the postmaster, Mr. A. S. Hamilton.

2 Cents	2 Cents	2 Cents
(7)	(8)	(9)

1885 (June). *Nos.* 18 *and* 10 *handstamped as T* 7.
23	1	2 c. on 8 c. carmine		75·00
24		2 c. on 16 c. blue	£700	£700

1885 (July). *No.* 20 *surch as T* 8.
25	1	2 c. on 16 c. blue	85·00	£120
		a. Surch double	—	£1400

1885 (Sept). *No.* 18 *handstamped diag as T* 9.
26	1	2 c. on 8 c. carmine	38·00	55·00

1885 (Sept)–86. *Wmk Crown CA. P* 14.
30	1	2 c. rose-red	1·50	4·75
		a. Pale rose-red (1886)	1·50	4·75
31		8 c. deep violet	12·00	7·00
		a. Mauve (1886)	15·00	8·00
32		10 c. sepia (1886)	4·50	14·00
33		16 c. grey (1886)	65·00	55·00
30/3			Set of 4 75·00	65·00
30/3 Optd "Specimen"			Set of 4 £350	

ISSUES OF BRITISH NORTH BORNEO COMPANY

From 1 January 1890 while remaining a Crown Colony, the administration of Labuan was transferred to the British North Borneo Co, which issued the following stamps.

6 Cents	Two Cents	Six Cents
(10)	(11)	(12)

1891 (July)–92. *Handstamped with T* 10.
34	1	6 c. on 8 c. deep violet (No. 31)	32·00	26·00
		a. Surch inverted	65·00	60·00
		b. Surch double	£170	
		c. Surch double, one inverted	£300	
		d. "Cents" omitted	£225	£225
		e. Imperf between (horiz pair)		
		f. Pair, one without surch, one surch inverted	£550	

35	1	6 c. on 8 c. mauve (No. 31a)	4·50	4·50
		a. Surch inverted	30·00	30·00
		b. Surch double, one inverted	£325	
		c. Surch double, both inverted	£325	
		d. "6" omitted	£300	
		e. Pair, one without surcharge	£450	£450
		f. Inverted. "Cents" omitted	£300	
		g. Pair, one without surch, one surch inverted	£550	
		h. Surch double	£160	
36		6 c. on 8 c. mauve (R.) (No. 31a) (2.92)	£375	£200
		a. Surch inverted	£475	£250
37		6 c. on 16 c. blue (No. 4) (3.92)	£1300	£1200
		a. Surch inverted	£2500	£2000
38		6 c. on 40 c. amber (No. 21)	£4000	£2500
		a. Surch inverted	£3000	£3000

There are two different versions of Type **10** with the lines of the surcharge either 1 mm or 2 mm apart.

(Recess D.L.R.)

1892–93. *No wmk. P* 14.

39	1	2 c. rose-lake	1·00	3·50
40		6 c. bright green	5·00	4·50
41		8 c. violet	2·25	4·50
		a. Pale violet (1893)	3·25	4·50
43		10 c. brown	3·75	7·00
		a. Sepia-brown (1893)	3·75	7·50
45		12 c. bright blue	3·25	6·00
		a. No right foot to second Chinese character	10·00	15·00
46		16 c. grey	3·25	6·00
47		40 c. ochre	16·00	24·00
		a. Brown-buff (1893)	17·00	30·00
39/47			*Set of* 7 30·00	50·00

The 6 c., 12 c., 16 c. and 40 c. are in sheets of 10, as are all the earlier issues. The other values are in sheets of 30.

1892 (Dec). *Nos.* 47 *and* 46 *surch locally as T* 11 *or* 12.

49	1	2 c. on 40 c. ochre (13 December)	£110	75·00
		a. Surch inverted	£250	£325
50		6 c. on 16 c. grey (20 December)	£190	£120
		a. Surch inverted	£225	£200

There are 10 slightly different versions of each of these surcharges.

CANCELLED-TO-ORDER. Prices are separately indicated, in a third price column, for stamps showing the recognisable black bars remainder cancellation. Earlier issues of the Company administration were also so treated, but, as postal cancellations were used, these cannot be identified.

(Litho D.L.R.)

1894 (April). *No wmk. P* 14.

51	1	2 c. carmine-pink	1·10	5·00	20
52		6 c. bright green	5·50	9·50	20
		a. Imperf between (horiz pair)	£3250		
53		8 c. bright mauve	5·00	8·00	20
54		10 c. brown	12·00	13·00	20
55		12 c. pale blue	13·00	20·00	25
		a. No right foot to second Chinese character	25·00	35·00	
56		16 c. grey	15·00	27·00	25
57		40 c. orange-buff	21·00	35·00	30
51/7			*Set of* 7 65·00	£100	1·25
51/7 H/S "Specimen"			*Set of* 7 £100		

Collectors are warned against forgeries of this issue.

PERFORATION. There are a number of small variations in the perforation of the Waterlow issues of 1894 to 1905 which we believe to be due to irregularity of the pins rather than different perforators.

In the following lists, stamps perf 12, 12½, 13 or compound are described as perf 12–13, stamps perf 13½, 14 or compound are described as perf 13½–14 and those perf 14½, 15 or compound are listed as perf 14½–15. In addition the 13½–14 perforation exists compound with 14½–15 and with 12–13, whilst perf 16 comes from a separate perforator.

LABUAN

40

CENTS

13 (14)

1894 (May)–**96.** *T* 24/32 *of North Borneo (colours changed), with* "LABUAN" *engraved on vignette plate as T* **13** (8, 12, 24 c.) *or horizontally (others). P* 14½–15.

(a) Name and central part of design in black

62	24	1 c. grey-mauve	1·50	3·75	20
		a. Imperf between (vert pair)	£400	—	£250
		b. Perf 13½–14	4·00	6·50	—
		c. Perf 13½–14, comp 14½–15	10·00		
		d. Perf 13½–14, comp 12–13	9·00	8·00	—
		e. Perf 12–13			
63	25	2 c. blue	2·50	4·25	20
		a. Imperf (pair)	£400		
		b. Perf 13½–14	3·00	4·75	—
		c. Perf 13½–14, comp 14½–15			
		d. Perf 13½–14, comp 12–13			
		e. Perf 12–13			
64	26	3 c. ochre	3·25	6·50	20
		a. Perf 13½–14	3·75	6·50	—
		b. Perf 13½–14, comp 14½–15			
		c. Perf 13½–14, comp 12–13			
		d. Perf 12–13			
65	27	5 c. green	15·00	13·00	20
		a. Perf 13½–14	15·00	7·50	—
		ab. Imperf between (horiz pair)			
		b. Perf 13½–14, comp 12–13	16·00		

67	28	6 c. brown-lake	2·50	6·00	20
		a. Imperf (pair)	£400	—	£225
		b. Perf 13½–14			1·25
		c. Perf 13½–14, comp 14½–15			70
		d. Perf 13½–14, comp 12–13			
		e. Perf 12–13			
68	29	8 c. rose-red	9·00	16·00	30
		a. Perf 13½–14	12·00	18·00	
69		8 c. pink (1896)	7·00	19·00	30
		a. Perf 13½–14	12·00		
70	30	12 c. orange-vermilion	16·00	32·00	30
		a. Perf 13½–14	28·00	35·00	2·00
		b. Perf 12–13			
		c. Perf 13½–14, comp 12–13			
71	31	18 c. olive-brown	22·00	35·00	30
		a. Perf 13½–14	26·00		
72		18 c. olive-bistre (1896)	28·00	38·00	30
		a. Perf 13½–14	26·00	35·00	—
		b. Perf 13½–14, comp 12–13			
		c. Imperf between (vert pair)	†	†	£400

(b) Name and central part in blue

73	32	24 c. pale mauve	13·00	28·00	30
74		24 c. dull lilac (1896)	13·00	28·00	30
		a. Perf 13½–14	13·00	28·00	—
62/74			*Set of* 9 75·00	£120	2·00
62/74 Optd "Specimen"			*Set of* 9 £120		

1895 (June). *No.* 83 *of North Borneo ($1 inscr* "STATE OF NORTH BORNEO") *surch as T* 14.

75	32c	4 c. on $1 scarlet	1·00	1·25	30
76		10 c. on $1 scarlet	1·25	1·40	30
77		20 c. on $1 scarlet	12·00	6·00	30
78		30 c. on $1 scarlet	15·00	18·00	30
79		40 c. on $1 scarlet	11·00	10·00	30
75/9			*Set of* 5 35·00	32·00	1·40
75/9 Optd "Specimen"			*Set of* 5 80·00		

No. 76 exists with the figures of the surcharge 2½ mm away from "CENTS". The normal setting has a space of 4 mm. Examples of the narrow setting have, so far, only been seen on cancelled-to-order stamps.

1846		4
	JUBILEE	
LABUAN	1896	**CENTS**
(15)	(16)	(17)

1896. *T* 32a *to* 32c *of North Borneo (as Nos.* 81 *to* 83, *but colours changed) optd with T* 15.

80		25 c. green	15·00	15·00	50
		a. Opt omitted	11·00	—	1·25
		b. Imperf (pair)			
		ba. Opt omitted	28·00		
		bb. Stamps ptd double, one inverted			
81		50 c. maroon	15·00	16·00	50
		a. Opt omitted	12·00	—	1·25
		b. Imperf (pair)			
		ba. Opt omitted	30·00		
		bb. Stamps ptd double			
82		$1 blue	30·00	22·00	50
		a. Opt omitted	15·00	—	1·25
		b. Imperf (pair)			
		ba. Opt omitted	32·00		
80/82 Optd "Specimen"			*Set of* 3 60·00		

Nos. 80bb and 81bb are from waste sheets subsequently sold by the British North Borneo Company to collectors.

1896 (24 Sept). *Jubilee of Cession of Labuan to Gt Britain. Nos.* 62 *to* 68 *optd with T* 16. *P* 14½–15.

83		1 c. black and grey-mauve	13·00	16·00	50
		b. Opt in orange	£170	£170	†
		c. "JEBILEE" (R. 8/7)	—	£375	£250
		d. "JUBILE" (R. 3/10)			
		e. Perf 13½–14	13·00	20·00	—
		ea. Opt double	£170	£170	—
		eb. Opt in orange	£170	£170	†
		f. Perf 13½–14, comp 12–13	17·00	13·00	—
		fa. Opt in orange	—	£170	†
		g. Perf 12–13			
84		2 c. black and blue	16·00	12·00	50
		a. Imperf horiz (vert pair)	£325	£375	†
		b. "JEBILEE" (R. 8/7)	£475	£475	—
		c. "JUBILE" (R. 3/10)			
		d. Perf 13½–14	18·00	12·00	—
		e. Perf 13½–14, comp 14½–15			—
		f. Perf 13½–14, comp 12–13	25·00		
85		3 c. black and ochre	18·00	20·00	50
		c. "JEBILEE" (R. 8/7)	—	£850	£600
		d. Perf 13½–14	25·00	25·00	—
		db. Opt double	£650		
		e. Perf 13½–14, comp 14½–15			—
		f. Perf 13½–14, comp 12–13			—
		fa. Opt double	£170	£170	£130
		fb. Opt treble	£650		
86		5 c. black and green	30·00	16·00	50
		a. Opt double	£200	£200	—
		b. Perf 13½–14	30·00	16·00	—
		c. Perf 13½–14, comp 12–13			
87		6 c. black and brown-lake	14·00	17·00	50
		a. Opt double	£250	£250	—
		b. "JUBILE" (R. 3/10)	£900		
		c. Perf 13½–14, comp 14½–15			
88		8 c. black and pink	21·00	11·00	50
		a. Perf 13½–14	19·00	11·00	—
		b. Perf 13½–14, comp 14½–15	30·00		
83/8			*Set of* 6 £100	80·00	2·75
83/8 Optd "Specimen"			*Set of* 6 £140		

No. 84b is known in a vertical strip of 3 imperf horizontally except at the base of the bottom stamp (*Price,* £3500 *unused*).

1897 (Apr)–**1901.** *T* 34/45 *of North Borneo (colours changed), with* "LABUAN" *engraved on vignette plate as T* **13** (8, 10, 12, 24 c.) *or horizontally (others). Name and central part in black (24 c. in blue). P* 13½–14.

89	34	1 c. greyish purple (p 14½–15)	2·25	3·50	20
		a. Perf 13½–14, comp 14½–15			
		b. Brown (1901)	3·00	5·50	—
		ba. Perf 14½–15	3·75		
		bb. Perf 16	9·00	13·00	

90	35	2 c. blue	5·50	3·25	20
		a. Imperf between (vert pair)	†	†	£275
		b. Imperf between (horiz pair)	†	†	£300
		c. Perf 14½–15	10·00		
		d. Perf 13½–14, comp 12–13	18·00	13·00	—
		e. Perf 16			5·00
91	36	3 c. ochre	8·50	9·50	20
		a. Imperf between (vert pair)	£400	†	—
		b. Perf 14½–15	7·00	5·00	—
		c. Perf 13½–14, comp 12–13			
92	38	5 c. green	23·00	25·00	25
		a. Perf 14½–15	20·00	24·00	—
		b. Perf 13½–14, comp 12–13			
93	39	6 c. brown-lake	6·00	15·00	50
		a. Perf 14½–15	3·50	15·00	—
		ba. Imperf between (vert pair)	†	†	£250
		b. Perf 13½–14, comp 12–13	—	—	3·00
94	40	8 c. rose-red			30
		a. Perf 14½–15	13·00	10·00	—
		b. Perf 13½–14, comp 12–13	17·00	—	2·75
		c. Vermilion	6·50	—	30
		ca. Perf 16			3·00
95	42	12 c. vermilion	32·00	42·00	40
		a. Perf 14½–15	19·00	30·00	—
96	44	18 c. olive-bistre	24·00	28·00	40
		a. Imperf between (vert pair)	†	†	—
		b. Perf 16	15·00	26·00	—
97	45	24 c. grey-lilac	13·00	30·00	40
		a. Perf 14½–15	10·00		
89/97			*Set of* 9 80·00	£130	2·25
89/97 Optd "Specimen"			*Set of* 9 £120		

The 12, 18 and 24 c. above were errors; in the 12 c., "LABUAN" is over the value at the top; the 18 c. has "POSTAL REVENUE" instead of "POSTAGE AND REVENUE", and the 24 c. is without "POSTAGE AND REVENUE".

1897 (Nov)–**98.** *(a) Types of North Borneo (colours changed), with* "LABUAN" *engraved on the vignette plate as in T* **13**. *P* 13½–14.

98	42	12 c. black and vermilion (3.98)	†	—	1·50
		a. Perf 14½–15	28·00	32·00	—
		b. Perf 13½–14, comp 14½–15			
		c. Perf 16	30·00	32·00	—
99	46	18 c. black and olive-bistre			
		a. Perf 14½–15	60·00	60·00	—
		b. Perf 16	†		6·50
100	47	24 c. blue and lilac-brown	15·00	38·00	
		a. Perf 14½–15	15·00	38·00	—
		b. Perf 13½–14, comp 12–13			
		c. Perf 16	18·00		
		d. Blue and ochre (p 14½–15)			
98/100 Optd "Specimen"			*Set of* 2 38·00		

In the 12 c. "LABUAN" is now correctly placed at foot of stamp. The 18 c. and 24 c. have the inscriptions on the stamps corrected, but the 18 c. still has "LABUAN" over the value at foot, and was further corrected as follows.

(b) As No. 99, but "LABUAN" at top

101	46	18 c. black and olive-bistre (Optd S. £25)	30·00	38·00	
		a. Perf 14½–15	23·00	40·00	
		b. Perf 13½–14, comp 12–13	22·00	35·00	
		c. Perf 12–13			

1899. *Surch with T* 17. *(a) P* 14½–15.

102	38	4 c. on 5 c. (No. 92a)	18·00	26·00	
103	39	4 c. on 6 c. (No. 93b)	15·00	19·00	
		a. Perf 13½–14	20·00		
		b. Perf 13½–14, comp 12–13			
104	40	4 c. on 8 c. (No. 94a)	30·00	32·00	
		a. Perf 13½–14	15·00	25·00	
		b. Perf 12–13	22·00		
105	42	4 c. on 12 c. (No. 98a)	23·00	29·00	
		a. Perf 13½–14	23·00		
		b. Perf 16	23·00	35·00	
		c. Perf 13½–14, comp 12–13			
106	46	4 c. on 18 c (No. 101a)	15·00	17·00	
		a. Surch double	£250	£300	
107	47	4 c. on 24 c. (No. 100a)	15·00	20·00	
		a. Perf 13½–14	14·00	25·00	
		b. Perf 13½–14, comp 12–13	18·00	22·00	
		c. Perf 16	25·00		

(b) P 14

108	32a	4 c. on 25 c. (No. 80)	5·50	7·50	
109	32b	4 c. on 50 c. (No. 81)	5·50	7·50	
110	32c	4 c. on $1 (No. 82)	5·50	7·50	
102/110 Optd "Specimen"			*Set of* 9 £120		

The 1 c., 2 c. and 3 c. values of this set were also surcharged "4 CENTS" but were not issued. They exist overprinted "Specimen" (*Price* £80 *the set of three*).

1900–02. *Types of North Borneo with* "LABUAN" *engraved on the vignette plate as in T* **13**, *in green on* 16 c *P* 13½–14.

111	35	2 c. black and green	3·50	2·50	20
		a. Perf 13½–14, comp 12–13			
112	37	4 c. black and yellow-brown	4·25	15·00	25
		a. Imperf between (vert pair)	£375		
		b. Perf 13½–14, comp 12–13			
113		4 c. black and carmine (8.1900)	7·00	2·75	20
		a. Perf 14½–15	6·00	4·50	—
		b. Perf 13½–14, comp 12–13	14·00	5·50	—
		c. Perf 16			
114	38	5 c. black and pale blue	18·00	18·00	50
		a. Perf 13½–14, comp 12–13	—	35·00	—
115	41	10 c. brown & slate-lilac (p 14½–15) (1902)	30·00	45·00	40
116	43	16 c. green and chestnut (1902)	40·00	48·00	1·50
		a. Perf 13½–14, comp 12–13	42·00	50·00	—
		b. Perf 12–13			
		c. Perf 14½–15			
111/16 Optd "Specimen"			*Set of* 6 £100		

No. 112 was printed in an incorrect frame colour and was not issued for postal purposes in Labuan. Used examples come from dealers' stock sent to the island for cancellation.

4 cents

18   (19)

(Recess Waterlow)

1902 (Sept)–03. *P* 13½–14.

116d	18	1 c. black and purple (10.03)	2·50	3·75	20
		da. Perf 14½–15	—	5·00	
117		2 c. black and green	2·50	2·75	20
		a. Perf 14½–15		4·00	
117b		3 c. black and sepia (10.03)	2·50	3·50	20
118		4 c. black and carmine	2·50	2·75	20
		a. Perf 14½–15	2·75		—
		b. Perf 13½–14, comp 12–13		25·00	—
119		8 c. black and vermilion	2·00	4·25	20
		a. Perf 14½–15	8·50		
120		10 c. brown and slate-blue	2·50	5·00	20
		b. Perf 14½–15	2·75		
		ba. Imperf between (vert pair)	†	†	£375
121		12 c. black and yellow	3·00	6·00	20
		a. Imperf between (vert strip of 3)	†	†	£2000
		b. Perf 16	3·00		
122		16 c. green and brown	2·50	7·50	20
		a. Imperf between (vert pair)	†	—	
123		18 c. black and pale brown	2·50	7·00	20
124		25 c. green and greenish blue	2·50	8·50	20
		a. Perf 14½–15	10·00		
		b. Error. Black and greenish blue	—	†	£225
125		50 c. dull purple and lilac	9·00	19·00	30
		a. Perf 13½–14, comp 12–13	14·00		
126		$1 claret and orange	4·00	21·00	40
		a. Perf 14½–15	11·00		
116d/26			Set of 12	35·00	80·00	2·40
116d/26		Optd "Specimen"	Set of 12	£160		

1904 (Dec). *Issues of 1895 and 1897–8 surch with T* 19.

(a) *P* 14½–15.

127	38	4 c. on 5 c. (No. 92a)	18·00	27·00	5·00
128	39	4 c. on 6 c. (No. 93b)	12·00	26·00	5·00
129	40	4 c. on 8 c. (No. 94a)	16·00	28·00	5·00
130	42	4 c. on 12 c. (No. 98a)	19·00	28·00	5·00
		a. Perf 16	20·00	30·00	
131	46	4 c. on 18 c. (No. 101) (p 13½–14)	15·00	26·00	5·00
		a. Perf 13½–14, comp 12–13	20·00		
		b. Perf 12–13			
132	47	4 c. on 24 c. (No. 100a)	13·00	26·00	5·00
		a. Perf 13½–14	13·00		
		b. Perf 13½–14, comp 12–13	20·00		
		c. Perf 16	26·00		

(b) *P* 14

133	32a	4 c. on 25 c. (No. 80)	8·50	18·00	5·00
134	32b	4 c. on 50 c. (No. 81)	8·50	18·00	5·00
		a. Surch double	£225		
		b. Surch triple			
135	32c	4 c. on $1 (No. 82)	8·50	18·00	5·00

LABUAN   LABUAN

(20)   (21)

1905 (Feb–Nov). *Nos. 81, 83 (in Labuan colour), and 84/6 of North Borneo optd locally with T* 20 (25 *c.,* $2) *or* 21 *others*).

136	32a	25 c. indigo	£700	†	—
137	32c	$1 blue	†	†	£425
138	32d	$2 dull green	£2250	£2250	—
139	14	$5 bright purple	£3000	†	£750
140	15	$10 brown (11.05)	£10000	†	£4000

Dangerous forgeries exist.
The overprint on No. 138 is 12 mm long.
No. 137 is said to have been issued in 1899.

POSTAGE DUE STAMPS

POSTAGE DUE

(D 1)

1901. *Optd with Type* D 1, *reading vertically upwards. P* 13½–14.

D1	35	2 c. black and green (111)	8·50	14·00	30
		a. Opt double	£200		
		b. Perf 13½–14, comp 12–13			
D2	36	3 c. black and ochre (91)	13·00	55·00	40
		a. Perf 13½–14, comp 12–13			
D3	37	4 c. black and carmine (113)	16·00	55·00	40
		a. Opt double	†	†	£200
		b. Perf 14½–15	18·00		
		c. Perf 13½–14, comp 12–13			
D4	38	5 c. black and pale blue (114)	22·00	55·00	40
		a. Perf 14½–15	26·00		
D5	39	6 c. black and brown-lake (93)	11·00	55·00	50
		a. Perf 14½–15	16·00		
		b. Perf 16	22·00		
D6	40	8 c. black and vermilion (94c)	27·00	55·00	60
		a. Frame inverted (p 14½–15)	†	†	£3750
		b. Perf 14½–15	20·00		75
		c. Perf 16	28·00		
		d. Black and rose-red (94)	32·00		
		da. Perf 14½–15			6·50
		db. Perf 13½–14, comp 12–13			
D7	42	12 c. black and vermilion (98)	45·00	55·00	2·00
		a. Opt reading downwards	†	†	£225
		b. Perf 14½–15	48·00		
D8	46	18 c. blk & ol-bistre (101) (p 14½–15)	13·00	55·00	1·00

D9	47	24 c. blue and lilac-brown (100)	22·00	55·00	1·00
		a. Perf 13½–14, comp 12–13			
		b. Perf 14½–15	22·00		
		ba. Blue and ochre	32·00		
		c. Perf 16	24·00	55·00	—
D1/9			Set of 9	£150	£400	6·00

The administration of Labuan reverted to Colonial Office control, as part of an agreement with Brunei, on 1 January 1906. By Letters Patent dated 30 October 1906 Labuan was incorporated with Straits Settlements and ceased issuing its own stamps. In 1946 it became part of the Colony of North Borneo.

XI. SABAH

(*formerly* North Borneo)

NORTH BORNEO

PRICES FOR STAMPS ON COVER TO 1945	
No. 1	from × 100
Nos. 2/3	from × 10
Nos. 4/5	
Nos. 6/19	from × 10
Nos. 19b/21b	
Nos. 22/8	from × 50
Nos. 29/35	
Nos. 36/44	from × 100
Nos. 45/50	
Nos. 51/2	from × 10
No. 54	
Nos. 55/65	from × 10
Nos. 66/79	from × 4
Nos. 81/6	
Nos. 87/91	from × 12
Nos. 92/111	from × 4
Nos. 112/26	from × 10
Nos. 127/40	from × 6
Nos. 141/5	—
Nos. 146/57	from × 5
Nos. 158/79	from × 8
Nos. 181/5	—
Nos. 186/8	from × 10
Nos. 189/230	from × 4
Nos. 231/4	
Nos. 235/49	from × 3
Nos. 250/2	
Nos. 253/75	from × 12
Nos. 276/92	from × 7
Nos. 293/4	
Nos. 295/300	from × 6
Nos. 301/2	
Nos. 303/17	from × 3
Nos. 318/19	from × 20
Nos. 320/34	from × 3
Nos. D1/26	from × 20
Nos. D27/8	
Nos. D29/35	from × 7
No. D35a	
Nos. D36/65	from × 20
Nos. D66/70	from × 5

BRITISH NORTH BORNEO COMPANY ADMINISTRATION

PRINTERS. The stamps of this country up to 1894 were designed by T. Macdonald and printed in lithography by Blades, East and Blades, London.

(1)   (2)   (3)

1883. *P* 12.

1	1	2 c. red-brown	15·00	30·00
		a. Imperf between (horiz pair)		

The figure "2" varies in size.

1883. *No.* 1 *surch as* T 2 *or* 3.

2	2	8 c. on 2 c. red-brown	£800	£550
3	3	8 c. on 2 c. red-brown	£350	£150
		a. Surch double	—	£3250

Type 2 was handstamped and stamps without stop are generally forgeries. Type 3 was a setting of 50 (10 × 5) providing ten varieties; it normally has a stop which sometimes failed to print.

CANCELLED-TO-ORDER—Prices are separately indicated in a third price column, for stamps showing the recognisable black bars remainder cancellation. The issues since 1916 have not been thus cancelled.

It should be noted, however, that a postmark of this form was in use for postal purposes up to this period, and was used at one or two of the smaller post-offices until 1949. A small oval with five bars was used to mark railway mail during 1945/55 and also as a paquebot mark at Jesselton c. 1950.

4   5   and Revenue

        (6)

1883. *P* 14.

4	4	50 c. violet	70·00	—	12·00
		a. Inverted "L" for first "F" in "FIFTY" (R.5/2)	£425	—	£100
5	5	$1 scarlet	50·00	—	8·00

1883. *P* 12.

6	1	4 c. pink	23·00	38·00
		a. Imperf (horiz pair)	†	—
7		8 c. green	45·00	45·00

1886. *P* 14.

8	1	½ c. magenta	50·00	£100
9		1 c. orange	£140	£200
		a. Imperf (pair)	£225	
		b. Imperf horiz (vert pair)		
10		2 c. brown	14·00	16·00
		a. Imperf between (horiz pair)	£450	
11		4 c. pink	14·00	38·00
12		8 c. green	16·00	38·00
		a. Imperf between (horiz pair)	£700	
13		10 c. blue	16·00	35·00
		a. Imperf (pair)	£250	
8/13			Set of 6	£200	£375

Imperforate examples of the 4 c. pink are listed under No. 6a.

1886. *Nos.* 8 *and* 13 *optd with* T 6.

14		½ c. magenta	50·00	£110
15		10 c. blue	90·00	£140

3 CENTS   5 CENTS   3 CENTS

(7)   (8)   Small "3" variety (R.3/1, 3/4, 3/7)

(Surchd by *North Borneo Herald*, Sandakan)

1886. T 1 *surch as* T 7/8. (a) *P* 12.

16	7	3 c. on 4 c. pink	75·00	£150
		a. Small "3"	—	£3500
17	8	5 c. on 8 c. green	£110	£160

(b) *P* 14

18	7	3 c. on 4 c. pink	48·00	85·00
		a. Small "3"	£950	
19	8	5 c. on 8 c. green	60·00	85·00
		a. Surch inverted	£1400	

9

10   11

12   13

1886–87. (a) *P* 14.

21b	9	½ c. magenta	11·00	28·00
22		½ c. rose	1·75	9·00
		a. Imperf (pair)	10·00	
23		1 c. orange-yellow	4·00	14·00
		a. Imperf between (vert pair)	£300	
		b. Imperf (pair)	9·00	
24		1 c. orange	1·50	6·00
		a. Imperf (pair)	6·00	
25		2 c. brown	1·50	6·50
		a. Imperf (pair)	6·00	

26	9	4 c. pink		1·50	6·50
		a. Imperf (pair)		6·00	
		b. Imperf between (horiz or vert pair)		£190	
		c. Imperf vert (horiz pair)		£225	
		d. Error. 1 c. pink (R. 2/3) (centre stamp of strip of 3)		£120	£250
		da. Imperf between (pair)			
		db. Imperf (pair)		£2000	
27		8 c. green		2·50	12·00
		a. Imperf (pair)		8·50	
28		10 c. blue		5·00	20·00
		a. Imperf between (vert pair)		£300	
		b. Imperf (pair)		8·50	
29	10	25 c. indigo		85·00	7·00
		a. Imperf between (vert pair)		70·00	10·00
30	11	50 c. violet		90·00	9·00
		a. Imperf (pair)		60·00	6·00
31	12	$1 scarlet		£140	7·00
		a. Imperf (pair)		75·00	6·00
32	13	$2 sage-green		£170	15·00
		a. Imperf (pair)		90·00	13·00
21b/32			Set of 10	£450	85·00

(b) P 12

34	9	½ c. magenta		90·00	£180
35		1 c. orange		70·00	£100

Nos. 21b/32 are known to have been sold as cancelled remainders, but these are difficult to distinguish from postally used. Values above 10 c. are infrequently found postally used so that the used prices quoted are for the remainders.

14

15   16

17   18

1887–92. *T* 14 (*as T* 9 *but inscr* "POSTAGE & REVENUE") *and T* 15/18 (*T* 10/13 *redrawn*). *P* 14.

36	14	½ c. magenta (1889)		2·50	13·00	—
		a. Imperf vert (horiz pair)		†	†	£200
		b. Rose		30	2·25	30
		ba. Imperf between (horiz pair)		£350	
37		1 c. orange (1892)		60	2·25	30
		a. Imperf vert (horiz pair)		£300	
38		2 c. brown (1889)		4·50	6·00	30
		a. Imperf between (horiz pair)			
		b. Lake-brown		1·00	6·00	30
39		3 c. violet		1·75	8·50	30
		a. Printed triple, one inverted			
40		4 c. rose-pink (1889)		2·50	15·00	30
		a. Imperf between (pair)		—	£120	—
41		5 c. slate		2·00	9·50	30
		a. Imperf between (pair)			
42		6 c. lake (1892)		4·50	12·00	45
43		8 c. blue-green (1891)		7·50	14·00	45
		a. Yellow-green		7·50	12·00	45
		b. Printed triple, one inverted			
44		10 c. blue (1891)		4·75	14·00	50
		a. Imperf between (vert pair)		†	£200	
		b. Dull blue		4·75	12·00	50
		ba. Imperf between (horiz pair)			
		c. Printed double			
45	15	25 c. indigo (1888)		20·00	65·00	50
		a. Imperf (pair)		80·00	—	3·00
		b. Imperf vert (horiz pair)		†	†	£250
46	16	50 c. violet (1888)		38·00	95·00	50
		a. Imperf (pair)		85·00	—	3·00
		b. Chalky blue		†	90·00	†
47	17	$1 scarlet (1888)		22·00	90·00	50
		a. Imperf (pair)		80·00	—	3·00
48	18	$2 dull green (1888)		70·00	£130	1·10
		a. Imperf (pair)		£100	—	3·50
36b/48			Set of 13	£160	£400	4·75

Nos. 36/44 also exist imperf (*Price* £6 *per pair unused*; £4 *cancelled*).

Nos. 39a, 43b and 44c are from waste sheets subsequently sold by the British North Borneo Company to collectors.

These stamps to the 10 c. value were forged on several occasions. Most forgeries of the ½ c. value can be identified by the presence of a diagonal line joining the top two horizontal strokes of the uppermost Chinese character.

The new 25 c. has the inscription "BRITISH NORTH BORNEO" in taller capitals. In the 50 c. the "0" of the numerals "50" in the two upper corners is square-shaped at the top and bottom instead of being oval. The 1 dollar has 14 pearls instead of 13 at each side, and on the 2 dollars the word "BRITISH" measures 10½ to 11 mm in length in place of 12 mm.

---

19   20

1889. *P* 14.

49	19	$5 bright purple		80·00	90·00	6·00
		a. Imperf (pair)		£150	—	16·00
50	20	$10 brown		£120	£160	9·00
		a. Imperf (pair)		£250	—	20·00
		b. "DOLLAPS" for "DOLLARS" (R.2/1)		£900	£1100	£325
		ba. Ditto. Imperf (pair)		£1500	—	£800

Two 6 1
Cents. cents. cent.

(21)   (22)   (23)

1890. *Surch as T* 21, *in red*.

51	15	2 c. on 25 c. indigo		40·00	65·00
		a. Surch inverted		£275	£275
52		8 c. on 25 c. indigo		60·00	80·00

The first printing of Nos. 51/2 had the two lines of the surcharge 3.5 mm apart. On a second printing of both values this gap widened to 5 mm.

1891–92. *Surch with T* 22.

54	9	6 c. on 8 c. green (1892)		£5000	£3500
		a. Large "s" in "cents"		£10000	
55	14	6 c. on 8 c. yellow-green		7·50	8·50
		a. Surch inverted		£180	£250
		b. Inverted "c" in "cents" (R.5/4)		£250	£300
		c. "cetns." for "cents" (R.3/7)		£275	£325
		d. Large "s" in "cents" (R.2/9 or 3/7)		95·00	95·00
56	9	6 c. on 10 c. blue		35·00	17·00
		a. Surch inverted		£130	£130
		b. Surch double			
		c. Surch treble		£275	
		d. Large "s" in "cents"		£120	£110
57	14	6 c. on 10 c. blue		70·00	24·00
		a. Large "s" in "cents"		£225	£140

Unused examples of Nos. 55 and 57 are normally without gum.

There were three settings of the surcharge for No. 55. On the first two the large "s" in "cents" occurred on R.2/9 with the other two listed varieties also included. Nos. 55b/c were corrected on the third setting and the large "s" in cents occurred on R.3/7.

1892. *Surch as T* 23 ("Cents." *with capital* "C" *as in T* 21 *on No.* 65), *in red*.

63	14	1 c. on 4 c. rose-pink		13·00	14·00
		a. Surch double		£650	
		b. Surch on back and on front		—	£500
		ba. As b, but with surch double on front			
64		1 c. on 5 c. slate		6·00	6·00
65	15	8 c. on 25 c. indigo		£110	£130

Unused examples of Nos. 63/5 are normally without gum.

24 Dyak Chief   25 Sambar Stag (*Cervus unicolor*)   26 Sago Palm

27 Great Argus Pheasant   28 Arms of the Company

29 Malay Dhow   30 Estuarine Crocodile

---

31 Mount Kinabalu   32 Arms of the Company with Supporters

PERFORATION. There are a number of small variations in the perforation of the Waterlow issues of 1894 to 1922 which we believe were due to irregularity of the pins rather than different perforators.

In the following lists, stamps perf 12, 12½, 13 or compound are described as perf 12–13, stamps perf 13½, 14 or compound are described as perf 13½–14 and those perf 14½, 15 or compound are listed as perf 14½–15. In addition the 13½–14 perforation exists compound with 14½–15 and with 12–13, whilst perf 15½–16 comes from a separate perforator.

(Recess Waterlow)

1894. *P* 14½–15.

66	24	1 c. black and olive-bistre		1·25	6·00	20
		a. Imperf between (horiz or vert pair)		£475		
		b. Perf 13½–14		1·25	6·00	20
		c. Perf 13½–14, comp 14½–15		24·00	35·00	
		d. Perf 13½–14, comp 12–13		11·00	28·00	
		e. Perf 12–13				
67		1 c. black and bistre-brown		1·00	6·50	20
		a. Perf 13½–14		1·25	6·50	20
		b. Perf 13½–14, comp 12–13		16·00	35·00	
		c. Perf 12–13				
68	25	2 c. black and rose-lake		3·50	4·50	30
		a. Imperf between (horiz or vert pair)		£400	£450	†
		b. Perf 13½–14		24·00	28·00	
69		2 c. black and lake		3·25	4·00	30
		a. Perf 13½–14		27·00	30·00	
		b. Perf 13½–14, comp 12–13		20·00	22·00	
		c. Imperf between (horiz pair)				
70	26	3 c. olive-green and mauve		2·25	7·00	30
		a. Imperf between (horiz pair)		—	£350	†
		b. Bronze-green and mauve				
		c. Perf 13½–14				
71		3 c. olive-green & violet (p 13½–14)		10·00	29·00	—
		a. Imperf between (horiz pair)				
72	27	5 c. black and vermilion		7·00	10·00	40
		a. Imperf between (horiz or vert pair)		£300		
		b. Perf 13½–14		32·00	55·00	
		c. Perf 13½–14, comp 12–13		—	60·00	
		d. Perf 13½–14, comp 14½–15				
		e. Perf 12–13				
73	28	6 c. black and bistre-brown		42·00	65·00	—
		a. Perf 13½–14		3·50	13·00	40
		b. Perf 13½–14, comp 12–13		—	50·00	—
		c. Perf 13½–14, comp 14½–15		45·00		
		d. Imperf between (horiz pair)				
74	29	8 c. black and dull purple		2·50	8·00	50
		a. Imperf between (vert pair)		£350		
		b. Perf 13½–14		7·00	22·00	50
		ba. Imperf between (vert pair)		£350	†	£300
		c. Perf 13½–14, comp 12–13				
75	30	12 c. black and blue		24·00	65·00	2·00
		a. Perf 13½–14		24·00	65·00	2·00
		b. Imperf between (horiz pair)		†	†	£400
76		12 c. black and ultramarine		32·00	70·00	2·00
		a. Perf 13½–14		30·00	70·00	2·00
		b. Imperf between (pair)				
78	31	18 c. black and deep green		15·00	40·00	2·00
		a. Perf 13½–14		20·00	40·00	2·00
79	32	24 c. blue and rose-lake		16·00	50·00	2·00
		a. Imperf between (vert pair)		—	—	£250
		b. Imperf between (vert strip of 3)		†	†	£350
		c. Perf 13½–14		16·00	50·00	2·00
		d. Perf 13½–14, comp 14½–15				
66/79			Set of 9	65·00	£180	7·50

32a   32b

32c   32d

(Litho Blades, East & Blades, London)

1894. *T* 32a *to* 32d, *and T* 19 *and* 20, *but inscribed* "THE STATE OF NORTH BORNEO". *P* 14.

81		25 c. indigo		8·00	26·00	70
		a. Imperf (pair)		16·00	—	2·75
		b. Imperf between (horiz or vert pair)		£550	—	75·00
		c. Printed double, one inverted		†	†	55·00
82		50 c. deep slate-purple		9·00	42·00	70
		a. Imperf (pair)		—	—	2·50
		b. Imperf between (horiz pair)				
		c. Printed double				
		d. Chalky blue		—	50·00	—

83	$1 scarlet	.. ..	.. 10·00	22·00	90
	a. Perf 14 × 11	..	.. £150		
	b. Imperf (pair)	..	.. 14·00	—	5·00
	c. Printed both sides		.. 25·00		
84	$2 dull green	.. ..	.. 13·00	55·00	90
	a. Imperf (pair)	..		—	4·50
	b. Printed double				
85	$5 bright purple	..	.. £130	£180	9·50
	a. Imperf (pair)	..	.. 85·00	—	14·00
	b. *Dull purple*	..	.. 65·00	£100	3·50
86	$10 brown	.. ..	.. £130	£190	5·00
	a. Imperf (pair)	..	.. 85·00	—	11·00
81/6			*Set of 6*	£200 £350	10·50
81/6 Optd "Specimen"			*Set of 6*	£120	

For Nos. 81 to 83 in other colours, see Labuan 80a, 81a and 82a.
Nos. 81c, 82c, 83c and 84b are from waste sheets subsequently sold by the British North Borneo Company to collectors.

4
CENTS

(33 (3½ mm between lines of surcharge))

(Surcharged by Waterlow)

1895 (June). *No. 83 surch as T 33.*

87	**32c**	4 cents on $1 scarlet	.. 2·50	1·50	30
		a. Surch double, one diagonal	£550		
88		10 cents on $1 scarlet	.. 5·50	1·75	30
89		20 cents on $1 scarlet	.. 18·00	10·00	30
90		30 cents on $1 scarlet	.. 11·00	14·00	30
91		40 cents on $1 scarlet	.. 16·00	25·00	30
87/91			*Set of 5* 48·00	48·00	1·40
87/91 Optd "Specimen"			*Set of 5* 85·00		

For 4 c. on $1 with wider spacing see No. 121.
No. 88 exists with the figures of the surcharge 2½ mm away from "CENTS". The normal setting has a space of 4 mm. Examples of the narrow setting have, so far, only been seen on cancelled-to-order stamps.

34	35	36
37 Orang-Utan	38	39
40	41 Sun Bear	
42	43 Borneo Railway Train	
44	45	

(Recess Waterlow)

1897 (Mar)–**1902.** *T 34 to 45. New frames. P 13½–14.*

92	1 c. black and bistre-brown		.. 4·50	2·50	20
	aa. Perf 16	..	..		
	a. Perf 14½–15	..	.. 4·00	2·00	20
	b. Perf 13½–14, comp 12–13		38·00	35·00	—
	c. Imperf between (horiz pair)		†	†	£325
93	1 c. black and ochre		.. 25·00	12·00	
	a. Perf 14½–15	..	.. 16·00	9·00	20
	ab. Imperf between (horiz pair)		†	†	£325
	b. Perf 13½–14, comp 12–13				
94	2 c. black and lake		.. 12·00	3·00	20
	a. Perf 14½–15	..	.. 6·50	2·75	20
	ab. Imperf between (horiz pair)		†	†	£325
	b. Perf 13½–14, comp 12–13		—	14·00	—
	c. Perf 12–13	..	..		
	d. Imperf between (vert pair)		†	†	£325

95	2 c. black and green (1900)	.. 24·00	1·50	20
	a. Perf 14½–15	.. 42·00	10·00	—
	b. Perf 13½–14, comp 12–13	.. 70·00	20·00	—
	c. Perf 12–13			
	d. Imperf between (pair)	— £425	†
96	3 c. green and rosy mauve	.. 19·00	7·00	30
	a. Perf 14½–15	.. 40·00	40·00	—
	b. Perf 13½–14, comp 12–13	.. 60·00	60·00	—
97	3 c. green & dull mauve (p 14½–15)	4·75	3·00	30
98	4 c. black and green (1900)	.. 6·00		40
	a. Perf 13½–14, comp 12–13			
99	4 c. black and carmine (1900)	.. 15·00	4·75	30
	a. Perf 16	.. 45·00	28·00	—
	b. Perf 14½–15	.. 25·00	2·00	30
	c. Perf 13½–14, comp 12–13	.. 20·00	22·00	—
	d. Perf 12–13			
100	5 c. black and orange-vermilion	.. 45·00	3·50	30
	a. Perf 14½–15	.. 48·00	2·75	30
	b. Perf 13½–14, comp 12–13	.. 48·00	12·00	—
	c. Perf 12–13			
101	6 c. black and bistre-brown	.. 18·00	11·00	30
	a. Perf 14½–15	.. 8·00	3·00	30
102	8 c. black and brown-purple	.. 40·00	38·00	—
	a. Perf 16	.. 75·00	13·00	40
	ab. Imperf between (vert pair)	£350	£350	—
	b. Perf 14½–15	.. 15·00	2·75	40
103	8 c. black and brown	.. 7·00	18·00	40
	a. Perf 14½–15	.. 35·00	40·00	—
	b. Perf 16			
104	10 c. brown and slate-lilac (1902)	.. 48·00	27·00	1·00
	a. Imperf between (vert pair)			
105	10 c. brown and slate-blue (1902)	.. 90·00	55·00	1·00
106	12 c. black and dull blue	.. 85·00	42·00	1·00
	a. Imperf between (vert pair)	†	†	£325
	b. Perf 14½–15	.. 48·00	28·00	1·00
	c. Perf 13½–14, comp 12–13	.. 95·00	55·00	—
107	16 c. green and chestnut (1902)	.. 80·00	75·00	2·50
	a. Perf 14½–15	.. 80·00	£110	—
108	18 c. black and green (p 16)	.. 12·00	30·00	50
	a. Imperf vert (horiz pair)	†	†	£60·00
	b. Imperf between (vert pair)	†	†	£200
	c. Imperf (pair)			
109	24 c. blue and lake	.. 8·50	50·00	1·00
	a. Perf 13½–14, comp 12–13	.. 24·00	70·00	—
	b. Perf 12–13	.. 70·00		
92/109	(one of each value)	*Set of 12* £250	£200	6·75
92/109	(excl 93, 97, 103) Optd "Specimen"			
		Set of 14 £170		

In the above the 18 c. has "POSTAL REVENUE" instead of "POSTAGE AND REVENUE" and the 24 c. has those words omitted. These stamps were replaced by others with corrected inscriptions; see Nos. 110 and 111.

46	47

1897. *Corrected inscriptions. P 13½–14.*

110	46	18 c. black and green	.. 45·00	14·00	75
		a. Imperf between (horiz pair)	†	†	£325
		b. Perf 14½–15	.. 48·00	12·00	75
		c. Perf 13½–14, comp 12–13	..		
111	47	24 c. blue and lake	.. 38·00	30·00	1·00
		a. Perf 16	.. 70·00	70·00	—
		b. Perf 14½–15	.. 28·00	45·00	1·00
		c. Perf 13½–14, comp 12–13	..		
		d. Perf 12–13	..		
110/11 Optd "Specimen"			*Set of 2* 45·00		

BRITISH
4
CENTS PROTECTORATE. cents

(48) (4½ mm between lines of surcharge) **(49)** **(50)**

1899. *Surch with T 48. (a) P 14½–15.*

112	4 c. on 5 c. (No. 100a)	..	27·00	
	a. Perf 13½–14	.. 11·00	10·00	
	b. Perf 13½–14, comp 12–13	.. 28·00	38·00	
113	4 c. on 6 c. (No. 101a)	.. 16·00	20·00	
	a. Perf 13½–14	.. 11·00	28·00	
114	4 c. on 8 c. (No. 102b)	.. 13·00	10·00	
115	4 c. on 12 c. (No. 106b)	.. 11·00	13·00	
	a. Imperf between (horiz pair)	£400		
	b. Imperf between (vert pair)	—	£400	
	c. Perf 13½–14	..		
	d. Perf 12–13	..		
	e. Perf 13½–14, comp 12–13	.. ¡22·00		
116	4 c. on 18 c. (No. 110a)	.. 9·50	13·00	
117	4 c. on 24 c. (No. 111b)	.. 11·00	12·00	
	a. Perf 16	.. 35·00	45·00	
	b. Perf 13½–14	.. 12·00	32·00	
	c. Perf 13½–14, comp 12–13	.. 26·00	35·00	
	d. Perf 12–13	.. 27·00	35·00	
	(b) P 14			
118	4 c. on 25 c. indigo (No. 81)	.. 5·00	8·50	
	a. Imperf between (horiz strip of 3)	£800		
119	4 c. on 50 c. deep slate-purple (No. 82)	.. 6·00	12·00	
	a. Chalky blue	.. 24·00	10·00	
121	4 c. on $1 scarlet (No. 83)	.. 5·00	8·50	
122	4 c. on $2 dull green (No. 84)	.. 5·00	12·00	
123	4 c. on $5 bright purple (No. 85)	.. £100	£170	
	a. Dull purple	.. 60·00	£130	

124	4 c. on $10 brown (No. 86)	.. 60·00	£130	
112/24		*Set of 12* £180	£350	
112/24 Optd "Specimen"	*Set of 12* £150		

No. 121 differs only from No. 87 in having the "4" and "cents" wider apart.
Examples of the Kudat postmark dated "AU 15 1899" struck on Nos. 112/24 are generally considered to be faked.
A new setting of the surcharge, with 5 mm between "4" and "CENTS", was used for the Specimen overprints, including unissued surcharges on the 1 c., 2 c. and 3 c. values (*price £90 the set of three*).

1899. *Surch as T 48 but 8½ mm between lines of surcharge. P 14.*

125	4 c. on $5 (No. 85)	..	5·50	11·00
126	4 c. on $10 (No. 86)	..	5·50	11·00

(Surcharged by Waterlow)

1901 (8 Oct)–05. *Optd as T 49. (a) P 13½–14.*

127	1 c. (No. 92) (R.)	.. 2·50	1·50	10
	a. Perf 14½–15	.. 1·50	1·60	10
128	2 c. (No. 95) (R.)	.. 2·25	1·75	10
	a. Perf 16	.. 3·50	5·00	15
	b. Perf 14½–15	.. 5·50	6·00	15
129	3 c. (No. 96)	.. 1·40	2·50	10
	a. Imperf between (vert pair)			
	b. Perf 14½–15	.. 5·50	2·00	10
	c. Perf 13½–14, comp 14½–15	.. 35·00		
130	4 c. (No. 99) (G.)	.. 4·75	1·50	10
	a. Perf 14½–15	.. 12·00	1·50	10
131	5 c. (No. 100) (G.)	.. 20·00	3·25	15
	a. Perf 14½–15	.. 4·75	2·25	15
132	6 c. (No. 101) (R.)	.. 27·00	45·00	—
	a. No stop after "Protectorate"	.. 65·00	65·00	—
	b. Perf 16	.. 2·50	6·00	20
133	8 c. (No. 103) (B.)	.. 2·75	3·00	20
	a. No stop after "Protectorate"	.. 3·00	18·00	—
	b. Perf 13½–14, comp 12–13	.. 38·00	14·00	—
	c. Imperf between (vert pair)	†	†	£300
134	10 c. (No. 104) (R.) (7.02)	.. 13·00	4·50	30
	a. Perf 14½–15	.. 50·00	22·00	—
	c. Perf 13½–14. No stop after "Protectorate"	.. 95·00		
	d. Opt double	.. £350	†	£225
	e. On 10 c. (No. 105)	.. 90·00		
	f. Imperf vert (horiz pair)	†	†	£300
135	12 c. (No. 106) (R.)	.. 25·00	12·00	1·00
136	16 c. (No. 107) (7.02)	.. 55·00	20·00	1·50
	a. Perf 14½–15	.. 60·00	28·00	1·50
	b. Perf 13½–14, comp 12–13	.. 95·00	48·00	—
137	18 c. (No. 110) (R.)	.. 8·00	19·00	60
	a. No stop after "Protectorate"			
	b. Perf 13½–14, comp 12–13	..		
138	24 c. (No. 111)	.. 14·00	28·00	1·00
	a. Perf 14½–15	.. 48·00	60·00	1·25
	b. Imperf between (horiz pair)			
	(b) P 14			
139	25 c. (No. 81) (R.)	.. 2·00	10·00	30
	a. No stop after "Protectorate"	.. 90·00	£110	—
	b. Overprints *tête-bêche* (horiz pair)			
	c. Overprint inverted	.. £350		
140	50 c. (No. 82) (R.)	.. 2·75	11·00	40
	a. No stop after "Protectorate"	.. 50·00	90·00	—
	b. *Chalky blue*	..		
141	$1 (No. 83) (R.) (1.04)	.. 10·00	55·00	—
142	$1 (No. 83)	.. 6·50	30·00	2·50
	a. Imperf horiz (vert pair)	£400		
	b. Opt double	†	†	£275
	c. Opt treble			
143	$2 (No. 84) (1903)	.. 25·00	80·00	3·50
	a. Opt double	.. £950	—	£325
144	$5 (No. 85b) (R.) (2.05)	.. £130	£300	4·00
145	$10 (No. 86) (R.) (2.05)	.. £190	£375	7·00
	a. Opt inverted	.. £1100		£350
127/45		*Set of 18* £425	£800	23·00
127/40 Optd "Specimen"	*Set of 14* £250		

There was more than one setting of the overprint for some of the values. Full sheets of the 6 c. and 8 c. are known, without stop throughout.

1904–5. *Surch locally with T 50. (a) P 14½–15.*

146	4 c. on 5 c. (No. 100a)	.. 18·00	28·00	3·00
	a. Surch omitted (in pair with normal)			
147	4 c. on 6 c. (No. 101a)	.. 6·00	16·00	2·00
	a. Surch inverted	.. £160		
148	4 c. on 8 c. (No. 102b)	.. 11·00	23·00	2·25
	a. Surch inverted	.. £180		
149	4 c. on 12 c. (No. 106b)	.. 20·00	35·00	2·50
	a. Perf 13½–14	.. 38·00	55·00	2·50
	b. Perf 13½–14, comp 12–13	.. 24·00	55·00	—
	c. Surch omitted (in pair with normal)			
150	4 c. on 18 c. (No. 110a)	.. 14·00	30·00	3·00
	a. Perf 13½–14			
151	4 c. on 24 c. (No. 111b)	.. 18·00	42·00	3·00
	a. Perf 16	.. 16·00	42·00	3·00
	b. Perf 13½–14	.. 19·00	42·00	3·00
	c. Perf 12–13	..		
	(b) P 14			
152	4 c. on 25 c. (No. 81)	.. 3·50	23·00	2·50
153	4 c. on 50 c. (No. 82)	.. 3·50	30·00	2·50
154	4 c. on $1 (No. 83)	.. 4·25	45·00	3·00
155	4 c. on $2 (No. 84)	.. 5·50	45·00	3·25
156	4 c. on $5 (No. 85)	.. 11·00	48·00	3·50
	a. Surch on No. 85b	.. 30·00	48·00	
157	4 c. on $10 (No. 86)	.. 11·00	48·00	3·50
	a. Surch inverted	.. £1200		
	b. Surch omitted (in pair with normal)			
146/57		*Set of 12* £110	£375	30·00

51 Malayan Tapir

52 Travellers' Tree

53 Railway at Jesselton

54 The Sultan of Sulu, his staff and W. C. Cowie, Managing Director of the Company

55 Indian Elephant

56 Sumatran Rhinoceros

57 Ploughing with Buffalo

58 Wild Boar

59 Palm Cockatoo

60 Rhinoceros Hornbill

61 Banteng

62 Dwarf Cassowary

(Recess Waterlow)

1909 (1 July)–24. *Centres in black.* P 13½–14.

158	51	1 c. chocolate-brown	..	3·25	80	10
		a. Perf 14½–15	..	17·00	8·50	—
159		1 c. brown	..	7·50	1·25	—
		a. Perf 14½–15	..	13·00	2·25	20
		b. Imperf between (vert pair)	£750		
160	52	2 c. green	..	75	40	10
		a. Imperf between (pair)			
		b. Perf 14½–15	..	2·00	60	10
161	53	3 c. lake	..	2·00	90	10
162		3 c. rose-lake	..	2·50	80	10
		a. Perf 14½–15	..	25·00	—	40
163		3 c. green (1924)	..	5·50	80	
164	54	4 c. scarlet	..	1·25	15	10
		a. Imperf between (vert pair)			
		b. Perf 14½–15	..	7·00	1·60	30
165	55	5 c. yellow-brown	..	6·50	3·25	10
		a. Perf 14½–15	..			
166		5 c. dark brown	..	7·50	2·25	—
167	56	6 c. olive-green	..	5·00	90	10
		a. Perf 14½–15	..	45·00	6·00	60
168		6 c. apple-green	..	15·00	2·00	—
169	57	8 c. lake	..	2·00	1·25	10
170	58	10 c. greyish blue	..	26·00	6·00	20
		a. Perf 14½–15	..	48·00	16·00	
171		10 c. blue	..	32·00	2·50	
172		10 c. turquoise-blue	..	13·00	1·75	
		a. Perf 14½–15	..	30·00	5·50	—
173	59	12 c. deep blue	..	18·00	1·60	20
		a. Perf 14½–15	..			
		b. Imperf between (horiz pair)	†	†	£350
173c		12 c. deep bright blue	..			
174	60	16 c. brown-lake	..	14·00	5·50	40
175	61	18 c. blue-green	..	60·00	27·00	50
176	62	24 c. deep rose-lilac	..	17·00	2·50	
		a. *Deep lilac*				
158/76			*Set of 13*	£130	40·00	
158/76 Optd "Specimen"			*Set of 13*	£275		

For this issue perf 12½ see Nos. 277, etc.

---

20 CENTS
(63)

64				65

1909 (7 Sept). *No.* 175 *surch with T* 63 *by Waterlow.* P 13½–14.

177	20 c. on 18 c. blue-green (R.) (Optd				
	S. £35)	..	4·50	50	10
	a. Perf 14½–15	..	£140	60·00	

(Recess Waterlow)

1911 (7 Mar). P 13½–14.

178	64	25 c. black and yellow-green	.	4·25	3·25	1·00
		a. Perf 14½–15	..	8·50	24·00	—
		b. Imperf (pair)	..	38·00		
178c		25 c. black and blue-green	..	30·00		
179		50 c. black and steel-blue	..	5·50	3·25	1·25
		a. Perf 14½–15	..	15·00	18·00	
		ab. Imperf between (horiz pair) £1000			
		c. Imperf (pair)	..	55·00		
180		$1 black and chestnut.	.	11·00	3·25	1·25
		a. Perf 14½–15	..	28·00	14·00	
		b. Imperf (pair)	..	70·00		
181		$2 black and lilac	..	27·00	11·00	3·00
182	65	$5 black and lake	..	60·00	65·00	20·00
		a. Imperf (pair)	..	£130		
183		$10 black and brick-red	..	£150	£180	40·00
		a. Imperf (pair)	..	£180		
178/83.			*Set of 6*	£225	£225	60·00
178/83 Optd "Specimen"			*Set of 6*	£225		

BRITISH

PROTECTORATE
(66)

2 cents
(67)

(68)

1912 (July). *Nos.* 85 *and* 86 *optd with T* 66.

184	$5 dull purple (R.)	..	£750	—	6·00
185	$10 brown (R.)	..	£900	—	6·00
	a. Opt inverted	..	†	†	—

1916 (Feb). *Stamps of* 1909–22 *surch as T* 67 *by Govt Printing Office, Sandakan.* P 13½–14.

186	2 c. on 3 c. black and rose-lake	..	11·00	8·00
	a. "s" inverted (R. 2/5)	..	85·00	85·00
	b. Surch double	..		
187	4 c. on 6 c. black and olive-green (R.)	..	11·00	10·00
	a. "s" inverted (R. 2/5)	..	85·00	85·00
	b. "s" inserted by hand	..	—	£550
	c. Perf 14½–15	..		
	ca. "s" inverted			
188	10 c. on 12 c. black and deep blue (R.)	..	27·00	38·00
	a. "s" inverted (R. 2/5)	..	90·00	90·00
186/8		*Set of 3*	45·00	50·00
186/8 Optd "Specimen"		*Set of 3*	£100	

Nos. 186/8 were surcharged from a setting of 25 (5×5) on which the required face values were inserted.

1916 (May). *Stamps of* 1909–11 *optd with T* 68 *by Waterlow.* P 13½–14. *Centres in black.* (a) *Cross in vermilion.*

189	51	1 c. brown	..	6·50	26·00
190	52	2 c. green	..	27·00	65·00
		a. Perf 14½–15	..	32·00	70·00
191	53	3 c. rose-lake	..	20·00	38·00
		a. Nos. 191 and 204 *se-tenant* (vert pair)	..	£750	
192	54	4 c. scarlet	..	5·50	24·00
		a. Perf 14½–15	..	£130	£110
193	55	5 c. yellow-brown	..	19·00	50·00
		a. Perf 14½–15	..		
194	56	6 c. apple-green	..	40·00	60·00
		a. Perf 14½–15	..	£130	
195	57	8 c. lake	..	17·00	50·00
196	58	10 c. blue	..	35·00	65·00
197	59	12 c. deep blue	..	60·00	70·00
198	60	16 c. brown-lake	..	60·00	70·00
199	61	20 c. on 18 c. blue-green	..	25·00	70·00
200	62	24 c. dull mauve	..	60·00	70·00
		a. Imperf between (vert pair)	..		
201	64	25 c. green (p 14½–15)	..	£250	£350
189/201			*Set of 13*	£500	£900

(b) *Cross in carmine*

202	51	1 c. brown	..	22·00	55·00
		a. Perf 14½–15	..	£130	
203	52	2 c. green	..	26·00	38·00
		b. Perf 14½–15	..	£130	
		ba. Opt double	..	†	—
204	53	3 c. rose-lake	..	26·00	55·00
204a	54	4 c. scarlet	..	£350	
205	55	5 c. yellow-brown	..	35·00	65·00
206	56	6 c. apple-green	..	27·00	65·00
		a. Perf 14½–15	..	£130	
207	57	8 c. lake	..	20·00	55·00
208	58	10 c. blue	..	32·00	60·00
209	59	12 c. deep blue	..	55·00	90·00
210	60	16 c. brown-lake	..	55·00	90·00
211	61	20 c. on 18 c. blue-green	..	55·00	90·00
212	62	24 c. dull mauve	..	65·00	£120
213	64	25 c. green	..	£600	
		a. Perf 14½–15	..	£400	£475
202/13 (ex 4 c.)			*Set of 12*	£650	£1100

The British North Borneo Company donated a proportion of the above issue to be sold by the National Philatelic War Fund for the benefit of the Red Cross and St. John's Ambulance Brigade.

RED CROSS

TWO CENTS (69) FOUR CENTS (70)

1918 (Aug). *Stamps of* 1909–11 *surch as T* 69. P 13½–14.

(a) *Lines of surcharge* 9 *mm apart*

214	51	1 c. + 2 c. brown	..	2·75	8·00
		a. Imperf between (horiz pair)	..£1000		
215	52	2 c. + 2 c. green	..	70	8·00
		a. Imperf between (horiz or vert pair) £1000		
		b. Imperf (pair)	..		
		c. Perf 14½–15	..		
216	53	3 c. + 2 c. rose-red	..	5·50	14·00
		a. Imperf between (horiz pair)	..£1000		
		b. Perf 14½–15	..	24·00	60·00
217		3 c. + 2 c. dull rose-carmine	..	£130	
		a. Perf 14½–15	..	£160	
218	54	4 c. + 2 c. scarlet	..	55	4·00
		a. Surch inverted	..	£275	
219	55	5 c. + 2 c. deep brown	..	5·00	16·00
220		5 c. + 2 c. pale brown	..	5·50	22·00
221	56	6 c. + 2 c. olive-green	..	4·00	17·00
		a. Perf 14½–15	..	£130	
221b		6 c. + 2 c. apple-green	..		
		c. Perf 14½–15	..	£225	
222	57	8 c. + 2 c. lake	..	4·50	7·00
		a. Inverted figure "3" for "C" in "CENTS"	..		
223	58	10 c. + 2 c. blue	..	6·50	22·00
224	59	12 c. + 2 c. deep bright blue	..	11·00	35·00
		a. Surch inverted	..	£500	
225	60	16 c. + 2 c. brown-lake	..	13·00	35·00
226	62	24 c. + 2 c. mauve	..	14·00	35·00

(b) *Lines of surch* 13–14 *mm apart*

227	52	2 c. + 2 c. green	..	55·00	£100
228	56	6 c. + 2 c. olive-green	..	£225	£500
229	64	25 c. + 2 c. green	..	10·00	38·00
230		50 c. + 2 c. steel-blue	..	12·00	38·00
231		$1 + 2 c. chestnut	..	38·00	48·00
232		$2 + 2 c. lilac	..	55·00	90·00
233	65	$5 + 2 c. lake	..	£250	£350
234		$10 + 2 c. brick-red	..	£250	£350
214/34			*Set of 17*	£600	£1000

The above stamps were dispatched from London in three consignments, of which two were lost through enemy action at sea. Only one sheet was found of No. 228.

These stamps were sold at a premium of 2 c. per stamp, which went to the Red Cross Society.

1918 (Oct). *Stamps of* 1909–11 *surch with T̄* 70, *in red.* P 13½–14.

235	51	1 c. + 4 c. chocolate	..	50	3·50
		a. Imperf between (horiz pair)	..£1000		
236	52	2 c. + 4 c. green	..	65	6·50
237	53	3 c. + 4 c. rose-lake	..	80	3·25
238	54	4 c. + 4 c. scarlet	..	40	4·50
239	55	5 c. + 4 c. brown	..	1·75	16·00
240	56	6 c. + 4 c. apple-green	..	1·75	11·00
		a. Imperf between (vert pair).	..£1000		
241	57	8 c. + 4 c. lake	..	1·10	9·00
242	58	10 c. + 4 c. turquoise-blue	..	2·50	12·00
242a		10 c. + 4 c. greenish blue	..	6·00	30·00
243	59	12 c. + 4 c. deep blue	..	7·00	12·00
		a. Surch double	..	£600	
244	60	16 c. + 4 c. brown-lake	..	5·00	16·00
245	62	24 c. + 4 c. mauve	..	5·00	20·00
246	64	25 c. + 4 c. yellow-green	..	3·50	42·00
247		25 c. + 4 c. blue-green	..	23·00	70·00
248		50 c. + 4 c. steel-blue	..	14·00	38·00
		a. Perf 14½–15	..	55·00	
249		$1 + 4 c. chestnut	..	14·00	50·00
		a. Perf 14½–15	..	60·00	
250		$2 + 4 c. lilac	..	40·00	75·00
251	65	$5 + 4 c. lake	..	£200	£375
252		$10 + 4 c. brick-red	..	£200	£375
235/52			*Set of 17*	£450	£1000

Nos. 235/52 were sold at face, plus 4 c. on each stamp for Red Cross Funds.

THREE

MALAYA-BORNEO EXHIBITION 1922.

■CENTS■
(71) (72)

1922 (31 Mar). *Malaya-Borneo Exhibition, Singapore. Stamps of* 1909–22 *optd as T* 71 *by Govt Printing Office, Sandakan.* P 13½–14.

253	51	1 c. brown (R.)	..	6·00	40·00
		a. "BORHEO"	..	£275	£325
		b. "BORNEQ"	..	£400	£450
		c. Stop after "EXHIBITION."	..	42·00	
		d. Raised stop after "1922"	..	£275	
		e. "EXHIBITICN." with stop	..	£400	
		f. Perf 14½–15	..	15·00	50·00
		fa. "BORHEO"	..	£375	
		fb. "BORNEQ"	..	£550	
		fc. Raised stop after "1922"	..	£375	
		fd. "EXHIBITICN." with stop	..	£550	
		fe. "MHLAYA" and stop after "EXHIBITION"			
		ff. Stop after "EXHIBITION."	..	50·00	
253g		1 c. brown (B.) (p 14½–15)	..	£700	
		ga. Vert pair, with and without opt	..	£2000	
		gb. Raised stop after "1922."	..	£1300	
		gc. "BORHEO"	..	£1300	
		gd. "BORNEQ"	..	£1700	
		gf. "EXHIBITICN." with stop	..	£1700	
		gg. "MHLAYA" and stop after "EXHIBITION"	..		

254	51	1 c. orange-brown (R.)	..	.. 15·00	45·00
255	52	2 c. green (R.)	..	.. 1·40	14·00
		a. Stop after "EXHIBITION."		20·00	
256	53	3 c. rose-lake (R.)	..	.. 5·00	30·00
		a. Stop after "EXHIBITION."		38·00	
		b. "EXHIBITICN." with stop	..	£1100	
		c. Raised stop after "1922"	..	£750	
257	54	4 c. scarlet (B.)	..	.. 1·40	24·00
		a. Stop after "EXHIBITION."		19·00	
		b. Perf 14½–15	..	..	
		ba. Stop after "EXHIBITION."			
258	55	5 c. orange-brown (B.)	..	.. 6·00	42·00
		a. Imperf between (vert pair)	..	£900	£900
		b. Stop after "EXHIBITION."		38·00	
		c. Opt double	..	£1600	
		d. Opt double (with stop)	..	£2750	
259		5 c. chestnut (B.)	..	.. 15·00	48·00
		a. Stop after "EXHIBITION."		55·00	
260	56	6 c. apple-green (R.)	..	.. 2·75	38·00
		a. Stop after "EXHIBITION."		30·00	
		b. Opt double	..	£1600	
		c. Opt double (with stop)	..	£2750	
261	57	8 c. dull rose (B.)	..	.. 4·00	38·00
		a. Stop after "EXHIBITION."		38·00	
262		8 c. deep rose-lake (B.)	..	.. 4·00	38·00
		a. Stop after "EXHIBITION."		38·00	
263	58	10 c. turquoise-blue (R.)	..	.. 4·50	38·00
		a. Stop after "EXHIBITION."		38·00	
		b. Perf 14½–15	..	.. 23·00	
		ba. Stop after "EXHIBITION."			
264		10 c. greenish blue (R.)	..	.. 6·00	45·00
		a. Stop after "EXHIBITION."		38·00	
265	59	12 c. deep blue (R.)	..	.. 3·75	20·00
		a. Stop after "EXHIBITION."		42·00	
266		12 c. deep bright blue (R.)	..	.. 26·00	
		a. Stop after "EXHIBITION."		£130	
267	60	16 c. brown-lake (B.)	..	.. 6·50	45·00
		a. Stop after "EXHIBITION."		42·00	
		b. Opt in red	..	£2500	
268	61	20 c. on 18 c. blue-green (B.)	..	.. 7·00	45·00
		a. Stop after "EXHIBITION."		80·00	
269		20 c. on 18 c. blue-green (R.)	..	.. 20·00	£130
		a. Stop after "EXHIBITION."		£200	£275
270	62	24 c. mauve (R.)	..	.. 16·00	48·00
		a. Stop after "EXHIBITION."		50·00	
271		24 c. lilac (R.)	..	.. 16·00	48·00
		a. Stop after "EXHIBITION."		50·00	
272		24 c. reddish lilac (R.)	..	.. 26·00	60·00
		a. Stop after "EXHIBITION."		75·00	
273	64	25 c. blue-green (R.)	..	.. 11·00	50·00
		a. Stop after "EXHIBITION."		45·00	
274		25 c. yellow-green (R.)	..	.. 3·75	45·00
		a. Stop after "EXHIBITION."		40·00	
		b. Opt double	..	£1300	
		c. Perf 14½–15	..	13·00	55·00
		ca. Stop after "EXHIBITION."		£200	
		cb. Opt double	..	£1100	
275		50 c. steel-blue (R.)	..	.. 6·00	35·00
		a. Stop after "EXHIBITION."		55·00	
		b. Perf 14½–15	..	20·00	
		ba. Stop after "EXHIBITION."		£100	
253/75				Set of 14 65·00	£450
253/75 Optd "Specimen"			.. Set of 14	£400	

These overprints were applied from a number of settings covering 10, 20, 25 or 30 stamps at a time.

Of the ten settings known for the horizontal stamps the earliest were only used for the 1 c. on which most of the varieties occur. Of the others the vast majority come from settings of 20 (10 × 2) with the stop after "EXHIBITION" variety on R. 2/7, or 25 (5 × 5) on which the same variety can be found on R. 5/4. In addition the 3 c. comes from a different setting of 20 (10 × 2) on which there is a raised stop after "1922" on R. 2/8 and "EXHIBITICN." on R. 2/9.

The 1 c. sequence is complicated, but additionally includes a setting of 10 with "BORHEO" on stamps 3 and 10, "BORNEQ" on stamp 4, raised stop on stamp 8 and "EXHIBITICN." on stamp 9. A setting of 20 repeats this sequence on its bottom line as does one of 30, although in this instance "MHLAYA" replaces "EXHIBITICN" as the variety on stamp 9.

For the vertical stamps (2, 6, 10, 12, 16 and 20 c. on 18 c.) the settings were of 20 (10 × 2) or 25 (5 × 5). The stop after "EXHIBITION" occurs on R. 2/7 of the former and R. 5/4 of the latter.

The 25 c. and 50 c. high values were overprinted from a setting of 20 (10 × 2), with the stop after "EXHIBITION" on R. 2/7, or 25 (5 × 5).

1923 (Oct). *T 54 surch with T 72.*

276		3 c. on 4 c. black and scarlet (Optd S. £50)	.. 1·00	4·25
		a. Surch double	..	.. £550	

1925–28. *As 1909–22. Centres in black, and some frame colours changed. P 12½.*

277	51	1 c. chocolate-brown	..	.. 85	70
		a. Imperf between (horiz pair)	..	£550	
278	52	2 c. claret	..	.. 35	50
		a. Imperf between (horiz or vert pair)	—	£450	
279	53	3 c. green (1925)	..	.. 2·00	1·25
		a. Imperf between (horiz pair)	..	..	
280	54	4 c. scarlet	..	.. 45	10
		a. Imperf between (vert pair)	..	£275	
		b. Imperf between (horiz pair)	..	£600	
281	55	5 c. yellow-brown	..	.. 3·00	2·00
		a. Imperf between (vert pair)	..	£400	
282	56	6 c. olive-green	..	.. 3·00	50
283	57	8 c. carmine	..	.. 1·75	15
		a. Imperf between (horiz or vert pair)	..	£350	
284	58	10 c. turquoise-blue	..	.. 1·75	50
		a. Imperf between (horiz or vert pair)	..	£500	
285	59	12 c. deep blue	..	.. 7·50	50
286	60	16 c. red-brown	..	.. 22·00	65·00
287	61	20 c. on 18 c. blue-green (R.)	..	.. 4·00	3·00
288	62	24 c. violet	..	.. 48·00	60·00
289	64	25 c. green	..	.. 4·50	4·25
290		50 c. steel-blue	..	.. 6·50	11·00
291		$1 chestnut	..	.. 15·00	85·00
292		$2 mauve	..	.. 48·00	£120
293	65	$5 lake (1928)	..	.. £110	£300
294		$10 orange-red (1928)	..	.. £200	£350
277/94				Set of 18 £425	£900

Examples of No. 278 were supplied for U.P.U. distribution punched with a 3½ mm diameter hole.

73 Head of a Murut   76 Mount Kinabalu

(Eng J. A. C. Harrison. Recess Waterlow)

1931 (1 Jan). *50th Anniv of British North Borneo Company. T 73, 76 and similar designs. P 12½.*

295		3 c. black and blue-green	..	.. 80	60
296		6 c. black and orange	..	.. 13·00	3·00
297		10 c. black and scarlet	..	.. 2·75	9·00
298		12 c. black and ultramarine	..	.. 3·75	7·00
299		25 c. black and violet	..	.. 30·00	28·00
300		$1 black and yellow-green	..	.. 16·00	60·00
301		$2 black and chestnut	..	.. 35·00	75·00
302		$5 black and purple	..	.. £110	£200
295/302				Set of 8 £180	£325
295/302 Optd "Specimen"			Set of 8 £275	

Designs: *Vert*—6 c. Orang-Utan; 10 c. Dyak warrior; $1 Badge of the Company; $5 Arms of the Company. *Horiz*—25 c. Clouded Leopard; $2 Arms of the Company.

81 Buffalo Transport   82 Palm Cockatoo

(Eng J. A. C. Harrison. Recess Waterlow)

1939 (1 Jan). *T 81/2 and similar designs. P 12½.*

303		1 c. green and red-brown	..	.. 30	30
304		2 c. purple and greenish blue	..	.. 2·00	30
305		3 c. slate-blue and green	..	.. 55	90
306		4 c. bronze-green and violet	..	.. 80	25
307		6 c. deep blue and claret	..	.. 45	1·50
308		8 c. scarlet	..	.. 4·50	75
309		10 c. violet and bronze-green	..	.. 28·00	4·50
310		12 c. green and royal blue	..	.. 8·50	2·75
		a. Green and blue	..	10·00	4·00
311		15 c. blue-green and brown	..	.. 11·00	4·25
312		20 c. violet and slate-blue	..	.. 6·00	3·00
313		25 c. green and chocolate	..	.. 7·00	4·50
314		50 c. chocolate and violet	..	.. 8·00	4·25
315		$1 brown and carmine	..	.. 45·00	15·00
316		$2 violet and olive-green	..	.. 70·00	60·00
317		$5 indigo and pale blue	..	.. £225	£160
303/17				Set of 15 £375	£225
303/17 Perf "Specimen"			Set of 15 £250	

Designs: *Vert*—3 c. Native; 4 c. Proboscis Monkey; 6 c. Mounted Bajaus; 10 c. Orang-Utan; 15 c. Dyak; $1, $2 Badge of the Company. *Horiz*—8 c. Eastern Archipelago; 12 c. Murut with blow-pipe; 20 c. River scene; 25 c. Native boat; 50 c. Mt Kinabalu; $5 Arms of the Company.

WAR TAX   **WAR TAX**

(96)   (97)

1941 (24 Feb). *Nos. 303/4 optd with T 96/7.*

318		1 c. green and red-brown	..	.. 15	50
319		2 c. purple and greenish blue	..	.. 1·25	2·00

BRITISH MILITARY ADMINISTRATION

North Borneo, including Labuan, was occupied by the Japanese in January 1942. Australian forces landed on Labuan on 10 June 1945 and by the end of the war against Japan on 14 August had liberated much of western North Borneo. The territory was placed under British Military Administration on 5 January 1946.

BMA   ℟

(98)   (99)

1945 (17 Dec). *Nos. 303/17 optd with T 98.*

320		1 c. green and red-brown	..	.. 2·50	40
321		2 c. purple and greenish blue	..	.. 6·00	1·00
		a. Opt double	..	.. £2750	
322		3 c. slate-blue and green	..	.. 1·25	1·00
323		4 c. bronze-green and violet	..	.. 14·00	9·50
324		6 c. deep blue and claret	..	.. 1·25	30
325		8 c. scarlet	..	.. 1·75	45
326		10 c. violet and bronze-green	..	.. 2·00	30
327		12 c. green and blue	..	.. 3·00	80
		a. Green and royal blue	..	..	
328		15 c. blue-green and brown	..	.. 1·25	1·00
329		20 c. violet and slate-blue	..	.. 1·50	1·00
330		25 c. green and chocolate	..	.. 2·75	75
331		50 c. chocolate and violet	..	.. 2·50	1·00
332		$1 brown and carmine	..	.. 22·00	17·00
333		$2 violet and olive-green	..	.. 22·00	17·00
		a. Opt double	..	.. £1700	
334		$5 indigo and pale blue	..	.. 8·00	8·00
320/34				Set of 15 80·00	55·00

These stamps and the similarly overprinted stamps of Sarawak were obtainable at all post offices throughout British Borneo (Brunei, Labuan, North Borneo and Sarawak), for use on local and overseas mail.

CROWN COLONY

North Borneo became a Crown Colony on 15 July 1946.

Lower bar broken   Lower bar broken
at right (R. 8/3)   at left (R. 8/4)

1947 (1 Sept–22 Dec). *Nos. 303 to 317 optd with T 99 and bars obliterating words* "THE STATE OF" *and* "BRITISH PROTECTORATE".

335		1 c. green and red-brown (15.12)	..	15	50
		b. Lower bar broken at right	..	8·00	
		c. Lower bar broken at left	..	8·00	
336		2 c. purple and greenish blue (22.12)	..	45	60
337		3 c. slate-blue and green (R.) (22.12)	..	15	15
338		4 c. bronze-green and violet	..	20	10
339		6 c. deep blue and claret (R.) (22.12)	..	15	20
340		8 c. scarlet	..	20	15
		b. Lower bar broken at right	..	10·00	
341		10 c. violet and bronze-green (15.12)	..	40	15
342		12 c. green and royal blue (22.12)	..	90	95
		a. Green and blue			
343		15 c. blue-green and brown (22.12)	..	1·25	30
344		20 c. violet and slate-blue (22.12)	..	35	30
		b. Lower bar broken at right	..	15·00	
345		25 c. green and chocolate (22.12)	..	40	30
		b. Lower bar broken at right	..	15·00	
346		50 c. chocolate and violet (22.12)	..	75	65
		b. Lower bar broken at right	..	25·00	
		c. Lower bar broken at left	..	25·00	
347		$1 brown and carmine (22.12)	..	60	85
348		$2 violet and olive-green (22.12)	..	2·50	4·50
349		$5 indigo and pale blue (R.) (22.12)	..	8·50	7·00
		b. Lower bar broken at right	..	55·00	
335/49				Set of 15 15·00	15·00
335/49 Perf "Specimen"			Set of 15 £250	

1948 (1 Nov). *Royal Silver Wedding. As Nos. 143/4 of Jamaica.*

350		8 c. scarlet	..	.. 30	50
351		$10 mauve	..	.. 12·00	26·00

1949 (10 Oct). *75th Anniv of U.P.U. As Nos. 145/8 of Jamaica.*

352		8 c. carmine	..	.. 30	30
353		10 c. brown	..	.. 60	30
354		30 c. orange-brown	..	.. 70	90
355		55 c. blue	..	.. 75	1·10
352/5				Set of 4 2·10	2·40

100 Mount Kinabalu   102 Coconut Grove

(Photo Harrison)

1950 (1 July)–52. *T 100, 102 and similar designs. Wmk Mult Script CA. Chalk-surfaced paper. P 13½ × 14½ (horiz), 14½ × 13½ (vert).*

356		1 c. red-brown	..	.. 15	40
357		2 c. blue	..	.. 15	20
358		3 c. green	..	.. 15	15
359		4 c. bright purple	..	.. 15	10
360		5 c. violet	..	.. 15	10
361		8 c. scarlet	..	.. 40	55
362		10 c. maroon	..	.. 30	10
363		15 c. ultramarine	..	.. 30	40
364		20 c. brown	..	.. 55	10
365		30 c. olive-brown	..	.. 55	10
366		50 c. rose-carmine ("JESSLETON")	..	45	2·00
366a		50 c. rose-carmine ("JESSELTON") (1.5.52)	..	3·00	65
367		$1 red-orange	..	.. 1·25	55
368		$2 grey-green	..	.. 2·00	6·50
369		$5 emerald-green	..	.. 9·50	12·00
370		$10 dull blue	..	.. 24·00	32·00
356/70				Set of 16 38·00	50·00

Designs: *Horiz*—2 c. Native musical instrument; 8 c. Map; 10 c. Log pond; 15 c. Malay prau, Sandakan; 20 c. Bajau Chief; $2 Murut with blowpipe; $5 Net-fishing; $10 Arms of North Borneo. *Vert*—4 c. Hemp drying; 5 c. Cattle at Kota Belud; 30 c. Suluk river canoe, Lahad Datu; 50 c. Clock tower, Jesselton; $1 Bajau horsemen.

1953 (3 June). *Coronation. As No. 153 of Jamaica.*

371		10 c. black and bright scarlet	..	.. 40	30

PRICES OF SETS

Set prices are given for many issues, generally those containing three stamps or more. Definitive sets include one of each value or major colour change, but do not cover different perforations, die types or minor shades. Where a choice is possible the set prices are based on the cheapest versions of the stamps included in the listings.

115 Log Pond

(Photo Harrison)

1954 (1 Mar)–59. *Designs previously used for King George VI issue, but with portrait of Queen Elizabeth II as in T* 115. *Chalk-surfaced paper. Wmk Mult Script CA. P* 14½×13½ (*vert*) *or* 13½×14½ (*horiz*).

372	1 c. red-brown (1.10.54)			10	30
373	2 c. blue (1.6.56)			30	15
374	3 c. green (1.2.57)			30	1·50
	a. Deep green (14.1.59)			1·00	2·00
375	4 c. bright purple (16.5.55)			30	20
376	5 c. reddish violet (1.7.54)			40	10
377	8 c. scarlet (1.10.54)			30	15
378	10 c. maroon			15	10
379	15 c. bright blue (16.5.55)			25	10
380	20 c. brown (3.8.54)			15	15
381	30 c. olive-brown (3.8.54)			40	15
382	50 c. rose-carm ("JESSELTON") (10.2.56)			2·75	10
	a. Rose (9.12.59)			4·50	55
383	$1 red-orange (1.4.55)			3·50	20
384	$2 deep green (1.10.55)			8·00	55
	a. Grey-green (22.1.58)			10·00	3·75
385	$5 emerald-green (1.2.57)			8·00	18·00
386	$10 deep blue (1.2.57)			20·00	30·00
372/86			*Set of* 15	40·00	45·00

Designs: *Horiz*—1 c. Mount Kinabalu; 2 c. Native musical instrument; 8 c. Map; 15 c. Native prahu, Sandakan; 20 c. Bajau chief; $2 Murut with blowpipe; $5 Net-fishing; $10 Arms of North Borneo. *Vert*—3 c. Coconut grove; 4 c. Hemp drying; 5 c. Cattle at Kota Belud; 30 c. Suluk boat, Lahad Datu; 50 c. Clock Tower, Jesselton; $1 Bajau horseman.

Plate 2 of the 30 c., released 10 August 1960, had a finer, 250 screen, instead of the previous 200 (*price* £1.75 *mint*).

116 Borneo Railway, 1902   119 Arms of Chartered Company

(Recess Waterlow)

1956 (1 Nov). *75th Anniv of British North Borneo Co. T* 116, 119 *and similar designs. Wmk Mult Script CA. P* 13 × 13½ (*horiz*) *or* 13½ × 13 (*vert*).

387	10 c. black and rose-carmine			1·00	30
388	15 c. black and red-brown			25	30
389	35 c. black and bluish green			30	90
390	$1 black and slate			65	1·50
387/90			*Set of* 4	2·00	2·75

Designs: *Horiz*—15 c. Malay prau; 35 c. Mount Kinabalu.

120 Sambar Stag   121 Orang-Utan

(Des Chong Yun Fatt. Recess Waterlow (until 1962), then D.L.R.)

1961 (1 Feb). *Horiz designs as T* 120 *or vert designs as T* 121. *W w* 12. *P* 13.

391	1 c. emerald and brown-red			10	10
392	4 c. bronze-green and orange			15	40
393	5 c. sepia and violet			15	10
394	6 c. black and blue-green			10	30
395	10 c. green and red			15	10
396	12 c. brown and grey-green			15	10
397	20 c. blue-green and ultramarine			2·75	10
398	25 c. grey-black and scarlet			45	50
399	30 c. sepia and olive			20	10
400	35 c. slate-blue and red-brown			55	20
401	50 c. emerald and yellow-brown			45	10
402	75 c. grey-blue and bright purple			4·00	90
403	$1 brown and yellow-green			6·50	55
404	$2 brown and slate			12·00	2·50
405	$5 emerald and maroon			22·00	12·00
406	$10 carmine and blue			20·00	17·00
391/406			*Set of* 16	60·00	30·00

Designs: *Horiz*—4 c. Sun Bear; 5 c. Clouded Leopard; 6 c. Dusun woman with gong; 10 c. Map of Borneo; 12 c. Banteng; 20 c. Butterfly orchid; 25 c. Sumatran Rhinoceros; 30 c. Murut with blow-pipe; 35 c. Mount Kinabalu; 50 c. Dusun and buffalo transport; 75 c. Bajau horsemen. *Vert*—$2 Rhinoceros Hornbill; $5 Crested Wood Partridge; $10 Arms of North Borneo.

1963 (4 June). *Freedom from Hunger. As No.* 80 *of Lesotho.*

407	12 c. ultramarine			70	15

North Borneo joined the Federation of Malaysia on 16 September 1963 and was renamed Sabah.

SABAH

STATE OF MALAYSIA

SABAH   **SABAH**
(136)   (137)

1964 (1 July)–65. *Nos.* 391/406 *of North Borneo* (*D.L.R. printings*), *optd with T* 136 (*Nos.* 408/19) *or T* 137 (*Nos.* 420/3).

408	1 c. emerald and brown-red			10	10
409	4 c. bronze-green and orange			15	50
410	5 c. sepia and violet			15	10
	a. Light sepia and deep violet (17.8.65)			55	30
411	6 c. black and blue-green			10	10
412	10 c. green and red			15	10
413	12 c. brown and grey-green			15	10
414	20 c. blue-green and ultramarine			1·75	10
415	25 c. grey-black and scarlet			45	80
416	30 c. sepia and olive			25	10
417	35 c. slate-blue and red-brown			30	20
418	50 c. emerald and yellow-brown			30	10
419	75 c. grey-blue and bright purple			2·25	65
420	$1 brown and yellow-green			3·50	50
421	$2 brown and slate			6·00	2·75
422	$5 emerald and maroon			8·00	11·00
423	$10 carmine and blue			13·00	16·00
408/23			*Set of* 16	32·00	29·00

Old stocks bearing Waterlow imprints of the 4 c., 5 c., 20 c. and 35 c. to $10 were used for overprinting, but in addition new printings of all values by De La Rue using the original plates with the De La Rue imprint replacing the Waterlow imprint were specially made for overprinting.

138 *Vanda hookeriana*   139 *Hebomoia glaucippe*

1965 (15 Nov)–68. *As Nos.* 166/72 *of Johore, but with Arms of Sabah inset as in T* 138. *W w* 13 (*upright*).

424	1 c. multicoloured			10	30
425	2 c. multicoloured			10	50
426	5 c. multicoloured			10	10
427	6 c. multicoloured			20	50
428	10 c. multicoloured			20	10
429	15 c. multicoloured (pale black panel)			1·50	10
	a. Brown-black panel (20.2.68)			1·75	10
430	20 c. multicoloured			1·75	40
424/30			*Set of* 7	3·50	1·75

The 5 c. to 15 c. exist with PVA gum as well as gum arabic. The higher values used with this issue were Nos. 20/27 of Malaysia (National Issues).

1970 (20 Nov). *As No.* 428, *but W w* 13 (*sideways*).

431	10 c. multicoloured			2·75	3·00

1971 (1 Feb)–78. *As Nos.* 175/87 *of Johore but with Arms of Sabah, as in T* 139. (*a*) *Litho by Bradbury, Wilkinson.*

432	1 c. multicoloured			10	60
433	2 c. multicoloured			30	60
434	5 c. multicoloured			45	10
435	6 c. multicoloured			45	55
436	10 c. multicoloured			45	10
437	15 c. multicoloured			60	10
438	20 c. multicoloured			70	50
432/8			*Set of* 7	2·75	2·25

(*b*) *Photo by Harrison* (1977–78)

439	1 c. multicoloured			1·50	3·00
440	2 c. multicoloured			1·50	3·50
441	5 c. multicoloured			7·50	2·75
442	10 c. multicoloured			2·25	50
443	15 c. multicoloured			2·25	45
444	20 c. multicoloured			6·00	1·75
439/44			*Set of* 6	19·00	11·00

For differences between litho and photo printings, see after Johore No. 187.

The higher values used with this issue were Nos. 64/71 of Malaysia (National Issues).

140 *Hibiscus rosa-sinensis*   141 Coffee

1979 (30 Apr). *As Nos.* 188/94 *of Johore but with Arms of Sabah as in T* 140.

445	1 c. *Rafflesia hasseltii*			10	30
446	2 c. *Pterocarpus indicus*			10	30
447	5 c. *Lagerstroemia speciosa*			10	10
448	10 c. *Durio zibethinus*			15	10
449	15 c. Type 140			25	10
450	20 c. *Rhododendron scortechinii*			30	10
451	25 c. *Etlingera elatior* (inscr "*Phaeomeria speciosa*")			30	10
445/51			*Set of* 7	1·10	75

For higher values used in conjunction with this series see Nos. 190/7 of Malaysia (National Issues).

1983–85. * *As Nos.* 447/8 *and* 450 *but without wmk.*

454	5 c. *Lagerstroemia speciosa* (1.85)			4·00	3·50
455	10 c. *Durio zibethinus* (1.85)			8·00	7·00
456	15 c. Type 140 (5.85)			6·00	3·50
457	20 c. *Rhododendron scortechinii* (blackish brown background) (1983)			12·00	2·00
457a	20 c. *Rhododendron scortechinii* (bronze-green background) (29.11.83)			9·50	1·00
454/7a			*Set of* 5	35·00	15·00

*There was no official release date for these stamps. Dates shown are the earliest recorded from postmarks and may be revised if earlier examples are reported.

For details of the shade differences between watermarked and unwatermarked printings see after Malaysia–Johore, No. 200a. On Nos. 454/6 and 457a the state crest is redrawn larger.

1986 (25 Oct). *As Nos.* 202/8 *of Johore but with Arms of Sabah as in T* 141.

459	1 c. Type 141			10	10
460	2 c. Coconuts			10	10
461	5 c. Cocoa			10	10
462	10 c. Black pepper			10	10
463	15 c. Rubber			10	10
464	20 c. Oil palm			10	10
465	30 c. Rice			15	20
459/65			*Set of* 7	40	45

POSTAL FISCALS

Three Cents. Revenue   **Ten Cents. Revenue**
(F 1)   (F 2)
(Raised stop)

1886. *Regular issues surch as Type F* 1 *or F* 2.

F1	1	3 c. on 4 c. pink (No. 6)		65·00	85·00
		a. Raised stop after "*Cents*"		60·00	80·00
F2		5 c. on 8 c. green (No. 7)		65·00	85·00
		a. Raised stop after "*Cents*"		60·00	80·00
F3	4	10 c. on 50 c. violet (No. 4)		75·00	£100
		a. Surch double		—	£650
		b. No stop after "*Cents*" *and stop after* "*Revenue.*"		£225	£300
		c. Inverted "*L*" *for first* "*F*" *in* "*FIFTY*" (R.5/2)		—	£400

It is believed that Nos. F1/2 were each surcharged from a horizontal setting of five so that the raised stop variety occurs on every stamp in the first, second, third, sixth, seventh and eighth vertical columns in the sheets of 50 (10×5).

POSTAGE DUE STAMPS

POSTAGE DUE
(D 1)

1895 (1 Aug). *Stamps of* 1894 *optd with Type D* 1. *P* 14½–15.

A. *Vertically* (*reading upwards*)

D 1	25	2 c. black and rose-lake		13·00	23·00	1·50
		a. Opt double		†	†	£225
		b. Opt reading downwards		†	†	£275
D 2		2 c. black and lake		10·00	16·00	60
		a. Perf 13½–14				
		b. Opt omitted (in vert pair with normal)		†		†£1000
D 3	26	3 c. olive-green and mauve		3·75	9·00	75
		a. Bronze-green and mauve				
		b. Opt reading downwards				
D 3c		3 c. olive-green and violet				
		ca. Opt double			†	£350
		cb. Perf 13½–14				
D 4	27	5 c. black and vermilion		22·00	22·00	1·50
		a. Printed double		†	—	
		b. Stop after "*DUE*"		50·00		
		c. Perf 13½–14		—	50·00	
		ca. Opt double				
		d. Perf 13½–14, *comp* 12–13		—	55·00	
D 5	28	6 c. black and bistre-brown		22·00	45·00	1·50
		a. Perf 13½–14		7·50	30·00	1·50
		b. Perf 12–13				
		c. Perf 13½–14, *comp* 12–13				
		d. Opt reading downwards				
D 6	31	18 c. black and deep green		42·00	70·00	3·00
		a. Opt reading downwards		£300	£200	†
D3/4 & D6 Optd "Specimen"			*Set of* 3	90·00		

B. *Horizontally*

D 7	29	8 c. black and dull purple		20·00	32·00	1·50
		a. Opt double		—	†	£300
		b. Perf 13½–14			†	£120
		ba. Opt inverted		†	†	£120
		c. Perf 13½–14, *comp* 12–13		35·00		
D 8	30	12 c. black and blue		—	38·00	1·50
		a. Opt double			†	£300
		b. Perf 13½–14		29·00	30·00	1·50
D 9		12 c. black & ultram (*p* 13½–14)		55·00	55·00	—
D10	31	18 c. black and deep green		35·00	60·00	3·00
		a. Opt inverted		£170	£350	
		b. Perf 13½–14		48·00	60·00	3·00
		ba. Opt double		†	†	£200
D11	32	24 c. blue and rose-lake		40·00	60·00	3·00
		a. Opt double		†	†	£250
		b. Perf 13½–14		16·00	45·00	
		c. Perf 13½–14, *comp* 14½–15				
D8 & D11 Optd "Specimen"			*Set of* 2	50·00		

1897. *Stamps of* 1897 *optd with Type D* 1. *P* 14½–15.

A. *Vertically*

D12		2 c. black and lake		4·25	6·50	50
		a. Perf 13½–14		19·00		

B. *Horizontally*

D13	2 c. black and lake		28·00 55·00
D14	8 c. black and brown-purple		28·00 38·00
	a. Stop after "DUE."		18·00 55·00
D12 & D14 Optd "Specimen"		*Set of 2* 45·00	

1901. *Issue of 1897–1902 optd with Type* D 1. *P* 13½–14.

A. Vertically (reading upwards)

D15	2 c. black and green		17·00 25·00	60
	a. Perf 13½–14, comp 12–13		— 50·00	—
	b. Perf 16			
	c. Perf 12–13			
	d. Opt reading downwards			
D16	3 c. green and rosy mauve		13·00 15·00	60
	a. Stop after "DUE"		38·00 60·00	—
	b. Perf 14½–15		5·00 13·00	40
	c. Perf 13½–14, comp 14½–15			
	d. Opt double			
	e. Opt double. Stop after "DUE"		£150	
D17	3 c. green & dull mauve (*p* 14½–15)		8·50 18·00	75
	a. Stop after "DUE"		38·00 60·00	—
	b. Opt double. Stop after "DUE"		£200 £225	—
D18	4 c. black and carmine		16·00 17·00	50
	a. Perf 14½–15			
D19	5 c. black and orange-vermilion		14·00 21·00	75
	a. Perf 14½–15		28·00 28·00	—
	b. Stop after "DUE"		35·00	
D20	6 c. black and bistre-brown (Optd "Specimen" £25)		— 20·00	40
	a. Perf 14½–15		3·00 14·00	40
	b. Perf 13½–14, comp 12–13			
D20*c*	8 c. black and brown-purple (*p* 16)			
D21	8 c. black and brown			
	a. Perf 14½–15		3·00 14·00	40
	ab. Opt reading downwards		† †	—
D22	12 c. black and dull blue		40·00 95·00	2·50
	a. Perf 14½–15			
D23	18 c. black and green (No. 108)			
D24	18 c. black and green (No. 110)		25·00 95·00	2·50
	a. Perf 13½–14, comp 12–13		40·00 95·00	2·50
D25	24 c. blue and lake (No. 109)		— 35·00	60
D26	24 c. blue and lake (No. 111)			
	a. Perf 14½–15		12·00 75·00	1·00

B. *Horizontally*

D27	2 c. black and green		55·00 70·00 3·00
D28	8 c. black and brown (*p* 14½–15)		65·00 75·00 4·00
	a. Stop after "DUE"			

An example of the 5 c. value, No. D19a, has been seen clearly postmarked 1899.

The stamp showing a stop after "DUE", Nos. D14a, D16a, D17a, D19b and D28a, may well represent a separate local overprint. Such stamps do not come cancelled-to-order.

1902–5. *Stamps of 1901–5 optd* "British Protectorate," *further optd with Type* D 1. *P* 13½–14. A. *Vertically* (1902).

D29	2 c. black and green (*p* 16)		£190 £140
D30	3 c. green and rosy mauve		70·00 85·00
D31	5 c. black and orange-vermilion (*p* 14½–15)		£100 85·00
D32	8 c. black and brown		90·00 75·00
D33	24 c. blue and lake		£110 70·00

B. Horizontally, at top of stamp (1904–5)

D34	2 c. black and green (*p* 14½–15)		80·00 50·00
	a. Perf 16		60·00 70·00
D35	4 c. black and carmine		60·00 19·00

C. Horizontally, at centre of stamp (1904–5)

D35*a*	1 c. black and bistre-brown		— 23·00
	b. Perf 14½–15		£200 — 23·00
D36	2 c. black and green		4·50 1·75 10
	a. Perf 14½–15		45·00 45·00 —
D37	3 c. green and rosy mauve		1·75 1·75 10
	a. Perf 14½–15		45·00 30·00 —
	ab. "POSTAGE DUE" double			
D38	4 c. black and carmine		4·50 4·25 20
	a. "POSTAGE DUE" double		— † £120
	b. Perf 14½–15		3·00 7·00 20
D39	5 c. black and orange-vermilion		5·50 3·00 20
	a. Perf 14½–15		30·00 22·00 —
D40	6 c. black and bistre-brown		6·50 6·00 25
	a. "POSTAGE DUE" inverted		£350 † 90·00
	b. "POSTAGE DUE" double		† —
	c. No stop after "PROTECTORATE"			
	d. Perf 16		26·00 26·00 —
D41	8 c. black and brown		13·00 4·00 40
	a. No stop after "PROTECTORATE"		38·00 35·00 —
D42	10 c. brown and slate-lilac		70·00 30·00 1·00
	a. No stop after "PROTECTORATE"			
D42*b*	10 c. brown and slate-blue		30·00 12·00 1·00
D43	12 c. black and blue		6·50 11·00 1·00
D44	16 c. green and chestnut		14·00 14·00 1·00
D45	18 c. black and green		4·00 11·00 1·00
	a. "POSTAGE DUE" double		£400 † 4·00
	b. Imperf between (vert pair)		— £350
D46	24 c. blue and lake		6·50 17·00 1·00
	a. Perf 14½–15		
	b. "POSTAGE DUE" double		£200 † 75·00

D. Horizontally. Optd locally, with stop after "DUE." (1902)

D47	1 c. black and bistre-brown		3·25 48·00
	a. With raised stop after "DUE."		4·75 48·00

No. D35a/b are usually found cancelled-to-order suggesting that they came from remainder stocks which were not issued, but we have also seen one unused example of No. D35a and several of No. D35b.

1919–24. *Stamps of 1909–22, optd with Type* D 1. *P* 13½–14.

A. Horizontally at top of stamp

D48	4 c. black and scarlet (1919)		60·00 12·00

B. Horizontally towards foot of stamp

D49	2 c. black and green (2.24)		6·00 50·00
	a. Perf 14½–15		18·00
D50	3 c. black and green		3·75 22·00
D51	3 c. black and scarlet		70 1·00
D52	5 c. black and yellow-brown		4·50 11·00
D53	6 c. black and olive-green		4·00 7·50

D53*a*	6 c. black and apple-green		
D54	8 c. black and rose-lake		1·25 1·25
	a. Opt double		£500
D55	10 c. black and turquoise-blue (7.24)		7·00 12·00
	a. Perf 14½–15		42·00 75·00
D56	12 c. black and deep blue (7.24)		22·00 50·00
	a. Horiz pair, one with opt omitted		£5000
D56*b*	16 c. black and red-brown		16·00 65·00
	ba. Black and brown-lake		6·00 42·00
D49/56*b*		*Set of 9* 50·00 £160	
D49 & D56*b* Optd "Specimen"		*Set of 2* 45·00	

Nos. D51/3 also exist with the overprint towards the centre of the stamp.

1926–31. *As* 1920–31, *but perf* 12½.

D57	2 c. black and claret		40 1·75
D58	3 c. black and green		2·50 12·00
D59	4 c. black and scarlet		70 9·00
D60	5 c. black and yellow-brown		4·00 45·00
D61	6 c. black and olive-green		3·50 2·25
D62	8 c. black and carmine		2·00 8·50
D63	10 c. black and turquoise-blue		4·75 45·00
D64	12 c. black and deep blue		12·00 80·00
D65	16 c. black and red-brown (1931)		28·00 £110
D57/65		*Set of 9* 50·00 £275	

Nos. D49/65 exist with two types of opt; A. Thick letters; pointed beard to "G". B. Thinner letters; "G" with square end to beard and "D" more open. No. D56a is Type B. and D56b, Type A.

D 2 Crest of the Company

(Recess Waterlow)

1939 (1 Jan). *P* 12½.

D66	D 2 2 c. brown		5·00 60·00
D67	4 c. scarlet		5·50 70·00
D68	6 c. violet		13·00 85·00
D69	8 c. green		13·00 £140
D70	10 c. blue		27·00 £190
D66/70		*Set of 5* 55·00 £500	
D66/70 Perf "Specimen"		*Set of 5* £140	

XII. JAPANESE OCCUPATION OF NORTH BORNEO

Japanese forces landed in Northern Borneo on 15 December 1941 and the whole of North Borneo had been occupied by 19 January 1942.

Brunei, North Borneo, Sarawak and, after a short period, Labuan, were administered as a single territory by the Japanese. Until September–October 1942, previous stamp issues, without overprint, continued to be used in conjunction with existing postmarks. From October 1942 onwards unoverprinted stamps of Japan were made available and examples can be found used from the area for much of the remainder of the War. Japanese Occupation issues for Brunei, North Borneo and Sarawak were equally valid throughout the combined territory but not, in practice, equally available.

PRICES FOR STAMPS ON COVER	
Nos. J1/17	*from* × 5
Nos. J18/19	*from* × 6
Nos. J20/32	*from* × 25
Nos. J33/4	*from* × 2
Nos. J35/48	*from* × 10

(1)	2 Mt Kinabalu	3 Borneo Scene

1942 (30 Sept). *Stamps of North Borneo handstamped with* T 1.

(a) In violet or black on Nos. 303/17

J 1	1 c. green and red-brown		90·00 £130
J 2	2 c. purple and greenish blue		85·00 £120
J 3	3 c. slate-blue and green		80·00 £120
J 4	4 c. bronze-green and violet		40·00 80·00
J 5	6 c. deep blue and claret		80·00 £120
J 6	8 c. scarlet		80·00 £120
	a. Pair, one without opt		£650
J 7	10 c. violet and bronze-green		80·00 £120
J 8	12 c. green and bright blue		£100 £180
J 9	15 c. blue-green and brown		£100 £180
J10	20 c. violet and slate-blue		£140 £225
J11	25 c. green and chocolate		£140 £225
J12	50 c. chocolate and violet		£190 £275
J13	$1 brown and carmine		£170 £325
J14	$2 violet and olive-green		£275 £425
	a. Pair, one without opt		£1200
J15	$5 indigo and pale blue		£325 £500

(b) In black on Nos. 318/19 ("WAR TAX")

J16	1 c. green and red-brown		£275 £170
J17	2 c. purple and greenish blue		£650 £250

(Litho Kolff & Co., Batavia)

1943 (29 Apr). *P* 12½.

J18	2 4 c. red		10·00 20·00
J19	3 8 c. blue		10·00 20·00

(4)   (5)

("Imperial Japanese Postal Service North Borneo")

1944 (30 Sept). *Nos.* 303/15 *of North Borneo optd as* T 4.

J20	1 c. green and red-brown		2·50 6·50
J21	2 c. purple and greenish blue		4·50 6·50
J22	3 c. slate-blue and green		2·00 3·75
J23	4 c. bronze-green and violet		2·75 5·50
J24	6 c. deep blue and claret		2·50 3·75
J25	8 c. scarlet		4·00 10·00
J26	10 c. violet and bronze-green		3·00 8·50
J27	12 c. green and bright blue		3·25 8·50
J28	15 c. blue-green and brown		3·25 9·50
J29	20 c. violet and slate-blue		9·50 22·00
J30	25 c. green and chocolate		9·50 22·00
J31	50 c. chocolate and violet		38·00 55·00
J32	$1 brown and carmine		50·00 85·00
J20/32		*Set of 13* £120 £225	

The spacing between the second and third lines of the overprint is 12 mm on the horizontal stamps, and 15 mm on the upright.

1944. *No.* J7 *with* T 4 *opt in addition.*

J32*a*	10 c. violet and bronze-green		£160 £325

The 2 c., 3 c., 8 c., 12 c. and 15 c. stamps of the 1942 issue are also known with Type 4 opt.

1945. *No.* J1 *surch with* T 5.

J33	81 $2 on 1 c. green and red-brown		£3500 £2750

(6)   7 Girl War-worker   (8) ("North Borneo")

1945 (?). *North Borneo No.* 315 *surch with* T 6.

J34	$5 on $1 brown and carmine		£3000 £2500

1945. *Contemporary stamps of Japan as* T 7 (*various subjects*) *optd with* T 8 *at Chinese Press, Kuching.*

J35	1 s. red-brown (No. 391)		2·50 7·00
J36	2 s. scarlet (No. 318)		2·75 7·00
J37	3 s. emerald-green (No. 319)		2·00 7·00
J38	4 s. yellow-green (No. 395)		3·00 7·00
J39	5 s. claret (No. 396)		3·25 8·00
J40	6 s. orange (No. 322)		3·25 9·00
J41	8 s. violet (No. 324)		2·00 9·00
J42	10 s. carmine and pink (No. 399)		3·00 9·00
J43	15 s. blue (No. 401)		3·00 9·00
J44	20 s. blue-slate (No. 328)		70·00 80·00
J45	25 s. brown and chocolate (No. 329)		60·00 65·00
J46	30 s. turquoise-blue (No. 330)		£160 95·00
J47	50 s. olive and bistre (No. 331)		55·00 60·00
J48	1 y. red-brown and chocolate (No. 332)		48·00 65·00
J35/48		*Set of 14* £375 £400	

Designs:—2 s. General Nogi; 3 s. Hydro-electric Works; 4 s. Hyuga Monument and Mt Fuji; 5 s. Admiral Togo; 6 s. Garambi Lighthouse, Formosa; 8 s. Meiji Shrine; 10 s. Palms and map of S.E. Asia; 15 s. Airman; 20 s. Mt Fuji and cherry blossoms; 25 s. Horyu Temple; 30 s. Torii, Itsukushima Shrine at Miyajima; 50 s. Kinkaku Temple; 1 y. Great Buddha, Kamakura.

Examples of some values have been found with hand-painted forged overprints.

XIII. SARAWAK

Sarawak was placed under British protection in 1888. It was ceded to Great Britain on 1 July 1946 and was administered as a Crown Colony until 16 September 1963 when it became a state of the Federation of Malaysia.

Stamps of INDIA were used in Sarawak from *circa* 1859. They were replaced by Sarawak issues from 1869, although these were only valid for "local" postage as far as Singapore. Mail for further afield needed a combination of Sarawak and STRAITS SETTLEMENTS stamps, a stock of the latter being kept by the Sarawak Post Office. This arrangement continued until 1 July 1897 when Sarawak joined the U.P.U.

PRICES FOR STAMPS ON COVER TO 1945	
No. 1	—
Nos. 2/7	*from* × 50
Nos. 8/21	*from* × 8
Nos. 22/6	*from* × 6
No. 27	*from* × 40
Nos. 28/35	*from* × 6
Nos. 36/47	*from* × 8
No. 48	†
No. 49	*from* × 10
Nos. 50/61	*from* × 6
No. 62	†
Nos. 63/71	*from* × 4
Nos. 72/3	*from* × 8
Nos. 74/5	—
Nos. 76/90	*from* × 7
Nos. 91/105	*from* × 5
Nos. 106/25	*from* × 3
Nos. 126/45	*from* × 2

BROOKE FAMILY ADMINISTRATION
Sir James Brooke. 1842–11 June 1868
Sir Charles Brooke. 11 June 1868–17 May 1917

UNUSED PRICES. Nos. 1/7, 27 and 32/5 in unused condition are normally found to be without gum. Prices in the unused column are for stamps in this state. Examples of these issues with original gum are worth considerably more.

1 Sir James Brooke   2 Sir Charles Brooke

The initials in the corners of T **1** and **2** stand for "James (Charles) Brooke, Rajah (of) Sarawak".

(T **1** and **2**. Die eng Wm. Ridgway. Litho Maclure, Macdonald & Co, Glasgow)

1869 (1 Mar). *P* 11.
1   1   3 c. brown/*yellow* .. .. .. 40·00 £200
Specimens are known printed from the engraved die in orange-brown on orange surface-coloured paper, and perf 12. These were submitted to the Sarawak authorities as examples of the stamps and exist both with and without obliterations.

1871 (1 Jan). *P* 11 (*irregular*).
2   2   3 c. brown/*yellow* .. .. 1·25 3·00
   a. Stop after "THREE" .. .. 35·00 48·00
   b. Imperf between (vert pair) .. £350
   c. Imperf between (horiz pair).. £475
The "stop" variety, No. 2a, which occurs on R. 10/7 is of no more philatelic importance than any of the numerous other variations, such as narrow first "A" in "SARAWAK" (R. 2/7) and "R" with long tail in left lower corner (R. 9/10), but it has been accepted by collectors for many years, and we therefore retain it. The papermaker's wmk "L N L" appears once or twice in sheets of No. 2.
Specimens are known, recess-printed, similar to those mentioned in the note after No. 1.

TWO CENTS

Copies of No. 2 surcharged as above were first reported in 1876 but following the discovery of dies for forgeries and faked postmarks in 1891 it was concluded that the issue was bogus, especially as the availability of the 2 c. of 1875 made it unnecessary to issue a provisional. It has now been established that a 2 c. postal rate was introduced from 1 August 1874 for the carriage of newspapers. Moreover four examples are known with a stop after "CENTS." and showing other minor differences from the forgery illustrated. This version could be genuine and if others come to light we will reconsider listing it.

1875 (1 Jan). *P* 11½–12.
3   2   2 c. mauve/*lilac* (*shades*) .. .. 2·50 12·00
4   4 c. red-brown/*yellow* .. .. 2·75 3·00
   a. Imperf between (vert pair) .. £475
5   6 c. green/*green* .. .. .. 2·75 3·50
6   8 c. bright blue/*blue* .. .. 2·50 3·50
7   12 c. red/*pale rose* .. .. .. 6·50 6·50
         Set of 5   15·00 26·00
Nos. 3, 4, 6 and 7 have the watermark "L N L" in the sheet, as No. 2. No. 5 is watermarked "L N T".
All values exist imperf and can be distinguished from the proofs by shade and impression. Stamps rouletted, pin-perf, or roughly perf 6½ to 7 are proofs clandestinely perforated.

The 12 c. "laid" paper, formerly listed, is not on a true laid paper, the "laid" effect being accidental and not consistent.

The lithographic stones for Nos. 3 to 7 were made up from strips of five distinct impressions hence there are five types of each value differing mainly in the lettering of the tablets of value. There are flaws on nearly every individual stamp, from which they can be plated.

4 Sir Charles Brooke

(Typo D.L.R.)

1888 (10 Nov)–**1897**. *No wmk. P* 14.
8   4   1 c. purple and black (6.6.92) 90 45
9   2 c. purple and carmine (11.11.88) .. 85 65
   a. Purple and rosine (1897) .. 4·00 1·75
10   3 c. purple and blue (11.11.88).. .. 1·25 1·25
11   4 c. purple and yellow .. .. 9·50 25·00
12   5 c. purple and green (12.6.91) .. 8·00 1·50
13   6 c. purple and brown (11.11.88) .. 7·00 30·00
14   8 c. green and carmine (11.11.88) .. 4·50 2·50
   a. Green and rosine (1897) .. 12·00 9·50
15   10 c. green and purple (12.6.91).. .. 23·00 14·00
16   12 c. green and blue (11.11.88) .. 4·50 6·50
17   16 c. green and orange (28.12.97) .. 30·00 45·00
18   25 c. green and brown (19.11.88).. .. 28·00 32·00
19   32 c. green and black (28.12.97) .. 24·00 35·00
20   50 c. green (26.7.97) .. .. 25·00 55·00
21    $1 green and black (2.11.97) .. 35·00 50·00
8/21   *Set of* 14   £170 £250

Prepared for use but not issued
21a $2 green and blue £350
21b $5 green and violet £350
21c $10 green and carmine £350
On No. 21 the value is in black on an uncoloured ground.
The tablet of value in this and later similar issues is in the second colour given.

One Cent.   **one cent.**
(5)   (6)

2^{C.}   **5^C**   **5^{C.}**
(7)   (8)   (9)

1889 (3 Aug)–**92**. *T* **4** *surch. P* 14.
22   5   1 c. on 3 c. (12.1.92) .. .. 20·00 23·00
   a. Surch double £400 £300
23   6   1 c. on 3 c. (2.92) .. .. 2·75 2·75
   a. No stop after "cent" (R. 2/6) .. 80·00
24   7   2 c. on 8 c. (3.8.89) .. .. 2·25 5·00
   a. Surch double £275
   b. Surch inverted £1800
   c. Surch omitted (in pair with normal) .. £2250
25   8   5 c. on 12 c. (with stop after "C") (17.2.91).. 17·00 28·00
   a. No stop after "C" .. .. 17·00 27·00
   b. "C" omitted £250 £250
   c. Surch double £900
   d. Surch double, one vertical £1700
   e. Surch omitted (in pair with normal) .. £5500
26   9   5 c. on 12 c. (17.2.91) .. .. 70·00 90·00
   a. No stop after "C" .. .. 60·00 75·00
   b. "C" omitted £325 £275
   c. Surch double £800

ONE CENT
———
(10)

1892 (23 May). *No.* 2 *surch with T* **10**.
27   2   1 c. on 3 c. brown/*yellow* 50 90
   a. Stop after "THREE." .. .. 16·00 24·00
   b. Imperf between (vert pair) .. £400
   c. Imperf horiz (vert pair) .. £400
   d. Bar omitted (1st ptg) £130
   e. Bar at top and bottom (1st ptg) .. £180
   f. Surch double (2nd ptg) .. £300 £325
No. 27 was surcharged with a setting of 100 (10 × 10). It was originally intended that there should be no bar at foot, but this was then added at a second operation before the stamps were issued. Subsequent supplies were surcharged with "ONE CENT" and bar at one operation.
Varieties with part of the surcharge missing are due to gum on the face of the unsurcharged stamps receiving part of the surcharge, which was afterwards washed off.

11   12

---

13 Sir Charles Brooke 14

(Die eng Wm. Ridgway. Recess P.B.)

1895 (1 Jan–Sept). *No wmk. P* 11½–12.
28   11   2 c. brown-red .. .. .. 4·00 5·50
   a. Imperf between (vert pair) .. £250
   b. Imperf between (horiz pair) .. £225
   c. Second ptg. Perf 12½ (Sept). .. 4·00 4·50
   ca. Perf 12½. Imperf between (horiz pair) £250
29   12   4 c. black .. .. .. 4·00 2·50
   a. Imperf between (horiz pair) .. £275
30   13   6 c. violet.. .. .. .. 3·50 7·00
31   14   8 c. green.. .. .. .. 13·00 6·00
28/31   *Set of* 4   22·00 18·00
Stamps of these types, printed in wrong colours, are trials and these, when surcharged with values in "pence", are from waste sheets that were used by Perkins, Bacon & Co as trial paper when preparing an issue of stamps for British South Africa.

4 CENTS.
(15)   16

1899. *Surch as T* **15**.
32   2   2 c. on 3 c. brown/*yellow* (19.9.99) .. 80 90
   a. Stop after "THREE" .. .. 35·00
   b. Imperf between (vert pair) .. £650
33   2 c. on 12 c. red/*pale rose* (29.6.99) .. 2·50 3·00
   a. Surch inverted £700 £900
34   4 c. on 6 c. green/*green* (R.) (16.11.99) .. 15·00 38·00
35   4 c. on 8 c. bright blue/*blue* (R.) (29.6.99) .. 2·75 4·50
32/5   *Set of* 4   19·00 42·00
A variety of surcharge with small "S" in "CENTS" may be found in the 2 c. on 12 c. and 4 c. on 8 c. and a raised stop after "CENTS" on the 4 c. on 6 c.
The omission of parts of the surcharge is due to gum on the surface of the stamps (see note after No. 27).
A block of 50 of No. 35 from the right of the pane is known line perforated 12.7 between the stamps and the margins at top and right.

(Typo D.L.R.)

1899 (10 Nov)–**1908**. *Inscribed* "POSTAGE POSTAGE." *No wmk. P* 14.
36   4   1 c. grey-blue and rosine (1.1.01) .. 30 60
   a. Grey-blue and red .. .. 1·50 60
   b. Ultramarine and rosine .. 3·25 1·25
   c. Dull blue and carmine .. 8·50 3·75
37   2 c. green (16.12.99) 50 40
38   3 c. dull purple (1.2.08) .. .. 2·75 15
39   4 c. rose-carmine (10.11.99) .. 3·75 1·60
   a. Aniline carmine .. .. 1·75 15
40   8 c. yellow and black (6.12.99) .. 1·75 70
41   10 c. ultramarine (10.11.99) .. 1·75 50
42   12 c. mauve (16.12.99) .. .. 2·00 1·75
   a. Bright mauve (1905) .. 11·00 6·00
43   16 c. chestnut and green (16.12.99) .. 1·75 1·50
44   20 c. bistre and bright mauve (4.00) .. 4·00 2·25
45   25 c. brown and blue (16.12.99) .. 2·75 3·50
46   50 c. sage-green and carmine (16.12.99) .. 11·00 18·00
47    $1 rose-carmine and green (16.12.99) .. 27·00 48·00
   a. Rosine and pale green .. 42·00 55·00
36/47   *Set of* 12   50·00 70·00

Prepared for use but not issued
48   4   5 c. olive-grey and green .. .. 12·00
The figures of value in the $1 are in colour on an uncoloured ground.

1902. *Inscribed* "POSTAGE POSTAGE". *W* **16**. *P* 14.
49   4   2 c. green .. .. 13·00 11·00

Sir Charles Vyner Brooke. 17 May 1917–1 June 1946

ONE cent
———

17 Sir Charles Vyner   (18)
     Brooke

(Typo D.L.R.)

1918 (26 Mar). *No wmk. Chalk-surfaced paper. P* 14.
50   17   1 c. slate-blue and red 40 60
   a. Dull blue and carmine .. 45 80
51   2 c. green .. .. .. 1·00 75
52   3 c. brown-purple .. .. 2·25 1·75
53   4 c. rose-carmine .. .. 2·25 1·60
   a. Rose-red .. .. .. 2·00 1·40
54   8 c. yellow and black .. .. 5·00 24·00
55   10 c. blue (*shades*) .. .. 2·00 2·25
56   12 c. purple .. .. .. 6·50 9·50
57   16 c. chestnut and green.. .. 5·00 4·50
58   20 c. olive and violet (*shades*) .. 3·50 4·75
59   25 c. brown and bright blue .. 4·00 7·50
60   50 c. olive-green and carmine .. 6·00 11·00
61    $1 bright rose and green .. 11·00 18·00
50/61   *Set of* 12   45·00 75·00
50/61 Optd "Specimen" .. .. *Set of* 12   £190

Prepared for use but not issued

62	17	1 c. slate-blue and slate		20·00	

On the $1 the figures of value are in colour on an uncoloured ground.

1922–23. *New colours and values. No wmk. Chalk-surfaced paper.* P 14.

63	17	2 c. purple (5.3.23)	75	1·25
64		3 c. dull green (23.3.22)	55	75
65		4 c. brown-purple (10.4.23)	70	30
66		5 c. yellow-orange	60	90
67		6 c. claret (1.22)	85	1·25
68		8 c. bright rose-red	1·75	17·00
69		10 c. black (1923)	1·75	2·25
70		12 c. bright blue (12.22)	7·00	16·00
		a. Pale dull blue	7·00	14·00
71		30 c. ochre-brown and slate	3·50	3·75
63/71		Set of 9	16·00	38·00

1923 (Jan). *Surch as T 18.* (a) *First printing. Bars 1¼ mm apart.*

72	17	1 c. on 10 c. dull blue	12·00	42·00
		a. "cnet" for "cent" (R. 9/5)	£300	£600
73		2 c. on 12 c. purple	5·00	24·00
		a. Thick, narrower "W" in "TWO"	17·00	55·00

(b) *Second printing. Bars ¾ mm apart*

74	17	1 c. on 10 c. dull blue	80·00	£150
		b. "cnet" for "cent" (R.9/5)		£8000
		c. "en" of "cent" scratched out and "ne" overprinted (R.9/5)		£3000
75		2 c. on 12 c. purple	45·00	85·00
		a. Thick, narrower "W" in "TWO"		£100

In the 2 c. on 12 c. the words of the surcharge are about 7½ mm from the bars.

The "cnet" error occurred on R.9/5 of all sheets from the first printing of the 1 c. on 10 c. A single example of the error, No. 74b, is known from the second printing, but the error was then corrected, as shown by the evidence of a surviving plate block, only to have the correct spelling scratched out, by a local employee, and "ne" substituted (No. 74c).

The thick "W" variety occurs on all stamps of the last two horizontal rows of the first printing (12 stamps per sheet), and in the last two vertical rows of the second printing (20 stamps per sheet).

1928 (Apr)–**29.** *W 16 (Multiple). Chalk-surfaced paper.* P 14.

76	17	1 c. slate-blue and carmine	45	35
77		2 c. bright purple	50	50
78		3 c. green	60	3·00
79		4 c. brown-purple	1·50	40
80		5 c. yellow-orange (5.8.29)	3·25	3·00
81		6 c. claret	80	10
82		8 c. bright rose-red	1·75	5·50
83		10 c. black	1·50	1·75
84		12 c. bright blue	1·75	7·50
85		16 c. chestnut and green	1·75	2·50
86		20 c. olive-bistre and violet	1·75	4·50
87		25 c. brown and bright blue	2·50	6·00
88		30 c. bistre-brown and slate	3·00	8·00
89		50 c. olive-green and carmine	3·75	5·50
90		$1 bright rose and green	9·00	18·00
76/90		Set of 15	30·00	60·00
76/90		Optd/Perf "Specimen" Set of 15	£200	

In the $1 the value is as before.

19 Sir Charles Vyner Brooke

20

(Recess Waterlow)

1932 (1 Jan). *W 20.* P 12½.

91	19	1 c. indigo	70	35
92		2 c. green	70	40
93		3 c. violet	2·25	70
94		4 c. red-orange	80	15
95		5 c. deep lake	2·25	70
96		6 c. scarlet	3·25	5·00
97		8 c. orange-yellow	3·00	5·00
98		10 c. black	2·25	2·50
99		12 c. deep ultramarine	2·75	5·50
100		15 c. chestnut	3·50	6·00
101		20 c. orange-red and violet	3·00	6·00
102		25 c. orange-yellow and chestnut	4·75	7·50
103		30 c. sepia and vermilion	4·75	13·00
104		50 c. carmine-red and olive-green	5·00	6·00
105		$1 green and carmine	8·00	19·00
91/105		Set of 15	42·00	70·00
91/105		Perf "Specimen" Set of 15	£200	

21 Sir Charles Vyner Brooke

BMA

(22)

(Recess B.W.)

1934 (1 May)–**41.** *No wmk.* P 12.

106	21	1 c. purple	15	10
107		2 c. green	15	10
107a		2 c. black (1.3.41)	80	1·40
108		3 c. black	15	10
108a		3 c. green (1.3.41)	70	1·50
109		4 c. bright purple	15	15
110		5 c. violet	20	10
111		6 c. carmine	15	50

111a	21	6 c. lake-brown (1.3.41)	1·75	5·00
112		8 c. red-brown	15	10
112a		8 c. carmine (1.3.41)	1·50	10
113		10 c. scarlet	75	40
114		12 c. blue	30	25
114a		12 c. orange (1.3.41)	80	3·75
115		15 c. orange	50	3·00
115a		15 c. blue (1.3.41)	1·75	5·00
116		20 c. olive-green and carmine	90	60
117		25 c. violet and orange	75	1·00
118		30 c. red-brown and violet	75	1·25
119		50 c. violet and scarlet	75	75
120		$1 scarlet and sepia	60	50
121		$2 bright purple and violet	4·50	6·00
122		$3 carmine and green	17·00	14·00
123		$4 blue and scarlet	17·00	17·00
124		$5 scarlet and red-brown	17·00	24·00
125		$10 black and yellow	17·00	28·00
106/25		Set of 26	75·00	£100
106/25		Perf "Specimen" Set of 26	£450	

For the 3 c. green, wmkd Mult Script CA, see No. 152a.

BRITISH MILITARY ADMINISTRATION

Following the Japanese surrender elements of the British Military Administration reached Kuching on 11 September 1945. From 6 November 1945 Australian stamps, initially the 3d. value and later the 1d., 6d. and 1s., were made available for civilian use until replaced by Nos. 126/45.

1945 (17 Dec). *Optd with T 22.*

126	21	1 c. purple	20	40
127		2 c. black (R.)	30	40
		a. Opt double	†	£2750
128		3 c. green	30	30
129		4 c. bright purple	30	30
130		5 c. violet (R.)	30	60
131		6 c. lake-brown	50	75
132		8 c. carmine	9·00	9·00
133		10 c. scarlet	50	60
134		12 c. orange	60	3·75
135		15 c. blue	85	40
136		20 c. olive-green and carmine	1·25	1·40
137		25 c. violet and orange (R.)	1·25	1·75
138		30 c. red-brown and violet	1·25	2·75
139		50 c. violet and scarlet	1·25	35
140		$1 scarlet and sepia	2·50	1·25
141		$2 bright purple and violet	9·00	4·50
142		$3 carmine and green	17·00	24·00
143		$4 blue and scarlet	25·00	25·00
144		$5 scarlet and red-brown	85·00	90·00
145		$10 black and yellow (R.)	90·00	£110
126/45		Set of 20	£225	£250

These stamps, and the similarly overprinted stamps of North Borneo, were obtainable at all post offices throughout British Borneo (Brunei, Labuan, North Borneo and Sarawak), for use on local and overseas mail.

The administration of Sarawak was returned to the Brooke family on 15 April 1946, but the Rajah, after consulting the inhabitants ceded the territory to Great Britain on 1 June 1946.

23 Sir James Brooke, Sir Charles Vyner (24)
Brooke and Sir Charles Brooke

(Recess B.W.)

1946 (18 May). *Centenary Issue.* P 12.

146	23	8 c. lake	30	30
147		15 c. blue	30	1·25
148		50 c. black and scarlet	40	80
149		$1 black and sepia	55	7·50
146/9		Set of 4	1·40	9·00
146/9		Perf "Specimen" Set of 4	90·00	

CROWN COLONY

1947 (16 Apr). *Optd with T 24, typo by B.W. in blue-black or red. Wmk Mult Script CA.* P 12.

150	21	1 c. purple	15	30
151		2 c. black (R.)	15	15
152		3 c. green (R.)	15	15
		a. Albino opt		£3000
153		4 c. bright purple	15	15
154		6 c. lake-brown (R.)	20	60
155		8 c. carmine	30	10
156		10 c. scarlet	20	20
157		12 c. orange	20	80
158		15 c. blue (R.)	20	40
159		20 c. olive-green and carmine (R.)	40	50
160		25 c. violet and orange (R.)	40	30
161		50 c. violet and scarlet (R.)	40	40
162		$1 scarlet and sepia	75	90
163		$2 bright purple and violet	1·00	3·00
164		$5 scarlet and red-brown	2·00	3·00
150/64		Set of 15	6·00	10·00
150/64		Perf "Specimen" Set of 15	£250	

No. 152a shows an uninked impression of T 24.

1948 (25 Oct). *Royal Silver Wedding. As Nos. 143/4 of Jamaica.*

165		8 c. scarlet	30	30
166		$5 brown	25·00	26·00

1949 (10 Oct). *75th Anniv of U.P.U. As Nos. 145/8 of Jamaica.*

167		8 c. carmine	80	50
168		15 c. deep blue	1·40	2·25
169		25 c. deep blue-green	1·40	1·50
170		50 c. violet	2·00	3·00
167/70		Set of 4	5·00	6·50

25 *Trogonoptera brookiana*   26 Western Tarsier

(Recess; Arms typo B.W.)

1950 (3 Jan). *T 25/6 and similar designs. Wmk Mult Script CA.* P 11½ × 11 (*horiz*) or 11 × 11½ (*vert*).

171		1 c. black	30	30
172		2 c. red-orange	20	40
173		3 c. green	10	60
174		4 c. chocolate	10	20
175		6 c. turquoise-blue	10	15
176		8 c. scarlet	10	30
177		10 c. orange	50	2·75
178		12 c. violet	1·75	1·50
179		15 c. blue	85	15
180		20 c. purple-brown and red-orange	60	30
181		25 c. green and scarlet	70	30
182		50 c. brown and violet	85	15
183		$1 green and chocolate	6·00	1·50
184		$2 blue and carmine	14·00	5·50
185		$5 black, yellow, red and purple	18·00	8·00
171/85		Set of 15	40·00	20·00

Designs: *Horiz*—8 c. Dayak dancer; 10 c. Malayan Pangolin; 12 c. Kenyah boys; 15 c. Fire-making; 20 c. Kelemantan rice barn; 25 c. Pepper vines; $1 Kelabit smithy; $2 Map of Sarawak; $5 Arms of Sarawak. *Vert*—3 c. Kayan tomb; 4 c. Kayan girl and boy; 6 c. Bead work; 50 c. Iban woman.

40 Map of Sarawak

(Recess B.W.)

1952 (1 Feb). *Wmk Mult Script CA.* P 11½ × 11.

186	40	10 c. orange	30	40

1953 (3 June). *Coronation. As No. 153 of Jamaica.*

187		10 c. black and deep violet-blue	85	75

41 Logging   44 Malabar Pied Hornbill

51 Queen Elizabeth II   52 Queen Elizabeth II
(after Annigoni)

(Des M. Thoma (1, 2 c.), R. Turrell (4 c.), J. D. Hughes (6, 12 c.), A. Hakim bin Moliti (8 c.), J. Woodcock (10 c.), J. Browning (15 c.), G. Gundersen (20 c.), K. Munich (25 c.). Recess, Arms typo ($5). B.W.)

1955 (1 June)–**59.** *T 41, 44, 51/2 and similar designs. Wmk Mult Script CA.* P 11×11½ (1 c., 2 c., 4 c.), 12×13 (30 c., 50 c., $1, $2) or 11½×11 (*others*).

188	41	1 c. green (1.10.57)	10	30
189		2 c. red-orange (1.10.57)	30	55
190		4 c. lake-brown (1.10.57)	45	30
		a. Brown-purple (18.3.59)	2·25	2·00
191	44	6 c. greenish blue (1.10.57)	3·00	55
192		8 c. rose-red (1.10.57)	30	30
193		10 c. deep green (1.10.57)	20	10
194		12 c. plum (1.10.57)	3·00	55
195		15 c. ultramarine (1.10.57)	80	20
196		20 c. olive and brown (1.10.57)	80	10
197		25 c. sepia and green (1.10.57)	6·00	15
198	51	30 c. red-brown and deep lilac	1·75	20
199		50 c. black and carmine (1.10.57)	2·00	15
200	52	$1 myrtle-green & orange-brn (1.10.57)	2·00	15
201		$2 violet and bronze-green (1.10.57)	5·50	2·00
202		$5 multicoloured (1.10.57)	13·00	5·50
188/202		Set of 15	38·00	10·00

Designs: *Horiz*—8 c. Shield with spears; 10 c. Kenyah ceremonial carving; 12 c. Barong panau (sailing prau); 25 c. Astana, Kuching; $5 Arms of Sarawak. *Vert* (as T 41)—2 c. Young Orang-Utan; 4 c. Kayan dancing; 50 c. Queen Elizabeth II; $2 Queen Elizabeth II (after Annigoni).

1963 (4 June). *Freedom from Hunger. As No. 80 of Lesotho.*

203		12 c. sepia	1·50	35

STATE OF MALAYSIA

1964–65. *As 1955–57 but wmk w 12. Perfs as before.*

204	41	1 c. green (8.9.64)			10	40
205	–	2 c. red-orange (17.8.65)			65	2·75
206	44	6 c. greenish blue (8.9.64)			3·75	2·75
207		10 c. deep green (8.9.64)			75	75
208		12 c. plum (8.9.64)			1·50	4·25
209		15 c. ultramarine (17.8.65)			1·25	8·00
210		20 c. olive and brown (9.6.64)			50	60
211		25 c. deep sepia and bluish green (8.9.64)		1·75	3·50
204/11				*Set of 8*	9·00	21·00

53 Vanda hookeriana   *54 Precis orithya*

1965 (15 Nov). *As Nos. 166/72 of Johore but with Arms of Sarawak inset as in T 53.*

212	1 c. multicoloured				10	60
	c. Grey omitted				35·00	
213	2 c. multicoloured				15	60
	a. Black (country name and shield) omitted			65·00	
	c. Yellow-olive (stems) omitted			30·00	
214	5 c. multicoloured				45	10
215	6 c. multicoloured				60	60
	a. Black (country name and shield) omitted			65·00	
216	10 c. multicoloured				65	10
	a. Red omitted				35·00	
217	15 c. multicoloured				1·50	10
218	20 c. multicoloured				1·75	50
212/18				*Set of 7*	4·75	2·25

The 1 c., 6 c., 10 c. and 15 c. exist with PVA gum as well as gum arabic.

No. 213a was formerly listed with Trengganu No. 101 but there is evidence that it was issued in Sarawak.

A used example of No. 218 is known with the bright purple (blooms) omitted.

The higher values used with this issue were Nos. 20/7 of Malaysia (National Issues).

(Litho B.W.)

1971 (1 Feb). *As Nos. 175/81 of Johore but with Arms of Sarawak inset as in T 54.*

219	1 c. multicoloured				15	65
220	2 c. multicoloured				35	75
221	5 c. multicoloured				65	10
222	6 c. multicoloured				80	60
223	10 c. multicoloured				80	10
224	15 c. multicoloured				1·25	10
225	20 c. multicoloured				1·50	60
219/25				*Set of 7*	5·00	2·50

The higher values used with this issue were Nos. 64/71 of Malaysia (National Issues).

55 Precis orithya (different crest at right)   *56 Rhododendron scortechinii*

(Photo Harrison)

1977 (12 Feb)–**78.** *As Nos. 219/21 and 223/5 but ptd in photogravure showing new State Crest as T 55.*

226	1 c. multicoloured (1978)				7·00	8·00
227	2 c. multicoloured (1978)				1·75	3·50
228	5 c. multicoloured				80	70
230	10 c. multicoloured (4.4.77)				65	30
231	15 c. multicoloured (19.4.77)				1·75	10
232	20 c. multicoloured (1978)				1·50	2·25
226/32				*Set of 6*	12·00	13·50

1979 (30 Apr). *As Nos. 188/94 of Johore but with Arms of Sarawak as in T 56.*

233	1 c. *Rafflesia hasseltii*				10	30
234	2 c. *Pterocarpus indicus*				10	30
235	5 c. *Lagerstroemia speciosa*				10	10
236	10 c. *Durio zibethinus*				10	10
237	15 c. *Hibiscus rosa-sinensis*				20	10
238	20 c. Type **56**				25	10
239	25 c. *Etlingera elatior* (inscr "*Phaeomeria speciosa*")			25	10
233/9				*Set of 7*	95	75

For higher values used in conjunction with this series see Nos. 190/7 of Malaysia (National Issues).

1983 (11 Oct)–**86.** *As Nos. 235/6 and 238 but without wmk.*

242	5 c. *Lagerstroemia speciosa* (4.4.86)			1·00	1·40
243	10 c. *Durio zibethinus* (9.9.85)			1·00	1·40
245	20 c. Type **56** (blackish brown background)		6·50	3·00
245a	20 c. Type **56** (bronze-green background) (2.8.84)		1·25	1·40
242/5a				*Set of 4*	9·00	6·50

* There was no official release date for these stamps. Dates shown are the earliest recorded from postmarks and may be revised if earlier examples are reported.

For details of the shade differences between watermarked and unwatermarked printings see after Malaysia–Johore No. 200a.

On Nos. 242/3 and 245a the crest is closer to the face value than on Nos. 235/6, 238 and 245.

---

57 Coffee

1986 (25 Oct). *As Nos. 202/8 of Johore but with Arms of Sarawak as in T 57.*

247	1 c. Type **57**				10	10
248	2 c. Coconuts				10	10
249	5 c. Cocoa				10	10
250	10 c. Black pepper				10	10
251	15 c. Rubber				10	10
252	20 c. Oil palm				10	10
253	30 c. Rice				15	20
247/53			*Set of 7*	40	45

XIV. JAPANESE OCCUPATION OF SARAWAK

Japanese forces landed in North Borneo in 16 December 1941 and Sarawak was attacked on 23 December 1941.

Brunei, North Borneo, Sarawak and, after a short period, Labuan, were administered as a single territory by the Japanese. Until September–October 1942, previous stamp issues, without overprint, continued to be used in conjunction with existing postmarks. From the Autumn of 1942 onwards unoverprinted stamps of Japan were made available and examples can be found used from the area for much of the remainder of the War. Japanese Occupation issues for Brunei, North Borneo and Sarawak were equally valid throughout the combined territory but not, in practice, equally available.

PRICES FOR STAMPS ON COVER	
Nos. J1/21	*from* ×8
Nos. J22/6	—

大日本帝国政府

(1)

("Imperial Japanese Government")

1942 (Oct). *Stamps of Sarawak handstamped with T 1 in violet.*

J 1	21	1 c. purple			24·00	29·00
		a. Pair, one without opt		£500	
J 2		2 c. green			65·00	85·00
J 3		2 c. black			40·00	55·00
J 4		3 c. black			£130	£150
J 5		3 c. green			35·00	40·00
J 6		4 c. bright purple			26·00	35·00
J 7		5 c. violet			30·00	32·00
J 8		6 c. carmine			50·00	60·00
J 9		6 c. lake-brown			32·00	40·00
J10		8 c. red-brown			£110	£140
J11		8 c. carmine			90·00	£110
J12		10 c. scarlet			32·00	40·00
J13		12 c. blue			80·00	85·00
J14		12 c. orange			80·00	£100
J15		15 c. orange			£140	£150
J16		15 c. blue			45·00	50·00
J17		20 c. olive-green and carmine		30·00	42·00
J18		25 c. violet and orange			38·00	40·00
J19		30 c. red-brown and violet		35·00	48·00
J20		50 c. violet and scarlet			35·00	45·00
J21		$1 scarlet and sepia			42·00	60·00
J22		$2 bright purple and violet		£100	£120
J23		$3 carmine and green			£550	£650
J24		$4 blue and scarlet			£110	£140
J25		$5 scarlet and red-brown		£110	£140
J26		$10 black and yellow			£120	£160

The overprint, being handstamped, exists inverted on all values. Stamps of T 21 optd with Japanese symbols within an oval frame are revenue stamps, while the same stamps overprinted with three Japanese characters between two vertical double rules, were used as seals.

Maldive Islands

BRITISH PROTECTORATE

MALDIVES

(1)   2 Minaret, Juma   3
           Mosque, Malé

1906 (9 Sept). *Nos. 277/9, 280a and 283/4 of Sri Lanka (Ceylon) optd with T 1. Wmk Mult Crown CA. P 14.*

1	44	2 c. red-brown	..	..	11·00	25·00
2	45	3 c. green	..	..	15·00	25·00
3		4 c. orange and ultramarine	..	32·00	65·00
4	46	5 c. dull purple	..	..	4·50	6·50
5	48	15 c. blue	..	..	50·00	95·00
6		25 c. bistre	..	..	60·00	£100
1/6			*Set of 6*	£150	£275

No further supplies of Nos. 1/6 were despatched to the Maldive Islands after 1907 and the stamps of CEYLON were used until 1909. Overseas mail to destinations other than Ceylon or India continued to be franked with Ceylon stamps until 1967 when Maldive Islands joined the U.P.U.

(Recess D.L.R.)

1909 (May). *T 2 (18½ × 22½ mm). W 3. P 14.*

7	2	2 c. orange-brown	..	..	2·25	70
8		3 c. deep myrtle	..	..	40	70
9		5 c. purple	..	..	40	35
10		10 c. carmine	..	..	3·25	80
7/10		..	..	*Set of 4*	5·75	2·25

4

(Photo Harrison)

1933. *T 2 redrawn (reduced to 18 × 21½ mm). W 4. P 15 × 14.*

11	2	2 c. grey	..	..	1·75	1·75
12		3 c. red-brown	..	..	70	1·75
13		5 c. claret (*sideways wmk*)	..	14·00	17·00
14		5 c. mauve (*upright wmk*)	..	6·50	10·00
15		6 c. scarlet	..	..	1·25	2·50
16		10 c. green	..	..	55	55
17		15 c. black	..	..	4·50	6·00
18		25 c. brown	..	..	4·75	6·00
19		50 c. purple	..	..	4·50	4·50
20		1 r. deep blue	..	..	6·00	2·75
11/20			*Set of 10*	40·00	48·00

The 2, 3, 6, 10, 15, 25, 50 c. and 1 r. values exist with both upright and sideways watermarks.

(New Currency. 100 larees=1 rupee)

5 Palm Tree and Dhow

(Recess B.W.)

1950 (24 Dec). *P 13.*

21	5	2 l. olive-green	..	..	65	40
22		3 l. blue	..	..	3·25	40
23		5 l. emerald-green	..	3·50	50
24		6 l. red-brown	..	..	35	30
25		10 l. scarlet	..	..	50	30
26		15 l. orange	..	..	50	30
27		25 l. purple	..	..	35	30
28		50 l. violet	..	..	40	30
29		1 r. chocolate	..	..	7·00	22·00
21/9			*Set of 9*	15·00	22·00

7 Fish   8 Native Products

(Recess B.W.)

1952. *P 13.*

30	7	3 l. blue	..	..	50	30
31	8	5 l. emerald	..	..	40	40

The Maldive Islands became a republic on 1 January 1953, but reverted to a sultanate in 1954.

9 Malé Harbour   10 Fort and Building

(Recess B.W.)

1956 (Feb). *P 13½ (T 9) or 11½ × 11 (T 10).*

32	9	2 l. purple	..	..	10	10
33		3 l. slate	..	..	10	10
34		5 l. red-brown	..	..	10	10
35		6 l. blackish violet	..	10	10
36		10 l. emerald	..	..	10	10
37		15 l. chocolate	..	..	10	10
38		25 l. rose-red	..	..	10	10
39		50 l. orange	..	..	10	10
40	10	1 r. bluish green	..	..	15	10
41		5 r. blue	..	..	60	20
42		10 r. magenta	..	..	85	40
32/42			*Set of 11*	1·75	80

11 Cycling   12 Basketball

(Des C. Bottiau. Recess and typo B.W.)

1960 (20 Aug). *Olympic Games. P 11½ × 11 (T 11) or 11 × 11½ (T 12).*

43	11	2 l. purple and green	..	10	10
44		3 l. greenish slate and purple	..	10	10
45		5 l. red-brown and ultramarine	10	10
46		10 l. emerald-green and brown	..	10	10
47		15 l. sepia and blue	..	10	10
48	12	25 l. rose-red and olive	..	10	10
49		50 l. orange and violet	..	10	10
50		1 r. emerald and purple	..	20	55
43/50		..	..	*Set of 8*	60	90

13 Tomb of Sultan   14 Custom House

(Recess B.W.)

1960 (15 Oct). *T 13, 14 and similar horiz designs. P 11½ × 11.*

51	2	2 l. purple	..	..	10	10
52		3 l. emerald-green	..	..	10	10
53		5 l. orange-brown	..	..	1·25	90
54		6 l. bright blue	..	..	10	10
55		10 l. carmine	..	..	10	10
56		15 l. sepia	..	..	10	10
57		25 l. deep violet	..	..	10	10
58		50 l. slate-grey	..	..	10	10
59		1 r. orange	..	..	15	10
60		5 r. deep ultramarine	..	1·75	60
61		10 r. grey-green	..	..	5·00	1·25
51/61		..		*Set of 11*	7·50	3·00

Designs:—5 l. Cowrie shells; 6 l. Old Royal Palace; 10 l. Road to Juma Mosque, Malé; 15 l. Council house; 25 l. New Government Secretariat; 50 l. Prime Minister's office; 1 r. Old Ruler's tomb; 5 r. Old Ruler's tomb (distant view); 10 r. Maldivian Port.
Higher values were also issued, intended mainly for fiscal use.

24 "Care of Refugees"

(Recess B.W.)

1960 (15 Oct). *World Refugee Year. P 11½ × 11.*

62	24	2 l. deep violet, orange and green	..	10	10
63		3 l. brown, green and red	..	10	10
64		5 l. deep green, sepia and red	..	10	10
65		10 l. bluish green, reddish violet and red	10	10
66		15 l. reddish violet, grey-green and red ..	10	10
67		25 l. blue, red-brown and bronze-green ..	10	10
68		50 l. yellow-olive, rose-red and blue	..	10	10
69		1 r. carmine, slate and violet	..	15	35
62/9		..	..	*Set of 8*	30	45

---

25 Coconuts   26 Map of Malé

(Photo Harrison)

1961 (20 Apr). *P 14 × 14½ (Nos. 70/74) or 14½ × 14 (others).*

70	25	2 l. yellow-brown and deep green	10	10
71		3 l. yellow-brown and bright blue	10	10
72		5 l. yellow-brown and magenta	10	10
73		10 l. yellow-brown and red-orange	10	10
74		15 l. yellow-brown and black	10	10
75	26	25 l. multicoloured	..	10	10
76		50 l. multicoloured	..	10	10
77		1 r. multicoloured	..	20	30
70/7			*Set of 8*	45	55

27 5 c. Stamp of 1906   30 Malaria Eradication
                                  Emblem

(Des M. Shamir. Photo Harrison)

1961 (9 Sept). *55th Anniv of First Maldivian Stamp. T 27 and similar horiz designs. P 14½ × 14.*

78		2 l. brown-purple, ultramarine & lt green	..	10	10
79		3 l. brown-purple, ultramarine & lt green	10	10
80		5 l. brown-purple, ultramarine & lt green	10	10
81		6 l. brown-purple, ultramarine & lt green	10	10
82		10 l. green, claret and maroon	..	10	10
83		15 l. green, claret and maroon	..	10	10
84		20 l. green, claret and maroon	..	10	10
85		25 l. claret, green and black	..	10	10
86		50 l. claret, green and black	..	20	50
87		1 r. claret, green and black	..	35	90
78/87			*Set of 10*	75	1·60

MS87a 114 × 88 mm. No. 87 (block of four). Imperf 1·50 2·75
Designs:—2 to 6 l. Type 27; 10 to 20 l. 1906 3 c. and posthorn; 25 l. to 1 r. 1906 2 c. and olive sprig.

(Recess B.W.)

1962 (7 Apr). *Malaria Eradication. P 13½ × 13.*

88	30	2 l. chestnut	..	..	10	10
89		3 l. emerald	..	..	10	10
90		5 l. turquoise-blue	..	..	10	10
91		10 l. red	..	..	10	10
92	—	15 l. deep purple-brown	..	15	10
93	—	25 l. deep blue	..	..	15	10
94	—	50 l. deep green	..	..	20	10
95	—	1 r. purple	..	..	45	25
88/95			*Set of 8*	90	45

Nos. 92/5 are as T 30, but have English inscriptions at the side.

31 Children of Europe and America   33 Sultan Mohamed
                                              Farid Didi

(Des C. Bottiau. Photo Harrison)

1962 (9 Sept). *15th Anniv of U.N.I.C.E.F. T 31 and similar horiz design. Multicoloured. P 14½ × 14.*

96		2 l. Type 31	..	..	10	10
97		6 l. Type 31	..	..	10	10
98		10 l. Type 31	..	..	10	10
99		15 l. Type 31	..	..	10	10
100		25 l. Children of Middle East and Far East	10	10
101		50 l. As 25 l.	..	..	10	10
102		1 r. As 25 l.	..	..	10	20
103		5 r. As 25 l.	..	..	45	2·00
96/103		..	..	*Set of 8*	70	2·25

(Photo Harrison)

1962 (29 Nov). *Ninth Anniv of Enthronement of Sultan. P 14 × 14½.*

104	33	3 l. orange-brown and bluish green	10	10
105		5 l. orange-brown and indigo	..	10	10
106		10 l. orange-brown and olive	..	10	10
107		20 l. orange-brown and olive-green	..	10	10
108		50 l. orange-brown and deep magenta	10	10
109		1 r. orange-brown and slate-lilac	..	15	25
104/9		..	..	*Set of 6*	35	45

34 Angel Fish

(Des R. Hegeman. Photo Enschedé)

1963 (2 Feb). *Tropical Fish. T 34 and similar triangular designs.
Multicoloured. P 13½.*

110	2 l.	Type 34	..	10	10
111	3 l.	Type 34	..	10	10
112	5 l.	Type 34	..	10	10
113	10 l.	Moorish Idol	..	10	10
114	25 l.	As 10 l.	..	10	10
115	50 l.	Soldier Fish	..	10	10
116	1 r.	Surgeon Fish	..	30	30
117	5 r.	Butterfly Fish	..	3·00	5·00
110/17		*Set of 8*		3·25	5·00

39 Fishes in Net   **40** Handful of Grain

(Photo State Ptg Wks, Vienna)

1963 (21 Mar). *Freedom from Hunger. P 12.*

118	**39**	2 l. brown and deep bluish green	..	30	60
119	**40**	5 l. brown and orange-red	..	50	50
120	**39**	7 l. brown and turquoise	..	70	50
121	**40**	10 l. brown and blue	..	85	50
122	**39**	25 l. brown and brown-red	..	3·00	2·75
123	**40**	50 l. brown and violet	..	4·75	5·50
124	**39**	1 r. brown and deep magenta	..	7·50	9·50
118/24		*Set of 7*		16·00	18·00

41 Centenary Emblem   **42** Maldivian Scout Badge

(Photo Harrison)

1963 (Oct). *Centenary of Red Cross. P 14 × 14½.*

125	**41**	2 l. red and deep purple	..	30	·90
126		15 l. red and deep bluish green	..	50	80
127		50 l. red and deep brown..		1·25	1·75
128		1 r. red and indigo	..	2·00	2·00
129		4 r. red and deep brown-olive	..	6·50	19·00
125/9		*Set of 5*		9·50	22·00

(Photo Enschedé)

1964. *World Scout Jamboree, Marathon (1963). P 13½.*

130	**42**	2 l. green and violet	..	10	10
131		3 l. green and bistre-brown	..	10	10
132		25 l. green and blue	..	15	10
133		1 r. green and crimson	..	55	1·10
130/3		*Set of 4*		70	1·25

43 Mosque, Malé   **44** Putting the Shot

(Recess B.W.)

1964 (10 Aug). *"Maldives Embrace Islam". W w 12. P 11½.*

134	**43**	2 l. purple	..	10	10
135		3 l. emerald-green	..	10	10
136		10 l. carmine	..	10	10
137		40 l. deep dull purple	..	20	15
138		60 l. blue ..	..	30	15
139		85 l. orange-brown	..	30	20
134/9		*Set of 6*		90	60

(Litho Enschedé)

1964 (Oct). *Olympic Games, Tokyo. T 44 and similar horiz design.
W w 12. P 14 × 13½.*

140	2 l. deep maroon and turquoise-blue		..	10	10
141	3 l. crimson and chestnut		..	10	10
142	5 l. bronze-green and deep green		..	15	10
143	10 l. slate-violet and reddish purple		..	20	10
144	15 l. sepia and yellow-brown		..	20	10
145	25 l. indigo and deep blue		..	30	10

146	50 l. deep olive-green and yellow-olive	55	20
147	1 r. deep maroon and olive-grey	95	40
140/7	*Set of 8*	2·25	70
MS147a	126 × 140 mm. Nos. 145/7. Imperf	2·25	2·25

Designs:—2 to 10 l. Type 44; 15 l. to 1 r. Running.

46 Telecommunications Satellite

(Des M. Shamir. Photo Harrison)

1965 (1 July). *International Quiet Sun Years. P 14½.*

148	**46**	5 l. blue ..		10	10
149		10 l. brown		15	10
150		25 l. green		30	10
151		1 r. deep magenta		60	45
148/51		*Set of 4*		1·00	60

On 26 July 1965, Maldive Islands became independent and left
the British Commonwealth.

INDEPENDENT SULTANATE

Sultan Mohamed Farid Didi
29 November 1953–10 November 1968

47 Isis (wall carving,   **48** President Kennedy
Abu Simbel)   and Doves

(Des M. and G. Shamir. Litho Harrison)

1965 (1 Sept). *Nubian Monuments Preservation. T 47 and similar
vert design. W w 12. P 14½.*

152	**47**	2 l. bluish green and brown-purple	..	10	10
153		3 l. lake and deep green	..	10	10
154	**47**	5 l. dull green and brown-purple	..	10	10
155		10 l. steel-blue and orange	..	10	10
156	**47**	15 l. red-brown and deep violet	..	10	10
157		25 l. reddish purple and deep blue	..	15	10
158	**47**	50 l. yellow-green and sepia	..	25	15
159		1 r. ochre and myrtle-green	..	50	30
152/9		*Set of 8*		1·00	70

Design:—3, 10, 25 l., 1 r. Rameses II on throne (wall carving, Abu
Simbel).

(Photo State Ptg Wks, Vienna)

1965 (10 Oct). *Second Death Anniv of President Kennedy. T 48
and similar horiz design. P 12.*

160	**48**	2 l. black and mauve	..	10	10
161		10 l. bistre-brown and mauve	..	10	10
162		25 l. indigo and mauve	..	10	10
163	—	1 r. brt reddish purple, yellow & bl-grn	25	25
164	—	2 r. bronze-green, yellow & blue-green	40	40
160/4		*Set of 5*		75	75
MS164a	150 × 130 mm. No. 164 in block of four. Imperf		2·75	3·00

Design:—1 r., 2 r. Pres. Kennedy and hands holding olive-
branch.

49 "XX" and U.N. Flag   **50** I.C.Y. Emblem

(Des O. Adler. Photo State Ptg Wks, Vienna)

1965 (24 Nov). *20th Anniv of U.N. P 12.*

165	**49**	3 l. turquoise-blue and red-brown	..	10	10
166		10 l. turquoise-blue and violet	..	10	10
167		1 r. turquoise-blue and bronze-green	..	35	35
165/7		*Set of 3*		40	40

(Des M. and G. Shamir. Photo State Ptg Wks, Vienna)

1965 (20 Dec). *International Co-operation Year. P 12.*

168	**50**	5 l. brown and yellow-bistre	..	15	10
169		15 l. brown and slate-lilac	..	20	10
170		50 l. brown and yellow-olive	..	45	30
171		1 r. brown and orange-red	..	1·25	1·50
172		2 r. brown and new blue	..	1·75	3·00
168/72		*Set of 5*		3·50	4·50
MS173	101 × 126 mm. Nos. 170/2. Imperf		6·50	6·50

---

51 Seashells

(Des M. and G. Shamir. Photo State Ptg Wks, Vienna)

1966 (1 June). *T 51 and similar multicoloured designs. P 12.*

174	2 l.	Type 51	..	20	40
175	3 l.	Yellow flowers	..	20	40
176	5 l.	Seashells (*different*)	..	30	15
177	7 l.	Camellias	..	30	15
178	10 l.	Type 51	..	50	15
179	15 l.	Crab Plover and Seagull..		1·75	30
180	20 l.	Yellow flowers	..	80	30
181	30 l.	Type 51	..	1·50	35
182	50 l.	Crab Plover and Seagull..		3·50	55
183	1 r.	Type 51	..	2·50	55
184	1 r.	Camellias	..	2·50	55
185	1 r. 50,	Yellow flowers	..	3·25	1·75
186	2 r.	Camellias	..	4·50	2·25
187	5 r.	Crab Plover and Seagull..		14·00	8·50
188	10 r.	Seashells (*different*)	..	15·00	12·00
174/88		*Set of 15*		45·00	26·00

The 3 l., 7 l., 20 l., 1 r. (No. 184), 1 r. 50 and 2 r. are diamond-
shaped (43½ × 43½ mm); the others are horizontal designs as
T 51.

52 Maldivian Flag

(Des M. and G. Shamir. Litho Harrison)

1966 (26 July). *First Anniv of Independence. P 14 × 14½.*

189	**52**	10 l. green, red and turquoise	..	15	10
190		1 r. green, red, brown & orange-yellow	60	40

53 "Luna 9" on Moon

(Des M. and G. Shamir. Litho Harrison)

1966 (1 Nov). *Space Rendezvous and Moon Landing. T 53 and
similar horiz designs. W w 12. P 15 × 14.*

191		10 l. light brown, grey-blue and bright blue	..	15	10
192		25 l. green and carmine	..	20	10
193		50 l. orange-brown and green..		25	15
194		1 r. turquoise-blue and chestnut	..	55	35
195		2 r. green and violet	..	85	65
196		5 r. rose-pink and deep turquoise-blue	1·75	1·60
191/6		*Set of 6*		3·25	2·50
MS197	108 × 126 mm. Nos. 194/6. Imperf		3·25	3·75

Designs:—25 l., 1 r., 5 r. "Gemini 6" and "7" rendezvous in space;
2 r. "Gemini" spaceship as seen from the other spaceship; 50 l.
Type 53.

54 U.N.E.S.C.O.   **55** Sir Winston Churchill
Emblem, and Owl   and Cortège
on Book

(Litho Harrison)

1966 (15 Nov). *20th Anniv of U.N.E.S.C.O. T 54 and similar vert
designs. W w 12. Multicoloured. P 15 × 14.*

198		1 l. Type 54		10	40
199		3 l. U.N.E.S.C.O. emblem, and globe and microscope		10	40
200		15 l. U.N.E.S.C.O. emblem, and mask, violin and palette		15	15
201		50 l. Type 54		90	45
202		1 r. Design as 3 l.		1·60	75
203		5 r. Design as 5 l.		6·50	8·50
198/203		*Set of 6*		8·00	9·50

(Des M. and G. Shamir. Litho Harrison)

1967 (1 Jan). *Churchill Commemoration. T* **55** *and similar horiz design. Flag in red and blue. P* 14½ × 13½.
204	**55**	2 l. olive-brown	..	..	15	40
205	—	10 l. turquoise-blue	..	..	50	10
206	**55**	15 l. green	..	..	75	10
207	—	25 l. violet	..	..	1·25	15
208	—	1 r. brown	..	..	3·25	75
209	**55**	2 r. 50, crimson	..	..	7·50	9·00
204/9				*Set of 6*	12·00	9·50

Design:—10 l., 25 l., 1 r. Churchill and catafalque.

IMPERFORATE STAMPS. From No. 210 onwards some sets and perforated miniature sheets exist imperforate from limited printings.

56 Footballers and Jules Rimet Cup

(Des M. and G. Shamir. Photo Govt Printer, Israel)

1967 (22 Mar). *England's Victory in World Cup Football Championship. T* **56** *and similar horiz designs. Multi-coloured. P* 14 × 13½.
210		2 l. Type **56**	..	..	10	40
211		3 l. Player in red shirt kicking ball	..	10	40
212		5 l. Scoring goal	..	..	10	10
213		25 l. As 3 l.	..	..	30	10
		a. Emerald (face value and inscr) omitted	£130	
214		50 l. Making a tackle	..	..	55	20
215		1 r. Type **56**	..	..	1·40	55
216		2 r. Emblem on Union Jack	..	2·50	3·00
210/16				*Set of 7*	4·50	4·25
MS217		100×121 mm. Nos. 214/16. Imperf	5·50	4·50

57 Clown Butterfly Fish

(Des M. and G. Shamir. Photo Govt Printer, Israel)

1967 (1 May). *Tropical Fishes. T* **57** *and similar horiz designs. Multicoloured. P* 14.
218		2 l.	..	..	10	30
219		3 l. Striped Puffer	..	..	10	30
220		5 l. Blue Spotted Boxfish	..	15	10
221		6 l. Picasso Fish	..	..	15	20
222		50 l. Blue Angelfish	..	..	1·75	30
223		1 r. Blue Spotted Boxfish	..	3·25	75
224		2 r. Blue Angelfish	..	..	5·50	6·00
218/24				*Set of 7*	10·00	7·00

58 Hawker Siddeley "HS748" over Airport Building

(Des M. and G. Shamir. Photo Govt Printer, Israel)

1967 (26 July). *Inauguration of Hulule Airport. T* **58** *and similar horiz design. P* 14 × 13½.
225		2 l. reddish violet and yellow-olive	..	10	40
226		5 l. deep green and lavender	..	10	10
227		10 l. reddish violet and light turquoise-green	15	10
228		15 l. deep green and yellow-ochre	..	20	10
229		30 l. deep ultramarine and light blue	..	50	10
230		50 l. deep brown and magenta	..	75	20
231		5 r. deep ultramarine and yellow-orange	3·25	4·00
232		10 r. deep brown and blue	..	5·50	6·50
225/32				*Set of 8*	9·50	10·00

Designs:—2 l., 10 l., 30 l., 5 r. T **58**; 5 l., 15 l., 50 l., 10 r. Airport building and aircraft. Higher values were also issued, intended mainly for fiscal use.

59 "Man and Music" Pavilion (**60**)

International Tourist Year 1967

(Des M. and G. Shamir. Photo Govt Printer, Israel)

1967 (Sept). *World Fair, Montreal. T* **59** *and similar horiz design. Multicoloured. P* 14 × 13½.
233		2 l. Type **59**	..	..	10	10
234		5 l. "Man and His Community" Pavilion	10	10
235		10 l. Type **59**	..	..	10	10

236		50 l. As 5 l.	..	..	25	20
237		1 r. Type **59**	..	..	50	40
238		2 r. As 5 l.	..	..	80	90
233/8				*Set of 6*	1·50	1·50
MS239		102 × 137 mm. Nos. 237/8. Imperf	2·50	2·25

1967 (1 Dec). *International Tourist Year. Nos. 225/32 optd as T* **60** (*in one or three lines*), *in gold.*
240		2 l. reddish violet and yellow-olive	..	10	30
241		5 l. deep green and lavender	..	10	15
242		10 l. reddish violet and light turquoise-green	15	15
243		15 l. deep green and yellow-ochre	..	15	15
244		30 l. deep ultramarine and light blue	..	20	20
245		50 l. deep brown and magenta	..	30	30
246		5 r. deep ultramarine and yellow-orange	2·50	3·25
247		10 r. deep brown and blue	..	3·75	5·00
240/7				*Set of 8*	6·50	8·50

61 Cub signalling and Lord Baden-Powell

62 French Satellite "A 1"

(Litho Harrison)

1968 (1 Jan). *Maldivian Scouts and Cubs. T* **61** *and similar vert design. P* 14 × 14½.
248	**61**	2 l. brown, green and yellow	..	10	30
249	—	3 l. carmine, bright blue and light blue	10	30
250	**61**	25 l. bluish violet, lake and orange-red	1·50	30
251	—	1 r. blackish green, chest & apple-green	3·50	1·60
248/51				*Set of 4*	4·50	2·25

Design:—3 l., 1 r. Scouts and Lord Baden-Powell.

(Des M. and G. Shamir. Photo Govt Printer, Israel)

1968 (27 Jan). *Space Martyrs. Triangular designs as T* **62**. *P* 14.
252		2 l. magenta and ultramarine	..	10	30
253		3 l. violet and yellow-brown	..	10	30
254		7 l. olive-brown and lake	..	15	30
255		10 l. deep blue, pale drab and black	..	15	15
256		25 l. bright emerald and reddish violet	..	40	15
257		50 l. blue and orange-brown	..	75	30
258		1 r. purple-brown and deep bluish green	1·10	50
259		2 r. deep brown, pale blue and black	..	1·75	1·75
260		5 r. magenta, light drab and black	..	2·75	3·00
252/60				*Set of 9*	6·50	6·00
MS261		110 × 155 mm. Nos. 258/9. Imperf	3·50	3·25

Designs:—2 l., 50 l. Type **62**; 3 l., 25 l. "Luna 10"; 7 l., 1 r. "Orbiter" and "Mariner"; 10 l., 2 r. Astronauts White, Grissom and Chaffee; 5 r. Cosmonaut V. M. Komarov.

63 Putting the Shot

64 "Adriatic Seascape" (Bonington)

(Des M. Shamir. Litho Harrison)

1968 (Feb). *Olympic Games, Mexico (1967) (1st issue). T* **63** *and similar vert design. Multicoloured. P* 14½.
262		2 l. Type **63**	..	..	10	15
263		6 l. Throwing the discus	..	10	15
264		10 l. Type **63**	..	..	10	10
265		15 l. As 6 l.	..	..	10	10
266		1 r. Type **63**	..	..	35	35
267		2 r. 50, As 6 l.	..	..	65	85
262/7				*Set of 6*	1·10	1·40

See also Nos. 294/7.

(Des M. Shamir. Litho Govt Printer, Israel)

1968 (1 Apr). *Paintings. T* **64** *and similar horiz designs. Multicoloured. P* 14.
268		50 l. Type **64**	..	..	50	30
269		1 r. "Ulysses deriding Polyphemus" (Turner)	80	45
270		2 r. "Sailing Boat at Argenteuil" (Monet)	1·40	1·40
271		5 r. "Fishing Boats at Les Saintes-Maries" (Van Gogh)	..	3·25	3·75
268/71				*Set of 4*	5·50	5·50

65 *Graf Zeppelin* and Montgolfier's Balloon

(Des M. Shamir. Photo Govt Printer, Israel)

1968 (1 June). *Development of Civil Aviation. T* **65** *and similar horiz designs. P* 14 × 13½.
272		2 l. orange-brown, yellow-green & ultram	15	40
273		3 l. turquoise-blue, violet & orange-brown	15	40
274		5 l. slate-green, crimson and turquoise-blue	15	15
275		7 l. bright blue, purple and red-orange	90	55
276		10 l. brown, turquoise-blue and bright purple	35	15
277		50 l. crimson, slate-green and yellow-olive	1·50	20
278		1 r. emerald, blue and vermilion	..	2·25	50
279		2 r. maroon, bistre and bright blue	..	14·00	10·00
272/9				*Set of 8*	18·00	11·00

Designs:—3 l., 1 r. Boeing "707" and Douglas "DC-3"; 5 l., 50 l. Wright Brothers aircraft and Lilienthal's glider; 7 l., 2 r. Projected Boeing Supersonic "733" and "Concorde"; 10 l. Type **65**.

66 W.H.O. Building, Geneva

International Boy Scout Jamboree, Farragut Park, Idaho, U.S.A. August 1-9, 1967

(**67**)

(Litho Harrison)

1968 (15 July). *20th Anniv of World Health Organisation. P* 14½ × 13½.
280	**66**	10 l. violet, turquoise-bl & lt greenish bl	50	10
281		25 l. bronze-green, yell-brn & orge-yell	90	15
282		1 r. deep brown, emerald & brt green	2·50	90
283		2 r. bluish violet, magenta and mauve	4·25	5·00
280/3				*Set of 4*	7·50	5·50

1968 (1 Aug). *First Anniv of Scout Jamboree, Idaho. Nos. 248/51 optd with T* **67**.
284		2 l. brown, green and yellow	..	10	40
285		3 l. carmine, bright blue and light blue	10	40
286		25 l. bluish violet, lake and orange-red	1·25	40
287		1 r. blackish green, chestnut & apple-green	4·00	2·10
284/7				*Set of 4*	4·75	3·00

68 Curlew and Redshank

1968 (24 Sept). *T* **68** *and similar horiz designs. Photo. Multicoloured. P* 14 × 13½.
288		2 l. Type **68**	..	..	40	60
289		10 l. Conches	..	..	1·00	20
290		25 l. Shells	..	..	1·50	25
291		50 l. Type **68**	..	..	4·50	90
292		1 r. Conches	..	..	4·50	95
293		2 r. Shells	..	..	4·75	4·50
288/93				*Set of 6*	15·00	6·75

69 Throwing the Discus

(Des M. Shamir. Photo Govt Printer, Israel)

1968 (12 Oct). *Olympic Games, Mexico (2nd issue). T* **69** *and similar multicoloured designs. P* 14.
294		10 l. Type **69**	..	..	10	10
295		50 l. Running	..	..	10	10
296		1 r. Cycling	..	..	35	35
297		2 r. Basketball	..	..	1·00	1·00
294/7				*Set of 4*	1·40	1·40

INDEPENDENT REPUBLIC

11 November 1968

70 Fishing Dhow

71 "The Thinker" (Rodin)

(Photo Harrison)

1968 (11 Nov). *Republic Day. T* **70** *and similar horiz design.*
P 14 × 14½.
298   10 l. brown, ultramarine and lt yellow-green   75   20
299   1 r. green, red and bright blue   ..   ..   2·25   80
Design:—1 r. National flag, crest and map.

(Des M. Shamir. Litho Rosenbaum Brothers, Vienna)

1969 (10 Apr). *U.N.E.S.C.O. "Human Rights". T* **71** *and similar*
vert designs, showing sculptures by Rodin. Multicoloured.
P 13½.
300   6 l. Type **71**   30   15
301   10 l. "Hands"   30   15
302   1 r. 50, "Eve"   ..   ..   2·00   2·00
303   2 r. 50, "Adam"   ..   ..   2·50   2·75
300/3 ..   ..   *Set of 4*   4·75   4·50
MS304   112 × 130 mm. Nos. 302/3. Imperf   ..   3·50   4·00

72 Module nearing Moon's Surface

(Des M. Shamir. Litho Govt Printer, Israel)

1969 (25 Sept). *First Man on the Moon. T* **72** *and similar square*
designs. Multicoloured. P 14.
305   6 l. Type **72**   15   15
306   10 l. Astronaut with hatchet   15   15
307   1 r. 50, Astronaut and module   ..   ..   1·10   1·10
308   2 r. 50, Astronaut using camera   ..   1·75   1·75
305/8 ..   ..   *Set of 4*   2·75   2·75
MS309   101 × 130 mm. Nos. 305/8. Imperf   ..   1·75   2·75

Gold Medal Winner
Mohamed Gammoudi
5000 m. run
Tunisia

REPUBLIC OF MALDIVES

(73)

1969 (1 Dec). *Gold-medal Winners, Olympic Games, Mexico*
(1968). Nos. 295/6 *optd with T* **73**, *or similar inscr honouring*
P. Trentin (cycling) of France.
310   50 l. multicoloured   40   40
311   1 r. multicoloured   60   60

74 Red-striped Butterfly Fish

(Des M. Shamir. Litho)

1970 (Jan). *Tropical Fish. T* **74** *and similar diamond-shaped*
designs. Multicoloured. P 10½.
312   2 l. Type **74**   40   60
313   5 l. Spotted Triggerfish   65   30
314   25 l. Scorpion Fish   ..   ..   ..   1·50   35
315   50 l. Forceps Fish   ..   ..   ..   2·25   85
316   1 r. Imperial Angelfish   ..   ..   3·25   1·00
317   2 r. Regal Angelfish ..   ..   ..   4·75   5·00
312/17 ..   ..   *Set of 6*   11·50   7·50

75 Columbia Dauman Victoria, 1899

(Des M. Shamir. Litho)

1970 (1 Feb). *"75 Years of the Automobile". T* **75** *and similar horiz*
designs. Multicoloured. P 12.
318   2 l. Type **75**   15   30
319   5 l. Duryea phaeton, 1902   20   30
320   7 l. Packard S-24, 1906   25   30
321   10 l. Autocar Runabout, 1907..   ..   30   30
322   25 l. Type **75**   75   30

323   50 l. As 5 l.   ..   ..   1·75   55
324   1 r. As 7 l.   ..   ..   2·75   90
325   2 r. As 10 l.   ..   ..   4·00   4·50
318/25 ..   ..   *Set of 8*   9·00   6·75
MS326   95 × 143 mm. Nos. 324/5. P 11½   ..   3·25   3·75

76 U.N. Headquarters, New York   **77** Ship and Light Buoy

(Des M. Shamir. Litho Rosenbaum Brothers, Vienna)

1970 (26 June). *25th Anniv of United Nations. T* **76** *and similar*
horiz designs. Multicoloured. P 13½.
327   2 l. Type **76**   10   50
328   10 l. Surgical operation (W.H.O.)   ..   55   15
329   25 l. Student,   actress   and   musician
          (U.N.E.S.C.O.)   ..   ..   ..   1·25   30
330   50 l. Children at work and play (U.N.I.C.E.F.)   1·50   60
331   1 r. Fish, corn and farm animals (F.A.O.)   1·75   90
332   2 r. Miner hewing coal (I.L.O.)   ..   3·50   4·00
327/32 ..   ..   *Set of 6*   7·75   5·75

(Des M. Shamir. Litho)

1970 (26 July). *10th Anniv of Inter-governmental Maritime*
Consultative Organization. T **77** *and similar vert design. Multi-*
coloured. P 13½.
333   50 l. Type **77**   45   40
334   1 r. Ship and lighthouse   ..   ..   1·00   85

78 "Guitar-player and   **79** Australian Pavilion
Masqueraders" (A. Watteau)

(Des M. Shamir. Litho Govt Printer, Israel)

1970 (1 Aug). *Famous Paintings showing the Guitar. T* **78** *and*
similar vert designs. Multicoloured. P 14.
335   3 l. Type **78**   10   30
336   7 l. "Spanish Guitarist" (E. Manet)   ..   10   30
337   50 l. "Costumed Player" (Watteau)   ..   50   35
338   1 r. "Mandoline-player" (Roberti)   ..   85   55
339   2 r. 50, "Guitar-player and Lady" (Watteau)   2·25   2·50
340   5 r. "Mandoline-player" (Frans Hals)   4·00   4·25
335/40 ..   ..   *Set of 6*   7·00   7·50
MS341   132 × 80 mm. Nos. 339/40. Roul   ..   4·25   4·75

(Des M. Shamir. Litho Rosenbaum Brothers, Vienna)

1970 (1 Aug). *"EXPO 70" World Fair, Osaka, Japan. T* **79** *and*
similar vert designs. Multicoloured. P 13½.
342   2 l. Type **79**   10   40
343   3 l. West German Pavilion   10   40
344   10 l. U.S.A. Pavilion   15   10
345   25 l. British Pavilion   25   15
346   50 l. Soviet Pavilion   40   35
347   1 r. Japanese Pavilion   75   65
342/7 ..   ..   *Set of 6*   1·50   1·75

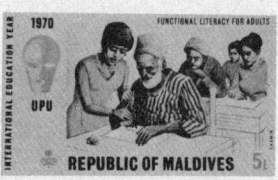

80 Learning the Alphabet

(Des M. Shamir. Litho Govt Printer, Israel)

1970 (7 Sept). *International Education Year. T* **80** *and similar*
horiz designs. Multicoloured. P 14.
348   5 l. Type **80**   15   15
349   10 l. Training teachers   20   10
350   25 l. Geography lesson   40   15
351   50 l. School inspector   60   45
352   1 r. Education by television   90   75
348/52 ..   ..   *Set of 5*   2·00   1·40

MINIMUM PRICE

The minimum price quote is 10p which represents
a handling charge rather than a basis for valuing
common stamps. For further notes about prices
see introductory pages.

Philympia
London 1970

(81)   **82** Footballers

1970 (18 Sept). *"Philympia 1970" Stamp Exhibition, London.*
Nos. 306/MS309 *optd with T* **81**, *in silver.*
353   10 l. multicoloured   10   10
354   1 r. 50, multicoloured   65   65
355   2 r. 50, multicoloured   ..   ..   1·00   1·25
353/5 ..   ..   *Set of 3*   1·50   1·75
MS356   101 × 130 mm. Nos. 305/8 optd. Imperf   6·00   7·00

(Des M. Shamir. Litho Rosenbaum Brothers, Vienna)

1970 (Dec). *World Cup Football Championships, Mexico. T* **82**
and similar vert designs, each showing football scenes and outline
of the Jules Rimet Trophy. P 13½.
357   3 l. multicoloured   10   40
358   6 l. multicoloured   10   40
359   7 l. multicoloured   10   30
360   25 l. multicoloured   60   20
361   1 r. multicoloured   ..   ..   ..   2·00   90
357/61 ..   ..   *Set of 5*   2·50   2·00

83 Little Boy and   **84** Astronauts Lovell, Haise
U.N.I.C.E.F. Flag   and Swigert

(Des M. Shamir. Litho State Printing Works, Budapest)

1971 (1 Apr). *25th Anniv of U.N.I.C.E.F. T* **83** *and similar vert*
design. Multicoloured. P 12.
362   5 l. Type **83**   10   15
363   10 l. Little girl with U.N.I.C.E.F. balloon   ..   10   15
364   1 r. Type **83**   ..   ..   ..   1·00   65
365   2 r. As 10 l.   ..   ..   2·00   2·25
362/5 ..   ..   *Set of 4*   2·75   2·75

(Des M. Shamir. Litho Govt Printer, Israel)

1971 (27 Apr). *Safe Return of "Apollo 13". T* **84** *and similar vert*
designs. Multicoloured. P 14.
366   5 l. Type **84**   15   15
367   20 l. Explosion in Space   15   15
368   1 r. Splashdown   50   50
366/8 ..   ..   *Set of 3*   70   70

85 "Multiracial Flower"   **86** "Mme. Charpentier and
her Children" (Renoir)

(Des M. Shamir. Litho)

1971 (3 May). *Racial Equality Year. P* 14.
369   85   10 l. multicoloured   10   15
370   25 l. multicoloured   20   15

1971 (Aug). *Famous Paintings showing "Mother and Child". T* **86**
and similar vert designs. Multicoloured. Litho. P 12.
371   5 l. Type **86**   10   10
372   7 l. "Susanna van Collen and her Daughter"
          (Rembrandt)   15   10
373   10 l. "Madonna nursing the Child" (Titian)   20   10
374   20 l. "Baroness Belleli and her Children"
          (Degas)   40   15
375   25 l. "The Cradle" (Morisot)   45   15
376   1 r. "Helena Fourment and her Children"
          (Rubens)   ..   ..   ..   1·50   75
377   3 r. "On the Terrace" (Renoir)   ..   3·50   3·75
371/7 ..   ..   *Set of 7*   5·75   4·50

87 Alan Shepard   88 "Ballerina" (Degas)

(Photo State Ptg Works, Vienna)

1971 (11 Nov). *Moon Flight of "Apollo 14". T 87 and similar vert designs. Multicoloured. P 12½.*

378	6 l. Type 87	..	..	30	10
379	10 l. Stuart Roosa	..	..	35	10
380	1 r. 50, Edgar Mitchell	..	..	2·75	2·00
381	5 r. Mission insignia	..	..	6·50	5·50
378/81			Set of 4	9·00	7·00

(Litho Rosenbaum Brothers, Vienna)

1971 (19 Nov). *Famous Paintings showing "Dancers". T 88 and similar vert designs. Multicoloured. P 14.*

382	5 l. Type 88	..	..	15	10
383	10 l. "Dancing Couple" (Renoir)	..	20	10
384	2 r. "Spanish Dancer" (Manet)	..	2·50	2·25
385	5 r. "Ballerinas" (Degas)	..	4·50	4·00
386	10 r. "La Goulue at the Moulin Rouge" (Toulouse-Lautrec)		6·50	5·75
382/6			Set of 5	12·50	11·00

(89)   90 Book Year Emblem

1972 (13 Mar). *Visit of Queen Elizabeth II and Prince Philip. Nos. 382/6 optd with T 89.*

387	5 l. multicoloured	..	..	15	10
388	10 l. multicoloured	..	..	20	10
389	2 r. multicoloured	..	..	4·00	3·50
390	5 r. multicoloured	..	..	7·00	6·00
391	10 r. multicoloured	..	..	8·50	8·00
387/91			Set of 5	18·00	16·00

(Des M. Shamir. Litho Bradbury, Wilkinson)

1972 (1 May). *International Book Year. P 13 × 13½.*

392	90	25 l. multicoloured	..	15	10
393		5 r. multicoloured	..	1·60	2·00

91 Scottish Costume   93 Cross-country Skiing

92 Stegosaurus

(Des M. Shamir. Litho State Printing Works, Budapest)

1972 (15 May). *National Costumes of the World. T 91 and similar vert designs. Multicoloured. P 12.*

394	10 l. Type 91	..	..	30	10
395	15 l. Netherlands	..	..	30	15
396	25 l. Norway	..	..	55	15
397	50 l. Hungary	..	..	90	55
398	1 r. Austria	..	..	1·50	80
399	2 r. Spain	..	..	3·00	2·50
394/9			Set of 6	6·00	3·75

(Des M. Shamir. Litho Rosenbaum Brothers, Vienna)

1972 (31 May). *Prehistoric Animals. T 92 and similar horiz designs. Multicoloured. P 14.*

400	2 l. Type 92	..	..	30	40
401	7 l. Dimetrodon (inscr "Edaphosaurus")	..	65	30
402	25 l. Diplodocus	..	..	1·25	40
403	50 l. Triceratops	..	..	1·50	75
404	2 r. Pteranodon	..	..	4·00	4·00
405	5 r. Tyrannosaurus	..	..	8·00	8·00
400/5			Set of 6	14·00	12·50

An imperforate miniature sheet containing Nos. 404/5 also exists, but was never made available.

(Des M. Shamir. Litho Rosenbaum Brothers, Vienna)

1972 (June). *Winter Olympic Games, Sapporo, Japan. T 93 and similar vert designs. Multicoloured. P 14.*

406	3 l. Type 93	..	..	10	30
407	6 l. Bob-sleighing	..	..	10	30
408	15 l. Speed-skating	..	..	20	20
409	50 l. Ski-jumping	..	..	1·00	45
410	1 r. Figure-skating (pair)	..	1·60	70
411	2 r. 50, Ice-hockey	..	..	5·00	3·25
406/11			Set of 6	7·00	4·75

94 Scout Saluting   95 Cycling

(Des M. Shamir. Litho Govt Printer, Israel)

1972 (1 Aug). *13th World Scout Jamboree, Asagiri, Japan (1971). T 94 and similar vert designs. Multicoloured. P 14.*

412	10 l. Type 92	..	..	65	20
413	15 l. Scout signalling	..	..	85	20
414	50 l. Scout blowing bugle	..	3·00	1·25
415	1 r. Scout beating drum	..	4·50	2·25
412/15			Set of 4	8·00	3·50

PRINTERS AND PROCESS. *Unless otherwise stated*, all the following issues to No. 1277 were lithographed by Format International Security Printers Ltd, London.

1972 (30 Oct). *Olympic Games, Munich. T 95 and similar vert designs. Multicoloured. P 14½ × 14.*

416	5 l. Type 95	..	..	10	10
417	10 l. Running	..	..	10	10
418	25 l. Wrestling	..	..	15	10
419	50 l. Hurdling	..	..	30	25
420	2 r. Boxing	..	..	1·00	1·25
421	5 r. Volleyball	..	..	2·10	2·50
416/21			Set of 6	3·25	3·75
MS422	92 × 120 mm. 3 r. As 50 l.; 4 r. As 10 l. P 15	5·25	6·00

96 Globe and Conference Emblem   97 "Flowers" (Van Gogh)

(Litho Harrison)

1972 (15 Nov). *U.N. Environmental Conservation Conference, Stockholm. P 14½.*

423	96	2 l. multicoloured	..	..	10	30
424		3 l. multicoloured	..	..	10	30
425		15 l. multicoloured	..	..	30	15
426		50 l. multicoloured	..	..	75	40
427		2 r. 50, multicoloured	..	3·25	3·75
423/7				Set of 5	4·00	4·50

(Des M. Shamir)

1973 (Mar). *Floral Paintings. T 97 and similar vert designs. Multicoloured. P 13½.*

428	1 l. Type 97	..	..	10	20
429	2 l. "Flowers in Jug" (Renoir)	..	10	20
430	3 l. "Chrysanthemums" (Renoir)	..	10	20
431	50 l. "Mixed Bouquet" (Bosschaert)	30	15
432	1 r. As 3 l.	..	..	55	40
433	5 r. As 2 l.	..	..	2·75	3·25
428/33			Set of 6	3·50	4·00
MS434	120 × 94 mm. 2 r. as 50 l.; 3 r. Type 97. P 15	5·00	6·00

LEMECHEV MIDDLE-WEIGHT GOLD MEDALLIST

(98)   99 Animal Care

1973 (Apr). *Gold-medal Winners, Munich Olympic Games. Nos. 420/MS422 optd with T 98 or similar commemorative inscr, in blue.*

435	2 r. multicoloured	..	..	2·25	1·75
436	5 r. multicoloured	..	..	3·25	2·75
MS437	92 × 120 mm. 3 r. multicoloured; 4 r. multicoloured		6·00	7·00

Overprints:—2 r. Type 98; 5 r. "JAPAN GOLD MEDAL WINNERS" (volleyball). Miniature sheet:—3 r. "EHRHARDT 100 METER HURDLES GOLD MEDALLIST"; 4 r. "SHORTER MARATHON GOLD MEDALLIST".

(Des M. Shamir)

1973 (Aug). *International Scouting Congress, Nairobi and Addis Ababa. T 99 and similar horiz designs. Multicoloured. P 14½.*

438	1 l. Type 99	..	..	10	20
439	2 l. Lifesaving	..	..	10	20
440	3 l. Agricultural training	..	10	20
441	4 l. Carpentry	..	..	10	20
442	5 l. Playing leapfrog	..	10	20
443	1 r. As 2 l.	..	..	2·50	75
444	2 r. As 4 l.	..	..	4·75	3·25
445	3 r. Type 99	..	..	6·50	4·50
438/45			Set of 8	12·50	8·50
MS446	101 × 79 mm. 5 r. As 3 l.	..	9·00	11·00

100 Makaira herscheli

1973 (Aug). *Fishes. T 100 and similar horiz designs. Multicoloured. P 14½.*

447	1 l. Type 100	..	..	10	20
448	2 l. Katsuwonus pelamys	..	10	20
449	3 l. Thunnus thynnus	..	10	20
450	5 l. Coryphaena hippurus	..	10	20
451	60 l. Lutjanus gibbus	..	40	30
452	75 l. As 60 l.	..	..	50	30
453	1 r. 50, Variola louti	..	1·10	1·10
454	2 r. 50, As 5 l.	..	..	1·60	1·75
455	3 r. Plectropoma maculatum	..	1·75	2·25
456	10 r. Scomberomorus commerson	4·75	6·50
447/56			Set of 10	9·00	11·50
MS457	119 × 123 mm. 4 r. As 2 l.; 5 r. Type 100	12·00	13·00

Nos. 451/2 are smaller, size 29 × 22 mm.

101 Golden-fronted Leafbird   102 Lantana camara

(Des M. Shamir)

1973 (Oct). *Fauna. T 101 and similar diamond-shaped designs. Multicoloured. P 14½.*

458	1 l. Type 101	..	..	10	15
459	2 l. Indian Flying Fox	..	10	15
460	3 l. Land tortoise	..	..	10	15
461	4 l. Kallima inachus (butterfly)	15	15
462	50 l. As 3 l.	..	..	40	25
463	2 r. Type 101	..	..	3·00	2·75
464	3 r. As 2 l.	..	..	3·00	2·75
458/64			Set of 7	6·25	5·75
MS465	66 × 74 mm. 5 r. As 4 l.	..	16·00	15·00

(Litho Questa)

1973 (19 Dec). *Flowers of the Maldive Islands. T 102 and similar vert designs. Multicoloured. P 14.*

466	1 l. Type 102	..	..	10	10
467	2 l. Nerium oleander	..	10	10
468	3 l. Rosa polyantha	..	10	10
469	4 l. Hibiscus manihot	..	10	10
470	5 l. Bougainvillea glabra	..	10	10
471	10 l. Plumera alba	..	..	10	10
472	50 l. Poinsettia pulcherrima	..	55	20
473	5 r. Ononis natrix	..	..	3·75	3·50
466/73			Set of 8	4·00	3·75
MS474	110 × 100 mm. 2 r. As 3 l.; 3 r. As 10 l.	3·25	4·25

103 "Tiros" Weather Satellite

(Des M. Shamir)

1974 (10 Jan). *Centenary of World Meteorological Organization.* T **103** *and similar horiz designs. Multicoloured.* P 14½.

475	1 l. Type **103**	..	10	10
476	2 l. "Nimbus" satellite	..	10	10
477	3 l. *Nomad* (weather ship)	..	10	10
478	4 l. Scanner, A.P.T. Instant Weather Picture equipment	..	10	10
479	5 l. Richard's wind-speed recorder	..	10	10
480	2 r. Type **103**	..	2·00	1·50
481	3 r. As 3 l.	..	2·25	1·75
475/81		Set of 7	4·00	3·25
MS482	110 × 79 mm. 10 r. As 2 l.	..	9·50	12·00

104 "Apollo" Spacecraft and Pres. Kennedy

(Des M. Shamir)

1974 (1 Feb). *American and Russian Space Exploration Projects.* T **104** *and similar horiz designs. Multicoloured.* P 14½.

483	1 l. Type **104**	..	10	15
484	2 l. "Mercury" capsule and John Glenn	..	10	15
485	3 l. "Vostok 1" and Yuri Gagarin	..	10	15
486	4 l. "Vostok 6" and Valentina Tereshkova	..	10	15
487	5 l. "Soyuz 11" and "Salyut" space-station	..	10	15
488	2 r. "Skylab" space laboratory	..	3·00	2·25
489	3 r. As 2 l.	..	3·50	2·75
483/9		Set of 7	6·00	5·25
MS490	103 × 80 mm. 10 r. Type **104**	..	9·00	11·00

105 Copernicus and "Skylab" Space Laboratory

106 "Maternity" (Picasso)

(Des G. Vasarhelyi)

1974 (10 Apr). *500th Birth Anniv of Nicholas Copernicus (astronomer).* T **105** *and similar horiz designs. Multicoloured.* P 14½.

491	1 l. Type **105**	..	10	15
492	2 l. Orbital space-station of the future	..	10	15
493	3 l. Proposed "Space-shuttle" craft	..	10	15
494	4 l. "Mariner 2" Venus probe	..	10	15
495	5 l. "Mariner 4" Mars probe	..	10	15
496	25 l. Type **105**	..	70	15
497	1 r. 50, As 2 l.	..	3·00	2·25
498	5 r. As 3 l.	..	7·50	7·00
491/8		Set of 8	10·00	9·00
MS499	106 × 80 mm. 10 r. "Copernicus" orbital observatory	..	12·00	14·00

(Des M. Shamir. Litho Questa)

1974 (May). *Paintings by Picasso.* T **106** *and similar vert designs. Multicoloured.* P 14.

500	1 l. Type **106**	..	10	10
501	2 l. "Harlequin and Friend"	..	10	10
502	3 l. "Pierrot Sitting"	..	10	10
503	20 l. "Three Musicians"	..	25	15
504	75 l. "L'Aficionado"	..	55	30
505	5 r. "Still Life"	..	3·50	3·00
500/5		Set of 6	4·00	3·25
MS506	100 × 101 mm. 2 r. As 20 l.; 3 r. As 5 r.	..	4·00	4·50

107 U.P.U. Emblem, Steam and Diesel Locomotives

108 Footballers

(Des M. Shamir)

1974 (May). *Centenary of Universal Postal Union.* T **107** *and similar horiz designs. Multicoloured.* P 14½.

507	1 l. Type **107**	..	10	10
508	2 l. Paddle-steamer and modern mailboat	..	10	10
509	3 l. Airship and Boeing "747" airliner	..	10	10
510	1 r. 50, Mailcoach and motor van	..	85	85
511	2 r. 50, As 2 l.	..	1·60	1·60
512	5 r. Type **107**	..	3·50	3·50
507/12		Set of 6	5·50	5·50
MS513	126 × 105 mm. 4 r. Type **107**	..	4·50	6·00

Nos. 507/12 were first issued in sheets of 50, but were later released in small sheets of five stamps and one label. These small sheets were perforated 13½.

(Des M. Shamir)

1974 (June). *World Cup Football Championships, West Germany.* T **108** *and similar vert designs, showing football scenes.* P 14½.

514	1 l. multicoloured	..	10	15
515	2 l. multicoloured	..	10	15
516	3 l. multicoloured	..	10	15
517	4 l. multicoloured	..	10	15
518	75 l. multicoloured	..	1·25	50
519	4 r. multicoloured	..	3·50	2·50
520	5 r. multicoloured	..	3·75	2·50
514/20		Set of 7	8·00	5·50
MS521	88 × 95 mm. 10 r. multicoloured	..	9·00	8·00

109 "Capricorn"

110 Churchill and Bomber Aircraft

(Des G. Vasarhelyi)

1974 (3 July). *Signs of the Zodiac.* T **109** *and similar horiz designs. Multicoloured.* P 14½.

522	1 l. Type **109**	..	10	15
523	2 l. "Aquarius"	..	10	15
524	3 l. "Pisces"	..	10	15
525	4 l. "Aries"	..	10	15
526	5 l. "Taurus"	..	10	15
527	6 l. "Gemini"	..	10	15
528	7 l. "Cancer"	..	10	15
529	10 l. "Leo"	..	15	15
530	15 l. "Virgo"	..	20	15
531	20 l. "Libra"	..	20	15
532	25 l. "Scorpio"	..	20	15
533	5 r. "Sagittarius"	..	10·00	7·00
522/33		Set of 12	10·00	7·75
MS534	119 × 99 mm. 10 r. "The Sun" (49 × 37 mm). P 13½	..	16·00	17·00

(Des M. Shamir)

1974 (30 Nov). *Birth Centenary of Sir Winston Churchill.* T **110** *and similar horiz designs. Multicoloured.* P 14½.

535	1 l. Type **110**	..	10	30
536	2 l. Churchill as pilot	..	10	30
537	3 l. Churchill as First Lord of the Admiralty	..	15	30
538	4 l. Churchill and H.M.S. *Indomitable* (aircraft carrier)	..	15	30
539	5 l. Churchill and fighter aircraft	..	15	30
540	60 l. Churchill and anti-aircraft battery	..	2·50	1·50
541	75 l. Churchill and tank in desert	..	2·75	1·50
542	5 r. Churchill and flying-boat	..	11·00	9·00
535/42		Set of 8	15·00	12·00
MS543	113 × 83 mm. 10 r. As 4 l.	..	17·00	17·00

111 *Cassia nana*

112 Royal Throne

(Des M. Shamir)

1975 (25 Jan). *Seashells and Cowries.* T **111** *and similar multicoloured designs.* P 14 × 13½ (60 l., 75 l.) or 14½ (others).

544	1 l. Type **111**	..	10	15
545	2 l. *Murex triremus*	..	10	15
546	3 l. *Harpa major*	..	10	15
547	4 l. *Lambis chiragra*	..	10	15
548	5 l. *Conus pennaceus*	..	10	15
549	60 l. *Cypraea diliculum* (22 × 30 mm)	..	2·00	1·00
550	75 l. *Clanculus pharaonis* (22 × 30 mm)	..	2·50	1·10
551	5 r. *Chicoreus ramosus*	..	8·00	6·50
544/51		Set of 8	11·50	8·50
MS552	152 × 126 mm. 2 r. As 3 l.; 3 r. as 2 l.	..	10·00	11·00

(Des M. Shamir. Litho Questa)

1975 (22 Feb). *Historical Relics and Monuments.* T **112** *and similar multicoloured designs.* P 14.

553	1 l. Type **112**	..	10	10
554	10 l. Candlesticks	..	10	10
555	25 l. Lamp-tree	..	15	10
556	60 l. Royal umbrellas	..	30	20
557	75 l. Eid-Miskith Mosque (*horiz*)	..	35	25
558	3 r. Tomb of Al-Hafiz Abu-al Barakath-al Barubari (*horiz*)	..	1·60	2·00
553/8		Set of 6	2·25	2·50

113 Guavas

114 *Phyllangia*

(Des M. Shamir)

1975 (Mar). *Fruits.* T **113** *and similar vert designs. Multicoloured.* P 14½.

559	2 l. Type **113**	..	10	15
560	4 l. Maldive mulberry	..	15	15
561	5 l. Mountain apples	..	15	15
562	10 l. Bananas	..	20	15
563	20 l. Mangoes	..	40	15
564	50 l. Papaya	..	80	30
565	1 r. Pomegranates	..	1·75	45
566	5 r. Coconut	..	8·00	8·00
559/66		Set of 8	10·50	8·50
MS567	136 × 102 mm. 2 r. As 10 l.; 3 r. As 2 l.	..	8·50	9·50

(Des M. Shamir)

1975 (6 June). *Marine Life.* T **114** *and similar triangular designs. Multicoloured.* P 14½.

568	1 l. Type **114**	..	10	10
569	2 l. *Madrepora oculata*	..	10	10
570	3 l. *Acropora gravida*	..	10	10
571	4 l. *Stylotella*	..	10	10
572	5 l. *Acrophora cervicornis*	..	10	10
573	60 l. *Strongylocentrotus purpuratus*	..	75	55
574	75 l. *Pisaster ochraceus*	..	85	65
575	5 r. *Marthasterias glacialis*	..	5·00	5·50
568/75		Set of 8	6·00	6·25
MS576	155 × 98 mm. 4 r. As 1 l. Imperf	..	10·00	12·00

115 Clock Tower and Customs Building within "10"

(116)

14th Boy Scout Jamboree July 29 – August 7, 1975

(Des M. Shamir)

1975 (26 July). *10th Anniv of Independence.* T **115** *and similar horiz designs. Multicoloured.* P 14½.

577	4 l. Type **115**	..	10	10
578	5 l. Government Offices	..	10	10
579	7 l. Waterfront	..	10	10
580	15 l. Mosque and minaret	..	10	10
581	10 r. Sultan Park and museum	..	4·00	6·00
577/81		Set of 5	4·00	6·00

1975 (26 July). *"Nordjamb 75" World Scout Jamboree, Norway.* Nos. 443/5 and MS446 optd with T **116**.

582	1 r. multicoloured	..	30	30
583	2 r. multicoloured	..	50	50
584	3 r. multicoloured	..	1·00	1·00
582/4		Set of 3	1·60	1·60
MS585	101 × 79 mm. 5 r. multicoloured	..	5·50	6·00

117 Madura Prau

118 *Brahmophthalma wallichi* (moth)

(Des M. Shamir)

1975 (Aug). *Ships.* T **117** *and similar multicoloured designs.* P 14½.

586	1 l. Type **117**	..	10	10
587	2 l. Ganges patela	..	10	10
588	3 l. Indian palla (*vert*)	..	10	10
589	4 l. Odhi (dhow) (*vert*)	..	10	10
590	5 l. Maldivian schooner	..	10	10
591	25 l. *Cutty Sark*	..	35	20
592	1 r. Maldivian baggala (*vert*)	..	85	70
593	5 r. Freighter *Maldive Courage*	..	3·75	4·25
586/93		Set of 8	4·75	5·00
MS594	99 × 85 mm. 10 r. As 1 l.	..	7·50	10·00

(Des M. Shamir)

1975 (7 Sept). *Butterflies and Moth.* T **118** *and similar horiz designs. Multicoloured.* P 14½.

595	1 l. Type **118**	..	10	10
596	2 l. *Teinopalpus imperialis*	..	10	10
597	3 l. *Cethosia biblis*	..	10	10
598	4 l. *Idea jasonia*	..	10	10
599	5 l. *Apatura ilia*	..	10	10
600	25 l. *Kallima horsfieldi*	..	55	35
601	1 r. 50, *Hebomoia leucippe*	..	2·50	2·50
602	5 r. *Papilio memnon*	..	7·00	6·00
595/602		Set of 8	9·00	8·00
MS603	134 × 97 mm. 10 r. As 25 l.	..	19·00	19·00

119 "The Dying Captive"

120 Beaker and Vase

1975 (9 Oct). *500th Birth Anniv of Michelangelo. T* 119 *and similar vert designs. Multicoloured. P* 14½.

604	1 l. Type 119	..	..	10	10
605	2 l. Detail of "The Last Judgement"	..	..	10	10
606	3 l. "Apollo"	..	..	10	10
607	4 l. Detail of Sistine Chapel ceiling	..	..	10	10
608	5 l. "Bacchus"	..	..	10	10
609	1 r. Detail of "The Last Judgement" (*different*)			80	30
610	2 r. "David"	..	..	1·75	1·25
611	5 r. "Cumaean Sibyl"	..	..	3·75	3·50
604/11			*Set of 8*	6·00	4·75
MS612	123 × 113 mm. 10 r. As 2 r.			7·50	9·00

The 1, 3, 5 l. and 2, 10 r. are sculptures; the other values show details of the frescoes in the Sistine Chapel.

(Des M. Shamir. Litho Questa)

1975 (Dec). *Maldivian Lacquerware. T* 120 *and similar vert designs. Multicoloured. P* 14.

613	2 l. Type 120	..	..	10	10
614	4 l. Boxes	..	..	10	10
615	50 l. Jar with lid	..	..	40	20
616	75 l. Bowls with covers	..	..	50	30
617	1 r. Craftsman at work	..	..	65	40
613/17		..	*Set of 5*	1·50	90

121 Map of Maldives

122 Cross-country Skiing

(Des M. Shamir. Litho Questa)

1975 (25 Dec). *Tourism. T* 121 *and similar horiz designs. Multicoloured. P* 14.

618	4 l. Type 121	..	..	10	10
619	5 l. Motor launch and small craft	..	..	10	10
620	7 l. Sailing boats	..	..	10	10
621	15 l. Underwater fishing	..	..	10	10
622	3 r. Hulule Airport	..	..	1·40	1·60
623	10 r. Motor cruisers	..	..	4·00	5·00
618/23		..	*Set of 6*	5·00	6·00

(Des M. Shamir)

1976 (10 Jan). *Winter Olympic Games, Innsbruck, Austria. T* 122 *and similar vert designs. Multicoloured. P* 15.

624	1 l. Type 122	..	..	10	10
625	2 l. Speed ice-skating	..	..	10	10
626	3 l. Pairs figure-skating	..	..	10	10
627	4 l. Four-man bobsleigh	..	..	10	10
628	5 l. Ski-jumping	..	..	15	10
629	25 l. Women's figure-skating	..	..	65	75
630	1 r. 15, Slalom skiing	..	..		
631	4 r. Ice-hockey	..	..	2·25	2·50
624/31			*Set of 8*	3·00	3·25
MS632	93 × 117 mm. 10 r. Downhill skiing			8·00	9·00

123 "General Burgoyne" (Reynolds)

124 Thomas Edison

1976 (15 Feb). *Bicentenary of American Revolution. T* 123 *and similar multicoloured designs. P* 15.

633	1 l. Type 123	..	..	10	10
634	2 l. "John Hancock" (Copley)	..	..	10	10
635	3 l. "Death of General Montgomery" (Trumbull) (*horiz*)			10	10
636	4 l. "Paul Revere" (Copley)	..	..	10	10
637	5 l. "Battle of Bunker Hill" (Trumbull) (*horiz*)			10	10
638	2 r. "The Crossing of the Delaware" (Sully) (*horiz*)			1·75	1·50
639	3 r. "Samuel Adams" (Copley)	..	..	2·25	2·00
640	5 r. "Surrender of Cornwallis" (Trumbull) (*horiz*)			2·75	2·50
633/40			*Set of 8*	6·25	5·75
MS641	147 × 95 mm. 10 r. "Washington at Dorchester Heights" (Stuart)			11·00	13·00

1976 (10 Mar). *Telephone Centenary. T* 124 *and similar horiz designs. Multicoloured. P* 15.

642	1 l. Type 124	..	..	10	10
643	2 l. Alexander Graham Bell	..	..	10	10
644	3 l. Telephones of 1919, 1937 and 1972	..		10	10
645	1 l. Cable entrance into station	..	..	10	10
646	20 l. Equaliser circuit assembly	..	..	15	10
647	1 r. *Salernum* (cable ship)	..	..	70	55
648	10 r. "Intelsat IV-A" and Earth Station	..		4·25	5·50
642/8			*Set of 7*	4·75	5·75
MS649	156 × 105 mm. 4 r. Early telephones			6·50	7·00

MAY 29TH–JUNE 6TH "INTERPHIL" 1976
(125)

126 Wrestling

1976 (29 May). *"Interphil 76" International Stamp Exhibition, Philadelphia. Nos.* 638/MS641 *optd with T* 125, *in blue* (5 r.) *or silver* (*others*).

650	2 r. multicoloured	..	..	1·25	1·50
651	3 r. multicoloured	..	..	1·75	2·00
652	5 r. multicoloured	..	..	2·25	2·50
650/2		..	*Set of 3*	4·75	5·50
MS653	147 × 95 mm. 10 r. multicoloured			9·00	11·00

(Des M. Shamir)

1976 (June). *Olympic Games, Montreal. T* 126 *and similar vert designs. Multicoloured. P* 15.

654	1 l. Type 126	..	..	10	10
655	2 l. Putting the shot	..	..	10	10
656	3 l. Hurdling	..	..	10	10
657	4 l. Hockey	..	..	10	10
658	5 l. Running	..	..	10	10
659	6 l. Javelin-throwing	..	..	10	10
660	1 r. 50, Discus-throwing	..	..	1·25	1·50
661	5 r. Volleyball	..	..	3·50	4·00
654/61			*Set of 8*	4·75	5·50
MS662	135 × 106 mm. 10 r. Throwing the hammer			7·50	10·00

127 *Dolichos lablab*

128 "Viking" approaching Mars

(Des M. Shamir. Litho Questa)

1976 (26 July)–77. *Vegetables. T* 127 *and similar vert designs. Multicoloured. P* 14.

663	2 l. Type 127	..	..	10	10
664	4 l. *Moringa pterygosperma*	..	..	10	10
665	10 l. *Solanum melongena*	..	..	10	10
666	20 l. *Moringa pterygosperma* (1977)	..		75	75
667	50 l. *Cucumis sativus*	..	..	80	65
668	75 l. *Trichosanthes anguina*	..	..	85	75
669	1 r. *Momordica charantia*	..	..	95	85
670	2 r. *Trichosanthes anguina* (1977)	..		3·00	3·50
663/70			*Set of 8*	6·00	6·00

1976 (2 Dec). *"Viking" Space Mission. T* 128 *and similar horiz design. Multicoloured. P* 14.

671	5 r. Type 128	..	..	2·50	2·75
MS672	121 × 89 mm. 20 r. Landing module on Mars			8·00	12·00

129 Coronation Ceremony

1977 (6 Feb). *Silver Jubilee of Queen Elizabeth II. T* 129 *and similar horiz designs. Multicoloured. P* 14 × 13½.

673	1 l. Type 129	..	..	10	10
674	2 l. Queen and Prince Philip	..	..	10	10
675	3 l. Royal couple with Princes Andrew and Edward			10	10
676	1 r. 15, Queen with Archbishops	..	..	35	25
677	3 r. State coach in procession	..	..	85	55
678	4 r. Royal couple with Prince Charles and Princess Anne			1·10	90
673/8			*Set of 6*	2·25	1·60
MS679	120 × 77 mm. 10 r. Queen and Prince Charles			3·00	3·25

Nos. 673/8 also exist perf 12 (*Price per set of 6 £1·75 mint or used*) from additional sheetlets of five stamps and one label in changed colours.

131 Printed Circuit and I.T.U. Emblem

132 "Miss Anne Ford" (Gainsborough)

(Des M. Shamir)

1977 (26 Mar). *150th Death Anniv of Ludwig van Beethoven* (*composer*). *T* 130 *and similar horiz designs. Multicoloured. P* 14.

680	1 l. Type 130	..	..	10	10
681	2 l. Portrait and manuscript of *Moonlight Sonata*			10	10
682	3 l. With Goethe at Teplitz	..	..	10	10
683	4 l. Portrait and string instruments	..		10	10
684	5 l. Beethoven's home, Heiligenstadt	..		10	10
685	25 l. Hands and gold medals	..	..	40	15
686	2 r. Portrait and part of *Missa solemnis*			2·00	1·60
687	5 r. Portrait and hearing-aids	..	..	3·75	3·00
680/7			*Set of 8*	5·75	4·50
MS688	121 × 92 mm. 4 r. Death mask and room where composer died			3·75	5·00

(Des M. Shamir. Litho Questa)

1977 (17 May). *Inauguration of Satellite Earth Station. T* 131 *and similar horiz designs. Multicoloured. P* 14.

689	10 l. Type 131	..	..	10	10
690	90 l. Central telegraph office	..	..	45	45
691	10 r. Satellite Earth station	..	..	5·00	6·50
689/91			*Set of 3*	5·00	6·50
MS692	100 × 85 mm. 5 r. "Intelsat IV-A" satellite over Maldives			2·75	3·50

(Des M. Shamir. Litho Questa)

1977 (20 May). *Artists' Birth Anniversaries. T* 132 *and similar vert designs. Multicoloured. P* 14.

693	1 l. Type 132 (250th anniv)	..	..	10	10
694	2 l. Group painting by Rubens (400th anniv)			10	10
695	3 l. "Girl with Dog" (Titian) (500th anniv)			10	10
696	4 l. "Mrs. Thomas Graham" (Gainsborough)			10	10
697	5 l. "Artist with Isabella Brant" (Rubens)	..		10	10
698	95 l. Portrait by Titian	..	..	40	40
699	1 r. Portrait by Gainsborough	..	..	40	40
700	10 r. "Isabella Brant" (Rubens)	..	..	3·50	5·00
693/700			*Set of 8*	4·00	5·50
MS701	152 × 116 mm. 5 r. "Self-portrait" (Titian)			2·25	3·00

133 Lesser Frigate Birds

134 Charles Lindbergh

(Des M. Shamir)

1977 (26 July). *Birds. T* 133 *and similar vert designs. Multicoloured. P* 14½.

702	1 l. Type 133	..	..	10	10
703	2 l. Crab Plover	..	..	10	10
704	3 l. White-tailed Tropic Bird	..		10	10
705	4 l. Wedge-tailed Shearwater	..	..	10	10
706	5 l. Grey Heron	..	..	10	10
707	20 l. White Tern	..	..	30	20
708	95 l. Cattle Egret	..	..	1·25	95
709	1 r. 25, Black-naped Tern	..	..	1·75	1·40
710	5 r. Pheasant Coucal	..	..	6·50	6·50
702/10			*Set of 9*	9·00	8·25
MS711	124 × 117 mm. 10 r. Green Heron			22·00	22·00

(Des M. Shamir)

1977 (31 Oct). *50th Anniv of Lindbergh's Transatlantic Flight and 75th Anniv of First Navigable Airships. T* 134 *and similar multicoloured designs. P* 14½.

712	1 l. Type 134	..	..	10	10
713	2 l. Lindbergh and *Spirit of St. Louis*			10	10
714	3 l. "Mohawk" aircraft (*horiz*)	..		10	10
715	4 l. Julliot's airship *Lebaudy I* (*horiz*)			10	10
716	5 l. Airship *Graf Zeppelin* and portrait of Zeppelin			10	10
717	1 r. Airship *Los Angeles* (*horiz*)	..		60	30
718	3 r. Lindbergh and Henry Ford	..	..	1·40	1·50
719	10 r. Vickers rigid airship	..	..	3·50	4·50
712/19			*Set of 8*	5·00	6·00
MS720	148 × 114 mm. 5 r. *Spirit of St. Louis*, Statue of Liberty and Eiffel Tower; 7 r. 50, Airship *L* 31 over German battleship			12·00	13·00

ALTERED CATALOGUE NUMBERS

Any Catalogue numbers altered from the last edition are shown as a list in the introductory pages.

135 Boat Building

136 Rheumatic Heart

(Des M. Shamir. Litho J.W.)

1977 (11 Nov). *Occupations. T 135 and similar multicoloured designs. P 13½ × 13 (2 r.) or 13 × 13½ (others).*
721	6 l. Type 135	..	..	30	15
722	15 l. Fishing	..	..	35	15
723	20 l. Cadjan weaving ..	..	..	40	15
724	90 l. Mat weaving	..	..	1·00	70
725	2 r. Lace making (vert)	..	..	2·25	2·50
721/5	..	..	Set of 5	3·75	3·25

(Des M. Shamir. Litho Questa)

1977 (Dec). *World Rheumatism Year. T 136 and similar vert designs. Multicoloured. P 14.*
726	1 l. Type 136	..	..	10	10
727	50 l. Rheumatic shoulder	..	..	20	15
728	2 r. Rheumatic fingers	..	..	85	1·00
729	3 r. Rheumatic knee	..	..	1·10	1·25
726/9	..	..	Set of 4	2·00	2·25

137 Lilienthal's Glider

138 Newgate Prison

(Des M. Shamir. Litho Questa)

1978 (27 Feb). *75th Anniv of First Powered Aircraft. T 137 and similar horiz designs. Multicoloured. P 13 × 13½.*
730	1 l. Type 137	..	..	10	15
731	2 l. Chanute's glider ..	..	..	10	15
732	3 l. Wright testing glider, 1900	..	10	15
733	4 l. Roe's aircraft	..	..	10	15
734	5 l. Wright demonstrating aircraft to King Alfonso of Spain	..	..	10	15
735	10 l. Roe's second biplane	..	..	15	15
736	20 l. Wright Brothers and A. G. Bell ..	..	15	15
737	95 l. Hadley's triplane	..	..	1·50	1·25
738	5 r. "BE 2"s at Upavon, 1914	..	5·50	5·50
730/8	..	..	Set of 9	7·00	7·00
MS739	98 × 82 mm. 10 r. Wright Brothers' Flyer	11·00	12·00

1978 (15 Mar). *World Eradication of Smallpox. T 138 and similar multicoloured designs. P 14.*
740	15 l. Foundling Hospital, London (horiz)	..	55	30
741	50 l. Type 138	..	..	1·25	50
742	2 r. Edward Jenner	..	..	3·25	2·50
740/2	..	..	Set of 3	4·50	3·00

139 Television Set

140 Mas Odi

(Des M. Shamir. Litho J.W.)

1978 (29 Mar). *Inauguration of Television in Maldives. T 139 and similar multicoloured designs. P 13 × 13½ (1 r. 50) or 13½ × 13 (others).*
743	15 l. Type 139	..	..	40	30
744	25 l. Television aerials	..	..	55	30
745	1 r. 50, Control desk (horiz)	..	1·90	1·90
743/5	..	..	Set of 3	2·50	2·25

(Des M. Shamir)

1978 (27 Apr). *Ships. T 140 and similar multicoloured designs. P 14½.*
746	1 l. Type 140 ..	..	..	10	10
747	2 l. Battela	..	..	10	10
748	3 l. Bandu odi (vert)	..	..	10	10
749	5 l. Maldive Trader (freighter)	..	10	10
750	1 r. Fath-hul Baaree (brigantine) (vert)	35	30
751	1 r. 25, Mas dhoni	..	..	40	40
752	3 r. Baggala (vert)	..	..	1·25	1·25
753	4 r. As No. 751	..	..	1·60	1·60
746/53	..	..	Set of 8	3·50	3·50
MS754	152 × 138 mm. 1 r. As No. 747; 4 r. As No. 751 ..	..	3·25	3·00

Nos. 746/8, 750 and 752/4 exist imperforate from stock dispersed by the liquidator of Format International Security Printers Ltd.

141 Ampulla

142 Capt. Cook

(Des M. Shamir. Litho Questa)

1978 (15 May). *25th Anniv of Coronation of Queen Elizabeth II. T 141 and similar vert designs. Multicoloured. P 14.*
755	1 l. Type 141 ..	..	..	10	10
756	2 l. Sceptre with dove	..	..	10	10
757	3 l. Golden orb	..	..	10	10
758	1 r. 15, St. Edward's Crown	..	15	15
759	2 r. Sceptre with cross	..	..	30	25
760	5 r. Queen Elizabeth II	..	..	80	70
755/60	..	..	Set of 6	1·10	1·00
MS761	108 × 106 mm. 10 r. Anointing spoon ..	2·00	2·00

Nos. 755/60 were also each issued in small sheets of three stamps and one label, perf 12, in changed colours.

(Des M. Shamir)

1978 (15 July). *250th Birth Anniv of Capt. James Cook and Bicentenary of Discovery of Hawaii. T 142 and similar multicoloured designs. P 14½.*
762	1 l. Type 142 ..	..	..	10	15
763	2 l. Statue of Kamehameha I of Hawaii	..	10	15
764	3 l. H.M.S. Endeavour	..	..	10	15
765	25 l. Route of Cook's third voyage	..	45	45
766	75 l. H.M.S. Resolution, H.M.S. Discovery and map of Hawaiian Islands (horiz) ..	1·25	1·25
767	1 r. 50, Cook meeting Hawaiian islanders on ship (horiz)	..	..	2·00	2·25
768	10 r. Death of Cook (horiz)	..	..	7·50	9·00
762/8	..	..	Set of 7	10·50	12·00
MS769	100 × 92 mm. 5 r. H.M.S. Endeavour (different)	..	..	18·00	18·00

Nos. 763/4 exist imperforate from stock dispersed by the liquidator of Format International Security Printers Ltd.

143 Schizophrys aspera

144 "Four Apostles"

1978 (30 Aug). *Crustaceans. T 143 and similar multicoloured designs. P 14.*
770	1 l. Type 143	..	..	10	10
771	2 l. Atergatis floridus	..	..	10	10
772	3 l. Perenon planissimum	..	..	10	10
773	90 l. Portunus granulatus	..	..	50	40
774	1 r. Carpilius maculatus	..	..	50	40
775	2 r. Huenia proteus	..	..	1·00	1·25
776	25 r. Etisus laevimanus	..	..	9·00	12·00
770/6	..	..	Set of 7	10·00	13·00
MS777	147 × 146 mm. 2 r. Panulirus longipes (vert)	1·75	2·50

(Des BG Studio. Litho Questa)

1978 (28 Oct). *450th Death Anniv of Albrecht Dürer (artist). T 144 and similar designs. P 14.*
778	10 l. multicoloured	..	..	10	10
779	20 l. multicoloured	..	..	10	10
780	55 l. multicoloured	..	..	20	20
781	1 r. black, cinnamon and brown	..	30	30
782	1 r. 80, multicoloured	..	..	50	60
783	3 r. multicoloured	..	..	1·00	1·25
778/83	..	..	Set of 6	1·90	2·25
MS784	141 × 122 mm. 10 r. multicoloured	..	5·00	6·00

Designs: Vert—20 l. "Self-portrait at 27", 55 l. "Madonna and Child with a Pear"; 1 r. 80, "Hare"; 3 r. "Great Piece of Turf"; 10 r. "Columbine". Horiz— 1 r. "Rhinoceros".

145 T.V. Tower and Building

146 Human Rights Emblem

(Des M. Shamir)

1978 (11 Nov). *Tenth Anniv of Republic. T 145 and similar horiz designs. Multicoloured. P 14½.*
785	1 l. Fishing boat	..	..	10	10
786	5 l. Montessori School	..	..	10	10
787	10 l. Type 145	..	..	10	10
788	25 l. Islet	..	..	15	15
789	50 l. Boeing "737"	..	..	20	15
790	95 l. Beach scene	..	..	30	30
791	1 r. 25, Dhow at night	..	..	50	45
792	2 r. President's official residence	..	75	90
793	5 r. Masjidh Afeefuddin (mosque)	..	1·75	2·00
785/93	..	..	Set of 9	3·50	3·50
MS794	119 × 88 mm. 3 r. Fisherman casting net	3·00	3·50

1978 (10 Dec). *30th Anniv of Declaration of Human Rights. P 14.*
795	146	30 l. pale magenta, dp mauve and green	15	15
796		90 l. yellow-ochre, red-brown and green	40	50
797		1 r. 80, lt greenish blue, dp blue & grn	70	85
795/7	..	..	Set of 3	1·10	1·40

147 Cypraea guttata

148 Delivery by Bellman

(Des M. Shamir. Litho Questa)

1979 (Jan). *Shells. T 147 and similar vert designs. Multicoloured. P 14.*
798	1 l. Type 147	..	..	10	10
799	2 l. Conus imperialis ..	..	..	10	10
800	3 l. Turbo marmoratus	..	..	10	10
801	10 l. Lambis truncata ..	..	..	20	10
802	1 r. Cypraea leucodon	..	..	1·00	40
803	1 r. 80, Conus figulinus	..	..	1·75	1·25
804	3 r. Conus gloria-maris	..	..	2·50	2·00
798/804	..	..	Set of 7	5·00	3·50
MS805	141 × 110 mm. 5 r. Vasum turbinellus · ·	5·50	5·50

(Des M. Shamir. Litho Questa)

1979 (28 Feb). *Death Centenary of Sir Rowland Hill. T 148 and similar multicoloured designs. P 14.*
806	1 l. Type 148 ..	..	..	10	10
807	2 l. Mail coach, 1840 (horiz)	..	10	10
808	3 l. First London letter box, 1855	..	10	10
809	1 r. 55, Penny Black stamps and posthorn	65	75
810	5 r. Maldives 15 c. stamp, 1906, and carrier pigeon	..	..	2·00	2·25
806/10	..	..	Set of 5	2·50	3·00
MS811	132 × 107 mm. 10 r. Sir Rowland Hill	..	4·00	4·50

Nos. 806/10 were also each issued in small sheets of five stamps and one label, perf 12, in changed colours.

149 Girl with Teddy Bear

150 "White Feathers"

(Des M. Sharmir. Litho Questa)

1979 (10 May). *International Year of the Child (1st issue). T 149 and similar vert designs. Multicoloured. P 14.*
812	5 l. Type 149	..	..	10	10
813	1 r. 25, Boy with model sailing boat ..	..	40	50
814	2 r. Boy with toy rocket	..	..	45	55
815	3 r. Boy with toy airship	..	..	60	75
812/15	..	..	Set of 4	1·40	1·60
MS816	108 × 109 mm. 5 r. Boy with toy train	..	1·60	2·00

See also Nos. 838/MS847.

(Des M. Shamir)

1979 (25 June). *25th Death Anniv of Henri Matisse (artist). T 150 and similar horiz designs. Multicoloured. P 14.*
817	20 l. Type 150	..	..	15	15
818	25 l. "Joy of Life"	..	..	15	15
819	30 l. "Eggplants"	..	..	15	15
820	1 r. 50, "Harmony in Red"	..	..	55	55
821	5 r. "Still-life"	..	..	1·75	60
817/21	..	..	Set of 5	2·50	2·75
MS822	135 × 95 mm. 4 r. "Water Pitcher"	..	2·50	2·75

151 Sari with Overdress

152 Gloriosa superba

(Des M. Shamir. Litho Questa)

1979 (22 Aug). *National Costumes.* T **151** *and similar vert designs. Multicoloured.* P 14.

823	50 l. Type **151**			25	25
824	75 l. Sashed apron dress			40	40
825	90 l. Serape			45	45
826	95 l. Ankle-length printed dress			55	55
823/6			*Set of 4*	1·50	1·50

(Des M. Shamir. Litho Questa)

1979 (29 Oct). *Flowers.* T **152** *and similar vert designs. Multicoloured.* P 14.

827	1 l. Type **152**			10	10
828	3 l. *Hibiscus tiliaceus*			10	10
829	50 l. *Barringtonia asiatica*			20	20
830	1 r. *Abutilon indicum*			40	40
831	5 r. *Guettarda speciosa*			1·75	2·00
827/31			*Set of 5*	2·10	2·40
MS832	94 × 85 mm. 4 r. *Pandanus odoratissimus*			1·75	2·25

153 Weaving

(Litho Questa)

1979 (11 Nov). *Handicraft Exhibition.* T **153** *and similar horiz designs. Multicoloured.* P 14.

833	5 l. Type **153**			10	10
834	10 l. Lacquerwork			10	10
835	1 r. 30, Tortoiseshell jewellery			45	50
836	2 r. Carved woodwork			70	80
833/6			*Set of 4*	1·10	1·25
MS837	125 × 85 mm. 5 r. Gold and silver jewellery			1·50	2·25

154 Mickey Mouse attacked by Bird

(Des Walt Disney Productions)

1979 (10 Dec). *International Year of the Child (2nd issue).* T **154** *and similar multicoloured designs.* P 11.

838	1 l. Goofy delivering parcel on motor-scooter (*vert*)			10	10
839	2 l. Type **154**			10	10
840	3 l. Goofy half-covered with letters			10	10
841	4 l. Pluto licking Minnie Mouse's envelopes			10	10
842	5 l. Mickey Mouse delivering letters on roller-skates (*vert*)			10	10
843	10 l. Donald Duck placing letter in mail-box			10	10
844	15 l. Chip and Dale carrying letter			10	10
845	1 r. 50, Donald Duck on monocycle (*vert*)			75	75
846	5 r. Donald Duck with ostrich in crate (*vert*)			2·25	2·50
838/46			*Set of 9*	3·00	3·25
MS847	127 × 102 mm. 4 r. Pluto putting parcel in mail-box. P 13½			5·50	4·25

155 Post-Ramadan Dancing

(Litho Questa)

1980 (19 Jan). *National Day.* T **155** *and similar horiz designs. Multicoloured.* P 14.

848	5 l. Type **155**			10	10
849	15 l. Musicians and dancer, Eeduu Festival			10	10
850	95 l. Sultan's ceremonial band			30	30
851	2 r. Dancer and drummers, Circumcision Festival			55	70
848/51			*Set of 4*	90	1·10
MS852	131 × 99 mm. 5 r. Swordsmen			1·40	1·75

156 Leatherback Turtle   157 Paul Harris
(*Dermochelys coriacea*)   (founder)

(Des M. Shamir. Litho Questa)

1980 (17 Feb). *Turtle Conservation Campaign.* T **156** *and similar horiz designs. Multicoloured.* P 14.

853	1 l. Type **156**			10	10
854	2 l. Flatback turtle (*Chelonia depressa*)			10	10
855	5 l. Hawksbill turtle (*Eretmochelys imbricata*)			10	10
856	10 l. Loggerhead turtle (*Caretta caretta*)			10	10
857	75 l. Olive Ridley turtle (*Lepidochelys olivacea*)			30	30
858	10 r. Atlantic Ridley turtle (*Lepidochelys kempii*)			3·25	3·50
853/8			*Set of 6*	3·25	3·50
MS859	85 × 107 mm. 4 r. Green turtle (*Chelonia mydas*)			1·50	2·25

(Des J.W. Litho Questa)

1980 (7 Apr). *75th Anniv of Rotary International.* T **157** *and similar vert designs. Multicoloured.* P 14.

860	75 l. Type **157**			25	10
861	90 l. Family (Humanity)			30	20
862	1 r. Wheat (Hunger)			30	25
863	10 r. Caduceus of Hermes (Health)			3·00	3·75
860/3			*Set of 4*	3·50	3·75
MS864	109 × 85 mm. 5 r. Globe			1·50	2·25

(158)   159 Swimming

1980 (6 May). *"London 1980" International Stamp Exhibition.* Nos. 809/MS811 *optd with* T **158**.

865	1 r. 55, multicoloured			1·25	75
866	5 r. multicoloured			2·50	2·00
MS867	132 × 107 mm. 10 r. multicoloured			6·50	7·00

On No. MS867 the overprint is horizontal.

(Des J.W. Litho Questa)

1980 (4 June). *Olympic Games, Moscow.* T **159** *and similar horiz designs. Multicoloured.* P 14.

868	10 l. Type **159**			10	10
869	50 l. Running			20	15
870	3 r. Putting the shot			90	1·00
871	4 r. High jump			1·10	1·25
868/71			*Set of 4*	2·00	2·25
MS872	105 × 85 mm. 5 r. Weightlifting			1·25	2·00

160 White-tailed Tropic Bird

(Des A. Abbas. Litho Questa)

1980 (10 July). *Birds.* T **160** *and similar horiz designs. Multicoloured.* P 14.

873	75 l. Type **160**			25	15
874	95 l. Sooty Tern			35	30
875	1 r. Common Noddy			35	30
876	1 r. 55, Curlew			50	40
877	2 r. Wilson's Petrel			60	50
878	4 r. Caspian Tern			1·10	1·00
873/8			*Set of 6*	2·75	2·40
MS879	124 × 85 mm. 5 r. Red-footed Booby and Brown Booby			5·50	6·00

161 Seal of Ibrahim II

(Litho Questa)

1980 (26 July). *Seals of the Sultans.* T **161** *and similar horiz designs. Each purple-brown and black.* P 14.

880	1 l. Type **161**			10	10
881	2 l. Mohammed Imadudeen II			10	10
882	5 l. Bin Haji Ali			10	10
883	1 r. Kuda Mohammed Rasgefaanu			30	30
884	2 r. Ibrahim Iskander I			50	60
880/4			*Set of 5*	80	90
MS885	131 × 95 mm. 3 r. Ibrahim Iskander I (*different*)			85	1·25

162 Queen Elizabeth the Queen Mother

(Des and litho Questa)

1980 (29 Sept). *Queen Mother's 80th Birthday.* P 14.

886	162	4 r. multicoloured		2·00	1·25
MS887		85 × 110 mm. **162** 5 r. multicoloured		2·75	2·75

163 Munnaru

(Des A. Abbas and M. Hassan)

1980 (9 Nov). *1400th Anniv of Hegira.* T **163** *and similar horiz designs. Multicoloured.* P 15.

888	5 l. Type **163**			10	10
889	10 l. Hukuru Miskiiy mosque			10	10
890	30 l. Medhuziyaaraiy (shrine of saint)			25	15
891	55 l. Writing tablets with verses of Koran			30	25
892	90 l. Mother teaching child Koran			50	45
888/92			*Set of 5*	1·10	85
MS893	124 × 101 mm. 2 r. Map of Maldives and coat of arms			80	1·25

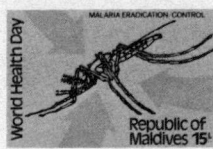

164 Malaria Eradication

(Des J.W. Litho Questa)

1980 (30 Nov). *World Health Day.* T **164** *and similar horiz designs.* P 14.

894	15 l. black, yellow and vermilion			10	10
895	25 l. multicoloured			15	10
896	1 r. 50, orange-brown, yellow-ochre & black			1·00	70
897	5 r. multicoloured			2·25	2·25
894/7			*Set of 4*	3·25	2·75
MS898	68 × 85 mm. 4 r. black, greenish blue and azure			1·25	1·75

Designs:—25 l. Food (Nutrition); 1 r. 50, Molar and toothbrush (Dental health); 4, 5 r. People and medical equipment (Clinics).

165 White Rabbit

(Des Walt Disney Productions)

1980 (22 Dec). *Scenes from Film "Alice in Wonderland".* T **165** *and similar horiz designs. Multicoloured.* P 11.

899	1 l. Type **165**			10	10
900	2 l. Alice falling into Wonderland			10	10
901	3 l. Alice too big to go through door			10	10
902	4 l. Alice and Tweedledum and Tweedledee			10	10
903	5 l. Alice and the caterpillar			10	10
904	10 l. Cheshire cat			10	10
905	15 l. Alice painting the roses			10	10
906	1 r. 50, Alice and the Queen of Hearts			1·50	1·25
907	4 r. Alice on trial			2·00	1·75
899/907			*Set of 9*	3·50	3·00
MS908	126 × 101 mm. 5 r. Alice at the Mad Hatter's tea-party. P 13½			5·00	4·25

166 Indian Ocean Ridley Turtle   167 Pendant Lamp

(Des A. Abbas and Maniku. Litho Questa)

1980 (29 Dec). *Marine Life.* T **166** *and similar horiz designs. Multicoloured.* P 14.

909	90 l. Type **166**			1·25	50
910	1 r. 25, Angel fishes			1·50	85
911	2 r. Spiny lobster			2·00	1·40
909/11			*Set of 3*	4·25	2·50
MS912	140 × 94 mm. 4 r. Fishes			1·50	2·00

1981 (7 Jan). *National Day.* T **167** *and similar multicoloured designs.* P 14½.

913	10 l. Tomb of Ghaazee Muhammad Thakuru-faan (*horiz*)			10	10
914	20 l. Type **167**			10	10
915	30 l. Chair used by Muhammad Thakurufaan			15	10
916	95 l. Muhammad Thakurufaan's palace (*horiz*)			35	40
917	10 r. Cushioned divan			2·75	3·50
913/17			*Set of 5*	3·00	3·75

168 Prince Charles and | 169 First Majlis Chamber
Lady Diana Spencer

(Des and litho J.W.)

1981 (22 June). *Royal Wedding. T* **168** *and similar vert designs. Multicoloured. P* 14.
918	1 r. Type 168	..	..	25	25
919	2 r. Buckingham Palace	..	..	40	40
920	5 r. Prince Charles, polo player	..	75	75
918/20			*Set of 3*	1·25	1·25
MS921	95×83 mm. 10 r. State coach	..	2·25	2·50

Nos. 918/20 also exist perforated 12 (*Price for set of 3* £1·25 *mint or used*) from additional sheets of five stamps and one label. These stamps have changed background colours.

(Des I. Azeez)

1981 (27 June). *50th Anniv of Citizens' Majlis* (*grievance rights*). *T* **169** *and similar multicoloured designs. P* 14½.
922	95 l. Type 169	..	..	30	30
923	1 r. Sultan Muhammed Shamsuddin III	..	35	35
MS924	137×94 mm. 4 r. First written constitution			
(*horiz*)			..	3·00	3·50

170 "Self-portrait with | 171 Airmail Envelope
a Palette"

(Des J.W. Litho Questa)

1981 (July). *Birth Centenary of Pablo Picasso. T* **170** *and similar vert designs. Multicoloured. P* 13½ × 14.
925	5 l. Type 170	..	..	10	10
926	10 l. "Woman in Blue"	..	..	15	10
927	25 l. "Boy with Pipe"	..	..	25	10
928	30 l. "Card Player"	..	..	25	10
929	90 l. "Sailor"	..	..	60	40
930	3 r. "Self-portrait"	..	..	1·25	1·00
931	5 r. "Harlequin"	..	..	1·75	1·40
925/31			*Set of 7*	3·75	2·75
MS932	106 × 130 mm. 10 r. "Child holding a Dove".			
Imperf			..	4·50	4·75

(Des and litho Questa)

1981 (9 Sept). *75th Anniv of Postal Service. P* 14.
933	171	25 l. multicoloured	..	15	10
934		75 l. multicoloured	..	35	30
935		5 r. multicoloured	..	1·25	1·40
933/5			*Set of 3*	1·60	1·60

172 Aircraft taking off | 173 Homer

(Des A. Abbas. Litho Questa)

1981 (11 Nov). *Male International Airport. T* **172** *and similar horiz designs. Multicoloured. P* 14.
936	5 l. Type 172	..	..	10	10
937	20 l. Passengers leaving aircraft	..	20	15
938	1 r. 80, Refuelling	..	..	75	75
939	4 r. Plan of airport	..	..	1·40	1·40
936/9			*Set of 4*	2·25	2·10
MS940	106 × 79 mm. 5 r. Aerial view of airport	..	1·50	2·25

(Des J.W.)

1981 (18 Nov). *International Year of Disabled People. T* **173** *and similar vert designs. Multicoloured. P* 14½.
941	2 l. Type 173	..	..	10	10
942	5 l. Miguel Cervantes	..	..	10	10
943	1 r. Beethoven	..	..	2·25	2·75
944	5 r. Van Gogh	..	..	3·75	2·75
941/4			*Set of 4*	5·50	3·25
MS945	116 × 91 mm. 4 r. Helen Keller and Anne			
Sullivan			..	4·00	4·25

174 Preparation of | 175 Collecting Bait
Maldive Fish

(Des Central Art Palace. Litho Questa)

1981 (25 Nov). *Decade for Women. T* **174** *and similar vert designs. Multicoloured. P* 14.
946	20 l. Type 174	..	..	10	10
947	90 l. 16th century Maldive women	..	25	25
948	1 r. Farming	..	..	30	30
949	2 r. Coir rope making	..	..	55	55
946/9			*Set of 4*	1·10	1·10

(Des I. Azeez. Litho Questa)

1981 (10 Dec). *Fishermen's Day. T* **175** *and similar horiz designs. Multicoloured. P* 14.
950	5 l. Type 175	..	..	30	15
951	15 l. Fishing boats	..	..	45	25
952	90 l. Fisherman with catch	..	90	50
953	1 r. 30, Sorting fish	..	..	1·25	65
950/3			*Set of 4*	2·50	1·40
MS954	147 × 101 mm. 3 r. Loading fish for export	1·00	1·50

176 Bread Fruit

(Des Design Images. Litho Questa)

1981 (30 Dec). *World Food Day. T* **176** *and similar horiz designs. Multicoloured. P* 14.
955	10 l. Type 176	..	..	15	10
956	25 l. Hen with chicks	..	..	40	15
957	30 l. Maize	..	..	40	20
958	75 l. Skipjack Tuna	..	..	85	40
959	1 r. Pumpkin	..	..	1·00	50
960	2 r. Coconuts	..	..	1·50	1·75
955/60			*Set of 6*	4·00	2·75
MS961	110 × 85 mm. 5 r. Eggplant	..	1·75	2·25

177 Pluto and Cat | 178 Balmoral

(Des Walt Disney Productions)

1982 (29 Mar). *50th Anniv of Pluto* (*Walt Disney cartoon character*). *T* **177** *and similar multicoloured design. P* 13½.
962	4 r. Type 177	..	..	2·50	2·00
MS963	127 × 101 mm. 6 r. Pluto (scene from *The Pointer*)			
			..	3·50	3·00

(Des PAD Studio. Litho Questa)

1982 (1 July). *21st Birthday of Princess of Wales. T* **178** *and similar vert designs. Multicoloured. P* 14½ × 14.
964	95 l. Type 178	..	..	20	20
965	3 r. Prince and Princess of Wales	..	55	55
966	5 r. Princess on aircraft steps	..	85	85
964/6			*Set of 3*	1·40	1·40
MS967	103 × 75 mm. 8 r. Princess of Wales	1·50	1·60

Nos. 964/6 also exist in sheetlets of 5 stamps and 1 label. Nos. 964/7 and the sheetlets exist imperforate from a restricted printing.

COMMONWEALTH MEMBER
9 July 1982

179 Scout saluting and Camp-site | 180 Footballer

(Des D. Miller. Litho Questa)

1982 (9 Aug). *75th Anniv of Boy Scout Movement. T* **179** *and similar horiz designs. Multicoloured. P* 14.
968	1 r. 30, Type 179	..	..	40	40
969	1 r. 80, Lighting a fire	..	..	50	50
970	4 r. Life-saving	..	..	1·10	1·10
971	5 r. Map-reading	..	..	1·40	1·40
968/71			*Set of 4*	3·00	3·00
MS972	128 × 66 mm. 10 r. Scout emblem and flag			
of the Maldives			..	2·00	2·50

(Des M. and S. Gerber Studio. Litho Questa)

1982 (4 Oct). *World Cup Football Championship, Spain. T* **180** *and similar square designs. P* 13½.
973	90 l. multicoloured	..	..	90	50
974	1 r. 50, multicoloured	..	..	1·40	70
975	3 r. multicoloured	..	..	2·25	1·25
976	5 r. multicoloured	..	..	2·75	2·00
973/6			*Set of 4*	6·50	4·00
MS977	94 × 63 mm. 10 r. multicoloured	..	3·50	3·50

1982 (18 Oct). *Birth of Prince William of Wales. Nos.* 964/7 *optd with T* **212a** *of Jamaica.*
978	95 l. Type 178	..	..	20	20
979	3 r. Prince and Princess of Wales	..	55	55
980	5 r. Princess on aircraft steps	..	85	85
978/80			*Set of 3*	1·40	1·40
MS981	103 × 75 mm. 8 r. Princess of Wales	2·25	2·50

Nos. 978/80 also exist in sheetlets of 5 stamps and 1 label. Nos. 978/81 and the sheetlets exist imperforate from a restricted printing.

181 Basic Education Scheme | 182 Koch isolates
the Bacillus

(Des and litho Harrison)

1982 (15 Nov). *National Education. T* **181** *and similar horiz designs. Multicoloured. P* 14.
982	90 l. Type 181	..	..	15	20
983	95 l. Primary education	..	..	15	20
984	1 r. 30, Teacher training	..	..	20	25
985	2 r. 50, Printing educational material	..	40	45
982/5			*Set of 4*	80	1·00
MS986	100 × 70 mm. 6 r. Thaana typewriter			
keyboard			..	1·00	1·60

(Des Artists International)

1982 (22 Nov). *Centenary of Robert Koch's Discovery of Tubercle Bacillus. T* **182** *and similar multicoloured designs. P* 14.
987	5 l. Type 182	..	..	10	10
988	15 l. Micro-organism and microscope	..	15	10
989	95 l. Dr. Robert Koch in 1905	..	35	35
990	3 r. Dr. Koch and plates from publication	..	85	1·00
987/90			*Set of 4*	1·25	1·40
MS991	77 × 61 mm. 5 r. Koch in his laboratory			
(*horiz*)			..	80	1·25

183 Blohm and Voss
"Ha 139" Seaplane

(Des W. Wright. Litho Questa)

1983 (28 July). *Bicentenary of Manned Flight. T* **183** *and similar horiz designs. Multicoloured. P* 14.
992	90 l. Type 183	..	..	1·50	50
993	1 r. 45, Macchi-Castoldi "MC.72"	..	2·00	1·25
994	4 r. Boeing "F4B-3"	..	..	3·50	2·50
995	5 r. *La France* airship	..	..	3·75	2·75
992/5			*Set of 4*	9·50	6·25
MS996	110 × 85 mm. 10 r. Nadar's *Le Geant*	3·00	4·00

184 "Curved Dash" Oldsmobile, 1902

(Des Publishers Graphics Inc)

1983 (Aug). *Classic Motor Cars. T* **184** *and similar horiz designs. Multicoloured. P* 14½.
997	5 l. Type 184	..	..	15	15
998	30 l. Aston Martin "Tourer", 1932	..	45	15
999	40 l. Lamborghini "Muira", 1966	..	50	20
1000	1 r. Mercedes-Benz "300SL", 1945	..	1·00	40
1001	1 r. 45, Stutz "Bearcat", 1913	..	1·40	90
1002	5 r. Lotus "Elite", 1958	..	..	3·50	3·50
997/1002			*Set of 6*	6·25	4·75
MS1003	132 × 103 mm. 10 r. Grand Prix			
"Sunbeam", 1924. *P* 14½			..	8·50	8·50

Nos. 997/1002 were each issued in sheets of 9, including one se-tenant label.

185 Rough-toothed Dolphin

(Des D. Miller. Litho Questa)

1983 (6 Sept). *Marine Mammals.* T **185** *and similar horiz designs. Multicoloured. P* 14.
1004	30 l. Type **185**	..	1·25	40
1005	40 l. Indo-Pacific Hump-backed Dolphin	..	1·40	45
1006	4 r. Finless Porpoise	..	4·50	2·50
1007	6 r. Pygmy Sperm Whale ..	..	6·50	4·00
1004/7		Set of 4	12·50	6·50
MS1008	82 × 90 mm. 5 r. Striped Dolphin	..	2·50	3·25

186 Dish Aerial

(Des PAD Studio. Litho Questa)

1983 (9 Oct). *World Communications Year.* T **186** *and similar horiz designs. Multicoloured. P* 14.
1009	50 l. Type **186**	..	15	10
1010	1 r. Land, sea and air communications	..	45	45
1011	2 r. Ship-to-shore communication	..	55	55
1012	10 r. Air traffic controller	..	1·90	2·50
1009/12		Set of 4	2·75	3·25
MS1013	91 × 76 mm. 20 r. Telecommunications		3·75	4·50

187 "La Donna Gravida"

(Des M. Diamond)

1983 (25 Oct). *500th Birth Anniv of Raphael.* T **187** *and similar vert designs showing paintings. Multicoloured. P* 13½.
1014	90 l. Type **187**	..	20	25
1015	3 r. "Giovanna d'Aragona" (detail)	..	60	65
1016	4 r. "Woman with Unicorn"	..	80	85
1017	6 r. "La Muta"	..	1·25	1·40
1014/17		Set of 4	2·50	2·75
MS1018	121 × 97 mm. 10 r. "The Knight's Dream" (detail)		1·90	2·75

Nos. 1014/17 exist imperforate from stock dispersed by the liquidator of Format International Security Printers Ltd.

188 Refugee Camp

(Litho Questa)

1983 (29 Nov). *Solidarity with the Palestinians.* T **188** *and similar horiz designs each showing the Dome of the Rock, Jerusalem. Multicoloured. P* 13½ × 14.
1019	4 r. Type **188**	..	1·50	1·50
1020	5 r. Refugee holding dead child	..	1·60	1·60
1021	6 r. Child carrying food	..	1·90	1·90
1019/21		Set of 3	4·50	4·50

189 Education Facilities   190 Baseball

(Des I. Azeez. Litho Questa)

1983 (10 Dec). *National Development Programme.* T **189** *and similar horiz designs. Multicoloured. P* 13½.
1022	7 l. Type **189**	..	10	10
1023	10 l. Health service and education	..	10	10
1024	5 r. Growing more food	..	1·25	1·25
1025	6 r. Fisheries development	..	1·50	1·50
1022/5		Set of 4	2·50	2·50
MS1026	134 × 93 mm. 10 r. Air transport		2·25	2·75

(Des PAD Studio. Litho Questa)

1984 (10 Mar). *Olympic Games, Los Angeles.* T **190** *and similar vert designs. Multicoloured. P* 14.
1027	50 l. Type **190**	..	15	15
1028	1 r. 55, Backstroke swimming	..	40	40
1029	3 r. Judo	..	80	90
1030	4 r. Shot-putting	..	1·25	1·40
1027/30		Set of 4	2·40	2·50
MS1031	85 × 105 mm. 10 r. Team Handball		2·40	2·75

Rf 1.45

19th UPU
CONGRESS HAMBURG
(191)   (192)

1984 (19 June). *Universal Postal Union Congress, Hamburg. Nos.* 994/6 *optd as* T **191**.
1032	4 r. Boeing "F4B-3"	..	1·40	1·40
1033	5 r. *La France* airship	..	1·60	1·60
MS1034	110 × 85 mm. 10 r. Nadar's *Le Geant*		2·75	3·75

1984 (20 Aug). *Surch as* T **192**. A. *In black.* B. *In gold.*
(a) On Nos. 964/7
			A		B	
1035	1 r. 45 on 95 l. Type **178**	5·00	3·00	5·00	3·00
1036	1 r. 45 on 3 r. Prince and Princess of Wales		5·00	3·00	5·00	3·00
1037	1 r. 45 on 5 r. Princess on aircraft steps		5·00	3·00	5·00	3·00
1035/7 ..		Set of 3	13·50	8·00	13·50	8·00
MS1038	103 × 75 mm. 1 r. 45 on 8 r. Princess of Wales	..	3·50	6·00	3·50	6·00

(b) On Nos. 978/81
			A		B	
1039	1 r. 45 on 95 l. Type **178**	5·00	3·00	5·00	3·00
1040	1 r. 45 on 3 r. Prince and Princess of Wales		5·00	3·00	5·00	3·00
1041	1 r. 45 on 5 r. Princess on aircraft steps		5·00	3·00	5·00	3·00
1039/41		Set of 3	13·50	8·00	13·50	8·00
MS1042	103 × 75 mm. 1 r. 45 on 8 r. Princess of Wales	..	3·50	6·00	3·50	6·00

Stamps from the sheetlets of five plus one label were also surcharged, either in black or gold, using a slightly different type.

193 Hands breaking Manacles   194 Island Resort and Common Terns

1984 (26 Aug). *Namibia Day.* T **193** *and similar horiz designs. Multicoloured. P* 15.
1043	6 r. Type **193**	..	1·50	1·60
1044	8 r. Namibia family	..	2·00	2·10
MS1045	129 × 104 mm. 10 r. Map of Namibia		2·40	2·75

(Litho Questa)

1984 (12 Sept). *Tourism.* T **194** *and similar vert designs. Multicoloured. P* 14.
1046	7 l. Type **194**	..	10	10
1047	15 l. Dhow	..	10	10
1048	20 l. Snorkelling	..	10	10
1049	2 r. Wind-surfing	..	40	40
1050	4 r. Aqualung diving	..	75	75
1051	6 r. Night fishing	..	1·25	1·25
1052	8 r. Game fishing	..	1·50	1·50
1053	10 r. Turtle on beach	..	1·75	1·75
1046/53		Set of 8	5·25	5·25

195 Frangipani

1984 (21 Sept). *"Ausipex" International Stamp Exhibition, Melbourne.* T **195** *and similar horiz designs showing flowers. Multicoloured. P* 14.
1054	5 r. Type **195**	..	2·25	1·75
1055	10 r. Cooktown Orchid	..	4·25	3·75
MS1056	105 × 77 mm. 15 r. Sun Orchid	..	8·50	5·50

196 Facade of the Malé Mosque

1984 (11 Nov). *Opening of Islamic Centre.* T **196** *and similar multicoloured design. P* 15.
1057	2 r. Type **196** ..		45	50
1058	5 r. Malé Mosque and minaret (*vert*).	..	1·10	1·25

197 Air Maldives Boeing "737"

(Des G. Drummond. Litho Questa)

1984 (19 Nov). *40th Anniv of International Civil Aviation Authority.* T **197** *and similar horiz designs. Multicoloured. P* 14.
1059	7 l. Type **197**	..	15	15
1060	4 r. Airlanka Lockheed "L-1011 TriStar"	..	1·25	1·25
1061	6 r. Air Alitalia McDonnell Douglas "DC10–30"		1·60	1·60
1062	8 r. L.T.U. Lockheed "L-1011 TriStar"	..	2·25	2·25
1059/62		Set of 4	4·75	4·75
MS1063	110 × 92 mm. 15 r. Air Maldives Shorts "SC7 Skyvan"	..	3·25	4·00

198 Daisy Duck

(Litho Questa)

1984 (26 Nov–1 Dec). *50th Anniv of Donald Duck (Walt Disney cartoon character).* T **198** *and similar horiz designs. Multicoloured. P* 12 (5 r.) *or* 14 × 13½ (*others*).
1064	3 l. Type **198**	..	10	10
1065	4 l. Huey, Dewey and Louie	..	10	10
1066	5 l. Ludwig von Drake	..	10	10
1067	10 l. Gyro Gearloose	..	10	10
1068	8 r. Uncle Scrooge painting self portrait	..	10	10
1069	25 l. Donald Duck with camera	..	10	10
1070	5 r. Donald Duck and Gus Goose (1.12)	..	1·00	1·00
1071	8 r. Gladstone Gander	..	1·60	1·60
1072	10 r. Grandma Duck	..	2·00	2·00
1064/72		Set of 9	4·25	4·25
MS1073	102 × 126 mm. 15 r. Uncle Scrooge and Donald Duck in front of camera	..	2·75	3·25
MS1074	126 × 102 mm. 15 r. Uncle Scrooge (1.12)	2·75	3·25

No. 1070 was printed in sheetlets of 8 stamps.

199 "The Day" (detail)   200 "Edmond Iduranty" (Degas)

(Litho Questa)

1984 (10 Dec). *450th Death Anniv of Correggio (artist).* T **199** *and similar vert designs. Multicoloured. P* 14.
1075	5 r. Type **199**	..	95	1·25
1076	10 r. "The Night" (detail)	..	1·60	2·00
MS1077	60 × 80 mm. 15 r. "Portrait of a Man"	..	2·75	3·25

(Litho Questa)

1984 (15 Dec). *150th Birth Anniv of Edgar Degas (artist).* T **200** *and similar vert designs. P* 14.
1078	75 l. Type **200** ..	..	15	20
1079	2 r. "James Tissot"	..	45	50
1080	5 r. "Achille de Gas in Uniform"	..	1·10	1·25
1081	10 r. "Lady with Chrysanthemums"	..	2·25	2·75
1078/81		Set of 4	3·50	4·25
MS1082	100 × 70 mm. 15 r. "Self-portrait"	..	3·25	3·75

201 Pale-footed
Shearwater

202 Squad Drilling

(Des I. MacLaury. Litho Questa)

1985 (9 Mar). *Birth Bicentenary of John J. Audubon (ornithologist) (1st issue). T* **201** *and similar multicoloured designs showing original paintings. P* 14.

1083	3 r. Type **201**..	..	1·25	80
1084	3 r. 50, Little Grebe (horiz)..	..	1·40	90
1085	4 r. Common Cormorant	..	1·50	1·00
1086	4 r. 50, White-faced Storm Petrel (horiz)	1·75	1·10
1083/6		Set of 4	5·50	3·50
MS1087	108×80 mm. 15 r. Red-necked Phalarope (horiz)	..	2·75	3·25

See also Nos. 1192/200.

(Des and litho Questa)

1985 (6 June). *National Security Service. T* **202** *and similar multicoloured designs. P* 13½×14 (No. 1092) or 14×13½ (others).

1088	15 l. Type **202**	..	20	10
1089	20 l. Combat patrol ..	..	20	10
1090	1 r. Fire fighting	..	50	25
1091	2 r. Coastguard cutter	..	90	55
1092	10 r. Independence Day Parade (vert)	2·25	2·50
1088/92		Set of 5	3·50	3·00
MS1093	128×85 mm. 10 r. Cannon on saluting base and National Security Service badge	2·25	2·25

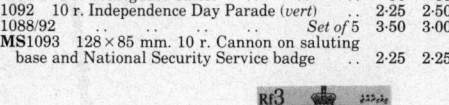

(203)

204 Queen Elizabeth the Queen
Mother, 1981

1985 (17 July). *Olympic Games Gold Medal Winners, Los Angeles. Nos.* 1027/31 *optd as T* **203** *or in larger capitals* (50 l., 10 r.).

1094	50 l. Type **190** (optd "JAPAN")	..	10	10
1095	1 r. 55, Backstroke swimming (opt T **203**)	30	35
1096	3 r. Judo (Optd "GOLD MEDALIST FRANK WIENEKE USA")	..	55	60
1097	4 r. Shot-putting (optd "GOLD MEDALIST CLAUDIA LOCH WEST GERMANY")	..	80	85
1094/7		Set of 4	1·60	1·75
MS1098	85×105 mm. 10 r. Team Handball (opt "U.S.A.")	..	1·90	2·00

(Des J.W. Litho Questa)

1985 (20 Aug). *Life and Times of Queen Elizabeth the Queen Mother. T* **204** *and similar multicoloured designs. P* 14.

1099	3 r. Type **204**..	..	55	60
1100	5 r. Visiting the Middlesex Hospital (horiz)	..	95	1·00
1101	7 r. The Queen Mother ..	..	1·40	1·50
1099/101		Set of 3	2·50	2·75
MS1102	56×85 mm. 15 r. With Prince Charles at Garter Ceremony ..	..	3·50	3·25

Stamps as Nos. 1099/101, but with face values of 1 r., 4 r. and 10 r., exist from additional sheetlets of 5 plus a label issued 4 January 1986. These also have changed background colours and are perforated 12½×12 (4 r.) or 12×12½ (others) (Price for set of 3 stamps £2.50 mint).

204a Liro da Braccio

205 Mas Odi (fishing boat)

(Des Susan David. Litho Questa)

1985 (3 Sept). *300th Birth Anniv of Johann Sebastian Bach (composer). T* **204a** *and similar vert designs. P* 14.

1103	15 l. multicoloured ..	..	10	10
1104	2 r. multicoloured ..	..	50	45
1105	4 r. multicoloured ..	..	90	85
1106	10 r. multicoloured ..	..	1·90	2·25
1103/6		Set of 4	3·00	3·25
MS1107	104×75 mm. 15 r. black and reddish orange	..	3·00	3·50

Designs:—2 r. Tenor oboe; 4 r. Serpent; 10 r. Table organ; 15 r. Johann Sebastian Bach.

(Des H. Afeef. Litho Questa)

1985 (23 Sept). *Maldives Ships and Boats. T* **205** *and similar horiz designs. Multicoloured. P* 14.

1108	3 l. Type **205**	..	10	10
1109	5 l. Battela (dhow)	..	10	10
1110	10 l. Addu odi (dhow)	..	10	10
1111	2 r. 60, Modern dhoni (fishing boat)	40	35
1112	2 r. 70, Mas dhoni (fishing boat) ..	40	35
1113	3 r. Baththeli dhoni	..	45	40
1114	5 r. Inter 1 (inter-island vessel) ..	75	80
1115	10 r. Dhoni-style yacht ..	..	1·40	1·75
1108/15		Set of 8	3·25	3·50

206 Windsurfing

207 United Nations
Building, New York

(Des H. Afeef. Litho Questa)

1985 (2 Oct). *10th Anniv of World Tourism Organization. T* **206** *and similar horiz designs. Multicoloured. P* 14.

1116	6 r. Type **206**..	..	1·10	1·40
1117	8 r. Scuba diving	..	1·50	1·75
MS1118	171×114 mm. 15 r. Kuda Hithi Resort	2·75	3·00

(Litho Questa)

1985 (24 Oct). *40th Anniv of United Nations Organization and International Year of Peace. T* **207** *and similar multicoloured designs. P* 14.

1119	15 l. Type **207**	..	10	10
1120	2 r. Hands releasing peace dove	40	45
1121	4 r. U.N. Security Council meeting (horiz)	80	85
1122	10 r. Lion and lamb ..	..	1·90	2·25
1119/22		Set of 4	2·75	3·25
MS1123	76×92 mm. 15 r. U.N. Building and peace dove ..	..	2·75	3·00

208 Maldivian Delegate voting
in U.N. General Assembly

(Des BG Studio. Litho Questa)

1985 (24 Oct). *20th Anniv of United Nations Membership. T* **208** *and similar horiz design. Multicoloured. P* 14.

1124	20 l. Type **208**	..	10	10
1125	15 r. U.N. and Maldivian flags, and U.N. Building, New York ..	..	2·75	3·25

209 Youths playing Drums

(Des BG Studio)

1985 (20 Nov). *International Youth Year. T* **209** *and similar multicoloured designs. P* 15.

1126	90 l. Type **209**	..	15	20
1127	6 r. Tug-of-war	..	1·10	1·40
1128	10 r. Community service (vert)	1·90	2·25
1126/8		Set of 3	2·75	3·50
MS1129	85×84 mm. 15 r. Raising the flag at youth camp (vert) ..	..	2·75	3·00

210 Quotation and Flags of
Member Nations

(Litho Questa)

1985 (8 Dec) *1st Summit Meeting of South Asian Association for Regional Co-operation, Dhaka, Bangladesh. P* 14.

1130	**210** 3 r. multicoloured ..	..	1·25	1·25

---

211 Frigate Tuna

212 Player running
with Ball

(Litho Questa)

1985 (10 Dec). *Fishermen's Day. Species of Tuna. T* **211** *and similar horiz designs. Multicoloured. P* 14.

1131	25 l. Type **211**	..	10	10
1132	75 l. Little Tuna ..	..	15	15
1133	3 r. Dogtooth Tuna	..	55	60
1134	5 r. Yellowfin Tuna	..	95	1·00
1131/4		Set of 4	1·50	1·60
MS1135	130×90 mm. 15 r. Skipjack Tuna	2·75	3·00

(Des Walt Disney Productions. Litho Questa)

1985 (21 Dec). *150th Birth Anniv of Mark Twain. Vert designs as T* **160a** *of Lesotho showing Walt Disney cartoon characters illustrating various Mark Twain quotations. Multicoloured. P* 12 (4 r.) or 13½×14 (others).

1136	2 l. Winnie the Pooh	..	10	10
1137	3 l. Gepetto and Figaro the cat	..	10	10
1138	4 l. Goofy and basket of broken eggs	..	10	10
1139	20 l. Goofy as doctor scolding Donald Duck	10	10
1140	4 r. Mowgli and King Louis	..	80	80
1141	13 r. The wicked Queen and mirror	3·00	3·00
1136/41		Set of 6	3·75	3·75
MS1142	126×101 mm. 15 r. Mickey Mouse as Tom Sawyer on comet's tail	..	3·00	3·00

No. 1140 was issued in sheetlets of 8 stamps.

(Des Walt Disney Productions. Litho Questa)

1985 (21 Dec). *Birth Bicentenaries of Grimm Brothers (folklorists). Multicoloured designs as T* **160b** *of Lesotho, but horiz, showing Walt Disney cartoon characters in scenes from "Dr. Knowall". P* 12 (3 r.) or 14×13½ (others).

1143	1 l. Donald Duck as Crabb driving oxcart..	10	10
1144	5 l. Donald Duck as Dr. Knowall ..	..	10	10
1145	10 l. Dr. Knowall in surgery	..	10	10
1146	15 l. Dr. Knowall with Uncle Scrooge as a lord	..	10	10
1147	3 r. Dr. and Mrs. Knowall in pony trap ..	55	65
1148	14 r. Dr. Knowall and thief..	..	2·75	3·25
1143/8		Set of 6	3·00	3·75
MS1149	126×101 mm. 15 r. Donald and Daisy Duck as Dr. and Mrs. Knowall ..	..	2·75	3·00

No. 1147 was printed in sheetlets of 8 stamps.

(Des W. Hanson. Litho Questa)

1986 (29 Apr). *Appearance of Halley's Comet (1st issue). Horiz designs as T* **162a** *of Lesotho. Multicoloured. P* 14.

1150	20 l. N.A.S.A. space telescope and Comet ..	50	25
1151	1 r. 50, E.S.A. Giotto spacecraft and Comet	1·25	1·10
1152	2 r. Japanese Planet A spacecraft and Comet ..	..	1·50	1·40
1153	4 r. Edmond Halley and Stonehenge	2·75	2·75
1154	5 r. Russian Vega spacecraft and Comet ..	3·00	3·00
1150/4		Set of 5	8·00	7·75
MS1155	101×70 mm. 15 r. Halley's Comet ..	7·00	7·00

See also Nos. 1206/11.

(Des J. Iskowitz. Litho Questa)

1986 (5 May). *Centenary of Statue of Liberty. Multicoloured designs as T* **163b** *of Lesotho showing the Statue of Liberty and immigrants to the U.S.A. P* 14.

1156	50 l. Walter Gropius (architect) ..	..	40	20
1157	70 l. John Lennon (musician) ..	..	1·50	80
1158	1 r. George Balanchine (choreographer) ..	1·50	80
1159	10 r. Franz Werfel (writer) ..	..	3·75	4·00
1156/9		Set of 4	6·50	5·25
MS1160	100×72 mm. 15 r. Statue of Liberty (vert) ..	..	5·00	5·50

(Des Walt Disney Productions)

1986 (22 May). *"Ameripex" International Stamp Exhibition, Chicago. Horiz designs as T* **163c** *of Lesotho showing Walt Disney cartoon characters and U.S.A. stamps. Multicoloured. P* 11.

1161	3 l. Johnny Appleseed and 1966 Johnny Appleseed stamp	..	10	10
1162	4 l. Paul Bunyan and 1958 Forest Conservation stamp	..	10	10
1163	5 l. Casey and 1969 Professional Baseball Centenary stamp	..	10	10
1164	10 l. Ichabod Crane and 1974 "Legend of Sleepy Hollow" stamp..	..	10	10
1165	15 l. John Henry and 1944 75th anniv of completion of First Transcontinental Railroad stamp	..	10	10
1166	20 l. Windwagon Smith and 1954 Kansas Territory Centenary stamp	..	10	10
1167	13 r. Mike Fink and 1970 Great Northwest stamp ..	..	3·25	3·00
1168	14 r. Casey Jones and 1950 Railroad Engineers stamp ..	..	3·50	3·25
1161/8		Set of 8	6·75	6·25
MS1169	Two sheets, each 127×101 mm. (a) 15 r. Davy Crockett and 1967 Davy Crockett stamp. (b) 15 r. Daisy Duck as Pocahontas saving Captain John Smith (Donald Duck). P 14×13½. .. Set of 2 sheets	7·00	8·00

(Litho Questa)

1986 (29 May). *60th Birthday of Queen Elizabeth II. Vert designs as T 163a of Lesotho. P 14.*

1170	1 r. black and chrome-yellow		35	25
1171	2 r. multicoloured ..		55	55
1172	12 r. multicoloured ..	..	2·75	2·75
1170/2		*Set of 3*	3·25	3·25
MS1173	120×85 mm. 15 r. black and grey-brown		3·75	4·25

Designs:—1 r. Royal Family at Girl Guides Rally, 1938; 2 r. Queen in Canada; 12 r. At Sandringham, 1970; 15 r. Princesses Elizabeth and Margaret at Royal Lodge, Windsor, 1940.
Nos. 1170/2 were each issued in sheetlets of five stamps and one stamp-size label.

(Des BG Studio. Litho Questa)

1986 (8 June). *World Cup Football Championship, Mexico. T 212 and similar vert designs. Multicoloured. P 14.*

1174	15 l. Type 212		30	20
1175	2 r. Player gaining control of ball	..	1·50	1·00
1176	4 r. Two players competing for ball		2·75	2·00
1177	10 r. Player bouncing ball on knee..		5·50	4·50
1174/7	.. .. ..	*Set of 4*	9·00	7·00
MS1178	95×114 mm. 15 r. Player kicking ball	..	3·00	4·00

(Litho Questa)

1986 (1 July). *Royal Wedding. Vert designs as T 170a of Lesotho. Multicoloured. P 14.*

1179	10 l. Prince Andrew and Miss Sarah Ferguson		10	10
1180	2 r. Prince Andrew..		60	60
1181	12 r. Prince Andrew in naval uniform	..	2·75	3·00
1179/81		*Set of 3*	3·00	3·25
MS1182	88×88 mm. 15 r. Prince Andrew and Miss Sarah Ferguson (*different*)..	..	4·00	4·25

WINNERS
Argentina 3
W.Germany 2

213 Moorish Idol and Sea Fan   (213*a*)

(Des Mary Walters)

1986 (22 Sept). *Marine Wildlife. T 213 and similar horiz designs. Multicoloured. P 15.*

1183	50 l. Type 213	..	60	30
1184	90 l. Regal Angelfish	..	80	45
1185	1 r. Anemone Fish ..	..	85	45
1186	2 r. Tiger Cowrie and Stinging Coral		1·40	1·00
1187	3 r. Emperor Angelfish and Staghorn Coral	..	1·75	1·25
1188	4 r. Black-naped Tern	..	2·50	2·00
1189	5 r. Fiddler Crab and Staghorn Coral		2·50	2·00
1190	10 r. Hawksbill Turtle	..	3·50	3·25
1183/90		*Set of 8*	12·50	9·50
MS1191	Two sheets, each 107×76 mm. (a) 15 r. Long Nosed Butterfly Fish. (b) 15 r. Trumpet Fish	*Set of 2 sheets*	7·00	8·50

(Litho Questa)

1986 (9 Oct). *Birth Bicentenary of John J. Audubon (ornithologist) (1985) (2nd issue). Multicoloured designs as T 201 showing original paintings. P 14.*

1192	3 l. Little Blue Heron (*horiz*)	..	10	10
1193	4 l. White-tailed Kite	..	10	10
1194	5 l. Greater Shearwater (*horiz*)	..	10	10
1195	10 l. Magnificent Frigate Bird	..	15	10
1196	15 l. Black-necked Grebe	..	25	20
1197	20 l. Goosander	..	30	20
1198	3 r. Peregrine Falcon (*horiz*)		4·50	4·50
1199	14 r. Prairie Chicken (*horiz*)	..	4·50	4·50
1192/9		*Set of 8*	9·00	8·50
MS1200	Two sheets, each 74×104 mm. (a) 15 r. Fulmar. (b) 15 r. White-fronted Goose (*horiz*)	*Set of 2 sheets*	15·00	16·00

Nos. 1192/9 were each issued in sheetlets of five stamps and one stamp-size label, which appears in the centre of the bottom row.

1986 (25 Oct). *World Cup Football Championship Winners, Mexico. Nos. 1174/8 optd with T 213a in gold.*

1201	15 l. Type 212	..	20	15
1202	2 r. Player gaining control of ball		75	55
1203	4 r. Two players competing for ball		1·25	1·00
1204	10 r. Player bouncing ball on knee..		2·50	2·25
1201/4		*Set of 4*	4·25	3·50
MS1205	95×114 mm. 15 r. Player kicking ball	..	2·75	3·50

(213*b*)   214 Servicing Aircraft

1986 (30 Oct). *Appearance of Halley's Comet (2nd issue). Nos. 1150/5 optd with T 213b in silver.*

1206	20 l. N.A.S.A. space telescope and Comet ..		20	15
1207	1 r. 50, E.S.A. Giotto spacecraft and Comet ..		50	45
1208	2 r. Japanese *Planet A* spacecraft and Comet ..		75	65
1209	4 r. Edmond Halley and Stonehenge		1·25	1·00
1210	5 r. Russian *Vega* spacecraft and Comet ..		1·40	1·25
1206/10		*Set of 5*	3·75	3·25
MS1211	101×70 mm. 15 r. Halley's Comet ..		3·00	3·50

1986 (4 Nov). *40th Anniv of U.N.E.S.C.O. T 214 and similar vert designs. Multicoloured. P 15.*

1212	1 r. Type 214..	..	20	25
1213	2 r. Boat building	..	40	45
1214	3 r. Children in classroom ..		55	60
1215	5 r. Student in laboratory	..	95	1·00
1212/15		*Set of 4*	1·90	2·10
MS1216	77×100 mm. 15 r. Diving bell on sea bed ..		2·75	3·50

215 *Hypholoma fasciculare*   216 *Ixora*

(Des Mary Walters)

1986 (31 Dec). *Fungi of the Maldives. T 215 and similar multicoloured designs. P 15.*

1217	15 l. Type 215	..	50	15
1218	50 l. Kuehneromyces mutabilis (*vert*)		85	30
1219	1 r. Amanita muscaria (*vert*)	..	1·25	50
1220	2 r. Agaricus campestris ..		1·75	1·00
1221	3 r. Amanita pantherina (*vert*)	..	2·00	1·25
1222	4 r. Coprinus comatus (*vert*)	..	2·25	1·75
1223	5 r. Pholiota spectabilis	..	2·40	2·25
1224	10 r. Pluteus cervinus	..	3·50	3·50
1217/24		*Set of 8*	13·00	9·50
MS1225	Two sheets, each 100×70 mm. (a) 15 r. Armillaria mellea. (b) 15 r. Stropharia aeruginosa (*vert*)	*Set of 2 sheets*	9·00	10·00

(Des Mary Walters)

1987 (29 Jan). *Flowers. T 216 and similar vert designs. Multicoloured. P 15.*

1226	10 l. Type 216	..	10	10
1227	20 l. Frangipani	..	10	10
1228	50 l. Crinum ..		25	15
1229	2 r. Pink Rose	..	50	50
1230	4 r. Flamboyant Flower	..	80	80
1231	10 r. Ground Orchid..		2·75	3·00
1226/31		*Set of 6*	4·00	4·25
MS1232	Two sheets, each 100×70 mm. (a) 15 r. Gardenia. (b) 15 r. Oleander	*Set of 2 sheets*	4·75	6·50

Similar 1, 7 and 12 r. stamps were prepared but not issued. They exist from stock dispersed by the liquidator of Format International Security Printers Ltd.

217 Guides studying Wild Flowers   218 *Thespesia populnea*

(Des R. Vigurs)

1987 (4 Apr). *75th Anniv of Girl Guide Movement (1985). T 217 and similar horiz designs. Multicoloured. P 15.*

1233	15 l. Type 217	..	10	10
1234	2 r. Guides with pet rabbits	..	40	40
1235	4 r. Guide observing White Spoonbill	..	80	90
1236	12 r. Lady Baden-Powell and Guide flag		2·50	3·00
1233/6		*Set of 4*	3·50	4·00
MS1237	104×78 mm. 15 r. Guides in sailing dinghy ..		2·75	3·00

(Litho Questa)

1987 (22 Apr). *Trees and Plants. T 218 and similar multicoloured designs. P 14.*

1238	50 l. Type 218	..	10	10
1239	1 r. Cocos nucifera ..		15	20
1240	2 r. Calophyllum mophyllum	..	30	35
1241	3 r. Xyanthosoma indica (*horiz*)	..	45	50
1242	5 r. Ipomoea batatas (*horiz*)	..	80	85
1243	7 r. Artocarpus altilis	..	1·10	1·25
1238/43		*Set of 6*	2·50	3·00
MS1244	75×109 mm. 15 r. Cocos nucifera (*different*) ..		2·25	2·75

218*a* Intrepid, 1970   219 *Precis octavia*

(Des J. Iskowitz)

1987 (4 May). *America's Cup Yachting Championship. T 218a and similar multicoloured designs. P 15.*

1245	15 l. Type 218a	..	10	10
1246	1 r. France II, 1974	..	20	20
1247	2 r. Gretel, 1962 ..		40	50
1248	12 r. Volunteer, 1887	..	2·00	2·50
1245/8		*Set of 4*	2·40	3·00
MS1249	113×83 mm. 15 r. Helmsman and crew on deck of Defender, 1895 (*horiz*)		2·25	2·75

1987 (16 Dec). *Butterflies. T 219 and similar vert designs. Multicoloured. P 15.*

1250	15 l. Type 219	..	45	30
1251	20 l. Atrophaneura hector	..	45	30
1252	50 l. Teinopalpus imperialis	..	75	40
1253	1 r. Kallima horsfieldi	..	1·00	45
1254	2 r. Cethosia biblis	..	1·60	1·00
1255	4 r. Idea jasonia	..	2·50	1·60
1256	7 r. Papilio memnon	..	3·50	3·00
1257	10 r. Aeropetes tulbaghia	..	4·00	4·00
1250/7		*Set of 8*	13·00	10·00
MS1258	Two sheets, each 135×102 mm. (a) 15 r. Acraea violae. (b) 15 r. Hebomoia leucippe	*Set of 2 sheets*	8·00	10·00

220 Isaac Newton experimenting with Spectrum

(Des J. Martin. Litho Questa)

1988 (10 Jan). *Great Scientific Discoveries. T 220 and similar multicoloured designs. P 14.*

1259	1 r. 50, Type 220	..	80	60
1260	3 r. Euclid composing Principles of Geometry (*vert*) ..		1·25	1·00
1261	4 r. Mendel formulating theory of Genetic Evolution (*vert*)	..	1·50	1·25
1262	5 r. Galileo and moons of Jupiter ..		1·75	1·50
1259/62		*Set of 4*	4·75	4·00
MS1263	102×72 mm. 15 r. "Apollo" lunar module (*vert*)		3·50	4·00

221 Donald Duck and Weather Satellite

(Des Walt Disney Co. Litho Questa)

1988 (15 Feb). *Space Exploration. T 221 and similar multicoloured designs showing Walt Disney cartoon characters. P 14×13½ (horiz) or 13½×14 (vert).*

1264	3 r. Type 221	..	10	10
1265	4 l. Minnie Mouse and navigation satellite		10	10
1266	5 l. Mickey Mouse's nephews talking via communication satellite	..	10	10
1267	10 l. Goofy in lunar rover (*vert*)	..	10	10
1268	20 l. Minnie Mouse delivering pizza to flying saucer (*vert*)	..	10	10
1269	13 r. Mickey Mouse directing spacecraft docking (*vert*)		1·60	1·75
1270	14 r. Mickey Mouse and "Voyager 2"		1·75	1·90
1264/70		*Set of 7*	3·25	3·50
MS1271	Two sheets, each 127×102 mm. (a) 15 r. Mickey Mouse at first Moon landing, 1969. (b) 15 r. Mickey Mouse and nephews in space station swimming pool (*vert*)	*Set of 2 sheets*	4·00	4·50

222 Syringe and Bacterium ("Immunization")

(Des Mary Walters. Litho Questa)

1988 (7 Apr). *40th Anniv of World Health Organization. T 222 and similar horiz design. Multicoloured. P 14.*

1272	2 r. Type 222	..	25	30
1273	4 r. Tap ("Clean Water")..	..	50	55

223 Water Droplet and Atoll   224 Globe, Carrier Pigeon and Letter

(Des I. Rasheed)

1988 (9 May). *World Environment Day (1987). T **223** and similar multicoloured designs.* P 15.
1274	15 l.	Type **223**	10	10
1275	75 l.	Coral reef	30	25
1276	2 r.	Audubon's Shearwaters in flight	1·25	1·00
1274/6		*Set of 3*	1·50	1·25
MS1277		105×76 mm. 15 r. Banyan Tree (*vert*)	2·25	2·75

(Litho Questa)

1988 (31 May). *Transport and Telecommunications Decade. T **224** and similar horiz designs, each showing central globe. Multicoloured.* P 14.
1278	2 r.	Type **224**	50	50
1279	3 r.	Dish aerial and girl using telephone	60	60
1280	5 r.	Satellite, television, telephone and antenna tower	1·00	1·00
1281	10 r.	Car, ship and airliner	2·00	2·25
1278/81		*Set of 4*	3·75	4·00

MALDIVES

40TH WEDDING ANNIVERSARY
H.M.QUEEN ELIZABETH II
H.R.H. THE DUKE OF EDINBURGH

(225)   226 Discus-throwing

1988 (7 July). *Royal Ruby Wedding. Nos. 1170/3 optd with T **225** in gold.*
1282	1 r.	black and chrome-yellow	30	20
1283	2 r.	multicoloured	45	35
1284	12 r.	multicoloured	2·25	2·75
1282/4		*Set of 3*	2·75	3·00
MS1285		120×85 mm. 15 r. black and grey-brown	2·75	3·00

(Des B. Bundock. Litho Questa)

1988 (16 July). *Olympic Games, Seoul. T **226** and similar multicoloured designs.* P 14.
1286	15 l.	Type **226**	10	10
1287	2 r.	100 metres race	35	35
1288	4 r.	Gymnastics (*horiz*)	65	65
1289	12 r.	Three-day equestrian event (*horiz*)	1·90	2·25
1286/9		*Set of 4*	2·75	3·00
MS1290		106×76 mm. 20 r. Tennis (*horiz*)	2·40	2·75

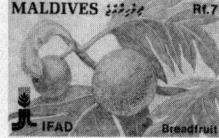

227 Immunization at Clinic   228 Breadfruit

(Des A. DiLorenzo. Litho Questa)

1988 (20 July). *International Year of Shelter for the Homeless. T **227** and similar vert designs. Multicoloured.* P 14.
1291	50 l.	Type **227**	30	30
1292	3 r.	Prefab housing estate	1·10	1·10
MS1293		63×105 mm. 15 r. Building site	1·75	2·25

(Des G. Watkins. Litho Questa)

1988 (30 July). *10th Anniv of International Fund for Agricultural Development. T **228** and similar multicoloured designs.* P 14.
1294	7 r.	Type **228**	85	90
1295	10 r.	Mangos (*vert*)	1·25	1·40
MS1296		103×74 mm. 15 r. Coconut palm, fishing boat and Yellowtail Tuna	1·75	2·25

(229)   230 Pres. Kennedy and Launch of "Apollo" Spacecraft

1988 (1 Dec). *World Aids Day. Nos. 1272/3 optd with T **229**.*
1297	2 r.	Type **222**	35	35
1298	4 r.	Tap ("Clean Water")	65	65

(Des A. Nahigian. Litho Questa)

1989 (13 Feb). *25th Death Anniv of John F. Kennedy (American statesman) (1988). U.S. Space Achievements. T **230** and similar vert designs. Multicoloured.* P 14.
1299	5 r.	Type **230**	60	65
		a. Horiz strip of 4. Nos. 1299/1302	2·10	
1300	5 r.	Lunar module and astronaut on Moon	60	65
1301	5 r.	Astronaut and buggy on Moon	60	65
1302	5 r.	President Kennedy and spacecraft	60	65
1299/1302		*Set of 4*	2·10	2·40
MS1303		108 × 77 mm. 15 r. President Kennedy making speech	1·75	2·25

Nos. 1299/1302 were printed together, *se-tenant*, in horizontal strips of 4 throughout the sheet.

	ASIA-PACIFIC
J. SCHULT DDR	TELECOMMUNITY 10 YEARS
(231)	(232)

1989 (29 Apr). *Olympic Medal Winners, Seoul. Nos. 1286/90 optd as T **231**.*
1304	15 l.	Type **226** (optd with T **231**)	10	10
1305	2 r.	100 metres race (optd "C. LEWIS USA")	20	25
1306	4 r.	Gymnastics (*horiz*) (optd "MEN'S ALL AROUND V. ARTEMOV USSR")	45	50
1307	12 r.	Three-day equestrian event (*horiz*) (optd "TEAM SHOW JUMPING W. GERMANY")	1·25	1·40
1304/7		*Set of 4*	1·75	2·00
MS1308		106×76 mm. 20 r. Tennis (*horiz*) (optd "OLYMPIC WINNERS MEN'S SINGLES GOLD M. MECIR CZECH. SILVER T. MAYOTTE USA BRONZE B. GILBERT USA")	2·25	2·40

On No. MS1308 the overprint appears on the sheet margin and not the 20 r. stamp.

(Litho Questa)

1989 (20 May). *500th Birth Anniv of Titian (artist). Vert designs as T **186a** of Lesotho showing paintings. Multicoloured.* P 13½×14.
1309	15 l.	"Benedetto Varchi"	10	10
1310	1 r.	"Portrait of a Young Man"	10	15
1311	2 r.	"King Francis I of France"	20	25
1312	5 r.	"Pietro Aretino"	55	60
1313	15 r.	"The Bravo"	1·60	1·75
1314	20 r.	"The Concert" (detail)	2·25	2·40
1309/14		*Set of 6*	4·25	4·75
MS1315		Two sheets. (a) 112×96 mm. 20 r. "An Allegory of Prudence" (detail). (b) 96×110 mm. 20 r. "Francesco Maria della Rovere"		
		Set of 2 sheets	4·50	4·75

(Litho Questa)

1989 (10 July). *10th Anniv of Asia-Pacific Telecommunity. Nos. 1279/80 optd with T **232** in silver.*
1316	3 r.	Dish aerial and girl using telephone	35	40
1317	5 r.	Satellite, television, telephone and antenna tower	55	60

(Litho Questa)

1989 (2 Sept–16 Oct). *Japanese Art. Paintings by Hokusai. Horiz designs as T **187a** of Lesotho. Multicoloured.* P 14×13½.
1318	15 l.	"Fuji from Hodogaya"	10	10
1319	50 l.	"Fuji from Lake Kawaguchi"	10	10
1320	1 r.	"Fuji from Owari"	10	15
1321	2 r.	"Fuji from Tsukudajima in Edo"	20	25
1322	4 r.	"Fuji from a Teahouse at Yoshida"	45	50
1323	6 r.	"Fuji from Tagonoura"	65	70
1324	10 r.	"Fuji from Mishima-goe"	1·10	1·25
1325	12 r.	"Fuji from the Sumida River in Edo"	1·25	1·40
1318/25		*Set of 8*	3·50	4·00
MS1326		Two sheets, each 101×77 mm. (a) 18 r. "Fuji from Inume Pass" (2 Sept). (b) 18 r. "Fuji from Fukagawa in Edo" (16 Oct) *Set of 2 sheets*	4·00	4·25

Nos. 1318/25 were each printed in sheetlets of 10 containing two horizontal strips of 5 stamps separated by printed labels commemorating Emperor Hirohito.

233 Clown Triggerfish

(Des L. Birmingham. Litho Questa)

1989 (16 Oct). *Tropical Fishes. T **233** and similar horiz designs. Multicoloured.* P 14.
1327	20 l.	Type **233**	15	15
1328	50 l.	Bluestripe Snapper	20	20
1329	1 r.	Blue Surgeonfish	25	25
1330	2 r.	Oriental Sweetlips	40	40
1331	3 r.	Wrasse	60	60
1332	8 r.	Threadfin Butterflyfish	1·60	1·60
1333	10 r.	Bicolour Parrotfish	1·90	1·90
1334	12 r.	Sabre Squirrelfish	2·10	2·10
1327/34		*Set of 8*	6·50	6·50
MS1335		Two sheets, each 101×73 mm. (a) 15 r. Butterfly Perch. (b) 15 r. Semicircle Angelfish		
		Set of 2 sheets	5·00	5·50

MALDIVES   15L

234 Goofy, Mickey and Minnie Mouse with Takuri "Type 3", 1907

(Des Walt Disney Co. Litho Questa)

1989 (17 Nov). *"World Stamp Expo '89" International Stamp Exhibition, Washington (1st issue). T **234** and similar horiz designs showing Walt Disney cartoon characters with Japanese cars. Multicoloured.* P 14×13½.
1336	15 l.	Type **234**	10	10
1337	50 l.	Donald and Daisy Duck in Mitsubishi "Model A", 1917	15	15
1338	1 r.	Goofy in Datsun "Roadstar", 1935	25	25
1339	2 r.	Donald and Daisy Duck with Mazda, 1940	35	35
1340	4 r.	Donald Duck with Nissan "Bluebird 310", 1959	65	65
1341	6 r.	Donald and Daisy Duck with Subaru "360", 1958	90	90
1342	10 r.	Mickey Mouse and Pluto in Honda "5800", 1966	1·50	1·50
1343	12 r.	Mickey Mouse and Goofy in Daihatsu "Fellow", 1966	1·60	1·60
1336/43		*Set of 8*	5·00	5·00
MS1344		Two sheets, each 127×102 mm. (a) 20 r. Daisy Duck with Chip n'Dale and Isuzu "Trooper II", 1981 (b) 20 r. Mickey Mouse with tortoise and Toyota "Supra", 1985 *Set of 2 sheets*	5·50	6·50

(Des Design Element. Litho Questa)

1989 (17 Nov). *"World Stamp Expo '89" International Stamp Exhibition, Washington (2nd issue). Landmarks of Washington. Sheet 62×78 mm containing multicoloured designs as T **193a** of Lesotho, but vert.* P 14.
MS1345		8 r. Marine Corps Memorial, Arlington National Cemetery	1·25	1·25

REPUBLIC OF MALDIVES   R.1

235 Lunar Module *Eagle*

(Des W. Hanson Studio. Litho Questa).

1989 (24 Nov). *20th Anniv of First Manned Landing on Moon. T **235** and similar multicoloured designs.* P 14.
1346	1 r.	Type **235**	20	15
1347	2 r.	Astronaut Aldrin collecting dust samples	35	35
1348	6 r.	Aldrin setting up seismometer	90	90
1349	10 r.	Pres. Nixon congratulating "Apollo 11" astronauts	1·40	1·60
1346/9		*Set of 4*	2·50	2·75
MS1350		107×75 mm. 18 r. Television picture of Armstrong about to step onto Moon (34×47 mm). P 13½×14	2·50	2·50

MALDIVES   20L   10L

236 Jawaharlal Nehru with Mahatma Gandhi   237 Sir William van Horne, Locomotive and Map of Canadian Pacific Railway, 1894

(Des Design Element. Litho B.D.T.)

1989 (20 Dec)–90. *Anniversaries and Events. T **236** and similar multicoloured designs.* P 14.
1351	20 l.	Type **236** (birth centenary)	15	15
1352	50 l.	Opium poppies and logo (anti-drugs campaign) (*vert*)	20	20
1353	1 r.	William Shakespeare (425th birth anniv) (15.2.90)	20	20
1354	2 r.	Storming the Bastille (bicent of French Revolution) (*vert*) (15.2.90)	30	30
1355	3 r.	"Concorde" (20th anniv of first flight) (15.2.90)	55	55
1356	8 r.	George Washington (bicent of inauguration)	1·40	1·40
1357	10 r.	William Bligh (bicent of mutiny on the Bounty)	1·60	1·60

1358 12 r. Hamburg Harbour (800th anniv) (vert) (15.2.90) .. 1·75 1·75
1351/8 *Set of 8* 5·50 5·50
MS1359 Two sheets. (a) 115×85 mm. 18 r. Baseball players (50th anniv of first televised game) (*vert*). (b) 110×80 mm. 18 r. Franz von Taxis (500th anniv of regular European postal services) (*vert*) (15.2.90) .. *Set of 2 sheets* 5·50 6·00

(Des A. Fagbohun. Litho Questa)

1989 (26 Dec). *Railway Pioneers. T 237 and similar vert designs. Multicoloured. P 14.*
1360 10 l. Type 237 10 10
1361 25 l. Matthew Murray and Middleton Colliery rack locomotive, 1811 10 10
1362 50 l. Louis Favre and locomotive entering tunnel, 1856 .. 10 10
1363 2 r. George Stephenson and *Locomotion*, 1825 .. 25 30
1364 6 r. Richard Trevithick and Pen-y-darran locomotive, 1804 70 75
1365 8 r. George Nagelmackers and "Orient Express" dining car, 1869 90 95
1366 10 r. William Jessop and horse-drawn line, 1770.. 1·10 1·25
1367 12 r. Isambard Brunel and G.W.R. train, 1833.. 1·40 1·50
1360/7 *Set of 8* 4·25 4·50
MS1368 Two sheets, each 71×103 mm. (a) 18 r. George Pullman (inventor of sleeping cars), 1864. (b) 18 r. Rudolf Diesel (inventor of diesel engine), 1892 .. *Set of 2 sheets* 4·25 4·50

238 Bodu Thakurufaanu Memorial Centre, Utheemu
239 "Louis XVI in Coronation Robes" (Duplessis)

(Litho B.D.T.)

1990 (1 Jan). *25th Anniv of Independence. T 238 and similar horiz designs. Multicoloured. P 14.*
1369 20 l. Type 238 10 10
1370 25 l. Islamic Centre, Malé 10 10
1371 50 l. National flag and logos of international organizations .. 10 10
1372 2 r. Presidential Palace, Malé .. 25 30
1373 5 r. National Security Service .. 55 60
1369/73 *Set of 5* 80 90
MS1374 128×90 mm. 10 r. National emblem .. 1·10 1·25

(Litho Questa)

1990 (11 Jan). *Bicentenary of French Revolution and "Philexfrance 89" International Stamp Exhibition, Paris. French Paintings. T 239 and similar multicoloured designs. P 13½×14.*
1375 15 l. Type 239 10 10
1376 50 l. "Monsieur Lavoisier and his Wife" (David) 10 10
1377 1 r. "Madame Pastoret" (David) .. 10 15
1378 2 r. "Oath of Lafayette, 14 July 1790" (anon) 25 30
1379 4 r. "Madame Trudaine" (David) 45 50
1380 6 r. "Chenard celebrating the Liberation of Savoy" (Boilly) 70 75
1381 10 r. "An Officer swears Allegiance to the Constitution" (anon) .. 1·10 1·25
1382 12 r. "Self Portrait" (David) 1·40 1·50
1375/82 *Set of 8* 3·75 4·25
MS1383 Two sheets. (a) 104×79 mm. 20 r. "The Oath of the Tennis Court, 20 June 1789" (David) (*horiz*). P 14×13½. (b) 79×104 mm. 20 r. "Rousseau and Symbols of the Revolution" (Jeaurat). P 13½×14 .. *Set of 2 sheets* 4·50 4·75

239a Donald Duck, Mickey Mouse and Goofy playing Rugby

(Des Walt Disney Co. Litho Questa)

1990 (3 May). *"Stamp World London 90" International Stamp Exhibition. T 239a and similar horiz designs showing Walt Disney cartoon characters playing British sports. Multicoloured. P 14×13½.*
1384 15 l. Type 239a 10 10
1385 50 l. Donald Duck and Chip-n-Dale curling 10 10
1386 1 r. Goofy playing polo 10 15
1387 2 r. Mickey Mouse and nephews playing soccer 25 30
1388 4 r. Mickey Mouse playing cricket 45 50
1389 6 r. Minnie and Mickey Mouse at Ascot races 70 75

1390 10 r. Mickey Mouse and Goofy playing tennis 1·10 1·25
1391 12 r. Donald Duck and Mickey Mouse playing bowls 1·40 1·50
1384/91 *Set of 8* 3·75 4·25
MS1392 Two sheets, each 126×101 mm. (a) 20 r. Minnie Mouse fox-hunting. (b) 20 r. Mickey Mouse playing golf .. *Set of 2 sheets* 4·50 4·75

240 Silhouettes of Queen Elizabeth II and Queen Victoria
241 Sultan's Tomb

(Des S. Pollard. Litho B.D.T.)

1990 (6 May). *150th Anniv of the Penny Black. T 240 and similar horiz designs. P 15×14.*
1393 8 r. black and olive-green .. 90 95
1394 12 r. black and deep dull blue .. 1·40 1·50
MS1395 109×84 mm. 18 r. black & yellow-brown 2·10 2·25
Designs:—12 r. As Type 240, but with position of silhouettes reversed; 18 r. Penny Black.

(Des Young Phillips Studio. Litho Questa)

1990 (8 July). *90th Birthday of Queen Elizabeth the Queen Mother. Vert designs as T 198a of Lesotho showing portraits, 1920–29. P 14.*
1396 6 r. brownish blk, brt mag & turquoise-bl 70 75
a. Strip of 3. Nos. 1396/8 1·90
1397 6 r. brownish blk, brt mag & turquoise-bl 70 75
1398 6 r. brownish blk, brt mag & turquoise-bl 70 75
1396/8 *Set of 3* 1·90 2·00
MS1399 90×75 mm. 18 r. multicoloured .. 2·10 2·25
Designs:—No. 1396, Lady Elizabeth Bowes-Lyon; No. 1397, Lady Elizabeth Bowes-Lyon wearing headband; No. 1398, Lady Elizabeth Bowes-Lyon leaving for her wedding; No. MS1399, Lady Elizabeth Bowes-Lyon wearing wedding dress. Nos. 1396/8 were printed together, horizontally and vertically *se-tenant*, in sheetlets of 9 (3×3).

(Litho Questa)

1990 (21 July). *Islamic Heritage Year. T 241 and similar horiz designs, each black and light cobalt. P 14.*
1400 1 r. Type 241 10 15
a. Block of 6. Nos. 1400/5 95
1401 1 r. Thakurufaan's Palace 10 15
1402 1 r. Malé Mosque 10 15
1403 2 r. Veranda of Friday Mosque 25 30
1404 2 r. Interior of Friday Mosque 25 30
1405 2 r. Friday Mosque and Monument 25 30
1400/5 *Set of 6* 95 1·25
Nos. 1400/5 were printed together, *se-tenant*, in blocks of 6 (3×2) within the sheet of 36.

242 Defence of Wake Island, 1941

(Des W. Wright. Litho Questa)

1990 (9 Aug). *50th Anniv of Second World War. T 242 and similar horiz designs. Multicoloured. P 14.*
1406 15 l. Type 242 10 10
1407 25 l. Stilwell's army in Burma, 1944 10 10
1408 50 l. Normandy offensive, 1944 10 10
1409 1 r. Capture of Saipan, 1944 10 15
1410 2 r. 50, D-Day landings, 1944 30 35
1411 3 r. 50, Allied landings in Norway, 1940 40 45
1412 4 r. Lord Mountbatten, Head of Combined Operations, 1943 45 50
1413 6 r. Japanese surrender, Tokyo Bay, 1945 70 75
1414 10 r. Potsdam Conference, 1945 .. 1·10 1·25
1415 12 r. Allied invasion of Sicily, 1943 1·40 1·50
1406/15 *Set of 10* 4·25 4·75
MS1416 115×87 mm. 18 r. Atlantic convoy .. 2·10 2·25

243 Crested Tern

(Des Mary Walters. Litho Questa)

1990 (9 Aug). *Birds. T 243 and similar horiz designs. Multicoloured. P 14.*
1417 15 l. Type 243 10 10
1418 50 l. Koel 10 10
1419 1 r. White Tern 10 15
1420 3 r. 50, Cinnamon Bittern 40 45
1421 6 r. Sooty Tern 70 75
1422 8 r. Audubon's Shearwater 90 95
1423 12 r. Common Noddy 1·40 1·50
1424 15 r. Lesser Frigate Bird .. 1·75 1·90
1417/24 *Set of 8* 5·00 5·25
MS1425 Two sheets, each 100×69 mm. (a) 18 r. Grey Heron. (b) 18 r. White-tailed Tropic Bird .. *Set of 2 sheets* 4·00 4·25

244 Emblem, Dish Aerial and Sailboards
245 *Spathoglottis plicata*

(Litho Questa)

1990 (21 Nov). *Fifth South Asian Association for Regional Co-operation Summit. T 244 and similar horiz designs. P 14.*
1426 75 l. black and brown-orange .. 15 15
1427 3 r. 50, multicoloured .. 60 60
MS1428 112×82 mm. 20 r. multicoloured .. 2·75 3·00
Designs:—3 r. 50, Flags of member nations; 20 r. Global warming diagram.

(Des Dot Barlowe. Litho Questa)

1990 (9 Dec). *"EXPO '90" International Garden and Greenery Exhibition, Osaka. Flowers. T 245 and similar multicoloured designs. P 14.*
1429 20 l. Type 245 10 10
1430 75 l. *Hippeastrum puniceum* .. 10 10
1431 2 r. *Tecoma stans* (*horiz*) .. 25 30
1432 3 r. 50 *Catharanthus roseus* (*horiz*) .. 40 45
1433 10 r. *Ixora coccinea* (*horiz*) .. 1·10 1·25
1434 12 r. *Clitorea ternatea* (*horiz*) .. 1·40 1·50
1435 15 r. *Caesalpinia pulcherrima* .. 1·75 1·90
1429/35 *Set of 7* 4·50 5·00
MS1436 Four sheets, each 111×79 mm. (a) 20 r. *Plumeria obtusa* (*horiz*). (b) 20 r. *Jasminum grandiflorum* (*horiz*). (c) 20 r. *Rosa sp* (*horiz*). (d) 20 r. *Hibiscus tiliaceous* (*horiz*) .. *Set of 4 sheets* 9·00 9·25

246 The Hare and the Tortoise

1990 (11 Dec). *International Literacy Year. T 246 and similar multicoloured designs showing Walt Disney cartoon characters illustrating fables by Aesop. P 14×13½.*
1437 15 l. Type 246 10 10
1438 50 l. The Town Mouse and the Country Mouse 10 10
1439 1 r. The Fox and the Crow .. 10 15
1440 3 r. 50, The Travellers and the Bear 40 45
1441 4 r. The Fox and the Lion 45 50
1442 6 r. The Mice Meeting .. 70 75
1443 10 r. The Fox and the Goat .. 1·10 1·25
1444 12 r. The Dog in the Manger .. 1·40 1·50
1437/44 *Set of 8* 4·00 4·25
MS1445 Two sheets, each 127×102 mm. (a) 20 r. The Miller, his Son and the Ass (*vert*). (b) 20 r. The Miser's Gold (*vert*). P 13½×14 *Set of 2 sheets* 4·50 4·75

247 East African Class "31" Locomotive
248 Ruud Gullit of Holland

(Des T. Agans. Litho Questa)

1990 (15 Dec). *Steam Railway Locomotives. T 247 and similar vert designs. Multicoloured. P 14.*
1446 20 l. Type 247 10 10
1447 50 l. Sudan Railways Class "Mikado" .. 10 10
1448 1 r. South African Beyer-Garratt Class "GM" 10 15
1449 3 r. Rhodesia Railways Class "7" .. 35 40
1450 5 r. U.S.A. Central Pacific Class "229" .. 55 60
1451 8 r. U.S.A. Reading Class "415".. 90 95
1452 10 r. Canada Porter narrow gauge .. 1·10 1·25
1453 12 r. U.S.A. Great Northern Class "515".. 1·40 1·50
1446/53 *Set of 8* 4·00 4·25
MS1454 Two sheets, each 90×65 mm. (a) 20 r. 19th-century standard American locomotive. (b) 20 r. East African Railways locomotive No. 5950 *Set of 2 sheets* 4·50 4·75

(Des Young Phillips Studio. Litho Questa)

1990 (27 Dec). *World Cup Football Championship, Italy. T* **248** *and similar multicoloured designs. P* 14.

1455	1 r. Type 248	.. ..	10	15
1456	2 r. 50, Paul Gascoigne of England		30	35
1457	3 r. 50, Brazilian challenging Argentine player		40	45
1458	5 r. Brazilian taking control of ball		55	60
1459	7 r. Italian and Austrian jumping for header		80	85
1460	10 r. Russian being chased by Turkish player		1·10	1·25
1461	15 r. Andres Brehme of West Germany		1·75	1·90
1455/61		*Set of 7*	4·50	5·00

MS1462 Four sheets, each 77×92 mm. (a) 18 r. Head of an Austrian player (*horiz*). (b) 18 r. Head of a South Korean player (*horiz*). (c) 20 r. Diego Maradona of Argentina (*horiz*). (d) 20 r. Schilacci of Italy (*horiz*).. .. *Set of 4 sheets* 8·50 8·75

249 Winged Euonymus   **250** "Summer" (Rubens)

(Des N. Waldman. Litho Questa)

1991 (29 Jan). *Bonsai Trees and Shrubs. T* **249** *and similar vert designs. Multicoloured. P* 14.

1463	20 l. Type 249	.. ..	10	10
1464	50 l. Japanese Black Pine		10	10
1465	1 r. Japanese Five Needle Pine		10	15
1466	3 r. 50, Flowering Quince		40	45
1467	5 r. Chinese Elm		55	60
1468	8 r. Japanese Persimmon		90	95
1469	10 r. Japanese Wisteria		1·10	1·25
1470	12 r. Satsuki Azalea		1·40	1·50
1463/70		*Set of 8*	4·00	4·50

MS1471 Two sheets, each 89×88 mm. (a) 20 r. Trident Maple. (b) 20 r. Sargent Juniper .. *Set of 2 sheets* 4·50 4·75

(Litho Questa)

1991 (7 Feb). *350th Death Anniv of Rubens. T* **250** *and similar horiz designs. Multicoloured. P* 14×13½.

1472	20 l. Type 250		10	10
1473	50 l. "Landscape with Rainbow" (detail)		10	10
1474	1 r. "Wreck of Aeneas"		10	15
1475	2 r. 50, "Château de Steen" (detail)		25	30
1476	3 r. 50, "Landscape with Herd of Cows"		40	45
1477	7 r. "Ruins on the Palantine"		80	85
1478	10 r. "Landscape with Peasants and Cows"		1·10	1·25
1479	12 r. "Wagon fording Stream"		1·40	1·50
1472/9		*Set of 8*	3·75	4·25

MS1480 Four sheets, each 100×71 mm. (a) 20 r. "Landscape at Sunset". (b) 20 r. "Peasants with Cattle by a Stream". (c) 20 r. "Shepherd with Flock". (d) 20 r. "Wagon in Stream" .. *Set of 4 sheets* 9·00 9·50

251 Greek Messenger from Marathon, 490 BC (2480th anniv)   **252** Arctic Iceberg and Maldives Dhoni

(Des W. Wright. Litho Questa)

1991 (11 Mar). *Anniversaries and Events (1990). T* **251** *and similar multicoloured designs. P* 14.

1481	50 l. Type 251		10	10
1482	1 r. Anthony Fokker in early aircraft (birth cent)		10	15
1483	3 r. 50, "Early Bird" satellite (25th anniv)		40	45
1484	7 r. Signing Reunification of Germany agreement (*horiz*)		80	85
1485	8 r. King John signing Magna Carta (775th anniv)		90	95
1486	10 r. Dwight D. Eisenhower (birth cent)		1·10	1·25
1487	12 r. Sir Winston Churchill (25th death anniv)		1·40	1·50
1488	15 r. Pres. Reagan at Berlin Wall (German reunification) (*horiz*)		1·75	1·90
1481/8		*Set of 8*	6·00	6·50

MS1489 Two sheets, each 180×81 mm. 20 r. German "Ju 88" bomber (50th anniv of Battle of Britain) (*horiz*). (b) 160×73 mm. 20 r. Brandenburg Gate (German reunification) (*horiz*) .. .. *Set of 2 sheets* 4·50 4·75

(Litho Questa)

1991 (10 Apr). *Global Warming. T* **252** *and similar horiz design. Multicoloured. P* 14.

1490	3 r. 50, Type 252		40	45
1491	7 r. Antarctic iceberg and *Maldive Trader* (freighter)		80	85

253 S.A.A.R.C. Emblem and Medal   **254** Children on Beach

(Litho Questa)

1991 (10 Apr). *Year of the Girl Child. P* 14.

1492	253 7 r. multicoloured	.. ..	80	85

(Litho Questa)

1991 (14 Apr). *Year of the Maldivian Child. Children's Paintings. T* **254** *and similar horiz designs. Multicoloured. P* 14.

1493	3 r. 50, Type 254		40	45
1494	5 r. Children in a park		55	60
1495	10 r. Hungry child dreaming of food		1·10	1·25
1496	25 r. Scuba diver		3·00	3·25
1493/6		*Set of 4*	4·50	5·00

255 "Still Life: Japanese Vase with Roses and Anemones" (Van Gogh)   **256** Boy painting

(Litho Walsall)

1991 (6 June). *Death Centenary of Vincent van Gogh (artist) (1990). T* **255** *and similar multicoloured designs. P* 13½.

1497	15 l. Type 255		10	10
1498	20 l. "Still Life: Red Poppies and Daisies"		10	10
1499	2 r. "Vincent's Bedroom in Arles" (*horiz*)		25	30
1500	3 r. 50, "The Mulberry Tree" (*horiz*)		40	45
1501	7 r. "Blossoming Chestnut Branches" (*horiz*)		80	85
1502	10 r. "Peasant Couple going to Work" (*horiz*)		1·10	1·25
1503	12 r. "Still Life: Pink Roses" (*horiz*)		1·40	1·50
1504	15 r. "Child with Orange" (*horiz*)		1·75	1·90
1497/1504		*Set of 8*	5·25	5·75

MS1505 Two sheets. (a) 77×101 mm. 25 r. "House in Auvers" (70×94 *mm*). (b) 101×77 mm. 25 r. "The Courtyard of the Hospital at Arles" (94×70 *mm*). Imperf .. *Set of 2 sheets* 6·00 6·25

(Des D. Miller. Litho Walsall)

1991 (4 July). *65th Birthday of Queen Elizabeth II. Horiz designs as T* **210** *of Lesotho. Multicoloured. P* 14.

1506	2 r. Queen at Trooping the Colour, 1990		25	30
1507	5 r. Queen with Queen Mother and Princess Margaret, 1973		55	60
1508	8 r. Queen and Prince Philip in open carriage (*horiz*)		90	95
1509	12 r. Queen at Royal Estates Ball		1·40	1·50
1506/9		*Set of 4*	2·75	3·00

MS1510 68×90 mm. 25 r. Separate photographs of Queen and Prince Philip .. .. 3·00 3·25

(Des D. Miller. Litho Walsall)

1991 (4 July). *10th Wedding Anniv of Prince and Princess of Wales. Horiz designs as T* **210** *of Lesotho. Multicoloured. P* 14.

1511	1 r. Prince and Princess skiing, 1986		10	10
1512	3 r. 50, Separate photographs of Prince, Princess and sons		40	45
1513	7 r. Prince Henry in Christmas play and Prince William watching polo		80	85
1514	15 r. Princess Diana at Ipswich, 1990, and Prince Charles playing polo		1·75	1·90
1511/14		*Set of 4*	2·75	3·00

MS1515 68×90 mm. 25 r. Prince and Princess of Wales in Hungary, and Princes William and Henry going to school .. .. .. 3·00 3·25

(Litho Questa)

1991 (25 July). *Hummel Figurines. T* **256** *and similar vert designs. Multicoloured. P* 14.

1516	10 l. Type 256		10	10
1517	25 l. Boy reading at table		10	10
1518	50 l. Boy with school satchel		10	10
1519	2 r. Girl with basket		25	30
1520	3 r. 50, Boy reading		40	45
1521	8 r. Girl and young child reading		90	95
1522	10 r. School girls		1·10	1·25
1523	25 r. School boys		3·00	3·25
1516/23		*Set of 8*	5·25	5·75

MS1524 Two sheets, each 97×127 mm. (a) 5 r. As No. 1519; 5 r. As No. 1520; 5 r. As No. 1521; 5 r. As No. 1522; (b) 8 r. As Type **256**; 8 r. As No. 1517; 8 r. As No. 1518; 8 r. As No. 1523 .. *Set of 2 sheets* 6·00 6·25

257 Class "C 57" Steam Locomotive   **258** Salamis temora and Vanda caerulea

(Litho B.D.T.)

1991 (25 Aug). *"Phila Nippon '91" International Stamp Exhibition, Tokyo. Japanese Steam Locomotives. T* **257** *and similar multicoloured designs. P* 14.

1525	15 l. Type 257		10	10
1526	25 l. Class "6250" locomotive (*horiz*)		10	10
1527	1 r. Class "D 51" locomotive		10	10
1528	3 r. 50, Class "8620" locomotive (*horiz*)		40	45
1529	5 r. Class "10" locomotive (*horiz*)		55	60
1530	7 r. Class "C 61" locomotive		80	85
1531	10 r. Class "9600" locomotive (*horiz*)		1·10	1·25
1532	12 r. Class "D 52" locomotive (*horiz*)		1·40	1·50
1525/32		*Set of 8*	4·00	4·50

MS1533 Two sheets, each 118×80 mm. (a) 20 r. Class "C 56" locomotive (*horiz*). (b) 20 r. Class "1080" locomotive (*horiz*) .. *Set of 2 sheets* 4·50 4·75

(Litho Questa)

1991 (2 Dec). *Butterflies and Flowers. T* **258** *and similar horiz designs. Multicoloured. P* 14.

1534	10 l. Type 258		10	10
1535	25 l. *Meneris tulbaghia* and *Incarvillea younghusbandii*		10	10
1536	50 l. *Polyommatus icarus* and *Campsis grandiflora*		10	10
1537	2 r. *Danaus plexippus* and *Thunbergia grandiflora*		25	30
1538	3 r. 50, *Colias interior* and *Medinilla magnifica*		40	45
1539	5 r. *Ascalapha ordorata* and *Meconopsis horridula*		55	60
1540	8 r. *Papilio memnon* and *Dillenia obovata*		90	95
1541	10 r. *Precis octavia* and *Thespesia populnea*		1·10	1·25
1534/41		*Set of 8*	3·00	3·50

MS1542 Two sheets, each 100×70 mm. (a) 20 r. *Bombax ceiba* and *Phyciodes tharos*. (b) 20 r. *Amauris niavius* and *Bombax insigne* .. *Set of 2 sheets* 4·50 4·75

259 "H-II" Rocket

(Des K. Gromell. Litho Questa)

1991 (11 Dec). *Japanese Space Programme. T* **259** *and similar multicoloured designs. P* 14.

1543	15 l. Type 259		10	10
1544	20 l. Projected "H-II" orbiting plane		10	10
1545	2 r. Satellite "GMS-5"		25	30
1546	3 r. 50, Satellite "MOMO-1"		40	45
1547	7 r. Satellite "CS-3"		80	85
1548	10 r. Satellite "BS-2a, 2b"		1·10	1·25
1549	12 r. "H-I" Rocket (*vert*)		1·40	1·50
1550	15 r. Space Flier unit and U.S. space shuttle		1·75	1·90
1543/50		*Set of 8*	5·25	5·75

MS1551 Two sheets. (a) 116×85 mm. 20 r. Dish aerial, Katsura Tracking Station (*vert*). (b) 85×116 mm. 20 r. "M-3SII" rocket (*vert*) .. .. *Set of 2 sheets* 4·50 4·75

260 Williams "FW-07"

(Litho B.D.T.)

1991 (28 Dec). *Formula 1 Racing Cars. T 260 and similar horiz designs. Multicoloured. P 14.*
1552	20 l.	Type 260	..	10	10
1553	50 l.	Brabham/BMW "BT50" turbo	..	10	10
1554	1 r.	Williams/Honda "FW-11"	..	10	10
1555	3 r. 50,	Ferrari "312 T3"	..	40	45
1556	5 r.	Lotus/Honda "99T"	..	55	60
1557	7 r.	Benetton/Ford "B188"	..	80	85
1558	10 r.	Tyrrell "P34" six-wheeler	..	1·10	1·25
1559	21 r.	Renault "RE-30B" turbo	..	2·40	2·50
1552/9			*Set of 8*	5·00	5·50

MS1560 Two sheets, each 84×56 mm. (a) 25 r. Brabham/BMW "BT50" turbo (*different*). (b) 25 r. Ferrari "F189" .. *Set of 2 sheets* 6·00 6·25

261 "Testa Rossa", 1957   262 Franklin D. Roosevelt

(Litho Questa)

1991 (28 Dec). *Ferrari Cars. T 261 and similar horiz designs. Multicoloured. P 14.*
1561	5 r.	Type 261	..	55	60
	a.	Sheetlet. Nos. 1561/9	..	4·50	
1562	5 r.	"275GTB", 1966	..	55	60
1563	5 r.	"Aspirarta", 1951	..	55	60
1564	5 r.	"Testarossa"	..	55	60
1565	5 r.	Enzo Ferrari	..	55	60
1566	5 r.	"Dino 246", 1958	..	55	60
1567	5 r.	"Type 375", 1952	..	55	60
1568	5 r.	Nigel Mansell's Formula 1 racing car	..	55	60
1569	5 r.	"312T", 1975	..	55	60
1561/9			*Set of 9*	4·50	4·75

Nos. 1561/9 were printed together, *se-tenant*, in sheetlets of 9 (3×3).

(Des R. Jung. Litho Questa)

1991 (30 Dec). *50th Anniv of Japanese Attack on Pearl Harbor. American War Leaders. T 262 and similar horiz designs. Multicoloured. P 14½.*
1570	3 r. 50,	Type 262	..	40	45
	a.	Sheetlet. Nos. 1570/9	..	3·50	
1571	3 r. 50,	Douglas MacArthur and map of Phillipines		40	45
1572	3 r. 50,	Chester Nimitz and Pacific island		40	45
1573	3 r. 50,	Jonathan Wainwright and barbed wire	..	40	45
1574	3 r. 50,	Ernest King and aircraft carrier		40	45
1575	3 r. 50,	Claire Chennault and "Flying Tiger" plane		40	45
1576	3 r. 50,	William Halsey and aircraft carrier	..	40	45
1577	3 r. 50,	Marc Mitscher and aircraft carrier		40	45
1578	3 r. 50,	James Doolittle and "B-25" bomber		40	45
1579	3 r. 50,	Raymond Spruance and dive bomber	..	40	45
1570/9			*Set of 10*	3·50	4·00

Nos. 1561/70 were printed together, *se-tenant*, in sheetlets of 10 with the stamps arranged in two horizontal strips of 5 separated by a gutter showing Japanese fighters attacking Pearl Harbor and Admiral Isoroku Yamamoto.

263 Boy Scouts exploring
Coral Reef

(Des W. Hanson Studio. Litho Questa)

1992 (30 Jan). *17th World Scout Jamboree, Korea. T 263 and similar designs. P 14.*
1580	10 r.	multicoloured	..	1·10	1·25
1581	11 r.	multicoloured	..	1·25	1·40

MS1582 Two sheets. (a) 90×117 mm. 18 r. brownish grey, black and magenta. (b) 117×90 mm. 20 r. multicoloured .. *Set of 2 sheets* 4·25 4·50
Designs: *Vert*—11 r. Scout salute and badge; 18 r. Postcard of Lord Baden-Powell carried by rocket, 1937; 20 r. Czechoslovakia 1918 10 h. "Scout Post" stamp.

(Des J. Iskowitz. Litho Questa)

1992 (30 Jan). *Birth Centenary of Charles de Gaulle (French statesman) (1990). Multicoloured designs as T 209 of Lesotho. P 14.*
1583	6 r.	de Gaulle and Normandy Landings, 1944		70	75
1584	10 r.	de Gaulle in Madagascar, 1958 (*horiz*)		1·10	1·25

MS1585 76×116 mm. 15 r. General de Gaulle during Second World War .. 1·75 1·90

(Des L. Fried. Litho Questa)

1992 (30 Jan). *Bicentenary of Brandenburg Gate, Berlin. T 264 and similar horiz designs. Multicoloured. P 14.*
1586	20 l.	Type 264	..	10	10
1587	1 r. 75,	Berlin Wall and man holding child	20	25
1588	4 r.	Demonstrator and border guards	..	45	50
1589	15 r.	Imperial German badges	..	1·75	1·90
1586/9			*Set of 4*	2·25	2·50

MS1590 Three sheets, each 101×72 mm. (a) 18 r. Ancient German helmet. (b) 18 r. 19th-century shako. (c) 18 r. Helmet of 1939 .. *Set of 3 sheets* 6·50 6·75

265 Schwarzenberg Palace 266 Modern
Trans-Siberian
Electric
Locomotive

(Des J. Iskowitz. Litho Questa)

1992 (30 Jan). *Death Bicentenary of Mozart (1991). T 265 and similar multicoloured designs. P 14.*
1591	50 l.	Type 265	..	10	10
1592	1 r.	Spa at Baden	..	10	10
1593	2 r.	Royal Palace, Berlin	..	25	30
1594	5 r.	Viennese masonic seal	..	55	60
1595	7 r.	St. Marx	..	80	85
1596	20 r.	Josepsplatz, Vienna	..	2·25	2·40
1591/6			*Set of 6*	3·75	4·00

MS1597 75×104 mm. 20 r. Bust of Mozart (*vert*) 2·25 2·40

(Des W. Wright. Litho Questa)

1992 (30 Jan). *Centenary of Trans-Siberian Railway. T 266 and similar multicoloured designs. P 14.*
1598	7 r.	Type 266	..	80	85
1599	12 r.	Steam locomotive (*horiz*)	..	1·40	1·50

MS1600 115×85 mm. 20 r. Steam locomotive stopped at signal (57×43 mm) .. 2·25 2·40

267 Lilienthal's Signature
and *Flugzeug Nr.16*

(Des W. Wright. Litho Questa)

1992 (30 Jan). *Centenary of Otto Lilienthal's First Gliding Experiments. P 14.*
1601	267	6 r. multicoloured	..	70	75

268 Kurt Schwitters (artist)
and Landesmuseum

(Des W. Wright. Litho Questa)

1992 (30 Jan). *750th Anniv of Hannover. P 14.*
1602	268	8 r. multicoloured	..	90	95

269 Map of Switzerland and 270 Mickey Mouse on
Man in Uri Traditional   Flying Carpet, Arabia
Costume

(Des W. Wright. Litho Questa)

1992 (30 Jan). *700th Anniv of Swiss Confederation. P 14.*
1603	269	9 r. multicoloured	..	1·00	1·10

(Des Walt Disney Co. Litho B.D.T.)

1992 (4 Feb). *Mickey's World Tour. T 270 and similar multicoloured designs showing Walt Disney cartoon characters in different countries. P 13.*
1604	25 l.	Type 270	..	10	10
1605	50 l.	Goofy and Big Ben, Great Britain	..	10	10
1606	1 r.	Mickey wearing clogs, Netherlands	..	10	10
1607	2 r.	Pluto eating pasta, Italy	..	25	30
1608	3 r.	Mickey and Donald doing Mexican hat dance		35	40
1609	3 r. 50,	Mickey, Goofy and Donald as tiki, New Zealand		40	45
1610	5 r.	Goofy skiing in Austrian Alps	..	55	60
1611	7 r.	Mickey and city gate, Germany	..	80	85
1612	10 r.	Donald as samurai, Japan	..	1·10	1·25
1613	12 r.	Mickey as heroic statue, Russia	..	1·40	1·50
1614	15 r.	Mickey, Donald, Goofy and Pluto as German band		1·75	1·90
1604/14			*Set of 11*	6·25	6·75

MS1615 Three sheets, each 83×104 mm. (a) 25 r. Donald chasing leprechaun, Ireland (*horiz*). (b) 25 r. Baby kangaroo surprising Pluto, Australia. (c) 25 r. Mickey and globe .. *Set of 3 sheets* 9·00 9·25

271 Whimbrel 272 Blue Surgeonfish

(Des D. Delouise. Litho Questa)

1992 (17 Feb). *Birds. T 271 and similar vert designs. Multicoloured. P 14½.*
1616	10 l.	Type 271	..	10	10
1617	25 l.	Great Egret	..	10	10
1618	50 l.	Grey Heron	..	10	10
1619	2 r.	Shag	..	25	30
1620	3 r. 50,	Roseate Tern	..	40	45
1621	5 r.	Greenshank	..	55	60
1622	8 r.	Hoopoe	..	90	95
1623	10 r.	Black-shouldered Kite	..	1·10	1·25
1624	25 r.	Scarlet Ibis	..	3·00	3·25
1625	50 r.	Grey Plover	..	6·00	6·25
1616/25			*Set of 10*	11·00	12·00

(Des D. Miller. Litho Questa)

1992 (3 Mar). *40th Anniv of Queen Elizabeth II's Accession. Horiz designs as T 214 of Lesotho. Multicoloured. P 14.*
1626	1 r.	Palm trees on beach	..	10	10
1627	3 r. 50,	Path leading to jetty	..	40	45
1628	7 r.	Tropical plant	..	80	85
1629	10 r.	Palm trees on beach (*different*)	..	1·10	1·25
1626/9			*Set of 4*	2·10	2·40

MS1630 Two sheets, each 74×97 mm. (a) 18 r. Dhow. (b) 18 r. Palm trees on beach (*different*)
Set of 2 sheets 4·00 4·25

(Litho B.D.T.)

1992 (23 Mar). *Fishes. T 272 and similar horiz designs. Multicoloured. P 14.*
1631	7 l.	Type 272	..	10	10
1632	20 l.	Bigeye	..	10	10
1633	50 l.	Yellowfin Tuna	..	10	10
1634	1 r.	Two-spot Red Snapper	..	10	10
1635	3 r. 50,	Sabre Squirrelfish	..	40	45
1636	5 r.	Picasso Triggerfish	..	55	60
1637	8 r.	Bennet's Butterfly Fish	..	90	95
1638	10 r.	Parrotfish	..	1·10	1·25
1639	12 r.	Grouper	..	1·40	1·50
1640	15 r.	Skipjack Tuna	..	1·75	1·90
1631/40			*Set of 10*	5·75	6·25

MS1641 Four sheets, each 116×76 mm. (a) 20 r. Threadfin Butterflyfish. (b) 20 r. Sweetlips. (c) 20 r. Clownfish. (d) 20 r. Clown Triggerfish
Set of 4 sheets 9·25 9·50

(Des Walt Disney Co. Litho Questa)

1992 (15 Apr). *International Stamp Exhibitions. Multicoloured designs as T 215 of Lesotho, showing Walt Disney cartoon characters. P 13½×14.*

(a) "Granada '92", Spain. The Alhambra
1642	2 r.	Minnie Mouse in Court of the Lions		25	30
1643	5 r.	Goofy in Lions Fountain	..	55	60
1644	8 r.	Mickey Mouse at the Gate of Justice		90	95
1645	12 r.	Donald Duck serenading Daisy at the Vermilion Towers		1·40	1·50
1642/5			*Set of 4*	2·75	3·00

MS1646 127×102 mm. 25 r. Goofy pushing Mickey in wheelbarrow .. 3·00 3·25

(b) "World Columbian Stamp Expo '92". Chicago Landmarks
1647	1 r.	Mickey meeting Jean Baptiste du Sable (founder)		10	10
1648	3 r. 50,	Donald Duck at Old Chicago Post Office		40	45
1649	7 r.	Donald at Old Fort Dearborn	..	80	85
1650	15 r.	Goofy in Museum of Science and Industry		1·75	1·90
1647/50			*Set of 4*	2·75	3·00

MS1651 127×102 mm. 25 r. Mickey and Minnie Mouse at Columbian Exposition, 1893 (*horiz*). P 14×13½. .. 3·00 3·25

NEW INFORMATION

The editor is always interested to correspond with people who have new information that will improve or correct the Catalogue.

273 Coastguard Patrol Boats

274 Flowers of the United States of America

(Litho Questa)

1992 (21 Apr). *Centenary of National Security Service. T 273 and similar horiz designs. Multicoloured. P 14.*
1652	3 r. 50, Type 273	..	..	40	45
1653	5 r. Infantry in training			55	60
1654	10 r. Aakoatey fort		..	1·10	1·25
1655	15 r. Fire Service ..		..	1·75	1·90
1652/5	..	..	Set of 4	3·50	3·75

MS1656 100×68 mm. 20 r. Ceremonial procession, 1892 .. .. .. 2·25 2·40

(Des W. Wright. Litho Questa)

1992 (26 Apr). *National Flowers. T 274 and similar multicoloured designs. P 14½.*
1657	25 l. Type 274	..	..	10	10
1658	50 l. Australia	..	..	10	10
1659	2 r. England	..	..	25	30
1660	3 r. 50, Brazil	..	..	40	45
1661	5 r. Holland	..	..	55	60
1662	8 r. France	..	..	90	95
1663	10 r. Japan	..	..	1·10	1·25
1664	15 r. Africa	..	..	1·75	1·90
1657/64	..	..	Set of 8	4·75	5·00

MS1665 Two sheets, each 114×85 mm. (a) 25 r. *Plumieria rubra, Classia fistula* and *Eugenia malaccensis* (57×43 *mm*). (b) 25 r. *Bauhinia variegata, Catharanthus roseus* and *Plumieria alba* (57×43 *mm*). P 14 .. .. Set of 2 sheets 6·00 6·25

275 *Laetiporus sulphureus*   **276** Hurdling

(Litho Walsall)

1992 (14 May). *Fungi. T 275 and similar vert designs. Multicoloured. P 14.*
1666	10 l. Type 275	..	..	10	10
1667	25 l. *Coprinus atramentarius*	..	..	10	10
1668	50 l. *Ganoderma lucidum*	..	..	10	10
1669	3 r. 50, *Russula aurata*	..	..	40	45
1670	5 r. *Polyporus umbellatus*	..	..	55	60
1671	8 r. *Suillus grevillei*	..	..	90	95
1672	10 r. *Clavaria zollingeri*	..	..	1·10	1·25
1673	25 r. *Boletus edulis*	..	..	3·00	3·25
1666/73	..	..	Set of 8	5·75	6·00

MS1674 Two sheets, each 100×70 mm. (a) 25 r. *Marasmius oreades.* (b) 25 r. *Trametes cinnabarina* .. .. Set of 2 sheets 6·00 6·25

(Litho Questa)

1992 (1 June–5 Oct). *Olympic Games, Albertville and Barcelona (1st issue). Multicoloured designs as T 216 of Lesotho. P 14.*
1675	10 l. Pole vault	..	..	10	10
1676	25 l. Men's pommel horse (*horiz*)	..	10	10
1677	50 l. Men's shot put	..	..	10	10
1678	1 r. Men's horizontal bar (*horiz*)	..	10	10
1679	2 r. Men's triple jump (*horiz*)	..	25	30
1680	3 r. 50, Table tennis	..	..	40	45
1681	5 r. Two-man bobsled (5 Oct)	..	55	60
1682	7 r. Freestyle wrestling (*horiz*)	..	80	85
1683	8 r. Freestyle ski-jump (5 Oct)	..	90	95
1684	9 r. Baseball	..	..	1·00	1·10
1685	10 r. Women's cross-country Nordic skiing (5 Oct)			1·10	1·25
1686	12 r. Men's 200 metres backstroke (*horiz*)		1·40	1·50
1675/86	..	..	Set of 12	3·75	4·00

MS1687 Three sheets. (a) 100×70 mm. 25 r. Decathlon (*horiz*). (b) 100×70 mm. 25 r. Women's slalom skiing (*horiz*) (5 Oct). (c) 70×100 mm. 25 r. Men's figure skating (5 Oct) Set of 3 sheets 9·00 9·25

(Litho Walsall)

1992 (1 June). *Olympic Games, Barcelona (2nd issue). T 276 and similar vert designs. Multicoloured. P 14.*
1688	10 l. Type 276	..	..	10	10
1689	1 r. Boxing	..	..	10	10
1690	3 r. 50, Women's sprinting	..	..	40	45
1691	5 r. Discus	..	..	55	60
1692	7 r. Basketball	..	..	80	85
1693	10 r. Long-distance running	..	..	1·10	1·25
1694	12 r. Aerobic gymnastics	..	..	1·40	1·50

1695	20 r. Fencing	..	..	2·25	2·40
1688/95			Set of 8	6·00	6·50

MS1696 Two sheets, each 70×100 mm. (a) 25 r. Olympic symbol and national flags. (b) 25 r. Olympic symbol and flame .. Set of 2 sheets 6·00 6·25

Z 7

Malta

Early records of the postal services under the British Occupation are fragmentary, but it is known that an Island Postmaster was appointed in 1802. A British Packet Agency was established in 1806 and it later became customary for the same individual to hold the two appointments together. The inland posts continued to be the responsibility of the local administration, but the overseas mails formed part of the British G.P.O. system.

The stamps of Great Britain were used on overseas mails from September 1857. Previously during the period of the Crimean War letters franked with Great Britain stamps from the Crimea were cancelled at Malta with a wavy line obliterator. Such postmarks are known between April 1855 and September 1856.

The British G.P.O. relinquished control of the overseas posts on 31 December 1884 when Great Britain stamps were replaced by those of Malta.

Z 1   Z 2

1855–56. *Stamps of GREAT BRITAIN cancelled with wavy lines obliteration, Type Z 1.*

Z1	1d. red-brown (1854), Die I, *wmk* Small Crown, *perf* 16	£800
Z2	1d. red-brown (1855), Die II, *wmk* Small Crown, *perf* 14	£800
	a. Very blued paper	
Z3	1d. red-brown (1855), Die II, *wmk* Large Crown, *perf* 16	£800
Z3a	1d. red-brown (1855), Die II, *wmk* Large Crown, *perf* 14	£800
Z4	2d. blue (1855), *wmk* Large Crown, *perf* 14 Plate No. 5	£4000
Z5	6d. (1854) embossed	£4000
Z6	1s. (1847) embossed	£4000

It is now established that this obliterator was sent to Malta and used on mail in transit emanating from the Crimea.

1857 (18 Aug)–59. *Stamps of GREAT BRITAIN cancelled "M", Type Z 2.*

Z 7	1d. red-brown (1841)	£1000
Z 8	1d. red-brown, Die I, *wmk* Small Crown, *perf* 16	75·00
Z 9	1d. red-brown, Die II, *wmk* Small Crown, *perf* 16	£800
Z10	1d. red-brown, Die II (1855) *wmk* Small Crown, *perf* 14	£170
Z11	1d. red-brown, Die II (1855) *wmk* Large Crown, *perf* 14	65·00
Z12	1d. rose-red (1857) *wmk* Large Crown, *perf* 14	17·00
Z13	2d. blue (1841), *imperf*	£2500
Z14	2d. blue (1854) *wmk* Small Crown, *perf* 16 Plate No. 4	£600
Z15	2d. blue (1855), *wmk* Large Crown, *perf* 14 *From* Plate Nos. 5, 6.	45·00
Z16	2d. blue (1858), *wmk* Large Crown, *perf* 16 Plate No. 6.	£225
Z17	2d. blue (1858) (Plate 7, 8, 9). *From*	35·00
Z18	4d. rose (1857)	35·00
	a. Thick glazed paper	£170
Z19	6d. violet (1854), embossed	£1600
Z20	6d. lilac (1856)	40·00
	a. Thick paper	£190
Z21	6d. lilac (1856) (blued *paper*)	£850
Z22	1s. green (1856)	£110
	a. Thick paper	£160

Z 3   Z 6

Z 4

Z 5

1859–84. *Stamps of GREAT BRITAIN cancelled "A 25" as in Types Z 3/7.*

Z23	½d. rose-red (1870–79) .. *From*	18·00
	Plate Nos. 4, 5, 6, 8, 9, 10, 11, 12, 13, 14, 15, 19, 20.	
Z24	1d. red-brown (1841), *imperf*	£2000
Z25	1d. red-brown (1854), *wmk* Small Crown, *perf* 16	£225
Z26	1d. red-brown (1855), *wmk* Large Crown, *perf* 14	55·00
Z27	1d. rose-red (1857), *wmk* Large Crown, *perf* 14	7·50
Z28	1d. rose-red (1861), Alphabet IV	£450
Z30	1d. rose-red (1864–79) .. *From*	12·00
	Plate Nos. 71, 72, 73, 74, 76, 78, 79, 80, 81, 82, 83, 84, 85, 86, 87, 88, 89, 90, 91, 92, 93, 94, 95, 96, 97, 98, 99, 100, 101, 102, 103, 104, 105, 106, 107, 108, 109, 110, 111, 112, 113, 114, 115, 116, 117, 118, 119, 120, 121, 122, 123, 124, 125, 127, 129, 130, 131, 132, 133, 134, 135, 136, 137, 138, 139, 140, 141, 142, 143, 144, 145, 146, 147, 148, 149, 150, 151, 152, 153, 154, 155, 156, 157, 158, 159, 160, 161, 162, 163, 164, 165, 166, 167, 168, 169, 170, 171, 172, 173, 174, 175, 176, 177, 178, 179, 180, 181, 182, 183, 184, 185, 186, 187, 188, 189, 190, 191, 192, 193, 194, 195, 196, 197, 198, 199, 200, 201, 202, 203, 204, 205, 206, 207, 208, 209, 210, 211, 212, 213, 214, 215, 216, 217, 218, 219, 220, 221, 222, 223, 224.	
Z31	1½d. lake-red (1870–79) (Plate Nos. 1, 3) .. *From*	£275
Z32	2d. blue (1841), *imperf*	£3500
Z33	2d. blue (1855) *wmk* Large Crown *perf* 14	55·00
Z34	2d. blue (1858–69).. .. *From*	15·00
	Plate Nos. 7, 8, 9, 12, 13, 14, 15.	
Z35	2½d. rosy mauve (1875) (blued *paper*) *From*	50·00
	Plate Nos. 1, 2.	
Z36	2½d. rosy mauve (1875–76) (Plate Nos. 1, 2, 3) *From*	27·00
Z37	2½d. rosy mauve (*Error of Lettering*)	£2250
Z38	2½d. rosy mauve (1876–79).. .. *From*	15·00
	Plate Nos. 3, 4, 5, 6, 7, 8, 9, 10, 11, 12, 13, 14, 15, 16, 17.	
Z39	2½d. blue (1880–81) (Plate Nos. 17, 18, 19, 20) *From*	9·00
Z40	2½d. blue (1881) (Plate Nos. 21, 22, 23) *From*	6·00
Z41	3d. carmine-rose (1862)	£100
Z42	3d. rose (1865) (Plate No. 4)	50·00
Z43	3d. rose (1867–73).. .. .. *From*	18·00
	Plate Nos. 4, 5, 6, 7, 8, 9, 10.	
Z44	3d. rose (1873–76).. .. *From*	22·00
	Plate Nos. 11, 12, 14, 15, 16, 17, 18, 19, 20.	
Z45	3d. rose (1881) (Plate Nos. 20, 21). .. *From*	£750
Z46	3d. on 3d. lilac (1883)	£450
Z47	4d. rose (or rose-carmine) (1857) ..	27·00
	a. Thick glazed paper	£110
Z48	4d. red (1862) (Plate Nos. 3, 4) *From*	30·00
Z49	4d. vermilion (1865–73) .. *From*	15·00
	Plate Nos. 7, 8, 9, 10, 11, 12, 13, 14.	
Z50	4d. vermilion (1876) (Plate No. 15)	£160
Z51	4d. sage-green (1877) (Plate Nos. 15, 16). *From*	85·00
Z52	4d. grey-brown (1880) *wmk* Large Garter Plate No. 17.	£120
Z53	4d. grey-brown (1880) *wmk* Crown *From* Plate Nos. 17, 18.	25·00
Z54	6d. violet (1854), embossed	£1500
Z55	6d. lilac (1856)	35·00
	a. Thick paper	
Z56	6d. lilac (1862) (Plate Nos. 3, 4) *From*	30·00
Z57	6d. lilac (1865–67) (Plate Nos. 5, 6) .. *From*	28·00
Z58	6d. lilac (1865–67) (*Wmk error*)	£1200
Z59	6d. lilac (1867) (Plate No. 6)	32·00
Z60	6d. violet (1867–70) (Plate Nos. 6, 8, 9) *From*	25·00
Z61	6d. buff (1872–73) (Plate Nos. 11, 12) *From*	£100
Z62	6d. chestnut (1872) (Plate No. 11)	30·00
Z63	6d. grey (1873) (Plate No. 12)	70·00
Z64	6d. grey (1873–80).. .. *From*	20·00
	Plate Nos. 13, 14, 15, 16, 17.	
Z65	6d. grey (1881–82) (Plate Nos. 17, 18) *From*	26·00
Z66	6d. on 6d. lilac (1883)	£110
Z67	8d. orange (1876)	£250
Z68	9d. straw (1862)	£475
Z69	9d. bistre (1862)	£475
Z70	9d. straw (1865)	£475
Z71	9d. straw (1867)	£600
Z72	10d. red-brown (1867)	£130
Z73	1s. (1847), embossed	£1500
Z74	1s. green (1856)	70·00
Z75	1s. green (1856) (thick *paper*)	£250
Z76	1s. green (1862)	60·00
Z77	1s. green ("K" *variety*)	£2250
Z78	1s. green (1865) (Plate No. 4)	35·00
Z79	1s. green (1867–73) (Plate Nos. 4, 5, 6, 7). *From*	10·00
Z80	1s. green (1873–77) .. *From*	30·00
	Plate Nos. 8, 9, 10, 11, 12, 13.	
Z81	1s. orange-brown (1880) (Plate No. 13)	£225
Z82	1s. orange-brown (1881) (Plate Nos. 13, 14) *From*	45·00
Z83	2s. blue (*shades*) (1867) .. *From*	90·00
Z84	2s. brown (1880)	£1700
Z85	5s. rose (1867–74) (Plate Nos. 1, 2) *From*	£300
Z86	5s. rose (1882) (Plate No. 4), blue *paper*..	£1100
Z87	5s. rose (1882) (Plate No. 4), white *paper*..	£1000
Z88	10s. grey-green (1878)	£1600

1880.

Z89	½d. deep green	8·50
Z90	½d. pale green	8·50
Z91	1d. Venetian red	7·50
Z92	1½d. Venetian red	£250
Z93	2d. pale rose	30·00
Z94	2d. deep rose	30·00
Z95	5d. indigo	50·00

1881.

Z96	1d. lilac (14 *dots*)	15·00
Z97	1d. lilac (16 *dots*)	6·00

1883–4.

Z 98–Z102	½d. slate-blue; 1½d., 2d, 2½d., 3d. *From*	8·50
Z103–Z107	4d. 5d., 6d., 9d., 1s. .. *From*	60·00
Z108	5s. rose (blued *paper*)	£1000
Z109	5s. rose (white *paper*)	£750

POSTAL FISCALS

Z110	1d. purple (1871) *wmk* Anchor	£750
Z111	1d. purple (1881) *wmk* Orb	£600

CROWN COLONY

PRINTERS. Nos. 1/156. Printed by De La Rue; typographed *except where otherwise stated.*

1

Type 1

The first Government local post was established on 10 June 1853 and, as an experiment, mail was carried free of charge. During 1859 the Council of Government decided that a rate of ½d. per ½ ounce should be charged for this service and stamps in Type I were ordered for this purpose. Both the new rate and the stamps were introduced on 1 December 1860. Until 1 January 1885 the ½d. stamps were intended for the local service only; mail for abroad being handled by the British Post Office on Malta, using G.B. stamps.

Specialists now recognise 29 printings in shades of yellow and one in green during the period to 1884. These printings can be linked to the changes in watermark and perforation as follows:

Ptg 1—Blued paper without wmk. P 14.
Ptgs 2 and 3—White paper without wmk. P 14.
Ptgs 4 to 9, 11, 13 to 19, 22 to 24—Crown CC wmk. P 14.
Ptg 10—Crown CC wmk. P 12½ (rough).
Ptg 12—Crown CC wmk. P 12½ (clean-cut).
Ptgs 20 and 21—Crown CC wmk. P 14 × 12½.
Ptgs 25 to 28, 30—Crown CA wmk. P 14.
Ptg 29—In green (No. 20).

1860 (1 Dec)–63. *No wmk. P 14. (a) Blued paper.*

1	½d. buff (1.12.60)	£850	£425

(b) Thin, hard white paper

2	½d. brown-orange (11.61)	£750	£325
3	½d. buff (1.63)	£550	£275
	a. Pale buff	£550	£275

No. 1 is printed in fugitive ink. It is known imperforate but was not issued in that state (*Price* £9000 *unused*).

The printing on No. 2 gives a very blurred and muddy impression; on Nos. 3/3a the impression is clear.

Specks of carmine can often be detected with a magnifying glass on Nos. 2/3a, and also on No. 4. Examples also exist on which parts of the design are in pure rose, due to defective mixing of the ink.

(Des E. Fuchs)

1863–81. *Wmk Crown CC. (a) P 14.*

4	½d. buff (6.63)	80·00	45·00
5	½d. bright orange (11.64)	£250	£100
6	½d. orange-brown (4.67)	£275	75·00
7	½d. dull orange (4.70)	£150	55·00
8	½d. orange-buff (5.72)	£130	55·00
9	½d. golden yellow (aniline) (10.74)	£250	£300
10	½d. yellow-buff (9.75)	60·00	55·00
11	½d. pale buff (3.77)	£120	55·00
12	½d. bright orange-yellow (4.80)	95·00	65·00
13	½d. yellow (4.81)	70·00	45·00

(b) P 12½ rough (No. 14) or clean-cut (No. 15)

14	½d. buff-brown (11.68)	80·00	70·00
	a. Imperf between (vert pair)		
15	½d. yellow-orange (5.71)	£225	£150

(c) P 14 × 12½

16	½d. yellow-buff (7.78)	£150	85·00
	a. Perf 12½ × 14		
17	½d. yellow (2.79)	£160	85·00

Examples of No. 4 from the 1863 printing are on thin, surfaced paper; later printings in the same shade were on unsurfaced paper. The ink used for No. 5 is mineral and, unlike that on No. 9, does not stain the paper.

Some variations of shade on No. 6 may be described as chestnut. The ink of No. 6 is clear and never muddy, although some examples are over-inked. Deeper shades of No. 4, with which examples of No. 6 might be confused, have muddy ink.

1882 (Mar)–84. *Wmk Crown CA. P* 14.
18	½d. orange-yellow	..	..	20·00	35·00
19	½d. red-orange (9.84)..	..	..	17·00	38·00

2

3

4

5

1885 (1 Jan)–90. *Wmk Crown CA. P* 14.
20	1	½d. green	..	..	1·25	35
21	2	1d. rose	..	..	70·00	25·00
22		1d. carmine (*shades*) (1890)	..	1·75	35
23	3	2d. grey	..	..	3·75	1·25
24	4	2½d. dull blue	..	..	30·00	1·25
25		2½d. bright blue	..	..	28·00	90
26		2½d. ultramarine	..	..	28·00	90
27	3	4d. brown	..	..	8·50	3·00
		a. Imperf (pair)	..	£3750	£4000
28		1s. violet	..	..	30·00	9·00
29		1s. pale violet (1890)	..	48·00	15·00
20/29			Set of 6	65·00	14·00
20/28	Optd "Specimen"		Set of 6	£2000	

Although not valid for postage until 1 January 1885 these stamps were available at the G.P.O., Valletta from 27 December 1884.

Three unused examples of the ½d. green, No. 20, are known line perforated 12. It is believed that these originated from proof books, the stamp not being issued for use with this perforation.

1886 (1 Jan). *Wmk Crown CC. P* 14.
30	5	5s. rose (Optd S. £450)	..	£110	80·00

6 Harbour of Valletta

7 Gozo Fishing Boat

8 Galley of Knights of St. John

9 Emblematic figure of Malta

10 Shipwreck of St. Paul

(T 6/10 recess)

1899 (4 Feb)–1901. *P* 14. (*a*) *Wmk Crown CA* (*sideways on* ¼d).
31	6	¼d. brown (4.1.01)	..	1·75	1·50
		a. Red-brown	..	90	40
32	7	4½d. sepia	..	..	11·00	8·50
33	8	5d. vermilion	..	..	25·00	13·00

(*b*) *Wmk Crown CC*
34	9	2s. 6d. olive-grey	..	35·00	12·00
35	10	10s. blue-black	..	75·00	60·00
31/5			Set of 5	£130	85·00
31/5	Optd "Specimen"		Set of 5	£225	

One Penny

(11)

12

1902 (4 July). *Nos. 24 and 25 surch locally at Govt Ptg Office with T* 11.
36	1d. on 2½d. dull blue (Optd S. £70)..		40	65
	a. Surch double	..	..	—	£3250
	b. "One Pnney" (R. 9/2)	..	28·00	50·00
	ba. Surch double, with "One Pnney"			
37	1d. on 2½d. bright blue	..	40	80
	a. "One Pnney" (R. 9/2)	..	30·00	50·00

(Des E. Fuchs)

1903 (12 Mar)–4. *Wmk Crown CA. P* 14.
38	12	½d. green	..	..	3·50	20
39		1d. black and red (7.5.03)	..	8·00	15
40		2d. purple and grey	..	14·00	6·00
41		2½d. maroon and blue (9.03)	..	13·00	2·00

42	12	3d. grey and purple (26.3.03)	..	80	50
43		4d. black and brown (19.5.04)	..	24·00	11·00
44		1s. grey and violet (6.4.03)	..	13·00	6·00
38/44			Set of 7	70·00	23·00
38/44	Optd "Specimen"		Set of 7	£130	

1904-14. *Wmk Mult Crown CA* (*sideways on* ¼d.). *P* 14.
45	6	¼d. red-brown (10.10.05)	..	75	15
		a. Deep brown (2.4.10*)	..	75	10
47	12	½d. green (6.11.04)	..	2·75	25
		a. Deep green (1909)	..	1·50	10
48		1d. black and red (24.4.05)	..	5·00	10
49		1d. red (2.4.07)	..	..	80	10
50		2d. purple and grey (22.2.05)	..	4·50	45
51		2d. grey (4.10.11)	..	1·25	3·25
52		2½d. maroon and blue (10.04)	..	10·00	40
53		2½d. bright blue (15.1.11)	..	4·00	1·25
54		4d. black and brown (1.4.06)	..	8·00	5·00
55		4d. black and red/yellow (21.11.11)	..	3·50	3·00
57	7	4½d. brown (27.2.05)	..	17·00	5·50
58		4½d. orange (2.8.12*)	..	3·00	3·25
59	8	5d. vermilion (20.2.05)	..	20·00	3·75
60		5d. pale sage-green (1909)	..	3·00	3·25
		a. Deep sage-green (1914)	..	9·50	14·00
61	12	1s. grey and violet (14.12.04)	..	45·00	1·75
62		1s. black/green (15.3.11)	..	6·00	2·00
63		5s. green and red/yellow (22.3.11)	..	60·00	65·00
45/63			Set of 17	£170	90·00
45a, 47a, 49, 51, 53, 55, 58, 60, 62,				
63 Optd "Specimen"			Set of 10	£300	

*These are the earliest known dates of use.

13

14

15

1914–21. *Wmk Mult Crown CA. Ordinary paper* (¼d. *to* 2½d., 2s. 6d.) *or chalk-surfaced paper* (*others*). *P* 14.
69	13	¼d. brown (2.1.14)	..	30	10
		a. Deep brown (1919)	..	30	30
71		½d. green (20.1.14)	..	1·25	10
		aa. Wmk sideways	..	† £3250	
		a. Deep green (1919)	..	60	15
73		1d. carmine-red (15.4.14)	..	60	10
		a. Scarlet (1915)	..	1·25	30
75		2d. grey (12.8.14)	..	4·50	2·50
		a. Deep slate (1919)	..	8·00	9·50
77		2½d. bright blue (11.3.14)	..	70	20
78	14	3d. purple/yellow (1.5.20)	..	2·50	5·00
		a. On orange-buff	..	18·00	32·00
79	6	4d. black (21.8.15)	..	10·00	2·50
		a. Grey-black (28.10.16)	..	18·00	7·50
80	13	6d. dull and bright purple (10.3.14)	..	7·00	11·00
		a. Dull purple and magenta (1918)	8·50	10·00
81	14	1s. black/green (*white back*) (2.1.14)	8·00	17·00
		a. On green, green back (Optd S. £45)		
		(1915)	..	10·00	13·00
		ab. Wmk sideways	..	† £1800	
		b. On blue-green, olive back (1918)	..	12·00	16·00
		c. On emerald surface (1920)	..	8·50	18·00
		d. On emerald back (1921)	..	22·00	30·00
86	15	2s. purple and bright blue/blue (15.4.14)	50·00	28·00
		a. Break in scroll	..	£190	
		b. Broken crown and scroll	..	£190	
		c. Dull purple and blue/blue (1921)	50·00	40·00
		ca. Break in scroll	..	£180	
		cb. Broken crown and scroll	..	£180	
87	9	2s. 6d. olive-grey (1919)	..	48·00	70·00
		a. Olive-grey (1920)	..	48·00	75·00
88	15	5s. green and red/yellow (21.3.17)	..	70·00	85·00
		a. Break in scroll	..	£275	
		b. Broken crown and scroll	..	£275	
69/88			Set of 12	£170	£190
69/88 (excl 87) Optd "Specimen"		Set of 11	£400	

The design of Nos. 79/a differs in various details from that of Type 6.

We have only seen one copy of No. 71aa; it is in used condition.

A 3d. purple on yellow on white back, Type 14, was prepared for use but not issued. It exists overprinted "Specimen" (*Price* £275).

For illustrations of the varieties on Nos. 86 and 88 see above No. 58 of Leeward Islands.

WAR TAX

(16)

17

18

(T 17 recess)

1917–18. *Optd with T* 16, *by De La Rue.*
92	13	½d. deep green (14.12.17*)	..	20	15
93	14	3d. grey and purple (15.2.18*)	..	1·75	6·50
92/3	Optd "Specimen"		Set of 2	£130	

*These are the earliest known dates of use.

1919 (6 Mar). *Wmk Mult Crown CA. P* 14.
96	17	10s. black (Optd S. £750)	..	£3000	£3500

Dark flaw on scroll (R. 2/4 1st state)   Lines omitted from scroll (R. 2/4 2nd state)

1921 (16 Feb)–22. *Wmk Mult Script CA. Chalk-surfaced paper* (6d., 2s.) *or ordinary paper* (*others*). *P* 14.
97	13	¼d. brown (12.1.22)	..	40	22·00
98		½d. green (19.1.22)	..	90	15·00
99		1d. scarlet (24.12.21)	..	40	65
100	18	2d. grey	..	..	2·50	80
101	13	2½d. bright blue (15.1.22)	..	2·75	17·00
102		6d. dull purple and brt purple (19.1.22)	25·00	48·00
103	15	2s. purple and blue/blue (19.1.22)	.60·00	£170
		a. Break in scroll	..	£200	
		b. Broken crown and scroll	..	£200	
		c. Dark flaw on scroll	..	£1500	
		d. Lines omitted from scroll	..	£275	
104	17	10s. black (19.1.22)	..	£300	£475
97/104			Set of 8	£350	£650
97/104 Optd "Specimen"		Set of 8	£400	

For illustrations of other varieties on No. 103 see above No. 58 of Leeward Islands.

(19)

(20)

1922 (12 Jan–Apr). *Optd with T* 19 *or T* 20 (*large stamps*), *at Govt Printing Office, Valletta.* (*a*) *On No. 35. Wmk Crown CC.*
105	10	10s. blue-black (R.)	..	£170	£275

(*b*) *On Nos. 71, 77, 78a, 80, 81d, 86c, 87a and 88. Wmk Mult Crown CA*
106	13	½d. green	..	..	20	45
107		2½d. bright blue	..	..	4·50	16·00
108	14	3d. purple/orange-buff	..	1·25	9·50
109	13	6d. dull and bright purple	..	1·25	9·50
110	14	1s. black/emerald	..	..	2·50	8·00
111	15	2s. dull purple and blue/blue (R.)	..	£200	£350
		a. Break in scroll	..	£550	
		b. Broken crown and scroll	..	£550	
112	9	2s. 6d. olive-grey	..	17·00	27·00
113	15	5s. green and red/yellow	..	50·00	75·00
		a. Break in scroll	..	£190	
		b. Broken crown and scroll	..	£190	
		c. Lines omitted from scroll	..	£225	
106/13			Set of 8	£250	£425

(*c*) *On Nos. 97/104. Wmk Mult Script CA*
114	13	¼d. brown	..	..	10	20
115		½d. green (29.4)	..	..	60	3·00
116		1d. scarlet	..	..	20	15
117	18	2d. grey	..	..	80	45
118	13	2½d. bright blue (15.1)	..	30	45
119		6d. dull and bright purple (19.4)	..	6·00	16·00
120	15	2s. purple and blue/blue (R.) (25.1)	.35·00	70·00
		a. Break in scroll	..	£140	
		b. Broken crown and scroll	..	£140	
		c. Lines omitted from scroll	..	£180	
121	17	10s. black (R.) (9.3)	..	£100	£150
114/21		..	..	Set of 8	£130	£200

One Farthing

(21)

22

23

1922 (15 Apr). *No. 100 surch with T* 21, *at Govt Printing Office, Valletta.*
122	18	¼d. on 2d. grey..	..	..	15	25

(Des C. Dingli (T 22) and G. Vella (23))

1922 (1 Aug)–26. *Wmk Mult Script CA* (*sideways on T* 22, *except No.* 140). *P* 14. (*a*) *Typo. Chalk-surfaced paper.*
123	22	¼d. brown (22.8.22)	..	40	45
		a. Chocolate-brown	..	30	15
124		½d. green	..	..	65	10
125		1d. orange and purple	..	1·25	15
126		1d. bright violet (25.4.24)	..	1·00	35
127		1½d. brown-red (1.10.23)	..	1·00	10
128		2d. bistre-brown and turquoise (28.8.22)	75	20
129		2½d. ultramarine (16.2.26)	..	1·00	4·50
130		3d. cobalt (28.8.22)	..	1·75	50
		a. Bright ultramarine	..	1·75	50
131		3d. black/yellow (16.2.26)	..	1·00	6·50

132	22	4d. yellow and bright blue (28.8.22)	..		1·25	1·60
133		6d. olive-green and reddish violet	..		1·75	1·25
134	23	1s. indigo and sepia	..	..	3·75	2·50
135		2s. brown and blue	..	..	5·50	8·50
136		2s. 6d. brt magenta & black (28.8.22)			7·00	8·50
137		5s. orange-yell & brt ultram (28.8.22)			15·00	25·00
138		10s. slate-grey and brown (28.8.22)			48·00	85·00

(b) Recess

139	22	£1 black and carmine-red (28.8.22)	..		£100	£200
140		£1 black and bright carmine (14.5.25)			£100	£200
123/39				Set of 17	£160	£300
123/39 Optd "Specimen"			Set of 17	£450	

No. 139 has the watermark sideways and No. 140 has it upright.

Two pence halfpenny   POSTAGE

(24)   (25)

1925. *Surch with T 24, at Govt Printing Office, Valletta.*

141	22	2½d. on 3d. cobalt (3 Dec)	..		30	1·00
142		2½d. on 3d. bright ultramarine (9 Dec)			40	1·00

1926 (1 April). *Optd with T 25, at Govt Printing Office, Valletta.*

143	22	¼d. brown	..	..	15	80
144		½d. green	..	..	15	15
145		1d. bright violet	..	..	40	25
146		1½d. brown-red	..	..	45	25
147		2d. bistre-brown and turquoise			30	20
148		2½d. ultramarine	..	..	55	40
149		3d. black/*yellow*	..	..	30	50
		a. Opt inverted	..	..	£190	£475
150		4d. yellow and bright blue	..		3·00	7·50
151		6d. olive-green and violet	..		1·50	1·40
152	23	1s. indigo and sepia	..	..	4·50	7·00
153		2s. brown and blue	..	..	35·00	85·00
154		2s. 6d. bright magenta and black			9·00	24·00
155		5s. orange-yellow & brt ultramarine			8·00	26·00
156		10s. slate-grey and brown	..		6·00	14·00
143/156				Set of 14	60·00	£150

26   27 Valletta Harbour

28 St. Publius   33 St. Paul

(T 26 typo, others recess Waterlow)

1926 (6 Apr)–**27.** *T 26/8, 33 and similar designs. Inscr "POSTAGE". Wmk Mult Script CA. P 15 × 14 (T 26) or 12½ (others).*

157	26	¼d. brown	..	..	30	15
158		½d. yellow-green (5.8.26)	..		30	15
159		1d. rose-red (1.4.27)	..		50	40
160		1½d. chestnut (7.10.26)	..		60	10
161		2d. greenish grey (1.4.27)	..		2·25	5·50
162		2½d. blue (1.4.27)	..		2·50	20
162a		3d. violet (1.4.27)	..		2·75	1·50
163		4d. black and red	..		2·75	7·00
164		4½d. lavender and ochre	..		2·50	2·50
165		6d. violet and scarlet (5.5.26)	..		2·50	2·00
166	27	1s. black	..	..	4·25	2·25
167	28	1s. 6d. black and green	..		5·00	9·00
168	–	2s. black and purple	..		5·50	13·00
169	–	2s. 6d. black and vermilion	..		10·00	29·00
170	–	3s. black and blue	..		13·00	26·00
171	–	5s. black and green (5.5.26)	..		20·00	42·00
172	33	10s. black and carmine (9.2.27)			55·00	90·00
157/72				Set of 17	£110	£200
157/72 Optd "Specimen"			Set of 17	£275	

Designs: *Vert*—2s. 6d. Gozo fishing boat; 3s. Neptune; *Horiz*—2s. Mdina (Notabile); 5s. Neolithic temple, Mnajdra.

POSTAGE

AIR MAIL	POSTAGE AND REVENUE	POSTAGE AND REVENUE.
(34)	(35)	(36)

1928 (1 Apr). *Air. Optd with T 34.*

173	26	6d. violet and scarlet	..		1·75	1·25

1928 (1 Oct–5 Dec). *As Nos. 157/72, optd.*

174	35	¼d. brown	..	..	40	10
175		½d. yellow-green	..		40	10
176		1d. rose-red	..	..	1·50	1·50
177		1d. chestnut (5.12.28)	..		2·50	10
178		1½d. chestnut	..	..	1·25	30
179		1½d. rose-red (5.12.28)	..		3·00	10
180		2d. greenish grey	..		3·25	8·00
181		2½d. blue	..	..	1·25	10
182		3d. violet	..	..	1·25	30
183		4d. black and red	..		1·25	1·00

184	35	4½d. lavender and ochre	..		2·25	1·50
185		6d. violet and scarlet	..		2·25	1·00
186	36	1s. black (R.)	..		2·25	2·00
187		1s. 6d. black and green (R.)			5·00	9·00
188		2s. black and purple (R.)	..		17·00	32·00
189		2s. 6d. black and vermilion (R.)			13·00	23·00
190		3s. black and blue (R.)	..		18·00	30·00
191		5s. black and green (R.)	..		26·00	60·00
192		10s. black and carmine (R.)	..		50·00	85·00
174/92				Set of 19	£120	£225
174/92 Optd "Specimen"			Set of 19	£300	

1930 (20 Oct). *As Nos. 157/172, but inscr "POSTAGE (&) REVENUE".*

193		¼d. brown	..	..	40	10
194		½d. yellow-green	..		40	10
195		1d. chestnut	..	..	40	10
196		1½d. rose-red	..		60	10
197		2d. greenish grey	..		90	20
198		2½d. blue	..	..	1·75	10
199		3d. violet	..	..	1·50	10
200		4d. black and red	..		1·25	2·25
201		4½d. lavender and ochre	..		2·00	1·50
202		6d. violet and scarlet	..		1·25	75
203		1s. black	..	..	4·00	8·00
204		1s. 6d. black and green	..		5·00	13·00
205		2s. black and purple	..		6·50	15·00
206		2s. 6d. black and vermilion			13·00	38·00
207		3s. black and blue	..		20·00	48·00
208		5s. black and green	..		25·00	55·00
209		10s. black and carmine	..		60·00	95·00
193/209				Set of 17	£130	£250
193/209 Perf "Specimen"			Set of 17	£275	

1935 (6 May). *Silver Jubilee. As Nos. 114/17 of Jamaica.*

210		½d. black and green	..		40	50
		a. Extra flagstaff	..		25·00	
		b. Short extra flagstaff			30·00	
		c. Lightning conductor	..		28·00	
211		2½d. brown and deep blue	..		2·50	2·75
		a. Extra flagstaff	..		£130	
		b. Short extra flagstaff			£130	
		c. Lightning conductor	..		£100	
212		6d. light blue and olive-green			5·00	3·25
		a. Extra flagstaff	..		£180	
		b. Short extra flagstaff			£160	
		c. Lightning conductor	..		£130	
213		1s. slate and purple	..		8·50	11·00
		a. Extra flagstaff	..		£425	
		b. Short extra flagstaff			£350	
		c. Lightning conductor	..		£250	
210/13				Set of 4	15·00	16·00
210/13 Perf "Specimen"			Set of 4	£130	

For illustrations of plate varieties see Omnibus section following Zimbabwe.

Sheets from the second printing of the ½d., 6d. and 1s. in November 1935 had the extra flagstaff partially erased from the stamp with a sharp point.

37 Grand Harbour, Valletta   38 H.M.S. *St. Angelo*

1937 (12 May). *Coronation. As Nos. 118/20 of Jamaica.*

214		½d. green	..	..	10	10
215		1½d. scarlet	..	..	50	15
		a. Brown-lake	..		£425	£450
216		2½d. bright blue	..		50	35
214/16				Set of 3	1·00	50
214/16 Perf "Specimen"			Set of 3	60·00	

39 Verdala Palace   40 Hypogeum, Hal Saflieni

Broken cross (Right pane R. 5/7)   Damaged value tablet (R. 4/9)

Semaphore flaw (R. 2/7)

(Recess Waterlow)

1938 (17 Feb*)–**43.** *T 37/40 and similar designs. Wmk Mult Script CA (sideways on No. 217). P 12½.*

217	37	¼d. brown	..	..	10	10
218	38	½d. green	..	..	40	10
218a		½d. red-brown (8.3.43)	..		30	10
219	39	1d. red-brown	..	..	3·75	20
219a		1d. green (8.3.43)	..		30	10
220	40	1½d. scarlet	..	..	40	15
		a. Broken cross	..		20·00	
220b		1½d. slate-black (8.3.43)	..		30	15
		ba. Broken cross	..		20·00	
221	–	2d. slate-black	..		30	70
221a	–	2d. scarlet (8.3.43)	..		40	10
222	–	2½d. greyish blue	..		30	30
222a	–	2½d. dull violet (8.3.43)	..		60	10
223	–	3d. dull violet	..		30	60
223a	–	3d. blue (8.3.43)	..		30	10
224	–	4½d. olive-green and yellow-brown			50	10
225	–	6d. olive-green and scarlet	..		50	15
226	–	1s. black	..	..	50	30
227	–	1s. 6d. black and olive-green	..		5·50	3·50
228	–	2s. green and deep blue	..		3·25	2·75
229	–	2s. 6d. black and scarlet	..		6·50	4·50
		a. Damaged value tablet	..		85·00	
230	–	5s. black and green	..		6·50	5·50
		a. Semaphore flaw	..		55·00	
231	–	10s. black and carmine	..		14·00	14·00
217/231				Set of 21	38·00	30·00
217/31 Perf "Specimen"			Set of 21	£350	

Designs: *Horiz* (as *T 39*)—2d. Victoria and citadel, Gozo; 2½d. De l'Isle Adam entering Mdina; 4½d. Ruins at Mnajdra; 1s. 6d. St. Publius; 2s. Mdina Cathedral; 2s. 6d. Statue of Neptune, *Vert* (as *T 40*)—3d. St. John's Co-Cathedral; 6d. Statue of Manoel de Vilhena; 1s. Maltese girl wearing faldetta; 5s. Palace Square, Valletta; 10s. St. Paul.

*This is the local date of issue but the stamps were released in London on 15 February.

1946 (3 Dec). *Victory. As Nos. 141/2 of Jamaica, but inscr "MALTA" between Maltese Cross and George Cross.*

232		1d. green	..	..	10	10
233		3d. blue	..	..	10	10
232/3 Perf "Specimen"			Set of 2	50·00	

SELF-GOVERNMENT

(52)   "NT" joined (R. 4/10)

Halation flaw (Pl 2 R. 2/5) (ptg of 8 Jan 1953)   Cracked plate (Pl 2 R. 5/1) (ptg of 8 Jan 1953)

(Optd by Waterlow)

1948 (25 Nov)–**53.** *New Constitution. As Nos. 217/31 but optd as T 52; reading up on ½d. and 5s., down on other values, and smaller on ¼d. value.*

234	37	¼d. brown	..	..	10	20
235	38	½d. red-brown	..		15	10
		a. "NT" joined	..		7·00	
236	39	1d. green	..	..	15	10
236a		1d. grey (R.) (8.1.53)	..		10	10
237	40	1½d. blue-black (R.)	..		40	10
		a. Broken cross	..		20·00	
237b		1½d. green (8.1.53)	..		10	10
		ba. Albino opt	..		†£10000	
238	–	2d. scarlet	..		40	10
238a	–	2d. yellow-ochre (8.1.53)	..		10	10
		ab. Halation flaw	..		65·00	
		ac. Cracked plate	..		75·00	
239	–	2½d. dull violet	..		60	10
239a	–	2½d. scarlet-vermilion (8.1.53)			30	65
240	–	3d. blue (R.)	..		30	15
240a	–	3d. dull violet (R.) (8.1.53)			35	10
241	–	4½d. olive-green and yellow-brown			1·50	1·50
241a	–	4½d. olive-green & dp ultram (R.) (8.1.53)			50	90

242	–	6d. olive-green and scarlet ..	..	50	15
243	–	1s. black ..	..	1·40	40
244	–	1s. 6d. black and olive-green ..		2·50	45
245	–	2s. green and deep blue (R.) ..	..	4·00	1·50
246	–	2s. 6d. black and scarlet ..	..	10·00	2·50
		a. Damaged value tablet ..	..	£110	
247	–	5s. black and green (R.) ..	..	16·00	5·50
		a. "NT" joined ..	..	£120	
248	–	10s. black and carmine ..	..	17·00	16·00
234/48			Set of 21	50·00	27·00

1949 (4 Jan). *Royal Silver Wedding. As Nos. 143/4 of Jamaica, but inscr "MALTA" between Maltese Cross and George Cross and with £1 ptd in recess.*

249		1d. green ..	..	45	10
250		£1 indigo ..	..	40·00	35·00

1949 (10 Oct). *75th Anniv of U.P.U. As Nos. 145/8 of Jamaica, but inscr "MALTA" in recess.*

251		2½d. violet ..	..	30	10
252		3d. deep blue ..	..	1·75	40
253		6d. carmine-red ..	..	1·75	40
254		1s. blue-black ..	..	1·75	1·50
251/4 ..			Set of 4	5·00	2·25

53 Queen Elizabeth II when Princess

54 "Our Lady of Mount Carmel" (attrib Palladino)

(T **53/4**. Recess B.W.)

1950 (1 Dec). *Visit of Princess Elizabeth to Malta. Wmk Mult Script CA. P 12 × 11½.*

255	**53**	1d. green ..	..	10	10
256		3d. blue ..	..	20	10
257		1s. black ..	..	55	45
255/7 ..			Set of 3	70	55

1951 (12 July). *Seventh Centenary of the Scapular. Wmk Mult Script CA. P 12 × 11½.*

258	**54**	1d. green ..	..	10	10
259		3d. violet ..	..	15	10
260		1s. black ..	..	40	40
258/60 ..			Set of 3	60	50

1953 (3 June). *Coronation. As No. 153 of Jamaica.*

261		1½d. black and deep yellow-green ..		30	10

55 St. John's Co-Cathedral

56 "Immaculate Conception" (Caruana) (altar-piece, Cospicua)

(Recess Waterlow)

1954 (3 May). *Royal Visit. Wmk Mult Script CA. P 12½.*

262	**55**	3d. violet ..	..	15	10

(Photo Harrison)

1954 (8 Sept). *Centenary of Dogma of the Immaculate Conception. Wmk Mult Script CA. Chalk-surfaced paper. P 14½ × 14.*

263	**56**	1½d. emerald ..	..	10	10
264		3d. bright blue ..	..	10	10
265		1s. grey-black ..	..	20	20
263/5 ..			Set of 3	30	30

57 Monument of the Great Siege, 1565

62 Auberge de Castile

(Recess Waterlow (2s. 6d. to £1). B.W. (others))

1956 (23 Jan).—**58**. *T **57**, **62** and similar designs. Wmk Mult Script CA. P 14×13½ (2s. 6d. to £1) or 11½ (others).*

266		¼d. violet ..		10	10
267		½d. orange ..	..	30	10
268		1d. black (9.2.56) ..	..	60	10
269		1½d. bluish green (9.2.56) ..		30	10
270		2d. brown (9.2.56) ..	..	60	10
		a. Deep brown (26.2.58) ..		50	10
271		2½d. orange-brown ..	..	30	30
272		3d. rose-red (22.3.56) ..	..	40	10

273		4½d. deep blue ..	..	50	20
274		6d. indigo (9.2.56) ..	..	30	10
275		8d. bistre-brown ..	..	1·00	1·00
276		1s. deep reddish violet ..		35	10
277		1s. 6d. deep turquoise-green ..		4·25	20
278		2s. olive-green ..	..	5·00	80
279		2s. 6d. chestnut (22.3.56) ..		5·50	2·25
280		5s. green (11.10.56) ..	..	9·00	2·75
281		10s. carmine-red (19.11.56) ..		35·00	8·00
282		£1 yellow-brown (5.1.57) ..		35·00	20·00
266/82 ..			Set of 17	85·00	32·00

Designs:—*Vert*—½d. Wignacourt aqueduct horsetrough; 1d. Victory church; 1½d. War memorial; 2d. Mosta dome; 3d. The King's scroll; 4½d. Roosevelt's scroll; 8d. Vedette; 1s. Mdina gate; 1s. 6d. "Les Gavroches" (statue); 2s. Monument of Christ the King; 2s. 6d. Grand Master Cottoner's monument; 5s. Grand Master Perellos's monument; 10s. St. Paul; £1 Baptism of Christ. *Horiz*—6d. Neolithic Temples at Tarxien.

See also Nos. 314/15.

74 "Defence of Malta"

75 Searchlights over Malta

(Des E. Cremona. Photo Harrison)

1957 (15 Apr). *George Cross Commemoration. Cross in silver. T **74/5** and similar design. Wmk Mult Script CA. P 14½ × 14 (3d.) or 14 × 14½ (others).*

283		1½d. deep dull green ..		15	10
284		3d. vermilion ..	..	15	10
285		1s. reddish brown ..	..	15	10
283/5 ..			Set of 3	40	20

Design: *Vert*—1s. Bombed buildings.

77 "Design"

(Des E. Cremona. Photo Harrison)

1958 (15 Feb). *Technical Education in Malta. T **77** and similar designs. W w **12**. P 14 × 14½ (3d.) or 14½ × 14 (others).*

286		1½d. black and deep green ..		10	10
287		3d. black, scarlet and grey ..		10	10
288		1s. grey, bright purple and black ..		15	10
286/8 ..			Set of 3	30	15

Designs: *Vert*—3d. "Construction". *Horiz*—1s. Technical School, Paola.

80 Bombed-out Family

81 Sea Raid on Grand Harbour, Valletta

(Des E. Cremona. Photo Harrison)

1958 (15 Apr). *George Cross Commemoration. Cross in first colour, outlined in silver. T **80/1** and similar design. W w **12**. P 14 × 14½ (3d.) or 14½ × 14 (others).*

289		1½d. blue-green and black ..		10	10
290		3d. red and black ..	..	10	10
291		1s. reddish violet and black ..		15	10
		a. Silver (outline) omitted	..	£250	
289/91 ..			Set of 3	30	15

Design: *Horiz*—1s. Searchlight crew.

83 Air Raid Casualties

84 "For Gallantry"

(Des E. Cremona. Photo Harrison)

1959 (15 Apr). *George Cross Commemoration. T **83/4** and similar design. W w **12**. P 14½ × 14 (3d.) or 14 × 14½ (others).*

292		1½d. grey-green, black and gold ..		15	10
293		3d. reddish violet, black and gold ..		15	10
294		1s. blue-grey, black and gold ..		55	55
292/4 ..			Set of 3	75	55

Design: *Vert*—1s. Maltese under bombardment.

86 Shipwreck of St. Paul   **87** Statue of St. Paul, Rabat, Malta (after Palombi)

(Des E. Cremona. Photo Harrison)

1960 (9 Feb). *19th Centenary of the Shipwreck of St. Paul. T **86/7** and similar designs. W w **12**. P 13 (1½d., 3d., 6d.) or 14 × 14½ (others).*

295		1½d. blue, gold and yellow-brown ..		15	10
		a. Gold (dates and crosses) omitted	..	55·00	
296		3d. bright purple, gold and blue ..		15	10
297		6d. carmine, gold and pale grey ..		25	10
298		8d. black and gold ..	..	30	40
299		1s. maroon and gold ..	..	25	10
300		2s. 6d. blue, deep bluish green and gold ..		1·00	1·50
		a. Gold omitted		£300	
295/300			Set of 6	1·90	1·90

Designs: *Vert as T* **86**—3d. Consecration of St. Publius (first Bishop of Malta) (after Palombi); 6d. Departure of St. Paul (after Palombi). *Diamond shaped as T* **87**—1s. Angel with *Acts of the Apostles*; 2s. 6d. St. Paul with *Second Epistle to the Corinthians*.

92 Stamp of 1860

(Centre litho; frame recess. Waterlow)

1960 (1 Dec). *Stamp Centenary. W w **12**. P 13½.*

301	**92**	1½d. buff, pale blue and green ..		25	10
		a. Buff, pale bl & myrtle (white paper)		3·00	1·50
302		3d. buff, pale blue and deep carmine		30	10
		a. Blank corner ..	..	£100	
303		6d. buff, pale blue and ultramarine ..		40	25
301/3 ..			Set of 3	85	40

No. 302a shows the right-hand bottom corner of the 1860 stamp blank. It occurs on R. 4/7 from early trial plates and sheets containing the error should have been destroyed, but some were sorted into good stock and issued at a post office.

93 George Cross

(Photo Harrison)

1961 (15 Apr). *George Cross Commemoration. T **93** and similar designs showing medal. W w **12**. P 15 × 14.*

304		1½d. black, cream and bistre ..		15	10
305		3d. olive-brown and greenish blue. ..		30	10
306		1s. olive-green, lilac & dp reddish violet ..		60	70
304/6 ..			Set of 3	95	75

96 "Madonna Damascena"

(Photo Harrison)

1962 (7 Sept). *Great Siege Commemoration. T **96** and similar vert designs. W w **12**. P 13 × 12.*

307		2d. bright blue ..	..	10	10
308		3d. red ..	..	10	10
309		6d. bronze-green ..	..	10	10
310		1s. brown-purple ..	..	15	20
307/10 ..			Set of 4	30	30

Designs:—3d. Great Siege Monument; 6d. Grand Master La Valette; 1s. Assault on Fort St. Elmo.

1963 (4 June). *Freedom from Hunger. As No. 80 of Lesotho.*

311		1s. 6d. sepia ..	..	4·50	2·75

1963 (2 Sept). *Red Cross Centenary. As Nos. 203/4 of Jamaica.*

312		2d. red and black ..	..	25	15
313		1s. 6d. red and blue ..	..	3·75	3·75

1963 (15 Oct)–**64.** *As Nos. 268 and 270, but wmk w* **12.**

314	**59**	1d. black	..	40	30
315	**61**	2d. deep brown (11.7.64*)	..	1·50	2·25

*This is the earliest known date recorded in Malta.

100 Bruce, Zammit and Microscope   101 Goat and Laboratory Equipment

(Des E. Cremona. Photo Harrison)

1964 (14 April). *Anti-Brucellosis Congress.* W w **12.** *P* 14.

316	**100**	2d. light brown, black and bluish green		10	10
		a. Black (microscope, etc) omitted		£250	
317	**101**	1s. 6d. black and maroon		55	20

102 "Nicola Cotoner tending Sick Man" (M. Preti)

105 Maltese Cross (*Upright*)

In this illustration the points of the crosses meet in a vertical line. When the watermark is sideways they meet in a horizontal line.

(Des E. Cremona. Photo Harrison)

1964 (5 Sept). *First European Catholic Doctors' Congress, Vienna.* T **102** *and similar horiz designs.* W **105** (*sideways*). *P* 13½ × 11½.

318	**102**	2d. red, black, gold and grey-blue	..	20	10
319		6d. red, black, gold and bistre	..	45	15
320		1s. 6d. red, black, gold and reddish violet	..	85	85
318/20		.. ..	*Set of* 3	1·40	1·00

Designs:—6d. St. Luke and Hospital; 1s. 6d. Sacra Infermeria, Valletta.

INDEPENDENT

106 Dove and British Crown   109 "The Nativity"

(Des E. Cremona. Photo Harrison)

1964 (21 Sept). *Independence.* T **106** *and similar vert designs.* W **105.** *P* 14½ × 13½.

321		2d. olive-brown, red and gold	..	30	10
		a. Gold omitted	..	70·00	
322		3d. brown-purple, red and gold	..	30	10
		a. Gold omitted	..	70·00	
323		6d. slate, red and gold	..	90	15
324		1s. blue, red and gold	..	90	15
325		1s. 6d. indigo, red and gold	..	2·50	1·50
326		2s. 6d. deep violet-blue, red and gold		2·50	2·75
321/6		.. ..	*Set of* 6	6·50	4·00

Designs:—2d., 1s. Type **106**; 3d., 1s. 6d. Dove and Pope's Tiara; 6d., 2s. 6d. Dove and U.N. emblem.

(Des E. Cremona. Photo D.L.R.)

1964 (3 Nov). *Christmas.* W **105** (*sideways*). *P* 13 × 13½.

327	**109**	2d. bright purple and gold	..	10	10
328		4d. bright blue and gold	..	20	15
329		8d. deep bluish green and gold	..	45	45
327/9		.. ..	*Set of* 3	65	60

110 Neolithic Era   117 Galleys of Knights of St. John

119 British Rule

(Des E. Cremona. Photo Harrison)

1965 (7 Jan)–**70.** *Chalk-surfaced paper.* T **110, 117, 119** *and similar designs.* W **105.** *P* 14 × 14½ (*vert*) or 14½ (*horiz*).

330		½d. multicoloured	..	10	10
		a. "½d" (white) printed twice†	..	10·00	
		b. White (face value) omitted	..	38·00	
331		1d. multicoloured	..	10	10
		a. Gold (ancient lettering) omitted	..	48·00	
		b. White (Greek lettering and "PUNIC") omitted	..	48·00	
		d. "PUNIC" omitted	..	80·00	
332		1½d. multicoloured	..	10	10
333		2d. multicoloured	..	10	10
		a. Gold omitted	..	28·00	
		b. Imperf (pair)	..	£275	
334		2½d. multicoloured	..	30	10
		a. Orange omitted*	..	55·00	
		b. Gold ("SARACENIC") omitted	..	50·00	
		c. Salmon printed twice†	..	50·00	
335		3d. multicoloured	..	10	10
		a. Gold (windows) omitted	..	65·00	
		b. "MALTA" (silver) omitted	..	32·00	
		c. "MALTA" (silver) printed twice			
		d. Bright lilac ("SICULO NORMAN") omitted	..		
		e. Imperf (pair)	..	£300	
336		4d. multicoloured	..	30	10
		a. "KNIGHTS OF MALTA" (silver) omitted	..	48·00	
		b. "MALTA" (silver) omitted	..	40·00	
		c. Black (shield surround) omitted	..	48·00	
		d. Imperf (pair)	..	£300	
337		4½d. multicoloured	..	40	40
		a. Silver ("MALTA", etc) omitted	..	£275	
337b		5d. multicoloured (1.8.70)	..	30	20
		ba. "FORTIFICATIONS" (gold) omitted		65·00	
338		6d. multicoloured	..	20	10
		a. "MALTA" (silver) omitted	..	42·00	
		b. Black omitted	..	60·00	
339		8d. multicoloured	..	20	10
		a. Gold (centre) omitted	..	32·00	
		b. Gold (frame) omitted	..	55·00	
339c		10d. multicoloured (1.8.70)	..	45	1·25
		ca. "NAVAL ARSENAL" (gold) omitted	..	75·00	
340		1s. multicoloured	..	30	10
		a. Gold (centre) omitted	..	80·00	
		b. Gold (framework) omitted	..	38·00	
341		1s. 3d. multicoloured	..	1·75	1·40
		a. Gold (centre) omitted	..	50·00	
		b. Gold (framework) omitted	..	80·00	
		c. Imperf (pair)	..	£350	
342		1s. 6d. multicoloured	..	60	10
		a. Head (black) omitted	..	£225	
		b. Gold (centre) omitted	..	38·00	
		c. Gold (framet) omitted	..	55·00	
343		2s. multicoloured	..	70	10
		a. Gold (centre) omitted	..	70·00	
		b. Gold (framework) omitted	..	42·00	
344		2s. 6d. multicoloured	..	70	50
345		3s. multicoloured	..	1·25	75
		a. Gold (framework) omitted	..	30·00	
346		5s. multicoloured	..	5·00	1·00
		a. Gold (HAFMED emblem) omitted	..	75·00	
		b. Gold (framework) omitted	..	60·00	
347		10s. multicoloured	..	3·50	3·00
		a. Gold (centre) omitted	..	80·00	
348		£1 multicoloured	..	3·75	5·00
		a. Pink omitted	..	26·00	
330/48		.. .. ..	*Set of* 21	18·00	12·50

Designs: *Vert*—1d. Punic era; 1½d. Roman era; 2d. Proto Christian era; 2½d. Saracenic era; 3d. Siculo Norman era; 4d. Knights of Malta; 5d. Fortifications; 6d. French occupation. *Horiz*—10d. Naval arsenal; 1s. Maltese corps of the British army; 1s. 3d. International Eucharistic congress, 1913; 1s. 6d. Self-government, 1921; 2s. Gozo civic council; 2s. 6d. State of Malta; 3s. Independence, 1964; 5s. HAFMED (Allied forces, Mediterranean); 10s. The Maltese Islands (map); £1 Patron saints.

*The effect of this is to leave the Saracenic pattern as a pink colour.

†On the ½d. the second impression is 6½ mm lower or 3 mm to the left, and on the 2½d. 1 mm lower so that it falls partly across "MALTA" and "2½d". Stamps with almost coincidental double impression are common.

The ½d. and 1d. had white printing plates. Two silver plates were used on the 4d., one for "KNIGHTS OF MALTA" and the other for "MALTA". Two gold plates were used for the 8d. to 10s., one for the framework and the other for the gold in the central part of the designs.

No. 337a comes from a sheet on which the silver printing was so misplaced that it missed the top horizontal row entirely.

The ½d. to 4d., 1s. and 1s. 6d. to 5s. values exist with PVA gum as well as gum arabic and the 5d. and 10d. have PVA gum only.

129 "Dante" (Raphael)

(Des E. Cremona. Photo Govt Ptg Works, Rome)

1965 (7 July). *700th Birth Anniv of Dante.* P 14.

349	**129**	2d. indigo		10	10
350		6d. bronze-green		15	10
351		2s. chocolate		50	70
349/51		.. ..	*Set of* 3	65	70

130 Turkish Camp   131 Turkish Fleet

(Des E. Cremona. Photo Harrison)

1965 (1 Sept). *400th Anniv of Great Siege.* T **130/1** *and similar designs.* W **105** (*sideways*). *P* 13 (6d., 1s.) or 14½ × 14 (*others*).

352		2d. olive-green, red and black		25	10
353		3d. olive-green, red, black and light drab		25	10
354		6d. multicoloured		50	10
		a. Gold (framework and dates) omitted	..	£180	
		b. Black (on hulls) omitted	..	£180	
355		8d. red, gold, indigo and blue		75	75
356		1s. red, gold and deep grey-blue	..	55	10
357		1s. 6d. ochre, red and black	..	1·00	30
358		2s. 6d. sepia, black, red and yellow-olive	..	1·75	2·00
352/8		.. ..	*Set of* 7	4·50	2·75

Designs: *Square* (as T **130**)—3d. Battle scene; 8d. Arrival of relief force; 1s. 6d. "Allegory of Victory" (from mural by M. Preti); 2s. 6d. Victory medal. *Vert* (as T **131**)—1s. Grand Master J. de La Valette's arms.

137 "The Three Kings"   138 Sir Winston Churchill

(Des E. Cremona. Photo Enschedé)

1965 (7 Oct). *Christmas.* W **105** (*sideways*). *P* 11 × 11½.

359	**137**	1s. slate-purple and red	..	10	10
360		4d. slate-purple and blue	..	30	25
361		1s. 3d. slate-purple and bright purple		30	30
359/61		.. ..	*Set of* 3	60	50

(Des E. Cremona. Photo Harrison)

1966 (24 Jan). *Churchill Commemoration.* T **138** *and similar square design.* W **105** (*sideways*). *P* 14½ × 14.

362	**138**	2d. black, red and gold	..	15	10
363	—	3d. bronze-green, yellow-olive and gold		15	10
364	**138**	1s. maroon, red and gold	..	20	10
		a. Gold (shading) omitted	..	£250	
365	—	1s. 6d. chalky blue, violet-blue and gold		35	40
362/5		.. ..	*Set of* 4	75	55

Design:—3d., 1s. 6d. Sir Winston Churchill and George Cross.

140 Grand Master La Valette   145 President Kennedy and Memorial

(Des E. Cremona. Photo State Ptg Works, Vienna)

1966 (28 Mar). *400th Anniv of Valletta.* T **140** *and similar square designs. Multicoloured.* W **105** (*sideways*). *P* 12.

366	**140**	2d. Type **140**	..	10	10
367		3d. Pope Pius V	..	10	10
		a. Gold omitted	..	£275	
368		6d. Map of Valletta	..	10	10
369		1s. Francesco Laparelli (architect)	..	10	10
370		2s. 6d. Girolamo Cassar (architect)	..	20	30
366/70		.. ..	*Set of* 5	40	45

(Des E. Cremona. Photo Harrison)

1966 (28 May). *President Kennedy Commemoration.* W **105** (*sideways*). *P* 15 × 14.
371 **145** 3d. olive, gold and black 10 10
    a. Gold inscr omitted .. £225
372 1s. 6d. Prussian blue, gold and black 10 10

146 "Trade"

(Des E. Cremona. Photo D.L.R.)

1966 (16 June). *Tenth Malta Trade Fair.* W **105** (*sideways*). *P* 13½.
373 **146** 2d. multicoloured 10 10
374 8d. multicoloured 20 25
375 2s. 6d. multicoloured 20 25
373/5 .. .. .. *Set of 3* 45 50

147 "The Child in the   148 George Cross
Manger"

(Des E. Cremona. Photo D.L.R.)

1966 (7 Oct). *Christmas.* W **105**. *P* 13½.
376 **147** 1d. black, gold, turquoise-bl & slate-pur 10 10
377 4d. black, gold, ultramarine & slate-pur 10 10
378 1s. 3d. black, gold, brt pur & slate-pur 10 10
    a. Gold omitted .. .. 70·00
376/8 .. .. *Set of 3* 15 10

(Des E. Cremona. Photo Harrison)

1967 (1 Mar). *25th Anniv of George Cross Award to Malta.* W **105** (*sideways*). *P* 14½ × 14.
379 **148** 2d. multicoloured 10 10
380 4d. multicoloured 10 10
381 3s. multicoloured 15 15
379/81 .. .. *Set of 3* 15 15

149 Crucifixion of St. Peter

150 Open Bible and Episcopal Emblems

(Des E. Cremona. Photo Harrison)

1967 (28 June). *1900th Anniv of Martyrdom of Saints Peter and Paul.* T **149/50** and similar design. W **105** (*sideways*). *P* 13½ × 14½ (8d.) or 14½ (*others*).
382 2d. chestnut, orange and black 10 10
383 8d. yellow-olive, gold and black 10 10
384 3s. blue, light blue and black 15 10
382/4 .. .. *Set of 3* 20 15
Design:—*Square as T* **149**—3s. Beheading of St. Paul.

152 "St. Catherine of Siena"   156 Temple Ruins, Tarxien

(Des E. Cremona. Photo Enschedé)

1967 (1 Aug). *300th Death Anniv of Melchior Gafa (sculptor).* T **152** and similar horiz designs. Multicoloured. W **105** (*sideways*). *P* 13½ × 13.
385 2d. Type **152** 10 10
386 4d. "St. Thomas of Villanova" .. 10 10
387 1s. 6d. "Baptism of Christ" (detail) .. 10 10
388 2s. 6d. "St. John the Baptist" (from "Baptism of Christ") 10 10
385/8 .. .. *Set of 4* 20 15

(Des E. Cremona. Photo Harrison)

1967 (12 Sept). *15th International Historical Architecture Congress, Valletta.* T **156** and similar square designs. Multicoloured. W **105**. *P* 15 × 14½.
389 2d. Type **156** 10 10
390 6d. Facade of Palazzo Falzon, Notabile 10 10
391 1s. Parish Church, Birkirkara .. 10 10
392 3s. Portal, Auberge de Castille .. 15 15
389/92 .. .. *Set of 4* 20 20

160 "Angels"   161 "Crib"   162 "Angels"

(Des E. Cremona. Photo D.L.R.)

1967 (20 Oct). *Christmas.* W **105** (*sideways*). *P* 14.
393 **160** 1d. multicoloured 10 10
    a. In triptych with Nos. 394/5 .. 10 10
    b. White stars (red omitted) .. 70·00
394 **161** 8d. multicoloured 10 10
395 **162** 1s. 4d. multicoloured 10 10
393/5 .. .. *Set of 3* 10 10
Nos. 393/5 were issued in sheets of 60 of each value (arranged *tête-bêche*), and also in sheets containing the three values *se-tenant*, thus forming a triptych of the Nativity.

163 Queen Elizabeth II and Arms of Malta

(Des E. Cremona. Photo Harrison)

1967 (13 Nov). *Royal Visit.* T **163** and similar designs. W **105** (*sideways on 2d., 3s.*). *P* 14 × 15 (4d.) or 15 × 14 (*others*).
396 2d. multicoloured 10 10
    a. Cream omitted* .. .. ..
397 4d. black, brown-purple and gold .. 10 10
398 3s. multicoloured 15 15
396/8 .. .. *Set of 3* 20 20
Designs: *Vert*—4d. Queen in Robes of Order of St. Michael and St. George. *Horiz*—3s. Queen and outline of Malta.
*This affects the Queen's face.

166   Human Rights Emblem and People   167

(Des E. Cremona. Photo Harrison)

1968 (2 May). *Human Rights Year.* W **105**. *P* 12½ (6d.) or 14½ (*others*).
399 **166** 2d. multicoloured 10 10
400 **167** 6d. multicoloured 10 10
401 2s. multicoloured 10 10
399/401 .. .. *Set of 3* 15 10
The design of the 2s. value is a reverse of Type **166**.

169 Fair "Products"

(Des E. Cremona. Photo Harrison)

1968 (1 June). *Malta International Trade Fair.* W **105** (*sideways*). *P* 14½ × 14.
402 **169** 4d. multicoloured 10 10
403 8d. multicoloured 10 10
404 3s. multicoloured 15 10
402/4 .. .. *Set of 3* 20 15

170 Arms of the Order of St. John   171 "La Valette"
and La Valette   (A. de Favray)

172 La Valette's Tomb   173 Angels and Scroll
bearing Date of Death

(Des E. Cremona. Photo Govt Printer, Israel)

1968 (1 Aug). *Fourth Death Centenary of Grand Master La Valette.* W **105** (*upright,* 1s. 6d.; *sideways, others*). *P* 13 × 14 (1d., 1s. 6d.) or 14 × 13 (*others*).
405 **170** 1d. multicoloured 10 10
406 **171** 8d. multicoloured 10 10
407 **172** 1s. 6d. multicoloured 10 10
408 **173** 2s. 6d. multicoloured 15 20
405/8 .. .. *Set of 4* 30 30

174 Star of Bethlehem and Angel   177 "Agriculture"
waking Shepherds

(Des E. Cremona. Photo Harrison)

1968 (3 Oct). *Christmas.* T **174** and similar shaped designs. Multicoloured. W **105** (*sideways*). *P* 14½ × 14.
409 Type **174** 10 10
410 8d. Mary and Joseph with shepherd watching over cradle 10 10
411 1s. 4d. Three Wise Men and Star of Bethlehem 10 10
409/11 .. .. *Set of 3* 15 15
The shortest side at top and the long side at the bottom both gauge 14½, the other three sides are 14. Nos. 409/11 were issued in sheets of 60 arranged in ten strips of six, alternately upright and inverted.

(Des E. Cremona. Photo Enschedé)

1968 (21 Oct). *Sixth Food and Agricultural Organization Regional Conference for Europe.* T **177** and similar vert designs. Multicoloured. W **105** (*sideways*). *P* 12½ × 12.
412 4d. Type **177** 10 10
413 1s. F.A.O. emblem and coin 10 10
414 2s. 6d. "Agriculture" sowing seeds 10 15
412/14 .. .. *Set of 3* 15 20

180 Mahatma Gandhi   181 I.L.O. Emblem

(Des E. Cremona. Photo Enschedé)

1969 (24 Mar). *Birth Centenary of Mahatma Gandhi.* W **105**. *P* 12 × 12½.
415 **180** 1s. 6d. blackish brown, black and gold 15 10

(Des E. Cremona. Photo Harrison)

1969 (26 May). *50th Anniv of International Labour Organization.* W **105** (*sideways*). *P* 13½ × 14½.
416 **181** 2d. indigo, gold and turquoise 10 10
417 6d. sepia, gold and chestnut 10 10

182 Robert Samut

(Des E. Cremona. Photo D.L.R.)

1969 (26 July). *Birth Centenary of Robert Samut (composer of Maltese National Anthem).* W **105** (*sideways*). P 13.

| 418 | 182 | 2d. multicoloured | .. | 10 | 10 |

183 Dove of Peace, U.N. Emblem and Sea-Bed

(Des E. Cremona. Photo D.L.R.)

1969 (26 July). *United Nations Resolution on Oceanic Resources.* W **105** (*sideways*). P 13.

| 419 | 183 | 5d. multicoloured | .. | 10 | 10 |

184 "Swallows" returning to Malta

(Des E. Cremona. Photo D.L.R.)

1969 (26 July). *Maltese Migrants' Convention.* W **105** (*sideways*). P 13.

| 420 | 184 | 10d. black, gold and yellow-olive | .. | 10 | 10 |

185 University Arms and Grand Master de Fonseca (founder)

(Des E. Cremona. Photo D.L.R.)

1969 (26 July). *Bicentenary of University of Malta.* W **105** (*sideways*). P 13.

| 421 | 185 | 2s. multicoloured | .. | 10 | 20 |

186 1919 Monument   **187** Flag of Malta and Birds

(Des E. Cremona. Photo Enschedé)

1969 (20 Sept). *Fifth Anniv of Independence.* T **186/7** and similar designs. W **105** (*upright on 5d., sideways others*). P 13½ × 12½ (2d.), 12 × 12½ (5d.), or 12½ × 12 (*others*).

422		2d. multicoloured	..	10	10
423		5d. black, red and gold	..	10	10
424		10d. black, turquoise-blue and gold	..	10	10
425		1s. 6d. multicoloured	..	10	20
426		2s. 6d. black, olive-brown and gold	..	15	25
422/6			*Set of 5*	30	55

Designs:—Vert as T **187**—10d. "Tourism"; 1s. 6d. U.N. and Council of Europe emblems; 2s. 6d. "Trade and Industry".

191 Peasants playing Tambourine and Bagpipes

(Des E. Cremona. Litho D.L.R.)

1969 (8 Nov). *Christmas. Children's Welfare Fund.* T **191** and similar horiz designs. Multicoloured. W **105** (*sideways*). P 12½.

427		1d. + 1d. Type 191	..	10	15
		a. Gold omitted	..	90·00	
		b. In triptych with Nos. 428/9	..	30	55
428		5d. + 1d. Angels playing trumpet and harp		15	15
429		1s. 6d. + 3d. Choir boys singing		15	30
427/9			*Set of 3*	30	55

Nos. 427/9 were issued in sheets of 60 of each value, and also in sheets containing the three values *se-tenant*, thus forming the triptych No. 427b.

194 "The Beheading of St. John" (Caravaggio)

(Des E. Cremona. Photo Enschedé)

1970 (21 Mar). *13th Council of Europe Art Exhibition.* T **194** and similar multicoloured designs. W **105** (*upright, 10d., 2s.; sideways, others*). P 14 × 13 (1d., 8d.), 12 (10d., 2s.) or 13 × 13½ (*others*).

430		1d. Type 194	..	10	10
431		2d. "St. John the Baptist" (M. Preti) (45 × 32 mm)		10	10
432		5d. Interior of St. John's Co-Cathedral, Valletta (39 × 39 mm)		10	10
433		6d. "Allegory of the Order" (Neapolitan School) (45 × 32 mm)		10	10
434		8d. "St. Jerome" (Caravaggio)		10	20
435		10d. Articles from the Order of St. John in Malta (63 × 21 mm)		10	10
436		1s. 6d. "The Blessed Gerard receiving Godfrey de Bouillon" (A. de Favray) (45 × 35 mm)		15	25
437		2s. Cape and Stolone (16th-century) (63 × 21 mm)		20	35
430/37			*Set of 8*	60	85

202 Artist's Impression of Fujiyama

(Des E. Cremona. Photo D.L.R.)

1970 (29 May). *World Fair, Osaka.* W **105** (*sideways*). P 15.

438	202	2d. multicoloured	..	10	10
439		2d. multicoloured	..	10	10
440		3s. multicoloured	..	15	15
438/40			*Set of 3*	15	15

203 "Peace and Justice"   **204** Carol-Singers, Church and Star

(Des J. Casha. Litho Harrison)

1970 (30 Sept). *25th Anniv of United Nations.* W **105**. P 14 × 14½.

441	203	2d. multicoloured	..	10	10
442		5d. multicoloured	..	10	10
443		2s. 6d. multicoloured	..	15	15
441/3			*Set of 3*	15	15

(Des E. Cremona. Photo Govt Printer, Israel)

1970 (7 Nov). *Christmas.* T **204** and similar vert designs. Multicoloured. W **105** (*sideways*). P 14 × 13.

444		1d. + ½d. Type 204	..	10	10
445		10d. + 2d. Church, star and angels with Infant		10	15
446		1s. 6d. + 3d. Church, star and nativity scene		15	25
444/6			*Set of 3*	20	40

207 Books and Quill   **208** Dun Karm, Books, Pens and Lamp

(Des H. Alden (1s. 6d.), A. Agius (2s.). Litho D.L.R.)

1971 (20 Mar). *Literary Anniversaries. Death Bicentenary* (1970) *of De Soldanis* (historian) (1s. 6d.) *and Birth Centenary of Dun Karm* (poet) (2s.). W **105** (*sideways*). P 13 × 13½.

| 447 | 207 | 1s. 6d. multicoloured | .. | 10 | 10 |
| 448 | 208 | 2s. multicoloured | .. | 10 | 15 |

209 Europa "Chain"

(Des H. Haflidason; adapted E. Cremona. Litho Harrison)

1971 (3 May). *Europa.* W **105** (*sideways*). P 13½ × 14½.

449	209	2d. orange, black and yellow-olive		10	10
450		5d. orange, black and vermilion		10	10
451		1s. 6d. orange, black and slate		20	65
449/51			*Set of 3*	30	65

210 "St. Joseph, Patron of the Universal Church" (G. Cali)   **211** *Centaurea spathulata*

(Des E. Cremona. Litho D.L.R.)

1971 (24 July). *Centenary of Proclamation of St. Joseph as Patron Saint of Catholic Church, and 50th Anniv of the Coronation of the Statue of "Our Lady of Victories".* T **210** and similar horiz design. Multicoloured. W **105** (*sideways*). P 13 × 13½.

452		Type 210	..	10	10
453		5d. Statue of "Our Lady of Victories" and galley		10	10
454		10d. Type 210	..	10	10
455		1s. 6d. As 5d.	..	20	40
452/5			*Set of 4*	30	50

(Des Reno Psaila. Litho Harrison)

1971 (18 Sept). *National Plant and Bird of Malta.* T **211** and similar horiz design. Multicoloured. W **105** (*sideways on 5d. and 10d.*). P 14½ × 14.

456		2d. Type 211	..	10	10
457		5d. Blue Rock Thrush	..	10	10
458		10d. As 5d.	..	25	15
459		1s. 6d. Type 211	..	25	1·00
456/9			*Set of 4*	60	1·25

212 Angel

(Des E. Cremona. Litho Format)

1971 (8 Nov). *Christmas.* T **212** and similar horiz designs. Multicoloured. W **105** (*sideways*). P 13½ × 14.

460		1d. + ½d. Type 212	..	10	10
461		10d. + 2d. Mary and the Child Jesus		15	20
462		1s. 6d. + 3d. Joseph lying awake		20	30
460/2			*Set of 3*	35	55
MS463		131 × 113 mm. Nos. 460/2. P 15	..	75	2·00

213 Heart and W.H.O. Emblem   **214** Maltese Cross

(Des A. Agius. Litho Format)

1972 (20 Mar). *World Health Day.* W **105**. P 13½ × 14.

464	213	2d. multicoloured	..	10	10
465		10d. multicoloured	..	15	10
466		2s. 6d. multicoloured	..	40	80
464/6			*Set of 3*	55	85

(New Currency. 10 mils = 1 cent; 100 cents = 1 Maltese pound)

(Des G. Pace. Litho Format)

1972 (16 May). *Decimal Currency.* T **214** and similar vert designs showing decimal coins. Multicoloured. W **105**. P 14 (2 m., 3 m., 2 c.), 14½ × 14 (5 m., 1 c., 5 c.) or 13½ (10 c., 50 c.).

467		2 m. Type 214	..	10	10
468		3 m. Bee on honeycomb	..	10	10
469		5 m. Earthen lampstand	..	10	10
470		1 c. George Cross	..	10	10
471		2 c. Classical head	..	10	10
472		5 c. Ritual altar	..	10	10
473		10 c. Grandmaster's galley	..	20	10
474		50 c. Great Siege Monument	..	80	1·25
467/74			*Set of 8*	1·25	1·25

Sizes:—2 m., 3 m. and 2 c. as T **214**; 5 m., 1 c. and 5 c. 22 × 27 mm; 10 c. and 50 c. 27 × 35 mm.

No. 467 exists imperforate from stock dispersed by the liquidator of Format International Security Printers Ltd.

= **1c3**

(215)   **216** "Communications"

1972 (30 Sept). *Nos. 337a, 339 and 341 surch as T 215, by Govt. Printing Works, Valletta.*

475	1 c. 3 on 5d. multicoloured	..	10	10
476	3 c. on 8d. multicoloured	..	15	10
	a. Surch inverted	..	50·00	
	b. Gold (frame) omitted	..	60·00	
477	5 c. on 1s. 3d. multicoloured	..	15	20
	a. Surch double	..	55·00	
	b. Surch inverted	..	30·00	
	c. Gold (centre) omitted	..	45·00	
475/7	..	*Set of 3*	30	35

PRINTERS. All stamps from No. 478 onwards were printed in lithography by Printex Ltd, Malta.

(Des P. Huovinen; adapted G. Pace)

1972 (11 Nov). *Europa.* **W 105** (*sideways*). *P 13.*

478	**216**	1 c. 3, multicoloured	..	10	10
479		3 c. multicoloured	..	10	10
480		5 c. multicoloured	..	15	35
481		7 c. 5, multicoloured	..	20	75
478/81			*Set of 4*	50	1·10

Nos. 478/81 were each printed in sheets including two *se-tenant* stamp-size labels.

217 Angel

(Des E. Cremona)

1972 (9 Dec). *Christmas. T 217 and similar horiz designs.* **W 105** (*sideways*). *P 13½.*

482	8 m. + 2 m. dull sepia, brownish grey and gold		10	10
483	3 c. + 1 c. plum, lavender and gold	..	15	35
484	7 c. 5 + 1 c. 5, indigo, azure and gold		20	45
482/4		*Set of 3*	35	75
MS485	137 × 113 mm. Nos. 482/4	..	1·90	3·50

Designs:—No. 483, Angel with tambourine; No. 484, Singing angel.

See also Nos. 507/10.

218 Archaeology   219 Europa "Posthorn"

(Des E. Cremona)

1973 (31 Mar)–76. *T 218 and similar designs. Multicoloured.* **W 105** (*sideways*). *P 13½ × 14* (*Nos. 500/a*) *or 13½* (*others*).

486	2 m. Type **218**	..	10	10
487	4 m. History	..	10	10
	a. Gold (inscr and decoration) omitted	75·00	
	b. Imperf (pair)	..	£325	
488	5 m. Folklore	..	10	10
489	8 m. Industry	..	10	10
490	1 c. Fishing industry	..	10	10
491	1 c. 3, Pottery	..	10	10
492	2 c. Agriculture	..	10	10
493	3 c. Sport	..	10	10
494	4 c. Yacht marina	..	15	10
495	5 c. Fiesta	..	15	10
496	7 c. 5, Regatta	..	25	10
497	10 c. Voluntary service	..	25	10
498	50 c. Education	..	75	1·00
499	£1 Religion	..	2·00	2·75
500	£2 Coat of arms (*horiz*)	..	15·00	16·00
	a. Gold omitted			
500b	£2 National Emblem (*horiz*) (28.1.76)	9·00	11·00
486/500b		*Set of 16*	25·00	28·00

Nos. 500/b are larger, 32 × 27 mm.

(Des L. Anisdahl; adapted G. Pace)

1973 (2 June). *Europa.* **W 105.** *P 14.*

501	**219**	3 c. multicoloured	..	15	10
502		5 c. multicoloured	..	15	35
503		7 c. 5, multicoloured	..	25	60
501/3			*Set of 3*	50	95

Nos. 501/3 were each printed in sheets containing two *se-tenant* stamp-size labels.

220 Emblem, and Woman   221 Girolamo Cassar
holding Corn   (architect)

(Des H. Alden)

1973 (6 Oct). *Anniversaries. T 220 and similar vert designs showing emblem and allegorical figures.* **W 105** (*sideways*). *P 13½.*

504	1 c. 3, multicoloured	..	10	10
505	7 c. 5, multicoloured	..	25	40
506	10 c. multicoloured	..	30	50
504/6		*Set of 3*	55	85

Anniversaries:—1 c. 3, Tenth Anniv of World Food Programme; 7 c. 5, 25th Anniv of W.H.O.; 10 c. 25th Anniv of Universal Declaration of Human Rights.

(Des E. Cremona)

1973 (10 Nov). *Christmas. Horiz designs as T 217. Multicoloured.* **W 105** (*sideways*). *P 13½.*

507	8 m. + 2 m. Angels and organ pipes		15	10
508	3 c. + 1 c. Madonna and Child	..	25	40
509	7 c. 5 + 1 c. 5, Buildings and Star	..	45	65
507/9		*Set of 3*	75	1·00
MS510	137 × 112 mm. Nos. 507/9	..	5·50	7·00

(Des E. Cremona)

1974 (12 Jan). *Prominent Maltese. T 221 and similar vert designs.* **W 105.** *P 14.*

511	1 c. 3, dull myrtle-grn, dull grey-grn & gold		10	10
512	3 c. deep turquoise, grey-blue and gold		10	10
513	5 c. dull sepia, deep slate-green and gold		15	15
514	7 c. 5, slate-blue, light slate-blue and gold		20	30
515	10 c. purple, dull purple and gold	..	20	40
511/15		*Set of 5*	60	85

Designs:—3 c. Giuseppe Barth (ophthalmologist); 5 c. Nicolo' Isouard (composer); 7 c. 5, John Borg (botanist); 10 c. Antonio Sciortino (sculptor).

222 "Air Malta" Emblem

(Des E. Cremona)

1974 (30 Mar). *Air. T 222 and similar horiz design. Multicoloured.* **W 105** (*sideways*). *P 13½.*

516	3 c. Type **222**	..	10	10
517	4 c. Boeing "707"	..	15	10
518	5 c. Type **222**	..	15	10
519	7 c. 5, As 4 c.	..	20	10
520	20 c. Type **222**	..	55	60
521	25 c. As 4 c.	..	55	60
522	35 c. Type **222**	..	1·00	1·40
516/22		*Set of 7*	2·40	2·50

223 Prehistoric Sculpture

(Des E. Cremona)

1974 (13 July). *Europa. T 223 and similar designs.* **W 105** (*sideways on Nos. 523 and 525*). *P 13½.*

523	1 c. 3, slate-blue, grey-black and gold		15	10
524	3 c. light bistre-brown, grey-black and gold		20	15
525	5 c. purple, grey-black and gold	..	25	45
526	7 c. 5, dull green, grey-black and gold		35	80
523/6		*Set of 4*	85	1·40

Designs: Vert—3 c. Old Cathedral Door, Mdina; 7 c. 5, "Vetlina" (sculpture by A. Sciortino). *Horiz*—5 c. Silver Monstrance.

Nos. 523/6 were each printed in sheets including two *se-tenant* stamp-size labels.

224 Heinrich von Stephan   225 Decorative Star
(founder) and Land Transport   and Nativity Scene

(Des S. and G. Sullivan)

1974 (20 Sept). *Centenary of Universal Postal Union. T 224 and similar horiz designs.* **W 105.** *P 13½ × 14.*

527	1 c. 3, blue-green, lt violet-blue & yell-orge		30	10
528	5 c. brown, dull vermilion and yellow-green		30	10
529	7 c. 5, dp dull blue, lt violet-blue & yell-grn		35	20
530	50 c. purple, dull vermilion and yellow-orange		1·00	1·25
527/30		*Set of 4*	1·75	1·50
MS531	126 × 91 mm. Nos. 527/30	..	3·75	5·00

Designs (each containing portrait as T 224):—5 c. *Washington* (paddle-steamer) and *Royal Viking Star* (liner); 7 c. 5, Balloon and Boeing "747"; 50 c. U.P.U. Buildings, 1874 and 1974.

(Des E. Cremona)

1974 (22 Nov). *Christmas. T 225 and similar vert designs, each with decorative star. Multicoloured.* **W 105** (*sideways*). *P 14.*

532	8 m. + 2 m. Type **225**	..	10	10
533	3 c. + 1 c. "Shepherds"	..	15	20
534	5 c. + 1 c. "Shepherds with gifts"		20	35
535	7 c. 5 + 1 c. 5, "The Magi"	..	30	40
532/5		*Set of 4*	65	95

REPUBLIC

226 Swearing-in of Prime Minister

(Des E. Cremona)

1975 (31 Mar). *Inauguration of Republic. T 226 and similar horiz designs.* **W 105** (*sideways*). *P 14.*

536	1 c. 3, multicoloured	..	10	10
537	5 c. rose-red and grey-black	..	20	10
538	25 c. multicoloured	..	60	60
536/8		*Set of 3*	75	1·10

Designs:—5 c. National flag; 25 c. Minister of Justice, President and Prime Minister.

227 Mother and Child ("Family Life")

(Des D. Friggieri)

1975 (30 May). *International Women's Year. T 227 and similar horiz design.* **W 105.** *P 13½ × 14.*

539	**227**	1 c. 3, light violet and gold		15	10
540	–	3 c. light blue and gold	..	20	10
541	**227**	5 c. dull olive-sepia and gold		50	20
542	–	20 c. chestnut and gold	..	2·25	3·00
539/42			*Set of 4*	2·75	3·00

Design:—3 c., 20 c. Office secretary ("Public Life").

228 "Allegory of Malta" (Francesco de Mura)

(Des E. Cremona)

1975 (15 July). *Europa. T 228 and similar horiz design. Multicoloured.* **W 105.** *P 14 × 13½.*

543	5 c. Type **228**	..	30	10
544	15 c. "Judith and Holofernes" (Valentin de Boulogne)		50	75

The 15 c. is a smaller design than the 5 c. (47 × 23 mm), though the perforated area is the same.

Nos. 543/4 were each printed in sheets including two *se-tenant* stamp-size labels.

229 Plan of Ggantija Temple

(Des R. England)

1975 (16 Sept). *European Architectural Heritage Year. T 229 and similar horiz designs.* **W 105** (*sideways*). *P 13½.*

545	1 c. 3, brownish black and light orange-red	..	10	10
546	3 c. dull purple, lt orange-red & blackish brn		20	10
547	5 c. blackish brown and light orange-red		40	35
548	25 c. dull grey-olive, light orange-red and brownish black		1·75	3·25
545/8		*Set of 4*	2·25	3·50

Designs:—3 c. Mdina skyline; 5 c. View of Victoria, Gozo; 25 c. Silhouette of Fort St. Angelo.

230 Farm Animals   231 "The Right to
Work"

(Des E. Cremona)

1975 (4 Nov). *Christmas. T 230 and similar multicoloured designs.* **W 105** (*sideways*). *P 13½.*

549	8 m. + 2 m. Type **230**	..	30	25
	In triptych with Nos. 550/1	..	2·25	5·00
550	3 c. + 1 c. Nativity scene (50 × 23 mm)		60	75
551	7 c. 5 + 1 c. 5, Approach of the Magi		1·50	1·75
549/51		*Set of 3*	2·25	2·50

Nos. 549/51 were issued in sheets of 50 of each value, and also in sheets containing the three values horizontally *se-tenant*, thus forming the triptych No. 549a which is a composite design of "The Nativity" by Master Alberto.

(Des A. de Giovanni)

1975 (12 Dec). *First Anniv of Republic. T 231 and similar vert designs.* **W 105.** *P 14.*

552	1 c. 3, multicoloured	..	10	10
553	5 c. multicoloured	..	20	10
554	25 c. deep rose, light steel-blue and black		70	1·00
552/4		*Set of 3*	80	1·10

Designs:—5 c. "Safeguarding the Environment"; 25 c. National Flag.

232 "Festa Tar-Rahal"   233 Waterpolo

(Des M. Camilleri)

1976 (26 Feb). *Maltese Folklore. T* **232** *and similar multicoloured designs. W* **105** (*sideways on 5 c. and 7 c. 5*). *P* 14.

555	1 c. 3, Type **232**	..	..	10	10
556	5 c. "L-Imnarja" (*horiz*)	..	..	15	10
557	7 c. 5, "Il-Karnival" (*horiz*)	..	..	45	70
558	10 c. "Il-Gimgha L-Kbira"	..	..	70	1·40
555/8	..	..	*Set of 4*	1·25	2·00

(Des H. Alden)

1976 (28 Apr). *Olympic Games, Montreal. T* **233** *and similar horiz designs. Multicoloured. W* **105**. *P* 13½ × 14.

559	1 c. 7, Type **233**	..	..	10	10
560	5 c. Sailing	..	..	20	10
561	30 c. Athletics	..	..	65	1·50
559/61	..	..	*Set of 3*	85	1·50

234 Lace-making

(Des F. Portelli)

1976 (8 July). *Europa. T* **234** *and similar horiz design. Multicoloured. W* **105** (*sideways*). *P* 13½ × 14.

562	7 c. Type **234**	..	..	20	30
563	15 c. Stone carving	..	..	25	40

Nos. 562/3 were each printed in sheets including two *se-tenant* stamp-size labels.

235 Nicola Cotoner

(Des E. Cremona)

1976 (14 Sept). *300th Anniv of School of Anatomy and Surgery. T* **235** *and similar horiz designs. Multicoloured. W* **105** (*sideways*). *P* 13½.

564	2 c. Type **235**	..	..	10	10
565	5 c. Arm	..	..	10	10
566	7 c. Giuseppe Zammit	..	..	15	10
567	11 c. Sacra Infermeria	..	..	25	65
564/7	..	..	*Set of 4*	50	75

1c7

236 St. John the   237 Jean de la   (238)
Baptist and St.   Valette's Armour
Michael

(Des E. Cremona)

1976 (23 Nov). *Christmas. Designs showing portions of "Madonna and Saints" by Domenico di Michelino. Multicoloured. W* **105** (*sideways on No. 571*). *P* 13½ × 14 (*No. 571*) *or* 13½ (*others*).

568	1 c. + 5 m. Type **236**	..	..	15	20
569	5 c. + 1 c. Madonna and Child	..	..	50	70
570	7 c. + 1 c. 5, St. Christopher and St. Nicholas		65	1·00
571	10 c. + 2 c. Complete painting (32 × 27 *mm*)	..	75	1·40
568/71	..	..	*Set of 4*	1·90	3·00

(Des J. Briffa)

1977 (20 Jan). *Suits of Armour. T* **237** *and similar vert designs. Multicoloured. W* **105**. *P* 13½.

572	2 c. Type **237**	..	..	10	10
573	7 c. Aloph de Wignacourt's armour	..	..	20	10
574	11 c. Jean Jacques de Verdelin's armour	..	25	50
572/4	..	..	*Set of 3*	45	60

1977 (24 Mar). *No.* 336 *surch with T* **238** *by Govt Printing Press, Malta.*

575	116	1 c. 7 on 4d. multicoloured	..	25	25
	a. "KNIGHTS OF MALTA" (silver) omitted	..	65·00	

---

239 "Annunciation"   240 Map and Radio
                                              Aerial

(Des E. Cremona)

1977 (30 Mar). *400th Birth Anniversary of Rubens. Flemish tapestries (1st series) showing his paintings as T* **239**. *Multicoloured. W* **105** (*sideways*). *P* 14.

576	2 c. Type **239**	..	..	10	10
577	7 c. "Four Evangelists"	..	..	20	10
578	11 c. "Nativity"	..	..	40	45
579	20 c. "Adoration of the Magi"	..	..	65	1·00
576/9	..	..	*Set of 4*	1·25	1·50

See also Nos. 592/5, 615/18 and 638/40.

(Des H. Borg)

1977 (17 May). *World Telecommunication Day. T* **240** *and similar design. W* **105** (*sideways on 1 and 6 c.*). *P* 14 × 13½ (*1 and 6 c.*) *or* 13½ × 14 (*others*).

580	240	1 c. black, green and vermilion	..	10	10
581		6 c. black, grey-blue and vermilion	..	15	10
582		8 c. black, chestnut and vermilion	..	15	10
583		17 c. black, dull mauve and vermilion	..	30	40
580/3		..	*Set of 4*	55	55

Design: *Horiz*—8 and 17 c. Map, aerial and aeroplane tail-fin.

241 Ta' L-Isperanza   242 "Aid to Handi-
                                              capped Workers"
                                              (detail from Workers'
                                              Monument)

(Des G. French)

1977 (5 July). *Europa. T* **241** *and similar horiz design. Multicoloured. W* **105** (*sideways*). *P* 13½.

584	7 c. Type **241**	..	..	30	15
585	20 c. Is-Salini	..	..	35	80

Nos. 584/5 were each printed in sheets including two *se-tenant* stamp-size labels.

(Des A. Agius)

1977 (12 Oct). *Maltese Worker Commemoration. T* **242** *and similar designs. W* **105** (*sideways on 20 c.*). *P* 13½.

586	2 c. orange-brown and light brown	..	..	10	10
587	7 c. chestnut and brown	..	..	15	10
588	20 c. multicoloured	..	..	40	60
586/8	..	..	*Set of 3*	55	60

Designs: *Vert*—7 c. "Stoneworker, modern industry and ship-building" (monument detail). *Horiz*—20 c. "Mother with Dead Son" and Service Medal.

243 The Shepherds   244 "Young Lady on
                                              Horseback and Trooper"

(Des E. Cremona)

1977 (16 Nov). *Christmas. T* **243** *and similar horiz designs. Multicoloured. W* **105** (*sideways*). *P* 13½ × 14.

589	1 c. + 5 m. Type **243**	..	..	10	20
	a. In triptych with Nos. 590/1	..	40	
590	7 c. + 1 c. The Nativity	..	..	15	30
591	11 c. + 1 c. 5, Flight into Egypt	..	20	45
589/91	..	..	*Set of 3*	40	85

Nos. 589/91 were issued in sheets of 50 of each value, and also in sheets containing the three values *se-tenant*, thus forming the triptych No. 589a.

(Des E. Cremona)

1978 (26 Jan). *Flemish Tapestries (2nd series). Horiz designs similar to T* **239**. *Multicoloured. W* **105** (*sideways*). *P* 14.

592	2 c. "The Entry into Jerusalem" (artist unknown)	..	..	10	10
593	7 c. "The Last Supper" (after Poussin)	..	20	10
594	11 c. "The Raising of the Cross" (after Rubens)	25	25
595	25 c. "The Resurrection" (after Rubens)	..	60	80
592/5	..	..	*Set of 4*	1·00	1·10

(Des A. Camilleri)

1978 (7 Mar). *450th Death Anniv of Albrecht Dürer. T* **244** *and similar vert designs. W* **105**. *P* 14.

596	1 c. 7, black, vermilion and deep blue	..	10	10
597	8 c. black, vermilion and slate	..	..	15	10
598	17 c. black, vermilion and deep slate	..	40	45
	a. Vermilion (monogram) omitted	..	75·00	
596/8	..	..	*Set of 3*	55	55

Designs:—8 c. "The Bag-piper"; 17 c. "The Virgin and Child with a Monkey".

245 Monument to Grand   246 Goalkeeper
Master Nicola Cotoner
(Foggini)

(Des E. Cremona)

1978 (26 Apr). *Europa. Monuments. T* **245** *and similar vert design. Multicoloured. W* **105**. *P* 14 × 13½.

599	7 c. Type **245**	..	..	15	10
600	25 c. Monument to Grand Master Ramon Perellos (Mazzuoli)	..	35	55

Nos. 599/600 were each printed in sheets including two *se-tenant* stamp-size labels.

(Des A. de Giovanni)

1978 (6 June). *World Cup Football Championship, Argentina. T* **246** *and similar vert designs. Multicoloured. W* **105** (*sideways*). *P* 14 × 13½.

601	2 c. Type **246**	..	..	10	10
602	11 c. Players heading ball	..	..	15	10
603	15 c. Tackling	..	..	25	35
601/3	..	..	*Set of 3*	45	45
MS604	125 × 90 mm. Nos. 601/3	..	1·50	2·25

247 Airliner over Megalithic Temple

(Des R. Caruana)

1978 (3 Oct). *Air. Horiz designs as T* **247**. *Multicoloured. W* **105** (*sideways*). *P* 13½.

605	5 c. Type **247**	..	..	15	10
606	7 c. Air Malta Boeing "720B"	..	..	15	10
607	11 c. Boeing "747" taking off from Luqa Airport	25	10
608	17 c. Type **247**	..	..	35	30
609	20 c. As 7 c.	..	..	50	40
610	75 c. As 11 c.	..	..	1·50	2·25
605/10	..	..	*Set of 6*	2·75	2·75

248 Folk Musicians   249 Luzzu
and Village Church   and Aircraft Carrier

(Des E. Cremona)

1978 (9 Nov). *Christmas. T* **248** *and similar multicoloured designs. W* **105** (*sideways*). *P* 13½ (*11 c.*) *or* 14 (*others*).

611	1 c. + 5 m. Type **248**	..	..	10	10
612	5 c. + 1 c. Choir of Angels	..	..	10	15
613	7 c. + 1 c. 5, Carol singers	..	..	15	20
614	11 c. + 3 c. Folk musicians, church, angels and carol singers (58 × 23 *mm*)	..	20	30
611/14	..	..	*Set of 4*	50	65

The 1, 5 and 7 c. values depict details of the complete design shown on the 11 c. value.

(Des E. Cremona)

1979 (24 Jan). *Flemish Tapestries (3rd series). Horiz designs as T* **239** *showing paintings by Rubens. Multicoloured. W* **105** (*sideways*). *P* 14.

615	2 c. "The Triumph of the Catholic Church"	..	10	10
616	7 c. "The Triumph of Charity"	..	..	15	10
617	11 c. "The Triumph of Faith"	..	..	25	20
618	25 c. "The Triumph of Truth"	..	..	70	55
615/18	..	..	*Set of 4*	1·10	80

(Des E. Cremona)

1979 (31 Mar). *End of Military Facilities Agreement. T* **249** *and similar vert designs. Multicoloured. W* **105** (*sideways*). *P* 13½.

619	2 c. Type **249**	..	..	10	10
620	5 c. Raising the flag ceremony	..	..	10	10
621	7 c. Departing soldier and olive sprig	..	15	10
622	8 c. Type **249**	..	..	30	40
623	17 c. As 5 c.	..	..	50	60
624	20 c. As 7 c.	..	..	50	60
619/24	..	..	*Set of 6*	1·40	1·60

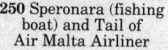

250 Speronara (fishing boat) and Tail of Air Malta Airliner

251 Children on Globe

(Des E. Cremona)

1979 (9 May). *Europa. Communications. T* **250** *and similar vert design. Multicoloured. W* **105** *(sideways). P* 14.

625	7 c. Type 250	..	15	10
626	25 c. Coastal watch tower and radio link towers		35	50

Nos. 625/6 were each printed in sheets including two *se-tenant* stamp-size labels.

(Des A. Bonnici (2 c.), A. Pisani (7 c.), M. French (11 c.))

1979 (13 June). *International Year of the Child. T* **251** *and similar multicoloured designs. W* **105** *(sideways). P* 14 × 13½ (2 c.) *or* 14 (*others*).

627	2 c. Type 251	..	10	10
628	7 c. Children flying kites (27 × 33 mm)	..	15	10
629	11 c. Children in circle (27 × 33 mm)	..	20	35
627/9		*Set of 3*	35	45

252 Shells (*Gibbula nivosa*)

(Des R. Pitré)

1979 (10 Oct). *Marine Life. T* **252** *and similar horiz designs. Multicoloured. W* **105**. *P* 13½.

630	2 c. Type 252	..	10	10
631	5 c. Loggerhead Turtle (*Garetta garetta*)	..	20	10
632	7 c. Dolphin Fish (*Coryphaena hippurus*)	..	25	10
633	25 c. Noble Pen Shell (*Pinna nobilis*)	..	90	1·25
630/3		*Set of 4*	1·25	1·25

253 "The Nativity" (detail)

(Des E. Cremona)

1979 (14 Nov). *Christmas. Paintings by G. Cali. T* **253** *and similar horiz designs. Multicoloured. W* **105**. *P* 14 × 13½.

634	1 c. + 5 m. Type 253	..	10	10
635	5 c. + 1 c. "The Flight into Egypt" (detail)	..	10	10
636	7 c. + 1 c. 5. "The Nativity"	..	15	20
637	11 c. + 3 c. "The Flight into Egypt"	..	25	50
634/7		*Set of 4*	50	85

(Des E. Cremona)

1980 (30 Jan). *Flemish Tapestries (4th series). Horiz designs as T* **239** *taken from paintings. Multicoloured. W* **105** *(sideways). P* 14.

638	2 c. "The Institution of Corpus Domini" (Rubens)	..	10	10
639	8 c. "The Destruction of Idolatry" (Rubens)	..	20	20
MS640	114 × 86 mm. 50 c. "Grand Master Perellos with St. Jude and St. Simon" (unknown Maltese artist) (*vert*)		80	1·40

254 Hal Saflieni Hypogeum, Paola

255 Dun Gorg Preca

1980 (15 Feb). *International Restoration of Maltese Monuments Campaign. T* **254** *and similar multicoloured designs. W* **105** *(sideways on* 8 *and* 12 c.). *P* 14.

641	2 c. 5, Type 254	..	10	15
642	6 c. Vilhena Palace, Mdina	..	25	20
643	8 c. Victoria Citadel, Gozo (*horiz*)	..	30	40
644	12 c. Fort St. Elmo, Valletta (*horiz*)	..	40	60
641/4		*Set of 4*	95	1·25

(Des R. Pitré)

1980 (12 Apr). *Birth Centenary of Dun Gorg Preca (founder of Society of Christian Doctrine). W* **105** *(sideways). P* 14 × 13½.

645	255	2 c. 5, black and grey	10	10

256 Ruzar Briffa (poet)

257 "Annunciation"

(Des V. Apap)

1980 (29 Apr). *Europa. Personalities. T* **256** *and similar horiz designs. W* **105** *(sideways). P* 13½ × 14.

646	8 c. black, brown-ochre and bronze-green	..	20	10
647	30 c. brown, brown-olive and brown-lake	..	55	70

Design:—30 c. Nikiol Anton Vassalli (scholar and patriot). Nos. 646/7 were each printed in sheets including two *se-tenant* stamp-size labels.

(Des R. Pitré)

1980 (7 Oct). *Christmas. Paintings by A. Inglott. T* **257** *and similar multicoloured designs. W* **105** *(sideways on* 12 c.). *P* 14 (12 c.) *or* 13½ (*others*).

648	2 c. + 5 m. Type 257	..	10	10
649	6 c. + 1 c. "Conception"	..	15	10
650	8 c. + 1 c. 5. "Nativity"	..	20	25
651	12 c. + 3 c. "Annunciation", "Conception" and "Nativity" (47 × 38 mm)	..	25	30
648/51		*Set of 4*	60	60

The paintings from the 2, 6 and 8 c. values are united to form the triptych on the 12 c. value.

258 Rook and Pawn

259 Barn Owl (*Tyto alba*)

(Des H. Borg)

1980 (20 Nov). *24th Chess Olympiad and International Chess Federation Congress, Malta. T* **258** *and similar multicoloured designs. W* **105** *(sideways on* 30 c.) *P* 14 × 13½ (30 c.) *or* 13½ × 14 (*others*).

652	2 c. 5, Type 258	..	20	10
653	8 c. Bishop and Pawn	..	50	15
654	30 c. King, Queen and Pawn (*vert*)	..	1·00	80
652/4		*Set of 3*	1·50	95

(Des M. Burlò)

1981 (20 Jan). *Birds. T* **259** *and similar vert designs. Multicoloured. W* **105** *(sideways). P* 13½.

655	3 c. Type 259	..	30	15
656	8 c. Sardinian Warbler (*Sylvia melanocephala*)		50	20
657	12 c. Woodchat Shrike (*Lanius senator*)		60	60
658	23 c. British Storm Petrel (*Hydrobates pelagicus*)	..	1·10	1·25
655/8		*Set of 4*	2·25	2·00

260 Traditional Horse Race

261 Stylised "25"

(Des H. Borg)

1981 (28 Apr). *Europa. Folklore. T* **260** *and similar vert design. Multicoloured. W* **105** *(sideways). P* 14.

659	8 c. Type 260	..	20	10
660	30 c. Attempting to retrieve flag from end of "gostra" (greasy pole)	..	40	65

The two values were each printed in sheets including two *se-tenant* stamp-size labels.

(Des A. de Giovanni)

1981 (12 June). *25th Maltese International Trade Fair. W* **105** *(sideways). P* 13½.

661	261	4 c. multicoloured	15	15
662		25 c. multicoloured	50	60

OMNIBUS ISSUES

Details, together with prices for complete sets, of the various Omnibus issues from the 1935 Silver Jubilee series to date are included in a special section following Zimbabwe at the end of Volume 2.

262 Disabled Artist at Work

263 Wheat Ear in Conical Flask

(Des A. Camilleri)

1981 (17 July). *International Year for Disabled Persons. T* **262** *and similar vert design. Multicoloured. W* **105** *(sideways). P* 13½.

663	3 c. Type 262	..	15	10
664	35 c. Disabled child playing football	..	55	75

(Des R. Caruana)

1981 (16 Oct). *World Food Day. W* **105** *(sideways). P* 14.

665	263	8 c. multicoloured	15	15
666		23 c. multicoloured	60	50

264 Megalithic Building

265 Children and Nativity Scene

(Des F. Portelli)

1981 (31 Oct). *History of Maltese Industry. Horiz designs as T* **264**. *Multicoloured. W* **105**. *P* 14.

667	5 m. Type 264	..	10	10
668	1 c. Cotton production	..	10	10
669	2 c. Early ship-building	..	15	10
670	3 c. Currency minting	..	20	10
671	5 c. "Art"	..	30	25
672	6 c. Fishing	..	30	25
673	7 c. Agriculture	..	30	30
674	8 c. Stone quarrying	..	30	35
675	10 c. Grape pressing	..	35	40
676	12 c. Modern ship-building	..	40	45
677	15 c. Energy	..	70	55
678	20 c. Telecommunications	..	70	75
679	25 c. "Industry"	..	90	95
680	50 c. Drilling for water	..	1·75	1·90
681	£1 Sea transport	..	3·50	4·25
682	£3 Air transport	..	10·50	13·00
667/82		*Set of 16*	18·00	21·00

(Des A. Bugeja)

1981 (18 Nov). *Christmas. T* **265** *and similar multicoloured designs. W* **105** *(sideways). P* 14.

683	2 c. + 1 c. Type 265	..	15	10
684	8 c. + 2 c. Christmas Eve procession (*horiz*)	..	25	20
685	20 c. + 3 c. Preaching midnight sermon	..	50	60
683/5		*Set of 3*	80	80

266 Shipbuilding

267 Elderly Man and Has-Serh (home for elderly)

(Des N. Attard)

1982 (29 Jan). *Shipbuilding Industry. T* **266** *and similar vert designs showing different scenes. W* **105** *(sideways). P* 13½.

686	3 c. multicoloured	..	15	10
687	8 c. multicoloured	..	30	30
688	13 c. multicoloured	..	55	55
689	27 c. multicoloured	..	1·25	1·25
686/9		*Set of 4*	2·00	2·00

(Des R. Pitré)

1982 (16 Mar). *Care of Elderly. T* **267** *and similar horiz design. Multicoloured. W* **105**. *P* 14 × 13½.

690	8 c. Type 267	..	40	20
691	30 c. Elderly woman and Has-Zmien (hospital for elderly)	..	1·40	1·40

268 Redemption of Islands by Maltese, 1428

(Des F. Portelli)

1982 (29 Apr). *Europa. Historical Events. T 268 and similar horiz design. Multicoloured. W 105. P 14 × 13½.*
692	8 c. Type 268	..	..	40	20
693	30 c. Declaration of rights by Maltese, 1802	..	1·00	1·40

Nos. 692/3 were each printed in sheets containing 2 *se-tenant* stamp-size labels.

269 Stylised Footballer

(Des R. Caruana)

1982 (11 June). *World Cup Football Championship, Spain. T 269 and similar horiz designs showing stylised footballers. W 105. P 14.*
694	3 c. multicoloured	..	..	20	10
695	12 c. multicoloured	..	..	60	55
696	15 c. multicoloured	..	..	70	65
694/6		..	*Set of 3*	1·40	1·25
MS697	125 × 90 mm. Nos. 694/6 ..	..	2·50	2·75

270 Angel appearing to Shepherds

(Des J. Mallia)

1982 (8 Oct). *Christmas. T 270 and similar multicoloured designs. W 105 (sideways). P 14 (No. 700) or 13½ (others).*
698	2 c. + 1 c. Type 270	..	..	15	10
699	8 c. + 2 c. Nativity and Three Wise Men bearing gifts	..	40	40
700	20 c. + 3 c. Nativity scene (*larger 45 × 37 mm*)	85	85
698/700			*Set of 3*	1·25	1·25

The designs from the 2 and 8 c. values are united to form the design of the 20 c. stamp.

271 Ta' Salvo Serafino (oared brigantine), 1531

(Des N. Attard)

1982 (13 Nov). *Maltese Ships (1st series). T 271 and similar horiz designs. Multicoloured. W 105. P 14 × 13½.*
701	3 c. Type 271	..	..	40	10
702	8 c. *La Madonna del Rosaria* (tartane), 1740	..	80	30
703	12 c. *San Paulo* (xebec), 1743	..	1·25	55
704	20 c. *Ta' Pietro Saliba* (xprunara), 1798	1·60	90
701/4			*Set of 4*	3·50	1·60

See also Nos. 725/8, 772/5, 792/5 and 809/12.

272 Manning Wardle, 1883

(Des R. Caruana)

1983 (21 Jan). *Centenary of Malta Railway. T 272 and similar horiz designs. Multicoloured. W 105. P 14 × 13½.*
705	3 c. Type 272	..	..	45	10
706	13 c. *Black Hawthorn*, 1884	..	1·00	65
707	27 c. *Beyer Peacock*, 1895	..	2·00	1·75
705/7	..	..	*Set of 3*	3·00	2·25

273 Peace Doves leaving Malta

(Des C. Cassar)

1983 (14 Mar). *Commonwealth Day. T 273 and similar multicoloured designs. W 105 (sideways on vert designs). P 14 × 13½ (8, 12 c.) or 13½ × 14 (others).*
708	8 c. Type 273	..	..	30	30
709	12 c. Tourist landmarks	..	..	40	50
710	15 c. Holiday beach (*vert*)	..	50	65
711	23 c. Ship-building (*vert*)	..	70	90
708/11	..	..	*Set of 4*	1·75	2·10

274 Ggantija Megalithic Temples, Gozo

(Des T. Bugeja (8 c.), R. Caruana (30 c.))

1983 (5 May). *Europa. T 274 and similar horiz design. Multicoloured. W 105. P 14 × 13½.*
712	8 c. Type 274	..	..	65	40
713	30 c. Fort St. Angelo	..	..	1·75	2·10

Nos. 712/13 were each printed in sheets including two *se-tenant* stamp-size labels.

275 Dish Aerials (World Communications Year)

(Des D. Friggieri)

1983 (14 July). *Anniversaries and Events. T 275 and similar horiz designs. Multicoloured. W 105 (sideways). P 13½ × 14.*
714	3 c. Type 275	..	..	35	15
715	7 c. Ships' prows and badge (25th anniv of I.M.O. Convention)	60	40
716	13 c. Container lorries and badge (30th anniv of Customs Co-operation Council)	80	60
717	20 c. Stadium and emblem (9th Mediterranean Games)	1·00	1·00
714/17	..	..	*Set of 4*	2·50	2·00

276 Monsignor Giuseppe de Piro   **277** Annunciation

(Des E. Barthet)

1983 (1 Sept). *50th Death Anniv of Monsignor Giuseppe de Piro. W 105 (sideways). P 14.*
718	**276** 3 c. multicoloured	..	..	15	15

(Des N. Attard)

1983 (6 Sept). *Christmas. T 277 and similar vert designs. Multicoloured. W 105 (sideways). P 13½ × 14.*
719	2 c. + 1 c. Type 277	..	..	30	15
720	8 c. + 2 c. The Nativity	..	75	50
721	20 c. + 3 c. Adoration of the Magi	..	1·40	1·10
719/21			*Set of 3*	2·25	1·60

278 Workers at Meeting

(Des F. Portelli)

1983 (5 Oct). *40th Anniv of General Workers' Union. T 278 and similar horiz designs. Multicoloured. W 105. P 14 × 13½.*
722	3 c. Type 278	..	..	25	10
723	8 c. Worker with family	..	..	50	40
724	27 c. Union H.Q. Building	..	1·50	1·75
722/4	..	..	*Set of 3*	2·00	2·00

(Des N. Attard)

1983 (17 Nov). *Maltese Ships (2nd series). Horiz designs as T 271. Multicoloured. W 105. P 14 × 13½.*
725	2 c. *Strangier* (full-rigged ship), 1813	..	20	15
726	12 c. *Tigre* (topsail schooner), 1839	..	90	75
727	13 c. *La Speranza* (brig), 1844	..	1·00	90
728	20 c. *Wignacourt* (barque), 1844	..	1·50	1·50
725/8	..	..	*Set of 4*	3·25	3·00

279 Boeing "737"

(Des R. Caruana)

1984 (26 Jan). *Air. T 279 and similar horiz designs. Multicoloured. W 105. P 14 × 13½.*
729	7 c. Type 279	..	..	25	30
730	8 c. Boeing "720B"	..	..	30	35
731	16 c. Vickers "Vanguard"	..	60	65
732	23 c. Vickers "Viscount"	..	85	90
733	27 c. Douglas "DC.3 Dakota"	..	95	1·00
734	38 c. A.W. "Atlanta"	..	..	1·40	1·50
735	75 c. Dornier "Wal"	..	..	2·75	3·00
729/35			*Set of 7*	6·50	7·00

280 C.E.P.T. 25th Anniversary Logo   **281** Early Policeman

(Des J. Larrivière and L. Borg)

1984 (27 Apr). *Europa. W 105. P 13½.*
736	**280** 8 c. green, black and gold	..	..	35	35
737	30 c. carmine-lake, black and gold	..	1·25	1·25

Nos. 736/7 were each printed in sheets including two *se-tenant* stamp-size labels.

(Des T. Bugeja)

1984 (14 June). *170th Anniv of Malta Police Force. T 281 and similar vert designs. Multicoloured. W 105. P 14 × 13½.*
738	3 c. Type 281	..	..	55	15
739	8 c. Mounted police	..	..	1·25	55
	a. Pale Venetian red (background) omitted	..	95·00	
740	11 c. Motorcycle policeman	..	..	1·50	1·25
741	25 c. Policeman and fireman	..	2·50	2·50
738/41			*Set of 4*	5·25	4·25

282 Running   **283** "The Visitation" (Pietro Caruana)

(Des L. Micallef)

1984 (26 July). *Olympic Games, Los Angeles. T 282 and similar vert designs. Multicoloured. W 105 (sideways). P 14.*
742	7 c. Type 282	..	..	25	30
743	12 c. Gymnastics	..	..	50	70
744	23 c. Swimming	..	..	85	1·25
742/4	..	..	*Set of 3*	1·50	2·00

(Des L. Micallef)

1984 (5 Oct). *Christmas. Paintings from Church of Our Lady of Porto Salvo, Valletta. T 283 and similar multicoloured designs. W 105 (sideways on horiz designs). P 14.*
745	2 c. + 1 c. Type 283	..	..	45	45
746	8 c. + 2 c. "The Epiphany" (Rafel Caruana) (*horiz*)	85	1·00
747	20 c. + 3 c. "Jesus among the Doctors" (Rafel Caruana) (*horiz*)	1·75	2·75
745/7	..	..	*Set of 3*	2·75	3·75

284 Dove on Map   **285** 1885 ½d. Green Stamp

(Des L. Micallef)

1984 (12 Dec). *10th Anniv of Republic. T 284 and similar vert designs. Multicoloured. W 105 (sideways). P 14.*
748	3 c. Type 284	..	..	40	20
749	8 c. Fort St. Angelo	..	..	75	60
750	30 c. Hands	..	..	2·50	3·75
748/50			*Set of 3*	3·25	4·00

(Des N. Attard)

1985 (2 Jan). *Centenary of Malta Post Office. T* **285** *and similar vert designs showing stamps of 1885. Multicoloured. W* **105**. *P* 14.
751	3 c. Type **285** ..	..	..	35	15
752	8 c. 1885 1d. rose	..	..	55	40
753	12 c. 1885 2½d. dull blue	..	..	75	1·10
754	20 c. 1885 4d. brown	..	..	1·25	2·25
751/4	..	..	*Set of 4*	2·50	3·50
MS755	165 × 90 mm. Nos. 751/4. Wmk sideways			2·75	3·75

286 Boy, and Hands planting Vine

(Des T. Bugeja)

1985 (7 Mar). *International Youth Year. T* **286** *and similar multicoloured designs. W* **105** *(sideways on 13 c.). P* 14.
756	2 c. Type **286**.	..	..	10	15
757	13 c. Young people and flowers (*vert*)	..	55	60
758	27 c. Girl holding flame in hand	..	1·25	1·40
756/8	..	..	*Set of 3*	1·75	1·90

287 Nicolo Baldacchino   288 Guzeppi Bajada and Manwel
(tenor)   Attard (victims)

(Des L. Micallef)

1985 (25 Apr). *Europa. European Music Year. T* **287** *and similar vert design. Multicoloured. W* **105**. *P* 14.
| 759 | 8 c. Type **287**. | .. | .. | 1·50 | 50 |
| 760 | 30 c. Francesco Azopardi (composer) | .. | 2·50 | 2·25 |

Nos. 759/60 were each printed in sheets including two *se-tenant* stamp-size labels.

(Des L. Micallef)

1985 (7 June). *66th Anniv of 7 June 1919 Demonstrations. T* **288** *and similar multicoloured designs. W* **105** *(sideways on 3 c., 7 c.). P* 14.
761	3 c. Type **288**.	..	..	35	15
762	7 c. Karmnu Abela and Wenzu Dyer (victims)	..	75	35
763	35 c. Model of projected Demonstration monument by Anton Agius (*vert*)	..	2·25	1·75
761/3	..	..	*Set of 3*	3·00	2·00

289 Stylized Birds   290 Giorgio Mitrovich
(nationalist) (Death Centenary)

(Des D. Friggieri)

1985 (26 July). *40th Anniv of United Nations Organization. T* **289** *and similar horiz designs. Multicoloured. W* **105** *(sideways). P* 13½ × 14.
764	4 c. Type **289**.	..	..	20	15
765	11 c. Arrow-headed ribbons ..	..	75	1·00
766	31 c. Stylized figures ..	..	1·75	3·00
764/6	..	..	*Set of 3*	2·40	3·75

(Des R. Pitre)

1985 (3 Oct). *Celebrities' Anniversaries. T* **290** *and similar vert design. Multicoloured. W* **105** *(sideways). P* 14.
| 767 | 8 c. Type **290**. | .. | .. | 70 | 35 |
| 768 | 12 c. Pietru Caxaru (poet and administrator) (400th death anniv) | .. | 1·40 | 1·25 |

COVER PRICES

Cover factors are quoted at the beginning of each country for most issues to 1945. An explanation of the system can be found on page x. The factors quoted do not, however, apply to philatelic covers.

291 The Three Wise Men   292 John XXIII Peace Laboratory
and Statue of St. Francis of Assisi

(Des G. Bonnici)

1985 (10 Oct). *Christmas. T* **291** *and similar vert designs showing details of terracotta relief by Ganni Bonnici. Multicoloured. W* **105** *(sideways). P* 14.
769	2 c. + 1 c. Type **291**	..	..	55	75
770	8 c. + 2 c. Virgin and Child	..	1·25	1·75
771	20 c. + 3 c. Angels ..	..	2·25	3·00
769/71	..	..	*Set of 3*	3·50	5·00

(Des N. Attard)

1985 (27 Nov). *Maltese Ships (3rd series). Steamships. Horiz designs as T* **271**. *Multicoloured. W* **105**. *P* 14.
772	3 c. *Scotia* (paddle-steamer), 1844 ..	55	20
773	7 c. *Tagliaferro* (screw steamer), 1882	1·00	80
774	15 c. *Gleneagles* (screw steamer), 1885	1·50	2·00
775	23 c. *L'Isle Adam* (screw steamer), 1886	2·25	2·75
772/5	..	..	*Set of 4*	4·75	5·25

(Des A. Agius (8 c.), T. Bugeja (11, 27 c.))

1986 (28 Jan). *International Peace Year. T* **292** *and similar horiz designs. Multicoloured. W* **105** *(sideways). P* 14 (8, 27 c.) *or* 13½ × 14 (11 c.).
776	8 c. Type **292**.	..	..	1·00	50
777	11 c. Dove and hands holding olive branch (40 × 19 mm) ..	..	1·50	1·75
778	27 c. Map of Africa, dove and two heads	3·00	3·75
776/8	..	..	*Set of 3*	5·00	5·50

293 Symbolic Plant   294 Heading the Ball
and *Cynthia cardui*,
Vanessa atalanta and
Polyommatus icarus
(butterflies)

(Des M. Burló)

1986 (3 Apr). *Europa. Environmental Conservation. T* **293** *and similar vert design. Multicoloured. W* **105**. *P* 14.
| 779 | 8 c. Type **293**. | .. | .. | 1·75 | 50 |
| 780 | 35 c. Island, Neolithic frieze, sea and sun .. | 3·25 | 5·00 |

Nos. 779/80 were each printed in sheets including two *se-tenant* stamp-size labels.

(Des T. Bugeja)

1986 (30 May). *World Cup Football Championship, Mexico. T* **294** *and similar horiz designs. Multicoloured. W* **105**. *P* 14.
781	3 c. Type **294**.	..	..	60	20
782	7 c. Saving a goal	..	..	1·25	80
783	23 c. Controlling the ball	..	4·00	5·00
781/3	..	..	*Set of 3*	5·25	5·50
MS784	125 × 90 mm. Nos. 781/3. Wmk sideways		5·25	6·50

295 Father Diegu   296 "Nativity"

(Des L. Micallef)

1986 (28 Aug). *Maltese Philanthropists. T* **295** *and similar vert designs. Multicoloured. W* **105**. *P* 14.
785	2 c. Type **295**.	..	..	40	30
786	3 c. Adelaide Cini	..	..	50	30
787	8 c. Alfonso Maria Galea	..	1·25	60
788	27 c. Vincenzo Bugeja	..	3·25	4·75
785/8	..	..	*Set of 4*	5·00	5·50

(Des L. Micallef)

1986 (10 Oct). *Christmas. T* **296** *and similar multicoloured designs showing paintings by Giuseppe D'Arena. W* **105** *(sideways on horiz designs). P* 14.
789	2 c. + 1 c. Type **296**	..	..	50	60
790	8 c. + 2 c. "Nativity" (detail) (*vert*) ..	1·50	1·75
791	20 c. + 3 c. "Epiphany"	..	2·75	3·75
789/91	..	..	*Set of 3*	4·25	5·50

(Des N. Attard)

1986 (19 Nov). *Maltese Ships (4th series). Horiz designs as T* **271**. *Multicoloured. W* **105**. *P* 14.
792	7 c. *San Paul* (freighter), 1921	..	1·25	50
793	10 c. *Knight of Malta* (cargo liner), 1930 ..	1·50	1·25
794	12 c. *Valetta City* (freighter), 1948 ..	1·75	2·00
795	20 c. *Saver* (freighter), 1959 ..	3·00	3·75
792/5	..	..	*Set of 4*	6·75	6·75

297 European Robin

(Des R. Caruana)

1987 (26 Jan). *25th Anniv of Malta Ornithological Society. T* **297** *and similar multicoloured designs. W* **105** *(sideways on* 3, 23 c.). *P* 14.
796	3 c. Type **297**. .	..	..	60	40
797	8 c. Peregrine Falcon (*vert*)..	..	1·50	75
798	13 c. Hoopoe (*vert*)	..	..	2·25	2·00
799	23 c. Cory's Shearwater	..	2·75	3·75
796/9	..	..	*Set of 4*	6·50	6·75

298 Aquasun Lido   299 16th-century Pikeman

(Des R. England)

1987 (15 Apr). *Europa. Modern Architecture. T* **298** *and similar vert design. Multicoloured. W* **105**. *P* 14.
| 800 | 8 c. Type **298**. | .. | .. | 1·25 | 75 |
| 801 | 35 c. Church of St. Joseph, Manikata .. | 3·50 | 4·75 |

Nos. 800/1 were each printed in sheets including two *se-tenant* stamp-size labels.

(Des L. Micallef)

1987 (10 June). *Maltese Uniforms (1st series). T* **299** *and similar vert designs. Multicoloured. W* **105** *(sideways). P* 14.
802	3 c. Type **299**.	..	..	55	40
803	7 c. 16th-century officer	..	1·00	80
804	10 c. 18th-century standard bearer	..	1·50	1·75
805	27 c. 18th-century General of the Galleys ..	3·25	4·00
802/5	..	..	*Set of 4*	5·75	6·25

See also Nos. 832/5, 851/4, 880/3 and 893/6.

300 Maltese Scenes, Wheat Ears and Sun
(European Environment Year)

(Des A. Camilleri)

1987 (18 Aug). *Anniversaries and Events. T* **300** *and similar horiz designs. Multicoloured. W* **105** *(sideways). P* 14.
806	5 c. Type **300**.	..	..	75	50
807	8 c. Esperanto star as comet (Centenary of Esperanto)	..	1·00	60
808	23 c. Family at house door (International Year of Shelter for the Homeless) ..	2·75	2·50
806/8	..	..	*Set of 3*	4·00	3·25

(Des N. Attard)

1987 (16 Oct). *Maltese Ships (5th series). Horiz designs as T* **271**. *Multicoloured. W* **105** *(sideways). P* 14.
809	2 c. *Medina* (freighter), 1969	..	40	40
810	11 c. *Rabat* (container ship), 1974 ..	1·40	1·75
811	13 c. *Ghawdex* (passenger ferry), 1979 ..	1·60	1·90
812	20 c. *Pinto* (car ferry), 1987 ..	2·25	2·75
809/12	..	..	*Set of 4*	5·00	6·00

301 "The Visitation"

(Des R. Caruana)

1987 (6 Nov). *Christmas. T* **301** *and similar horiz designs, each showing illuminated illustration, score and text from 16th-century choral manuscript. Multicoloured. W* **105** *(sideways). P* 14.

813	2 c. + 1 c. Type **301** ..		40	40
814	8 c. + 2 c. "The Nativity" ..		1·25	1·75
815	20 c. + 3 c. "The Adoration of the Magi" ..		2·50	3·00
813/15		*Set of 3*	3·75	4·50

302 Dr. Arvid Pardo (U.N. representative)   **303 Ven. Nazju Falzon** (Catholic catechist)

(Des S. Mallia)

1987 (18 Dec). *20th Anniv of United Nations Resolution on Peaceful Use of the Seabed. T* **302** *and similar vert design. Multicoloured. W* **105.** *P* 14.

816	8 c. Type **302**..		1·00	75
817	12 c. U.N. emblem and sea ..		1·75	2·25
MS818	125 × 90 mm. Nos. 816/17. Wmk sideways. P 13 × 13½ ..		2·75	3·25

(Des E. Barthet)

1988 (23 Jan). *Maltese Personalities. T* **303** *and similar vert designs. Multicoloured. W* **105.** *P* 14.

819	2 c. Type **303**		25	30
820	3 c. Mgr. Sidor Formosa (philanthropist) ..		25	30
821	4 c. Sir Luigi Preziosi (ophthalmologist) ..		30	30
822	10 c. Fr. Anastasju Cuschieri (poet) ..		70	75
823	25 c. Mgr. Pietru Pawl Saydon (Bible translator) ..		2·00	2·75
819/23		*Set of 5*	3·25	4·00

304 "St. John Bosco with Youth" (statue) (Death Centenary)   **305 Bus, Ferry and Airplane**

(Des F. Portelli)

1988 (5 Mar). *Religious Anniversaries. T* **304** *and similar vert designs. Multicoloured. W* **105** *(sideways). P* 14.

824	10 c. Type **304** ..		80	80
825	12 c. "Assumption of Our Lady" (altarpiece by Perugino, Ta' Pinu, Gozo) (Marian Year) ..		1·00	1·00
826	14 c. "Christ the King" (statue by Sciortino) (75th anniv of International Eucharistic Congress, Valletta) ..		1·50	2·00
824/6		*Set of 3*	3·00	3·50

(Des F. Fenech)

1988 (9 Apr). *Europa. Transport and Communications. T* **305** *and similar vert design. Multicoloured. W* **105** *(sideways). P* 13½.

827	10 c. Type **305** ..		1·00	75
828	35 c. Control panel, dish aerial and pylons		2·75	3·50

Nos. 827/8 were each printed in sheets including two *se-tenant* stamp-size labels.

---

306 Globe and Red Cross Emblems (125th anniv of International Red Cross)   **307 Athletics**

(Des M. Cremona)

1988 (28 May). *Anniversaries and Events. T* **306** *and similar horiz designs. Multicoloured. W* **105.** *P* 13½.

829	4 c. Type **306**		40	40
830	18 c. Divided globe (Campaign for North-South Interdependence and Solidarity)		1·75	2·00
831	19 c. Globe and symbol (40th anniv of World Health Organization) ..		1·75	2·00
829/31		*Set of 3*	3·50	4·00

(Des L. Micallef)

1988 (23 July). *Maltese Uniforms (2nd issue). Vert designs as T* **299.** *Multicoloured. W* **105** *(sideways). P* 14.

832	3 c. Private, Maltese Light Infantry, 1800		30	30
833	4 c. Gunner, Malta Coast Artillery, 1802 ..		35	35
834	10 c. Field Officer, 1st Maltese Provincial Battalion, 1805		85	95
835	25 c. Subaltern, Royal Malta Regiment, 1809 ..		2·25	2·75
832/5		*Set of 4*	3·25	4·00

(Des R. Gauci)

1988 (17 Sept). *Olympic Games, Seoul. T* **307** *and similar vert designs. Multicoloured. W* **105** *(sideways). P* 14×13½.

836	4 c. Type **307** ..		30	30
837	10 c. Diving ..		70	80
838	35 c. Basketball ..		2·00	2·75
836/8		*Set of 3*	2·75	3·50

308 Shepherd with Flock   **309 Commonwealth Emblem**

(Des R. Gauci)

1988 (5 Nov). *Christmas. T* **308** *and similar vert designs. Multicoloured. W* **105.** *P* 14.

839	3 c. + 1 c. Type **308** ..		25	30
840	10 c. + 2 c. The Nativity ..		60	75
841	25 c. + 3 c. Three Wise Men ..		1·50	2·00
839/41		*Set of 3*	2·10	2·75

(Des F. Portelli)

1989 (28 Jan). *25th Anniv of Independence. T* **309** *and similar multicoloured designs. W* **105** *(sideways). P* 14 (25 c.) *or* 13½ *(others).*

842	3 c. Type **309** ..		25	25
843	3 c. Council of Europe flag ..		25	25
844	4 c. U.N. flag ..		30	30
845	10 c. Workers hands gripping ring and national flag ..		75	85
846	12 c. Scales and allegorical figure of Justice		90	1·10
847	25 c. Prime Minister Borg Olivier with Independence constitution (42 × 28 mm) ..		1·90	2·75
842/7		*Set of 6*	4·00	5·00

310 New State Arms   **311 Two Boys flying Kite**

(Des F. Portelli)

1989 (25 Mar). *W* **105.** *P* 14.

848	**310** £1 multicoloured ..		4·00	4·25

(Des R. Gauci)

1989 (6 May). *Europa. Children's Games. T* **311** *and similar vert design. Multicoloured. W* **105** *(sideways). P* 13½.

849	10 c. Type **311** ..		1·25	75
850	35 c. Two girls with dolls ..		3·25	4·00

Nos. 849/50 were each printed in sheets including two *se-tenant* stamp-size labels.

(Des L. Micallef)

1989 (24 June). *Maltese Uniforms (3rd series). Vert designs as T* **299.** *Multicoloured. W* **105** *(sideways). P* 14.

851	3 c. Officer, Maltese Veterans, 1815		35	35
852	4 c. Subaltern, Royal Malta Fencibles, 1839		40	40
853	10 c. Private, Malta Militia, 1856 ..		1·00	1·25
854	25 c. Colonel, Royal Malta Fencible Artillery, 1875 ..		2·25	3·00
851/4		*Set of 4*	3·50	4·50

312 Human Figures and Buildings   **313 Angel and Cherub**

(Des L. Casha)

1989 (17 Oct). *Anniversaries and Commemorations. T* **312** *and similar horiz designs showing logo and stylized human figures. Multicoloured. W* **105** *(sideways). P* 14.

855	3 c. Type **312** (20th anniv of U.N. Declaration on Social Progress and Development)		30	30
856	4 c. Workers and figure in wheelchair (Malta's Ratification of European Social Charter) ..		35	35
857	10 c. Family (40th anniv of Council of Europe) ..		80	90
858	14 c. Teacher and children (70th anniv of Malta Union of Teachers) ..		1·00	1·40
859	25 c. Symbolic knights (Knights of the Sovereign Military Order of Malta Assembly) ..		2·25	2·75
855/9		*Set of 5*	4·25	5·25

(Des J. Mallia)

1989 (11 Nov). *Christmas. T* **313** *and similar horiz designs showing vault paintings by Mattia Preti from St. John's Co-Cathedral, Valletta. Multicoloured. W* **105.** *P* 13½.

860	3 c. + 1 c. Type **313** ..		40	40
861	10 c. + 2 c. Two angels ..		90	1·00
862	20 c. + 3 c. Angel blowing trumpet ..		1·60	2·00
860/2		*Set of 3*	2·50	3·00

314 Presidents Bush and Gorbachev   **315 General Post Office, Auberge d'Italie, Valletta**

1989 (2 Dec). *U.S.A.–U.S.S.R. Summit Meeting, Malta. W* **105.** *P* 14.

863	**314** 10 c. multicoloured ..		1·00	1·25

(Des R. Caruana)

1990 (9 Feb). *Europa. Post Office Buildings. T* **315** *and similar multicoloured design. W* **105** *(sideways on 10 c.). P* 14.

864	10 c. Type **315** ..		75	50
865	5 c. Branch Post Office, Zebbug (horiz) ..		2·25	3·00

Nos. 864/5 were each printed in sheets including two *se-tenant* stamp-size labels.

316 Open Book and Letters from Different Alphabets (International Literacy Year)   **317 Samuel Taylor Coleridge (poet) and Government House**

(Des T. Bugeja)

1990 (7 Apr). *Anniversaries and Events. T* **316** *and similar multicoloured designs. W* **105** *(sideways on 4, 19 c.). P* 14.

866	3 c. Type **316** ..		25	25
867	4 c. Count Roger of Sicily and Norman soldiers (900th anniv of Sicilian rule) (horiz) ..		30	30
868	19 c. Communications satellite (25th anniv of International Telecommunication Union membership) (horiz) ..		1·50	2·00
869	20 c. Football and map of Malta (Union of European Football Associations 20th Ordinary Congress, Malta) ..		1·50	2·00
866/9		*Set of 4*	3·25	4·00

(Des A. Grech)

1990 (3 May). *British Authors. T* **317** *and similar horiz designs. Multicoloured. W* **105** *(sideways). P* 13½.

870	4 c.	Type **317**		25	30
871	10 c.	Lord Byron (poet) and map of Valletta		50	70
872	12 c.	Sir Walter Scott (novelist) and Great Siege		60	85
873	25 c.	William Makepeace Thackeray (novelist) and Naval Arsenal ..		1·25	2·00
870/3		.. .. ..	*Set of* 4	2·40	3·50

318 St. Paul   319 Flags and Football

(Des N. Bason)

1990 (25 May). *Visit of Pope John Paul II. T* **318** *and similar vert design showing bronze bas-reliefs. W* **105** *(sideways). P* 14.

874	4 c. brownish black, flesh and carmine ..	50	90
	a. Pair. Nos. 874/5	2·00	2·50
875	25 c. brownish black, flesh and carmine	1·50	1·75

Design:—25 c. Pope John Paul II.
Nos. 874/5 were printed together in a sheet of 12 (4×3) containing 10 stamps, *se-tenant* horizontally or vertically, and two stamp-size labels on R. 2/1 and 2/4.

(Des T. Bugeja)

1990 (8 June). *World Cup Football Championship, Italy. T* **319** *and similar horiz designs. Multicoloured. W* **105**. *P* 14.

876	5 c.	Type **319**		35	30
877	10 c.	Football in net		65	85
878	14 c.	Scoreboard and football		1·00	1·40
876/8		..	*Set of* 3	1·75	2·25
MS879		123×90 mm. Nos. 876/8. Wmk sideways	1·75	2·50

(Des L. Micallef)

1990 (25 Aug). *Maltese Uniforms (4th series). Vert designs as T* **299**. *Multicoloured. W* **105** *(sideways). P* 14.

880	3 c.	Captain, Royal Malta Militia, 1889		30	30
881	4 c.	Field officer, Royal Malta Artillery, 1905		35	35
882	10 c.	Labourer, Malta Labour Corps, 1915		65	75
883	25 c.	Lieutenant, King's Own Malta Regiment of Militia, 1918		1·50	1·75
880/3		..	*Set of* 4	2·50	2·75

320 Innkeeper   321 1899 10s. Stamp under Magnifying Glass

(Des J. Smith)

1990 (10 Nov). *Christmas. Figures from Crib by Austin Galea, Marco Bartolo and Rosario Zammit. T* **320** *and similar multicoloured designs. W* **105** *(sideways). P* 14×14½ (10 c.) or 13½×14 (*others*).

884	3 c. + 1 c.	Type **320**		30	40
885	10 c. + 2 c.	Nativity (41×28 *mm*)		70	90
886	25 c. + 3 c.	Shepherd with sheep		1·60	2·00
884/6		.. ..	*Set of* 3	2·40	3·00

(Des J. Mallia)

1991 (6 Mar). *25th Anniv of Philatelic Society of Malta. W* **105** *(sideways). P* 14.

887	**321**	10 c. multicoloured	60	70

322 "Eurostar" Satellite and V.D.U. Screen   323 St. Ignatius Loyola (founder of Jesuits) (500th birth anniv)

(Des R. Caruana)

1991 (16 Mar). *Europa. Europe in Space. T* **322** *and similar vert design. Multicoloured. W* **105** *(sideways). P* 14.

888	10 c. Type **322**	75	70
889	35 c. "Ariane 4" rocket and projected HOTOL aerospaceplane ..	2·00	2·10

Nos. 888/9 were each printed in sheets including two *se-tenant* stamp-size labels.

(Des J. Mallia)

1991 (29 Apr). *Religious Commemorations. T* **323** *and similar multicoloured designs. W* **105** *(sideways on* 3, 30 c.). *P* 14.

890	3 c.	Type **323**		30	20
891	4 c.	Abbess Venerable Maria Adeodata Pisani (185th birth anniv) (*vert*)		35	25
892	30 c.	St. John of the Cross (400th death anniv)		2·00	2·25
890/2		.. ..	*Set of* 3	2·40	2·40

(Des L. Micallef)

1991 (13 Aug). *Maltese Uniforms (5th series). Vert designs as T* **299**. *Multicoloured. W* **105** *(sideways). P* 14.

893	3 c.	Officer with colour, Royal Malta Fencibles, 1860		30	25
894	10 c.	Officer with colour, Royal Malta Regiment of Militia, 1903		70	60
895	19 c.	Officer with Queen's colour, King's Own Malta Regiment, 1968		1·40	1·40
896	25 c.	Officer with colour, Malta Armed Forces, 1991		1·75	1·75
893/6			*Set of* 4	3·75	3·50

324 Interlocking Arrows   325 Honey Buzzard

(Des N. Attard)

1991 (23 Sept). *25th Anniv of Union Haddiema Maghqudin (public services union). W* **105** *(sideways). P* 13½.

897	**324**	4 c. multicoloured		30	30

(Des H. Borg)

1991 (3 Oct). *Endangered Species. Birds. T* **325** *and similar vert designs. Multicoloured. W* **105**. *P* 14.

898	4 c.	Type **325**		45	50
	a.	Horiz strip of 4. Nos. 898/901		2·25	
899	4 c.	Marsh Harrier		45	50
900	10 c.	Eleonora's Falcon		80	90
901	10 c.	Lesser Kestrel		80	90
898/901			*Set of* 4	2·25	2·50

Nos. 898/901 were printed together, *se-tenant*, in horizontal strips of 4 throughout the sheet.

326 Three Wise Men   327 Ta' Hagrat Neolithic Temple

(Des H. Borg)

1991 (6 Nov). *Christmas. T* **326** *and similar vert designs. Multicoloured. W* **105**. *P* 14.

902	3 c. + 1 c.	Type **326**		25	25
903	10 c. + 2 c.	Holy Family		65	70
904	25 c. + 3 c.	Two shepherds		1·25	1·50
902/4			*Set of* 3	2·00	2·25

(Des F. Portelli)

1991 (9 Dec). *National Heritage of the Maltese Islands. T* **327** *and similar multicoloured designs. W* **105** *(sideways on* £2). *P* 13½.

905	1 c.	Type **327**	10	10
906	2 c.	Cottoner Gate	10	10
907	3 c.	St. Michael's Bastion, Valletta	10	15
908	4 c.	Spinola Palace, St. Julian's ..	15	15
909	5 c.	Birkirkara Church	20	25
910	10 c.	Mellieha Bay ..	35	40
911	12 c.	Wied iz-Zurrieq	40	45
912	14 c.	Mgarr harbour, Gozo ..	50	55
913	20 c.	Yacht marina	70	75
914	50 c.	Gozo Channel ..	1·75	1·90
915	£1	"Arab Horses" (sculpture by Antonio Sciortino) ..	3·50	3·75
916	£2	Independence Monument (Ganni Bonnici) (*vert*) ..	7·00	7·25
905/16		.. .. ..	*Set of* 12	13·50	14·50

MINIMUM PRICE

The minimum price quote is 10p which represents a handling charge rather than a basis for valuing common stamps. For further notes about prices see introductory pages.

---

328 Aircraft Tailfins and Terminal

(Des. H. Borg)

1992 (8 Feb). *Opening of International Air Terminal. T* **328** *and similar horiz design. W* **105** *(sideways). P* 14.

917	4 c.	Type **328**		30	30
918	10 c.	National flags and terminal ..		55	65

329 Ships of Columbus   330 George Cross and Anti-aircraft Gun Crew

(Des H. Borg)

1992 (20 Feb). *Europa. 500th Anniv of Discovery of America by Columbus. T* **329** *and similar horiz design. W* **105** *(sideways). P* 14.

919	10 c. Type **329**	55	55
920	35 c. Columbus and map of Americas ..	2·00	2·25

Nos. 919/20 were each printed in sheets including two *se-tenant* stamp-size labels.

(Des H. Borg)

1992 (15 Apr). *50th Anniv of Award of George Cross to Malta. T* **330** *and similar vert designs. Multicoloured. W* **105**. *P* 14.

921	4 c.	Type **330**		25	25
922	10 c.	George Cross and memorial bell		55	55
923	50 c.	Tanker *Ohio* entering Grand Harbour		2·50	2·75
921/3			*Set of* 3	3·00	3·25

331 Running   332 Church of the Flight into Egypt

(Des H. Borg)

1992 (24 June). *Olympic Games, Barcelona. T* **331** *and similar horiz designs. Multicoloured. W* **105** *(sideways). P* 14.

924	3 c.	Type **331**		20	20
925	10 c.	High jumping		55	55
926	30 c.	Swimming		1·75	1·75
924/6		..	*Set of* 3	2·25	2·25

(Des N. Attard)

1992 (5 Aug). *Rehabilitation of Historical Buildings. T* **332** *and similar designs. W* **105** *(sideways on* 4, 25 c.). *P* 14.

927	3 c.	black, pale stone and bluish grey		15	15
928	4 c.	black, pale stone and flesh		20	20
929	19 c.	black, pale stone and pale rose-lilac		1·25	1·25
930	25 c.	black, pale stone and pale grey-olive		1·50	1·50
927/30			*Set of* 4	2·75	2·75

Designs: *Horiz*—4 c. St. John's Co-Cathedral; 25 c. Auberge de Provence. *Vert*—19 c. Church of Madonna del Pillar.

333 "The Nativity" (Giuseppe Cali)   334 Malta College Building, Valletta

(Des L. Buttigieg)

1992 (22 Oct). *Christmas. Religious Paintings by Giuseppe Cali from Mosta Church. T **333** and similar horiz designs. Multicoloured. W **105** (sideways). P 14.*

931	3 c. + 1 c. Type **333**	15	20
932	10 c. + 2 c. "Adoration of the Magi"	40	45
933	25 c. + 3 c. "Christ with the Elders in the Temple"	95	1·00
931/3	.. .. *Set of 3*	1·40	1·50

(Des L. Buttigieg)

1992 (12 Nov). *400th Anniv of University of Malta. T **334** and similar multicoloured design. W **105** (sideways on 30 c.). P 14.*

934	4 c. Type **334**	15	20
935	30 c. Modern University complex, Tal-Qroqq (horiz)	1·00	1·10

335 Lions Club Emblem

(Des H. Borg)

1993 (4 Feb). *75th Anniv of International Association of Lions Club. T **335** and similar horiz design. Multicoloured. W **105**. P 13½.*

936	4 c. Type **335**	15	20
937	50 c. Eye (Sight First Campaign) ..	1·75	1·90

POSTAGE DUE STAMPS

D 1   D 2   D 3 Maltese Lace

1925 (16 Apr). *Type-set by Govt. Printing Office, Valletta. Imperf.*

D 1	D 1	½d. black	1·25	3·75
D 2		1d. black	2·50	2·50
D 3		1½d. black	2·50	3·50
D 4		2d. black	3·50	6·50
D 5		2½d. black	2·75	2·75
		a. "2" of "½" omitted ..	£900	£1200
D 6		3d. black/*grey*	8·50	11·00
D 7		4d. black/*buff*	4·75	9·00
D 8		6d. black/*buff*	4·75	11·00
D 9		1s. black/*buff*	7·50	15·00
D10		1s. 6d. black/*buff* ..	13·00	38·00
D1/10		.. .. .. *Set of 10*	45·00	90·00

Nos. D1/10 were each issued in sheets containing 4 panes (6 × 7) printed separately. Examples exist in *tête-bêche* pairs from the junction of the panes, price about four times that of a single stamp.

No. D5a occurred on R. 4/4 of the last 2½d. pane position to be printed. Forgeries exist, but can be detected by comparison with a normal example under ultra-violet light. They are often found in pair with normal, showing forged cancellations of "VALLETTA AP20 25" or "G.P.O" MY 7 25".

(Typo B.W.)

1925 (20 July). *Wmk Mult Script CA (sideways). P 12.*

D11	D 2	½d. green	1·25	60
D12		1d. violet	1·25	45
D13		1½d. brown	1·50	1·25
D14		2d. grey	11·00	1·50
D15		2½d. orange	2·00	1·25
D16		3d. blue	3·25	1·25
D17		4d. olive-green	12·00	11·00
D18		6d. purple	2·50	3·25
D19		1s. black	5·50	10·00
D20		1s. 6d. carmine	7·00	16·00
D11/20		.. .. .. *Set of 10*	42·00	42·00
D11/20	Optd "Specimen" ..	*Set of 10*	£200	

1953 (5 Nov)–**63**. *Wmk Mult Script CA (sideways). Chalk-surfaced paper. P 12.*

D21	D 2	½d. emerald	70	1·25
D22		1d. purple	70	1·25
		a. *Deep purple* (17.9.63) ..	75	2·50
D23		1½d. yellow-brown ..	4·00	6·50
D24		2d. grey-brown (20.3.57) ..	7·00	7·00
		a. *Blackish brown* (3.4.62) ..	11·00	13·00
D25		3d. deep slate-blue ..	1·50	2·00
D26		4d. yellow-olive ..	6·00	8·00
D21/6		.. .. *Set of 6*	18·00	23·00

1966 (Oct). *As No. D24, but wmk w **12** (sideways).*

D27	D 2	2d. grey-brown	25·00	25·00

1967–70. *Ordinary paper. W **105** (sideways).*

(a) P 12, line (9.11.67)

D28	D 2	½d. emerald	4·00	9·00
D29		1d. purple	4·00	9·00
D30		2d. blackish brown ..	4·00	9·00
D31		4d. yellow-olive ..	60·00	£100
D28/31		.. .. *Set of 4*	65·00	£120

(b) P 12½, comb (30.5.68–70)

D32	D 2	½d. emerald	35	1·00
D33		1d. purple	30	65
D34		1½d. yellow-brown ..	35	1·50
		a. *Orange-brown* (23.10.70)..	90	2·00
D35		2d. blackish brown ..	85	70
		a. *Brownish black* (23.10.70) ..	1·25	2·00
D36		2½d. yellow-orange ..	60	70
D37		3d. deep slate-blue ..	60	60
D38		4d. yellow-olive ..	1·00	80
D39		6d. purple	75	1·00
D40		1s. black	2·25	4·25
D41		1s. 6d. carmine	90	1·50
D32/41		.. .. *Set of 10*	7·00	11·50

The above are the local release dates. In the 12½ perforation the London release dates were 21 May for the ½d. to 4d. and 4 June for the 6d. to 1s. 6d.

Nos. D34a and D35a are on glazed paper.

(Des G. Pace. Litho Printex Ltd, Malta)

1973 (28 Apr). *W **105**. P 13 × 13½.*

D42	D 3	2 m. grey-brown and reddish brown	10	10
D43		3 m. dull orange and Indian red	10	10
D44		5 m. rose and bright scarlet ..	10	10
D45		1 c. turquoise and bottle green	15	15
D46		2 c. slate and black	15	15
D47		3 c. light yellow-brown and red-brown	15	15
D48		5 c. dull blue and royal blue ..	25	25
D49		10 c. reddish lilac and plum ..	45	45
D42/9		.. .. *Set of 8*	1·25	1·25

D 4

(Des M. Bonavia)

1993 (4 Jan). *W **105** (sideways). P 14.*

D50	D 4	1 c. magenta and pale magenta ..	10	10
D51		2 c. new blue and pale blue ..	10	10
D52		5 c. blue-green & pale turquoise-green	20	25
D53		10 c. yellow-orange and greenish yellow	35	40
D50/3		.. .. .. *Set of 4*	65	75

Mauritius

GREAT BRITAIN STAMPS USED IN MAURITIUS. We no longer list the Great Britain stamps with obliteration "B 53" as there is no evidence that British stamps were available from the Mauritius Post Office.

See under SEYCHELLES for stamps of Mauritius used at Victoria with "B 64" cancellations between 1861 and 1890.

A similar "B 65" cancellation was used on the island of Rodrigues, a dependency of Mauritius, from 11 December 1861 onwards.

PRICES FOR STAMPS ON COVER TO 1945
The classic issues, Nos. 1/25 and 36/44, are rare used on cover

Nos. 26/9	from × 2
Nos. 32/5	from × 3
Nos. 48/72	from × 3
Nos. 76/81	from × 5
Nos. 83/91	from × 6
Nos. 92/100	from × 4
Nos. 101/11	from × 3
Nos. 117/24	from × 8
Nos. 127/32	from × 7
No. 133	from × 4
Nos. 134/5	from × 10
No. 136	from × 8
Nos. 137/56	from × 6
Nos. 157/63	from × 5
Nos. 164/221	from × 3
No. 222	—
Nos. 223/41	from × 3
Nos. 242/4	from × 10
Nos. 245/8	from × 3
Nos. 249/63	from × 2
Nos. E1/6	from × 10
Nos. D1/7	from × 40
Nos. R1/4	from × 15

CROWN COLONY

Nos. 1/25b and 36/44 were printed in Mauritius.

1	2
("POST OFFICE")	("POST PAID")

(Engraved on copper by J. O. Barnard)

1847 (21 Sept.). *Head of Queen on groundwork of diagonal and perpendicular lines. Imperf.*

1	1	1d. orange-red	£600000	£250000
2		2d. deep blue	£400000	£275000

A single plate contained one example of each value.

It is generally agreed that fifteen examples of No. 1 have survived (including two unused) and twelve of No. 2 (including four unused).

NOTE. Our prices for early Mauritius are for stamps in very fine condition. Exceptional copies are worth more, poorer copies considerably less.

(Engraved on copper by J. O. Barnard)

1848 (June)–**59.** *Imperf.*

A. *Earliest impressions. Design deep, sharp and clear. Diagonal lines predominate. Thick paper (Period of use: 1d. 1853–54, 2d. 1848–49)*

3	2	1d. orange-vermilion/*yellowish*	£19000	£13000
4		2d. indigo-blue/*grey to bluish*	£23000	£13000
		a. "PENOE" for "PENCE" (R. 3/1)	£34000	£23000
5		2d. deep blue/*grey to bluish*	£25000	£13000
		a. "PENOE" for "PENCE" (R. 3/1)	—	£26000

B. *Early impressions. Design sharp and clear but some lines slightly weakened. Paper not so thick, grey to yellowish white or bluish (Period of use: 1d. 1853–55, 2d. 1849–54).*

6	2	1d. vermilion	£11000	£5000
7		1d. orange-vermilion	£12000	£5000
8		2d. blue	£15000	£5500
		a. "PENOE" for "PENCE" (R. 3/1)	£18000	£9000
9		2d. deep blue	£19000	£6000

C. *Intermediate impressions. White patches appear where design has worn. Paper yellowish white, grey or bluish, of poorish quality (Period of use: 1d and 2d. 1854–57)*

10	2	1d. bright vermilion	£7500	£2000
11		1d. dull vermilion	£7500	£2000
12		1d. red	£7500	£1900
13		2d. deep blue	£7000	£2000
14		2d. blue	£5000	£2000
		a. "PENOE" for "PENCE" (R. 3/1)	from £10000	£4000
15		2d. light blue	£5000	£2000

D. *Worn impressions. Much of design worn away but some diagonal lines distinct. Paper yellowish, grey or bluish, of poorish quality (Period of use: 1d. 1857–59, 2d. 1855–58)*

16	2	1d. red/*yellowish or grey*	£1500	£325
17		1d. red-brown/*yellowish or grey*	£1500	£325
18		1d. red/*bluish*	£900	£325
19		1d. red-brown/*bluish*	£850	£325
20		2d. blue (*shades*)/*yellowish or grey*	£1500	£650
		a. "PENOE" for "PENCE" (R. 3/1) *from*	—	£900
21		2d. grey-blue/*yellowish or grey*	£1700	£650
22		2d. blue (*shades*)/*bluish*	£1500	£600
		a. Doubly printed		

E. *Latest impressions. Almost none of design showing except part of Queen's head and frame. Paper yellowish, grey or bluish, of poorish quality (Period of use: 1d. 1859, 2d. 1856–58)*

23	2	1d. red	£850	£325
24		1d. red-brown	£900	£325
25		2d. grey-blue/*bluish*	£950	£375
		a. "PENOE" for "PENCE" (R. 3/1)	£1600	£700

F. *Retouched impression. Retouching to Queen's head and frame. Paper bluish of poor quality (Period of use of 2d. 1857–58)*

25b	2	2d. greyish blue/*bluish*		

Earliest known use of the 2d. value is on 19 June 1848, but the 1d. value is not known used before 27 September 1853.

There were separate plates for the 1d. and 2d. values, each of 12 (3×4).

3	(4)	5

(Recess P.B.)

1858*. *Surch with T 4. Imperf.*

26	3	4d. green	£650	£350

*Although originally gazetted for use from 8 April 1854, research into the archives indicates that No. 26 was not actually issued until 1858, when the stamps were mentioned in an ordinance of 30 April. The earliest dated postmark known is 27 March 1858.

1858–62. *No value expressed. Imperf.*

27	3	(4d.) green	£400	£200
28		(6d.) vermilion	18·00	26·00
29		(9d.) dull magenta (1859)	£475	£200
		a. Reissued as (1d.) value (11.62)	†	£160

Use of the dull magenta as a 1d. value can be confirmed by the presence of the "B 53" cancellation which was first introduced in 1861.

Prepared for use, but not issued

30	3	(No value), red-brown	6·00	
31		(No value), blue	2·75	

Remainders of these were overprinted "L.P.E. 1890" in red, perforated at the London Philatelic Exhibition and sold as souvenirs.

(Recess P.B.)

1859–61. *Imperf.*

32	5	6d. blue	£425	28·00
33		6d. dull purple-slate (1861)	15·00	22·00
34		1s. vermilion	£1800	45·00
35		1s. yellow-green (1861)	£180	70·00

The 1859 printings had the colours transposed by mistake.

6	7	8

(Engraved on copper by J. Lapirot)

1859 (Mar–Oct). *Imperf.* (a) *Early impressions.*

36	6	2d. deep blue	£3500	£1700
37		2d. blue	£2500	£1500

(b) *Intermediate prints. Lines of background, etc, partly worn away* (July)

38	6	2d. blue	£1800	£600

(c) *Worn impressions, bluish-paper* (Oct)

39	6	2d. blue	£800	£375

Nos. 36/9 were printed from a plate of 12 (4×3).

(1848 plate re-engraved by R. Sherwin)

1859 (Oct). *Bluish paper. Imperf.*

40	7	2d. deep blue	£22000	£3000

The 1d. plate was also re-engraved, but was not put into use. Reprints in black were made in 1877 from both 1d. and 2d. re-engraved plates. Coloured autotype illustrations were prepared from these reprints and 600 were included in the R.P.S.L. handbook on *British Africa* in 1900. Further reprints in black were made in 1911 after the plates had been presented to the R.P.S.L. and defaced.

(Lithographed by L. A. Dardenne)

1859 (Dec). *White laid paper. Imperf.*

41	8	1d. deep red	£2000	£900
41a		1d. red	£1600	£600
42		1d. dull vermilion	£1100	£550
43		2d. slate-blue	£2000	£600
43a		2d. blue	£950	£400
44		2d. pale blue	£850	£300
		a. Heavy retouch on neck		—£1000
		b. Slight retouches (several varieties)		—£550

9	10

(Typo D.L.R.)

1860 (Apr)–**63.** *No wmk. P 14.*

46	9	1d. purple-brown	85·00	15·00
47		2d. blue	£110	23·00
48		4d. rose	£100	18·00
49		6d. green (1862)	£475	95·00
50		6d. slate (1863)	£120	70·00
51		9d. dull purple	65·00	30·00
52		1s. buff (1862)	£180	55·00
53		1s. green (1863)	£450	£130

1862. *Intermediate perf 14 to 16.*

54	5	6d. slate	14·00	25·00
		a. Imperf between (horiz pair)	£2750	
55		1s. deep green	£1400	£300

1863–72. *Wmk Crown CC. P 14.*

56	9	1d. purple-brown	35·00	6·50
57		1d. brown	48·00	5·00
58		1d. bistre (1872)	70·00	5·00
59		2d. pale blue	55·00	4·50
60		2d. bright blue	55·00	4·50
		a. Imperf (pair)	£1000	£1100
61		3d. deep red	85·00	21·00
61a		3d. dull red	32·00	8·50
62		4d. rose	60·00	1·75
63		6d. dull violet	95·00	23·00
64		6d. yellow-green (1865)	90·00	9·00
65		6d. blue-green	75·00	3·75
66		9d. yellow-green (1872)	£100	£110
67	10	10d. maroon (1872)	£110	22·00
68	9	1s. yellow	£100	12·00
69		1s. blue (1866)	£120	18·00
70		1s. orange (1872)	95·00	12·00
71		5s. rosy mauve	£110	35·00
72		5s. bright mauve (1865)	£130	35·00

HALF PENNY   ½   d

(11)	(12)
HALF PENNY	HALF PENNY

1876. (a) *Nos. 51 and 67 surch with T 11 locally.*

76	9	½d. on 9d. dull purple	2·75	6·50
		a. Surch inverted	£275	
		b. Surch double		
77	10	½d. on 10d. maroon	80	9·00

(b) *Prepared for use, but not issued. No. 51 surch with T 12.*

78	9	½d. on 9d. dull purple (R.)	£550	
		a. "PRNNY"		
		b. Black surch	£650	

HALF PENNY   **One Penny**   **One Shilling**

(13)	(14)	(15)

1877 (Apr–Dec). *Nos. 62, 67 (colour changed) and 71/2 surch with T 13/15 locally.*

79	10	½d. on 10d. rose	2·00	22·00
80	9	1d. on 4d. rose-carmine (6 Dec)	7·50	12·00
81		1s. on 5s. rosy mauve (6 Dec)	£180	85·00
82		1s. on 5s. bright mauve (6 Dec)	£200	£100

(New Currency. 100 cents = 1 rupee)

"CANCELLED" OVERPRINTS. Following the change of currency in 1878 various issues with face values in sterling were overprinted "CANCELLED" in serifed type and sold as remainders. The stamps involved were Nos. 51, 56/62, 65, 67/8, 71/2, 76, 78/b, 79 and 81/2.

Examples of such overprints on stamps between Nos. 51 and 72 are worth about the same as the prices quoted for used, on Nos. 78/b they are worth 12% of the unused price, on No. 79 65% and on Nos. 81/2 20%.

---

2 CENTS   **2 Rs. 50 C.**

(16)	(17)

1878 (3 Jan). *Surch as T 16 or 17 (No. 91). Wmk Crown CC. P 14.*

83	10	2 c. dull rose (lower label blank)	5·00	4·50
84	9	4 c. on 1d. bistre	7·00	3·75
85		8 c. on 2d. blue	60·00	75
86	13	13 c. on 3d. orange-red	7·00	18·00
87		17 c. on 4d. rose	85·00	1·50
88		25 c. on 6d. slate-blue	£120	4·75
89		38 c. on 9d. pale violet	18·00	35·00
90		50 c. on 1s. green	75·00	2·50
91		2 r. 50 on 5s. bright mauve	12·00	9·00
83/91			*Set of 9* £350	70·00

NEW INFORMATION

The editor is always interested to correspond with people who have new information that will improve or correct the Catalogue.

18

19

20

21

22

23

24

25

26

(Typo D.L.R.)

1879 (Mar)–80. *Wmk Crown CC. P* 14.
92	18	2 c. Venetian red (1.80)	..	..	30·00	11·00
93	19	4 c. orange	..	..	50·00	3·25
94	20	8 c. blue (1.80)	..	..	12·00	1·00
95	21	13 c. slate (1.80)	..	..	£110	£120
96	22	17 c. rose (1.80)	..	..	38·00	4·00
97	23	25 c. olive-yellow		..	£170	8·00
98	24	38 c. bright purple (1.80)	..	£130	£150
99	25	50 c. green (1.80)	..	..	2·75	1·75
100	26	2 r. 50, brown-purple (1.80)	..	24·00	42·00
92/100		..	..	*Set of* 9	£500	£300

27

(Typo D.L.R.)

1883–94. *Wmk Crown CA. P* 14.
101	18	1 c. pale violet (1893)	..	..	40	45
102		2 c. Venetian red	..	..	20·00	4·75
103		2 c. green (1885)	..	..	1·25	40
104	19	4 c. orange	..	..	50·00	2·50
105		4 c. carmine (1885)	..	..	1·25	30
106	20	8 c. blue (1891)	..	..	80	80
107	27	15 c. chestnut (1893)	..	..	1·50	55
108		15 c. blue (1894)	..	..	5·50	40
109		16 c. chestnut (1885)	..	..	2·25	55
110	23	25 c. olive-yellow	..	..	3·50	1·50
111	25	50 c. orange (1887)	..	..	26·00	8·00
101/11		..	..	*Set of* 11	£100	18·00
101, 103, 105, 107/9, 111 Optd "Specimen"		*Set of* 7	£300	

16 CENTS
(28)

SIXTEEN CENTS
(29)

(*a*) Surcharge 14 mm long and 3 high.
(*b*) Surcharge 15 mm long and 3½ high.
(*c*) Surcharge 15 mm long and 2½ high.

1883 (26 Feb). *No.* 96 *surch as T* **28** *locally.*
112	22	16 c. on 17 c. rose (*a*)	..	..	80·00	40·00
		a. Surch double				
113		16 c. on 17 c. rose (*b*)	..	..	85·00	40·00
114		16 c. on 17 c. rose (*c*)	..	..	£160	90·00

1883 (14 July). *Surch with T* **29** *by D.L.R. Wmk Crown CA. P* 14.
115	22	16 c. on 17 c. rose	..	..	35·00	80

PRICES OF SETS

Set prices are given for many issues, generally those containing three stamps or more. Definitive sets include one of each value or major colour change, but do not cover different perforations, die types or minor shades. Where a choice is possible the set prices are based on the cheapest versions of the stamps included in the listings.

---

2 CENTS
(30)

2 CENTS
(31)

1885 (11 May). *No.* 98 *surch with T* **30** *locally.*
116	24	2 c. on 38 c. bright purple	..	..	65·00	32·00
		a. Without bar			—	80·00
		b. Surch inverted	..	..	£275	£275
		c. Surch double	..	..	£325	

1887 (6 July). *No.* 95 *surch with T* **31** *locally.*
117	21	2 c. on 13 c. slate (R.)	..	..	26·00	45·00
		a. Surch inverted	..	..	85·00	£100
		b. Surch double	..	..	—	£300
		c. Surch double, one on back of stamp	£350	

TWO CENTS

TWO CENTS
(32)

TWO CENTS
(33)

1891 (10–16 Sept). *Nos.* 88, 96, 98 *and* 105 *surch locally as T* **32** (*Nos.* 118/19, 121) *or T* **33** (*No.* 120).
118	19	2 c. on 4 c. carmine (No. 105) (12 Sept)	35	20
		a. Surch inverted	..	..	60·00	
		b. Surch double	..	..	65·00	60·00
		c. Surch double, one inverted ..	65·00	60·00	
119	22	2 c. on 17 c. rose (No. 96) (16 Sept)	60·00	60·00
		a. Surch inverted	..	..	£160	
		b. Surch double	..	..	£275	£275
120	9	2 c. on 38 c. on 9d. pale violet (No. 89) (16 Sept)	..	..	1·00	3·50
		a. Surch inverted	..	..	£120	
		b. Surch double	..	..	£300	£300
		c. Surch double, one inverted ..	60·00	
121	24	2 c. on 38 c. bright purple (No. 98)	2·00	2·75
		a. Surch inverted	..	..	£275	
		b. Surch double	..	..	70·00	
		c. Surch double, one inverted ..	70·00	

Minor varieties are also known with portions of the surcharge missing, due to defective printing.

ONE CENT
(34)

ONE CENT
(35)

1893 (1–7 Jan). *Surch with T* **34** *by D.L.R. or T* **35** *locally. Wmk Crown CA. P* 14.
123	18	1 c. on 2 c. pale violet (Optd S. £27)	45	50
124	27	1 c. on 16 c. chestnut (7 Jan)	..	..	45	1·00

36

37

(Typo D.L.R.)

1895–9. *Wmk Crown CA. P* 14.
127	36	1 c. dull purple and ultramarine (8.7.97)	50	50
128		2 c. dull purple and orange (8.7.97)	..	2·00	10
129		3 c. dull purple and deep purple	..	60	30
130		4 c. dull purple and emerald (8.7.97)	..	3·50	30
131		6 c. green and rose-red (1899)	..	3·00	2·25
132		18 c. green and ultramarine (8.7.97)	..	6·50	5·00
128/32				*Set of* 6	14·50	7·50
128/32 Optd "Specimen"	..	..	*Set of* 6	75·00	

(Des L. Duvergé. Typo D.L.R.)

1898 (15 Apr). *Diamond Jubilee. Wmk CA over Crown (sideways). P* 14.
133	37	36 c. orange & ultramarine (Optd S. £40)	9·00	13·00

6
CENTS
(38)

15
CENTS
(39)

1899 (23–28 May). *Nos.* 132/3 *surcharged with T* **38/9** *locally.*
134	36	6 c. on 18 c. green and ultramarine (R.)	50	60
		a. Surch inverted	..	..	£200	£160
135	37	15 c. on 36 c. orge & ultram (B.) (28 May)	1·00	90
		a. Bar of surch omitted	..	..	£160	

The space between "6" and "CENTS" varies from 2½ to 4 mm.

40 Admiral Mahé de Labourdonnais, Governor of Mauritius, 1735–46

4
Cents
(41)

(Recess D.L.R.)

1899 (13 Dec). *Birth Bicentenary of Labourdonnais. Wmk Crown CC. P* 14.
136	40	15 c. ultramarine (Optd S. £60)..	..	10·00	1·75

1900. *No.* 109 *surch with T* **41** *locally.*
137	27	4 c. on 16 c. chestnut	..	..	1·00	3·50

42

12
CENTS
(43)

(Typo D.L.R.)

1900–05. *Wmk Crown CC* (1 r.) *or Crown CA* (*others*) (*sideways on* 2 r. 50, 5 r.). *Ordinary paper. P* 14.
138	36	1 c. grey and black (1901)	..	50	10
139		2 c. dull purple and bright purple (4.01)	30	10
140		3 c. green and carmine/*yellow* (1902)	..	1·50	40
141		4 c. purple and carmine/*yellow*	..	1·25	10
142		4 c. grey-green and violet (1903)	..	60	85
143		4 c. black and carmine/*blue* (14.10.04)	3·00	20
144		5 c. dull purple & brt pur/*buff* (8.10.02)	3·25	38·00
145		5 c. dull purple and black/*buff* (2.03)	1·60	1·75
146		6 c. purple and carmine/*red* (1902)	..	1·25	20
147		8 c. green and black/*buff* (16.7.02)	..	1·00	3·25
148		12 c. grey-black and carmine (16.7.02)	..	1·50	85
149		15 c. green and orange	..	..	6·00	6·00
150		15 c. black and blue/*blue* (1905)	..	32·00	1·25
151		25 c. green and carmine/*green* (1902)	..	4·25	8·50
		a. Chalk-surfaced paper	..	..	2·25	7·50
152		50 c. dull green & dp green/*yellow* (1902)	8·50	17·00
153	42	1 r. grey-black and carmine (1902)	..	40·00	25·00
154		2 r. 50, green and black/*blue* (1902)	..	11·00	45·00
155		5 r. purple and carmine/*red* (1902)	..	48·00	75·00
138/55				*Set of* 18	£140	£200
138/55 Optd "Specimen"	..	..	*Set of* 18	£180	

1902. *No.* 132 *surch with T* **43**.
156	36	12 c. on 18 c. green and ultramarine	..	80	5·00

The bar cancelling the original value seems in some cases to be one thick bar and in others two thin ones.

Postage & Revenue.

(44)

1902 (7 July). *Various stamps optd with T* **44** *locally.*
157	36	4 c. purple and carmine/*yellow* (No. 141)	20	20
158		6 c. green and rose-red (No. 131)	..	35	2·25
159		15 c. green and orange (No. 149)	..	65	30
160	23	25 c. olive-yellow (No. 110)	..	75	2·25
161	25	50 c. green (No. 99)	..	..	3·75	1·00
162	26	2 r. 50, brown-purple (No. 100)	..	50·00	60·00
157/62				*Set of* 6	50·00	60·00

Nos. 157/62 were overprinted to make surplus stocks of postage stamps available for revenue (fiscal) purposes also.

1902 (22 Sept). *No.* 133 *surch as T* **43**, *but with longer bar.*
163	37	12 c. on 36 c. orange and ultramarine	..	1·25	1·00
		a. Surch inverted	..	..	£300	£250

The note below No. 156 also applies to No. 163.
Forged double surcharge errors show a straight, instead of a curved, serif to the "1" of "12".

1904–7. *Wmk Mult Crown CA. Ordinary paper* (2 c., 4 c., 6 c.) *or chalk-surfaced paper* (*others*). *P* 14.
164	36	1 c. grey and black (1907)	..	8·00	1·40
165		2 c. dull and bright purple (1905)	..	7·50	50
		a. Chalk-surfaced paper	..	..	7·50	30
166		3 c. green and carmine/*yellow*	..	19·00	3·75
167		4 c. black and carmine/*blue*	..	4·00	30
		a. Chalk-surfaced paper	..	..	1·00	10
168		6 c. purple and carmine/*red*	..	2·00	10
		a. Chalk-surfaced paper	..	..	1·25	10
171		15 c. black and blue/*blue* (1907)	..	4·00	35
174		50 c. green and deep green/*yellow*	..	1·40	2·25
175		1 r. grey-black and carmine (1907)	..	19·00	30·00
164/75				*Set of* 8	55·00	35·00

46

47

(Typo D.L.R.)

1910 (17 Jan). *Wmk Mult Crown CA. Ordinary paper (1 c. to 15 c.) or chalk-surfaced paper (25 c. to 10 r.). P 14.*

181	46	1 c. black	..	..	75	10
182		2 c. brown	..	..	1·75	10
183		3 c. green	..	..	1·00	10
184		4 c. pale yellow-green and carmine		1·10	10
185	47	5 c. grey and carmine	..	..	75	1·75
186	46	6 c. carmine-red	..	..	70	10
		a. Pale red	..	..	2·50	45
187		8 c. orange	..	..	1·50	1·25
188	47	12 c. greyish slate	..	..	60	65
189	46	15 c. blue	..	..	7·50	10
190	47	25 c. black and red/*yellow*	..	1·75	8·50
191		50 c. dull purple and black	..	1·75	11·00
192		1 r. black/*green*	..	..	3·75	6·50
193		2 r. 50, black and red/*blue*	..	7·50	40·00
194		5 r. green and red/*yellow*	..	24·00	60·00
195		10 r. green and red/*green*	..	80·00	£140
181/95				*Set of 15*	£110	£250
181/95 Optd "Specimen"			*Set of 15*	£200	

On Nos. 188, 190 and 195 the value labels are as in T **49**.

48

49

(Typo D.L.R.)

1913–21. *Wmk Mult Crown CA. Ordinary paper (5 c., 12 c.) or chalk-surfaced paper (others). P 14.*

196	48	5 c. grey and carmine (5.8.15) ..		1·00	1·25
		a. Slate-grey and carmine	..	8·50	7·00
198	49	12 c. greyish slate (1915)	..	2·00	30
199		25 c. black and red/*yellow* (1913)	40	1·40
		a. White back (1916) ..		50	11·00
		b. On orange-buff	..	30·00	60·00
		c. On pale yellow (Die I) (Optd S. £25)	30·00	40·00
		d. On pale yellow (Die II) (Optd S. £25)	50	13·00
200	48	50 c. dull purple and black (Die I) (1921)	20·00	38·00
201		1 r. black/*blue-green* (olive back) (1917)	1·75	10·00
		a. On emerald surface	..	7·50	35·00
		b. On emerald back (Die II) (Optd S. £25)	1·25	6·00
202		2 r. 50, black and red/*blue* (1916)	..	16·00	30·00
203		5 r. green and red/*orange-buff* (1921)	40·00	65·00
		a. On pale yellow (Die I)		40·00	65·00
		b. On pale yellow (Die II)		35·00	75·00
204	49	10 r. green and red/*green* (1913)	45·00	80·00
		a. On blue-green, olive back ..		£700	
		b. On emerald surface	..	45·00	80·00
		c. On emerald back (Die I)	..	40·00	75·00
		d. On emerald back (Die II) (Optd S. £28)	24·00	65·00
196/204				*Set of 8*	90·00	£180
196/204 Optd "Specimen" (Die I) ..		*Set of 8*	£150	

1921–26. *Wmk Mult Script CA. Chalk-surfaced paper (50 r.). P 14.*

205	46	1 c. black	..	..	50	90
206		2 c. brown	..	..	60	10
207		2 c. purple/*yellow* (1926)	..	50	20
208		3 c. green (1926)	..	..	2·00	10
209		4 c. pale olive-green and carmine		1·50	1·75
210		4 c. green (1922)	..	..	90	10
211		4 c. brown (1926)	..	..	1·25	70
212		6 c. carmine	..	..	10·00	6·00
213		6 c. bright mauve (1922)	..	1·00	10
214		8 c. orange (1925)	..	..	2·25	9·00
215		10 c. grey (1922)	..	..	2·00	3·25
216		10 c. carmine-red (1926)	..	2·25	80
217		12 c. carmine-red (1922)	..	1·00	40
218		12 c. grey (1926)	..	..	75	1·50
219		15 c. blue	..	..	5·50	2·75
		a. Cobalt (1926)	..	..	60	25
220		20 c. blue (1922)	..	..	2·00	50
221		20 c. purple (1926)	..	..	5·50	9·00
222	–	50 r. dull pur & grn (1924) (Optd S. £170)	£700	£1300
205/21			..	*Set of 17*	30·00	32·00
205/21 Optd "Specimen"			*Set of 17*	£225	

No. 222 is as Type **46**, but measures 25×35 mm.

A

B

Two types of duty plate in the 12 c. In Type B the letters of "MAURITIUS" are larger; the extremities of the downstroke and the tail of the "2" are pointed, instead of square, and the "c" is larger.

1921–34. *Wmk Mult Script CA. Chalk-surfaced paper (25 c. to 10 r.). P 14.*

223	49	1 c. black (1926)	..	..	45	35
224		2 c. brown (1926)	..	..	45	10
225		3 c. green (1926)	..	..	60	30
226		4 c. sage-green & carm (Die II) (1926)	45	30
		a. Die I (1932)	..	..	5·50	23·00
226b		4 c. green (Die I) (1932)	..	2·00	45
227	48	5 c. grey and carmine (Die II) (1922)	60	10
		a. Die I (1932)	..	..	2·50	1·25
228	49	6 c. sepia (1927)	..	..	50	60
229		8 c. orange (1926)	..	..	50	6·00
230		10 c. carmine-red (Die II) (1926)	65	20
		a. Die I (1932)	..	..	3·75	4·25
231		12 c. grey (Type A)	..	..	30	6·50
232		12 c. carmine-red (Type A) (1922)	30	2·50
232a		12 c. pale grey (Type A) (1926) (Optd S. £24)	50	5·00
232b		12 c. grey (Type B) (1934)	..	1·25	20
233		15 c. Prussian blue (1926)	..	60	20
234		20 c. purple (1927)	..	..	45	40
235		20 c. Prussian blue (Die I) (1932)	8·50	80
		a. Die II (1934)	..	..	10·00	30
236		25 c. black & red/*pale yell* (Die II) (1922)	30	15
		a. Die I (1932)	..	..	2·00	19·00
237	48	50 c. dull purple and black (Die II) (1922)	7·00	3·50
238		1 r. black/*emerald* (Die II) (1922)	90	40
		a. Die I (1932)	..	..	8·50	17·00
239		2 r. 50, black and red/*blue* (1922)	15·00	6·00
240		5 r. green and red/*yellow* (1924)	18·00	50·00
241	49	10 r. green and red/*emerald* (1924)	48·00	85·00
223/41				*Set of 20*	95·00	£140
223/41 Optd/Perf "Specimen" ..		*Set of 20*	£300	

3

Cents

——————

(50)

51

1925 (25 Nov). *Nos. 210, 217 and 220 surch locally as T* **50.**

242	46	3 c. on 4 c. green	..	..	2·50	3·50
243		10 c. on 12 c. carmine-red	..	20	10
244		15 c. on 20 c. blue	..	55	15
242/4			..	*Set of 3*	3·00	3·50
242/4 Optd "Specimen" ..		*Set of 3*	65·00	

1935 (6 May). *Silver Jubilee. As Nos. 114/17 of Jamaica but ptd by D.L.R. P* 13½×14.

245		5 c. ultramarine and grey	..	30	10
		f. Diagonal line by turret	..	27·00	
		g. Dot to left of chapel ..		30·00	
		h. Dot by flagstaff	..	30·00	
246		12 c. green and indigo	..	2·00	10
		g. Dot to left of chapel ..		50·00	
247		20 c. brown and deep blue ..		3·00	20
		g. Dot to left of chapel ..		60·00	
248		1 r. slate and purple	..	26·00	28·00
		h. Dot by flagstaff	..	£150	
245/8			..	*Set of 4*	28·00	28·00
245/8 Perf "Specimen" ..		*Set of 4*	75·00	

For illustrations of plate varieties see Omnibus section following Zimbabwe.

Line by sceptre (R. 5/3)

1937 (12 May). *Coronation. As Nos. 118/20 of Jamaica.*

249		5 c. violet	..	..	45	10
250		12 c. scarlet	..	..	45	60
251		20 c. bright blue	..	..	45	10
		a. Line by sceptre	..	27·00	
249/51				*Set of 3*	1·25	70
249/251 Perf "Specimen"		*Set of 3*	45·00	

Sliced "S" (R. 8/4 of right pane, Duty Plate 1)

"IJ" flaw (R. 3/6 of right pane)   Battered "A" (R. 6/1 of right pane)

(Typo D.L.R.)

1938–49. *T* **51** *and similar types. Wmk Mult Script CA. Chalk-surfaced paper (25 c. to 10 r.). P 14.*

252		2 c. olive-grey (9.3.38)	..	15	10
		a. Perf 15×14 (1942)	..	1·00	10
253		3 c. reddish purple and scarlet (27.10.38)	1·50	70
		a. Reddish lilac and red (4.43) ..		1·00	90
254		4 c. dull green (26.2.38)	..	1·75	10
		a. Deep dull green (4.43)	..	75	70
255		5 c. slate-lilac (23.2.38)	..	3·00	30
		a. Pale lilac (shades) (4.43)	..	1·25	10
		b. Perf 15×14 (1942)	..	23·00	10
256		10 c. rose-red (9.3.38)	..	1·50	15
		a. Sliced "S"	..	..	40·00	
		b. Deep reddish rose (shades) (4.43)	1·50	10
		ba. Sliced "S"	..	..	40·00	
		c. Perf 15×14. *Pale reddish rose* (1942)	23·00	30
		ca. Sliced "S"	..	..	£120	
257		12 c. salmon (shades) (26.2.38)	..	80	10
		a. Perf 15×14 (1942)	..	50·00	75
258		20 c. blue (23.2.38)	..	1·00	10
259		25 c. brown-purple (2.3.38)	..	3·00	10
		a. "IJ" flaw	..	..	70·00	
		b. Ordinary paper (8.4.43)	..	2·00	10
		ba. "IJ" flaw	..	..	55·00	

260	1 r. grey-brown (2.3.38)	..	..	8·50	1·25
	a. Battered "A"	..	..	£100	
	b. Ordinary paper (8.4.43)	..	5·50	60	
	ba. Battered "A"	..	..	80·00	
	c. Drab (4.49)	..	..	8·50	2·25
261	2 r. 50, pale violet (2.3.38)	..	25·00	6·50	
	a. Ordinary paper (8.4.43)	..	17·00	6·50	
	b. Slate-violet (4.48)	..	32·00	16·00	
262	5 r. olive-green (2.3.38)	..	35·00	18·00	
	a. Ordinary paper. Sage-green (8.4.43)	26·00	17·00		
263	10 r. reddish purple (shades) (2.3.38)	..	30·00	17·00	
	a. Ordinary paper (8.4.43)	..	8·50	13·00	
252/63			Set of 12	60·00	35·00
252/63 Perf "Specimen"			Set of 12	£140	

The stamps perf 15 × 14 were printed by Bradbury, Wilkinson from De La Rue plates and issued only in the colony in 1942. De La Rue printings of the 2 c. to 20 c. in 1943–45 were on thin, whiter paper. 1943–45 printings of the 25 c. to 10 r. were on unsurfaced paper.

1946 (20 Nov). *Victory. As Nos. 141/2 of Jamaica.*
264	5 c. lilac	..	..	10	10
265	20 c. blue	..	..	10	10
264/5 Perf "Specimen"			Set of 2	45·00	

52 1d. "Post Office" Mauritius and King George VI

(Recess B.W.)

1948 (22 Mar). *Centenary of First British Colonial Postage Stamp. Wmk Mult Script CA. P 11½×11.*
266	52	5 c. orange and magenta	..	10	30
267		12 c. orange and green	..	10	10
268	—	20 c. blue and light blue	..	10	10
269	—	1 r. blue and red-brown	..	15	30
266/9			Set of 4	40	60
266/9 Perf "Specimen"			Set of 4	90·00	

Design—20 c., 1 r. As T 52 but showing 2d. "Post Office" Mauritius.

1948 (25 Oct). *Royal Silver Wedding. As Nos. 143/4 of Jamaica.*
270	5 c. violet	..	..	10	10
271	10 r. magenta	..	..	9·00	13·00

1949 (10 Oct). *75th Anniv of U.P.U. As Nos. 145/8 of Jamaica.*
272	12 c. carmine	..	..	60	65
273	20 c. deep blue	..	..	60	10
274	35 c. purple	..	..	60	50
275	1 r. sepia	..	..	60	20
272/5			Set of 4	2·25	1·90

53 Labourdonnais Sugar Factory   55 Aloe Plant

(Photo Harrison)

1950 (1 July). *T 53, 55 and similar designs. Wmk Mult Script CA. Chalk surfaced paper. P 13½ × 14½ (horiz), 14½ × 13½ (vert).*
276	1 c. bright purple	..	..	10	50
277	2 c. rose-carmine	..	..	15	10
278	3 c. yellow-green	..	..	60	1·75
279	4 c. green	..	..	20	50
280	5 c. blue	..	..	15	10
281	10 c. scarlet	..	..	30	75
282	12 c. olive-green	..	..	1·25	40
283	20 c. ultramarine	..	..	50	15
284	25 c. brown-purple	..	..	85	40
285	35 c. violet	..	..	30	10
286	50 c. emerald-green	..	..	1·50	50
287	1 r. deep blue	..	..	3·00	10
288	2 r. 50, orange	..	..	10·00	5·50
289	5 r. red-brown	..	..	11·00	10·00
290	10 r. dull blue	..	..	13·00	14·00
276/290			Set of 15	38·00	32·00

Designs: Horiz—2 c. Grand Port; 5 c. Rempart Mountain; 10 c. Transporting cane; 12 c. Mauritius Dodo and map; 35 c. Government House, Reduit; 1 r. Timor Deer; 2 r. 50, Port Louis; 5 r. Beach scene; 10 r. Arms of Mauritius. Vert—4 c. Tamarind Falls; 20 c. Legend of Paul and Virginie (inscr "VIRGINIA"); 25 c. Labourdonnais statue; 50 c. Pieter Both Mountain.
The latitude is incorrectly shown on No. 282. This was corrected before the same design was used for No. 302a.

1953 (2 June). *Coronation. As No. 153 of Jamaica.*
291	10 c. black and emerald	..	..	45	15

68 Tamarind Falls   69 Historical Museum, Mahebourg

(Photo Harrison)

1953 (3 Nov)–**58**. *Designs previously used for King George VI issue, but with portrait of Queen Elizabeth II as in T 68/9. Wmk Mult Script CA. Chalk-surfaced paper. P 13½×14½ (horiz) or 14½×13½ (vert).*
293	2 c. bright carmine (1.6.54)	..	..	10	10
294	3 c. yellow-green (1.6.54)	..	30	40	
295	4 c. bright purple	..	..	10	50
296	5 c. Prussian blue (1.6.54)	..	10	10	
297	10 c. bluish green	..	..	10	10
	a. Yellowish green (9.2.55)	..	20	10	
298	15 c. scarlet	..	..	10	10
299	20 c. brown-purple	..	..	15	20
300	25 c. bright ultramarine	..	45	10	
	a. Bright blue (19.6.57)	..	45	10	
301	35 c. reddish violet (1.6.54)	..	20	10	
302	50 c. bright green	..	..	45	35
302a	60 c. deep green (2.8.54)	..	7·50	10	
	ab. Bronze-green (27.8.58)	..	9·00	10	
303	1 r. sepia	..	..	30	10
	a. Deep grey-brown (19.6.57)	..	90	65	
304	2 r. 50, orange (1.6.54)	..	9·00	4·50	
305	5 r. red-brown (1.6.54)	..	8·00	4·00	
	a. Orange-brown (19.6.57)	..	15·00	4·50	
306	10 r. deep grey-blue (1.6.54)	..	10·00	60	
293/306			Set of 15	32·00	9·50

Designs: Horiz—2 c. Grand Port; 4 c. Sugar factory; 5 c. Rempart Mountain; 35 c. Government House; 60 c. Mauritius Dodo and map; 1 r. Timor Deer; 2 r. 50, Port Louis; 5 r. Beach scene; 10 r. Arms of Mauritius. Vert—3 c. Aloe plant; 20 c. Labourdonnais statue; 25 c. Legend of Paul and Virginie; 50 c. Pieter Both Mountain.
Nos. 296 and 300 exist in coils, constructed from normal sheets.
See also Nos. 314/16.

70 Queen Elizabeth II and King George III (after Lawrence)

(Litho Enschedé)

1961 (11 Jan). *150th Anniv of British Post Office in Mauritius. W w 12. P 13½ × 14.*
307	70	10 c. black and brown-red	..	10	10
308		20 c. ultramarine and light blue	..	20	25
309		35 c. black and yellow	..	25	25
310		1 r. deep maroon and green	..	25	25
307/10			Set of 4	70	70

1963 (4 June). *Freedom from Hunger. As No. 80 of Lesotho.*
311	60 c. reddish violet	..	..	40	10

1963 (2 Sept). *Red Cross Centenary. As Nos. 203/4 of Jamaica.*
312	10 c. red and black	..	..	15	10
313	60 c. red and blue	..	..	60	20

1963 (12 Nov)–**65**. *As Nos. 297, 302a and 304 but wmk w 12.*
314	68	10 c. bluish green (1964)	..	15	10
	a. Yellowish green (21.1.65)	..	25	10	
315	—	60 c. bronze-green (28.5.64)	..	1·50	10
316	—	2 r. 50, orange	..	2·75	5·50
314/16			Set of 3	4·00	5·50

71 Bourbon White Eye

(Des D. M. Reid-Henry. Photo Harrison)

1965 (16 Mar). *Horiz designs as T 71. W w 12 (upright). Multi-coloured; background colours given. P 14½ × 14.*
317	2 c. lemon	..	..	10	15
	a. Grey (leg) omitted	..	50·00		
318	3 c. brown	..	..	10	15
	a. Black (eye and beak) omitted	..	45·00		
319	4 c. light reddish purple	..	10	15	
	a. Mauve-pink omitted*	..	35·00		
	b. Pale grey omitted	..	60·00		
	c. Orange omitted	..	£100		
320	5 c. grey-brown	..	..	1·25	10
321	10 c. light grey-green	..	30	10	
322	15 c. pale grey	..	..	85	30
	a. Red (beak) omitted	..	45·00		
323	20 c. light yellow-bistre	..	80	10	
324	25 c. bluish grey	..	..	1·00	10
325	35 c. greyish blue	..	..	1·25	10
326	50 c. light yellow-buff	..	35	35	
327	60 c. light greenish yellow	..	40	10	
328	1 r. light yellow-olive	..	1·00	10	
	a. Pale orange omitted	..	80·00		
	b. Light grey (ground) omitted	..	80·00		
329	2 r. 50, pale stone	..	..	4·50	5·50
330	5 r. pale grey-blue	..	..	13·00	6·00
	a. Brown-red omitted	..	80·00		
331	10 r. pale bluish green	..	22·00	9·00	
317/31			Set of 15	42·00	20·00

Designs:—3 c. Rodriguez Fody; 4 c. Olive White-eye; 5 c. Mascarene Paradise Flycatcher; 10 c. Mauritius Fody; 15 c. Mauritius Parakeet; 20 c. Mauritius Greybird; 25 c. Mauritius Kestrel; 35 c. Pink Pigeon; 50 c. Reunion Bulbul; 60 c. Mauritius Blue Pigeon

(extinct); 1 r. Mauritius Dodo (extinct); 2 r. 50, Rodriguez Solitaire (extinct); 5 r. Mauritius Red Rail (extinct); 10 r. Broad-billed Parrot (extinct).
*On the 4 c. the background is printed in two colours so that in No. 319a the background colour is similar to that of the 5 c.
On No. 317a it is the deep grey which is missing, affecting the leg, beak and part of the branch. On No. 319c the missing orange affects the under breast of the bird, which appears much paler. On No. 328a the omission affects the legs and part of the body and on No. 330a the whole of the bird appears in the same colour as the legs.
The 50 c. and 2 r. 50 exist with PVA gum as well as gum arabic. Nos. 320 and 324 exist in coils, constructed from normal sheets.
See also Nos. 340/1 and 370/5.

1965 (17 May). *I.T.U. Centenary. As Nos. 98/9 of Lesotho.*
332	10 c. red-orange and apple-green	..	15	10	
333	60 c. yellow and bluish violet	..	40	20	

1965 (25 Oct). *International Co-operation Year. As Nos. 100/1 of Lesotho.*
334	10 c. reddish purple and turquoise-green	15	10		
335	60 c. deep bluish green and lavender	..	30	20	

1966 (24 Jan). *Churchill Commemoration. As Nos. 102/5 of Lesotho.*
336	2 c. new blue	..	..	10	60
337	10 c. deep green	..	..	25	10
338	60 c. brown	..	..	1·10	15
339	1 r. bluish violet	..	..	1·25	15
336/9			Set of 4	2·40	90

1966–67. *As Nos. 320, 325 but wmk w 12 sideways.*
340	5 c. grey-brown (1966)	..	..	10	15
341	35 c. greyish blue (27.6.67)	..	20	15	

No. 340 exists in coils, constructed from normal sheets.

72 "Education"

73 "Science"

74 "Culture"

(Des Jennifer Toombs. Litho Harrison)

1966 (1 Dec). *20th Anniv of U.N.E.S.C.O. W w 12 (sideways). P 14.*
342	72	5 c. slate-violet, red, yellow and orange	15	30
343	73	10 c. orange-yellow, violet and deep olive	25	10
344	74	60 c. black, bright purple and orange	50	15
342/4			Set of 3	80	45

SELF-GOVERNMENT

86 Red-tailed Tropic Bird

(Des D. M. Reid-Henry. Photo Harrison)

1967 (1 Sept). *Self-Government. T 86 and similar horiz designs. Multicoloured. W w 12. P 14½.*
345	2 c. Type 86	..	..	10	35
346	10 c. Rodriguez Brush Warbler	..	15	10	
347	60 c. Rose-ringed Parakeet (extinct)	..	20	10	
348	1 r. Grey-rumped Swiftlet	..	25	10	
345/8			Set of 4	65	40

NEW INFORMATION

The editor is always interested to correspond with people who have new information that will improve or correct the Catalogue.

SELF GOVERNMENT 1967

(90)

1967 (1 Dec). *Self-Government. As Nos. 317/31 but wmk sideways on Nos. 352/3 and 357. Optd with T* **90**. *P* 14 × 14½.

349	2 c. lemon		10	50
350	3 c. brown		10	50
351	4 c. light reddish purple		10	50
	a. Orange omitted		35·00	
352	5 c. grey-brown		10	10
353	10 c. light grey-green		10	10
354	15 c. pale grey		10	30
355	20 c. light yellow-bistre		15	10
356	25 c. bluish grey		15	10
357	35 c. greyish blue		20	10
358	50 c. light yellow-buff		25	15
359	60 c. light greenish yellow		25	10
360	1 r. light yellow-olive		35	10
361	2 r. 50, pale stone		1·00	2·00
362	5 r. pale grey-blue		3·00	3·25
363	10 r. pale bluish green		5·50	8·00
349/63		*Set of* 15	10·00	13·00

INDEPENDENT

91 Flag of Mauritius

(Litho D.L.R.)

1968 (12 Mar). *Independence. T* **91** *and similar horiz design. P* 13½ × 13.

364	**91**	2 c. multicoloured		10	45
365	—	3 c. multicoloured		10	45
366	**91**	15 c. multicoloured		10	10
367	—	20 c. multicoloured		10	10
368	**91**	60 c. multicoloured		20	10
369	—	1 r. multicoloured		30	10
364/9			*Set of* 6	65	1·10

Design:—3 c., 20 c. and 1 r. Arms and Mauritius Dodo emblem.

1968 (12 July). *As Nos.* 317/18, 322/3 *and* 327/8 *but background colours changed as below.*

370	2 c. olive-yellow		20	1·00
371	3 c. cobalt		1·50	2·00
372	15 c. cinnamon		55	20
	a. Greenish blue omitted		90·00	
373	20 c. buff		3·00	90
374	60 c. rose		90	15
375	1 r. reddish purple		1·75	1·00
370/5		*Set of* 6	7·00	4·75

93 Dominique rescues Paul and Virginie

(Des V. Whiteley, from prints. Litho Format)

1968 (2 Dec). *Bicentenary of Bernardin de St. Pierre's Visit to Mauritius. Multicoloured designs as T* **93**. *P* 13½.

376	2 c. Type **93**		10	50
377	15 c. Paul and Virginie crossing the river		20	10
378	50 c. Visit of Labourdonnais to Madame de la Tour (*horiz*)		30	10
379	60 c. Meeting of Paul and Virginie in Confidence (*vert*)		30	10
380	1 r. Departure of Virginie for Europe (*horiz*)		40	20
381	2 r. 50, Bernardin de St. Pierre (*vert*)		1·10	2·50
376/81		*Set of* 6	2·25	3·00

99 Batardé

(Des J. Vinson (3 c., 20 c., 1 r.), R. Granger Barrett (others). Photo Harrison)

1969 (12 Mar)–73. W w **12** (*sideways on* 2, 3, 4, 5, 10, 15, 60 *and* 75 c.). *Chalk-surfaced paper. P* 14.

382	2 c. multicoloured		10	40
	a. Pale green printed double*		25·00	
383	3 c. multicoloured		10	70
384	4 c. multicoloured		90	1·50
385	5 c. multicoloured		30	10
386	10 c. scarlet, black and flesh		1·00	10
387	15 c. ochre, black and cobalt		30	10
388	20 c. multicoloured		65	40
	a. Glazed ordinary paper (20.2.73)		30	2·00

389	25 c. red, black and pale apple-green		30	65
	a. Glazed ordinary paper (22.1.71)		3·50	2·00
390	30 c. multicoloured		1·50	1·00
	a. Glazed, ordinary paper (20.2.73)		4·50	4·25
391	35 c. multicoloured		65	50
	a. Glazed ordinary paper (3.2.71)		90	60
392	40 c. multicoloured		35	1·25
	a. Glazed ordinary paper (20.2.73)		3·75	3·75
393	50 c. multicoloured		1·00	10
	a. Red omitted		50·00	
	b. Glazed ordinary paper (22.1.71)		1·50	10
	ba. Red printed double			
394	60 c. black, rose and ultramarine		1·50	10
395	75 c. multicoloured		1·50	1·50
396	1 r. multicoloured		60	10
	a. Glazed ordinary paper (22.1.71)		2·00	15
397	2 r. 50, multicoloured		2·75	4·50
	a. Glazed ordinary paper (20.2.73)		2·00	7·00
398	5 r. multicoloured		6·50	6·00
	a. Glazed ordinary paper (22.1.71)		10·00	5·50
399	10 r. multicoloured		2·50	4·00
382/99		*Set of* 18	20·00	20·00
388a/98a		*Set of* 9	25·00	23·00

Designs:—3 c. Red Reef Crab; 4 c. Episcopal Mitre; 5 c. Bourse; 10 c. Starfish; 15 c. Sea Urchin; 20 c. Fiddler Crab; 25 c. Spiny Shrimp; 30 c. Single Harp Shells, and Double Harp Shell; 35 c. Argonaute; 40 c. Nudibranch; 50 c. Violet and Orange Spider Shells; 60 c. Blue Marlin; 75 c. *Conus clytospira*; 1 r. Dolphin; 2 r. 50, Spiny Lobster, 5 r. Sacré Chien Rouge; 10 r. Croissant Queue Jaune.

*No. 382a. occurs from a sheet on which a second printing of the pale green appears above the normal.

Nos. 385/6 and 389 exist in coils constructed from normal sheets.

See also Nos. 437/54 and 475/91.

117 Gandhi as Law Student   124 Frangourinier Cane-crusher (18th cent)

(Des J. W. Litho Format)

1969 (1 July). *Birth Centenary of Mahatma Gandhi. T* **117** *and similar vert designs. Multicoloured. W w* **12**. *P* 13½.

400	2 c. Type **117**		10	10
401	15 c. Gandhi as stretcher-bearer during Zulu Revolt		25	10
402	50 c. Gandhi as Satyagrahi in South Africa		30	20
403	60 c. Gandhi at No. 10 Downing Street, London		30	10
404	1 r. Gandhi in Mauritius, 1901		40	10
405	2 r. 50, Gandhi, the "Apostle of Truth and Non-Violence"		90	1·00
400/5		*Set of* 6	2·00	1·25
MS406	153 × 153 mm. Nos. 400/5		3·75	6·50

(Des V. Whiteley. Photo Enschedé)

1969 (22 Dec).* *150th Anniv of Telfair's Improvements to the Sugar Industry. T* **124** *and similar multicoloured designs. W w* **12** (*sideways on* 2 c. *to* 1 r.), *P* 11½ × 11 (2 r. 50) *or* 11 × 11½ (*others*).

407	2 c. Three-roller Vertical Mill		10	20
408	15 c. Type **124**		10	10
409	60 c. Beau Rivage Factory, 1867		10	10
410	1 r. Mon Désert-Alma Factory, 1969		10	10
411	2 r. 50, Dr. Charles Telfair (*vert*)		25	50
407/11		*Set of* 5	45	60
MS412	159 × 88 mm. Nos. 407/11†. Wmk sideways. P 11 × 11½.		1·50	2·00

*This was the local release date but the Crown Agents issued the stamps on 15 December.

† In the miniature sheet the 2 r. 50 is perf 11 at the top and imperf on the other three sides.

EXPO '70 OSAKA

(128)   129 Morne Plage, Mountain and Lufthansa Airliner

1970 (7 Apr). *World Fair, Osaka. Nos.* 394 *and* 396 *optd with T* **128** *by Harrison & Sons.*

413	60 c. black, rose and ultramarine		10	10
414	1 r. multicoloured		10	10

(Des H. Rose. Litho G. Gehringer, Kaiserslautern, Germany)

1970 (2 May). *Inauguration of Lufthansa Flight, Mauritius-Frankfurt. T* **129** *and similar multicoloured design. P* 14.

415	25 c. Type **129**		10	10
416	50 c. Airliner and Map (*vert*)		10	10

131 Lenin as a Student   133 2d. "Post Office" Mauritius and original Post Office

(Photo State Ptg Works, Moscow)

1970 (15 May). *Birth Centenary of Lenin. T* **131** *and similar vert design. P* 12 × 11½.

417	15 c. blackish green and silver		10	10
418	75 c. blackish brown and gold		20	20

Design:—75 c. Lenin as Founder of U.S.S.R.

(Des and litho D.L.R.)

1970 (15 Oct). *Port Louis, Old and New. T* **133** *and similar horiz designs. Multicoloured. W w* **12** (*sideways*). *P* 14.

419	5 c. Type **133**		10	10
420	15 c. G.P.O. Building (built 1870)		10	10
421	50 c. Mail Coach (c. 1870)		20	10
422	75 c. Port Louis Harbour (1970)		30	10
423	2 r. 50, Arrival of Pierre A. de Suffren (1783)		50	70
419/23		*Set of* 5	1·00	80
MS424	165 × 95 mm. Nos. 419/23		2·75	6·50

138 U.N. Emblem and Symbols

(Des Jennifer Toombs. Litho Format)

1970 (24 Oct). *25th Anniv of United Nations. W w* **12** (*sideways*). *P* 14½.

425	**138**	10 c. multicoloured	10	10
426		60 c. multicoloured	30	10

139 Rainbow over Waterfall

(Des R. Granger Barrett from local ideas (60 c.), R. Granger Barrett from local ideas and adapted by N. Mossae (others). Litho Format)

1971 (12 Apr). *Tourism. T* **139** *and similar horiz designs. Multicoloured. W w* **12** (*sideways*). *P* 14.

427	10 c. Type **139**		25	10
428	15 c. Trois Mamelles Mountains		25	10
429	60 c. Beach scene		45	10
430	2 r. 50, Marine life		1·50	1·50
427/30		*Set of* 4	2·25	1·50

Nos. 427/30 are inscribed on the reverse with details of tourist attractions in Mauritius.

140 "Crossroads" of Indian Ocean

(Des R. Granger Barrett (60 c.) or V. Whiteley (others). Litho Harrison)

1971 (23 Oct). *25th Anniv of Plaisance Airport. T* **140** *and similar horiz designs. Multicoloured. W w* **12** (*sideways on* 15 c.). *P* 14.

431	15 c. Type **140**		15	10
432	60 c. "Boeing 707" and Terminal Buildings		30	10
433	1 r. Air Hostesses on gangway		35	10
434	2 r. 50, *Roland Garros* (aeroplane), Choisy Airfield. 1937		1·75	2·75
431/4		*Set of* 4	2·25	2·75

141 Princess Margaret Orthopaedic Centre

(Des and litho Harrison)

1971 (2 Nov). *Third Commonwealth Medical Conference. T 141 and similar horiz design. Multicoloured.* W w 12. *P* 14 × 13½.
435   10 c. Type 141   10   10
436   75 c. Operation Theatre in National Hospital   20   20

1972–74. *As Nos. 382/99 but W w 12 upright* (2, 3, 4, 5, 10, 15, 60, 75 c.) *or sideways* (others).

A. *Glazed, ordinary paper.* B. *Chalk-surfaced paper*

		A		B	
437	2 c. multicoloured	10	50	40	1·50
438	3 c. multicoloured	1·25	2·75	30	1·25
439	4 c. multicoloured	†		4·00	4·00
440	5 c. multicoloured	3·00	30	30	10
441	10 c. scarlet, black and flesh ..	3·50	30	4·25	60
442	15 c. ochre, black and cobalt ..	50	80	35	10
443	20 c. multicoloured	†		35	75
444	25 c. red, black & apple-green..	†		35	80
445	30 c. multicoloured	†		3·00	3·25
446	35 c. multicoloured	†		4·50	60
	a. Orange-brown omitted ..	†		60·00	—
447	40 c. multicoloured	†		4·50	4·75
448	50 c. multicoloured	†		45	10
	a. Red omitted	†		55·00	—
449	60 c. black, rose & ultramarine	60	60	65	10
	a. Rose omitted	†		50·00	—
450	75 c. multicoloured	1·75	6·00	3·00	1·10
451	1 r. multicoloured	†		1·25	20
452	2 r. 50, multicoloured	†		2·00	3·50
453	5 r. multicoloured	†		3·00	2·00
	a. Greenish blue printed double	†		35·00	—
454	10 r. multicoloured	†		5·00	8·00
437/450A	*Set of* 7	9·50	10·00		
437/454B	*Set of* 18			35·00	29·00

Nos. 440B and 444B exist in coils, constructed from normal sheets.
Dates of issue:
Glazed paper—10.1.72, 5 c., 10 c.; 20.2.73, 2 c., 3 c., 15 c., 60 c., 75 c.
Chalk-surfaced paper—8.11.73, 10 c., 20 c., 30 c., 35 c., 40 c., 75 c., 1 r., 10 r.; 12.12.73, 25 c., 50 c., 2 r. 50, 5 r.; 25.2.74, 5 c., 15 c., 60 c.; 13.6.74, 2 c., 3 c., 4 c.

142 Queen Elizabeth and Prince Philip

(Des and photo Harrison)

1972 (24 Mar). *Royal Visit. T 142 and similar multicoloured design.* W w 12. *P* 14.
455   15 c. Type 142   15   10
456   2 r. 50, Queen Elizabeth II (vert) ..   ..   2·50   2·50

143 Theatre Façade

(Des and litho Harrison)

1972 (26 June). *150th Anniversary of Port Louis Theatre. T 143 and similar horiz design. Multicoloured.* W w 12. *P* 14.
457   10 c. Type 143   10   10
458   1 r. Theatre Auditorium   30   10

144 Pirate Dhow

(Des and litho Harrison)

1972 (17 Nov). *Pirates and Privateers. T 144 and similar multicoloured designs.* W w 12 (*sideways on* 60 c. *and* 1 r.). *P* 14½ × 14 (60 c., 1 r.) *or* 14 × 14½ (others).
459   15 c. Type 144   55   10
460   60 c. Treasure chest (vert)   85   15
461   1 r. Lemene and L'Hirondelle (vert) ..   1·00   15
462   2 r. 50, Robert Surcouf ..   ..   ..   4·00   6·50
459/62   ..   ..   *Set of* 4   5·75   6·50

145 Mauritius University   146 Map and Hands

(Des and litho Harrison)

1973 (10 Apr). *Fifth Anniv of Independence. T 145 and similar horiz designs. Multicoloured.* W w 12 (*sideways*). *P* 14.
463   15 c. Type 145   10   10
464   60 c. Tea Development   15   15
465   1 r. Bank of Mauritius   15   15
463/5   ..   ..   *Set of* 3   30   30

(Des and litho Harrison)

1973 (25 Apr). *O.C.A.M.* Conference. T 146 and similar multicoloured design.* W w 12 (*sideways on* 10 c.). *P* 14½ × 14 (10 c.) *or* 14 × 14½ (2 r. 50).
466   10 c. O.C.A.M. emblem (horiz)   10   10
467   2 r. 50, Type 146   40   45
*O.C.A.M. = Organisation Commune Africaine Malgache et Mauricienne.

147 W.H.O. Emblem

(Des and litho Harrison)

1973 (20 Nov). *25th Anniv of W.H.O.* W w 12. *P* 14.
468   147   1 r. multicoloured   10   10
         a. Wmk sideways   20   10

148 Meteorological Station, Vacoas.

(Des and litho Harrison)

1973 (27 Nov). *I.M.O./W.M.O. Centenary.* W w 12 (*sideways*). *P* 14.
469   148   75 c.   multicoloured   30   40

149 Capture of the *Kent*, 1800   150 P. Commerson (naturalist)

(Des and litho Harrison)

1974 (21 Mar). *Birth Bicent of Robert Surcouf (privateer).* W w 12 (*sideways*). *P* 14.
470   149   60 c.   multicoloured   50   70

(Des and litho Harrison)

1974 (18 Apr). *Death Bicent of Philibert Commerson* (1973). W w 12. *P* 14½.
471   150   2 r. 50, multicoloured   30   40

PRICES OF SETS

Set prices are given for many issues, generally those containing three stamps or more. Definitive sets include one of each value or major colour change, but do not cover different perforations, die types or minor shades. Where a choice is possible the set prices are based on the cheapest versions of the stamps included in the listings.

151 Cow being Milked

(Des and litho Harrison)

1974 (23 Oct). *Eighth F.A.O. Regional Conference for Africa, Mauritius.* W w 12 (*sideways*). *P* 14.
472   151   60 c. multicoloured   10   10

152 Mail Train

(Des and litho Harrison)

1974 (4 Dec). *Centenary of Universal Postal Union. T 152 and similar horiz design. Multicoloured.* W w 12. *P* 14.
473   15 c. Type 152   40   15
474   1 r. New G.P.O., Port Louis   40   20

1975–77. *As Nos. 382/99 but W w 14 (sideways on* 2 *to* 15 c., 60 c. *and* 75 c.). *Chalk-surfaced paper.*
475   2 c. multicoloured (16.8.77) ..   ..   2·00   50
476   2 c. multicoloured (16.8.77) ..   ..   2·00   50
477   4 c. multicoloured (16.8.77) ..   ..   2·50   50
478   5 c. multicoloured (19.3.75)   55   40
479   15 c. ochre, black and cobalt (21.1.75)   1·60   65
480   20 c. multicoloured (19.3.76)   30   30
         a. Grey (background) omitted £120
481   25 c. red, black and apple-green (19.3.75)   60   2·00
482   30 c. multicoloured (21.1.75)   35   2·75
         a. Yellow omitted ..   ..   70·00
483   35 c. multicoloured (19.3.76)   60   15
         a. Orange-brown omitted ..   ..   45·00
484   40 c. multicoloured (19.3.76)   75   60
485   50 c. multicoloured (19.3.76)   75   10
486   60 c. black, rose and ultramarine (16.8.77)   3·75   25
487   75 c. multicoloured (19.4.77) ..   ..   1·25   40
488   1 r. multicoloured (19.3.76)   75   20
         a. Deep bluish green (fin and tail markings) omitted ..   ..   80·00
489   2 r. 50, multicoloured (16.8.77) ..   14·00   4·00
490   5 r. multicoloured (21.1.75) ..   ..   5·00   13·00
491   10 r. multicoloured (21.1.75) ..   ..   7·50   12·00
475/91   ..   ..   ..   *Set of* 17   40·00   35·00
No. 492 is vacant.

153 "Cottage Life" (F. Leroy)

(Des and litho Harrison)

1975 (6 Mar). *Aspects of Mauritian Life. T 153 and similar multicoloured designs showing paintings.* W w 14 (*sideways on* 15 c., 60 c. *and* 2 r. 50). *P* 14.
493   15 c. Type 153   10   10
494   60 c. "Milk Seller" (A. Richard) (vert) ..   35   10
         a. Brown and stone (ornaments and frame) double ..   ..
495   1 r. "Entrance of Port Louis Market" (Thuillier)   35   10
496   2 r. 50, "Washerwoman" (Max Boulleé) (vert)   95   80
493/6   ..   ..   *Set of* 4   1·60   85

154 Mace across Map

(Des Harrison. Litho Questa)

1975 (21 Nov). *French-speaking Parliamentary Assemblies Conference. Port Louis.* W w 14 (*sideways*). *P* 14.
497   154   75 c. multicoloured   30   50

155 Woman with Lamp ("The Light of the World")

(Des A. H. Abdoolah; adapted Harrison. Litho Questa)

1975 (5 Dec). *International Women's Year.* W w **14** (*sideways*). P 14½.
498 **155** 2 r. 50, multicoloured .. .. .. 35 1·00

156 Parched Landscape

(Des Harrison (50 c.), J.W. Ltd (60 c.) Litho Questa)

1976 (26 Feb). *Drought in Africa. T* **156** *and similar design. Multicoloured.* W w **14** (*sideways on* 50 c.). P 14.
499 50 c. Type **156** 15 15
500 60 c. Map of Africa and carcass (*vert*).. .. 15 15

157 *Pierre Loti*, 1953–70

(Des J. W. Litho Questa)

1976 (2 July). *Mail Carriers to Mauritius. T* **157** *and similar horiz designs. Multicoloured.* W w **14** (*sideways*). P 14½ × 14.
501 10 c. Type **157** 20 10
502 15 c. *Secunder*, 1907 .. .. .. 25 10
503 50 c. *Hindostan*, 1842 .. .. .. 55 15
504 60 c. *St. Geran*, 1740 .. .. .. 60 15
505 2 r. 50, *Maën*, 1638 .. .. 2·00 4·50
501/5 .. .. .. *Set of* 5 3·25 4·50
MS506 115×138 mm. Nos. 501/5 .. .. 4·50 6·00

158 "The Flame of Hindi carried   **159** Conference Logo and
across the Seas"   Map of Mauritius

(Des N. Nagalingum (Type **158**), C. R. Prakashi and R. B. Kailash (1 r. 20); adapted J. W. Litho Questa)

1976 (28 Aug). *Second World Hindi Convention. T* **158** *and similar horiz design. Multicoloured.* W w **14** (*sideways*). P 14.
507 10 c. Type **158** 10 10
508 75 c. Type **158** 10 15
509 1 r. 20, Hindi script 20 40
507/9 .. .. .. *Set of* 3 30 50

(Des J. W. Litho Questa)

1976 (22 Sept). *22nd Commonwealth Parliamentary Association Conference. T* **159** *and similar vert design. Multicoloured.* W w **14**. P 14.
510 1 r. Type **159** 30 10
511 2 r. 50, Conference logo 80 80

160 King Priest and   **161** Sega Scene
Breastplate

(Des J. W. Litho Walsall)

1976 (15 Dec). *Moenjodaro Excavations, Pakistan. T* **160** *and similar vert designs. Multicoloured.* W w **14**. P 14.
512 60 c. Type **160** 25 10
513 1 r. House with well and goblet .. 40 10
514 2 r. 50, Terracotta figurine and necklace .. 1·00 65
512/14 .. .. .. *Set of* 3 1·50 70

(Des BG Studio. Litho J.W.)

1977 (20 Jan). *Second World Black and African Festival of Arts and Culture, Nigeria.* W w **14** (*sideways*). P 13.
515 **161** 1 r. multicoloured 30 15

162 The Queen with Sceptre   **163** *Hugonia tomentosa*
and Rod

(Des L. Curtis. Litho Harrison)

1977 (7 Feb). *Silver Jubilee. T* **162** *and similar vert designs. Multicoloured.* W w **14** (*sideways*). P 14½ × 14.
516 50 c. The Queen at Mauritius Legislative
    Assembly, 1972 .. .. 20 10
517 75 c. Type **162** 25 10
518 5 r. Presentation of Sceptre and Rod .. 75 75
516/18 .. .. .. *Set of* 3 1·10 75

(Des Jennifer Toombs. Litho Questa)

1977 (22 Sept). *Indigenous Flowers. T* **163** *and similar multicoloured designs.* W w **14** (*sideways on* 20 c. *and* 1 r. 50). P 14.
519 20 c. Type **163** 10 10
520 1 r. *Ochna mauritiana* (*vert*).. .. .. 20 10
521 1 r. 50, *Dombeya acutangula.* 30 20
522 5 r. *Trochetia blackburniana* (*vert*) .. 1·00 1·25
519/22 .. .. *Set of* 4 1·40 1·40
MS523 130 × 130 mm. Nos. 519/22. Wmk sideways 3·00 6·00

164 "Twin Otter"   **165** Portuguese Map of
Mauritius, 1519

(Des A. Theobald. Litho Questa)

1977 (31 Oct). *Inaugural International Flight of Air Mauritius. T* **164** *and similar horiz designs. Multicoloured.* W w **14** (*sideways*). P 14½ × 14.
524 25 c. Type **164** 25 10
525 50 c. "Twin Otter" and Air Mauritius emblem 40 10
526 75 c. Piper "Navajo" and Boeing "747" .. 55 10
527 5 r. Boeing "707" .. .. 2·00 1·50
524/7 .. .. .. *Set of* 4 3·00 1·50
MS528 110 × 152 mm. Nos. 524/7 .. 3·50 3·75

(Des Harrison. Litho J.W.)

1978 (12 Mar)–84. *Designs as T* **165** *in light brown, chestnut and black* (25 r.) *or multicoloured* (*others*). W w **14** (*sideways on horiz designs*). P 13½. A. *Without imprint.* B. *With imprint date at foot.*

		A		B	
529	10 c. Type **165** ..	30	30	40	40
530	15 c. Dutch Occupation, 1638–1710 (*horiz*)..	40	40	†	
531	20 c. Van Keulen's map, *c.* 1700 (*horiz*)	50	45	†	
532	25 c. Settlement on Rodriguez, 1691	30	30	70	30
533	35 c. French charter, 1715	30	30	80	20
534	50 c. Construction of Port Louis, *c.* 1736 (*horiz*)	30	30	75	20
535	60 c. Pierre Poivre, *c.* 1767 ..	40	40	†	
536	70 c. Bellin's map, 1763 (*horiz*) ..	45	45	†	
537	75 c. First coinage, 1794	60	40	60	20
538	90 c. Battle of Grand Port, 1810 (*horiz*)	55	55	†	
539	1 r. British landing, 1810 (*horiz*)	40	20	70	20
540	1 r. 20, Government House, *c.* 1840 (*horiz*)	60	60	†	
541	1 r. 25, Lady Gomm's ball, 1847	70	20	70	20
542	1 r. 50, Indian immigration, 1835 (*horiz*)	60	30	†	
543	2 r. Race course, *c.* 1870 (*horiz*)	60	30	1·00	30
544	3 r. Place d'Armes, *c.* 1880 (*horiz*)	60	30	†	
545	5 r. Royal Visit postcard, 1901 (*horiz*)	60	50	1·50	1·50
546	10 r. Royal College, 1914 (*horiz*)	90	90	†	
547	15 r. Unfurling Mauritian flag, 1968	1·00	1·10	†	
548	25 r. First Mauritian Governor-General and Prime Minister (*horiz*)	2·00	2·25	†	
529A/48A	..	*Set of* 20	11·00	9·50	
529B/45B	..	*Set of* 9		6·50	3·25

Dates of issue:—12.3.78, Nos. 529A/48A; 15.6.83, Nos. 537B, 541B, 543B; 1.84, No. 533B; 11.84, Nos. 529B, 532B, 534B; 4.85, No. 539B; 8.5.85, No. 545B.
Nos. 533B, 537B, 541B and 543B exist with different imprint dates.
For 35 c. as Nos. 533B, but perforated 14½ see No. 737 and for values watermarked w **16** see Nos. 740/57.

166 Mauritius Dodo   **167** Problem of Infection, World War I

(Des Jennifer Toombs. Litho Questa)

1978 (21 Apr). *25th Anniv of Coronation. T* **166** *and similar vert designs.* P 15.
549 3 r. grey-blue, black and new blue .. 25 45
    a. Sheetlet, Nos. 549/51, each × 2 .. .. 1·75
550 3 r. multicoloured 25 45
551 3 r. grey-blue, black and new blue .. 25 45
549/51 .. .. .. *Set of* 3 65 1·25
Designs:—No. 549, Antelope of Bohun; 550, Queen Elizabeth II. Nos. 549/51 were printed together in small sheets of 6, containing two *se-tenant* strips of 3 with horizontal gutter margin between.

(Des Jennifer Toombs. Litho Enschedé)

1978 (3 Aug). *50th Anniv of Discovery of Penicillin. T* **167** *and similar horiz designs.* W w **14** (*sideways*). P 13½ × 14.
552 20 c. multicoloured 30 10
553 1 r. multicoloured 70 10
554 1 r. 50, black, olive-bistre & dp bluish grn .. 1·00 30
555 5 r. multicoloured .. .. 1·75 2·75
552/5 .. .. .. *Set of* 4 3·25 3·00
MS556 150 × 90 mm. Nos. 552/5 .. 3·25 4·25
Designs:—1 r. First mould-growth, 1928; 1 r. 50, *Penicillium notatum*; 5 r. Sir Alexander Fleming.

168 *Papilio manlius* (butterfly)   **169** Ornate Table

(Des G. Drummond. Litho Walsall)

1978 (21 Sept). *World Wildlife. T* **168** *and similar horiz designs. Multicoloured.* W w **14** (*sideways*). P 13½ × 14.
557 20 c. Type **168** 30 10
558 1 r. Geckos 30 10
559 1 r. 50 Greater Mascarene Flying Fox .. 40 30
560 5 r. Mauritius Kestrel .. .. 2·75 3·00
557/60 .. .. *Set of* 4 3·25 3·00
MS561 154 × 148 mm. Nos. 557/60 .. 6·00 6·50

(Des C. Abbott. Litho Questa)

1978 (21 Dec). *Bicentenary of Reconstruction of Chateau Le Réduit. T* **169** *and similar vert designs. Multicoloured.* W w **14**. P 14½ × 14.
562 15 c. Type **169** 10 10
563 75 c. Chateau Le Réduit 10 10
564 3 r. Le Réduit gardens 30 45
562/4 .. .. .. *Set of* 3 40 50

170 Whitcomb Diesel Locomotive   **171** Father Laval and
"65H.P.", 1949   Crucifix

(Des G. Hutchins. Litho Questa)

1979 (1 Feb). *Railway Locomotives. T* **170** *and similar horiz designs. Multicoloured.* W w **14** (*sideways*). P 14½.
565 20 c. Type **170** 15 10
566 1 r. *Sir William*, 1922 .. .. 30 10
567 1 r. 50, Kitson type, 1930 .. .. 40 45
568 2 r. Garratt type, 1927 .. .. 60 85
565/8 .. .. .. *Set of* 4 1·25 1·25
MS569 128 × 128 mm. Nos. 565/8 .. 1·75 2·50

(Des J. W. Litho Questa)

1979 (30 Apr). *Beatification of Father Laval* (*missionary*). *T* **171** *and similar multicoloured designs.* W w **14** (*sideways on* 5 r.). P 14.
570 20 c. Type **171** 10 10
571 1 r. 50, Father Laval 10 10
572 5 r. Father Laval's tomb (*horiz*) .. 35 50
570/2 .. .. .. *Set of* 3 40 55
MS573 150 × 96 mm. Nos. 570/2 (wmk upright) .. 90 1·40

172 Astronaut descending
from Lunar Module
173 Great Britain 1855 4d. Stamp
and Sir Rowland Hill

(Manufactured by Walsall)

1979 (20 July). *10th Anniv of Moon Landing. T* **172** *and similar vert designs. Multicoloured. Imperf × roul 5*. Self-adhesive (from booklets).*
574	20 c. Type **172** ..		15	15
	a. Booklet pane. Nos. 574/6 ..		2·25	
	b. Booklet pane. Nos. 574/5, each × 3		2·25	
575	3 r. Astronaut performing experiment on Moon		70	90
576	5 r. Astronaut on Moon		2·00	3·25
574/6 ..		*Set of 3*	2·50	4·00

*Nos. 574/6 are separated by various combinations of rotary-knife (giving a straight edge) and roulette.

(Des J. W. Litho Questa)

1979 (27 Aug). *Death Centenary of Sir Rowland Hill. T* **173** *and similar vert designs showing stamps and Sir Rowland Hill. Multicoloured. W w* **14**. *P* **14**.
577	25 c. Type **173**		10	10
578	2 r. 1954 60 c. definitive ..		45	50
579	5 r. 1847 1d. "POST OFFICE" ..		90	1·25
577/9 ..		*Set of 3*	1·25	1·60
MS580	120 × 89 mm. 3 r. 1847 2d. "POST OFFICE"		95	1·10

174 Young Child being Vaccinated

(Des V. Whiteley Studio. Litho Questa)

1979 (11 Oct). *International Year of the Child. T* **174** *and similar designs in black, ultramarine and bright blue* (1 r.) *or multicoloured (others). W w* **14** *(sideways on 15, 25 c., 1 r. 50, and 3 r.). P 14½ × 14.*
581	15 c. Type **174** ..		10	10
582	25 c. Children playing..		10	10
583	1 r. I.Y.C. emblem (*vert*)		15	10
584	1 r. 50, Girls in chemistry laboratory		25	20
585	3 r. Boy operating lathe ..		45	50
581/5 ..		*Set of 5*	90	75

175 The Liénard Obelisk
176 *Emirne*

(Des L. Curtis. Litho Questa)

1980 (24 Jan). *Pamplemousses Botanical Gardens. T* **175** *and similar horiz designs. Multicoloured. W w* **14** *(sideways). P 14 × 14½.*
586	20 c. Type **175**		10	10
587	25 c. Poivre Avenue ..		10	10
588	1 r. Varieties of Vacoas ..		20	10
589	2 r. Giant Water Lilies ..		35	45
590	5 r. Mon Plaisir (mansion) ..		60	1·25
586/90		*Set of 5*	1·25	1·75
MS591	152 × 105 mm. Nos. 586/90 ..		2·50	2·75

(Des J. W. Litho Walsall)

1980 (6 May). *"London 1980" International Stamp Exhibition. Mail-carrying Ships. T* **176** *and similar horiz designs. Multicoloured. W w* **14** *(sideways). P 14½ × 14.*
592	25 c. Type **176** ..		15	10
593	1 r. *Boissevain* ..		25	10
594	2 r. *La Boudeuse* ..		45	20
595	5 r. *Sea Breeze* ..		65	80
592/5 ..		*Set of 4*	1·40	1·00

PRICES OF SETS

Set prices are given for many issues, generally those containing three stamps or more. Definitive sets include one of each value or major colour change, but do not cover different perforations, die types or minor shades. Where a choice is possible the set prices are based on the cheapest versions of the stamps included in the listings.

177 Blind Person
Basket-making
178 Prime Minister
Sir Seewoosagur Ramgoolam

(Des J. W. Litho Harrison)

1980 (27 June). *Birth Centenary of Helen Keller (campaigner for the handicapped). T* **177** *and similar vert designs. Multicoloured. W w* **14**. *P* **14**.
596	25 c. Type **177** ..		15	10
597	1 r. Deaf child under instruction		35	10
598	2 r. 50, Helen reading braille		55	35
599	5 r. Helen at graduation, 1904		1·00	90
596/9 ..		*Set of 4*	1·90	1·25

(Des Walsall. Litho and gold foil embossed Questa)

1980 (18 Sept). *80th Birthday and 40th Year in Parliament of Prime Minister Sir Seewoosagur Ramgoolam. W w* **14**. *P* 13½.
600	**178** 15 r. multicoloured		1·25	1·40

No. 600 was printed in sheets of 4 stamps.

179 Headquarters, Mauritius Institute

(Des BG Studio. Litho J.W.)

1980 (1 Oct). *Centenary of Mauritius Institute. T* **179** *and similar horiz designs. Multicoloured. W w* **14** *(sideways). P* 13.
601	25 c. Type **179** ..		15	10
602	2 r. Rare copy of Veda ..		30	15
603	2 r. 50, Rare cone ..		35	20
604	5 r. "Le Torrent" (painting by Harpignies) ..		55	60
601/4 ..		*Set of 4*	1·25	90

180 *Hibiscus liliiflorus*
181 Beau-Bassin/Rose Hill

(Des Jennifer Toombs. Litho Questa)

1981 (15 Jan). *Flowers. T* **180** *and similar vert designs. Multicoloured. W w* **14**. *P* **14**.
605	25 c. Type **180** ..		15	10
606	2 r. *Erythrospermum monticolum* ..		40	45
607	2 r. 50, *Chasalia boryana* ..		50	55
608	5 r. *Hibiscus columnaris* ..		95	1·50
605/8 ..		*Set of 4*	1·75	2·25

(Des L. Curtis. Litho J.W.)

1981 (10 Apr). *Coats of Arms of Mauritius Towns. T* **181** *and similar vert designs. Multicoloured. W w* **14**. *P* 13½ × 13.
609	25 c. Type **181** ..		10	10
610	1 r. 50, Curepipe ..		30	20
611	2 r. Quatre-Bornes ..		35	25
612	2 r. 50, Vacoas/Phoenix ..		40	30
613	5 r. Port Louis ..		75	75
609/13 ..		*Set of 5*	1·75	1·40
MS614	130 × 130 mm. Nos. 609/13. *P* 14..		2·00	3·25

182 Prince Charles
as Colonel-in-Chief,
Royal Regiment of Wales
183 Emmanuel Anquetil
and Guy Rozemont

(Des J. W. Litho Questa)

1981 (22 July). *Royal Wedding. T* **182** *and similar vert designs. Multicoloured. W w* **14**. *P* 14.
615	25 c. Wedding bouquet from Mauritius ..		10	10
616	2 r. 50, Type **182** ..		55	15
617	10 r. Prince Charles and Lady Diana Spencer		1·40	90
615/17 ..		*Set of 3*	1·75	1·00

(Des G. Vasarhelyi. Litho Questa)

1981 (27 Aug). *Famous Politicians and Physician* (5 r). *T* **183** *and similar horiz designs. W w* **14** *(sideways). P* 14½.
618	20 c. black and carmine ..		10	10
619	25 c. black and lemon ..		10	10
620	1 r. 25, black and emerald ..		30	15
621	1 r. 50, black and rose-red ..		35	15
622	2 r. black and ultramarine ..		45	20
623	2 r. 50, black and orange-brown ..		50	30
624	5 r. black and turquoise-blue ..		90	90
618/24		*Set of 7*	2·40	1·60

Designs:—25 c. Remy Ollier and Sookdeo Bissoondoyal; 1 r. 25, Maurice Curé and Barthélemy Ohsan; 1 r. 50, Sir Guy Forget and Renganaden Seeneevassen; 2 r. Sir Abdul Razak Mohamed and Jules Koenig; 2 r. 50, Abdoollatiff Mahomed Osman and Dazzi Rama (Pandit Sahadeo); 5 r. Sir Thomas Lewis and electrocardiogram.

184 Drummer and Piper
185 "Skills"

(Des Jennifer Toombs. Litho Format)

1981 (16 Sept). *Religion and Culture. T* **184** *and similar multicoloured designs. W w* **14** *(sideways on 20 c. and 5 r.). P 14 × 13½ (20 c.), 13½ × 14 (2 r.) or 13½ (5 r.).*
625	20 c. Type **184** ..		10	10
626	2 r. Swami Sivananda (*vert*) ..		55	65
627	5 r. Chinese Pagoda ..		90	1·90
625/7 ..		*Set of 3*	1·40	2·40

The 20 c. value commemorates the World Tamil Culture Conference (1980).

(Des BG Studio. Litho Questa)

1981 (15 Oct). *25th Anniv of Duke of Edinburgh Award Scheme. T* **185** *and similar vert designs. Multicoloured. W w* **14**. *P* 14.
628	25 c. Type **185** ..		10	10
629	1 r. 25, "Service" ..		10	10
630	5 r. "Expeditions" ..		25	30
631	10 r. Duke of Edinburgh ..		50	70
628/31 ..		*Set of 4*	75	1·00

186 Ka'aba (sacred shrine,
Great Mosque of Mecca)
187 Scout Emblem

(Des Jennifer Toombs. Litho Questa)

1981 (26 Nov). *Moslem Year 1400 A.H. Commemoration. T* **186** *and similar vert designs. Multicoloured. W w* **14**. *P* 14½ × 14.
632	25 c. Type **186** ..		10	10
633	2 r. Mecca ..		50	60
634	5 r. Mecca and Ka'aba ..		1·00	1·75
632/4 ..		*Set of 3*	1·40	2·25

(Des C. Abbott. Litho Walsall)

1982 (22 Feb). *75th Anniv of Boy Scout Movement and 70th Anniv of Scouting in Mauritius. T* **187** *and similar horiz designs. W w* **14** *(sideways). P 14 × 14½.*
635	25 c. deep lilac and light green ..		10	10
636	2 r. deep brown and brown-ochre ..		30	30
637	5 r. deep green and yellow-olive ..		70	1·00
638	10 r. deep green and new blue ..		1·25	2·00
635/8 ..		*Set of 4*	2·00	3·00

Designs:—2 r. Lord Baden-Powell and Baden-Powell House; 5 r. Grand Howl; 10 r. Ascent of Pieter Both.

188 Charles Darwin
189 Bride and Groom at
Buckingham Palace

(Des L. Curtis. Litho Questa)

1982 (19 Apr). *150th Anniv of Charles Darwin's Voyage. T* **188** *and similar horiz designs. Multicoloured. W w* **14** *(sideways). P* 14.

639	25 c. Type **188**	10	10
	a. Yellow (background to side panels) omitted		
640	2 r. Darwin's telescope	30	45
641	2 r. 50, Darwin's elephant ride ..	35	55
642	10 r. H.M.S. *Beagle* beached for repairs ..	1·40	2·50
639/42	.. .. *Set of* 4	1·90	3·25

(Des Jennifer Toombs. Litho J. W.)

1982 (1 July). *21st Birthday of Princess of Wales. T* **189** *and similar vert designs. Multicoloured. W w* **14**. *P* 13.

643	25 c. Mauritius coat of arms ..	10	10
644	2 r. 50, Princess Diana in Chesterfield, November 1981	45	35
645	5 r. Type **189**	75	80
646	10 r. Formal portrait	1·25	1·75
643/6	.. .. *Set of* 4	2·25	2·75

190 Prince and Princess of Wales with Prince William   **191** Bois Fandamane Plant

(Des Harrison. Litho Walsall)

1982 (22 Sept). *Birth of Prince William of Wales. W w* **14** *(sideways). P* 14 × 14½.

647	**190** 2 r. 50, multicoloured	65	30

(Des Harrison. Litho Format)

1982 (15 Dec). *Centenary of Robert Koch's Discovery of Tubercle Bacillus. T* **191** *and similar vert designs. Multicoloured. W w* **14**. *P* 14.

648	25 c. Type **191**	10	10
649	1 r. 25, Central market, Port Louis ..	35	30
650	2 r. Bois Banane plant	55	55
651	5 r. Platte de Lézard plant	1·10	1·60
652	10 r. Dr. Robert Koch	2·00	2·75
648/52	.. .. *Set of* 5	3·50	4·75

192 Arms and Flag of Mauritius   **193** Early Wall-mounted Telephone

(Des and litho J.W.)

1983 (14 Mar). *Commonwealth Day. T* **192** *and similar horiz designs. Multicoloured. W w* **14** *(sideways). P* 13.

653	25 c. Type **192**	10	10
654	2 r. 50, Satellite view of Mauritius ..	15	30
655	5 r. Harvesting sugar cane	30	75
656	10 r. Port Louis harbour	70	1·50
653/6	.. .. *Set of* 4	1·10	2·40

(Des G. Vasarhelyi. Litho Format)

1983 (24 June). *World Communications Year. T* **193** *and similar multicoloured designs. W w* **14** *(sideways on 1 r. 25 and 10 r.). P* 14.

657	25 c. Type **193**	10	10
658	1 r. 25, Early telegraph apparatus (*horiz*) ..	50	20
659	2 r. Earth satellite station	90	50
660	10 r. First hot air balloon in Mauritius, 1784 (*horiz*)	2·25	2·75
657/60	.. .. *Set of* 4	3·25	3·25

194 Map of Namibia   **195** Fish Trap

(Des J. W. Litho Questa)

1983 (26 Aug). *Namibia Day. T* **194** *and similar vert designs. Multicoloured. W w* **14**. *P* 14.

661	25 c. Type **194**	30	10
662	2 r. 50, Hands breaking chains ..	1·00	65
663	5 r. Family and settlement ..	1·60	1·75
664	10 r. Diamond mining..	2·75	3·00
661/4	.. .. *Set of* 4	5·00	5·00

(Des Walsall. Litho Format)

1983 (25 Sept). *Fishery Resources. T* **195** *and similar multicoloured designs. W w* **14** *(sideways on 1 r. and 10 r.). P* 14.

665	25 c. Type **195**	15	10
666	1 r. Fishing boat (*horiz*) ..	55	15
667	5 r. Game fishing	1·50	1·75
668	10 r. Octopus drying (*horiz*) ..	2·00	2·75
665/8	.. .. .. *Set of* 4	3·75	4·25

196 Swami Dayananda   **197** Adolf von Plevitz

(Des A. Theobald. Litho Questa)

1983 (3 Nov). *Death Centenary of Swami Dayananda. T* **196** *and similar vert designs. Multicoloured. W w* **14**. *P* 14.

669	25 c. Type **196**	10	10
670	35 c. Last meeting with father ..	10	10
671	2 r. Receiving religious instruction ..	40	45
672	5 r. Swami demonstrating strength ..	80	1·40
673	10 r. At a religious gathering.. ..	1·25	2·75
669/73	.. .. .. *Set of* 5	2·40	4·25

(Des L. Curtis. Litho Harrison)

1983 (8 Dec). *125th Anniv of the Arrival in Mauritius of Adolf von Plevitz (social reformer). T* **197** *and similar horiz designs. Multicoloured. W w* **14** *(sideways). P* 14 × 14½.

674	25 c. Type **197**	10	10
675	30 r. La Laura Government school ..	30	30
676	5 r. Von Plevitz addressing 1872 Commission of Enquiry	90	1·25
677	10 r. Von Plevitz with Indian farm workers	1·50	2·25
674/7	.. .. .. *Set of* 4	2·50	3·50

198 Courtship Chase   **199** Wreck of S.S. *Tayeb*

(Des N. Arlott. Litho Format)

1984 (26 Mar). *Mauritius Kestrel. T* **198** *and similar multicoloured designs. W w* **14** *(sideways on 25 c. and 2 r. 50). P* 14.

678	25 c. Type **198**	45	10
679	2 r. Kestrel in tree (*vert*)	1·00	65
680	2 r. 50, Young Kestrel	1·25	90
681	10 r. Head (*vert*)	2·75	4·00
678/81	.. .. *Set of* 4	5·00	5·00

(Des M. Joyce. Litho Questa)

1984 (23 May). *250th Anniv of "Lloyd's List" (newspaper). T* **199** *and similar vert designs. Multicoloured. W w* **14**. *P* 14½ × 14.

682	25 c. Type **199**	20	10
683	1 r. S.S. *Taher*	65	15
684	5 r. East Indiaman *Triton* ..	1·75	2·25
685	10 r. M.S. *Astor*	2·25	3·50
682/5	.. .. .. *Set of* 4	4·25	5·50

200 Blue Latan Palm   **201** Slave Girl

(Des Jennifer Toombs. Litho Format)

1984 (23 July). *Palm Trees. T* **200** *and similar vert designs. Multicoloured. W w* **14**. *P* 14½.

686	25 c. Type **200**	10	10
687	50 c. *Hyophorbe vaughanii* ..	20	15
688	2 r. 50, *Tectiphiala ferox* ..	1·25	65
689	5 r. Round Island Bottle-palm ..	2·00	2·25
690	10 r. *Hyophorbe amaricaulis* ..	3·25	3·75
686/90	.. .. .. *Set of* 5	6·25	6·25

(Des C. Abbott. Litho Walsall)

1984 (20 Aug). *150th Anniv of the Abolition of Slavery and of the Introduction of Indian Immigrants. T* **201** *and similar designs. W w* **14** *(sideways on 2 r., 10 r.). P* 14½.

691	25 c. deep rose-lilac, rose-lilac and bistre	15	10
692	1 r. deep rose-lilac, rose-lilac and bistre ..	50	10
693	2 r. deep rose-lilac and rose-lilac ..	85	60
694	10 r. deep rose-lilac and rose-lilac ..	2·75	3·25
691/4	.. .. .. *Set of* 4	3·75	3·50

Designs: *Vert*—1 r. Slave market. *Horiz*—2 r. Indian immigrant family; 10 r. Arrival of Indian immigrants.

202 75th Anniversary Production of *Faust* and Leoville L'Homme   **203** The Queen Mother on Clarence House Balcony, 1980

(Des Walsall. Litho Questa)

1984 (10 Sept). *Centenary of Alliance Francaise (cultural organization). T* **202** *and similar horiz designs. Multicoloured. W w* **14** *(sideways). P* 14½ × 14.

695	25 c. Type **202**	15	10
696	1 r. 25, Prize-giving ceremony and Aunauth Beejadbur	50	40
697	5 r. First headquarters and Hector Clarenc ..	1·50	2·00
698	10 r. Lion Mountain and Labourdonnais ..	2·00	3·00
695/8	.. .. .. *Set of* 4	3·75	5·00

(Des A. Theobald (15 r.), C. Abbott (others). Litho Questa)

1985 (7 June). *Life and Times of Queen Elizabeth the Queen Mother. T* **203** *and similar vert designs. Multicoloured. W w* **16**. *P* 14½ × 14.

699	25 c. The Queen Mother in 1926 ..	10	10
700	2 r. With Princess Margaret at Trooping the Colour	30	30
701	5 r. Type **203**	60	1·00
702	10 r. With Prince Henry at his christening (from photo by Lord Snowdon).. ..	1·10	1·75
699/702	.. .. .. *Set of* 4	1·90	2·75
MS703	91 × 73 mm. 15 r. Reopening the Stratford Canal, 1964. Wmk sideways	2·75	2·00

204 High Jumping   **205** Adult and Fledgling Pink Pigeons

(Des Joan Thompson. Litho Walsall)

1985 (24 Aug). *2nd Indian Ocean Islands Games. T* **204** *and similar vert designs. Multicoloured. W w* **14**. *P* 14½.

704	25 c. Type **204**..	20	10
705	50 c. Javelin-throwing	35	15
706	1 r. 25, Cycling	65	55
707	10 r. Wind surfing	3·00	4·00
704/7	.. .. .. *Set of* 4	3·75	4·25

(Des N. Arlott. Litho Walsall)

1985 (2 Sept). *Pink Pigeon. T* **205** *and similar vert designs. Multicoloured. W w* **16**. *P* 14.

708	25 c. Type **205**..	60	15
709	2 r. Pink Pigeon displaying at nest ..	1·50	1·00
710	2 r. 50, On nest	1·75	1·40
711	5 r. Pair preening	2·75	3·25
708/11	.. .. .. *Set of* 4	6·00	5·25

206 Caverne Patates, Rodrigues

(Des D. Miller. Litho Walsall)

1985 (27 Sept). *10th Anniv of World Tourism Organization T* **206** *and similar horiz designs. Multicoloured. W w* **16** *(sideways). P* 14½.

712	25 c. Type **206**..	30	10
713	35 c. Coloured soils, Chamarel ..	30	10
714	5 r. Serpent Island	2·00	2·25
715	10 r. Coin de Mire Island	3·25	3·50
712/15	.. .. .. *Set of* 4	5·25	5·50

207 Old Town Hall, Port Louis

(Des Jennifer Toombs. Litho J.W.)

1985 (22 Nov). *250th Anniv of Port Louis. T 207 and similar horiz designs. Multicoloured. W w 16 (sideways). P 13 × 13½.*
716 25 c. Type **207**. 10 10
717 1 r. Al-Aqsa Mosque (180th anniv) . . 35 10
718 2 r. 50, Vase and trees (250th anniv of settlement of Tamil-speaking Indians) 70 50
719 10 r. Port Louis Harbour . . . . 2·25 2·75
716/19 . . . . . . *Set of 4* 3·00 3·00

208 Edmond Halley and Diagram   **209** Maize (World Food Day)

(Des D. Hartley. Litho Walsall)

1986 (21 Feb). *Appearance of Halley's Comet. T 208 and similar horiz designs. Multicoloured. W w 16 (sideways). P 14.*
720 25 c. Type **208**. 10 10
721 1 r. 25, Halley's Comet (1682) and Newton's Reflector 35 20
722 3 r. Halley's Comet passing Earth. . 70 50
723 10 r. *Giotto* spacecraft . . . . 2·25 2·50
720/3 . . . . . . *Set of 4* 3·00 3·00

(Des A. Theobald. Litho Harrison)

1986 (21 Apr). *60th Birthday of Queen Elizabeth II. Vert designs as T 230a of Jamaica. Multicoloured. W w 16. P 14½×14.*
724 25 c. Princess Elizabeth wearing badge of Grenadier Guards, 1942 . . 10 10
725 75 c. Investiture of Prince of Wales, 1969 . . 10 10
726 2 r. With Prime Minister of Mauritius, 1972 20 25
727 3 r. In Germany, 1978 . . . . 30 35
728 15 r. At Crown Agents Head Office, London, 1983 . . . . . . 1·50 1·75
724/8 . . . . . . *Set of 5* 1·90 2·25

(Des O. Bell. Litho Walsall)

1986 (25 July). *International Events. T 209 and similar vert designs. Multicoloured. W w 16. P 14.*
729 25 c. Type **209**. 10 10
730 1 r. African Regional Industrial Property Organization emblem (10th anniv) . . 30 10
731 1 r. 25, International Peace Year emblem . . 45 25
732 10 r. Footballer and Mauritius Football Association emblem (World Cup Football Championship, Mexico) . . 2·50 2·50
729/32 . . . . . . *Set of 4* 3·00 2·75

210 *Cryptopus elatus*   **211** Hesketh Bell Bridge

(Des Harrison. Litho Walsall)

1986 (3 Oct). *Orchids. T 210 and similar vert designs. Multicoloured. W w 16. P 14½ × 14.*
733 25 c. Type **210**. 30 10
734 2 r. *Jumellea recta* 90 40
735 2 r. 50, *Angraecum mauritianum* . . 1·10 50
736 10 r. *Bulbophyllum longiflorum* . . 2·25 2·50
733/6 . . . . . . *Set of 4* 4·00 3·25

1986 (Nov). *As No. 533B, but printed litho by Questa. P 14½.*
737 35 c. French charter, 1715 . . 60 60

(Litho Questa)

1987 (11 Jan)–**89**. *As Nos. 531/2, 534, 543/5 and 548 but W w 16 (sideways on horiz designs). P 14½.*
740 20 c. Van Keulen's map, c. 1700 (horiz) 30 30
741 25 c. Settlement on Rodriguez, 1691 . . 40 40
743 50 c. Construction of Port Louis, c. 1736 (horiz) (16.1.89) 45 30
752 2 r. Race course, c. 1870 (horiz) . . 60 30
753 3 r. Place d'Armes, c. 1880 (horiz) (16.1.89) 1·00 85
754 5 r. Royal Visit postcard, 1901 (horiz) (16.1.89) 1·40 1·40
757 25 r. First Mauritian Governor-General and Prime Minister (horiz) (16.1.89) 3·00 3·50
740/57 . . . . . . *Set of 7* 6·50 6·25
No. 752 exists with different imprint dates below the design.

(Des D. Hartley. Litho Format)

1987 (22 May). *Mauritius Bridges. T 211 and similar horiz designs. Multicoloured. W w 16 (sideways). P 14½.*
758 25 c. Type **211**. 20 10
759 50 c. Sir Colville Deverell Bridge . . 25 10
760 2 r. 50, Cavendish Bridge . . 80 45
761 5 r. Tamarin Bridge. . . . 1·40 1·25
762 10 r. Grand River North West Bridge 2·00 2·25
758/62 . . . . . . *Set of 5* 4·25 3·75

212 Supreme Court, Port Louis   **213** Dodo Mascot

(Des N. Shewring. Litho Walsall)

1987 (2 June). *Bicentenary of the Mauritius Bar. T 212 and similar horiz designs. Multicoloured. W w 16 (sideways). P 14×14½.*
763 25 c. Type **212**. 10 10
764 1 r. District Court, Flacq 25 10
765 1 r. 25, Statue of Justice 35 20
766 10 r. Barristers of 1787 and 1987 . . 1·40 1·50
763/6 . . . . . . *Set of 4* 1·90 1·75

(Des O. Bell. Litho Format)

1987 (5 Sept). *International Festival of the Sea. T 213 and similar multicoloured designs. W w 16 (sideways on 25 c, 5 r.). P 14×14½ (vert) or 14½×14 (horiz).*
767 25 c. Type **213**. 15 10
768 1 r. 50, Yacht regatta (horiz) . . 60 40
769 3 r. Water skiing (horiz) . . . . 1·25 80
770 5 r. *Svanen* (barquentine) . . . . 1·75 2·00
767/70 . . . . . . *Set of 4* 3·25 3·00

214 Toys   **215** Maison Ouvriere (Int Year of Shelter for the Homeless)

(Des G. Vasarhelyi. Litho Walsall)

1987 (30 Oct). *Industrialisation. T 214 and similar horiz designs. Multicoloured. W w 14 (sideways). P 14.*
771 20 c. Type **214**. 10 10
772 35 c. Spinning factory 10 10
773 50 c. Rattan furniture 10 10
774 2 r. 50, Spectacle factory . . 75 60
775 10 r. Stone carving . . . . 2·00 2·25
771/5 . . . . . . *Set of 5* 2·75 2·75

(Des D. Miller. Litho Walsall)

1987 (30 Dec). *Art and Architecture. T 215 and similar horiz designs. W w 16 (sideways). P 14×14½.*
776 25 c. multicoloured 10 10
777 1 r. black and brownish grey . . 15 10
778 1 r. 25, multicoloured 20 20
779 2 r. multicoloured 35 40
780 5 r. multicoloured . . . . 85 1·00
776/80 . . . . . . *Set of 5* 1·50 1·60
Designs:—1 r. "Paul et Virginie" (lithograph); 1 r. 25, Chateau de Rosnay; 2 r. "Vielle Ferme" (Boulle); 5 r. "Trois Mamelles".

216 University of Mauritius   **217** Breast Feeding

(Des A. Theobald. Litho B.D.T.)

1988 (11 Mar). *20th Anniv of Independence. T 216 and similar horiz designs. Multicoloured. W w 14 (sideways). P 13½.*
781 25 c. Type **216**. 10 10
782 75 c. Anniversary gymnastic display 15 10
783 2 r. 50, Hurdlers and aerial view of Sir Maurice Rault Stadium 55 45
784 5 r. Air Mauritius aircraft at Sir Seewoosagur Ramgoolam International Airport 1·10 1·00
785 10 r. Governor-General Sir Veerasamy Ringadoo and Prime Minister Aneerood Jugnauth . . . . 2·00 2·00
781/5 . . . . . . *Set of 5* 3·50 3·25

(Des D. Ashby. Litho B.D.T.)

1988 (1 July). *40th Anniv of World Health Organization. T 217 and similar vert designs. Multicoloured. W w 14. P 13½.*
786 20 c. Type **217**. 10 10
787 2 r. Baby under vaccination umbrella and germ droplets 80 50
788 3 r. Nutritious food 95 80
789 10 r. W.H.O. logo . . . . 2·25 2·50
786/9 . . . . . . *Set of 4* 3·50 3·50

218 Modern Bank Building   **219** Olympic Rings and Athlete

(Des N. Shewring (25 r.). Litho B.D.T.)

1988 (1 Sept). *150th Anniv of Mauritius Commercial Bank Ltd. T 218 and similar multicoloured designs. W w 14 (sideways on 1, 25 r.). P 13½.*
790 25 c. black, blue-green and new blue 10 10
791 1 r. black and brown-lake . . 15 10
792 1 r. 25, multicoloured . . 30 30
793 25 r. multicoloured . . . . 4·50 4·50
790/3 . . . . . . *Set of 4* 4·50 4·50
Designs: Horiz—1 r. Mauritius Commercial Bank, 1897; 25 r. Fifteen dollar bank note of 1838. Vert—1 r. 25, Bank arms.

(Des P. Broadbent. Litho B.D.T.)

1988 (1 Oct). *Olympic Games, Seoul. T 219 and similar horiz designs. Multicoloured. W w 14 (sideways). P 14.*
794 25 c. Type **219**. 10 10
795 35 c. Wrestling 10 10
796 1 r. 50, Long distance running . . 50 40
797 10 r. Swimming . . . . 2·00 2·50
794/7 . . . . . . *Set of 4* 2·50 2·75

220 Nature Park   **221** La Tour Sumeire, Port Louis

(Des D. Miller. Litho Harrison (40 c. (No. 807), 3 r., 4 r., 6 r., 10 r.) or B.D.T. (others))

1989 (11 Mar)–**91**. *Protection of the Environment. T 220 and similar multicoloured designs. P 14. (a) W w 14 (sideways on horiz designs)*
799 15 c. Underwater view (29.11.90) . . 10 10
800 40 c. Type **220** (19.2.91) . . 10 10
801 1 r. 50, Whimbrel (29.11.90) . . 10 15
802 3 r. Marine life 25 30
803 4 r. Fern Tree (vert) 30 35
804 6 r. Ecological scenery (vert) . . 50 55
805 25 r. Migratory birds and map (vert) (29.11.90) . . . . 2·00 2·10
(b) W w 16 (sideways on horiz designs)
806 30 c. Greenshank (29.11.90) . . 10 10
807 40 c. Type **220** 30 30
808 50 c. Round Island (vert) (4.10.91) 10 10
809 75 c. Bassin Blanc (4.10.91) . . 10 10
810 1 r. Mangrove (vert) (29.11.90) . . 10 10
811 2 r. Le Morne (4.10.91) . . 15 20
812 5 r. Rivière du Poste estuary (4.10.91) 40 45
813 10 r. *Phelsuma ornata* (gecko) on plant (vert) 80 85
814 15 r. Benarès waves (4.10.91) . . 1·25 1·40
799/814 . . . . . . *Set of 16* 5·75 6·25
No. 800, unlike No. 807, shows an imprint date.

(Des A. Theobald. Litho B.D.T.)

1989 (14 July). *Bicentenary of the French Revolution. T 221 and similar vert designs. W w 14. P 14.*
818 30 c. black, emerald & pale greenish yellow 10 10
819 1 r. black, orange-brown and cinnamon . . 20 10
820 8 r. multicoloured . . . . 1·25 1·25
821 15 r. multicoloured . . . . 2·00 2·00
818/21 . . . . . . *Set of 4* 3·25 3·00
Designs:—1 r. Salle de Spectacle du Jardin; 8 r. Portrait of Comte de Malartic; 15 r. Bicentenary logo.

222 Cardinal Jean Margeot   **223** Nehru

(Des L. Curtis. Litho B.D.T.)

1989 (13 Oct). *Visit of Pope John Paul II. T 222 and similar vert designs. Multicoloured. W w 14. P 14×13½.*
822 30 c. Type **222**. 20 10
823 40 c. Pope John Paul II and Prime Minister Jugnauth, Vatican, 1988 . . 30 15

824	3 r.	Mère Marie Magdeleine de la Croix and Chapelle des Filles de Marie, Port Louis, 1864	75	55
825	6 r.	St. Francois d'Assise Church, Pamplemousses, 1756	1·40	1·40
826	10 r.	Pope John Paul II	2·50	2·75
822/6		Set of 5	4·75	4·50

(Des K. Clarkson. Litho B.D.T.)

1989 (14 Nov). *Birth Centenary of Jawaharlal Nehru (Indian statesman). T* **223** *and similar horiz designs. Multicoloured. W* w **16** *(sideways). P* 14.

827	40 c.	Type **223**	20	10
828	1 r. 50,	Nehru with daughter, Indira, and grandsons	40	30
829	3 r.	Nehru and Gandhi	1·00	90
830	4 r.	Nehru with Presidents Nasser and Tito	1·25	1·25
831	10 r.	Nehru with children	2·75	3·00
827/31		Set of 5	5·00	5·00

224 Cane cutting   225 Industrial Estate

(Des D. Miller. Litho B.D.T.)

1990 (10 Jan). *350th Anniv of Introduction of Sugar Cane to Mauritius. T* **224** *and similar horiz designs. Multicoloured. W* w **16** *(sideways). P* 13½.

832	30 c.	Type **224**	10	10
833	40 c.	Sugar factory, 1867	10	10
834	1 r.	Mechanical loading of cane	15	10
835	25 r.	Modern sugar factory	3·50	4·00
832/5		Set of 4	3·50	4·00

(Des L. Curtis. Litho B.D.T.)

1990 (29 Mar). *60th Birthday of Prime Minister Sir Anerood Jugnauth. T* **225** *and similar horiz designs. Multicoloured. W* w **14** *(sideways). P* 13½.

836	35 c.	Type **225**	10	10
837	40 c.	Sir Anerood Jugnauth at desk	10	10
838	1 r. 50,	Mauritius Stock Exchange symbol	20	20
839	4 r.	Jugnauth with Governor-General Sir Seewoosagur Ramgoolam	75	75
840	10 r.	Jugnauth greeting Pope John Paul II	1·75	2·00
836/40		Set of 5	2·50	2·75

226 Desjardins (naturalist) (150th death anniv)   227 Letters from Alphabets

(Des D. Miller. Litho B.D.T.)

1990 (5 July). *Anniversaries. T* **226** *and similar multicoloured designs. W* w **14** *(sideways on 35 c., 8 r.). P* 14.

841	30 c.	Type **226**	10	10
842	35 c.	Logo on TV screen (25th anniv of Mauritius Broadcasting Corporation) (horiz)	10	10
843	6 r.	Line Barracks (now Police Headquarters) (250th anniv)	1·00	1·00
844	8 r.	Town Hall, Curepipe (centenary of municipality) (horiz)	1·40	1·40
841/4		Set of 4	2·25	2·25

(Des G. Vasarhelyi. Litho B.D.T.)

1990 (28 Sept). *International Literacy Year. T* **227** *and similar horiz designs. Multicoloured. W* w **14** *(sideways). P* 14.

845	30 c.	Type **227**	10	10
846	1 r.	Blind child reading Braille	20	10
847	3 r.	Open book and globe	55	55
848	10 r.	Book showing world map with quill pen	1·75	2·00
845/8		Set of 4	2·40	2·50

(Des D. Miller. Litho Questa)

1991 (17 June). *65th Birthday of Queen Elizabeth II and 70th Birthday of Prince Philip. Vert designs as T* **58** *of Kiribati. Multicoloured. W* w **16** *(sideways). P* 14½×14.

849	8 r.	Queen Elizabeth II	1·00	1·25
		a. Horiz pair. Nos. 849/50 separated by label	2·00	2·50
850	8 r.	Prince Philip in Grenadier Guards ceremonial uniform	1·00	1·25

Nos. 849/50 were printed together in a similar sheet format to Nos. 366/7 of Kiribati.

NEW INFORMATION

The editor is always interested to correspond with people who have new information that will improve or correct the Catalogue.

228 City Hall, Port Louis (25th anniv of City status)   229 *Euploea euphon*

(Des G. Vasarhelyi. Litho Questa)

1991 (18 Aug). *Anniversaries and Events. T* **228** *and similar multicoloured designs. W* w **14** *(sideways on 40 c., 10 r.). P* 14.

851	40 c.	Type **228**	10	10
852	4 r.	Colonel Draper (race course founder) (150th death anniv) (vert)	65	65
853	6 r.	Joseph Barnard (engraver) and "POST PAID" 2d. stamp (175th birth anniv) (vert)	85	85
854	10 r.	Spitfire *Mauritius II* (50th anniv of Second World War)	1·75	2·00
851/4		Set of 4	3·00	3·25

(Des I. Loe. Litho Walsall)

1991 (15 Nov). *"Phila Nippon '91" International Stamp Exhibition, Tokyo. Butterflies. T* **229** *and similar horiz designs. W* w **14** *(sideways). P* 14×14½.

855	40 c.	Type **229**	15	10
856	3 r.	*Hypolimnas misippus* (female)	35	35
857	8 r.	*Papilio manlius*	90	1·00
858	10 r.	*Hypolimnas misippus* (male)	1·10	1·25
855/8		Set of 4	2·25	2·40

230 Green Turtle, Tromelin

(Des G. Vasarhelyi. Litho Walsall)

1991 (13 Dec). *Indian Ocean Islands. T* **230** *and similar horiz designs. Multicoloured. W* w **14** *(sideways). P* 14.

859	40 c.	Type **230**	10	10
860	1 r.	Glossy Ibis, Agalega	15	10
861	2 r.	Takamaka flowers, Chagos Archipelago	25	30
862	15 r.	*Lambis violacea* sea shell, St. Brandon	1·75	1·90
859/62		Set of 4	2·00	2·10

231 Pres. Veerasamy Ringadoo and President's Residence   232 Ticolo (mascot)

(Des G. Vasarhelyi. Litho Walsall)

1992 (12 Mar). *Proclamation of Republic. T* **231** *and similar horiz designs. W* w **14** *(sideways). P* 13½×14.

863	40 c.	Type **231**	10	10
864	4 r.	Prime Minister Anerood Jugnauth and Government House	50	60
865	8 r.	Children and rainbow	90	1·00
866	10 r.	Presidential flag	1·10	1·25
863/6		Set of 4	2·40	2·75

(Des G. Vasarhelyi. Litho B.D.T.)

1992 (25 June). *8th African Athletics Championships, Port Louis. T* **232** *and similar multicoloured designs. W* w **14** *(sideways on 4, 5 r.). P* 13½.

867	40 c.	Type **232**	10	10
868	4 r.	Sir Anerood Jugnauth Stadium (horiz)	45	45
869	5 r.	High jumping (horiz)	55	55
870	6 r.	Championships emblem	70	80
867/70		Set of 4	1·60	1·75

233 Bouquet (25th anniv of Fleurir Maurice)   234 Bank of Mauritius Headquarters

(Des D. Miller. Litho B.D.T.)

1992 (13 Aug). *Local Events and Anniversaries. T* **233** *and similar multicoloured designs. W* w **14** *(sideways on 2, 3, 15 r.). P* 13½.

871	40 c.	Type **233**	10	10
872	1 r.	Swami Krishnanandji Maharaj (25th anniv of arrival)	10	10
873	2 r.	Boy with dog (humane education) (horiz)	15	10
874	3 r.	Commission Headquarters (10th anniv of Indian Ocean Commission) (horiz)	25	30
875	15 r.	Radio telescope antenna, Bras d'Eau (project inauguration) (horiz)	1·25	1·40
871/5		Set of 5	1·75	1·90

(Des D. Miller. Litho Walsall)

1992 (29 Oct). *25th Anniv of Bank of Mauritius. T* **234** *and similar multicoloured designs. W* w **14** *(sideways on horiz designs). P* 14½.

876	40 c.	Type **234**	10	10
877	4 r.	Dodo gold coin (horiz)	30	35
878	8 r.	First bank note issue (horiz)	65	70
879	15 r.	Graph of foreign exchange reserves, 1967–92 (horiz)	1·25	1·40
876/9		Set of 4	2·10	2·25

235 Housing Development

(Des G. Vasarhelyi. Litho B.D.T.)

1993 (12 Mar). *25th Anniv of National Day. T* **235** *and similar vert designs. Multicoloured. W* w **14**. *P* 15×14.

880	30 c.	Type **235**	10	10
881	40 c.	Gross domestic product graph on computer screen	10	10
882	3 r.	National colours on map of Mauritius	25	30
883	4 r.	Ballot box	30	35
884	15 r.	Grand Commander's insignia for Order of Star and Key of the Indian Ocean	1·25	1·40
880/4		Set of 5	1·75	2·00

EXPRESS DELIVERY STAMPS

EXPRESS DELIVERY 15c.
(E 1)

EXPRESS DELIVERY (INLAND) 15c.
(E 2)

EXPRESS DELIVERY (INLAND) 15 c.
(E 3)

EXPRESS DELIVERY (INLAND) 15 c
(E 4)

Type E 2. "(INLAND)" was inserted at a second printing on stamps already surcharged with Type E 1 (No. E1).

Type E 3. New setting made at one printing. More space above and below "(INLAND)".

Type E 4. New setting with smaller "15 c" and no stop.

1903 (10 Aug)–04. *No.* 136 *surch locally in red.*

E1	E 1	15 c. on 15 c. ultramarine	4·25	15·00
E2	E 2	15 c. on 15 c. ultramarine (28.3.04)	15·00	22·00
		a. "A" inverted	£300	£275
E3	E 3	15 c. on 15 c. ultramarine (4.04)	4·25	85
		a. Surch inverted		£200
		b. Surch double, both inverted		
		c. Imperf between (vert pair)		£1900
E4	E 4	15 c. on 15 c. ultramarine (1904)	£170	£180
		a. Surch inverted		
		b. Surch double		
		c. Surch double, both inverted		
		d. "c" omitted		—£1000

(FOREIGN)
EXPRESS
DELIVERY
18 CENTS
(E 5)

1904. *T* **42** (*without value in label*), *surch with Type* E **5** *locally.*
Wmk Crown CC. P 14.
E5	18 c. green	1·50	12·00
	a. Exclamation mark for "I" in "FOREIGN"	£250	

1904. *T* **42** (*without value in label*) *surch with Type* E **3** *locally.*
E6	15 c. grey-green (R.)	1·25	1·25
	a. Surch inverted	£250	£250
	b. Surch double	£200	
	c. Surch double, one "LNIAND"	£200	£200

POSTAGE DUE STAMPS

POSTAGE
DUE
10c

D 1   (D 2)

(Typo Waterlow)

1933–54. *Wmk Mult Script CA. P* 15 × 14.
D1	D 1	2 c. black		35	50
D2		4 c. violet		40	65
D3		6 c. scarlet		40	80
D4		10 c. green		40	70
D5		20 c. bright blue		50	90
D6		50 c. deep magenta (1.3.54)		55	7·00
D7		1 r. orange (1.3.54)		70	10·00
D1/7			Set of 7	3·00	18·00
D1/5	Perf "Specimen"		Set of 5	60·00	

(Typo D.L.R.)

1966–72. *Wmk w* **12.** *Chalk-surfaced paper. P* 13½×14 (2 *c*.) *or*
15×14 (*others*).
D 8	D 1	2 c. black (11.7.67)		1·50	2·25
D 9		4 c. slate-lilac (7.1.69)		1·75	4·25
D10		6 c. red-orange (7.1.69)		3·50	10·00
		a. Perf 13½×14		18·00	
D11		10 c. yellow-green (16.2.67)		30	1·00
D12		20 c. blue (3.1.66)		1·50	4·00
		a. Deep blue (7.1.69)		2·00	5·00
D13		50 c. deep magenta (7.1.69)		75	7·00
		a. Magenta (10.1.72)		1·00	9·00
D8/13			Set of 6	8·50	26·00

1982 (25 Oct). *Nos.* 530A/1A, 535A, 540A, 542A *and* 547A *optd*
as Type D **2,** *by J. W. Dunn Printers Ltd.*
D14	10 c. on 15 c. Dutch Occupation, 1638–1710	10	10
D15	20 c. on 20 c. Van Keulen's map, circa 1700	10	10
D16	50 c. on 60 c. Pierre Poivre, circa 1767	10	10
D17	1 r. on 1 r. 20, Government House, circa 1840	10	10
D18	1 r. 50 on 1 r. 50, Indian immigration, 1835	10	10
D19	5 r. on 15 r. Unfurling Mauritian flag, 1968	40	45
D14/19	Set of 6	60	70

FISCALS USED FOR POSTAGE

INLAND
REVENUE
(F 1)

INLAND (F 2)
REVENUE

F 3

1889. *T* **19,** *wmk Crown CA, optd. P* 14.
R1	F 1	4 c. carmine	4·50	5·00
R2	F 2	4 c. lilac	2·50	10·00

(Typo D.L.R.)
1896. *Wmk Crown CA. P* 14.
R3	F 3	4 c. dull purple	16·00

Montserrat

A local post office operated on Montserrat from some time early in the 18th century, although the first recorded postal marking does not occur until 1791. A branch of the British G.P.O. was established at Plymouth, the island capital, in 1852.

The stamps of Great Britain were used from 1858 until the overseas postal service reverted to local control on 1 April 1860. In the interim period between 1860 and the introduction of Montserrat stamps in 1876 No. CC1 and a similar "uncrowned" handstamp were again used.

PLYMOUTH
CROWNED-CIRCLE HANDSTAMPS

C 1

CC1 C 1 MONTSERRAT (R.) (15.7.1852) *Price on cover* £2500
No. CC1 was used as an emergency measure, struck in black, during 1886.

Stamps of GREAT BRITAIN *cancelled* "A 08" *as Type Z 1 of Jamaica.*

1858 (8 May) *to* **1860.**

Z1	1d. rose-red (1857), *perf* 14		£1100
Z2	4d. rose (1857)		
Z3	6d. lilac (1856)		
Z4	1s. green (1856)		£450

PRICES FOR STAMPS ON COVER TO 1945

Nos. 1/2	*from* × 40
No. 3	†
Nos. 4/5	*from* × 8
Nos. 6/13	*from* × 12
Nos. 14/22	*from* × 4
No. 23	—
Nos. 24/33	*from* × 4
Nos. 35/47	*from* × 3
No. 48	—
Nos. 49/59	*from* × 3
Nos. 60/2	*from* × 15
Nos. 63/83	*from* × 3
Nos. 84/93	*from* × 4
Nos. 94/7	*from* × 3
Nos. 98/100	*from* × 8
Nos. 101/12	*from* × 5

MONTSERRAT

1	(2)	3 (Die I)
	ONE PENNY	HALF PENNY

(T 1 recess D.L.R.)

1876 (Sept). *Stamps of Antigua optd with T 2. Wmk Crown CC. P 14.*

1	1	1d. red		19·00 15·00
		a. Bisected (½d.) (on cover)		† £1400
		b. Inverted "S"		£1200 £1000
2		6d. green		55·00 40·00
		a. Bisect (used as 2½d.) (on cover)		† £5000
		b. Inverted "S"		£1500 £1300
3		6d. blue-green		£1100
		a. Inverted "S"		£5500

Nos. 1/3 were overprinted either from a setting of 120 (12×10) or from a setting of 60 (6×10) applied twice to each sheet. This setting of 60 had an inverted "S" on R. 3/3. The same setting was subsequently used for some sheets of Nos. 7 and 13.

No. 1 was bisected and used for a ½d. in 1883. This bisected stamp is found surcharged with a small "½" in *black* and also in *red*; both were unofficial and they did not emanate from the Montserrat P.O.

The 6d. in blue-green is only known unused.

(T 3 typo D.L.R.)

1880 (Jan). *Wmk Crown CC. P 14.*

4	3	2½d. red-brown		£250 £180
5		4d. blue		£140 40·00

1884–85. *Wmk Crown CA. P 14.*

6	3	½d. dull green		1·00 5·50
7	1	1d. red		9·00 17·00
		a. Inverted "S"		£1000 £1000
		b. Rose-red (1885)		13·00 14·00
		ba. Bisected vert (½d.) (on cover)		† £1300
		bb. Inverted "S"		£1100 £1100
9	3	2½d. red-brown		£225 65·00
10		2½d. ultramarine (1885)		14·00 16·00
11		4d. blue		£2250 £250
12		4d. mauve (1885)		3·25 3·00
10, 12 Optd "Specimen"			*Set of 2* £275

1884 (May). *Wmk Crown CA. P 12.*

13	1	1d. red		70·00 45·00
		a. Inverted "S"		£2250 £1500
		b. Bisected (½d.) (on cover)		† £1600

The stamps for Montserrat were superseded by the general issue for Leeward Islands in November 1890, but the following issues were in concurrent use with the stamps inscribed "LEEWARD ISLANDS" until 1 July 1956, when Leeward Islands stamps were withdrawn and invalidated.

4 Device of the Colony	5

(Typo D.L.R.)

1903 (Aug). *(a) Wmk Crown CA. P 14.*

14	4	½d. grey-green and green		65 6·00
15		1d. grey-black and red		60 40
16		2d. grey and brown		5·00 13·00
17		2½d. grey and blue		1·50 1·75
18		3d. dull orange and deep purple		4·00 16·00
19		6d. dull purple and olive		4·00 26·00
20		1s. green and bright purple		10·00 16·00
21		2s. green and brown-orange		23·00 16·00
22		2s. 6d. green and black		15·00 30·00

(b) *Wmk Crown CC. P 14*

23	5	5s. black and scarlet		80·00 £140
14/23			*Set of 10*	£120 £225
14/23 Optd "Specimen"			*Set of 10*	£160

1904–08. *Wmk Mult Crown CA. Ordinary paper* (½d., 2d., 3d., 6d.) *or chalk-surfaced paper* (others). *P 14.*

24	4	½d. grey-green and green		80 80
		a. Chalk-surfaced paper (3.06)		40 75
25		1d. grey-black and red (1905)		12·00 20·00
26		2d. grey and brown		65 2·25
		a. Chalk-surfaced paper (5.06)		90 1·00
27		2½d. grey and blue (1905)		2·50 6·50
28		3d. dull orange and deep purple		3·25 3·25
		a. Chalk-surfaced paper (1908)		3·25 2·50
29		6d. dull purple and olive		2·50 8·00
		a. Chalk-surfaced paper (1908)		3·00 5·00
30		1s. green and bright purple (1908)		8·50 5·50
31		2s. green and orange (1908)		23·00 35·00
32		2s. 6d. green and black (1908)		35·00 35·00
33	5	5s. black and red (1907)		65·00 £100
24/33			*Set of 10*	£120 £180

1908 (June)–**14.** *Wmk Mult Crown CA. Ordinary paper* (½d. to 2½d.) *or chalk-surfaced paper* (3d. to 5s.). *P 14.*

35	4	½d. deep green (4.10)		1·75 80
36		1d. rose-red		1·40 30
38		2d. greyish slate (9.09)		1·75 8·00
39		2½d. blue		2·25 3·50
40		3d. purple/*yellow* (9.09)		1·00 11·00
		a. *White back* (1.14) (Optd S. £25)		2·50 22·00
43		6d. dull and deep purple (9.09)		6·50 30·00
		a. *Dull and bright purple* (1914)		7·50 30·00
44		1s. black/*green* (9.09)		3·50 16·00
45		2s. purple and bright blue/*blue* (9.09)		24·00 38·00
46		2s. 6d. black and red/*blue* (9.09)		30·00 48·00
47	5	5s. red and green/*yellow* (9.09)		48·00 60·00
35/47			*Set of 10*	£100 £190
35/47 Optd "Specimen"			*Set of 10*	£190

7	8	WAR STAMP (9)

(T 7/8 typo D.L.R.)

1914. *Wmk Mult Crown CA. Chalk-surfaced paper. P 14.*

48	7	5s. red and green/*yellow*		48·00 75·00
48 Optd "Specimen"				75·00

1916 (10 Oct)–**23.** *Wmk Mult Crown CA. Ordinary paper* (½d. to 2½d.) *or chalk-surfaced paper* (3d. to 5s.). *P 14.*

49	8	½d. green		30 1·75
50		1d. scarlet		35 75
		a. Carmine-red		7·50 5·00
51		2d. grey		1·00 4·00
52		2½d. bright blue		1·50 9·00
53		3d. purple/*yellow*		75 5·00
		a. On pale yellow (1922) (Optd S. £20)		75 6·00
54		4d. grey-black and red/*pale yellow* (1923)		4·75 17·00
55		6d. dull and deep purple		2·75 15·00
56		1s. black/*blue-green* (olive back)		3·00 14·00
57		2s. purple and blue/*blue*		10·00 16·00
58		2s. 6d. black and red/*blue*		22·00 32·00
59		5s. green and red/*yellow*		38·00 48·00
49/59			*Set of 11*	70·00 £150
49/59 Optd "Specimen"			*Set of 11*	£160

1917 (Oct)–**18.** *No. 49 optd with T 9.*

60	8	½d. green (R.)		10 1·00
61		½d. green (Blk.) (6.18)		15 1·25
		a. Deep green (10.18)		15 1·00
		ab. "C" and "A" missing from wmk		

No. 61ab shows the "C" omitted from one impression and the "A" missing from the next.

1919 (Mar). *T 8. Special printing in orange. Value and "WAR STAMP" as T 9 inserted in black at one printing.*

62		1½d. black and orange		10 30
60/2 Optd "Specimen"			*Set of 3*	80·00

1922 (13 July)–**29.** *Wmk Mult Script CA. Ordinary paper* (¼d. to 3d. (No. 73) *or chalk-surfaced paper* (others). *P 14.*

63	8	¼d. brown		15 3·25
64		½d. green (5.4.23)		20 30
65		1d. bright violet (5.4.23)		30 30
66		1d. carmine (1929)		75 70
67		1½d. orange-yellow		1·75 9·50
68		1½d. carmine (5.4.23)		30 1·75
69		1½d. red-brown (1929)		70 50
70		2d. grey		45 1·00
71		2½d. deep bright blue		6·50 13·00
		a. *Pale brt blue* (17.8.26) (Optd S. £30)		60 90
72		2½d. orange-yellow (5.4.23)		1·25 18·00
73		3d. dull blue (5.4.23)		50 11·00
74		3d. purple/*yellow* (2.1.27)		1·10 4·75
75		4d. black and red/*pale yellow*		60 5·00
76		5d. dull purple and olive		2·50 10·00
77		6d. pale and bright purple (5.4.23)		1·00 6·00
78		1s. black/*emerald* (5.4.23)		3·00 7·00
79		2s. purple and blue/*blue*		3·50 11·00
80		2s. 6d. black and red/*blue* (5.4.23)		11·00 30·00
81		3s. green and violet		12·00 17·00
82		4s. black and scarlet		13·00 22·00
83		5s. green and red/*pale yellow* (6.23)		19·00 27·00
63/83			*Set of 21*	60·00 £160
63/83 Optd/Perf "Specimen"			*Set of 21*	£275

10 Plymouth

(Recess D.L.R.)

1932 (18 April). *Tercentenary. Wmk Mult Script CA. P 14.*

84	10	½d. green		75 3·25
85		1d. scarlet		75 2·75
86		1½d. red-brown		1·25 2·00
87		2d. grey		1·25 11·00
88		2½d. ultramarine		1·25 9·50
89		3d. orange		1·50 9·00
90		6d. violet		2·25 18·00
91		1s. olive-brown		8·50 25·00
92		2s. 6d. purple		48·00 60·00
93		5s. chocolate		£100 £130
84/93			*Set of 10*	£150 £225
84/93 Perf "Specimen"			*Set of 10*	£225

1935 (6 May). *Silver Jubilee. As Nos. 114/17 of Jamaica, but ptd by Waterlow & Sons. P 11×12.*

94		1d. deep blue and scarlet		85 1·75
95		1½d. ultramarine and grey		75 2·50
96		2½d. brown and deep blue		2·25 1·25
97		1s. slate and purple		3·00 7·50
94/7			*Set of 4*	6·25 11·50
94/7 Perf "Specimen"			*Set of 4*	75·00

1937 (12 May). *Coronation. As Nos. 118/20 of Jamaica.*

98		1d. scarlet		30 40
99		1½d. yellow-brown		40 25
100		2½d. bright blue		40 60
98/100			*Set of 3*	1·00 1·10
98/100 Perf "Specimen"			*Set of 3*	50·00

11 Carr's Bay	12 Sea Island Cotton

13 Botanic Station

(Recess D.L.R.)

1938 (2 Aug)–**48.** *Wmk Mult Script CA. P 12* (10s., £1) *or 13* (others).

101	11	½d. blue-green		70 85
		a. Perf 14 (1942)		10 15
102	12	1d. carmine		60 40
		a. Perf 14 (1943)		20 20
103		1½d. purple		9·00 50
		a. Perf 14 (1942)		20 40
104	13	2d. orange		5·50 60
		a. Perf 14 (1942)		30 50
105	12	2½d. ultramarine		55 40
		a. Perf 14 (1943)		40 30
106	11	3d. brown		70 40
		a. Perf 14, *Red-brown* (1942)		40 50
		ab. *Deep brown* (1943)		7·50 4·75
107	13	6d. violet		3·00 60
		a. Perf 14 (1943)		75 40
108	11	1s. lake		5·50 70
		a. Perf 14 (1942)		50 30

109	13	2s. 6d. slate-blue	11·00	70
		a. Perf 14 (1943)	12·00	2·25
110	11	5s. rose-carmine	17·00	7·50
		a. Perf 14 (1942)	13·00	2·75
111	13	10s. pale blue (1948)	13·00	16·00
112	11	£1 black (1948)	13·00	23·00
101a/12		*Set of 12*	48·00	40·00
101/12	Perf "Specimen"	*Set of 12*	£250	

1946 (1 Nov). *Victory. As Nos. 141/2 of Jamaica.*

113	1½d. purple		10	10
114	3d. chocolate		10	10
113/14	Perf "Specimen"	*Set of 2*	55·00	

1949 (3 Jan). *Royal Silver Wedding. As Nos. 143/4 of Jamaica.*

115	2½d. ultramarine		10	10
116	5s. carmine		4·50	2·75

1949 (10 Oct). *75th Anniv of U.P.U. As Nos. 145/8 of Jamaica.*

117	2½d. ultramarine		15	30
118	3d. brown		30	30
119	6d. purple		30	30
120	1s. purple		35	30
117/20		*Set of 4*	1·00	1·10

(New Currency. 100 cents = 1 dollar)

1951 (16 Feb). *Inauguration of B.W.I. University College. As Nos. 149/50 of Jamaica.*

121	3 c. black and purple		20	15
122	12 c. black and violet		20	20

14 Government House   **18** Badge of Presidency

(Recess B.W.)

1951 (17 Sept). *T **14**, **18** and similar horiz designs. Wmk Mult Script CA. P 11½ × 11.*

123	14	1 c. black		10	45
124	—	2 c. green		15	40
125	—	3 c. orange-brown		30	45
126	—	4 c. carmine		30	20
127	—	5 c. reddish violet		30	40
128	18	6 c. olive-brown		30	20
129	—	8 c. deep blue		35	20
130	—	12 c. blue and chocolate		35	30
131	—	24 c. carmine and yellow-green		60	30
132	—	60 c. black and carmine		3·25	1·75
133	—	$1.20, yellow-green and blue		5·50	2·75
134	—	$2.40, black and green		4·50	12·00
135	18	$4.80, black and purple		15·00	16·00
123/135		*Set of 13*		28·00	32·00

Designs:—2 c., $1.20, Sea Island cotton: cultivation; 3 c. Map of colony; 4, 24 c. Picking tomatoes; 5, 12 c. St. Anthony's Church; 8, 60 c. Sea Island cotton: ginning; $2.40, Government House.

1953 (2 June). *Coronation. As No. 153 of Jamaica.*

136	2 c. black and deep green		10	10

19 Government House   **20** Shakespeare and Memorial Theatre, Stratford-upon-Avon

Types **16** and **18**: I. inscr "PRESIDENCY". II. inscr "COLONY".

(Recess B.W.)

1953 (15 Oct)–**62.** *As King George VI issue, but with portrait of Queen Elizabeth II as in T **19**. Wmk Mult Script CA. P 11½ × 11.*

136a	—	½ c. deep violet (I) (3.7.56)		30	10
136b	—	½ c. deep violet (II) (1.9.58)		30	10
137	19	1 c. black		10	10
138	—	2 c. green		10	10
139	—	3 c. orange-brown (I)		30	10
139a	—	3 c. orange-brown (II) (1.9.58)		35	15
140	—	4 c. carmine-red (1.6.55)		30	15
141	—	5 c. reddish lilac (1.6.55)		30	30
142	18	6 c. deep bistre-brown (I) (1.6.55)		20	10
142a	—	6 c. deep bistre-brown (II) (1.9.58)		40	15
		ab. Deep sepia-brown (30.7.62)		2·25	1·25
143	—	8 c. deep bright blue (1.6.55)		40	10
144	—	12 c. blue and red-brown (1.6.55)		75	10
145	—	24 c. carmine-red and green (1.6.55)		1·00	10
145a	—	48 c. yellow-olive and purple (15.10.57)		9·00	2·00
146	—	60 c. black and carmine (1.6.55)		4·50	1·25
147	—	$1.20, green and greenish blue (1.6.55)		8·50	4·00
148	—	$2.40, black and bluish green (1.6.55)		5·50	8·50
149	18	$4.80, black & deep purple (I) (1.6.55)		6·00	10·00
149a	—	$4.80, black & deep purple (II) (1.9.58)		6·00	7·00
136a/149a		*Set of 15*		35·00	21·00

Extra designs:—½, 3 c. Map of colony; 48 c. Sea Island cotton: cultivation.

See also No. 157.

1958 (22 Apr). *Inauguration of British Caribbean Federation. As Nos. 175/7 of Jamaica.*

150	3 c. deep green		40	20
151	6 c. blue		55	35
152	12 c. scarlet		70	15
150/2		*Set of 3*	1·50	60

1963 (8 July). *Freedom from Hunger. As No. 80 of Lesotho.*

153	12 c. reddish violet		30	15

1963 (2 Sept). *Red Cross Centenary. As Nos. 203/4 of Jamaica.*

154	4 c. red and black		10	10
155	12 c. red and blue		25	25

(Des R. Granger Barrett. Photo Harrison)

1964 (23 Apr). *400th Birth Anniv of William Shakespeare. W w 12. P 14 × 14½.*

156	20	12 c. indigo	10	10

1964 (29 Oct). *As No. 138 but wmk w **12**.*

157	2 c. green		15	15

1965 (17 May). *I.T.U. Centenary. As Nos. 98/9 of Lesotho.*

158	4 c. vermilion and violet		15	10
159	48 c. light emerald and carmine		30	20

21 Pineapple   **22** Avocado

(Des Sylvia Goaman. Photo Harrison)

1965 (16 Aug). *T **21**/2 and similar vert designs showing vegetables, fruit or plants. Multicoloured. W w **12** (upright). P 15×14.*

160	1 c. Type **21**		10	10
161	2 c. Type **22**		10	10
162	3 c. Soursop		10	10
163	4 c. Pepper		10	10
164	5 c. Mango		10	10
165	6 c. Tomato		10	10
166	8 c. Guava		10	10
167	10 c. Ochro		10	10
168	12 c. Lime		15	10
169	20 c. Orange		20	10
170	24 c. Banana		20	10
171	42 c. Onion		75	60
172	48 c. Cabbage		1·25	75
173	60 c. Pawpaw		2·00	90
174	$1.20, Pumpkin		2·00	1·75
175	$2.40, Sweet potato		5·50	2·50
176	$4.80, Egg plant		5·50	6·00
160/76		*Set of 17*	16·00	12·00

See also Nos. 213/22.

1965 (25 Oct). *International Co-operation Year. As Nos. 100/1 of Lesotho.*

177	2 c. reddish purple and turquoise-green		10	20
178	12 c. deep bluish green and lavender		25	10

1966 (26 Jan). *Churchill Commemoration. As Nos. 102/5 of Lesotho.*

179	1 c. new blue		10	10
	a. Cerise (sky) omitted		£180	
180	2 c. deep green		10	10
181	24 c. brown		15	10
182	42 c. bluish violet		20	15
179/82		*Set of 4*	40	30

23 Queen Elizabeth II and Duke of Edinburgh

(Des H. Baxter. Litho B.W.)

1966 (4 Feb). *Royal Visit. W w **12**. P 11×12.*

183	23	14 c. black and ultramarine	40	15
184		24 c. black and magenta	60	15

24 W.H.O. Building

(Des M. Goaman. Litho Harrison)

1966 (20 Sept). *Inauguration of W.H.O. Headquarters, Geneva. W w **12** (sideways). P 14.*

185	24	12 c. black, yellow-green and light blue	10	10
186		60 c. black, light purple and yellow-brown	25	20

1966 (1 Dec). *20th Anniv of U.N.E.S.C.O. As Nos. 342/4 of Mauritius.*

187	4 c. slate-violet, red, yellow and orange		10	10
	a. Orange omitted		50·00	
188	60 c. orange-yellow, violet and deep olive		20	10
189	$1.80, black, bright purple and orange		70	70
187/9	*Set of 3*		80	75

On No. 187a the omission of the orange only affects the squares of the lower case letters so that they appear yellow, the same as the capital squares.

   $1.00

25 Yachting   (26)

(Des and photo Harrison)

1967 (29 Dec). *International Tourist Year. T **25** and similar multicoloured designs. W w **12** (sideways on 15 c.). P 14.*

190	5 c. Type **25**		10	10
191	15 c. Waterfall near Chance Mountain (vert)		15	10
192	16 c. Fishing, skin-diving and swimming		15	15
193	24 c. Playing golf		50	15
190/3	*Set of 4*		80	40

1968 (6 May). *Nos. 168, 170, 172 and 174/6 surch as T **26**. W w 12 (upright).*

194	15 c. on 12 c. Lime		20	15
195	25 c. on 24 c. Banana		25	15
196	50 c. on 48 c. Cabbage		45	15
197	$1 on $1.20, Pumpkin		1·50	40
198	$2.50 on $2.40, Sweet potato		2·00	3·00
199	$5 on $4.80, Egg plant		2·50	3·75
194/9	*Set of 6*		6·00	7·00

See also Nos. 219 etc.

27 Sprinting   **28** Sprinting, and Aztec Pillars

(Des G. Vasarhelyi. Photo Harrison)

1968 (31 July). *Olympic Games, Mexico. T **27**/8 and similar designs. W w **12** (sideways on $1). P 14.*

200	15 c. deep claret, emerald and gold		10	10
201	25 c. blue, orange and gold		10	10
202	50 c. green, red and gold		10	10
203	$1 multicoloured		20	20
200/3	*Set of 4*		35	30

Designs: *Horiz as T **27***—25 c. Weightlifting; 50 c. Gymnastics.

31 Alexander Hamilton

(Des and photo Harrison)

1968 (6 Dec*). *Human Rights Year. T **31** and similar horiz designs. Multicoloured. W w **12**. P 14 × 14½.*

204	5 c. Type **31**		10	10
205	15 c. Albert T. Marryshow		10	10
206	25 c. William Wilberforce		10	10
207	50 c. Dag Hammarskjöld		10	10
208	$1 Dr. Martin Luther King		25	30
204/8	*Set of 5*		40	45

*Although first day covers were postmarked 2 December, these stamps were not put on sale in Montserrat until 6 December.

32 "The Two Trinities" (Murillo)   **33** "The Adoration of the Kings" (detail, Botticelli)

(Des and photo Harrison)

1968 (16 Dec). *Christmas.* W w **12** (sideways). P 14½ × 14.
209	32	5 c. multicoloured				10	10
210	33	15 c. multicoloured				10	10
211	32	25 c. multicoloured				10	10
212	33	50 c. multicoloured				15	20
209/12					Set of 4	30	30

1969–70. *As Nos. 160/4, 167, 169 and 194/6 but wmk w* **12** *sideways.*
213		1 c. Type **21** (24.6.69)				10	10
214		2 c. Type **22** (23.4.70)				60	75
215		3 c. Soursop (24.6.69)				20	15
216		4 c. Pepper (24.6.69)				35	15
217		5 c. Mango (23.4.70)				80	85
218		10 c. Ochro (24.6.69)				50	25
219		15 c. on 12 c. Lime (24.6.69)				60	40
220		20 c. Orange (17.3.69)				65	45
221		25 c. on 24 c. Banana (24.6.69)				90	85
222		50 c. on 48 c. Cabbage (24.6.69)				4·00	6·00
213/22					Set of 10	8·00	9·00

The 1 c., 3 c., 4 c., 10 c., 15 c. and 20 c. exist with PVA gum as well as gum arabic, but the 2 c. and 5 c. exist with PVA gum only.

34 Map showing "CARIFTA" Countries

35 "Strength in Unity"

(Des J. Cooter. Photo Harrison)

1969 (27 May). *First Anniv of CARIFTA (Caribbean Free Trade Area).* W w **12** (sideways on T **34**). P 14.
223	34	15 c. multicoloured				10	10
224		20 c. multicoloured				10	10
225	35	35 c. multicoloured				10	10
226		50 c. multicoloured				15	15
223/6					Set of 4	30	30

36 Telephone Receiver and Map of Montserrat

40 Dolphin

(Des R. Reid, adapted by V. Whiteley. Litho P.B.)

1969 (29 July). *Development Projects.* T **36** *and similar vert designs. Multicoloured.* W w **12**. P 13½.
227	36	15 c. Type **36**				10	10
228		25 c. School symbols and map				10	10
229		50 c. "HS 748" aircraft and map				15	10
230		$1 Electricity pylon and map				25	20
227/30					Set of 4	35	30

(Des Harrison. Photo Enschedé)

1969 (1 Nov). *Game Fish.* T **40** *and similar horiz designs. Multicoloured.* P 13 × 13½.
231	40	5 c. Type **40**				20	10
232		15 c. Atlantic sailfish				35	10
233		25 c. Blackfin tuna				40	10
234		40 c. Spanish mackerel				65	30
231/4					Set of 4	1·40	50

41 King Caspar before the Virgin and Child (detail) (Norman 16th-cent stained glass window)

42 "Nativity" (Leonard Limosin)

(Des J. Cooter. Litho D.L.R.)

1969 (10 Dec). *Christmas. Paintings multicoloured; frame colours given.* W w **12** (sideways on 50 c.). P 13.
235	41	15 c. black, gold and violet				10	10
236		25 c. black and vermilion				10	10
237	42	50 c. black, ultramarine & yellow-orange				15	15
235/7					Set of 3	30	20

43 "Red Cross Sale"

(Des and litho J.W.)

1970 (13 Apr). *Centenary of British Red Cross.* T **43** *and similar horiz designs. Multicoloured.* W w **12** (sideways). P 14½ × 14.
238		3 c. Type **43**				10	10
239		4 c. School for deaf children				10	10
240		15 c. Transport services for disabled				10	10
241		20 c. Workshop				10	20
238/41					Set of 4	30	30

44 Red-footed Booby

45 "Madonna and Child with Animals" (Brueghel the Elder, after Dürer)

(Des V. Whiteley. Photo Harrison)

1970 (2 July)–**74.** *Birds.* T **44** *and similar multicoloured designs.* W w **12** (sideways on vert designs and upright on horiz designs). P 14 × 14½ (horiz) or 14½ × 14 (vert).

A. *Chalk-surfaced paper* (2.7.70).
B. *Glazed, ordinary paper* (30.10.74, $10; 22.1.71, others).

			A		B	
242	1 c. Type **44**		10	10	†	
243	2 c. American Kestrel		15	15	80	1·50
244	3 c. Magnificent Frigate Bird		15	15	†	
245	4 c. Great Egret		40	15	†	
246	5 c. Brown Pelican		80	10	80	1·00
247	10 c. Bananaquit		30	10	1·00	1·50
248	15 c. Smooth-billed Ani		30	15	3·75	3·75
249	20 c. Red-billed Tropic Bird		35	15	1·50	1·75
250	25 c. Montserrat Oriole		50	50	4·00	4·50
251	50 c. Green-throated Carib		3·50	1·00	4·00	4·00
252	$1 Antillean Crested Hummingbird		3·50	1·00	4·25	4·50
253	$2.50, Little Blue Heron		3·50	4·00	8·00	9·50
254	$5 Purple-throated Carib		7·50	9·00	13·00	16·00
254a	$10 Forest Thrush		†		15·00	15·00
242A/54A		Set of 13	19·00	15·00		
243B/54aB		Set of 11			50·00	55·00

The 1 c. 15 c., 20 c., 25 c., $1, $5 and $10 are horizontal, and the remainder are vertical designs.

See also Nos. 295/302.

(Des G. Drummond. Litho D.L.R.)

1970 (1 Oct).* *Christmas.* T **45** *and similar multicoloured design.* W w **12**. P 14½ × 14.
255		5 c. Type **45**				10	10
256		15 c. "The Adoration of the Shepherds" (Domenichino)				10	10
257		20 c. Type **45**				10	10
258		$1 As 15 c.				35	60
255/8					Set of 4	55	70

*This was the local date of issue but the stamps were released by the Crown Agents on 21 September.

46 War Memorial

47 Girl Guide and Badge

(Des V. Whiteley. Litho J.W.)

1970 (30 Nov). *Tourism.* T **46** *and similar horiz designs. Multicoloured.* W w **12** (sideways). P 14½ × 14.
259		5 c. Type **46**				10	10
260		15 c. Plymouth from Fort St. George				10	10
261		25 c. Carr's Bay				15	10
262		50 c. Golf Fairway				55	30
259/62					Set of 4	75	45
MS263	135 × 109 mm. Nos. 259/62					1·50	2·00

(Des V. Whiteley. Litho Questa)

1970 (31 Dec). *Diamond Jubilee of Montserrat Girl Guides.* T **47** *and similar vert design. Multicoloured.* W w **12**. P 14.
264		10 c. Type **47**				10	10
265		15 c. Brownie and Badge				10	10
266		25 c. As 15 c.				15	10
267		40 c. Type **47**				20	20
264/7					Set of 4	50	30

48 "Descent from the Cross" (Van Hemessen)

49 D.F.C. and D.F.M. in Searchlights

(Des J.W. Photo Enschedé)

1971 (22 Mar). *Easter.* T **48** *and similar vert design. Multicoloured.* W w **12**. P 13½.
268		5 c. Type **48**				10	10
269		15 c. "Noli me tangere" (Orcagna)				10	10
270		20 c. Type **48**				10	10
271		40 c. As 15 c.				15	15
268/71					Set of 4	30	30

(Des Col. A. Maynard. Litho Questa)

1971 (8 July). *Golden Jubilee of Commonwealth Ex-Services League.* T **49** *and similar vert designs. Multicoloured.* W w **12**. P 14.
272		10 c. Type **49**				10	10
273		20 c. M.C., M.M. and jungle patrol				15	10
274		40 c. D.S.C., D.S.M. and submarine action				20	15
275		$1 V.C. and soldier attacking bunker				50	70
272/5					Set of 4	85	85

50 "The Nativity with Saints" (Romanino)

51 Piper "Apache"

(Des G. Drummond. Litho Questa)

1971 (16 Sept). *Christmas.* T **50** *and similar vert design. Multicoloured.* W w **12**. P 14 × 13½.
276		5 c. Type **50**				10	10
277		15 c. "Choir of Angels" (Simon Marmion)				10	10
278		20 c. Type **50**				10	10
279		$1 As 15 c.				35	40
276/9					Set of 4	50	50

(Des and litho J.W.)

1971 (16 Dec). *14th Anniv of Inauguration of L.I.A.T. (Leeward Islands Air Transport).* T **51** *and similar horiz designs. Multicoloured.* W w **12** (sideways). P 13½.
280		5 c. Type **51**				10	10
281		10 c. Beech "Twin Bonanza"				15	15
282		15 c. De Havilland "Heron"				30	15
283		20 c. Britten Norman "Islander"				35	15
284		40 c. De Havilland "Twin Otter"				65	45
285		75 c. Hawker Siddeley "748"				2·00	2·25
280/5					Set of 6	3·25	3·00
MS286	203 × 102 mm. Nos. 280/5					10·00	11·00

52 "Chapel of Christ in Gethsemane", Coventry Cathedral

53 Lizard

(Des G. Drummond. Litho A. & M.)

1972 (9 Mar). *Easter.* T **52** *and similar horiz design. Multicoloured.* W w **12**. P 13.
287		5 c. Type **52**				10	10
288		10 c. "The Agony in the Garden" (Bellini)				10	10
289		20 c. Type **52**				10	10
290		75 c. As 10 c.				35	50
287/90					Set of 4	45	60

(Des G. Drummond. Litho Questa)

1972 (20 July). *Reptiles.* T **53** *and similar multicoloured designs.* W w **12** (sideways on 40 c. and $1). P 14½.
291		15 c. Type **53**				15	10
292		20 c. Mountain Chicken (frog)				20	10
293		40 c. Iguana (horiz)				35	20
294		$1 Tortoise (horiz)				2·00	2·00
291/4					Set of 4	2·40	2·00

1972 (21 July)–74. *As No. 242 etc., but W w* **12**, *sideways on horiz designs* (1, 15, 20, 25 c.) *and upright on vert designs* (others). *Glazed, ordinary paper.*

295	1 c. Type **44**		50	45
	a. Chalk-surfaced paper (4.2.74)		60	45
296	2 c. American Kestrel		60	45
	a. Chalk-surfaced paper (4.2.74)		2·25	45
297	3 c. Magnificent Frigate Bird		9·00	6·50
298	4 c. Great Egret (*chalk-surfaced paper*) (4.2.74)		1·00	2·50
299	5 c. Brown Pelican (8.3.73)		40	30
	a. Chalk-surfaced paper (4.2.74)		60	55
300	15 c. Smooth-billed Ani (8.3.73)		50	45
	a. Chalk-surfaced paper (2.10.73)		85	1·00
301	20 c. Red-billed Tropic Bird (*chalk-surfaced paper*) (2.10.73)		1·40	1·50
302	25 c. Montserrat Oriole (*chalk-surfaced paper*) (17.5.74)		3·25	3·50
295/302		*Set of 8*	15·00	14·00

In 1973–74, during shortages of the 5 c. value, letters can be found posted unstamped and franked with a "postage paid" mark. Other covers exist with the word "paid" in manuscript.

54 "Madonna of the Chair" (Raphael)

(Des J. Cooter. Litho Format)

1972 (18 Oct). *Christmas. T* **54** *and similar horiz designs. Multicoloured. W w* **12**. *P* 13½.

303	10 c. Type **54**		10	10
304	35 c. "Virgin and Child with Cherub" (Fungai)		15	10
305	50 c. "Madonna of the Magnificat" (Botticelli)		25	30
306	$1 "Virgin and Child with St. John and an Angel" (Botticelli)		40	65
303/6		*Set of 4*	70	90

55 Lime, Tomatoes and Pawpaw 56 *Passiflora herbertiana*

(Des (from photographs by D. Groves) and photo Harrison)

1972 (20 Nov). *Royal Silver Wedding. Multicoloured; background colour given. W w* **12**. *P* 14 × 14½.

307	**55**	35 c. rose	10	10
308		$1 bright blue	20	20

(Des J. Cooter. Litho Walsall)

1973 (9 Apr). *Easter. T* **56** *and similar vert designs showing passion-flowers. Multicoloured. W w* **12**. *P* 13½.

309	20 c. Type **56**		25	10
310	35 c. *P. vitifolia*		35	10
311	75 c. *P. amabilis*		1·40	1·40
312	$1 *P. alata-caerulea*		1·75	1·75
309/12		*Set of 4*	3·50	3·00

Nos. 309/12 are inscribed on the reverse with information about the passion-flower.

57 Montserrat Monastery, Spain 58 "Virgin and Child" (School of Gerard David)

(Des J. Cooter. Litho Format)

1973 (9 July). *480th Anniv of Columbus's Discovery of Montserrat. T* **57** *and similar horiz designs. Multicoloured. W w* **12**. *P* 13½.

313	10 c. Type **57**		15	10
314	35 c. Columbus sighting Montserrat		30	15
315	60 c. Columbus's ship off Montserrat		1·50	1·50
316	$1 Colony badge and map of voyage		1·75	1·75
313/16		*Set of 4*	3·50	3·00
MS317	126 × 134 mm. Nos. 313/16		16·00	16·00

58a Princess Anne and Captain Mark Phillips 59 Steel Band

(Des PAD Studio. Litho Questa)

1973 (14 Nov). *Royal Wedding. Centre multicoloured. W w* **12** (*sideways*). *P* 13½.

322	58a	35 c. sage-green	10	10
323		$1 violet-blue	20	20

(Des J. W. Litho Questa)

1974 (8 Apr). *25th Anniv of University of West Indies. T* **59** *and similar designs. Multicoloured. W w* **12** (*sideways on* 20 c., $1 *and* MS328).

324	20 c. Type **59**		15	10
325	35 c. Masqueraders (*vert*)		20	10
326	60 c. Student weaving (*vert*)		1·00	1·00
327	$1 University Centre, Montserrat		1·10	1·25
324/7		*Set of 4*	2·25	2·25
MS328	130 × 89 mm. Nos. 324/7		4·00	7·50

60 Hands with Letters (61)

(Des P. Powell. Litho Walsall)

1974 (3 July). *Centenary of Universal Postal Union. T* **60** *and similar horiz design. W w* **12**. *P* 14½ × 14.

329	**60**	1 c. multicoloured	10	10
330		2 c. lt rose-red, orange-verm & blk	10	10
331	**60**	3 c. multicoloured	10	10
332		5 c. lt yellow-orange, reddish orge & blk	10	10
333	**60**	50 c. multicoloured	20	20
334		$1 pale blue, turquoise-blue and black	40	65
329/34		*Set of 6*	75	90

Designs:—2 c., 5 c., $1 Figures from U.P.U. Monument.

1974 (2 Oct). *Various stamps surch as T* **61**.

335	2 c. on $1 (No. 252B)		30	50
336	5 c. on 50 c. (No. 333)		40	60
337	10 c. on 60 c. (No. 326)		1·75	2·25
338	20 c. on $1 (No. 252B)		30	40
	a. "2" with seriffs (Pl 1B R. 3/1)		10·00	
	b. Bottom bar of surch omitted (Pl 1B R. 5/1-5)		5·00	
339	35 c. on $1 (No. 334)		75	1·25
335/9		*Set of 5*	3·25	4·50

62 Churchill and Houses of Parliament 63 Carib "Carbet"

(Des R. Granger Barrett. Litho D.L.R.)

1974 (30 Nov). *Birth Centenary of Sir Winston Churchill. T* **62** *and similar vert design. Multicoloured. No wmk. P* 13 × 13½.

340	35 c. Type **62**		15	10
341	70 c. Churchill and Blenheim Palace		20	20
MS342	81 × 85 mm. Nos. 340/1		50	70

(Des C. Abbott. Litho Walsall)

1975 (3 Mar). *Carib Artefacts. T* **63** *and similar horiz designs.*

(a) W w **12** (*sideways*). *From sheets. P* 14

343	5 c. lake-brown, yellow and black		10	10
344	20 c. black, lake-brown and yellow		10	10
345	35 c. black, yellow and lake-brown		15	10
346	70 c. yellow, lake-brown and black		25	40
343/6		*Set of 4*	50	60

(b) No wmk. Self-adhesive with advertisements on the reverse. From booklets. Rouletted

347	5 c. lake-brown, yellow and black		15	25
	a. Booklet pane. Nos. 347/50 se-tenant		90	
348	20 c. black, lake-brown and yellow		15	25
	a. Booklet pane. Nos. 348 × 3 and No. 349 × 3		90	
349	35 c. black, yellow and lake-brown		15	25
350	70 c. yellow, lake-brown and black		15	25
347/50		*Set of 4*	90	1·25

Designs:—20 c. "Caracoli"; 35 c. Club or mace; 70 c. Canoe.

64 One-Bitt Coin

(Des J. Cooter. Litho Questa)

1975 (1 Sept). *Local Coinage, 1785–1801. T* **64** *and similar diamond-shaped designs. W w* **14** (*sideways*). *P* 13½.

351	5 c. black, light violet-blue and silver		10	10
352	10 c. black, salmon and silver		15	10
353	35 c. black, light blue-green and silver		20	15
354	$2 black, bright rose and silver		1·25	1·50
351/4		*Set of 4*	1·50	1·60
MS355	142 × 142 mm. Nos. 351/4		1·75	2·75

Designs:—10 c. Eighth dollar; 35 c. Quarter dollar; $2 One dollar.

No. MS355 has details of the coins depicted printed on the reverse side, beneath the gum.

65 1d. and 6d. Stamps of 1876 66 "The Trinity"

(Des J. Cooter. Litho J. W.)

1976 (5 Jan). *Centenary of First Montserrat Postage Stamp. T* **65** *and similar horiz designs. W w* **12** (*sideways*). *P* 13.

356	5 c. deep carmine, yellowish green and black		10	10
357	10 c. light yellow-ochre, scarlet and black		15	10
358	40 c. multicoloured		40	40
359	55 c. deep mauve, yellowish green and black		50	50
360	70 c. multicoloured		70	70
361	$1.10, yellowish green, brt blue & grey-blk		1·00	1·00
356/61		*Set of 6*	2·50	2·50
MS362	170 × 159 mm. Nos. 356/61		3·50	4·50

Designs:—10 c. G.P.O. and bisected 1d. stamp; 40 c. Bisects on cover; 55 c. G.B. 6d. used in Montserrat and local 6d. of 1876; 70 c. Stamps for 2½d. rate, 1876; $1.10, Packet boat *Antelope* and 6d. stamp.

(Des J. Cooter. Litho Questa)

1976 (5 Apr). *Easter. Unissued stamps prepared for Easter 1975 with values and date obliterated by black bars. T* **66** *and similar vert designs showing paintings by Orcagna. Multicoloured. W w* **14**. *P* 13½.

363	15 c. on 5 c. Type **66**		10	10
	a. Surch omitted		50·00	
364	40 c. on 35 c. "The Resurrection"		15	15
	a. Surch omitted		50·00	
365	55 c. on 70 c. "The Ascension"		15	15
	a. Surch omitted		50·00	
366	$1.10 on $1 "Pentecost"		30	40
	a. Surch omitted		50·00	
363/6		*Set of 4*	55	65
MS367	160 × 142 mm. Nos. 363/6		1·25	2·00
	a. Surch omitted		£200	

For No. 363 the "1" was added to the original 5 c. to make 15 c.

(67) 68 White Frangipani

1976 (12 Apr). *Nos. 244A, 246A and 247A surch as T* **67**.

368	2 c. on 5 c. Brown Pelican	..	10	15
369	30 c. on 10 c. Bananaquit	..	30	20
370	45 c. on 3 c. Magnificent Frigate Bird	..	40	25
	a. Surch triple	..		
	b. Surch double	..	40·00	
368/70		*Set of 3*	70	55

(Des J. Cooter. Litho Questa)

1976 (5 July)–**80**. *Various horiz designs showing Flowering Trees as T* **68**. *Multicoloured. Ordinary paper. W* w **14** *(sideways). P* 13½.

371	1 c. Type **68**	..	10	10
372	2 c. Cannon-ball Tree	..	10	10
373	3 c. Lignum vitae	..	10	10
374	5 c. Malay apple	..	15	10
375	10 c. Jacaranda	..	20	10
376	15 c. Orchid Tree	..	25	10
	a. Chalk-surfaced paper (8.80)	..	1·25	1·75
377	20 c. Manjak	..	25	10
	a. Chalk-surfaced paper (8.80)	..	1·25	1·75
378	25 c. Tamarind	..	25	10
379	40 c. Flame of the Forest	..	35	20
380	55 c. Pink Cassia	..	40	25
381	70 c. Long John	..	50	30
382	$1 Saman	..	65	40
383	$2.50, Immortelle	..	1·25	1·50
384	$5 Yellow Poui	..	2·00	2·25
385	$10 Flamboyant	..	3·00	4·25
371/85		*Set of 15*	8·00	8·50

69 Mary and Joseph   **70** Hudson River Review, 1976

(Des L. Curtis. Litho Format)

1976 (4 Oct). *Christmas. T* **69** *and similar vert designs. Multicoloured. W* w **14**. *P* 14.

386	15 c. Type **69**	..	10	10
387	20 c. The Shepherds	..	10	10
388	55 c. Mary and Jesus	..	15	15
389	$1.10, The Magi	..	30	50
386/9		*Set of 4*	50	65
MS390	95 × 135 mm. Nos. 386/9	..	60	1·75

(Des and litho J.W.)

1976 (13 Dec). *Bicentenary of American Revolution. T* **70** *and similar vert designs. Multicoloured. W* w **14**. *P* 13.

391	15 c. Type **70**	..	30	15
392	40 c. } The *Raleigh* attacking	,	60	40
393	75 c. } H.M.S. *Druid*, 1777*	..	60	40
394	$1.25, Hudson River Review	..	1·10	40
391/4		*Set of 4*	2·40	1·40
MS395	95 × 145 mm. Nos. 391/4. P 13½.	..	2·50	2·75

*The date is wrongly given on the stamps as "1776".

Nos. 392/3 and 391 and 394 were printed in horizontal *se-tenant* pairs throughout the sheet, each pair forming a composite design.

71 The Crowning   **72** Ipomoea alba

(Des G. Vasarhelyi. Litho J.W.)

1977 (7 Feb). *Silver Jubilee. T* **71** *and similar horiz designs. Multicoloured. W* w **14** *(sideways). P* 13.

396	30 c. Royal Visit, 1966..	..	15	15
397	45 c. Cannons firing salute	..	20	20
398	$1 Type **71**	..	35	60
396/8		*Set of 3*	60	85

(Des J. Cooter. Litho Questa)

1977 (1 June). *Flowers of the Night. T* **72** *and similar multicoloured designs. W* w **14** *(sideways on 40 and 55 c.). P* 14.

399	15 c. Type **72**	..	15	10
400	40 c. *Epiphyllum hookeri* (*horiz*)	..	40	30
401	55 c. *Cereus hexagonus* (*horiz*)	..	55	45
402	$1.50, *Cestrum nocturnum*	..	1·50	1·95
399/402		*Set of 4*	2·40	1·90
MS403	126 × 130 mm. Nos. 399/402. Wmk sideways		2·25	3·25

73 Princess Anne laying Foundation Stone of Glendon Hospital

(Des BG Studio. Litho Questa)

1977 (3 Oct). *Development. T* **73** *and similar horiz designs. Multicoloured. W* w **14** *(sideways). P* 14½ × 14.

404	20 c. Type **73**	..	15	10
405	40 c. *Statesman* (freighter) at Plymouth	..	25	15
406	55 c. Glendon Hospital	..	30	20
407	$1.50, Jetty at Plymouth Port	..	80	1·00
404/7		*Set of 4*	1·40	1·25
MS408	146 × 105 mm. Nos. 404/7	..	2·00	2·50

━━ ═══

$1.00

SILVER JUBILEE 1977

ROYAL VISIT

TO THE CARIBBEAN

(74)

1977 (28 Oct). *Royal Visit. Nos.* 380/1 *and* 383 *surch locally with T* **74**.

409	$1 on 55 c. Pink Cassia	..	30	45
410	$1 on 70 c. Long John	..	30	45
411	$1 on $2.50, Immortelle	..	30	45
	a. Surch double	..		
409/11		*Set of 3*	80	1·25

75 The Stable at Bethlehem   **76** Four-eye Butterflyfish

(Des L. Curtis. Litho Walsall)

1977 (14 Nov). *Christmas. T* **75** *and similar vert designs. Multicoloured. W* w **14**. *P* 14 × 14½.

412	5 c. Type **75**	..	10	10
413	40 c. The Three Kings..	..	15	10
414	55 c. Three Ships	..	20	10
415	$2 Three Angels	..	55	75
412/15		*Set of 4*	80	85
MS416	119 × 115 mm. Nos. 412/15	..	1·00	1·75

(Des J.W. Litho Walsall)

1978 (15 Mar). *Fish. T* **76** *and similar horiz designs. Multicoloured. W* w **14** *(sideways). P* 14.

417	30 c. Type **76**	..	20	10
418	40 c. French Angelfish	..	25	15
419	55 c. Blue Tang	..	35	15
420	$1.50, Queen Triggerfish	..	80	90
417/20		*Set of 4*	1·40	1·10
MS421	152 × 102 mm. Nos. 417/20	..	2·25	3·00

77 St. Paul's Cathedral   **78** Alpinia speciosa

(Des G. Drummond. Litho J.W.)

1978 (2 June). *25th Anniv of Coronation. T* **77** *and similar horiz designs. Multicoloured. W* w **14** *(sideways). P* 13.

422	40 c. Type **77**	..	10	10
423	55 c. Chichester Cathedral	..	10	10
424	$1 Lincoln Cathedral	..	20	25
425	$2.50, Llandaff Cathedral	..	30	50
422/5		*Set of 4*	55	75
MS426	130 × 102 mm. Nos. 422/5. P 13½ × 14	..	70	1·25

Nos. 422/5 were each printed in sheets including two *se-tenant* stamp-size labels.

(Des J. Cooter. Litho J.W.)

1978 (18 Sept). *Flowers. T* **78** *and similar vert designs. Multicoloured. W* w **14**. *P* 13½ × 13.

427	40 c. Type **78**	..	20	10
428	55 c. *Allamanda cathartica*	..	25	15
429	$1 *Petrea volubilis*	..	45	45
430	$2 *Hippeastrum puniceum*	..	70	80
427/30		*Set of 4*	1·40	1·40

79 Private, 21st (Royal North British Fusiliers), 1796   **80** Cub Scouts

(Des J.W. Litho Questa)

1978 (20 Nov). *Military Uniforms (1st series). T* **79** *and similar vert designs showing soldiers from British infantry regiments. Multicoloured. W* w **14**. *P* 14 × 14½.

431	30 c. Type **79**	..	15	15
432	40 c. Corporal, 86th (Royal County Down), 1831	..	20	15
433	55 c. Sergeant, 14th (Buckinghamshire) 1837	..	30	20
434	$1.50, Officer, 55th (Westmorland), 1784	..	75	80
431/4		*Set of 4*	2·00	1·75
MS435	140 × 89 mm. Nos. 431/4	..	2·00	2·75

See also Nos. 441/5.

(Des J. W. Litho Walsall)

1979 (2 Apr). *50th Anniv of Boy Scout Movement on Montserrat. T* **80** *and similar multicoloured designs. W* w **14** *(sideways on 40 and 55 c). P* 14.

436	40 c. Type **80**	..	25	10
437	55 c. Scouts with signalling equipment	..	35	20
438	$1.25, Camp fire (*vert*)	..	60	55
439	$2 Oath ceremony (*vert*)	..	1·00	1·00
436/9		*Set of 4*	2·00	1·75
MS440	120 × 110 mm. Nos. 436/9	..	2·25	2·25

(Des J.W. Litho Questa)

1979 (4 June). *Military Uniforms (2nd series). Vert designs as T* **79** *showing soldiers from infantry regiments. Multicoloured. W* w **14**. *P* 14 × 14½.

441	30 c. Private, 60th (Royal American), 1783	..	15	15
442	40 c. Private, 1st West India, 1819	..	20	15
443	55 c. Officer, 5th (Northumberland), 1819	..	30	25
444	$2.50, Officer, 93rd (Sutherland Highlanders), 1830	..	1·00	1·10
441/4		*Set of 4*	1·50	1·50
MS445	139 × 89 mm. Nos. 441/4	..	2·00	2·50

81 Child reaching out to Adult

(Des G. Vasarhelyi. Litho Questa)

1979 (17 Sept). *International Year of the Child. W* w **14** *(sideways). P* 13½ × 14.

446	81	$2 black, orange-brown and flesh	..	50	55
MS447	85 × 99 mm. No. 446	..	50	2·00

82 Sir Rowland Hill with Penny Black and Montserrat 1876 1d. Stamp   **83** Plume Worm

(Des G. Vasarhelyi. Litho Questa)

1979 (1 Oct). *Death Centenary of Sir Rowland Hill and Centenary of U.P.U. Membership. T* **82** *and similar horiz designs. Multicoloured. W* w **14** *(sideways). P* 14.

448	40 c. Type **82**	..	20	10
449	55 c. U.P.U. emblem and notice announcing Leeward Islands entry into Union	..	25	15
450	$1 1883 Letter following U.P.U. membership	..	35	50
451	$2 Great Britain Post Office Regulations notice and Sir Rowland Hill	..	60	80
448/51		*Set of 4*	1·25	1·40
MS452	135 × 154 mm. Nos. 448/51	..	3·25	3·25

(Des G. Drummond. Litho Walsall)

1979 (26 Nov). *Marine Life. T* **83** *and similar vert designs. Multicoloured. W* w **14**. *P* 14.

453	40 c. Type **83**	..	30	15
454	55 c. Sea Fans	..	40	20
455	$2 Coral and Sponge	..	1·00	1·00
453/5		*Set of 3*	1·50	1·25

84 Tree Frog

(Des J. Cooter. Litho Rosenbaum Bros, Vienna)

1980 (4 Feb). *Reptiles and Amphibians. T* **84** *and similar horiz designs. Multicoloured. W* w **14** (*sideways*). *P* 13½.

456	40 c. Type 84		20	15
457	55 c. Tree Lizard		25	25
458	$1 Crapaud		45	50
459	$2 Wood Slave		80	90
456/9		Set of 4	1·50	1·60

75th Anniversary of
Rotary International

85 *Marquess of Salisbury*
and 1838 Handstamps   (86)

(Des BG Studio. Litho Questa)

1980 (14 Apr). *"London 1980" International Stamp Exhibition. T* **85** *and similar horiz designs. Multicoloured. W* w **14** (*sideways*). *P* 13½.

460	40 c. Type 85		20	15
461	55 c. "H.S. 748" aircraft and 1976 55 c. definitive		25	25
462	$1.20, *La Plata* (liner) and 1903 5s. stamp		45	45
463	$1.20, *Lady Hawkins* (packet steamer) and 1932 Tercentenary 5s. commemorative		45	45
464	$1.20, *Avon* (paddle-steamer) and Penny Red stamp with "A 08" postmark		45	45
465	$1.20, "Aeronca" aeroplane and 1953 $1.20 definitive		45	45
460/5		Set of 6	2·00	2·00
MS466	115 × 110 mm. Nos. 460/5. P 12		1·60	2·50

Nos. 460/5 were each printed in sheets of 4 stamps and two *se-tenant* stamp-size labels.
Some sheets of No. 462 showed the red colour omitted from the map in the right-hand label.

1980 (7 July). *75th Anniv of Rotary International. No.* 383 *optd with T* **86**.

467	$2.50, Immortelle		70	85

87 Greek, French and U.S.A. Flags

(Des A. Theobald. Litho Questa)

1980 (7 July). *Olympic Games, Moscow. T* **87** *and similar horiz designs. Multicoloured. W* w **14** (*sideways*). *P* 13½ × 14.

468	40 c. Type 87		15	15
469	55 c. Union, Swedish and Belgian flags		15	15
470	70 c. French, Dutch and U.S.A. flags		20	20
471	$1 German, Union and Finnish flags		25	25
472	$1.50, Australian, Italian and Japanese flags		30	40
473	$2 Mexican, West German and Canadian flags		35	55
474	$2.50, "The Discus Thrower" (sculpture by Miron)		40	75
468/74		Set of 7	1·60	2·25
MS475	150 × 100 mm. Nos. 468/74		1·60	3·00
	a. Bottom row of stamps in miniature sheet imperf on 3 sides			£475

Nos. 468/74 were each printed in small sheets of 4 including one *se-tenant* stamp-size label.
No. **MS**475a shows the three stamps in the bottom row of the miniature sheet imperforate vertically and with no perforations between the stamps and the bottom margin.

XX 5¢   Montserrat   40c

(88)   89 S.S. *Lady Nelson*, 1928

1980 (30 Sept). *Nos.* 371, 373, 376 *and* 379 *surch as T* **88**.

476	5 c. on 3 c. Lignum vitae		10	10
	a. Surch double, one inverted		45·00	
477	35 c. on 1 c. Type 68		20	15
	a. Surch omitted (in vert pair with normal)		50·00	
478	35 c. on 3 c. Lignum vitae		20	15
479	35 c. on 15 c. Orchid Tree		20	15

480	55 c. on 40 c. Flame of the Forest		25	15
	a. Surch inverted		60·00	
481	$5 on 40 c. Flame of the Forest		1·25	2·00
476/81		Set of 6	2·00	2·25

The surcharge omitted error, No. 477a, occurs on the lower stamp of a vertical pair. On the upper stamp the surcharge is at the foot of the design.

(Des J.W. Litho Walsall)

1980 (3 Nov). *Mail Packet Boats* (1st series). *T* **89** *and similar horiz designs. Multicoloured. W* w **14** (*sideways*). *P* 14.

482	40 c. Type 89		20	15
483	55 c. R.M.S.P. *Chignecto*, 1913		30	25
484	$1 R.M.S.P. *Solent*, 1878		50	50
485	$2 R.M.S.P. *Dee*, 1841		75	85
482/5		Set of 4	1·60	1·60

See also Nos. 615/19.

90 *Heliconius charitonia*   91 Spadefish

(Des J.W. Litho Questa)

1981 (2 Feb). *Butterflies. T* **90** *and similar square designs. Multicoloured. W* w **14** (*inverted*). *P* 14.

486	50 c. Type 90		60	40
487	65 c. *Pyrgus oileus*		70	45
488	$1.50, *Phoebis agarithe*		90	85
489	$2.50, *Danaus plexippus*		1·25	1·10
486/9		Set of 4	3·00	2·50

Nos. 486/9 were each printed in sheets including two *se-tenant* stamp-size labels.

(Des G. Drummond. Litho J.W.)

1981 (20 Mar). *Fishes. Vert designs as T* **91**. *Multicoloured. W* w **14**. *P* 13½ × 13.

490	5 c. Type 91		40	10
491	10 c. Hogfish		40	10
492	15 c. Creole Wrasse		50	10
493	20 c. Yellow Damselfish		60	10
494	25 c. Sergeant Major		60	10
495	35 c. Clown Wrasse		50	20
496	45 c. Schoolmaster		50	25
497	55 c. Striped Parrotfish		95	30
498	65 c. Bigeye		50	30
499	75 c. French Grunt		60	40
500	$1 Rock Beauty		75	55
501	$2 Blue Chromis		1·75	1·10
502	$3 Fairy Basslet and Blueheads		1·90	1·75
503	$5 Cherubfish		2·75	2·75
504	$7.50, Longspine Squirrelfish		5·50	4·75
505	$10 Longsnout Butterflyfish		6·50	6·50
490/505		Set of 16	22·00	17·00

For stamps watermarked with W w **15** see Nos. 555/70.

92 Fort St. George

(Des J. Cooter. Litho Format)

1981 (18 May). *Montserrat National Trust. T* **92** *and similar horiz designs. Multicoloured. W* w **14** (*sideways*). *P* 13½ × 14.

506	50 c. Type 92		30	20
507	65 c. Bird sanctuary, Fox's Bay		45	35
508	$1.50, Museum		85	75
509	$2.50, Bransby Point Battery, *circa* 1780		1·40	1·40
506/9		Set of 4	2·75	2·40

(Des D. Shults. Litho Questa)

1981 (17 July–19 Nov). *Royal Wedding. Horiz designs as T* **26/27** *of Kiribati. Multicoloured.* (a) W w **15**. *P* 14.

510	90 c. *Charlotte*		25	25
	a. Sheetlet. No. 510 × 6 and No. 511		2·10	
511	90 c. Prince Charles and Lady Diana Spencer		85	85
512	$3 *Portsmouth*		60	60
	a. Sheetlet. No. 512 × 6 and No. 513		4·50	
513	$3 As No. 511		1·50	1·50
514	$4 *Britannia*		75	75
	a. Sheetlet. No. 514 × 6 and No. 515		5·50	
515	$4 As No. 511		1·75	1·75
510/15		Set of 6	5·25	5·25
MS516	120 × 109 mm. $5 As No. 511. Wmk sideways. P 12 (19 Nov)		1·50	1·50

(b) *Booklet stamps. No wmk. P* 12 (19 Nov)

517	90 c. As No. 510		45	45
	a. Booklet pane. No. 517 × 4		1·75	
518	$3 As No. 513		1·60	1·75
	a. Booklet pane No. 518 × 2		3·25	

Nos. 510/15 were printed in sheetlets of seven stamps of the same face value, each containing six of the "Royal Yacht" design and one of the larger design showing Prince Charles and Lady Diana.
Nos. 517/18 come from $13.20 stamp booklets.

93 H.M.S. *Dorsetshire* and Seaplane   94 Methodist Church, Bethel

(Des Court House Advertising Ltd. Litho Questa)

1981 (31 Aug). *50th Anniv of Montserrat Airmail Service. T* **93** *and similar horiz designs. Multicoloured. W* w **14** (*sideways*). *P* 14.

519	50 c. Type 93		40	30
520	65 c. Beechcraft "Twin Bonanza" aeroplane		55	50
521	$1.50, De Havilland "Dragon Rapide" R.M. *Lord Shaftesbury* aeroplane		95	1·25
522	$2.50, Hawker Siddeley Avro "748" aeroplane and maps of Montserrat and Antigua		1·40	2·00
519/22		Set of 4	3·00	3·50

(Des J. Cooter. Litho Walsall)

1981 (16 Nov). *Christmas. Churches. T* **94** *and similar vert designs. Multicoloured. W* w **14**. *P* 14 × 13½.

523	50 c. Type 94		20	15
524	65 c. St George's Anglican Church, Harris		25	15
525	$1.50, St Peter's Anglican Church, St Peters		60	60
526	$2.50, St Patrick's R.C. Church, Plymouth		75	1·00
523/6		Set of 4	1·75	1·75
MS527	176 × 120 mm. Nos. 523/6		3·00	3·50

95 Rubiaceae
(*Rondeletia buxifolia*)   96 Plymouth

(Des local artist. Litho Questa)

1982 (18 Jan). *Plant Life. T* **95** *and similar multicoloured designs. W* w **14** (*sideways on* 65 c. *and* $2.50). *P* 14½.

528	50 c. Type 95		30	30
529	65 c. Boraginaceae (*Heliotropium ternatum*) (*horiz*)		40	40
530	$1.50, Simarubaceae (*Picramnia pentandra*)		85	85
531	$2.50, Ebenaceae (*Diospyrus revoluta*) (*horiz*)		1·25	1·25
528/31		Set of 4	2·50	2·50

(Litho Format)

1982 (17 Apr). *350th Anniv of Settlement of Montserrat by Sir Thomas Warner. W* w **14** (*sideways*). *P* 14½.

532	**96** 40 c. green		30	30
533	55 c. red		35	35
534	65 c. chestnut		40	40
535	75 c. olive-grey		45	50
536	85 c. bright blue		50	60
537	95 c. bright orange		55	65
538	$1 bright reddish violet		60	70
539	$1.50, brown-olive		80	1·00
540	$2 deep claret		1·10	1·25
541	$2.50, bistre-brown		1·40	1·60
532/41		Set of 10	5·75	6·50

Nos. 532/41 are based on the 1932 Tercentenary set.

97 Catherine of Aragon, Princess of Wales, 1501   98 Local Scout

(Des D. Shults and J. Cooter. Litho Format)

1982 (16 June). *21st Birthday of Princess of Wales. T* **97** *and similar vert designs. Multicoloured. W* w **15**. *P* 13½ × 14.

542	75 c. Type 97		20	15
543	$1 Coat of Arms of Catherine of Aragon		30	20
544	$5 Diana, Princess of Wales		1·50	1·75
542/4		Set of 3	1·75	1·90

(Des D. Shults. Litho Format)

1982 (13 Sept). *75th Anniv of Boy Scout Movement. T* **98** *and similar vert design. Multicoloured. W* w **15**. *P* 14.

545	$1.50, Type **98**	..	..	85	70
546	$2.50, Lord Baden-Powell	..	..	1·25	1·10

99 Annunciation

(Des Jennifer Toombs. Litho Walsall)

1982 (18 Nov). *Christmas. T* **99** *and similar horiz designs. Multicoloured. W* w **14** (*sideways*). *P* 14.

547	35 c. Type **99**	..	..	20	15
548	75 c. Shepherd's Vision	..	..	40	35
549	$1.50, The Stable	..	..	85	85
550	$2.50, Flight into Egypt	..	..	1·00	1·10
547/50	.. .. ..	..	*Set of 4*	2·25	2·25

100 *Lepthemis vesiculosa*   **101** Blue-headed Hummingbird

(Des J. Cooter. Litho Walsall)

1983 (19 Jan). *Dragonflies. T* **100** *and similar horiz designs. Multicoloured. W* w **14** (*sideways*). *P* 13½ × 14.

551	50 c. Type **100**	..	..	25	20
552	65 c. *Orthemis ferruginea*	..	..	30	25
553	$1.50, *Triacanthagyna trifida*	..	..	70	75
554	$2.50, *Erythrodiplax umbrata*	..	..	1·25	1·25
551/4	.. .. ..	..	*Set of 4*	2·25	2·25

1983 (12 Apr). *As Nos.* **490/505**, *but W* w **15** *and imprint date* "1983" *added. P* 13½ × 13.

555	5 c. Type **91**	..	..	20	10
556	10 c. Hogfish	..	..	25	10
559	25 c. Sergeant Major	..	..	35	20
560	35 c. Clown Wrasse	..	..	45	30
564	75 c. French Grunt	..	..	75	55
565	$1 Rock Beauty	..	..	85	65
568	$5 Cherubfish	..	..	2·75	3·00
570	$10 Longsnout Butterflyfish	..	..	5·50	6·00
555/70	.. .. ..	..	*Set of 8*	10·00	10·00

(Des G. Drummond. Litho Format)

1983 (24 May). *Hummingbirds. T* **101** *and similar vert designs. Multicoloured. W* w **14**. *P* 14.

571	35 c. Type **101**	..	..	1·25	35
572	75 c. Green-throated Carib	..	..	1·50	55
573	$2 Antillean Crested Hummingbird	..	2·50	1·40
574	$3 Purple-throated Carib	..	..	3·00	1·75
571/4	..	..	*Set of 4*	7·50	3·50

102 Montserrat Emblem   (**103**)

(Litho Harrison)

1983 (25 July). *W* w **14**. *P* 14½.

575	**102**	$12 royal blue and rose	..	4·25	5·00
576		$30 rose and royal blue	..	11·00	12·00

1983 (15 Aug). *Various stamps surch as T* **103**. (*a*) *Nos.* **491, 498, 501** (*all W* w **14**), **559, 564** (*both W* w **15**).

577	40 c. on 25 c. Sergeant Major (No. **559**)	..	20	20
	a. Surch inverted	..	..	30·00
	b. Surch on No. **494**..	..	9·00	10·00
	c. Error. Surch on 10 c. (No. **491**)	..	22·00
	d. Surch double	..	..	40·00
578	70 c. on 10 c. Hogfish (No. **491**)	..	35	35
	a. Surch inverted	..	..	30·00
	b. Surch on No. **556**..	..	24·00	24·00
	c. Surch omitted (in pair with normal)	..	£130
	d. Surch double	..	..	35·00

579	90 c. on 65 c. Bigeye (No. **498**). .	..	50	55
	a. Error. Surch on 10 c. (No. **491**)	..	
	b. Error. Surch on 75 c. (No. **499**)	..	80·00
	c. Surch double	..	..	40·00
580	$1.15 on 75 c. French Grunt (No. **564**)	60	65
	a. Surch on No. **499**.	..	11·00	11·00
	b. Error. Surch on 25 c. (No. **559**)	..	40·00
	c. Surch inverted	..	..	38·00
581	$1.50 on $2 Blue Chromis (No. **501**)	..	80	85
	a. Surch inverted	..	..	60·00
	b. Error. Surch on 75 c. (No. **499**)	..	80·00
	c. Error. Surch on 75 c. (No. **564**)	..	

(*b*) *Nos.* **512/15**

582	70 c. on $3 Portsmouth	..	60	70
	a. Sheetlet. No. **582** × 6 and No. **583**	4·00	
	b. Surch double	..	..	5·00
	c. Surch inverted	..	..	17·00
	d. Surch inverted (horiz pair)	..	35·00
583	70 c. on $3 Prince Charles and Lady Diana Spencer	..	60	70
	b. Surch double	..	..	38·00
	c. Surch inverted	..	..	90·00
584	$1.15 on $4 Britannia	..	1·00	1·10
	a. Sheetlet. No. **584** × 6 and No. **585**	7·00	
	b. Surch double	..	..	20·00
	c. Surch inverted	..	..	12·00
	d. Surch inverted (horiz pair)	..	25·00
	e. Error. Surch on $3 (No. **512**)	..	6·50
585	$1.15 on $4 As No. **583**	..	1·00	1·10
	b. Surch double	..	..	35·00
	c. Surch inverted	..	..	65·00
	e. Error. Surch on $3 (No. **513**)	..	70·00
577/85	..	*Set of 9*	4·75	5·25

Nos. **582d** and **584d** show the long surcharge intended for Nos. **583** or **585** inverted across horizontal pairs of the smaller design. Nos. **583c** and **585c** show two examples of the smaller surcharge inverted.

104 Montgolfier Balloon, 1783   **105** Boys dressed as Clowns

(Des A. Theobald. Litho Format)

1983 (19 Sept). *Bicentenary of Manned Flight. T* **104** *and similar multicoloured designs. W* w **14** (*sideways on 75 c. to $2*). *P* 14.

586	35 c. Type **104**	..	..	15	15
587	75 c. De Havilland "Twin Otter" (*horiz*)	35	30
588	$1.50, Lockheed "Vega" (*horiz*)	..	70	75
589	$2 R 34 airship (*horiz*)	..	1·00	1·25
586/9	..	*Set of 4*	2·00	2·25
MS590	109 × 145 mm. Nos. **586/9**. Wmk sideways	2·10	2·50

Nos. **586/9** were re-issued on 15 December 1983 overprinted "INAUGURAL FLIGHT Montserrat-Nevis-St. Kitts". It is understood nearly all of these overprints were used on Flown First Flight/Day Covers (Price for set of 4 on First Flight Cover £30).

(Des Jennifer Toombs. Litho Format)

1983 (18 Nov). *Christmas. Carnival. T* **105** *and similar horiz designs. Multicoloured. W* w **15** (*sideways*). *P* 14.

591	55 c. Type **105** ..	..	..	25	20
592	90 c. Girls dressed as silver star bursts	40	35
593	$1.15, Flower girls	..	..	50	60
594	$2 Masqueraders	..	..	95	1·00
591/4	..	*Set of 4*	1·90	1·90

106 Statue of Discus-thrower   **107** Cattle Egret

(Des Court House Studio. Litho Questa)

1984 (26 Mar). *Olympic Games, Los Angeles. T* **106** *and similar vert designs. Multicoloured. W* w **15** (*sideways*). *P* 14.

595	90 c. Type **106**	..	..	35	35
596	$1 Olympic torch	..	..	40	45
597	$1.15, Olympic stadium, Los Angeles	45	50
598	$2.50, Olympic and American flags	..	80	1·00
595/8	..	*Set of 4*	1·75	2·10
MS599	110 × 110 mm. Nos. **595/8**. Wmk upright	1·75	2·25

(Des G. Drummond. Litho Walsall)

1984 (28 May). *Birds of Montserrat. T* **107** *and similar multi-coloured designs. W* w **15** (*sideways on 5 c. to 90 c.*). *P* 14.

600	5 c. Type **107**	..	..	15	20
601	10 c. Carib Grackle	..	..	15	20
602	15 c. Moorhen ("Common Gallinule")	15	20
603	20 c. Brown Booby	..	..	20	20
604	25 c. Black-whiskered Vireo	..	20	20
605	40 c. Scaly-breasted Thrasher. .	..	35	25

606	55 c. Laughing Gull	..	..	50	30
607	70 c. Glossy Ibis	..	..	60	45
608	90 c. Green Heron	..	..	75	50
609	$1 Belted Kingfisher (*vert*)	..	90	65
610	$1.15, Bananaquit (*vert*)	..	1·10	1·40
611	$3 American Kestrel ("Sparrow Hawk") (*vert*). .	..	..	2·25	3·50
612	$5 Forest Thrush (*vert*)	..	3·50	6·00
613	$7.50, Black-crowned Night Heron (*vert*)	5·50	9·50
614	$10 Bridled Quail Dove (*vert*)	..	7·00	12·00
600/14	..	*Set of 15*	21·00	32·00

(Des J.W. Litho Format)

1984 (9 July). *Mail Packet Boats (2nd series). Multicoloured designs as T* **89**. *W* w **15** (*sideways*). *P* 14.

615	55 c. R.M.S.P. *Tagus*, 1907	..	50	40
616	90 c. R.M.S.P. *Cobequid*, 1913	..	75	65
617	$1.15, S.S. *Lady Drake*, 1942	..	1·00	1·00
618	$2 M.V. *Factor*, 1948	..	1·75	2·00
615/18	..	*Set of 4*	3·50	3·50
MS619	152 × 100 mm. Nos. **615/18**.	..	3·25	4·25

No. **MS619** also commemorates the 250th anniversary of *Lloyd's List* (newspaper).

108 Hermit Crab and Top Shell

(Des G. Drummond. Litho Questa)

1984 (24 Sept). *Marine Life. T* **108** *and similar horiz designs. Multicoloured. W* w **15** (*sideways*). *P* 14.

620	90 c. Type **108**	..	..	1·00	75
621	$1.15, Rough File Shell	..	1·25	95
622	$1.50, True Tulip Snail	..	1·75	1·40
623	$2.50, West Indian Fighting Conch	2·50	2·50
620/3	..	*Set of 4*	6·00	5·00

109 "Bull Man"   **110** Mango

(Des Jennifer Toombs. Litho Questa)

1984 (12 Nov). *Christmas. Carnival Costumes. T* **109** *and similar horiz designs. Multicoloured. W* w **15** (*sideways*). *P* 14.

624	55 c. Type **109**	..	..	40	25
625	$1.15, Masquerader Captain	..	1·25	90
626	$1.50, "Fantasy" Carnival Queen	..	1·50	1·25
627	$2.30, "Ebony and Ivory" Carnival Queen	2·25	2·25
624/7	..	*Set of 4*	4·75	4·25

(Des G. Drummond. Litho Format)

1985 (8 Feb). *National Emblems. T* **110** *and similar vert designs. Multicoloured. W* w **15**. *P* 14.

628	$1.15, Type **110**	..	..	1·00	75
629	$1.50, Lobster Claw	..	..	1·50	95
630	$3 Montserrat Oriole	..	..	2·75	1·90
628/30	..	*Set of 3*	4·75	3·75

IMPERFORATES AND MISSING COLOURS. Various issues between Nos. **631** and **695** exist either imperforate or with colours omitted. Such items are not listed as there is no evidence that they fulfil the criteria outlined on page xi of this catalogue.

111 *Oncidium urophyllum*   **112** Queen Elizabeth the Queen Mother

(Des J. Cooter. Litho Format)

1985 (9 May). *Orchids of Montserrat. T* **111** *and similar vert designs. Multicoloured. W* w **15**. *P* 14.

631	90 c. Type **111**. .	..	..	80	55
632	$1.15, *Epidendrum difforme*	..	90	70
633	$1.50, *Epidendrum ciliare*. .	..	1·00	85
634	$2.50, *Brassavola cucullata*	..	1·40	1·40
631/4	..	*Set of 4*	3·75	3·25
MS635	120 × 140 mm. Nos. **631/4**	..	4·25	5·00

(Des D. Ewart ($2), Maxine Marsh (others). Litho Format)

1985 (7 Aug). *Life and Times of Queen Elizabeth the Queen Mother. Various vertical portraits as T* **112**. *P* 12½.

636	55 c. multicoloured		30	35
	a. Horiz pair. Nos. 636/7		60	70
637	55 c. multicoloured		30	35
638	90 c. multicoloured		35	55
	a. Horiz pair. Nos. 638/9		70	1·10
639	90 c. multicoloured		35	55
640	$1.15, multicoloured		40	65
	a. Horiz pair. Nos. 640/1		80	1·25
641	$1.15, multicoloured		40	65
642	$1.50, multicoloured		50	70
	a. Horiz pair. Nos. 642/3		1·00	1·40
643	$1.50, multicoloured		50	70
636/43		Set of 8	3·00	4·00
MS644	85×113 mm. $2 multicoloured; $2 multicoloured		1·40	1·90

The two designs of each value were issued, *se-tenant*, in horizontal pairs within the sheets. Each *se-tenant* pair shows a floral pattern across the bottom of the portraits which stops short of the left-hand edge on the left-hand stamp and of the right-hand edge on the right-hand stamp.

Designs as Nos. 636/7 and 642/3 but with face values of $3.50×2 and $6×2, also exist in additional miniature sheets from a restricted printing issued 10 January 1986.

Nos. 636/43 and an unissued 15 c. also exist in separate miniature sheets, combining the two designs for each value, from stock dispersed by the liquidator of Format International Security Printers Ltd.

113 Cotton Plants

(Des G. Drummond. Litho Format)

1985 (18 Oct). *Montserrat Sea Island Cotton Industry. T* **113** *and similar horiz designs. Multicoloured. W w* **15**. *P* 15.

645	90 c. Type **113**.		75	75
646	$1 Operator at carding machine		80	80
647	$1.15, Threading loom		95	95
648	$2.50, Weaving with hand loom		2·00	2·25
645/8		Set of 4	4·00	4·25
MS649	148×103 mm. Nos. 645/8. Wmk sideways		3·50	3·75

CARIBBEAN ROYAL VISIT 1985

(114)   115 Black-throated Blue Warbler

1985 (25 Oct). *Royal Visit. Nos.* 514/15, 543, 587/8 *and* 640/1 *optd as T* **114** *or surch also.*

650	75 c. multicoloured (No. 587)		2·50	2·50
651	$1 multicoloured (No. 543)		4·00	3·00
652	$1.15, multicoloured (No. 640)		4·00	3·00
	a. Horiz pair. Nos. 652/3		8·00	7·00
653	$1.15, multicoloured (No. 641)		4·00	3·50
654	$1.50, multicoloured (No. 588)		5·50	5·00
655	$1.60 on $4 multicoloured (No. 514)		3·50	3·50
	a. Sheetlet. No. 655×6 and No. 656		28·00	
	ab. Sheetlet No. 655×6 and No. 656a		28·00	
656	$1.60 on $4 multicoloured (No. 515) (surch $1.60 only)		10·00	10·00
	a. Additionally optd "CARIBBEAN ROYAL VISIT—1985"		10·00	10·00
650/6		Set of 7	30·00	28·00

No. 656 shows a new face value only; "CARIBBEAN ROYAL VISIT" being omitted from the surcharge. No. 656a is the corrected version issued subsequently.

(Des R. Vigurs. Litho Format)

1985 (29 Nov). *Leaders of the World. Birth Bicentenary of John J. Audubon (ornithologist). T* **115** *and similar vert designs showing original paintings. Multicoloured. P* 12½.

657	15 c. Type **115**.		15	15
	a. Horiz pair. Nos. 657/8		30	30
658	15 c. Palm Warbler		15	15
659	30 c. Bobolink		20	20
	a. Horiz pair. Nos. 659/60		40	40
660	30 c. Lark Sparrow		20	20
661	55 c. Chipping Sparrow		30	30
	a. Horiz pair. Nos. 661/2		60	60
662	55 c. Northern Oriole		30	30
663	$2.50, American Goldfinch		1·00	1·00
	a. Horiz pair. Nos. 663/4		2·00	2·00
664	$2.50, Blue Grosbeak		1·00	1·00
657/64		Set of 8	3·00	3·00

Nos. 657/8, 659/60, 661/2 and 663/4 were printed together, *se-tenant*, in horizontal pairs throughout the sheets.

NEW INFORMATION

The editor is always interested to correspond with people who have new information that will improve or correct the Catalogue.

116 Herald Angel appearing to   117 Lord Baden-Powell Goatherds

(Des Jennifer Toombs. Litho Format)

1985 (2 Dec). *Christmas. T* **116** *and similar horiz designs showing a Caribbean Nativity. Multicoloured. P* 15.

665	70 c. Type **116**.		40	45
666	$1.15, Three Wise Men following the Star		65	70
667	$1.50, Carol singing around War Memorial, Plymouth		80	85
668	$2.30, Praying to "Our Lady of Montserrat" Church of Our Lady, St. Patrick's Village		1·25	1·40
665/8		Set of 4	2·75	3·00

(Des G. Vasarhelyi. Litho Format)

1986 (11 Apr). *50th Anniv of Montserrat Girl Guide Movement. T* **117** *and similar vert designs. Multicoloured. W w* **15** *(sideways). P* 15.

669	20 c. Type **117**.		25	25
	a. Horiz pair. Nos. 669/70.		50	50
670	20 c. Girl Guide saluting		25	25
671	75 c. Lady Baden-Powell		65	65
	a. Horiz pair. Nos. 671/2		1·25	1·25
672	75 c. Guide assisting in old people's home		65	65
673	90 c. Lord and Lady Baden-Powell		80	80
	a. Horiz pair. Nos. 673/4		1·60	1·60
674	90 c. Guides serving meal in old people's home		80	80
675	$1.15, Girl Guides of 1936.		1·00	1·00
	a. Horiz pair. Nos. 675/6		2·00	2·00
676	$1.15, Two Guides saluting		1·00	1·00
669/76		Set of 8	4·75	4·75

Nos. 669/70, 671/2, 673/4 and 675/6 were each printed together, *se-tenant*, in horizontal pairs throughout the sheets.

117a Queen Elizabeth II

(Des Court House Studio. Litho Format)

1986 (21 Apr). *60th Birthday of Queen Elizabeth II. T* **117a** *and similar multicoloured designs. P* 12½.

677	10 c. Type **117a**.		10	10
678	$1.50, Princess Elizabeth in 1928		60	60
679	$3 In Antigua, 1977		1·00	1·00
680	$6 In Canberra, 1982 (*vert*)		2·00	2·00
677/80		Set of 4	3·25	3·25
MS681	85×115 mm. $8 Queen with bouquet		4·50	5·00

The 10 c., $1.50 and $3 also exist watermarked w **16** (sideways), but no examples of these used from Montserrat have been seen.

Nos. 677/80 also exist in individual miniature sheets from stock dispersed by the liquidator of Format International Security Printers Ltd.

118 King Harold and Halley's Comet, 1066 (from Bayeux Tapestry)

(Des Court House Studio. Litho Format)

1986 (9 May). *Appearance of Halley's Comet. T* **118** *and similar horiz designs. Multicoloured. P* 14×13½.

682	35 c. Type **118**.		30	30
683	50 c. Comet of 1301 (from Giotto's "Adoration of the Magi")		40	40
684	70 c. Edmond Halley and Comet of 1531		55	55
685	$1 Comets of 1066 and 1910		70	70
686	$1.15, Comet of 1910		80	80
687	$1.50, E.S.A. *Giotto* spacecraft and Comet		95	95
688	$2.30, U.S. Space Telescope and Comet		1·40	1·40
689	$4 Computer reconstruction of 1910 Comet		2·50	2·50
682/9		Set of 8	7·00	7·00
MS690	Two sheets, each 140×115 mm. (a) 40 c. Type 118; $1.75, As No. 683; $2 As No. 684; $3 As No. 685. (b) 55 c. As No. 686; 60 c. As No. 687; 80 c. As No. 688; $5 As No. 689 Set of 2 sheets		7·00	8·00

118a Prince Andrew   119 Antelope (1793)

(Des Court House Studio. Litho Format)

1986 (23 July–15 Oct). *Royal Wedding (1st issue). T* **118a** *and similar multicoloured designs. P* 12½.

691	70 c. Type **118a**		30	35
	a. Pair. Nos. 691/2		60	70
692	70 c. Miss Sarah Ferguson.		30	35
693	$2 Prince Andrew wearing stetson (*horiz*)		75	90
	a. Pair. Nos. 693/4		1·50	1·75
694	$2 Miss Sarah Ferguson on skiing holiday (*horiz*)		75	90
691/4		Set of 4	2·00	2·25
MS695	115×85 mm. $10 Duke and Duchess of York on Palace balcony after wedding (*horiz*) (15.10)		3·50	3·75

Nos. 691/2 and 693/4 were printed together, *se-tenant*, in horizontal and vertical pairs throughout the sheets.

Nos. 691/4 imperforate come from souvenir stamp booklets.

See also Nos. 705/8.

A set of eight was prepared for the 1986 World Cup Football Championships, but was not issued. Examples exist from stock dispersed by the liquidator of Format International Security Printers Ltd.

(Des T. Hadler. Litho Questa)

1986 (29 Aug). *Mail Packet Sailing Ships. T* **119** *and similar horiz designs. Multicoloured. W w* **15**. *P* 14.

696	90 c. Type **119**.		1·50	1·25
697	$1.15, *Montagu* (1810)		1·75	1·50
698	$1.50, *Little Catherine* (1813)		2·25	2·25
699	$2.30, *Hinchingbrook* (1813)		2·75	3·00
696/9		Set of 4	7·50	7·25
MS700	165×123 mm. Nos. 696/9. Wmk sideways		9·00	9·50

120 Radio Montserrat Building, Dagenham

(Des G. Vasarhelyi. Litho Questa)

1986 (29 Sept). *Communications. T* **120** *and similar horiz designs. Multicoloured. W w* **15**. *P* 14.

701	70 c. Type **120**.		1·00	70
702	$1.15, Radio Gem dish aerial, Plymouth		1·50	1·25
703	$1.50, Radio Antilles studio, O'Garro's		1·75	1·75
704	$2.30, Cable and Wireless building, Plymouth		2·25	3·00
701/4		Set of 4	6·00	6·00

(121)   121a Statue of Liberty

1986 (14 Nov). *Royal Wedding (2nd issue). Nos.* 691/4 *optd as T* **121** *in silver.*

705	70 c. Type **118a**		50	50
	a. Pair. Nos. 705/6		1·00	1·00
706	70 c. Miss Sarah Ferguson		50	50
707	$2 Prince Andrew wearing stetson (*horiz*)		1·25	1·25
	a. Pair. Nos. 707/8.		2·50	2·50
708	$2 Miss Sarah Ferguson on skiing holiday (*horiz*)		1·25	1·25
705/8		Set of 4	3·25	3·25

(Des Court House Studio. Litho Format)

1986 (18 Nov). *Centenary of Statue of Liberty. Vert views of Statue as T* **121a** *in separate miniature sheets. Multicoloured. P* 14×13½.

MS709	Three sheets, each 85×115 mm. $3; $4.50; $5 Set of 3 sheets		7·00	8·00

122 Sailing and Windsurfing

123 Christmas Rose

(Des J. Cooter. Litho Format)

1986 (10 Dec). *Tourism. T* **122** *and similar horiz designs. Multicoloured. P* 15.

710	70 c. Type **122**. .	..	..	1·00	70
711	$1.15, Golf ..	..	..	2·50	1·50
712	$1.50, Plymouth market	..	..	2·50	2·25
713	$2.30, Air Recording Studios	..	..	2·75	3·25
710/13	..	..	*Set of* 4	8·00	7·00

(Des Jennifer Toombs. Litho Questa)

1986 (12 Dec). *Christmas. Flowering Shrubs. T* **123** *and similar vert designs. Multicoloured. P* 14.

714	70 c. Type **123**. .	..	..	60	40
715	$1.15, Candle Flower	..	..	85	70
716	$1.50, Christmas Tree Kalanchoe	..	1·25	1·00
717	$2.30, Snow on the Mountain	..	1·75	2·00
714/17	..	..	*Set of* 4	4·00	3·75
MS718	150×110 mm. Nos. 714/17. P 12	..	5·00	6·00

124 Tiger Shark

(125)

(Des M. Hillier. Litho Questa)

1987 (2 Feb). *Sharks. T* **124** *and similar horiz designs. Multicoloured. W w* 15. *P* 14.

719	40 c. Type **124**. .	..	..	1·00	55
720	90 c. Lemon Shark	..	..	1·75	1·10
721	$1.15, White Shark	..	..	2·00	1·75
722	$3.50, Whale Shark	..	..	4·00	4·25
719/22	..	..	*Set of* 4	8·00	7·00
MS723	150×102 mm. Nos. 719/22. Wmk sideways. P 12. .	..	..	8·50	9·00

1987 (6 Apr). *Nos.* 601, 603, 607/8 *and* 611 *surch as T* **125**.

724	5 c. on 70 c. Glossy Ibis	..	20	15
725	$1 on 20 c. Brown Booby	..	1·00	80
726	$1.15 on 10 c. Carib Grackle	..	1·10	90
727	$1.50 on 90 c. Green Heron. .	..	1·40	1·40
728	$2.30 on $3 American Kestrel (*vert*)	..	2·25	2·75
724/8	..	..	*Set of* 5	5·50	5·50

127 *Phoebis trite*

(126)

1987 (13 June). *"Capex '87" International Stamp Exhibition, Toronto. No.* **MS**690 *optd with T* **126** *in black and red.*

MS729 Two sheets. As No. MS690

Set of 2 *sheets* 6·50 7·00

No. MS729 also carries an overprint commemorating the exhibition on the lower sheet margins.

(Des M. Hillier. Litho Questa)

1987 (10 Aug). *Butterflies. T* **127** *and similar square designs. Multicoloured. W w* 15. *P* 14.

730	90 c. Type **127**	..	..	1·50	80
731	$1.15, *Biblis hyperia*	..	..	2·00	1·25
732	$1.50, *Polygonus leo*	..	..	2·50	2·00
733	$2.50, *Hypolimnas misippus*	..	4·00	4·25
730/3	..	..	*Set of* 4	9·00	7·50

128 *Oncidium variegatum*

(Des R. Vigurs. Litho Questa)

1987 (13 Nov). *Christmas. Orchids. T* **128** *and similar multicoloured designs. P* 14×13½ (90 c., $1.50) *or* 13½×14 (*others*).

734	90 c. Type **128**. .	..	..	60	45
735	$1.15, *Vanilla planifolia* (*horiz*)	..	85	55
736	$1.50, *Gongora quinquenervis*	..	1·10	75
737	$3.50, *Brassavola nodosa* (*horiz*)	..	2·00	1·75
734/7	..	..	*Set of* 4	4·00	3·25
MS738	100×75 mm. $5 *Oncidium lanceanum* (*horiz*)	..	..	6·00	7·00

40th Wedding Anniversary
HM Queen Elizabeth II
HRH Duke of Edinburgh.
November 1987.
$2.30 ==

(129)

1987 (29 Nov). *Royal Ruby Wedding. Nos* 601. 604/5 *and* 608 *surch as T* **129**. A. *Surch* "Edinburgh". B. *Surch* "Edinburgh".

		A		B	
739	5 c. on 90 c. Green Heron	1·50	1·50	15	15
740	$1.15 on 10 c. Carib Grackle ..	3·25	3·25	65	65
741	$2.30 on 25 c. Black-whiskered Vireo	6·00	6·00	1·40	1·40
742	$5 on 40 c. Scaly-breasted Thrasher ..	9·00	9·00	2·75	3·00
739/42	*Set of* 4	18·00	18·00	4·50	4·75

Nos. 739A/42A were from the first printing using Type **129**. After the spelling mistake was noticed it was corrected on sheets subsequently surcharged.

(Des M. Pollard. Litho Questa)

1988 (8 Feb). *Bats. T* **130** *and similar vert designs. Multicoloured. W w* 15 (*sideways*). *P* 14.

743	55 c. Type **130**. .	..	..	50	35
744	90 c. *Chiroderma improvisum* (fruit bat)	..	80	65
745	$1.15, Fisherman Bat	..	..	1·10	1·10
746	$2.30, *Brachyphylla cavernarum* (fruit bat)	2·25	2·50
743/6	..	..	*Set of* 4	4·25	4·25
MS747	133×110 mm. $2.50, Funnel-eared Bat. Wmk upright	..	..	3·00	3·50

131 Magnificent Frigate Bird

132 Discus throwing

(Des R. Vigurs. Litho Questa)

1988 (2 Apr). *Easter. Birds. T* **131** *and similar vert designs. Multicoloured. P* 14×13½.

748	90 c. Type **131**	..	..	60	45
749	$1.15, Caribbean Elaenia	..	..	80	65
750	$1.50, Glossy Ibis	..	..	1·00	1·00
751	$3.50, Purple-throated Carib	..	2·00	2·25
748/51	..	..	*Set of* 4	4·00	4·00
MS752	100 × 75 mm. $5 Brown Pelican	..	2·50	3·25

(Des R. Vigurs. Litho Questa)

1988 (29 July). *Olympic Games, Seoul. T* **132** *and similar horiz designs. Multicoloured. P* 13½×14.

753	90 c. Type **132**	..	..	40	45
754	$1.15, High jumping	..	..	50	55
755	$3.50, Athletics ..	..	..	1·60	1·75
753/5	..	..	*Set of* 3	2·25	2·50
MS756	103×77 mm. $5 Rowing	..	2·25	2·75

133 Golden Tulip

134 University Crest

(Des R. Vigurs. Litho Questa)

1988 (30 Aug). *Sea Shells. T* **133** *and similar horiz designs. Multicoloured. P* 14.

757	5 c. Type **133**	..	..	10	10
758	10 c. Little Knobby Scallop	..	15	15
759	15 c. Sozoni's Cone ..	..	15	15
760	20 c. Globular Coral Shell ..	..	20	20
761	25 c. Sundial	..	..	20	20
762	40 c. King Helmet ..	..	30	30
763	55 c. Channelled Turban	..	40	40
764	70 c. True Tulip Shell	..	55	55
765	90 c. Music Volute ..	..	65	65
766	$1 Flame Auger	..	..	70	70
767	$1.15, Rooster Tail Conch	..	80	80
768	$1.50, Queen Conch	..	95	95
769	$3 Teramachi's Slit Shell	..	1·75	2·00
770	$5 Florida Crown Conch ..	..	3·25	3·50
771	$7.50, Beau's Murex	..	5·00	5·50
772	$10 Triton's Trumpet	..	7·00	7·50
757/72	..	..	*Set of* 16	20·00	21·00

(Des R. Vigurs. Litho Questa)

1988 (14 Oct). *40th Anniv of University of West Indies. P* 14×13½.

773	**134** $5 multicoloured	..	2·40	2·50

= HRH PRINCESS
ALEXANDRA'S VISIT
NOVEMBER 1988
40¢

(135)

1988 (4 Nov). *Princess Alexandra's Visit. Nos.* 763, 766 *and* 769/70 *surch as T* **135**.

774	40 c. on 55 c. Channelled Turban	..	35	35
775	90 c. on $1 Flame Auger	..	55	55
776	$1.15 on $3 Teramachi's Slit Shell	..	70	70
	a. Surch double ..	..	55·00	
777	$1.50 on $5 Florida Crown Conch	..	85	85
774/7	..	..	*Set of* 4	2·25	2·25

136 Spotted Sandpiper

(Des R. Vigurs. Litho Questa)

1988 (4 Dec). *Christmas. Sea Birds. T* **136** *and similar horiz designs. Multicoloured. P* 13½×14.

778	90 c. Type **136**	..	..	70	55
779	$1.15, Turnstone	..	..	85	70
780	$3.50, Red-footed Booby ..	..	2·00	2·25
778/80	..	..	*Set of* 3	3·25	3·25
MS781	105×79 mm. $5 Audubon's Shearwater	2·75	3·25

137 Handicapped Children in Classroom

(Des R. Vigurs. Litho Questa)

1988 (16 Dec). *125th Anniv of International Red Cross. P* 13½ × 14.

782	**137** $3.50, multicoloured	..	1·50	1·60

138 Drum Major in Ceremonial Uniform

139 Amazon Lily

(Des R. Vigurs. Litho Questa)

1989 (24 Feb). *75th Anniv of Montserrat Defence Force* (1988). *Uniforms. T* **138** *and similar vert designs. Multicoloured. P* 14×13½.

783	90 c. Type **138**	..	..	70	55
784	$1.15, Field training uniform	..	85	75
785	$1.50, Cadet in ceremonial uniform	..	1·25	1·25
786	$3.50, Gazetted Police Officer in ceremonial uniform	..	2·50	2·75
783/6	..	..	*Set of* 4	4·75	4·75
MS787	102×76 mm. $5 Island Girl Guide Commissioner and Brownie	..	3·25	4·00

(Litho Questa)

1989 (21 Mar). *Easter. Lilies. T* **139** *and similar multicoloured designs. P* 13½×14 (90 c.) *or* 14×13½ (others).

788	90 c. Type **139**		50	50
789	$1.15, Salmon Blood Lily (*vert*)		70	70
790	$1.50, Amaryllis (*Hippeastrum vittatum*) (*vert*)		85	85
791	$3.50, Amaryllis (*Hippeastrum* hybrid) (*vert*)		1·90	1·90
788/91		*Set of* 4	3·50	3·50
MS792	103×77 mm. $5 Resurrection Lily (*vert*)		3·50	4·00

140 *Morning Prince* (schooner), 1942

141 The Scarecrow

(Des R. Vigurs. Litho Questa)

1989 (30 June). *Shipbuilding in Montserrat. T* **140** *and similar horiz designs. Multicoloured. P* 13½×14.

793	90 c. Type **140**		40	45
794	$1.15, *Western Sun* (inter-island freighter)		55	60
795	$1.50, *Kim G* (inter-island freighter) under construction		70	75
796	$3.50, *Romaris* (island ferry), c. 1942		1·60	1·75
793/6		*Set of* 4	3·00	3·25

(Litho Questa)

1989 (22 Sept). *50th Anniv of The Wizard of Oz* (film). *T* **141** *and similar multicoloured designs. P* 14.

797	90 c. Type **141**		40	45
798	$1.15, The Lion		55	60
799	$1.50, The Tin Man		70	75
800	$3.50, Dorothy		1·60	1·75
797/800		*Set of* 4	3·00	3·25
MS801	113×84 mm. $5 Characters from film (*horiz*)		2·40	2·50

Hurricane Hugo
Relief Surcharge $2.50

(142)

1989 (20 Oct). *Hurricane Hugo Relief Fund. Nos.* 795/6 *surch with T* **142**.

802	$1.50 + $2.50, *Kim G* (inter-island freighter) under construction		1·90	2·00
803	$3.50 + $2.50, *Romaris* (island ferry), c. 1942		2·75	3·00

143 "Apollo 11" above Lunar Surface

(Litho Questa)

1989 (19 Dec). *20th Anniv of First Manned Landing on Moon. T* **143** *and similar multicoloured designs. P* 13½×14.

804	90 c. Type **143**		35	40
805	$1.15, Astronaut alighting from lunar module *Eagle*		45	50
806	$1.50, *Eagle* and astronaut conducting experiment		60	65
807	$3.50, Opening "Apollo 11" hatch after splashdown		1·40	1·50
804/7		*Set of* 4	2·50	2·75
MS808	101×76 mm. $5 Astronaut on Moon. P 14 ×13½		2·75	3·00

144 *Yamato* (Japanese battleship)

145 The Empty Tomb

(Litho Questa)

1990 (12 Feb). *World War II Capital Ships. T* **144** *and similar horiz designs. Multicoloured. P* 14.

809	70 c. Type **144**		50	40
810	$1.15, U.S.S. *Arizona* at Pearl Harbour		70	60
811	$1.50, *Bismarck* (German battleship) in action		1·00	90
812	$3.50, H.M.S. *Hood* (battle cruiser)		1·75	2·00
809/12		*Set of* 4	3·50	3·50
MS813	118×90 mm. $5 *Bismarck* and map of North Atlantic		3·75	4·25

(Des R. Vigurs. Litho Questa)

1990 (12 Apr). *Easter. T* **145** *and similar vert designs showing stained glass windows from St. Michael's Parish Church, Bray, Berkshire. Multicoloured. P* 14×15.

814	$1.15, Type **145**		45	50
	a. Horiz strip of 3. Nos. 814/16		2·25	
815	$1.50, The Ascension		60	65
816	$3.50, The Risen Christ with Disciples		1·40	1·50
814/16		*Set of* 3	2·25	2·40
MS817	65×103 mm. $5 The Crucifixion		2·50	3·00

Nos. 814/16 were printed together, *se-tenant*, in sheets of 6 (3×2).

(146)

1990 (3 May). *"Stamp World London 90" International Stamp Exhibition. Nos.* 460/4 *surch as T* **146** *in bright purple.*

818	70 c. on 40 c. Type **85**		40	40
819	90 c. on 55 c. "H.S. 748" aircraft and 1976 55 c. definitive		55	55
820	$1 on $1.20, *La Plata* (liner) and 1903 5s. stamp		65	65
821	$1.15 on $1.20, *Lady Hawkins* (packet steamer) and 1932 Tercentenary 5s. commemorative		75	75
822	$1.50 on $1.20, *Avon* (paddle-steamer) and Penny Red stamp with "A 08" postmark		1·00	1·00
818/22		*Set of* 5	3·00	3·00

Nos. 818/22 also show the "Stamp World London 90" emblem overprinted on one of the *se-tenant* labels.

147 General Office, Montserrat, and 1884 ½d. Stamp

(Litho Questa)

1990 (1 June). *150th Anniv of the Penny Black. T* **147** *and similar multicoloured designs. P* 13½×14 (*horiz*) *or* 14×13½ (*vert*).

823	90 c. Type **147**		55	55
824	$1.15, Sorting letters and Montserrat 1d. stamp of 1876 (*vert*)		75	75
825	$1.50, Posting letters and Penny Black (*vert*)		1·00	1·00
826	$3.50, Postman delivering letters and 1840 Twopence Blue		2·50	2·50
823/6		*Set of* 4	4·25	4·25
MS827	102×75 mm. $5 Montserrat soldier's letter of 1836 and Penny Black		3·50	3·75

148 Montserrat v. Antigua Match

(Litho Questa)

1990 (8 July). *World Cup Football Championship, Italy. T* **148** *and similar multicoloured designs. P* 14.

828	90 c. Type **148**		55	55
829	$1.15, U.S.A v. Trinidad match		75	75
830	$1.50, Montserrat team		1·00	1·00
831	$3.50, West Germany v. Wales match		2·00	2·00
828/31		*Set of* 4	3·75	3·75
MS832	77×101 mm. $5 World Cup trophy (*vert*)		3·00	3·50

COVER PRICES

Cover factors are quoted at the beginning of each country for most issues to 1945. An explanation of the system can be found on page x. The factors quoted do not, however, apply to philatelic covers.

---

149 Spinner Dolphin

(Des Jennifer Toombs. Litho Questa)

1990 (25 Sept). *Dolphins. T* **149** *and similar horiz designs. Multicoloured. P* 14.

833	90 c. Type **149**		55	55
834	$1.15, Common Dolphin		75	75
835	$1.50, Striped Dolphin		1·00	1·00
836	$3.50, Atlantic Spotted Dolphin		2·00	2·00
833/6		*Set of* 4	3·75	3·75
MS837	103×76 mm. $5 Atlantic White-sided Dolphin		2·75	3·25

150 Spotted Goatfish

(151)

(Litho Questa)

1991 (7 Feb). *Tropical Fishes. T* **150** *and similar horiz designs. Multicoloured. P* 13½×14.

838	90 c. Type **150**		55	55
839	$1.15, Cushion Star		75	75
840	$1.50, Rock Beauty		1·00	1·00
841	$3.50, French Grunt		2·25	2·25
838/41		*Set of* 4	4·00	4·00
MS842	103×76 mm. $5 Trunkfish		3·00	3·50

1991 (27 Feb). *Nos.* 760/1, 768 *and* 771 *surch as T* **151**.

843	5 c. on 20 c. Globular Coral Shell		15	15
844	5 c. on 25 c. Sundial		15	15
845	$1.15 on $1.50, Queen Conch		90	90
846	$1.15 on $7.50, Beau's Murex		90	90
843/6		*Set of* 4	1·90	1·90

152 Duck

153 *Panaeolus antillarum*

(Des K. West. Litho Questa)

1991 (29 May). *Domestic Birds. T* **152** *and similar horiz designs. Multicoloured. P* 14.

847	90 c. Type **152**		60	60
848	$1.15, Hen and chicks		80	80
849	$1.50, Rooster		1·10	1·10
850	$3.50, Helmet Guineafowl		2·40	2·40
847/50		*Set of* 4	4·50	4·50

(Des M. Pollard. Litho Questa)

1991 (13 June). *Fungi. T* **153** *and similar square designs. P* 14.

851	90 c. olive-grey		70	70
852	$1.15, rosine		90	90
853	$1.50, yellow-brown		1·25	1·25
854	$2 maroon		1·75	1·75
855	$3.50, dull ultramarine		2·75	2·75
851/5		*Set of* 5	6·50	6·50

Designs:—$1.15, *Cantharellus cinnabarinus*; $1.50, *Gymnopilus chrysopellus*; $2, *Psilocybe cubensis*; $3.50, *Leptonia caeruleocapitata*.

154 Red Water Lily

155 Tree Frog

(Des M. Pollard. Litho Questa)

1991 (8 Aug). *Lilies. T* **154** *and similar vert designs. Multicoloured. P* 14.

856	90 c. Type **154**		65	65
857	$1.15, Shell Ginger		75	75
858	$1.50, Early Day Lily		1·00	1·00
859	$3.50, Anthurium		2·50	2·50
856/9		*Set of* 4	4·50	4·50

(Des M. Pollard. Litho B.D.T.)

1991 (9 Oct). *Frogs and Toad. T* **155** *and similar multi-coloured designs. P* 14.

860	$1.15, Type 155 ..	80	80
861	$2 Crapaud Toad ..	1·40	1·40
862	$3.50, Mountain Chicken (frog) ..	2·50	2·50
860/2	*Set of* 3	4·25	4·25

MS863 110×110 mm. $5 Tree Frog, Crapaud Toad and Mountain Chicken (76½×44 *mm*). P 15×14 .. .. 3·50 3·75

156 Black British Shorthair Cat

(Des M. Pollard. Litho B.D.T.)

1991 (5 Dec). *Cats. T* **156** *and similar horiz designs. Multicoloured. P* 14.

864	90 c. Type 156 ..	60	60
865	$1.15, Seal Point Siamese ..	80	80
866	$1.50, Silver Tabby Persian ..	1·00	1·00
867	$2.50, Birman Temple Cat ..	1·60	1·60
868	$3.50, Egyptian Mau ..	1·90	1·90
864/8	*Set of* 5	5·50	5·50

157 Navigational Instruments

158 Runner with Olympic Flame

(Des M. Pollard. Litho Questa)

1992 (16 Jan). *500th Anniv of Discovery of America by Columbus. T* **157** *and similar horiz designs. Multicoloured. P* 14.

869	$1.50, Type 157 ..	80	90
	a. Sheetlet. Nos. 869/75 ..	5·75	
870	$1.50, Columbus and coat of arms ..	80	90
871	$1.50, Landfall on the Bahamas ..	80	90
872	$1.50, Petitioning Queen Isabella ..	80	90
873	$1.50, Tropical birds ..	80	90
874	$1.50, Tropical fruits ..	80	90
875	$3 Ships of Columbus (81×26 *mm*)	1·50	1·75
869/75	*Set of* 7	5·75	6·50

Nos. 869/75 were printed together, *se-tenant*, in sheetlets of 7 with decorative margins.

(Des M. Pollard. Litho B.D.T.)

1992 (10 Apr). *Olympic Games, Barcelona. T* **158** *and similar square designs. Multicoloured. P* 14.

876	$1 Type 158 ..	60	60
877	$1.15, Montserrat, Olympic and Spanish flags ..	75	75
878	$2.30, Olympic flame on map of Montserrat	1·25	1·25
879	$3.60, Olympic events ..	1·75	1·75
876/9	*Set of* 4	4·00	4·00

159 Tyrannosaurus

(Des M. Pollard. Litho Questa)

1992 (1 May). *Death Centenary of Sir Richard Owen (zoologist). T* **159** *and similar multicoloured designs. P* 14.

880	$1 Type 159 ..	70	70
881	$1.15, Diplodocus ..	80	80
882	$1.50, Apatosaurus ..	1·00	1·00
883	$3.45, Dimetrodon ..	2·25	2·25
880/3	*Set of* 4	4·25	4·25

MS884 114×84 mm. $4.60, Sir Richard Owen and dinosaur bone (*vert*) .. .. 3·50 3·75

160 Male Montserrat Oriole

(Des R. Vigurs. Litho Questa)

1992 (30 June). *Montserrat Oriole. T* **160** *and similar horiz designs. Multicoloured. P* 14.

885	$1 Type 160 ..	60	60
886	$1.15, Male and female Orioles ..	75	75
887	$1.50, Female Oriole with chicks ..	1·00	1·00
888	$3.60, Map of Montserrat and male Oriole	1·75	1·75
885/8	*Set of* 4	3·75	3·75

161 *Psophus stridulus* (grasshopper)

(Des M. Pollard. Litho B.D.T.)

1992 (20 Aug). *Insects. T* **161** *and similar horiz designs. Multicoloured. P* 15×14.

889	5 c. Type 161 ..	10	10
890	10 c. *Gryllus campestris* (field cricket)	10	10
891	15 c. *Lepthemis vesiculosa* (dragonfly)	10	10
892	20 c. *Orthemis ferruginea* (red skimmer)	10	10
893	25 c. *Gerris lacustris* (pond skater)	10	10
894	40 c. *Byctiscus betulae* (leaf weevil)	15	20
895	55 c. *Atta texana* (leaf-cutter ants)	20	25
896	70 c. *Polistes fuscatus* (paper wasp)	30	35
897	90 c. *Sparmopolius fulvus* (bee fly)	40	45
898	$1 *Chrysopa carnea* (lace wing)	45	50
899	$1.15, *Phoebis philea* (butterfly)	50	55
900	$1.50, *Cynthia cardui* (butterfly)	65	70
901	$3 *Utetheisa bella* (moth)	1·25	1·40
902	$5 *Alucita pentadactyla* (moth)	2·25	2·50
903	$7.50, *Anartia jatropha* (butterfly)	3·25	3·50
904	$10 *Heliconius melpomene* (butterfly)	4·25	4·50
889/904	*Set of* 16	12·50	13·50

162 Adoration of the Magi

(Des M. Pollard. Litho Questa)

1992 (26 Nov). *Christmas. T* **162** *and similar horiz design. Multicoloured. P* 13½×14.

905	$1.15, Type 162 ..	50	55
906	$4.60, Appearance of angel to shepherds ..	2·00	2·25

OFFICIAL STAMPS

O.H.M.S.   **O.H.M.S.**

(O 1)   (O 2)

1976 (12 Apr). *Various stamps, some already surcharged, optd locally with Type* O 1.

O1	5 c. multicoloured (No. 246A) ..	†	65
O2	10 c. multicoloured (No. 247A) ..	†	75
	a. Opt double ..	†	18·00
	b. Horiz pair, one stamp without opt	†	£250
O3	30 c. on 10 c. multicoloured (No. 369)..	†	1·50
	a. Opt double ..	†	40·00
O4	45 c. on 3 c. multicoloured (No. 370) ..	†	2·00
O5	$5 multicoloured (No. 254A) ..	†	£100
O6	$10 multicoloured (No. 254aB) ..	†	£550
O1/6	*Set of* 6	†	£600

These stamps were issued for use on mail from the Montserrat Philatelic Bureau. They were not available for sale in either unused or used condition.

1976 (1 Oct)–**80**. *Nos.* 374/8, 380/2 *and* 384/5 *optd with Type* O 2 locally.

O 7	5 c. Malay Apple ..	†	15
	a. Opt inverted ..	†	—
	b. Missing stop after "S" ..	†	1·50
O 8	10 c. Jacaranda ..	†	20
	a. Missing stop after "S" ..	†	1·50
O 9	15 c. Orchid Tree ..	†	25
	a. Opt inverted ..	†	70·00
	b. Missing stop after "S" ..	†	1·50
O10	20 c. Manjak ..	†	30
	a. Opt inverted ..	†	70·00
	b. Chalk-surfaced paper (1980) ..	†	—
	c. Missing stop after "S" ..	†	1·50
O11	25 c. Tamarind ..	†	35
	a. Missing stop after "S" ..	†	1·50
O12	55 c. Pink Cassia ..	†	55
	a. Opt inverted ..	†	—
	b. Missing stop after "S" ..	†	2·50
O13	70 c. Long John ..	†	60
	a. Missing stop after "S" ..	†	3·50
O14	$1 Saman ..	†	95
	a. Opt inverted ..	†	—
	b. Missing stop after "S" ..	†	5·00
O15	$5 Yellow Poui ..	†	4·50
	a. Missing stop after "S" ..	†	13·00
O16	$10 Flamboyant (14.4.80) ..	†	7·50
	a. Missing stop after "S" ..	†	20·00
O7/16	*Set of* 10	†	14·00

Nos. O7/16 were not available in an unused condition, but were sold to the public cancelled-to-order.

The missing stop after "S" variety occurs on R. 1/3 and 3/5.

O.H.M.S.

O.H.M.S.   O.H.M.S.   45¢

(O 3)   (O 4)   (O 5)

1980 (7 July). *Nos.* 374/8, 380/2 *and* 384/5 *optd with Type* O 3 *in Great Britain.*

O17	5 c. Malay Apple ..	†	10
	a. Opt double ..	†	—
O18	10 c. Jacaranda ..	†	10
O19	15 c. Orchid Tree ..	†	10
O20	20 c. Manjak ..	†	10
	a. Opt double ..	†	70·00
O21	25 c. Tamarind ..	†	15
O22	55 c. Pink Cassia ..	†	35
	a. Opt double ..	†	15·00
O23	70 c. Long John ..	†	45
O24	$1 Saman ..	†	60
O25	$5 Yellow Poui ..	†	2·75
O26	$10 Flamboyant ..	†	5·50
O17/26	*Set of* 10	†	9·00

Nos. O17/26 were not available in an unused condition, but were sold to the public cancelled-to-order. At least two values, the 20 c. and $1 are, however, known uncancelled.

These stamps were originally intended for issue on 3 November 1980, but certain values were placed on sale from 7 July onwards to meet shortages. Bulk supplies did not arrive on the island until early December 1980.

O.H. M.S.

Spaced "H" and "M" (R. 3/4)

1980 (30 Sept). *Nos.* 374/82, 384/5 *and* 476, *together with surcharges on Nos.* 372, 376 *and* 379, *optd as Type* O 4 *locally.*

O27	5 c. Malay Apple ..	†	10
O28	5 c. on 3 c. Lignum vitae ..	†	10
O29	10 c. Jacaranda ..	†	10
O30	15 c. Orchid Tree ..	†	10
	a. Opt double ..	†	—
O31	20 c. Manjak ..	†	15
	a. Opt double ..	†	15·00
O32	25 c. Tamarind ..	†	15
O33	30 c. on 15 c. Orchid Tree ..	†	20
O34	35 c. on 2 c. Cannon-ball Tree ..	†	20
	a. Spaced "H" and "M" ..	†	3·50
O35	40 c. Flame of the Forest ..	†	25
O36	55 c. Pink Cassia ..	†	35
O37	70 c. Long John ..	†	60
O38	$1 Saman ..	†	70
O39	$2.50 on 40 c. Flame of the Forest ..	†	2·00
	a. "O.H.M.S." opt omitted ..	£160	
O40	$5 Yellow Poui ..	†	4·00
O41	$10 Flamboyant ..	†	7·00
	a. Opt double ..	†	75·00
O27/41	*Set of* 15	†	14·00

Nos. O27/41 were not available in an unused condition, but were sold to the public cancelled-to-order. No. O39a was, however, found amongst supplies of the postage series.

1981 (20 Mar). *Nos. 490/4, 496, 498, 500, 502/3 and 505 optd with Type O 4.*

O42	5 c. Type **91**	..	10	10
	a. Opt inverted ..	..	17·00	
O43	10 c. Hogfish	..	10	10
O44	15 c. Creole Wrasse	..	10	10
	a. Opt double	..	†	—
O45	20 c. Yellow Damselfish	..	15	15
O46	25 c. Sergeant Major	..	15	15
O47	45 c. Schoolmaster	..	25	20
	a. Opt double	..	22·00	
	ab. Opt double, one on reverse	..	16·00	
	b. Opt inverted ..	..	22·00	
O48	65 c. Bigeye	..	35	30
	a. Opt inverted ..	..	65·00	
O49	$1 Rock Beauty ..	..	65	65
O50	$3 Fairy Basslet and Blueheads	..	1·75	1·75
O51	$5 Cherubfish	..	3·00	3·00
O52	$10 Longsnout Butterflyfish	..	5·50	3·50
O42/52	..	*Set of 11*	11·00	9·00

1982 (17 Nov). *Nos. 510/15 surch as Type O 5 (in one line on Nos. O54, O56 and O58).*

O53	45 c. on 90 c. *Charlotte*	..	25	30
	a. Sheetlet. No. O53 × 6 and No. O54	1·75		
	b. Surch double	..	25·00	
	c. Surch inverted	..	16·00	
	d. Surch inverted (horiz pair)	..	32·00	
	e. Horiz pair, one without surch	..	70·00	
O54	45 c. on 90 c. Prince Charles and Lady Diana Spencer	..	30	30
	b. Surch double	..	70·00	
	c. Surch inverted	..	50·00	
O55	75 c. on $3 *Portsmouth*	..	35	35
	a. Sheetlet. No. O55 × 6 and No. O56	2·25		
	b. Surch double	..	30·00	
	c. Surch inverted	..	18·00	
	d. Surch inverted (horiz pair)	..	23·00	
	e. Horiz pair, one without surch	..	70·00	
	f. Error. Surch on $4 (No. 514)	..	15·00	
	fa. Sheetlet. No. O55f × 6 and No. O56f	£150		
O56	75 c. on $3 Prince Charles and Lady Diana Spencer	..	45	45
	b. Surch double	..	75·00	
	c. Surch inverted	..	25·00	
	f. Error. Surch on $4 (No. 515)	..	70·00	
O57	$1 on $4 *Britannia*	..	50	50
	a. Sheetlet. No. O57 × 6 and No. O58	3·50		
	b. Surch double	..	32·00	
	c. Surch inverted	..	10·00	
	d. Surch inverted (horiz pair)	..	24·00	
	e. Horiz pair, one without surch	..		
O58	$1 on $4 Prince Charles and Lady Diana Spencer	..	60	60
	b. Surch double	..	80·00	
	c. Surch inverted	..	27·00	
O53/8	.. ..	*Set of 6*	2·00	2·10

Nos. O53d, O55d and O57d show the long surcharge, intended for Nos. O54, O56 or O58, inverted across horizontal pairs of the smaller design. Nos. O54c, O56c and O58c show two examples as Type O 5 inverted on the same stamp.

70¢

		O	O
		O H M S	O H M S
O.H.M.S.			
(O 6)		(O 7)	(O 8)

1983 (19 Oct). *Nos. 542/4 surch as Type O 6 or optd only ($1).*

O59	70 c. on 75 c. Type **97**	..	60	40
O60	$1 Coat of Arms of Catherine of Aragon ..		70	50
	a. Opt inverted ..	..	40·00	
O61	$1.50 on $5 Diana, Princess of Wales	..	1·00	80
O59/61	.. ..	*Set of 3*	2·10	1·60

1985 (12 Apr). *Nos. 600/12 and 614 opt with Type O 7 (horizontally on Nos. O71/5).*

O62	5 c. Type **107**	..	..	20	20
O63	10 c. Carib Grackle	..	..	20	20
O64	15 c. Moorhen	..	..	20	20
O65	20 c. Brown Booby	..	..	20	20
O66	25 c. Black-whiskered Vireo	..		25	25
O67	40 c. Scaly-breasted Thrasher	..		35	30
	a. Opt double	..	..	†	—
O68	55 c. Laughing Gull ..		..	45	30
O69	70 c. Glossy Ibis	..	..	60	40
O70	90 c. Green Heron ..		..	75	40
O71	$1 Belted Kingfisher	..	..	90	45
O72	$1.15, Bananaquit..		..	1·25	70
O73	$3 American Kestrel	..	..	2·25	2·25
O74	$5 Forest Thrush ..		..	3·25	3·50
O75	$10 Bridled Quail Dove	..		5·50	3·75
O62/75	.. ..	..	*Set of 14*	15·00	11·50

1989 (9 May). *Nos. 757/70 and 772 optd with Type O 8.*

O76	5 c. Type **133**	..	..	20	20
O77	10 c. Little Knobby Scallop	..		20	20
O78	15 c. Sozoni's Cone	..	..	20	20
O79	20 c. Globular Coral Shell ..		..	20	20
O80	25 c. Sundial	..	..	25	25
O81	40 c. King Helmet ..		..	30	30
O82	55 c. Channelled Turban	..		40	40
O83	70 c. True Tulip Shell	..		50	50
	a. Horiz pair, left-hand stamp without opt	..		..	
O84	90 c. Music Volute	..	..	65	65
O85	$1 Flame Auger ..		..	70	70
O86	$1.15, Rooster Tail Conch	..		80	80

O87	$1.50, Queen Conch	..	..	95	95
O88	$3 Teramachi's Slit Shell	..		1·75	1·75
O89	$5 Florida Crown Conch	..		3·00	3·00
O90	$10 Triton's Trumpet	..		5·50	5·50
O76/90	..	*Set of 15*	14·00	14·00

 70¢

OHMS

OHMS	70¢
(O 9)	(O 10)

1989 (26 May). *Nos. 578 and 580/1 surch with Type O 9.*

O91	70 c. on 10 c. Hogfish	..	40	40
O92	$1.15 on 75 c. French Grunt	..	70	70
O93	$1.50 on $2 Blue Chromis	..	85	85
O91/3	..	*Set of 3*	1·75	1·75

1992 (3 July). *Nos. 838/41, 847/50 and 856/9 surch or optd only as Type O 10 ("OHMS" vert on Nos. O96, O98/9, O102/3 and O105) by Benjies Printery, Antigua.*

O94	70 c. on 90 c. Type **150**	..	30	35
O95	70 c. on 90 c. Type **152**	..	30	35
O96	70 c. on 90 c. Type **154**	..	30	35
O97	70 c. on $3.50, French Grunt	..	30	35
O98	$1 on $3.50, Helmet Guineafowl	..	45	50
O99	$1 on $3.50, Anthurium	..	45	50
O100	$1.15, Cushion Star	..	50	55
O101	$1.15, Hen and Chicks	..	50	55
O102	$1.15, Shell Ginger	..	50	55
O103	$1.50, Rock Beauty	..	65	70
O104	$1.50, Rooster ..	..	65	70
O105	$1.50, Early Day Lily ..	..	65	70
O94/105	..	*Set of 12*	5·00	5·50

Morocco Agencies
(British Post Offices)

With the growth of trade and commerce during the 19th century European powers opened post offices or postal agencies in various ports along the Moroccan coast from the early 1850's onwards. French and, in the north, Spanish influence eventually became predominant, leading to the protectorates of 1912. The British, who had inaugurated a regular postal service between Gibraltar and Tangier or Tetuan in May 1778, established their first postal agency in 1857. German offices followed around the turn of the century.

Before 1892 there was no indigenous postal service and those towns where there was no foreign agency were served by a number of private local posts which continued to flourish until 1900. In November 1892 the Sultan of Morocco established the Cherifian postal service, but this was little used until after its reorganization at the end of 1911. The Sultan's post was absorbed by the French postal service on 1 October 1913. Issues of the local posts and of the Sultan's post can occasionally be found used on cover in combination with stamps of Gibraltar or the Morocco Agencies.

In 1857 the first British postal agency was established at Tangier within the precincts of the Legation and was run by the official interpreter. From 1 March 1858 all letters for Great Britain sent via the British mail packets from Gibraltar required franking with Great Britain stamps.

In 1872 the Tangier office was relocated away from the Legation and the interpreter was appointed British Postal Agent. At the same time the agency was placed under the control of the Gibraltar postmaster. When the colonial posts became independent of the British G.P.O. on 1 January 1886 Gibraltar retained responsibility for the Morocco Agencies. Further offices, each under the control of the local Vice-Consul, were opened from 1886 onwards.

I. GIBRALTAR USED IN MOROCCO

Details of the various agencies are given below. Type C, the "A26" killer, is very similar to postmarks used at Gibraltar during this period. In addition to the town name postmarks as Types A, B and D from Fez, Mazagan, Saffi and Tetuan were also inscribed "MOROCCO".

Postmark Types used on Gibraltar issues.

Type A	Type C
Circular datestamp	"A26" killer

Type B
Duplex cancellation

Type D
Registered oval

BISECTS. The 10 c., 40 c. and 50 c. values of the 1889 surcharges and of the 1889–96 issue are known bisected and used for half their value from various of the Morocco Agencies. These bisects were never authorised by the Gibraltar Post Office.

CASABLANCA
The British postal agency opened on 1 January 1887 and was initially supplied with ½d., 4d. and 6d. stamps from the Gibraltar 1886 overprinted on Bermuda issue and 1d., 2d. and 2½d. values from the 1886–87 set.

Stamps of GIBRALTAR cancelled with Types A (without code or code "C"), B (without code, code "C" or code "A") or D.

1886. *Optd on Bermuda (Nos. 1/7).*
Z1	½d. dull green	..	..	..	45·00
Z2	4d. orange-brown	..	..	..	£250
Z3	6d. deep lilac	..	..	..	£250

1886–87. *Queen Victoria £sd issue (Nos. 8/14).*
Z 4	½d. dull green	..	..	..	20·00
Z 5	1d. rose	..	..	..	22·00
Z 6	2d. brown-purple	..	..	..	45·00
Z 7	2½d. blue	..	..	..	30·00
Z 8	4d. orange-brown	..	..	..	70·00
Z10	1s. bistre	..	..	..	£250

1889. *Surch in Spanish currency (Nos. 15/21).*
Z11	5 c. on ½d. green	..	..	..	35·00
Z12	10 c. on 1d. rose	..	..	..	30·00
Z13	25 c. on 2d. brown-purple	..	..	..	40·00
Z14	25 c. on 2½d. bright blue	..	..	..	25·00
Z15	40 c. on 4d. orange-brown	..	..	..	75·00
Z16	50 c. on 6d. bright lilac	..	..	..	65·00
Z17	75 c. on 1s. bistre	..	..	..	£100

1889–96. *Queen Victoria Spanish currency issue (Nos. 22/33).*
Z18	5 c. green	..	..	..	10·00
Z19	10 c. carmine	..	..	..	10·00
Z20	20 c. olive-green and brown	..	..	20·00
Z22	25 c. ultramarine	..	..	..	10·00
Z23	40 c. orange-brown	..	..	..	25·00
Z24	50 c. bright lilac	..	..	..	20·00
Z25	75 c. olive-green	..	..	..	55·00
Z26	1 p. bistre	..	..	..	50·00
Z28	1 p. bistre and ultramarine	..	..	25·00
Z29	2 p. black and carmine	..	..	..	35·00

FEZ
The British postal agency in this inland town opened on 24 February 1892 and was initially supplied with stamps up to the 50 c. value from the Gibraltar 1889–96 issue.

Stamps of GIBRALTAR cancelled with Types A (without code) or D.

1889–96. *Queen Victoria Spanish currency issue (Nos. 22/33).*
Z31	5 c. green	..	..	..	20·00
Z32	10 c. carmine	..	..	..	22·00
Z33	20 c. olive-green and brown	..	..	40·00
Z35	25 c. ultramarine	..	..	..	35·00
Z36	40 c. orange-brown	..	..	..	60·00
Z37	50 c. bright lilac	..	..	..	45·00

LARAICHE
The British postal agency at Laraiche opened in March 1886, although the first postmark, an "A26" killer, was not supplied until May.

Stamps of GIBRALTAR cancelled with Types B (without code) or D.

1886. *Optd on Bermuda (Nos. 1/7).*
Z39	½d. dull green	..	..	..	
Z40	1d. rose-red	..	..	..	
Z41	2½d. ultramarine	..	..	..	

1886–87. *Queen Victoria £sd issue (Nos. 8/14).*
Z42	½d. dull green	..	..	..	75·00
Z43	1d. rose	..	..	..	75·00
Z45	2½d. blue	..	..	..	80·00

1889. *Surch in Spanish currency (Nos. 15/21).*
Z47	5 c. on ½d. green	..	..	..	50·00
Z48	10 c. on 1d. rose	..	..	..	
Z49	25 c. on 2½d. bright blue	..	..	

It is believed that the other surcharges in this series were not supplied to Laraiche.

1889–96. *Queen Victoria Spanish currency issue (Nos. 22/33).*
Z50	5 c. green	..	..	..	20·00
Z51	10 c. carmine	..	..	..	30·00
Z52	20 c. olive-green and brown	..	..	
Z54	25 c. ultramarine	..	..	..	30·00
Z55	40 c. orange-brown	..	..	..	
Z56	50 c. bright-lilac	..	..	..	65·00
Z57	1 p. bistre and ultramarine	..	..	

MAZAGAN
This was the main port for the inland city of Marrakesh. The British postal agency opened on 1 March 1888 and was initially supplied with stamps from the Gibraltar 1886–87 series.

Stamps of GIBRALTAR cancelled with Types A (codes "A" or "C") or D (without code, code "A" or code "C").

1886–87. *Queen Victoria £sd issue (Nos. 8/14).*
Z58	½d. dull green	..	..	..	18·00
Z59	1d. rose	..	..	..	18·00
Z60	2d. brown-purple	..	..	..	
Z61	2½d. blue	..	..	..	25·00
Z62	4d. orange-brown	..	..	..	75·00
Z63	6d. lilac	..	..	..	90·00

1889. *Surch in Spanish currency (Nos. 15/21).*
Z64	5 c. on ½d. green	..	..	..	
Z65	10 c. on 1d. rose	..	..	..	
Z66	25 c. on 2½d. bright blue	..	..	

It is believed that the other surcharges in this series were not supplied to Mazagan.

1889–96. *Queen Victoria Spanish currency issue (Nos. 22/33).*
Z67	5 c. green	..	..	..	14·00
Z68	10 c. carmine	..	..	..	12·00
Z69	20 c. olive-green and brown	..	..	38·00
Z70	25 c. ultramarine	..	..	..	35·00
Z71	40 c. orange-brown	..	..	..	
Z72	50 c. bright lilac	..	..	..	
Z74	1 p. bistre and ultramarine	..	..	
Z75	2 p. black and carmine	..	..	..	

MOGADOR
The British postal agency at this port opened in May 1887 and was initially supplied with stamps from the Gibraltar 1886–87 series.

Stamps of GIBRALTAR cancelled with Types A (code "C"), B (code "C") or D.

1886–87. *Queen Victoria £sd issue (Nos. 8/14).*
Z76	½d. dull green	..	..	..	22·00
Z77	1d. rose	..	..	..	30·00
Z78	2d. brown-purple	..	..	..	45·00
Z79	2½d. blue	..	..	..	30·00

1889. *Surch in Spanish currency (Nos. 15/21).*
Z80	5 c. on ½d. green	..	..	..	35·00
Z81	10 c. on 1d. rose	..	..	..	35·00
Z82	25 c. on 2½d. bright blue	..	..	35·00

It is believed that the other surcharges in this series were not supplied to Mogador.

1889–96. *Queen Victoria Spanish currency issue (Nos. 22/33).*
Z83	5 c. green	..	..	..	10·00
Z84	10 c. carmine	..	..	..	12·00
Z85	20 c. olive-green and brown	..	..	
Z87	25 c. ultramarine	..	..	..	16·00
Z88	40 c. orange-brown	..	..	..	25·00
Z89	50 c. bright lilac	..	..	..	25·00

RABAT
The British postal agency at this port on the north-west coast of Morocco opened in March 1886, although the first cancellation, an "A26" killer, was not supplied until May. The initial stock of stamps was from the Gibraltar 1886 overprinted on Bermuda issue.

Stamps of GIBRALTAR cancelled with Types B (code "O") or D.

1886. *Optd on Bermuda (Nos. 1/7).*
Z92	½d. dull green	..	..	..	
Z93	1d. rose-red	..	..	..	
Z94	2½d. ultramarine	..	..	..	£100

1886–87. *Queen Victoria £sd issue (Nos. 8/14).*
Z 95	½d. dull green	..	..	..	20·00
Z 96	1d. rose	..	..	..	20·00
Z 97	2d. brown-purple	..	..	..	50·00
Z 98	2½d. blue	..	..	..	30·00
Z101	1s. bistre	..	..	..	£300

1889. *Surch in Spanish currency (Nos. 15/21).*
Z102	5 c. on ½d. green	..	..	..	38·00
Z103	10 c. on 1d. rose	..	..	..	35·00
Z104	25 c. on 2½d. bright blue	..	..	38·00

It is believed that the other surcharges in this series were not supplied to Rabat.

1889–96. *Queen Victoria Spanish currency issue (Nos. 22/33).*
Z105	5 c. green	..	..	..	14·00
Z106	10 c. carmine	..	..	..	14·00
Z107	20 c. olive-green and brown	..	..	28·00
Z108	25 c. ultramarine	..	..	..	15·00
Z109	40 c. orange-brown	..	..	..	35·00
Z110	50 c. bright lilac	..	..	..	32·00

SAFFI
The British postal agency at this port opened on 1 July 1891 and was supplied with stamps from the Gibraltar 1889–96 series.

Stamps of GIBRALTAR cancelled with Types B (code "C") or D (code "C").

1889–96. *Queen Victoria Spanish currency issue (Nos. 22/33).*
Z111	5 c. green	..	..	..	14·00
Z112	10 c. carmine	..	..	..	14·00
Z113	20 c. olive-green and brown	..	..	30·00
Z115	25 c. ultramarine	..	..	..	16·00
Z116	40 c. orange-brown	..	..	..	
Z117	50 c. bright lilac	..	..	..	40·00
Z118	1 p. bistre and ultramarine	..	..	45·00
Z119	2 p. black and carmine	..	..	..	50·00

TANGIER
The British postal agency in Tangier opened on 1 April 1857 and from 1 March of the following year letters from it sent via the packet service to Great Britain required franking with Great Britain stamps.

No identifiable postmark was supplied to Tangier until 1872 and all earlier mail was cancelled with one of the Gibraltar marks. In April 1872 a postmark as Type A was supplied on which the "N" of "TANGIER" was reversed. A corrected version, with code letter "A", followed in 1878, but both were used as origin or arrival marks and the Great Britain stamps continued to be cancelled with Gibraltar obliterators. The Type A postmarks generally fell into disuse after 1880 and very few identifiable marks occur on mail from Tangier until the introduction of Gibraltar stamps in 1886.

Stamps of GIBRALTAR cancelled with Types A (codes "A" or "C"), B (code "A") or D.

1886. *Optd on Bermuda (Nos. 1/7).*
Z120	½d. dull green	..	..	..	40·00
Z121	1d. rose-red	..	..	..	50·00
Z122	2d. purple-brown	..	..	..	£130
Z123	2½d. ultramarine	..	..	..	40·00
Z124	4d. orange-brown	..	..	..	£160
Z125	6d. deep lilac	..	..	..	£200
Z126	1s. yellow-brown	..	..	..	£500

1886–87. *Queen Victoria £sd issue (Nos. 8/14).*
Z127	½d. dull green	..	..	..	15·00
Z128	1d. rose	..	..	..	15·00
Z129	2d. brown-purple	..	..	..	40·00
Z130	2½d. blue	..	..	..	25·00
Z131	4d. orange-brown	..	..	..	65·00
Z132	6d. lilac	..	..	..	£100
Z133	1s. bistre	..	..	..	£225

1889. *Surch in Spanish currency (Nos. 15/21).*

Z134	5 c. on ½d. green		24·00
Z135	10 c. on 1d. rose		17·00
Z136	25 c. on 2d. brown-purple		30·00
Z137	25 c. on 2½d. bright blue		25·00
Z138	40 c. on 4d. orange-brown		75·00
Z139	50 c. on 6d. bright lilac		60·00
Z140	75 c. on 1s. bistre		£100

1889–96. *Queen Victoria Spanish currency issue (Nos. 22/33).*

Z141	5 c. green		5·00
Z142	10 c. carmine		5·00
Z143	20 c. olive-green and brown		16·00
Z144	20 c. olive-green		18·00
Z145	25 c. ultramarine		8·00
Z146	40 c. orange-brown		10·00
Z147	50 c. bright lilac		9·00
Z148	75 c. olive-green		40·00
Z149	1 p. bistre		50·00
Z150	1 p. bistre and ultramarine		15·00
Z151	2 p. black and carmine		35·00
Z152	5 p. slate-grey		80·00

TETUAN

The British postal agency in this northern town was opened in 1890 and was supplied with stamps from the Gibraltar 1889–96 series.

Stamps of GIBRALTAR cancelled with Types A (code "C"), B (code "C" often inverted) or D (code "C").

1889–96. *Queen Victoria Spanish currency issue (Nos. 22/33).*

Z153	5 c. green		15·00
Z154	10 c. carmine		22·00
Z155	20 c. olive-green and brown		35·00
Z157	25 c. ultramarine		25·00
Z158	40 c. orange-brown		40·00
Z159	50 c. bright lilac		45·00
Z161	1 p. bistre and ultramarine		

PRICES FOR STAMPS ON COVER TO 1945

Nos. 1/16	from × 7
Nos. 17/30	from × 3
Nos. 31/74	from × 3
Nos. 75/6	from × 4
Nos. 112/24	from × 4
No. 125	—
Nos. 126/35	from × 5
Nos. 136/42	from × 2
Nos. 143/59	from × 3
Nos. 160/75	from × 8
Nos. 191/9	from × 5
Nos. 200/1	from × 3
Nos. 202/11	from × 4
Nos. 212/15	from × 5
Nos. 216/24	from × 8
Nos. 225/6	from × 2
Nos. 227/30	from × 6
Nos. 231/52	from × 6

The above prices apply to stamps used on cover from Morocco. Examples of Nos. 31/76 and 231/52 used on cover in Great Britain after 1950 have little additional value.

II. GIBRALTAR ISSUES OVERPRINTED

With the reversion of Gibraltar to sterling in 1898 it became necessary to provide separate issues for the Morocco Agencies which continued to use Spanish currency.

The following were used in all the British postal agencies.

Morocco Agencies (1)

Morocco Agencies (2)

Agencies — Inverted "V" for "A" (Right-hand pane R.6/6)

Agencies — Long tail to "S" (Right-hand pane R.8/2)

1898 (1 June)–**1900.** *Nos. 22/8 and 31/2 (Queen Victoria) of Gibraltar optd with T 1 (wide "M" and ear of "g" projecting upwards), in black at Gibraltar Chronicle office.*

1	5 c. green	30	40
	a. Inverted "V" for "A"	20·00	24·00
	b. Long tail to "S"	20·00	24·00
2	10 c. carmine	30	20
	b. Bisected (5 c.) (on cover)	† £1100	
	c. Inverted "V" for "A"	£225	£275
	d. Long tail to "S"	£225	
	e. Lines of opt 5 mm apart (6.00)	2·00	1·00
	ea. Opt double	£550	
3	20 c. olive-green	2·75	3·00
	a. Opt double	£450	
	b. Inverted "V" for "A"	27·00	32·00
	c. Long tail to "S"	27·00	32·00
	d. Olive-green and brown	1·50	1·25
	db. Inverted "V" for "A"	24·00	26·00
	dc. Long tail to "S"	24·00	26·00
4	25 c. ultramarine	1·50	60
	a. Inverted "V" for "A"	£100	£120
	b. Long tail to "S"	£100	£120
	c. Blue opt (7.98)	26·00	32·00
5	40 c. orange-brown (2.6.98)	2·50	3·25
	a. Inverted "V" for "A"	£150	£180
	b. Long tail to "S"	£150	£180
	c. Blue opt (7.98)	8·00	12·00
6	50 c. bright lilac (2.6.98)	14·00	23·00
	a. Inverted "V" for "A"	£250	£275
	b. Long tail to "S"	£250	£275
	c. Blue opt (7.98)	8·00	12·00
7	1 p. bistre and ultramarine (2.6.98)	8·00	20·00
	a. Inverted "V" for "A"	£180	£250
	b. Long tail to "S"	£180	£250
	c. Blue opt (7.98)	£140	£150

8	2 p. black and carmine (4.6.98)	5·00	20·00
	a. Inverted "V" for "A"	£225	£275
	b. Long tail to "S"	£225	£275
1/8		Set of 8	24·00 60·00

The blue overprint can be easily distinguished by looking through the stamp in front of a strong light.

The listed varieties of overprint occur from the first setting. They were corrected on the second setting of July 1898, which produced Nos. 5c, 6c, 7c and further supplies of No. 8. The corrected type was subsequently used to produce additional stocks of Nos. 1/2. Numerous more minor varieties exist from these settings.

No. 2e comes from two further printings in 1900 using a third setting on which the two lines of the overprint were 5 mm apart instead of the 4 mm space used previously.

Agencies — "CD" sideways flaw (Left-hand pane R.1/5)

Morocco — Broad top to "M" (Left-hand pane R.7/3)

Agencies — Hyphen between "nc" (Right-hand pane R.3/5)

1899 (Feb)–**1902.** *Nos. 22/3, 25/8 and 31/2 (Queen Victoria) of Gibraltar optd with T 2 (narrow "M" and ear of "g" horizontal), in black by D.L.R., London.*

9	5 c. green (4.99)	25	15
	a. "CD" sideways	8·00	8·00
	b. Broad top to "M"	7·00	7·00
	c. Hyphen between "nc"	7·00	7·00
10	10 c. carmine	35	15
	a. "CD" sideways	8·00	8·00
	b. Broad top to "M"	7·00	7·00
	c. Hyphen between "nc"	7·00	7·00
	d. Opt double	£700	£700
11	20 c. olive-green (5.02)	1·50	70
	b. Broad top to "M"	19·00	19·00
	c. Hyphen between "nc"	19·00	19·00
12	25 c. ultramarine (10.99)	3·00	90
	a. "CD" sideways	24·00	24·00
	b. Broad top to "M"	20·00	20·00
	c. Hyphen between "nc"	20·00	20·00
13	40 c. orange-brown (3.02)	22·00	16·00
	b. Broad top to "M"	£100	£110
	c. Hyphen between "nc"	£100	£110
14	50 c. bright lilac (4.99)	5·50	3·50
	b. Broad top to "M"	90·00	£100
	c. Hyphen between "nc"	90·00	£100
15	1 p. bistre and ultramarine (4.99)	13·00	20·00
	b. Broad top to "M"	£110	£140
	c. Hyphen between "nc"	£110	£140
16	2 p. black and carmine (3.01)	20·00	38·00
	b. Broad top to "M"	£250	£325
	c. Hyphen between "nc"	£250	£325
9/16		Set of 8	60·00 70·00
9/16 Optd "Specimen"		Set of 8	£180

1903–5. *As Nos. 46/51 (King Edward VII) of Gibraltar, but with value in Spanish currency, optd with T 2. Wmk Crown CA. P 14.*

17	5 c. grey-green and green (1.03)	2·75	80
	a. "CD" sideways	22·00	22·00
	b. Broad top to "M"	22·00	22·00
	c. Hyphen between "nc"	22·00	22·00
18	10 c. dull purple/red (8.03)	2·00	30
	a. "CD" sideways	22·00	22·00
	b. Broad top to "M"	22·00	22·00
	c. Hyphen between "nc"	22·00	22·00
19	20 c. grey-green and carmine (9.04)	7·00	32·00
	a. "CD" sideways	55·00	£100
	b. Broad top to "M"	55·00	£100
	c. Hyphen between "nc"	55·00	£100
20	25 c. purple and black/blue (1.7.03)	1·00	15
	a. "CD" sideways	32·00	32·00
	b. Broad top to "M"	32·00	32·00
	c. Hyphen between "nc"	35·00	35·00
21	50 c. purple and violet (3.7.05)	55·00	£110
	a. "CD" sideways	£250	£400
	b. Broad top to "M"	£250	£400
	c. Hyphen between "nc"	£250	£400
22	1 p. black and carmine (19.11.05)	45·00	£120
	a. "CD" sideways	£225	£425
	b. Broad top to "M"	£225	£425
	c. Hyphen between "nc"	£225	£425
23	2 p. black and blue (19.11.05)	48·00	95·00
	a. "CD" sideways	£250	£400
	b. Broad top to "M"	£250	£400
	c. Hyphen between "nc"	£250	£400
17/23		Set of 7	£140 £325
17/23 Optd "Specimen"		Set of 7	£180

1905 (Jan)–**06.** *As Nos. 17/23 but wmk Mult Crown CA. Ordinary paper (5, 10, 20 c.) or chalk-surfaced paper (others).*

24	5 c. grey-green and green (4.05)	1·00	1·00
	a. "CD" sideways	20·00	22·00
	b. Broad top to "M"	20·00	22·00
	c. Hyphen between "nc"	£600	£650
	d. Chalk-surfaced paper (1.06)	1·00	1·00
	da. "CD" sideways	20·00	22·00
	db. Broad top to "M"	20·00	22·00
25	10 c. dull purple/red	1·50	40
	a. "CD" sideways	22·00	20·00
	b. Broad top to "M"	22·00	20·00
	d. Chalk-surfaced paper (12.05)	65	40
	da. "CD" sideways	20·00	20·00
	db. Broad top to "M"	20·00	20·00
26	20 c. grey-green and carmine (1.06)	1·50	20·00
	a. "CD" sideways	27·00	70·00
	b. Broad top to "M"	27·00	70·00
27	25 c. purple and black/blue (6.06)	22·00	5·00
	a. "CD" sideways	£140	£110
	b. Broad top to "M"	£140	£110
28	50 c. purple and violet (7.06)	6·00	20·00
	a. "CD" sideways	£130	£180
	b. Broad top to "M"	£130	£180
29	1 p. black and carmine (11.05)	22·00	65·00
	a. "CD" sideways	£180	£275
	b. Broad top to "M"	£180	£275
30	2 p. black and blue (11.05)	15·00	32·00
	a. "CD" sideways	£160	£225
	b. Broad top to "M"	£160	£225
24/30		Set of 7	60·00 £130

Control of the British postal agencies in Morocco returned to the G.P.O., London, from 1 January 1907.

All the following issues are overprinted on Great Britain

III. BRITISH CURRENCY

Stamps overprinted "MOROCCO AGENCIES" only were primarily intended for use on parcels (and later, air-mail correspondence), and were on sale at British P.Os throughout Morocco including Tangier, until 1937.

PRICES. Our prices for used stamps with these overprints are for specimens used in Morocco. These stamps could be used in the United Kingdom, with official sanction, from the summer of 1950 onwards with U.K. postmarks are worth about 50 per cent less.

MOROCCO AGENCIES (4)

MOROCCO AGENCIES (5)

MOROCCO AGENCIES (6)

1907 (30 Apr)–**13.** *King Edward VII optd as T 4 or 5 (2s. 6d.).*

(a) De La Rue printings. Ordinary paper (½d., 1d., 4d. (No. 35) or chalk-surfaced paper (others)

31	½d. pale yellowish green (1.6.07)	75	6·00
32	1d. scarlet (5.5.07)	2·50	3·00
33	2d. pale grey-green and carmine	2·50	4·50
34	4d. green and chocolate-brown (29.10.07)	3·75	3·25
35	4d. pale orange (3.12)	3·75	3·50
	a. Orange-red	3·75	3·50
36	6d. pale dull purple (5.5.07)	4·75	7·50
	a. Dull purple	4·75	7·50
37	1s. dull green and carmine (5.5.07)	13·00	16·00
38	2s. 6d. pale dull purple (5.5.07)	48·00	75·00
	a. Dull purple	48·00	80·00

(b) Harrison printing. Ordinary paper

40	4d. bright orange (No. 286) (1913)	8·00	18·00

(c) Somerset House printing. Ordinary paper

41	2s. 6d. dull greyish purple (No. 315) (1913)	65·00	£110

1914–31. *King George V.*

(a) W 100 (Simple Cypher). Optd with T 4

42	½d. green	30	45
43	1d. scarlet	50	10
44	1½d. red-brown (1921)	1·00	11·00
45	2d. orange (Die I)	1·00	35
46	3d. bluish violet (1921)	1·00	35
47	4d. grey-green (1921)	1·00	70
48	6d. reddish purple (chalk-surfaced paper) (1921)	3·00	13·00
49	1s. bistre-brown (1917)	5·00	75
	a. Opt triple, two albino	90·00	

(b) W 110 (Single Cypher). Optd with T 6.

50	2s. 6d. sepia-brown (Waterlow ptg) (No. 400) (1914)	28·00	40·00
	a. Re-entry	£450	£450
	b. Opt double, one albino	£150	
51	2s. 6d. yellow-brown (D.L.R. ptg) (No. 406) (1917)	28·00	28·00
	a. Opt double	£1500	£1000
	b. Pale brown (No. 407)	25·00	42·00
53	2s. 6d. chocolate-brown (B.W. ptg) (No. 414)	28·00	25·00
	a. Opt double, one albino*	£150	
54	5s. rose-red (B.W. ptg) (No. 416) (1931)	48·00	70·00
	a. Opt triple, two albino		
42/54		Set of 10	80·00 £110
49/50, 54 Optd "Specimen"		Set of 3	£200

*The albino overprint is quite clear, with the "MOROCCO" appearing just below "AGENCIES" of the normal overprint and a little to the right as seen from the back. There is also a second faint albino impression just below the normal overprint.

MOROCCO AGENCIES (7) S (A)

MOROCCO AGENCIES (8) S (B)

(A) Opt 14 mm long; ends of "s" cut off diagonally.
(B) Opt 15½ mm long; ends of "s" cut off horizontally

1925–36. *King George V (W 111 (Block Cypher) optd with T 7 (A) or T 8 (B).*

		A	B
55	½d. green	60 30	1·50 22·00
56	1½d. chestnut (1931)	9·00 13·00	†
57	2d. orange	2·00 1·00	†
58	2½d. blue	2·00 5·00	£100 30·00
59	4d. grey-green (1.36)	†	3·50 30·00
60	6d. purple (1931)	2·00 8·50	40 60
61	1s. bistre-brown	15·00 50·00	48·00 55·00
55/61 (cheapest)		Set of 7	29·00 50·00
61A Optd "Specimen"			60·00

1935 (8 May). *Silver Jubilee (Nos. 453/6) optd "MOROCCO AGENCIES" only, as in T 17.*

62	½d. green (B.)	1·25	2·00
63	1d. scarlet (B.)	1·25	3·25
64	1½d. red-brown (B.)	1·50	7·00
65	2½d. blue (R.)	1·50	2·50
62/5		Set of 4	5·00 13·00

1935–37. *King George V. (a) Harrison photo ptgs (Nos. 440/5 and 449). W 111 (Block Cypher) optd with T 8.*

66	1d. scarlet (4.35)	3·00	2·50
67	1½d. red-brown (28.4.36)	2·00	10·00
68	2d. orange (1.5.36)	35	80
69	2½d. ultramarine (11.2.36)	1·75	4·25
70	3d. violet (2.3.36)	40	15
71	4d. deep grey-green (14.5.36)	40	15
72	1s. bistre-brown (31.8.36)	80	1·00

(b) Waterlow re-engraved ptgs. W 110 (Single Cypher) optd with T 6

73	2s. 6d. chocolate-brown (No. 450)	32·00	32·00
74	5s. bright rose-red (No. 451) (2.3.37)	22·00	60·00
66/74		Set of 9	55·00 £100
72/3 Optd "Specimen"		Set of 2	£130

1936 (26 Oct)–**37**. *King Edward VIII, optd "MOROCCO AGENCIES" only, as in T* 18.
A. MOROCCO 14½ mm long.
B. MOROCCO 15¼ mm long (5.1.37)

			A		B	
75	1d. scarlet	..	10	30	2·50	7·50
76	2½d. bright blue	..	10	15	80	4·25

The first two printings of both values showed all the stamps with the short overprint, Nos. 75A/6A.

On 5 January 1937 a further printing of both values was placed on sale in London which had all stamps, 24 in all, from the bottom two horizontal rows (Rows 19 and 20) with the long overprint, Nos. 75B/6B. Subsequent printings increased the number of long overprints in the sheet to 25 by the addition of R. 8/9, and, finally, to 31 (R. 1/7, R. 7/1, R. 8/1, R. 13/3, 4 and 10, R 14/6, but without R. 8/9).

For the 1d. value all sheets from cylinder 2 show the first setting. Sheets from cylinder 6 were also used for the first, and for all subsequent settings. The 2½d. value was overprinted on sheets from cylinder 2 throughout.

From 3 June 1937 unoverprinted stamps of Great Britain were supplied to the post offices at Tangier and Tetuan (Spanish Zone) as local stocks of issues overprinted "MOROCCO AGENCIES" were exhausted.

Type E   Type F

Stamps of GREAT BRITAIN cancelled as Types E *or* F *at Tangier.*

1937. *King George V photo and re-engraved issues.*
Z170	1½d. red-brown (No. 441)	..	..
Z171	2d. orange (No. 442)	..	..
Z172	3d. violet (No. 444)	..	..
Z173	4d. deep grey-green (No. 445)	..	..
Z174	6d. purple (No. 426a)	..	..
Z175	1s. bistre-brown (No. 449)	..	..
Z176	2s. 6d. chocolate-brown (No. 450)	..	..
Z177	5s. bright rose-red (No. 451)	..	..

1937–39. *King George VI (Nos. 462/75).*
Z178	½d. green
Z179	1d. scarlet
Z180	1½d. red-brown
Z181	2d. orange
Z182	2½d. ultramarine
Z183	3d. violet
Z184	4d. grey-green
Z185	5d. brown
Z186	6d. purple
Z187	7d. emerald-green
Z188	8d. bright carmine
Z189	9d. deep olive-green
Z190	10d. turquoise-blue
Z191	1s. bistre-brown

1939–42. *King George VI (Nos. 476/8a).*
Z192	2s. 6d. brown
Z193	2s. 6d. yellow-green
Z194	5s. red
Z195	10s. dark blue
Z196	10s. ultramarine

1941–42. *King George VI pale colours (Nos. 485/90).*
Z197	½d. pale green
Z198	1d. pale scarlet
Z199	1½d. pale red-brown
Z200	2d. pale orange
Z201	2½d. light ultramarine
Z202	3d. pale violet

1946. *Victory (Nos. 491/2).*
Z203	2½d. ultramarine
Z204	3d. violet

Type G

Stamps of GREAT BRITAIN cancelled as Type G *at Tetuan.*

1937. *King George V.*
Z210	6d. purple (No. 426a)	..	..

1937–39. *King George VI (Nos. 465/75).*
Z211	2d. orange
Z212	2½d. ultramarine
Z213	3d. violet
Z214	4d. grey-green
Z215	6d. purple
Z216	9d. deep olive-green
Z217	1s. bistre-brown

1939–42. *King George VI (Nos. 476/7).*
Z218	2s. 6d. brown	..	..
Z219	2s. 6d. yellow-green	..	..
Z220	5s. red	..	..

1941. *King George VI pale colours (Nos. 485/90).*
Z221	½d. pale green
Z222	2d. pale orange
Z223	2½d. light ultramarine
Z224	3d. pale violet

Other unoverprinted stamps of Great Britain are known with Morocco Agencies postmarks during this period, but it is believed that only Nos. Z170/224 were sold by the local post offices.

The use of unoverprinted stamps in Tangier ceased with the issue of Nos. 261/75 on 1 January 1949. Stamps overprinted "MOROCCO AGENCIES" replaced the unoverprinted values at Tetuan on 16 August 1949.

MOROCCO AGENCIES (9)	MOROCCO AGENCIES (10)

1949 (16 Aug). *King George VI, optd with* T **9** *or* **10** *(2s. 6d., 5s.).*
77	½d. pale green	..	..	1·50	1·50
78	1d. pale scarlet	..	..	2·25	4·00
79	1½d. pale red-brown	..	..	2·50	3·25
80	2d. pale orange	..	..	2·50	4·00
81	2½d. light ultramarine	..	..	2·75	4·00
82	3d. pale violet	..	..	1·00	45
83	4d. grey-green	..	..	45	50
84	5d. brown	..	..	2·50	6·50
85	6d. purple	..	..	80	1·00
86	7d. emerald-green	..	..	40	9·00
87	8d. bright carmine	..	..	2·25	4·50
88	9d. deep olive-green	..	..	40	7·50
89	10d. turquoise-blue	..	..	40	4·25
90	11d. plum	..	..	70	4·00
91	1s. bistre-brown	..	..	2·25	4·00
92	2s. 6d. yellow-green	..	..	9·50	19·00
93	5s. red	..	..	28·00	35·00
77/93	..	..	*Set of* 17	55·00	£100

1951 (3 May). *King George VI (Nos. 503/7, 509/10), optd with* T **9** *or* **10** *(2s. 6d., 5s.).*
94	½d. pale orange	..	..	90	30
95	1d. light ultramarine	..	..	90	30
96	1½d. pale green	..	..	90	65
97	2d. pale red-brown	..	..	90	1·00
98	2½d. pale scarlet	..	..	90	60
99	2s. 6d. yellow-green (H.M.S. *Victory*)	..	9·00	14·00
100	5s. red (Dover)	..	..	11·00	16·00
94/100	..	..	*Set of* 7	22·00	30·00

1952–55. *Queen Elizabeth II. W* **153** *(Tudor Crown). Optd with* T **9**.
101	½d. orange-red (31.8.53)	..	10	10
102	1d. ultramarine (31.8.53)	..	15	50
103	1½d. green (5.12.52)	..	15	10
104	2d. red-brown (31.8.53)	..	20	60
105	2½d. carmine-red (5.12.52)	..	25	10
106	4d. ultramarine (1.3.55)	..	60	1·75
107	5d. brown (6.7.53)	..	65	60
108	6d. reddish purple (1.3.55)	..	50	1·75
109	8d. magenta (6.7.53)	..	1·25	1·00
110	1s. bistre-brown (6.7.53)	..	70	60
101/10	..	..	*Set of* 10	4·00	6·25

1956 (10 Sept). *Queen Elizabeth II. W* **165** *(St. Edward's Crown). Optd with* T **9**.
111	2½d. carmine-red (No. 544)	..	55	2·50

Stamps overprinted "MOROCCO AGENCIES" were withdrawn from sale on 31 December 1956.

IV. SPANISH CURRENCY

Stamps surcharged in Spanish currency were sold at British P.Os. throughout Morocco until the establishment of the French Zone and the Tangier International Zone, when their use was confined to the Spanish Zone.

During this period further British postal agencies were opened at Alcazar (1907–1916), Fez–Mellah (Jewish quarter) (1909), Marrakesh (1909), Marrakesh–Mellah (Jewish quarter) (1912–14), and Mequinez (1907–1916).

MOROCCO AGENCIES	MOROCCO AGENCIES
5 CENTIMOS (11)	6 PESETAS (12)

1907 (1 Jan)–**12**. *King Edward VII surch as* T **11** *(5 c. to 1 p.) or* **12** *(3 p. to 12 p.).*
(a) *De La Rue printings. Ordinary paper (Nos. 112/13, 116, 118, 122/3) or chalk-surfaced paper (others)*
112	5 c. on ½d. pale yellowish green	..	55	15
	a. Yellowish green	..	55	15
113	10 c. on 1d. scarlet	..	1·25	10
	a. Bright scarlet	..	1·25	10
114	15 c. on 1½d. pale purple and green	..	70	15
	a. Slate-purple and bluish green	..	70	15
	b. "1" of "15" omitted	..	£2750	

115	20 c. on 2d. pale grey-green and carmine-red	60	15
	a. Pale grey-green and scarlet	60	15
116	25 c. on 2½d. ultramarine	85	15
	a. Pale ultramarine	85	15
117	40 c. on 4d. green & chocolate-brn (29.10.07)	90	1·75
	a. Deep green and chocolate-brown	90	1·75
118	40 c. on 4d. pale orange (12.5.10)	35	60
	a. Orange-red	35	60
119	50 c. on 5d. dull purple and ultramarine	1·10	80
	a. Slate-purple and ultramarine	1·10	80
120	1 p. on 10d. dull purple and carmine	6·50	5·50
	a. Slate-purple and carmine	6·50	5·50
	b. No cross on crown		
121	3 p. on 2s. 6d. pale dull purple	17·00	23·00
	a. Dull purple	17·00	23·00
122	6 p. on 5s. bright carmine	35·00	45·00
	a. Deep bright carmine	35·00	45·00
123	12 p. on 10s. ultramarine (30.4.07)	75·00	75·00
112/23	*Set of* 12	£120	£130
117, 123 Optd "Specimen"	*Set of* 2	£140	

(b) *Harrison printing. Ordinary paper*
124	25 c. on 2½d. bright blue (No. 283) (1912)	16·00	15·00
	a. Dull blue	16·00	15·00

(c) *Somerset House printing. Ordinary paper*
125	12 p. on 10s. blue (No. 319) (1912)	..	£140	£200

1912. *King George V (W* **49** *(Imperial Crown)) surch as* T **11**.
126	5 c. on ½d. green (No. 339)	..	90	10
127	10 c. on 1d. scarlet (No. 342)	..	50	10
	a. No cross on crown	..	£110	55·00

MOROCCO AGENCIES 3 CENTIMOS (13)	MOROCCO AGENCIES 10 CENTIMOS (14)
MOROCCO AGENCIES 15 CENTIMOS (15)	MOROCCO AGENCIES 6 PESETAS (16)

1914–26. *King George V.* (a) *W* **100** *(Simple Cypher). Surch as* T **11** *(5 c.),* **13** *(3 c. and 40 c.)*,* **15** *(15 c.) and* **14** *(remainder).*
128	3 c. on ½d. green (1917)	..	..	20	2·50
129	5 c. on ½d. green	..	..	30	10
130	10 c. on 1d. scarlet	..	..	30	10
131	15 c. on 1½d. red-brown (1915)	..	..	30	10
	a. Surch double, one albino	..	75·00	
132	20 c. on 2d. orange (Die I)	..	..	25	25
	a. Surch double, one albino	..	75·00	
133	25 c. on 2½d. blue (*shades*)	..	..	50	10
134	40 c. on 4d. grey-green (1917)	..	..	1·50	4·00
	a. Surch double, one albino	..		
135	1 p. on 10d. turquoise-blue	..	..	1·25	3·00

*The surcharge on Nos. 134, 148 and 158 is as T **13** for the value and T **15** for "MOROCCO AGENCIES".

(b) *W* **110** *(Single Cypher). Surch as* T **16**. (i) *Waterlow printings*
136	6 p. on 5s. rose-carmine	..	27·00	48·00
	a. Surch double, one albino	..	£110	
137	6 p. on 5s. pale rose-carmine	..	£130	£180
	a. Surch double, one albino	..	£150	
138	12 p. on 10s. indigo-blue (R.)	..	£100	£150
	a. Surch double, one albino	..	£250	
	b. Surch triple, two albino	..		
136, 138 Optd "Specimen"	*Set of* 2	£180	

(ii) *De La Rue printings*
139	3 p. on 2s. 6d. grey-brown (1918)	..	25·00	70·00
	a. Surch double, one albino			
140	3 p. on 2s. 6d. yellow-brown	..	25·00	85·00
	a. Surch double, one albino			
141	12 p. on 10s. blue (R.)	..	£110	£160
	a. Surch double, one albino	..	£300	

(iii) *Bradbury Wilkinson printings*
142	3 p. on 2s. 6d. chocolate-brown (1926)	..	23·00	50·00
128/42	*Set of* 11	£140	£225

1925–31. *King George V (W* **111** *(Block Cypher)), surch as* T **11, 13, 14** *or* **15**.
143	5 c. on ½d. green (1931)	..	..	40	7·00
144	10 c. on 1d. scarlet (1929)	..	..	9·00	14·00
145	15 c. on 1½d. red-brown	..	..	7·00	14·00
146	20 c. on 2d. orange (1931)	..	..	3·00	5·50
	a. Surch double, one albino	..	85·00	
147	25 c. on 2½d. blue	..	..	65	30
148	40 c. on 4d. grey-green (1930)	..	..	65	30
	a. Surch double, one albino			
143/8	..	..	*Set of* 6	18·00	35·00

MOROCCO AGENCIES 10 CENTIMOS (17)	MOROCCO AGENCIES 10 CENTIMOS (18)

1935 (8 May). *Silver Jubilee (Nos. 453/6). Surch as T 17.*
149	5 c. on ½d. green (B.)	..	1·00	45
150	10 c. on 1d. scarlet (B.)	..	2·75	2·25
	a. Pair, one with "CENTIMES"		£1100	
151	15 c. on 1½d. red-brown (B.)	..	1·90	8·00
152	25 c. on 2½d. blue (R.)	..	5·50	2·25
149/52		*Set of 4*	10·00	11·50

No. 150a occurred on R. 5/4 of a small second printing made in June 1935. The error can only be identified when *se-tenant* with a normal No. 150. Beware of forgeries.

1935–37. *King George V Harrison photo ptgs (Nos. 439/43, 445 and 448). W 111 (Block Cypher). Surch as T 11, 13, 14 or 15.*
153	5 c. on ½d. green	..	75	6·50
154	10 c. on 1d. scarlet (11.36)	..	2·50	2·75
155	15 c. on 1½d. red-brown (4.35)	..	2·50	3·25
156	20 c. on 2d. orange (26.10.36)	..	30	25
157	25 c. on 2½d. ultramarine (8.9.36)	..	1·25	3·75
158	40 c. on 4d. deep grey-green (18.5.37)	..	35	3·00
159	1 p. on 10d. turquoise-blue (14.4.37)	..	70	30
153/9	.. .. ..	*Set of 7*	7·50	18·00

1936 (26 Oct)–**37.** *King Edward VIII, surch as T 18.*
A. "MOROCCO" 14¼ mm long.
B. "MOROCCO" 15¼ mm long (5.1.37).
			A		B	
160	5 c. on ½d. green	..	10	10		
161	10 c. on 1d. scarlet	..	50	50	2·00	3·75
162	15 c. on 1½d. red-brown	..	10	10		†
163	25 c. on 2½d. bright blue	..	10	10		†
160/3		*Set of 4*	65	65		

The first three printings of the 10 c. on 1d. (from cyls 4, 5 and 6) showed all stamps with the short surcharge (No. 161A).

On 5 January 1937 a further printing was placed on sale in London which had 49 stamps in the sheet (R. 1/2 to 11, R. 2/1, 5 and 6, 8 and 9, R. 3/5, R. 4/5, R. 5/4 and 5, 10, R. 6/6 and 7, R. 7/8, R. 8/8, R. 9/8, R. 11/7, 9, R.13/2 to 5, 7 and 8, R. 14/1, 7, R. 15/7, 11, R. 16/5, 10, R. 17/4, 10 and 11, R. 18/1, R. 19/2, R. 20/1 and 2, 3, 7, 9) with the long surcharge (No. 161B). The next printing increased the number of long surcharges in the sheet to 50 (R. 10/2), but the final version, although retaining 50 long surcharges, showed them on R. 1/2 to 11, R. 17/5 to 8 and the entire rows 18, 19 and 20. The first two printings with long surcharges were from cylinder 6 and the last from cylinder 13.

(19)

1937 (13 May). *Coronation (No. 461), surch as T 19.*
164	15 c. on 1½d. maroon (B.)	..	30	20

(20) (21)

1937 (June)–**52.** *King George VI (Nos. 462/4, 466, 468, 471 and 474), surch as T 20.*
165	5 c. on ½d. green (B.)	..	45	15
166	10 c. on 1d. scarlet	..	40	10
167	15 c. on 1½d. red-brown (B.) (4.8.37)	..	45	25
168	25 c. on 2½d. ultramarine	..	50	50
169	40 c. on 4d. grey-green (9.40)	..	8·00	6·00
170	70 c. on 7d. emerald-green (9.40)	..	50	5·00
171	1 p. on 10d. turquoise-blue (16.6.52)	..	30	3·50
165/71		*Set of 7*	9·50	14·00

1949 (6 May). *Centenary of First Adhesive Postage Stamps (Nos. 479/81 and 483), surch as T 21.*
172	5 c. on ½d. green (B.)	..	30	1·25
173	10 c. on 1d. scarlet	..	1·40	1·75
174	15 c. on 1½d. red-brown (B.)	..	30	1·50
175	25 c. on 2½d. ultramarine	..	70	1·50
172/5		*Set of 4*	2·10	4·50

(22) (23)

1948 (26 Apr). *Silver Wedding (Nos. 493/4), surch with T 22 or 23.*
176	25 c. on 2½d. ultramarine	..	30	15
177	45 p. on £1 blue	..	15·00	22·00

1948 (29 July). *Olympic Games (Nos. 495/8), variously surch as T 22.*
178	25 c. on 2½d. ultramarine	..	40	50
179	30 c. on 3d. violet	..	40	50
180	60 c. on 6d. bright purple	..	40	50
181	1 p. 20 c. on 1s. brown	..	55	50
	a. Surch double		£550	
178/81		*Set of 4*	1·60	1·75

1951 (3 May)–**52.** *King George VI (Nos. 503/5 and 507/8), surch as T 20.*
182	5 c. on ½d. pale orange	..	1·50	1·25
183	10 c. on 1d. light ultramarine	..	2·50	1·00
184	15 c. on 1½d. pale green	..	1·50	4·00
185	25 c. on 2½d. pale scarlet	..	1·50	1·75
186	40 c. on 4d. light ultramarine (26.5.52)	..	50	8·50
182/6		*Set of 5*	6·75	15·00

1954–55. *Queen Elizabeth II. W 153 (Tudor Crown). Surch as T 20.*
187	5 c. on ½d. orange-red (1.9.54)	..	10	60
188	10 c. on 1d. ultramarine (1.3.55)	..	30	50

1956. *Queen Elizabeth II. W 165 (St. Edward's Crown). Surch as T 20.*
189	5 c. on ½d. orange-red (June)	..	15	30
190	40 c. on 4d. ultramarine (15 Aug)	..	70	1·75

The British postal agency at Laraiche closed on 30 June 1938. Stamps surcharged in Spanish currency were withdrawn from sale when the Tetuan agency closed on 31 December 1956.

V. FRENCH CURRENCY

For use in the British postal agencies at Casablanca (closed 14.8.37), Fez (closed 8.1.38), Fez–Mellah (closed after 1930), Marrakesh (closed 14.8.37), Mazagan (closed 14.8.37), Mogador (closed 31.10.33), Rabat (closed 8.1.38) and Saffi (closed 14.8.37).

(24) (25)

1917–24. *King George V (W 100 (Simple Cypher)), surch as T 24 or 25 (1 f.).*
191	3 c. on ½d. green (R.)	..	20	2·50
192	5 c. on ½d. green	..	15	10
193	10 c. on 1d. scarlet	..	75	15
194	15 c. on 1½d. red-brown	..	80	15
195	25 c. on 2½d. blue	..	30	15
196	40 c. on 4d. slate-green	..	80	30
197	50 c. on 5d. yellow-brown (1923)	..	70	2·50
198	75 c. on 9d. olive-green (1924)	..	50	75
199	1 f. on 10d. turquoise-blue	..	1·75	85
	a. Surch double, one albino		85·00	
191/9		*Set of 9*	5·50	6·75

1924–32. *King George V (B. W. ptg). W 110 (Single Cypher), surch as T 25, but closer vertical spacing.*
200	3 f. on 2s. 6d. chocolate-brown	..	7·50	2·00
	a. Major re-entry	..	£275	£275
	b. Surch double, one albino			
	c. Reddish brown	..	20·00	10·00
201	6 f. on 5s. rose-red (1932)	..	38·00	40·00
200/1 Optd "Specimen"		*Set of 2*	£120	

1925–34. *King George V (W 111 (Block Cypher)), surch as T 24 or 25 (1 f.).*
202	5 c. on ½d. green	..	30	5·00
203	10 c. on 1d. scarlet	..	30	30
204	15 c. on 1½d. red-brown	..	85	1·75
205	25 c. on 2½d. blue	..	30	25
206	40 c. on 4d. grey-green	..	50	70
207	50 c. on 5d. yellow-brown	..	50	10
208	75 c. on 9d. olive-green	..	1·50	15
209	90 c. on 9d. olive-green	..	2·75	3·00
210	1 f. on 10d. turquoise-blue	..	70	10
211	1 f. 50 on 1s. bistre-brown (Optd S. £50)	..	3·50	2·25
202/11		*Set of 10*	10·00	12·00

1935 (8 May). *Silver Jubilee (Nos. 453/6), surch as T 17, but in French currency.*
212	5 c. on ½d. green (B.)	..	15	15
213	10 c. on 1d. scarlet (B.)	..	60	50
214	15 c. on 1½d. red-brown (B.)	..	15	50
215	25 c. on 2½d. blue (R.)	..	20	15
212/15		*Set of 4*	1·00	1·10

1935–37. *King George V (Harrison photo ptgs. W 111 (Block Cypher)), surch as T 24 or 25 (1 f.).*
216	5 c. on ½d. green (10.35)	..	45	1·50
217	10 c. on 1d. scarlet (2.3.36)	..	35	30
218	15 c. on 1½d. red-brown	..	1·25	1·50
219	25 c. on 2½d. ultramarine (25.9.36)	..	30	15
220	40 c. on 4d. deep grey-green (2.12.36)	..	30	15
221	50 c. on 5d. yellow-brown (15.9.36)	..	30	15
222	90 c. on 9d. deep olive-green (15.2.37)	..	35	65
223	1 f. on 10d. turquoise-blue (10.2.37)	..	30	30
224	1 f. 50 on 1s. bistre-brown (20.7.37) (Optd S. £50)	..	30	65

1935–36. *King George V (Waterlow re-engraved ptgs). W 100 (Single Cypher), surch as T 25, but closer vertical spacing.*
225	3 f. on 2s. 6d. chocolate-brown (No. 450)	..	4·75	12·00
226	6 f. on 5s. bright rose-red (No. 451) (17.6.36)	..	6·00	20·00
216/26		*Set of 11*	13·00	35·00
225/6 Optd "Specimen"		*Set of 2*	£120	

1936 (26 Oct). *King Edward VIII, surch as T 18, but in French currency.*
227	5 c. on ½d. green	..	10	15
	a. Bar through "POSTAGE"		£400	
228	15 c. on 1½d. red-brown	..	10	15

1937 (13 May). *Coronation (No. 461), surch as T 19, but in French currency.*
229	15 c. on 1½d. maroon (B.)	..	30	20

1937 (June). *King George VI, surch as T 20, but in French currency.*
230	5 c. on ½d. green (B.)	..	30	85

Stamps surcharged in French currency were withdrawn from sale on 8 January 1938.

VI. TANGIER INTERNATIONAL ZONE

By an agreement between Great Britain, France and Spain Tangier was declared an international zone in 1924. Stamps overprinted "Morocco Agencies" or surcharged in Spanish currency were used there until replaced by Nos. 231/4.

PRICES. Our note *re* U.K. usage (at beginning of Section III) also applies to "TANGIER" optd stamps.

(26) (27)

1927. *King George V (W 111 (Block Cypher)), optd with T 26.*
231	½d. green	..	50	10
	a. Opt double, one albino			
232	1d. scarlet	..	40	10
	a. Inverted "Q" for "O" (R. 20/3)	..	£800	
233	1½d. chestnut	..	2·00	2·00
234	2d. orange	..	3·25	10
	a. Opt double, one albino		75·00	
231/4		*Set of 4*	5·50	2·00

1934 (Dec)–**35.** *King George V (Harrison photo ptgs. W 111 (Block Cypher)), optd with T 26.*
235	½d. green (2.35)	..	1·00	1·40
236	1d. scarlet	..	65	10
237	1½d. red-brown	..	15	10
235/7		*Set of 3*	1·60	2·00

1935 (8 May). *Silver Jubilee (Nos. 453/5), optd with T 27.*
238	½d. green (B.)	..	1·00	85
239	1d. scarlet	..	5·50	3·75
240	1½d. red-brown (B.)	..	1·25	15
238/40		*Set of 3*	7·00	4·25

1936 (26 Oct). *King Edward VIII, optd with T 26.*
241	½d. green	..	10	15
242	1d. scarlet	..	10	10
243	1½d. red-brown	..	15	10
241/3		*Set of 3*	30	30

(28) (29)

1937 (13 May). *Coronation (No. 461), optd with T 28.*
244	1½d. maroon (B.)	..	40	15

1937. *King George VI (Nos. 462/4), optd with T 29.*
245	½d. green (B.) (June)	..	40	20
246	1d. scarlet (June)	..	95	30
247	1½d. red-brown (B.) (4 Aug)	..	60	10
245/7		*Set of 3*	1·75	50

(30) (31)

1940 (6 May). *Centenary of First Adhesive Postage Stamps (Nos. 479/81), optd with T 30.*
248	½d. green (B.)	..	30	2·00
249	1d. scarlet	..	45	30
250	1½d. red-brown (B.)	..	1·25	65
248/50		*Set of 3*	1·75	2·75

1944. *King George VI pale colours (Nos. 485/6), optd with T 29.*
251	½d. pale green (B.)	..	2·50	75
252	1d. pale scarlet	..	3·00	1·00

1946 (11 June). *Victory (Nos. 491/2), optd as T 31.*
253	2½d. ultramarine	..	30	20
254	3d. violet	..	30	20

The opt on No. 254 is smaller (23×2½ mm).

1948 (26 Apr). *Royal Silver Wedding (Nos. 493/4), optd with T 30.*
255	2½d. ultramarine	..	30	15
	a. Opt omitted (in vert pair with stamp optd at top)	..	£2250	
256	£1 blue	..	24·00	28·00

No. 255a comes from a sheet in which the overprint is misplaced downwards resulting in the complete absence of the opt from the six stamps of the top row. On the rest of the sheet the opt falls at the top of each stamp instead of at the foot.

1948 (29 July). *Olympic Games (Nos. 495/8), optd with T 30.*
257	2½d. ultramarine ..			65	60
258	3d. violet	..	..	65	40
259	6d. bright purple			65	60
260	1s. brown			65	60
257/60	..		*Set of 4*	2·40	1·60

1949 (1 Jan). *King George VI, optd with T 29.*
261	2d. pale orange			2·50	2·25
262	2½d. light ultramarine	..	..	35	80
263	3d. pale violet			35	20
264	4d. grey-green			2·50	4·50
265	5d. brown			1·00	5·50
266	6d. purple			35	30
267	7d. emerald-green			70	5·50
268	8d. bright carmine			1·25	5·00
269	9d. deep olive-green			50	7·00
270	10d. turquoise-blue			50	7·50
271	11d. plum ..			50	6·50
272	1s. bistre-brown ..			60	85
273	2s. 6d. yellow-green			4·00	7·50
274	5s. red	..	..	9·00	28·00
275	10s. ultramarine ..			35·00	70·00
261/75	..		*Set of 15*	55·00	£130

1949 (10 Oct). *75th Anniv of U.P.U. (Nos. 499/502), optd with T 30.*
276	2½d. ultramarine ..			50	60
277	3d. violet			50	60
278	6d. bright purple			50	50
279	1s. brown			50	1·25
276/9	..		*Set of 4*	1·75	2·75

1950 (2 Oct)–**51.** *King George VI, optd with T 29 or 30 (shilling values).*
280	½d. pale orange (3.5.51)	..		30	30
281	1d. light ultramarine (3.5.51)	..		50	75
282	1½d. pale green (3.5.51)	..		50	4·50
283	2d. pale red-brown (3.5.51)	..		50	90
284	2½d. pale scarlet (3.5.51) ..			55	45
285	4d. light ultramarine			55	2·25
286	2s. 6d. yell-grn (H.M.S. *Victory*) (3.5.51)			3·75	2·75
287	5s. red (Dover) (3.5.51)	..		9·50	11·00
288	10s. ultramarine (St. George) (3.5.51)	..	14·00	13·00
280/8	..		*Set of 9*	27·00	32·00

1952–54. *Queen Elizabeth II (W 153 (Tudor Crown)), optd with T 29.*
289	½d. orange-red (31.8.53)	..		10	20
290	1d. ultramarine (31.8.53)			15	20
291	1½d. green (5.12.52)			10	20
292	2d. red-brown (31.8.53) ..			20	20
293	2½d. carmine-red (5.12.52)	..		10	20
294	3d. deep lilac (B.) (18.1.54)			20	20
295	4d. ultramarine (2.11.53)			45	1·00
296	5d. brown (6.7.53) ..			60	90
297	6d. reddish purple (18.1.54)			45	15
298	7d. bright green (18.1.54)			80	1·60
299	8d. magenta (6.7.53) ..			80	1·50
300	9d. bronze-green (8.2.54)			1·25	75
301	10d. Prussian blue (8.2.54)			1·40	2·75
302	11d. brown-purple (8.2.54)	..		1·40	3·25
303	1s. bistre-brown (6.7.53)	..		50	30
304	1s. 3d. green (2.11.53)	..		65	55
305	1s. 6d. grey-blue (2.11.53)	..		80	1·75
289/305	..		*Set of 17*	9·00	14·00

1953 (3 June). *Coronation (Nos. 532/5), optd with T 30.*
306	2½d. carmine-red	..		50	30
307	4d. ultramarine	..		1·00	30
308	1s. 3d. deep yellow-green	..		1·25	1·25
309	1s. 6d. deep grey-blue	..		1·25	60
306/9	..		*Set of 4*	3·50	2·25

1955 (23 Sept). *Queen Elizabeth II, Castle high values (W 165 (St. Edward's Crown)), optd with T 30.*
310	2s. 6d. black-brown	..		3·25	4·50
311	5s. rose-red	..		5·00	8·50
312	10s. ultramarine ..			18·00	20·00
310/12			*Set of 3*	24·00	30·00

1956. *Queen Elizabeth II (W 165 St. Edward's Crown)), optd with T 29.*
313	½d. orange-red (21 March)	..		10	10
314	1d. ultramarine (13 April)	..		20	20
315	1½d. green (22 Oct)			40	75
316	2d. red-brown (25 July)	..		90	1·50
317	2d. light red-brown (10 Dec)	..		50	30
318	2½d. carmine-red (19 Dec)	..		40	30
319	3d. deep lilac (B.) (22 Oct)	..		40	50
320	4d. ultramarine (25 June)	..		65	2·00
321	6d. reddish purple (22 Oct)	..		50	55
322	1s. 3d. green (26 Nov)	..		1·75	12·00
313/22	..		*Set of 10*	5·00	16·00

1857·1957

1857·1957
TANGIER

TANGIER
(32)   (33)

1957 (1 Apr). *Centenary of British Post Office in Tangier.*

(*a*) *Nos. 540/2 and 543b/56 (W 165 (St. Edward's Crown)), optd as T 32 or 33 (7d)*
323	½d. orange-red	..		10	10
324	1d. ultramarine ..			10	10
325	1½d. green			10	10
326	2d. light red-brown	..		10	10
327	2½d. carmine-red ..			15	20

328	3d. deep lilac (B.)	..		15	10
329	4d. ultramarine ..	..		30	20
330	5d. brown	..		30	35
331	6d. reddish purple	..		30	15
332	7d. bright green ..			30	30
333	8d. magenta	..	..	30	50
334	9d. bronze-green	..		30	30
	a. "TANGIER" omitted	..		£3500	
335	10d. Prussian blue	..		30	30
336	11d. brown-purple	..		30	30
337	1s. bistre-brown ..			30	30
338	1s. 3d. green	..		45	50
339	1s. 6d. grey-blue	..		50	55

(*b*) *Nos. 536/8 (W 165 (St. Edward's Crown)), optd as T 32.*
340	2s. 6d. black-brown	..		2·00	2·25
	a. Hyphen omitted	..		60·00	
	b. Hyphen inserted	..		20·00	
341	5s. rose-red	..		2·75	2·25
	a. Hyphen omitted	..		60·00	
	b. Hyphen inserted	..		10·00	
342	10s. ultramarine ..			3·75	3·50
	a. Hyphen omitted	..		70·00	
	b. Hyphen inserted	..		15·00	
323/42			*Set of 20*	11·00	10·50

Nos. 340a/b, 341a/b and 342a/b occur on R.9/2 in the sheet of 40 (4×10). They are best collected in marginal blocks of four from the bottom left corner of the sheet. Specialists recognise two forms of No. 340b; one where the hyphen on R.9/2 was inserted separately to correct the error, No. 340a; the other from a later printing where a new and corrected overprinting plate was used. (*Price £10 un.*)

All stamps overprinted "TANGIER" were withdrawn from sale on 30 April 1957.

Mosul
see Iraq

Muscat

An independent Arab Sultanate in Eastern Arabia with an Indian postal administration.

The Indian post office at Muscat town is officially recorded as having opened on 1 May 1864. Stamps of India were provided for its use, most surviving examples being of the ½ a. value, although others to the 8 a. are known.

The office was initially included in the Bombay Postal Circle and the first postmark, so far only recorded on stampless covers, was a single circle, 21½ mm in diameter, broken at the top by "MUSCAT" and with the date in two lines across the centre. This was followed by a cancellation showing the post office number, "309", within a diamond of 13, later 16, bars. It is believed that this was used in conjunction with a single ring date stamp inscribed "MUSCAT".

1864 Diamond

In 1869 the office was transferred to the Sind Circle, assigned a new number, "23", and issued with a duplex cancellation. Major reorganisation of the postal service in 1873 resulted in Muscat becoming office "K-4". For ten years from 1873 the cancellations do not, very confusingly, carry any indication of the year of use.

1869 Duplex

1873 Duplex

Muscat rejoined the Bombay Circle in 1879 and was issued with a cancellation showing a "B" within a square of horizontal bars. The date used at this time was unique in that it carried the inscription "MASKAT", although the spelling reverted to the more usual form by 1882. The square cancellation had been replaced by a similar circular mark by 1884.

Subsequent postmarks were of various circular types, all inscribed "MUSCAT".

There was only one Indian post office in Muscat, but a further office did exist, from 12 April 1868, at the Muscat dependency of Guadur, a port on the Mekran coast of Baluchistan.

No cancellations have been reported from Guadur before its transfer to the Sind Circle in 1869. Cancellations are all similar in style to those for Muscat, Guadur being initially assigned number "24", although an office in Southern India is also known to have used this numeral. The 1869 duplex is interesting in that it is inscribed "GWADUR". Under the 1873 reorganisation the office became "4/K-1", this postmark using the "GUADUR" spelling.

1869 Duplex

PRICES FOR STAMPS ON COVER
Nos. 1/15   *from* × 100
Nos. O1/10   *from* × 100

(1)   (2)

1944 (20 Nov). *Bicentenary of Al-Busaid Dynasty. Nos. 259/60, 265/8 and 269a/77 (King George VI) of India optd ("AL BUSAID 1363" in Arabic script) as T 1 or 2 (rupee values).*
1	3 p. slate			30	2·50
2	½ a. purple	..	..	30	2·50
3	9 p. green ..			30	2·50
4	1 a. carmine			30	2·50
5	1½ a. dull violet			30	2·50
6	2 a. vermilion			30	2·50
7	3 a. bright violet ..			30	2·50
8	3½ a. bright blue	..		30	2·50
9	4 a. brown			30	2·50
10	6 a. turquoise-green			45	2·50
11	8 a. slate-violet	..		40	3·00
12	12 a. lake ..			70	3·75
13	14 a. purple			40	5·00
14	1 r. grey and red-brown	..		45	7·00
15	2 r. purple and brown			50	12·00
1/15	..		*Set of 15*	5·00	50·00

OFFICIAL STAMPS

1944 (20 Nov). *Bicentenary of Al-Busaid Dynasty. Nos. O138, O143, O144a/6 and 146b/50 of India optd as T 1 or 2.*
O 1	3 p. slate	..		50	5·00
O 2	½ a. purple	..		50	5·00
O 3	9 p. green	..		50	5·00
O 4	1 a. carmine	..		50	5·00
O 5	1½ a. dull violet	..		50	5·00
O 6	2 a. vermilion	..		50	5·00
O 7	2½ a. bright violet	..		50	5·00
O 8	4 a. brown	..		50	5·50
O 9	8 a. slate-violet ..			50	6·00
O10	1 r. grey and red-brown	..		2·00	14·00
O1/10			*Set of 10*	6·00	55·00

From December 1947 there was a Pakistani postal administration and stamps of Pakistan were used until 31 March 1948. The subsequent British administration operated from 1 April 1948 to 29 April 1966 when the stamps of the BRITISH POSTAL AGENCIES IN EASTERN ARABIA were used.

Later issues for this area will be found listed under OMAN in Part 19 (*Middle East*) of this catalogue.

Nagaland

Labels inscribed "NAGALAND" with currency in cents and chaplees are considered to be propaganda labels.

Namibia

(*formerly* South West Africa)

SOUTH WEST AFRICA

The stamps of Germany were used in the colony from July 1886 until the introduction of issues for GERMAN SOUTH-WEST AFRICA in May 1897. Following occupation by South African forces in 1914–15 the issues of SOUTH AFRICA were used, being replaced by the overprinted issues in 1923.

Walvis (or Walfish) Bay, the major anchorage on the South West Africa coast, was claimed by Great Britain as early as 1796. In 1878 the 430 sq mile area around the port, together with a number of offshore islands, was annexed to Cape Province, passing to the Union of South Africa in 1910.
Stamps of the Cape of Good Hope and South Africa were used at Walfish Bay, often cancelled with numeral obliterator 300, until the enclave was transferred to the South West Africa administration on 1 October 1922.
The Walfish Bay territory reverted to South Africa on 30 August 1977 and from that date the stamps of South Africa were, once again, in use.

PRICES FOR STAMPS ON COVER TO 1945
Nos. 1/40a	*from* × 6
Nos. 41/133	*from* × 2
Nos. D1/5	*from* × 10
Nos. D6/51	*from* × 20
Nos. O1/4	*from* × 3
Nos. O5/20	*from* × 15
No. O21	—
No. O22	*from* × 15

INSCRIPTIONS. Most of the postage stamps up to No. 140 are inscribed alternately in English and Afrikaans throughout the sheets and the same applies to all the Official stamps and to Nos. D30/33.

PRICES for Nos. 1/140 are for unused horizontal pairs, used horizontal pairs or used singles (either inscr), *unless otherwise indicated.*

OVERPRINT SETTINGS. Between 1923 and 1928 the King George V definitives of South Africa, Types 2 and 3, and the various postage due stamps were issued overprinted for use in South West Africa. A number of overprint settings were used:

Setting I – Overprint Types 1 and 2 ("Zuid-West Afrika"). 14 mm between lines of overprint. See Nos. 1/12 and D1/9

Setting II – As Setting I, but 10 mm between lines of overprint. See Nos. 13/15 and D10/13

Setting III – Overprint Types 3 ("Zuidwest Afrika") and 4. "South West" 14 mm long. "Zuidwest" 11 mm long. 14 mm between lines of overprint. See Nos. 16/27 and D14/17

Setting IV – As Setting III, but "South West" 16 mm long, "Zuidwest" 12 mm long and 14 mm between lines of overprint. See Nos. 28 and D17a/20

Setting V – As Setting IV, but 12 mm between lines of overprint. See Nos. D21/4

Setting VI – As Setting IV, but 9½ mm between lines of overprint. See Nos. 29/40 and D25/32.

South West **Zuid-West**

Africa. Afrika.
(1) (2)

1923 (1 Jan–17 June). *Nos. 3/4, 6 and 9/17 of South Africa optd alternately with T 1 and 2 by typography.*

			Un pair	Us pair	Us single
	(a) Setting I (14 mm between lines of opt)				
1	½d. green		1·50	5·50	1·00
	a. "Wes" for "West" (R. 20/8)		80·00	£110	
	b. "Afr ica" (R. 20/2)		£120		
	c. Litho opt in shiny ink (17 June)		8·50	35·00	4·00
2	1d. rose-red		1·75	5·50	1·00
	a. Opt inverted		£450		
	b. "Wes" for "West" (R. 12/2)		£150		
	c. "Af.rica" for "Africa" (R. 20/6)		£140	£160	
	d. Opt double		£750		
	e. "Afr ica" (R. 20/2)		£120		
	f. "Afrika" without stop (R. 17/8)		£225		
3	2d. dull purple		2·50	8·00	1·50
	a. Opt inverted		£500	£550	
	b. "Wes" for "West" (R. 20/8)		£225		
	c. Litho opt in shiny ink (30 Mar)		22·00	55·00	8·00
4	3d. ultramarine		7·50	16·00	2·75
5	4d. orange-yellow and sage-green		13·00	38·00	4·00
	a. Litho opt in shiny ink (19 Apr)		35·00	60·00	8·00
6	6d. black and violet		8·00	35·00	4·00
	a. Litho opt in shiny ink (19 Apr)		35·00	65·00	7·50
7	1s. orange-yellow		23·00	48·00	5·00
	a. Litho opt in shiny ink (19 Apr)		60·00	95·00	11·00
8	1s. 3d. pale violet		30·00	55·00	5·50
	a. Opt inverted		£250		
	b. Litho opt in shiny ink (19 Apr)		75·00	£120	14·00

9	2s. 6d. purple and green		70·00	£130	18·00
	a. Litho opt in shiny ink (19 Apr)		£150	£250	35·00
10	5s. purple and blue		£160	£325	50·00
11	10s. blue and olive-green		£1600	£2500	£400
12	£1 green and red		£900	£1600	£250
1/12		*Set of 12*	£2500	£4250	£650
1/12 Optd "Specimen"		*Set of 12 singles*	£1500		

Nos. 1/12 were overprinted in complete sheets of 240 (4 panes 6×10).
No. 3b shows traces of a type spacer to the right of where the "t" should have been. This spacer is not visible on Nos. 1a and 2b.
Minor varieties, such as broken "t" in "West", were caused by worn type. Stamps showing one line of overprint only or with the lower line above the upper line due to overprint misplacement may also be found. All values exist showing a faint stop after "Afrika" on R.17/8, but only the 1d. has been confirmed as existing with it omitted.

	(b) Setting II (10 mm between lines of opt) (31 Mar)				
13	5s. purple and blue		£160	£300	60·00
	a. "Afrika" without stop (R.6/1)		£1700	£1700	
14	10s. blue and olive-green		£550	£950	£180
	a. "Afrika" without stop (R.6/1)		£3000	£3500	
15	£1 green and red		£1100	£1600	£250
	a. "Afrika" without stop (R.6/1)		£6000	—£1100	
13/15		*Set of 3*	£1600	£2500	£450

Nos. 13/15 were overprinted in separate panes of 60 (6×10).

Zuidwest **South West**

Afrika. **Africa.**
(3) (4)

1923 (15 July)–26. *Nos. 3/4, 6 and 9/17 of South Africa optd as T 3 ("Zuidwest" in one word, without hyphen) and 4 alternately.*

	(a) Setting III ("South West" 14 mm long, "Zuidwest" 11 mm long, 14 mm between lines of opt)				
16	½d. green (5.9.24)		3·75	20·00	3·25
	a. "outh" for "South" (R.1/1)		£1300		
17	1d. rose-red (28.9.23)		3·50	7·50	1·40
	a. "outh" for "South" (R.1/1)		£1300		
18	2d. dull purple (28.9.23)		3·50	5·50	1·00
	a. Opt double		£850		
19	3d. ultramarine		3·75	6·00	1·25
20	4d. orange-yellow and sage-green		4·75	16·00	2·75
21	6d. black and violet (28.9.23)		11·00	32·00	4·00
22	1s. orange-yellow		14·00	42·00	5·00
23	1s. 3d. pale violet		28·00	45·00	5·50
24	2s. 6d. purple and green		45·00	80·00	10·00
25	5s. purple and blue		£200	£300	50·00
26	10s. blue and olive-green		£200	£300	50·00
27	£1 green and red (28.9.23)		£350	£475	70·00
16/27		*Set of 12*	£650	£1000	£150

Nos. 16/27 were overprinted in complete sheets of 240 (4 panes 6×10).
Two sets may be made with this overprint, one with bold lettering, and the other from September 1924, with thinner lettering and smaller stops.

	(b) Setting IV ("South West" 16 mm long, "Zuidwest" 12 mm long, 14 mm between lines of opt)				
28	2s. 6d purple and green (29.6.24)		80·00	£150	28·00

No. 28 was overprinted on two panes of 60 horizontally side by side.

	(c) Setting VI ("South West" 16 mm long, "Zuidwest" 12 mm long, 9½ mm between lines of opt)				
29	½d. green (16.12.25)		5·00	30·00	4·50
30	1d. rose-red (9.12.24)		2·25	7·50	1·40
31	2d. dull purple (9.12.24)		3·75	14·00	1·75
32	3d. ultramarine (31.1.26)		3·75	20·00	2·75
	a. Deep bright blue (20.4.26)		55·00	85·00	12·00
33	4d. orge-yellow & sage-grn (9.12.24)		5·50	27·00	3·50
34	6d. black and violet (9.12.24)		7·00	35·00	4·50
35	1s. orange-yellow (9.12.24)		11·00	40·00	4·50
36	1s. 3d. pale violet (9.12.24)		14·00	42·00	5·00
37	2s. 6d. purple and green (9.12.24)		35·00	70·00	10·00
38	5s. purple and blue (31.1.26)		55·00	£100	14·00
39	10s. blue and olive-green (9.12.24)		85·00	£130	20·00
40	£1 green and red (9.1.26)		£300	£450	70·00
	a. Pale olive-green and red (8.11.26)		£250	£450	90·00
29/40a		*Set of 12*	£425	£850	£140
35, 39/40 H/S "Specimen"		*Set of 3*	£500		

Nos. 29/40 were overprinted in complete sheets of 240 (4 panes of 6×10), with, initially, "South West Africa" 16½ mm long on the upper two panes and 16 mm long on the lower two. This order was subsequently reversed. For printings from 8 November 1926 all four panes showed the 16½ mm measurement. No. 40a only comes from this printing.

Suidwes **Afrika.** **South West** **Africa.**
(5) (6)

1926 (1 Jan–1 May). *Nos. 30/2 of South Africa optd with T 5 (on stamps inscr in Afrikaans) and 6 (on stamps inscr in English) sideways, alternately in black.*

41	½d. black and green		2·50	8·50	1·00
42	1d. black and carmine		2·50	7·00	75
43	6d. green and orange (1 May)		26·00	48·00	7·00
41/3		*Set of 3*	28·00	55·00	8·00

SOUTH WEST AFRICA **SUIDWES-AFRIKA**
(7) (8)

1926. *No. 33 of South Africa, imperf, optd with T 7 (E.) or T 8 (A.).*

				Single stamps	
				E	A
44	4d. grey-blue			65 2·00,	65 2·00

1927. *As Nos. 41/3, but Afrikaans opt on stamp inscr in English and vice versa.*

45	½d. black and green		1·40	5·00	80
	a. "Africa" without stop (R.13/8)		£150		
46	1d. black and carmine		1·40	2·50	50
	a. "Africa" without stop (R.13/8)		£225		
47	6d. green and orange		13·00	25·00	3·00
	a. "Africa" without stop (R.13/8)		£170		
45/7		*Set of 3*	14·50	29·00	3·75

SOUTH WEST AFRICA **S.W.A.** **S.W.A.**
(9) (10) (11)

1927. *As No. 44E, but overprint T 9.*

			Single stamps	
48	4d. grey-blue (H/S S. £70)		7·50	19·00

1927 (Apr). *Nos. 34/9 of South Africa optd alternately as T 5 and 6, in blue, but with lines of overprint spaced 16 mm.*

49	2d. grey and purple		3·75	15·00	1·75
50	3d. black and red		3·75	23·00	2·50
51	1s. brown and blue		14·00	32·00	4·00
52	2s. 6d. green and brown		45·00	65·00	12·00
53	5s. black and green		75·00	£120	20·00
54	10s. blue and bistre-brown		85·00	£130	20·00
49/54		*Set of 6*	£200	£350	50·00
49/51, 54 H/S "Specimen"		*Set of 4*	£350		

A variety of Nos. 49, 50, 51 and 54, with spacing 16½ mm between lines of overprint, occurs in the third vertical row of each sheet.

1927. *As No. 44, but perf 11½ by John Meinert, Ltd, Windhoek.*

			Single stamps			
			E		A	
55	4d. grey-blue		70	3·50	70	3·50
	a. Imperf between (pair)		30·00	60·00	30·00	60·00
55 H/S "Specimen"			70·00		70·00	

1927 (Aug)–30. *Optd with T 10. (a) On Nos. 13 and 17a of South Africa.*

			Single stamps	
56	1s. 3d. pale violet (H/S S. £70)		1·25	6·00
	a. Without stop after "A" (R.3/4)		90·00	
57	£1 pale olive-green and red		£120	£180
	a. Without stop after "A" (R.3/4)		£2250	£3000

(b) On Nos. 30/2 and 34/9 of South Africa

			Un pair	Us pair	Us single
58	½d. black and green		1·50	4·25	70
	a. Without stop after "A"		50·00	75·00	
	b. "S.W.A." opt above value		2·75	13·00	2·25
	c. As b, in vert pair, top stamp without opt		£450		
59	1d. black and carmine		1·25	3·25	55
	a. Without stop after "A"		50·00	75·00	
	b. "S.W.A." opt at top (30.4.30)		1·75	11·00	1·60
	c. As b, vert pair, top stamp without opt		£375		
60	2d. grey and maroon		4·50	8·50	1·10
	a. Without stop after "A"		75·00	£110	
	b. Opt double, one inverted		£650	£850	
61	3d. black and red		6·00	23·00	3·25
	a. Without stop after "A"		75·00	£120	
62	4d. brown (4.28)		18·00	48·00	7·00
	a. Without stop after "A"		85·00	£130	
63	6d. green and orange		13·00	22·00	2·75
	a. Without stop after "A"		£110		
64	1s. brown and deep blue		24·00	42·00	5·00
	a. Without stop after "A"		£1700		
65	2s. 6d. green and brown		45·00	75·00	10·00
	a. Without stop after "A"		£160	£250	
66	5s. black and green		65·00	£100	18·00
	a. Without stop after "A"		£225	£350	
67	10s. bright blue and brown		£120	£180	28·00
	a. Without stop after "A"		£325	£500	
58/67		*Set of 10*	£250	£425	70·00
58/61, 63/7 H/S "Specimen"		*Set of 9*	£550		

On the ½d., 1d. and 6d. the missing stop variety occurs three times on each sheet, R.1/7, 13/4 and one position not yet identified. For the other values it comes on R.2/3 of the right pane and, for the 2s. 6d., 5s. and 10s., on R.8/1 of the left pane. The overprint is normally found at the base of the ½d., 1d., 6d., 1s. 3d. and £1 values and at the top on the remainder.

1930–31. *Nos. 42 and 43 of South Africa (rotogravure printing) optd with T 10.*

68	½d. black and green (1931)		7·00	18·00	2·50
69	1d. black and carmine		6·00	18·00	2·50

1930 (27 Nov–Dec). *Air. Nos. 40/1 of South Africa optd.*

(a) As T 10.

				Un single	Us single
70	4d. green (*first printing*)			12·00	25·00
	a. No stop after "A" of "S.W.A."			80·00	£110
	b. Later printings			7·00	25·00
71	1s. orange (*first printing*)			70·00	£110
	a. No stop after "A" of "S.W.A."			£400	£500
	b. Later printings			15·00	48·00

First printing: Thick letters, blurred impression. Stops with rounded corners.
Later printings: Thinner letters, clear impression. Clean cut, square stops.

(b) As T 11 (12.30)

72	4d. green			1·25	5·50
	a. Opt double			£140	
	b. Opt inverted			£130	
73	1s. orange			1·50	14·00
	a. Opt double				

12 Kori Bustard

13 Cape Cross

14 Bogenfels

15 Windhoek

16 Waterberg

17 Luderitz Bay

18 Bush Scene

19 Elands

20 Mountain Zebra and Blue Wildebeests

21 Herero Huts

22 Welwitschia Plant

23 Okuwahaken Falls

24 Monoplane over Windhoek

25 Biplane over Windhoek

(Recess B.W.)

1931 (5 Mar). *T* **12** to **25** (*inscr alternately in English and Afrikaans*). *W* **9** *of South Africa. P* 14 × 13½. (*a*) *Postage*.

74	½d. black and emerald	..	1·40	1·25	10
75	1d. indigo and scarlet	..	1·25	2·00	10
76	2d. blue and brown ..		50	2·25	15
77	3d. grey-blue and blue	..	50	2·50	15
78	4d. green and purple	..	90	5·50	20
79	6d. blue and brown ..		60	7·00	20
80	1s. chocolate and blue	..	1·00	7·00	25
81	1s. 3d. violet and yellow	..	8·50	11·00	50
82	2s. 6d. carmine and grey	..	20·00	22·00	1·75
83	5s. sage-green and red-brown	..	20·00	40·00	2·75
84	10s. red-brown and emerald ..		55·00	60·00	7·00
85	20s. lake and blue-green	..	£110	£110	12·00

(*b*) *Air*

86	3d. brown and blue ..		32·00	40·00	3·50
87	10d. black and purple-brown	..	55·00	85·00	9·00
74/87	.. .. ..	*Set of* 14	£275	£350	32·00

26

(Recess B.W.)

1935 (1 May). *Silver Jubilee. Inscr bilingually. W* **9** *of South Africa. P* 14 × 13½.

					Un	Us
					single	single
88	**26**	1d. black and scarlet	..	..	60	25
89		2d. black and sepia	..	..	1·00	25
90		3d. black and blue	..	..	11·00	14·00
91		6d. black and purple	..	..	5·00	3·50
88/91	..			*Set of* 4	16·00	16·00

1935–36. *Voortrekker Memorial Fund. Nos.* 50/3 *of South Africa optd with T* **10**.

92	½d. + ½d. black and green	..	1·00	4·50	65
	a. Opt inverted	..		£225	
93	1d. + ½d. grey-black and pink	..	1·50	3·25	40
94	2d. + 1d. grey-green and purple	..	5·00	6·00	80
	a. Without stop after "A"	..		£190	
	b. Opt double	..		£180	
95	3d. + 1½d. grey-green and blue	..	15·00	25·00	3·50
	a. Without stop after "A"	..		£200	£225
92/5	.. ..	*Set of* 4	20·00	35·00	4·75

27 Mail Train   **28**

(Recess B.W.)

1937 (1 Mar). *W* **9** *of South Africa. P* 14 × 13½.

96	**27**	1½d. purple-brown	..	9·50	2·00	15

(Recess B.W.)

1937 (12 May). *Coronation. W* **9** *of South Africa* (*sideways*). *P* 13½ × 14.

97	**28**	½d. black and emerald	..	60	15	10
98		1d. black and scarlet	..	70	15	10
99		1½d. black and orange	..	70	15	10
100		2d. black and brown	..	70	15	10
101		3d. black and blue	..	70	15	10
102		4d. black and purple	..	70	20	10
103		6d. black and yellow	..	80	1·75	20
104		1s. black and grey-black	..	1·25	1·50	20
97/104			*Set of* 8	5·50	3·75	60

1938 (14 Dec). *Voortrekker Centenary Memorial. Nos.* 76/9 *of South Africa optd as T* **11**.

105	½d. + ½d. blue and green ..		6·50	8·00	1·00
106	1d. + 1d. blue and carmine	..	14·00	4·50	75
107	1½d. + 1½d. chocolate & blue-green	18·00	17·00	2·50
108	3d. + 3d. bright blue	..	40·00	30·00	4·50
105/8		*Set of* 4	70·00	55·00	8·00

1938 (14 Dec). *Voortrekker Commemoration. Nos.* 80/1 *of South Africa optd as T* **11**.

109	1d. blue and carmine	..	7·50	7·00	1·00
110	1½d. greenish blue and brown	..	9·50	9·00	1·25

1939 (17 July). *250th Anniv of Landing of Huguenots in South Africa and Huguenot Commemoration Fund. Nos.* 82/4 *of South Africa optd as T* **11**.

111	½d. + ½d. brown and green	..	5·50	5·00	70
112	1d. + 1d. green and carmine	..	9·50	7·50	1·00
113	1½d. + 1½d. blue-green and purple	..	13·00	9·50	1·25
111/13		*Set of* 3	25·00	20·00	2·50

SWA (29)   **SWA** (30)   **SWA** (31)   **S W A** (32)

1941 (1 Oct)–43. *War Effort. Nos.* 88/96 *of South Africa optd with T* **29** *or* **30** (3d. *and* 1s.). (*a*) *Inscr alternately*.

114	½d. green (1.12.41)	..	75	1·50	15
	a. Blue-green (1942)	..	65	1·00	15
115	1d. carmine (1.11.41)	..	55	1·25	15
	a. "Stain" on uniform	..			
116	1½d. myrtle-green (21.1.42)	..	55	1·25	15
117	3d. blue	..	13·00	5·50	75
118	4d. orange-brown	..	6·50	6·50	75
	a. Red-brown	..	10·00	17·00	2·75
119	6d. red-orange	..	2·50	3·00	50
120	1s. 3d. olive-brown (15.1.43)	..	7·00	6·50	95

(*b*) *Inscr bilingually*

			Un	Us
			single	single
121	2d. violet	..	40	30
122	1s. brown (17.11.41)	..	60	40
114/22	*Set of* 7 *pairs and* 2 *singles*	29·00	23·00

1943–44. *War Effort (reduced sizes). Nos.* 97/104 *of South Africa, optd with T* **29** (1½d. *and* 1s., *No.* 130), *or T* **31** (*others*).

(*a*) *Inscr alternately*

			Un	Us	Us
			unit	unit	single
123	½d. blue-green (T) ..	..	40	1·50	10
	a. Green	..	2·50	2·75	15
	b. Greenish blue	..	1·75	1·75	10
124	1d. carmine-red (T)	..	70	1·40	10
	a. Bright carmine ..		1·75	2·00	10
125	1½. red-brown (P)	..	45	50	10
126	2d. violet (P)	..	2·50	1·75	10
	a. Reddish violet ..		3·00	1·75	10
127	3d. blue (T) ..		2·75	6·00	35
128	6d. red-orange (P)	..	2·00	2·25	30
	a. Opt inverted	..		£375	

(*b*) *Inscr bilingually*

129	4d. slate-green (T)	..	2·00	6·50	40
	a. Opt inverted	..	£350	£275	50·00
130	1s. brown (opt T 29) (P)	..	11·00	15·00	1·60
	a. Opt inverted	..	£375	£300	
	b. Opt T 31 (1944)	..	3·25	3·75	30
	c. Opt T 31 inverted	..	£350	£275	40·00
123/30b		*Set of* 8	13·00	20·00	2·75

The "units" referred to above consist of pairs (P) or triplets (T). No. 128 exists with another type of opt as Type **31**, but with broader "s", narrower "w" and more space between the letters.

1945. *Victory. Nos.* 108/10 *of South Africa optd with T* **30**.

131	1d. brown and carmine	..	25	40	10
	a. Opt inverted	..	£200	£225	
132	2d. slate-blue and violet	..	30	45	10
133	3d. deep blue and blue	..	65	70	10
131/3		*Set of* 3 · 1·10	1·40	20

1947 (17 Feb). *Royal Visit. Nos.* 111/13 *of South Africa optd as T* **31**, *but* 8½ × 2 *mm*.

134	1d. black and carmine	..	10	10	10
135	2d. violet	..	10	15	10
	a. "Bird" on "2" ..				
136	3d. blue	..	15	15	10
134/6		*Set of* 3	30	35	15

1948 (26 Apr). *Royal Silver Wedding. No.* 125 *of South Africa, optd as T* **31**, *but* 4 × 2 *mm*.

137	3d. blue and silver ..		1·50	35	10

1949 (1 Oct). *75th Anniv of U.P.U. Nos.* 128/30 *of South Africa optd as T* **30**, *but* 13 × 4 *mm*.

138	½d. blue-green	..	1·25	1·50	20
139	1½d. brown-red	..	1·25	80	15
140	3d. bright blue	..	1·75	1·00	20
	a. "Lake" in East Africa	..	20·00		
138/40		*Set of* 3	3·75	3·00	50

1949 (1 Dec). *Inauguration of Voortrekker Monument, Pretoria. Nos.* 131/3 *of South Africa optd with T* **32**.

			Un	Us
			single	single
141	1d. magenta..	..	10	10
142	1½d. blue-green	..	10	10
143	3d. blue	..	10	20
141/3 ..	..	*Set of* 3	20	25

1952 (14 Mar). *Tercentenary of Landing of Van Riebeeck. Nos.* 136/40 *of South Africa optd as T* **30**, *but* 8 × 3½ *mm* (1d., 4½d.) *or* 11 × 4 *mm* (*others*).

144	½d. brown-purple and olive-grey	..	10	40
145	1d. deep blue-green	..	10	10
146	2d. deep violet	..	50	10
147	4½d. blue	..	30	1·25
148	1s. brown	..	1·25	1·75
144/8		*Set of* 5	2·00	1·75

PRINTERS. The following stamps were printed by the Government Printer, Pretoria, in photogravure (Nos. 149/234) or lithography (subsequent issues), *unless stated otherwise*.

33 Queen Elizabeth II and *Catophracies Alexandri*

1953 (2 June). *Coronation. T* **33** *and similar horiz designs. W* **9** *of South Africa. P* 14.

149	1d. bright carmine	..	..	75	10
150	2d. deep bluish green	..		75	10
151	4d. magenta	..		1·60	55
152	6d. dull ultramarine ..			1·75	1·25
153	1s. deep orange-brown	..		1·75	40
149/53			*Set of* 5	6·00	2·75

Designs:—2d. *Bauhinia macrantha*, 4d. *Caralluma nebrownii*, 6d. *Gloriosa virescens*, 1s. *Rhigozum tricholotum*.

34 "Two Bucks" (rock painting)

36 "Rhinoceros Hunt" (rock painting)

38 Karakul Lamb

39 Ovambo Woman blowing Horn

(Des O. Schroeder (1d. to 4d.), M. Vandenschen (4½d. to 10s.))

1954 (15 Nov). *T* **34**, **36**, **38**/**9** *and similar designs. W* **9** *of South Africa* (*sideways on vert designs*). *P* 14.

154	1d. brown-red	..	..	30	10
155	2d. deep brown	..	..	35	10
156	3d. dull purple	..	..	2·25	10
157	4d. blackish olive	..	..	2·25	10
158	4½d. deep blue	..	..	1·25	15
159	6d. myrtle-green	..	..	1·25	10
160	1s. deep mauve	..	..	1·25	30
161	1s. 3d. cerise	..	..	6·00	30
162	1s. 6d. purple	..	..	6·00	35
163	2s. 6d. bistre-brown	..	..	10·00	60
164	5s. deep bright blue	..	..	15·00	2·75
165	10s. deep myrtle-green	..	..	48·00	15·00
154/65			*Set of* 12	85·00	18·00

Designs: *Vert* (as *T* **34**)—2d. "White Lady" (rock painting). (As *T* **38**)—2s. 6d. Gemsbok; 5s. African Elephant. (As *T* **39**)—1s. Ovambo woman; 1s. 3d. Herero woman; 1s. 6d. Ovambo girl. *Horiz* (as *T* **36**)—4d. "White Elephant and Giraffe" (rock painting).

1960. *As Nos. 154/7, 162, but W* **102** *of South Africa (sideways on vert designs). P* 14.

166		1d. brown-red	.. ..	55	65
167		2d. deep brown	.. ..	70	70
168		3d. dull purple	.. ..	1·40	2·00
169		4d. blackish olive	.. ..	4·25	4·50
170		1s. 6d. purple	.. ..	22·00	15·00
166/70		.. ..	*Set of 5*	26·00	21·00

(New Currency. 100 cents=1 rand)

46 G.P.O. Windhoek **47** Finger Rock

48 Mounted Soldier Monument **49** Quivertree

50 S.W.A. House, Windhoek **50a** Greater Flamingoes and Swakopmund Lighthouse

51 Fishing Industry **52** Greater Flamingo **53** German Lutheran Church, Windhoek

54 Diamond **55** Fort Namutoni

55a Hardap Dam **56** Topaz

57 Tourmaline **58** Heliodor

1961 (14 Feb)**–63**. *Unsurfaced paper. W* **102** *of South Africa (sideways on vert designs). P* 14.

171	46	½ c. brown and pale blue	.. ..	60	10
172	47	1 c. sepia and reddish lilac	.. ..	15	10
173	48	1½ c. slate-violet and salmon	.. ..	20	10
174	49	2 c. deep green and yellow	.. ..	75	10
175	50	2½ c. red-brown and light blue	.. ..	35	10
176	50a	3 c. ultramarine and rose-red (1.10.62)		3·75	15
177	51	3½ c. indigo and blue-green	.. ..	70	15
178	52	5 c. scarlet and grey-blue	.. ..	3·75	10
179	53	7½ c. sepia and pale lemon	.. ..	70	15
180	54	10 c. blue and greenish yellow	.. ..	1·75	15
181	55	12½ c. indigo and lemon	.. ..	85	30
182	55a	15 c. chocolate and light blue (16.3.63)		14·00	3·25
183	56	20 c. brown and red-orange	.. ..	7·00	30
184	57	50 c. deep bluish green & yellow-orge		11·00	1·50
185	58	1 r. yellow, maroon and blue	.. ..	20·00	13·00
171/185			*Set of 15*	60·00	17·00

See also Nos. 186/91, 202/16, 224/6 and 240.

1962–66. *As No. 171, etc., but without watermark.*

186	46	½ c. brown and pale blue (8.62)	..	50	1·50
187	48	1½ c. slate-violet and salmon (9.62)	..	5·00	35
188	49	2 c. deep green and yellow (5.62)	..	2·25	2·25
189	50	2½ c. red-brown and light blue (1964)	..	4·00	3·50
190	51	3½ c. indigo and blue-green (1966)	..	9·50	4·00
191	52	5 c. scarlet and grey-blue (9.62)	..	6·00	50
186/91			*Set of 6*	25·00	11·00

59 "Agricultural Development" **60** Centenary Emblem and Map **61** Centenary Emblem and part of Globe

1963 (16 Mar). *Opening of Hardap Dam. W* **102** *of South Africa (sideways). P* 14.

192	59	3 c. chocolate and light green	..	30	15

1963 (30 Aug). *Centenary of Red Cross. P* 14.

193	60	7½ c. red, black and light blue	..	7·00	4·00
194	61	15 c. red, black and orange-brown	..	10·00	6·00

62 Interior of Assembly Hall **63** Calvin

1964 (14 May). *Opening of Legislative Assembly Hall, Windhoek. W* **102** *of South Africa. P* 14.

195	62	3 c. ultramarine and salmon	.. ..	50	30

1964 (1 Oct). *400th Death Anniv of Calvin (Protestant reformer). P* 14.

196	63	2½ c. brown-purple and gold	..	50	15
197		15 c. deep bluish green and gold	..	2·75	1·75

64 Mail Runner of 1890 **65** Kurt von François (founder) **66** Dr. H. Vedder

(Des D. Aschenborn)

1965 (18 Oct). *75th Anniv of Windhoek. Chalk-surfaced paper. W* **127** *of South Africa (sideways). P* 14.

198	64	3 c. sepia and scarlet	..	50	15
199	65	15 c. red-brown and blue-green	.. ..	1·25	1·10

1966 (4 July). *90th Birth Anniv of Dr. H. Vedder (philosopher and writer). Chalk-surfaced paper. W* **127** *of South Africa (sideways). P* 14.

200	66	3 c. blackish green and salmon	..	50	15
201		15 c. deep sepia and light blue	..	1·25	65

Nos. 200/1 exist on Swiss-made paper with *tête-bêche* watermark from a special printing made for use in presentation albums for delegates to the U.P.U. Congress in Tokyo in 1969, as supplies of the original Harrison paper were by then exhausted (*Set of 2 price* £17 *mint*).

1966–72. *As 1961–66 but chalk-surfaced paper and W* **127** *of South Africa* (sideways on vert designs).*

202	46	½ c. brown and pale blue (1967)	..	1·25	10
203	47	1 c. sepia and light reddish lilac (1967)		1·25	10
		a. Grey-brown and lilac (9.72)	..	1·75	10
204	48	1½ c. slate-violet and salmon (1968)	..	6·50	30
205	49	2 c. deep bluish green and yellow	..	3·00	10
206	50	2½ c. dp red-brown & lt turquoise-blue		2·50	10
		a. Dp red-brown & pale blue (1967)		70	10
207	50a	3 c. ultramarine and rose-red (1970)		8·00	50
208	51	3½ c. indigo and blue-green (1967)	..	4·00	1·75
209	50	4 c. dp red-brown & lt turq-bl (1.4.71)		1·50	1·50
210	52	5 c. scarlet and grey-blue (1968)	..	4·00	10
211	53	6 c. sepia & greenish yellow (31.8.71)		8·50	8·50
212		7½ c. sepia and pale lemon (1967)	..	2·50	30
213	55	9 c. indigo & greenish yellow (1.7.71)		8·50	8·50
214	54	10 c. brt blue & greenish yellow (6.70)		17·00	1·50
		a. Whiter background† (9.72)	..	17·00	2·25
215	55a	15 c. chocolate and light blue (1.72)		17·00	6·50
216	56	20 c. brown and red-orange (1968)	..	16·00	1·75
202/16			*Set of 15*	90·00	28·00

*The watermark in this issue is indistinct but the stamps can be distinguished from the stamps without watermark by their shades and the chalk-surfaced paper which is appreciably thicker and whiter. The 1, 1½, 3, 4, 5, 6, 9, 10, 15 and 20 c. are known only with the watermark *tête-bêche* but the ½ c. and 2½ c. exist with both forms, the remainder being as illustrated.

† No. 214a, printed from sheets, has a much whiter background around the value and behind "SOUTH WEST AFRICA" compared with No. 214, which was issued in coils only.

See also Nos. 224/6 and 240.

---

67 Camelthorn Tree

(Des D. Aschenborn (2½ c., 3 c.), Govt Printer, Pretoria (15 c.))

1967 (6 Jan). *Verwoerd Commemoration. Chalk-surfaced paper. T* **67** *and similar designs. W* **127** *of South Africa (sideways on vert designs). P* 14.

217		2½ c. black and emerald-green	.. ..	20	10
218		3 c. brown and new blue	.. ..	30	10
219		15 c. blackish brown and reddish purple		1·10	45
217/19			*Set of 3*	1·40	60

Designs: *Vert.*—3 c. Waves breaking against rock; 15 c. Dr. H. F. Verwoerd.

70 President Swart **71** President and Mrs. Swart

1968 (2 Jan). *Swart Commemoration. Chalk-surfaced paper. W* **127** *of South Africa (tête-bêche, sideways). P* 14 × 15.

220	70	3 c. orange-red, black & turquoise-blue			
		G. Inscribed in German	..	45	15
		A. Inscribed in Afrikaans	..	45	15
		E. Inscribed in English	..	45	15
221	71	15 c. red, blackish olive and dull green			
		G. Inscribed in German	..	1·50	1·75
		A. Inscribed in Afrikaans	..	1·50	1·75
		E. Inscribed in English	..	1·50	1·75
		a. Red, brownish olive & bronze-green			
		G. Inscribed in German	..	3·00	2·25
		A. Inscribed in Afrikaans	..	3·00	2·25
		E. Inscribed in English	..	3·00	2·25
220/1		.. *Set of 2 values in strips of three*		12·00	
		Set of 6 singles		5·00	5·00

The three languages appear, *se-tenant*, both horizontally and vertically, throughout the sheet.

1970 (14 Feb). *Water 70 Campaign. As Nos. 299/300 of South Africa, but without phosphor band and inscr* "SWA".

222		2½ c. green, bright blue and chocolate		75	30
223		3 c. Prussian blue, royal blue and buff	..	75	30

72 G.P.O., Windhoek **73** "Red Sand-dunes, Eastern South West Africa"

1970–71. *As Nos. 202 and 204/5 but* "POSGELD INKOMSTE" *omitted and larger figure of value as in T* **72**. *W* **127** *of South Africa (tête-bêche, sideways on* 1½ *and* 2 *c.)*.

224	72	½ c. brown and pale blue (6.70)..	..	1·50	30
225		1½ c. slate-violet and salmon (1.6.71)		13·00	14·00
226		2 c. deep bluish green and lemon (11.70)		5·00	40
224/6			*Set of 3*	18·00	14·00

1970 (24 Aug). *150th Anniv of Bible Society of South Africa. As Nos. 301/2 of South Africa, but inscr* "SWA".

228		2½ c. multicoloured	..	1·50	10
229		12½ c. gold, black and blue	.. ..	8·00	6·50

No. 228 has a phosphor frame, probably added in error.
A mint example of No. 229 exists with a second, blind, impression of the die-stamped features.

1971 (31 May). *"Interstex" Stamp Exhibition, Cape Town. As No. 303A of South Africa, but without phosphor frame and inscr* "SWA".

230		5 c. light greenish blue, black and pale yellow		4·75	1·50

1971 (31 May). *Tenth Anniv of Antarctic Treaty. As No. 304 of South Africa, but without phosphor frame, and inscr* "SWA".

231		12½ c. blue-black, greenish blue & orge-red		45·00	25·00

1971 (31 May). *Tenth Anniv of the South African Republic. As Nos. 305/6 of South Africa, but without phosphor frame, and inscr* "SWA".

232		2 c. pale flesh and brown-red..	..	3·25	75
233		4 c. green and black	..	3·25	75

1972 (19 Sept). *Centenary of S.P.C.A. As No. 312 of South Africa, but inscr* "SWA".

234		5 c. multicoloured	.. ..	3·50	55

WATERMARK. All issues from this date are on unwatermarked paper.

(Lettering by E. de Jong)

1973 (1 May). *Scenery. T* **73** *and similar multicoloured designs showing paintings by Adolph Jentsch.* P 11½ × 12½ (10 and 15 c.) *or* 12½ × 11½ (others).
235	2 c. Type 73		75	75
236	4 c. "After the Rain"		1·25	1·25
237	5 c. "Barren Country"		1·50	1·50
238	10 c. "Schaap River" (*vert*)		2·75	2·75
239	15 c. "Namib Desert" (*vert*)		4·00	4·00
235/9		Set of 5	9·00	9·00

1973 (28 May). *As Nos.* 207 *but without wmk. Phosphorised paper.*
240	*50a* 3 c. ultramarine and rose-red		2·50	1·25

No. 240 is also distinguishable in that the lettering of "SOUTH WEST AFRICA" is whiter.

74 *Sarcocaulon rigidum*   **75** *Euphorbia virosa*

(Des D. Findlay)

1973 (1 Sept)–**79**. *Succulents. Various multicoloured designs as T* **74/5**. *Phosphorised glossy paper (original printing of all values) or ordinary paper* (1, 2, 3, 4, 5, 9, 10, 15, 20, 30, 50 c.).

(*a*) *As T* **74**. *P* 12½.
241	1 c. Type 74		15	10
	a. Black (face value, etc.) omitted		£120	
242	2 c. *Lapidaria margaretae*		90	50
	a. Perf 14 × 13½ (4.8.79)		20	10
243	3 c. *Titanopsis schwantesii*		20	10
	a. Black (face value, etc.) omitted		£120	
	b. Perf 14 × 13½ (8.8.79)		30	15
244	4 c. *Lithops karasmontana*		25	10
245	5 c. *Caralluma lugardii*		40	30
	a. Black (face value, etc.) omitted		£120	
	b. Perf 14 × 13½ (12.12.79)		40	20
246	6 c. *Dinteranthus microspermus*		1·00	60
247	7 c. *Conophytum gratum*		70	70
248	9 c. *Huernia oculata*		65	60
249	10 c. *Gasteria pillansii*		80	45
	a. Black (face value, etc.) omitted		£200	
	b. Perf 14 × 13½ (13.8.79)		40	30
250	14 c. *Stapelia pedunculata*		1·50	90
251	15 c. *Fenestraria aurantiaca*		65	30
252	20 c. *Decabelone grandiflora*		4·00	1·00
253	25 c. *Hoodia bainii*		2·50	1·25

(*b*) *As T* **75**. *P* 11½ × 12½ (30 c., 1 r.) *or* 12½ × 11½ (50 c.)
254	30 c. Type 75		1·00	65
	a. Perf 13½ × 14 (27.12.79)		90	90
255	50 c. *Pachypodium namaquanum* (*vert*)		1·25	2·25
	a. Perf 14 × 13½ (18.12.79)		1·50	1·50
256	1 r. *Welwitschia bainesii*		2·00	5·00
241/56		Set of 16	15·00	12·00

1973 (1 Sept)–**80**. *Coil stamps. As Nos.* 241/2 *and* 245 *but photo, colours changed.* P 14.
257	1 c. black and light mauve		60	45
	a. Chalk-surfaced paper (7.76?)		70	30
	b. Imperf × perf 14. Chalk-surfaced paper (1980)		3·50	3·75
258	2 c. black and yellow		40	40
	a. Chalk-surfaced paper (7.76?)		75	40
	b. Imperf × perf 14. Chalk-surfaced paper (1.79)		85	40
259	5 c. black and light rose-red		1·50	45
	a. Imperf × perf 14. Chalk-surfaced paper (8.2.78)		1·00	45
257/9		Set of 3	1·75	1·10

Coils of Nos. 257b, 258b and 259a come with every fifth stamp numbered on the reverse.

76 Chat-shrike   **77** Giraffe, Antelope and Spoor

(Des D. Findlay)

1974 (13 Feb). *Rare Birds. T* **76** *and similar vert designs. Multicoloured.* P 12½ × 11½.
260	4 c. Type 76		3·00	75
261	5 c. Peach-faced Lovebirds		4·00	1·25
262	10 c. Damaraland Rock Jumper		10·00	4·50
263	15 c. Rüppell's Parrots		14·00	8·50
260/3		Set of 4	28·00	13·50

(Des O. Schröder)

1974 (10 Apr). *Twyfelfontein Rock-engravings. T* **77** *and similar multicoloured designs.* P 11½ × 12½ (15 c.) *or* 12½ × 11½ (others).
264	4 c. Type 77		1·50	50
265	5 c. Elephant, hyena, antelope and spoor		1·50	80
	a. Black (value and "SWA") omitted		£550	
266	15 c. Kudu Cow (38 × 21 *mm*)		7·00	6·00
264/6		Set of 3	9·00	6·50

---

78 Cut Diamond   **79** Wagons and Map of the Trek

(Des M. Barnett)

1974 (30 Sept). *Diamond Mining. T* **78** *and similar vert design. Multicoloured.* P 12½ × 11½.
267	10 c. Type 78		4·50	3·50
268	15 c. Diagram of shore workings		5·00	4·50

(Des K. Esterhuysen)

1974 (13 Nov). *Centenary of Thirstland Trek.* P 11½ × 12½.
269	**79** 4 c. multicoloured		1·00	75

80 Peregrine Falcon   **81** Kolmannskop (ghost town)

(Des D. Findlay)

1975 (19 Mar). *Protected Birds of Prey. T* **80** *and similar vert designs. Multicoloured.* P 12½ × 11½.
270	4 c. Type 80		2·00	1·00
271	5 c. Verreaux's Eagle		2·25	1·50
272	10 c. Martial Eagle		6·00	4·50
273	15 c. Egyptian Vulture		7·50	7·50
270/3		Set of 4	16·00	13·00

(Des A. H. Barrett)

1975 (23 July). *Historic Monuments. T* **81** *and similar horiz designs. Multicoloured.* P 11½ × 12½.
274	5 c. Type 81		30	15
275	9 c. "Martin Luther" (steam tractor)		50	50
276	15 c. Kurt von François and Old Fort, Windhoek		1·00	80
274/6		Set of 3	1·60	1·25

82 "View of Lüderitz"

(Des J. Hoekstra)

1975 (15 Oct). *Otto Schröder. T* **82** *and similar horiz designs showing his paintings. Multicoloured.* P 11½ × 12½.
277	15 c. Type 82		55	45
	a. Block of 4. Nos. 277/80		2·00	
278	15 c. "View of Swakopmund"		55	45
279	15 c. "Harbour Scene"		55	45
280	15 c. "Quayside, Walvis Bay"		55	45
277/80		Set of 4	2·00	1·60
MS281	122 × 96 mm. Nos. 277/80		2·25	4·50

Nos. 277/80 were printed together, in *se-tenant* blocks of four within the sheet.

83 Elephants

(Des H. Pager)

1976 (31 Mar). *Prehistoric Rock Paintings. T* **83** *and similar horiz designs. Multicoloured.* P 11½ × 12½.
282	4 c. Type 83		40	10
283	10 c. Rhinoceros		65	30
284	15 c. Antelope		80	60
285	20 c. Man with bow and arrow		1·10	85
282/5		Set of 4	2·75	1·60
MS286	121 × 95 mm. Nos. 282/5		2·75	4·00

84 Schwerinsburg

(Des H. Pager)

1976 (14 May). *Castles. T* **84** *and similar horiz designs. Multicoloured.* P 11½ × 12½.
287	10 c. Type 84		50	30
288	15 c. Schloss Duwisib		70	50
289	20 c. Heynitzburg		1·00	80
287/9		Set of 3	2·00	1·40

85 Large-toothed Rock Hyrax

(Des D. Findlay)

1976 (16 July). *Fauna Conservation. T* **85** *and similar horiz designs. Multicoloured.* P 11½ × 12½.
290	4 c. Type 85		50	20
291	10 c. Kirk's Dik-Dik		1·50	90
292	15 c. Kuhl's Tree Squirrel		2·25	2·00
290/2		Set of 3	3·75	2·75

86 The Augustineum, Windhoek

(Des H. Pager)

1976 (17 Sept). *Modern Buildings. T* **86** *and similar horiz design.* P 11½ × 12½.
293	15 c. black and yellow		40	50
294	20 c. black and light yellow		50	60

Design:—20 c. Katutura Hospital, Windhoek.

87 Ovambo Water Canal System

(Des A. H. Barrett)

1976 (19 Nov). *Water and Electricity Supply. T* **87** *and similar horiz design. Multicoloured.* P 11½ × 12½.
295	15 c. Type 87		30	30
296	20 c. Ruacana Falls Power Station		40	40

88 Coastline near Pomona

(Des A. H. Barrett)

1977 (29 Mar). *Namib Desert. T* **88** *and similar horiz designs. Multicoloured.* P 11½ × 12½.
297	4 c. Type 88		20	15
298	10 c. Bush and dunes, Sossusvlei		30	30
299	15 c. Plain near Brandberg		50	50
300	20 c. Dunes, Sperr Gebiet		60	60
297/300		Set of 4	1·40	1·40

89 Kraal

(Des A. H. Barrett)

1977 (15 July). *The Ovambo People. T* **89** *and similar horiz designs.* P 11½ × 12½.
301	4 c. multicoloured		10	10
302	10 c. black, dull orange and cinnamon		30	20
303	15 c. multicoloured		30	25
304	20 c. multicoloured		35	45
301/4		Set of 4	95	90

Designs—10 c. Grain baskets; 15 c. Pounding grain; 20 c. Women in tribal dress.

90 Terminal Buildings

(Des H. Pager and A. H. Barrett)

1977 (22 Aug). *J. G. Strijdom Airport, Windhoek. P* 12½.
305   90   20 c. multicoloured   30   30

91 Drostdy, Lüderitz

92 Side-winding Adder

(Des A. H. Barrett)

1977 (4 Nov). *Historic Houses. T* **91** *and similar horiz designs. Multicoloured. P* 12 × 12½.
306   5 c. Type **91**   15   10
307   10 c. Woermannhaus, Swakopmund ..   40   30
308   15 c. Neu-Heusis, Windhoek   45   35
309   20 c. Schmelenhaus, Bethanie   65   40
306/9 ..   ..   *Set of* 4   1·50   1·10
MS310   122 × 96 mm. Nos. 306/9 ..   ..   1·50   2·25

(Des D. Findlay)

1978 (6 Feb). *Small Animals. T* **92** *and similar horiz designs. Multicoloured. P* 12½.
311   4 c. Type **92**   15   10
312   10 c. Grant's Desert Golden Mole   ..   30   30
313   15 c. Palmato Gecko   50   30
314   20 c. Namaqua Chameleon   65   40
311/14 ..   ..   *Set of* 4   1·40   1·00

93 Ostrich Hunting

(Des A. H. Barrett)

1978 (14 Apr). *The Bushmen. T* **93** *and similar horiz designs in light grey-brown, stone and black. P* 12 × 12½.
315   4 c. Type **93**   15   10
316   10 c. Woman carrying fruit   25   20
317   15 c. Hunters kindling fire   35   30
318   20 c. Woman with musical instrument   ..   40   40
315/18 ..   ..   *Set of* 4   1·00   90

94 Lutheran Church, Windhoek

ALGEMENE STEMREG

(**95**)

(Des A. H. Barrett)

1978 (16 June). *Historic Churches. T* **94** *and similar horiz designs. P* 12½.
319   4 c. grey-black and cinnamon   10   10
320   10 c. grey-black and ochre   15   20
321   15 c. grey-black and light brown-rose   ..   20   25
322   20 c. grey-black and light grey-blue   ..   30   35
319/22   ..   ..   *Set of* 4   65   80
MS323   125 × 90 mm. Nos. 319/22 ..   ..   1·00   1·75
Designs:—10 c. Lutheran Church, Swakopmund; 15 c. Rhenish Mission Church, Otjimbingwe; 20 c. Rhenish Missionary Church, Keetmanshoop.

1978 (1 Nov). *Universal Suffrage. Designs as Nos.* 244/5, 249 *and* 251/3 *optd with T* **95** (*or similar inscr in English or German*).
324   4 c. Lithops karasmontana   ..
   A. Opt in Afrikaans..   10   10
   E. Opt in English   10   10
   G. Opt in German   10   10
325   5 c. Caralluma lugardii   ..
   A. Opt in Afrikaans..   10   10
   E. Opt in English   10   10
   G. Opt in German   10   10
326   10 c. Gasteria pillansii..
   A. Opt in Afrikaans..   10   10
   E. Opt in English   10   10
   G. Opt in German   10   10
327   15 c. Fenestraria aurantiaca   ..
   A. Opt in Afrikaans..   15   15
   E. Opt in English   15   15
   G. Opt in German   15   15
328   20 c. Decabelone grandiflora   ..
   A. Opt in Afrikaans..   20   20
   E. Opt in English   20   20
   G. Opt in German   20   20
329   25 c. Hoodia bainii
   A. Opt in Afrikaans..   25   25
   E. Opt in English   25   25
   G. Opt in German   25   25
324/9 ..   ..   ..   *Set of* 18 (6 *strips of* 3)   2·40   2·40
   Nos. 324A/G, 325A/G, 326A/G, 327A/G, 328A/G and 329A/G were each printed together, *se-tenant*, in horizontal and vertical strips of 3 throughout the sheets.

NEW INFORMATION

The editor is always interested to correspond with people who have new information that will improve or correct the Catalogue.

---

96 Greater Flamingo

97 Silver Topaz

(Des D. Findlay)

1979 (5 Apr). *Water Birds. T* **96** *and similar vert designs. Multicoloured. P* 14.
330   4 c. Type **96**   20   10
331   15 c. White-breasted Cormorant   45   25
332   20 c. Chestnut-banded Sand Plover   50   35
333   25 c. Eastern White Pelican   55   40
330/3 ..   ..   *Set of* 4   1·50   1·00

(Des H. Botha)

1979 (26 Nov). *Gemstones. T* **97** *and similar horiz designs. Multicoloured. P* 14.
334   4 c. Type **97**   25   10
335   15 c. Aquamarine   55   20
336   20 c. Malachite   60   25
337   25 c. Amethyst   60   30
334/7 ..   ..   *Set of* 4   1·75   75

98 Killer Whale

99 Impala

(Des A. H. Barrett)

1980 (25 Mar). *Whales. T* **98** *and similar multicoloured designs. P* 14.
338   4 c. Type **98**   35   10
339   5 c. Humpback Whale (38 × 22 *mm*)   ..   40   10
340   10 c. Black Right Whale (38 × 22 *mm*)   ..   55   30
341   15 c. Sperm Whale (58 × 22 *mm*)   ..   1·00   60
342   20 c. Fin Whale (58 × 22 *mm*)   ..   1·25   80
343   25 c. Blue Whale (88 × 22 *mm*)   ..   1·60   1·10
338/43   ..   ..   ..   *Set of* 6   4·50   2·75
MS344   202 × 95 mm. Nos. 338/43 .   ..   5·50   6·00

(Des P. Bosman)

1980 (25 June). *25th Anniv of Division of Nature Conservation and Tourism. Antelopes. T* **99** *and similar horiz designs. Multicoloured. P* 14.
345   5 c. Type **99**   15   10
346   10 c. Topi   20   10
347   15 c. Roan Antelope   40   15
348   20 c. Sable Antelope   50   20
345/8 ..   ..   *Set of* 4   1·10   45

100 Black-backed Jackal

101 Meerkat

(Des Sheila Nowers (11, 12, 14, 16 c.), P. Bosman (others))

1980 (1 Oct)–89. *Wildlife. Multicoloured designs as T* **100**. *Ordinary paper. P* 14.
349   1 c. Type **100**   15   10
   a. Chalk-surfaced paper (11.6.85)   ..   70   70
350   2 c. Hunting Dog   30   10
   a. Chalk-surfaced paper (4.6.86)   ..   75   75
351   3 c. Brown Hyena   20   10
   a. Chalk-surfaced paper (10.2.88)   ..   70   80
352   4 c. Springbok   20   10
   a. Chalk-surfaced paper (29.7.87)   ..   70   80
353   5 c. Gemsbok   20   10
   a. Chalk-surfaced paper (11.6.85)   ..   90   90
354   6 c. Greater Kudu   20   10
   a. Chalk-surfaced paper (8.8.88)   ..   1·00   1·00
355   7 c. Mountain Zebra (*horiz*)   ..   40   20
   a. Chalk-surfaced paper (19.3.86)   ..   75   85
356   8 c. Cape Porcupine (*horiz*)   ..   30   10
   a. Chalk-surfaced paper (11.6.85)   ..   1·00   1·00
357   9 c. Ratel (*horiz*)..   30   10
   a. Chalk-surfaced paper (10.2.88)   ..   1·00   1·00
358   10 c. Cheetah (*horiz*)   30   10
358a   11 c. Blue Wildebeest (2.4.84)   ..   40   30
358b   12 c. African Buffalo (*horiz*) (1.4.85)   80   80
   ba. Booklet pane of 10 with margins all round (1.8.85)   ..   ..   8·00
358c   14 c. Caracal (*horiz*) (*chalk-surfaced paper*) (1.4.86)   ..   ..   ..   2·00   1·40

102 Von Bach

359   15 c. Hippopotamus (*horiz*)   ..   30   10
   a. Chalk-surfaced paper (10.2.88)   ..   70   85
359b   16 c. Warthog (*horiz*) (*chalk-surfaced paper*) (1.4.87)   ..   1·50   1·40
   ba. Ordinary paper (15.2.89)   ..   1·25   1·25
360   20 c. Eland (*horiz*)..   30   10
   a. Chalk-surfaced paper (11.6.85)   ..   70   85
361   25 c. Black Rhinoceros (*horiz*)   ..   40   20
   a. Chalk-surfaced paper (11.6.85)   ..   70   85
362   30 c. Lion (*horiz*)   70   20
   a. Chalk-surfaced paper (4.6.86)   ..   1·00   1·00
363   50 c. Giraffe   50   30
   a. Chalk-surfaced paper (21.4.88)   ..   1·00   1·25
364   1 r. Leopard   90   55
   a. Chalk-surfaced paper (4.6.86)   ..   1·75   2·00
365   2 r. African Elephant   ..   ..   1·00   90
   a. Chalk-surfaced paper (10.2.88)   ..   2·00   2·25
349/65   ..   ..   *Set of* 21   10·00   6·50
   Some printings of the 4, 15 and 25 c. from 1983/4 were on phosphorescent paper. The same paper was used for printings of the 1, 2, 3, 8, 9, 10, 16 c. (No. 359ba), 20, 30 c. and 1 r. during 1989.

(Des P. Bosman. Photo)

1980 (1 Oct). *Coil stamps. Wildlife. Vert designs as T* **101**. *Imperf × perf* 14.
366   1 c. yellow-brown   10   10
367   2 c. deep dull blue   10   10
368   5 c. yellow-olive   15   15
366/8   ..   ..   ..   *Set of* 3   30   30
Designs:—2 c. Savanna Monkey; 5 c. Chacma Baboon.

(Des A. H. Barrett)

1980 (25 Nov). *Water Conservation. Dams. T* **102** *and similar horiz designs. Multicoloured. P* 14.
369   5 c. Type **102**   10   10
370   10 c. Swakoppoort   15   10
371   15 c. Naute   20   20
372   20 c. Hardap   25   25
369/72   ..   ..   ..   *Set of* 4   60   60

103 View of Fish River Canyon

104 *Aloe erinacea*

(Des A. H. Barrett)

1981 (20 Mar). *Fish River Canyon. T* **103** *and similar horiz designs showing various views of canyon. P* 14.
373   5 c. multicoloured   10   10
374   15 c. multicoloured   20   20
375   20 c. multicoloured   25   25
376   25 c. multicoloured   30   30
373/6 ..   ..   *Set of* 4   75   70

(Des D. Findlay)

1981 (14 Aug). *Aloes. T* **104** *and similar vert designs. Multicoloured. P* 14 × 13½.
377   5 c. Type **104**   10   10
378   15 c. *Aloe viridiflora*   30   30
379   20 c. *Aloe pearsonii*   35   25
380   25 c. *Aloe littoralis*   40   30
377/80 ..   ..   *Set of* 4   1·00   75

105 Paul Weiss-Haus

(Des A. H. Barrett)

1981 (16 Oct). *Historic Buildings of Lüderitz. T* **105** *and similar horiz designs. Multicoloured. P* 14.
381   5 c. Type **105**   10   10
382   15 c. Deutsche Afrika Bank   20   20
383   20 c. Schroederhaus   30   30
384   25 c. Altes Postamt   30   35
381/4 ..   ..   *Set of* 4   75   80
MS385   125 × 90 mm. Nos. 381/4   85   90

106 Salt Pan

107 Kalahari Starred Tortoise
(*Psammobates oculifer*)

(Des A. H. Barrett)

1981 (4 Dec). *Salt Industry. T* **106** *and similar horiz designs. Multicoloured. P* 14.

386	5 c. Type 106	..	..	..	10	10
387	15 c. Dumping and washing	..	..	20	20
388	20 c. Loading by conveyor	..	..	25	30
389	25 c. Dispatch to refinery	..	..	30	35
386/9	..	..	..	*Set of* 4	70	80

(Des A. H. Barrett)

1982 (12 Mar). *Tortoises. T* **107** *and similar horiz designs. Multicoloured. P* 14.

390	5 c. Type 107	..	..	..	10	10
391	15 c. Leopard Tortoise (*Geochelone pardalis*)	..	20	20
392	20 c. Angulate Tortoise (*Chersina angulata*)	..	25	30
393	25 c. Speckled Padloper (*Homopus signatus*)	..	30	35
390/3	..	..	..	*Set of* 4	70	80

108 Mythical Sea-monster

(Des Sheila Nowers)

1982 (28 May). *Discoverers of South West Africa.* (1st series). *Bartolomeu Dias. T* **108** *and similar horiz designs. Multicoloured. P* 14.

394	15 c. Type 108	..	..	20	20
395	20 c. Bartolomeu Dias and map of Africa showing voyage	..	..	30	30
396	25 c. Dias' caravel	..	..	55	40
397	30 c. Dias erecting commemorative cross, Angra das Voltas, 25 July 1488	..	55	45
394/7	..	..	..	*Set of* 4	1·40	1·25

See also Nos. 455/8.

109 Brandberg

110 Otjikaeva Head-dress of Herero Woman

(Des A. H. Barrett)

1982 (3 Aug). *Mountains of South West Africa. T* **109** *and similar horiz designs. Multicoloured. P* 13½ × 14.

398	6 c. Type 109	..	..	..	10	10
399	15 c. Omatako	..	..	..	20	20
400	20 c. Die Nadel	..	..	..	25	30
401	25 c. Spitzkuppe	..	..	..	30	35
398/401	..	..	*Set of* 4	75	85

(Des A. H. Barrett)

1982 (15 Oct). *Traditional Head-dresses of South West Africa.* (1st series). *T* **110** *and similar vert designs. Multicoloured. P* 14.

402	6 c. Type 110	..	..	..	10	10
403	15 c. Ekori head-dress of Himba	..	..	25	35
404	20 c. Oshikoma hair-piece and iipando plaits of Ngandjera	..	..	35	45
405	25 c. Omhatela head-dress of Kwanyama	..	35	60
402/5	..	..	..	*Set of* 4	95	1·40

See also Nos. 427/30.

111 Fort Vogelsang

112 Searching for Diamonds, Kolmanskop, 1908

(Des J. van Ellinckhuijzen)

1983 (16 Mar). *Centenary of Lüderitz. T* **111** *and similar designs. P* 14.

406	6 c. brownish black and deep carmine-red	..	10	10
407	20 c. brownish black and yellow-brown	..	25	30
408	25 c. brownish black and chestnut	..	30	35
409	30 c. brownish black and brown-purple	..	35	40
410	40 c. brownish black and bright green	..	50	55
406/10	..	..	*Set of* 5	1·40	1·50

Designs: *Vert* (23 × 29 *mm*)—20 c. Chief Joseph Fredericks; 30 c. Heinrich Vogelsang (founder); 40 c. Adolf Lüderitz (colonial promoter). *Horiz* (*As T* **111**)—25 c. Angra Pequena.

1983 (8 June). *75th Anniv of Discovery of Diamonds. T* **112** *and similar designs. P* 13½ × 14 (10, 20 c.) *or* 14 × 13½ (*others*).

411	10 c. deep brown and pale stone	..	15	15
412	20 c. maroon and pale stone	..	30	30
413	25 c. Prussian blue and pale stone	..	35	35
414	40 c. brownish black and pale stone	..	55	55
411/14	..	..	*Set of* 4	1·25	1·25

Designs: *Horiz* (34 × 19 *mm*)—20 c. Digging for diamonds, Kolmanskop, 1908. *Vert* (19 × 26 *mm*)—25 c. Sir Ernest Oppenheimer (industrialist); 40 c. August Stauch (prospector).

113 "Common Zebras drinking" (J. van Ellinckhuijzen)

114 The Rock Lobster

1983 (1 Sept). *Painters of South West Africa. T* **113** *and similar horiz designs. Multicoloured. P* 13½ × 14.

415	10 c. Type 113	..	..	15	15
416	20 c. "Rossing Mountain" (H. Henckert)	..	25	30
417	25 c. "Stampeding African Buffalo" (F. Krampe)	..	..	30	35
418	40 c. "Erongo Mountains" (J. Blatt)	..	50	55
415/18	..	..	*Set of* 4	1·10	1·25

(Des J. van Ellinckhuijzen)

1983 (23 Nov). *Lobster Industry. T* **114** *and similar horiz designs. Multicoloured. P* 13½ × 14.

419	10 c. Type 114	..	..	15	15
420	20 c. Mother ship and fishing dinghies	..	25	30
421	25 c. Netting lobsters from dinghy	..	30	35
422	40 c. Packing lobsters	..	..	50	55
419/22	..	..	*Set of* 4	1·10	1·25

115 Hohenzollern House

(Des A. H. Barrett)

1984 (8 Mar). *Historic Buildings of Swakopmund. T* **115** *and similar horiz designs. P* 14.

423	10 c. grey-black and orange-brown	..	15	15
424	20 c. grey-black and new blue	..	30	25
425	25 c. grey-black and yellow-green	..	30	30
426	30 c. grey-black and ochre	..	35	30
423/6	..	..	*Set of* 4	1·00	90

Designs:—20 c. Railway Station; 25 c. Imperial District Bureau; 30 c. Ritterburg.

(Des A. H. Barrett)

1984 (25 May). *Traditional Head-dresses of South West Africa* (2nd series). *Multicoloured designs as T* **110**. *P* 14.

427	11 c. Eendjushi head-dress of Kwambi	..	25	15
428	20 c. Bushman woman	..	..	40	25
429	25 c. Omulenda head-dress of Kwaluudhi	..	45	30
430	30 c. Mbukushu women	..	..	45	30
427/30	..	..	*Set of* 4	1·40	90

116 Map and German Flag

117 Sweet Thorn

(Des J. van Ellinckhuijzen)

1984 (7 Aug). *Centenary of German Colonisation. T* **116** *and similar horiz designs. Multicoloured. P* 14 × 14½.

431	11 c. Type 116	..	..	25	15
432	25 c. Raising the German flag, 1884	..	50	50
433	30 c. German Protectorate boundary marker	50	60
434	45 c. *Elizabeth* and *Leipzig* (German corvettes)	..	..	1·25	1·60
431/4	..	..	*Set of* 4	2·25	2·50

(Des Eva-Maria Linsmayer)

1984 (22 Nov). *Spring in South West Africa. T* **117** *and similar vert designs. Multicoloured. P* 14.

435	11 c. Type 117	..	..	20	15
436	25 c. Camel Thorn	..	..	40	35
437	30 c. Hook Thorn	..	..	45	35
438	45 c. Candle-pod Acacia	..	..	60	50
435/8	..	..	*Set of* 4	1·50	1·25

NEW INFORMATION

The editor is always interested to correspond with people who have new information that will improve or correct the Catalogue.

118 Head of Ostrich

(Des J. van Ellinckhuijzen)

1985 (15 Mar). *Ostriches. T* **118** *and similar horiz designs. Multicoloured. P* 14.

439	11 c. Type 118	..	..	40	10
440	25 c. Ostrich on eggs	..	..	70	30
441	30 c. Newly-hatched chick and eggs	..	80	50
442	50 c. Mating dance	..	..	1·10	75
439/42	..	..	*Set of* 4	2·75	1·50

119 Kaiserstrasse

(Des A. H. Barrett)

1985 (6 June). *Historic Buildings of Windhoek. T* **119** *and similar horiz designs. P* 14.

443	12 c. black and brown-ochre	..	..	25	10
444	25 c. black and grey-olive	..	..	45	25
445	30 c. black and brown	..	..	45	30
446	50 c. black and yellow-brown	..	90	70
443/6	..	..	*Set of* 4	1·90	1·25

Designs:—25 c. Turnhalle; 30 c. Old Supreme Court Building; 50 c. Railway Station.

120 Zwilling Locomotive

121 Lidumu-dumu (keyboard instrument)

(Des J. van Ellinckhuijzen)

1985 (2 Aug). *Narrow-gauge Railway Locomotives. T* **120** *and similar horiz designs. Multicoloured. P* 14.

447	12 c. Type 120	..	..	30	10
448	25 c. Feldspur side-tank locomotive	..	60	25
449	30 c. Jung and Henschel side-tank locomotive	..	..	70	35
450	50 c. Henschel Hd locomotive	..	90	60
447/50	..	..	*Set of* 4	2·25	1·10

(Des J. van Ellinckhuijzen)

1985 (17 Oct). *Traditional Musical Instruments. T* **121** *and similar horiz designs. Multicoloured. P* 14.

451	12 c. Type 121	..	..	10	10
452	25 c. Ngoma (drum)	..	..	20	20
453	30 c. Okambulumbumbwa (stringed instrument)	..	..	25	25
454	50 c. // Gwashi (stringed instrument)	..	35	35
451/4	..	..	*Set of* 4	80	80

122 Erecting Commemorative Pillar at Cape Cross, 1486

123 Ameib, Erongo Mountains

(Des J. van Ellinckhuijzen)

1986 (24 Jan). *Discoverers of South West Africa* (2nd series). *Diogo Cao. T* **122** *and similar horiz designs. P* 14.

455	12 c. black, brownish grey & deep dull green	35	10
456	20 c. black, brownish grey & pale red-brown	55	25
457	25 c. black, brownish grey and dull blue	..	70	35
458	30 c. black, brownish grey & dull reddish pur	85	60
455/8	..	..	*Set of* 4	2·25	1·10

Designs:—20 c. Diogo Cao's coat of arms; 25 c. Caravel; 30 c. Diogo Cao.

(Des J. van Niekerk)

1986 (24 Apr). *Rock Formations. T* **123** *and similar horiz designs. Multicoloured. P* 14.

459	14 c. Type 123	..	..	60	15
460	20 c. Vingerklip, near Outjo	..	..	70	25
461	25 c. Petrified sand dunes, Kuiseb River	..	85	40
462	30 c. Orgelpfeifen, Twyfelfontein	..	95	55
459/62	..	..	*Set of* 4	2·75	1·25

124 Model wearing Swakara Coat

125 Pirogue, Lake Liambezi

(Des J. van Ellinckhuijzen)

1986 (10 July). *Karakul Industry. T* **124** *and similar vert designs. Multicoloured. P* 14.
463	14 c. Type 124..	35	15
464	20 c. Weaving karakul wool carpet ..	55	30
465	25 c. Flock of karakul ewes on veld..	55	45
466	30 c. Karakul rams	75	60
463/6	.. .. .. Set of 4	2·00	1·40

1986 (6 Nov). *Life in the Caprivi Strip. T* **125** *and similar horiz designs. Multicoloured. P* 14.
467	14 c. Type 125..	50	15
468	20 c. Ploughing with oxen ..	80	65
469	25 c. Settlement in Eastern Caprivi	1·00	90
470	30 c. Map of Caprivi Strip ..	1·25	1·25
467/70	.. .. Set of 4	3·25	2·75

126 "Gobabis Mission Station", 1863

127 *Garreta nitens* (beetle)

1987 (19 Feb). *Paintings by Thomas Baines. T* **126** *and similar horiz designs. Multicoloured. P* 14.
471	14 c. Type 126..	50	15
472	20 c. "Outspan at Koobie", 1861 ..	80	65
473	25 c. "Outspan under Oomahaama Tree", 1862	1·00	90
474	30 c. "Swakop River", 1861 ..	1·25	1·25
471/4	.. .. .. Set of 4	3·25	2·75

(Des E. Holm)

1987 (7 May). *Useful Insects. T* **127** *and similar horiz designs. Multicoloured. P* 14.
475	16 c. Type 127	55	15
476	20 c. *Alcimus stenurus* (fly) ..	85	65
477	25 c. *Anthophora caerulea* (bee) ..	1·10	90
478	30 c. *Hemiempusa capensis* (mantid) ..	1·40	1·25
475/8	.. .. .. Set of 4	3·50	2·75

128 Okaukuejo

(Des J. van Niekerk)

1987 (23 July). *Tourist Camps. T* **128** *and similar horiz designs. Multicoloured. P* 14½ × 14.
479	16 c. Type 128..	55	15
480	20 c. Daan Viljoen	70	60
481	25 c. Ai-Ais	80	75
482	30 c. Hardap	85	85
479/82	.. .. .. Set of 4	2·50	2·10

129 Wreck of *Hope* (whaling schooner), 1804

130 Bartolomeu Dias

(Des Sheila Nowers)

1987 (15 Oct). *Shipwrecks. T* **129** *and similar horiz designs. Multicoloured. P* 14.
483	16 c. Type 129..	60	15
484	30 c. *Tilly,* 1885	1·00	85
485	40 c. *Eduard Bohlen,* 1909 ..	1·25	1·25
486	50 c. *Dunedin Star,* 1942 ..	1·50	1·50
483/6	.. .. .. Set of 4	4·00	3·25

(Des Sheila Nowers)

1988 (7 Jan). *500th Anniv of Discovery of Cape of Good Hope by Bartolomeu Dias. T* **130** *and similar vert designs. Multicoloured. P* 14.
487	16 c. Type 130..	35	15
488	30 c. Caravel	70	55
489	40 c. Map of South West Africa, *c.* 1502 ..	80	70
490	50 c. King João II of Portugal ..	85	75
487/90	.. .. .. Set of 4	2·40	2·00

131 Sossusvlei

(Des J. van Niekerk)

1988 (3 Mar). *Landmarks of South West Africa. T* **131** *and similar horiz designs. Multicoloured. P* 14.
491	16 c. Type 131..	40	15
492	30 c. Sesriem Canyon ..	75	55
493	40 c. Hoaruseb "clay castles" ..	85	70
494	50 c. Hoba meteorite	90	75
491/4	.. .. .. Set of 4	2·50	2·00

MACHINE LABELS. From 30 March 1988 gummed labels in the above design numbered "PT01", ranging in value from 1 c. to 99 r. 99, were available from a machine located at the Windhoek Post Office. During March 1989 three further machines at Ausspanplatz (PT02), Swakopmund (PT03) and Keetmanshoop (PT04) were added.

132 First Postal Agency, Otyimbingue, 1888

133 Herero Chat

(Des H. Pulon)

1988 (7 July). *Centenary of Postal Service in South West Africa. T* **132** *and similar horiz designs. Multicoloured. P* 14.
495	16 c. Type 132	45	15
496	30 c. Post Office, Windhoek, 1904 ..	75	55
497	40 c. Mail-runner and map ..	80	70
498	50 c. Camel mail, 1904 ..	85	75
495/8	.. .. .. Set of 4	2·50	2·00

(Des G. Arnott)

1988 (3 Nov). *Birds of South West Africa. T* **133** *and similar vert designs. Multicoloured. P* 14.
499	16 c. Type 133	40	15
500	30 c. Gray's Lark	70	50
501	40 c. Rüppell's Bustard ..	80	65
502	50 c. Monteiro's Hornbill ..	85	70
499/502	.. .. Set of 4	2·50	1·75

134 Dr. C. H. Hahn and Gross-Barmen Mission

135 Beechcraft "1900"

(Des H. Pulon)

1989 (16 Feb). *Missionaries. T* **134** *and similar horiz designs. Multicoloured. P* 14.
503	16 c. Type 134	40	10
504	30 c. Revd. J. G. Krönlein and Berseba Mission ..	70	50
505	40 c. Revd. F. H. Kleinschmidt and Rehoboth Mission ..	80	65
506	50 c. Revd. J. H. Schmelen and Bethanien Mission ..	85	70
503/6	.. .. Set of 4	2·50	1·75

(Des M. Botha)

1989 (18 May). *75th Anniv of Aviation in South West Africa. T* **135** *and similar horiz designs. Multicoloured. P* 14.
507	18 c. Type 135	30	15
508	30 c. Ryan "Navion" ..	50	40
509	40 c. Junkers "F13" ..	55	45
510	50 c. Pfalz "Otto" biplane ..	60	55
507/10	.. .. Set of 4	1·75	1·40

136 Barchan Dunes

(Des A. H. Barrett)

1989 (14 Aug). *Namib Desert Sand Dunes. T* **136** *and similar horiz designs. Multicoloured. P* 14.
511	18 c. Barchan dunes ..	30	15
512	30 c. Star dunes (36×20 *mm*) ..	50	40
513	40 c. Transverse dunes ..	65	60
514	50 c. Crescentic dunes (36×20 *mm*) ..	80	80
511/14	.. .. Set of 4	2·00	1·75

137 Ballot Box and Outline Map of South West Africa

1989 (24 Aug). *South West Africa Constitutional Election. P* 14.
515	137 18 c. purple-brown and salmon ..	30	15
516	35 c. deep grey-blue and pale emerald	50	40
517	45 c. plum and lemon ..	70	60
518	60 c. dull green and deep yellow-ochre	85	80
515/18	.. .. Set of 4	2·10	1·75

138 Gypsum

139 Oranjemund Alluvial Diamond Field

(Des J. van Niekerk)

1989 (16 Nov)–**90**. *Minerals. T* **138/9** *and similar multicoloured designs. Phosphorised paper* (25 *c.*) *or chalk-surfaced paper* (30, 35, 50 *c.*, 1 *r.*). *P* 14.
519	1 c. Type 138 ..	10	10
520	2 c. Fluorite ..	10	10
521	5 c. Mimetite ..	10	10
522	7 c. Cuprite ..	10	10
523	10 c. Azurite ..	10	10
524	18 c. Boltwoodite (inscr "K (H3O) (UO2) (SiO4)") ..	20	10
	a. Formula corrected to "K2 (UO2) 2 (SiO3) 2 (OH) 2 5 H2O" (25.10.90)	2·00	1·50
525	20 c. Dioptase ..	20	15
526	25 c. Type 139 ..	25	15
527	30 c. Tsumeb lead and copper complex ..	35	20
528	35 c. Rosh Pinah zinc mine ..	35	20
529	40 c. Diamonds ..	50	30
530	45 c. Wulfenite ..	50	30
531	50 c. Uis tin mine ..	60	30
532	1 r. Rössing uranium mine ..	1·10	80
533	2 r. Gold ..	1·50	1·50
519/33	.. .. Set of 15	5·50	4·00

The 1, 2, 5, 7, 10, 18, 20, 40, 45 c. and 2 r. are vertical as T **138**, and the 25, 30, 35, 50 c. and 1 r. horizontal as T **139**.

140 Arrow Poison

(Des Eva-Maria Linsmayer)

1990 (1 Feb). *Flora. T* **140** *and similar vert designs. Multicoloured. P* 14.
534	18 c. Type 140 ..	40	10
535	35 c. Baobab flower ..	75	40
536	45 c. Sausage Tree flowers ..	85	50
537	60 c. Devil's Claw ..	1·10	90
534/7	.. .. Set of 4	2·75	1·75

South West Africa became independent on 21 March 1990 and was renamed Namibia.

NAMIBIA

PRINTERS. The following stamps were printed in lithography by the Government Printer, Pretoria, South Africa.

141 Pres. Sam Nujoma, Map of Namibia and National Flag

142 Fish River Canyon

(Des T. Marais)

1990 (21 Mar). *Independence. T 141 and similar multicoloured designs. P 14.*

538	18 c. Type 141		30	15
539	45 c. Hands releasing dove and map of Namibia (*vert*)		60	60
540	60 c. National flag and map of Africa		90	1·00
538/40		Set of 3	1·60	1·60

(Des J. van Ellinckhuijzen)

1990 (26 Apr). *Namibia Landscapes. T 142 and similar horiz designs. Multicoloured. P 14.*

541	18 c. Type 142		20	20
542	35 c. Quiver-tree forest, Keetmanshoop		35	35
543	45 c. Tsaris Mountains		40	40
544	60 c. Dolerite boulders, Keetmanshoop		50	50
541/4		Set of 4	1·25	1·25

143 Stores on Kaiser Street, c. 1899

144 Maizefields

(Des J. van Ellinckhuijzen)

1990 (26 July). *Centenary of Windhoek. T 143 and similar horiz designs. Multicoloured. P 14.*

545	18 c. Type 143		15	15
546	35 c. Kaiser Street, 1990		25	25
547	45 c. City Hall, 1914		30	30
548	60 c. City Hall, 1990		40	40
545/8		Set of 4	1·00	1·00

1990 (11 Oct). *Farming. T 144 and similar horiz designs. Multicoloured. P 14.*

549	20 c. Type 144		15	15
550	35 c. Sanga bull		25	25
551	50 c. Damara ram		35	35
552	65 c. Irrigation in Okavango		45	45
549/52		Set of 4	1·10	1·10

145 Gypsum

146 Radiosonde Weather Balloon

(Des J. van Niekerk)

1991 (2 Jan–14 June). *Minerals. Designs as Nos. 519/21 and 523/33, some with values changed, and new design (5 r.), inscr "Namibia" as T 145. Multicoloured. Chalk-surfaced paper (25, 30, 35, 50 c., 1 r.). P 14.*

553	1 c. Type 145		10	10
554	2 c. Fluorite		10	10
555	5 c. Mimetite		10	10
556	10 c. Azurite		10	10
557	20 c. Dioptase		10	10
558	25 c. Type 139		10	15
	a. Ordinary paper (14 June)		10	15
559	30 c. Tsumeb lead and copper complex		15	20
560	35 c. Rosh Pinah zinc mine		15	20
561	40 c. Diamonds		20	25
562	50 c. Uis tin mine		20	25
563	65 c. Boltwoodite		30	35
564	1 r. Rössing uranium mine		45	50
565	1 r. 50, Wulfenite		65	70
566	2 r. Gold		85	90
567	5 r. Willemite (vert as T 145)		2·25	2·40
553/67		Set of 15	5·00	5·50

Printings of the 5 c. and 10 c. in 1992 were on phosphorescent paper.

(Des L. Kriedemann)

1991 (1 Feb). *Centenary of Weather Service. T 146 and similar horiz designs. Multicoloured. P 14.*

568	20 c. Type 146		20	20
569	35 c. Sunshine recorder		30	30
570	50 c. Measuring equipment		40	40
571	65 c. Meteorological station, Gobabeb		50	50
568/71		Set of 4	1·25	1·25

147 Herd of Zebras

148 Karas Mountains

1991 (18 Apr). *Endangered Species. Mountain Zebra. T 147 and similar horiz designs. Multicoloured. P 14.*

572	20 c. Type 147		35	35
573	25 c. Mare and foal		40	40
574	45 c. Zebras and foal		70	70
575	60 c. Two zebras		90	90
572/5		Set of 4	2·10	2·10

(Des A. H. Barrett)

1991 (18 July). *Mountains of Namibia. T 148 and similar horiz designs. Multicoloured. P 14.*

576	20 c. Type 148		30	20
577	25 c. Gamsberg Mountains		35	30
578	45 c. Mount Brukkaros		60	55
579	60 c. Erongo Mountains		75	65
576/9		Set of 4	1·75	1·50

149 Bernabe de la Bat Camp

150 Artist's Pallet

(Des J. van Niekerk)

1991 (24 Oct). *Tourist Camps. T 149 and similar horiz designs. Multicoloured. P 14.*

580	20 c. Type 149		30	30
581	25 c. Von Bach Dam Recreation Resort		35	35
582	45 c. Gross Barmen Hot Springs		55	55
583	60 c. Namutoni Rest Camp		70	70
580/3		Set of 4	1·75	1·75

(Des H. Pulon)

1992 (30 Jan). *21st Anniv of Windhoek Conservatoire. T 150 and similar horiz designs. Multicoloured. P 14.*

584	20 c. Type 150		15	15
585	25 c. French horn and cello		15	15
586	45 c. Theatrical masks		30	30
587	60 c. Ballet dancers		45	45
584/7		Set of 4	95	95

151 Blue Kurper

152 Old Jetty

(Des B. Jackson)

1992 (16 Apr). *Freshwater Angling. T 151 and similar horiz designs. Multicoloured. P 14.*

588	20 c. Type 151		20	20
589	25 c. Largemouthed Yellow Fish		20	20
590	45 c. Carp		40	40
591	60 c. Sharptoothed Catfish		60	60
588/91		Set of 4	1·25	1·25

1992 (2 July). *Centenary of Swakopmund. T 152 and similar horiz designs. Multicoloured. P 14.*

592	20 c. Type 152		20	20
593	25 c. Recreation centre		20	20
594	45 c. State House and lighthouse		40	40
595	60 c. Sea front		55	55
592/5		Set of 4	1·25	1·25
MS596	118×93 mm. Nos. 592/5		1·25	1·40

153 Running

154 Wrapping English Cucumbers

(Des B. Jackson)

1992 (24 July). *Olympic Games, Barcelona. T 153 and similar horiz designs. Multicoloured. P 14.*

597	20 c. Type 153		20	20
598	25 c. Map of Namibia, Namibian flag and Olympic rings		20	20
599	45 c. Swimming		40	40
600	60 c. Olympic Stadium, Barcelona		55	55
597/600		Set of 4	1·25	1·25
MS601	115×75 mm. Nos. 597/600		1·25	1·40

1992 (10 Sept). *Integration of the Disabled. T 154 and similar horiz designs. Multicoloured. P 14.*

602	20 c. Type 154		15	15
603	25 c. Weaving mats		15	15
604	45 c. Spinning thread		30	30
605	60 c. Preparing pot plants		40	50
602/5		Set of 4	90	1·00

155 Elephants in Desert

(Des D. Murphy)

1993 (25 Feb). *Namibia Nature Foundation. Rare and Endangered Species. T 155 and similar horiz designs. Multicoloured. P 14.*

606	20 c. Type 155		15	15
607	25 c. Sitatunga in swamp		15	15
608	45 c. Black Rhinoceros		30	30
609	60 c. Hunting Dogs		40	40
606/9		Set of 4	90	1·00
MS610	217×59 mm. Nos. 606/9		1·00	1·10

POSTAGE DUE STAMPS

PRICES for Nos. D1/39 are for unused horizontal pairs, used horizontal pairs and used singles.

1923 (1 Jan–July). *Optd with T 1 and 2 alternately.*

(a) Setting I (14 mm between lines of overprint) (i) On Nos. D5/6 of Transvaal

D1	5d. black and violet		4·00	32·00	9·00
	a. "Wes" for "West" (R. 8/6, 10/2 left pane)	..	£120		
	b. "Afrika" without stop (R. 6/1)	80·00			
D2	6d. black and red-brown ..		17·00	35·00	9·50
	a. "Wes" for "West" (R. 10/2)	£225			
	b. "Afrika" without stop (R. 6/1, 7/2) ..	£130			

(ii) On Nos. D3/4 and D6 of South Africa (De La Rue printing)

D3	2d. black and violet	..	16·00	32·00	9·00
	a. "Wes" for "West" (R. 10/2)	£140	£170		
	b. "Afrika" without stop (R. 6/1, 7/2) ..	£140			
D4	3d. black and blue	..	8·00	32·00	9·00
	a. "Wes" for "West" (R. 10/2)	£100			
D5	6d. black and slate (20 Apr)		23·00	40·00	11·00
	a. "Wes" for "West" (R. 8/6)	£140			

(iii) On Nos. D9/10, D11 and D14 of South Africa (Pretoria printings)

D6	½d. black and green (p 14)	..	4·00	19·00	5·00
	a. Opt inverted	£300			
	b. Opt double ..	£550	£600		
	c. "Wes" for "West" (R. 10/2)	70·00			
	d. "Afrika" without stop (R. 6/1, 7/2)	70·00			
D7	1d. black and rose (roul) ..		6·50	19·00	5·00
	a. "Wes" for "West" (R. 10/2)	80·00			
	b. "Afrika" without stop (R. 6/1)	80·00			
	c. Imperf between (horiz pair) ..	£900			
D8	1½d. black and yellow-brown (roul)	1·00	9·50	2·50	
	a. "Wes" for "West" (R. 8/6, 10/2)	65·00			
	b. "Afrika" without stop (R. 6/1)	65·00			
D9	2d. black and violet (p 14) (21 June)	2·00	17·00	4·50	
	a. "Wes" for "West" (R. 8/6)	80·00			
	b. "Afrika" without stop (R. 6/1)	80·00			

Nos. D1/9 were initially overprinted as separate panes of 60, but some values were later done as double panes of 120.

A variety of Nos. D1, D4/5 and D9 with 15 mm between the lines of overprint occurs on four positions in each pane from some printings.

(b) Setting II (10 mm between lines of overprint). (i) On No. D5 of Transvaal

D10	5d. black and violet (20 Apr)	..	55·00	£110	

(ii) On Nos. D3/4 of South Africa (De La Rue printing)

D11	2d. black and violet (20 Apr)	..	12·00	27·00	8·00
	a. "Afrika" without stop (R.6/1)	£120			
D12	3d. black and blue (20 Apr)	..	7·00	21·00	5·50
	a. "Afrika" without stop (R.6/1)	75·00			

(iii) On No. D9 of South Africa (Pretoria printing). Roul

D13	1d. black and rose (July)	..	£8000	— £1500

1923 (30 July)–**26**. *Optd as T 3 ("Zuidwest" in one word without hyphen) and 4.*

(a) Setting III ("South West" 14 mm long, "Zuidwest" 11 mm long and 14 mm between lines of overprint).

(i) On No. D6 of Transvaal

D14	6d. black and red-brown ..		19·00	60·00	19·00

(ii) On Nos. D9 and D11/12 of South Africa (Pretoria printing)

D15	½d. black and green (p 14)	..	6·50	18·00	4·25
D16	1d. black and rose (roul)	..	2·00	15·00	3·75
D17	1d. black and rose (p 14) (2.8.23)	6·50	17·00	4·00	

(b) Setting IV ("South West" 16 mm long, "Zuidwest" 12 mm long and 14 mm between lines of overprint).

(i) On No. D5 of Transvaal

D17a	5d. black and violet (1.7.24)	..	£400	£650

(ii) On Nos. D11/12 and D16 of South Africa (Pretoria printing). P 14

D18	½d. black and green (1.7.24)	..	3·50	17·00	4·00
D19	1d. black and rose (1.7.24)	..	5·00	18·00	4·25
D20	6d. black and slate (1.7.24)	..	2·25	28·00	8·50
	a. "Africa" without stop (R.9/5)	£100			

(c) Setting V (12 mm between lines of overprint).

(i) On No. D5 of Transvaal

D21	5d. black and violet (6.8.24)	..	2·50	24·00	7·50

(ii) On No. D4 of South Africa (De La Rue printing)

D22	3d. black and blue (6.8.24)	..	10·00	35·00	9·50

(iii) On Nos. D11 and D13 of South Africa (Pretoria printing). P 14

D23	½d. black and green (6.8.24)	..	2·00	20·00	5·00
D24	1½d. black & yellow-brown (6.8.24)	4·50	20·00	5·00	

(d) Setting VI (9½ mm between lines of overprint).

(i) On No. D5 of Transvaal

D25	5d. black and violet (7.9.24)	..	2·25	12·00	3·00
	a. "Africa" without stop (R. 9/5)	60·00			

(ii) On No. D4 of South Africa (De La Rue printing)

D26	3d. black and blue (3.2.26)	..	6·00	32·00	9·00

(iii) On Nos. D11/16 of South Africa (Pretoria printing). P 14

D27	½d. black and green (1.3.26)	..	4·50	22·00	5·50
D28	1d. black and rose (16.3.25)	..	1·40	6·50	1·50
	a. "Africa" without stop (R. 9/5 right pane) ..	65·00			
D29	1½d. black & yellow-brown (1.10.26)	2·50	19·00	4·75	
	a. "Africa" without stop (R. 9/5 right pane) ..	65·00			
D30	2d. black and violet (7.9.24)	..	2·50	11·00	2·75
	a. "Africa" without stop (R. 9/5 right pane) ..	55·00			
D31	3d. black and blue (6.5.26)	..	2·75	12·00	3·00
	a. "Africa" without stop (R. 9/5 right pane) ..	60·00			
D32	6d. black and slate (1.10.26)	..	8·50	24·00	12·00
	a. "Africa" without stop (R. 9/5 right pane) ..	£110			
D27/32	.. ..	Set of 6	20·00	£100	27·00

For Setting VI the overprint was applied to sheets of 120 (2 panes of 60) of the 1d., 3d. and 6d., and to individual panes of 60 for the other values. The two measurements of "South West", as detailed under No. 40, also occur on the postage dues. Nos. D25 and D31/2 show 16 mm long, No. 27 16½ mm long and the other stamps can be found with either measurement. In addition to the complete panes the 16½ mm long "South West" also occurs on R.2/4 in the 16 mm left pane for Nos. D28 and D30/2.

Suidwes	**South West**
(D 1)	(D 2)

Afrika.	**Africa.**
(D 1)	(D 2)

1927 (14 May–27 Sept). *Optd as Types D 1 and D 2, alternately, 12 mm between lines of overprint. (a) On No. D5 of Transvaal.*

D33	5d. black and violet (27 Sept)	..	17·00	60·00	19·00

(b) On Nos. D13/16 of South Africa (Pretoria printing). P 14

D34	1½d. black and yellow-brown		70	11·00	3·00
D35	2d. black and pale violet (27 Sept)	2·75	11·00	2·50	
	a. Black and deep violet ..	3·25	12·00	2·75	
D37	3d. black and blue (27 Sept)	..	10·00	35·00	9·50
D38	6d. black and slate (27 Sept)	..	6·00	25·00	7·00

(c) On No. D18 of South Africa (Pretoria printing). P 14

D39	1d. black and carmine	..	1·00	8·50	2·25
D33/9	..	Set of 6	32·00	£130	38·00

No. D33 was overprinted in panes of 60 and the remainder as complete sheets of 120.

Examples of all values can be found with very small or very faint stops from various positions in the sheet.

1928–29. *Optd with T 10. (a) On Nos. D15/16 of South Africa*

				Un Single	Us Single
D40	3d. black and blue	..		50	11·00
	a. Without stop after "A" (R.3/6)	25·00			
D41	6d. black and slate	..		8·00	22·00
	a. Without stop after "A" (R.3/6)	£120			

(b) On Nos. D17/21 of South Africa

D42	½d. black and green	..		40	7·00
D43	1d. black and carmine	..		40	3·25
	a. Without stop after "A" (R.3/6)	40·00			
D44	2d. black and mauve	..		40	3·50
	a. Without stop after "A" (R.3/6)	55·00			
D45	3d. black and blue	..		1·75	18·00
D46	6d. black and slate	..		1·00	18·00
	a. Without stop after "A" (R.3/6)	40·00			
D42/6	.. ..	Set of 5	3·50	45·00	

D 3	D 4	D 5

(Litho B.W.)

1931 (23 Feb). *Inscribed bilingually. W 9 of South Africa. P 12.*

D47	D 3	½d. black and green	..	60	6·00
D48		1d. black and scarlet	..	60	1·25
D49		2d. black and violet	..	70	2·50
D50		3d. black and blue	..	2·00	14·00
D51		6d. black and slate	..	8·00	22·00
D47/51		Set of 5		10·50	40·00

PRINTER. The following issues have been printed by the South African Government Printer, Pretoria.

1959 (18 May). *Centre typo; frame roto. W 9 of South Africa. P 15 × 14.*

D52	D 4	1d. black and scarlet	..	1·25	10·00
D53		2d. black and reddish violet ..		1·25	11·00
D54		3d. black and blue	..	1·25	12·00
D52/4 ..		Set of 3		3·25	30·00

1960 (Dec). *As Nos. D52 and D54 but W 102 of South Africa.*

D55	1d. black and scarlet..	..		2·50	4·50
D56	3d. black and blue	..		2·50	6·50

1961 (14 Feb). *As Nos. D52 etc, but whole stamp roto, and value in cents. W 102 of South Africa.*

D57	1 c. black and blue-green	..		40	3·00
D58	2 c. black and scarlet..	..		40	3·00
D59	4 c. black and reddish violet ..		50	3·00	
D60	5 c. black and light blue	..		80	3·50
D61	6 c. black and green	..		80	5·00
D62	10 c. black and yellow ..			1·75	6·50
D57/62		Set of 6		4·25	22·00

1972 (22 Mar). *W 127 (sideways tête-bêche). Phosphorised chalk-surfaced paper. P 14 × 13½.*

D63	D 5	1 c. emerald	..	75	3·75
D64		8 c. ultramarine	..	3·00	7·00

The use of Postage Due stamps ceased in April 1975.

NEW INFORMATION

The editor is always interested to correspond with people who have new information that will improve or correct the Catalogue.

OFFICIAL STAMPS

OFFICIAL	**OFFISIEEL**
South West	Africa.
Suidwes	Afrika.
(O 1)	(O 2)

1926 (Dec). *Nos. 30, 31, 6 and 32 of South Africa optd with Type O·1 on English stamp and O 2 on Afrikaans stamp alternately.*

				Un pair	Us pair	Us single
O1	½d. black and green..	..		65·00	£150	30·00
O2	1d. black and carmine	..		65·00	£150	30·00
O3	2d. dull purple	..		£150	£225	45·00
O4	6d. green and orange	..		85·00	£140	30·00
O1/4		Set of 4		£325	£600	£120

OFFICIAL	**OFFISIEEL**
S.W.A.	**S.W.A.**
(O 3)	(O 4)

1929 (May). *Nos. 30, 31, 32 and 34 of South Africa optd with Type O 3 on English stamp and O 4 on Afrikaans stamp.*

O5	½d. black and green		1·00	11·00	2·75
O6	1d. black and carmine		1·00	11·00	2·75
O7	2d. grey and purple		1·50	13·00	3·25
	a. Pair, stamp without stop after "OFFICIAL"		5·00	35·00	
	b. Pair, stamp without stop after "OFFISIEEL"		5·00	35·00	
	c. Pair, comprising a and b		16·00	75·00	
O8	6d. green and orange		3·00	14·00	3·50
O5/8		Set of 4	6·00	45·00	11·00

Types O 3 and O 4 are normally spaced 17 mm between lines on all except the 2d. value, which is spaced 13 mm.

Except on No. O7, the words "OFFICIAL" or "OFFISIEEL" normally have no stops after them.

OFFICIAL	**OFFISIEEL**
S.W.A.	**S.W.A.**
(O 5)	(O 6)

OFFICIAL.	**OFFISIEEL.**
S.W.A.	**S.W.A.**
(O 7)	(O 8)

1929 (Aug). *Nos. 30, 31 and 32 of South Africa optd with Types O 5 and O 6, and No. 34 with Types O 7 and O 8, languages to correspond.*

O 9	½d. black and green		65	11·00	2·75
O10	1d. black and carmine		75	11·00	2·75
O11	2d. grey and purple		90	13·00	3·25
	a. Pair, one stamp without stop after "OFFICIAL"		3·75	35·00	
	b. Pair, one stamp without stop after "OFFISIEEL"		3·75	35·00	
	c. Pair, comprising a and b		18·00	75·00	
O12	6d. green and orange		3·00	27·00	6·50
O9/12		Set of 4	4·75	55·00	13·50

OFFICIAL	**OFFISIEEL**
(O 9)	(O 10)

1931. *English stamp optd with Type O 9 and Afrikaans stamp with Type O 10 in red.*

O13	12	½d. black and emerald	..	7·00	15·00	3·50
O14	13	1d. indigo and scarlet ..	..	75	15·00	3·50
O15	14	2d. blue and brown	..	70	10·00	2·25
O16	17	6d. blue and brown	..	2·25	14·00	3·25
O13/16		Set of 4		9·75	48·00	11·50

OFFICIAL	**OFFISIEEL**
(O 11)	(O 12)

1938 (1 July). *English stamp optd with Type O 11 and Afrikaans with Type O 12 in red.*

O17	27	1½d. purple-brown	..	23·00	32·00	5·50

OFFICIAL	**OFFISIEEL**
(O 13)	(O 14)

1945–50. *English stamp optd with Type O 13, and Afrikaans stamp with Type O 14 in red.*

O18	12	½d. black and emerald ..	..	7·00	20·00	4·25
O19	13	1d. indigo and scarlet (1950)	..	2·25	13·00	3·00
		a. Opt double	..	£400		
O20	27	1½d. purple-brown	..	28·00	26·00	4·75
O21	14	2d. blue and brown (1947?)	..	£425	£600	£100
O22	17	6d. blue and brown	..	7·00	25·00	4·75
O18/20, O22		Set of 4		40·00	75·00	15·00

OFFICIAL   OFFISIEEL
(O 15)   (O 16)

1951 (16 Nov)–**52.** *English stamp optd with Type O 15 and Afrikaans stamp with Type O 16, in red.*

O23	12	½d. black and emerald (1952)	10·00	14·00	3·75
O24	13	1d. indigo and scarlet	1·50	10·00	1·75
		a. Opts transposed	55·00	80·00	
O25	27	1½d. purple-brown	22·00	20·00	4·50
		a. Opts transposed	65·00	80·00	
O26	14	2d. blue and brown	1·00	13·00	3·25
		a. Opts transposed	35·00	85·00	
O27	17	6d. blue and brown	2·75	30·00	7·00
		a. Opts transposed	22·00	85·00	
O23/7		*Set of 5*	32·00	80·00	18·00

The above errors refer to stamps with the English overprint on Afrikaans stamp and *vice versa*.

The use of official stamps ceased in January 1955.

Natal
see South Africa

Nauru

Stamps of MARSHALL ISLANDS were used in Nauru from the opening of the German Colonial Post Office on 14 July 1908 until 8 September 1914.

Following the occupation by Australian forces the "N.W. PACIFIC ISLANDS" overprints on Australia (see NEW GUINEA) were used during the early months of 1916.

PRICES FOR STAMPS ON COVER TO 1945
Nos. 1/12	*from* × 10
Nos. 13/16	*from* × 3
Nos. 17/25	—
Nos. 26/39	*from* × 6
Nos. 40/3	*from* × 10
Nos. 44/7	*from* × 15

BRITISH MANDATE

NAURU (1)   **NAURU** (2)   **NAURU** (3)

1916 (2 Sept)–**23.** *Stamps of Great Britain* (1912–22) *overprinted at Somerset House.*

(a) With T 1 (12½ *mm long) at foot*

1	½d. green		30	3·50
	a. "NAUP.U"		£275	
	b. Double opt, one albino		60·00	
2	1d. bright scarlet		80	2·75
	a. "NAUP.U"		£450	
2b	1d. carmine-red		10·00	
	bb. Double opt, one albino		£200	
3	1½d. red-brown (1923)		55·00	80·00
4	2d. orange (Die I)		1·75	8·50
	a. "NAUP.U"		£300	£325
	b. Double opt, one albino		£100	
5	2d. orange (Die II) (1923)		70·00	£100
6	2½d. blue		2·75	5·00
	a. "NAUP.U"		£375	£400
	b. Double opt, one albino		£200	
7	3d. bluish violet		2·00	3·50
	a. NAUP.U"		£375	£400
	b. Double opt, one albino		£200	
8	4d. slate-green		2·00	8·00
	a. "NAUP.U"		£500	£550
	b. Double opt, one albino		£200	
9	5d. yellow-brown		2·25	8·50
	a. "NAUP.U"		£650	
	b. Double opt, one albino		£140	
10	6d. purple (*chalk-surfaced paper*)		3·25	10·00
	a. "NAUP.U"		£550	
	b. Double opt, one albino		£225	
11	9d. agate		8·50	19·00
	a. Double opt, one albino		£225	
12	1s. bistre-brown (Optd S. £130)		7·00	19·00
	a. Double opt, one albino		£250	
1/12	*Set of 11*		75·00	£140

(b) With T 2 (13½ *mm long) at centre* (1923)

13	½d. green		4·50	55·00
14	1d. scarlet		24·00	45·00
15	1½d. red-brown		28·00	55·00
	a. Double opt, one albino		£140	
16	2d. orange (Die II)		45·00	80·00
13/16	*Set of 4*		90·00	£200

The "NAUP.U" errors occur on R.6/2 from Control I 16 only. The ink used on this batch of overprints was shiny jet-black.

There is a constant variety consisting of short left stroke to "N" which occurs on Nos. 1, 2, 2b, 4 (£30 *each*); 3 (£175); 5 (£200); 6,7 (£40 *each*); 8, 9, 10 (£60 *each*); 11, 12 (£75 *each*). All unused prices.

(c) With T 3. (i) *Waterlow printing*

17	5s. rose-carmine		£2500	£2000
18	10s. indigo-blue (R.) (Optd S. £1400)		£6000	£5000
	a. Double opt, one albino		£8000	£8000

(ii) *De La Rue printing*

19	2s. 6d. deep brown (Optd S. £250)		£550	£650
	a. Double opt, one albino		£1200	
	b. Treble opt, two albino		£1300	
20	2s. 6d. yellow-brown		65·00	90·00
21	2s. 6d. pale brown (worn plate) (Optd S. £250)		70·00	85·00
	a. Re-entry			
22	5s. bright carmine (*shades*) (Optd S. £250)	£100	£140
	a. Treble opt, two albino		£550	
23	10s. pale blue (R.)		£250	£325
	a. Treble opt. (Blk. + R. + albino)		£500	£550
23b	10s. deep bright blue (R.)		£500	£550

(iii) *Bradbury, Wilkinson printing* (1919)

24	2s. 6d. chocolate-brown		75·00	£100
	a. Major re-entry			
	b. Double opt, one albino		£325	
25	2s. 6d. pale brown		60·00	85·00
	a. Double opt, one albino		£300	

AUSTRALIAN MANDATE

4 *Century* (freighter)

(Des R. A. Harrison. Eng T. S. Harrison. Recess Note Printing Branch of the Treasury, Melbourne and from 1926 by the Commonwealth Bank of Australia)

1924–48. *T 4. No wmk. P 11.*
  I. Rough surfaced, greyish paper (1924–34).
  II. Shiny surfaced, white paper (1937–48).

			I		II	
26	½d. chestnut		60	2·75	7·50	13·00
	a. Perf 14 (1947)		†		1·25	6·50
27	1d. green		1·50	2·75	2·50	3·00
28	1½d. scarlet		2·25	3·50	90	1·50
29	2d. orange		2·25	6·50	1·50	7·50
30	2½d. slate-blue		4·00	13·00	†	
30a	2½d. greenish blue (1934)		4·00	11·00	†	
30b	2½d. dull blue (1948)		†		1·25	3·50
	ba. Imperf between (vert pair)		†		£4000	£4000
	bb. Imperf between (horiz pair)		†		£4000	£4000
31	3d. pale blue		2·50	7·50	†	
31a	3d. greenish grey (1947)		†		1·50	6·50
32	4d. olive-green		3·75	9·00	3·50	6·50
33	5d. brown		2·50	6·00	3·25	3·75
34	6d. dull violet		3·00	11·00	3·00	3·50
35	9d. olive-brown		5·50	17·00	7·50	16·00
36	1s. brown-lake		6·00	13·00	5·00	2·75
37	2s. 6d. grey-green		25·00	35·00	24·00	28·00
38	5s. claret		50·00	75·00	35·00	48·00
39	10s. yellow		90·00	£110	85·00	85·00
26I/39I		*Set of 14*	£180	£275	†	
26II/39II		*Set of 15*	†		£160	£190

HIS MAJESTY'S JUBILEE.

1910 - 1935

(5)   6

1935 (12 July). *Silver Jubilee. T 4* (*shiny surfaced, white paper*) *optd with T 5.*

40	1½d. scarlet		60	80
41	2d. orange		1·00	4·00
42	2½d. dull blue		1·50	1·50
43	1s. brown-lake		4·00	3·50
40/3		*Set of 4*	6·50	9·00

(Recess John Ash, Melbourne)

1937 (10 May). *Coronation. P 11.*

44	6	1½d. scarlet		45	50
45		2d. orange		45	90
46		2½d. blue		45	30
47		1s. purple		85	75
44/7			*Set of 4*	2·00	2·25

7 Nauruan Netting Fish

8 Anibare Bay

15 Map of Nauru

(Recess Note Printing Branch, Commonwealth Bank, Melbourne, and from 1960 by Note Ptg Branch, Reserve Bank of Australia, Melbourne)

1954 (6 Feb)–**65.** *T 7/8, 15 and similar designs. Toned paper. P 13½×14½ (horiz) or 14½×13½ (vert).*

48	½d. deep violet			20	20
	a. *Violet* (8.5.61)			20	30
49	1d. bluish green			30	30
	a. *Emerald-green* (8.5.61)			20	30
	b. *Deep green* (1965)			50	40
50	3½d. scarlet			1·50	30
	a. *Vermilion* (1958)			2·25	60
51	4d. grey-blue			1·50	80
	a. *Deep blue* (1958)			3·25	1·75
52	6d. orange			70	20
53	9d. claret			60	20
54	1s. deep purple			30	20
55	2s. 6d. deep green			2·50	60
56	5s. magenta			8·00	2·00
48/56		*Set of 9*		14·00	4·25

Designs: *Horiz*—3½d. Loading phosphate from cantilever; 4d. Great Frigate Bird; 6d. Nauruan canoe; 9d. Domaneab (meeting-house); 2s. 6d. Buada lagoon. *Vert*—1s. Palm trees. Nos. 48a, 49a/b, 50a and 51a are on white paper.

16 Micronesian Pigeon   **17** Poison Nut

20 Capparis   **21** White Tern

(Recess (10d., 2s. 3d.) or photo (others) Note Ptg Branch, Reserve Bank of Australia, Melbourne)

1963–65. *T 16/17, 20/1 and similar designs. P 13½ × 13 (5d.), 13 × 13½ (8d.), 14 × 13½ (10d.), 15 × 14½ (1s. 3d.) or 13½ (others).*

57	2d. black, blue, red-brn & orge-yell (3.5.65)		1·00	1·75
58	3d. multicoloured (16.4.64)		75	35
59	5d. multicoloured (22.4.63)		75	75
60	8d. black and green (1.7.63)		2·50	80
61	10d. black (16.4.64)		50	30
62	1s. 3d. blue, black & yellow-green (3.5.65)		3·50	2·00
63	2s. 3d. ultramarine (16.4.64)		3·25	55
64	3s. 3d. multicoloured (3.5.65)		4·50	2·50
57/64		*Set of 8*	15·00	8·00

Designs: *Vert*—5d. "Iyo" (*calophyllum*). *Horiz*—8d. Black Lizard; 2s. 3d. Coral pinnacles; 3s. 3d. Finsch's Reed Warbler.

22 "Simpson and his Donkey"

(Des C. Andrew (after statue, Shrine of Remembrance, Melbourne. Photo Note Ptg Branch, Reserve Bank of Australia, Melbourne)

1965 (14 Apr). *50th Anniv of Gallipoli Landing. P 13½.*

65	22	5d. sepia, black and emerald		15	10

(New Currency. 100 cents = $1 Australian)

24 Anibare Bay   **25** "Iyo" (*calophyllum*)

(Recess (1, 2, 3, 5, 8, 19, 25 c. and $1) or photo (others))

1966 (14 Feb–25 May). *Decimal Currency. Various stamps with values in cents and dollars as T 24/5 and some colours changed. Recess printed stamps on helecon paper.*

66	24	1 c. deep blue		15	10
67	7	2 c. brown-purple (25 May)		15	10
68	—	3 c. bluish green (as 3½d.) (25 May)		30	40
69	25	4 c. multicoloured		25	10
70	—	5 c. deep ultramarine (as 1s.) (25 May)		25	40
71	—	7 c. black and chestnut (as 8d.)		30	10
72	20	8 c. olive-green		30	10
73	—	10 c. red (as 4d.)		40	10

74	21	15 c. blue, black & yellow-green (25 May)		80	1·25
75	–	25 c. deep brown (as 2s. 3d.) (25 May)		45	40
76	17	30 c. multicoloured		70	30
77	–	35 c. multicoloured (as 3s. 3d.) (25 May)		1·25	35
78	16	50 c. multicoloured		2·50	80
79	–	$1 magenta (as 5s.)		2·00	1·00
66/79			Set of 14	8·50	5·00

The 25 c. is as No. 63, but larger, 27½ × 24½ mm.

REPUBLIC

Nauru became independent on 31 January 1968 and was later admitted into special membership of the Commonwealth.

REPUBLIC OF NAURU
(26)

1968 (31 Jan–15 May). *Nos. 66/79 optd with T 26.*

80	24	1 c. deep blue (R.)		10	30
81	7	2 c. brown-purple		10	10
82	–	3 c. bluish green		15	10
83	25	4 c. multicoloured (15.5.68)		15	10
84	–	5 c. deep ultramarine (R.)		15	10
85	–	7 c. black and chestnut (R.) (15.5.68)		25	10
86	20	8 c. olive-green (R.)		25	10
87	–	10 c. red		30	15
88	21	15 c. blue, black and yellow-green		2·75	2·50
89	–	25 c. deep brown (R.)		30	15
90	17	30 c. multicoloured (15.5.68)		55	15
91	–	35 c. multicoloured (15.5.68)		1·25	30
92	16	50 c. multicoloured		2·00	50
93	–	$1 magenta		1·25	75
80/93			Set of 14	8·00	4·50

27 "Towards the Sunrise"   28 Planting Seedling, and Map

(Des H. Fallu (5 c.), Note Ptg Branch (10 c.). Photo Note Ptg Branch, Reserve Bank of Australia, Melbourne)

1968 (11 Sept). *Independence. P* 13½.

94	27	5 c. black, slate-lilac, orange-yellow and yellow-green		10	10
95	28	10 c. black, yellow-green and new blue		10	10

29 Flag of Independent Nauru   30 Island, "C" and Stars

(Des J. Mason. Photo Note Ptg Branch, Reserve Bank of Australia, Melbourne)

1969 (31 Jan). *P* 13½.

96	29	15 c. yellow, orange and royal blue		15	15

This is a definitive issue which was put on sale on the first anniversary of Independence.

(Des R. Brooks, Litho Format)

1972 (7 Feb). *25th Anniv of South Pacific Commission. P* 14½ × 14.

97	30	25 c. multicoloured		30	25

Independence 1968-1973
(31)

1973 (31 Jan). *Fifth Anniv of Independence. No. 96 optd with T 31 in gold.*

98	29	15 c. yellow, orange and royal blue		20	30

32 Denea   33 Artefacts and Map

(Des locally; adapted G. Vasarhelyi. Litho Format)

1973 (28 Mar*–25 July). *Various multicoloured designs as T 32 (1 to 5 c.) or T 33 (others). P* 14 (1 to 5 c.), 14½ × 14 (7, 8, 10, 30, 50 c.) *or* 14 × 14½ (*others*).

99		1 c. Ekwenababae		50	20
100		2 c. Kauwe Iud		65	20
101		3 c. Rimone		65	20
102		4 c. Type 32		65	30
103		5 c. Erekogo		65	30
104		7 c. Ikimago (fish) (25.7)		30	20

105		8 c. Catching flying-fish (23.5)		30	20
106		10 c. Itsibweb (ball game) (23.5)		30	20
107		15 c. Naruian wrestling (23.5)		35	20
108		20 c. Snaring Frigate Birds (23.5)		50	30
109		25 c. Nauruan girl (25.7)		50	30
110		30 c. Catching Noddy Birds (25.7)		85	40
111		50 c. Great Frigate Birds (25.7)		1·75	75
112		$1 Type 33		2·00	75
99/112			Set of 14	9·00	4·00

The 1 to 5 c. show flowers, and the 7, 8, 10, 30, 50 c. are horiz designs.
*This is the local release date but the Crown Agents issued the stamps on 21 March.

34 Co-op Store   35 Phosphate Mining

(Des G. Vasarhelyi. Litho Format)

1973 (20 Dec). *50th Anniv of Nauru Co-operative Society. T 34 and similar multicoloured designs. P* 14 × 14½ (50 c.) *or* 14½ × 14 (*others*).

113		5 c. Type 34		20	30
114		25 c. Timothy Detudamo (founder)		20	15
115		50 c. N.C.S. trademark (*vert*)		45	55
113/15			Set of 3	75	90

(Des G. Vasarhelyi (7 c. from original by J. Mason; 10 c. from original by K. Depaune). Litho Format)

1974 (21 May). *175th Anniv of First Contact with the Outside World. T 35 and similar horiz designs. Multicoloured. P* 13 × 13½ (7, 35, 50 c.) *or* 13½ × 13 (*others*).

116		7 c. M.V. *Eigamoiya* (bulk carrier)		1·25	90
117		10 c. Type 29		1·00	25
118		15 c. Fokker Friendship *Nauru Chief*		1·00	30
119		25 c. Nauruan chief in early times		1·25	35
120		35 c. Capt. Fearn and H.M.S. *Hunter*		5·50	2·50
121		50 c. H.M.S. *Hunter* off Nauru		2·50	1·40
116/121			Set of 6	11·00	5·25

The 7, 35 and 50 c. are larger, 70 × 22 mm.

36 Map of Nauru   37 Rev. P. A. Delaporte

(Des G. Vasarhelyi. Litho Format)

1974 (23 July). *Centenary of Universal Postal Union. T 36 and similar multicoloured designs. P* 13½ × 14 (5 c.), 13 × 13½ ($1) *or* 13½ × 13 (*others*).

122		5 c. Type 36		20	20
123		8 c. Nauru Post Office		20	20
124		20 c. Nauruan postman		20	10
125		$1 U.P.U. Building and Nauruan flag		50	60
122/5			Set of 4	1·00	1·00
MS126		157 × 105 mm. Nos. 122/5. Imperf		3·50	5·50

The 8 and 20 c. are horiz (33 × 21 mm), and the $1 is vert (21 × 33 mm).

(Des J.W. Litho Format)

1974 (10 Dec). *Christmas and 75th Anniv of Rev. Delaporte's Arrival. P* 14½.

127	37	15 c. multicoloured		20	20
128		20 c. multicoloured		30	30

38 Map of Nauru, Lump of Phosphate Rock and Albert Ellis   39 Micronesian Outrigger

(Des M. and Sylvia Goaman. Litho Format)

1975 (23 July). *Phosphate Mining Anniversaries. T 38 and similar horiz designs. Multicoloured. P* 14½ × 14.

129		5 c. Type 38		30	30
130		7 c. Coolies and mine.		40	35
131		15 c. Electric railway, barges and ship		1·25	1·25
132		25 c. Modern ore extraction		1·50	1·40
129/32			Set of 4	3·00	3·00

Anniversaries:—5 c. 75th Anniv of discovery; 7 c. 70th Anniv of Mining Agreement; 15 c. 55th Anniv of British Phosphate Commissioners; 25 c. 5th Anniv of Nauru Phosphate Corporation.

(Des M. and Sylvia Goaman. Litho Format)

1975 (1 Sept). *South Pacific Commission Conference, Nauru (1st issue). T 39 and similar horiz designs. Multicoloured. P* 13½ × 14.

133		20 c. Type 39		75	40
		a. Block of 4. Nos. 133/6		2·75	
134		20 c. Polynesian double-hull		75	40
135		20 c. Melanesian outrigger		75	40
136		20 c. Polynesian outrigger		75	40
133/6			Set of 4	2·75	1·40

Nos. 133/6 were printed in *se-tenant* blocks of four throughout the sheet.

40 New Civic Centre   41 "Our Lady" (Yaren Church)

(Des M. and Sylvia Goaman. Litho Format)

1975 (29 Sept). *South Pacific Commission Conference, Nauru (2nd issue). T 40 and similar horiz design. Multicoloured. P* 14.

137		30 c. Type 40		15	15
138		50 c. Domaneab (meeting-house)		30	30

(Des M. and Sylvia Goaman. Litho Format)

1975 (7 Nov). *Christmas. T 41 and similar vert design showing stained-glass window. Multicoloured. P* 14½ × 14.

139		5 c. Type 41		15	10
140		7 c. "Suffer little children…" (Orro Church)		15	10
141		15 c. As 7 c.		30	20
142		25 c. Type 41		45	35
139/42			Set of 4	95	65

42 Flowers floating towards Nauru

(Des M. and Sylvia Goaman. Litho Format)

1976 (31 Jan*). *Christmas. 30th Anniv of the Return from Truk. T 42 and similar horiz designs. Multicoloured. P* 14½.

143		10 c. Type 42		10	10
144		14 c. Nauru encircled by garland		15	10
145		25 c. Finsch's Reed Warbler and maps		35	25
146		40 c. Return of the islanders		45	35
143/6			Set of 4	95	65

*This is the local date of issue; the Crown Agents released the stamps one day earlier.
Nos. 143/6 exist imperforate from sets of progressive proofs.

43 3d. and 9d. Stamps of 1916

(Des M. and Sylvia Goaman. Litho Format)

1976 (6 May). *60th Anniv of Nauruan Stamps. T 43 and similar horiz designs. Multicoloured. P* 13½.

147		10 c. Type 43		15	15
148		15 c. 6d. and 1s. stamps		20	15
149		25 c. 2s. 6d. stamp		30	25
150		50 c. 5s. "Specimen" stamp		40	35
147/50			Set of 4	95	80

Nos. 147/8 show stamps with errors; the 3d. "Short N" and the 6d. "P" for "R".
Nos. 147/50 exist imperforate from sets of progressive proofs.

44 *Pandanus mei* and *Enna G* (cargo liner)

(Des M. and Sylvia Goaman. Litho Format)

1976 (26 July). *South Pacific Forum, Nauru. T 44 and similar horiz designs. Multicoloured. P* 13½.

151		10 c. Type 44		15	10
152		20 c. *Tournefortia argentea* and Nauruan aircraft		20	15
153		30 c. *Thespesia populnea* and Nauru Tracking Station		25	15
154		40 c. *Cordia subcordata* and produce		35	25
151/4			Set of 4	85	60

Nos. 151/4 exist imperforate from sets of progressive proofs.

45 Nauruan Choir **46** Nauru House and Coral Pinnacles

(Des G. Vasarhelyi. Litho Format)

1976 (17 Nov). *Christmas. T 45 and similar vert designs. Multicoloured. P 13½.*
155	15 c. Type 45	..	..	10	10
	a. Horiz pair. Nos. 155/6	..	..	20	20
156	15 c. Nauruan choir	..	..	10	10
157	20 c. Angel in white dress	..	..	15	15
	a. Horiz pair. Nos. 157/8	..	..	30	30
158	20 c. Angel in red dress	..	..	15	15
155/8	..	..	Set of 4	50	50

Nos. 155/6 and 157/8 were printed horizontally *se-tenant* throughout the sheet, both forming composite designs.

(Des D. Gentleman. Photo Harrison)

1977 (25 Apr*). *Opening of Nauru House, Melbourne. T 46 and similar vert design. Multicoloured. P 14.*
159	15 c. Type 46	..	..	15	15
160	30 c. Nauru House and Melbourne skyline	..	25	25

*This is the local release date. The London agency released the stamps on 14 April.

47 Cable Ship *Anglia* **48** Father Kayser and First Catholic Church

(Des D. Gentleman. Photo Harrison)

1977 (7 Sept). *75th Anniv of First Trans-Pacific Cable and 20th Anniv of First Artificial Earth Satellite. T 47 and similar vert designs. P 14 × 14½.*
161	7 c. multicoloured	..	..	25	10
162	15 c. light blue, grey and black	..	35	15
163	20 c. light blue, grey and black	..	35	15
164	25 c. multicoloured	..	..	35	20
161/4	..	..	Set of 4	1·10	60

Designs:—15 c. Tracking station, Nauru; 20 c. Stern of *Anglia*; 25 c. Dish aerial.

(Des D. Gentleman. Photo Harrison)

1977 (28 Nov). *Christmas. T 48 and similar vert designs. Multicoloured. P 14½.*
165	15 c. Type 48	..	..	10	10
166	25 c. Congregational Church, Orro	..	15	15
167	30 c. Catholic Church, Arubo	..	15	15
165/7	..	..	Set of 3	30	30

No. 165 also commemorates the 75th anniversary of the Catholic Church on Nauru.

49 Arms of Nauru **(50)**

(Des G. Vasarhelyi. Litho Format)

1978 (31 Jan). *Tenth Anniv of Independence. P 14½.*
168	**49**	15 c. multicoloured	..	20	15
169		60 c. multicoloured	..	35	30

1978 (29 Mar). *Nos. 159/60 surch as T 50 by Format.*
170	4 c. on 15 c. Type 46	..	1·75	3·25
171	5 c. on 15 c. Type 46	..	1·75	3·25
172	8 c. on 30 c. No. 160	..	1·75	3·25
173	10 c. on 30 c. No. 160	..	1·75	3·25
170/3	..	..	Set of 4	6·25	11·50

COVER PRICES

Cover factors are quoted at the beginning of each country for most issues to 1945. An explanation of the system can be found on page x. The factors quoted do not, however, apply to philatelic covers.

51 Collecting Shellfish **52** A.P.U. Emblem

(Des D. Gentleman. Photo Harrison)

1978 (17 May)–**79.** *Horiz designs as T 51 in brown, blue and black (4 c.), grey, black and light blue (20 c., $5) or multicoloured (others). P 14½.*
174	1 c. Type 51	..	..	30	20
175	2 c. Coral outcrop (6.6.79)	..	30	20
176	3 c. Reef scene (6.6.79)	..	30	20
177	4 c. Girl with fish (6.6.79)	..	35	20
178	5 c. Eastern Reef Heron (6.6.79)	..	80	30
179	7 c. Catching fish, Buada Lagoon	..	20	10
180	10 c. Ijuw Lagoon	..	..	20	15
181	15 c. Girl framed by coral	..	20	30
182	20 c. Pinnacles, Anibare Bay reef	..	30	25
183	25 c. Pinnacle at Meneng	..	30	30
184	30 c. Head of Great Frigate Bird	..	1·25	45
185	32 c. White-capped Noddy in coconut palm	85	35
186	40 c. Wandering Tattler	..	1·50	55
187	50 c. Great Frigate Birds on perch	..	85	45
188	$1 Old coral pinnacles at Topside	..	70	55
189	$2 New pinnacles at Topside	..	95	1·00
190	$5 Blackened pinnacles at Topside ..	1·75	2·25
174/90	..	..	Set of 17	10·00	7·00

(Litho Toppan Ptg Co, Ltd)

1978 (28 Aug). *14th General Assembly of Asian Parliamentarians' Union. T 52 and similar vert design. P 13.*
191	15 c. multicoloured	..	..	20	25
192	20 c. black, deep ultramarine and gold	20	25

Design:—20 c. As T 52 but different background.

53 Virgin and Child **54** Baden-Powell and Cub Scout

(Des R. Vigurs. Litho Format)

1978 (1 Nov). *Christmas. T 53 and similar multicoloured design. P 14.*
193	7 c. Type 53	..	..	10	10
194	15 c. Angel in sun-rise scene (*horiz*)	..	10	10
195	20 c. As 15 c.	..	..	15	15
196	30 c. Type 53	..	..	20	20
193/6	..	..	Set of 4	40	40

(Des J. Charles. Litho Format)

1978 (1 Dec). *70th Anniv of Boy Scout Movement. T 54 and similar horiz designs. Multicoloured. P 13½.*
197	20 c. Type 54	..	..	20	15
198	30 c. Baden-Powell and Boy Scout	..	25	20
199	50 c. Baden-Powell and Rover Scout	..	35	30
197/9	..	..	Set of 3	70	60

55 Wright *Flyer* over Nauru

(Des D. Gentleman. Litho Format)

1979 (24 Jan). *Flight Anniversaries. T 55 and similar horiz designs. Multicoloured. P 14.*
200	10 c. Type 55	..	..	15	10
201	15 c. *Southern Cross* superimposed on nose of Boeing "727"	..	..	25	15
	a. Pair. Nos. 201/2	..	..	50	30
202	15 c. *Southern Cross* and Boeing "727" (front view)	..	..	25	15
203	30 c. Wright *Flyer* over Nauru airfield	..	35	20
200/3	..	..	Set of 4	90	55

Commemorations:—10, 30 c. 75th anniversary of powered flight; 15 c. 50th anniversary of Kingsford-Smith's Pacific flight.

Nos. 201/2 were printed together, *se-tenant*, in horizontal and vertical pairs throughout the sheet.

56 Sir Rowland Hill and Marshall Islands 10 pf. Stamp of 1901

(Des R. Granger Barrett. Litho Format)

1979 (27 Feb). *Death Centenary of Sir Rowland Hill. T 56 and similar horiz designs showing stamps and Sir Rowland Hill. Multicoloured. P 14½.*
204	5 c. Type 56	..	..	15	10
	a. Imperf (pair)	..	..	£375	
205	15 c. "NAURU" opt on Great Britain 10s. "Seahorse" of 1916–23	..	25	20
	a. Imperf (pair)	..	..	£375	
206	60 c. 1978 10th Anniversary of Independence 60 c. commemorative	..	55	40
	a. Imperf (pair)	..	..		
204/6	..	..	Set of 3	85	60
MS207	159 × 101 mm. Nos. 204/6 .	..	85	1·25
	a. Error. Imperf	..	..	£650	

57 Dish Antenna, Transmitting Station and Radio Mast **58** Smiling Child

(Des G. Vasarhelyi. Litho Format)

1979 (22 Aug). *50th Anniv of International Consultative Radio Committee. T 57 and similar horiz designs. Multicoloured. P 14½.*
208	7 c. Type 57	..	..	15	10
209	32 c. Telex operator	..	..	35	25
210	40 c. Radio operator	..	..	40	25
208/10	..	..	Set of 3	80	55

(Des G. Vasarhelyi. Litho Format)

1979 (3 Oct). *International Year of the Child. T 58 and similar vert designs showing smiling children. P 14½.*
211	8 c. multicoloured	..	..	10	10
	a. Horiz strip of 5. Nos. 211/15	..	70	
212	15 c. multicoloured	..	..	15	15
213	25 c. multicoloured	..	..	20	20
214	32 c. multicoloured	..	..	20	20
215	50 c. multicoloured	..	..	25	25
211/15	..	..	Set of 5	70	70

Nos. 211/15 were printed together, *se-tenant*, in horizontal strips of 5 throughout the sheet, forming a composite design.

59 Ekwenababae (flower), Scroll inscribed "Peace on Earth" and Star

(Des G. Vasarhelyi. Litho Format)

1979 (14 Nov). *Christmas. T 59 and similar horiz designs. Multicoloured. P 14½.*
216	7 c. Type 59	..	..	10	10
217	15 c. *Thespia populnea* (flower), scroll inscribed "Goodwill toward Men" and star	..	10	10
218	20 c. Denea (flower), scroll inscribed "Peace on Earth" and star	..	10	10
219	30 c. Erekogo (flower), scroll inscribed "Goodwill toward Men" and star	..	20	20
216/19	..	..	Set of 4	40	40

Nos. 216/19 exist imperforate from sets of progressive proofs.

60 Dassault "Falcon" over Melbourne

(Des G. Vasarhelyi. Litho Format)

1980 (28 Feb). *10th Anniv of Air Nauru. T 60 and similar horiz designs. Multicoloured. P 14½.*
220	15 c. Type 60	..	..	40	15
221	20 c. Fokker "F28 (Fellowship)" over Tarawa	45	15
222	25 c. Boeing "727" over Hong Kong	..	45	15
223	30 c. Boeing "737" over Auckland	..	45	15
220/3	..	..	Set of 4	1·60	55

61 Steam Locomotive

(Des G. Vasarhelyi. Litho Format)

1980 (6 May). *10th Anniv of Nauru Phosphate Corporation. Railway Locomotives.* T **61** *and similar horiz designs. Multicoloured.* P 14½.

224	8 c. Type **61**				10	10
225	32 c. Electric locomotives	..	..		20	20
226	60 c. Diesel locomotive	..	..		35	35
224/6			*Set of 3*		60	60
MS227	168 × 118 mm. Nos. 224/6. P 13 ..				2·00	1·75

No. **MS**227 also commemorates the "London 1980" International Stamp Exhibition.

62 Verse 10 from Luke, Chapter 2 in English

(Des C. Abbott. Litho Format)

1980 (24 Sept). *Christmas.* T **62** *and similar square designs showing verses from Luke, chapter 2. Multicoloured.* P 14½.

228	20 c. Type **62**	..	..		10	10
	a. Horiz pair. Nos. 228/9	..	..		20	20
229	20 c. Verse 10 in Nauruan				10	10
230	30 c. Verse 14 in English	..	..		15	15
	a. Horiz pair. Nos. 230/1	..	..		30	30
231	30 c. Verse 14 in Nauruan				15	15
228/31			*Set of 4*		50	50

Nos. 228/9 and 230/1 were each printed together, *se-tenant*, in horizontal pairs throughout the sheet.
See also Nos. 248/51.

63 Nauruan, Australian, Union and New Zealand Flags on Aerial View of Nauru

(Des H. Woods. Litho Format)

1980 (3 Dec)–**81**. *20th Anniv of U.N. Declaration on the Granting of Independence to Colonial Countries and Peoples.* T **63** *and similar multicoloured designs.* P 14½ (25 c.) or 13½ (others).

232	25 c. Type **63**				15	15
233	30 c. U.N. Trusteeship Council (72 × 23 mm)				15	15
	(11.2.81)					
234	50 c. Nauru independence ceremony, 1968 (72 × 23 mm)				25	25
232/4			*Set of 3*		50	50

The 25 c. value was printed in sheets including 5 *se-tenant* stamp-size labels; the other two values were each printed in sheets including 5 *se-tenant* half stamp-size labels.

Nos. 233/4 exist imperforate from stock dispersed by the liquidator of Format International Security Printers Ltd.

64 Timothy Detudamo

(Des R. Granger Barrett. Litho Format)

1981 (11 Feb). *30th Anniv of Nauru Local Government Council. Head Chiefs.* T **64** *and similar horiz designs. Multicoloured.* P 14½.

235	20 c. Type **64**	..	..		15	15
236	30 c. Raymond Gadabu	..	..		15	15
237	50 c. Hammer DeRoburt	..	..		25	25
235/7 ..			*Set of 3*		50	50

65 Casting Net by Hand

(Litho Questa)

1981 (22 May). *Fishing.* T **65** *and similar horiz designs. Multicoloured.* P 12 × 11½.

238	8 c. Type **65**	..	..		10	10
239	20 c. Outrigger canoe.	..	..		20	15
240	32 c. Outboard motor boat	..	..		25	20
241	40 c. Trawler ..	..	..		30	25
238/41			*Set of 4*		75	60
MS242	167 × 116 mm. No. 241 × 4. P 14				1·90	2·00

No. **MS**242 was issued to commemorate the "WIPA 1981" International Stamp Exhibition, Vienna.

---

66 Bank of Nauru Emblem and Building   67 Inaugural Speech

(Des H. Woods. Litho Harrison)

1981 (21 July). *Fifth Anniv of Bank of Nauru.* P 14 × 14½.

243	**66**	$1 multicoloured	60	60

(Des G. Vasarhelyi. Litho Questa)

1981 (24 Oct). *U.N. Day. E.S.C.A.P. (United Nations Economic and Social Commission for Asia and the Pacific) Events.* T **67** *and similar square designs. Multicoloured.* P 14 × 14½.

244	15 c. Type **67**				15	15
245	20 c. Presenting credentials	..			15	15
246	25 c. Unveiling plaque				20	20
247	30 c. Raising U.N. flag				25	25
244/7			*Set of 4*		65	65

(Des C. Abbott. Litho Format)

1981 (14 Nov). *Christmas. Bible Verses. Square designs as* T **62**. *Multicoloured.* P 14½.

248	20 c. Matthew 1, 23 in English	..			15	15
	a. Horiz pair. Nos. 248/9	..			30	30
249	20 c. Matthew 1, 23 in Nauruan	..			15	15
250	30 c. Luke 2, 11 in English	..			20	20
	a. Horiz pair. Nos. 250/1	..			40	40
251	30 c. Luke 2, 11 in Nauruan	..			20	20
248/51			*Set of 4*		70	70

Nos. 248/9 and 250/1 were each printed together, *se-tenant*, in horizontal pairs throughout the sheet.

68 Earth Satellite Station

(Des M. Rickards. Litho Format)

1981 (9 Dec). *Tenth Anniv of South Pacific Forum.* T **68** *and similar horiz designs. Multicoloured.* P 13½ × 14.

252	10 c. Type **68**				30	20
253	20 c. *Enna G* (cargo liner)				35	25
254	30 c. Airliner				35	30
255	40 c. Local produce				40	40
252/5 ..			*Set of 4*		1·25	1·00

69 Nauru Scouts leaving for 1935 Frankston Scout Jamboree

(Des C. Abbott. Litho Format)

1982 (23 Feb). *75th Anniv of Boy Scout Movement.* T **69** *and similar multicoloured designs.* P 14.

256	7 c. Type **69**				15	15
257	8 c. Two Nauru scouts on *Nauru Chief*, 1935 (*vert*)				15	15
258	15 c. Nauru scouts making pottery, 1935 (*vert*)				20	20
259	20 c. Lord Huntingfield addressing Nauru scouts, Frankston Jamboree, 1935				25	25
260	25 c. Nauru cub and scout, 1982				30	30
261	40 c. Nauru cubs, scouts and scouters, 1982 ..				45	45
256/61			*Set of 6*		1·40	1·40
MS262	152 × 114 mm. Nos. 256/61. Imperf				1·75	2·00

No. **MS**262 also commemorates Nauru's participation in the "Stampex" National Stamp Exhibition, London.

Nos. 256/61 were each printed in sheets including four *se-tenant* stamp-size labels.

70 100kw Electricity Generating Plant under Construction (left side)

(Litho Irish Security Stamp Printing Ltd)

1982 (10 June). *Ocean Thermal Energy Conversion.* T **70** *and similar horiz designs. Multicoloured.* P 13½.

263	25 c. Type **70**				50	30
	a. Horiz pair. Nos. 263/4				1·00	60
264	25 c. 100kw Electricity Generating Plant under construction (right side) ..				50	30
265	40 c. Completed plant (left)				70	40
	a. Horiz pair. Nos. 265/6				1·40	80
266	40 c. Completed plant (right)				70	40
263/6 ..			*Set of 4*		2·25	1·25

Nos. 263/4 and 265/6 were printed together, *se-tenant*, in horizontal pairs forming composite designs throughout sheets which also included two stamp-size and twelve half stamp-size labels.

---

71 S.S. *Fido*   72 Queen Elizabeth II on Horseback

(Des R. Littleford (5 c.), Debbie Ryder (10, 30 c.), Cecilia Eales (60 c.), Jane Evans ($1). Litho Format)

1982 (11 Oct). *75th Anniv of Phosphate Shipments.* T **71** *and similar horiz designs. Multicoloured.* P 14.

267	5 c. Type **71**				50	10
268	10 c. Steam locomotive *Nellie*				85	20
269	30 c. Modern "Clyde" class diesel loco				1·25	50
270	60 c. M.V. *Eigamoiya* (bulk carrier)				1·50	80
267/70			*Set of 4*		3·75	1·40
MS271	165 × 107 mm. $1 *Eigamoiya*, *Rosie-D* and *Kolle-D* (bulk carriers) (67 × 27 mm)				2·00	1·75

No. **MS**271 was issued to commemorate "ANPEX 82" National Stamp Exhibition, Brisbane.

(Des G. Vasarhelyi. Litho Format)

1982 (21 Oct). *Royal Visit.* T **72** *and similar multicoloured designs.* P 14½.

272	20 c. Type **72**				40	30
273	50 c. Prince Philip, Duke of Edinburgh				75	60
274	$1 Queen Elizabeth II and Prince Philip (*horiz*)				1·40	1·25
272/4 ..			*Set of 3*		2·25	1·90

73 Father Bernard Lahn   74 Speaker of the Nauruan Parliament

(Des G. Vasarhelyi. Litho Format)

1982 (17 Nov). *Christmas.* T **73** *and similar horiz designs. Multicoloured.* P 14½.

275	20 c. Type **73**				35	30
276	30 c. Reverend Itubwa Amram				40	45
277	40 c. Pastor James Aingimen ..				45	60
278	50 c. Bishop Paul Mea ..				50	90
275/8 ..			*Set of 4*		1·50	2·00

Nos. 275/8 were printed in sheets of 25 including 5 *se-tenant*, stamp-size, labels.

(Des G. Vasarhelyi. Litho Walsall)

1983 (23 Mar). *15th Anniv of Independence.* T **74** *and similar multicoloured designs.* W w 14 (sideways on 30, 50 c.). P 14.

279	15 c. Type **74**				15	15
280	20 c. Family Court in session ..				20	20
281	30 c. Law Courts building (*horiz*)				25	25
282	50 c. Parliamentary chamber (*horiz*) ..				40	40
279/82 ..			*Set of 4*		90	90

75 Nauru Satellite Earth Station

(Des C. Abbott. Litho Questa)

1983 (11 May). *World Communications Year.* T **75** *and similar horiz designs. Multicoloured.* W w 14 (sideways). P 14.

283	5 c. Type **75**				10	10
284	10 c. Omni-directional range installation				15	15
285	20 c. Emergency short-wave radio				20	25
286	25 c. Radio Nauru control room				30	30
287	40 c. Unloading air mail				45	45
283/7 ..			*Set of 5*		1·00	1·10

76 Return of Exiles from Truk on M.V. *Trienza*, 1946   77 "The Holy Virgin, the Holy Child and St. John" (School of Raphael)

(Des D. Slater. Litho Format)

1983 (14 Sept). *Angam Day. T 76 and similar multicoloured designs. W w 14 (sideways on 15 c.). P 13½ (15 c.) or 14 (others).*

288	15 c. Type 76		20	25
289	20 c. Mrs. Elsie Agio (exile community leader)		20	25
290	30 c. Child on scales		35	40
291	40 c. Nauruan children		45	50
288/91		Set of 4	1·10	1·25

Nos. 289/91 are vertical designs, each 25 × 41 mm.

(Des L. Curtis. Litho Questa)

1983 (16 Nov). *Christmas. T 77 and similar multicoloured designs. W w 14 (sideways on 50 c.). P 14 × 14½ (50 c.) or 14½ × 14 (others).*

292	5 c. Type 77		10	10
293	15 c. "Madonna on the Throne surrounded by Angels" (School of Seville)		15	15
294	50 c. "The Mystical Betrothal of St. Catherine with Jesus" (School of Veronese) (*horiz*)		40	40
292/4		Set of 3	55	55

78 S.S. *Ocean Queen*   79 1974 U.P.U. $1 Stamp

(Des Beverley Barnard and L. Curtis. Litho Questa)

1984 (23 May). *250th Anniv of "Lloyd's List" (newspaper). T 78 and similar vert designs. Multicoloured. W w 14. P 14½ × 14.*

295	20 c. Type 78		45	30
296	25 c. M.V. *Enna G*		50	35
297	30 c. M.V. *Baron Minto*		55	40
298	40 c. Sinking of M.V. *Triadic*, 1940		75	55
295/8		Set of 4	2·00	1·40

(Des L. Curtis. Litho Format)

1984 (4 June). *Universal Postal Union Congress, Hamburg. W w 14. P 14.*

299	79 $1 multicoloured	1·10	1·25

80 *Hypolimnas bolina* (female)

(Des I. Loe. Litho B.D.T.)

1984 (24 July). *Butterflies. T 80 and similar horiz designs. Multicoloured. W w 14 (sideways). P 14.*

300	25 c. Type 80		50	40
301	30 c. *Hypolimnas bolina* (male)		55	55
302	50 c. *Danaus plexippus*		70	85
300/2		Set of 3	1·60	1·60

81 Coastal Scene   82 Buada Chapel

(Des A. Theobald. Litho Enschedé)

1984 (21 Sept). *Life in Nauru. T 81 and similar multicoloured designs. W w 14 (sideways on horiz designs). P 13½ × 14 (1, 5, 10, 25, 40 c., $2) or 14 × 13½ (others).*

303	1 c. Type 81		10	20
304	3 c. Nauruan woman (*vert*)		15	20
305	5 c. Modern trawler		20	20
306	10 c. Golfer on the links		50	30
307	15 c. Excavating phosphate (*vert*)		55	40
308	20 c. Surveyor (*vert*)		40	40
309	25 c. Air Nauru airliner		45	35
310	30 c. Elderly Nauruan (*vert*)		45	35
311	40 c. Loading hospital patient on to aircraft		50	40
312	50 c. Skin-diver with fish (*vert*)		70	55
313	$1 Tennis player (*vert*)		1·75	1·75
314	$2 Anabar Lagoon		2·00	2·25
303/14		Set of 12	7·00	6·50

Nos. 303/14 were each issued in sheets of 9 with decorative margins.

(Des L. Curtis. Litho Format)

1984 (14 Nov). *Christmas. T 82 and similar multicoloured designs. W w 14 (sideways on 50 c.). P 14.*

315	30 c. Type 82		60	50
316	40 c. Detudamo Memorial Church		80	65
317	50 c. Candle-light service, Kayser College (*horiz*)		90	70
315/17		Set of 3	2·10	1·75

84 Open Cut Mining   85 Mother and Baby on Beach

83 Air Nauru Jet on Tarmac

(Des L. Curtis. Litho Walsall)

1985 (26 Feb). *15th Anniv of Air Nauru. T 83 and similar multicoloured designs. W w 14 (sideways on 20 c., 40 c.). P 14.*

318	20 c. Type 83		55	35
319	30 c. Stewardess on aircraft steps (*vert*)		70	60
320	40 c. Fokker "F28" over Nauru		85	75
321	50 c. Freight being loaded onto Boeing "727" (*vert*)		1·00	85
318/21		Set of 4	2·75	2·25

(Des L. Curtis. Litho B.D.T.)

1985 (31 July). *15th Anniv of Nauru Phosphate Corporation. T 84 and similar horiz designs. Multicoloured. W w 14 (sideways). P 14.*

322	20 c. Type 84		70	60
323	25 c. Locomotive hauling crushed ore		1·25	1·00
324	30 c. Phosphate drying plant		1·25	1·00
325	50 c. Early steam locomotive		2·00	1·75
322/5		Set of 4	4·75	4·00

(Des A. Theobald. Litho Questa)

1985 (15 Nov). *Christmas. T 85 and similar vert design. Multicoloured. W w 16 (sideways). P 14.*

326	50 c. Beach scene		1·25	1·50
	a. Horiz pair. Nos. 326/7		2·50	3·00
327	50 c. Type 85		1·25	1·50

Nos. 326/7 were printed in sheets of 16 made up of two strips of four *se-tenant* pairs, each pair forming a composite design. The two strips were divided by a horizontal gutter.

86 Adult Common Noddy with Juvenile

(Des N. Arlott. Litho Questa)

1985 (31 Dec). *Birth Bicentenary of John J. Audubon (ornithologist). Common "Brown" Noddy. T 86 and similar horiz designs. Multicoloured. W w 16. P 14.*

328	10 c. Type 86		35	35
329	20 c. Adult and immature birds in flight		50	70
330	30 c. Adults in flight		65	85
331	50 c. "Brown Noddy" (John J. Audubon)		80	1·10
328/31		Set of 4	2·10	2·75

87 Douglas Motor Cycle

(Des M. Joyce. Litho Questa)

1986 (5 Mar). *Early Transport on Nauru. T 87 and similar horiz designs. Multicoloured. W w 16. P 14.*

332	15 c. Type 87		70	70
333	20 c. Primitive lorry		85	85
334	30 c. German 2 ft gauge locomotive (1910)		1·25	1·25
335	40 c. "Baby" Austin car		1·50	1·50
332/5		Set of 4	4·00	4·00

88 Island and Bank of Nauru   89 *Plumeria rubra*

(Des G. Vasarhelyi. Litho Format)

1986 (21 July). *10th Anniv of Bank of Nauru. Children's Paintings. T 88 and similar horiz designs. Multicoloured. W w 16 (sideways). P 14.*

336	20 c. Type 88		30	30
337	25 c. Borrower with notes and coins		35	35
338	30 c. Savers		40	40
339	40 c. Customers at bank counter		55	55
336/9		Set of 4	1·40	1·40

(Des Doreen McGuinness. Litho Questa)

1986 (30 Sept). *Flowers. T 89 and similar horiz designs. Multicoloured. W w 16. P 14.*

340	20 c. Type 89		55	70
341	25 c. *Tristellateia australis*		65	85
342	30 c. *Bougainvillea cultivar*		75	1·00
343	40 c. *Delonix regia*		1·00	1·25
340/3		Set of 4	2·75	3·50

90 Carol Singers   91 Young Girls Dancing

(Des M. Joyce. Litho Questa)

1986 (8 Dec). *Christmas. T 90 and similar horiz design. Multicoloured. W w 16 (sideways). P 14.*

344	20 c. Type 90		45	30
345	$1 Carol singers and hospital patient		2·00	1·75

(Des Joan Thompson. Litho Questa)

1987 (31 Jan). *Nauruan Dancers. T 91 and similar multicoloured designs. Multicoloured. W w 16 (sideways on 20, 30 c.). P 14.*

346	20 c. Type 91		70	70
347	30 c. Stick dance		90	1·00
348	50 c. Boy doing war dance (*vert*)		1·50	1·75
346/8		Set of 3	2·75	3·50

92 Hibiscus Fibre Skirt   93 U.P.U. Emblem and Air Mail Label

(Des L. Curtis. Litho B.D.T.)

1987 (30 July). *Personal Artifacts. T 92 and similar horiz designs. Multicoloured. W w 16 (sideways). P 14.*

349	25 c. Type 92		75	75
350	30 c. Headband and necklets		85	85
351	45 c. Decorative necklets		1·10	1·10
352	60 c. Pandanus leaf fan		1·60	1·60
349/52		Set of 4	3·75	3·75

(Des D. Miller. Litho Format)

1987 (20 Oct). *World Post Day. T 93 and similar multicoloured design. W w 16. P 14½ × 14.*

353	40 c. Type 93		65	65
MS354	122 × 82 mm. $1 U.P.U. emblem and map of Pacific showing mail routes (114 × 74 mm). Wmk sideways. Imperf		1·75	2·00

94 Open Bible   95 Nauruan Children's Party

(Des Janet Boschen. Litho Walsall)

1987 (5 Nov). *Centenary of Nauru Congregational Church. W w 14. P 13 × 13½.*

355	94 40 c. multicoloured	65	80

(Des M. Joyce. Litho Format)

1987 (27 Nov). *Christmas. T 95 and similar horiz design. Multicoloured. W w 16 (sideways). P 14.*

356	20 c. Type 95		75	35
357	$1 Nauruan Christmas dinner		2·75	2·75

96 Loading Phosphate on Ship   97 Map of German Marshall Is. and 1901 5 m. Yacht Definitive

(Des B. Clinton. Litho CPE Australia Ltd, Melbourne)

1988 (31 Jan). *20th Anniv of Independence. T* **96** *and similar multicoloured designs. P* 13½×14 (25 c.), 14×13½ (40, 55 c.) *or* 13 ($1).
358	25 c. Type **96**			80	80
359	40 c. Tomano flower (*vert*)			1·50	1·50
360	55 c. Great Frigate Bird (*vert*)			2·00	2·00
361	$1 Arms of Republic (35×35 *mm*)			2·25	2·50
358/61			Set of 4	6·00	6·25

(Des O. Bell. Litho Format)

1988 (29 July). *80th Anniv of Nauru Post Office. T* **97** *and similar horiz designs. Multicoloured. W w* **16** *(sideways). P* 14.
362	30 c. Type **97**			30	35
363	50 c. Letter and post office of 1908			50	55
364	70 c. Nauru Post Office and airmail letter		65	70
362/4			Set of 3	1·25	1·40

98 "Itubwer" (mat)

99 U.P.U. Emblem and National Flag

(Des Jennifer Toombs. Litho CPE Australia Ltd, Melbourne)

1988 (1 Aug). *String Figures. T* **98** *and similar horiz designs. Multicoloured. P* 13½ × 14.
365	25 c. Type **98**			25	30
366	40 c. "Etegerer–the Pursuer"			40	45
367	55 c. "Holding up the Sky"			50	55
368	80 c. "Manujie's Sword"			75	80
365/8			Set of 4	1·75	1·90

(Des Elisabeth Innes. Litho CPE Australia Ltd, Melbourne)

1988 (1 Oct). *Centenary of Nauru's Membership of Universal Postal Union. P* 13½ × 14.
369	**99**	$1 multicoloured	95	1·00

100 "Hark the Herald Angels"

101 Logo (15th anniv of Nauru Insurance Corporation)

(Des Elisabeth Innes. Litho CPE Australia Ltd, Melbourne)

1988 (28 Nov). *Christmas. T* **100** *and similar square designs showing words and music from "Hark the Herald Angels Sing". P* 13.
370	20 c. black, orange-vermilion and lemon		20	25
371	60 c. black, orange-vermilion and mauve		55	60
372	$1 black, orange-vermilion & bright green	95	1·00
370/2		Set of 3	1·50	1·60

(Litho Note Ptg Branch, Reserve Bank of Australia)

1989 (19 Nov). *Anniversaries and Events. T* **101** *and similar vert designs. Multicoloured. P* 14×15.
373	15 c. Type **101**		15	30
374	50 c. Logos (World Telecommunications Day and 10th anniv of Asian Pacific Tele-community)		50	75
375	$1 Photograph of island scene (150 years of photography)		95	1·40
376	$2 Capitol and U.P.U. emblem (20th U.P.U. Congress, Washington)		1·90	2·50
373/6		Set of 4	3·25	4·50

102 Mother and Baby

103 Eigigu working while Sisters play

(Des Robin White. Litho Note Ptg Branch, Reserve Bank of Australia)

1989 (15 Dec). *Christmas. T* **102** *and similar vert design. Multicoloured. P* 14×15.
377	20 c. Type **102**		30	30
378	$1 Children opening presents		1·50	1·75

(Des Anita Cecil. Litho Note Ptg Branch, Reserve Bank of Australia)

1989 (22 Dec). *20th Anniv of First Manned Landing on Moon. Legend of Eigigu, the Girl in the Moon. T* **103** *and similar vert designs. Multicoloured. P* 14×15.
379	25 c. Type **103**		80	80
380	30 c. Eigigu climbing tree		90	90
381	50 c. Eigigu stealing toddy from blind woman		1·75	1·75
382	$1 Eigigu on Moon		3·00	3·00
379/82		Set of 4	5·75	5·75

104 Early Mining by Hand

105 Sunday School Class

(Des Robin White. Litho Note Ptg Branch. Reserve Bank of Australia)

1990 (3 July). *20th Anniv of Nauru Phosphate Corporation. T* **104** *and similar vert design. Multicoloured. P* 14×15.
383	50 c. Type **104**		65	65
384	$1 Modern mining by excavator		1·25	1·25

(Litho Note Ptg Branch, Reserve Bank of Australia)

1990 (26 Nov). *Christmas. T* **105** *and similar vert design. Multicoloured. P* 14×15.
385	25 c. Type **105**		40	40
	a. Horiz pair. Nos. 385/6		80	80
386	25 c. Teacher telling Christmas story		40	40

Nos. 385/6 were printed together, *se-tenant*, in horizontal pairs throughout the sheet, each pair forming a composite design.

106 Eoiyepiang laying Baby on Mat

107 Oleander

(Des Robin White. Litho Note Ptg Branch, Reserve Bank of Australia)

1990 (24 Dec). *Legend of "Eoiyepiang, the Daughter of Thunder and Lightning". T* **106** *and similar vert designs. Multicoloured. P* 14×15.
387	25 c. Type **106**		30	30
388	30 c. Eoiyepiang making floral decoration		35	35
389	50 c. Eoiyepiang left on snow-covered mountain		60	60
390	$1 Eoiyepiang and warrior		1·10	1·10
387/90		Set of 4	2·10	2·10

(Litho Leigh-Mardon Ltd, Melbourne)

1991 (22 July). *Flowers. T* **107** *and similar multicoloured designs. P* 14½.
391	15 c. Type **107**		15	10
392	20 c. Lily		15	20
393	25 c. Passion Flower		20	25
394	30 c. Lily (*different*)		25	30
395	35 c. Caesalpinia		30	35
396	40 c. Clerodendron		35	40
397	45 c. *Baubina pinnata*		40	45
398	50 c. Hibiscus (*vert*)		45	50
399	75 c. Apocynaceae		65	70
400	$1 Bindweed (*vert*)		85	90
401	$2 Tristellateia (*vert*)		1·75	1·90
402	$3 Impala Lily (*vert*)		2·50	2·75
391/402		Set of 12	7·25	8·00

108 Jesus Christ and Children (stained glass window)

109 Star and Symbol of Asian Development Bank

(Des R. Varma. Litho Leigh-Mardon Ltd, Melbourne)

1991 (12 Dec). *Christmas. Sheet* 124×82 *mm. P* 14.
MS403	**108**	$2 multicoloured	2·50	2·50

(Des R. Varma. Litho Leigh-Mardon Ltd, Melbourne)

1992 (4 May). *25th Annual Meeting of Asian Development Bank. P* 14×14½.
404	**109**	$1.50, multicoloured	1·75	1·75

110 Gifts under Christmas Tree

111 Hammer DeRoburt

(Des B. Clinton. Litho Printset Cambec Pty Ltd, Australia)

1992 (23 Nov). *Christmas. Children's Paintings. T* **110** *and similar horiz design. Multicoloured. P* 14½×14.
405	45 c. Type **110**		55	55
406	60 c. Father Christmas in sleigh		70	70

(Des B. Clinton. Litho Printset Cambec Pty Ltd, Australia)

1993 (31 Jan). *25th Anniv of Independence and Hammer DeRoburt (former President) Commemoration. P* 14×14½.
407	**111**	$1 multicoloured	85	90

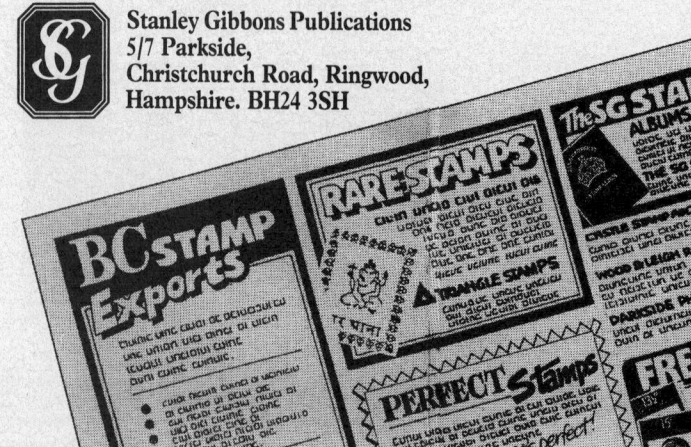

Nevis
see St. Kitts-Nevis

New Brunswick
see Canada

Newfoundland
see Canada

New Guinea
see Papua New Guinea

New Hebrides
see Vanuatu

New Republic
see South Africa

New South Wales
see Australia

New Zealand

From 1831 mail from New Zealand was sent to Sydney, New South Wales, routed through an unofficial postmaster at Kororareka.

The first official post office opened at Kororareka in January 1840 to be followed by others at Auckland, Britannia, Coromandel Harbour, Hokianga, Port Nicholson, Russell and Waimate during the same year. New South Wales relinquished control of the postal service when New Zealand became a separate colony on 3 May 1841.

The British G.P.O. was responsible for the operation of the overseas mails from 11 October 1841 until the postal service once again passed under colonial control on 18 November 1848.

CC 1

CC 2

AUCKLAND
CROWNED-CIRCLE HANDSTAMPS
CC1 CC 1 AUCKLAND NEW ZEALAND (R.) (31.10.1846) .. .. *Price on cover* £250

NELSON
CROWNED-CIRCLE HANDSTAMPS
CC2 CC 1 NELSON NEW ZEALAND (R.) (31.10.1846)
Price on cover £900

NEW PLYMOUTH
CROWNED-CIRCLE HANDSTAMPS
CC3 CC 1 NEW PLYMOUTH NEW ZEALAND (R. *or* Black) (31.10.1846) .. *Price on cover* £1500
CC3a CC 2 NEW PLYMOUTH NEW ZEALAND (R. *or* Black) (1854) .. .. *Price on cover* · £2000

OTAGO
CROWNED-CIRCLE HANDSTAMPS
CC4 CC 2 OTAGO NEW ZEALAND (R.) (1851)
Price on cover £1500

PETRE
CROWNED-CIRCLE HANDSTAMPS
CC5 CC 1 PETRE NEW ZEALAND (R.) (31.10.1846)
Price on cover £1200

PORT VICTORIA
CROWNED-CIRCLE HANDSTAMPS
CC6 CC 2 PORT VICTORIA NEW ZEALAND (R.) (1851) .. .. .. *Price on cover* £1000

RUSSELL
CROWNED-CIRCLE HANDSTAMPS
CC7 CC 1 RUSSELL NEW ZEALAND (R.) (31.10.1846)
Price on cover £3000

WELLINGTON
CROWNED-CIRCLE HANDSTAMPS
CC8 CC 1 WELLINGTON NEW ZEALAND (R.) (31.10.1846) .. .. *Price on cover* £300

A similar mark for Christchurch as Type CC **2** is only known struck, in black, as a cancellation after the introduction of adhesive stamps.

No. CC3a is a locally-cut replacement with the office name around the circumference, but a straight "PAID AT" in the centre.

PRICES FOR STAMPS ON COVER TO 1945

Nos. 1/125	*from* × 2
Nos. 126/36	*from* × 3
Nos. 137/9	*from* × 2
No. 140	—
No. 141	*from* × 2
No. 142	—
Nos. 143/8	*from* × 2
Nos. 149/51	*from* × 10
Nos. 152/84	*from* × 2
Nos. 185/6	—
Nos. 187/203	*from* × 3
Nos. 205/7e	—
Nos. 208/13	*from* × 2
Nos. 214/16j	—
Nos. 217/58	*from* × 3
No. 259	—
Nos. 260/9	*from* × 3
No. 270	—
Nos. 271/6	*from* × 3
Nos. 277/307	*from* × 2
Nos. 308/16	*from* × 3
No. 317	—
Nos. 318/28	*from* × 3
Nos. 329/48	—
No. 349	*from* × 5
Nos. 350/1	—
No. 352	*from* × 5
Nos. 353/69	—
Nos. 370/86	*from* × 2
No. 387	*from* × 4
Nos. 388/99	*from* × 3
Nos. 400/666	*from* × 2
Nos. E1/5	*from* × 5
No. E6	*from* × 10
Nos. D1/8	*from* × 3
Nos. D9/16	*from* × 5
Nos. D17/20	*from* × 3
Nos. D21/47	*from* × 6
Nos. O1/24	*from* × 12
Nos. O59/66	*from* × 4
Nos. O67/8	—
Nos. O69/81	*from* × 5
Nos. O82/7	—
Nos. O88/93	*from* × 20
Nos. O94/9	*from* × 12
Nos. O100/11	*from* × 5
Nos. O112/13	—
Nos. O115/19	*from* × 5
Nos. O120/33	*from* × 10
Nos. O134/51	*from* × 4
Nos. P1/7	*from* × 8
Nos. L1/9	*from* × 10
Nos. L8a/12	—
Nos. L13/20	*from* × 15
Nos. L21/3	—
Nos. L24/41	*from* × 12
No. F1	—
No. F2	*from* × 5
Nos. F3/144	—

Nos. F145/58	*from* × 3
Nos. F159/68	*from* × 3
Nos. F169/79	*from* × 3
Nos. F180/6	—
Nos. F187/90	*from* × 2
Nos. F191/203	*from* × 3
Nos. F204/11	—
Nos. F212/18	*from* × 2
Nos. A1/3	*from* × 2

CROWN COLONY

1

2

(Eng by Humphreys. Recess P.B.)

1855 (18 July). *Wmk Large Star,* W w **1.** *Imperf.*

1	1	1d. dull carmine (*white paper*)	..	£27000	£8000
2		2d. dull blue (*blued paper*)		£14000	£550
3		1s. pale yellow-green (*blued paper*)	..	£25000	£5000
		a. Bisected (6d.) (on cover)	..	†	£20000

The 2d. and 1s. on white paper formerly listed are now known to be stamps printed on blued paper which have had the bluing washed out.

Nos. 3a and 6a. were used at Dunedin from March 1857 when the rate for ½ oz letters to Great Britain was reduced to 6d. All known examples are bisected vertically.

(Printed by J. Richardson, Auckland, N.Z.)

1855 (Dec). *First printing. Wmk Large Star. White paper. Imperf.*

3b	1	1d. orange..	..	..	£15000

1855 (Dec)–57. *No wmk. Blue paper. Imperf.*

4	1	1d. red	..	..	£6500	£1400
5		2d. blue (3.56)	..	..	£2250	£300
		a. Without value	..	..		
6		1s. green (9.57)	..	..	£15000	£3500
		a. Bisected (6d.) (on cover)	..		†	£15000

These stamps on blue paper may occasionally be found watermarked double-lined letters, being portions of the paper-maker's name.

No. 6a was used at Otago during November 1858 on letters to Great Britian.

1857 (Jan). *Wmk Large Star. White paper similar to the issue of July* 1855.

7	1	1d. dull orange	..	—	£12000

This stamp is in the precise shade of the 1d. of the 1858 printing by Richardson on *no wmk* white paper. An unsevered pair is known with Dunedin cancellation on a cover front showing an Auckland arrival postmark of 19.1.1857.

1858–63. *Hard or soft white paper. No wmk.* (a) *Imperf.*

8	1	1d. dull orange (1858)	..	..	£1600	£375
8a		2d. deep ultramarine (1858)	..	..	£1500	£750
9		2d. pale blue	..	..	£750	£180
10		2d. blue	..	..	£750	£180
11		2d. dull deep blue	..		—	£250
12		6d. bistre-brown (Aug 1859)	..	£2250	£500
13		6d. brown	..	..	£1100	£300
14		6d. pale brown	..	..	£1100	£400
15		6d. chestnut	..	..	£2500	£550
16		1s. dull emerald-green	..		£7000	£1000
17		1s. blue-green	..	..	£7000	£1200

(b) *Pin-roulette, about* 10 *at Nelson* (1862)

18	1	1d. dull orange	..	—	£4500
19		2d. blue	..	..	—	£3500
20		6d. brown	..	..	—	£3750
21		1s. blue-green	..		—	£6500

(c) *Serrated perf about* 16 *or* 18 *at Nelson* (1862)

22	1	1d. dull orange	..	—	£3250
23		2d. blue	..	..	—	£2750
24		6d. brown	..	..	—	£2750
25		6d. chestnut	..		—	£5500
26		1s. blue-green	..		—	£4750

(d) *Rouletted* 7 *at Auckland* (April 1859)

27	1	1d. dull orange	..	£4500	£3250
28		2d. blue	..	..	£5500	£2750
29		6d. brown	..	..	£3750	£2250
		a. Imperf between (pair)		£10000	£9000
30		1s. dull emerald-green	..	£5500	£3500
31		1s. blue-green	..		£6500	£3500

(e) *P* 13 *at Dunedin* (1863)

31a	1	1d. dull orange	..	—	£3250
31b		2d. pale blue	..	..	£2750	£1800
32		6d. pale brown	..		—	£5000

Other forms of separation, in addition to those shown above, are known, both on the stamps of this issue and on those of 1862. Some of the varieties are extremely rare, only single copies being known.

The 2d. in a distinctive deep bright blue on white paper wmkd. Large Star is believed by experts to have been printed by Richardson in 1861 or 1862. This also exists doubly printed and with serrated perf.

(Printed by John Davies at the G.P.O., Auckland, N.Z.)

1862 (Feb–Dec). *Wmk Large Star.* (a) *Imperf.*

33	1	1d. orange-vermilion	..	..	£400	£120
34		1d. vermilion	..	..	£400	£130
35		1d. carmine-vermilion	..	..	£350	£150
36		2d. deep blue (Plate I)	..	..	£300	65·00
		a. Double print	..	..		£2500
37		2d. slate-blue (Plate I)	..	£1500	£180
37a		2d. milky blue (Plate I, worn)	..		£225
38		2d. pale blue (Plate I, worn)	..	£225	70·00
39		2d. blue (*to* deep) (Plate I, very worn)	..	£225	70·00
40		3d. brown-lilac (Dec 1862)	..	..	£300	£100

41	1	6d. black-brown	.. .. ..	£650	80·00
42		6d. brown	.. .. ..	£650	80·00
43		6d. red-brown	.. .. ..	£500	70·00
44		1s. green	.. .. ..	£750	£160
45		1s. yellow-green	.. ..	£700	£150
46		1s. deep green	.. ..	£850	£190

Nos. 37a/38 show some signs of wear on right of Queen's head and shades of No. 39 show moderate to advanced states of wear.

(b) Rouletted 7 at Auckland (5.62)

47	1	1d. orange-vermilion	.. ..	£3000	£650
48		1d. vermilion	.. ..	£1800	£600
48a		1d. carmine-vermilion	..	£2750	£800
49		2d. deep blue	.. ..	£1700	£400
50		2d. slate-blue	.. ..	£2750	£700
51		2d. pale blue	.. ..	£1500	£500
52		3d. brown-lilac	.. ..	£1700	£650
53		6d. black-brown	.. ..	£2000	£400
54		6d. brown	.. .. ..	£1700	£500
55		6d. red-brown	.. ..	£1700	£400
56		1s. green	.. .. ..	£2000	£550
57		1s. yellow-green	.. ..	£3000	£550
58		1s. deep green	.. ..	£3000	£650

(c) Serrated perf 16 or 18 at Nelson (8.62)

59	1	1d. orange-vermilion	..	—	£1300
60		1d. deep blue	.. ..	—	£850
		a. Imperf between (pair)	..	£5500	£2750
61		2d. slate-blue	.. ..	—	
62		3d. brown-lilac	.. ..	£2750	£1400
63		6d. black-brown	.. ..	—	£1500
64		6d. brown	.. .. ..	—	£1500
65		1s. yellow-green	.. ..	—	£2500

(d) Pin-perf 10 at Nelson (8.62)

66	1	2d. deep blue	.. ..	—	£1800
67		6d. black-brown	.. ..	—	£3000

The dates put to above varieties are the earliest that have been met with.

1862. *Wmk Large Star. P 13 (at Dunedin).*

68	1	1d. orange-vermilion	.. ..	£600	£160
69		1d. carmine-vermilion	..	£600	£160
70		2d. deep blue (Plate I)	..	£300	50·00
71		2d. slate-blue (Plate I)	..	—	£700
72		2d. blue (Plate I)	..	£225	35·00
72a		2d. milky blue (Plate I)	..	—	£500
73		2d. pale blue (Plate I)	..	£225	35·00
74		3d. brown-lilac	.. ..	£550	£140
75		6d. black-brown	.. ..	£550	£110
		a. Imperf between (horiz pair)			
76		6d. brown	.. .. ..	£500	55·00
77		6d. red-brown	.. ..	£400	32·00
78		1s. dull green	.. ..	£500	£200
79		1s. deep green	.. ..	£550	£180
80		1s. yellow-green	.. ..	£550	£160

See also Nos. 110/125 and the note that follows these.

1862–63. *Pelure paper. No wmk. (a) Imperf.*

81	1	1d. orange-vermilion (1863)	..	£5500	£1700
82		2d. ultramarine	.. ..	£3250	£750
83		2d. pale ultramarine	..	£3250	£750
84		3d. lilac	.. .. ..	£25000	†
85		6d. black-brown	.. ..	£1400	£250
86		1s. deep green	.. ..	£6000	£850

The 3d. is known only unused.

(b) Rouletted 7 at Auckland

87	1	1d. orange-vermilion	..	—	£4000
88		6d. black-brown	.. ..	£2000	£450
89		1s. deep green	.. ..	£3500	£1100

(c) P 13 at Dunedin

90	1	1d. orange-vermilion	..	£9500	£3000
91		2d. ultramarine	.. ..	£4500	£600
92		2d. pale ultramarine	..	£4500	£600
93		6d. black-brown	.. ..	£3500	£325
94		1s. deep green	.. ..	£7000	£1200

(d) Serrated perf 15 at Nelson

95	1	6d. black-brown	.. ..	—	£4000

1863 (early). *Hard or soft white paper. No wmk. (a) Imperf.*

96	1	2d. dull deep blue (shades)..	..	£2250	£800

(b) P 13

96a	1	2d. dull deep blue (shades)	..	£1600	£475

These stamps show slight beginnings of wear of the printing plate in the background to right of the Queen's ear. By the early part of 1864, the wear of the plate had spread, more or less, all over the background of the circle containing the head. The major portion of the stamps of this printing appears to have been consigned to Dunedin and to have been there perforated 13.

1864. *Wmk "N Z", W 2. (a) Imperf.*

97	1	1d. carmine-vermilion	..	£700	£200
98		2d. pale blue (Plate I worn)	..	£750	£200
99		6d. red-brown	.. ..	£2000	£475
100		1s. green	.. .. ..	£900	£250

(b) Rouletted 7 at Auckland

101	1	1d. carmine-vermilion	..	£4500	£2750
102		2d. pale blue (Plate I worn)	..	£1400	£700
103		6d. red-brown	.. ..	£4250	£2200
104		1s. green	.. ..	£2750	£1000

(c) P 13 at Dunedin

104a	1	1d. carmine-vermilion	..	£5000	£3500
105		2d. pale blue (Plate I worn)	..	£550	£160
106		1s. green	.. .. ..	£1100	£450
		a. Imperf between (horiz pair)	..	£7500	

(d) P 12½ at Auckland

106b	1	1d. carmine-vermilion	..	£4000	£2250
107		2d. pale blue (Plate I worn)	..	£225	50·00
108		6d. red-brown	.. ..	£225	30·00
109		1s. yellow-green	.. ..	£4000	£2000

1864–67. *Wmk Large Star. P 12½ (at Auckland).*

110	1	1d. carmine-vermilion (1864)	..	80·00	18·00
111		1d. pale orange-vermilion	..	£100	18·00
		a. Imperf (pair)	..	£1700	£1100
112		1d. orange	.. ..	£250	48·00
113		2d. pale blue (Plate I worn) (1864)		85·00	15·00
114		2d. deep blue (Plate II) (1866)		90·00	14·00
		a. Imperf vert (horiz pair)	..	—	£2500

115	1	2d. blue (Plate II)	..	90·00	17·00
		a. Retouched (Plate II) (1867)	..	£130	24·00
		c. Imperf (pair) (Plate II)	..	£1200	£1200
		d. Retouched. Imperf (pair)	..	£1700	£1900
116		3d. brown-lilac (1864)	..	£750	£500
117		3d. lilac	.. ..	65·00	17·00
		a. Imperf (pair)	..	£1800	£1200
118		3d. deep mauve	..	£325	45·00
		a. Imperf (pair)	..	£1800	£1200
119		4d. deep rose (1865)	..	£1800	£250
120		4d. yellow (1865)	..	90·00	50·00
121		4d. orange	..	£1100	£800
122		6d. red-brown (1864)	..	85·00	18·00
122a		6d. brown	..	95·00	20·00
		b. Imperf (pair)	..	£1100	£1000
123		1s. deep green (1864)	..	£500	£160
124		1s. green	.. ..	£275	55·00
125		1s. yellow-green	..	£100	45·00

The above issue is sometimes difficult to distinguish from Nos. 68/80 because the vertical perforations usually gauge 12¾ and sometimes a full 13. However stamps of this issue invariably gauge 12½ horizontally, whereas the 1862 stamps measure a full 13.

Nos. 111a, 115c/d, 117a, 118a and 122b were issued during problems with the perforation machine which occurred in 1866–67, 1869–70 and 1871–73. Imperforate sheets of the 1s. were also released, but these stamps are very similar to Nos. 44/6.

The 1d., 2d. and 6d. were officially reprinted imperforate, without gum, in 1884 for presentation purposes. They can be distinguished from the errors listed by their shades which are pale orange, dull blue and dull chocolate-brown respectively, and by the worn state of the plates from which they were printed.

1871. *Wmk Large Star. (a) P 10.*

126	1	1d. brown	.. ..	£375	50·00

(b) P 12½ × 10

127	1	1d. deep brown	.. ..	—	£800

(c) P 10 × 12½

128	1	1d. brown	.. ..	£110	23·00
		a. Perf 12½ comp 10 (1 side)	..	£225	60·00
129		2d. deep blue (Plate II)	..	—	£5500
		a. Perf 10*	..	†	£9500
130		2d. vermilion	.. ..	£120	17·00
		a. Retouched	..	£160	24·00
		b. Perf 12½ comp 10 (1 side)	..	£650	£275
		c. Perf 10*	..	†	£9500
131		6d. deep blue	.. ..	£1100	£550
		a. Blue	.. ..	£750	£275
		b. Imperf between (vert pair)	..	—	£4250
		c. Perf 12½ comp 10 (1 side)	..	£700	£200
		ca. Imperf vert (horiz pair)			

(d) P 12½

132	1	1d. red-brown	.. ..	90·00	20·00
		a. Brown (shades, worn plate)	..	90·00	20·00
		b. Imperf horiz (vert pair)	..	—	£2750
133		2d. orange	.. ..	50·00	15·00
		a. Retouched	..	£110	40·00
134		2d. vermilion	.. ..	85·00	17·00
		a. Retouched	..	£150	50·00
135		6d. blue	.. ..	85·00	28·00
136		6d. pale blue	.. ..	55·00	28·00

*Only one used copy each of Nos. 129a and 130c have been reported.

1872. *No wmk. P 12½.*

137	1	1d. brown	.. ..	£275	40·00
138		2d. vermilion	..	48·00	18·00
		a. Retouched	..	£150	27·00
139		4d. orange-yellow	..	£120	£450

1872. *Wmk "N Z", W 2. P 12½.*

140	1	1d. brown	.. ..	—	£2500
141		2d. vermilion	.. ..	£300	75·00
		a. Retouched	..	£600	£120

In or about 1872 1d., 2d. and 4d. stamps were printed on paper showing sheet watermarks of either "W. T. & Co." (Wiggins Teape & Co.) in script letters or "T. H. Saunders" in double-lined capitals; portions of these letters are occasionally found on stamps.

1872. *Wmk Lozenges, with "INVICTA" in double-lined capitals four times in the sheet. P 12½.*

142	1	2d. vermilion	.. ..	£2750	£500
		a. Retouched	..	£3750	£700

3

4

(Des John Davies. Die eng on wood in Melbourne. Printed from electrotypes at Govt Ptg Office, Wellington)

1873 (1 Jan). *(a) Wmk "NZ", W 2.*

143	3	½d. pale dull rose (p 10)..	..	60·00	14·00
144		½d. pale dull rose (p 12½)	..	£180	60·00
145		½d. pale dull rose (p 12½ × 10)	..	£110	50·00

(b) No wmk

146	3	½d. pale dull rose (p 10)	..	80·00	26·00
147		½d. pale dull rose (p 12½)	..	£200	70·00
148		½d. pale dull rose (p 12½ × 10)	..	£150	60·00

As the paper used for Nos. 143/5 was originally intended for fiscal stamps which were more than twice as large, about one-third of the impressions fall on portions of the sheet showing no watermark, giving rise to varieties Nos. 146/8. In later printings of No. 151 a few stamps in each sheet are without watermark. These can be distinguished from No. 147 by the shade.

1875 (Jan). *Wmk Star, W 4.*

149	3	½d. pale dull rose (p 12½)	..	11·00	90
		a. Imperf horiz (vert pair)	..	£600	£325
		b. Imperf between (horiz pair)	..	†	£500
150		½d. dull pale rose (p nearly 12)	..	60·00	5·50

1892 (May). *Wmk "NZ and Star". W 12b. P 12½.*

151	3	½d. bright rose (shades)	..	5·00	40
		a. No wmk	.. ..	7·50	2·25

5

6

7

8

9

10

11

12

12a 6 mm

12b 7 mm

12c 4 mm

(T **5/10** eng De La Rue. T **11** and **12** des, eng & plates by W. R. Bock. Typo Govt Ptg Office, Wellington)

1874 (2 Jan)–78. *W 12a. A. White paper. (a) P 12½.*

152	5	1d. lilac	.. ..	45·00	3·50
		a. Imperf	..	£400	
153	6	2d. rose	.. ..	45·00	1·75
154	7	3d. brown	.. ..	95·00	55·00
155	8	4d. maroon	.. ..	£250	50·00
156	9	6d. blue	.. ..	£180	10·00
157	10	1s. green	.. ..	£650	25·00

(b) Perf nearly 12

158	6	2d. rose (1878)	.. ..	£600	£180

(c) Perf compound of 12½ and 10

159	5	1d. lilac	.. ..	£150	40·00
160	6	2d. rose	.. ..	£350	65·00
161	7	3d. brown	.. ..	£160	60·00
162	8	4d. maroon	.. ..	£350	£100
163	9	6d. blue	.. ..	£225	45·00
164	10	1s. green	.. ..	£650	£100
		aa. Imperf between (vert pair)	..	†	—

(d) Perf nearly 12 × 12½

164a	5	1d. lilac (1875)	.. ..	£650	£250
165	6	2d. rose (1878)	.. ..	£650	£190

B. Blued paper. (a) P 12½

166	5	1d. lilac	.. ..	70·00	29·00
167	6	2d. rose	.. ..	95·00	29·00
168	7	3d. brown	.. ..	£225	75·00
169	8	4d. maroon	.. ..	£425	£100
170	9	6d. blue	.. ..	£325	48·00
171	10	1s. green	.. ..	£1000	£190

(b) Perf compound of 12½ and 10

172	5	1d. lilac	.. ..	£180	50·00
173	6	2d. rose	.. ..	£500	80·00
174	7	3d. brown	.. ..	£190	65·00
175	8	4d. maroon	.. ..	£450	£110
176	9	6d. blue	.. ..	£300	90·00
177	10	1s. green	.. ..	£1000	£200

1875. *Wmk Large Star, W w 1. P 12½.*

178	5	1d. deep lilac	.. ..	£500	£100
179	6	2d. rose	.. ..	£300	15·00

1878. *W 12a. P 12 × 11½ (comb).*

180	5	1d. mauve-lilac	.. ..	35·00	2·75
181	6	2d. rose	.. ..	35·00	1·40
182	8	4d. maroon	.. ..	£130	38·00
183	9	6d. blue	.. ..	80·00	10·00
184	10	1s. green	.. ..	£110	27·00
185	11	2s. deep rose (1 July)	..	£300	£275
186	12	5s. grey (1 July)	..	£325	£275

This perforation is made by a horizontal "comb" machine, giving a gauge of 12 horizontally and about 11¾ vertically. Single specimens can be found apparently gauging 11½ all round or 12 all round, but these are all from the same machine. The perforation described above as "nearly 12" was from a single-line machine.

ALTERED CATALOGUE NUMBERS

Any Catalogue numbers altered from the last edition are shown as a list in the introductory pages.

13   14   15

16   17   18

19   20   21

22

Description of Watermarks

W 12a. 6 mm between "N Z" and star; broad irregular star; comparatively wide "N"; "N Z" 11½ mm wide.

W 12b. 7 mm between "N Z" and star; narrower star; narrow "N"; "N Z" 10 mm wide.

W 12c. 4 mm between "N Z" and star; narrow star; wide "N"; "N Z" 11½ mm wide.

Description of Papers

1882–88. Smooth paper with horizontal mesh. W **12a.**
1888–98. Smooth paper with vertical mesh. W **12b.**
1890–91. Smooth paper with vertical mesh. W **12c.**
1898. Thin yellowish toned, coarse paper with clear vertical mesh. W **12b.** Perf 11 only.

In 1899–1900 stamps appeared on medium to thick white coarse paper but we do not differentiate these (except where identifiable by shade) as they are more difficult to distinguish.

PAPER MESH. This shows on the back of the stamp as a series of parallel grooves, either vertical or horizontal. It is caused by the use of a wire gauze conveyor-belt during paper-making.

Description of Dies

1d.

Die 1

Die 2

Die 3

1882. Die 1. Background shading complete and heavy.
1886. Die 2. Background lines thinner. Two lines of shading weak or missing left of Queen's forehead.
1889. Die 3. Shading on head reduced; ornament in crown left of chignon clearer, with unshaded "arrow" more prominent.

PRICES OF SETS

Set prices are given for many issues, generally those containing three stamps or more. Definitive sets include one of each value or major colour change, but do not cover different perforations, die types or minor shades. Where a choice is possible the set prices are based on the cheapest versions of the stamps included in the listings.

2d.

Die 1

Die 2

Die 3

1882. Die 1. Background shading complete and heavy.
1886. Die 2. Weak line of shading left of forehead and missing shading lines below "TA".
1889. Die 3. As Die 2 but with comma-like white notch in hair below "&".

6d.

Die 1

Die 2

1882. Die 1. Shading heavy. Top of head merges into shading.
1892. Die 2. Background lines thinner. Shading on head more regular with clear line of demarcation between head and background shading.

STAMPS WITH ADVERTISEMENTS. During November 1891 the New Zealand Post Office invited tenders for the printing of advertisements on the reverse of the current 1d. to 1s. stamps. The contract was awarded to Messrs Miller, Truebridge & Reich and the first sheets with advertisements on the reverse appeared in February 1893.

Different advertisements were applied to the backs of the individual stamps within the sheets of 240 (four panes of 60).

On the first setting those in a vertical format were inverted in relation to the stamps and each of the horizontal advertisements had its base at the left-hand side of the stamp when seen from the back. For the second and third settings the vertical advertisements were the same way up as the stamps and the bases of those in the horizontal format were at the right as seen from the back. The third setting only differs from the second in the order of the individual advertisements.

The experiment was not, however, a success and the contract was cancelled at the end of 1893.

(Des F. W. Sears (½d.), A. E. Cousins (2½d.), A. W. Jones (5d.); others adapted from 1874 issue by W. H. Norris. Dies eng A. E. Cousins (½d., 2½d., 5d.), W. R. Bock (others). Typo Govt Ptg Office)

1882–1900. Inscr "POSTAGE & REVENUE".

A. W 12a. Paper with horiz mesh (1.4.82–86). (a) P 12 × 11½

187	14	1d. rose to rose-red (Die 1)	..	35·00	4·50
		a. Imperf (pair)	..	£275	
		b. Imperf between (vert pair)	..	£300	
		c. Die 2. Pale rose to carmine-rose (1886)	30·00	4·50
188	15	2d. lilac to lilac-purple (Die 1)	..	40·00	4·00
		a. Imperf (pair)	..	£300	
		b. Imperf between (vert pair)	..	£300	
		c. Die 2. Lilac (1886)	..	55·00	5·00
189	17	3d. yellow (1884)	..	48·00	4·75
190	18	4d. blue-green	..	65·00	4·50
191	20	6d. brown (Die I)	..	70·00	3·75
192	21	8d. blue (1885)	..	65·00	45·00
193	22	1s. red-brown	..	75·00	12·00

(b) P 12½ (1884?)

193a	14	1d. rose to rose-red (Die 1)	..	£170	75·00

B. W 12b. Paper with vert mesh (1888–95)

(a) P 12×11½ (1888–95)

194	13	½d. black (1.4.95)	..	25·00	60·00

195	14	1d. rose to rosine (Die 2)	40·00	3·50
		a. Die 3. Rose to carmine (1889)	40·00	3·50
		ab. Red-brn advert (1st setting) (2.93)		
		ac. Red advert (1st setting) (3.93)	50·00	10·00
		ad. Blue advert (2nd setting) (4.93)	60·00	25·00
		ae. Mauve advert (2nd setting) (5.93)	38·00	6·00
		af. Green advert (2nd setting) (6.93)		
		ag. Brn-red advert (3rd setting) (9.93)	38·00	6·00
196	15	2d. lilac (Die 2)	40·00	4·00
		a. Die 3. Lilac to purple (1889)	40·00	4·00
		ab. Red advert (1st setting) (3.93)	60·00	15·00
		ac. Mauve advert (2nd setting) (5.93)	50·00	
		ad. Sepia advert (2nd setting) (5.93)	50·00	20·00
		ae. Green advert (2nd setting) (6.93)	—	75·00
		af. Brn-red advert (3rd setting) (9.93)		
197	16	2½d. pale blue (1891)	45·00	5·50
		a. Brn-red advert (2nd setting) (4.93)	45·00	11·00
		b. Ultramarine (green advert. 2nd setting) (6.93)	55·00	13·00
198	17	3d. yellow	40·00	6·00
		a. Brn-red advert (2nd setting) (4.93)	60·00	10·00
		b. Sepia advert (2nd setting) (5.93)		
199	18	4d. green to bluish green	50·00	2·75
		a. Sepia advert (2nd setting) (5.93)	60·00	10·00
200	19	5d. olive-black (1.2.91)	40·00	9·00
		a. Imperf (pair)	£300	
		b. Brn-pur advert (3rd setting) (9.93)	60·00	25·00
201	20	6d. brown (Die 1)	60·00	2·25
		a. Die 2 (1892)	£110	50·00
		ab. Sepia advert (2nd setting) (5.93)		
		ac. Brn-red advert (3rd setting) (9.93)	£140	60·00
202	21	8d. blue	65·00	45·00
203	22	1s. red-brown	75·00	6·00
		a. Black advert (2nd setting) (5.93)	£300	£150
		b. Brn-pur advert (3rd setting) (9.93)	£100	15·00

(b) P 12×12½ (1888–91)

204	14	1d. rose (Die 2)	..	£190	75·00
		a. Die 3 (1889)			

(c) P 12½ (1888–89)

205	14	1d. rose (Die 3) (1889)	..	£160	90·00
		a. Mauve advert (2nd setting) (5.93)		
206	15	2d. lilac (Die 2)	..	£120	80·00
		a. Die 3. Deep lilac (1889)	90·00	65·00
		ab. Brn-red advert (3rd setting) (9.93)	£160	80·00
207	16	2½d. blue (1891)	..	£170	90·00

(d) Mixed perfs 12×11½ and 12½ (1891–93)

207b	14	1d. rose (Die 3) (brn-red advert. 3rd setting)	..	—	50·00
207b	15	2d. lilac (Die 3)			
		ba. Brn-red advert (3rd setting) (9.93)		
207c	18	4d. green	..	—	50·00
207d	19	5d. olive-black	..	—	95·00
207e	20	6d. brown (Die I)	..	—	£100
		ea. Die 2	..	—	£150

C. W 12c. Paper with vert mesh (1890). (a) P 12 × 11½

208	14	1d. rose (Die 3)	..	65·00	6·00
209	15	2d. purple (Die 3)	..	65·00	6·00
210	16	2½d. ultramarine (27.12)	..	60·00	9·50
211	17	3d. yellow	..	65·00	11·00
		a. Lemon-yellow	..	65·00	12·00
212	20	6d. brown (Die I)	..	£110	22·00
213	22	1s. deep red-brown	..	£130	40·00

(b) P 12½

214	14	1d. rose (Die 3)	..	£170	£100
215	15	2d. purple (Die 3)	..	£150	£100
216	16	2½d. ultramarine	..	£200	£100

(c) P 12×12½

216a	20	6d. brown (Die I)	..	£180	£130

D. Continuation of W **12b.** Paper with vert mesh (1891–1900)

(a) P 10×12½ (1891–94)

216b	14	1d. rose (Die 3)	£180	85·00
		ba. Perf 12½×10	£200	85·00
		bb. Red-brn advert (1st setting) (2.93)	£180	£100
		bc. Brn-red advert (2nd setting) (4.93)	£150	70·00
		bd. Mauve advert (2nd setting) (5.93)	£150	70·00
		be. Green advert (2nd setting) (6.93)	£200	£120
216c	15	2d. lilac (Die 3)	£150	55·00
216d	16	2½d. blue (1893)	£130	60·00
216e	17	3d. yellow	£150	70·00
216f	18	4d. green	£170	£140
216g	19	5d. olive-black (1894)	£180	£170
		ga. Perf 12½×10		
216h	20	6d. brown (Die I)	£190	£190
		i. Die 2 (1892)	£150	£150
		ia. Brn-pur advert (3rd setting) (9.93)	£180	£180
216j	22	1s. red-brown	£170	£160

(b) P 10 (1891–95)

217	13	½d. black (1895)	3·00	30
218	14	1d. rose (Die 3)	6·50	1·25
		a. Carmine	£250	£250
		b. Imperf (pair)	£275	
		c. Imperf between (pair)	£200	
		d. Imperf horiz (vert pair)	£250	£120
		e. Mixed perfs 10 and 12½		
		f. Red-brown advert (1st setting) (2.93)	14·00	4·00
		g. Red advert (1st setting) (3.93)	14·00	5·00
		h. Brown-red advert (2nd and 3rd settings) (4.93)	7·00	2·50
		i. Blue advert (2nd setting) (4.93)	50·00	20·00
		j. Mauve advert (2nd setting) (5.93)	7·00	2·50
		k. Green advert (2nd setting) (6.93)	50·00	16·00
		l. Brown-purple advert (3rd setting) (9.93)	7·00	2·50
219	15	2d. lilac (Die 3)	7·50	30
		a. Purple	8·50	30
		b. Imperf between (pair)	£225	
		c. Mixed perfs 10 and 12½	—	90·00
		d. Red-brown advert (1st setting) (2.93)	22·00	5·00
		e. Red advert (1st setting) (3.93)	22·00	5·00
		f. Brown-red advert (2nd and 3rd settings) (4.93)	11·00	2·50
		g. Sepia advert (2nd setting) (5.93)	15·00	3·00
		h. Green advert (2nd setting) (6.93)	32·00	8·00
		i. Brown-purple advert (3rd setting) (9.93)	11·00	2·50

220	16	2½d. blue (1892)	42·00	3·50
		a. *Ultramarine* ..	42·00	4·00
		b. Mixed perfs 10 and 12½	£170	90·00
		c. Mauve advert (2nd setting) (5.93)	42·00	6·00
		d. Green advert (2nd setting) (6.93)	70·00	9·00
		e. Brown-purple advert (3rd setting) (9.93) ..	42·00	6·00
221	17	3d. pale orange-yellow ..	35·00	7·00
		a. *Orange*	35·00	7·50
		b. *Lemon-yellow* ..	42·00	8·50
		c. Mixed perfs 10 and 12½	£160	£120
		d. Brown-red advert (2nd and 3rd settings) (4.93)	38·00	11·00
		e. Sepia advert (3rd setting) (5.93)	75·00	24·00
		f. Brown-purple advert (3rd setting) (9.93) ..	35·00	8·00
222	18	4d. green (1892) ..	45·00	2·50
		a. *Blue-green* ..	50·00	3·50
		b. Mixed perfs 10 and 12½	£190	80·00
		c. Brown-red advert (2nd setting) (4.93)	60·00	4·00
		d. Brown-purple advert (3rd setting) (9.93) ..	55·00	4·00
223	19	5d. olive-black (1893) ..	42·00	10·00
		a. Brown-purple advert (3rd setting) (9.93)	65·00	14·00
224	20	6d. brown (Die 1) ..	80·00	16·00
		a. Mixed perfs 10 and 12½	45·00	5·00
		b. Die 2 (1892) ..	45·00	5·00
		ba. *Black-brown* ..	48·00	5·00
		bb. Imperf (pair) ..	£225	
		bc. Mixed perfs 10 and 12½	90·00	50·00
		bd. Sepia advert (2nd setting) (4.93)	60·00	9·50
		be. Brown-red advert (3rd setting) (9.93)	60·00	9·50
		bf. Brown-purple advert (3rd setting) (9.93)	60·00	9·50
225	21	8d. blue (brown-purple advert. 3rd setting) (9.93)	65·00	45·00
226	22	1s. red-brown	75·00	5·00
		a. Imperf between (pair) ..	£400	
		b. Mixed perfs 10 and 12½	£150	£110
		c. Sepia advert (2nd setting) (5.93)	£100	12·00
		d. Black advert (2nd setting) (5.93)	£180	£110
		e. Brown-red advert (3rd setting) (9.93)	£100	12·00
		f. Brown-purple advert (3rd setting) (9.93)	£100	12·00

(c) P 10×11 (1895–97)

227	13	½d. black (1896) ..	3·25	40
		a. Mixed perfs 10 and 11 ..	80·00	26·00
		b. Perf 11×10 ..	24·00	9·50
228	14	1d. rose (Die 3) ..	4·50	15
		a. Mixed perfs 10 and 11 ..	85·00	50·00
		b. Perf 11×10 ..	50·00	5·50
229	15	2d. purple (Die 3) ..	7·50	20
		a. Mixed perfs 10 and 11 ..	60·00	50·00
230	16	2½d. blue (1896) ..	38·00	3·50
		a. *Ultramarine* ..	38·00	4·25
		b. Mixed perfs 10 and 11 ..	—	65·00
231	17	3d. lemon-yellow (1896) ..	60·00	7·00
232	18	4d. pale green (1896) ..	70·00	6·50
		a. Mixed perfs 10 and 11 ..	—	80·00
233	19	5d. olive-black (1897) ..	48·00	10·00
234	20	6d. deep brown (Die 2) (1896)	55·00	4·00
		a. Mixed perfs 10 and 11 ..	£160	50·00
		b. Perf 11×10 ..		
235	22	1s. red-brown (1896) ..	75·00	8·00
		a. Mixed perfs 10 and 11 ..	£140	70·00

(d) P 11 (1895–1900)

236	13	½d. black (1897) ..	2·50	15
		a. Thin coarse toned paper (1898)	22·00	1·25
		b. Ditto. Wmk sideways ..	—	£150
237	14	1d. rose (Die 3) ..	3·50	10
		a. *Deep carmine* ..	5·50	1·25
		b. Imperf between (pair) ..	£300	
		c. *Deep carmine/thin coarse toned* (1898)	8·00	1·25
		d. Ditto. Wmk sideways ..	—	£200
238	15	2d. mauve (Die 3) ..	7·00	30
		a. *Purple*	7·00	30
		b. *Deep purple/thin coarse toned* (1898)	8·00	1·25
		c. Ditto. Wmk sideways ..	—	£180
239	16	2½d. blue (1897) ..	38·00	3·50
		a. Thin coarse toned paper (1898)	50·00	12·00
240	17	3d. pale yellow (1897) ..	48·00	4·50
		a. *Pale dull yellow/thin coarse toned* (1898)	55·00	7·50
		b. *Orange* (1899) ..	40·00	5·50
		c. *Dull orange-yellow* (1900) ..	48·00	7·50
241	18	4d. yellowish green ..	48·00	3·25
		a. *Bluish green* (1897)..	48·00	3·00
242	19	5d. olive-black/*thin coarse toned* (1899)	50·00	17·00
243	20	6d. brown (Die 2) (1897) ..	55·00	3·00
		a. *Black-brown* ..	55·00	3·00
		b. *Brown/thin coarse toned* (1898)	60·00	4·50
244	21	8d. blue (1898) ..	65·00	45·00
245	22	1s. red-brown (1897) ..	70·00	5·50

Only the more prominent shades have been included.

Stamps perf compound of 11 and 12½ exist but we do not list them as there is some doubt as to whether they are genuine.

For the ½d. and 2d. with double-lined watermark, see Nos. 271/2.

PRICES OF SETS

Set prices are given for many issues, generally those containing three stamps or more. Definitive sets include one of each value or major colour change, but do not cover different perforations, die types or minor shades. Where a choice is possible the set prices are based on the cheapest versions of the stamps included in the listings.

23 Mount Cook or Aorangi

24 Lake Taupo and Mount Ruapehu

25 Pembroke Peak, Milford Sound

26 Lake Wakatipu and Mount Earnslaw, inscribed "WAKITIPU"

27 Lake Wakatipu and Mount Earnslaw, inscribed "WAKATIPU"

28 Sacred Huia Birds

29 White Terrace, Rotomahana

30 Otira Gorge and Mount Ruapehu

31 Brown Kiwi

32 Maori War Canoe

33 Pink Terrace, Rotomahana

34 Kea and Kaka

35 Milford Sound

36 Mount Cook

(Des H. Young (½d.), J. Gaut (1d.), W. Bock (2d., 3d., 9d., 1s.), E. Howard (4d., 6d., 8d.), E. Luke (others). Eng A. Hill (2½d., 1s.), J. A. C. Harrison (5d.), Rapkin (others). Recess Waterlow)

1898 (5 Apr). *No wmk. P 12 to 16.*

246	23	½d. purple-brown ..	4·00	40
		a. Imperf between (pair) ..	£650	£650
		b. *Purple-slate* ..	4·50	55
		c. *Purple-black*.. ..	7·00	1·75
247	24	1d. blue and yellow-brown ..	2·75	20
		a. Imperf between (pair) ..	£600	
		b. Imperf vert (horiz pair) ..	£450	£500
		c. Imperf horiz (vert pair) ..	£450	£500
		d. *Blue and brown* ..	3·50	65
		da. Imperf between (pair) ..	£600	
248	25	2d. lake	22·00	20
		a. Imperf vert (horiz pair) ..	£400	
		b. *Rosy lake* ..	22·00	20
		ba. Imperf between (pair) ..	£550	
		bb. Imperf vert (horiz pair) ..	£400	
249	26	2½d. sky-blue (inscr "WAKITIPU")	6·50	18·00
		a. *Blue*	6·50	18·00
250	27	2½d. blue (inscr "WAKATIPU")..	14·00	1·25
		a. *Deep blue* ..	14·00	1·50
251	28	3d. yellow-brown ..	20·00	6·00
252	29	4d. bright rose ..	12·00	14·00
		a. *Lake-rose* ..	14·00	15·00
		b. *Dull rose* ..	12·00	14·00
253	30	5d. sepia	55·00	£120
		a. *Purple-brown* ..	30·00	12·00
254	31	6d. green	48·00	22·00
		a. *Grass-green* ..	55·00	35·00
255	32	8d. indigo	38·00	26·00
		a. *Prussian blue* ..	38·00	20·00
256	33	9d. purple	35·00	22·00
257	34	1s. vermilion	55·00	15·00
		a. *Dull red* ..	55·00	15·00
		b. Imperf between (pair) ..	£1200	
258	35	2s. grey-green ..	90·00	60·00
		a. Imperf between (vert pair) ..	£1200	£1200
259	36	5s. vermilion ..	£170	£200
246/59		*Set of 13*	£475	£350

37 Lake Taupo and Mount Ruapehu

(Recess Govt Printer, Wellington)

1899 (May)–03. *Thick, soft ("Pirie") paper. No wmk. P 11.*

260	27	2½d. blue (6.99) ..	11·00	1·75
		a. Imperf between (pair) ..	£500	
		b. Imperf horiz (vert pair) ..	£300	
		c. *Deep blue* ..	11·00	1·75
261	28	3d. yellow-brown (5.00) ..	22·00	1·50
		a. Imperf between (pair) ..	£650	
		b. Imperf vert (horiz pair) ..	£350	
		c. *Deep brown* ..	22·00	1·50
		ca. Imperf between (pair) ..	£650	
262	37	4d. indigo and brown (8.99) ..	7·00	1·25
		a. *Bright blue and chestnut* ..	7·00	1·25
		b. *Deep blue and bistre-brown*	7·00	1·25
263	30	5d. purple-brown (6.99) ..	18·00	2·50
		a. *Deep purple-brown* ..	18·00	2·25
		ab. Imperf between (pair) ..	£700	
264	31	6d. deep green ..	48·00	48·00
		a. *Yellow-green*..	65·00	75·00
265		6d. pale rose (5.5.00) ..	35·00	2·50
		a. Imperf vert (horiz pair) ..	£350	
		b. *Rose-red* ..	35·00	2·50
		ba. Printed double ..	£350	
		bb. Imperf between (pair) ..	£500	
		bc. Imperf vert (horiz pair) ..	£200	
		bd. Showing part of sheet wmk (7.02)* ..	65·00	27·00
		c. *Scarlet* ..	45·00	8·00
		ca. Imperf vert (horiz pair) ..	£375	
266	32	8d. indigo	26·00	9·00
		a. *Prussian blue* ..	26·00	9·00
267	33	9d. deep purple (8.99) ..	40·00	22·00
		a. *Rosy purple* ..	27·00	8·50
268	34	1s. red (5.00) ..	48·00	6·50
		a. *Dull orange-red* ..	48·00	3·00
		b. *Dull brown-red* ..	48·00	6·50
		c. *Bright red* ..	60·00	22·00
269	35	2s. blue-green (7.99) ..	75·00	30·00
		a. *Laid paper* (1.03) ..	£170	£200
		b. *Grey-green* ..	75·00	38·00
270	36	5s. vermilion (7.99) ..	£170	£180
		a. *Carmine-red*..	£250	£275
260/70		*Set of 11*	£425	£250

*No. 265bd is on paper without general watermark, but showing the words "LISBON SUPERFINE" wmkd once in the sheet; the paper was obtained from Parsons Bros, an American firm with a branch at Auckland.

38

1900. *Thick, soft ("Pirie") paper. Wmk double-lined "NZ" and Star, W 38 (sideways). P 11.*

271	13	½d. black	4·50	3·00
272	15	2d. bright purple ..	10·50	3·00

39 White Terrace, Rotomahana

41

40 Commemorative of the New Zealand Contingent in the South African War

(Des J. Nairn (1½d.). Recess Govt Printer, Wellington)

1900 (Mar–Dec). *Thick, soft ("Pirie") paper. W 38. P 11.*

273	23	½d. pale yellow-green (7.3.00) ..	8·00	2·75
		a. *Yellow-green*.. ..	5·50	20
		b. *Green* ..	4·50	10
		ba. Imperf between (pair) ..	£275	
		c. *Deep green* ..	4·50	10
274	39	1d. crimson (7.3.00) ..	11·00	10
		a. *Rose-red* ..	11·00	10
		ab. Imperf between (pair) ..	£550	£550
		ac. Imperf vert (horiz pair) ..	£275	
		b. *Lake* ..	20·00	2·75
275	40	1½d. khaki (7.12.00) ..	£65·00	£475
		a. *Brown* ..	50·00	50·00
		ab. Imperf vert (horiz pair) ..	£450	
		ac. Imperf (pair).. ..	£550	
		b. *Chestnut* ..	7·50	4·00
		ba. Imperf vert (horiz pair) ..	£450	
		bb. Imperf horiz (vert pair) ..	£550	
		c. *Pale chestnut* ..	7·50	4·00
		ca. Imperf (pair).. ..	£550	

276	41	2d. dull violet (3.00)	..	7·00	45
		a. Imperf between (pair)		£650	
		b. Mauve	..	8·00	1·50
		c. Purple	..	7·00	45
		ca. Imperf between (pair)		£500	

The above ½d. stamps are slightly smaller than those of the previous printing. A new plate was made to print 240 stamps instead of 120 as previously, and to make these fit the watermarked paper the border design was redrawn and contracted, the centre vignette remaining as before. The 2d. stamp is also from a new plate providing smaller designs.

42

(Des G. Bach. Eng J. A. C. Harrison. Recess Waterlow)

1901 (1 Jan). *Universal Penny Postage. No wmk. P 12 to 16.*

277	42	1d. carmine..	..	5·00	2·50

All examples of No. 277 show a small dot above the upper left corner of the value tablet which is not present on later printings.

(Recess Govt Printer, Wellington)

1901 (Feb–Dec). *Thick, soft ("Pirie") paper. W 38. (a) P 11.*

278	42	1d. carmine	..	6·00	15
		a. Imperf vert (horiz pair)		£250	
		b. Deep carmine	..	6·00	15
		ba. Imperf horiz (vert pair)		£250	
		c. Carmine-lake	..	20·00	7·50

(b) P 14

279	23	½d. green (11.01)	..	10·00	2·75
280	42	1d. carmine	..	38·00	9·00
		a. Imperf vert (horiz pair)		£225	

(c) P 14×11

281	23	½d. green	..	8·00	4·00
		a. Deep green		8·00	4·00
		b. Perf 11×14		9·00	9·00
282	42	1d. carmine	..	£250	75·00
		a. Perf 11×14		£1100	£250

(d) P 11 and 14 mixed*

283	23	½d. green	..	30·00	35·00
284	42	1d. carmine	..	£250	75·00

*The term "mixed" is applied to stamps from sheets which were at first perforated 14, or 14×11, and either incompletely or defectively perforated. These sheets were patched on the back with strips of paper, and re-perforated 11 in those parts where the original perforation was defective.

Nos. 278/84 were printed from new plates supplied by Waterlow. These were subsequently used for Nos. 285/307 with later printings on Cowan paper showing considerable plate wear.

(Recess Govt Printer, Wellington)

1901 (Dec). *Thin, hard ("Basted Mills") paper. W 38. (a) P 11.*

285	23	½d. green	..	40·00	50·00
286	42	1d. carmine	..	60·00	60·00

(b) P 14

287	23	½d. green	..	20·00	11·00
		a. Imperf vert (horiz pair)		£325	
288	42	1d. carmine	..	12·00	2·25
		a. Imperf vert (horiz pair)		£250	
		b. Imperf horiz (vert pair)		£250	

(c) P 14×11

289	23	½d. green	..	20·00	30·00
		a. Deep green		20·00	30·00
		b. Perf 11×14		20·00	30·00
290	42	1d. carmine	..	14·00	4·00
		a. Perf 11×14		12·00	2·75

(d) Mixed perfs

291	23	½d. green	..	40·00	50·00
292	42	1d. carmine	..	75·00	50·00

(Recess Govt Printer, Wellington)

1902 (Jan). *Thin, hard ("Cowan") paper. No wmk. (a) P 11.*

293	23	½d. green	..	90·00	

(b) P 14

294	23	½d. green	..	9·00	3·50
295	42	1d. carmine	..	12·00	1·25

(c) P 14×11

296	23	½d. green	..	60·00	
		a. Perf 11×14		70·00	
297	42	1d. carmine	..	£110	£110
		a. Perf 11×14		£110	£110

(d) Mixed perfs

298	23	½d. green	..	90·00	
299	42	1d. carmine	..	£120	£120

43 "Single" Wmk

(Recess Govt Printer, Wellington)

1902 (Apr). *Thin, hard ("Cowan") paper. W 43. (a) P 11.*

300	23	½d. green	..	60·00	70·00
301	42	1d. carmine	..	£550	£400

(b) P 14

302	23	½d. green	..	3·00	15
		a. Imperf vert (horiz pair)		£170	
		b. Deep green	..	3·50	30
		ba. Imperf vert (horiz pair)		£170	
		c. Yellow-green		3·00	30
		d. Pale yellow-green		12·00	2·25
303	42	1d. carmine	..	3·00	10
		a. Imperf horiz (vert pair)		£170	
		b. Booklet pane of 6 (21.8.02)		£200	
		c. Pale carmine	..	3·00	10
		ca. Imperf horiz (vert pair)		£170	
		cb. Booklet pane of 6		£200	
		d. Deep carmine*		32·00	4·00

(c) P 14×11

304	23	½d. green	..	14·00	
		a. Deep green	..	20·00	
		b. Perf 11×14	..	14·00	
305	42	1d. carmine	..	£100	80·00
		a. Perf 11×14	..	£120	90·00
		ab. Deep carmine*		£400	£300

(d) Mixed perfs

306	23	½d. green	..	20·00	
		a. Deep green	..	25·00	
307	42	1d. carmine	..	20·00	20·00
		a. Pale carmine	..	20·00	20·00
		b. Deep carmine*		£250	£250

*Nos. 303*b*, 305*a* and 307*b* were printed from a plate made by Waterlow & Sons, known as the "Reserve" plate. The stamps do not show evidence of wearing and the area surrounding the upper part of the figure is more deeply shaded. This plate was subsequently used to produce Nos. 362, 364, and 366/9.

A special plate, made by W. R. Royle & Sons, showing a minute dot between the horizontal rows, was introduced in 1902 to print the booklet pane, No. 303*b*. A special characteristic of the booklet pane was that the pearl in the top left-handed corner was large. Some panes exist with the outer edges imperforate.

(Recess Govt Printer, Wellington)

1902 (28 Aug)–09. *Thin, hard ("Cowan") paper. W 43 (sideways on 3d., 5d., 6d., 8d., 1s. and 5s.). (a) P 11*

308	27	2½d. blue (5.03)	..	11·00	11·00
		a. Deep blue	..	13·00	11·00
309	28	3d. yellow-brown	..	17·00	60
		a. Bistre-brown..	..	17·00	60
		b. Pale bistre	..	27·00	2·75
310	37	4d. deep blue and deep brown/*bluish* (27.11.02)	..	8·50	45·00
		a. Imperf vert (horiz pair)	..	£450	
311	30	5d. red-brown (4.03)	..	16·00	5·50
		a. Deep brown	..	16·00	3·00
		b. Sepia ..	..	32·00	12·00
312	31	6d. rose (9.02)	..	35·00	3·50
		a. Rose-red	..	35·00	4·50
		ab. Wmk upright	..	£475	£300
		b. Rose-carmine	..	40·00	4·50
		ba. Imperf vert (horiz pair)	..	£400	
		bb. Imperf horiz (vert pair)	..		
		c. Bright carmine-pink	..	50·00	6·00
		d. Scarlet	..	50·00	15·00
313	32	8d. blue (2.03)	..	26·00	6·00
		a. Steel-blue	..	26·00	6·00
		ab. Imperf vert (horiz pair)	..	£500	
		ac. Imperf horiz (vert pair)	..	£500	
314	33	9d. purple (5.03)	..	28·00	10·00
315	34	1s. brown-red (11.02)	..	48·00	5·50
		a. Bright red	..	48·00	6·00
		b. Orange-red	..	48·00	3·25
		ba. Error. Wmk W 12b (inverted)		† £1200	
		c. Orange-brown	..	60·00	8·00
316	35	2s. green (4.03) ..	..	70·00	35·00
		a. Blue-green	..	70·00	35·00
317	36	5s. deep red (6.03)	..	£170	£180
		a. Wmk upright	..	£200	£225
		b. Vermilion	..	£170	£180
		ba. Wmk upright	..	£200	£225

(b) P 14

318	40	1½d. chestnut (2.07) ..	..	12·00	35·00
319	41	2d. grey-purple (12.02)	..	5·50	60
		a. Purple	..	5·50	60
		ab. Imperf vert (horiz pair) ..		£350	
		ac. Imperf horiz (vert pair) ..		£350	
		b. Bright reddish purple	..	6·50	1·25
320	27	2½d. blue (1906)	..	7·00	1·50
		a. Deep blue..	..	7·00	1·75
321	28	3d. bistre-brown (1906)	..	23·00	1·25
		a. Imperf vert (horiz pair) ..		£450	
		b. Bistre	..	23·00	1·25
		c. Pale yellow-bistre	..	48·00	8·00
322	37	4d. deep blue and deep brown/*bluish* (1903)	..	6·00	2·00
		a. Imperf vert (horiz pair)	..	£400	
		b. Imperf horiz (vert pair)	..	£400	
		c. Centre inverted ..	..	† £50000	
		d. Blue and chestnut/*bluish*	..	6·00	70
		e. Blue and ochre-brown/*bluish*	..	6·00	70
323	30	5d. black-brown (1906)	..	50·00	15·00
		a. Red-brown	..	23·00	5·50
324	31	6d. bright carmine-pink (1906)	..	50·00	6·00
		a. Imperf vert (horiz pair)	..	£400	
		b. Rose-carmine	..	50·00	6·50
325	32	8d. steel-blue (1907)..	..	25·00	5·50
326	33	9d. purple (1906)	..	25·00	6·00
327	34	1s. orange-brown (1906)	..	60·00	4·50
		a. Orange-red	..	55·00	4·50
		b. Pale red	..	75·00	24·00
328	35	2s. green (1.06)	..	65·00	20·00
		a. Blue-green	..	65·00	20·00
329	36	5s. deep red (1906)	..	£170	£180
		a. Wmk upright	..	£200	£225
		b. Dull red	..	£170	£180
		ba. Wmk upright	..	£180	£200

(c) Perf compound of 11 and 14

330	40	1½d. chestnut (1907) ..	..	£600	
331	41	2d. purple (1903)	..	£275	
332	28	3d. bistre-brown (1906)	..	£500	£450
333	37	4d. blue and yellow-brown (1903) ..		£300	£300
334	30	5d. red-brown (1906)	..	£425	£450
335	31	6d. rose-carmine (1907)	..	£300	£200
336	32	8d. steel-blue (1907)..	..	£600	
337	33	9d. purple (1906)	..	£700	£700
338	36	5s. deep red (1906)	..	£1500	

(d) Mixed perfs

339	40	1½d. chestnut (1907) ..	..	£600	
340	41	2d. purple (1903)	..	£150	
341	28	3d. bistre-brown (1906)	..	£500	£450
342	37	4d. blue and chestnut/*bluish* (1904)	..	£250	£250
		a. Blue and yellow-brown/*bluish* ..		£250	£250
343	30	5d. red-brown (1906)	..	£400	£400
344	31	6d. rose-carmine (1907)	..	£250	£200
		a. Bright carmine-pink	..	£275	£200
345	32	8d. steel-blue (1907)..	..	£550	
346	33	9d. purple (1906)	..	£700	£700
347	35	2s. blue-green (1906)	..	£800	£800
348	36	5s. vermilion (1906)..	..	£1400	

Two sizes of paper were used for the above stamps:—

(1) A sheet containing 240 wmks, with a space of 9 mm between each.

(2) A sheet containing 120 wmks, with a space of 24 mm between each vertical row.

Size (1) was used for the ½d., 1d., 2d., and 4d., and size (2) for 2½d., 5d., 9d., and 2s. The paper in each case exactly fitted the plates, and had the watermark in register, though in the case of the 4d., the plate of which contained only 80 stamps, the paper was cut up to print it. The 3d., 6d., 8d., and 1s. were printed on variety (1), but with watermark sideways: by reason of this, specimens from the margins of the sheets show parts of the words "NEW ZEALAND POSTAGE" in large letters, and some copies have no watermark at all. For the 1½d. and 5s. stamps variety (1) was also used, but two watermarks appear on each stamp.

(Recess Govt Printer, Wellington)

1904 (Feb). *Printed from new "dot" plates made by W.R. Royle & Sons. Thin, hard ("Cowan") paper. W 43 (a) P 14.*

349	42	1d. rose-carmine	..	7·50	40
		a. Pale carmine	..	7·50	40

(b) P 11×14

350	42	1d. rose-carmine	..	£120	£110

(c) Mixed perfs

351	42	1d. rose-carmine	..	20·00	20·00
		a. Pale carmine	..	20·00	20·00

These plates have a minute dot in the horizontal margins between the rows, centred under each stamp, but it is frequently cut out by the perforations. However, they can be further distinguished by the notes below.

In 1906 fresh printings were made from four new plates, two of which, marked in the margin "W1" and "W2", were supplied by Waterlow Bros and Layton, and the other two, marked "R1" and "R2", by W. R. Royle & Son. The intention was to note which pair of plates wore the best and produced the best results. They can be distinguished as follows:—

(a)	*(b)*	*(c)*
(d)	*(e)*	*(f)*

(a) Four o'clock flaw in rosette at top right corner. Occurs in all these plates but not in the original Waterlow plates.

(b) Pearl at right strong.

(c) Pearl at right weak.

(d) Dot at left and S-shaped ornament unshaded.

(e) S-shaped ornament with one line of shading within.

(f) As (e) but with line from left pearl to edge of stamp.

"Dot" plates comprise (a) and (d).

Waterlow plates comprise (a), (b) and (e).

Royle plates comprise (a), (c) and (e) and the line in (f) on many stamps but not all.

(Recess Govt Printer, Wellington)

1906. *Thin, hard ("Cowan") paper. W 43.*

(a) Printed from new Waterlow plates. (i) P 14

352	42	1d. deep rose-carmine	..	18·00	1·00
		a. Imperf horiz (vert pair)	..	£200	
		b. Aniline carmine	..	17·00	1·00
		ba. Imperf vert (horiz pair)	..	£200	
		c. Rose-carmine	..	17·00	1·00

(ii) P 11

353	42	1d. aniline carmine	..	£500	

(iii) P 11×14

354	42	1d. rose-carmine	..	£400	

(iv) Mixed perfs

355	42	1d. deep rose-carmine	..	£400	

(b) Printed from new Royle plates. (i) P 14

356	42	1d. rose-carmine	..	10·00	1·25
		a. Imperf horiz (vert pair)	..	£225	£225
		b. Bright rose-carmine	..	12·00	1·40

(ii) P 11

357	42	1d. bright rose-carmine	..	£100	

(iii) P 11×14

358	42	1d. rose-carmine	..	85·00	
		a. Perf 14×11	..		

(iv) Mixed perfs

359	42	1d. rose-carmine	..	£100	

(v) P 14×14½ (comb)

360	42	1d. bright rose-carmine	..	60·00	42·00
		a. Rose-carmine	..	60·00	42·00

Nos. 360/a are known both with and without the small dot. See also No. 386.

1905 (15 June)–06. *Stamps supplied to penny-in-the-slot machines.*

(i) *"Dot" plates of 1904.* (ii) *Waterlow "reserve" plate of 1902*

(a) Imperf top and bottom; zigzag roulette 9½ on one or both sides, two large holes at sides

361	42	1d. rose-carmine (i)	£120
362		1d. deep carmine (ii)	£140

(b) As last but rouletted 14½ (8.7.05)

363	42	1d. rose-carmine (i)	£140
364		1d. deep carmine (ii)	£250

(c) Imperf all round, two large holes each side (6.3.06)

365	42	1d. rose-carmine (i)	£100
366		1d. deep carmine (ii)	£100

(d) Imperf all round (21.6.06)

367	42	1d. deep carmine (ii)	£130

(e) Imperf all round. Two small indentations on back of stamp (1.06)

368	42	1d. deep carmine (ii)	£160	£130

(f) Imperf all round; two small pin-holes in stamp (21.6.06)

369	42	1d. deep carmine (ii)	£140	£130

No. 365 only exists from strips of Nos. 361 or 363 (resulting from the use of successive coins) which have been separated by scissors. Similarly strips of Nos. 362 and 364 can produce single copies of No. 366 but this also exists in singles from a different machine.

Most used copies of Nos. 361/7 are forgeries and they should only be collected on cover.

44 Maori Canoe, *Te Arawa*

(Des L. J. Steele. Eng W. R. Bock. Typo Govt Printer, Wellington)

1906 (1–17 Nov). *New Zealand Exhibition, Christchurch.* T **44** *and similar horiz designs.* W **43** *(sideways).* P 14.

370		½d. emerald-green	16·00	23·00
371		1d. vermilion	13·00	15·00
	a.	Claret	£7000	£8000
372		3d. brown and blue	45·00	55·00
373		6d. pink and olive-green (17.11)	£140	£225
370/3		*Set of 4*	£200	£275

Designs:—1d. Maori art; 3d. Landing of Cook; 6d. Annexation of New Zealand.

The 1d. in claret was the original printing, which was considered unsatisfactory.

47 (T **28** reduced)   **48** (T **31** reduced)   **49** (T **34** reduced)

(New plates (except 4d.), supplied by Perkins Bacon. Recess Govt Printer, Wellington).

1907–8. *Thin, hard ("Cowan") paper.* W **43**. (a) *P* 14 *(line).*

374	23	½d. green (1907)	24·00	7·00
	a.	Imperf (pair)	£120	
	b.	Yellow-green	16·00	2·50
	c.	Deep yellow-green	14·00	1·75
375	47	3d. brown (6.07)	42·00	19·00
376	48	6d. carmine-pink (3.07)	38·00	6·00
	a.	Red	65·00	28·00

(b) P 14×13, 13½ *(comb)*

377	23	½d. green (1907)	12·00	5·00
	a.	Yellow-green	8·00	85
378	47	3d. brown (2.08)	42·00	23·00
	a.	Yellow-brown	42·00	25·00
379	37	4d. blue and yellow-brown/bluish (6.08)	27·00	20·00
380	48	6d. pink (2.08)	£250	85·00
381	49	1s. orange-red (12.07)	£130	48·00

(c) P 14×15 *(comb)*

382	23	½d. yellow-green (1907)	8·00	60
383	47	3d. brown (8.08)	35·00	7·00
	a.	Yellow-brown	35·00	7·00
384	48	6d. carmine-pink (8.08)	38·00	9·50
385	49	1s. orange-red (8.08)	£120	24·00
	a.	Deep orange-brown	£300	

The ½d. stamps of this 1907–8 issue have a minute dot in the margin between the stamps, where not removed by the perforation. (See note after No. 351a.) Those perforated 14 can be distinguished from the earlier stamps, Nos. 302/d, by the absence of plate wear. This is most noticeable on the 1902 printings as a white patch at far left, level with the bottom of the "P" in "POSTAGE". Such damage is not present on the new plates used for Nos. 374/c.

Stamps of T **47**, **48** and **49** also have a small dot as described in note after No. 351a.

TYPOGRAPHY PAPERS. 1908–30. De La Rue paper is chalk-surfaced and has a smooth finish. The watermark is as illustrated. The gum is toned and strongly resistant to soaking. **Jones paper** is chalk-surfaced and has a coarser texture, is poorly surfaced and the ink tends to peel. The outline of the watermark commonly shows on the surface of the stamp. The gum is colourless or only slightly toned and washes off readily. **Cowan paper** is chalk-surfaced and is white and opaque. The watermark is usually smaller than in the "Jones" paper and is often barely visible.

Wiggins Teape paper is chalk-surfaced and is thin and hard. It has a vertical mesh with a narrow watermark, whereas the other papers have a horizontal mesh and a wider watermark.

50

(Typo Govt Printer, Wellington, from Perkins Bacon plate).

1908 (1 Dec). *De La Rue chalk-surfaced paper.* W **43**. P 14×15 *(comb).*

386	50	1d. carmine	30·00	50

The design of Type **50** differs from Type **42** by alterations in the corner rosettes and by the lines on the globe which are diagonal instead of vertical.

51   **52**   **53**

(Eng P.B. Typo Govt Printer, Wellington)

1909 (8 Nov)–12. *De La Rue chalk-surfaced paper with toned gum.* W **43**. P 14×15 *(comb).*

387	51	½d. yellow-green	3·25	10
	aa.	Deep green	3·25	20
	a.	Imperf (pair)	£140	
	b.	Booklet pane. Five stamps plus label in position 1 (4.10)	£475	
	c.	Ditto, but label in position 6 (4.10)	£475	
	d.	Booklet pane of 6 (4.10)	£150	
	e.	Ditto, but with coloured bars on selvedge (5.12)	£140	

Stamps with blurred and heavy appearance are from booklets.

(Eng W. R. Royle & Son, London. Recess Govt Printer, Wellington)

1909 (8 Nov)–16. T **52** *and similar portraits.*

(a) W **43**. *P* 14×14½ *(comb)*

388		2d. mauve	14·00	5·00
	a.	Deep mauve	18·00	5·00
389		3d. chestnut	18·00	30
390		4d. orange-red	22·00	22·00
	a.	Orange-yellow (1912)	7·00	2·00
391		5d. brown (1910)	14·00	80
	a.	Red-brown	12·00	80
392		6d. carmine (1910)	28·00	40
	a.	Deep carmine (29.10.13)	28·00	85
393		8d. indigo-blue	10·00	65
	a.	Deep bright blue	13·00	65
394		1s. vermilion (1910)	48·00	1·75
388/94		*Set of 8*	£140	28·00

(b) W **43**. *P* 14 *(line)**

395		3d. chestnut (1910)	40·00	4·00
396		4d. orange (1910)	15·00	5·50
397		5d. brown	23·00	3·00
	a.	Red-brown (15.9.11)	25·00	3·50
398		6d. carmine	40·00	6·50
399		1s. vermilion	48·00	6·50
395/9		*Set of 5*	£150	23·00

(c) W **43** *(sideways) (paper with widely spaced watermark as used for Nos. 308 and 320 – see note below No. 348).* P 14 *(line)**

400		8d. indigo-blue (8.16)	14·00	38·00
	a.	No wmk	55·00	90·00

(d) W **43**. *P* 14×13½ *(comb)†*

401		3d. chestnut (1915)	60·00	65·00
	a.	Vert pair. P 14×13½ and 14×14½	£225	£275
402		5d. red-brown (1916)	18·00	1·75
	a.	Vert pair. P 14×13½ and 14×14½	50·00	70·00
403		6d. carmine (1915)	70·00	70·00
	a.	Vert pair. P 14×13½ and 14×14½	£225	£275
404		8d. indigo-blue (3.16)	24·00	1·75
	a.	Vert pair. P 14×13½ and 14×14½	50·00	70·00
	b.	Deep bright blue	24·00	1·75
	ba.	Vert pair. P 14×13½ and 14×14½	50·00	70·00
401/4		*Set of 4*	£150	£120

*In addition to showing the usual characteristics of a line perforation, these stamps may be distinguished by their vertical perforation which measures 13.8. Nos. 388/94 generally measure vertically 14 to 14.3. An exception is 13.8 one vertical side but 14 the other.

†The 3d. and 6d. come in full sheets perf 14×13½. The 3d., 5d. and 6d. values also exist in two combinations: (a) five top rows perf 14×13½ with five bottom rows perf 14×14½ and (b) four top rows perf 14×13½ with six bottom rows perf 14×14½. The 8d. perf 14×13½ only exists from combination (b).

(Eng P.B. Typo Govt Printer, Wellington)

1909 (8 Nov)–26. *P* 14×15 *(comb).*

(a) W **43**. *De La Rue chalk-surfaced paper with toned gum*

405	53	1d. carmine	1·25	10
	a.	Imperf (pair)	£200	
	b.	Booklet pane of 6 (4.10)	£140	
	c.	Ditto, but with coloured bars on selvedge (5.12)	£110	

(b) W **43**. *Jones chalk-surfaced paper with white gum*

406	53	1d. deep carmine (1924)	12·00	4·00
	a.	On unsurfaced paper. Pale carmine	£275	
	b.	Booklet pane of 6 with bars on selvedge (1.12.24)	£100	

(c) W **43**. *De La Rue unsurfaced medium paper with toned gum*

407	53	1d. rose-carmine (4.25)	26·00	60·00

(d) W **43** *(sideways). De La Rue chalk-surfaced paper with toned gum*

408	53	1d. bright carmine (4.25)	6·50	22·00
	a.	No wmk	20·00	40·00
	b.	Imperf (pair)	50·00	

(e) No wmk, but bluish "NZ" and Star lithographed on back. Art paper

409	53	1d. rose-carmine (1925)	2·25	1·25
	a.	"NZ" and Star in black	10·00	
	b.	"NZ" and Star colourless	24·00	

(f) W **43**. *Cowan thick, opaque, chalk-surfaced paper with white gum*

410	53	1d. deep carmine (8.25)	4·25	1·00
	a.	Imperf (pair)	65·00	70·00
	b.	Booklet pane of 6 with bars and adverts on selvedge	£100	

(g) W **43**. *Wiggins Teape thin, hard, chalk-surfaced paper with white gum*

411	53	1d. rose-carmine (6.26)	24·00	9·00

Examples of No. 405 with a blurred and heavy appearance are from booklets.

No. 406a comes from a sheet on which the paper coating was missing from the right-hand half.

Many stamps from the sheets of No. 408 were without watermark or showed portions of "NEW ZEALAND POSTAGE" in double-lined capitals.

AUCKLAND EXHIBITION, 1913.

(**59**)

60

1913 (1 Dec). *Auckland Industrial Exhibition. Nos. 387aa, 389, 392 and 405 optd with T* **59** *by Govt Printer, Wellington.*

412	51	½d. deep green	10·00	24·00
413	53	1d. carmine	16·00	27·00
414	52	3d. chestnut	£100	£170
415		6d. carmine	£110	£200
412/15		*Set of 4*	£200	£375

These overprinted stamps were only available for letters in New Zealand and to Australia.

(Des H. L. Richardson. Recess Govt Printer, Wellington, from plates made in London by P.B.)

1915 (30 July)–29. *P* 14×14½, *comb (See notes below).*

(a) W **43**. *Cowan unsurfaced paper*

416	60	1½d. grey-slate	3·00	50
	a.	Perf 14×13½	2·00	50
	b.	Vert pair, 416/a	35·00	50·00
417		2d. bright violet	7·00	17·00
	a.	Perf 14×13½	7·00	17·00
	b.	Vert pair, 417/a	24·00	50·00
418		2d. yellow (15.1.16)	4·50	13·00
	a.	Perf 14×13½	4·50	13·00
	b.	Vert pair, 418/a	18·00	48·00
419		2½d. blue	8·50	5·00
	a.	Perf 14×13½ (1916)	3·25	1·50
	b.	Vert pair, 419/a	35·00	65·00
420		3d. chocolate	7·50	75
	a.	Perf 14×13½	7·50	70
	b.	Vert pair, 420/a	35·00	55·00
421		4d. yellow	4·25	30·00
	a.	Perf 14×13½	4·25	30·00
	b.	Vert pair, 421/a	26·00	£120
	c.	Re-entry (Pl 20 R. 1/6)	30·00	
	d.	Re-entry (Pl 20 R. 4/10)	35·00	
422		4d. bright violet (7.4.16)	7·00	30
	a.	Perf 14×13½	5·00	30
	b.	Imperf (pair)	£750	
	c.	Vert pair, 422/a	35·00	65·00
	d.	Re-entry (Pl 20 R. 1/6)	35·00	
	e.	Re-entry (Pl 20 R. 4/10)	40·00	
423		4½d. deep green	19·00	15·00
	a.	Perf 14×13½	12·00	3·00
	b.	Vert pair, 423/a	48·00	65·00
424		5d. light blue (4.22)	18·00	20·00
	a.	Perf 14×13½	6·00	70
	b.	Imperf (pair)	£110	£120
	c.	Pale ultramarine (5.29)	12·00	8·50
	ca.	Perf 14×13½	8·00	3·75
	cb.	Vert pair, 424c/ca	55·00	75·00
425		6d. carmine	7·00	30
	a.	Perf 14×13½	5·50	30
	b.	Vert pair, 425/a (1916)	65·00	95·00
	c.	Imperf three sides (pair)	£1200	
	d.	Carmine-lake. Perf 14×13½ (11.27)	£500	£325
426		7½d. red-brown	32·00	38·00
	a.	Perf 14×13½ (10.20)	13·00	18·00
	b.	Vert pair, 426/a	50·00	80·00
427		8d. indigo-blue (19.4.21)	17·00	35·00
	a.	Perf 14×13½	16·00	35·00
	b.	Vert pair, 427/a	38·00	80·00
428		8d. red-brown (p 14×13½) (2.22)	15·00	90
429		9d. sage-green	17·00	4·50
	a.	Perf 14×13½	13·00	1·00
	b.	Vert pair, 429/a	70·00	£100
	c.	Imperf three sides (pair)	£1300	
	d.	Imperf (pair)	£1000	
	e.	Yellowish ol. Perf 14×13½ (12.25)	28·00	7·00
430		1s. vermilion	13·00	30
	a.	Perf 14×13½	13·00	1·25
	b.	Imperf (pair)	£2250	
	c.	Vert pair, 430/a	75·00	£100
	d.	Pale orange-red (1925)	30·00	6·50
416/30		*Set of 15*	£850	£425
	db.	Orange-brown (1.2.28)	£325	

(b) W **43** *(sideways on 2d., 3d. and 6d.). Thin paper with widely spaced watermark as used for Nos. 308 and 320 – see note below No. 348).*

431	60	1½d. grey-slate (3.16)	1·50	4·00
	a.	No wmk	2·00	7·00
	b.	Perf 14×13½	1·50	4·00
	ba.	No wmk	2·00	7·00
	c.	Vert pair, 431/b	20·00	35·00
	ca.	Vert pair, 431a/ba	28·00	50·00
432		2d. yellow (p 14, line) (6.16)	4·50	35·00
	a.	No wmk	30·00	65·00
433		3d. chocolate (p 14, line) (6.16)	6·00	11·00
	a.	No wmk	26·00	55·00

434 60 6d. carmine (p 14, line) (8.16) .. 6·00 42·00
a. No wmk .. .. .. 35·00 80·00
431/4 .. .. Set of 4 16·00 80·00

The 1½d., 2½d., 4½d. and 7½d. have value tablets as shown in T 60. In the other values, the tablets are shortened, and the ornamental border at each side of the crown correspondingly extended.

During the laying-down of plate 20 for the 4d., from the roller-die which also contained dies of other values, an impression of the 4½d. value was placed on R.1/6 and of the 2½d. on R.4/10. These errors were subsequently corrected by re-entries of the 4d. impression, but on R.1/6 traces of the original impression can be found in the right-hand value tablet and above the top frame line, while on R.4/10 the foot of the "2" is visible in the left-hand value tablet with traces of "½" to its right.

Of this issue the 1½d., 2½d., 4d. (both), 4½d., 5d., 6d., 7½d., 9d. and 1s are known from sheets perforated 14×13½ throughout and the 4d. violet, 5d., 6d. and 1s. from sheets perforated 14×14½ throughout.

All values from 1½d. to 1s. were also produced showing the use of the two different perforations within the same sheet as described beneath No. 404ba. In most instances the top four rows were perforated 14×13½ and the bottom six 14×14½. For one printing of the 4d. violet and for all printings of the 5d. pale ultramarine with two perforations on the same sheet the arrangement differed in that the top five rows were perforated 14×14½ and the bottom five 14×13½.

With the exception of Nos. 432/4 any with perforations measuring 14×14 or nearly must be classed as 14×14½, this being an irregularity of the comb machine, and not a product of the 14-line machine.

WAR STAMP

61 62 (63)

Type 62 (from local plates) can be identified from Type 61 (prepared by Perkins Bacon) by the shading on the portrait. This is diagonal on Type 62 and horizontal on Type 61.

(Die eng W. R. Bock. Typo Govt Printer, Wellington, from plates made by P.B. (T 61) or locally (T 62))

1915 (30 July)–34. P 14×15.
(a) W 43. De La Rue chalk-surfaced paper with toned gum.
435 61 ½d. green 70 10
a. Booklet pane of 6 with bars on
selvedge £110
b. Yellow-green .. .. 3·25 60
ba. Booklet pane of 6 with bars on
selvedge .. .. 90·00
c. Very thick, hard, highly surfaced
paper with white gum (12.15) .. 12·00 23·00
436 62 1½d. grey-black (4.16) .. .. 3·25 50
a. Black .. .. 4·50 55
437 61 1½d. slate (5.9.16) .. 6·50 10
438 1½d. orange-brown (9.18) .. 1·75 10
439 2d. yellow (9.16) .. 1·00 10
a. Pale yellow .. .. 3·75 60
440 3d. chocolate (5.19) .. .. 6·00 40
435/40 .. Set of 6 17·00 85

(b) W 43. Jones chalk-surfaced paper with white gum
441 61 ½d. green (10.24) .. .. 6·50 4·00
a. Booklet pane of 6 with bars on
selvedge (1.12.24).. .. £100
442 2d. dull yellow (7.24) .. .. 4·00 18·00
443 3d. deep chocolate (3.25) .. 18·00 6·00
441/3 .. Set of 3 26·00 25·00

(c) No wmk, but bluish "NZ" and Star lithographed on back. Art paper
444 61 ½d. apple-green (4.25) .. .. 1·50 1·25
a. "NZ" and Star almost colourless.. 4·25
445 2d. yellow (7.25) .. .. 6·00 35·00

(d) W 43. Cowan thick, opaque, chalk-surfaced paper with white gum
446 61 ½d. green (8.25) 40 10
a. Booklet pane of 6 with bars and
adverts on selvedge .. 90·00
ab. Booklet pane of 6 with bars on
selvedge (1934) 50 20
b. Perf 14 (1927) 50 20
ba. Booklet pane of 6 with bars on
selvedge (1928) .. 65·00
bb. Booklet pane of 6 with bars and
adverts on selvedge (1928) .. 65·00
447 1½d. orange-brown (p 14) (8.29) .. 8·50 12·00
a. Perf 14×15 (7.33) .. 45·00 50·00
448 2d. yellow (8.25) .. .. 3·50 20
a. Perf 14 (1929) .. .. 2·75 10
449 3d. chocolate (8.25) .. 6·50 20
a. Perf 14 (1929) .. 7·50 1·50
446/9 .. Set of 4 17·00 12·00

(e) W 43. Wiggins Teape thin, hard, chalk-surfaced paper
450 61 1½d. orange-brown (p 14) (1930) .. 30·00 60·00
451 2d. yellow (5.26) .. .. 7·50 15·00
a. Perf 14 (10.27) .. .. 6·50 15·00
The designs of these stamps also differ as described beneath No. 434.
Stamps from booklet panes often have blurred, heavy impressions. Different advertisements can be found on the listed booklet panes.

1915 (24 Sept). No. 435 optd with T 63.
452 61 ½d. green .. .. .. 1·60 20

64 "Peace" and Lion   65 "Peace" and Lion

(Des and typo D.L.R. from plates by P.B., Waterlow and D.L.R.)
1920 (27 Jan). Victory. T 64/5 and similar designs. W 43 (sideways on ½d., 1½d., 3d. and 1s.). De La Rue chalk-surfaced paper. P 14.
453 ½d. green .. .. .. 2·00 1·60
a. Pale yellow-green .. 24·00 16·00
454 1d. carmine-red .. .. 4·00 30
a. Bright carmine .. 6·00 40
455 1½d. brown-orange .. .. 3·50 20
456 3d. chocolate .. .. 13·00 11·00
457 6d. violet .. .. 13·00 14·00
458 1s. orange-red .. .. 24·00 42·00
453/8 .. Set of 6 55·00 60·00
Designs: Horiz (as T 65)—1½d. Maori chief. (As T 64)—3d. Lion; 1s. King George V. Vert (as T 64)—6d. "Peace" and "Progress".
The above stamps were placed on sale in London in November, 1919.

2d.   2d.

TWOPENCE
(68)   69

1922 (Mar). Surch with T 68.
459 64 2d. on ½d. green (R.) .. .. 2·00 75

(Des and eng W. R. Bock. Typo Govt Printer, Wellington)
1923 (1 Oct)–25. Restoration of Penny Postage. W 43. P 14×15.
(a) De La Rue chalk-surfaced paper with toned gum.
460 69 1d. carmine .. .. 1·75 30
(b) Jones chalk-surfaced paper with white gum
461 69 1d. carmine (3.24) .. .. 4·00 2·75
(c) Cowan unsurfaced paper with very shiny gum
462 69 1d. carmine-pink (4.25) .. 27·00 25·00
The paper used for No. 462 is similar to that of Nos. 416/30.

70 Exhibition Buildings

(Des H. L. Richardson. Eng and typo Govt Printer, Wellington)
1925 (17 Nov). Dunedin Exhibition. W 43. Cowan chalk-surfaced paper. P 14×15.
463 70 ½d. yellow-green/green.. .. 2·00 11·00
464 1d. carmine/rose .. .. 2·50 5·00
465 4d. mauve/pale mauve .. .. 38·00 65·00
a. "POSTAGF" at right (R.1/2, R.10/1) £120 £170
463/5 .. Set of 3 38·00 75·00

71   72

(Des H. L. Richardson; plates by B.W. (1d. from sheets), P.B. (1d. from booklets), Royal Mint, London (others). Typo Govt Printer, Wellington)
1926 (12 July)–34. W 43. P 14. (a) Jones chalk-surfaced paper with white gum.
466 72 2s. deep blue .. .. 45·00 50·00
467 3s. mauve .. .. 70·00 90·00
(b) Cowan thick, opaque, chalk-surfaced paper with white gum
468 71 1d. rose-carmine (15.11.26) .. 40 10
a. Imperf (pair).. .. 60·00
b. Booklet pane of 6 with bars on
selvedge (1928) .. 65·00
c. Booklet pane of 6 with bars and
adverts on selvedge (1928) .. 65·00
d. Perf 14×15 (3.27) .. 45 10
da. Booklet pane of 6 with bars and
adverts on selvedge (1934) .. 75·00
469 72 2s. light blue (5.27) .. 45·00 15·00
470 3s. pale mauve (9.27) .. 70·00 85·00
468/70 .. Set of 3 £100 90·00
(c) Wiggins Teape thin, hard, chalk-surfaced paper with white gum
471 71 1d. rose-carmine (6.30) .. .. 14·00 6·50
No. 468 exists in a range of colours including scarlet and deep carmine to magenta but we have insufficient evidence to show that these were issued.

73 Nurse   74 Smiling Boy

(Typo Govt Printing Office, Wellington)
1929–30. Anti-Tuberculosis Fund. T 73 and similar type. W 43. P 14. (a) Inscribed "HELP STAMP OUT TUBERCULOSIS".
544 1d. + 1d. scarlet (11.12.29) .. 11·00 14·00
(b) Inscribed "HELP PROMOTE HEALTH"
545 1d. + 1d. scarlet (29.10.30) .. 17·00 22·00

(Des L. C. Mitchell. Dies eng and plates made Royal Mint, London (1d.), Govt Ptg Office, Wellington from W. R. Bock die (2d.). Typo Govt Ptg Office, Wellington)
1931 (31 Oct). Health Stamps. W 43 (sideways). P 14½×14.
546 74 1d. + 1d. scarlet .. 75·00 75·00
547 2d. + 1d. blue .. 75·00 65·00

75 New Zealand Lake Scenery   (76)

FIVE PENCE

(Des L. C. Mitchell. Plates, Royal Mint, London. Typo Govt Ptg Office)
1931 (10 Nov)–35. Air. W 43. P 14×14½.
548 75 3d. chocolate .. .. 18·00 12·00
a. Perf 14×15 (4.35) .. £190 £425
549 4d. blackish purple .. 20·00 12·00
550 7d. brown-orange .. 22·00 7·50
548/50 .. Set of 3 55·00 28·00

1931 (18 Dec). Air. Surch with T 76.
551 75 5d. on 3d. green (R.) .. .. 9·00 6·50

77 Hygeia,   78 The Path to Health
Goddess of Health

(Des R. E. Tripe and W. J. Cooch. Eng H. T. Peat. Recess Govt Printing Office, Wellington)
1932 (18 Nov). Health Stamp. W 43. P 14.
552 77 1d. + 1d. carmine .. .. 20·00 22·00

(Des J. Berry. Eng H. T. Peat. Recess Govt Printing Office, Wellington)
1933 (8 Nov). Health Stamp. W 43. P 14.
553 78 1d. + 1d. carmine .. .. 7·50 13·00

TRANS-TASMAN
AIR MAIL
"FAITH IN AUSTRALIA."
(79)   80 Crusader

1934 (17 Jan). Air. T 75 in new colour optd with T 79. W 43. P 14×14½.
554 75 7d. light blue (B.) .. .. 38·00 38·00

(Des J. Berry. Recess D.L.R.)
1934 (25 Oct). Health Stamp. W 43. P 14×13½.
555 80 1d. + 1d. carmine .. .. 6·00 7·00

81 Collared Grey   82 Brown Kiwi   83 Maori Woman
Fantail

84 Maori Carved House   85 Mt Cook

86 Maori Girl   87 Mitre Peak

88 Swordfish

89 Harvesting

90 Tuatara Lizard

91 Maori Panel

92 Tui

93 Capt. Cook at Poverty Bay

94 Mt Egmont

Die I   Die II

CAPTAIN COQK
AT POVERTY BAY
OCTOBER 8ᵀᴴ 1769

"Captain Coqk"
(R. 1/4)

(Des J. Fitzgerald (½d., 4d.), C. H. and R. J. G. Collins (1d.),
M. Matthews (1½d.), H. W. Young (2d.), L. C. Mitchell (2½d.,
3d., 8d., 1s., 3s.), W. J. Cooch and R. E. Tripe (5d.), T. I. Archer
(6d.), I. F. Calder (9d.) and I. H. Jenkins (2s.). Litho Waterlow
(9d.). Recess D.L.R. (remainder))

1935 (1 May). *W* **43**.
556	81	½d. bright green, p 14 × 13½..	..		1·50	30
557	82	1d. scarlet (Die I), p 14 × 13½	..		1·50	20
		a. Perf 13½ × 14	..	..	55·00	24·00
		b. Die II. Perf 14 × 13½	..		5·00	1·50
		ba. Booklet pane of 6 with adverts on				
		selvedge	..	..	35·00	
558	83	1½d. red-brown, p 14 × 13½	..		4·25	5·00
		a. Perf 13½ × 14	..		4·25	3·75
559	84	2d. orange, p 14 × 13½	..		1·50	30
560	85	2½d. chocolate and slate, p 13–14 × 13½	4·50	14·00
		a. Perf 13½ × 14	..		4·00	12·00
561	86	3d. brown, p 14 × 13½	..		8·00	90
562	87	4d. black and sepia, p 14	..		2·25	55
563	88	5d. ultramarine, p 13–14 × 13½		9·00	15·00
		a. Perf 13½ × 14	..		16·00	16·00
564	89	6d. scarlet, p 13½ × 14	..		4·00	3·25
565	90	8d. chocolate, p 14 × 13½	..		4·00	3·25
566	91	9d. scarlet and black, p 14 × 14½		9·00	2·50
567	92	1s. deep green, p 14 × 13½	..		14·00	4·25
568	93	2s. olive-green, p 13–14 × 13½		24·00	18·00
		a. "CAPTAIN COQK"	..		42·00	
		b. Perf 13½ × 14	..		35·00	22·00
		ba. "CAPTAIN COQK"	..		55·00	
569	94	3s. chocolate & yell-brn, p 13–14 ×			
		13½	..		15·00	32·00
		a. Perf 13½ × 14	..		15·00	32·00
556/69a				*Set of 14*	90·00	85·00

Some stamps from sheets perforated 14×13½ by De La Rue
sometimes show the horizontal perforations nearer 13½.

In the 2½d., 5d., 2s. and 3s. perf 13–14×13½ the horizontal
perforations of each stamp are in two sizes, one half of each
horizontal side measuring 13 and the other 14.

See also Nos. 577/90 and 630/1.

95 Bell Block Aerodrome

96 King George V
and Queen Mary

(Des J. Berry. Eng Stamp Printing Office, Melbourne. Recess Govt
Printing Office, Wellington)

1935 (4 May). *Air. W* **43**. *P* **14**.
570	95	1d. carmine	..		40	40
571		3d. violet	..	..	2·75	2·75
572		6d. blue ..	..	..	6·00	1·75
570/2				*Set of 3*	8·00	4·50

(Frame by J. Berry. Recess B.W.)

1935 (7 May). *Silver Jubilee. W* **43**. *P* 11 × 11½.
573	96	½d. green	..	..	1·00	70
574		1d. carmine	..	..	1·40	50
575		6d. red-orange ..	..		12·00	17·00
573/5		..	..	*Set of 3*	13·00	17·00

97 "The Key to Health"   98 "Multiple Wmk"

(Des S. Hall. Recess John Ash, Melbourne)

1935 (30 Sept). *Health Stamp. W* **43**. *P* 11.
576	97	1d. + 1d. scarlet	..	..	1·50	2·25

WATERMARKS. In W **43** the wmk units are in vertical columns
widely spaced and the sheet margins are unwatermarked or wmkd
"NEW ZEALAND POSTAGE" in large letters.

In W **98** the wmk units are arranged alternately in horizontal
rows closely spaced and are continued into the sheet margins.

(Litho Govt Ptg Office, Wellington (9d.). Recess Waterlow or D.L.R.
(others))

1936–43. *W* **98**.
577	81	½d. bright green, p 14×13½	..		1·00	10
578	82	1d. scarlet (Die II), p 14×13½	..		55	10
579	83	1½d. red-brown, p 14×13½	..		6·00	2·00
580	84	2d. orange, p 14×13½	..		20	10
		b. Perf 12½† (6.41)	..		2·75	10
		c. Perf 14 (6.41)	..		13·00	70
		d. Perf 14×15 (6.41)	..		24·00	6·00
581	85	2½d. chocolate and slate, p 13–14×13½		75	3·75
		a. Perf 14	..		2·00	1·25
		b. Perf 14×13½ (1942)	..		50	1·75
582	86	3d. brown, p 14×13½	..		28·00	15
583	87	4d. black and sepia, p 14×13½	..		3·25	10
		a. Perf 12½* (1941)	..		17·00	90
		b. Perf 14, line (1941)	..		55·00	45·00
		c. Perf 14×14½ comb (7.42)	..		80	10
584	88	5d. ultramarine, p 13–14×13½	..		6·00	1·40
		b. Perf 12½*† (7.41, 1942)	..		20·00	95
		c. Perf 14×13½ (1942)	..		2·50	65
585	89	6d. scarlet, p 13½×14	..		6·50	40
		a. Perf 12½* (1941)	..		2·75	60
		b. Perf 14½×14 (1942)	..		75	10
586	90	8d. choc, p 14×13½ (*wmk sideways*)		5·00	1·25
		a. Wmk upright (1939)	..		3·00	1·25
		b. Perf 12½* (*wmk sideways*) (1941)		2·50	90
		c. Perf 14×14½ (*wmk sideways*)			
		(1943)	..		3·00	2·00
587	91	9d. red & grey, p 14×15 (*wmk sideways*)	35·00	2·00
		a. *Red and grey-black. Perf* 13½×14			
		(1.3.38)	..		42·00	1·75
588	92	1s. deep green, p 14×13½	..		2·25	30
		b. Perf 12½* (11.41)	..		55·00	8·50
589	93	2s. olive-green, p 13–14×13½	..		20·00	2·00
		a. "CAPTAIN COQK"	..		45·00	
		b. Perf 13½×14 (1938)	..		£170	2·00
		ba. "CAPTAIN COQK"	..		£180	
		c. Perf 12½*† (1941, 1942)	..		35·00	3·00
		ca. "CAPTAIN COQK"	..		55·00	
		d. Perf 14×13½ (1942)	..		14·00	1·25
		da. "CAPTAIN COQK"	..		55·00	
590	94	3s. chocolate & yell-brn, p 13–14×13½		28·00	4·00
		a. Perf 12½* (1941)	..		60·00	27·00
		b. Perf 14×13½ (1942)	..		6·00	1·50
577/90b			..	*Set of 14*	90·00	8·50

*†Stamps indicated with an asterisk were printed and perforated
by Waterlow; those having a dagger were printed by D.L.R. and
perforated by Waterlow. No. 580d was printed by D.L.R. and perforated by Harrison and No. 583b was printed by Waterlow and
perforated by D.L.R. These are all known as "Blitz perfs" because
De La Rue were unable to maintain supplies after their works were
damaged by enemy action. All the rest, except the 9d., were printed
and perforated by D.L.R.

On stamps printed and perforated by De La Rue the perf
14 × 13½ varies in the sheet and is sometimes nearer 13½. 2d.
perf 14 × 15 is sometimes nearer 14 × 14½.

2½d., 5d., 2s. and 3s. In perf 13–14 × 13½ one half the length of
each horizontal perforation measures 13 and the other 14. In perf
14 × 13½ the horizontal perforation is regular.

4d. No. 583b is line-perf measuring 14 exactly and has a blackish
sepia frame. No. 583c is a comb-perf measuring 14 × 14.3 or
14 × 14.2 and the frame is a warmer shade.

2s. No. 589b is comb-perf and measures 13.5 × 13.75.

For 9d. typographed, see Nos. 630/1.

99 N.Z. Soldier at
Anzac Cove

100 Wool

(Des L. C. Mitchell. Recess John Ash, Melbourne)

1936 (27 Apr). *Charity. 21st Anniv of "Anzac" Landing at Gallipoli. W* **43**. *P* 11.
591	99	½d. + ½d. green	..		35	1·40
592		1d. + 1d. scarlet	..		35	90

(Des L. C. Mitchell. Recess John Ash, Melbourne)

1936 (1 Oct). *Congress of British Empire Chambers of
Commerce, Wellington. Industries Issue. T* **100** *and similar
horiz designs. W* **43** (*sideways*). *P* 11½.
593		½d. emerald-green	..		30	30
594		1d. scarlet	..	..	30	20
595		2½d. blue	..	..	1·00	6·00
596		4d. violet	..	..	80	4·75
597		6d. red-brown	..	..	1·25	3·75
593/7				*Set of 5*	3·25	13·50

Designs:—1d. Butter; 2½d. Sheep; 4d. Apples; 6d. Exports.

105 Health Camp

106 King George VI and
Queen Elizabeth

(Des J. Berry. Recess John Ash, Melbourne)

1936 (2 Nov). *Health Stamp. W* **43**. *P* 11.
598	105	1d. + 1d. scarlet	..	..	1·00	3·25

(Recess B.W.)

1937 (13 May). *Coronation. W* **98**. *P* 14 × 13½.
599	106	1d. carmine	..	..	30	10
600		2½d. Prussian blue	..		1·75	1·60
601		6d. red-orange ..	..		2·40	1·25
599/601				*Set of 3*	4·00	2·50

107 Rock climbing

108   King George VI

108a

(Des G. Bull and J. Berry. Recess John Ash, Melbourne)

1937 (1 Oct). *Health Stamp. W* **43**. *P* 11.
602	107	1d. + 1d. scarlet	..	..	1·50	2·50

Broken ribbon flaw (R. 6/6 of Pl 8)

(Des W. J. Cooch. Recess B.W.)

1938–44. *W* **98**. *P* 14 × 13½.
603	108	½d. green (1.3.38)	..		6·50	10
604		½d. brown-orange (10.7.41)..		20	10
605		1d. scarlet (1.7.38)	..		5·00	10
		a. Broken ribbon	..		40·00	
606		1d. green (21.7.41)	..		20	10
607	108a	1½d. purple-brown (26.7.38)	..		24·00	1·25
608		1½d. scarlet (1.2.44)	..		20	10
609		3d. blue (26.9.41)	..		20	10
603/9				*Set of 7*	32·00	1·25

For other values see Nos. 680/9.

109 Children playing   110 Beach Ball

(Des J. Berry. Recess B.W.)

1938 (1 Oct). *Health Stamp. W* **98**. *P* 14 × 13½.
610	109	1d. + 1d. scarlet	..	..	3·00	1·60

(Des S. Hall. Recess Note Printing Branch, Commonwealth Bank
of Australia, Melbourne)

1939 (16 Oct). *Health Stamps. Surcharged with new value. W* **43**.
P 11.
611	110	1d. on ½d. + ½d. green	..		1·50	3·25
612		2d. on 1d. + 1d. scarlet	..		2·50	3·25

111 Arrival of the Maoris, 1350

115 Signing Treaty of Waitangi, 1840

(Des L. C. Mitchell (½d., 3d., 4d.); J. Berry (others). Recess B.W.)

1940 (2 Jan–8 Mar). *Centenary of Proclamation of British Sovereignty. T* **111, 115** *and similar designs. W* **98.** *P* 14 × 13½ (2½d.), 13½ × 14 (5d.) *or* 13½ (*others*).

613	½d. blue-green	..	..	30	10
614	1d. chocolate and scarlet	..	..	2·75	10
615	1½d. light blue and mauve	..	..	30	20
616	2d. blue-green and chocolate	..	..	1·50	10
617	2½d. blue-green and blue	..	..	1·00	35
618	3d. purple and carmine	..	..	2·50	25
619	4d. chocolate and lake	..	..	12·00	50
620	5d. pale blue and brown	..	..	5·00	2·25
621	6d. emerald-green and violet	..	..	12·00	45
622	7d. black and red	..	..	1·25	3·50
623	8d. black and red (8.3)	..	..	12·00	1·50
624	9d. olive-green and orange	..	..	7·00	75
625	1s. sage-green and deep green	..	..	13·00	2·50
613/25		*Set of* 13		60·00	11·00

Designs: *Horiz* (as *T* **111**)—1d. H.M.S. *Endeavour*, chart of N.Z., and Capt. Cook; 1½d. British Monarchs; 2d. Tasman with *Heemskerk* and chart; 3d. Landing of immigrants, 1840; 4d. Road, Rail, Sea and Air transport; 6d. *Dunedin* and "Frozen Mutton Route" to London; 7d., 8d. Maori council; 9d. Gold mining in 1861 and 1940. (As *T* **115**)—5d. H.M.S. *Britomart* at Akaroa, 1840. *Vert* (as *T* **111**)—1s. Giant Kauri tree.

1940 (1 Oct). *Health Stamps. As T* **110,** *but without extra surcharge. W* **43.** *P* 11.

626	110	1d. + ½d. blue-green	..	5·00	8·00
627		2d. + 1d. brown-orange	..	5·00	8·00

1ᴰ 1ᴰ **2ᴅ** **1941**
(123)   Inserted "2"   (124)

1941. *Surch as T* **123.**

628	108	1d. on ½d. green (1.5.41)	..	30	10
629	108a	2d. on 1½d. purple-brown (4.41)	..	30	10
		a. Inserted "2"	..	£475	£300

The surcharge on No. 629 has only one figure, at top left, and there is only one square to obliterate the original value at bottom right.

The variety "Inserted 2" occurs on the 10th stamp, 10th row. It is identified by the presence of remnants of the damaged "2", and by the spacing of "2" and "D" which is variable and different from the normal.

(Typo Govt Printing Office, Wellington)

1941. *As T* **91,** *but smaller* (17½ × 20½ mm). *P* 14 × 15. (*a*) W **43.**

630	91	9d. scarlet and black (5.41)	..	70·00	14·00

(*b*) W **98**

631	91	9d. scarlet and black (29.9.41)	..	2·25	1·50

1941 (4 Oct). *Health Stamps. Nos.* 626/7 *optd with T* **124.**

632	110	1d. + ½d. blue-green	..	25	1·40
633		2d. + 1d. brown-orange	..	25	1·40

125 Boy and Girl on Swing

126 Princess Margaret

(Des S. Hall. Recess Note Printing Branch, Commonwealth Bank of Australia, Melbourne)

1942 (1 Oct). *Health Stamps. W* **43.** *P* 11.

634	125	1d. + ½d. blue-green	..	15	35
635		2d. + 1d. orange-red	..	15	30

(Des J. Berry. Recess B.W.)

1943 (1 Oct). *Health Stamps. T* **126** *and similar triangular design. W* **98.** *P* 12.

636		1d. + ½d. green	..	10	50
		a. Imperf between (vert pair)	..	£4000	
637		2d. + 1d. red-brown	..	10	10
		a. Imperf between (vert pair)	..	£4000	£4000

Design:—2d. Queen Elizabeth II as Princess.

✚ **TENPENCE** ✚
(128)

1944 (1 May). *No.* 615 *surch with T* **128.**

662	10d. on 1½d. light blue and mauve	..	10	10

---

129 Queen Elizabeth II as Princess and Princess Margaret

130 Statue of Peter Pan, Kensington Gardens

(Recess B.W.)

1944 (9 Oct). *Health Stamps. W* **98.** *P* 13½.

663	129	1d. + ½d. green	..	10	15
664		2d. + 1d. blue	..	10	15

(Des J. Berry. Recess B.W.)

1945 (1 Oct). *Health Stamps. W* **98.** *P* 13½.

665	130	1d. + ½d. green and buff	..	10	10
666		2d. + 1d. carmine and buff	..	10	10

131 Lake Matheson

132 King George VI and Parliament House, Wellington

133 St. Paul's Cathedral

139 "St. George" (Wellington College War Memorial Window)

Printer's guide mark (R. 12/3)

Completed rudder (R. 2/4 of Pl 42883 and R. 3/2 of Pl 42796)

(Des J. Berry. Photo Harrison (1½d. and 1s.). Recess B.W. (1d. and 2d.) and Waterlow (others))

1946 (1 Apr). *Peace issue. T* **131/3, 139** *and similar designs. W* **98** (*sideways on* 1½d.). *P* 13 (1d., 2d.), 14 × 14½ (1½d., 1s.), 13½ (*others*).

667	½d. green and brown	..	..	15	20
	a. Printer's guide mark	..	..	4·00	
668	1d. green	..	..	10	10
669	1½d. scarlet	..	..	10	10
670	2d. purple	..	..	15	10
671	3d. ultramarine and grey	..	..	20	10
	a. Completed rudder	..	..	5·00	
672	4d. bronze-green and orange	..	20	20
673	5d. green and ultramarine	..	20	15
674	6d. chocolate and vermilion	..	15	10
675	8d. black and carmine	..	15	10
676	9d. blue and black	..	..	15	10
677	1s. grey-black	..	..	15	15
667/77		*Set of* 11		1·50	1·25

Designs: *Horiz* (as *T* **132**)—2d. The Royal Family. (As *T* **131**)—3d. R.N.Z.A.F. badge and aeroplanes; 4d. Army badge, tank and plough; 5d. Navy badge, H.M.N.Z.S. *Achilles* (cruiser) and *Dominion Monarch* (liner); 6d. N.Z. coat of arms, foundry and farm; 9d. Southern Alps and Franz Josef Glacier. *Vert* (as *T* **139**)—1s. National Memorial Campanile.

142 Soldier helping Child over Stile

(Des J. Berry. Recess Waterlow)

1946 (24 Oct). *Health Stamps. W* **98.** *P* 13½.

678	142	1d. + ½d. green and orange-brown	..	10	10
		a. Yellow-green and orange-brown	..	3·75	3·75
679		2d. + 1d. chocolate and orange-brown	..	10	10

144 King George VI

145 Statue of Eros

Plate 1

Plate 2

(Des W. J. Cooch. Recess T **108a**, B.W.; T **144**, D.L.R.)

1947–52. W **98** (*sideways on* "*shilling*" *values*). (*a*) P 14 × 13½.

680	108a	2d. orange	..	15	10
681		4d. bright purple	..	45	30
682		5d. slate	..	50	40
683		6d. carmine	..	40	10
684		8d. violet	..	65	30
685		9d. purple-brown	..	70	30

(*b*) P 14

686	144	1s. red-brown and carmine (Plate 1)	..	1·40	40
		a. Wmk upright (Plate 1)	..	50	40
		b. Wmk upright (Plate 2)	..	2·00	40
687		1s. 3d. red-brown and blue (Plate 2)	..	70	50
		a. Wmk upright (14.1.52)	..	2·00	3·00
688		2s. brown-orange and green (Plate 1)	..	1·50	1·00
		a. Wmk upright (Plate 1)	..	2·00	2·25
689		3s. red-brown and grey (Plate 2)	..	1·75	2·00
680/9		*Set of* 10		6·50	4·75

In head-plate 2 the diagonal lines of the background have been strengthened and result in the upper corners and sides appearing more deeply shaded.

(Des J. Berry. Recess Waterlow)

1947 (1 Oct). *Health Stamps. W* **98** (*sideways*). *P* 13½.

690	145	1d. + ½d. green	..	10	10
691		2d. + 1d. carmine	..	10	10

146 Port Chalmers, 1848

148 First Church, Dunedin

(Des J. Berry. Recess B.W.)

1948 (23 Feb). *Centennial of Otago. T* **146, 148** *and similar designs. W* **98** (*sideways on* 3d.). *P* 13½.

692		1d. blue and green	..	10	10
693		2d. green and brown	..	10	10
694		3d. purple	..	10	15
695		6d. black and rose	..	10	15
692/5		*Set of* 4		30	45

Designs: *Horiz*—2d. Cromwell, Otago; 6d. University of Otago.

150 Boy Sunbathing and Children Playing

151 Nurse and Child

(Des E. Linzell. Recess B.W.)

1948 (1 Oct). *Health Stamps. W* **98.** *P* 13½.

696	150	1d. + ½d. blue and green	..	10	10
697		2d. + 1d. purple and scarlet	..	10	10

1949 ROYAL VISIT ISSUE. Four stamps were prepared to commemorate this event: 2d. Treaty House, Waitangi; 3d. H.M.S. *Vanguard*; 5d. Royal portraits; 6d. Crown and sceptre. The visit did not take place and the stamps were destroyed, although a few examples of the 3d. later appeared on the market. A similar set was prepared in 1952, but was, likewise, not issued.

(Des J. Berry. Photo Harrison)

1949 (3 Oct). *Health Stamps.* W **98**. P 14 × 14½.
698	151	1d. + ½d. green	..	..	10	10
699		2d. + 1d. ultramarine	..	..	10	10
		a. No stop below "D" of "1D." (R.1/2)		6·50	13·00

1½d.

POSTAGE

(152)

153 Queen Elizabeth II and Prince Charles

1950 (28 July). *As Type F* **6**, *but without value, surch with T* **152**. W **98** (*inverted*). *Chalk-surfaced paper.* P 14.
700	F 6	1½d. carmine	..	..	10	10

Originally issued with the watermark inverted, this later appeared with it upright.

(Des J. Berry and R. S. Phillips. Photo Harrison)

1950 (2 Oct). *Health Stamps.* W **98**. P 14 × 14½.
701	153	1d. + ½d. green	..	..	10	10
702		2d. + 1d. plum	..	..	10	10

154 Christchurch Cathedral   **155** Cairn on Lyttleton Hills

(Des L. C. Mitchell (2d.), J. A. Johnstone (3d.) and J. Berry (others). Recess B.W.)

1950 (20 Nov). *Centennial of Canterbury, N.Z. T* **154**/5 *and similar designs.* W **98** (*sideways on* 1d. *and* 3d.). P 13½.
703		1d. green and blue	..	..	15	10
704		2d. carmine and orange	..	..	15	10
705		3d. dark blue and blue	..	..	20	10
706		6d. brown and blue	..	..	20	25
707		1s. reddish purple and blue	..	20	30
703/7				*Set of* 5	80	80

Designs: *Vert* (*as T* **154**)—3d. John Robert Godley. *Horiz* (*as T* **155**)—6d. Canterbury University College; 1s. Aerial view of Timaru.

159 "Takapuna" class Yachts

(Des J. Berry and R. S. Phillips. Recess B.W.)

1951 (1 Nov). *Health Stamps.* W **98**. P 13½.
708	159	1½d. + ½d. scarlet and yellow.	..	10	30
709		2d. + 1d. deep green and yellow	..	10	10

160 Princess Anne   **161** Prince Charles

(From photographs by Marcus Adams. Photo Harrison)

1952 (1 Oct). *Health Stamps.* W **98**. P 14 × 14½.
710	160	1½d. + ½d. carmine-red	..	..	10	10
711	161	2d. + 1d. brown	..	..	10	10

1952–53. *Nos.* 604 *and* 606 *surch as T* **162**.
712	108	1d. on ½d. brown-orange (11.9.53)	20	30
		a. "D" omitted			†	—
713		3d. on 1d. green (12.12.52*)	..	10	10

*Earliest known date used.

3D

(162)

---

163 Buckingham Palace   **164** Queen Elizabeth II

(Des L. C. Mitchell (1s. 6d.), J. Berry (others). Recess D.L.R. (2d., 4d.), Waterlow (1s. 6d.) Photo Harrison (3d., 8d.))

1953 (25 May). *Coronation. T* **163**/4 *and similar designs.* W **98**. P 13 (2d., 4d.), 13½ (1s. 6d.) *or* 14 × 14½ (3d., 8d.).
714		2d. deep bright blue	..	..	30	20
715		3d. brown	..	..	..	30	10
716		4d. carmine	..	..	1·00	1·75
717		8d. slate-grey	..	..	80	80
718		1s. 6d. purple and ultramarine	..	1·50	1·00
714/18				*Set of* 5	3·50	3·50

Designs: *Horiz* (*as T* **163**)—4d. Coronation State Coach; 1s. 6d. St. Edward's Crown and Royal Sceptre. *Vert* (*as T* **164**)—8d. Westminster Abbey.

168 Girl Guides   **169** Boy Scouts

(Des J. Berry. Photo Harrison)

1953 (7 Oct). *Health Stamps.* W **98**. P 14 × 14½.
719	168	1½d. + ½d. blue	..	..	10	10
720	169	2d. + 1d. deep yellow-green	..	10	20
		a. Imperf 3 sides (block of 4)			

No. 720a shows the left-hand vertical pair imperforate at right and the right-hand pair imperforate at left, top and bottom.

170 Queen Elizabeth II   **171** Queen Elizabeth II and Duke of Edinburgh

(Des L. C. Mitchell. Recess Waterlow)

1953 (9 Dec). *Royal Visit.* W **98**. P 13 × 14 (3d.) *or* 13½ (4d.).
721	170	3d. dull purple	..	..	10	10
722	171	4d. deep ultramarine	..	..	10	25

172   **173** Queen Elizabeth II   **174**

Die I   Die II

(Des L. C. Mitchell (T **172**/3), J. Berry (T **174**). Recess D.L.R. (T **173**), B.W. (others))

1953 (15 Dec)–58. W **98**. P 14 × 13½ (T **172**), 14 (T **173**) *or* 13½ (T **174**).
723	172	½d. slate-black (1.3.54)	..	..	15	30
724		1d. orange (1.3.54)	..	..	15	10
725		1½d. brown-lake	..	..	15	10
726		2d. bluish green (1.3.54)	..	..	20	10
727		3d. vermilion (1.3.54)	..	..	20	10
728		4d. blue (1.3.54)	..	..	40	40
729		6d. purple (1.3.54)	..	..	70	1·00
730		8d. carmine (1.3.54)	..	..	60	40
731	173	9d. brown and bright green (1.3.54)	60	30
732		1s. black & carm-red (Die I) (1.3.54)	65	10
		a. Die II (1958)		..	60·00	11·00
733		1s. 6d. black and bright blue (1.3.54) ..	1·75	40
733a		1s. 9d. black and red-orange (1.7.57) ..	5·50	85

733b	174	2s. 6d. brown (1.7.57) ..	..	23·00	5·50
734		3s. bluish green (1.3.54)	..	11·00	30
735		5s. carmine (1.3.54)	..	17·00	2·50
736		10s. deep ultramarine (1.3.54) ..	45·00	15·00
723/36			*Set of* 16	95·00	24·00

1s. Dies I and II. The two dies of the Queen's portrait differ in the shading on the sleeve at right. The long lines running upwards from left to right are strong in Die I and weaker in Die II. In the upper part of the shading the fine cross-hatching is visible in Die I only between the middle two of the four long lines, but in Die II it extends clearly across all four lines.

In the lower part of the shading the strength of the long lines in Die I makes the cross-hatching appear subdued, whereas in Die II the weaker long lines make the cross-hatching more prominent.

Centre plates 1A, 1B and 2B are Die I; 3A and 3B are Die II.

For stamps as T **172** but with larger figures of value see Nos. 745/51.

1958 NEW PAPER. A new white opaque paper first came into use in August 1958 and was used for later printings of Nos. 733a, 745, 747/9, O159, O161, O163/4, O166 and L54. It is slightly thicker than the paper previously used, but obviously different in colour (white, against cream) and opacity (the previous paper being *relatively* transparent).

175 Young Climber and Mts Aspiring and Everest

(Des J. Berry. Recess; vignette litho B.W.)

1954 (4 Oct). *Health Stamps.* W **98**. P 13½.
737	175	1½d. + ½d. sepia and deep violet	..	10	10
738		2d. + 1d. sepia and blue-black	..	10	10

176 Maori Mail-carrier   **177** Queen Elizabeth II

178 Douglas "DC 3" Airliner

(Des R. M. Conly (2d.), J. Berry (3d.), A. G. Mitchell (4d.). Recess D.L.R.)

1955 (18 July). *Centenary of First New Zealand Postage Stamps.* W **98**. P 14 (2d.), 14 × 14½ (3d.) *or* 13 (4d.).
739	176	2d. sepia and deep green	..	..	10	10
740	177	3d. brown-red	..	..	..	10	10
741	178	4d. black and bright blue	..	15	25
739/41		..	..	*Set of* 3	30	35

179 Children's Health Camps Federation Emblem   **180**

(Des E. M. Taylor. Recess B.W.)

1955 (3 Oct). *Health Stamps.* W **98** (*sideways*). P 13½ × 13.
742	179	1½d. + ½d. sepia and orange-brown	10	25
743		2d. + 1d. sepia and brown	..	10	10
744		3d. + 1d. sepia and deep rose-red	15	10
		a. Centre omitted	..		
742/4				*Set of* 3	30	45

1955–59. *As Nos.* 724/30 *but larger figures of value and stars omitted from lower right corner.*
745	180	1d. orange (12.7.56)	..	..	50	10
746		1½d. brown-lake (1.12.55)	..	60	40
747		2d. bluish green (19.3.56)	..	40	10
748		3d. vermilion (1.5.56)	..	1·10	10
749		4d. blue (3.2.58)	..	..	1·75	35
750		6d. purple (20.10.55)	..	7·50	10
751		8d. chestnut (1.12.59)	..	1·75	10
745/51				*Set of* 7	15·00	5·50

See note re white opaque paper after No. 736. No. 751 exists only on white paper.

181 "The Whalers of Foveaux Strait"

183 Takahe

(Des E. R. Leeming (2d.), L. C. Mitchell (3d.), M. R. Smith (8d.). Recess D.L.R.)

1956 (16 Jan). *Southland Centennial. T* **181, 183** *and similar design.* W **98.** *P* 13½ × 13 (8*d.*) or 13 × 12½ (*others*).

752	2d. deep blue-green	..	10	10
753	3d. sepia	..	10	10
754	8d. slate-violet and rose-red	..	40	60
752/4		*Set of* 3	50	70

Design: *Horiz*—3d. "Farming".

184 Children picking Apples

(Des L. C. Mitchell, after photo by J. F. Louden. Recess B.W.)

1956 (24 Sept). *Health Stamps.* W **98.** *P* 13 × 13½.

755	**184** 1½d. + ½d. purple-brown	..	15	20
	a. Blackish brown	..	60	4·50
756	2d. + 1d. blue-green	..	15	15
757	3d. + 1d. claret	..	15	10
755/7	..	*Set of* 3	40	40

185 New Zealand Lamb and Map

186 Lamb, *Dunedin* and *Port Brisbane* (refrigerated freighter)

(Des M. Goaman. Photo Harrison)

1957 (15 Feb). *75th Anniv of First Export of N.Z. Lamb.* W **98** (*sideways on* 4*d.*). *P* 14 × 14½ (4*d.*) or 14½ × 14 (8*d.*).

758	**185** 4d. blue	..	40	45
759	**186** 8d. deep orange-red	..	60	65

187 Sir Truby King

(Des M. R. Smith. Recess B.W.)

1957 (14 May). *50th Anniv of Plunket Society.* W **98.** *P* 13.

760	**187** 3d. bright carmine-red	..	10	10

188 Life-savers in Action

189 Children on Seashore

(Des L. Cutten (2d.), L. C. Mitchell (3d.). Recess Waterlow)

1957 (25 Sept). *Health Stamps.* W **98** (*sideways*). *P* 13½.

761	**188** 2d. + 1d. black and emerald	..	15	20
762	**189** 3d. + 1d. ultramarine and rose-red	..	15	10
MS762b	Two sheets each 112 × 96 mm with Nos. 761 and 762 in blocks of 6 (2 × 3)..	*Per pair*	12·00	18·00
MS762c	As last but with wmk upright	*Per pair*	16·00	32·00

2d

(190)

191 Girls' Life Brigade Cadet

192 Boys' Brigade Bugler

1958 (6 Jan–Mar). *No.* 746 *surch as T* **190.**

763	**180** 2d. on 1½d. brown-lake	..	..	50	10
	a. Smaller dot in surch			15	10
	b. Error. Surch on No. 725 (3.58)			£110	£150

Diameter of dot on No. 763 is 4¼ mm; on No. 763a 3¾ mm.
Forgeries of No. 763b are known.

(Des J. Berry. Photo Harrison)

1958 (20 Aug). *Health Stamps.* W **98.** *P* 14 × 14½.

764	**191** 2d. + 1d. green	..	20	15
765	**192** 3d. + 1d. blue	..	20	15
MS765a	Two sheets each 104 × 124 mm with Nos. 764/5 in blocks of 6 (3 × 2).	*Per pair*	14·00	12·00

193 Sir Charles Kingsford Smith and *Southern Cross*

194 Seal of Nelson

(Des J. E. Lyle. Eng F. D. Manley. Recess Commonwealth Bank of Australia Note Ptg Branch)

1958 (27 Aug). *30th Anniv of First Air Crossing of the Tasman Sea.* W **98** (*sideways*). *P* 14 × 14½.

766	**193** 6d. deep ultramarine	..	30	30

(Des M. J. Macdonald. Recess B.W.)

1958 (29 Sept). *Centenary of City of Nelson.* W **98.** *P* 13½×13.

767	**194** 3d. carmine	..	10	10

195 "Pania" Statue, Napier

196 Australian Gannets on Cape Kidnappers

(Des M. R. Smith (2d.), J. Berry (3d.), L. C. Mitchell (8d.). Photo Harrison)

1958 (3 Nov). *Centenary of Hawke's Bay Province. T* **195/6** *and similar design.* W **98** (*sideways on* 3*d.*). *P* 14½×14 (3*d.*) or 13½×14½ (*others*).

768	2d. yellow-green	..	..	10	10
769	3d. blue	..	..	15	10
770	8d. red-brown	..	..	45	75
768/70			*Set of* 3	60	80

Design:—*Vert* 8d. Maori sheep-shearer.

197 "Kiwi" Jamboree Badge

198 Careening H.M.S. *Endeavour* at Ship Cove

(Des Mrs. S. M. Collins. Recess B.W.)

1959 (5 Jan). *Pan-Pacific Scout Jamboree, Auckland.* W **98.** *P* 13½×13.

771	**197** 3d. sepia and carmine	..	10	10

(Des G. R. Bull and G. R. Smith. Photo Harrison)

1959 (2 Mar). *Centenary of Marlborough Province. T* **198** *and similar horiz designs.* W **98** (*sideways*). *P* 14½ × 14.

772	2d. green	..	15	10
773	3d. deep blue	..	15	10
774	8d. light brown	..	60	60
772/4	..	*Set of* 3	80	70

Designs:—3d. Shipping wool, Wairau Bar, 1857; 8d. Salt industry. Grassmere.

201 Red Cross Flag

(Photo Harrison)

1959 (3 June). *Red Cross Commemoration.* W **98** (*sideways*). *P* 14½×14.

775	**201** 3d. + 1d. red and ultramarine	..	10	10
	a. Red Cross omitted			£1000	

---

202 Grey Teal

203 New Zealand Stilt

(Des Display Section, G.P.O. Photo Harrison)

1959 (16 Sept). *Health Stamps.* W **98** (*sideways*). *P* 14 × 14½.

776	**202** 2d. + 1d. greenish yellow, ol & rose-red	15	20
777	**203** 3d. + 1d. black, pink and light blue	15	20
	a. Pink ptg omitted		£100	
MS777c.	Two sheets each 95 × 109 mm. with Nos. 776/7 in blocks of 6 (3 × 2).	*Per pair*	6·50	14·00

204 "The Explorer"

205 "The Gold Digger"

(Des G. R. Bull and G. R. Smith. Photo Harrison)

1960 (16 May). *Centenary of Westland Province. T* **204/5** *and similar vert design.* W **98.** *P* 14 × 14½.

778	2d. deep dull green	..	15	10
779	3d. orange-red	..	15	10
780	8d. grey-black	..	40	1·75
778/80		*Set of* 3	60	1·75

Design:—8d. "The Pioneer Woman".

207 Manuka (Tea Tree)

214 National Flag

216 Trout

219 Taniwha (Maori Rock Drawing)

220 Butter Making

221 Tongariro National Park and Château

221a Tongariro National Park and Château

(Des Harrison (½d.), G. F. Fuller (1d., 3d., 6d.), A. G. Mitchell (2d., 4d., 5d., 8d., 3s., 10s., £1), P.O. Public Relations Division (7d.), P.O. Publicity Section (9d.), J. Berry (1s., 1s. 6d.), R. E. Barwick (1s. 3d.), J. C. Boyd (1s. 9d.), D. F. Kee (2s.), L. C. Mitchell (2s. 6d., 5s.). Photo D.L.R. (½d., 1d., 2d., 3d., 4d., 6d., 8d.) or Harrison (others))

1960 (11 July)–66. *T* **207, 214, 216, 219/21a** *and similar designs. Chalk-surfaced paper* (2½d., 5d., 7d., 1s. 9d. (No. 795), 3s. (No. 799)). W **98** (*sideways on* 2½d., 5d., 1s. 3d., 1s. 6d., 2s. 6d., 3s. *and* 10s.)). *P* 14×14½ (1s. 3d., 1s. 6d., 2s., 5s., £1) *or* 14½×14 (*others*).

781	**207** ½d. grey, green and cerise (1.9.60)	10	10
	a. Grey omitted	..	40·00	
	b. Green omitted		90·00	
782	— 1d. orge, green, lake & brn (1.9.60)	10	10
	a. Orange omitted		£160	
	b. Coil. Perf 14½×13. Wmk sideways (11.63)		1·25	2·00
	c. Chalk-surfaced paper (1965?)	..	10	40
783	— 2d. carmine, black, yellow & green	10	10
	a. Black omitted	..	£160	
	b. Yellow omitted		£200	
784	— 2½d. red, yellow, blk & grn (1.11.61)	70	10
	a. Red omitted		£300	
	b. Yellow omitted		90·00	
	c. Green omitted		£110	
	d. Red and green omitted		£400	

785	–	3d. yellow, green, yellow-brown and deep greenish blue (1.9.60) ..	30	10
		a. Yellow omitted ..	90·00	
		b. Green omitted ..	90·00	
		c. Yellow-brown omitted ..	90·00	
		e. Coil. Perf 14½×13. Wmk sideways (3.10.63) ..	1·25	1·75
		f. Chalk-surfaced paper (1965?) ..	30	50
786	–	4d. purple, buff, yellow-green & lt bl	40	10
		a. Purple omitted ..	£160	
		b. Buff omitted ..	£200	
		d. Chalk-surfaced paper (1965?) ..	£300	9·00
787	–	5d. yell, dp grn, blk & vio (14.5.62)	60	10
		a. Yellow omitted ..	£130	
788	–	6d. lilac, green and deep bluish green (1.9.60) ..	50	10
		a. No wmk ..	20·00	13·00
		ab. Lilac omitted ..	90·00	
		ac. Green omitted ..	70·00	
		c. Chalk-surfaced paper (1966?) ..	65	1·25
788d	–	7d. red, green, yellow and pale red (16.3.66) ..	35	1·00
789	–	8d. rose-red, yellow and grey (1.9.60) ..	40	10
790	214	9d. red and ultramarine (1.9.60) ..	30	10
		a. Red omitted ..	£180	
791	–	1s. brown and deep green..	25	10
792	216	1s. 3d. carmine, sepia & bright blue	4·00	50
		a. Carmine omitted ..	£170	
		b. Carmine, sepia and greyish blue	1·00	10
793	–	1s. 6d. olive-green & orange-brown	60	10
794	–	1s. 9d. bistre-brown ..	19·00	15
795	–	1s. 9d. orange-red, blue, green and yellow (4.11.63) ..	7·00	50
796	219	2s. black and orange-buff ..	3·25	10
		a. Chalk-surfaced paper (1966) ..	2·25	1·50
797	220	2s. 6d. yellow and light brown ..	1·75	65
		a. Yellow omitted ..	£275	
798	221	3s. blackish brown ..	55·00	65
799	221a	3s. bistre, blue and green (1.4.64)	7·50	1·50
800	–	5s. blackish green ..	5·50	80
		a. Chalk-surfaced paper (1966) ..	2·25	4·50
801	–	10s. steel-blue ..	9·00	1·25
		a. Chalk-surfaced paper (1966) ..	4·00	10·00
802	–	£1 deep magenta ..	9·00	6·00
		781/802	*Set of 23* 90·00	11·00

Designs: *Vert* (as *T 207*)—1d. Karaka; 2d. Kowhai Ngutu–kaka (Kaka Beak); 2½d. Titoki; 3d. Kowhai; 4d. Puarangi (Hibiscus); 5d. Matua Tikumu (Mountain Daisy); 6d. Pikiarero (Clematis); 7d. Koromiko; 8d. Rata. (As *T 216*)—1s. 6d. Tiki. (As *T 219*)—5s. Sutherland Falls; £1 Pohutu Geyser. *Horiz* (as *T 214*)—1s. Timber industry—1s. 9d. Aerial top dressing. (As *T 221*)—10s. Tasman Glacier.

Nos. 782b and 785e were replaced by coils with upright watermark perf 14½ × 14 in 1966.

CHALKY PAPER. The chalk-surfaced paper is not only whiter but also thicker, making the watermark difficult to see. Examples of the 4d. value can be found on a thick surfaced paper. These should not be confused with the rare chalk-surfaced printing, No. 786d, which can be identified by its positive reaction to the silver test.

225 Sacred Kingfisher   226 New Zealand Pigeon

(Des Display Section, G.P.O. Recess B.W.)

1960 (10 Aug). *Health Stamps. W 98. P 13½.*

803	225	2d. + 1d. sepia and turquoise-blue ..	40	40
804	226	3d. + 1d. deep purple-brown and orange	40	40
MS804b		Two sheets each 95 × 107 mm with Nos.		
		803 and 804 in blocks of 6. *P* 11½ × 11 *Per pair* 30·00 32·00		

227 "The Adoration of the Shepherds" (Rembrandt)

(Photo Harrison)

1960 (1 Nov). *Christmas. W 98. P 13½.*

805	227	2d. red and deep brown/cream ..	15	10
		a. Red omitted..	£250	

MINIMUM PRICE

The minimum price quote is 10p which represents a handling charge rather than a basis for valuing common stamps. For further notes about prices see introductory pages.

---

228 Great Egret   229 New Zealand Falcon

(Des Display Section, G.P.O. Recess B.W.)

1961 (2 Aug). *Health Stamps. W 98. P 13½.*

806	228	2d. + 1d. black and purple ..	30	20
807	229	3d. + 1d. deep sepia and yellow-green	30	20
MS807a		Two sheets each 97 × 121 mm with Nos.		
		806/7 in blocks of 6 (3 × 2)	*Per pair* 25·00 25·00	

(230)   (231)   232 "Adoration of the Magi" (Dürer)

1961 (1 Sept). *No. 748 surch with T 230 (wide setting).*

808	180	2½d. on 3d. vermilion ..	15	15
		a. Narrow setting (T 231) ..	15	15
		b. Pair, wide and narrow ..	16·00	25·00

The difference in the settings is in the overall width of the new value, caused by two different spacings between the "2", "½" and "d".

(Photo Harrison)

1961 (16 Oct). *Christmas. W 98 (sideways). P 14½ × 14.*

809	232	2½d. multicoloured ..	10	10

233 Morse Key and Port Hills, Lyttelton

(Des A. G. Mitchell (3d.) and L. C. Mitchell (8d.). Photo Harrison)

1962 (1 June). *Telegraph Centenary. T 233 and similar horiz design. W 98 (sideways). P 14½ × 14.*

810		3d. sepia and bluish green ..	10	10
		a. Green omitted ..	£350	
811		8d. black and brown-red ..	35	55
		a. Imperf (pair) ..	£800	
		b. Black omitted ..	£325	

Design:—8d. Modern teleprinter.
No. 811a comes from a sheet with the two top rows imperforate and the third row imperforate on three sides.

235 Red-fronted Parakeet   236 Tieke Saddleback

(Des Display Section, G.P.O. Photo D.L.R.)

1962 (3 Oct). *Health Stamps. W 98. P 15 × 14.*

812	235	2½d. + 1d. multicoloured ..	20	30
		a. Orange omitted ..		
813	236	3d. + 1d. multicoloured ..	20	30
		a. Orange omitted ..	£900	
MS813b		Two sheets each 96 × 101 mm with Nos.		
		812/3 in blocks of 6 (3 × 2) ..	*Per pair* 45·00 32·00	

237 "Madonna in Prayer" (Sassoferrato)

(Photo Harrison)

1962 (15 Oct). *Christmas. W 98. P 14½ × 14.*

814	237	2½d. multicoloured ..	10	10

238   Prince Andrew   239

(Design after photographs by Studio Lisa, London. Recess D.L.R.)

1963 (7 Aug). *Health Stamps. W 98. P 14.*

815	238	2½d. + 1d. dull ultramarine	10	30
		a. Ultramarine ..	30	30
		b. Deep blue ..	30	35
816	239	3d. + 1d. carmine ..	10	10
MS816a		Two sheets each 93×100 mm with Nos.		
		815/16 in blocks of 6 (3 × 2)	*Per pair* 21·00 24·00	

240 "The Holy Family" (Titian)

(Photo Harrison)

1963 (14 Oct). *Christmas. W 98 (sideways). P 12½.*

817	240	2½d. multicoloured ..	10	10
		a. Imperf (pair) ..	£160	
		b. Yellow omitted ..	£250	

241 Steam Locomotive *Pilgrim* and "DG" Diesel Electric Loco   242 Diesel Express and Mt Ruapehu

(Des Commercial Art Section, N.Z. Railways. Photo D.L.R.)

1963 (25 Nov). *Railway Centenary. W 98 (sideways). P 14.*

818	241	3d. multicoloured ..	30	10
		a. Blue (sky) omitted ..	£250	
819	242	1s. 9d. multicoloured ..	1·60	80
		a. Red (value) omitted ..	£650	

243 "Commonwealth Cable"

(Des P. Morriss. Photo Note Printing Branch, Reserve Bank of Australia)

1963 (3 Dec). *Opening of COMPAC (Trans-Pacific Telephone Cable). No wmk. P 13½.*

820	243	8d. red, blue and yellow..	50	90

244 Road Map and Car Steering-wheel   245 Silver Gulls

(Des L. C. Mitchell. Photo Harrison)

1964 (1 May). *Road Safety Campaign. W 98. P 15 × 14.*

821	244	3d. black, ochre-yellow and blue ..	15	10

(Des Display Section G.P.O., after Miss T. Kelly. Photo Harrison)

1964 (5 Aug). *Health Stamps. T 245 and similar horiz design. Multicoloured. W 98. P 14½.*

822		2½d. + 1d. Type 245 ..	25	15
		a. Red (beak and legs) omitted ..	£110	
823		3d. + 1d. Little Penguin ..	25	15
MS823a		Two sheets each 171 × 84 mm with Nos.		
		822/3 in blocks of 8 (4 × 2) ..	*Per pair* 45·00 48·00	

7D

POSTAGE

(247)

246 Rev. S. Marsden taking first
Christian service at Rangihoua
Bay, 1814

(Des L. C. Mitchell. Photo Harrison)

1964 (12 Oct). *Christmas.* W 98 (*sideways*). *P* 14 × 13½.
824   246   2½d. multicoloured   10   10

1964 (14 Dec). *As Type F 6, but without value, surch with T 247.*
W 98. *Unsurfaced paper. P* 14 × 13½.
825   F 6   7d. carmine-red   30   80

248 Anzac Cove

(Des R. M. Conly. Photo Harrison)

1965 (14 Apr). *50th Anniv of Gallipoli Landing. T* 248 *and
similar horiz design.* W 98. *P* 12½.
826   4d. yellow-brown   10   10
827   5d. green and red   10   30
Design:—5d. Anzac Cove and poppy.

249 I.T.U. Emblem and   250 Sir Winston
Symbols   Churchill

(Photo Harrison)

1965 (17 May). *I.T.U. Centenary.* W 98. *P* 14½×14.
828   249   9d. blue and pale chocolate   30   35

(Des P. Morriss from photograph by Karsh. Photo Note Ptg
Branch, Reserve Bank of Australia)

1965 (24 May). *Churchill Commemoration. P* 13½.
829   250   7d. black, pale grey and light blue   15   50

251 Wellington Provincial Council Building

(Des from painting by L. B. Temple (1867). Photo Harrison)

1965 (26 July). *Centenary of Government in Wellington.* W 98
(*sideways*). *P* 14½ × 14.
830   251   4d. multicoloured   10   10

252 Kaka   253 Collared Grey Fantail
                        (after Miss T. Kelly)

(Des Display Section, G.P.O. Photo Harrison)

1965 (4 Aug). *Health Stamps.* W 98. *P* 14 × 14½.
831   252   3d. + 1d. multicoloured   30   15
832   253   4d. + 1d. multicoloured   30   15
   a. Green ("POSTAGE HEALTH" and
      on leaves) omitted £140
MS832b   Two sheets each 100 × 109 mm with Nos.
   831/2 in blocks of 6 (3 × 2)   ..   *Per pair* 32·00 35·00

254 I.C.Y. Emblem   255 "The Two Trinities"
                              (Murillo)

(Litho D.L.R.)

1965 (28 Sept). *International Co-operation Year.* W 98 (*sideways*).
P 14.
833   254   4d. carmine-red and light yellow-olive   15   10

(Photo Harrison)

1965 (11 Oct). *Christmas.* W 98. *P* 13½ × 14.
834   255   3d. multicoloured   10   10
   a. Gold (frame) omitted £600

256 Arms of New Zealand   259 "Progress"
                                    Arrowhead

(Des Display Section, G.P.O. Photo D.L.R.)

1965 (30 Nov). *11th Commonwealth Parliamentary Conference.
T* 256 *and similar horiz designs. Multicoloured. P* 14.
835   4d. Type 256   25   20
   a. Blue (incl value) omitted £325
836   9d. Parliament House, Wellington and Badge   45   90
837   2s. Wellington from Mt Victoria   ..   80   2·50
   a. Carmine omitted £275
835/7   ..   ..   *Set of* 3   1·40   3·25

(Des Display Section, G.P.O. Photo Harrison)

1966 (5 Jan). *Fourth National Scout Jamboree, Trentham.* W 98.
P 14 × 15.
838   259   4d. gold and myrtle-green   ..   10   10
   a. Gold (arrowhead) omitted   ..   £475

260 New Zealand   262 "The Virgin with Child"
Bell Bird   (Maratta)

(Des Display Section, G.P.O. Photo Harrison)

1966 (3 Aug). *Health Stamps. T* 260 *and similar vert design.
Multicoloured.* W 98 (*sideways*). *P* 14 × 14½.
839   3d. + 1d. Type 260   15   20
840   4d. + 1d. Weka Rail   15   20
   a. Deep brown (values and date) omitted   ..   £650
MS841   Two sheets each 107 × 91 mm. Nos. 839/40
   in blocks of 6 (3 × 2)   ..   *Per pair* 18·00 35·00
In No. 840a besides the value, "1966" and "Weka" are also
omitted and the bird, etc. appears as light brown.

(Photo Harrison)

1966 (3 Oct). *Christmas.* W 98 (*sideways*). *P* 14½.
842   262   3d. multicoloured   10   10
   a. Red omitted £100

263 Queen Victoria and   264 Half-sovereign of
Queen Elizabeth II   1867 and Commemorative
                                    Dollar Coin

(Des Display Section, G.P.O. Photo Harrison)

1967 (3 Feb). *Centenary of New Zealand Post Office Savings
Bank.* W 98 (*sideways on 4d.*). *P* 14 × 14½.
843   263   4d. black, gold and maroon   ..   10   10
844   264   9d. gold, silver, black, lt blue & dp grn   10   15

(New Currency. 100 cents = 1 dollar)

265 Manuka (Tea Tree)   266 Pohutu Geyser

1967 (10 July)–70. *Decimal Currency. Designs as 1960–66
issue, but with values inscr in decimal currency as T* 265/6.
Chalky paper. W 98 (*sideways on 8 c., 10 c., 20 c., 50 c. and $2).
P* 13½ × 14 (*½ c. to 3 c., 5 c. and 7 c.*), 14 × 14½ (*4 c., 6 c., 8 c.,
10 c., 25 c., 30 c. and $1*) *or* 14 × 14½ (*15 c., 20 c., 50 c. and $2*).
845   265   ½ c. pale blue, yellow-green and cerise   10   10
846   —   1 c. yellow, carmine, green & lt brown
            (as 1d.)   10   10
   a. Booklet pane. Five stamps plus
      one printed label   ..   ..   1·75
847   —   2 c. carmine, black, yellow and green
            (as 2d.)   10   10
848   —   2½ c. yellow, green, yellow-brown and
            deep bluish green (as 3d.)   10   10
   a. Deep bluish green omitted*   £425
   b. Imperf (pair)† £100
849   —   3 c. purple, buff, yellow-green and
            light greenish blue (as 4d.)   10   10
850   —   4 c. yellow, deep green, black and
            violet (as 5d.)   30   10
851   —   5 c. lilac, yellow-olive and bluish green
            (as 6d.)   65   10
852   —   6 c. red, green, yellow and light pink
            (as 7d.)   70   10
853   —   7 c. rose-red, yellow, green and grey
            (as 8d.)   85   20
854   214   8 c. red and ultramarine   ..   85   10
   a. Red omitted £190
855   —   10 c. brown and deep green (as 1s.)   80   10
856   —   15 c. olive-green and orange-brown (as
            1s. 6d.)   60   60
857   219   20 c. black and buff   ..   ..   2·50
858   220   25 c. yellow and light brown   ..   6·00   90
859   221a   30 c. olive-yellow, green & greenish
            blue   ..   ..   ..   5·00   25
   a. No wmk (1970)   ..   ..   3·50   3·75
860   —   50 c. blackish green (as 5s.)   ..   5·00   75
861   — $1 Prussian blue (as 10s.)   ..   20·00   1·25
862   266 $2 deep magenta   ..   ..   11·00 12·00
845/62   ..   ..   ..   *Set of* 18   45·00 15·00
*This occurred on one horizontal row of ten, affecting the back-
ground colour so that the value is also missing. In the row above
and the row below, the colour was partially omitted. The price is for
a vertical strip.
The 2½ c. value has been seen with the yellow omitted, but only
on a used example.
†This comes from a sheet of which the six right-hand vertical
rows were completely imperforate and the top, bottom and left-
hand margins had been removed.
The 4 c., 30 c. and 50 c. exist with PVA gum as well as gum
arabic. No. 859a exists with PVA gum only.
For $4 to $10 in the "Arms" type, see under Postal Fiscal stamps.
See also Nos. 870, etc.

268 Running with Ball

(Des L. C. Mitchell. Photo Harrison)

1967 (2 Aug). *Health Stamps. Rugby Football. T* 268 *and similar
multicoloured design.* W 98 (*sideways on 2½ c.*). *P* 14½ × 14
(*2½ c.*) *or* 14 × 14½ (*3 c.*).
867   2½ c. + 1 c. Type 268   15   10
868   3 c. + 1 c. Positioning for a place-kick (*horiz*)   15   10
MS869   Two sheets; (*a*) 76 × 130 mm (867); (*b*)
   130 × 76 mm (868). Containing blocks of
   six   ..   ..   *Per pair* 23·00 25·00

270 *Kaita* (trawler)   271 Brown Trout
and Catch

276 Dairy Farm, Mt Egmont and Butter Consignment

277 Fox Glacier, Westland National Park

(Des Display Section, G.P.O. (7, 8, 10, 18, 20, 25 c. and 28 c. from photo), R. M. Conly (7½ c.). Litho B.W. (7, 8, 18, 20 c.) or photo D.L.R. (7½ c.) and Harrison (10, 25, 28 c.). Others (15 c., $2) as before)

1967–69. T 270/1, 276/7 and similar designs. Chalky paper (except 7, 8, 18, 20 c.). No wmk (7, 8, 20 c.) or W 98 (sideways on 7½, 10, 15, 25 c., upright on 18, 28 c., $2). P 13½ (7, 7½ c.), 13 × 13½ (8, 18, 20 c.), 14½ × 14 (10, 25 c.) or 14 × 14½ (15, 28 c., $2).

870	7 c. multicoloured (3.12.69)..	..	..	1·50	90
871	7½ c. multicoloured* (29.8.67)	..	..	30	70
	a. Wmk upright (10.68)	..	..	50	75
872	8 c. multicoloured (8.7.69)	..	..	75	70
873	10 c. multicoloured (2.4.68)	..	..	50	10
	a. Green (background) omitted	..	£275	
874	15 c. apple-green, myrtle-green and carmine (as No. 856†) (19.3.68)	..	..	1·00	50
875	18 c. multicoloured (8.7.69)	..	..	1·40	55
876	20 c. multicoloured (8.7.69)	..	..	1·40	20
877	25 c. multicoloured (10.12.68)	..	..	6·00	2·00
878	28 c. multicoloured (30.7.68)..	..	..	60	10
879	$2 black, ochre & pale blue (as No. 862) (10.12.68)	..	..	35·00	19·00
870/79			Set of 10	42·00	22·00

Designs: Horiz—8 c. Apples and orchard; 10 c. Forest and timber; 18 c. Sheep and the "Woolmark"; 20 c. Consignments of beef and herd of cattle.

*No. 871 was originally issued to commemorate the introduction of the brown trout into New Zealand.

† No. 874 is slightly larger than No. 856, measuring 21 × 25 mm and the inscriptions and numerals differ in size.

278 "The Adoration of the Shepherds" (Poussin)

279 Mount Aspiring, Aurora Australis and Southern Cross

280 Sir James Hector (founder)

(Photo Harrison)

1967 (3 Oct). Christmas. W 98 (sideways). P 13½ × 14.
880 278 2½ c. multicoloured 10 10

(Des J. Berry. Litho D.L.R.)

1967 (10 Oct). Centenary of the Royal Society of New Zealand. W 98 (sideways on 4 c.). P 14 (4 c) or 13 × 14 (8 c.).
881 279 4 c. multicoloured 25 20
882 280 8 c. multicoloured 25 40

281 Open Bible

282 Soldiers and Tank

(Des Display Section, G.P.O. Litho D.L.R.)

1968 (23 Apr). Centenary of Maori Bible. W 98. P 13½.
883 281 3 c. multicoloured 10 10
a. Gold (inscr etc.) omitted £110

(Des L. C. Mitchell. Litho D.L.R.)

1968 (7 May). New Zealand Armed Forces. T 282 and similar horiz designs. Multicoloured. W 98 (sideways). P 14 × 13½.
884 4 c. Type 282 .. .. .. 30 15
885 10 c. Airmen, "Canberra" and "Kittyhawk" aircraft 50 25
886 28 c. Sailors and H.M.N.Z.S. Achilles, 1939, and H.M.N.Z.S. Waikato, 1968 .. 70 1·40
884/6 .. .. Set of 3 1·40 1·60

285 Boy breasting Tape, and Olympic Rings

287 Placing Votes in Ballot Box

(Des L. C. Mitchell. Photo Harrison)

1968 (7 Aug). Health Stamps. T 285 and similar horiz design. Multicoloured. P 14½ × 14.
887 2½ c. + 1 c. Type 285 .. .. 10 10
888 3 c. + 1 c. Girl swimming and Olympic rings 10 10
a. Red (ring) omitted £750
b. Blue (ring) omitted £350
MS889 Two sheets each 145×95 mm. Nos. 887/8 in blocks of six .. .. Per pair 15·00 25·00
No. 888a occurred in one miniature sheet. Six examples are known, one being used. No. 888b occurred from a second miniature sheet.

(Des J. Berry. Photo Japanese Govt Ptg Bureau, Tokyo)

1968 (19 Sept). 75th Anniv of Universal Suffrage in New Zealand. P 13.
890 287 3 c. ochre, olive-green and light blue .. 10 10

288 Human Rights Emblem

289 "Adoration of the Holy Child" (G. van Honthorst)

(Photo Japanese Govt Ptg Bureau, Tokyo)

1968 (19 Sept). Human Rights Year. P 13.
891 288 10 c. scarlet, yellow and deep green .. 10 30

(Photo Harrison)

1968 (1 Oct). Christmas. W 98 (sideways). P 14 × 14½.
892 289 2½ c. multicoloured 10 10

290 I.L.O. Emblem

(Photo Harrison)

1969 (11 Feb). 50th Anniv of International Labour Organization. W 98 (sideways). P 14½ × 14.
893 290 7 c. black and carmine-red 15 30

291 Supreme Court Building, Auckland

292 Law Society's Coat of Arms

(Des R. M. Conly. Litho B.W.)

1969 (8 Apr). Centenary of New Zealand Law Society. T 291/2 and similar design. P 13½ × 13 (3 c.) or 13 × 13½ (others).
894 3 c. multicoloured (shades) 10 10
895 10 c. multicoloured 35 45
896 18 c. multicoloured (shades) 45 70
894/6 .. .. Set of 3 80 1·10
Design:—Vert—18 c. "Justice" (from Memorial Window in University of Canterbury, Christchurch).

295 Student being conferred with Degree

(Des R. M. Conly. Litho B.W.)

1969 (3 June). Centenary of Otago University T 295 and similar multicoloured design. P 13 × 13½ (3 c.) or 13½ × 13 (10 c.).
897 3 c. Otago University (vert) 10 10
898 10 c. Type 295 .. .. .. 20 25

OMNIBUS ISSUES

Details, together with prices for complete sets, of the various Omnibus issues from the 1935 Silver Jubilee series to date are included in a special section following Zimbabwe at the end of Volume 2.

296 Boys playing Cricket

298 Dr. Elizabeth Gunn (founder of First Children's Health Camp)

(Des R. M. Conly (4 c.); L. C. Mitchell (others). Litho B.W.)

1969 (6 Aug). Health Stamps. T 296 and similar horiz design and T 298. P 12½ × 13 (No. 901) or 13 × 12½ (others).
899 2½ c. + 1 c. multicoloured 40 40
900 3 c. + 1 c. multicoloured 40 40
901 4 c. + 1 c. brown and ultramarine .. 40 1·40
899/901 .. .. Set of 3 1·10 2·00
MS902 Two sheets each 144 × 84 mm. Nos. 899/900 in blocks of six .. .. Per pair 20·00 38·00
Design:—3 c. Girls playing cricket.

299 Oldest existing House in New Zealand, and Old Stone Mission Store, Kerikeri

(Litho D.L.R.)

1969 (18 Aug). Early European Settlement in New Zealand, and 150th Anniv of Kerikeri. T 299 and similar horiz design. Multi-coloured. W 98 (sideways). P 13 × 13½.
903 4 c. Type 299 .. .. .. 20 25
904 6 c. View of Bay of Islands .. .. 30 1·00

301 "The Nativity" (Federico Fiori (Barocci))

302 Captain Cook, Transit of Venus and "Octant"

(Photo Harrison)

1969 (1 Oct). Christmas. P 13 × 14. A. W 98. B. No wmk.
				A		B	
905	301	2½ c. multicoloured	..	10	10	10	10

(Des Eileen Mayo. Photo; portraits embossed Harrison)

1969 (9 Oct). Bicentenary of Captain Cook's Landing in New Zealand. T 302 and similar horiz designs. P 14½ × 14.
906 4 c. black, cerise and blue .. .. 1·00 35
907 6 c. slate-green, purple-brown & black .. 1·25 2·75
908 18 c. purple-brown, slate-green & black .. 2·75 2·75
909 28 c. cerise, black and blue .. .. 4·50 4·75
906/9 .. .. Set of 4 8·50 9·50
MS910 109 × 90 mm. Nos. 906/9 .. .. 18·00 30·00
Designs:—6 c. Sir Joseph Banks (naturalist) and outline of H.M.S. Endeavour; 18 c. Dr. Daniel Solander (botanist) and his plant; 28 c. Queen Elizabeth II and Cook's chart, 1769.
The miniature sheet exists additionally inscribed on the selvedge at bottom. "A SOUVENIR FROM NEW ZEALAND STAMP EXHIBITION, NEW PLYMOUTH 6TH–11TH OCTOBER. 1969". These were not sold from Post Offices.

306 Girl, Wheat Field and C.O.R.S.O. Emblem

307 Mother feeding her Child, Dairy Herd and C.O.R.S.O. Emblem

(Des L. C. Mitchell. Photo Japanese Govt Printing Bureau, Tokyo)

1969 (18 Nov). 25th Anniv of C.O.R.S.O. (Council of Organiz-ations for Relief Services Overseas). P 13.
911 306 7 c. multicoloured 20 90
912 307 8 c. multicoloured 20 90

308 "Cardigan Bay" (champion trotter)

(Des L. C. Mitchell. Photo Courvoisier)

1970 (28 Jan). *Return of "Cardigan Bay" to New Zealand. P* 11½.
913 **308** 10 c. multicoloured 20 25

309 *Vanessa gonerilla* (butterfly) **310** Queen Elizabeth II and New Zealand Coat of Arms

(Des Enid Hunter (½ c., 1 c., 2 c., 18 c., 20 c.), Eileen Mayo (2½ c. to 7 c.), D. B. Stevenson (7½ c., 8 c.), M. Cleverley (10 c., 15 c., 25 c., 30 c., $1, $2), M. V. Askew (23 c., 50 c.). Photo Harrison (½ c. to 20 c.), Enschedé (23 c., 50 c.), Courvoisier ($1, $2) or Litho B.W. (25 c., 30 c.))

1970 (12 Mar)–76. *Various designs at T* **309**/10. *W* 98 (*sideways on* 10, 15 *and* 20 *c.) or No wmk* (23 c., to $2).

(a) Size as T **309**. *P* 13½ × 13
914 ½ c. multicoloured (2.9.70) 10 20
915 1 c. multicoloured (2.9.70) 10 10
    a. Wmk sideways (booklets) (6.7.71) 80 1·25
    b. Booklet pane. No. 915a × 3 with three *se-
    tenant* printed labels (6.7.71) .. 2·25
916 2 c. multicoloured (2.9.70) 10 10
    a. Black (inscr, etc.) omitted .. £110
917 2½ c. multicoloured (2.9.70) 40 10
918 3 c. black, brown and orange (2.9.70) 15 10
    a. Wmk sideways (booklets) (6.7.71) 55 85
919 4 c. multicoloured (2.9.70) 15 10
    a. Wmk sideways (booklets) (6.7.71) 55 85
920 5 c. multicoloured (4.11.70) 45 10
921 6 c. blackish grn, yell-grn & carm (4.11.70) 45 20
922 7 c. multicoloured (4.11.70) 55 40
923 7½ c. multicoloured (4.11.70) .. .. 1·00 1·50
924 8 c. multicoloured (4.11.70) 65 50

(b) Size as T **310**. *Various Perfs*
925 10 c. multicoloured (p 14½ × 14) .. 40 15
926 15 c. black, flesh and pale brown
    (p 13½ × 13) (20.1.71) .. 1·50 50
927 18 c. chestnut, black and apple-green
    (p 13 × 13½) (20.1.71) .. 1·50 40
928 20 c. black & yell-brn (p 13½ × 13) (20.1.71) 1·50 15
929 23 c. multicoloured (p 13½ × 12½) (1.12.71) 80 20
930 25 c. multicoloured (p 13 × 13½) (1.9.71) 1·75 35
    b. Perf 14 (11.76?) 70 40
931 30 c. multicoloured (p 13 × 13½) (1.9.71) 3·00 15
    a. Perf 14 (9.76?) .. .. 3·00 2·25
932 50 c. multicoloured (p 13½ × 12½) (1.9.71) 80 20
    a. Apple green (hill) omitted .. 25·00
    b. Buff (shore) omitted .. 55·00
933 $1 multicoloured (p 11½) (14.4.71) 2·00 85
934 $2 multicoloured (p 11½) (14.4.71) 5·50 1·25
914/34 *Set of* 21 19·00 6·50
Designs: *Vert*—½ c. *Lycaena salustius* (butterfly); 2 c. *Argyrophenga antipodum* (butterfly); 2½ c. *Nyctemera annulata* (moth); 3 c. *Detunda egregia* (moth); 4 c. *Charagia virescens* (moth); 5 c. Scarlet Parrot Fish; 6 c. Sea Horses; 7 c. Leather Jacket (fish); 7½ c. Garfish; 8 c. John Dory (fish); 18 c. Maori club; 25 c. Hauraki Gulf Maritime Park; 30 c. Mt Cook National Park. *Horiz*—10 c. Type **310**: 15 c. Maori fish hook; 20 c. Maori tattoo pattern; 23 c. Egmont National Park; 50 c. Abel Tasman National Park; $1 Geothermal Power; $2 Agricultural Technology.
Although issued as a definitive No. 925 was put on sale on the occasion of the Royal Visit to New Zealand.
See also Nos. 1008, etc.

311 Geyser Restaurant **312** U.N. H.Q. Building

(Des M. Cleverley. Photo Japanese Govt Printing Bureau, Tokyo)

1970 (8 Apr). *World Fair, Osaka. T* **311** *and similar horiz designs. Multicoloured. P* 13.
935 7 c. Type **311** 40 75
936 8 c. New Zealand Pavilion 40 75
937 18 c. Bush Walk 60 75
935/7 .. .. .. *Set of* 3 1·25 2·00

(Des R. M. Conly (3 c.), L. C. Mitchell (10 c.). Litho D.L.R.)

1970 (24 June). *25th Anniv of United Nations. T* **312** *and similar vert design. P* 13½.
938 3 c. multicoloured 10 10
939 10 c. scarlet and yellow 20 20
Design:—10 c. Tractor on horizon.

313 Soccer

(Des L. C. Mitchell. Litho D.L.R.)

1970 (5 Aug). *Health Stamps. T* **313** *and similar multicoloured design. P* 13½.
940 2½ c. + 1 c. Netball (*vert*) 10 15
941 3 c. + 1 c. Type **313** 10 15
MS942 Two sheets: (*a*) 102 × 125 mm (940); (*b*) 125 × 102 mm (941), containing blocks of six *Per pair* 17·00 25·00

314 "The Virgin adoring the Child" (Correggio) **315** "The Holy Family" (stained glass window, Invercargill Presbyterian Church)

(Litho D.L.R.)

1970 (1 Oct). *Christmas. T* **314**/15 *and similar design. P* 12½.
943 2½ c. multicoloured 10 10
944 3 c. multicoloured 10 10
    a. Green (inscr and value) omitted .. £150
945 10 c. black, orange and silver .. 30 75
943/5 .. .. .. *Set of* 3 35 75
Design: *Horiz*—10 c. Tower of Roman Catholic Church, Sockburn.
No. 943 exists as an imperforate proof with the country inscription and face value omitted.

316 Chatham Islands Lily

(Des Eileen Mayo. Photo Japanese Govt Printing Bureau, Tokyo)

1970 (2 Dec). *Chatham Islands. T* **316** *and similar horiz design. Multicoloured. P* 13.
946 1 c. Type **316** 10 15
947 2 c. Shy Albatross 30 25

317 Country Women's Institute Emblem

(Des L. C. Mitchell. Photo Japanese Govt Ptg Bureau, Tokyo)

1971 (10 Feb). *50th Anniversaries of Country Women's Institutes and Rotary International in New Zealand. T* **317** *and similar horiz design. Multicoloured. P* 13.
948 4 c. Type **317** 10 10
949 10 c. Rotary emblem and map of New Zealand 10 20

318 Rainbow II (yacht)

(Des J. Berry (5 c.), G. F. Fuller (8 c.). Litho B.W.)

1971 (3 Mar). *One Ton Cup Racing Trophy. T* **318** *and similar horiz design. Multicoloured. P* 13½ × 13.
950 5 c. Type **318** 15 20
951 8 c. One Ton Cup 25 65

319 Civic Arms of Palmerston North

(Des R. M. Conly. Photo Japanese Govt Ptg Bureau, Tokyo)

1971 (12 May). *City Centenaries. T* **319** *and similar horiz designs. Multicoloured. P* 13.
952 3 c. Type **319** 10 10
953 4 c. Arms of Auckland 10 10
954 5 c. Arms of Invercargill 15 40
952/4 .. .. .. *Set of* 3 30 50

320 Antarctica on Globe **321** Child on Swing

(Des Eileen Mayo. Photo Japanese Govt Ptg Bureau, Tokyo)

1971 (9 June). *Tenth Anniv of Antarctic Treaty. P* 13.
955 **320** 6 c. multicoloured .. .. 1·50 1·50

(Des Eileen Mayo. Photo Japanese Govt Ptg Bureau, Tokyo)

1971 (9 June). *25th Anniv of U.N.I.C.E.F. P* 13.
956 **321** 7 c. multicoloured 50 70

(322) (322a) (322b)

T **322**. Photo, showing screening dots; thin bars, wide apart.
T **322a**. Typo, without screening dots; thick bars, closer together.
T **322b**. Typo; bars similar to T **322**.

1971–73. *No.* 917 *surcharged.*
(a) In photogravure, by Harrison (23.6.71*)
957 **322** 4 c. on 2½ c. multicoloured .. 15 10
(b) Typographically, by Harrison (13.7.72*)
957a **322a** 4 c. on 2½ c. multicoloured .. 45 10
    ab. Albino surch £110
    ac. Surch double, one albino .. 15·00
(c) Typographically, locally (18.6.73*)
957b **322b** 4 c. on 2½ c. multicoloured .. 15 10
*Earliest known postmarks.

323 Satellite-tracking Aerial

(Des M. Cleverley. Photo Courvoisier)

1971 (14 July). *Opening of Satellite Earth Station. T* **323** *and similar horiz design. P* 11½.
958 8 c. black, drab-grey and vermilion .. 60 1·00
959 10 c. black, turquoise-grn & pale bluish vio .. 65 1·00
Design:—10 c. Satellite.

324 Girls playing Hockey

(Des L. C. Mitchell. Litho Harrison)

1971 (4 Aug). *Health Stamps. T* **324** *and similar horiz designs. Multicoloured. W* 98 (*sideways on* 5 c.). *P* 13½ × 13.
960 3 c. + 1 c. Type **324** 45 50
961 4 c. + 1 c. Boys playing hockey .. 45 50
962 5 c. + 1 c. Dental Health .. .. 1·10 2·00
960/2 .. .. .. *Set of* 3 1·75 2·75
MS963 Two sheets each 122 × 96 mm. Nos. 960/1 in blocks of six .. .. *Per pair* 22·00 32·00

325 "Madonna bending over the Crib" (Maratta) **326** "Tiffany" Rose

(Des Enid Hunter (10 c.), D. A. Hatcher (others). Photo Harrison)

1971 (6 Oct). *Christmas. T* **325** *and similar vert designs. Multicoloured. P* 13 × 13½.
964 3 c. Type **325** 10 10
965 4 c. "The Annunciation" (stained-glass window) (21½ × 38 mm) .. 10 10
966 10 c. "The Three Kings" (21½ × 38 mm) 70 1·00
964/6 .. .. .. *Set of* 3 80 1·25

(Des A. G. Mitchell. Photo Courvoisier)

1971 (3 Nov). *First World Rose Convention, Hamilton. T 326 and similar vert designs showing roses. Multicoloured. P 11½.*
967 2 c. Type 326 .. .. 15 30
968 5 c. "Peace" 35 35
969 8 c. "Chrysler Imperial" .. .. 60 1·10
967/9 .. .. *Set of 3* 1·00 1·60

327 Lord Rutherford and   **328** Benz (1895)
Alpha Particles

(Des M. Cleverley. Litho B.W.)

1971 (1 Dec). *Birth Centenary of Lord Rutherford (scientist). T 327 and similar horiz design. Multicoloured. P 13½ × 13.*
970 1 c. Type 327 .. .. .. 25 40
971 7 c. Lord Rutherford and formula .. 85 1·40

(Des A. G. Mitchell. Litho B.W.)

1972 (2 Feb). *International Vintage Car Rally. T 328 and similar horiz designs. Multicoloured. P 14.*
972 3 c. Type 328 .. .. .. 20 10
973 4 c. Oldsmobile (1904) 25 10
974 5 c. Ford "Model T" (1914) .. 35 10
975 6 c. Cadillac Service car (1915) .. 55 45
976 8 c. Chrysler (1924) .. .. 1·25 1·25
977 10 c. Austin "7" (1923) .. .. 1·25 1·25
972/7 .. .. .. *Set of 6* 3·50 2·75

329 Coat of Arms of   **330** Black Scree
Wanganui   Cotula

(Des M. Cleverley. Litho Harrison)

1972 (5 Apr). *Anniversaries. T 329 and similar designs. P 13 × 13½ (3, 5 and 8 c.) or 13½ × 13 (others).*
978 3 c. multicoloured 15 10
979 4 c. red-orange, brown-bistre and black .. 15 10
980 5 c. multicoloured 25 10
981 8 c. multicoloured .. .. 1·50 1·60
982 10 c. multicoloured .. .. 1·50 1·60
978/82 .. .. .. *Set of 5* 3·25 3·25
Designs and Events: *Vert*—3 c. Type 329 (Centenary of Wanganui Council govt); 5 c. De Havilland DH89 "Rapide" Dominie and Boeing "737" (25th Anniv National Airways Corp); 8 c. French frigate and Maori palisade (Bicent of landing by Marion du Fresne). *Horiz*—4 c. Postal Union symbol (Tenth Anniv of Asian-Oceanic Postal Union); 10 c. Stone cairn (150th Anniv of New Zealand Methodist Church).

(Des Eileen Mayo. Litho Harrison)

1972 (7 June). *Alpine Plants. T 330 and similar vert designs. Multicoloured. P 13½.*
983 4 c. Type 330 .. .. .. 30 10
984 6 c. North Island Eidelweiss .. 75 60
985 8 c. Haast's Buttercup .. .. 1·25 1·25
986 10 c. Brown Mountain Daisy .. 1·75 1·75
983/6 .. .. .. *Set of 4* 3·50 3·25

331 Boy playing   **332** "Madonna with
Tennis   Child" (Murillo)

(Des L. C. Mitchell. Litho Harrison)

1972 (2 Aug). *Health Stamps. T 331 and similar vert design. P 13 × 13½.*
987 3 c. + 1 c. light grey and chestnut .. 30 45
988 4 c. + 1 c. light red-brown, grey and lemon .. 30 45
MS989 Two sheets each 107 × 123 mm. Nos. 987/8 in blocks of six .. .. *Per pair* 20·00 30·00
Design:—No. 988, Girl playing tennis.

(Des D. A. Hatcher. Photo Courvoisier)

1972 (4 Oct). *Christmas. T 332 and similar vert designs. Multicoloured. P 11½.*
990 3 c. Type 332 .. .. .. 10 10
991 5 c. "The Last Supper" (stained-glass window, St. John's Church, Levin) .. 15 10
992 10 c. Pohutukawa flower .. .. 55 1·00
990/2 .. .. .. *Set of 3* 70 1·00

6c

New Zealand 3c

333 Lake   **334** Old Pollen Street
Waikaremoana

(Des D. A. Hatcher. Photo Courvoisier)

1972 (6 Dec). *Lake Scenes. T 333 and similar vert designs. Multicoloured. P 11½.*
993 6 c. Type 333 .. .. .. 1·00 1·25
994 8 c. Lake Hayes .. .. .. 1·10 1·25
995 18 c. Lake Wakatipu .. .. 2·00 2·25
996 23 c. Lake Rotomahana .. .. 2·25 2·75
993/6 .. .. .. *Set of 4* 5·75 6·75

(Des Miss V. Jepsen (3 c.), B. Langford (others). Litho Harrison)

1973 (7 Feb). *Commemorations. T 334 and similar horiz designs. Multicoloured (except 8 c.). P 13½ × 13.*
997 3 c. Type 334 .. .. .. 15 10
998 4 c. Coal-mining and pasture .. 15 10
999 5 c. Cloister 15 15
1000 6 c. Forest, birds and lake .. 50 80
1001 8 c. Rowers (light grey, indigo and gold) .. 45 1·00
1002 10 c. Graph and people .. .. 50 1·60
997/1002 .. .. .. *Set of 6* 1·75 3·25
Events:—3 c. Centennial of Thames Borough; 4 c. Centennial of Westport Borough; 5 c. Centennial of Canterbury University; 6 c. 50th Anniv of Royal Forest and Bird Protection Society; 8 c. Success of N.Z. Rowers in 1972 Olympics; 10 c. 25th Anniv of E.C.A.F.E.

New Zealand 3c
NEW ZEALAND 5c

335 Class "W" Locomotive   **336** "Maori Woman
and Child"

(Des R. M. Conly. Litho Harrison)

1973 (4 Apr). *New Zealand Steam Locomotives. T 335 and similar horiz designs. Multicoloured. P 14 × 14½.*
1003 3 c. Type 335 .. .. .. 50 10
1004 4 c. Class "X" 65 10
1005 5 c. Class "Ab" 65 10
1006 10 c. Class "Ja" .. .. .. 2·50 1·75
1003/6 .. .. .. *Set of 4* 3·75 1·75

1973–76. *As Nos. 914 etc., but no wmk.*
1008 1 c. multicoloured (7.9.73) .. 90 65
   a. Booklet pane. No. 1008 × 3 with three *se-tenant* printed labels (8.74) .. 2·40
   b. Red (wing markings) omitted .. £130
   c. Blue (spots on wings) omitted .. 60·00
1009 2 c. multicoloured (6.73?) .. 30 10
1010 3 c. black, light brown and orange (1974) 2·25 80
1011 4 c. multicoloured (7.9.73) .. 70 10
   a. Bright green (wing veins) inverted £275
   b. Purple-brown omitted .. £170
   c. Orange-yellow omitted .. £200
   d. Greenish blue (background) omitted £150
   e. Bright green (wing veins) omitted 6·00
   f. Apple green (wings) omitted £130
1012 5 c. multicoloured (1973) .. 1·75 1·25
1013 6 c. blackish green, yellow-green and rose-carmine (7.9.73) .. 40 30
   a. Yellow-grn (part of sea horse) omitted £170
1014 7 c. multicoloured (1974) .. 3·50 2·50
1015 8 c. multicoloured (1974) .. 4·75 1·50
   a. Blue-green (background) omitted £200
1017 10 c. multicoloured, *p* 13½×13 (6.73?) 80 10
   a. Silver (Arms) omitted .. £110
   b. Imperf (vert pair) .. £180
   c. Deep blue (Queen's head, face value etc.) omitted £180
   d. Red (hair ribbon) omitted .. 20·00
1018 15 c. black, flesh & pale brown, *p* 13½×13 (2.8.76) .. .. 2·00 10
1019 18 c. chestnut, black & apple-green (1974) 1·00 90
   a. Black (inscr, etc.) omitted .. £160
1020 20 c. black and yellow-brown (1974) 80 10
1008/20 .. .. .. *Set of 12* 17·00 7·50

(Des and photo Courvoisier)

1973 (6 June). *Paintings by Frances Hodgkins. T 336 and similar vert designs. Multicoloured. P 11½.*
1027 5 c. Type 336 .. .. .. 40 15
1028 8 c. "Hilltop" 75 75
1029 10 c. "Barn in Picardy" .. .. 1·00 1·50
1030 18 c. "Self Portrait Still Life" .. 1·50 2·50
1027/30 .. .. .. *Set of 4* 3·25 2·50

COVER PRICES

Cover factors are quoted at the beginning of each country for most issues to 1945. An explanation of the system can be found on page x. The factors quoted do not, however, apply to philatelic covers.

Postage + Health 3c 1c 1973 **New Zealand**
CHRISTMAS 1973 NEW ZEALAND 3c

337 Prince Edward   **338** "Tempi Madonna"
(Raphael)

(Des and litho Harrison)

1973 (1 Aug). *Health Stamps. P 13 × 13½.*
1031 **337** 3 c. + 1 c. dull yellowish green and reddish brown .. 30 30
1032 4 c. + 1 c. rose-red and blackish brown 30 30
MS1033 Two sheets each 96 × 121 mm with Nos. 1031/2 in blocks of 6 (3 × 2) .. *Per pair* 18·00 27·00

(Des A. G. Mitchell. Photo Enschedé)

1973 (3 Oct). *Christmas. T 338 and similar vert designs. Multicoloured. P 12½ × 13½.*
1034 3 c. Type 338 .. .. .. 10 10
1035 5 c. "Three Kings" (stained-glass window, St. Theresa's Church, Auckland) .. 10 10
1036 10 c. Family entering church 25 60
1034/6 .. .. .. *Set of 3* 40 50

6c **New Zealand** MITRE PEAK
New Zealand 4c

339 Mitre Peak   **340** Hurdling

(Des D. A. Hatcher. Photo Enschedé)

1973 (5 Dec). *Mountain Scenery. T 339 and similar multicoloured designs. P 13 × 13½ (6, 8 c.) or 13½ × 13 (others).*
1037 6 c. Type 339 .. .. .. 80 90
1038 8 c. Mt Ngauruhoe .. .. 1·00 1·50
1039 18 c. Mt Sefton (*horiz*) .. .. 1·75 3·00
1040 23 c. Burnett Range (*horiz*) .. 2·00 3·00
1037/40 .. .. .. *Set of 4* 5·00 7·50

(Des M. Cleverley. Litho Harrison)

1974 (9 Jan). *Tenth British Commonwealth Games, Christchurch. T 340 and similar vert designs. 5 c. black and violet-blue, others multicoloured. P 13 × 14.*
1041 4 c. Type 340 .. .. .. 10 10
1042 5 c. Ball-player 15 10
1043 10 c. Cycling 20 15
1044 18 c. Rifle-shooting 35 65
1045 23 c. Bowls 50 85
1041/5 .. .. .. *Set of 5* 1·10 1·60
No. 1042 does not show the Games emblem, and commemorates the Fourth Paraplegic Games, held at Dunedin.

New Zealand Day 1974
NEW ZEALAND 4c CENTENARY OF NAPIER 1874~1974

341 Queen Elizabeth II   **342** "Spirit of Napier"
Fountain

(Des D. A. Hatcher and A. G. Mitchell. Litho Harrison)

1974 (5 Feb). *New Zealand Day. Sheet 131 × 74 mm. containing T 341 and similar horiz designs, size 37 × 20 mm. Multicoloured. P 13.*
MS1046 4 c. × 5 Treaty House, Waitangi; Signing Waitangi Treaty; Type 341; Parliament Buildings Extensions; Children in Class .. .. 60 2·00

(Des Miss V. Jepsen. Photo Courvoisier)

1974 (3 Apr). *Centenaries of Napier and U.P.U. T 342 and similar vert designs. Multicoloured. P 11½.*
1047 4 c. Type 342 .. .. .. 10 10
1048 5 c. Clock Tower, Berne 10 15
1049 8 c. U.P.U. Monument, Berne .. 35 90
1047/9 .. .. .. *Set of 3* 50 1·00

343 Boeing Seaplane, 1919

344 Children, Cat and Dog

(Des R. M. Conly. Litho Harrison)

1974 (5 June). *History of New Zealand Airmail Transport.* T **343** *and similar horiz designs. Multicoloured.* P 14 × 13.

1050	3 c. Type **343**	25	10
1051	4 c. Lockheed "Electra", 1937	30	10
1052	5 c. Bristol Freighter, 1958	35	10
1053	23 c. Empire "S 30" flying-boat, 1940	1·50	1·50
1050/3	*Set of 4*	2·25	1·60

(Des B. Langford. Litho Harrison)

1974 (7 Aug). *Health Stamps.* P 13 × 13½.

1054	**344** 3 c. + 1 c. multicoloured	20	30
1055	— 4 c. + 1 c. multicoloured	25	30
1056	— 5 c. + 1 c. multicoloured	1·00	1·25
1054/6	*Set of 3*	1·25	1·75
MS1057	145 × 123 mm. No. 1055 in block of ten	21·00	30·00

Nos. 1055/6 are as T **344**, showing children and pets.

345 "The Adoration" of the Magi" (Konrad Witz)

346 Great Barrier Island

(Des Eileen Mayo. Photo Courvoisier)

1974 (2 Oct). *Christmas.* T **345** *and similar horiz designs. Multicoloured.* P 11½.

1058	3 c. Type **345**	10	10
1059	5 c. "The Angel Window" (stained-glass window, Old St. Pauls Church, Wellington)	10	10
1060	10 c. Madonna Lily	30	50
1058/60	*Set of 3*	40	55

(Des D. A. Hatcher. Photo Enschedé)

1974 (4 Dec). *Off-shore Islands.* T **346** *and similar horiz designs. Multicoloured.* P 13½ × 13.

1061	6 c. Type **346**	30	40
1062	8 c. Stewart Island	40	80
1063	18 c. White Island	70	1·50
1064	23 c. The Brothers	1·00	2·00
1061/4	*Set of 4*	2·25	4·25

347 Crippled Child

(Des Miss V. Jepsen (3 c., 5 c.), A. G. Mitchell (10 c., 18 c.). Litho Harrison)

1975 (5 Feb). *Anniversaries and Events.* T **347** *and similar horiz designs. Multicoloured.* P 13½.

1065	3 c. Type **347**	10	10
1066	5 c. Farming family	15	10
1067	10 c. I.W.Y. symbols	20	55
1068	18 c. Medical School Building, Otago University	35	80
1065/8	*Set of 4*	70	1·40

Commemorations:—3 c. 40th Anniv of N.Z. Crippled Children Society; 5 c. 50th Anniv of Women's Division, Federated Farmers of N.Z.; 10 c. International Women's Year; 18 c. Centenary of Otago Medical School.

348 Scow *Lake Erie*

(Des R. M. Conly. Litho Harrison)

1975 (2 Apr). *Historic Sailing Ships.* T **348** *and similar horiz designs.* P 13½ × 13.

1069	4 c. black and red	30	10
1070	5 c. black and turquoise-blue	30	10
1071	8 c. black and yellow	45	35
1072	10 c. black and olive-yellow	50	40
1073	18 c. black and light brown	80	90
1074	23 c. black and slate-lilac	95	1·25
1069/74	*Set of 6*	3·00	2·75

Ships:—5 c. Schooner *Herald*; 8 c. Brigantine *New Zealander*; 10 c. Topsail schooner *Jessie Kelly*; 18 c. Barque *Tory*; 23 c. Full-rigged clipper *Rangitiki*.

349 Lake Summer Forest Park

(Des and photo Enschedé)

1975 (4 June). *Forest Park Scenes.* T **349** *and similar horiz designs. Multicoloured.* P 13.

1075	6 c. Type **349**	50	70
1076	8 c. North-west Nelson	60	1·00
1077	18 c. Kaweka	1·25	1·75
1078	23 c. Coromandel	1·50	2·00
1075/8	*Set of 4*	3·50	5·00

350 Girl feeding Lamb

351 "Virgin and Child" (Zanobi Machiavelli)

(Des Margaret Chapman. Litho Harrison)

1975 (6 Aug). *Health Stamps.* T **350** *and similar horiz designs. Multicoloured.* P 13½ × 13.

1079	3 c. + 1 c. Type **350**	20	25
1080	4 c. + 1 c. Boy with hen and chicks	20	25
1081	5 c. + 1 c. Boy with duck and duckling	60	1·10
1079/81	*Set of 3*	90	1·40
MS1082	123 × 146 mm. No. 1080 × 10	14·00	25·00

(Des Enid Hunter. Photo Harrison)

1975 (1 Oct). *Christmas.* T **351** *and similar horiz designs. Multicoloured.* P 13 × 13½ (3 c.) or 13½ × 13 (others).

1083	3 c. Type **351**	10	10
	a. Red omitted*	£150	
1084	5 c. "Cross in Landscape" (stained-glass window, Greendale Church)	10	10
	a. Brown (face value) omitted	£160	
1085	10 c. "I saw three ships . . ." (carol)	35	65
1083/5	*Set of 3*	60	65

*This occurred in the last two vertical rows of the sheet with the red partially omitted on the previous row.

Used copies of No. 1083 have been seen with the orange ("Christmas 1975") omitted.

352 "Sterling Silver"

353 Queen Elizabeth II (photograph by W. Harrison)

353a Maripi (knife)

353b Paua

353c "Beehive" (section of Parliamentary Buildings, Wellington)

(Des A. G. Mitchell (1 to 14 c.), I. Hulse (20 c. to $2), R. Conly ($5). Photo Harrison (1 to 10 c.), Courvoisier (11 to 14 c.), Heraclio Fournier (20 c. to $5))

1975 (26 Nov)–**81**. (a) *Vert designs as T* **352** *showing garden roses. Multicoloured.* P 14½ (6 to 8 c.) or 14½ × 14 (others).

1086	1 c. Type **352**	10	10
1087	2 c. "Lilli Marlene"	10	10
1088	3 c. "Queen Elizabeth"	60	10
	a. Perf 14½ (6.79)	85	10
1089	4 c. "Super Star"	10	10
1090	5 c. "Diamond Jubilee"	10	10
1091	6 c. "Cresset"	90	85
	a. Perf 14½ × 14 (8.76?)	40	30
1092	7 c. "Michele Meilland"	2·00	50
	a. Perf 14½ × 14 (6.76?)	40	10
1093	8 c. "Josephine Bruce"	2·00	90
	a. Perf 14½ × 14 (8.76?)	65	10
1094	9 c. "Iceberg"	15	15

(b) *Type* **353**. P 14½ × 14 (7.12.77)

1094a	10 c. multicoloured	85	20
	ab. Perf 14½ (2.79)	30	10

(c) *Vert designs as T* **353a** *showing Maori artefacts.* P 11½ (24.11.76)

1095	11 c. reddish brown, lemon & blackish brown	45	30
1096	12 c. reddish brown, lemon & blackish brown	30	10
1097	13 c. reddish brown, greenish blue and blackish brown	60	30
1098	14 c. reddish brown, lemon & blackish brown	30	20

Designs:—12 c. Putorino (flute); 13 c. Wahaika (club); 14 c. Kotiate (club).

(d) *Horiz designs as T* **353b** *showing seashells. Multicoloured.* P 13

1099	20 c. Type **353b** (29.11.78)	15	20
1100	30 c. Toheroa (29.11.78)	25	30
1101	40 c. Coarse Dosinia (29.11.78)	30	35
1102	50 c. Spiny Murex (29.11.78)	40	45
1103	$1 Scallop (26.11.79)	70	85
	a. Imperf between (vert pair)	£400	
1104	$2 Circular Saw (26.11.79)	1·00	1·75

(e) *Type* **353c**. P 13 (2.12.81)

1105	$5 multicoloured	3·00	2·00
	a. Imperf (vert pair)		
1086/105	*Set of 21*	9·00	6·75

Faked "missing colour errors" exist of No. 1094a, involving parts of the portrait.

A used example of No. 1099 exists with the black colour omitted so that the body of the shell appears in blue instead of green.

No. 1103a occurs on the top two rows of the sheet; the lower stamp being imperforate on three edges except for two perforation holes at the foot of each vertical side.

354 Family and League of Mothers Badge

(Des A. P. Derrick. Litho J.W.)

1976 (4 Feb). *Anniversaries and Metrication.* T **354** *and similar horiz designs. Multicoloured.* P 13½ × 14.

1110	6 c. Type **354**	10	10
1111	7 c. Weight, temperature, linear measure and capacity	10	10
1112	8 c. William Bryan (immigrant ship), mountain and New Plymouth	15	10
1113	10 c. Two women shaking hands and Y.W.C.A. badge	15	40
1114	25 c. Map of the world showing cable links	30	1·25
1110/14	*Set of 5*	70	1·60

Anniversaries:—6 c. League of Mothers, 50th Anniv; 7 c. Metrication; 8 c. Centenary of New Plymouth; 10 c. 50th Anniv of New Zealand Y.W.C.A.; 25 c. Centenary of link with International Telecommunications Network.

355 Gig

356 Purakaunui Falls

(Des G. F. Fuller. Litho Harrison)

1976 (7 Apr). *Vintage Farm Transport.* T **355** *and similar horiz designs. Multicoloured.* P 13½ × 13.

1115	6 c. Type **355**	15	20
1116	7 c. Thorneycroft lorry	20	10
1117	8 c. Scandi wagon	50	20
1118	9 c. Traction engine	30	40
1119	10 c. Wool wagon	30	75
1120	25 c. Cart	80	1·75
1115/20	*Set of 6*	2·00	2·75

(Des and photo Courvoisier)

1976 (2 June). *Waterfalls.* T **356** *and similar vert designs. Multicoloured.* P 11½.

1121	10 c. Type **356**	40	10
1122	14 c. Marakopa Falls	75	55
1123	15 c. Bridal Veil Falls	80	60
1124	16 c. Papakorito Falls	90	70
1121/4	*Set of 4*	2·50	1·75

357 Boy and Pony

358 "Nativity" (Spanish carving)

(Des Margaret Chapman. Litho Harrison)

1976 (4 Aug). *Health Stamps.* T **357** *and similar vert designs. Multicoloured.* P 13 × 13½.

1125	7 c. + 1 c. Type **357**	25	30
1126	8 c. + 1 c. Girl and calf	25	30
1127	10 c. + 1 c. Girls and bird	50	75
1125/7	*Set of 3*	90	1·25
MS1128	96 × 121 mm. Nos. 1125/7 × 2	7·00	9·00

(Des Margaret Chapman (18 c.), D. A. Hatcher (others). Photo Harrison)

1976 (6 Oct). *Christmas. T 358 and similar horiz designs. Multicoloured. P 14 × 14½ (7 c.) or 14½ × 14 (others).*

1129	7 c. Type **358**			15	10
1130	11 c. "Resurrection" (stained-glass window, St. Joseph's Catholic Church, Grey Lynn)			25	30
1131	18 c. Angels			40	60
1129/31			*Set of 3*	70	85

359 Arms of Hamilton   **360** Queen Elizabeth II

(Des P. L. Blackie. Litho Harrison)

1977 (19 Jan). *Anniversaries. T 359 and similar vert designs. Multicoloured. P 13 × 13½.*

1132	8 c. Type **359**			15	10
	a. Horiz strip of 3, Nos. 1132/4			45	
1133	8 c. Arms of Gisborne			15	10
1134	8 c. Arms of Masterton			15	10
1135	10 c. A.A. emblem			15	30
	a. Horiz pair. Nos. 1135/6			30	90
1136	10 c. Arms of the College of Surgeons			15	30
1132/6			*Set of 5*	75	80

Events:—Nos. 1132/4, City Centenaries; No. 1135, 75th Anniv of the Automobile Association in New Zealand; No. 1136, 50th Anniv of Royal Australasian College of Surgeons.

Designs of each value were printed in the same sheet horizontally *se-tenant.*

(Des and photo Harrison from photographs by Warren Harrison)

1977 (23 Feb). *Silver Jubilee. Sheet 178 × 82 mm containing T 360 and similar vert designs showing different portraits. P 14 × 14½.*

MS1137	8 c. × 5 multicoloured			80	1·50
	a. Imperf			£1400	
	ab. Ditto, and silver omitted			£2000	
	b. Silver omitted			£550	
	c. Indian red omitted			£250	

361 Physical Education   **(362)**
and Maori Culture

(Des A. G. Mitchell. Litho Harrison)

1977 (6 Apr). *Education. T 361 and similar vert designs. Multicoloured. P 13 × 13½.*

1138	8 c. Type **361**			30	60
	a. Horiz strip of 5, Nos. 1138/42			1·40	
1139	8 c. Geography, science and woodwork			30	60
1140	8 c. Teaching the deaf, kindergarten and woodwork			30	60
1141	8 c. Tertiary and language classes			30	60
1142	8 c. Home science, correspondence school and teacher training			30	60
1138/42			*Set of 5*	1·40	2·75

Nos. 1138/42 were printed horizontally *se-tenant* throughout the sheet.

1977 (Apr). *Coil Stamps. Nos. 1010/11 surch as T 362 by Govt Printer, Wellington.*

1143	7 c. on 3 c. *Detunda egregia* (moth) (19.4)			40	65
1144	8 c. on 4 c. *Charagia virescens* (moth) (21.4)			40	65
	a. Bright green (wing veins) omitted			85·00	

Forged "7 c." surcharges, similar to No. 1143, but in smaller type, are known applied to Nos. 918 and 1010.

363 Karitane Beach   **364** Girl with Pigeon

(Des D. A. Hatcher. Photo Heraclio Fournier)

1977 (1 June). *Seascapes. T 363 and similar horiz designs. Multicoloured. P 14½.*

1145	10 c. Type **363**			20	10
1146	16 c. Ocean Beach, Mount Maunganui			35	35
1147	18 c. Piha Beach			40	40
1148	30 c. Kaikoura Coast			50	50
1145/8			*Set of 4*	1·25	1·25

(Des A. P. Derrick. Litho Harrison)

1977 (3 Aug). *Health Stamps. T 364 and similar vert designs. Multicoloured. P 13 × 13½.*

1149	7 c. + 2 c. Type **364**			20	30
1150	8 c. + 2 c. Boy with frog			25	35
1151	10 c. + 2 c. Girl with butterfly			45	70
1149/51			*Set of 3*	80	1·25
MS1152	97 × 120 mm. Nos. 1149/51 × 2			5·50	10·00

Stamps from the miniature sheet are without white border and together form a composite design.

365 "The Holy Family" (Correggio)

(Des Margaret Chapman (23 c.), graphics for all values produced by printer. Photo Courvoisier)

1977 (5 Oct). *Christmas. T 365 and similar vert designs. Multicoloured. P 11½.*

1153	7 c. Type **365**			15	10
1154	16 c. "Madonna and Child" (stained-glass window, St. Michael's and All Angels, Dunedin)			25	20
1155	23 c. "Partridge in a Pear Tree"			40	45
1153/5			*Set of 3*	70	65

366 Merryweather Manual   **367** Town Clock and
Pump, 1860   Coat of Arms,
Ashburton

(Des R. M. Conly. Litho Harrison)

1977 (7 Dec). *Fire Fighting Appliances. T 366 and similar horiz designs. Multicoloured. P 14 × 13.*

1156	10 c. Type **366**			15	10
1157	11 c. 2-wheel hose, reel and ladder, 1880			15	10
1158	12 c. Shand Mason steam fire engine, 1873			20	15
1159	23 c. Chemical fire engine, 1888			30	30
1156/9			*Set of 4*	70	60

(Des P. L. Blackie (No. 1162), Harrison (No. 1163), P. J. Durrant (others), Litho Harrison)

1978 (8 Mar). *Centenaries. T 367 and similar multicoloured designs. P 14.*

1160	10 c. Type **367**			15	10
	a. Horiz pair. Nos. 1160/1			30	50
1161	10 c. Stratford and Mt Egmont			15	10
1162	12 c. Early telephone			15	15
1163	20 c. Bay of Islands (*horiz*)			20	30
1160/3			*Set of 4*	60	85

Centenaries commemorated are those of the towns of Ashburton and Stratford, of the telephone in New Zealand, and of the Bay of Islands County.

The 10 c. values were printed together, *se-tenant*, in horizontal pairs throughout the sheet.

368 Students and   **369**   **370** Maui Gas
Ivey Hall, Lincoln   Drilling Platform
College

(Des A. P. Derrick. Litho Harrison)

1978 (26 Apr). *Land Resources and Centenary of Lincoln College of Agriculture. T 368 and similar vert designs. Multicoloured. P 14½.*

1164	10 c. Type **368**			15	10
1165	12 c. Sheep grazing			20	25
1166	15 c. Fertiliser ground spreading			20	30
1167	16 c. Agricultural Field Days			20	30
1168	20 c. Harvesting grain			25	40
1169	30 c. Dairy farming			40	70
1164/9			*Set of 6*	1·25	1·90

(Photo Harrison)

1978 (3 May–9 June). *Coil Stamps. P 14½ × 14 (10 c.) or 14 × 13 (others).*

1170	**369**	1 c. bright purple (9.6)			10	30
1171		2 c. bright orange (9.6)			10	30
1172		5 c. red-brown (9.6)			10	35
1173		10 c. bright blue			30	70
1170/3				*Set of 4*	45	1·50

(Des R. M. Conly. Litho Harrison)

1978 (7 June). *Resources of the Sea. T 370 and similar vert designs. Multicoloured. P 13 × 14.*

1174	12 c. Type **370**			20	15
1175	15 c. Trawler			30	25
1176	20 c. Map of 200 mile fishing limit			40	35
1177	23 c. Humpback Whale and Bottle-nosed Dolphins			50	40
1178	35 c. Kingfish, snapper, grouper and squid			75	75
1174/8			*Set of 5*	1·90	1·75

371 First Health   **372** "The Holy   **373** Sir Julius
Charity Stamp   Family" (El Greco)   Vogel

(Des A. G. Mitchell. Litho Harrison)

1978 (2 Aug). *Health Stamps. Health Services Commemorations. T 371 and similar vert design. P 13 × 14.*

1179	10 c. + 2 c. black, red and gold			25	35
1180	12 c. + 2 c. multicoloured			25	40
MS1181	97 × 124 mm. Nos. 1179/80 × 3			3·50	4·75

Designs and commemorations:—10 c. Type **371** (50th anniversary of health charity stamps); 12 c. Heart operation (National Heart Foundation).

(Des R. M. Conly. Photo Courvoisier)

1978 (4 Oct). *Christmas. T 372 and similar multicoloured designs. P 11½.*

1182	7 c. Type **372**			10	10
1183	10 c. All Saints' Church, Howick			25	30
1184	23 c. Beach scene			30	45
1182/4			*Set of 3*	60	70

(Des A. G. Mitchell. Litho J.W.)

1979 (7 Feb). *Statesmen. T 373 and similar vert designs in sepia and drab. P 13 × 13½.*

1185	10 c. Type **373**			30	55
	a. Horiz strip of 3, Nos. 1185/7			90	
1186	10 c. Sir George Grey			30	55
1187	10 c. Richard John Seddon			30	55
1185/7			*Set of 3*	90	1·50

Nos. 1185/7 were printed together, *se-tenant*, in horizontal strips of 3 throughout the sheet.

Nos. 1185/7 have matt, almost invisible gum.

374 Riverlands Cottage,   **375** Whangaroa Harbour
Blenheim

(Des P. Leitch. Litho Enschedé)

1979 (4 Apr). *Architecture (1st series). T 374 and similar horiz designs. P 13½ × 13.*

1188	10 c. black, new blue and deep blue			10	10
1189	12 c. black, pale green and bottle green			15	25
1190	15 c. black and grey			20	30
1191	20 c. black, yellow-brown and sepia			25	30
1188/91			*Set of 4*	65	90

Designs:—12 c. The Mission House, Waimate North; 15 c. "The Elms", Tauranga; 20 c. Provincial Council Buildings, Christchurch.

See also Nos. 1217/20 and 1262/5.

(Photo Heraclio Fournier)

1979 (6 June). *Small Harbours. T 375 and similar multicoloured designs. P 13.*

1192	15 c. Type **375**			20	10
1193	20 c. Kawau Island			25	30
1194	23 c. Akaroa Harbour (*vert*)			30	35
1195	35 c. Picton Harbour (*vert*)			45	50
1192/5			*Set of 4*	1·10	1·10

376 Children with Building Bricks

(Des W. Kelsall. Litho J.W.)

1979 (6 June). *International Year of the Child. P 14.*

1196	**376**	10 c. multicoloured			15	10

377 Demoiselle (378)

4c

(Des P. Blackie (12 c.), G. Fuller (others). Litho Harrison)

1979 (25 July). *Health Stamps. Marine Life. T 377 and similar multicoloured designs. P 13 × 13½ (12 c.) or 13½ × 13 (others).*
1197	10 c. + 2 c. Type **377**			40	50
	a. Horiz pair. Nos. 1197/8			80	1·00
1198	10 c. + 2 c. Sea Urchin			40	50
1199	12 c. + 2 c. Fish and underwater cameraman				
	(vert)			40	50
1197/9			*Set of 3*	1·10	1·40

MS1200 144 × 72 mm. Nos. 1197/9, each × 2.
P 14 × 14½ (12 c.) or 14½ × 14 (others) .. .. 4·00 5·50

Nos. 1197/8 were printed together, *se-tenant*, in horizontal pairs throughout the sheet.

1979 (31 Aug)–80. *Nos. 1091a, 1092a, 1093a and 1094ab surch as T 378 by Govt Printer, Wellington.*
1201	4 c. on 8 c. "Josephine Bruce" (24.9.79)			10	20
1202	14 c. on 10 c. Type **353**			40	20
	a. Surch double, one albino				
1203	17 c. on 6 c. "Cresset" (9.10.79)			40	70
1203a	20 c. on 7 c. "Michele Meilland" (29.9.80)			35	10
1201/3a			*Set of 4*	1·10	1·10

379 "Madonna and Child" (sculpture by Ghiberti)

380 Chamber, House of Representatives

(Des D. Hatcher. Photo Courvoisier)

1979 (3 Oct). *Christmas. T 379 and similar vert designs. Multicoloured. P 11½.*
1204	10 c. Type **379**			15	10
1205	25 c. Christ Church, Russell			30	40
1206	35 c. Pohutukawa (tree)			40	55
1204/6			*Set of 3*	75	90

(Des D. Hatcher. Litho J.W.)

1979 (26 Nov). *25th Commonwealth Parliamentary Conference, Wellington. T 380 and similar vert designs. Multicoloured. P 13½.*
1207	14 c. Type **380**			15	10
1208	20 c. Mace and Black Rod			20	20
1209	30 c. Wall hanging from the "Beehive"			30	45
1207/9			*Set of 3*	60	60

381 1855 1d. Stamp

(Des D. Hatcher (14 c. (all designs)), R. Conly (others). Litho Harrison)

1980 (7 Feb). *Anniversaries and Events. T 381 and similar designs. P 13½×13 (14 c. (all designs)) or 14 (others).*
1210	14 c. black, brown-red and yellow			20	20
	a. Horiz strip of 3. Nos. 1210/12			60	
	ab. Black (inscription) omitted *(strip of 3)*			£120	
1211	14 c. black, deep turquoise-blue and yellow			20	20
1212	14 c. black, dull yellowish green and yellow			20	20
1213	17 c. multicoloured			20	25
1214	25 c. multicoloured			25	30
1215	30 c. multicoloured			25	35
1210/15			*Set of 6*	1·10	1·40

MS1216 146×96 mm. Nos. 1210/12 (as horiz strip). P 14½×14 *(sold at 52 c.)* .. 2·75 4·50

Designs and commemorations; (38 × 22 *mm*)—No. 1210, Type 381; No. 1211, 1855 2d. stamp; No. 1212, 1855 1s. stamp (125th anniversary of New Zealand stamps). (40 × 23 *mm*)—No. 1213, Geyser, wood-carving and building (centenary of Rotorua (town)); No. 1214, *Earina autumnalis* and *thelymitra venosa* (International Orchid Conference, Auckland); No. 1215; Ploughing and Golden Plough Trophy (World Ploughing Championships, Christchurch).
The premium on No. **MS**1216 was used to help finance the "Zeapex 80" International Stamp Exhibition, Auckland.
Nos. 1210/12 were printed together, *se-tenant*, in horizontal strips of 3 throughout the sheet.

382 Ewelme Cottage, Parnell

383 Auckland Harbour

(Des P. Leitch. Litho Enschedé)

1980 (2 Apr). *Architecture (2nd series). T 382 and similar horiz designs. Multicoloured. P 13½ × 12½.*
1217	14 c. Type **382**			15	10
1218	17 c. Broadgreen, Nelson			25	35
1219	25 c. Courthouse, Oamaru			30	45
1220	30 c. Government Buildings, Wellington			35	45
1217/20			*Set of 4*	95	1·25

(Des D. Hatcher. Photo Heraclio Fournier)

1980 (4 June). *Large Harbours. T 383 and similar horiz designs. Multicoloured. P 13.*
1221	25 c. Type **383**			30	25
1222	30 c. Wellington Harbour			35	30
1223	35 c. Lyttelton Harbour			40	40
1224	50 c. Port Chalmers			65	65
1221/4			*Set of 4*	1·50	1·40

384 Surf-fishing

385 "Madonna and Child with Cherubim" (sculpture by Andrea della Robbia)

(Des Margaret Chapman. Litho Enschedé)

1980 (6 Aug). *Health Stamps. Fishing. T 384 and similar horiz designs. Multicoloured. P 13 × 12½.*
1225	14 c. + 2 c. Type **384**			45	70
	a. Horiz pair. Nos. 1225/6			90	1·40
1226	14 c. + 2 c. Wharf-fishing			45	70
1227	17 c. + 2 c. Spear-fishing			45	55
1225/7			*Set of 3*	1·25	1·75

MS1228 148 × 75 mm. Nos. 1225/7 each × 2
P 13½ × 13 .. .. .. 2·50 3·50

Nos. 1225/6 were printed together, *se-tenant*, in horizontal pairs throughout the sheet.

(Des P. Durrant. Photo Courvoisier)

1980 (1 Oct). *Christmas. T 385 and similar vert designs. Multicoloured. P 11½.*
1229	10 c. Type **385**			15	10
1230	25 c. St. Mary's Church, New Plymouth			25	25
1231	35 c. Picnic scene			40	45
1229/31			*Set of 3*	70	70

386 Te Heu Heu (chief)

387 Lt.-Col. the Hon W. H. A. Feilding and Borough of Feilding Crest

(Des R. Conly. Litho Heraclio Fournier)

1980 (26 Nov). *Maori Personalities. Vert designs as T 386. Multicoloured. P 12½ × 13.*
1232	15 c. Type **386**			10	10
1233	25 c. Te Hau (chief)			15	10
1234	35 c. Te Puea (princess)			20	10
1235	45 c. Ngata (politician)			30	15
1236	60 c. Te Ata-O-Tu (warrior)			35	20
1232/6			*Set of 5*	1·00	50

(Des R. Conly. Litho Harrison)

1981 (4 Feb). *Commemorations. T 387 and similar horiz design. P 14½.*
1237	20 c. multicoloured			20	20
1238	25 c. black and brown-ochre			25	25

Designs and Commemorations:—20 c. Type **387** (Centenary of Feilding (town)); 25 c. I.Y.D. emblem and cupped hands (International Year of the Disabled).

388 The Family at Play

389 Kaiauai River

(Des A. Derrick. Litho J.W.)

1981 (1 Apr). *"Family Life." T 388 and similar vert designs. Multicoloured. P 13½ × 13.*
1239	20 c. Type **388**			20	10
1240	25 c. The family, young and old			25	25
1241	30 c. The family at home			30	30
1242	35 c. The family at church			35	40
1239/42			*Set of 4*	1·00	95

(Des D. Hatcher. Photo Heraclio Fournier)

1981 (3 June). *River Scenes. T 389 and similar multicoloured designs. P 13½ × 13 (30, 35 c.) or 13 × 13½ (others).*
1243	30 c. Type **389**			30	30
1244	35 c. Mangahao			40	40
1245	40 c. Shotover *(horiz)*			45	45
1246	60 c. Cleddau *(horiz)*			75	75
1243/6			*Set of 4*	1·75	1·75

390 St. Paul's Cathedral   391 Girl with Starfish

(Des and litho Harrison)

1981 (29 July). *Royal Wedding. T 390 and similar horiz design. Multicoloured. P 14½.*
1247	20 c. Type **390**			20	30
	a. Pair. Nos. 1247/8			40	60
	ab. Deep grey (inscriptions and date) omitted			£800	
1248	20 c. Prince Charles and Lady Diana Spencer			20	30

Nos. 1247/8 were printed together, *se-tenant*, in horizontal and vertical pairs throughout the sheet.

(Des P.O. Litho Harrison)

1981 (5 Aug). *Health Stamps. Children playing by the Sea. T 391 and similar vert designs. Multicoloured. P 14½.*
1249	20 c. + 2 c. Type **391**			25	50
	a. Horiz pair. Nos. 1249/50			50	1·00
1250	20 c. + 2 c. Boy fishing			25	50
1251	25 c. + 2 c. Children exploring rock pool			25	35
1249/51			*Set of 3*	70	1·25

MS1252 100 × 125 mm. Nos. 1249/51, each × 2 .. 2·00 2·50

The 20 c. values were printed together, *se-tenant*, in horizontal pairs throughout the sheet, forming a composite design.
The stamps from No. **MS**1252 were printed together, *se-tenant*, in two horizontal strips of 3, each forming a composite design.

392 "Madonna Suckling the Child" (painting, d'Oggiono)

393 Tauranga Mission House

(Des Margaret Chapman. Photo Courvoisier)

1981 (7 Oct). *Christmas. T 392 and similar vert designs. Multicoloured. P 11½.*
1253	14 c. Type **392**			15	10
1254	30 c. St. John's Church, Wakefield			35	25
1255	40 c. Golden Tainui (flower)			45	35
1253/5			*Set of 3*	85	60

(Des A. Derrick. Litho Walsall)

1982 (3 Feb). *Commemorations. T 393 and similar vert designs. Multicoloured. P 14½.*
1256	20 c. Type **393**			25	10
	a. Horiz pair. Nos. 1256/7			50	60
1257	20 c. Water tower, Hawera			25	10
1258	25 c. Cat			35	35
1259	30 c. *Dunedin* (refrigerated sailing ship)			35	40
1260	35 c. Scientific research equipment			40	45
1256/60			*Set of 5*	1·40	1·60

Commemorations:—No. 1256, Centenary of Tauranga (town); No. 1257, Centenary of Hawera (town); No. 1258, Centenary of S.P.C.A. (Society for the Prevention of Cruelty to Animals in New Zealand); No. 1259, Centenary of Frozen Meat Exports; No. 1260, International Year of Science.
The 20 c. values were printed together, *se-tenant*, in horizontal pairs throughout the sheet.

394 Map of New Zealand   395 Alberton, Auckland

(Des A. G. Mitchell. Litho Leigh-Mardon Ltd, Melbourne)

1982 (1 Apr–13 Dec). P 12½.

1261	**394**	24 c. pale yellowish green and ultram		30	10
		a. Perf 14½ × 14 (13.12.82)	..	35	10

(Des P. Leitch. Litho Walsall)

1982 (7 Apr). *Architecture (3rd series). T 395 and similar horiz designs. Multicoloured. P 14 × 14½.*

1262	20 c. Type **395**			20	15
1263	25 c. Caccia Birch, Palmerston North			25	25
1264	30 c. Railway station, Dunedin			30	30
1265	35 c. Post Office, Ophir	..		35	40
1262/5			*Set of 4*	1·00	1·00

396 Kaiteriteri Beach, Nelson (Summer)   397 Labrador

(Des D. Hatcher. Photo Heraclio Fournier)

1982 (2 June). *"The Four Seasons". New Zealand Scenes. T 396 and similar horiz designs. Multicoloured. P 13 × 13½.*

1266	35 c. Type **396**			40	40
1267	40 c. St. Omer Park, Queenstown (Autumn)			45	45
1268	45 c. Mt Ngauruhoe, Tongariro National Park (Winter)	..		50	50
1269	70 c. Wairarapa farm (Spring)	..		75	75
1266/9			*Set of 4*	1·90	1·90

(Des R. Conly. Litho Enschedé)

1982 (4 Aug). *Health Stamps. Dogs. T 397 and similar vert designs. Multicoloured. P 13 × 13½.*

1270	24 c. + 2 c. Type **397**			75	80
	a. Horiz pair. Nos. 1270/1 ..			1·50	1·60
1271	24 c. + 2 c. Border Collie			75	80
1272	30 c. + 2 c. Cocker Spaniel			75	80
1270/2			*Set of 3*	2·00	2·25
MS1273	98 × 125 mm. Nos. 1270/2, each × 2. P 14 × 13½			4·00	4·50

The 24 c. values were printed together, *se-tenant*, in horizontal pairs throughout the sheet.

398 "Madonna with Child and Two Angels" (paintings by Piero di Cosimo)

(Des Margaret Chapman. Photo Heraclio Fournier)

1982 (6 Oct). *Christmas. T 398 and similar vert designs. Multicoloured. P 14 × 13½.*

1274	18 c. Type **398**	..		20	10
1275	35 c. Rangiatea Maori Church, Otaki			35	30
1276	45 c. Surf life-saving	..		50	40
1274/6			*Set of 3*	95	65

399 Nephrite   399a Grapes

399b Kokako

(Des P. Durrant (Nos. 1277/82), D. Little (Nos. 1283/7), Janet Marshall (Nos. 1288/97). Litho Leigh-Mardon Ltd. Melbourne)

1982 (1 Dec)–89. *Multicoloured. P 14½×14 (Nos. 1277/87) or 14½ (Nos. 1288/97).*

(a) *Minerals. T 399 and similar vert designs*

1277	1 c. Type **399**	..		10	10
	a. Perf 12½			50	10
1278	2 c. Agate	..		10	10
	a. Perf 12½			1·75	75
1279	3 c. Iron Pyrites	..		10	10
1280	4 c. Amethyst			10	10
1281	5 c. Carnelian			10	10
1282	9 c. Native Sulphur	..		20	10

(b) *Fruits. T 399a and similar vert designs*

1283	10 c. Type **399a** (7.12.83)			75	10
1284	20 c. Citrus Fruit (7.12.83)			35	10
1285	30 c. Nectarines (7.12.83)			30	10
1286	40 c. Apples (7.12.83) ..			35	10
1287	50 c. Kiwifruit (7.12.83)			40	10

(c) *Native Birds. T 399b and similar vert designs*

1288	30 c. Kakapo (1.5.86)	..		50	25
1289	40 c. Mountain ("Blue") Duck (2.2.87)			60	35
1290	45 c. New Zealand Falcon (1.5.86)			1·00	35
1291	60 c. New Zealand Teal (2.2.87)	..		1·00	40
1292	$1 Type **399b** (24.4.85)			1·25	30
1293	$2 Chatham Island Robin (24.4.85)			1·60	50
1294	$3 Stitchbird (23.4.86)			2·00	1·40
1295	$4 Saddleback (23.4.86)	..		2·75	3·00
1296	$5 Takahe (20.4.88)	..		3·25	3·50
1297	$10 Little Spotted Kiwi (19.4.89)			6·50	6·75
1277/97			*Set of 21*	21·00	15·00
1292/7	Optd "Specimen" ..		*Set of 6*	7·50	

Nos. 1292/7 overprinted "Specimen" come from a special "NEW ZEALAND 1990" Presentation Pack issued on 19 April 1989.

A miniature sheet containing No. 1293 was only available from the New Zealand stand at "PHILEXFRANCE '89" International Stamp Exhibition or the Philatelic Bureau at Wanganui.

400 Old Arts Building, Auckland University   401 Queen Elizabeth II

(Des G. Emery (35 c.), P. Durrant (others). Litho Cambec Press, Melbourne (35 c.), J.W. (others))

1983 (2 Feb). *Commemorations. T 400 and similar vert designs. Multicoloured. P 13 × 13½ (35 c.) or 14 × 13½ (others).*

1303	24 c. Salvation Army Centenary logo	..		30	10
1304	30 c. Type **400**			40	35
1305	35 c. Stylised Kangaroo and Kiwi			45	35
1306	40 c. Rainbow Trout			50	45
1307	45 c. Satellite over Earth	..		55	50
1303/7			*Set of 5*	2·00	1·50

Commemorations:—24 c. Centenary of Salvation Army; 30 c. Centenary of Auckland University; 35 c. Closer Economic Relationship agreement with Australia; 40 c. Centenary of introduction of Rainbow Trout into New Zealand; 45 c. World Communications Year.

(Des P. Durrant. Litho Harrison)

1983 (14 Mar). *Commonwealth Day. T 401 and similar horiz designs. Multicoloured. P 13½.*

1308	24 c. Type **401**			20	10
1309	35 c. Maori rock drawing			30	40
1310	40 c. Woolmark and wool-scouring symbols	..		35	45
1311	45 c. Coat of arms	..		40	55
1308/11			*Set of 4*	1·10	1·40

402 "Boats, Island Bay" (Rita Angus)   403 Mt Egmont

(Des D. Hatcher. Litho Leigh-Mardon Ltd, Melbourne)

1983 (6 Apr). *Paintings by Rita Angus. T 402 and similar vert designs. Multicoloured. P 14½.*

1312	24 c. Type **402**			30	10
1313	30 c. "Central Otago Landscape"			35	45
1314	35 c. "Wanaka Landscape"			45	50
1315	45 c. "Tree"	..		55	70
1312/15			*Set of 4*	1·50	1·60

(Des P. Durrant. Photo Heraclio Fournier)

1983 (1 June). *Beautiful New Zealand. T 403 and similar multi-coloured designs. P 13.*

1316	35 c. Type **403**			30	35
1317	40 c. Cooks Bay			35	40
1318	45 c. Lake Matheson (*horiz*)	..		40	45
1319	70 c. Lake Alexandrina (*horiz*)			65	70
1316/19			*Set of 4*	1·50	1·75

---

404 Tabby   405 "The Family of the Holy Oak Tree" (Raphael)

(Des R. Conly. Litho Harrison)

1983 (3 Aug). *Health Stamps. Cats. T 404 and similar vert designs. Multicoloured. P 14.*

1320	24 c. + 2 c. Type **404**			30	25
	a. Horiz pair. Nos. 1320/1 ..			60	50
1321	24 c. + 2 c. Siamese			30	25
1322	30 c. + 2 c. Persian			50	30
1320/2			*Set of 3*	1·00	60
MS1323	100 × 126 mm. Nos. 1320/2, each × 2			2·00	1·75

The 24 c. values were printed together, *se-tenant*, in horizontal pairs throughout the sheet.

(Des R. Conly (45 c.), M. Wyatt (others). Photo Courvoisier)

1983 (5 Oct). *Christmas. T 405 and similar vert designs. Multi-coloured. P 12 × 11½.*

1324	18 c. Type **405**			10	10
1325	35 c. St. Patrick's Church, Greymouth			30	35
1326	45 c. "The Glory of Christmas" (star and flowers) ..	..		40	45
1324/6			*Set of 3*	75	75

406 Geology

(Des R. Conly. Litho Cambec Press, Melbourne)

1984 (1 Feb). *Antarctic Research. T 406 and similar horiz designs. Multicoloured. P 13½ × 13.*

1327	24 c. Type **406**			25	10
1328	40 c. Biology			35	40
1329	58 c. Glaciology			50	55
1330	70 c. Meteorology			60	70
1327/30			*Set of 4*	1·60	1·60
MS1331	126 × 110 mm. Nos. 1327/30			1·75	3·00

407 *Mountaineer*, Lake Wakatipu   408 Mount Hutt

(Des M. Wyatt. Litho Cambec Press, Melbourne)

1984 (4 Apr). *New Zealand Ferry Boats. T 407 and similar horiz designs. Multicoloured. P 13½ × 13.*

1332	24 c. Type **407**			30	10
1333	40 c. *Waikana*, Otago ..			40	40
1334	58 c. *Britannia*, Waitemata	..		55	55
1335	70 c. *Wakatere*, Firth of Thames			65	65
1332/5			*Set of 4*	1·75	1·60

(Des D. Little. Litho Cambec Press, Melbourne)

1984 (6 June). *Ski-slope Scenery. T 408 and similar horiz designs. Multicoloured. P 13½ × 13.*

1336	35 c. Type **408**			40	40
1337	40 c. Coronet Park			45	45
1338	45 c. Turoa			50	50
1339	70 c. Whakapapa			75	75
1336/9			*Set of 4*	1·90	1·90

409 Hamilton's Frog

(Des A. G. Mitchell. Litho Cambec Press, Melbourne)

1984 (11 July). *Amphibians and Reptiles. T 409 and similar horiz designs. Multicoloured. P 13½.*

1340	24 c. Type **409**			30	30
	a. Horiz pair. Nos. 1340/1 ..			60	60
1341	24 c. Great Barrier Skink	..		30	30
1342	30 c. Harlequin Gecko			35	35
1343	58 c. Otago Skink			70	70
1344	70 c. Gold-striped Gecko			75	75
1340/4			*Set of 5*	2·25	2·25

Nos. 1340/1 were printed together, *se-tenant*, in horizontal pairs throughout the sheet.

410 Clydesdales ploughing Field

(Des Margaret Chapman. Litho Harrison)

1984 (1 Aug). *Health Stamps. Horses. T* **410** *and similar horiz designs. Multicoloured. P* 14½.

1345	24 c. + 2 c. Type **410**	..	..	30	30
	a. Horiz pair. Nos. 1345/6 ..	..		60	60
1346	24 c. + 2 c. Shetland ponies	..		30	30
1347	30 c. + 2 c. Thoroughbreds	..		45	35
1345/7			*Set of 3*	1·00	85

MS1348 148 × 75 mm. Nos. 1345/7, each × 2 .. 1·60 1·75
Nos. 1345/6 were printed together, *se-tenant*, in horizontal pairs throughout the sheet.

MACHINE LABELS. An automatic machine dispensing labels, ranging in value from 1 c. to $99.99, was installed at the Queen Street Post Office, Auckland, on 3 September 1984 for a trial period. The oblong designs, framed by simulated perforations at top and bottom and vertical rules at the sides, showed the "Southern Cross", face value and vertical column of six horizontal lines between the "NEW ZEALAND" and "POST-AGE" inscriptions. The trial period ended abruptly on 16 October 1984.

Similar labels, with the face value and inscriptions within a plain oblong, were introduced on 12 February 1986 and from 22 August 1988 they were printed on paper showing New Zealand flags. On 12 September 1990 the design printed on the paper was changed to show seaplanes.

411 "Adoration of the Shepherds"
(Lorenzo di Credi)

(Des R. Conly (45 c.), P. Durrant (others). Photo Heraclio Fournier)

1984 (26 Sept). *Christmas. T* **411** *and similar multicoloured designs. P* 13½ × 14 (18 c.) *or* 14 × 13½ (*others*).

1349	18 c. Type **411**	..	..	20	10
1350	35 c. Old St. Paul's, Wellington (*vert*)	..	40	35
1351	45 c. "The Joy of Christmas" (*vert*)	..	50	45
1349/51	..	..	*Set of 3*	1·00	80

412 Mounted Riflemen, South Africa, 1901

(Des R. Conly. Litho Harrison)

1984 (7 Nov). *New Zealand Military History. T* **412** *and similar horiz designs. Multicoloured. P* 15 × 14.

1352	24 c. Type **412**	..	..	30	10
1353	40 c. Engineers, France, 1917	..	..	45	45
1354	58 c. Tanks of 2nd N.Z. Divisional Cavalry, North Africa, 1942			60	60
1355	70 c. Infantryman in jungle kit, and 25-pounder gun, Korea and South-East Asia, 1950–72	..		70	75
1352/5			*Set of 4*	1·90	1·75

MS1356 122 × 106 mm. Nos. 1352/5 .. .. 1·75 1·90

413 St. John Ambulance Badge

(Des Lindy Fisher. Litho J.W.)

1985 (16 Jan). *Centenary of St. John Ambulance in New Zealand. P* 14.

1357	**413**	24 c. black, gold and bright rosine	..	25	10
1358		30 c. black, sil & bright ultram	..	35	30
1359		40 c. black and grey	..	..	40	45
1357/9		..	..	*Set of 3*	90	75

The colours of the badge depicted are those for Bailiffs and Dames Grand Cross (24 c.), Knights and Dames of Grace (30 c.) and Serving Brothers and Sisters (40 c.).

MINIMUM PRICE

The minimum price quote is 10p which represents a handling charge rather than a basis for valuing common stamps. For further notes about prices see introductory pages.

---

414 Nelson Horse-drawn Tram, 1862   **415** Shotover Bridge

(Des. R. Conly. Litho Cambec Press, Melbourne)

1985 (6 Mar). *Vintage Trams. T* **414** *and similar horiz designs. Multicoloured. P* 13½.

1360	24 c. Type **414**	..	..	25	10
1361	30 c. Graham's Town steam tram, 1871	..	35	50
1362	35 c. Dunedin cable car, 1881	..	35	60
1363	40 c. Auckland electric tram, 1902	..	35	60
1364	45 c. Wellington electric tram, 1904 ..		40	70
1365	58 c. Christchurch electric tram, 1905	..	50	1·10
1360/5			*Set of 6*	2·00	3·25

TARAPEX '86. To support this National Philatelic Exhibition the New Zealand Post Office co-operated with the organisers in the production of a set of "postage imprint labels". Five of the designs showed drawings of Maoris, taken from originals by Arthur Herbert Messenger and the sixth the Exhibition logo.

The sheetlets of 6 gummed and perforated labels were released by the Exhibition organisers on 3 April 1985. Although such labels were valid for postage, and could be so used by the general public, the sheetlets were not available from any New Zealand post office or from the Philatelic Bureau.

(Des R. Freeman. Photo Courvoisier)

1985 (12 June). *Bridges of New Zealand. T* **415** *and similar multicoloured designs. Granite paper. P* 11½.

1366	35 c. Type **415**	..	..	40	50
1367	40 c. Alexandra Bridge	..	..	45	60
1368	45 c. South Rangitikei Railway Bridge (*vert*)	50	75
1369	70 c. Twin Bridges (*vert*)	..	..	70	1·10
1366/9			*Set of 4*	1·90	2·75

416 Queen Elizabeth II   **417** Princess of Wales
(from photo by Camera   and Prince William
Press)

(Des B. Clinton. Litho Leigh-Mardon Ltd, Melbourne)

1985 (1 July). *Multicoloured, background colours given. P* 14½ × 14.

1370	**416**	25 c. rosine	..	..	50	10
1371		35 c. new blue..	..	..	90	10

Examples of the 25 c. value exist with the orders on the sash omitted. These are believed to originate from unissued sheets sent for destruction in March 1986.

(Des D. Little. Litho Cambec Press, Melbourne)

1985 (31 July). *Health Stamps. T* **417** *and similar vert designs showing photographs by Lord Snowdon. Multicoloured. P* 13½.

1372	25 c. + 2 c. Type **417**	..	35	55
	a. Horiz pair. Nos. 1372/3 ..		70	1·10
1373	25 c. + 2 c. Princess of Wales and Prince Henry	..	35	55
1374	35 c. + 2 c. Prince and Princess of Wales with Princes William and Henry	35	55
1372/4		*Set of 3*	95	1·50

MS1375 118 × 84 mm. Nos. 1372/4, each × 2 .. 1·75 3·00
Nos. 1372/3 were printed together, *se-tenant*, in horizontal pairs throughout the sheet.

418 The Holy Family in   **419** H.M.N.Z.S. *Philomel*
the Stable   (1914–47)

(Des Eileen Mayo. Photo Enschedé)

1985 (18 Sept). *Christmas. T* **418** *and similar vert designs. Multicoloured. P* 13½ × 12½.

1376	18 c. Type **418**	..	..	20	10
1377	40 c. The shepherds	..	..	40	75
1378	50 c. The angels	..	..	45	90
1376/8			*Set of 3*	95	1·60

Examples of the 18 c. and 50 c. stamps exist showing the spelling error "CRISTMAS". These are believed to originate from unissued sheets sent for destruction in March 1986. The New Zealand Post Office has stated that no such stamps were issued and that existing examples "were removed unlawfully during the destruction process".

(Des P. Durrant. Litho Cambec Press, Melbourne)

1985 (6 Nov). *New Zealand Naval History. T* **419** *and similar horiz designs. Multicoloured. P* 13½.

1379	25 c. Type **419**	..	..	70	15
1380	45 c. H.M.N.Z.S. *Achilles* (1936–46)	..	1·10	1·40
1381	60 c. H.M.N.Z.S. *Rotoiti* (1949–65)..	1·40	1·75
1382	75 c. H.M.N.Z.S. *Canterbury* (from 1971)	1·75	2·00
1379/82			*Set of 4*	4·50	4·25

MS1383 124 × 108 mm. Nos. 1379/82 .. 4·50 4·75

420 Police Computer   **421** Indian "Power Plus"
Operator   1000cc Motor Cycle (1920)

(Des A. Mitchell. Litho Leigh-Mardon Ltd, Melbourne)

1986 (15 Jan). *Centenary of New Zealand Police. T* **420** *and similar vert designs, each showing historical aspects above modern police activities. Multicoloured. P* 14½ × 14.

1384	25 c. Type **420**	..	..	35	50
	a. Horiz strip of 5. Nos. 1384/8 ..		1·60	
1385	25 c. Detective and mobile control room	..	35	50
1386	25 c. Policewoman and badge	..	35	50
1387	25 c. Forensic scientist, patrol car and policeman with child	..	35	50
1388	25 c. Police College, Porirua, Patrol boat *Lady Elizabeth II* and dog handler	..	35	50
1384/8			*Set of 5*	1·60	2·25

Nos. 1384/8 were printed together, *se-tenant*, in horizontal strips of 5 throughout the sheet.

(Des M. Wyatt. Litho J.W.)

1986 (5 Mar). *Vintage Motor Cycles. T* **421** *and similar horiz designs. Multicoloured. P* 13 × 12½.

1389	35 c. Type **421**	..	..	40	30
1390	45 c. Norton "CS1" 500cc (1927)	..	50	45
1391	60 c. B.S.A. "Sloper" 500cc (1930) ..	65	65
1392	75 c. Triumph "Model H" 550cc (1915)	75	85
1389/92			*Set of 4*	2·10	2·00

422 Tree of Life   **423** Knights Point

(Des Margaret Clarkson. Litho J.W.)

1986 (5 Mar). *International Peace Year. T* **422** *and similar horiz design. Multicoloured. P* 13 × 12½.

1393	25 c. Type **422**	..	..	30	30
	a. Horiz pair. Nos. 1393/4 ..		60	60
1394	25 c. Peace dove	..	..	30	30

Nos. 1393/4 were printed together, *se-tenant*, in horizontal pairs throughout the sheet.

(Des P. Durrant. Photo Heraclio Fournier)

1986 (11 June). *Coastal Scenery. T* **423** *and similar horiz designs. Multicoloured. P* 14.

1395	55 c. Type **423**	..	..	55	45
1396	60 c. Becks Bay	..	..	55	45
1397	65 c. Doubtless Bay ..	..	..	60	50
1398	80 c. Wainui Bay	..	..	75	65
1395/8			*Set of 4*	2·25	1·90

MS1399 124 × 99 mm. No. 1398 (*sold at* $1.20) .. 85 90
The 40 c. premium on No. **MS**1399 was to support "New Zealand 1990" International Stamp Exhibition, Auckland.

No. **MS**1399 exists overprinted for "Stockholmia". Such miniature sheets were only available at this International Stamp Exhibition in Stockholm and were not placed on sale in New Zealand.

424 "Football"   **425** "A Partridge
(Kylie Epapara)   in a Pear Tree"

(Litho Leigh-Mardon Ltd, Melbourne)

1986 (30 July). *Health Stamps. Children's Paintings (1st series). T* **424** *and similar multicoloured designs.* P 14½×14 (30 c.) or 14×14½ (45 c.).

1400	30 c.+3 c. Type **424**	.. ..	30	40
	a. Horiz pair. Nos. 1400/1		60	80
1401	30 c.+3 c. "Children at Play" (Phillip Kata)		30	40
1402	45 c.+3 c. "Children Skipping" (Mia Flannery) (*horiz*)		40	50
1400/2	*Set of 3*		90	1·10
MS1403	144×81 mm. Nos. 1400/2, each×2		2·00	2·25

Nos. 1400/1 were printed together, *se-tenant*, in horizontal pairs throughout the sheet.

No. **MS**1403 exists overprinted for "Stockholmia". Such miniature sheets were only available at this International Stamp Exhibition in Stockholm and were not placed on sale in New Zealand.

See also Nos. 1433/6.

(Des Margaret Halcrow-Cross. Photo Heraclio Fournier)

1986 (17 Sept). *Christmas. "The Twelve Days of Christmas" (carol). T* **425** *and similar vert designs.* Multicoloured. P 14½.

1404	25 c. Type **425**	..	20	10
1405	55 c. "Two turtle doves"	..	45	45
1406	65 c. "Three French hens"	..	50	50
1404/6	*Set of 3*		1·00	95

426 Conductor and Orchestra   **427** Jetboating

(Des R. Freeman. Litho Leigh-Mardon Ltd, Melbourne)

1986 (5 Nov). *Music in New Zealand. T* **426** *and similar vert designs.* P 14½×14.

1407	30 c. multicoloured ..	..	25	10
1408	60 c. black, new blue and yellow-orange ..		45	50
1409	80 c. multicoloured ..	..	70	75
1410	$1 multicoloured ..	..	80	85
1407/10	*Set of 4*		2·00	2·00

Designs:—60 c. Cornet and brass band; 80 c. Piper and Highland pipe band; $1 Guitar and country music group.

(Des M. Wyatt. Litho Leigh-Mardon Ltd, Melbourne)

1987 (14 Jan). *Tourism. T* **427** *and similar vert designs.* Multicoloured. P 14½×14.

1411	60 c. Type **427**	.. ..	50	50
1412	70 c. Sightseeing flights	.. ..	60	60
1413	80 c. Camping	.. ..	70	75
1414	85 c. Windsurfing	.. ..	70	75
1415	$1.05, Mountaineering	.. ..	90	1·00
1416	$1.30, River rafting	.. ..	1·10	1·25
1411/16	*Set of 6*		4·00	4·25

428 Southern Cross Cup

(Des R. Proud. Litho Leigh-Mardon Ltd, Melbourne)

1987 (2 Feb). *Yachting Events. T* **428** *and similar horiz designs showing yachts.* Multicoloured. P 14×14½.

1417	40 c. Type **428**	.. ..	35	15
1418	80 c. Admiral's Cup ..	..	70	80
1419	$1.05, Kenwood Cup	.. ..	85	1·00
1420	$1.30, America's Cup	.. ..	1·10	1·40
1417/20	*Set of 4*		2·75	3·25

429 Hand writing Letter and Postal Transport

(Des Communication Arts Ltd. Litho C.P.E. Australia Ltd, Melbourne)

1987 (1 Apr). *New Zealand Post Ltd Vesting Day. T* **429** *and similar horiz design.* Multicoloured. P 13½.

1421	40 c. Type **429**	..	90	1·00
	a. Horiz pair. Nos. 1421/2	..	1·75	2·00
1422	40 c. Posting letter, train and mailbox	90	1·00

Nos. 1421/2 were printed together, *se-tenant*, in horizontal pairs throughout the sheet.

430 Avro "626" and Wigram Airfield, 1937   **431** Urewera National Park and Fern Leaf

(Des P. Leitch. Litho Leigh-Mardon Ltd, Melbourne)

1987 (15 Apr). *50th Anniv of Royal New Zealand Air Force. T* **430** *and similar horiz designs.* Multicoloured. P 14×14½.

1423	40 c. Type **430**	..	35	15
1424	70 c. "P-40 Kittyhawk" over World War II Pacific airstrip..	..	55	60
1425	80 c. Short "Sunderland" flying boat and Pacific lagoon ..	..	60	70
1426	85 c. A-4 "Skyhawk" and Mt Ruapehu	65	75
1423/6	*Set of 4*		2·00	2·00
MS1427	115×105 mm. Nos. 1423/6 ..		3·00	2·50

No. **MS**1427 overprinted on the selvedge with the "CAPEX" logo was only available from the New Zealand stand at this International Philatelic Exhibition in Toronto.

(Des Tracey Purkis. Litho Leigh-Mardon Ltd, Melbourne)

1987 (17 June). *Centenary of National Parks Movement. T* **431** *and similar vert designs.* Multicoloured. P 14½.

1428	70 c. Type **431**	..	70	55
1429	80 c. Mt Cook and buttercup	..	75	60
1430	85 c. Fiordland and pineapple shrub	..	80	65
1431	$1.30, Tongariro and tussock	..	1·40	95
1428/31	*Set of 4*		3·25	2·50
MS1432	123×99 mm. No. 1431 (*sold at* $1.70)	1·75	1·75

The 40 c. premium on No. **MS**1432 was to support "New Zealand 1990" International Stamp Exhibition, Auckland.

No. **MS**1432 overprinted on the selvedge with the "CAPEX" logo was only available from the New Zealand stand at this International Philatelic Exhibition in Toronto.

432 "Kite Flying" (Lauren Baldwin)   **433** "Hark the Herald Angels Sing"

(Adapted D. Little. Litho Leigh-Mardon Ltd, Melbourne)

1987 (29 July). *Health Stamps. Children's Paintings (2nd series). T* **432** *and similar multicoloured designs.* P 14½.

1433	40 c. + 3 c. Type **432**	..	80	1·00
	a. Horiz pair. Nos. 1433/4		1·60	2·00
1434	40 c. + 3 c. "Swimming" (Ineke Schoneveld)	80	1·00
1435	60 c. + 3 c. "Horse Riding" (Aaron Tylee) (*vert*) ..		1·25	1·40
1433/5	*Set of 3*		2·50	3·00
MS1436	100×117 mm. Nos. 1433/5, each×2	5·00	6·00

Nos. 1433/4 were printed together, *se-tenant*, in horizontal pairs throughout the sheet.

(Des Ellen Giggenbach. Litho Leigh-Mardon Ltd, Melbourne)

1987 (16 Sept). *Christmas. T* **433** *and similar vert designs.* Multicoloured. P 14½.

1437	35 c. Type **433**	..	45	10
1438	70 c. "Away in a Manger" ..	..	90	55
1439	85 c. "We Three Kings of Orient Are"	1·10	65
1437/9	*Set of 3*		2·25	1·25

434 Knot ("Pona")   **435** "Geothermal"

(Des Nga Puna Waihanga. Litho Security Printers (M), Malaysia)

1987 (4 Nov). *Maori Fibre-work. T* **434** *and similar vert designs.* Multicoloured. W **138** of Malaysia. P 12.

1440	40 c. Type **434**	..	35	10
1441	60 c. Binding ("Herehere")	..	45	45
1442	80 c. Plait ("Whiri")..	..	60	65
1443	85 c. Cloak weaving ("Korowai") with flax fibre ("Whitau") ..	..	65	70
1440/3	*Set of 4*		1·90	1·75

(Des Fay McAlpine. Litho Leigh-Mardon Ltd, Melbourne)

1988 (13 Jan). *Centenary of Electricity. T* **435** *and similar horiz designs, each showing radiating concentric circles representing energy generation.* Multicoloured. P 14×14½.

1444	40 c. multicoloured ..	..	30	35
1445	60 c. black, rosine and brownish black	..	40	45
1446	70 c. multicoloured ..	..	50	55
1447	80 c. multicoloured ..	..	60	65
1444/7	*Set of 4*		1·60	1·75

Designs:—60 c. "Thermal"; 70 c. "Gas"; 80 c. "Hydro".

436 Queen Elizabeth II and 1882 Queen Victoria 1d. Stamp   **437** "Mangopare"

(Des A. G. Mitchell (40 c.), M. Conly and M. Stanley ($1). Litho Leigh-Mardon Ltd, Melbourne)

1988 (13 Jan). *Centenary of Royal Philatelic Society of New Zealand. T* **436** *and similar multicoloured designs.* P 14×14½.

1448	40 c. Type **436**	..	35	40
	a. Horiz pair. Nos. 1448/9		70	80
1449	40 c. As Type **436**, but 1882 Queen Victoria 2d. ..		35	40
MS1450	107×160 mm. $1 "Queen Victoria" (Chalon) (*vert*). P 14½×14	90	75

Nos. 1448/9 were printed together, *se-tenant*, in horizontal pairs throughout the sheet.

No. **MS**1450 overprinted on the selvedge with the "SYDPEX" logo was only available from the New Zealand stand at this International Philatelic Exhibition in Sydney and from the Philatelic Bureau at Wanganui.

(Des S. Adsett. Litho Leigh-Mardon Ltd, Melbourne)

1988 (2 Mar). *Maori Rafter Paintings. T* **437** *and similar vert designs.* Multicoloured. P 14½.

1451	40 c. Type **437**	..	40	40
1452	40 c. "Koru" ..	..	40	40
1453	40 c. "Raupunga"	..	40	40
1454	60 c. "Koiri" ..	..	55	65
1451/4	*Set of 4*		1·60	1·75

438 "Good Luck"   **439** Paradise Shelduck

(Des Communication Arts Ltd. Litho CPE Australia Ltd, Melbourne)

1988 (18 May). *Greetings Booklet Stamps. T* **438** *and similar multicoloured designs.* P 13½.

1455	40 c. Type **438**	..	25	30
	a. Booklet pane. Nos. 1455/9 ..	1·10	
1456	40 c. "Keeping in touch"	..	25	30
1457	40 c. "Happy birthday"	..	25	30
1458	40 c. "Congratulations" (41 × 27 mm)	25	30
1459	40 c. "Get well soon" (41 × 27 mm)	25	30
1455/9	*Set of 5*		1·10	1·40

Nos. 1455/9 only exist from $2 stamp booklets.

(Des Pauline Morse. Litho Leigh-Mardon Ltd, Melbourne)

1988 (7 June)–**91**. *Native Birds.* Multicoloured. P 14½×14.

1459a	5 c. Sooty Crake (1.7.91)	..	10	10
1460	10 c. Double-banded Plover ("Banded Dotterel") (2.11.88) ..		10	10
1461	20 c. Yellowhead (2.11.88)	..	10	15
1462	30 c. Grey-backed White Eye ("Silvereye") (2.11.88) ..		20	25
1463	40 c. Brown Kiwi (2.11.88)	..	25	30
	a. Perf 13½×13 (8.11.89)	..	80	1·00
	ab. Pack pane. No. 1463a/10 with margins all round		8·00	
1463b	45 c. Rock Wren (1.7.91)	..	30	35
	ba. Booklet pane. No. 1463b×10 with horiz sides of pane imperf (1.10.91)	3·25	
1464	50 c. Sacred Kingfisher (2.11.88)	..	35	40
1465	60 c. Spotted Cormorant ("Spotted Shag") (2.11.88) ..		40	45
1466	70 c. Type **439**	..	45	50
1467	80 c. Fiordland Crested Penguin (2.11.88)	55	60
1468	90 c. New Zealand Robin (2.11.88)	..	60	65
1459a/68	*Set of 11*		3·00	3·50

No. 1463a was only issued in panes of ten with margins on all four sides. These panes were initially included in "Stamp Pads" of 50 such panes, but subsequently appeared in $4 stamp packs.

No. 1463ba comes from the $4.50 "hanging" booklet.

A miniature sheet containing No. 1466 was only available from the New Zealand stand at "WORLD STAMP EXPO '89" International Stamp Exhibition or the Philatelic Bureau, Wanganui. It was subsequently overprinted with the "New Zealand 1990" emblem.

For 40 c. and 45 c. stamps in similar designs, but self-adhesive, see Nos. 1589/a.

440 Milford Track   **441** Kiwi and Koala at Campfire

(Des H. Thompson. Litho Leigh-Mardon Ltd, Melbourne)

1988 (8 June). *Scenic Walking Trails.* T **440** *and similar vert designs. Multicoloured.* P 14½.

1469	70 c. Type **440**			50	60
1470	80 c. Heaphy Track			55	70
1471	85 c. Copland Track			60	75
1472	$1.30, Routeburn Track			90	1·10
1469/72			*Set of 4*	2·25	2·75
MS1473	124 × 99 mm. No. 1472 (*sold at* $1.70)			1·50	1·50

The 40 c. premium on No. **MS**1473 was to support "New Zealand 1990" International Stamp Exhibition, Auckland.

(Des R. Harvey. Litho Leigh-Mardon Ltd, Melbourne)

1988 (21 June). *Bicentenary of Australian Settlement.* P 14½.

1474	**441** 40 c. multicoloured			60	35

A stamp in a similar design was also issued by Australia.

442 Swimming   **443** "O Come All Ye Faithful"

(Des R. Proud. Litho Leigh-Mardon Ltd, Melbourne)

1988 (27 July). *Health Stamps. Olympic Games, Seoul.* T **442** *and similar horiz designs.* Multicoloured. P 14½.

1475	40 c. + 3 c. Type **442**			35	45
1476	60 c. + 3 c. Athletics			50	65
1477	70 c. + 3 c. Canoeing			60	75
1478	80 c. + 3 c. Show-jumping			70	85
1475/8			*Set of 4*	1·90	2·40
MS1479	120 × 90 mm. Nos. 1475/8			1·90	2·40

(Des Fay McAlpine. Litho Leigh-Mardon Ltd, Melbourne)

1988 (14 Sept). *Christmas. Carols.* T **443** *and similar vert designs, each showing illuminated verses. Multicoloured.* P 14½.

1480	35 c. Type **443**			30	30
1481	60 c. "Hark the Herald Angels Sing"			55	65
1482	80 c. "Ding Dong Merrily on High"			60	70
1483	85 c. "The First Nowell"			65	80
1480/3			*Set of 4*	1·90	2·25

444 "Lake Pukaki" (John Gully)   **445** Brown Kiwi

(Litho Leigh-Mardon Ltd, Melbourne)

1988 (5 Oct). *New Zealand Heritage (1st issue). The Land.* T **444** *and similar horiz designs showing 19th-century paintings. Multicoloured.* P 14 × 14½.

1484	40 c. Type **444**			35	35
1485	60 c. "On the Grass Plain below Lake Arthur" (William Fox)			45	45
1486	70 c. "View of Auckland" (John Hoyte)			55	55
1487	80 c. "Mt. Egmont from the Southward" (Charles Heaphy)			60	60
1488	$1.05, "Anakiwa, Queen Charlotte Sound" (John Kinder)			80	80
1489	$1.30, "White Terraces, Lake Rotoma-hana" (Charles Barraud)			95	95
1484/9			*Set of 6*	3·25	3·25

See also Nos. 1505/10, 1524/9, 1541/6, 1548/53 and 1562/7.

(Des A. Mitchell. Eng. G. Prosser of B.A.B.N. Recess Leigh-Mardon Ltd, Melbourne)

1988 (19 Oct)–**91**. P 14½ (*and around design*).

1490	**445** $1 bronze-green			2·00	2·25
	a. Booklet pane. No. 1490×6			11·00	
1490*b*	$1 bright scarlet (17.4.91)			65	70

No. 1490 was only issued in $6 stamp booklets with the horizontal edges of the booklet pane imperforate. Each circular stamp was also separated by vertical perforations.

No. 1490*b* was printed in sheets of 24 (6×4).

446 Humpback Whale and Calf   **447** Clover

(Des Lindy Fisher. Litho Govt Ptg Office, Wellington)

1988 (2 Nov). *Whales.* T **446** *and similar horiz designs. Multicoloured.* P 13½.

1491	60 c. Type **446**			75	55
1492	70 c. Killer Whales			90	65
1493	80 c. Southern Right Whale			1·00	70
1494	85 c. Blue Whale			1·10	75

1495	$1.05, Southern Bottlenose Whale and calf			1·40	90
1496	$1.30, Sperm Whale			1·50	1·10
1491/6			*Set of 6*	6·00	4·25

Although inscribed "ROSS DEPENDENCY" Nos. 1491/6 were available from post offices throughout New Zealand.

(Des Heather Arnold. Litho Leigh-Mardon Ltd, Melbourne)

1989 (18 Jan). *Wild Flowers.* T **447** *and similar horiz designs. Multicoloured.* P 14½.

1497	40 c. Type **447**			40	35
1498	60 c. Lotus			50	55
1499	70 c. Montbretia			60	65
1500	80 c. Wild Ginger			70	75
1497/1500			*Set of 4*	2·00	2·10

448 Katherine Mansfield   **449** Moriori Man and Map of Chatham Islands

(Des A. G. Mitchell. Litho Harrison)

1989 (1 Mar). *New Zealand Authors.* T **448** *and similar vert designs. Multicoloured.* P 12½.

1501	40 c. Type **448**			30	35
1502	60 c. James K. Baxter			40	50
1503	70 c. Bruce Mason			50	60
1504	80 c. Ngaio Marsh			55	70
1501/4			*Set of 4*	1·60	1·90

(Des D. Gunson. Litho Leigh-Mardon Ltd, Melbourne)

1989 (17 May). *New Zealand Heritage (2nd issue). The People.* T **449** *and similar horiz designs.* P 14×14½.

1505	40 c. multicoloured			45	35
1506	60 c. orge-brn, brownish grey & reddish brn			60	70
1507	70 c. yellow-grn, brownish grey & dp olive			65	75
1508	80 c. bright greenish blue, brownish grey and deep dull blue			75	85
1509	$1.05, grey, brownish grey & grey-black			1·00	1·10
1510	$1.30, bright rose-red, brownish grey, and lake-brown			1·25	1·40
1505/10			*Set of 6*	4·25	4·50

Designs:—60 c. Gold prospector; 70 c. Settler ploughing; 80 c. Whaling; $1.05, Missionary preaching to Maoris; $1.30, Maori village.

450 White Pine (Kahikatea)   **451** Duke and Duchess of York with Princess Beatrice

(Des D. Gunson. Litho Questa)

1989 (7 June). *Native Trees.* T **450** *and similar vert designs. Multicoloured.* P 14×14½.

1511	80 c. Type **450**			75	80
1512	85 c. Red Pine (Rimu)			80	85
1513	$1.05, Totara			1·00	1·10
1514	$1.30, Kauri			1·25	1·40
1511/14			*Set of 4*	3·50	3·75
MS1515	102×125 mm. No. 1514 (*sold at* $1.80)			1·75	1·75

The 50 c. premium on No. **MS**1515 was to support "New Zealand 1990" International Stamp Exhibition, Auckland.

(Des and litho Leigh-Mardon Ltd, Melbourne)

1989 (26 July). *Health Stamps.* T **451** *and similar vert designs. Multicoloured.* P 14½.

1516	40 c. + 3 c. Type **451**			50	55
	a. Horiz pair. Nos. 1516/17			1·00	1·10
1517	40 c. + 3 c. Duchess of York with Princess Beatrice			50	55
1518	80 c. + 3 c. Princess Beatrice			1·25	90
1516/18			*Set of 3*	2·00	1·75
MS1519	120×89 mm. Nos. 1516/18, each ×2			5·50	4·25

Nos. 1516/17 were printed together, *se-tenant*, in horizontal pairs throughout the sheet.

No. **MS**1519 overprinted on the selvedge with the "WORLD STAMP EXPO '89" logo was only available from the New Zealand stand at this International Stamp Exhibition and from the Philatelic Bureau at Wanganui.

MINIMUM PRICE

The minimum price quote is 10p which represents a handling charge rather than a basis for valuing common stamps. For further notes about prices see introductory pages.

---

452 One Tree Hill, Auckland, through Bedroom Window   **453** Windsurfing

(Des H. Chapman. Litho Leigh-Mardon Ltd, Melbourne)

1989 (13 Sept). *Christmas.* T **452** *and similar vert designs showing Star of Bethlehem. Multicoloured.* P 14½.

1520	35 c. Type **452**			35	30
1521	65 c. Shepherd and dog in mountain valley			65	70
1522	80 c. Star over harbour			85	90
1523	$1 Star over globe			1·25	1·40
1520/3			*Set of 4*	2·75	3·00

(Des M. Bailey. Litho Leigh-Mardon Ltd, Melbourne)

1989 (11 Oct). *New Zealand Heritage (3rd issue). The Sea.* T **453** *and similar horiz designs. Multicoloured.* P 14×14½.

1524	40 c. Type **453**			40	35
1525	60 c. Fishes of many species			60	70
1526	65 c. Marlin and game fishing launch			65	75
1527	80 c. Rowing boat and yachts in harbour			80	85
1528	$1 Coastal scene			1·00	1·10
1529	$1.50, Container ship and tug			1·50	1·60
1524/9			*Set of 6*	4·50	4·75

454 Games Logo

(Des Heather Arnold. Litho Leigh-Mardon Ltd, Melbourne)

1989 (8 Nov)–**90**. *14th Commonwealth Games. Auckland.* T **454** *and similar horiz designs. Multicoloured.* P 14½.

1530	40 c. Type **454**			40	35
1531	40 c. Goldie (games kiwi mascot)			40	35
1532	40 c. Gymnastics			40	35
1533	50 c. Weightlifting			50	55
1534	65 c. Swimming			65	70
1535	80 c. Cycling			80	90
1536	$1 Lawn bowling			1·00	1·25
1537	$1.80, Hurdling			1·75	1·90
1530/7			*Set of 8*	5·50	5·75
MS1538	Two sheets, each 105×92 mm. with different margin designs. (a) Nos. 1530/1 (horiz pair). (b) Nos. 1530/1 (vert pair) (24.1.90)				
			Set of 2 sheets	1·10	1·25

455 Short "S.30" Empire Flying Boat and Boeing "747"   **456** Chief Kawiti signing Treaty

(Des R. Proud. Litho Enschedé)

1990 (17 Jan). *50th Anniv of Air New Zealand.* P 13×14½.

1539	**455** 80 c. multicoloured			1·40	80

(Des A. G. Mitchell from painting by L. C. Mitchell. Litho Enschedé)

1990 (17 Jan). *150th Anniv of Treaty of Waitangi. Sheet* 80×118 mm, *containing* T **456** *and similar multicoloured design.* P 13½.

MS1540	40 c. Type **456**; 40 c. Chief Hone Heke (first signatory) and Lieut-Governor Hobson (horiz)			80	80

457 Maori Voyaging Canoe   **458** *Thelymitra pulchella*

(Des G. Fuller. Litho Leigh-Mardon Ltd, Melbourne)

1990 (7 Mar). *New Zealand Heritage (4th issue). The Ships.*
T **457** *and similar horiz designs. Multicoloured.* P 14×14½.

1541	40 c. Type **457**				60	35
1542	50 c. H.M.S. *Endeavour* (Cook), 1769				75	50
1543	60 c. *Tory* (barque), 1839				85	60
1544	80 c. *Crusader* (full-rigged immigrant ship), 1871				1·25	85
1545	$1 *Edwin Fox* (full-rigged immigrant ship), 1873				1·40	1·10
1546	$1.50, *Arawa* (steamer), 1884				2·00	1·75
1541/6				*Set of 6*	6·25	4·50

A miniature sheet containing No. 1542 was only available from the New Zealand stand at "Stamp World London '90" International Stamp Exhibition or from the Philatelic Bureau, Wanganui.

(Des Lindy Fisher. Litho Leigh-Mardon Ltd, Melbourne)

1990 (18 Apr). *"New Zealand 1990" International Stamp Exhibition, Auckland. Native Orchids. Sheet* 179×80 *mm. containing* T **458** *and similar vert designs. Multicoloured.* P 14½.

MS1547	40 c. Type **458**; 40 c. *Corybas macranthus*; 40 c. *Dendrobium cunninghamii*; 40 c. *Pterostylis banksii*; 80 c. *Aporostylis bifolia* (sold at $4.90)		4·25	4·25

The stamps in No. **MS1547** form a composite design.
The $2.50 premium on No. **MS1547** was used to support the Exhibition.
Miniature sheets as No. **MS1547**, but imperforate are from a limited printing distributed to those purchasing season tickets for the exhibition.

459 Grace Neill (social reformer) and Maternity Hospital, Wellington   **460** Akaroa

(Des Elspeth Williamson. Litho Leigh-Mardon Ltd, Melbourne)

1990 (16 May). *New Zealand Heritage (5th issue). Famous New Zealanders.* T **459** *and similar horiz designs. Multicoloured.* P 14×14½.

1548	40 c. Type **459**				40	30
1549	50 c. Jean Batten (pilot) and Percival "Gull" aircraft				45	45
1550	60 c. Katherine Sheppard (suffragette) and 19th-century women				60	60
1551	80 c. Richard Pearse (inventor) and early flying machine				75	75
1552	$1 Lt.-Gen. Sir Bernard Freyberg and tank				95	95
1553	$1.50, Peter Buck (politician) and Maori pattern				1·25	1·40
1548/53				*Set of 6*	4·00	4·00

(Des Lindy Fisher. Litho Leigh-Mardon Ltd, Melbourne)

1990 (13 June). *150th Anniversary of European Settlements.* T **460** *and similar vert designs. Multicoloured.* P 14½.

1554	80 c. Type **460**				75	75
1555	$1 Wanganui				95	95
1556	$1.50, Wellington				1·40	1·40
1557	$1.80, Takapuna Beach, Auckland				1·60	1·60
1554/7				*Set of 4*	4·25	4·25
MS1558	125×100 mm. No. 1557 (sold at $2.30)				3·25	3·50

The 50 c. premium on No. **MS1558** was to support "New Zealand 1990" International Stamp Exhibition, Auckland.

461 Jack Lovelock (athlete) and Race   **462** Creation Legend of Rangi and Papa

(Des T. Crilley. Litho Questa)

1990 (25 July). *Health Stamps. Sportsmen (1st series).* T **461** *and similar horiz design. Multicoloured.* P 14½×13½.

1559	40 c. + 5 c. Type **461**				50	50
1560	80 c. + 5 c. George Nepia (rugby player) and match				75	75
MS1561	115×96 mm. Nos. 1559/60, each ×2				2·25	2·25

See also Nos. 1687/9.

(Des K. Hall. Litho Leigh-Mardon Ltd, Melbourne)

1990 (24 Aug). *New Zealand Heritage (6th issue). The Maori.* T **462** *and similar horiz designs. Multicoloured.* P 14×14½.

1562	40 c. Type **462**				40	30
	a. Violet-blue (face value) omitted					
1563	50 c. Pattern from Maori feather cloak				55	50
1564	60 c. Maori women's choir				60	60
1565	80 c. Maori facial tattoos				75	75
1566	$1 War canoe prow (detail)				90	95
1567	$1.50, Maori haka				1·40	1·50
1562/7				*Set of 6*	4·25	4·25

463 Queen Victoria   **464** Angel

(Des A. G. Mitchell. Recess Leigh-Mardon Ltd, Melbourne)

1990 (29 Aug). *150th Anniv of the Penny Black. Sheet* 169×70 *mm containing* T **463** *and similar vert designs.* P 14½×14.

MS1568	40 c.×6 indigo (Type **463**, King Edward VII, King George V, King Edward VIII, King George VI, Queen Elizabeth II)		1·90	1·90

(Des Sally Simons. Litho Leigh-Mardon Ltd, Melbourne)

1990 (12 Sept). *Christmas.* T **464** *and similar vert designs showing angels.* P 14½.

1569	40 c. purple, dp greenish bl & dp yellow-brn			40	30
1570	$1 purple, blue-green & dp yellow-brown			80	80
1571	$1.50, pur, brt crimson & dp yellow-brn			1·40	1·60
1572	$1.80, purple, red and deep yellow-brown			1·60	1·75
1569/72			*Set of 4*	3·75	4·00

465 Antarctic Petrel   **466** Coopworth Ewe and Lambs

(Des Janet Luxton. Litho Heraclio Fournier)

1990 (7 Nov). *Antarctic Birds.* T **465** *and similar vert designs. Multicoloured.* P 13½×13.

1573	40 c. Type **465**				40	30
1574	50 c. Wilson's Petrel				50	50
1575	60 c. Snow Petrel				60	60
1576	80 c. Southern Fulmar				75	75
1577	$1 Chinstrap Penguin				85	85
1578	$1.50, Emperor Penguin				1·40	1·50
1573/8				*Set of 6*	4·00	4·00

Although inscribed "Ross Dependency" Nos. 1573/8 were available from post offices throughout New Zealand.

(Des Lindy Fisher. Litho Leigh-Mardon Ltd, Melbourne)

1991 (23 Jan). *New Zealand Farming and Agriculture. Sheep Breeds.* T **466** *and similar vert designs. Multicoloured.* P 14½×14.

1579	40 c. Type **466**				40	30
1580	60 c. Perendale				55	55
1581	80 c. Corriedale				70	70
1582	$1 Drysdale				85	85
1583	$1.50, South Suffolk				1·25	1·25
1584	$1.80, Romney				1·50	1·60
1579/84				*Set of 6*	4·75	4·75

467 Moriori, Royal Albatross, Nikau Palm and Artefacts   **468** Goal and Footballers

(Des K. Hall. Litho Southern Colour Print Ltd, Dunedin)

1991 (6 Mar). *Bicentenary of Discovery of Chatham Islands.* T **467** *and similar vert design. Multicoloured.* P 13½.

1585	40 c. Type **467**				40	40
1586	80 c. Carvings, H.M.S. *Chatham*, Moriori house of 1870, and Tommy Solomon				70	70

(Des T. Crilley. Litho Southern Colour Print Ltd, Dunedin)

1991 (6 Mar). *Centenary of New Zealand Football Association.* T **468** *and similar horiz design. Multicoloured.* P 13½.

1587	80 c. Type **468**				75	75
	a. Horiz pair. Nos. 1587/8				1·50	1·50
1588	80 c. Five footballers and referee				75	75

Nos. 1587/8 were printed together, *se-tenant*, in horizontal pairs throughout the sheet, each pair forming a composite design.

(Des Pauline Morse. Litho Printset, Australia)

1991 (17 Apr–1 July). *As Nos. 1463/b, but self-adhesive.* P 11½.

1589	40 c. Brown Kiwi				45	45
1589a	45 c. Rock Wren (1.7.91)				30	35

Nos. 1589/a were only available in coils of 100, each stamp, with die-cut perforations, being separate on the imperforate backing paper. Initially the 45 c. showed the surplus surface paper removed, but from November 1991 supplies had the stamps surrounded by white selvedge. The format was changed again in October 1992 when the coils again appeared without the white selvedge. In the 1992 version, however, the stamps interlock and there is no backing paper visible between them, as was the case with the initial stock in July 1991.

A limited quantity of the 45 c. in sheets of 200 (8×25) was produced for use on official first day covers. It is reported that a small number of such sheets were subsequently sold by a few post offices.

469 Tuatara on Rocks   **470** Clown

(Des Pauline Morse. Litho Leigh-Mardon Ltd, Melbourne)

1991 (17 Apr). *Endangered Species. The Tuatara.* T **469** *and similar horiz designs. Multicoloured.* P 14½.

1590	40 c. Type **469**				40	45
1591	40 c. Tuatara in crevice				40	45
1592	40 c. Tuatara with foliage				40	45
1593	40 c. Tuatara in dead leaves				40	45
1590/3				*Set of 4*	1·40	1·60

(Des Helen Crawford. Litho Leigh-Mardon Ltd, Melbourne)

1991 (15 May–1 July). *Booklet Stamps. "Happy Birthday".* T **470** *and similar multicoloured designs.* P 13½.

1594	40 c. Type **470**				35	45
	a. Booklet pane. Nos. 1594/8				1·60	
1595	40 c. Balloons				35	45
1596	40 c. Party hat				35	45
1597	40 c. Birthday present (41×27 mm)				35	45
1598	40 c. Birthday cake (41×27 mm)				35	45
1599	45 c. Type **470**				30	35
	a. Booklet pane. Nos. 1599/1603				1·50	
1600	45 c. As No. 1595 (1 July)				30	35
1601	45 c. As No. 1596 (1 July)				30	35
1602	45 c. As No. 1597 (1 July)				30	35
1603	45 c. As No. 1598 (1 July)				30	35
1594/1603				*Set of 10*	3·00	3·50

The above were only issued in $2 (Nos. 1594/8) or $2.25 (Nos. 1599/603) stamp booklets.

471 Cat at Window   **472** Punakaiki Rocks

(Des Jennifer Lautusi. Litho Leigh-Mardon Ltd, Melbourne)

1991 (15 May–1 July). *Booklet Stamps. "Thinking of You".* T **471** *and similar multicoloured designs.* P 13½.

1604	40 c. Type **471**				35	45
	a. Booklet pane. Nos. 1604/8				1·60	
1605	40 c. Cat playing with slippers				35	45
1606	40 c. Cat with alarm clock				35	45
1607	40 c. Cat in window (41×27 mm)				35	45
1608	40 c. Cat at door (41×27 mm)				35	45
1609	45 c. Type **471** (1 July)				30	35
	a. Booklet pane. Nos. 1609/13				1·50	
1610	45 c. As No. 1605 (1 July)				30	35
1611	45 c. As No. 1606 (1 July)				30	35
1612	45 c. As No. 1607 (1 July)				30	35
1613	45 c. As No. 1608 (1 July)				30	35
1604/13				*Set of 10*	3·00	3·50

The above were only issued in $2 (Nos. 1604/8) or $2.25 (Nos. 1609/13) stamp booklets.

(Des H. Thompson. Litho Leigh-Mardon Ltd, Melbourne)

1991 (12 June). *Scenic Landmarks.* T **472** *and similar horiz designs. Multicoloured.* P 14½.

1614	40 c. Type **472**				35	30
1615	50 c. Moeraki Boulders				50	45
1616	80 c. Organ Pipes				75	75
1617	$1 Castle Hill				85	85
1618	$1.50, Te Kaukau Point				1·40	1·50
1619	$1.80, Ahuriri River Clay Cliffs				1·60	1·75
1614/19				*Set of 6*	5·00	5·00

473 Dolphins Underwater   **474** Children's Rugby

(Des Heather Arnold. Litho Leigh-Mardon Ltd, Melbourne)

1991 (24 July). *Health Stamps. Hector's Dolphin. T 473 and similar horiz design.* Multicoloured. P 14½.

1620	45 c. + 5 c. Type 473	50	50
1621	80 c. + 5 c. Dolphins leaping	90	90
MS1622	115×100 mm. Nos. 1620/1, each × 2	2·75	2·75

(Des A.G. Mitchell. Litho Leigh-Mardon Ltd, Melbourne)

1991 (21 Aug). *World Cup Rugby Championship. T 474 and similar vert designs.* Multicoloured. P 14½×14.

1623	80 c. Type 474	75	75
1624	$1 Women's rugby	85	85
1625	$1.50, Senior rugby	1·40	1·40
1626	$1.80, "All Blacks" (national team)	1·60	1·60
1623/6	Set of 4	4·25	4·25
MS1627	113×90 mm. No. 1626 (sold at $2.40)	2·00	2·25

No. MS1627 additionaly inscribed "PHILA NIPPON '91" was available, at $1·80, from the New Zealand stand at this International Stamp Exhibition in Tokyo and from the Philatelic Bureau at Wanganui.

475 Three Shepherds   476 *Dodonidia helmsii*

(Des Designworks Communications. Litho Southern Colour Print, Dunedin)

1991 (18 Sept). *Christmas. T 475 and similar vert designs.* Multicoloured. P 13½.

1628	45 c. Type 475	45	45
	a. Block of four. Nos 1628/31	1·60	
1629	45 c. Two Kings on camels	45	45
1630	45 c. Mary and Baby Jesus	45	45
1631	45 c. King with gift	45	45
1632	65 c. Star of Bethlehem	60	60
1633	$1 Crown	85	85
1634	$1.50, Angel	1·40	1·40
1628/34	Set of 7	4·00	4·00

Nos. 1628/31 were printed together, *se-tenant*, in blocks of four throughout the sheet.

(Des Pauline Morse. Litho Leigh-Mardon Ltd, Melbourne)

1991 (6 Nov). *Butterflies. T 476 and similar vert designs.* Multicoloured. P 14½.

1635	$1 Type 476	65	70
1636	$2 Zizina otis oxleyi	1·25	1·40
1637	$3 Vanessa itea	2·00	2·10
1635/7	Set of 3	3·50	3·75

A miniature sheet containing No. 1637 was only available from the New Zealand stand at "PHILA NIPPON '91" International Stamp Exhibition, Tokyo, or the Philatelic Bureau, Wanganui.

479 Yacht *Kiwi Magic*, 1987   480 *Heemskerk*

(Des R. Proud. Litho Leigh-Mardon Ltd, Melbourne)

1992 (22 Jan). *New Zealand Challenge for America's Cup. T 479 and similar horiz designs.* Multicoloured. P 14.

1655	45 c. Type 479	40	35
1656	80 c. Yacht New Zealand, 1988	70	70
1657	$1 Yacht America, 1851	85	85
1658	$1.50, Yacht New Zealand, 1992	1·25	1·40
1655/8	Set of 4	3·00	3·00

(Des G. Fuller. Litho Enschedé)

1992 (12 Mar). *Great Voyages of Discovery. T 480 and similar horiz designs.* Multicoloured. P 13×14½.

1659	45 c. Type 480	40	35
1660	80 c. Zeehan	70	70
1661	$1 Santa Maria	85	85
1662	$1.50, Pinta and Nina	1·25	1·40
1659/62	Set of 4	3·00	3·00

Nos. 1659/60 commemorate the 350th anniversary of Tasman's discovery of New Zealand and Nos. 1661/2 the 500th anniversary of discovery of America by Columbus.

A miniature sheet containing stamps as Nos. 1661/2, but perforated 14, was only available from the New Zealand stand at "World Columbian Stamp Expo '92", Chicago, and from the Philatelic Bureau at Wanganui.

ALTERED CATALOGUE NUMBERS

Any Catalogue numbers altered from the last edition are shown as a list in the introductory pages.

---

481 Sprinters   482 Weddell Seal and Pup

(Des Sheryl McCammon. Litho Southern Colour Print, Dunedin)

1992 (3 Apr). *Olympic Games, Barcelona (1st issue).* P 13½.

1663	481 45 c. multicoloured	40	40

See also Nos. 1670/4.

(Des Lindy Fisher. Litho Southern Colour Print, Dunedin)

1992 (8 Apr). *Antarctic Seals. T 482 and similar horiz designs.* Multicoloured. P 13½.

1664	45 c. Type 482	40	35
1665	50 c. Crabeater Seals swimming	45	45
1666	65 c. Leopard Seal and penguins	60	60
1667	80 c. Ross Seal	75	75
1668	$1 Southern Elephant Seal and harem	85	90
1669	$1.80, Hooker's Sea Lion and pup	1·50	1·60
1664/9	Set of 6	4·00	4·25

Although inscribed "Ross Dependency" Nos. 1664/9 were available from post offices throughout New Zealand.

483 Cycling   484 Ice Pinnacles, Franz Josef Glacier

(Des M. Bailey. Litho Southern Colour Print, Dunedin)

1992 (13 May). *Olympic Games, Barcelona (2nd issue). T 483 and similar horiz designs.* P 13½.

1670	45 c. Type 483	40	35
1671	80 c. Archery	70	70
1672	$1 Equestrian three-day eventing	85	85
1673	$1.50, Sailboarding	1·40	1·40
1670/3	Set of 4	3·00	3·00
MS1674	125×100 mm. Nos. 1670/3. P 14×14½	3·25	3·25

No. MS1674 exists overprinted with the emblem of the "World Columbian, Stamp Expo '92" and was only available from the New Zealand stand at this International Stamp Exhibition in Chicago and from the Philatelic Bureau at Wanganui.

(Des A. Hollows. Litho Southern Colour Print, Dunedin)

1992 (12 June). *Glaciers. T 484 and similar horiz designs.* Multicoloured. P 13½.

1675	45 c. Type 484	40	35
1676	50 c. Tasman Glacier	50	45
1677	80 c. Snowball glacier, Marion Plateau	70	70
1678	$1 Brewster Glacier	85	85
1679	$1.50, Fox Glacier	1·40	1·40
1680	$1.80, Franz Josef Glacier	1·50	1·60
1675/80	Set of 6	4·75	4·75

485 "Grand Finale" Camellia   486 Tree and Hills

(Des Pat Medearis Altman. Litho Leigh-Mardon Ltd, Melbourne)

1992 (8 July). *Camellias. T 485 and similar vert designs.* Multicoloured. P 14½.

1681	45 c. Type 485	40	35
1682	50 c. "Showa-No-Sakae"	50	45
1683	80 c. "Sugar Dream"	70	70
1684	$1 "Night Rider"	85	85
1685	$1.50, "E.G. Waterhouse"	1·40	1·40
1686	$1.80, "Dr. Clifford Parks"	1·50	1·50
1681/6	Set of 6	4·75	4·75

(Des T. Crilley. Litho Southern Colour Print, Dunedin)

1992 (12 Aug). *Health Stamps. Sportsmen (2nd series).* Horiz designs as T 461. Multicoloured. P 13½.

1687	45 c. + 5 c. Anthony Wilding (tennis player) and match	55	60
1688	80 c. + 5 c. Stewie Dempster (cricketer) and batsman	70	80
MS1689	115×96 mm. Nos. 1687/8, each × 2. P 14	2·50	2·75

(Des Van de Roer Design. Litho Leigh-Mardon Ltd, Melbourne)

1992 (1 Sept). *Booklet Stamps. Landscapes. T 486 and similar horiz designs.* Multicoloured. P 14×14½.

1690	45 c. Type 486	30	35
	a. Booklet pane. Nos. 1690/9	2·75	
1691	45 c. River and hills	30	35
1692	45 c. Hills and mountain	30	35
1693	45 c. Glacier	30	35
1694	45 c. Hills and waterfall	30	35
1695	45 c. Tree and beach	30	35
1696	45 c. Estuary and cliffs	30	35
1697	45 c. Fjord	30	35
1698	45 c. River delta	30	35
1699	45 c. Ferns and beach	30	35
1690/9	Set of 10	2·75	3·25

Nos. 1690/9 were only issued in $4.50 stamp booklets with the pane forming a composite design.

487 Reindeer over Houses   488 1920's Fashions

(Des K. Hall. Litho Leigh-Mardon Ltd, Melbourne)

1992 (16 Sept). *Christmas. T 487 and similar vert designs.* Multicoloured. P 14½.

1700	45 c. Type 487	30	35
	a. Block of 4. Nos. 1700/3	1·10	
1701	45 c. Santa Claus on sleigh over houses	30	35
1702	45 c. Christmas tree in window	30	35
1703	45 c. Christmas wreath and children at window	30	35
1704	65 c. Candles and fireplace	45	50
1705	$1 Family going to church	65	70
1706	$1.50, Picnic under Pohutukawa tree	1·00	1·10
1700/6	Set of 7	3·00	3·25

Nos. 1700/3 were printed together, *se-tenant*, in blocks of four throughout the sheet.

(Des T. Crilley. Litho Southern Colour Print, Dunedin)

1992 (4 Nov). *New Zealand in the 1920's. T 488 and similar vert designs.* Multicoloured. P 13½.

1707	45 c. Type 488	30	35
1708	50 c. Dr. Robert Jack and early radio announcer	35	40
1709	80 c. "All Blacks" rugby player, 1924	55	60
1710	$1 Swaggie and dog	65	70
1711	$1.50, Ford "Model A" car and young couple	1·00	1·10
1712	$1.80, Amateur aviators and biplane	1·25	1·40
1707/12	Set of 6	3·75	4·00

489 "Old Charley" Toby Jug   490 Women's Fashions of the 1930's

(Des Brand New Ltd. Litho Leigh-Mardon Ltd, Melbourne)

1993 (20 Jan). *Royal Doulton Ceramics Exhibition, New Zealand. T 489 and similar vert designs.* Multicoloured. P 13.

1713	45 c. Type 489	30	35
1714	50 c. "Bunnykins" nursery plate	35	40
1715	80 c. "Maori Art" tea set	55	60
1716	$1 "Ophelia" handpainted plate	65	70
1717	$1.50, "St. George" figurine	1·00	1·10
1718	$1.80, "Lambeth" saltglazed stoneware vase	1·25	1·40
1713/18	Set of 6	3·75	4·00
MS1719	125×100 mm. No. 1718	1·25	1·40

(Des R. Jones. Litho Leigh-Mardon Ltd, Melbourne)

1993 (17 Feb). *New Zealand in the 1930's. T 490 and similar vert designs.* Multicoloured. P 14½×14.

1720	45 c. Type 490	30	35
1721	50 c. Unemployed protest march	35	40
1722	80 c. "Phar Lap" (racehorse)	55	60
1723	$1 State housing project	65	70
1724	$1.50, Boys drinking free school milk	1·00	1·10
1725	$1.80, Cinema queue	1·25	1·40
1720/5	Set of 6	3·75	4·00

Index to New Zealand Stamp Designs from 1946

The following index is intended to facilitate the identification of all New Zealand stamps from 1946 onwards. Portrait stamps are usually listed under surnames only, views under the name of the town or city and other issues under the main subject or a prominent word and date chosen from the inscription. Simple abbreviations have occasionally been resorted to and when the same design or subject appears on more than one stamp, only the first of each series is indicated.

EXPRESS DELIVERY STAMPS

E 1

(Typo Govt Printing Office, Wellington)

1903 (9 Feb). *Value in first colour. W 43 (sideways). P 11.*
E1　E 1　6d. red and violet　.. .. 32·00 20·00

1926–36. *Thick, white, opaque chalk-surfaced "Cowan" paper. W 43.*

　　　　　(a) P 14 × 14½
E2　E 1　6d. vermilion and bright violet　.. 35·00 18·00
　　　　　(b) P 14 × 15 (1936)
E3　E 1　6d. carmine and bright violet　.. 32·00 48·00

1937–39. *Thin, hard, chalk-surfaced "Wiggins Teape" paper.*

　　　　　(a) P 14 × 14½
E4　E 1　6d. carmine and bright violet .. 60·00 38·00
　　　　　(b) P 14 × 15 (1939)
E5　E 1　6d. vermilion and bright violet .. 90·00 £100

E 2 Express Mail Delivery Van

(Des J. Berry. Eng Stamp Ptg Office, Melbourne Recess Govt Ptg Office, Wellington)

1939 (16 Aug). *W 43. P 14.*
E6　E 2　6d. violet　.. .. .. 1·50 1·75

POSTAGE DUE STAMPS

D 1　　　　　　(I)

3D.　　5D.
(a)　　　*(b)*
Large "D"　　Small "D"

(Typo Govt Printing Office, Wellington)

1899 (1 Dec). *W 12b. Coarse paper. P 11.*

I. Type I. *Circle of 14 ornaments, 17 dots over "N.Z.", "N.Z." large.*

　　　　　(a) Large "D"
D1　D 1　½d. carmine and green　.. .. 12·00 24·00
　　　　a. No stop after "D" (Right pane R. 2/3) 80·00 £130
D2　　1s. carmine and green　.. .. 60·00 75·00
D3　　1s. carmine and green　.. .. 65·00 80·00
D4　　2s. carmine and green　.. .. £110 £130
D1/4　　　　　.. *Set of 4* £225 £250
To avoid further subdivision the 1s. and 2s. are placed with the *pence* values, although the two types of "D" do not apply to the higher values.

　　　　　(b) Small "D"
D6　D 1　5d. carmine and green .. .. 20·00 18·00
D7　　6d. carmine and green .. .. 23·00 18·00
D8　　10d. carmine and green .. .. 70·00 80·00
D6/8　　　　.. *Set of 3* £100 £100

II. Type II. *Circle of 13 ornaments, 15 dots over "N.Z.", "N.Z." small.*

　　　　　(a) Large "D"
D 9　D 1　½d. vermilion and green　.. 2·50 15·00
　　　a. No stop after "D" (Right pane
　　　R. 2/3)　.. .. 50·00 85·00
D10　　1d. vermilion and green　.. 8·50 1·00
D11　　2d. vermilion and green　.. 48·00 9·00
D12　　3d. vermilion and green　.. 12·00 3·50
D9/12　　　.. *Set of 4* 65·00 23·00

　　　　　(b) Small "D"
D14　D 1　1d. vermilion and green　.. 13·00 1·50
D15　　2d. vermilion and green　.. 28·00 4·75
D16　　4d. vermilion and green　.. 26·00 9·00
D14/16　　　.. *Set of 3* 60·00 14·00

Nos. D9/16 were printed from a common frame plate of 240 (4 panes of 60) used in conjunction with centre plates of 120 (2 panes of 60) for the ½d. and 4d. or 240 for the other values. Sheets of the 1d. and 2d. each contained two panes with large "D" and two panes with small "D".

D 2　　　　　D 3

(Des W. R. Bock. Typo Govt Printing Office)

1902 (28 Feb). *No wmk. P 11.*
D17　D 2　½d. red and deep green　.. 1·25 6·00

1904–08. *"Cowan" unsurfaced paper. W 43 (sideways). (a) P 11.*
D18　D 2　½d. red and green (4.04)　.. 1·50 1·50
　　　a. Imperf between (horiz pair)　.. £600
D19　　1d. red and green (5.12.05)　.. 8·50 3·25
D20　　2d. red and green (5.4.06)　.. 90·00 95·00
D18/20　　　.. *Set of 3* 90·00 95·00

　　　　　(b) P 14
D21　D 2　1d. carmine and green (12.06)　.. 12·00 1·25
　　　a. Rose-pink and green (9.07)　.. 11·00 1·25
D22　　2d. carmine and green (10.06)　.. 9·00 5·50
　　　a. Rose-pink and green (6.08)　.. 5·00 1·25

1919 (Jan)–**20.** *"De La Rue" chalky paper. Toned gum. W 43. P 14 × 15.*
D23　D 2　½d. carmine and green (6.19)..　.. 3·25 3·00
D24　　1d. carmine and green　.. 4·50 30
D25　　2d. carmine and green (8.20)..　.. 8·00 2·50
D23/5　　　.. *Set of 3* 14·00 5·25

1925 (May). *"Jones" chalky paper. White gum. W 43. P 14 × 15.*
D26　D 2　½d. carmine and green　.. 35·00 35·00

1925 (July). *No wmk, but bluish "N Z" and Star lithographed on back. P 14 × 15.*
D27　D 2　½d. carmine and green　.. 2·00 20·00
D28　　2d. carmine and green　.. 3·00 15·00

1925 (Nov)–**35.** *"Cowan" thick, opaque chalky paper. W 43.*

　　　　　(a) P 14 × 15
D29　D 2　½d. carmine and green (12.26)　.. 1·75 8·00
D30　　1d. carmine and green　.. 3·25 80
D31　　2d. carmine and green (6.26)..　.. 18·00 3·75
D32　　3d. carmine and green (6.35)..　.. 48·00 55·00
D29/32　　　.. *Set of 4* 65·00 60·00

　　　　　(b) P 14
D33　D 2　½d. carmine and green (10.28)　.. 27·00 28·00
D34　　1d. rose and pale yellow-green (6.28)　.. 4·00 1·25
D35　　2d. carmine and green (10.29)..　.. 7·00 2·75
D36　　3d. carmine and green (5.28)　.. 15·00 42·00
D33/6　　　.. *Set of 4* 48·00 65·00

1937–38. *"Wiggins Teape" thin, hard chalky paper. W 43. P 14 × 15.*
D37　D 2　½d. carmine and yellow-green (2.38) .. 18·00 30·00
D38　　1d. carmine and yellow-green (1.37) .. 11·00 3·75
D39　　2d. carmine and yellow-green (6.37) .. 20·00 8·50
D40　　3d. carmine and yellow-green (11.37) .. 75·00 55·00
D37/40　　　.. *Set of 4* £110 85·00

(Des J. Berry. Typo Govt Printing Office, Wellington)

1939–49. *P 15 × 14. (a) W 43 (sideways) (16.8.39).*
D41　D 3　½d. turquoise-green　.. .. 3·50 4·25
D42　　1d. carmine　.. .. 1·50 30
D43　　2d. bright blue　.. .. 4·50 2·75
D44　　3d. orange-brown　.. .. 13·00 22·00
D41/4　　　.. *Set of 4* 20·00 26·00

　　　　　(b) W 98 sideways
D45　D 3　1d. carmine (4.49)　.. .. 6·00 5·00*
D46　　2d. bright blue (12.46)　.. 1·50 80
D47　　3d. orange-brown (6.45)　.. 4·25 5·00
　　　a. Wmk upright (1943)　.. 38·00 30·00
D45/6..　　　.. *Set of 3* 10·50 9·75*
*The use of Postage Due stamps ceased in 1951, our used price for No. D45 being for stamps postmarked after this date (*price for examples clearly cancelled 1949–51, £25*).

OFFICIAL STAMPS

1891 (Dec)–**1906.** *Contemporary issues handstamped "O.P. S.O." diagonally. (a) Stamps of 1873 type. W 12b. P 12½.*
O 1　3　½d. rose (V.)　.. .. — £450

　　　　(b) Stamps of 1882–97 optd in rose or magenta. W 12b.
O 2　13　½d. black (p 10)　.. .. — £170
　　　a. Violet opt　.. .. — £200
O 3　　½d. black (p 10 × 11)　.. — £170
O 4　14　1d. rose (p 12 × 11½)　.. — £180
O 5　　1d. rose (p 11)　.. .. — £180
O 6　15　2d. purple (p 11)　.. .. — £325
O 7　　2d. mauve-lilac (p 10)　.. — £325
　　　a. Violet opt　.. .. — £375
O 8　16　2½d. blue (p 11)　.. .. — £225
O 9　　2½d. ultramarine (p 10)　.. — £225
O10　　2½d. ultramarine (p 10 × 11)　.. — £225
O11　19　5d. olive-black (p 11½ × 11½) .. — £375
O12　20　6d. brown (p 12 × 11½)　.. — £500

　　　　(c) Stamps of 1898–1903 optd in violet. P 11. (i) No wmk
O13　23　½d. green (p 14) (No. 294)　.. — £160
O14　26　2½d. blue (p 12–16) (No. 249a)..　.. — £400
O15　27　2½d. blue (No. 260)　.. .. — £325
O16　37　4d. indigo and brown (No. 262)　.. — £375
O17　30　5d. purple-brown (No. 263)　.. — £400
　　　a. Green opt　.. .. — £375
O18　32　8d. indigo (No. 266)　.. — £475

　　　　　(ii) W 38
O19　42　1d. carmine (No. 278)　.. — £180

　　　　(iii) W 43 (sideways on 3d., 1s.)
O20　42　1d. carmine (p 14) (No. 303)　.. — £180
　　　a. Green opt　.. .. — £180
O21　27　2½d. blue (No. 308)　.. .. — £275
O22　28　3d. yellow-brown (No. 309)　.. — £400
O23　34　1s. orange-red (No. 315b)　.. — £750
O24　35　2s. green (No. 316)　.. .. — £1100
The letters signify "On Public Service Only", and stamps so overprinted were used by the Post Office Department on official correspondence between the department and foreign countries.

(O 3)

1907–08. *Stamps of 1902–6 optd with Type O 3 (vertically upwards). W 43 (sideways on 3d., 6d., 1s. and 5s.). P 14.*
O59　23　½d. yellow-green　.. .. 7·50 50
　　　a. Perf 11 × 14　.. .. 65·00
　　　b. Mixed perfs　.. .. 65·00
O60　42　1d. carmine (No. 303) (1908)*　.. 7·00 7·00
　　　a. Booklet pane of 6　.. 35·00
O60b　　1d. rose-carmine (Waterlow) (No. 352) 7·50 30
　　　ba. Perf 11 × 14　.. .. — £225
　　　bb. Mixed perfs　.. .. — £225
O60c　　1d. carmine (Royle)　.. .. 7·50 30
　　　ca. Perf 11 × 14　.. .. £200
　　　cb. Mixed perfs　.. .. £200
O61　41　2d. purple　.. .. 8·00 1·40
　　　a. Bright reddish purple　.. 7·00 1·00
　　　ab. Mixed perfs　.. .. £180 £180
O63　28　3d. bistre-brown　.. .. 35·00 1·75
O64　31　6d. bright carmine-pink　.. £110 15·00
　　　a. Imperf vert (horiz pair)　.. £750
　　　b. Mixed perfs　.. .. £400 £350
O65　34　1s. orange-red　.. .. 85·00 15·00
O66　35　2s. blue-green　.. .. 70·00 48·00
　　　a. Imperf between (pair)　.. £1100
　　　b. Imperf vert (horiz pair)　.. £900
O67　36　5s. deep red　.. .. £150 £170
　　　a. Wmk upright　.. .. £700 £750
*Though issued in 1908, a large quantity of booklets was mislaid and not utilized until they were found in 1930.

1908–09. *Optd as Type O 3. W 43.*
O69　23　½d. green (p 14 × 15)　.. .. 6·50 1·50
O70　50　1d. carmine (p 14 × 15)　.. 60·00 1·75
O71　48　6d. pink (p 14 × 13, 13½)　.. £140 38·00
O72　　6d. pink (p 14 × 15) (1909)　.. £110 35·00
O72a　F 4　£1 rose-pink (p 14) (No. F89)　.. £500 £400

1910. *No. 387 optd with Type O 3.*
O73　51　½d. yellow-green　.. .. 3·75 30
　　　a. Opt inverted (reading downwards)　† £1200

1910–16. *Nos. 389 and 392/4 optd with Type O 3. P 14 × 14½.*
O74　52　3d. chestnut　.. .. .. 14·00 80
　　　a. Perf 14 × 13½ (1915)　.. 60·00 70·00
　　　ab. Vert pair, O74/a　.. .. £300 £350
O75　—　6d. carmine　.. .. 18·00 3·75
　　　a. Deep carmine (1913)　.. 24·00 4·25
O76　—　8d. indigo-blue (R.) (5.16)　.. 14·00 18·00
　　　a. Perf 14 × 13½　.. 14·00 18·00
　　　ab. Vert pair, O76/a　.. 45·00 60·00
O77　—　1s. vermilion　.. .. 45·00 12·00
O74/7　　　.. *Set of 4* 80·00 30·00

1910–25. *Optd with Type O 3. (a) W 43. De La Rue chalk-surfaced paper with toned gum.*
O78　53　1d. carmine (No. 405)　.. .. 3·00 10
　　　(b) W 43. Jones chalk-surfaced paper with white gum
O79　53　1d. deep carmine (No. 406) (1925)　.. 9·50 4·00
(c) No wmk, but bluish "NZ" and Star lithographed on back. Art paper
O80　53　1d. rose-carmine (No. 409) (1925)　.. 6·00 9·00
(d) W 43. Cowan thick, opaque, chalk-surfaced paper with white gum
O81　53　1d. deep carmine (No. 410) (1925)　.. 8·00 1·25

1913–25. *Postal Fiscal stamps optd with Type O 3.*
　　(i) Chalk-surfaced De La Rue paper. (a) P 14 (1913–14)
O82　F 4　2s. blue (30.9.14)　.. .. 42·00 28·00
O83　　5s. yellow-green (13.6.13)　.. 70·00 75·00
O84　　£1 rose-carmine (1913)　.. £550 £450
O82/4 ..　　　.. *Set of 3* £600 £600

　　　(b) P 14½ × 14, comb (1915)
O85　F 4　2s. deep blue (Aug)　.. .. 45·00 25·00
　　　a. No stop after "OFFICIAL"　.. £120 80·00
O86　　5s. yellow-green (Jan)　.. 65·00 65·00
　　　a. No stop after "OFFICIAL"　.. £200 £200
　　(ii) Thick, white, opaque chalk-surfaced Cowan paper. P 14½ × 14 (1925)
O87　F 4　2s. blue　.. .. 55·00 60·00
　　　a. No stop after "OFFICIAL"　.. £160 £160
The overprint on these last, and on Nos. O69 and O72a, is from a new set of type, giving a rather sharper impression than Type O 3, but otherwise resembling it closely.

1915 (12 Oct)–**34.** *Optd with Type O 3. P 14 × 15. (a) On Nos. 435/40 (De La Rue chalk-surfaced paper with toned gum).*
O88　61　½d. green　.. .. 1·25 10
O89　62　1½d. grey-black (6.16)　.. 5·50 2·50
O90　61　1½d. slate (12.16)　.. 3·75 40
O91　　1½d. orange-brown (4.19)　.. 3·75 30
O92　　2d. yellow (4.17)　.. 3·75 10
O93　　3d. chocolate (11.19) .. .. 9·00 35
O88/93　　　.. *Set of 6* 24·00 3·50
(b) On Nos. 441 and 443 (Jones chalk-surfaced paper with white gum)
O94　61　½d. green (1924)　.. .. 4·00 2·50
O95　　3d. deep chocolate (1924)　.. 35·00 4·50
(c) On Nos. 446/7 and 448a/9 (Cowan thick, opaque, chalk-surfaced paper with white gum)
O96　61　½d. green (1925)　.. .. 65 10
　　　a. Perf 14 (1929)　.. .. 2·25 35
　　　ab. No stop after "OFFICIAL"　.. 22·00 25·00
O97　　1½d. orange-brown (p 14) (1929)　.. 9·50 11·00
　　　a. No stop after "OFFICIAL"　.. 40·00 55·00
　　　b. Perf 14 × 15 (1934)　.. 20·00 25·00
O98　　2d. yellow (p 14) (1931)　.. 1·50 30
　　　a. No stop after "OFFICIAL"　.. 32·00 22·00

O99	61	3d. chocolate (1925)	3·50	40
		a. No stop after "OFFICIAL"	50·00	35·00
		b. Perf 14 (1930)	26·00	1·75
		ba. No stop after "OFFICIAL"	90·00	42·00
O96/9		Set of 4	13·50	11·00

1915 (Dec)–**27**. *Optd with Type O 3. P 14×14½. (a) Nos. 420, 422, 425, 428 and 429a/30 (Cowan unsurfaced paper).*

O100	60	3d. chocolate	3·00	70
		a. Perf 14×13½	3·00	70
		ab. Vert pair, O100/a	35·00	50·00
O101		4d. bright violet (p 14×13½) (4.25)	12·00	2·00
		a. Re-entry (Pl 20 R. 1/6)	40·00	
		b. Re-entry (Pl 20 R. 4/10)	45·00	
		c. Perf 14×14½ (4.27)	22·00	1·00
O102		6d. carmine (6.16)	4·50	75
		a. Perf 14×13½	3·75	60
		ab. Vert pair, O102/a	50·00	60·00
O103		8d. red-brown (p 14×13½) (8.22)	70·00	85·00
O104		9d. sage-green (p 14×13½) (4.25)	35·00	32·00
O105		1s. vermilion (9.16)	5·50	2·00
		a. Perf 14×13½	16·00	11·00
		ab. Vert pair, O105/a	65·00	90·00
		c. Pale orange-red	28·00	11·00
O100/5		Set of 6	£120	£110

(b) No. 433 (Thin paper with widely spaced sideways wmk)

| O106 | 60 | 3d. chocolate (p 14) (7.16) | 3·00 | 4·25 |
| | | a. No wmk | 30·00 | 50·00 |

1927–33. *Optd with Type O 3. W 43. P 14.*

O111	71	1d. rose-carmine (No. 468)	1·25	10
		a. No stop after "OFFICIAL"	22·00	15·00
		b. Perf 14×15	1·25	10
O112	72	2s. light blue (No. 469) (2.28)	70·00	80·00
O113	F 6	5s. green (1933)	£250	£250
O111/13		Set of 3	£300	£275

Official   Official

(O 4)   (O 5)

1936–61. *Pictorial issue optd horiz or vert (2s.) with Type O 4.*

(a) W 43 (Single "N Z" and Star)

O115	82	1d. scarlet (Die 1) (p 14×13½)	1·25	50
		a. Perf 13½×14	75·00	40·00
O116	83	1½d. red-brown (p 13½×14)	17·00	18·00
		a. Perf 14×13½	£4500	
O118	92	1s. deep green (p 14×13½)	19·00	23·00
O119	F 6	5s. green (p 14) (12.38)	85·00	24·00
O115/19		Set of 4	£110	60·00

The watermark of No. O119 is almost invisible.

Only four examples of No. O116a exist. The error occurred when a sheet of No. 558a was found to have a block of four missing. This was replaced by a block of No. 558 and the sheet was then sent for overprinting.

(b) W 98 (Mult "N Z" and Star)

O120	81	½d. bright green, p 14×13½ (7.37)	4·75	3·75
O121	82	1d. scarlet (Die II), p 14×13½ (11.36)	3·00	20
O122	83	1½d. red-brown, p 14×13½ (7.36)	9·00	40
O123	84	2d. orange, p 14×13½ (1.38)	1·50	10
		a. Perf 12½ (1942)	£170	50·00
		c. Perf 14 (1938)	32·00	7·50
O124	85	2½d. chocolate and slate, p 13–14 × 13½ (26.7.38)	40·00	45·00
		a. Perf 14 (1938)	12·00	10·00
O125	86	3d. brown, p 14×13½ (1.3.38)	45·00	2·00
O126	87	4d. black and sepia, p 14×13½ (8.36)	8·00	85
		a. Perf 12½ (1941)	3·75	1·50
		b. Perf 12½ (1941)	3·25	2·00
		c. Perf 14×13½ (10.42)	3·25	40
O127	89	6d. scarlet, p 13½×14 (12.37)	9·00	40
		a. Perf 12½ (1941)	9·00	3·50
		b. Perf 14½×14 (7.42)	4·50	10
O128	90	8d. chocolate, p 12½ (wmk sideways) (1942)	11·00	11·00
		a. Perf 14 × 14½ (wmk sideways) (1945)	5·50	10·00
		b. Perf 14×13½	†£1600	
O129	91	9d. red and grey-black (G.) (No. 587a), p 13½×14 (1.3.38)	48·00	35·00
O130		9d. scarlet and black (Blk.)(No.631), p 14×15 (1943)	15·00	18·00
O131	92	1s. deep green, p 14×13½ (2.37)	35·00	85
		a. Perf 12½ (1942)	17·00	85
O132	93	2s. olive-green, p 13–14 × 13½ (5.37)	60·00	22·00
		a. "CAPTAIN COQK"	70·00	
		b. Perf 13½×14 (1939)	£100	5·50
		ba. "CAPTAIN COQK"	£120	
		c. Perf 12½ (1942)	90·00	24·00
		ca. "CAPTAIN COQK"	£110	
		d. Perf 14×13½ (1944)	35·00	7·00
		da. "CAPTAIN COQK"	£150	
O133	F 6	5s. green, C, p 14 (3.43)	27·00	5·00
		a. Perf 14 × 13½. Yellow-green, O (10.61)	15·00	23·00
O120/33		Set of 14	£200	85·00

The opt on No. O127a was sometimes applied at the top of the stamp, instead of always at the bottom, as on No. O127.

All examples of No. O128b were used by a government office in Whangerei.

See notes on perforations after No. 590b.

1938–51. *Nos. 603 etc., optd with Type O 4.*

O134	108	½d. green (1.3.38)	9·00	1·25
O135		½d. brown-orange (1946)	1·25	1·50
O136		1d. scarlet (1.7.38)	10·00	15
O137		1d. green (10.7.41)	1·75	10
O138	108a	1½d. purple-brown (26.7.38)	65·00	18·00
O139		1½d. scarlet (2.4.51)	8·00	2·75
O140		3d. blue (16.10.41)	1·75	10
O134/40		Set of 7	85·00	21·00

1940 (2 Jan–8 Mar). *Centennial. Nos. 613, etc., optd with Type O 5.*

O141		½d. blue-green (R.)	75	35
		a. "ff" joined, as Type O 4	40·00	45·00
O142		1d. chocolate and scarlet	3·25	10
		a. "ff" joined, as Type O 4	50·00	50·00
O143		1½d. light blue and mauve	1·50	10
O144		2d. blue-green and chocolate	3·25	10
		a. "ff" joined, as Type O 4	50·00	45·00

O145		2½d. blue-green and ultramarine	3·00	2·75
		a. "ff" joined, as Type O 4	50·00	50·00
O146		3d. purple and carmine (R.)	7·00	80
		a. "ff" joined, as Type O 4	35·00	45·00
O147		4d. chocolate and lake	40·00	2·00
		a. "ff" joined, as Type O 4	£100	55·00
O148		6d. emerald-green and violet	20·00	2·00
		a. "ff" joined, as Type O 4	65·00	55·00
O149		8d. black and red (8.3)	23·00	16·00
		a. "ff" joined, as Type O 4	65·00	80·00
O150		9d. olive-green and vermilion	8·00	7·00
O151		1s. sage-green and deep green	40·00	4·00
O141/51		Set of 11	£130	32·00

1947–49. *Nos. 680, etc., optd with Type O 4.*

O152	108a	2d. orange	1·00	10
O153		4d. bright purple	2·75	50
O154		6d. carmine	8·00	40
O155		8d. violet	8·00	6·00
O156		9d. purple-brown	9·00	6·50
O157	144	1s. red-brown and carmine (wmk upright) (Plate 1)	11·00	85
		a. Wmk sideways (Plate 1) (1949)	8·00	4·00
		b. Wmk upright (Plate 2)	17·00	6·00
O158		2s. brown-orange and green (wmk sideways) (Plate I)	19·00	15·00
		a. Wmk upright (Plate 1)	29·00	26·00
O152/8		Set of 7	50·00	26·00

O 6   (O 7)
Queen Elizabeth II

(Des J. Berry. Recess B.W.)

1954 (1 Mar)–**63.** *W 98. P 14×13½.*

O159	O 6	1d. orange	45	20
O160		1½d. brown-lake	75	2·50
O161		2d. bluish green	30	15
O162		2½d. olive (1.3.63)	4·00	1·50
O163		3d. vermilion	40	10
O164		4d. blue	70	15
O165		9d. carmine	3·50	60
O166		1s. purple	50	10
O167		3s. slate (1.3.63)	48·00	48·00
O159/67		Set of 9	42·00	48·00

See note re white opaque paper after No. 736. Nos. O162 and O167 exist only on white paper.

1959 (1 Oct). *No. O160 surch with Type O 7.*

| O168 | O 6 | 6d. on 1½d. brown-lake | 20 | 85 |

1961 (1 Sept). *No. O161 surch as Type O 7.*

| O169 | O 6 | 2½d. on 2d. bluish green | 35 | 1·00 |

Owing to the greater use of franking machines by Government Departments, the use of official stamps was discontinued on 31 March 1965, but they remained on sale at the G.P.O. until 31 December 1965.

PROVISIONALS ISSUED AT REEFTON AND USED BY THE POLICE DEPARTMENT

1907 (Jan). *Current stamps of 1906, overwritten "Official," in red ink, and marked "Greymouth—PAID—3" inside a circular postmark stamp. P 14.*

P1	23	½d. green	£450	£650
P2	40	1d. carmine	£450	£700
P3	38a	2d. purple	£700	£850
P4	28	3d. bistre	£650	£800
P5	31	6d. pink	£850	£950
P6	34	1s. orange-red	£1100	£1300
P7	35	2s. green	—	£5000

LIFE INSURANCE DEPARTMENT

L 1   Lighthouse   L 2

(Des W. B. Hudson and J. F. Rogers; eng A. E. Cousins. Typo Govt Printing Office, Wellington)

1891 (2 Jan)–**98.** A. W 12c. P 12×11½.

L 1	L 1	½d. bright purple	55·00	7·00
L 2		1d. blue	55·00	9·00
		a. Wmk 12b	90·00	20·00
L 3		2d. brown-red	85·00	4·00
		a. Wmk 12b	95·00	12·00
L 4		3d. deep brown	£190	20·00
L 5		6d. green	£275	60·00
L 6		1s. rose	£650	£120
L1/6		Set of 6	£1100	£200

B. W 12b (1893–98). (a) P 10 (1893)

L 7	L 1	½d. bright purple	55·00	7·00
L 8		1d. blue	55·00	1·25
L 9		2d. brown-red	75·00	3·75
L7/9		Set of 3	£160	11·00

(b) P 11×10

L10	L 1	½d. bright purple (1896)	90·00	26·00
		a. Perf 10×11	—	60·00
L11		1d. blue (1897)	55·00	11·00
		a. Perf 10×11		

(c) Mixed perfs 10 and 11 (1897)

| L12 | L 1 | 2d. brown-red | £550 | £550 |

(d) P 11 (1897–98)

L13	L 1	½d. bright purple	55·00	2·75
		a. Thin coarse toned paper (1898)	65·00	5·50
L14		1d. blue	55·00	75
		a. Thin coarse toned paper (1898)	65·00	1·50
L15		2d. brown-red	70·00	3·50
		a. Chocolate	£110	24·00
		b. Thin coarse toned paper (1898)	70·00	3·50
L13/15		Set of 3	£160	6·25

1902–04. W 43 (sideways). (a) P 11.

L16	L 1	½d. bright purple (1903)	55·00	4·25
L17		1d. blue (1902)	55·00	1·00
L18		2d. brown-red (1904)	80·00	4·50
L16/18		Set of 3	£170	8·75

(b) P 14×11

| L19 | L 1 | ½d. bright purple (1903) | £1100 | |
| L20 | | 1d. blue (1904) | 90·00 | 10·00 |

Nos. L16/17 and L20 are known without watermark from the margins of the sheet.

1905–6. Redrawn, with "V.R." omitted. W 43 (sideways). (a) P 11.

| L21 | L 2 | 2d. brown-red (12.05) | £1200 | 80·00 |

(b) P 14

| L22 | L 2 | 1d. blue (1906) | £150 | 30·00 |

(c) P 14×11

| L23 | L 2 | 1d. blue (1906) | £475 | £150 |
| | | a. Mixed perfs | — | £375 |

Between January 1907 and the end of 1912 the Life Insurance Department used ordinary Official stamps.

1913 (2 Jan)–**37.** New values and colours. W 43.

(a) "De La Rue paper". P 14×15

L24	L 2	½d. green	7·00	80
		a. Yellow-green	7·00	80
L25		1d. carmine	8·00	1·00
		a. Carmine-pink	14·00	1·40
L26		1½d. black (1917)	38·00	6·50
L27		1½d. chestnut-brown (1919)	1·25	2·25
L28		2d. bright purple	45·00	23·00
L29		2d. yellow (1920)	3·50	2·00
L30		3d. yellow-brown	45·00	23·00
L31		6d. carmine-pink	30·00	17·00
L24/31		Set of 8	£160	65·00

(b) "Cowan" paper. (i) P 14×15

| L31a | L 2 | ½d. yellow-green (1925) | 22·00 | 4·00 |
| L31b | | 1d. carmine-pink (1925) | 23·00 | 3·25 |

(ii) P 14

L32	L 2	½d. yellow-green (1926)	9·00	1·50
L33		1d. scarlet (1931)	7·00	1·50
L34		2d. yellow (1937)	5·50	4·00
L35		3d. brown-lake (1931)	18·00	22·00
L36		6d. pink (1925)	23·00	26·00
L32/6		Set of 5	55·00	50·00

(c) "Wiggins Teape" paper. P 14 × 15

L36a	L 2	½d. yellow-green (3.37)	6·00	6·50
L36b		1d. scarlet (3.37)	10·00	2·75
L36c		6d. pink (7.37)	22·00	35·00
L36a/c		Set of 3	32·00	40·00

For descriptions of the various types of paper, see after No. 518. In the 1½d. the word "POSTAGE" is in both the side-labels instead of at left only.

1944–47. W 98. P 14 × 15.

L37	L 2	½d. yellow-green (7.47)	2·75	4·50
L38		1d. scarlet (6.44)	1·50	1·50
L39		2d. yellow (1946)	6·50	8·00
L40		3d. brown-lake (10.46)	12·00	15·00
L41		6d. pink (7.47)	8·00	22·00
L37/41		Set of 5	28·00	45·00

L3 Castlepoint Lighthouse   L 6 Cape Campbell Lighthouse

(Des J. Berry. Recess B.W.)

1947 (1 Aug)–**65.** Type L 3, L 6 and similar designs. W 98 (sideways on 1d., 2d., 2½d.). P 13½.

L42		½d. grey-green and orange-red	80	60
L43		1d. olive-green and pale blue	50	30
L44		2d. deep blue and grey-black	70	25
L45		2½d. black and bright blue (white opaque paper) (4.11.63)	9·50	13·00
L46		3d. mauve and pale blue	2·25	35
L47		4d. brown and yellow-orange	1·75	40
		a. Wmk sideways (white opaque paper) (13.10.65)	5·00	13·00
L48		9d. chocolate and blue	1·75	1·25
L49		1s. red-brown and blue	2·50	1·25
L42/49		Set of 8	18·00	15·00

Designs: Horiz (as Type L 3)–1d Taiaroa lighthouse; 2d. Cape Palliser lighthouse; 6d. The Brothers lighthouse. Vert (as Type L 6)–3d. Eddystone lighthouse; 4d. Stephens Island lighthouse; 1s. Cape Brett lighthouse.

(L 11)   (L 12)

1967 (10 July)–**68.** *Decimal currency. Stamps of 1947–65, surch as Type L 12 or L 11 (2 c.).*

L50	1 c. on 1d. (No. L43)	2·25	4·25
	a. Wmk upright (*white opaque paper*) (10.5.68)	2·25	3·50
L51	2 c. on 2½d. (No. L45)	7·00	9·00
L52	2½ c. on 3d. (No. L46)	1·75	4·50
	a. Horiz pair, one without surcharge .. £1700		
	b. Wmk sideways (*white opaque paper*) (4.68?)	2·50	4·75
L53	3 c. on 4d. (No. L47a)	4·50	5·00
L54	5 c. on 6d. (No. L48)	2·00	6·50
L55	10 c. on 1s. (No. L49)	3·00	11·00
	a. Wmk sideways (*white opaque paper*)	1·25	4·00
L50/55a	Set of 6	17·00	29·00

See note *re* white opaque paper below No. 736.
No. L54 exists on both ordinary and whiter paper.

L 13 Moeraki Point Lighthouse L 14 Puyesegur Point Lighthouse

(Des J. Berry. Litho B.W.)

1969 (27 Mar)–**77.** *Types L 13/14 and similar designs. No wmk. Chalk-surfaced paper* (8, 10 c.), *ordinary paper* (*others*). *P 14* (8, 10 c.) *or* 13½ (*others*).

L56	½ c. greenish yellow, red and deep blue	2·00	2·00
L57	2½ c. ultramarine, green and pale buff	1·00	1·25
L58	3 c. reddish brown and yellow	75	75
	a. Chalk-surfaced paper (16.6.77)	80	2·25
L59	4 c. lt new blue, yellowish grn & apple-grn	1·00	1·00
	a. Chalk-surfaced paper (16.6.77)	65	2·25
L60	8 c. multicoloured (17.11.76)	45	2·50
L61	10 c. multicoloured (17.11.76)	45	2·50
L62	15 c. black, light yellow and ultramarine	60	1·75
	a. Perf 14. Chalk-surfaced paper (24.12.76)	1·50	2·00
L56/62	Set of 7	5·00	10·50

Designs: *Horiz*—4 c. Cape Egmont Lighthouse; *Vert*—3c. Baring Head Lighthouse; 8 c. East Cape; 10 c. Farewell Spit; 15 c. Dog Island Lighthouse.

(L 16) L 17

1978 (8 Mar). *No. L 57 surch with Type L 16. Chalky paper.*
L63	L 14 25 c. on 2½ c. ultramarine, grn & buff	75	1·75

(Des A. G. Mitchell. Litho Harrison)

1981 (3 June). *P 14½.*
L64	L 17 5 c. multicoloured	10	10
L65	10 c. multicoloured	10	10
L66	20 c. multicoloured	15	15
L67	30 c. multicoloured	25	25
L68	40 c. multicoloured	35	30
L69	50 c. multicoloured	45	35
L64/9	Set of 6	1·25	1·00

Issues for the Government Life Insurance Department were withdrawn on 1 December 1989 when it became the privatised Tower Corporation.

POSTAL FISCAL STAMPS

As from 1 April 1882 fiscal stamps were authorised for postal use and conversely postage stamps became valid for fiscal use. Stamps in the designs of 1867 with "STAMP DUTY" above the Queen's head were withdrawn and although some passed through the mail quite legitimately they were mainly "philatelic" and we no longer list them. The issue which was specifically authorised in 1882 was the one which had originally been put on sale for fiscal use in 1880.

Although all fiscal stamps were legally valid for postage only values between 2s. and £1 were stocked at ordinary post offices. Other values could only be obtained by request from the G.P.O., Wellington or from offices of the Stamp Duties Department. Later the Arms types above £1 could also be obtained from the head post offices in Auckland, Christchurch, Dunedin and also a branch post office at Christchurch North where there was a local demand for them.

It seems sensible to list under Postal Fiscals the Queen Victoria stamps up to the £1 value and the Arms types up to the £5 because by 1931 the higher values were genuinely needed for postal purposes. Even the £10 was occasionally used on insured airmail parcels.

Although 2s. and 5s. values were included in the 1898 pictorial issue, it was the general practice for the Postal Department to limit the postage issues to 1s. until 1926 when the 2s. and 3s. appeared. These were then dropped from the fiscal issues and when in turn the 5s. and 10s. were introduced in 1953 and the £1 in 1960 no further printings of these values occurred in the fiscal series.

FORGED POSTMARKS. Our prices are for stamps with genuine postal cancellations. Beware of forged postmarks on stamps from which fiscal cancellations have been cleaned off.

Many small post offices acted as agents for government departments and it was the practice to use ordinary postal date-stamps on stamps used fiscally, so that when they are removed from documents they are indistinguishable from postally used specimens unless impressed with the embossed seal of the Stamp Duties Department.

Date-stamps very similar to postal date-stamps were sometimes supplied to offices of the Stamp Duties Department and it is not clear when this practice ceased. Prior to the Arms types the only sure proof of the postal use of off-cover fiscal stamps is when they bear a distinctive duplex, registered or parcel post cancellation, but beware of forgeries of the first two.

F 1 F 2 F 3

(Die eng W. R. Bock. Typo Govt Ptg Office)

1882 (Feb). *W 12a. P 12 × 11½.*
F1	F 1	1d. lilac	£160	£300
F2		1d. blue	75·00	25·00

The 1d. fiscal was specifically authorised for postal use in February 1882 owing to a shortage of the 1d. Type 5 and pending the introduction of the 1d. Type 14 on 1 April.

The 1d. lilac fiscal had been replaced by the 1d. blue in 1878 but postally used copies with 1882 duplex postmarks are known although most postally used examples are dated from 1890 and these must have been philatelic.

(Des and dies eng W. R. Bock. Typo Govt Ptg Office)

1882 (early). *W 12a. P 12 × 11½.*
F3	F 2	1s. grey green	
F4	F 3	1s. grey-green and red	

Copies of these are known postally used in 1882 and although not specifically authorised for postal use it is believed that their use was permitted where there was a shortage of the 1s. postage stamp.

The 2s. value Type F 3 formerly listed is not known with 1882–83 postal date-stamps.

WMK TYPE F 5. The balance of the paper employed for the 1867 issue was used for early printings of Type F 4 introduced in 1880 before changing over to the "N Z" and Star watermark. The values we list with this watermark are known with 1882–83 postal date stamps. Others have later dates and are considered to be philatelic but should they be found with 1882–83 postal dates we would be prepared to add them to the list.

In the following list the 4d., 6d., 8d. and 1s. are known with early 1882 postal date-stamps and, like Nos. F3/4, it is assumed that they were used to meet a temporary shortage of postage stamps.

F 4 F 5

The 12s. 6d. value has the head in an oval (as Type 10), and the 15s. and £1 values have it in a broken circle (as Type 7).

(Dies eng W. R. Bock. Typo Govt Ptg Office)

1882 (1 Apr). *Type F 4 and similar types. "De La Rue" paper.*

A. W 12a (6 mm). (a) P 12 (1882)
F 5	4d. orange-red (*Wmk F 5*)	—	£130
F 6	6d. lake-brown	—	£130
F 7	8d. green (*Wmk F 5*)		
F 8	1s. pink		
F 9	2s. blue	50·00	4·50
F10	2s. 6d. grey-brown	85·00	4·50
	a. Wmk F 5		
F11	3s. mauve	£110	5·50
F12	4s. brown-rose	£110	11·00
F13	5s. green	£140	11·00
	a. Yellow-green	£140	11·00
F14	6s. rose	£150	27·00
F15	7s. ultramarine	£160	40·00
F16	7s. 6d. bronze-grey	£160	45·00
F17	8s. deep blue	£160	40·00
F18	9s. orange	£150	45·00
F19	10s. brown-red	£140	14·00
	a. Wmk F 5		
F20	15s. green	£190	45·00
F21	£1 rose-pink	£190	45·00

(b) P 12½ (1886)
F22	2s. blue	50·00	4·50
F23	2s. 6d. grey-brown	85·00	4·50
F24	3s. mauve	£110	5·50
F25	4s. purple-claret	£110	11·00
	a. Brown-rose	£110	11·00
F26	5s. green	£140	11·00
	a. Yellow-green	£140	11·00
F27	6s. rose	£150	27·00
F28	7s. ultramarine	£160	40·00
F29	8s. deep blue	£160	40·00
F30	9s. orange	£150	45·00
F31	10s. brown-red	£140	14·00
F32	15s. green	£190	45·00
F33	£1 rose-pink	£190	45·00

B. W 12b (7 mm). P 12½ (1888)
F34	2s. blue	45·00	4·50
F35	2s. 6d. grey-brown	80·00	4·50
F36	3s. mauve	£100	5·50
F37	4s. brown-rose	£100	11·00
	a. Brown-red	£100	11·00
F38	5s. green	£130	11·00
	a. Yellow-green	£130	11·00
F39	6s. rose	£150	27·00
F40	7s. ultramarine	£160	40·00
F41	7s. 6d. bronze-grey	£160	45·00
F42	8s. deep blue	£160	40·00
F43	9s. orange	£150	45·00
F44	10s. brown-red	£140	12·00
	a. Maroon	£140	12·00
F45	£1 pink	£190	45·00

C. W 12c (4 mm). P 12½ (1890)
F46	2s. blue	75·00	11·00
F47	3s. mauve	£150	27·00
F48	4s. brown-red	£120	15·00
F49	5s. green	£140	12·00
F50	6s. rose	£160	27·00
F51	7s. ultramarine	£170	40·00
F52	8s. deep blue	£170	40·00
F53	9s. orange	£150	45·00
F54	10s. brown-red	£140	13·00
F55	15s. green	£250	60·00

D. Continuation of W 12b. P 11 (1895–1901)
F56	2s. blue	27·00	5·50
F57	2s. 6d. grey-brown	80·00	4·50
	a. Inscr "COUNTERPART" (1901)*	£150	£110
F58	3s. mauve	£100	5·50
F59	4s. brown-red	£100	10·00
F60	5s. yellow-green	£130	12·00
F61	6s. rose	£140	27·00
F62	7s. pale blue	£160	40·00
F63	7s. 6d. bronze-grey	£160	45·00
F64	8s. deep blue	£160	40·00
F65	9s. orange	£150	45·00
	a. Imperf between (horiz pair)	£700	
F66	10s. brown-red	£140	12·00
	a. Maroon	£140	12·00
F67	15s. green	£190	45·00
F68	£1 rose-pink	£190	45·00

*The plate normally printed in yellow and inscribed "COUNTERPART" just above the bottom value panel, for use on the counterparts of documents but was issued in error in the colour of the normal fiscal stamp and accepted for use.

E. W 43 (sideways)
(i) Unsurfaced "Cowan" paper. (a) P 11 (1903)
F69	2s. 6d. grey-brown	80·00	4·50
F70	3s. mauve	£100	5·50
F71	4s. orange-red	£100	10·00
F72	6s. rose	£140	27·00
F73	7s. pale blue	£160	40·00
F74	8s. deep blue	£150	40·00
F75	10s. brown-red	£130	14·00
	a. Maroon	£130	14·00
F76	15s. green	£190	45·00
F77	£1 rose-pink	£170	45·00

(b) P 14 (1906)
F78	2s. 6d. grey-brown	80·00	4·50
F79	3s. mauve	£100	5·50
F80	4s. orange-red	£100	7·50
F81	5s. yellow-green	70·00	7·50
F82	6s. rose	£140	27·00
F83	7s. pale blue	£150	40·00
F84	7s. 6d. bronze-grey	£150	45·00
F85	8s. deep blue	£150	40·00
F86	9s. orange	£140	45·00
F87	10s. maroon	£130	12·00
F88	15s. green	£190	45·00
F89	£1 rose-pink	£170	45·00

(c) P 14½ × 14, comb (clean-cut) (1907)
F90	2s. blue	25·00	4·00
F91	2s. 6d. grey-brown	80·00	4·50
F92	3s. mauve	£100	5·50
F93	4s. orange-red	90·00	7·50
F94	6s. rose	£140	27·00
F95	10s. maroon	£130	12·00
F96	15s. green	£170	45·00
F97	£1 rose-pink	£170	45·00

(ii) Chalk-surfaced "De La Rue" paper. (a) P 14 (1913)
F 98	2s. blue	25·00	4·00
F 99	2s. 6d. grey-brown	27·00	4·50
F100	3s. purple	70·00	5·50
F101	4s. orange-red	70·00	7·00
F102	5s. yellow-green	70·00	7·50
F103	6s. rose	£100	14·00
F104	7s. pale blue	£100	15·00
F105	7s. 6d. bronze-grey	£150	45·00
F106	8s. deep blue	£130	24·00
F107	9s. orange	£140	45·00
F108	10s. maroon	£130	12·00
F109	15s. green	£170	40·00
F110	£1 rose-carmine	£170	45·00

(b) P 14½ × 14, comb (1913–21)
F111	2s. deep blue	25·00	4·00
F112	2s. 6d. grey-brown	27·00	4·50
F113	3s. purple	70·00	5·50
F114	4s. orange-red	70·00	7·00
F115	5s. yellow-green	70·00	7·50
F116	6s. rose	£100	14·00
F117	7s. pale blue	£100	15·00
F118	8s. deep blue	£130	24·00
F119	9s. orange	£130	45·00
F120	10s. maroon	£130	12·00
F121	12s. 6d. deep plum (1921)	£2500	£750
F122	15s. green	£170	40·00
F123	£1 rose-carmine	£170	45·00

The "De La Rue" paper has a smooth finish and has toned gum which is strongly resistant to soaking.

(iii) Chalk-surfaced "Jones" paper. P 14½ × 14, comb (1924)
F124	2s. deep blue	30·00	4·00
F125	2s. 6d. deep grey-brown	32·00	4·50
F126	3s. purple	80·00	5·50
F127	5s. yellow-green	80·00	7·50
F128	10s. brown-red	£140	12·00
F129	12s. 6d deep purple	£2500	£750
F130	15s. green	£190	40·00

The "Jones" paper has a coarser texture, is poorly surfaced and the ink tends to peel. The outline of the watermark commonly shows on the surface of the stamp. The gum is colourless or only slightly toned and washes off readily.

(iv) Thick, opaque, chalk-surfaced "Cowan" paper. P 14½ × 14, comb (1925–30)
F131	2s. blue	25·00	4·00
F132	2s. 6d. deep grey-brown	27·00	4·50
F133	3s. mauve	£100	10·00

F134	4s. orange-red	..	..	70·00	7·00
F135	5s. yellow-green	..	..	70·00	7·50
F136	6s. rose	..	..	£100	14·00
F137	7s. pale blue	..	..	£100	15·00
F138	8s. deep blue	..	..	£130	24·00
	a. Error. Blue (as 2s.) (1930)		..	£500	
F139	10s. brown-red	..	..	£130	12·00
F140	12s. 6d. blackish purple	..		£2500	£750
F141	15s. green	..	..	£170	40·00
F142	£1 rose-pink	..	..	£170	45·00

The "Cowan" paper is white and opaque and the watermark, which is usually smaller than in the "Jones" paper, is often barely visible.

(v) Thin, hard, chalk-surfaced "Wiggins Teape" paper. P 14½ × 14, comb (1926)

F143	4s. orange-red	..	..	75·00	7·00
F144	£1 rose-pink	..	..	£180	80·00

The "Wiggins Teape" paper has a vertical mesh with narrow watermark, whereas other chalk-surfaced papers with this perforation have a horizontal mesh and wider watermark.

F 6   (F 7)

(Des H. L. Richardson. Typo Govt Ptg Office)

1931–40. *As Type F 6 (various frames). W 43. P 14.*

(i) Thick, opaque, chalk-surfaced "Cowan" paper, with horizontal mesh (1931–35)

F145	1s. 3d. lemon (4.31)	..	..	10·00	35·00
F146	1s. 3d. orange-yellow	..	..	4·00	3·25
F147	2s. 6d. deep brown	..	..	13·00	2·75
F148	4s. red	..	..	14·00	3·50
F149	5s. green	..	..	15·00	5·00
F150	6s. carmine-rose	..	..	24·00	8·50
F151	7s. blue	..	..	27·00	12·00
F152	7s. 6d. olive-grey	..	..	55·00	70·00
F153	8s. slate-violet	..	..	28·00	23·00
F154	9s. brown-orange	..	..	30·00	23·00
F155	10s. carmine-lake	..	..	24·00	7·50
F156	12s. 6d. deep plum (9.35)	..	..	£140	£140
F157	15s. sage-green	..	..	60·00	18·00
F158	£1 pink	..	..	60·00	15·00
F159	25s. greenish blue	..	..	£225	£325
F160	30s. brown (1935)	..	..	£250	£120
F161	35s. orange-yellow	..	..	£2000	£2250
F162	£2 bright purple	..	..	£300	55·00
F163	£2 10s. red	..	..	£180	£225
F164	£3 green	..	..	£300	£150
F165	£3 10s. rose (1935)	..	..	£1200	£950
F166	£4 light blue (1935)	..	..	£300	£120
F167	£4 10s. deep olive-grey (1935)	..	£1300	£1000
F168	£5 indigo-blue	..	..	£325	90·00

(ii) Thin, hard "Wiggins Teape" paper with vertical mesh (1936–40)

(a) Chalk-surfaced (1936–39)

F169	1s. 3d. pale orange-yellow	..	..	4·50	1·50
F170	2s. 6d. dull brown	..	..	19·00	1·60
F171	4s. pale red-brown	..	..	30·00	3·75
F172	5s. green	..	..	30·00	5·00
F173	6s. carmine-rose	..	..	32·00	13·00
F174	7s. pale blue	..	..	35·00	18·00
F175	8s. slate-violet	..	..	55·00	35·00
F176	9s. brown-orange	..	..	60·00	40·00
F177	10s. pale carmine-lake	..	..	50·00	6·50
F178	15s. sage-green	..	..	85·00	32·00
F179	£1 pink	..	..	70·00	23·00
F180	30s. brown (1.39)	..	..	£275	95·00
F181	35s. orange-yellow	..	..	£2500	£2500
F182	£2 bright purple (1937)	..	..	£325	60·00
F183	£3 green (1937)	..	..	£325	£150
F184	£5 indigo-blue (1937)	..	..	£400	£120

(b) Unsurfaced (1940)

F185	7s. 6d. olive-grey	..	..	£120	90·00

Not all values listed above were stocked at ordinary post offices as some of them were primarily required for fiscal purposes but all were valid for postage.

1939. *No. F161 surch with Type F 7.*

F186	35/- on 35s. orange-yellow	..	..	£325	£200

Because the 35s. orange-yellow could so easily be confused with the 1s. 3d. in the same colour it was surcharged.

1940 (June). *New values surch as Type F 7. W 43. "Wiggins Teape" chalk-surfaced paper. P 14.*

F187	3/6 on 3s. 6d. grey-green	..	..	40·00	12·00
F188	5/6 on 5s. 6d. lilac	..	..	55·00	32·00
F189	11/- on 11s. yellow	..	..	£110	75·00
F190	22/- on 22s. scarlet	..	..	£250	£180
F187/90			Set of 4	£400	£250

These values were primarily needed for fiscal purposes.

1940–58. *As Type F 6 (various frames). W 98.*

(i) P 14. "Wiggins Teape" chalk-surfaced paper with vertical mesh (1940–56)

F191	1s. 3d. orange-yellow	..	..	4·00	80
F192	1s. 3d. yell & blk (wmk inverted) (14.6.55)	1·00	30
	b. Error. Yellow & bl (wmk inverted) (7.56)	3·00	5·50
F193	2s. deep brown	..	..	5·00	30
F194	4s. red-brown	..	..	11·00	50
F195	5s. green	..	..	12·00	60
F196	6s. carmine-rose	..	..	25·00	2·50
F197	7s. pale blue	..	..	27·00	4·25
F198	7s. 6d. olive-grey (wmk inverted) (21.12.50)	55·00	48·00
F199	8s. slate-violet	..	..	35·00	16·00
F200	9s. brown-orange (1.46)	..	..	20·00	28·00
F201	10s. carmine-lake	..	..	20·00	2·25
F202	15s. sage-green	..	..	38·00	17·00
F203	£1 pink	..	..	24·00	3·50
F204	25s. greenish blue (1946)	..	..	£300	£325

F205	30s. brown (1946)	..	..	£190	95·00
F206	£2 bright purple (1946)	..	..	70·00	18·00
F207	£2 10s. red (wmk inverted) (9.8.51)	..	£225	£190
F208	£3 green (1946)	..	..	85·00	45·00
F209	£3 10s. rose (11.48)	..	..	£1200	£1000
F210	£4 light blue (wmk inverted) (12.2.52)	£100	60·00
F211	£5 indigo-blue	..	..	£130	45·00
F191/211			Set of 21	£2250	£1600

THREE SHILLINGS	I.
THREE SHILLINGS	II.

3s. 6d.

Type I. Broad serifed capitals

Type II. Taller capitals, without serifs

Surcharged as Type F 7

F212	3/6 on 3s. 6d. grey-green (I) (1942)	..	20·00	5·00
F213	3/6 on 3s. 6d. grey-green (II) (6.53)	..	12·00	27·00
F214	5/6 on 5s. 6d. lilac (1944)	..	..	22·00	12·00
F215	11/- on 11s. yellow (1942)	..	..	60·00	40·00
F216	22/- on 22s. scarlet (1945)	..	..	£180	£120
F212/16			Set of 5	£250	£180

(ii) P 14 × 13½. "Wiggins Teape" unsurfaced paper with horizontal mesh (1956–58)

F217	1s. 3d. yellow and black (11.56)	..	1·50	1·00
F218	£1 pink (20.10.58)	..	..	32·00	15·00

No. F192b had the inscription printed in blue in error but as many as 378,000 were printed.

From about 1949–53 inferior paper had to be used and for technical reasons it was necessary to feed the paper into the machine in a certain way which resulted in whole printings with the watermark inverted for most values. These are fully listed in the *New Zealand Concise Catalogue*. In the above list the prices are for the cheapest form.

F 8

1967 (10 July). *Decimal currency. W 98 (sideways). Unsurfaced paper. P 14.*

F219	F 8	$4 deep reddish violet	..	2·00	55
F220		$6 emerald	..	3·00	1·50
F221		$8 light greenish blue	..	4·00	3·50
F222		$10 deep ultramarine	..	5·00	3·50
F219/22			Set of 4	12·50	8·00

The original printings were line perf on paper with the sideways watermark inverted ("N Z" to right of star when viewed from the front). From 1968 the stamps were comb perforated with the sideways watermark normal. The prices quoted are for the cheaper printings. Both are listed in the *New Zealand Concise Catalogue*.

1986 (Apr). *As Nos. F220/2 but without wmk. Chalk-surfaced paper.*

F223	F 8	$6 bright green	..	5·50	5·50
F224		$8 light greenish blue	..	7·00	8·00
F225		$10 deep ultramarine	..	8·00	9·00
F223/5			Set of 3	18·00	20·00

No further printings were made of the $4 after the introduction of a $5 postage stamp in 1981.

ANTARCTIC EXPEDITIONS

VICTORIA LAND

These issues were made under authority of the New Zealand Postal Department and, while not strictly necessary, they actually franked correspondence to New Zealand. They were sold to the public at a premium.

1908 (15 Jan). *Shackleton Expedition. T 42 of New Zealand (p 14), optd "King Edward VII Land", in two lines, reading up, by Coulls, Culling and Co., Wellington.*

A1	1d. rose-carmine (No. 356 Royle) (G.)	..	£400	35·00
	a. Opt double	..	..	—	£1500
A1b	1d. rose-carmine (No. 352c Waterlow) (G.)	..	£1300	£800

Nos. A1/1b were used on board the expedition ship, *Nimrod*, and at the Cape Royds base in McMurdo Sound. Due to adverse conditions Shackleton landed in Victoria Land rather than King Edward VII Land the intended destination.

1911 (9 Feb)–13. *Scott Expedition. Stamps of New Zealand optd "VICTORIA LAND.", in two lines by Govt Printer, Wellington.*

A2	50	½d. deep green (No. 387aa) (18.1.13)	..	£500	£500
A3	52	1d. carmine (No. 405)	..	45·00	75·00
		a. No stop after "LAND"	..	£375	£550

Nos. A2/3 were used at the Cape Evans base on McMurdo Sound or on the *Terra Nova*.

ROSS DEPENDENCY

This comprises a sector of the Antarctic continent and a number of islands. It was claimed by Great Britain on 30 July 1923 and soon afterward put under the jurisdiction of New Zealand.

1 H.M.S. *Erebus*

2 Shackleton and Scott

3 Map of Ross Dependency and New Zealand

4 Queen Elizabeth II

(Des E. M. Taylor (3d.), L. C. Mitchell (4d.), R. Smith (8d.), J.Berry (1s. 6d.). Recess D.L.R.)

1957 (11 Jan). *W 98 of New Zealand (Mult N Z and Star). P 13 (1s. 6d.) or 14 (others).*

1	1	3d. indigo	..	2·50	75
2	2	4d. carmine-red	..	2·50	75
3	3	8d. bright carmine-red and ultramarine	2·50	1·00
		a. Bright carmine-red and blue	..	7·50	6·00
4	4	1s. 6d. slate-purple	..	2·50	1·25
1/4			Set of 4	9·00	3·25

(New Currency. 100 cents = 1 dollar)

5 H.M.S. *Erebus*

1967 (10 July). *Decimal currency. As Nos. 1/4 but with values inscr in decimal currency as T 5. Chalky paper (except 15 c.). W 98 of New Zealand (sideways on 7 c.). P 13 (15 c.) or 14 (others).*

5	5	2 c. indigo	..	8·00	4·75
		a. Deep blue	..	12·00	7·00
6	2	3 c. carmine-red	..	7·00	4·75
7	3	7 c. bright carmine-red and ultramarine	11·00	7·50
8	4	15 c. slate-purple	..	12·00	12·00
5/8			Set of 4	35·00	26·00

6 McCormick's Skua   7 Scott Base

(Des M. Cleverley. Litho B.W.)

1972 (18 Jan)–79. *Horiz design as T 6 (3 to 8 c.) or 7 (10, 18 c.). Ordinary paper. P 14½ × 14 (10, 18 c.) or 13 (others).*

9		3 c. black, brownish grey and pale blue	..	1·25	1·25
		a. Chalk-surfaced paper (2.79)	..	65	90
10		4 c. black, royal blue and violet	..	80	1·00
		a. Chalk-surfaced paper (2.79)	..	40	90
11		5 c. black, brownish grey and rose-lilac	..	70	1·00
		a. Chalk-surfaced paper (2.79)	..	30	90
12		8 c. black, yellow-brown and brownish grey	70	1·10
		a. Chalk-surfaced paper (2.79)	..	40	90
13		10 c. black, turquoise-green and slate-green	..	1·00	1·50
		a. Perf 13½ × 13. Chalk-surfaced paper (2.79)	40	1·00
14		18 c. black, violet and bright violet	..	2·25	2·50
		a. Perf 13½ × 13. Chalk-surfaced paper (2.79)	50	1·40
9/14			Set of 6	6·00	7·50
9a/14a			Set of 6	2·40	5·50

Designs:—4 c. "Hercules" aeroplane at Williams Field; 5 c. Shackleton's Hut; 8 c. Supply ship H.M.N.Z.S. *Endeavour*; 18 c. Tabular ice floe.

8 Adelie Penguins

(Des R. Conly. Litho Asher and Co, Melbourne)

1982 (20 Jan). *Horiz designs as T 8. Multicoloured. P 15½.*

15		5 c. Type 8	..	..	75	60
16		10 c. Tracked vehicles	..	..	40	30
17		20 c. Scott Base	..	..	50	30
18		30 c. Field party	..	..	50	30
19		40 c. Vanda Station	..	..	50	30
20		50 c. Scott's hut, Cape Evans	..	55	35
15/20			Set of 6	2·75	1·75

The post office at Scott Base closed on 30 September 1987 and Nos. 15/20 were withdrawn from sale at philatelic counters in New Zealand on 31 December 1987. Local stamps were subsequently issued by the Armed Forces Canteen Council to cover the cost of mail carriage from Scott Base to New Zealand. These are not listed as they had no national or international validity.

TOKELAU

Formerly known as the Union Islands, and administered as part of the Gilbert and Ellice Islands Colony, they were transferred to New Zealand on 4 November 1925 and then administered by Western Samoa. The islands were finally incorporated in New Zealand on 1 January 1949 and became a dependency. The name Tokelau was adopted on 7 May 1946.

Stamps of GILBERT AND ELLICE ISLANDS were used in Tokelau from February 1911 until June 1926 when they were replaced by those of SAMOA. These were current until 1948.
The post office on Atafu opened in 1911, but the cancellations for the other two islands, Fakaofo and Nukunono, did not appear until 1926.

1 Atafu Village and Map

(Des J. Berry from photographs by T. T. C. Humphrey. Recess B.W.)

1948 (22 June). *T* 1 *and similar horiz designs. Wmk T* 98 *of New Zealand (Mult N Z and Star). P* 13½.
1	½d. red-brown and purple	..	..	15	20
2	1d. chestnut and green	..	..	15	20
3	2d. green and ultramarine	..	..	15	20
1/3			*Set of 3*	40	55

Designs:–1d. Nukunono hut and map; 2d. Fakaofo village and map.
Covers are known postmarked 16 June 1948, but this was in error for 16 July.

1953 (15 June*). *Coronation. As No.* 715 *of New Zealand, but inscr* "TOKELAU ISLANDS".
4	164	3d. brown	..	3·00	3·00

*This is the date of issue in Tokelau. The stamps were released in New Zealand on 25 May.

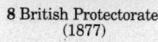

(4) (5)

1956 (27 Mar). *No.* 1 *surch with T* 4 *by Govt Printer, Wellington.*
5	1	1s. on ½d. red-brown and purple	..	4·00	3·50

1966 (8 Nov). *Postal fiscal stamps of New Zealand (Type F* 6), *but without value, surch as T* 5 *by Govt Printer, Wellington. W* 98 *of New Zealand. P* 14.
6	6d. light blue	..	..	65	1·25
7	8d. light emerald	..	..	75	1·00
8	2s. light pink	..	..	85	1·40
6/8			*Set of 3*	2·00	3·25

(New Currency. 100 cents = 1 dollar (New Zealand))

(6) (7)

1967 (4 Sept*). *Decimal currency.*

(a) *Nos.* 1/3 *surch in decimal currency as T* 6 *by Govt Printer, Wellington*
9	1c. on 1d.	..	..	60	60
10	2 c. on 2d.	..	..	1·00	1·00
11	10 c. on ½d.	..	..	2·00	2·00

(b) *Postal Fiscal stamps of New Zealand (Type F* 6), *but without value, surch as T* 7 *by Govt Printer, Wellington. W* 98 *of New Zealand (sideways). P* 14 *(line or comb)*
12	F 6	3 c. reddish lilac	..	50	30
13		5 c. light blue	..	50	30
14		7 c. light emerald	..	50	30
15		20 c. light pink	..	65	40
9/15			*Set of 7*	5·25	4·50

*This is the date of issue in Tokelau. The stamps were released in New Zealand on 10 July.

8 British Protectorate (1877)

12 H.M.S. *Dolphin,* 1765

(Des New Zealand P.O. artists from suggestions by Tokelau Administration. Litho B.W.)

1969 (8 Aug). *History of Tokelau. T* 8 *and similar horiz designs. W* 98 *of New Zealand. P* 13 × 12½.
16	5 c. ultramarine, yellow and black	..		25	10
17	10 c. vermilion, yellow and black	..		30	10
18	15 c. green, yellow and black	..		35	15
19	20 c. yellow-brown, yellow and black	..		40	15
16/19			*Set of 4*	1·10	45

Designs:—10 c. Annexed to Gilbert and Ellice Islands, 1916; 15 c. New Zealand Administration, 1925; 20 c. New Zealand Territory, 1948.

1969 (1 Oct). *Christmas. As T* 301 *of New Zealand, but inscr* "TOKELAU ISLANDS". *W* 98 *of New Zealand. P* 13½ × 14½.
20	301	2 c. multicoloured	..	10	15

1970 (1 Oct). *Christmas. As T* 314 *of New Zealand but inscr* "TOKELAU ISLANDS". *P* 12½.
21	341	2 c. multicoloured	..	10	20

(Des D. B. Stevenson. Litho B.W.)

1970 (9 Dec). *Discovery of Tokelau. T* 12 *and similar multicoloured designs. P* 13½.
22	5 c. Type 12	..		1·50	35
23	10 c. H.M.S. Pandora, 1791	..		1·50	35
24	25 c. General Jackson, 1835 (horiz)	..		3·25	70
22/4			*Set of 3*	5·75	1·25

13 Fan

14 Windmill Pump

(Des Enid Hunter. Litho Harrison)

1971 (20 Oct). *Various horiz designs as T* 13 *showing handicrafts. Multicoloured. P* 14.
25	1 c. Type 13	..	..	20	20
26	2 c. Hand-bag	..	..	30	30
27	3 c. Basket	..	..	40	40
28	5 c. Hand-bag	..	..	50	65
29	10 c. Shopping-bag	..	..	60	80
30	15 c. Fishing box	..	..	1·00	1·50
31	20 c. Canoe	..	..	1·25	1·25
32	25 c. Fishing hooks	..	..	1·25	2·00
25/32			*Set of 8*	5·00	7·00

(Des A. G. Mitchell. Litho Questa)

1972 (6 Sept). *25th Anniversary of South Pacific Commission. T* 14 *and similar vert designs. Multicoloured. P* 14 × 13½.
33	5 c. Type 14	..	..	35	60
34	10 c. Community well	..	..	45	75
35	15 c. Pest eradication	..	..	55	1·00
36	20 c. Flags of member nations	..	..	60	1·25
33/6			*Set of 4*	1·75	3·25

On No. 35 "PACIFIC" is spelt "PACFIC".

15 Horny Coral

16 Hump-back Cowrie

(Des Eileen Mayo. Litho B.W.)

1973 (12 Sept). *Coral. T* 15 *and similar vert designs. Multicoloured P.* 13.
37	3 c. Type 15	..	..	1·00	80
38	5 c. Soft Coral	..	..	1·00	90
39	15 c. Mushroom Coral	..	..	1·75	1·50
40	25 c. Staghorn Coral	..	..	2·00	1·75
37/40	..		*Set of 4*	5·25	4·50

(Des G. F. Fuller. Litho Questa)

1974 (13 Nov). *"Shells of the Coral Reef". T* 16 *and similar horiz designs. Multicoloured. P* 14.
41	3 c. Type 16	..	..	1·25	1·25
42	5 c. Tiger Cowrie	..	..	1·50	1·50
43	15 c. Mole Cowrie	..	..	2·50	3·00
44	25 c. Eyed Cowrie	..	..	3·00	3·50
41/4			*Set of 4*	7·50	8·25

17 Moorish Idol

18 Canoe Building

(Des Eileen Mayo. Litho Questa)

1975 (19 Nov). *Fishes. T* 17 *and similar vert designs. Multicoloured. P* 14.
45	5 c. Type 17	..	..	50	1·00
46	10 c. Long-nosed Butterfly-fish	..		70	1·25
47	15 c. Lined Butterfly-fish	..		85	1·75
48	25 c. Red Fire-fish	..		1·10	2·00
45/8	..		*Set of 4*	2·75	5·50

(Des F. Paulo. Litho Questa)

1976 (27 Oct)–81. *T* 18 *and similar multicoloured designs showing local life. P* 14 × 13½ *(9 c. to $1) or* 13½ × 14 *(others).*
49	1 c. Type 18	..		20	50
	a. Perf 14½ × 15 (15.7.81)			10	15
50	2 c. Reef fishing	..		20	1·00
51	3 c. Weaving preparation	..		25	50
	a. Perf 14½ × 15 (15.7.81)			10	15
52	5 c. Umu (kitchen)	..		30	50
	a. Perf 14½ × 15 (15.7.81)			10	15
53	9 c. Carving (vert)	..		10	55
	a. Perf 15 × 14½ (15.7.81)			10	15
54	20 c. Husking coconuts (vert)	..		15	45
	a. Perf 15 × 14½ (15.7.81)			15	20
55	50 c. Wash day (vert)	..		20	70
	a. Perf 15 × 14½ (15.7.81)			20	20
56	$1 Meal time (vert)	..		35	1·50
	a. Perf 15 × 14½ (15.7.81)			20	20
49/56	..		*Set of 8*	1·25	5·00
49a/56a	..		*Set of 7*	95	1·10

19 White Tern

20 Westminster Abbey

(Des F. Paulo. Litho Questa)

1977 (16 Nov). *Birds of Tokelau. T* 19 *and similar horiz designs. Multicoloured. P* 14½.
57	8 c. Type 19	..	..	30	40
58	10 c. Turnstone	..	..	35	45
59	15 c. White-capped Noddy	..	..	60	70
60	30 c. Common Noddy	..	..	90	1·25
57/60	..		*Set of 4*	2·00	2·50

(Des Eileen Mayo. Litho Questa)

1978 (28 June). *25th Anniv of Coronation. T* 20 *and similar vert designs. Multicoloured. P* 14.
61	8 c. Type 20	..	..	20	20
62	10 c. King Edward's Chair	..		20	20
63	15 c. Coronation regalia	..		30	35
64	30 c. Queen Elizabeth II	..		50	60
61/4	..		*Set of 4*	1·10	1·25

21 Canoe Race

22 Rugby

(Des F. Paulo. Photo Heraclio Fournier)

1978 (8 Nov). *Canoe Racing. T* 21 *and similar horiz designs showing races. P* 13½ × 14.
65	8 c. multicoloured	..	..	20	20
66	12 c. multicoloured	..	..	25	25
67	15 c. multicoloured	..	..	30	30
68	30 c. multicoloured	..	..	50	50
65/8	..		*Set of 4*	1·10	1·10

(Des F. Paulo. Photo Heraclio Fournier)

1979 (7 Nov). *Sports. T* 22 *and similar horiz designs. Multicoloured. P* 13½.
69	10 c. Type 22	..	..	15	15
70	15 c. Cricket	..	..	40	60
71	20 c. Rugby (different)	..		40	65
72	30 c. Cricket (different)	..		60	80
69/72			*Set of 4*	1·40	2·00

23 Surfing

24 Pole Vaulting

(Des F. Paulo. Litho J.W.)

1980 (5 Nov). *Water Sports. T* 23 *and similar horiz designs. Multicoloured. P* 13.
73	10 c. Type 23	..	..	10	10
74	20 c. Surfing (different)	..		15	15
75	30 c. Swimming	..	..	20	25
76	50 c. Swimming (different)	..		25	35
73/6	..		*Set of 4*	60	60

(Des F. Paulo. Photo Heraclio Fournier)

1981 (4 Nov). *Sports. T* **24** *and similar vert designs. Multicoloured. P* 14 × 13½.

77	10 c. Type **24**	10	10
78	20 c. Volleyball	20	20
79	30 c. Running	25	30
80	50 c. Volleyball (*different*)	30	35
77/80	*Set of* 4	75	85

25 Wood Carving   26 Octopus Lure

(Des R. Conly. Litho Enschedé)

1982 (5 May). *Handicrafts. T* **25** *and similar vert designs. Multicoloured. P* 14 × 13½.

81	10 s. Type **25**	10	10
82	22 s. Bow-drilling sea shell	15	25
83	34 s. Bowl finishing	20	35
84	60 s. Basket weaving	35	50
81/4	*Set of* 4	70	1·10

(Des R. Conly. Litho Questa)

1982 (3 Nov). *Fishing Methods. T* **26** *and similar vert designs. Multicoloured. P* 14.

85	5 c. Type **26**	15	10
86	18 s. Multiple-hook fishing	35	20
87	23 s. Ruvettus fishing	40	25
88	34 s. Netting flying fish	45	30
89	63 s. Noose fishing	55	40
90	75 s. Bonito fishing	60	45
85/90	*Set of* 6	2·25	1·50

27 Outrigger Canoe   28 Javelin Throwing

(Des R. Conly. Litho Cambec Press, Melbourne)

1983 (4 May). *Transport. T* **27** *and similar horiz designs. Multicoloured. P* 13 × 13½.

91	5 s. Type **27**	10	10
92	18 s. Wooden whaleboat	15	15
93	23 s. Aluminium whaleboat	15	20
94	34 s. *Alia* (fishing catamaran)	25	25
95	63 s. M.V. *Frysna* (freighter)	35	40
96	75 s. McKinnon "Goose" flying boat	45	50
91/6	*Set of* 6	1·25	1·40

(Des R. Conly. Litho Questa)

1983 (2 Nov). *Traditional Pastimes. T* **28** *and similar horiz designs. Multicoloured. P* 14.

97	5 s. Type **28**	10	10
98	18 s. String game	15	15
99	23 s. Fire making	15	20
100	34 s. Shell throwing	25	25
101	63 s. Hand-ball game	35	40
102	75 s. Mass wrestling	45	50
97/102	*Set of* 6	1·25	1·40

29 Planting and Harvesting   30 Convict Tang ("Manini")

(Des R. Conly. Litho J.W.)

1984 (2 May). *Copra Industry. T* **29** *and similar vert designs. Multicoloured. P* 13½ × 13.

103	48 s. Type **29**	40	45
	a. Horiz strip of 5. Nos. 103/7	1·90	
104	48 s. Husking and splitting	40	45
105	48 s. Drying	40	45
106	48 s. Bagging	40	45
107	48 s. Shipping	40	45
103/7	*Set of* 5	1·90	2·00

Nos. 103/7 were printed together, *se-tenant*, in horizontal strips of 5 throughout the sheet.

(Des R. Conly. Litho B.D.T.)

1984 (5 Dec). *Fishes. T* **30** *and similar horiz designs. Multicoloured. P* 15 × 14.

108	1 s. Type **30**	10	10
109	2 s. Flying Fish ("Hahave")	10	10
110	5 s. Fire Wrasse ("Uloulo")	10	10
111	9 s. Unicorn Fish ("Ume ihu")	10	10
112	23 s. Napoleon Fish ("Lafilafi")	15	20

113	34 s. Red Snapper ("Fagamea")	20	25
114	50 s. Yellow Fin Tuna ("Kakahi")	35	40
115	75 s. Castor-oil Fish ("Palu po")	50	55
116	$1 Grey Shark ("Mokoha")	65	70
117	$2 Black Marlin ("Hakula")	1·25	1·40
108/17	*Set of* 10	3·00	3·25

Examples of Nos. 108/17 are known postmarked at Nukunonu on 23 November 1984.

The 50 s., No. 114 was sold at the "STAMPEX 86" Stamp Exhibition, Adelaide, overprinted "STAMPEX 86 4–10 AUGUST 1986" in three lines. These overprinted stamps were not available from post offices in Tokelau. Used examples come from dealers' stocks subsequently sent to the islands for cancellation.

31 *Ficus tinctoria* ("Mati")   32 Administration Centre, Atafu

(Des R. Conly. Litho Wyatt and Wilson Ltd, Christchurch, N.Z.)

1985 (26 June). *Native Trees. T* **31** *and similar vert designs. Multicoloured. P* 13.

118	5 c. Type **31**	10	10
119	18 c. *Morinda citrifolia* ("Nonu")	15	15
120	32 c. Breadfruit Tree ("Ulu")	20	25
121	48 c. *Pandanus tectorius* ("Fala")	35	40
122	60 c. *Cordia subcordata* ("Kanava")	40	45
123	75 c. Coconut Palm ("Niu")	50	55
118/23	*Set of* 6	1·50	1·60

Nos. 118/23 were issued with matt, almost invisible PVA gum.

(Des R. Conly. Litho Questa)

1985 (4 Dec). *Tokelau Architecture (1st series). Public Buildings. T* **32** *and similar horiz designs. Multicoloured. P* 14.

124	5 c. Type **32**	10	10
125	18 c. Administration Centre, Nukunonu	15	15
126	32 c. Administration Centre, Fakaofo	20	25
127	48 c. Congregational Church, Atafu	35	40
128	60 c. Catholic Church, Nukunonu	40	45
129	75 c. Congregational Church, Fakaofo	50	55
124/9	*Set of* 6	1·50	1·60

33 Atafu Hospital

(Des R. Conly. Litho Cambec Press, Melbourne)

1986 (7 May). *Tokelau Architecture (2nd series). Hospitals and Schools. T* **33** *and similar horiz designs. Multicoloured. P* 13½.

130	5 c. Type **33**	10	10
131	18 c. St. Joseph's Hospital, Nukunonu	10	10
132	32 c. Fenuafala Hospital, Fakaofo	20	25
133	48 c. Matauala School, Atafu	35	40
134	60 c. Matiti School, Nukunonu	40	45
135	75 c. Fenuafala School, Fakaofo	55	60
130/5	*Set of* 6	1·50	1·60

34 Coconut Crab

(Des R. Conly. Litho Questa)

1986 (3 Dec). *Agricultural Livestock. T* **34** *and similar horiz designs. Multicoloured. P* 14.

136	5 c. Type **34**	10	10
137	18 c. Pigs	15	15
138	32 c. Chickens	25	25
139	48 c. Reef Hawksbill Turtle	40	40
140	60 c. Goats	45	45
141	75 c. Ducks	60	60
136/41	*Set of* 6	1·75	1·75

35 *Scaevola taccada* ("Gahu")

(Des R. Conly. Litho Questa)

1987 (6 May). *Tokelau Flora. T* **35** *and similar horiz designs. Multicoloured. P* 14.

142	5 c. Type **35**	35	35
143	18 c. *Hernandia nymphaeifolia* ("Puka")	60	60
144	32 c. *Pandanus tectorius* ("Higano")	90	90
145	48 c. *Gardenia taitensis* ("Tialetiale")	1·10	1·10
146	60 c. *Pemphis acidula* ("Gagie")	1·40	1·40
147	75 c. *Guettarda speciosa* ("Puapua")	1·50	1·50
142/7	*Set of* 6	5·25	5·25

36 Javelin-throwing

(Des F. Paulo. Litho Leigh-Mardon Ltd, Melbourne)

1987 (2 Dec). *Tokelau Olympic Sports. T* **36** *and similar horiz designs. Multicoloured. P* 14 × 14½.

148	5 c. Type **36**	20	20
149	18 c. Shot-putting	40	40
150	32 c. Long jumping	60	60
151	48 c. Hurdling	75	75
152	60 c. Sprinting	1·00	1·00
153	75 c. Wrestling	1·25	1·25
148/53	*Set of* 6	3·75	3·75

37 Small Boat Flotilla in Sydney Harbour   38 Island Maps and Ministerial Representatives

(Des and litho CPE Australia Ltd, Melbourne)

1988 (30 July). *Bicentenary of Australian Settlement and "Sydpex '88" National Stamp Exhibition, Sydney. T* **37** *and similar square designs. Multicoloured. P* 13.

154	50 c. Type **37**	1·00	1·00
	a. Horiz strip of 5. Nos. 154/8	4·50	
155	50 c. Sailing ships and liners	1·00	1·00
156	50 c. Sydney skyline and Opera House	1·00	1·00
157	50 c. Sydney Harbour Bridge	1·00	1·00
158	50 c. Sydney waterfront	1·00	1·00
154/8	*Set of* 5	4·50	4·50

Nos. 154/8 were printed together, *se-tenant*, in horizontal strips of five throughout the sheet, forming a composite aerial view of the re-enactment of First Fleet's arrival.

(Des F. Paulo. Litho Leigh-Mardon Ltd, Melbourne)

1988 (10 Aug). *Political Development. T* **38** *and similar horiz designs. Multicoloured. P* 14½.

159	5 c. Type **38** (administration transferred to N.Z. Foreign Affairs Ministry, 1975)	10	10
160	18 c. General Fono (island assembly) meeting, 1977	15	15
161	32 c. Arms of New Zealand (first visit by New Zealand Prime Minister, 1985)	20	25
162	48 c. U.N. logo (first visit by U.N. representative, 1976)	35	40
163	60 c. Canoe and U.N. logo (first Tokelau delegation to U.N., 1987)	40	45
164	75 c. Secretary and N.Z. flag (first islander appointed as Official Secretary, 1987)	50	55
159/64	*Set of* 6	1·50	1·60

39 Three Wise Men in Canoe and Star

(Des F. Paulo. Litho Govt Ptg Office, Wellington)

1988 (7 Dec). *Christmas. T* **39** *and similar horiz designs showing Christmas in Tokelau. Multicoloured. P* 13½.

165	5 c. Type **39**	10	10
166	20 c. Tokelau Nativity	20	20
167	40 c. Flight to Egypt by canoe	35	35
168	60 c. Children's presents	45	45
169	70 c. Christ child in Tokelauan basket	55	55
170	$1 Christmas parade	75	75
165/70	*Set of* 6	2·10	2·10

40 Launching Outrigger Canoe   41 Basketwork

(Des F. Paulo. Litho Leigh-Mardon Ltd, Melbourne)

1989 (28 June). *Food Gathering. T* **40** *and similar horiz designs. Multicoloured. P* 14×14½.

171	50 c. Type **40**	..	85	85
	a. Horiz strip of 3. Nos. 171/3	..	2·25	
172	50 c. Paddling canoe away from shore		85	85
173	50 c. Fishing punt and sailing canoe	..	85	85
174	50 c. Canoe on beach	..	85	85
	a. Horiz strip of 3. Nos. 174/6	..	2·25	
175	50 c. Loading coconuts into canoe	..	85	85
176	50 c. Tokelauans with produce	..	85	85
171/6		*Set of* 6	4·50	4·50

Nos. 171/3 and 174/6 were each printed together, *se-tenant*, in horizontal strips of three throughout the sheets, forming composite designs.

A $3 miniature sheet commemorating the 150th anniversary of the Penny Black and "Stamp World London 90" International Stamp Exhibition exists, but was not issued or used by the New Zealand Post offices on the islands.

(Litho Leigh-Mardon Ltd, Melbourne)

1990 (2 May). *Women's Handicrafts. T* **41** *and similar horiz designs. Multicoloured. P* 14½.

177	5 c. Type **41**	..	..	30	30
178	20 c. Preparing cloth	..	..	65	65
179	40 c. Tokelau fabrics	..	..	90	90
180	60 c. Mat weaving	..	..	1·40	1·40
181	80 c. Weaving palm fronds	..	..	1·75	1·75
182	$1 Basket making	..	..	1·90	1·90
177/82		..	*Set of* 6	6·25	6·25

42 Man with Adze and Wood
Blocks   43 Swimming

(Des F. Paulo. Litho Wyatt & Wilson, Christchurch)

1990 (1 Aug). *Men's Handicrafts. T* **42** *and similar horiz designs. Multicoloured. P* 13½.

183	50 c. Type **42**	..	85	85
	a. Horiz strip of 3. Nos. 183/5	..	2·25	
184	50 c. Making fishing boxes	..	85	85
185	50 c. Fixing handles to fishing boxes	..	85	85
186	50 c. Two men decorating fishing boxes	..	85	85
	a. Horiz strip of 3. Nos. 186/8	..	2·25	
187	50 c. Canoe building (two men)	..	85	85
188	50 c. Canoe building (three men)	..	85	85
183/8		*Set of* 6	4·50	4·50

Nos. 183/5 and 186/8 were each printed together, *se-tenant*, in horizontal strips of 3 throughout the sheets, and have matt, almost invisible, gum.

Under the terms of the Tokelau Post Office Regulations which came into force on 1 March 1991 the responsibility for providing postage stamps for the islands passed from New Zealand Post to the Administrator of Tokelau, based at the Ministry of External Relations, Wellington.

(Des R. Roberts. Litho Southern Colour Print, Dunedin)

1992 (8 July). *Olympic Games, Barcelona. T* **43** *and similar vert designs. Multicoloured. P* 13½.

189	40 c. Type **43**	..	..	..	35	35
190	60 c. Longjumping	..	..	..	50	50
191	$1 Volleyball	..	..	..	80	80
192	$1.80, Running	..	..	..	1·50	1·50
189/92			*Set of* 4		2·75	2·75

44 Santa Maria

(Des R. Roberts. Litho Southern Colour Print, Dunedin)

1992 (18 Dec). *500th Anniv of Discovery of America by Columbus. T* **44** *and similar horiz designs. Multicoloured. P* 13½.

193	40 c. Type **44**	..	25	30
194	60 c. Christopher Columbus	..	40	45
195	$1.20, Fleet of Columbus	..	80	85
196	$1.80, Columbus landing in the New World	..	1·25	1·40
193/6	.. .. ..	*Set of* 4	2·50	2·75

Nigeria

LAGOS

A British Consul was established at Lagos during 1853 as part of the anti-slavery policy, but the territory was not placed under British administration until the treaty of August 1861. From 1866 Lagos was administered with Sierra Leone and from July 1874 as part of Gold Coast. It became a separate colony in January 1886.

Although a postal service had been established by the British G.P.O. in 1851 no postal markings were supplied to Lagos until 1859. The British G.P.O. retained control of the postal service until 1874, when it became the responsibility of the colonial authorities.

CROWNED-CIRCLE HANDSTAMPS

CC 1

CC1 CC 1 LAGOS (19.2.1859) .. .. *Price on cover* £1500

PRICES FOR STAMPS ON COVER	
Nos. 1/9	*from* × 6
Nos. 10/41	*from* × 5
No. 42	*from* × 15
Nos. 44/53	*from* × 5
Nos. 54/63	*from* × 4

PRINTERS. All the stamps of Lagos were typographed by D.L.R.

1

1874 (10 June)–**75.** *Wmk Crown CC. P 12½.*
1	1	1d. lilac-mauve..	..	..	50·00	28·00
2		2d. blue ..	..	..	50·00	26·00
3		3d. red-brown (3.75)	..	..	90·00	40·00
4		3d. red-brown and chestnut	..	75·00	48·00
5		4d. carmine ..	..	..	60·00	40·00
6		6d. blue-green ..	..	..	75·00	10·00
8		1s. orange (value 15½ mm) (3.75)	£300	£130
9		1s. orange (value 16½ mm)	£225	60·00
1/9		..	..	*Set of 6*	£475	£180

1876. *Wmk Crown CC. P 14.*
10	1	1d. lilac-mauve..	..	..	32·00	14·00
11		2d. blue ..	..	..	35·00	12·00
12		3d. red-brown	..	..	90·00	18·00
13		3d. chestnut	..	..	£110	30·00
14		4d. carmine	..	..	£160	11·00
		a. Wmk sideways	..	..	£850	£130
15		6d. green ..	..	..	75·00	6·00
16		1s. orange (value 16½ mm long)	£450	65·00
10/16		..	..	*Set of 6*	£750	£110

1882 (June). *Wmk Crown CA. P 14.*
17	1	1d. lilac-mauve..	..	..	15·00	10·00
18		2d. blue ..	..	..	£110	4·75
19		3d. chestnut	..	..	10·00	5·00
20		4d. carmine	..	..	£100	11·00
17/20		..	..	*Set of 4*	£200	28·00

1884 (Dec)–**86.** *New values and colours. Wmk Crown CA. P 14.*
21	1	½d. dull green (2.86)	..	..	75	20
22		1d. rose-carmine	..	..	85	25
23		2d. grey ..	..	..	38·00	5·00
24		4d. pale violet	..	..	70·00	8·50
25		6d. olive-green ..	..	..	5·00	22·00
26		1s. orange (3.85)	..	..	5·00	13·00
27		2s. 6d. olive-black (10.86)	..	£275	£250
28		5s. blue (10.86) ..	..	£450	£400
29		10s. purple-brown (10.86)	..	£1200	£800
21/9		..	*Set of 9*	£1800	£1300
27/9 Optd "Specimen"		*Set of 3*	£400	

We would warn collectors against clever forgeries of Nos. 27 to 29 on genuinely watermarked paper.

2½ PENNY   A

2½ PENNY   B

1887 (Mar)–**1902.** *Wmk Crown CA. P 14.*
30	1	2d. dull mauve and blue	..	1·25	1·00
31		2½d. ultramarine (A) (12.90)	..	1·25	1·75
		a. Larger letters of value (B) ..	..	18·00	17·00
		b. *Blue* (A)	..	..	80·00	50·00

32	1	3d. dull mauve and chestnut (4.91)	..	2·50	3·25
33		4d. dull mauve and black	..	2·00	1·75
34		5d. dull mauve and green (2.94)	..	2·00	11·00
35		6d. dull mauve and mauve	..	4·50	3·00
		a. *Dull mauve and carmine* (10.02)	..	4·50	12·00
36		7½d. dull mauve and carmine (2.94)	..	2·00	23·00
37		10d. dull mauve and yellow (2.94)	..	2·75	13·00
38		1s. yellow-green and black	..	3·00	14·00
		a. *Blue-green and black*	..	4·00	16·00
39		2s. 6d. green and carmine	..	22·00	55·00
40		5s. green and blue	..	32·00	95·00
41		10s. green and brown	..	60·00	£140
30/41		..	*Set of 12*	£120	£325
30/41 Optd "Specimen"		..	*Set of 12*	£250	

HALF PENNY

(2)   3

1893 (Aug). *No. 33 surch with T 2.*
42	1	½d. on 4d. dull mauve and black	..	2·75	2·50
		a. Surch double	..	..	55·00	55·00
		b. Surch treble	..	..	85·00	
		c. Error. ½d. on 2d. (No. 30)	..	—£11000	

There were four settings of this surcharge, a scarce setting in which "HALF PENNY" is 16½ mm and three others in which the length is 16 mm. Of No. 42c, one copy is known unused and one used.

1904 (22 Jan–Nov). *Wmk Crown CA. P 14.*
44	3	½d. dull green and green	..	1·50	5·50
45		1d. purple and black/*red*	..	60	15
46		2d. dull purple and blue	..	6·00	12·00
47		2½d. dull purple and blue/*blue* (B)	1·00	1·50
		a. Smaller letters of value as A	3·00	8·00
48		3d. dull purple and brown	..	1·00	2·75
49		6d. dull purple and mauve	..	35·00	10·00
50		1s. green and black	..	35·00	30·00
51		2s. 6d. green and carmine	..	80·00	£160
52		5s. green and blue	..	£150	£275
53		10s. green and brown (Nov)	..	£250	£750
44/53		..	*Set of 10*	£500	£1100
44/53 Optd "Specimen"		..	*Set of 10*	£200	

1904–06. *Wmk Mult Crown CA. Ordinary paper. P 14.*
54	3	½d. dull green and green (30.10.04)	..	4·50	1·75
		a. Chalk-surfaced paper (12.3.06)	..	4·25	1·75
55		1d. purple and black/*red* (22.10.04)	..	2·00	10
		a. Chalk-surfaced paper (21.9.05)	..	75	10
56		2d. dull purple and blue (2.05)	..	1·75	75
		a. Chalk-surfaced paper (25.9.06)	..	5·50	2·25
57		2½d. dull purple and blue/*blue* (B) (chalk-surfaced paper) (13.10.05)	..	1·50	15·00
		a. Smaller letters of values as A	..	55·00	£100
58		3d. dull purple and brown (27.4.05)	..	2·75	90
		a. Chalk-surfaced paper (2.8.06)	..	7·50	1·75
59		6d. dull purple and mauve (31.10.05)	..	3·75	1·25
		a. Chalk-surfaced paper (1.3.06)	..	3·75	1·25
60		1s. green and black (15.10.04)	..	3·50	5·00
		a. Chalk-surfaced paper (4.06)	..	9·00	2·25
61		2s. 6d. green and carmine (3.12.04)	..	10·00	24·00
		a. Chalk-surfaced paper (21.10.06)	..	17·00	24·00
62		5s. green and blue (1.05)	..	17·00	65·00
		a. Chalk-surfaced paper (21.10.06)	..	26·00	80·00
63		10s. green and brown (3.12.04)	..	48·00	£120
		a. Chalk-surfaced paper (12.3.06)	..	55·00	£120
54/63		..	*Set of 10*	80·00	£200

Lagos was incorporated into the Colony and Protectorate of Southern Nigeria, previously formed from Niger Coast Protectorate and part of the Niger Company territories, on 16 February 1906. Stamps of Lagos were then authorised for use throughout Southern Nigeria.

NIGER COAST PROTECTORATE

OIL RIVERS PROTECTORATE

A British consulate for the Bights of Benin and Biafra was established in 1849 on the off-shore Spanish island of Fernando Poo. In 1853 the appointment was divided with a consul for the Bight of Benin at Lagos. The consulate for the Bight of Biafra was transferred to Old Calabar in 1882.

A British protectorate was proclaimed over the coastal area, with the exceptions of the colony of Lagos and the centre of the Niger delta, in June 1885. It was not, however, until 1891 that steps were taken to set up an adminintration with a consul-general at Old Calabar and vice-consuls at some of the river ports.

The consulate-general at Old Calabar and the vice-consulates at Benin, Bonny, Brass, Forcados and Opobo acted as collection and distribution centres for mail from November 1891, but were not recognised as post offices until 20 July 1892.

For a few months from July 1892 local administrative handstamps, as Type Z 1, were in use either as obliterators or in conjunction with the c.d.s.

Z 1

These oval handstamps are usually found on the 1892 overprinted issue, but the following are known on unoverprinted stamps of Great Britain:

1892

BENIN

Stamps of GREAT BRITAIN *cancelled with oval postmark, Type* Z 1, *inscribed* "BENIN".
Z1	2½d. purple/*blue* (V.) ..	..	..	£1000

BONNY

Stamps of GREAT BRITAIN *cancelled with oval postmark, Type* Z 1, *inscribed* "BONNY".
Z2	2½d. purple/*blue* (V.) ..	..	..	

BRASS RIVER

Stamps of GREAT BRITAIN *cancelled with oval postmark, Type* Z 1, *inscribed* "BRASS".
Z3	2½d. purple/*blue* (Blk.)	..	..	£750

OLD CALABAR RIVER

Stamps of GREAT BRITAIN *cancelled with oval postmark, Type* Z 1, *inscribed* "OLD CALABAR".
Z4	2½d. purple/*blue* (Blk.)	..	..	

Stamps of GREAT BRITAIN *cancelled* "BRITISH VICE-CONSULATE OLD CALABAR" *within double-lined circle.*
Z5	2½d. purple/*blue* (V.) ..	..	..	£400
Z6	5d. dull purple and blue (V.)	..		

For later use of Type Z 1 and the circular Vice-Consulate marks see note beneath No. 6.

Z 2.

Unoverprinted stamps of Great Britain remained officially valid for postage in the Protectorate until 30 September 1892, but were available from post offices in the Niger Company Territories up to the end of 1899. The two areas were so closely linked geographically that offices in the Protectorate continued to accept letters franked with Great Britain stamps until the reorganisation of 1900. The listing below covers confirmed examples, known on cover or piece, the prices quoted being for the latter.

1892 to 1899

Stamps of GREAT BRITAIN *cancelled with circular postmarks as Type* Z 2.

BENIN RIVER
Z 7	2d. green and carmine		
Z 8	2½d. purple/*blue*		
Z 9	3d. purple/*yellow*		
Z10	5d. dull purple and blue		
Z11	1s. green		

BONNY RIVER
Z12	½d. vermilion		
Z13	2½d. purple/*blue*		£250
Z14	5d. dull purple and blue		£350
Z15	6d. deep purple/*red* ..		£350

BRASS RIVER
Z16	1½d. dull purple and green	..	
Z17	2½d. purple/*blue*		£850
Z17a	2½d. purple/*blue* (squared-circle cancellation)	
Z18	6d. purple/*red*		£700

FORCADOS RIVER
Z19	1d. lilac ..	..		£550
Z20	2½d. purple/*blue*		
Z21	5d. dull purple and blue (m/s cancellation)	
Z22	10d. dull purple and carmine		

OLD CALABAR RIVER
Z23	½d. vermilion..	..		£300
Z24	1d. lilac		£250
Z25	1½d. dull purple and green	..	
Z26	2d. green and vermilion		
Z27	2½d. purple/*blue*		£250
Z28	5d. dull purple and blue		
Z29	6d. purple/*red*		
Z30	1s. green		

OPOBO RIVER
Z31	2½d. purple/*blue*		
Z32	10d. dull purple and carmine	..	

Some later covers are known franked with G.B. stamps, but the origin of the stamps involved is uncertain.

PRICES FOR STAMPS ON COVER	
Nos. 1/6	*from* × 10
Nos. 7/36	*from* × 3
Nos. 37/44	
Nos. 45/50	*from* × 10
Nos. 51/6	*from* × 12
Nos. 57/65	*from* × 3
Nos. 66/73	*from* × 12

BRITISH PROTECTORATE

OIL RIVERS

(1)	(2)

1892 (20 July)**–94.** *Nos. 172, 197, 200/1, 207a and 211 of Great Britain optd by D.L.R. with T 1.*

1	½d. vermilion	5·50	4·50
2	1d. lilac	5·50	4·50
	a. Opt reversed "OIL RIVERS" at top	£4000	
	b. Bisected (½d.) (on cover)	† £2500	
3	2d. grey-green and carmine	14·00	8·00
	a. Bisected (1d.) (on cover)	† £4000	
4	2½d. purple/*blue*	6·50	2·00
5	5d. dull purple and blue (Die II (No. 207a))	7·50	7·50
	a. On Die I (No. 207)		
6	1s. dull green	45·00	55·00
1/6		Set of 6	75·00 70·00
1/6	H/S "Specimen"	Set of 6	£300

Nos. 2b and 3a were used at Bonny River during August and September 1894.

Die II of the 5d. shows thin vertical lines to the right of "5d.". On Die I there are square dots in this position.

OVAL HANDSTAMPS. In addition to Nos. Z1/4 postmarks as Type Z 1 are also known used on the 1892–94 overprinted issue from the following offices:

Bakana (Nos. 2, 4/6)
Benin (Nos. 1/6)
Bonny (No. 2)
Brass (Nos. 3/5)
Buguma (Nos. 4 and 6)
Old Calabar (No. 4)
Opobo (Nos. 1/3)
Sombreiro River (Nos. 1/6)

The Vice-Consulate marks, as Nos. Z5/6, are also known struck on examples of No. 4 from Bonny, Forcados or Old Calabar.

Nos. 2 to 6 surcharged locally

1893 (3 Sept). *Issued at Old Calabar. Surch with T 2 and then bisected.*

7	½d. on half of 1d. (R.)	£150	£140
	a. Unsevered pair	£450	£425
	ab. Surch inverted and dividing line reversed (unsevered pair)	— £6500	
	b. Surch reversed (dividing line running from left to right) (unsevered pair)	— £6500	
	c. Straight top to "1" in "½"	£350	£350
	d. "½" omitted		
	e. Surch double (unsevered pair with normal)	— £1500	
	f. *Se-tenant* pair. Nos. 7a/8a	— £8500	
8	½d. on half of 1d. (V.)	£3000	£2750
	a. Unsevered pair	£7000	£6500
	b. Surch double (pair)	£10000	

The surcharge was applied in a setting covering one horizontal row at a time. Violet ink was used for the top row in the first sheet, but was then replaced with red.

HALF PENNY.	HALF PENNY.
(3)	(4)

1893 (Dec). *Issued at Old Calabar. Nos. 3/6 handstamped.*

(a) With T 3

9	½d. on 2d. (V.)	£500	£300
	a. Surch inverted	£3000	
	b. Surch diagonal (up or down)	£2250	
	c. Surch vertical (up or down)	£2250	
10	½d. on 2½d. (Verm.)	£6500	
	a. Surch in carmine	£10000	

(b) With T 4

11	½d. on 2½d. (G.)	£225	£200
	a. Surch double	£2000	£2000
	b. Surch diagonally inverted	£2000	
12	½d. on 2½d. (Verm)	£425	£300
13	½d. on 2½d. (C.)	£275	£300
	a. Surch omitted (in pair)		
14	½d. on 2½d. (B.)	£300	£325
15	½d. on 2½d. (Blk.)	£2750	
	a. Surch inverted	£4000	
	b. Surch diagonal inverted (up or down)	£3000	
16	½d. on 2½d. (B.-Blk.)	£3000	

In T 3 "HALF" measures 9½ mm and "PENNY" 12½ mm with space 1½ mm between the words. Bar 14½ mm ending below the stop. The "F" is nearly always defective.

In T 4 "HALF" is 8½ mm, "PENNY" 12½ mm, spacing 2½ mm, and bar 16 mm, extending beyond the stop.

HALF PENNY.	HALF PENNY
5 (Stop after "N")	6 (No stop after "N")

(c) With T 5

17	½d. on 2½d. (Verm.)	£350	£200
	a. Surch double	— £1300	
	b. Surch vertical (up)	— £2000	

(d) With T 6

18	½d. on 2d. (V.)	£550	£350
19	½d. on 2½d. (Verm.)	£225	£250
	a. Surch inverted	£1400	
	b. Surch double	— £1600	
	c. Surch diagonal (up or down)	£1200	
	d. Surch omitted (in strip of 3)	£6500	
	e. Surch vertical (up or down)	£1400	
	f. Surch diagonal, inverted (up or down)	£1600	

In T 5 the "P" and "Y" are raised, and the space between the words is about 4 mm. Bar is short, approx 13½ mm. T 6 is similar but without the stop after "N".

Half Penny	*Half Penny*
(7)	(8)

(e) With T 7

20	½d. on 2d. (V.)	£275	£225
	a. Surch double	— £5500	
	b. Surch vertical (up or down)	£1600	
	c. Surch diagonal (up or down)	£1500	
	d. Surch diagonal (inverted)	£3000	
21	½d. on 2½d. (Verm.)	£200	£180
	a. Surch double	£4000	
	b. Surch vertical (up or down)	£1400	
	c. Surch inverted	£1600	
	d. Surch diagonal (up or down)	£1200	
	e. Surch diagonal, inverted (up)	£3000	
22	½d. on 2½d. (B.)	£6500	£6500
23	½d. on 2½d. (C.)	£5500	
24	½d. on 2½d. (V.)	£3500	

(f) With T 8

25	½d. on 2½d. (Verm.)	£325	£350
	a. Surch diagonal (up)	£1800	
26	½d. on 2½d. (B.)	£7500	
27	½d. on 2½d. (G.)	£275	£350
	a. Surch double	£5000	
28	½d. on 2½d. (C.)	£10000	£10000

In T 7 the "a" and "e" are narrow and have a short upward terminal hook. The "l" has a very small hook. The letters "nny" have curved serifs, and the distance between the words is 5½ mm.

In T 8 the "a" and "e" are wider. The "l" has a wider hook. The letters "nny" have straight serifs, and the distance between the words is 4¼ mm.

HALF PENNY.	*HALF PENNY*
(9)	(10)

(g) With T 9

29	½d. on 2d. (V.)	£300	£300
30	½d. on 2d. (B.)	£900	£550
	a. Surch double		
31	½d. on 2½d. (Verm.)	£400	£500
	a. Surch double		
32	½d. on 2½d. (B.)	£300	£300
33	½d. on 2½d. (G.)	£300	£300
	a. Surch double (G.)	£1600	
	b. Surch double (G. + Verm.)		
34	½d. on 2½d. (V.)	£3250	

(h) With T 10

35	½d. on 2½d. (G.)	£400	£450
36	½d. on 2½d. (Verm.)	£4250	

One Shilling	5/-
(11)	(12)

(i) With T 11

37	1s. on 2d. (V.)	£400	£350
	a. Surch inverted	£2750	
	b. Surch vertical (up or down)	£2500	
	c. Surch diagonal (up or down)	£2250	
	d. Surch diagonal, inverted (up or down)	£2750	
38	1s. on 2d. (Verm.)	£550	£700
	a. Surch inverted	£3750	
	b. Surch diagonal (up or down)	£3250	
	c. Surch vertical (up or down)	£3750	
39	1s. on 2d. (Blk.)	£5000	
	a. Surch inverted	£8000	
	b. Surch vertical (up or down)	£6500	

There are two main types of the "One Shilling" surcharge:—

Type A. The "O" is over the "hi" of "Shilling" and the downstrokes of the "n" in "One", if extended, would meet the "ll" of "Shilling". The "g" is always raised. Type A is known in all three colours.

Type B. The "O" is over the first "i" of "Shilling" and the downstrokes of the "n" would meet the "li" of "Shilling". Type B is known in violet and vermilion.

There is a third, minor type of the black surcharge, but the differences are very slight.

Various types of the surcharges on Nos. 9 to 39 were printed on the same sheet, and different types in different colours may be found *se-tenant*. These are of great rarity.

(j) As T 12

40	5s. on 2d. (V.)	£7000	£8000
	a. Surch inverted	£10000	
	b. Surch vertical (up or down)	£10000	£10000
	c. Surch diagonal (down)	£10000	
41	10s. on 5d. (Verm.)	£6000	£8000
	a. Surch inverted	£10000	
	b. Surch vertical (up or down)	£10000	
	c. Surch diagonal (up or down)		
42	20s. on 1s (V.)	£65000	
	a. Surch inverted	£80000	
43	20s. on 1s. (Verm.)	£65000	
44	20s. on 1s. (Blk.)	£65000	

NIGER COAST PROTECTORATE

The name of the protectorate was changed on 12 May 1893.

PERFORATION. There are a number of small variations in the perforation of the Waterlow issues of 1893 to 1898 which were due to irregularity of the pins rather than different perforators.

In the following lists, stamps perf 12, 12½, 13 or compound are described as perf 12–13, stamps perf 13½, 14 or compound are described as perf 13½–14 and those perf 14½, 15 or compound are listed as perf 14½–15. In addition the 13½–14 perforation exists compound with 14½–15 and with 12–13, whilst perf 15½–16 comes from a separate perforator.

13	14

(Des G. D. Drummond. Recess Waterlow)

1894 (1 Jan). *T 13 (with "OIL RIVERS" obliterated and "NIGER COAST" in top margin). Various frames. No wmk. Thick and thin papers. P 14½–15.*

45	½d. vermilion	4·00	3·75
	a. Perf 13½–14	4·00	
46	1d. pale blue	3·75	3·25
	a. Bisected (½d.) (on cover)	† £550	
	b. *Dull blue*	3·75	3·25
	ba. Bisected (½d.) (on cover)	† £450	
	c. Perf 13½–14	4·00	
	d. Perf 13½–14, comp 12–13		
47	2d. green	15·00	13·00
	a. Imperf between (horiz pair)	† £3000	
	b. Bisected (1d.) (on cover)	† £700	
	c. Perf 14½–15, comp 12–13		
	d. Perf 13½–14, comp 12–13	14·00	13·00
	e. Perf 13½–14, comp 12–13	20·00	18·00
	f. Perf 12–13		
48	2½d. carmine-lake	3·75	3·50
	a. Perf 13½–14	5·50	5·00
	b. Perf 13½–14, comp 12–13		
	c. Perf 12–13		
49	5d. grey-lilac	11·00	9·00
	a. *Lilac* (1894)	10·00	12·00
	b. Perf 13½–14	10·00	
50	1s. black	14·00	12·00
	a. Perf 14½–15, comp 12–13		
	b. Perf 13½–14		
	c. Perf 13½–14, comp 12–13	25·00	
45/50		Set of 6	45·00 42·00

There were three printings of each value, in November 1893, Jan 1894 and March 1894.

Nos. 46a, 46ba and 47b were used at Bonny River during August and September 1894.

(Recess Waterlow)

1894 (June). *T 14 (various frames). No wmk. P 14½–15.*

51	½d. yellow-green	1·40	2·50
	a. *Deep green*	2·00	3·50
	b. Perf 14½–15, comp 13½–14		
	c. Perf 13½–14	3·00	
	d. Perf 13½–14, comp 12–13	10·00	
52	1d. orange-vermilion	8·00	6·50
	a. *Vermilion*	7·00	3·25
	b. Bisected diagonally (½d.) (on cover)	† £500	
	c. Perf 15½–16		
	d. Perf 13½–14	8·00	
	e. Perf 13½–14, comp 12–13		
53	2d. lake	8·50	3·75
	a. Bisected diagonally (1d.) (on cover)		
	b. Perf 13½–14	9·00	3·25
54	2½d. blue	8·50	3·50
	a. *Pale blue*	8·00	5·00
	b. Perf 13¼–14	10·00	
55	5d. purple	5·00	5·50
	a. *Deep violet*	5·00	5·50
56	1s. black	12·00	
	a. Perf 13½–14	12·00	7·00
	b. Perf 13½–14, comp 12–13	20·00	
51/6		Set of 6	38·00 22·00

Nos. 52b and 53a were used at Bonny River during August and September 1894.

1/2	1	ONE = HALF PENNY =
(15)	(16)	(17)

1894. *Provisionals. Issued at Opobo.*

(a) Nos. 46b and 46 bisected vertically and surch with T 15 (May–June)

57	."½" on half of 1d dull blue (R.) (May)	£750	£250
	a. Surch inverted (in strip of 3 with normals)	£6500	
58	"½" on half of 1d. pale blue (R.) (June)	£550	£225
	a. Surch *tête-bêche* (pair)		
	b. Surcharge inverted	£2500	

(b) No. 3 bisected vertically and surch

(i) With T 16 (12 mm high) (June–Oct)

59	"1" on half of 2d. (Verm.)	£500	£250
	a. Surch double	£1100	£950
	b. Surch inverted	— £1100	

(ii) Smaller "1" (4¾ mm high)

60	"1" on half of 2d. (C.)	— £2500	

(iii) *Smaller "1" (3¾ mm high)*
61   "1" on half on 2d. (C.)
Nos. 60 and 61 exist *se-tenant*. (Price £18000 used.)

(c) *No. 52a bisected, surch with* T 15 *(Aug–Sept)*
62   ½ on half of 1d. vermilion (Blk.) .. £1700 £450
63   ½ on half of 1d. vermilion (V.) .. £1500 £325
64   ½ on half of 1d. vermilion (B.) .. £1200 £250
    a. "½" double .. .. .. — £2000
The stamp is found divided down the middle and also diagonally.

1894 (10 Aug). *Issued at Old Calabar. No. 54 surch with T 17 and two bars through value at foot.*
65   ½d. on 2½d. blue £275 £200
    a. Surch double £1600 £1300
    b. "OIE" for "ONE" £1400 £1000
    c. Ditto. Surch double .. — £2250
There are eight types in the setting of T 17.

(Recess Waterlow)

1897 (Mar)–**98**. *As T 14 (various frames). Wmk Crown CA. P 14½–15.*
66   ½d. green (7.97) .. .. 1·75 1·00
    a. Sage-green .. .. 2·25 1·75
    b. Perf 13½–14 .. .. 2·25 2·25
    c. Perf 15½–16 .. .. 10·00 5·00
67   1d. orange-vermilion .. .. 2·25 1·00
    a. Vermilion .. .. 2·50 1·00
    b. Imperf between (pair) .. £2250
    c. Perf 15½–16 .. .. 6·00
    d. Perf 13½–14 .. .. 2·50 1·75
68   2d. lake (7.97) .. .. 1·75 1·00
    a. Perf 15½–16 .. .. 4·00 2·00
69   2½d. slate-blue (8.97) .. 3·25 2·00
    a. Deep bright blue .. 3·25 1·00
    b. Perf 13½–14 .. .. 6·00 3·00
70   5d. red-violet (p 13½–14) (1898) 8·00 45·00
    a. Purple .. .. 8·00 48·00
    b. Perf 13½–14, comp 12–13 .. 18·00
71   6d. yellow-brown (6.98) .. 7·00 6·50
    a. Perf 13½–14 .. .. 8·50
72   1s. black (1898) .. .. 15·00 14·00
    a. Perf 13½–14 .. .. 14·00 14·00
73   2s. 6d. olive-bistre (6.98) .. 30·00
    a. Perf 15½–16 .. .. 30·00
    b. Perf 13½–14 .. .. 22·00 60·00
74   10s. deep violet (6.98) .. 75·00 £140
    a. Bright violet .. .. 80·00 £140
    b. Perf 13½–14 .. .. 80·00 £140
66/74 .. .. .. *Set of 9* £120 £225
71, 73/4 Optd "Specimen" .. *Set of 3* £225

Owing to temporary shortages in Southern Nigeria, the above issue was again in use at various times from 1902 until 1907.

On 1 January 1900 the Niger Coast Protectorate together with the southern portion of the Niger Company Territories became the protectorate of Southern Nigeria.

NIGER COMPANY TERRITORIES

Following the development of trade along the Niger, British commercial interests formed the United African Company in 1879 which became, in 1886, the Royal Niger Company. A charter was granted to the Company in the same year to administer territory along the Rivers Niger and Benue over which a British protectorate had been proclaimed. The Company's territories extended to the Niger delta to provide access to the interior.

Post Offices were opened at Akassa (1887), Burutu (1896), Lokoja (1898) and Abutshi (1899). The stamps of Great Britain were used from 1888.

On the establishment of postal services in 1887 the Company arranged with the British G.P.O. that unstamped mail marked with their handstamps would be delivered in Great Britain, the recipients only being charged the normal rate of postage from West Africa. This system was difficult to administer, however, so the British authorities agreed in 1888 to the supply of G.B. stamps for use at the Company post offices.

Initially the stamps on such covers were left uncancelled until the mail arrived in the United Kingdom, the Company handstamp being struck elsewhere on the address side. This method continued to be used until early 1896, although a number of covers from the twelve months prior to that date do show the Company handstamp cancelling the stamps. Some of these covers were later recancelled on arrival in Great Britain. From May 1896 the postage stamps were cancelled in the Niger Territories.

In the following listings no attempt has been made to cover the use of the Company marks on the reverse of envelopes.

Dates given are those of earliest known postmarks. Colour of postmarks in brackets. Where two or more colours are given, price is for cheapest. Illustrations are reduced to two-thirds linear of the actual size.

Stamps of GREAT BRITAIN cancelled as indicated below.

ABUTSHI

1899 (4 Oct *to* 31 Dec). *Cancelled as T 8, but inscribed "THE ROYAL NIGER CO. C. & L. ABUTSHI" with "CUSTOMS (date) OFFICE" in central oval.*
Z1   ½d. vermilion (V.) £275
Z2   1d. lilac (V.) £190
Z3   2½d. purple/*blue* (V.) .. £300
Z4   5d. dull purple and blue (V.) .. £325
Z5   10d. dull purple and carmine (V.) .. £375
Z6   2s. 6d. deep lilac (V.) .. £425

AKASSA

The listings for Nos. Z7/15 are for *covers* on which the Akassa handstamp appears on the front, but is *not* used as a cancellation for the G.B. stamps. Examples of Nos. Z16/26 occur, from 1895–96, with the handstamp struck on the front of the cover away from the stamps, or, from 1896, used as a cancellation. The prices quoted are for *single* stamps showing the cancellation; covers from either period being worth considerably more. On Nos. Z27/42 the handstamp was used as a cancellation and the prices quoted are for *single stamps.*

1

2

1888. *Cancelled as T 3 but with Maltese cross each side of "AKASSA". Size 36 × 22 mm.*
Z 7   6d. deep purple/*red* ..

1890 (24 June). *Size 39 × 24 mm.*
Z 8 1 2½d. purple/*blue* (V.) ..
Z 9   3d. purple/*yellow* (V.) ..
Z10   5d. dull purple and blue (V.) ..
Z11   6d. deep purple/*red* (V.) ..
Z12   10d. dull purple and carmine (V.) ..
Z12a   1s. green (V.) ..
Z13   2s. 6d. lilac (V.) ..

1894.
Z14 2 1d. lilac (V.) (July) .. 85·00
Z15   2½d. purple/*lilac* (V.) (3 Oct) ..

3

4

1895 (7 March). *Size 39 × 25 mm.*
Z16 3 2½d. purple/*blue* (V.) .. ..

1895 (1 June)–**99**.
Z17 4 ½d. vermilion (V.) .. .. 29·00
Z18   1d. lilac (V.) .. .. 27·00
Z19   2d. green and vermilion (V.) .. £190
Z20   2½d. purple/*blue* (V.) .. 26·00
Z21   3d. purple/*yellow* (V.) .. £140
Z22   5d. dull purple and blue (V.) .. 30·00
Z23   6d. deep purple/*red* (V.) .. 70·00
Z24   9d. dull purple and blue (V.) .. £140
Z25   10d. dull purple and carmine (V.) .. 70·00
Z26   2s. 6d. deep lilac (V.) £130

1899 (20 May). *Cancelled as T 4, but "CUSTOMS DEPT" in place of "POST OFFICE".*
Z27   1d. lilac (V.) .. £200
Z28   2½d. purple/*blue* (V.).. £200

5

1897 (Jan) *to* **1899** (Dec).
Z29 5 ½d. vermilion (V.) .. .. 29·00
Z30   1d. lilac (V.) .. .. 28·00
    a. "RECD" for year in postmark
Z31   2d. green and vermilion (V.) .. 75·00
Z32   2½d. purple/*blue* (V.) .. 38·00
    a. "RECD" for year in postmark (1898) ..
Z33   3d. purple/*yellow* (V.) .. £110
Z34   4d. green and brown (V.) .. 75·00
Z35   4½d. green and carmine (V.) .. £475
Z36   5d. dull purple and blue (V.) .. 48·00
Z37   6d. deep purple/*red* (V.) .. £110
Z38   9d. dull purple and blue (V.) .. £160
Z39   10d. dull purple and carmine (V.) .. 70·00
Z40   1s. green (V.) £250
Z41   2s. 6d. deep lilac (V.) .. £130

1899 (9 Jan). *Cancelled as T 7, but inscribed "AKASSA".*
Z42   5d. dull purple and blue (V.) ..

BURUTU

1897 (20 Jan) *to* **1898** (30 Oct). *Cancelled as T 6, "BURUTU" in sans-serif caps. Size 44 × 24 mm.*
Z43 6 ½d. vermilion (V.) .. .. 45·00
Z44   1d. lilac (V.) .. .. 42·00
Z45   1½d. dull purple and green (V.) .. £130
Z46   2d. green and carmine (V.) .. 80·00
Z47   2½d. purple/*blue* (V.) .. 28·00
Z48   3d. purple/*yellow* (V.) .. 90·00
Z49   4d. green and brown (V.) .. 70·00
Z50   5d. dull purple and blue (V.) .. 48·00
Z51   6d. deep purple/*red* (V.).. .. 95·00
Z52   9d. dull purple and blue (V.) .. £130

Z53 6 10d. dull purple and carmine (V.) .. 70·00
Z54   1s. green (V.) £300
Z55   2s. 6d. lilac (V.) £120
The 2½d. is also known with this postmark in blue (6.9.97) and violet-black (Apr 1898) and the ½d., 2½d., 3d., 5d. and 10d. with it in black.

1898 *to* **1899**. *Cancelled as T 4, but inscribed "BURUTU" in serifed caps. Size 44 × 27 mm.*
Z56   ½d. vermilion (V., Blk.) .. 48·00
Z57   1d. lilac (V., Blk.) .. 45·00
Z58   2d. green and vermilion (V.) .. £130
Z59   2½d. purple/*blue* (V., Blk.) .. 40·00
Z60   3d. purple/*yellow* (V.) .. £110
Z61   4d. green and brown (V.) .. 90·00
Z62   4½d. green and carmine (V.).. .. £500
Z63   5d. dull purple and blue (V.) .. 50·00
Z64   6d. deep purple/*red* (V.) .. £130
Z65   9d. dull purple and blue (V.) .. £160
Z66   10d. dull purple and carmine (V., Blk.) .. 70·00
Z67   2s. 6d. lilac (V., Blk.) £160

7

1898 (9 July) *to* **1899** (Feb).
Z68 7 1d. lilac (V.) ..
Z69   2½d. purple/*blue* (V.) £200

1899 (20 May). *Cancelled as T 4, but inscribed "CUSTOM DEPT. BURUTU".*
Z70   1d. lilac (V.) ..
There is some doubt as to the use of this cancellation for postal purposes.

LOKOJA

8

1899 (30 June *to* 31 Dec).
Z71 8 ½d. vermilion (V.) .. .. 65·00
Z72   1d. lilac (V.) .. .. 55·00
Z73   2½d. purple/*blue* (V.) .. £170
Z74   5d. dull purple and blue (V.) .. £180
Z75   10d. dull purple and carmine (V.) .. £180
Z76   2s. 6d. deep lilac (V.) £375

AGENT GENERAL NIGER TERRITORIES

The listings for Nos. Z78/9 are for covers showing a handstamp struck on the address side, but *not* used as a cancellation for the G.B. stamp.

1894. *Cancelled as T 8 but inscribed "AGENT GENERAL NIGER TERRITORIES".*
Z78   2½d. purple/*blue* (V.) (3.10.94) .. £1000

1895 (4 Aug). *Cancelled as T 7 but inscribed as last.*
Z79   2½d. purple/*blue* (V.).. .. .. £1000
It is now believed that these cancellations may have been used at Asaba.

The British Government purchased the Royal Niger Company territories and from 1 January 1900 they were incorporated into the protectorates of Northern and Southern Nigeria. Of the post offices listed above only Lokoja was then situated in Northern Nigeria, the remainder joining Niger Coast in forming Southern Nigeria.

Issues for Northern Nigeria did not reach Lokoja until sometime in March 1900 and the post office there continued to use unoverprinted stamps of Great Britain until these supplies arrived.

NORTHERN NIGERIA

The Protectorate of Northern Nigeria was formed on 1 January 1900 from the northern part of the Niger Company Territories. Only one post office existed in this area, at Lokoja, and this continued to use unoverprinted stamps of GREAT BRITAIN until the arrival of Nos. 1/9 during March 1900.

PRICES FOR STAMPS ON COVER		
Nos. 1/7	*from × 6*	
Nos. 8/9		
Nos. 10/16	*from × 5*	
Nos. 17/19		
Nos. 20/6	*from × 5*	
No. 27		
Nos. 28/37	*from × 5*	
Nos. 38/9		
Nos. 40/9	*from × 5*	
Nos. 50/2	—	

NIGERIA / Northern Nigeria

PRINTERS. All issues were typographed by De La Rue & Co.

1   2

1900 (Mar). *Wmk Crown CA. P* 14.

1	1	½d. dull mauve and green	1·25	6·00
2		1d. dull mauve and carmine	1·90	2·25
3		2d. dull mauve and yellow	3·25	18·00
4		2½d. dull mauve and ultramarine	6·00	18·00
5	2	5d. dull mauve and chestnut	10·00	25·00
6		6d. dull mauve and violet	13·00	18·00
7	1	1s. green and black	14·00	38·00
8		2s. 6d. green and ultramarine	60·00	£160
9		10s. green and brown	£160	£375
1/9		*Set of* 9	£225	£600
1/9 Optd "Specimen"		*Set of* 9	£180	

3   4

1902 (1 July). *Wmk Crown CA. P* 14.

10	3	½d. dull purple and green	80	60
11		1d. dull purple and carmine	1·00	20
12		2d. dull purple and yellow	80	1·60
13		2½d. dull purple and ultramarine	75	3·25
14	4	5d. dull purple and chestnut	1·50	4·50
15		6d. dull purple and violet	3·25	4·50
16	3	1s. green and black	2·75	3·75
17		2s. 6d. green and ultramarine	8·00	22·00
18		10s. green and brown	45·00	48·00
10/18		*Set of* 9	55·00	80·00
10/18 Optd "Specimen"		*Set of* 9	£150	

1904 (April). *Wmk Mult Crown CA. P* 14.

19	4	£25 green and carmine	£25000	

1905 (Aug)–06. *Wmk Mult Crown CA. Ordinary paper. P* 14.

20	3	½d. dull purple and green (10.05)	5·50	3·50
		a. Chalk-surfaced paper (1906)	2·75	2·75
21		1d. dull purple and carmine	3·25	30
		a. Chalk-surfaced paper (1906)	2·00	60
22		2d. dull purple and yellow (10.05)	7·00	14·00
		a. Chalk-surfaced paper (1906)	6·50	8·50
23		2½d. dull purple and ultramarine (10.05)	4·25	3·75
24	4	5d. dull purple and chestnut (10.05)	10·00	22·00
		a. Chalk-surfaced paper (1906)	15·00	22·00
25		6d. dull purple and violet (10.05)	13·00	20·00
		a. Chalk-surfaced paper (1906)	15·00	15·00
26	3	1s. green and black (10.05)	28·00	45·00
		a. Chalk-surfaced paper (1906)	17·00	26·00
27		2s. 6d. green and ultramarine (10.05)	38·00	42·00
		a. Chalk-surfaced paper (1906)	25·00	32·00
20/7		*Set of* 8	70·00	£100

1910 (Jan)–11. *Wmk Mult Crown CA. Ordinary paper* (½d. to 2½d.) *or chalk-surfaced paper* (others). *P* 14.

28	3	½d. green (4.10)	80	40
29		1d. carmine (1.10)	70	20
30		2d. grey (10.11)	1·25	2·25
31		2½d. blue (10.10)	75	3·25
32	4	3d. purple/*yellow* (9.11)	1·25	30
34		5d. dull purple and olive-green (2.11)	2·50	4·25
35		6d. dull purple and purple (11.10)	5·00	9·00
		a. *Dull and bright purple* (1911)	1·50	4·00
36	3	1s. black/*green* (11.10)	1·00	55
37		2s. 6d. black and red/*blue* (3.11)	8·00	16·00
38	4	5s. green and red/*yellow* (9.11)	17·00	48·00
39	3	10s. green and red/*green* (3.11)	42·00	45·00
28/39		*Set of* 11	70·00	£110
28/39 Optd "Specimen"		*Set of* 11	£180	

5   6

1912. *Wmk Mult Crown CA. Ordinary paper* (½d., 1d., 2d.) *or chalk-surfaced paper* (others). *P* 14.

40	5	½d. deep green	30	20
41		1d. red	30	15
42		2d. grey	1·50	2·50
43	6	3d. purple/*yellow*	80	75
44		4d. black and red/*yellow*	50	70
45		5d. dull purple and olive-green	1·75	4·00
46		6d. dull and bright purple	1·75	3·25
47		9d. dull purple and carmine	1·25	6·00
48	5	1s. black/*green*	1·75	75
49		2s. 6d. black and red/*blue*	7·00	22·00
50	6	5s. green and red/*yellow*	16·00	55·00
51	5	10s. green and red/*green*	30·00	45·00
52	6	£1 purple and black/*red*	£170	£130
40/52		*Set of* 13	£200	£225
40/52 Optd "Specimen"		*Set of* 13	£200	

On 1 January 1914 Northern Nigeria became part of Nigeria.

SOUTHERN NIGERIA

The Colony and Protectorate of Southern Nigeria was formed on 1 January 1900 by the amalgamation of Niger Coast Protectorate with the southern part of the Niger Territories. Lagos was incorporated into the territory on 16 February 1906.

The stamps of NIGER COAST PROTECTORATE were used in Southern Nigeria until the introduction of Nos. 1/9, and also during a shortage of these values in mid-1902. The issues of LAGOS were utilized throughout Southern Nigeria after 16 February 1906 until supplies were exhausted.

PRICES FOR STAMPS ON COVER

Nos. 1/7	*from* × 8	
Nos. 8/9	—	
Nos. 10/18	*from* × 4	
Nos. 19/20	—	
Nos. 21/30	*from* × 4	
Nos. 31/2	—	
Nos. 33/42	*from* × 4	
Nos. 43/4	—	
Nos. 45/53	*from* × 4	
Nos. 55/6	—	

PRINTERS. All issues of Southern Nigeria were typographed by De La Rue & Co, Ltd, London.

1   2   3

1901 (Mar)–02. *Wmk Crown CA. P* 14.

1	1	½d. black and pale green	70	75
		a. *Black and green* (1902)	60	50
2		1d. black and carmine	70	50
3		2d. black and red-brown	1·75	3·50
4		4d. black and sage-green	1·75	6·50
5		6d. black and purple	1·75	3·75
6		1s. green and black	7·00	15·00
7		2s. 6d. black and brown	30·00	55·00
8		5s. black and orange-yellow	38·00	75·00
9		10s. black and purple/*yellow*	65·00	£130
1/9		*Set of* 9	£130	£250
1/9 Optd "Specimen"		*Set of* 9	£120	

1903 (Mar)–04. *Wmk Crown CA. P* 14.

10	2	½d. grey-black and pale green	70	15
11		1d. grey-black and carmine	1·25	15
12		2d. grey-black and chestnut	2·50	90
13		2½d. grey-black and blue (1904)	2·00	75
14		4d. grey-black and olive-green	1·75	3·50
15		6d. grey-black and purple	3·25	8·00
16		1s. green and black	17·00	10·00
17		2s. 6d. grey-black and brown	12·00	32·00
		a. *Grey and yellow-brown*	60·00	80·00
18		5s. grey-black and yellow	38·00	80·00
19		10s. grey-black and purple/*yellow*	25·00	65·00
20		£1 green and violet	£225	£375
10/20		*Set of* 11	£300	£500
10/20 Optd "Specimen"		*Set of* 11	£160	

1904 (June)–08. *Wmk Mult Crown CA. Ordinary paper. P* 14.

21	2	½d. grey-black and pale green	40	10
		a. Chalk-surfaced paper (1905)	50	20
22		1d. grey-black and carmine	4·00	20
		a. Chalk-surfaced paper (1905)	5·00	10
23		2d. grey-black and chestnut	2·25	45
		a. *Pale grey and chestnut* (1907)	3·25	40
24		2½d. grey-black and bright blue (1905)	80	95
25		3d. orange-brown & bright purple (*chalk-surfaced paper*) (1907) (Optd S. £20)	8·50	1·25
26		4d. grey-black and olive-green (1905)	14·00	16·00
		a. Chalk-surfaced paper (1906)	17·00	17·00
		ab. *Grey-black & pale olive-green* (1907)	16·00	17·00
27		6d. grey-black and bright purple (1905)	5·50	1·00
		a. Chalk-surfaced paper (1905)	7·00	1·00
28		1s. grey-green and black	2·50	1·50
		a. Chalk-surfaced paper (1907)	7·50	1·25
29		2s. 6d. grey-black and brown (1905)	15·00	9·00
		a. Chalk-surfaced paper (1905)	20·00	8·50
30		5s. grey-black and yellow (1905)	30·00	50·00
		a. Chalk-surfaced paper (1907)	38·00	50·00
31		10s. grey-black and purple/*yellow* (*chalk-surfaced paper*) (1908)	75·00	£120
32		£1 green and violet (1905)	£130	£170
		a. Chalk-surfaced paper (1905)	£100	£140
21/32		*Set of* 12	£225	£300

I   II

Die I. Thick "1"; small "d".
Die II. Thinner "1"; larger "d".

1907–11. *Colours changed. Ordinary paper* (½d. to 2½d.) *or chalk-surfaced paper* (others). *Wmk Mult Crown CA. P* 14.

33	2	½d. pale green	60	20
		a. *Blue-green* (1910)	40	20
34		1d. carmine (I)	90	15
		a. *Die II. Carmine-red* (1910)	30	10
35		2d. greyish slate (1909)	80	70
36		2½d. blue (1909)	1·00	3·50
37		3d. purple/*yellow* (1909)	1·00	30

38	2	4d. black and red/*yellow* (1909)	60	80
39		6d. dull purple and purple (1909)	11·00	3·00
		a. *Dull purple and bright purple* (1911)	14·00	2·50
40		1s. black/*green* (1909)	6·50	40
41		2s. 6d. black and red/*blue* (1909)	4·50	90
42		5s. green and red/*yellow* (1909)	25·00	45·00
43		10s. green and red/*green* (1909)..	55·00	85·00
44		£1 purple and black/*red* (1909)	£140	£150
33/44		*Set of* 12	£200	£250
33/44 Optd "Specimen"		*Set of* 12	£225	

It was formerly believed that the plate used for printing the head was retouched in 1907 but the fact that the 1d. Die II, which did not appear until 1910, only exists in the first state of the head threw some doubts on this theory. Specialists now recognise that two dies of the head existed and that plates from both were used in Southern Nigeria.

The differences are very small and we refrain from listing them until more research is done, both in this country and in others where they may have been used. The differences are illustrated below:

A   B

In Head A the fifth line of shading on the king's cheek shows as a line of dots and the lines of shading up to the king's hair are broken in places. In Head B the lines of shading are more regular, especially the fifth line.

The following stamps are known:
Ordinary colours: 21 ordinary and chalky, A; 22 ordinary and chalky, A; 23, A; 23a, B; 24, A; 25, B; 26 ordinary and chalky, A; 27 ordinary, A; 27 chalky, B; 28 ordinary, A; 28 chalky, B; 29 ordinary, A; 29 chalky, A and B; 30 ordinary, A; 30 chalky, B; 31, B; 32 ordinary, A; 32 chalky, B.

New colours: 33, A and B; 33a, B; 34, A and B; 34a, A; 35/44, B.

1912. *Wmk Mult Crown CA. P* 14.

45	3	½d. green	60	10
46		1d. red	60	10
47		2d. grey	60	85
48		2½d. bright blue	2·50	2·75
49		3d. purple/*yellow*	75	30
50		4d. black and red/*yellow*	70	2·00
51		6d. dull and bright purple	75	1·00
52		1s. black/*green*	2·25	60
53		2s. 6d. black and red/*blue*	4·50	11·00
54		5s. green and red/*yellow*	11·00	45·00
55		10s. green and red/*green*	35·00	75·00
56		£1 purple and black/*red*	£140	£150
45/56		*Set of* 12	£180	£225
45/56 Optd "Specimen"		*Set of* 12	£200	

On 1 January 1914 Southern Nigeria became part of Nigeria.

NIGERIA

Nigeria was formed on 1 January 1914 from the former protectorates of Northern and Southern Nigeria.

PRICES FOR STAMPS ON COVER TO 1945

Nos. 1/10	*from* × 3	
Nos. 11/13	—	
Nos. 15/24	*from* × 3	
No. 25	—	
Nos. 25a/9d	*from* × 3	
No. 29e	—	
Nos. 30/3	*from* × 3	
Nos. 34/59	*from* × 2	

CROWN COLONY

1   2

(Typo D.L.R.)

1914–27. *Wmk Mult Crown CA. Ordinary paper* (½d. to 2½d.) *or chalk-surfaced paper* (others). *P* 14.

    A. *Die I.* (1.6.14–21)

1	1	½d. green	75	30
2		1d. carmine-red	1·50	10
		a. *Scarlet* (6.17)	2·25	10
3		2d. grey	2·25	85
		a. *Slate-grey* (1918)	2·75	75
4		2½d. bright blue	1·25	90
		a. *Dull blue* (1915)		
5	2	3d. purple/*yellow* (*white back*)	1·75	5·00
		a. *On yellow* (*lemon back*) (8.15)	1·25	1·25
		b. *On deep yellow* (*yellow back, thick paper*) (1915) (Optd S. £30)	16·00	7·50
		c. *On pale yellow* (*orange-buff back*) (12.20)	4·50	16·00
		d. *On pale yellow* (*pale yellow back*) (1921)	4·50	15·00

6	2	4d. black and red/*yellow* (*white back*) ..			1·00	4·75
		a. On yellow (*lemon back*) (8.15) ..			80	3·00
		b. On deep yellow (*yellow back, thick paper*) (1915) (Optd S. £30)			15·00	6·00
		c. On pale yellow (*orange-buff back*) (1921)			6·00	6·50
		d. On pale yellow (*pale yellow back*) (1921)			7·00	16·00
7	1	6d. dull and bright purple (*shades*) ..			2·25	3·00
8	1	1s. black /*pale blue-green* (*white back*) ..			80	5·00
		a. On yellow-green (*white back*)				
		b. On pale blue-green (*yellow-green back*) (1915)			10·00	15·00
		c. On pale blue green (*blue-green back*) (1915) (Optd S. £30)			1·00	3·75
		d. On pale blue-green (*pale olive back*) (1918)			12·00	15·00
		e. On emerald-green (*pale olive back*) (12.20)			4·50	16·00
		f. On emerald-green (*emerald-green back*) (1921) ..			1·00	8·50
9		2s. 6d. black and red/*blue*			5·50	3·00
10	2	5s. green and red/*yellow* (*white back*)			6·50	19·00
		a. On yellow (*lemon back*) (8.15) ..			16·00	35·00
		b. On deep yellow (*yellow back, thick paper*) (1915) (Optd S. £30)			24·00	50·00
		c. On yellow (*orange-buff back*) (1921)			25·00	60·00
		d. On pale yellow (*pale yellow back*) (1921)			45·00	85·00
11	1	10s. green and red/*blue-green* (*white back*)			38·00	80·00
		a. On blue-green (*blue-green back*) (8.15) (Optd S. £35)			35·00	65·00
		b. On blue-green (*pale olive back*) (1918)			£600	£1100
		c. On emerald green (*pale olive back*) (12.20)			75·00	95·00
		d. On emerald-green (*emerald back*) (1921)			28·00	70·00
12	2	£1 deep purple and black/*red*			£150	£180

B. Change to Die II (19.1.27)

13	2	£1 purple and black/*red*		£160	£200
1/12			Set of 12	£180	£225
1/12 Optd "Specimen"			Set of 12	£300	

1921–32. *Wmk Mult Script CA. Ordinary paper (½d. to 3d.) or chalk-surfaced paper (others). P 14.*

A. The basic issue. Die I for the ½d., 1d., 2d., 2½d., 3d and 6d., Die II remainder (1921–26)

15	1	½d. green (1921) ..		60	40
16		1d. rose-carmine (1921)..		65	30
17		2d. grey (5.21) ..		1·50	2·00
18		2½d. bright blue (5.21) ..		70	2·00
19	2	3d. bright violet (1.24) ..		3·75	3·25
20		4d. black and red/*pale yellow* (10.23)		50	55
21		6d. dull and bright purple (5.21)		4·75	5·50
22	1	1s. black/*emerald* (7.24)..		80	80
23		2s. 6d. black and red/*blue* (8.25)		6·00	15·00
24	2	5s. green and red/*yellow* (10.26)		12·00	45·00
25	1	10s. green and red/*green* (4.26)		48·00	£110
15/25			Set of 11	70·00	£160
15/25 Optd "Specimen"			Set of 11	£250	

B. Change to Die II (1924–25)

25a	1	½d. green (5.25)..		1·50	85
25b		1d. rose-carmine (5.25)..		75	55
25c		2d. grey (1924) ..		3·00	40
25d	2	3d. bright violet (5.25) ..		6·00	1·50
25e		6d. dull and bright purple (7.24)		4·50	4·75
25a/e			Set of 5	14·00	7·25

C. New value and colours changed. Die II (1927–31)

26	2	1½d. orange (1.4.31) ..		1·75	15
27	1	2d. chestnut (1.10.27) ..		1·75	1·00
28		2d. chocolate (1.7.28) ..		65	15
29	2	3d. bright blue (1.4.31) ..		2·50	2·00
26/7, 29			Set of 3	6·00	3·00
26/7, 29 Optd/Perf "Specimen"			Set of 3	75·00	

D. Reappearance of Die I (Key Plate 23) (Mar to Aug 1932)

29a	1	2d. chocolate (Mar) ..		4·50	75
29b		4d. black and red/*pale yellow*		5·50	7·00
29c	1	2s. 6d. black and red/*blue*		29·00	35·00
29d	2	5s. green and red/*yellow*		48·00	85·00
29e	1	10s. green and red/*green* ..		80·00	£180
29a/e			Set of 5	£150	£275

A Key Plate 23 printing was also made for the £1 value, but this does not differ from the 1914 issue, No. 12.

1935 (6 May). *Silver Jubilee. As Nos. 114/17 of Jamaica, but ptd by Waterlow. P 11×12.*

30		1½d. ultramarine and grey ..		60	40
31		2d. green and indigo ..		1·50	40
		j. Kite and vertical log ..		45·00	
32		3d. brown and deep blue ..		2·75	5·00
33		1s. slate and purple ..		2·75	13·00
30/3			Set of 4	7·00	17·00
30/3 Perf "Specimen" ..			Set of 4	75·00	

For illustration of plate variety see Omnibus section following Zimbabwe.

3 Apapa Wharf   4 Fishing Village

5 Victoria-Buea Road

(Recess D.L.R.)

1936 (1 Feb). *Designs as T 3/5. Wmk Mult Script CA.*

(a) P 11½ × 13

34		½d. green ..		85	85
35		1d. carmine ..		40	35
36		1½d. brown ..		40	30
		a. Perf 12½ × 13½ ..		27·00	2·00
37		2d. black ..		40	70
38		3d. blue ..		70	75
		a. Perf 12½ × 13½ ..		70·00	24·00
39		4d. red-brown ..		1·25	2·00
40		6d. dull violet ..		40	60
41		1s. sage-green ..		1·10	4·50

(b) P 14

42		2s. 6d. black and ultramarine ..		3·50	13·00
43		5s. black and olive-green ..		6·00	18·00
44		10s. black and grey ..		45·00	60·00
45		£1 black and orange..		75·00	£120
34/45			Set of 12	£120	£190
34/45 Perf "Specimen"			Set of 12	£225	

Designs: *Vert as T 3/4*—1d. Cocoa; 1½d. Tin dredger; 2d. Timber industry; 4d. Cotton ginnery; 6d. Habe minaret; 1s. Fulani Cattle. *Horiz as T 5*—5s. Oil Palms; 10s. River Niger at Jebba; £1, Canoe pulling.

1937 (12 May). *Coronation. As Nos. 118/20 of Jamaica, but ptd by B.W. & Co. P 11×11½.*

46		1d. carmine ..		30	75
47		1½d. brown ..		75	75
48		3d. blue ..		1·25	1·75
46/8			Set of 3	2·10	3·00
46/8 Perf "Specimen"			Set of 3	55·00	

15 King George VI   16 Victoria-Buea Road

(Recess B.W. (T 15), D.L.R. (others))

1938 (1 May)**–51.** *Designs as T 15/16. Wmk Mult Script CA. P 12 (T 15) or 13 × 11½ (others).*

49	15	½d. green ..		10	10
		a. Perf 11½ (15.2.50) ..		30	10
50		1d. carmine ..		18·00	2·50
		a. Rose-red (1941) ..		30	10
50b		1d. bright carmine (1.12.44)		10	10
		ba. Perf 11½ (15.2.50) ..		10	20
51		1½d. brown ..		20	10
		a. Perf 11½ (15.11.50) ..		10	10
52		2d. black ..		10	50
52aa		2d. rose-red (1.12.44) ..		10	40
		ab. Perf 11½ (15.2.50) ..		10	40
52a		2½d. orange (4.41) ..		10	45
53		3d. blue ..		10	10
		a. Wmk sideways ..		†	—
53b		3d. black (1.12.44) ..		10	10
54		4d. orange ..		48·00	2·50
54a		4d. blue (1.12.44) ..		15	1·00
55		6d. blackish purple ..		20	10
		a. Perf 11½ (17.4.51) ..		30	40
56		1s. sage-green ..		50	10
		a. Perf 11½ (15.2.50) ..		15	10
57		1s. 3d. light blue (1940)..		40	10
		a. Perf 11½ (14.6.50) ..		30	60
		b. Wmk sideways (Perf 11½) ..		—£1500	
58	16	2s. 6d. black and blue ..		50·00	9·00
		a. Perf 13½ (6.42) ..		2·00	2·75
		ab. Perf 13½. *Black and deep blue* (1946)		30·00	25·00
		b. Perf 14 (1942) ..		1·50	1·50
		c. Perf 12 (15.8.51) ..		1·50	1·50
59	—	5s. black and orange ..		85·00	9·50
		a. Perf 13½ (8.42) ..		3·75	3·00
		b. Perf 14 (1948) ..		4·00	3·00
		c. Perf 12 (19.5.49) ..		4·00	1·75
49/59c			Set of 16	50·00	7·50
49/52aa, 53/9 Perf "Specimen"			Set of 15	£200	

Design: *Horiz as T 16*—5s. R. Niger at Jebba.

1946 (21 Oct). *Victory. As Nos. 141/2 of Jamaica.*

60		1½d. chocolate ..		15	10
61		4d. blue ..		15	50
60/1 Perf "Specimen"			Set of 2	55·00	

1948 (20 Dec). *Royal Silver Wedding. As Nos. 143/4 of Jamaica.*

62		1d. bright purple ..		35	10
63		5s. brown-orange ..		5·00	7·00

1949 (10 Oct). *75th Anniv of U.P.U. As Nos. 145/8 of Jamaica.*

64		1d. bright reddish purple ..		15	10
65		3d. deep blue ..		35	65
66		6d. purple ..		50	1·25
67		1s. olive ..		70	1·50
64/7			Set of 4	1·50	3·25

1953 (2 June). *Coronation. As No. 153 of Jamaica, but ptd by B.W.*

68		1½d. black and emerald ..		30	10

18 Old Manilla Currency   21 "Tin"

Die I   Die Ia
Flat-bed   Rotary

Two types of 1d.:
The Belgian rotary printings have thicker lines of shading giving blotches of black colour instead of fine lines, particularly in the stirrups.

Major re-entry showing duplication of steps of the terraces (Pl 3, R. 1/5)

Type A   Type B
Gap in row of dots   Unbroken row of dots

Two types of 2d. slate-violet:
Nos. 72c/cc. The original cylinder used was Type A (July 1956); later Type B (Sept 1957). The above illustrations will help classification, but two stamps per sheet of 60 of Type A show faint dots. However, one of these has the "2d." re-entry which does not exist in Type B sheets, and shades are distinctive.

Die I Flat-bed

Die Ia Rotary

Two types of 3d.:
As in the 1d. the Belgian rotary printings have thicker lines of shading and this is particularly noticeable in the dark hills in the background.

24 Ife Bronze   26 Victoria Harbour

29 New and Old Lagos

(Des M. Fievet. Recess Waterlow)

1953 (1 Sept)–58. T **18, 21, 24, 26, 29** and similar designs. Wmk Mult Script CA. P 14.

69	18	½d. black and orange	..	15	30
70	–	1d. black and bronze-green (Die I)	..	20	10
		a. Die Ia (1.9.58)	..	20	10
71	–	1½d. blue-green	..	35	40
72	21	2d. black and yellow-ochre	..	3·75	20
		a. Black and ochre (18.8.54)	..	4·25	20
		b. Re-entry	..	70·00	
72c		2d. slate-violet (Type A) (23.7.56)	..	3·00	85
		ca. Slate-blue (shades) (Type A)	..	4·50	30
		cb. Bluish grey (Type B) (25.9.57)	..	3·00	30
		cc. Grey (shades) (Type B)	..	3·00	20
73	–	3d. black and purple (Die I)	..	55	10
		a. Die Ia. Black & reddish pur (1.9.58)	..	55	10
		b. Imperf (pair)	..	£200	
74	–	4d. black and blue	..	1·75	20
75	24	6d. orange-brown and black	..	30	10
		a. Chestnut and black (18.8.54)	..	30	10
76	–	1s. black and maroon	..	40	10
77	26	2s. 6d. black and green	..	4·00	30
		a. Black and deep green (18.8.54)	..	5·00	30
78	–	5s. black and red-orange	..	3·25	75
79	–	10s. black and red-brown	..	6·50	1·50
80	29	£1 black and violet	..	11·00	5·00
69/80			Set of 13	30·00	8·00

Designs: Horiz (as T **18**)—1d. Bornu horsemen; 1½d. "Groundnuts"; 3d. Jebba bridge and R. Niger; 4d. "Cocoa"; 1s. "Timber". (As T **26**)—5s. "Palm-oil"; 10s. "Hides and skins".

Nos. 70a, 72c/cc and 73a were printed on rotary machines by a subsidary company, Imprimerie Belge de Sécurité, in Belgium. Nos. 72ca and 72cc were only available in Nigeria.

ROYAL VISIT 1956

(30)

31 Victoria Harbour

1956 (28 Jan). Royal Visit. No. 72 optd with T **30**.

81	21	2d. black and ochre	..	40	20
		a. Opt inverted	..	£160	

(Recess Waterlow)

1958 (1 Dec). Centenary of Victoria. W w **12**. P 13½ × 14.

82	31	3d. black and purple	..	20	20

32 Lugard Hall

(Recess Waterlow)

1959 (14 Mar). Attainment of Self-Government, Northern Region of Nigeria. T **32** and similar horiz design. W w **12**. P 13½ (3d.) or 13½ × 14 (1s.).

83		3d. black and purple	..	15	10
84		1s. black and green	..	45	50

Design:—1s. Kano Mosque.

INDEPENDENT FEDERATION

34

35 Legislative Building

38 Dove, Torch and Map

(Des L. J. Wittington (1d.), R. Crawford (3d.), R. D. Baxter (6d.), J. White (1s. 3d.), Photo Waterlow)

1960 (1 Oct). Independence. T **35, 38** and similar horiz designs. W **34**. P 13½ (1s. 3d.) or 14 (others).

85		1d. black and scarlet	..	10	10
86		3d. black and greenish blue	..	15	10
87		6d. green and red-brown	..	20	15
88		1s. 3d. bright blue and yellow	..	30	15
85/8			Set of 4	60	40

Designs: (As T **35**)—3d. African paddling canoe; 6d. Federal Supreme Court.

39 Groundnuts

48 Central Bank

1961 (1 Jan). T **39, 48,** and similar designs. W **34**. P 15 × 14 (½d. to 1s 3d.) or 14½ (others).

89		½d. emerald	..	10	50
90		1d. reddish violet	..	50	10
91		1½d. carmine-red	..	50	1·75
92		2d. deep blue	..	30	10
93		3d. deep green	..	30	10
94		4d. blue	..	40	45
95		6d. yellow and black	..	55	10
		a. Yellow omitted	..	—	£300
96		1s. yellow-green	..	2·25	10
97		1s. 3d. orange	..	30	10
98		2s. 6d. black and yellow	..	1·00	15
99		5s. black and emerald	..	50	35
100		10s. black and ultramarine	..	75	1·25
101		£1 black and carmine-red	..	5·00	4·75
89/101			Set of 13	11·00	8·75

Designs: Vert (as T **39**)—1d. Coal mining; 1½d. Adult education; 2d. Pottery; 3d. Oyo carver; 4d. Weaving; 6d. Benin mask; 1s. Yellow-casqued Hornbill; 1s. 3d. Camel train. Horiz (as T **48**)—5s. Nigeria Museum; 10s. Kano airport; £1 Lagos railway station.

PRINTERS. The above and all following issues to No. 206 were printed in photogravure by Harrison & Sons, except where otherwise stated.

52 Globe and Railway Locomotive

56 Coat of Arms

(Des M. Goaman)

1961 (25 July). Admission of Nigeria into U.P.U. T **52** and similar horiz designs. W **34**. P 14½.

102		1d. red-orange and blue	..	10	10
103		3d. olive-yellow and black	..	10	10
104		1s. 3d. blue and carmine-red	..	20	10
105		2s. 6d. deep green and blue	..	30	45
102/5			Set of 4	55	50

Designs:—3d. Globe and mail-van; 1s. 3d. Globe and aircraft; 2s. 6d. Globe and liner.

(Des S. Bodo (3d.), R. Hopeman (4d.), C. Adesina (6d.), M. Shamir (1s. 6d.), B. Enweonwu (2s. 6d.))

1961 (1 Oct). First Anniv of Independence. T **56** and similar designs. W **34**. P 14½.

106		3d. multicoloured	..	10	10
107		4d. yellow-green and yellow-orange	..	10	10
108		6d. emerald-green	..	20	10
109		1s. 3d. grey, emerald and blue	..	25	10
110		2s. 6d. green and grey-blue	..	30	30
106/10			Set of 5	80	45

Designs: Horiz—4d. Natural resources and map; 6d. Nigerian Eagle; 1s. 3d. Eagles in flight; 2s. 6d. Nigerians and flag.

A used copy of No. 106 has been seen with both the silver (large "Y" appearing grey) and the yellow (appearing white) omitted.

61 "Health"

66 Malaria Eradication Emblem and Parasites

(Des M. Shamir)

1962 (25 Jan). Lagos Conference of African and Malagasy States. T **61** and similar vert designs. W **34**. P 14 × 14½.

111		1d. yellow-bistre	..	10	10
112		3d. deep reddish purple	..	10	10
113		6d. deep green	..	15	10
114		1s. brown	..	20	10
115		1s. 3d. blue	..	25	20
111/15			Set of 5	65	40

Designs:—3d. "Culture"; 6d. "Commerce"; 1s. "Communications"; 1s. 3d. "Co-operation".

1962 (7 Apr). Malaria Eradication. T **66** and similar horiz designs. W **34**. P 14½.

116		3d. green and orange-red	..	10	10
117		6d. blue and bright purple	..	15	10
118		1s. 3d. magenta and violet-blue	..	20	10
119		2s. 6d. blue and yellow-brown	..	30	20
116/19			Set of 4	65	30

Designs:—6d. Insecticide spraying; 1s. 3d. Aerial spraying; 2s. 6d. Mother, child and microscope.

70 National Monument

71 Benin Bronze

(Des S. Bodo (3d.), B. Enweonwu (5s.))

1962 (1 Oct). Second Anniv of Independence. W **34**. P 14½ × 14 (3d.) or 14 × 14½ (5s.).

120	70	3d. emerald and blue	..	10	10
		a. Emerald omitted			
121	71	5s. red, emerald and violet	..	1·00	45

72 Fair Emblem

73 "Cogwheels of Industry"

(Des M. Goaman (1d., 2s. 6d.), J. O. Gbagbeolu and M. Goaman (6d.), R. Hegeman (1s.))

1962 (27 Oct). International Trade Fair, Lagos. W **34**. T **72/3** and similar designs. P 14½.

122		1d. olive-brown and orange-red	..	15	10
123		6d. carmine-red and black	..	15	10
124		1s. orange-brown and black	..	15	10
125		2s. 6d. ultramarine and yellow	..	30	30
122/5			Set of 4	60	30

Designs: Horiz as T **73**—1s. "Cornucopia of Industry; 2s. 6d. Oilwells and tanker.

76 "Arrival of Delegates"

77 Mace as Palm Tree

(Des S. Akosile (2½d.), M. Goaman (others))

1962 (5 Nov). Eighth Commonwealth Parliamentary Conference, Lagos. T **76/77** and similar design. W **34**. P 14½.

126		2½d. greenish blue	..	15	15
127		4d. indigo and rose-red	..	15	10
128		1s. 3d. sepia and lemon	..	20	20
126/8			Set of 3	45	35

Design: Horiz—4d. National Hall.

80 Tractor and Maize

81 Mercury Capsule and Kano Tracking Station

(Des M. Goaman)

1963 (21 Mar). Freedom from Hunger. T **80** and similar design. W **34**. P 14.

129		3d. olive-green	..	50	20
130		6d. magenta	..	1·00	20

Design: Vert—3d. Herdsman.

(Des R. Hegeman)

1963 (21 June). "Peaceful Use of Outer Space". T **81** and similar vert design. W **34**. P 14½ × 14.

131		6d. blue and yellow-green	..	25	10
132		1s. 3d. black and blue-green	..	35	20

Design:—1s. 3d. Satellite and Lagos Harbour.

83 Scouts shaking Hands

(Des S. Apostolou (3d.), G. Okiki (1s.))

1963 (1 Aug). *11th World Scout Jamboree, Marathon. T 83 and similar triangular-shaped design.* W 34. P 14.
133   3d. red and bronze-green 20   15
134   1s. black and red 50   50
MS134a   93 × 95 mm. Nos. 133/4 .. 1·75 1·75
   ab. Red omitted (on 3d. value) .. £225
Design:—1s. Campfire.

85 Emblem and First Aid Team   88 President Azikiwe and State House

(Des M. Goaman)

1963 (1 Sept). *Red Cross Centenary. T 85 and similar horiz designs.* W 34. P 14½.
135   3d. red and deep ultramarine .. 55   10
136   6d. red and deep green 85   10
137   1s. 3d. red and deep sepia .. 1·50 60
135/7   .. .. *Set of 3* 2·50 70
MS137a   102 × 102 mm. No. 137 (block of four) .. 7·00 7·00
Designs:—6d. Emblem and "Hospital Services"; 1s. 3d. Patient and emblem.

(Des M. Shamir. Photo Govt Printer, Israel)

1963 (1 Oct). *Republic Day. T 88 and similar vert designs showing administrative buildings and President Azikiwe.* P 14 × 13.
138   3d. yellow-olive and grey-green .. 10   10
139   1s. 3d. yellow-brown and sepia .. 10   10
   a. Yellow-brown (portrait) omitted ..
140   2s. 6d. turquoise-blue and deep violet-blue .. 15   15
138/40   .. .. *Set of 3* 30   30
Designs:—1s. 3d. Federal Supreme Court Building; 2s. 6d. Parliament Building.

89 Charter and Broken Whip   90 "Freedom of Worship"

(Des S. Apostolou (3d.), Mrs. F. P. Effiong (others). Photo D.L.R.)

1963 (10 Dec). *15th Anniv of Declaration of Human Rights. T 89/90 and similar designs.* W 34. P 13.
141   3d. vermilion 10   10
142   6d. blue-green 10   10
143   1s. 3d. ultramarine 20   10
144   2s. 6d. bright purple 35   30
141/4   .. .. *Set of 4* 60   35
Designs: Vert as T 90—1s. 3d. "Freedom from want"; 2s. 6d. "Freedom of speech".

93 Queen Nefertari   94 Rameses II

(Des M. Shamir)

1964 (8 Mar). *Nubian Monuments Preservation.* W 34. P 14½.
145   93   6d. yellow-olive and emerald .. 50   10
146   94   2s. 6d. brown, deep olive and emerald 1·50 1·75

NEW INFORMATION

The editor is always interested to correspond with people who have new information that will improve or correct the Catalogue.

95 President Kennedy

(Des M. Shamir (1s. 3d.), M. Goaman (2s. 6d.), Mr. Bottiau (5s.). Photo Govt Printer, Israel (1s. 3d.); litho Lewin-Epstein, Bat Yam, Israel (others))

1964 (27 Aug). *President Kennedy Memorial Issue. T 95 and similar horiz designs.* P 13 × 14 (1s. 3d.) or 14 (others).
147   1s. 3d. light violet and black .. 40   15
148   2s. 6d. black, red, blue and green .. 60   55
149   5s. black, deep blue, red and green .. 95   1·40
147/9   .. .. *Set of 3* 1·75 1·90
MS149a   154 × 135 mm. No. 149 (block of four).
   Imperf .. .. 9·00 10·00
Designs:—2s. 6d. President Kennedy and flags; 5s. President Kennedy (U.S. coin head) and flags.

98 President Azikiwe   99 Herbert Macaulay

(Des S. Apostolou (3d.), W. H. Irvine (others). Photo Govt Printer, Israel (3d.); Harrison (others))

1964 (1 Oct). *First Anniv of Republic. T 98 or 99 and similar vert design.* P 14 × 13 (3d.) or 14½ (others).
150   3d. red-brown 10   10
151   1s. 3d. green 25   10
152   2s. 6d. deep grey-green 40   30
150/2   .. .. *Set of 3* 65   40
Design:—2s. 6d. King Jaja of Opobo.

101 Boxing Gloves

102 Hurdling

(Des A. Adalade (3d.), S. Medahunsi (6d.), M. Shamir (1s. 3d.), M. Goaman (2s. 6d.))

1964 (10 Oct). *Olympic Games, Tokyo. T 101 and similar designs, and T 102.* W 34. P 14 (2s. 6d.) or 14½ (others).
153   3d. sepia and olive-green .. 15   10
154   6d. emerald and indigo .. 20   10
155   1s. 3d. sepia and yellow-olive .. 45   15
156   2s. 6d. sepia and chestnut .. 1·00 1·25
153/6   .. .. *Set of 4* 1·60 1·40
MS156a   102 × 102 mm. No. 156 (block of four).
   Imperf .. .. 2·75 4·25
Designs: Horiz—6d. High-jumping. Vert—1s. 3d. Running.

105 Scouts on Hill-top

(Des S. Apostolou (1d., 1s. 3d.), H. N. G. Cowham and Eagle Scout N. A. Lasisi (3d.), W. H. Irvine (6d.))

1965 (1 Jan). *50th Anniv of Nigerian Scout Movement. T 105 and similar vert designs.* P 14 × 14½.
157   1d. brown 10   10
158   3d. red, black and emerald .. 15   10
159   6d. red, sepia and yellow-green .. 25   15
160   1s. 3d. bistre-brown, greenish yellow and black-green 40   55
157/60   .. .. *Set of 4* 75   75
MS160a   76 × 104 mm. No. 160 (block of four).
   Imperf .. .. 6·00 8·00
Designs:—3d. Scout badge on shield; 6d. Scout badges; 1s. 3d. Chief Scout and Nigerian scout.

109 "Telstar"   110 Solar Satellite

(Des M. Shamir. Photo Govt Printer, Israel)

1965 (1 Apr). *International Quiet Sun Years.* P 14 × 13.
161   109   6d. reddish violet and turquoise-blue .. 10   10
162   110   1s. 3d. green and reddish lilac.. .. 10   10

111 Native Tom-tom and Modern Telephone

(Des C. Botham (5s.), H. N. G. Cowham (others). Photo Enschedé)

1965 (2 Aug). *I.T.U. Centenary. T 111 and similar designs.* P 11½ × 11 (1s. 3d.) or 11 × 11½ (others).
163   3d. black, carmine and yellow-brown .. 15   10
164   1s. 3d. black, blue-green and chalky blue .. 1·25 1·00
165   5s. black, carmine, blue & brt greenish blue 3·75 4·50
163/5   .. .. *Set of 3* 4·50 5·00
Designs: Vert—1s. 3d. Microwave aerial. Horiz—5s. Telecommunications satellite and part of globe.

114 I.C.Y. Emblem and Diesel Locomotive   117 Carved Frieze

(Des W. H. Irvine. Photo D.L.R.)

1965 (1 Sept). *International Co-operation Year. T 114 and similar horiz designs.* W 34. P 14 × 15.
166   3d. green, red and orange .. .. 2·00 10
167   1s. black, bright blue and lemon .. 2·00 40
168   2s. 6d. green, bright blue and yellow .. 7·00 4·00
166/8   .. .. *Set of 3* 10·00 4·00
Designs:—1s. Students and Lagos Teaching Hospital; 2s. 6d. Kainji (Niger) Dam.

(Des S. Apostolou (3d.), W. H. Irvine (others). Photo D.L.R.)

1965 (1 Oct). *2nd Anniv of Republic. T 117 and similar designs.* P 14 × 15 (3d.) or 15 × 14 (others).
169   3d. black, red and orange-yellow .. 10   10
170   1s. 3d. red-brown, dp green & lt ultramarine 65   20
171   5s. brown, blackish brown and light green .. 1·75 2·00
169/71   .. .. *Set of 3* 2·25 2·00
Designs: Vert—1s. 3d. Stone images at Ikom; 5s. Tada bronze.

120 Lion and Cubs   121 African Elephants

132 Hippopotamus   133 African Buffalo

(Des M. Fievet. Photo Harrison (1d., 2d., 3d., 4d. (No. 177a), 9d.) or Delrieu (others))

1965 (1 Nov)—**66**. *T 120/1, 132/3 and similar designs. Without printer's imprint. Chalk-surfaced paper (1d., 2d., 3d., 4d., 9d.).* P 12 × 12½ (½d., 6d.), 12½ × 12 (1½d., 4d.), 14 × 13½ (1d., 2d., 3d., 9d.) or 12½ (others).
172   ½d. multicoloured (1.11.65) 50   70
173   1d. multicoloured (1.11.65) 30   15
174   1½d. multicoloured (2.5.66) .. .. 3·75 4·00
175   2d. multicoloured (1.4.66) .. .. 2·00 15

176	3d.	multicoloured (17.10.66)	..	1·00	15
177	4d.	multicoloured (2.5.66)	..	50	1·75
	a.	Perf 14 × 13½ (1966)	..	30	55
178	6d.	multicoloured (2.5.66)	..	1·00	30
179	9d.	Prussian blue and orange-red (17.10.66)		2·25	40
180	1s.	multicoloured (2.5.66)	..	1·50	40
181	1s. 3d.	multicoloured (2.5.66)	..	6·50	45
182	2s. 6d.	orange-brown, buff and brown (2.5.66)	..	75	30
183	5s.	chestnut, light yellow and brown (2.5.66)		1·50	1·50
	a.	Pale chestnut, yellow and brown-purple (1966)	..	1·50	1·50
184	10s.	multicoloured (2.5.66)	..	5·50	3·00
185	£1	multicoloured (2.5.66)	..	13·00	8·50
172/85			Set of 14	35·00	18·00

Designs: *Horiz* (as *T* 121)—1½d. Splendid Sunbird; 2d. Village Weaver and Red-headed Malimbe; 3d. Cheetah; 4d. Leopards; 9d. Grey Parrots. (As *T* 133)—1s. Blue-breasted Kingfishers; 1s. 3d. Crowned Cranes; 2s. 6d. Kobs; 5s. Giraffes. *Vert* (as *T* 120)—6d. Saddle-bill Stork.

The 2d. and 3d. exist with PVA gum as well as gum arabic. See also Nos. 220, etc.

The 1d., 3d., 4d. (No. 177a) 1s., 1s. 3d., 2s. 6d., 5s. and £1 values exist overprinted "F.G.N." (Federal Government of Nigeria) twice in black. They were prepared in November 1968 at the request of one of the State Governments for use as official stamps but the scheme was abandoned and meter machines were used instead. Some stamps held at Lagos Post Office were sold over the counter in error and passed through the post. The Director of Posts made limited stocks of all values, except the 1s., available from the Philatelic Bureau from 11 April 1969 "in order not to create an artificial scarcity", but they had no postal validity. Covers do, however, exist showing the 4d. value used by Lagos Federal Income Tax Office in April 1969 and others from the Office of the Secretary to the Military Government in 1973 carry the 3d., 4d. and 2s. 6d. values.

(134)

COMMONWEALTH
P. M. MEETING
11. JAN. 1966

135 Y.M.C.A. Emblem and H.Q., Lagos

1966 (11 Jan). *Commonwealth Prime Ministers' Meeting, Lagos. No 98 optd with T* 134 *by the Nigerian Security Printing and Minting Co, Lagos, in red.*

186	48	2s. 6d. black and yellow	..	30	30

(Des S. B. Ajayi. Litho Nigerian Security Printing & Minting Co Ltd)

1966 (1 Sept). *Nigerian Y.W.C.A.'s Diamond Jubilee. P* 14.

187	135	4d. yellow-orange, ultramarine, orange-brown and yellow-green		15	10
188		9d. yellow-orange, ultramarine, brown and turquoise-green		15	40

137 Telephone Handset and Linesman

139 "Education, Science and Culture"

(Des S. B. Ajayi (4d.), N. Lasisi (1s. 6d.), B. Enweonwu (2s. 6d))

1966 (1 Oct). *Third Anniv of Republic. T* 137 *and similar designs. W* 34. *P* 14½ × 14.

189		4d. green		10	10
190		1s. 6d. black, brown and reddish violet	..	45	50
191		2s. 6d. indigo, blue, yellow and green		1·25	2·00
189/91			Set of 3	1·60	2·25

Designs: *Vert*—4d. Dove and flag. *Horiz*—2s. 6d. Niger Bridge, Jebba.

(Des V. Whiteley from sketch by B. Salisu)

1966 (4 Nov). *20th Anniv of U.N.E.S.C.O. W* 34 *(sideways). P* 14½ × 14.

192	139	4d. black, lake and orange-yellow		40	10
193		1s. 6d. black, lake and turquoise-green		1·50	2·00
194		2s. 6d. black, lake and rose-pink		2·50	4·50
192/4	..	..	Set of 3	4·00	6·00

140 Children drinking

(Des V. Whiteley, after M. O. Afamefuna (4d.), I. U. Anawanti (1s. 6d.) and S. Adeyemi (2s. 6d.))

1966 (1 Dec). *Nigerian Red Cross. T* 140 *and similar designs. W* 34. *P* 14 × 14½ (1s. 6d.) or 14½ × 14 (others).

195		4d. + 1d. black, reddish violet and red		30	25
196		1s. 6d. + 3d. multicoloured	..	1·00	3·50
197		2s. 6d. + 3d. multicoloured		1·25	4·00
195/7	..	..	Set of 3	2·25	7·00

Designs: *Vert*—1s. 6d. Tending patient. *Horiz*—2s. 6d. Tending casualties, and badge.

143 Surveying

(Des M. Goaman)

1967 (1 Feb). *International Hydrological Decade. T* 143 *and similar multicoloured design. W* 34. *P* 14½ × 14 (4d.) or 14 × 14½ (2s. 6d.).

198		4d. Type 143	..	10	10
199		2s. 6d. Water gauge on dam (*vert*)	..	25	60

145 Globe and Weather Satellite   147 Eyo Masqueraders

(Des M. Shamir (4d.), S. Bodo (1s. 6d.))

1967 (23 Mar). *World Meteorological Day. T* 145 *and similar horiz design. W* 34. *P* 14½ × 14.

200		4d. magenta and blue	..	15	10
201		1s. 6d. black, yellow and blue	..	50	50

Design:—1s. 6d. Passing storm and sun.

(Des G. A. Okiki (4d.), A. B. Saka Lawal (1s. 6d.), S. Bodo (2s. 6d.). Photo Enschedé)

1967 (1 Oct). *4th Anniv of Republic. T* 147 *and similar multicoloured designs. P* 11½ × 11 (2s. 6d.) or 11 × 11½ (others).

202		4d. Type 147	..	20	10
203		1s. 6d. Crowd watching acrobat		1·25	1·25
204		2s. 6d. Stilt dancer (*vert*)		1·50	2·25
202/4	..		Set of 3	2·75	3·25

150 Tending Sick Animal   151 Smallpox Vaccination

(Des G. Drummond)

1967 (1 Dec). *Rinderpest Eradication Campaign. P* 14½ × 14.

205	150	4d. multicoloured	..	15	10
206		1s. 6d. multicoloured	..	55	65

PRINTERS AND PROCESS. Nos. 207/89 were printed in photogravure by the Nigerian Security Printing and Minting Co Ltd, *unless otherwise stated.*

(Des J. Owei. Litho)

1968 (7 Apr). *20th Anniv of World Health Organization. T* 151 *and similar horiz design. P* 14.

207		4d. magenta and black	..	15	10
208		1s. 6d. orange, lemon and black	..	55	40

Design:—1s. 6d. African and mosquito.

153 Chained Hands and Outline of Nigeria   155 Hand grasping at Doves of Freedom

(Des Jennifer Toombs)

1968 (1 July). *Human Rights Year. T* 153 *and similar design. P* 14.

209		4d. greenish blue, black and yellow	..	10	10
210		1s. 6d. myrtle-green, orange-red and black	..	20	30

Design: *Vert*—1s. 6d. Nigerian flag and Human Rights emblem.

(Des G. Vasarhelyi)

1968 (1 Oct). *5th Anniv of Federal Republic. P* 13½ × 14.

211	155	4d. multicoloured	..	10	10
212		1s. 6d. multicoloured	..	20	20

156 Map of Nigeria and Olympic Rings   158 G.P.O., Lagos

(Des J. Owei)

1968 (14 Oct). *Olympic Games, Mexico. T* 156 *and similar horiz design. P* 14.

213		4d. black, green and scarlet	..	10	10
214		1s. 6d. multicoloured		20	20

Design:—1s. 6d. Nigerian athletes, flag and Olympic rings.

(Des D.L.R.)

1969 (11 Apr). *Inauguration of Philatelic Service. P* 14.

215	158	4d. black and green		10	10
216		1s. 6d. black and blue	..	20	20

159 Yakubu Gowon and Victoria Zakari

(Des adapted from photo by Jackie Phillips. Litho)

1969 (20 Sept). *Wedding of General Gowon. P* 13 × 13½.

217	159	4d. chocolate and emerald		10	10
218		1s. 6d. black and emerald	..	30	20

1969–72. (*a*) *As No.* 173 *etc, but printed by Nigerian Security Printing and Minting Co Ltd. With printer's imprint* "N.S.P. & M. CO. LTD." *P* 13½ (6d.) *or P* 13 × 13½ (*others*).

220	1d.	multicoloured	..	2·00	60
222	2d.	multicoloured	..	1·25	70
	a.	Smaller imprint* (13.1.71)		1·25	1·25
223	3d.	multicoloured (7.71)		65	55
	a.	Larger imprint* (22.10.71)		1·00	1·25
224	4d.	multicoloured		6·00	90
	a.	Smaller imprint*			
225	6d.	multicoloured (1971)		1·00	90
226	9d.	Prussian blue and orange-red (1970)	5·50	3·00
	a.	"TD" of "LTD" omitted from imprint (Pl. 1B, R. 10/2)	..	27·00	
227	1s.	multicoloured (8.71)	..	2·00	50
228	1s. 3d.	multicoloured (1971)		8·00	3·50
229	2s. 6d.	multicoloured (1972)		4·00	7·00
230	5s.	multicoloured (1972)		8·00	8·00
220/30			Set of 10	30·00	23·00

*On No. 222a the designer's name measures 4¾ mm. On No. 223a the imprints measure 9 and 8½ mm respectively. The normal imprints on Nos. 222/3 both measure 5½ mm.

The date given for Nos. 222a and 223a are for the earliest known used copies.

†No. 224 has the left-hand imprint 6 mm long and the right-hand 5½ mm. On No. 224a the imprints are 5½ mm and 4½ mm respectively. The width of the design is also ½ mm smaller.

Imperforate proofs of similar 10s. and £1 values are known.

(*b*) *As Nos.* 222 *and* 224, *but redrawn, and printed by Enschedé. No printer's imprint; designer's name at right. P* 14½ × 13.

231	2d.	multicoloured (9.70)	..	25·00	6·00
232	4d.	multicoloured (3.71)	..	1·50	2·00

In the 2d. the face value is white instead of yellow, and in the 4d. the white lettering and value are larger.

160 Bank Emblem and "5th Anniversary"   161 Bank Emblem and Rays

(Des J. Owei (4d.), B. Salisu (1s. 6d.). Litho)

1969 (18 Oct). *Fifth Anniv of African Development Bank. P* 14.

233	160	4d. orange, black and blue	..	10	10
234	161	1s. 6d. lemon, black and plum	..	20	20

162 I.L.O. Emblem   164 Olumo Rock

(Des D. West)

1969 (15 Nov). *50th Anniv of International Labour Organisation. T* 162 *and similar horiz design. P* 14.

235		4d. black and bright reddish violet	..	10	10
236		1s. 6d. emerald and black	..	30	25

Design:—1s. 6d. World map and I.L.O. emblem.

(Des A. Onwudimegwu)

1969 (30 Dec). *International Year of African Tourism. T* 164 *and similar designs. P* 14.

237		4d. multicoloured		10	10
238		1s. black and bright emerald	..	20	10
239		1s. 6d. multicoloured	..	40	20
237/9	..	..	Set of 3	60	30

Designs: *Vert*—1s. Traditional musicians; 1s. 6d. Assob Falls.

167 Symbolic Tree   **168** U.P.U. H.Q. Building

(Des E. Emokpae (4d., 1s., 2s.), B. Onobrakpeya (1s. 6d.). Photo Enschedé)

1970 (28 May). *"Stamp of Destiny"; End of Civil War.* T **167** and similar designs. P 11 × 11½ (2s.) or 11½ × 11 (others).
240	4d. gold, new blue and black .		..	10	10
241	1s. multicoloured		..	10	10
242	1s. 6d. yellow-green and black		..	10	10
243	2s. multicoloured	..	..	15	20
240/3	..	..	Set of 4	30	30

Designs: *Vert*—1s. Symbolic Wheel; 1s. 6d. United Nigerians supporting Map. *Horiz*—2s. Symbolic Torch.

(Des A. Onwudimegwu)

1970 (29 June). *New U.P.U. Headquarters Building.* P 14.
244	**168**	4d. reddish violet and greenish yellow ..	10	10
245		1s. 6d. light greenish blue and deep blue ..	20	20

169 Scroll   **170** Oil Rig

(Des A. Onwudimegwu)

1970 (1 Sept). *25th Anniv of United Nations.* T **169** and similar vert design. P 14.
246	4d. orange-brown, buff and black ..	10	10
247	1s. 6d. steel-blue, cinnamon and gold ..	20	20

Design:—1s. 6d. U.N. Building.

(Des E. Emokpae. Litho Enschedé)

1970 (30 Sept). *Tenth Anniv of Independence.* T **170** and similar vert designs. Multicoloured. P 13½ × 13.
248	2d. Type **170**		10	10
249	4d. University Graduate		15	10
250	6d. Durbar Horsemen		15	10
251	9d. Servicemen raising Flag..		20	10
252	1s. Footballer		20	10
253	1s. 6d. Parliament Building..		25	25
254	2s. Kainji Dam		60	70
255	2s. 6d. Agricultural Produce		60	75
248/55	..	.. Set of 8	2·00	1·75

171 Children and Globe   **172** Ibibio Face Mask

(Des E. Emokpae and A. Onwudimegwu. Photo Enschedé)

1971 (21 Mar). *Racial Equality Year.* T **171** and similar multicoloured designs. P 13 × 13½ (4d., 2s.) or 13½ × 13 (others).
256	4d. Type **171**	10	10
257	1s. Black and white men uprooting "Racism" (vert)	10	10
258	1s. 6d. The world in black and white (vert)	15	50
259	2s. Black and white men united	15	75
256/9	.. .. .. Set of 4	35	1·25

(Des A. Onwudimegwu)

1971 (30 Sept). *Antiquities of Nigeria.* T **172** and similar vert designs. P 13½ × 14.
260	4d. black and pale blue	10	10
261	1s. 3d. blackish brown and ochre ..	15	30
262	1s. 9d. emerald, sepia and olive-yellow ..	20	80
260/2	.. Set of 3	35	1·00

Designs:—1s. 3d. Benin bronze; 1s. 9d. Ife bronze.

MINIMUM PRICE

The minimum price quote is 10p which represents a handling charge rather than a basis for valuing common stamps. For further notes about prices see introductory pages.

---

173 Children and Symbol   **174** Mast and Dish Aerial

(Des E. Emokpae)

1971 (11 Dec). *25th Anniv of U.N.I.C.E.F.* T **173** and similar vert designs, each incorporating the U.N.I.C.E.F. symbol. P 13½ × 14.
263	4d. multicoloured	10	10
264	1s. 3d. yellow-orange, orge-red & carm-lake	15	40
265	1s. 9d. pale greenish blue & dp greenish blue	15	85
263/5	.. Set of 3	30	1·25

Designs:—1s. 3d. Mother and child; 1s. 9d. Mother carrying child.

(Des A. Onwudimegwu)

1971 (30 Dec). *Opening of Nigerian Earth Satellite Station.* T **174** and similar horiz designs. P 14.
266	**174**	4d. multicoloured	15	10
267	—	1s. 3d. green, blue and black ..	30	50
268	—	1s. 9d. brown, orange and black ..	40	1·00
269	—	3s. mauve, black and magenta ..	85	2·00
266/9		.. Set of 4	1·50	3·25

Designs:—Nos. 267/9, as T **174**, but showing different views of the Satellite Station.

The 4d. has been seen on a cover from Ilorin, postmarked 23.12.71.

175 Trade Fair Emblem   **176** Traffic

(Des E. Emokpae (4d.), A. Onwudimegwu (others). Litho D.L.R.)

1972 (23 Feb). *All-Africa Trade Fair.* T **175** and similar designs. P 13.
270	4d. multicoloured	10	10
271	1s. 3d. deep lilac, lemon and gold ..	15	35
272	1s. 9d. yellow-orange, orange-yellow & black	15	90
270/2	.. Set of 3	30	1·25

Designs: *Horiz*—1s. 3d. Map of Africa with pointers to Nairobi. *Vert*—1s. 9d. Africa on globe.

(Des A. Onwudimegwu (4d., 3s.), E. Emokpae (1s. 3d.), J. Owei (1s. 9d.). Litho D.L.R.)

1972 (23 June). *Change to Driving on the Right.* T **176** and similar horiz designs. Multicoloured (except 4d.). P 13.
273	4d. Type **176** (yellow-orge, dp chest & black)	15	10
274	1s. 3d. Roundabout	70	70
275	1s. 9d. Highway	80	1·25
276	3s. Road junction	2·00	3·00
273/6	.. .. .. Set of 4	3·25	4·50

177 Nok Style Terracotta Head   **178** Hides and Skins

(Des G. Okiki (1s. 3d.), A. Aiyegbusi (others). Litho D.L.R.)

1972 (1 Sept). *All-Nigeria Arts Festival.* T **177** and similar multicoloured designs. P 13.
277	4d. Type **177**	10	10
278	1s. 3d. Bronze pot from Igbo-Ukwu ..	25	60
279	1s. 9d. Bone harpoon (horiz).. ..	30	1·00
277/9	.. Set of 3	60	1·50

(New Currency. 100 kobo = 1 naira)

(Des E. Emokpae (8, 25, 30, 50 k., 1 n.), A. Onwudimegwu (others))

1973–74. T **178** and similar designs. P 14.

(a) *Photo. Left-hand imprint 5¼ mm long* (2 Jan–2 Apr)
280	1 k. multicoloured (deep green foliage) ..		50	50
	a. Light emerald foliage* (2.4.73) ..		20	10
281	2 k. black, pale turquoise-blue and bright purple ..		35	10
282	5 k. multicoloured (emerald hills) ..		60	40
	a. Bright yellow-green hills* (2.4.73) ..		50	10

283	10 k. black, orange-yellow and lilac ..	..	70	40
284	12 k. black, pale emerald and deep cobalt ..		8·00	7·00
285	18 k. multicoloured		7·00	2·00
286	20 k. multicoloured		9·50	3·00
287	30 k. black, chrome-yellow and new blue ..		9·50	6·00
288	50 k. multicoloured (black background and figure) ..		5·00	2·75
	a. Deep chocolate background and figure* (2.4.73)		1·50	90
289	1 n. multicoloured		10·00	10·00
280/9	..	.. Set of 10	42·00	26·00

(b) *Litho. Left-hand imprint 6 mm long* (2 Apr 1973†–74)
290	1 k. multicoloured (8.73) ..	..	10	10
291	2 k. black, pale turquoise-blue and bright purple (27.6.74)** ..		2·00	75
292	3 k. multicoloured		15	10
293	5 k. multicoloured (shades) (2.74) ..		3·00	80
294	7 k. multicoloured		30	65
295	8 k. multicoloured		40	10
296	10 k. black, orange-yellow and lilac (8.73) ..		4·00	15
297	12 k. black, green and cobalt (shades) ..		30	85
298	15 k. multicoloured		30	50
299	18 k. multicoloured		50	30
300	20 k. multicoloured		65	30
301	25 k. multicoloured		85	45
302	30 k. black, chrome-yellow and new blue ..		40	80
303	35 k. multicoloured		3·50	2·50
305	1 n. multicoloured (shades).. ..		1·25	1·10
306	2 n. multicoloured (shades)		3·50	3·75
290/306	..	.. Set of 16	19·00	12·00

Designs: *Horiz*—2 k. Natural gas tanks; 3 k. Cement works; 5 k. Cattle-ranching; 7 k. Timber mill; 8 k. Oil refinery; 10 k. Cheetahs, Yankari Game Reserve; 12 k. New Civic Building; 15 k. Sugar-cane harvesting; 20 k. Vaccine production; 25 k. Modern wharf; 35 k. Textile machinery; 1 n. Eko Bridge; 2 n. Teaching Hospital, Lagos. *Vert*—18 k. Palm oil production; 30 k. Argungu Fishing Festival; 50 k. Pottery.

*On Nos. 280a, 282a and 288a other colours also differ, but the shades can best be identified by the distinctive features noted.

Used copies of No. 282a have been seen with orange omitted.

†Although First Day Covers of Nos. 290/306 were dated 1 April the stamps were not placed on sale until 2 April. Later, post-dated, covers included No. 291.

**This is the earliest known postmark date. No. 291 was not released by the Crown Agents in London until 11 September 1975.

Differences between printings:
1 k. In photogravure printings the stretched hide at left is in brownish black; on the litho stamps this hide is brown and yellow.
2 k. On the litho stamp the line of division between the black and pale blue colours of the gas tanks is a regular curve; on the photogravure printing it is horizontal and irregular. The litho stamp also has a wider mauve border at top.
5 k. The litho printing differs from the photogravure (Nos. 282/a) in having brown on the herdsman, instead of black.
10 k. The litho version has much less black on the cheetahs and tree trunk. It also shows black details at the left-hand end of the trunk, which do not appear on the photogravure version.
12 k. No. 284 is much darker than the litho version, especially within the building and amongst the trees at right.
18 k. The lithographed printing shows two oildrums in the foreground which are not present on the photogravure stamp.
20 k. The lithographed printing includes a brown plate not present on the photogravure version and this shows on the chemist. The liquid in the flasks is grey-blue instead of black. On the watermarked version, No. 348, the liquid is turquoise-blue.
30 k. No. 287 is much darker, with greater use of black in the design.
50 k. The litho version (No. 352) has solid shading on the potter's upper arm and lacks a black inner frame-line beneath the potter's wheel. No. 352 has a green printer's imprint at foot (instead of black) and its background is similar to that of No. 288a.
1 n. On the photogravure stamp the traffic is shown driving on the left. For the litho version the traffic is corrected to show it driving on the right.

See also Nos. 338/54.

PROCESS. From No. 307 onwards all stamps were lithographed by the Nigerian Security Printing and Minting Co Ltd.

179 Athlete

1973 (8 Jan). *Second All-African Games, Lagos.* T **179** and similar multicoloured designs (except 5 k.). P 13.
307	5 k. Type **179** (lt lilac, lt greenish bl & blk) ..	15	10
308	12 k. Football	25	50
309	18 k. Table-tennis	60	1·00
310	25 k. National Stadium (vert) ..	70	1·50
307/10	.. Set of 4	1·50	2·75

180 All-Africa House, Addis Ababa   **181** Dr. Hansen

1973 (25 May). *Tenth Anniv of O.A.U. T* **180** *and similar vert designs. Multicoloured. P* 14.

311	5 k.	Type **180**	10	10
312	18 k.	O.A.U. flag	30	40
313	30 k.	O.A.U. emblem and symbolic flight of ten stairs	50	80
311/13		*Set of* 3	70	1·10

(Des A. Onwudimegwu)

1973 (30 July). *Centenary of Discovery of Leprosy Bacillus. P* 14.

314	**181**	5 k. + 2 k. lt red-brown, flesh & black	30	70

182 W.M.O. Emblem and Weather-vane   183 University Complex

(Des O. I. Oshiga)

1973 (4 Sept.). *I.M.O./W.M.O. Centenary. P* 14.

315	**182**	5 k. multicoloured	15	10
316		30 k. multicoloured	1·25	2·00

(Des A. Onwudimegwu (5, 18 k.), C. Okechukwu (12 k.), O. I. Oshiga (30 k.))

1973 (17 Nov). *25th Anniv of Ibadan University. T* **183** *and similar multicoloured designs. P* 13½ × 14 (12 k.) *or* 14 × 13½ (*others*).

317	5 k.	Type **183**	10	10
318	12 k.	Students' population growth (*vert*)	25	30
319	18 k.	Tower and students	35	55
320	30 k.	Teaching Hospital	50	85
317/20		*Set of* 4	1·10	1·50

184 Lagos 1d. Stamp of 1874

(Des A. Onwudimegwu (30 k.), S. Eluare (others))

1974 (10 June). *Stamp Centenary. T* **184** *and similar horiz designs. P* 14 × 13½.

321	5 k.	light emerald, yellow-orange and black	15	10
322	12 k.	multicoloured	40	60
323	18 k.	light yellowish green, mauve and black	70	1·00
324	30 k.	multicoloured	1·60	2·50
321/4		*Set of* 4	2·50	3·75

Designs:—5 k. Graph of mail traffic growth; 12 k. Northern Nigeria £25 stamp of 1904; 30 k. Forms of mail transport.

185 U.P.U. Emblem on Globe   186 Starving and Well-fed Children

(Des S. Eluare (5 k.). A. Onwudimegwu (18 k.), O. I. Oshiga (30 k.))

1974 (9 Oct). *Centenary of Universal Postal Union. T* **185** *and similar horiz designs. P* 14.

325	5 k.	lt greenish blue, yellow-orange & black	15	10
326	18 k.	multicoloured	1·25	60
327	30 k.	bistre-brown, lt greenish blue & black	1·75	1·75
325/7		*Set of* 3	2·75	2·25

Designs:—18 k. World transport map; 30 k. U.P.U. emblem and letters.

(Des A. Onwudimegwu (12 k.), S. Eluare (others))

1974 (25 Nov). *Freedom from Hunger Campaign. T* **186** *and similar designs. P* 14.

328	5 k.	apple-green, buff and grey-black	10	10
329	12 k.	multicoloured	40	50
330	30 k.	multicoloured	1·10	1·75
328/30		*Set of* 3	1·40	2·00

Designs: *Horiz*—12 k. Poultry battery. *Vert*—30 k. Water-hoist.

187 Telex Network and Teleprinter   188 Queen Amina of Zaria

(Des S. Eluare)

1975 (3 July). *Inauguration of Telex Network. T* **187** *and similar vert designs. P* 13½ × 14.

331	5 k.	black, yellow-orange & light olive-green	10	10
332	12 k.	black, lemon and orange-brown	20	20
333	18 k.	multicoloured	30	30
334	30 k.	multicoloured	50	50
331/4		*Set of* 4	1·00	1·00

Nos. 332/4 are as T **187** but have the motifs arranged differently.

(Des A. Onwudimegwu)

1975 (18 Aug). *International Women's Year. P* 14.

335	**188**	5 k. deep olive, light yellow and azure	15	10
336		18 k. purple, pale blue and light mauve	50	65
337		30 k. multicoloured	60	1·10
335/7		*Set of* 3	1·10	1·75

189

1975–82*. *As Nos.* 290 *etc., but W* **189** (*sideways on* 18, 50 k.).

338	1 k.	multicoloured (6.4.77)	40	55
339	2 k.	black, pale turq-bl & bright purple (9.75)	75	10
340	3 k.	multicoloured (10.75)	15	10
341	5 k.	multicoloured (1.76)	80	10
342	7 k.	multicoloured (16.5.80)	1·50	85
343	8 k.	multicoloured (12.76)	1·25	80
344	10 k.	blk, orange-yell & lilac (*shades*) (7.4.76)	1·00	20
346	15 k.	multicoloured (5.82)	—	1·50
347	18 k.	multicoloured (12.78)	2·25	2·00
348	20 k.	multicoloured (9.79)	2·50	2·00
349	25 k.	multicoloured (21.3.77)	2·50	25
352	50 k.	multicoloured (2.9.77)	3·50	3·25
354	2 n.	multicoloured (11.77)	6·00	6·00

*Earliest known dates of use.

190 Alexander Graham Bell   191 Child Writing

(Des A. Onwudimegwu)

1976 (10 Mar). *Telephone Centenary. T* **190** *and similar designs. W* **189** (*sideways on* 5 *and* 25 k.). *P* 13½.

355	5 k.	multicoloured	10	10
356	18 k.	multicoloured	40	55
357	25 k.	royal blue, pale blue and blackish brown	70	1·00
		a. No wmk	10·00	
355/7		*Set of* 3	1·10	1·50

Designs: *Horiz*—18 k. Gong and modern telephone system. *Vert*—25 k. Telephones, 1876 and 1976.

(Des A. Onwudimegwu (5 k.), S. Eluare (18 k.), N. Lasisi (25 k.))

1976 (20 Sept). *Launching of Universal Primary Education. T* **191** *and similar designs. W* **189** (*sideways on* 18 *and* 25 k.). *P* 14.

358	5 k.	lemon, light violet and bright mauve	10	10
359	18 k.	multicoloured	45	60
360	25 k.	multicoloured	70	85
358/60		*Set of* 3	1·10	1·40

Designs: *Vert*—18 k. Children entering school; 25 k. Children in class.

192 Festival Emblem

(Des O. I. Oshiga (5 k., 30 k.), A. Onwudimegwu (10 k., 12 k.), N. Lasisi (18 k.))

1976–77. *Second World Black and African Festival of Arts and Culture, Nigeria. T* **192** *and similar horiz designs. W* **189**. *P* 14.

361	5 k.	gold and blackish brown (1.11.76)	15	10
362	10 k.	lt red-brown, lt yellow & black (15.1.77)	35	40
363	12 k.	multicoloured (15.1.77)	40	55
364	18 k.	chrome-yellow, lt brown & blk (1.11.76)	60	80
365	30 k.	magenta and black (15.1.77)	1·00	1·50
361/5		*Set of* 5	2·25	3·00

Designs:—10 k. National Arts Theatre; 12 k. African hair styles; 18 k. Musical instruments; 30 k. "Nigerian arts and crafts".

193 General Murtala Muhammed and Map of Nigeria   194 Scouts Saluting

(Des A. Onwudimegwu (5, 18 k.), O. I. Oshiga (30 k.))

1977 (12 Feb). *First Death Anniv of General Muhammed* (*Head of State*). *T* **193** *and similar vert designs. Multicoloured. W* **189** (*sideways on* 18 *and* 30 k.). *P* 14.

366	5 k.	Type **193**	10	10
367	18 k.	General in dress uniform	20	35
368	30 k.	General in battle dress	30	70
366/8		*Set of* 3	50	1·00

(Des N. Lasisi (18 k.), A. Onwudimegwu (others))

1977 (2 Apr). *First All-Africa Scout Jamboree, Jos, Nigeria. T* **194** *and similar horiz designs. Multicoloured. W* **189** (*sideways on* 5 k.). *P* 14.

369	5 k.	Type **194**	15	10
370	18 k.	Scouts cleaning street	70	70
371	25 k.	Scouts working on farm	85	95
372	30 k.	Jamboree emblem and map of Africa	1·10	1·40
369/72		*Set of* 4	2·50	2·75

195 Trade Fair Complex

(Des S. Eluare (5 k.), A. Onwudimegwu (others))

1977 (27 Nov). *1st Lagos International Trade Fair. T* **195** *and similar horiz designs. W* **189**. *P* 14.

373	5 k.	black, new blue and yellow-green	10	10
374	18 k.	black, new blue and magenta	20	25
375	30 k.	multicoloured	30	45
373/5		*Set of* 3	50	70

Designs:—18 k. Globe and Trade Fair emblem; 30 k. Weaving and basketry.

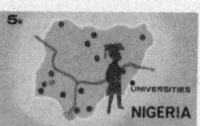

196 Map showing Nigerian Universities

(Des M. O. Shadare (5 k.), C. Okechukwu (12 k.), A. Onwudimegwu (18 k.), N. Lasisi (30 k.))

1978 (28 Apr). *Global Conference on Technical Co-operation between Developing Countries, Buenos Aires. T* **196** *and similar horiz designs. W* **189**. *P* 14.

376	5 k.	multicoloured	10	10
377	12 k.	multicoloured	15	15
378	18 k.	multicoloured	25	25
379	30 k.	yellow, bluish violet and black	45	60
376/9		*Set of* 4	80	1·00

Designs:—12 k. Map of West African highways and telecommunications; 18 k. Technologists undergoing training; 30 k. World map.

197 Microwave Antenna

1978 (17 May). *10th World Telecommunications Day. W* **189**. *P* 14.

380	**197**	30 k. multicoloured	50	60

198 Students on "Operation Feed the Nation"   199 Mother with Infected Child

(Des J. Salisu (5 k.), N. Lasisi (18 k.), A. Onwudimegwu (30 k.))

1978 (7 July). *"Operation Feed the Nation" Campaign. T* **198** *and similar multicoloured designs. W* **189** (*sideways on* 30 k.). *P* 14.

381	5 k.	Type **198**	10	10
382	18 k.	Family backyard farm	20	20
383	30 k.	Plantain farm (*vert*)	35	60
381/3		*Set of* 3	55	75

(Des G. Osuji (30 k.), N. Lasisi (others))

1978 (31 Aug). *Global Eradication of Smallpox. T* **199** *and similar designs.* W **189** *(sideways on 30 k.).* P 14.
384 5 k. black, orange-brown and rose-lilac .. 15 10
385 12 k. multicoloured 30 20
386 18 k. black, lake-brown and greenish yellow .. 50 40
387 30 k. black, silver and rose-pink .. 70 70
384/7 .. .. *Set of* 4 1·50 1·25
Designs: *Horiz*—12 k. Doctor and infected child; 18 k. Group of children being vaccinated. *Vert*—30 k. Syringe.

200 Nok Terracotta Human Figure, Bwari (900 B.C.–200 A.D.)   **201** Anti-Apartheid Emblem

(Des local artists)

1978 (27 Oct). *Antiquities. T* **200** *and similar designs.* W **189** *(sideways on 5, 18 and 30 k.).* P 14.
388 5 k. black, new blue and carmine-red .. 10 10
389 12 k. multicoloured 10 10
390 18 k. black, greenish blue and carmine-red .. 15 15
391 30 k. multicoloured 20 20
388/91 .. .. *Set of* 4 45 45
Designs: *Horiz*—12 k. Igbo-Ukwu bronze snail shell, Igbo Isaiah (9th-century A.D.). *Vert*—18 k. Ife bronze statue of king (12th–15th century A.D.); 30 k. Benin bronze equestrian figure (about 1700 A.D.).

(Des A. Onwudimegwu)

1978 (10 Dec). *International Anti-Apartheid Year.* W **189** *(sideways).* P 14.
392 **201** 18 k. black, greenish yellow & vermilion 15 15

202 Wright Brothers and *Flyer*   **203** Murtala Muhammed Airport

(Des A. Onwudimegwu)

1978 (28 Dec). *75th Anniv of Powered Flight. T* **202** *and similar horiz design.* W **189**. P 14.
393 5 k. multicoloured 15 10
394 18 k. black, ultramarine and light blue .. 50 20
Design:—18 k. Nigerian Air Force formation.

(Des A. Onwudimegwu)

1979 (15 Mar). *Opening of Murtala Muhammed Airport.* W **189**. P 14.
395 **203** 5 k. black, grey-blk & brt greenish blue 30 30

204 Child with Stamp Album   **205** Mother and Child

1979 (11 Apr). *10th Anniv of National Philatelic Service.* W **189**. P 14.
396 **204** 5 k. multicoloured 10 10

1979 (28 June). *International Year of the Child. T* **205** *and similar multicoloured designs.* W **189** *(sideways on 25 k.).* P 14.
397 5 k. Type **205** 15 10
398 18 k. Children studying 40 30
399 25 k. Children playing *(vert)* 50 50
397/9 .. .. *Set of* 3 95 80

206 Trainee Teacher making Audio Visual Aid Materials   **207** Necom House

(Des M. Shadare and O. Oshiga)

1979 (25 July). *50th Anniv of International Bureau of Education. T* **206** *and similar vert design. Multicoloured.* W **189** *(sideways).* P 14.
400 10 k. Type **206** 10 10
401 30 k. Adult education class 25 30

(Des A. Onwudimegwu)

1979 (20 Sept). *50th Anniv of Consultative Committee of International Radio.* W **189** *(sideways).* P 14.
402 **207** 10 k. multicoloured 15 20

208 Trainees of the Regional Aerial Survey School, Ile-Ife

(Des A. Onwudimegwu)

1979 (12 Dec). *21st Anniv of the Economic Commission for Africa.* W **189**. P 14.
403 **208** 10 k. multicoloured 20 20

209 Football, Cup and Map of Nigeria   **210** Wrestling

(Des G. Akinola (10 k.), Mrs. O. Adeyeye (30 k.))

1980 (8 Mar). *African Cup of Nations Football Competition, Nigeria. T* **209** *and similar multicoloured design.* W **189** *(sideways on 30 k.).* P 14.
404 10 k. Type **209** 15 10
405 30 k. Footballer *(vert)* 50 50

(Des M. Shadare (10 k.), Mrs. O. Adeyeye (others))

1980 (19 July). *Olympic Games, Moscow. T* **210** *and similar designs.* W **189** *(sideways on 10, 20 and 45 k.).* P 14.
406 10 k. multicoloured 10 10
407 20 k. black and bright yellow-green 10 10
408 30 k. black, reddish orange and blue .. 15 15
409 45 k. multicoloured 20 20
406/9 .. .. *Set of* 4 45 45
Designs: *Vert*—20 k. Long jump; 45 k. Netball. *Horiz*—30 k. Swimming.

211 Figures supporting O.P.E.C. Emblem   **212** Steam Locomotive

(Des G. Oluwasegun)

1980 (15 Sept). *20th Anniv of O.P.E.C. (Organization of Petroleum Exporting Countries). T* **211** *and similar design.* W **189** *(sideways on 45 k.).* P 14.
410 10 k. black, ultramarine and greenish yellow 15 10
411 45 k. black, deep turquoise-blue and magenta 55 60
Design:—*Vert*—45 k. O.P.E.C. emblem on globe.

1980 (2 Oct). *25th Anniv of Nigerian Railway Corporation. T* **212** *and similar horiz designs. Multicoloured.* W **189**. P 14.
412 10 k. Type **212** 55 10
413 20 k. Loading goods train .. .. 1·25 85
414 30 k. Freight train .. .. 1·50 1·00
412/14 .. .. .. *Set of* 3 3·00 1·75

213 Metric Scales   **214** "Communications" Symbols and Map of West Africa

(Des G. Akinola (10 k.), M. Shadare (30 k.))

1980 (14 Oct). *World Standards Day. T* **213** *and similar design.* W **189** *(sideways on 10 k.).* P 14.
415 10 k. red and b'ack 10 10
416 30 k. multicoloured 35 40
Design:—*Horiz*—30 k. Quality control.

1980 (5 Nov). *5th Anniv of E.C.O.W.A.S. (Economic Community of West African States). T* **214** *and similar horiz designs showing symbols of economic structure and map of West Africa.* W **189**. P 14.
417 10 k. black, yellow-orange and grey-olive .. 10 10
418 25 k. black, emerald and bright rose .. 10 10
419 30 k. black, greenish yellow and yellow-brown 15 15
420 45 k. black, turquoise-blue and bright blue .. 20 25
417/20 .. .. *Set of* 4 45 50
Designs:—25 k. "Transport"; 30 k. "Agriculture"; 45 k. "Industry".

215 Disabled Woman Sweeping   **216** President launching "Green Revolution" (food production campaign)

(Des N. Lasisi (10 k.), G. Akinola (30 k.))

1981 (25 June). *International Year for Disabled Persons. T* **215** *and similar vert design.* W **189** *(sideways).* P 14.
421 10 k. multicoloured 20 10
422 30 k. black, chestnut and new blue .. 65 65
Design:—30 k. Disabled man filming.

(Des Mrs. A. Adeyeye (10 k.), G. Akinola (30 k.), S. Eluare (others))

1981 (16 Oct). *World Food Day. T* **216** *and similar designs.* W **189** *(sideways on 25 and 30 k.).* P 14.
423 10 k. multicoloured 10 10
424 25 k. black, greenish yellow and emerald .. 20 50
425 30 k. multicoloured 25 55
426 45 k. black, yellow-brown and orange-yellow .. 45 85
423/6 .. .. *Set of* 4 85 1·75
Designs: *Vert*—25 k. Food crops; 30 k. Harvesting tomatoes. *Horiz*—45 k. Pig farming.

217 Rioting in Soweto   **218** "Preservation of Wildlife"

(Des G. Osuji)

1981 (10 Dec). *Anti-Apartheid Movement. T* **217** *and similar design.* W **189** *(sideways on 45 k.).* P 14.
427 30 k. multicoloured 35 45
428 45 k. black, vermilion and light green .. 50 80
Design: *Vert*—45 k. "Police brutality".

(Des G. Akinola)

1982 (22 Feb). *75th Anniv of Boy Scout Movement. T* **218** *and similar horiz design. Multicoloured.* W **189**. P 14.
429 30 k. Type **218** 75 55
430 45 k. Lord Baden-Powell taking salute .. 1·00 95

219 Early Inoculation   **220** "Keep Your Environment Clean"

(Des G. Osuji (10 k.), C. Ogbebor (30 k.), N. Lasisi (45 k.))

1982 (24 Mar). *Centenary of Robert Koch's Discovery of Tubercle Bacillus. T* **219** *and similar designs.* W **189** *(sideways on 45 k.).* P 14.
431 10 k. multicoloured 25 15
432 30 k. grey-black, brown and turquoise-green .. 65 55
433 45 k. grey-black, light brown and bright green 1·10 85
431/3 .. .. *Set of* 3 1·75 1·40
Designs: *Horiz*—30 k. Technician and microscope. *Vert*—45 k. Patient being X-rayed.

(Des C. Ogbebor (10 k.), N. Lasisi (others))

1982 (10 June). *10th Anniv of U.N. Conference on Human Environment. T* **220** *and similar horiz designs.* W **189**. P 14.
434 10 k. multicoloured 15 10
435 20 k. yellow-orange, greenish grey and black .. 40 40
436 30 k. multicoloured 55 60
437 45 k. multicoloured 80 85
434/7 .. .. *Set of* 4 1·75 1·75
Designs:—20 k. "Check air pollution"; 30 k. "Preserve natural environment"; 45 k. "Reafforestation concerns all".

COVER PRICES
Cover factors are quoted at the beginning of each country for most issues to 1945. An explanation of the system can be found on page x. The factors quoted do not, however, apply to philatelic covers.

221 *Salamis parhassus*

222 Carving of "Male and Female Twins"

(Des G. Akinola)

1982 (15 Sept). *Nigerian Butterflies. T* **221** *and similar horiz designs. Multicoloured.* W **189**. P 14.

438	10 k. Type **221**		..	15	10
439	20 k. *Iterus zalmoxis*	..	..	30	30
440	30 k. *Cymothoe beckeri*	..	..	40	40
441	45 k. *Papilio hesperus*	..	..	70	70
438/41			*Set of 4*	1·40	1·40

(Des C. Ogbebor (10 k.), G. Akinola (20 k.), S. Eluare (30 k.), N. Lasisi (45 k.))

1982 (18 Nov). *25th Anniv of National Museum. T* **222** *and similar multicoloured designs.* W **189** *(sideways on 10, 30, 45 k.).* P 14.

442	10 k. Type **222**		..	25	10
443	20 k. Royal bronze leopard (*horiz*)	..		50	55
444	30 k. Soapstone seated figure	..		80	1·25
445	45 k. Wooden helmet mask	..	..	1·25	1·75
442/5		..	*Set of 4*	2·50	3·25

223 Three Generations

224 Satellite View of Globe

(Des G. Akinola)

1983 (8 Mar). *Family Day. T* **223** *and similar multicoloured design.* W **189** *(sideways on 30 k.).* P 14.

446	10 k. Type **223**		..	15	10
447	30 k. Parents with three children (*vert*)		50	65

(Des N. Lasisi (30 k.), C. Ogbebor (others))

1983 (14 Mar). *Commonwealth Day. T* **224** *and similar designs.* W **189** *(sideways on 30, 45 k.).* P 14.

448	10 k. yellow-brown and black	..		10	10
449	25 k. multicoloured		..	30	30
450	30 k. black, magenta and pale grey	..		35	35
451	45 k. multicoloured	..	..	45	45
448/51		..	*Set of 4*	1·10	1·10

Designs:—*Horiz*—25 k. National Assembly Buildings. *Vert*—30 k. Drilling for oil; 45 k. Athletics.

225 Corps Members on Building Project

226 Postman on Bicycle

(Des Mrs. A. Adeyeye (25 k.), G. Akinola (others))

1983 (25 May). *10th Anniv of National Youth Service Corps. T* **225** *and similar multicoloured designs.* W **189** *(sideways on 25, 30 k.).* P 14.

452	10 k. Type **225**		..	15	10
453	25 k. On the assault-course (*vert*)	..		30	30
454	30 k. Corps members on parade (*vert*)..		40	40
452/4		..	*Set of 3*	75	70

(Des N. Lasisi (25 k.), O. Ogunfowora (30 k.), Mrs. A. Adeyeye (others))

1983 (20 July). *World Communications Year. T* **226** *and similar multicoloured designs.* W **189** *(sideways on 10 k.).* P 14.

455	10 k. Type **226**		..	15	10
456	25 k. Newspaper kiosk (*horiz*)..	..		30	40
457	30 k. Town crier blowing elephant tusk (*horiz*)	35	45
458	45 k. T.V. newsreader (*horiz*)	..	..	45	55
455/8		..	*Set of 4*	1·10	1·25

227 Pink Shrimp

228 On Parade

(Des Hilda Woods (10 k.), G. Osuji (25 k.), Mrs. A. Adeyeye (30 k.), O. Ogunfowora (45 k.))

1983 (22 Sept). *World Fishery Resources. T* **227** *and similar horiz designs.* W **189**. P 14.

459	10 k. rose, new blue and black..		..	15	10
460	25 k. multicoloured	..	..	30	40
461	30 k. multicoloured	..	..	30	45
462	45 k. multicoloured	..	..	40	70
459/62			*Set of 4*	1·00	1·40

Designs:—25 k. Long Neck Croaker; 30 k. Barracuda; 45 k. Fishing techniques.

(Des F. Nwaije (10 k.), Mrs A. Adeyeye (30 k.), G. Osuji (45 k.))

1983 (14 Oct). *Boys' Brigade Centenary and 75th Anniv of Movement in Nigeria. T* **228** *and similar multicoloured designs.* W **189** *(sideways on 10 k.).* P 14.

463	10 k. Type **228**		..	40	10
464	30 k. Members working on cassava plantation (*horiz*)	..	1·25	1·25
465	45 k. Skill training (*horiz*)	..	,	2·00	2·25
463/5	..	..	*Set of 3*	3·25	3·25

229 Crippled Child

230 Waterbuck

(Des S. Eluare (10 k.), G. Osuji (others))

1984 (29 Feb). *Stop Polio Campaign. T* **229** *and similar designs.* W **189** *(sideways on 10 k. and 30 k.).* P 14.

466	10 k. light blue, black and light brown	..	20	15
467	25 k. pale orange, black and greenish yellow	45	60
468	30 k. carmine-rose, black and orange-brown	55	75
466/8			*Set of 3*	1·10	1·40

Designs:—*Horiz*—25 k. Child receiving vaccine. *Vert*—30 k. Healthy child.

(Des O. Ogunfowora (30 k.), Mrs. A. Adeyeye (45 k.), N. Lasisi (others))

1984 (25 May). *Nigerian Wildlife. T* **230** *and similar designs.* W **189** *(inverted on 30 k., sideways on 10 k., 45 k.).* P 14.

469	10 k. light green, light brown and black	..	20	10
470	25 k. multicoloured		..	50	50
471	30 k. yellow-brown, black and light green	..	60	70
472	45 k. new blue, pale orange and black	..	80	95
469/72			*Set of 4*	1·90	2·00

Designs:—*Horiz*—25 k. Hartebeest; 30 k. African Buffalo. *Vert*—45 k. Diademed Monkey ("African Golden Monkey").

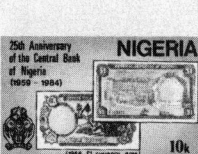

231 Obverse and Reverse of 1969 £1 Note

232 Boxing

1984 (2 July). *25th Anniv of Nigerian Central Bank. T* **231** *and similar horiz designs.* W **189** *(inverted on 30 k.).* P 14.

473	10 k. multicoloured	..		20	10
474	25 k. deep cinnamon, black and light green	..	45	50
475	30 k. light rose, black and grey-olive	..	55	60
473/5	..	..	*Set of 3*	1·10	1·10

Designs:—25 k. Central Bank; 30 k. Obverse and reverse of 1959 £5 note.

1984 (20 July). *Olympic Games, Los Angeles. T* **232** *and similar vert designs. Multicoloured.* W **189** *(sideways).* P 14.

476	10 k. Type **232**		..	15	10
477	25 k. Discus-throwing	..	..	35	50
478	30 k. Weightlifting	..	..	40	60
479	45 k. Cycling	..	..	60	90
476/9	..	..	*Set of 4*	1·40	1·90

233 Irrigation Project, Lesotho

234 Pin-tailed Whydah

(Des Mrs. A. Adeyeye (10 k.), S. Eluare (25 k.), Hilda Woods (30 k.), O. Ogunfowora (45 k.))

1984 (10 Sept). *20th Anniv of African Development Bank. T* **233** *and similar designs.* W **189** *(sideways on 10 k.).* P 14.

480	10 k. multicoloured	..		20	10
481	25 k. multicoloured		..	50	50
482	30 k. black, chrome yell & bright greenish bl	60	60
483	45 k. black, orange-brn & bright greenish bl	..	1·75	90
480/3	..	..	*Set of 4*	2·75	1·90

Designs: *Horiz*—25 k. Bomi Hills Road, Liberia; 30 k. School building project, Seychelles; 45 k. Coal mining, Niger.

(Des S. Eluare (25 k.), O. Ogunfowora (45 k.), F. Isibor (others))

1984 (24 Oct). *Rare Birds. T* **234** *and similar vert designs. Multicoloured.* W **189** *(sideways).* P 14.

484	10 k. Type **234**		..	65	10
485	25 k. Spur-winged Plover	..		1·25	50
486	30 k. Red Bishop	..		1·25	90
487	45 k. Double-spurred Francolin	..		1·50	1·40
484/7	..	..	*Set of 4*	4·25	2·50

235 Aircraft taking-off

236 Office Workers and Clocks ("Punctuality")

(Des F. Isibor (10 k.), O. Ogunfowora (45 k.))

1984 (7 Dec). *40th Anniv of International Civil Aviation Organization. T* **235** *and similar horiz design. Multicoloured.* W **189** *(inverted on 45 k.).* P 14.

488	10 k. Type **235**		..	50	10
489	45 k. Aircraft circling globe ..		..	1·75	1·50

(Des O. Ogunfowora)

1985 (27 Feb). *"War against Indiscipline". T* **236** *and similar horiz design. Multicoloured.* W **189** *(inverted on 20 k.).* P 14.

490	20 k. Type **236**		..	30	35
491	50 k. Cross over hands passing banknotes ("Discourage Bribery")..	..		70	75

237 Footballers receiving Flag from Major-General Buhari

238 Globe and O.P.E.C. Emblem

(Des F. Isibor (50 k.), G. Akinola (others))

1985 (5 June). *International Youth Year. T* **237** *and similar multicoloured designs.* W **189** *(sideways on 50, 55 k.).* P 14.

492	20 k. Type **237**		..	30	35
493	50 k. Girls of different tribes with flag (*vert*)	..	..	70	75
494	55 k. Members of youth organizations with flags (*vert*)	..	..	75	80
492/4	..	..	*Set of 3*	1·60	1·75

1985 (15 Sept). *25th Anniv of Organization of Petroleum Exporting Countries. T* **238** *and similar design.* W **189** *(sideways on 20 k.).* P 14.

495	20 k. greenish blue and orange-vermilion ..	1·00	35
496	50 k. black and ultramarine..	..		1·75	75

Design: *Horiz*—50 k. World map and O.P.E.C. emblem.

239 Rolling Mill

240 Waterfall

1985 (25 Sept). *25th Anniv of Independence. T* **239** *and similar horiz designs. Multicoloured.* W **189**. P 14.

497	20 k. Type **239**	..		40	10
498	50 k. Map of Nigeria	..		60	35
499	55 k. Remembrance Arcade ..			60	40
500	60 k. Eleme, first Nigerian oil refinery		85	50
497/500			*Set of 4*	2·25	1·25
MS501	101×101 mm. Nos. 497/500. Wmk sideways	..	..	4·00	4·75

(Des S. Eluare (55 k.), F. Isibor (60 k.), Mrs. A. Adeyeye (others))

1985 (27 Sept). *World Tourism Day. T* **240** *and similar multicoloured designs.* W **189** *(sideways on 20, 55, 60 k., inverted on 50 k.).* P 14.

502	20 k. Type **240**			45	10
503	50 k. Pottery, carved heads and map of Nigeria (*horiz*)	..		55	40
504	55 k. Calabash carvings and Nigerian flag ..		55	40
505	60 k. Leather work	..	..	55	45
502/5	..	..	*Set of 4*	1·90	1·25

241 Map of Nigeria and National Flag   242 Rock Python

(Des N. Lasisi (20 k.), Mrs. A. Adeyeye (50 k.), O. Ogunfowora (55 k.))

1985 (7 Oct). *40th Anniv of United Nations Organization and 25th Anniv of Nigerian Membership. T 241 and similar designs. W 189 (sideways on 20 k., inverted on 50 k.). P 14.*
506	20 k. black, light green and pale blue	15	10
507	50 k. black, dull ultramarine and cerise	30	30
508	55 k. black, new blue and carmine	30	30
506/8	*Set of 3*	65	65

Designs: *Horiz*—50 k. United Nations Building, New York; 55 k. United Nations logo.

IMPERFORATE STAMPS. Nos. 509/12, 528/38, 543/6, 555/7, 560/7, 572/9, 582/94, 599/603 and 607/16 exist imperforate from restricted printings. Such printings may also exist for other issues.

(Des Hilda Woods (10, 30 k.), G. Akinola (20 k.), F. Isibor (25 k.))

1986 (15 Apr). *African Reptiles. T 242 and similar horiz designs. W 189 (inverted on 10 k.). P 14.*
509	10 k. multicoloured	35	10
510	20 k. black, orange-brown and pale new blue	65	50
511	25 k. multicoloured	70	65
512	30 k. multicoloured	70	85
509/12	*Set of 4*	2·25	1·90

Designs:—20 k. Long Snouted Crocodile; 25 k. Gopher Tortoise; 30 k. Chameleon.

243 Social Worker with Children   244 Emblem and Globe

(Des G. Akinola (1, 35 k.), S. Eluare (5 k.), O. Ogunfowora (10, 15 k.), Mrs. A. Adeyeye (40, 45 k.), G. Osuji (50 k.), C. Ogbebor (others))

1986 (16 June). *Nigerian Life. T 243 and similar multicoloured designs. W 189 (sideways on 1, 10, 20, 40 k. and inverted on 2, 5, 25, 50 k.). 1, 2 n.). P 14.*
513	1 k. Type 243	10	10
514	2 k. Volkswagen motor assembly line (*horiz*)	10	10
515	5 k. Modern housing estate (*horiz*)	10	10
516	10 k. Harvesting oil palm fruit	10	10
517	15 k. Unloading freighter (*horiz*)	10	10
518	20 k. Tecoma stans (flower)	10	10
519	25 k. Hospital ward (*horiz*)	10	10
519a	30 k. Birom dancers	10	10
520	35 k. Telephonists operating switchboard (*horiz*)	10	10
521	40 k. Nkpokiti dancers	10	10
522	45 k. Hibiscus (*horiz*)	10	10
523	50 k. Post Office counter (*horiz*)	10	10
524	1 n. Stone quarry (*horiz*)	10	15
525	2 n. Students in laboratory (*horiz*)	10	10
513/25	*Set of 14*	70	75

Nos. 513/25 were originally scheduled for issue during 1984, but were delayed. The 5 k. and 20 k. appear to have been released for postal purposes during 1984 and are known postmarked from 2 November (5 k.) or 3 July (20 k.). The 30 k. value, No. 519a, was not included in the 1986 philatelic release.

(Des Mrs. A. Adeyeye)

1986 (20 June). *International Peace Year. T 244 and similar horiz design. Multicoloured. W 189. P 14.*
526	10 k. Type 244	10	10
527	20 k. Hands of five races holding globe	10	10

245 *Goliathus goliathus* (beetle)   246 Oral Rehydration Therapy

(Des Hilda Woods (25 k.), S. Eluare (others))

1986 (14 July). *Nigerian Insects. T 245 and similar horiz designs. Multicoloured. W 189 (inverted on 20 k.). P 14.*
528	10 k. Type 245	35	10
529	20 k. Vespa vulgaris (wasp)	45	40
530	25 k. Acheta domestica (cricket)	55	55
531	30 k. Anthrenus verbasci (beetle)	75	85
528/31	*Set of 4*	1·90	1·75
MS532	119×101 mm. Nos. 528/31. Wmk sideways	4·00	4·75

(Des N. Lasisi (10 k.), F. Isibor (30 k.), Mrs. A. Adeyeye (others))

1986 (11 Nov). *40th Anniv of United Nations Children's Fund. T 246 and similar vert designs. W 189 (sideways). P 14.*
533	10 k. multicoloured	30	10
534	20 k. black, reddish brown & greenish yellow	50	30
535	25 k. multicoloured	55	40
536	30 k. multicoloured	70	55
533/6	*Set of 4*	1·75	1·25

Designs:—20 k. Immunisation; 25 k. Breast feeding; 30 k. Mother and child.

247 Stylized Figures on Wall ("International Understanding")   248 Freshwater Clam

(Des S. Eluare (20 k.), Hilda Woods (30 k.))

1986 (12 Dec). *25th Anniv of Nigerian Institute of International Affairs. T 247 and similar design. W 189 (sideways on 30 k.). P 14.*
537	20 k. black, greenish blue and light green	50	40
538	30 k. multicoloured	75	1·00

Design: *Vert*—30 k. "Knowledge" (bronze sculpture).

(Des G. Osuji (20 k.), F. Isibor (others))

1987 (31 Mar). *Shells. T 248 and similar horiz designs. W 189 (inverted on 10, 25 k.). P 14.*
539	10 k. multicoloured	50	10
540	20 k. black, reddish brown & pale rose-pink	80	80
541	25 k. multicoloured	90	80
542	30 k. multicoloured	1·00	1·25
539/42	*Set of 4*	3·00	2·75

Design:—20 k. Periwinkle; 25 k. Bloody Cockle (inscr "BLODDY COCKLE"); 30 k. Mangrove Oyster.

249 *Clitoria ternatea*   250 Doka Hairstyle

(Des S. Eluare (10 k.), Hilda Woods (20 k.), Mrs. A. Adeyeye (others))

1987 (28 May). *Nigerian Flowers. T 249 and similar vert designs. W 189 (sideways). P 14.*
543	10 k. multicoloured	10	10
544	20 k. lake-brown, greenish yellow & emerald	15	15
545	25 k. multicoloured	15	15
546	30 k. multicoloured	20	20
543/6	*Set of 4*	45	45

Designs:—20 k. Hibiscus tiliaceus; 25 k. Acanthus montanus; 30 k. Combretum racemosum.

(Des G. Akinola (25 k.), S. Eluare (30 k.), Mrs. A. Adeyeye (others))

1987 (15 Sept). *Women's Hairstyles. T 250 and similar vert designs. W 189 (sideways). P 14.*
547	10 k. black, orange-brown and olive-grey	10	10
548	20 k. multicoloured	10	10
549	25 k. black, brown and vermilion	10	10
550	30 k. multicoloured	10	10
547/50	*Set of 4*	30	30

Designs:—20 k. Eting; 25 k. Agogo; 30 k. Goto.

251 Family sheltering under Tree   252 Red Cross Worker distributing Food

(Des S. Nwasike (20 k.), Mrs. A. Adeyeye (30 k.))

1987 (10 Dec). *International Year of Shelter for the Homeless. T 251 and similar vert design. Multicoloured. W 189 (sideways). P 14.*
551	20 k. Type 251	15	10
552	30 k. Family and modern house	15	20

(Des G. Osuji)

1988 (17 Feb). *125th Anniv of International Red Cross. T 252 and similar vert designs. Multicoloured. W 189 (sideways). P 14.*
553	20 k. Type 252	15	10
554	30 k. Carrying patient to ambulance	15	40

253 Doctor vaccinating Baby   254 O.A.U. Logo

(Des C. Ogbebor (10 k.), G. Osuji (others))

1988 (7 Apr). *40th Anniv of World Health Organization. T 253 and similar horiz designs. Multicoloured. W 189 (inverted). P 14.*
555	10 k. Type 253	10	10
556	20 k. W.H.O. logo and outline map of Nigeria	15	15
557	30 k. Doctor and patients at mobile clinic	15	15
555/7	*Set of 3*	30	30

(Des O. Ojo (10 k.), Mrs. A. Adeyeye (20 k.))

1988 (25 May). *25th Anniv of Organization of African Unity. T 254 and similar vert design. W 189 (sideways). P 14.*
558	10 k. olive-bistre, emerald and bright orange	15	15
559	20 k. multicoloured	15	15

Design:—20 k. Four Africans supporting map of Africa.

255 Pink Shrimp   256 Weightlifting

(Des S. Eluare)

1988 (2 June). *Shrimps. T 255 and similar horiz designs. W 189. P 14.*
560	10 k. multicoloured	15	10
561	20 k. black and pale yellow-olive	20	10
562	25 k. black, orange-vermilion & yell-brown	20	10
563	30 k. reddish orange, olive-bistre and black	25	10
560/3	*Set of 4*	70	30
MS564	120 × 101 mm. Nos. 560/3. Wmk sideways	40	50

Designs:—20 k. Tiger Shrimp; 25 k. Deepwater Roseshrimp; 30 k. Estuarine Prawn.

(Des G. Osuji (30 k.), Mrs. A. Adeyeye (others))

1988 (6 Sept). *Olympic Games, Seoul. T 256 and similar multicoloured designs. W 189 (sideways on 30 k.). P 14.*
565	10 k. Type 256	15	10
566	20 k. Boxing	20	10
567	30 k. Athletics (*vert*)	30	15
565/7	*Set of 3*	60	30

257 Banknote Production Line

(Des Mrs. A. Adeyeye (25 k.), G. Akinola (30 k.), O. Ojo (others))

1988 (28 Oct). *25th Anniv of Nigerian Security Printing and Minting Co Ltd. T 257 and similar designs. W 189 (inverted on 10 k.). P 14.*
568	10 k. multicoloured	10	10
569	20 k. black, silver and emerald	10	10
570	25 k. multicoloured	10	10
571	30 k. multicoloured	15	15
568/71	*Set of 4*	30	30

Designs: *Horiz (as T 257)*—20 k. Coin production line. *Vert (37 × 44 mm)*—25 k. Montage of products; 30 k. Anniversary logos.

258 Tambari   259 Construction of Water Towers, Mali

(Des S. Nwasike (10 k.), N. Lasisi (20 k.), S. Eluare (others))

1989 (29 June). *Nigerian Musical Instruments. T 258 and similar horiz designs. W 189 (inverted). P 14.*
572	10 k. multicoloured	10	10
573	20 k. multicoloured	10	10
574	25 k. chestnut, bronze-green and black	10	10
575	30 k. red-brown and black	15	15
572/5	*Set of 4*	30	30

Designs:—20 k. Kundung, 25 k. Ibid; 30 k. Dundun.

(Des Hilda Woods (10 k.), F. Abdul (20, 25 k.), S. Eluare (30 k.))

1989 (10 Sept). *25th Anniv of African Development Bank. T* **259** *and similar multicoloured designs. W* **189** *(inverted on 10, 25 k. and sideways on 30 k.). P 14.*

576	10 k. Type **259**			10	10
577	20 k. Paddy field, Gambia			10	10
578	25 k. Bank Headquarters, Abidjan, Ivory Coast			10	10
579	30 k. Anniversary logo (*vert*)			15	15
576/9			*Set of 4*	30	30

260 Lighting Camp Fire   **261** Etubom Costume

(Des F. Abdul (10 k.), Mrs. A. Adeyeye (20 k.))

1989 (16 Sept). *70th Anniv of Nigerian Girl Guides Association. T* **260** *and similar multicoloured design. W* **189** *(inverted on 10 k. and sideways on 20 k.). P 14.*

580	10 k. Type **260**			15	10
581	20 k. Guide on rope bridge (*vert*)			15	20

(Des S. Eluare (10 k.), Mrs. A. Adeyeye (20 k.), F. Abdul (others))

1989 (26 Oct). *Traditional Costumes. T* **261** *and similar vert designs. Multicoloured. W* **189** *(sideways). P 14.*

582	10 k. Type **261**			15	10
583	20 k. Fulfulde			20	10
584	25 k. Aso-Ofi			25	10
585	30 k. Fuska Kura			30	15
582/5			*Set of 4*	80	30

262 Dove with Letter and Map of Africa   **263** Oil Lamps

1990 (18 Jan). *10th Anniv of Pan African Postal Union. T* **262** *and similar vert design. Multicoloured. W* **189** *(sideways). P 14.*

586	10 k. Type **262**			15	10
587	20 k. Parcel and map of Africa			15	20

1990 (24 May). *Nigerian Pottery. T* **263** *and similar horiz designs. W* **189** *(inverted on 10 k.). P 14.*

588	10 k. brownish black, orange-brn & slate-vio			10	10
589	20 k. brownish black, red-brown & slate-vio			10	10
590	25 k. reddish brown and slate-violet			10	10
591	30 k. multicoloured			15	10
588/91			*Set of 4*	30	30
MS592	120×100 mm. Nos. 588/91. Wmk sideways			30	35

Designs:—20 k. Water pots; 25 k. Musical pots; 30 k. Water jugs.

264 Teacher and Class

(Des Mrs. A. Adeyeye (20 k.), G. Osuji (30 k.))

1990 (8 Aug). *International Literacy Year. T* **264** *and similar horiz design. W* **189** *(inverted). P 14.*

593	20 k. multicoloured			10	10
594	30 k. blackish brn, greenish bl & orange-yell			15	15

Design:—30 k. Globe and book.

265 Globe and OPEC Logo   **266** Grey Parrot

1990 (14 Sept). *30th Anniv of the Organisation of Petroleum Exporting Countries. T* **265** *and similar multicoloured designs. W* **189** *(inverted on 10, 25 k. and sideways on others). P 14.*

595	10 k. Type **265**			10	10
596	20 k. Logo and flags of member countries (*vert*)			10	10
597	25 k. World map and logo			15	15
598	30 k. Logo within inscription "Co-operation for Global Energy Security" (*vert*)			15	15
595/8			*Set of 4*	35	35

(Des C. Ogbebor (20 k.), G. Osuji (30 k, 2 n. 50), S. Eluare (1 n. 50))

1990 (8 Nov). *Wildlife. T* **266** *and similar vert designs. Multicoloured. W* **189** *(sideways). P 14.*

599	20 k. Type **266**			10	10
600	30 k. Roan Antelope			10	10
601	1 n. 50, Grey-necked Bald Crow ("Rock-fowl")			20	25
602	2 n. 50, Mountain Gorilla			35	40
599/602			*Set of 4*	55	60
MS603	118×119 mm. Nos. 599/602. Wmk inverted			65	75

267 Eradication Treatment   **268** Hand holding Torch (Progress)

(Des C. Ogbebor (20 k.), G. Osuji (others))

1991 (20 Mar). *National Guineaworm Eradication Day. T* **267** *and similar multicoloured designs. W* **189** *(sideways on 10, 30 k.). P 14.*

604	10 k. Type **267**			10	10
605	20 k. Women collecting water from river (*horiz*)			10	10
606	30 k. Boiling pot of water			10	10
604/6			*Set of 3*	15	15

1991 (26 May). *Organization of African Unity Heads of State and Governments Meeting, Abuja. T* **268** *and similar vert designs each showing outline map of Africa. Multicoloured. W* **189** *(sideways). P 14.*

607	20 k. Type **268**			10	10
608	30 k. Cogwheel (Unity)			10	10
609	50 k. O.A.U. flag (Freedom)			10	10
607/9			*Set of 3*	15	15

269 National Flags   **270** Electric Catfish

(Des G. Osuji)

1991 (4 July). *Economic Community of West African States Summit Meeting, Abuja. T* **269** *and similar horiz design. Multicoloured. W* **189** *(inverted). P 14.*

610	20 k. Type **269**			10	10
611	50 k. Map showing member states			10	10

(Des R. Adeyemi (10 k.), C. Ogbebor (20 k.), N. Lasisi (others))

1991 (30 July). *Nigerian Fishes. T* **270** *and similar horiz designs. Multicoloured. W* **189** *(inverted on 20 k.). P 14.*

612	10 k. Type **270**			10	10
613	20 k. Niger Perch			10	10
614	30 k. Talapia			10	10
615	50 k. African Catfish			10	10
612/15			*Set of 4*	20	20
MS616	121×104 mm. Nos. 612/15. Wmk sideways			10	10

271 Telecom '91 Emblem   **272** Boxing

(Des S. Eluare)

1991 (7 Oct). *"Telecom '91" 6th World Telecommunication Exhibition, Geneva. T* **271** *and similar design. W* **189** *(sideways on 50 k.). P 14.*

617	20 k. black, deep green and deep violet			10	10
618	50 k. multicoloured			10	10

Design: *Vert*—50 k. Emblem and patchwork.

(Des G. Akinola (2 n.), G. Osuji (others))

1992 (24 Jan). *Olympic Games, Barcelona (1st issue). T* **272** *and similar horiz designs. W* **189** *(2 n.) or no wmk (others). Multicoloured. P 14.*

619	50 k. Type **272**			10	10
620	1 n. Nigerian athlete winning race			10	10
621	1 n. 50, Table tennis			10	10
622	2 n. Taekwondo			10	10
619/22			*Set of 4*	25	30
MS623	120×117 mm. Nos. 619/22. W **189** (sideways)			30	35

273 Football   **274** Blood Pressure Gauge

(Des A. Olusola)

1992 (3 Apr). *Olympic Games, Barcelona (2nd issue). W* **189** *(sideways). P 14.*

624	**273** 1 n. 50, multicoloured			10	10

(Des Mrs. A. Adeyeye (50 k., 1 n.), G. Osuji (others))

1992 (7 Apr). *World Health Day. T* **274** *and similar vert designs. No wmk. Multicoloured. P 14.*

625	50 k. Type **274**			10	10
626	1 n. World Health Day '92 emblem			10	10
627	1 n. 50, Heart and lungs			10	10
628	2 n. Interior of heart			10	10
625/8			*Set of 8*	25	30
MS629	123×111 mm. Nos. 625/8			30	35

POSTAGE DUE STAMPS

D 1

(Litho B.W.)

1959 (4 Jan). *Wmk Mult Script CA. P* 14½ × 14.

D1	D 1	1d. red-orange			10	55
D2		2d. red-orange			15	70
D3		3d. red-orange			20	1·00
D4		6d. red-orange			20	3·00
D5		1s. grey-black			45	4·25
D1/5				*Set of 5*	1·00	8·50

1961 (1 Aug). *W* **34**. *P* 14½ × 14.

D 6	D 1	1d. red			10	25
D 7		2d. light blue			10	30
D 8		3d. emerald			15	50
D 9		6d. yellow			30	70
D10		1s. blue (*shades*)			45	1·75
D6/10				*Set of 5*	1·00	3·25

(Typo Nigerian Security Printing & Minting Co)

1973 (3 May)–**90**. *New Currency. No wmk. P* 12½×13½.

D11	D 1	2 k. red			10	10
		a. Roul 9 (1990)			1·50	
D12		3 k. blue			10	10
D13		5 k. orange-yellow (*shades*)			10	10
D14		10 k. light apple-green (*shades*)			10	10
		a. Roul 9. Emerald (1987)			4·00	
D11/14				*Set of 4*	20	20

Nos. D11a and D14a are known postally used at Ibadan in January 1990 and August 1987.

BIAFRA

The following stamps were issued by Biafra (the Eastern Region of Nigeria) during the civil war with the Federal Government, 1967–70.

They were in regular use within Biafra from the time when supplies of Nigerian stamps were exhausted; and towards the end of the conflict they began to be used on external mail carried by air via Libreville.

1 Map of Republic

2 Arms, Flag and Date of Independence

3 Mother and Child

(Typo and litho Mint, Lisbon)

1968 (5 Feb). *Independence.* P 12½.

1	1	2d. multicoloured		10	40
2	2	4d. multicoloured		10	50
3	3	1s. multicoloured		15	1·10
1/3			*Set of 3*	30	1·75

SOVEREIGN BIAFRA

(4)

1968 (Apr). *Nos. 172/5 and 177/85 of Nigeria optd as T 4 (without "SOVEREIGN" on 10s.).*

4		½d. multicoloured (No. 172)		90	2·25
5		1d. multicoloured (No. 173)		1·25	3·50
		a. Opt double		£150	
		b. Opt omitted (in pair with normal)		£325	
6		1½d. multicoloured (No. 174)		3·75	7·00
7		2d. multicoloured (No. 175)		17·00	45·00
8		4d. multicoloured (No. 177a)		17·00	45·00
9		6d. multicoloured (No. 178)		3·50	6·00
10		9d. Prussian blue and orange-red (No. 179)		1·50	2·50
11		1s. multicoloured (Blk. + R.) (No. 180)		50·00	90·00
12		1s. 3d. multicoloured (Blk. + R.) (No. 181)		32·00	50·00
13		2s. 6d. orange-brown, buff and brown (Blk. + R.) (No. 182)		1·75	5·50
		a. Red opt omitted		£160	
14		5s. chestnut, lt yell & brn (Blk. + R.) (No. 183)		1·75	5·50
		a. Red opt omitted		£160	
		b. Black opt omitted		£150	
		c. Pale chestnut, yellow & brn-pur (No. 183a)		2·25	5·50
15		10s. multicoloured (No. 184)		10·00	25·00
16		£1 multicoloured (Blk. + R.) (No. 185)		10·00	25·00
		a. Black ("SOVEREIGN BIAFRA") omitted		£170	
		b. Red (coat of arms) omitted		£170	
4/16			*Set of 13*	£120	£275

Nos. 172/3 of Nigeria also exist surcharged "BIAFRA – FRANCE FRIENDSHIP 1968 SOVEREIGN BIAFRA", clasped hands and "+5/-" (½d.) or "+£1" (1d.). There is no evidence that these two surcharges were used for postage within Biafra (*Price for set of 2 £20 mint*).

5 Weapon Maintenance

8 Biafran Arms and Banknote

9 Orphaned Child

(Litho Mint, Lisbon)

1968 (30 May). *First Anniv of Independence. T 5, 8/9 and similar vert designs.* P 12½.

17		4d. multicoloured		15	10
18		1s. multicoloured		20	20
19		2s. 6d. multicoloured		45	1·25
20		5s. multicoloured		60	2·00
		a. Indigo (banknote) omitted		40·00	
		b. Red (from flag) omitted		40·00	
21		10s. multicoloured		1·00	3·00
		a. Bright green (from flag) omitted		30·00	
17/21			*Set of 5*	2·10	6·00

Designs:—1s. Victim of atrocity; 2s. 6d. Nurse and refugees.

Nos. 17/21 also exist surcharged "HELP BIAFRAN CHILDREN" and different charity premium ranging from 2d. on the 4d. to 2s. 6d. on the 10s. There is no evidence that these surcharges were used for postage within Biafra (*Price for set of 5 £1.50 mint*).

In late 1968 a set of four values, showing butterflies and plants, was offered for sale outside Biafra. The same stamps also exist overprinted "MEXICO OLYMPICS 1968" and Olympic symbol. There is no evidence that either of these issues were used for postage within Biafra (*Price for set of 4 £4* (*Butterflies and Plants*) *or £3.50* (*Olympic overprints*), both mint).

CANCELLED-TO-ORDER. Many issues of Biafra, including the three unissued sets mentioned above, were available cancelled-to-order with a special "UMUAHIA" handstamp. This was the same diameter as postal cancellations, but differed from them by having larger letters, 3 mm. high, and the year date in full. Where such cancellations exist on issued stamps the used prices quoted are for c-t-o examples. Postally used stamps are worth considerably more.

16 Child in Chains and Globe

17 Pope Paul VI, Map of Africa and Papal Arms

1969 (30 May). *Second Anniv of Independence. Multicoloured; frame colours given.* Litho. P 13 × 13½.

35	16	2d. yellow-orange		75	2·50
36		4d. red-orange		75	2·50
		a. Green (wreath) and orange (Sun) omitted			
37		1s. new blue		1·00	4·00
38		2s. 6d. emerald		1·75	8·50
35/8			*Set of 4*	3·75	16·00

A miniature sheet with a face value of 10s. was also released.

1969 (1 Aug). *Visit of Pope Paul to Africa. T 17 and similar vert designs. Multicoloured.* Litho. P 13×13½.

39		4d. Type 17		40	2·00
40		6d. Pope Paul VI, Map of Africa and arms of the Vatican		55	4·00
41		9d. Pope Paul VI, map of Africa and St. Peter's Basilica, Vatican.		75	5·50
42		3s. Pope Paul VI, map of Africa and Statue of St. Peter		2·25	11·00
39/42			*Set of 4*	3·50	20·00

A miniature sheet with a face value of 10s. was also released.

No. 42 has a magenta background. This value is also known with the background in brown-red or brown.

Biafra was overrun by Federal troops on 10 January 1970 and surrender took place on 15 January.

On 17 December the French Agency released a Christmas issue consisting of Nos. 39/42 overprinted "CHRISTMAS 1969 PEACE ON EARTH AND GOODWILL TO ALL MEN" together with the miniature sheet overprinted "CHRISTMAS 1969" and surcharged £1. Later Nos. 35/38 were released overprinted in red "SAVE BIAFRA 9TH JAN 1970" with a premium of 8d., 1s. 4d., 4s., and 10s. respectively together with the miniature sheet with a premium of £1. We have no evidence that these issues were actually put on sale in Biafra before the collapse, but it has been reported that the 4d. Christmas issue and 2d. + 8d. Save Biafra exist genuinely used before capitulation.

Nos. 40/41 have been seen surcharged "+ 10/–HUMAN RIGHTS" and the United Nations emblem but it is doubtful if they were issued.

No. 81 of Nigeria has also been reported with the original "ROYAL VISIT 1956" overprint, together with "NIGERIA" from the basic stamp, obliterated and a "SERVICE" overprint added. Such stamps were not used for official mail in Biafra, although an example is known with the "UMUAHIA" c-t-o mark.

Niue

Niue became a British Protectorate on 20 April 1900 and was transferred to New Zealand control on 11 June 1901. There was considerable local resentment at attempts to incorporate Niue into the Cook Islands and, in consequence, the island was recognised as a separate New Zealand dependency from 1902.

PRICES FOR STAMPS ON COVER TO 1945	
No. 1	*from* × 2
Nos. 2/5	*from* × 8
Nos. 6/7	—
Nos. 8/9	*from* × 30
Nos. 10/12	—
Nos. 13/31	*from* × 3
Nos. 32/7c	—
Nos. 38/47	*from* × 5
Nos. 48/9	—
No. 50	*from* × 15
Nos. 51/4	—
Nos. 55/61	*from* × 8
Nos. 62/8	*from* × 12
Nos. 69/71	*from* × 3
Nos. 72/4	*from* × 10
Nos. 75/8	*from* × 8
Nos. 79/88	—
Nos. 89/97	*from* × 2

NEW ZEALAND DEPENDENCY
Stamps of New Zealand overprinted

NIUE

(1)

1902 (4 Jan). *Handstamped with T 1, in green or bluish green. Pirie paper. Wmk double-lined "N Z" and Star, W 38 of New Zealand.* P 11.

1	42	1d. carmine		£350	£350

A few overprints were made with a *greenish violet* ink. These occurred only in the first vertical row and part of the second row of the first sheet overprinted owing to violet ink having been applied to the pad (*Price £1400 un*).

NIUE. ½ PENI.	NIUE. TAHA PENI.	NIUE. 2½ PENI.
(2)	(3) 1d.	(4)

1902 (4 Apr). *Type-set surcharges. T 2, 3, and 4.*

(i) Pirie paper. No wmk. P 11.

2	27	2½d. blue (R.)		1·25	2·75
		a. No stop after "PENI"		25·00	40·00
		b. Surch double		£2000	

(ii) Basted Mills paper. Wmk double-lined "N Z" and Star, W 38 of New Zealand.

(a) P 14

3	23	½d. green (R.)		75	2·75
		a. Spaced "U" and "E" (R. 3/3, 3/6, 8/3, 8/6)		6·00	12·00
		b. Surch inverted		£250	£400
		c. Surch double			
4	42	1d. carmine (B.)		7·50	8·50
		a. Spaced "U" and "E" (R. 3/3, 3/6, 8/6)		55·00	70·00
		b. No stop after "PENI" (R. 9/3)		£140	£150
		c. Varieties a. and b. on same stamp (R. 8/3)		£140	£150

(b) P 14×11

5	42	1d. carmine (B.)		1·00	1·40
		a. Spaced "U" and "E" (R. 3/3, 3/6, 8/6)		8·50	9·00
		b. No stop after "PENI" (R. 9/3)		28·00	35·00
		c. Varieties a. and b. on same stamp (R. 8/3)		28·00	35·00

(c) Mixed perfs

6	23	½d. green (R.)			£650
7	42	1d. carmine (B.)			£450

1902 (2 May). *Type-set surcharges, T 2, 3. Cowan paper. Wmk single-lined "N Z" and Star, W 43 of New Zealand. (a) P 14.*

8	23	½d. green (R.)		65	80
		a. Spaced "U" and "E" (R. 3/3, 3/6, 8/3, 8/6)		5·50	6·00
9	42	1d. carmine (B.)		50	65
		a. Surch double		£750	
		b. Spaced "U" and "E" (R. 3/3, 3/6, 8/6)		9·00	11·00
		c. No stop after "PENI" (R. 5/3, 7/3, 9/3, 10/3, 10/6)		9·00	11·00
		d. Varieties b. and c. on same stamp (R. 8/3)		28·00	35·00
		e. "I" of "NIUE" omitted (R. 6/5 from end of last ptg)			

(b) P 14×11

10	23	½d. green (R.)			

(c) Mixed perfs

11	23	½d. green (R.)			£650
12	42	1d. carmine (B.)			£180
		a. Spaced "U" and "E" (R. 3/3, 3/6, 8/3, 8/6)			£350
		b. No stop after "PENI" (R. 5/3, 7/3, 9/3, 10/3, 10/6)			£300

NIUE. (5)	Tolu e Pene. (6) 3d.
Ono e Pene. (7) 6d.	**Taha e Sileni.** (8) 1s.

1903 (2 July). *Optd with name at top, T 5, and values at foot, T 6/8, in blue. W 43 of New Zealand.* P 11.

13	28	3d. yellow-brown		5·50	5·00
14	31	6d. rose-red		6·00	10·00
15	34	1s. brown-red ("Tahae" joined)			£650
16		1s. bright red		25·00	25·00
		a. Orange-red		32·00	35·00
13/16			*Set of 3*	32·00	35·00

NIUE. ½ PENI.	NIUE.
(9)	(10)

1911 (30 Nov). *½d. surch with T 9, others optd at top as T 5 and values at foot as T 7, 8. W 43 of New Zealand.* P 14 × 14½.

17	51	½d. green (C.)		45	40
18	52	6d. carmine (B.)		2·00	7·00
19		1s. vermilion (B.)		6·50	38·00
17/19			*Set of 3*	8·00	40·00

1915 (Sept). *Surch as T 4. W 43 of New Zealand.* P 14.

20	27	2½d. deep blue (C.)		9·00	17·00

1917 (Aug). *1d. surch as T 3, 3d. optd as T 5 with value as T 6. W 43 of New Zealand.*

21	53	1d. carmine (p 14×15) (Br.)		5·50	5·50
		a. No stop after "PENI" (R.10/16)		£150	
22	60	3d. chocolate (p 14×14½) (B.)		48·00	75·00
		a. No stop after "PENE" (R.10/4)		£475	
		b. Perf 14×13½		60·00	85·00
		c. Vert pair, Nos. 22/b		£180	

1917-21. *Optd with T 10. W 43 of New Zealand.* (a) P 14×15.

23	61	½d. green (R.) (2.20)	..	50	95
24	53	1d. carmine (B.) (10.17)	..	2·75	3·75
25	61	1½d. slate (R.) (11.17)	..	80	1·75
26		1½d. orange-brown (R.) (2.19)	..	70	2·00
27		3d. chocolate (B.) (6.19)	..	1·40	15·00

(b) P 14×14½

28	60	2½d. deep blue (R.) (10.20)	..	90	2·75
		a. Perf 14×13½	..	1·75	4·00
		b. Vert pair, Nos. 28/a	..	18·00	35·00
29		3d. chocolate (B.) (10.17)	..	1·25	1·50
		a. Perf 14×13½	..	1·60	2·50
		b. Vert pair, Nos. 29/a	..	27·00	40·00
30		6d. carmine (B.) (8.21)	..	4·25	16·00
		a. Perf 14×13½	..	4·75	16·00
		b. Vert pair, Nos. 30/a	..	38·00	65·00
31		1s. vermilion (B.) (10.18)	..	4·75	16·00
		a. Perf 14×13½	..	7·50	16·00
		b. Vert pair, Nos. 31/a	..	42·00	70·00
23/31			Set of 9	15·00	55·00

1918-29. *Postal Fiscal stamps as Type F 4 of New Zealand optd with T 10. W 43 of New Zealand (sideways).*

(i) *Chalk-surfaced "De La Rue" paper.* (a) P 14

32	5s. yellow-green (R.) (7.18)	..	80·00	90·00

(b) P 14½ × 14, comb

33	2s. deep blue (R.) (9.18)	..	15·00	32·00
34	2s. 6d. grey-blue (B.) (2.23)	..	17·00	40·00
35	5s. yellow-green (R.) (10.18)	..	20·00	48·00
36	10s. maroon (B.) (2.23)	..	70·00	90·00
37	£1 rose-carmine (B.) (2.23)	..	£130	£150
33/7		Set of 5	£225	£300

(ii) *Thick, opaque, white chalk-surfaced "Cowan" paper. P 14½ × 14.*

37a	5s. yellow-green (R.) (10.29)	..	22·00	48·00
37b	10s. brown-red (B.) (2.27)	..	75·00	90·00
37c	£1 rose-pink (B.) (2.28)	..	£130	£150
37a/c		Set of 3	£200	£250

11 Landing of	12 Landing of
Captain Cook	Captain Cook

(Des, eng and recess P.B.)

1920 (23 Aug). *T 11 and similar designs. No wmk. P 14.*

38	½d. black and green	..	2·75	3·25
39	1d. black and dull carmine	..	1·75	1·25
40	1½d. black and red	..	2·50	3·75
41	3d. black and blue	..	60	5·50
42	6d. red-brown and green	..	80	11·00
43	1s. black and sepia	..	1·50	11·00
38/43		Set of 6	9·00	32·00

Designs: *Vert*—1d. Wharf at Avarua; 1½d. "Capt Cook (Dance)"; 3d. Palm tree. *Horiz*—6d. Huts at Arorangi; 1s. Avarua Harbour.

Examples of the 6d. with inverted centre were not supplied to the Post Office.

1925-27. *As Nos. 38/9 and new values. W 43 of New Zealand. P 14.*

44	½d. black and green (1927)..	..	1·25	4·75
45	1d. black and deep carmine (1925)	..	75	75
46	2½d. black and blue (10.27)	..	1·75	6·50
47	4d. black and violet (10.27)	..	3·00	8·50
44/7		Set of 4	6·00	18·00

Designs: *Vert*—2½d. Te Po, Rarotongan chief. *Horiz*—4d. Harbour, Rarotonga, and Mount Ikurangi.

1927-28. *Admiral type of New Zealand optd as T 10. W 43 of New Zealand. P 14.*

(a) "*Jones*" paper

48	72	2s. deep blue (2.27) (R.)	..	15·00	42·00

(b) "*Cowan*" paper

49	72	2s. light blue (R.) (2.28)	..	16·00	30·00

1931 (Apr). *No. 40 surch as T 18 of Cook Is.*

50	2d. on 1½d. black and red	..	1·50	1·00

1931 (12 Nov). *Postal Fiscal stamps as Type F 6 of New Zealand optd as T 10. W 43 of New Zealand. Thick, opaque, chalk-surfaced "Cowan" paper. P 14.*

51	2s. 6d. deep brown (B.)	..	5·50	11·00
52	5s. green (R.)	..	26·00	55·00
53	10s. carmine-lake (B.)	..	35·00	70·00
54	£1 pink (B.)	..	55·00	95·00
51/4		Set of 4	£110	£200

See also Nos. 79/82 for different type of overprint.

(Des L. C. Mitchell. Recess P.B.)

1932 (16 Mar). *T 12 and similar designs inscr "NIUE" and "COOK ISLANDS". No wmk. P 13.*

55	½d. black and emerald	..	5·50	11·00
	a. Perf 13×14×13×13	..	£250	
56	1d. black and deep lake	..	1·00	30
57	2d. black and red-brown	..	75	2·75
	a. Perf 14×13×13×13	..	90·00	£150
58	2½d. black and slate-blue	..	5·50	30·00
59	4d. black and greenish blue	..	7·50	27·00
	a. Perf 14	..	8·50	23·00
60	6d. black and orange-vermilion	..	2·00	2·00
61	1s. black and purple (p 14)	..	2·00	5·00
55/61		Set of 7	22·00	65·00

Designs: *Vert*—1d. Capt. Cook; 1s. King George V. *Horiz*—2d. Double Maori canoe; 2½d. Islanders working cargo; 4d. Port of Avarua; 6d. R.M.S. *Monowai*.

Examples of the 2½d. with inverted centre were not supplied to the Post Office.

Nos. 55a and 57a are mixed perforations, each having one side perforated 14 where the original perforation, 13, was inadequate.

(Recess from Perkins, Bacon's plates at Govt Ptg Office, Wellington, N.Z.)

1932-36. *As Nos. 55/61, but W 43 of New Zealand. P 14.*

62	½d. black and emerald	..	50	90
63	1d. black and deep lake	..	50	30
64	2d. black and yellow-brown (1.4.36)	..	40	70
65	2½d. black and slate-blue	..	40	2·75
66	4d. black and greenish blue	..	1·25	1·25
67	6d. black and red-orange (1.4.36)	..	70	65
68	1s. black and purple (1.4.36)	..	4·50	14·00
62/68		Set of 7	7·50	18·00

Imperforate proofs of No. 65 are known used on registered mail from Niue postmarked 30 August 1945 or 29 October 1945.

See also Nos. 89/97.

SILVER JUBILEE OF KING GEORGE V. 1910-1935.	Normal letters	B K E N
(12)	Narrow letters	B K E N

1935 (7 May). *Silver Jubilee. Designs as Nos. 63, 65 and 67 (colours changed) optd with T 12 (wider vertical spacing on 6d.). W 43 of New Zealand. P 14.*

69	1d. red-brown and lake	..	60	1·50
	a. Narrow "K" in "KING"..	..	2·75	8·00
	b. Narrow "B" in JUBILEE	..	2·75	8·00
70	2½d. dull and deep blue (R.)	..	3·25	2·50
	a. Narrow first "E" in "GEORGE"	..	4·00	12·00
71	6d. green and orange	..	3·25	5·00
	a. Narrow "N" in "KING"..	..	14·00	32·00
69/71		Set of 3	6·50	8·00

Examples of No. 70 imperforate horizontally are from proof sheets not issued through the Post and Telegraph Department (*Price £350 for vert pair*).

NIUE (13)	14 King George VI	15 Tropical Landscape

1937 (13 May). *Coronation Issue. Nos. 599/601 of New Zealand optd with T 13.*

72	1d. carmine	..	30	10
73	2½d. Prussian blue	..	40	30
74	6d. red-orange	..	40	20
72/4		Set of 3	1·00	50

1938 (2 May). *T 14 and similar designs inscr "NIUE COOK ISLANDS". W 43 of New Zealand. P 14.*

75	1s. black and violet	..	3·50	4·00
76	2s. black and red-brown	..	9·50	9·00
77	3s. light blue and emerald-green	..	22·00	13·00
75/7		Set of 3	32·00	23·00

Designs: *Vert*—2s. Island village. *Horiz*—3s. Cook Islands canoe.

1940 (2 Sept). *Surch as in T 15. W 98 of New Zealand. P 13½×14.*

78	3d. on 1½d. black and purple	..	10	10

NIUE.
(16)

1941-67. *Postal Fiscal stamps as Type F 6 of New Zealand with thin opt, T 16. P 14.*

(i) *Thin, hard, chalk-surfaced "Wiggins Teape" paper with vertical mesh (1941-43).* (a) W 43 of New Zealand

79	2s. 6d. deep brown (B.) (4.41)	..	40·00	35·00
80	5s. green (R.) (4.41)	..	£170	£140
81	10s. pale carmine-lake (B.) (6.42)	..	£100	£150
82	£1 pink (B.) (2.43?)	..	£170	£200
79/82		Set of 4	£425	£475

(b) W 98 of New Zealand (1944-45)

83	2s. 6d. deep brown (B.) (3.45)	..	3·00	6·50
84	5s. green (R.) (11.44)	..	6·50	9·00
85	10s. carmine-lake (B.) (11.45)	..	50·00	70·00
86	£1 pink (B.) (6.42)	..	40·00	48·00
83/6		Set of 4	90·00	£120

(ii) *Unsurfaced "Wiggins Teape" paper with horizontal mesh. W 98 of New Zealand (1957-67)*

87	2s. 6d. deep brown (p 14 × 13½) (1.11.57)	..	4·25	5·50
88	5s. pale yellowish green (wmk sideways) (6.67)	..	50·00	75·00

Nos. 83/5 were later printed with the watermark inverted for technical reasons and the prices quoted are for the cheapest form. They are fully listed in the *Two Reigns Catalogue*.

No. 88 came from a late printing made to fill demands from Wellington, but no supplies were sent to Niue. It exists in both line and comb perf.

1944-46. *As Nos. 62/7 and 75/7, but W 98 of New Zealand (sideways on ½d., 1d., and 2s.).*

89	12	½d. black and emerald	..	50	80
90	—	1d. black and deep lake	..	50	60
91	—	2d. black and red-brown	..	3·50	3·25
92	—	2½d. black and slate-blue (1946)	..	60	95
93	—	4d. black and greenish blue	..	85	90
94	—	6d. black and red-orange	..	70	1·40
95	14	1s. black and violet	..	1·25	60
96	—	2s. black and red-brown (1945)	..	5·00	2·75
97	—	3s. light blue and emerald-green (1945)	..	9·50	6·00
89/97			Set of 9	20·00	16·00

1946 (4 June). *Peace. Nos. 668, 670, 674/5 of New Zealand optd as T 16 without stop (twice, reading up and down on 2d.).*

98	1d. green (B.)	..	10	10
99	2d. purple (B.)	..	10	10
100	6d. chocolate and vermilion (Blk.)	..	10	10
	a. Opt double, one albino	..	£200	
101	8d. black and carmine (B.)	..	10	10
98/101		Set of 4	35	30

Nos. 102/112 are no longer used.

17 Map of Niue	18 H.M.S. *Resolution*
23 Bananas	24 Matapa Chasm

(Des J. Berry. Recess B.W.)

1950 (3 July). *T 17/18, 23/24 and similar designs. W 98 of New Zealand (sideways inverted on 1d., 2d., 3d., 4d., 6d. and 1s.). P 13½×14 (horiz) or 14×13½ (vert).*

113	½d. orange and blue	..	10	15
114	1d. brown and blue-green	..	2·25	80
115	2d. black and carmine	..	15	15
116	3d. blue and violet-blue	..	10	15
117	4d. olive-green and purple-brown	..	10	15
118	6d. green and brown-orange	..	60	20
119	9d. orange and brown	..	10	20
120	1s. purple and black	..	10	20
121	2s. brown-orange and dull green	..	75	2·50
122	3s. blue and black	..	4·00	3·75
113/22		Set of 10	7·50	7·25

Designs: *Horiz* (as T 18)—2d. Alofi landing; 3d. Native hut; 4d. Arch at Hikutavake; 6d. Alofi bay; 1s. Cave, Makefu. *Vert* (as T 17)—9d. Spearing fish.

1953 (25 May). *Coronation. As Nos. 715 and 717 of New Zealand, but inscr "NIUE".*

123	3d. brown	..	65	30
124	6d. slate-grey	..	95	30

(New Currency. 100 cents = 1 dollar)

1c	50c NIUE
(25)	26

1967 (10 July-7 Aug). *Decimal currency.* (a) *Nos. 113/22 surch as T 25.*

125	½ c. on ½d.	..	10	10
126	1 c. on 1d.	..	80	15
127	2 c. on 2d.	..	10	10
128	2½ c. on 3d.	..	10	10
129	3 c. on 4d.	..	10	10
130	5 c. on 6d.	..	10	10
131	8 c. on 9d.	..	10	10
132	10 c. on 1s.	..	10	10
133	20 c. on 2s.	..	60	1·25
134	30 c. on 3s.	..	1·50	1·75
125/34		Set of 10	2·75	3·00

(b) *Arms type of New Zealand without value, surch as in T 26. W 98 of New Zealand (sideways). P 14.*

135	26	25 c. deep yellow-brown	..	65	65
		a. Rough perf 11	..	8·00	14·00
136		50 c. pale yellowish green	..	1·00	1·00
		a. Rough perf 11	..	9·00	16·00
137		$1 magenta	..	80	1·50
		a. Rough perf 11	..	13·00	15·00
138		$2 light pink	..	1·40	2·50
		a. Rough perf 11	..	15·00	10·00
135/8			Set of 4	3·50	5·00
135a/8a			Set of 4	40·00	60·00

The 25 c., $1 and $2 perf 14 exist both line and comb perforated. The 50 c. is comb perforated only. The perf 11 stamps resulted from an emergency measure in the course of printing.

1967 (3 Oct). *Christmas. As T 278 of New Zealand, but inscr "NIUE".*

139	2½ c. multicoloured	..	10	10

1969 (1 Oct). *Christmas. As T 301 of New Zealand, but inscr "NIUE". W 98 of New Zealand. P 13½ × 14½.*

140	2½ c. multicoloured	..	10	10

NEW INFORMATION

The editor is always interested to correspond with people who have new information that will improve or correct the Catalogue.

27 "Pua"　　27 Kalahimu

(Des Mrs. K. W. Billings. Litho Enschedé)

1969 (27 Nov). *T* **27** *and similar vert designs. Multicoloured.*
P 12½ × 13½.
141	½ c. Type 27		10	10
142	1 c. "Golden Shower"		10	10
143	2 c. Flamboyant		10	10
144	2½ c. Frangipani		10	10
145	3 c. Niue Crocus		10	10
146	5 c. Hibiscus		10	10
147	8 c. "Passion Fruit"		10	10
148	10 c. "Kampui"		10	10
149	20 c. Queen Elizabeth II (after Anthony Buckley)		1·00	1·25
150	30 c. Tapeu Orchid		1·75	1·75
141/150		*Set of 10*	3·00	3·00

(Des G. F. Fuller. Photo Enschedé)

1970 (19 Aug). *Indigenous Edible Crabs. T* **37** *and similar horiz*
designs. Multicoloured. P 13½ × 12½.
151	3 c. Type 37		10	10
152	5 c. Kalavi		10	10
153	30 c. Unga		30	25
151/3		*Set of 3*	45	40

1970 (1 Oct). *Christmas. As T* **314** *of New Zealand, but inscr*
"NIUE".
154	2½ c. multicoloured		10	10

38 Outrigger Canoe and　　39 Spotted Triller
Aircraft over Jungle

(Des L. C. Mitchell. Litho B.W.)

1970 (9 Dec). *Opening of Niue Airport. T* **38** *and similar horiz*
designs. Multicoloured. P 13½.
155	3 c. Type 38		10	10
156	5 c. Cargo liner, and aircraft over harbour		15	10
157	8 c. Aircraft over Airport		15	20
155/7		*Set of 3*	35	35

(Des A. G. Mitchell. Litho B.W.)

1971 (23 June). *Birds. T* **39** *and similar horiz designs. Multi-*
coloured. P 13½.
158	5 c. Type 39		15	10
159	10 c. Purple-capped Fruit Dove		70	15
160	20 c. Blue-crowned Lory		80	20
158/60		*Set of 3*	1·50	40

1971 (6 Oct). *Christmas. As T* **325** *of New Zealand, but inscr*
"NIUE".
161	3 c. multicoloured		10	10

40 Niuean Boy　　41 Octopus Lure

(Des L. C. Mitchell. Litho Harrison)

1971 (17 Nov). *Niuean Portraits. T* **40** *and similar vert designs.*
Multicoloured. P 13 × 14.
162	4 c. Type 40		10	10
163	6 c. Girl with garland		10	10
164	9 c. Man		10	10
165	14 c. Woman with garland		15	20
162/5		*Set of 4*	35	35

(Des A. G. Mitchell. Litho B.W.)

1972 (3 May). *South Pacific Arts Festival, Fiji. T* **41** *and similar*
multicoloured designs. P 13½.
166	3 c. Type 41		10	10
167	5 c. War weapons		15	10
168	10 c. Sika throwing (*horiz*)		20	10
169	25 c. Vivi dance (*horiz*)		30	20
166/9		*Set of 4*	65	40

42 Alofi Wharf

(Des A. G. Mitchell. Litho Questa)

1972 (6 Sept). *25th Anniversary of South Pacific Commission.*
T **42** *and similar horiz designs. Multicoloured. P* 14.
170	4 c. Type 42		10	10
171	5 c. Medical Services		15	10
172	6 c. Schoolchildren		15	10
173	18 c. Dairy cattle		25	20
170/3		*Set of 4*	60	40

1972 (4 Oct). *Christmas. As T* **332** *of New Zealand but inscr*
"NIUE".
174	3 c. multicoloured		10	10

43 Kokio　　44 "Large Flower Piece"
(Jan Brueghel)

(Des G. F. Fuller. Litho Harrison)

1973 (27 June). *Fishes. T* **43** *and similar horiz designs. Multi-*
coloured. P 14 × 13½.
175	8 c. Type 43		25	25
176	10 c. Loi		30	30
177	15 c. Malau		40	40
178	20 c. Palu		45	45
175/8		*Set of 4*	1·25	1·25

(Des and litho Enschedé)

1973 (21 Nov). *Christmas. T* **44** *and similar vert designs showing*
flower studies by the artists listed. Multicoloured. P 14 × 13½.
179	4 c. Type 44		10	10
180	5 c. Bollongier		10	10
181	10 c. Ruysch		20	20
179/81		*Set of 3*	30	30

45 Capt. Cook and Bowsprit　　46 King Fataaiki

(Des A. G. Mitchell. Litho Questa)

1974 (20 June). *Bicentenary of Capt. Cook's Visit. T* **45** *and*
similar horiz designs each showing Cook's portrait. Multi-
coloured. P 13½ × 14.
182	2 c. Type 45		30	20
183	3 c. Niue landing place		30	25
184	8 c. Map of Niue		50	40
185	20 c. Ensign of 1774 and Administration Building		70	80
182/5		*Set of 4*	1·60	1·50

SELF-GOVERNMENT

(Des A. G. Mitchell. Litho Questa)

1974 (19 Oct). *Self-Government. T* **46** *and similar multicoloured*
designs. P 14 × 13½ (4 *and* 8 c.) *or* 13½ × 14 (*others*).
186	4 c. Type 46		10	10
187	8 c. Annexation Ceremony, 1900		10	10
188	10 c. Legislative Assembly Chambers (*horiz*)		10	10
189	20 c. Village meeting (*horiz*)		15	15
186/9		*Set of 4*	35	30

47 Decorated Bicycles　　48 Children going to Church

(Des B. C. Strong. Litho D.L.R.)

1974 (13 Nov). *Christmas. T* **47** *and similar vert designs. P* 12½.
190	3 c. multicoloured		10	10
191	10 c. multicoloured		10	10
192	20 c. dull red-brown, slate and black		20	20
190/2		*Set of 3*	30	30
Designs:—10 c. Decorated motorcycles; 20 c. Motor transport to
church.

(Des Enid Hunter. Litho Questa)

1975 (29 Oct). *Christmas. T* **48** *and similar horiz designs. Multi-*
coloured. P 14.
193	4 c. Type 48		10	10
194	5 c. Child with balloons on bicycle		10	10
195	10 c. Balloons and gifts on tree		20	20
193/5		*Set of 3*	30	30

49 Hotel Buildings　　50 Preparing Ground for Taro

(Des B. C. Strong. Litho Harrison)

1975 (19 Nov). *Opening of Tourist Hotel. T* **49** *and similar horiz*
design. Multicoloured. P 13½ × 13.
196	8 c. Type 49		10	10
197	20 c. Ground-plan and buildings		20	20

(Des A. G. Mitchell. Litho Questa)

1976 (3 Mar). *T* **50** *and similar horiz designs showing food gath-*
ering. Multicoloured. P 13½ × 14.
198	1 c. Type 50		10	10
199	2 c. Planting taro		10	10
200	3 c. Banana gathering		10	10
201	4 c. Harvesting taro		10	10
202	5 c. Gathering shell fish		30	10
203	10 c. Reef fishing		20	10
204	20 c. Luku gathering		20	15
205	50 c. Canoe fishing		40	60
206	$1 Coconut husking		60	80
207	$2 Uga gathering		1·00	1·40
198/207		*Set of 10*	2·75	2·75
See also Nos. 249/58 and 264/73.

51 Water　　52 Christmas Tree, Alofi

(Des A. G. Mitchell. Litho Questa)

1976 (7 July). *Utilities. T* **51** *and similar vert designs. Multi-*
coloured. P 14.
208	10 c. Type 51		10	10
209	15 c. Telecommunications		15	15
210	20 c. Power		15	15
208/10		*Set of 3*	30	30

(Des A. G. Mitchell. Litho Questa)

1976 (15 Sept). *Christmas. T* **52** *and similar horiz design. Multi-*
coloured. P 14.
211	9 c. Type 52		15	15
212	15 c. Church Service, Avatele		15	15

53 Queen Elizabeth II and Westminster Abbey

(Des and photo Heraclio Fournier)

1977 (7 June). *Silver Jubilee. T* **53** *and similar horiz design.*
Multicoloured. P 13½.
213	$1 Type 53		1·25	75
214	$2 Coronation regalia		1·50	1·00
MS215	72 × 104 mm. Nos. 213/14		2·50	2·50
Stamps from the miniature sheet have a blue border.

54 Child Care　　55 "The Annunciation"

(Des R. M. Conly. Litho Questa)

1977 (29 June). *Personal Services. T 54 and similar horiz designs. Multicoloured. P 14½.*

216	10 c. Type **54**	..	..	..	15	10
217	15 c. School dental clinic	..	..	..	20	20
218	20 c. Care of the aged ..	..	..	..	20	20
216/18	..	..	..	*Set of 3*	50	45

(Des and photo Heraclio Fournier)

1977 (15 Nov). *Christmas. T 55 and similar vert designs showing paintings by Rubens. Multicoloured. P 13.*

219	10 c. Type **55**	..	..	..	20	10
220	15 c. "Adoration of the Magi"	..	..	20	10
221	20 c. "Virgin in a Garland	..	..	35	20
222	35 c. "The Holy Family"	..	..	55	35
219/22	..	..	..	*Set of 4*	1·10	65
MS223	82 × 129 mm. Nos. 219/22	..	..	1·50	2·25

(56)

1977 (15 Nov). *Nos. 198 etc., 214, 216 and 218 surch as T 56 by New Zealand Govt Printer.*

224	12 c. on 1 c. Type **50**	..	..	..	25	25
225	16 c. on 2 c. Planting taro	..	..	30	30
226	30 c. on 3 c. Banana gathering	..	..	40	40
227	35 c. on 4 c. Harvesting taro	..	..	45	45
228	40 c. on 5 c. Gathering shell fish	..	50	50
229	60 c. on 20 c. Luku gathering..	..	70	65
230	70 c. on $1 Coconut husking	..	..	75	65
231	85 c. on $2 Uga gathering	..	..	80	65
232	$1.10 on 10 c. Type **54**	..	..	90	65
233	$2.60 on 20 c. Care of the aged	..	1·25	1·00
234	$3.20 on $2 Coronation regalia (Gold)	1·50	1·25
224/34	..	..	..	*Set of 11*	7·00	6·00

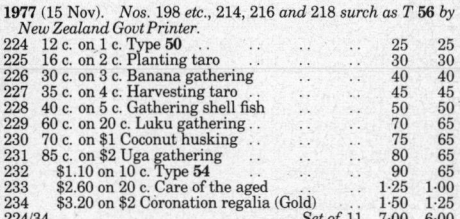

57 "An Island View in Atooi"

(Photo Heraclio Fournier)

1978 (18 Jan). *Bicentenary of Discovery of Hawaii. T 57 and similar horiz designs showing paintings by John Webber. Multicoloured. P 13.*

235	12 c. Type **57**	..	85	30
236	16 c. "View of Karakaooa, in Owhyhee"	95	40
237	20 c. "Offering before Capt. Cook in the Sandwich Islands"	1·25	45
238	30 c. "Tereoboo, King of Owhyhee bringing presents to Capt. Cook"	1·40	50
239	35 c. "Canoe in the Sandwich Islands, the rowers masked"	1·50	55
235/9	..	..	*Set of 5*	5·50	2·00
MS240	121 × 121 mm. Nos. 235/9	..	5·50	4·25

Nos. 235/9 were each printed in small sheets of 6, including 1 se-tenant stamp-size label.

58 "The Deposition of Christ" (Caravaggio)   **59** Flags of Niue and U.K.

(Photo Heraclio Fournier)

1978 (15 Mar). *Easter. Paintings from the Vatican Galleries. T 58 and similar vert design. Multicoloured. P 13.*

241	10 c. Type **58**	..	..	15	10
242	20 c. "The Burial of Christ" (Bellini) ..	..	35	35
MS243	102 × 68 mm. Nos. 241/2	..	..	60	75

1978 (15 Mar). *Easter. Children's Charity. Designs as Nos. 241/2 in separate miniature sheets 64 × 78 mm, each with a face value of 70 c. + 5 c. P 13.*

MS244	As Nos. 241/2	..	*Set of 2 sheets*	1·75	2·00

(Photo Heraclio Fournier)

1978 (26 June). *25th Anniv of Coronation. T 59 and similar horiz designs. Multicoloured. A. White border. B. Turquoise-green border. P 13.*

		A		B	
245	$1.10 Type **59** ..	1·25	1·00	1·25	1·00
246	$1.10 Coronation portrait by Cecil Beaton	1·25	1·00	1·25	1·00
247	$1.10 Queen's personal flag for New Zealand	1·25	1·00	1·25	1·00
245/7	..	*Set of 3*	3·25	2·75	3·25	2·75
MS248	87 × 98 mm. Nos. 245/7	..	4·25	3·50		†

Nos. 245/7 were printed together in small sheets of 6, containing two se-tenant strips of 3, with horizontal gutter margin between. The upper strip has white borders, the lower turquoise-green.

(Litho Questa)

1978 (27 Oct). *Designs as Nos. 198/207 but margin colours changed and silver frame. P 13½ × 14.*

249	12 c. Type **50**	..	..	..	20	20
250	16 c. Planting taro	..	..	..	20	20
251	30 c. Banana gathering	..	..	30	25
252	35 c. Harvesting taro	..	..	30	30
253	40 c. Gathering shell fish	..	..	40	30
254	60 c. Reef fishing	..	..	..	45	35
255	75 c. Luku gathering ..	..	..	50	40
256	$1.10, Canoe fishing..	..	..	1·10	80
257	$3.20, Coconut husking	..	..	1·25	1·25
258	$4.20, Uga gathering	..	..	1·40	1·40
249/58	..	..	..	*Set of 10*	5·50	5·00

See also Nos. 264/73.

60 "Festival of the Rosary"

(Des and photo Heraclio Fournier)

1978 (30 Nov). *Christmas. 450th Death Anniv of Dürer. T 60 and similar horiz designs. Multicoloured. P 13.*

259	20 c. Type **60**	..	..	40	20
260	30 c. "The Nativity"	..	..	50	30
261	35 c. "Adoration of the Magi"	..	60	35
259/61	..	..	*Set of 3*	1·40	75
MS262	143 × 82 mm. Nos. 259/61	..	1·50	1·75

Nos. 259/61 were each printed in small sheets of 6.

1978 (30 Nov). *Christmas. Children's Charity. Designs as Nos. 259/61 in separate miniature sheets 74 × 66 mm., each with a face value of 60 c. + 5 c. P 13.*

MS263	As Nos. 259/61	..	*Set of 3 sheets*	2·00	2·00

(Litho Questa)

1979 (26 Feb–28 May). *Air. Designs as Nos. 249/58 but gold frames and additionally inscr "AIRMAIL". P 13½ × 14.*

264	15 c. Planting taro	..	..	..	20	15
265	20 c. Banana gathering	..	..	25	15
266	23 c. Harvesting taro	..	..	30	15
267	50 c. Canoe fishing	..	..	70	20
268	90 c. Reef fishing	..	..	85	35
269	$1.35, Type **50** (30.3)	..	..	1·25	1·50
270	$2.10, Gathering shell fish (30.3)	..	2·00	2·25
271	$2.60, Luku gathering (30.3)	..	2·00	2·50
272	$5.10, Coconut husking (28.5)	..	2·25	3·50
273	$6.35, Uga gathering (28.5)..	..	2·50	4·50
264/73	..	..	*Set of 10*	11·00	14·00

PRINTERS. The following stamps were printed in photogravure by Heraclio Fournier, Spain, *except where otherwise stated.*

61 "Pietà" (Gregorio Fernandez)   **62** "The Nurse and Child" (Franz Hals)

1979 (2 Apr). *Easter. Paintings. T 61 and similar horiz design. Multicoloured. P 13.*

274	30 c. Type **61**	..	..	30	25
275	35 c. "Burial of Christ" (Pedro Roldan)	35	25
MS276	82 × 82 mm. Nos. 274/5	..	1·75	1·75

1979 (2 Apr). *Easter. Children's Charity. Designs as Nos. 274/5 in separate miniature sheets 86 × 69 mm., each with a face value of 70 c. + 5 c. P 13.*

MS277	As Nos. 274/5	..	*Set of 2 sheets*	1·75	1·75

1979 (31 May). *International Year of the Child. Details of Paintings. T 62 and similar vert designs. Multicoloured. P 14 × 13½.*

278	16 c. Type **62**	..	..	30	15
279	20 c. "Child of the Duke of Osuna" (Goya)	35	20
280	30 c. "Daughter of Robert Strozzi" (Titian)	55	35
281	35 c. "Children eating Fruit" (Murillo)	65	40
278/81	..	..	*Set of 4*	1·60	1·00
MS282	80 × 115 mm. Nos. 278/81. P 13 ..	1·60	2·25

1979 (31 May). *International Year of the Child. Children's Charity. Designs as Nos. 278/81 in separate miniature sheets 99 × 119 mm, each with a face value of 70 c. + 5 c. P 13.*

MS283	As Nos. 278/81	..	*Set of 4 sheets*	2·50	2·50

---

63 Penny Black Stamp   **64** Cook's Landing at Botany Bay

1979 (3 July). *Death Centenary of Sir Rowland Hill. T 63 and similar vert designs. Multicoloured. P 14 × 13½.*

284	20 c. Type **63**	..	..	20	15
285	20 c. Sir Rowland Hill and original Bath mail coach	..	20	15
286	30 c. Basel 1845 2½ r. stamp ..	..	30	20
287	30 c. Sir Rowland Hill and Alpine village coach	30	20
288	35 c. U.S.A. 1847 5 c. stamp ..	..	35	25
289	35 c. Sir Rowland Hill and first Transatlantic U.S.A. mail vessel	35	25
290	50 c. France 1849 20 c. stamp.	..	50	35
291	50 c. Sir Rowland Hill and French Post Office railway van, 1849	50	35
292	60 c. Bavaria 1849 1 k. stamp.	..	55	40
293	60 c. Sir Rowland Hill and Bavarian coach with mail	..	55	40
284/93	..	..	*Set of 10*	3·50	2·50
MS294	143 × 149 mm. Nos. 284/93	..	3·50	3·75

Nos. 284/5, 286/7, 288/9, 290/1 and 292/3 were each printed together, se-tenant, in horizontal pairs throughout the sheet forming composite designs.

1979 (30 July). *Death Bicentenary of Captain Cook. T 64 and similar horiz designs. Multicoloured. P 14.*

295	20 c. Type **64**	..	..	55	30
296	30 c. Cook's men during a landing on Erromanga	..	75	40
297	35 c. H.M.S. *Resolution* and H.M.S. *Discovery* in Queen Charlotte's Sound	85	45
298	75 c. Death of Captain Cook, Hawaii	1·50	70
295/8	..	..	*Set of 4*	3·25	1·75
MS299	104 × 80 mm. Nos. 295/8. P 13½..	3·25	3·00

65 Launch of "Apollo 11"   **66** "Virgin of Tortosa" (P. Serra)

1979 (27 Sept). *10th Anniv of Moon Landing. T 65 and similar vert designs. Multicoloured. P 13½.*

300	30 c. Type **65**	..	..	25	20
301	35 c. Lunar module on Moon ..	..	30	25
302	60 c. Helicopter, recovery ship and command module after splashdown	40	40
300/2	..	..	*Set of 3*	85	75
MS303	120 × 82 mm. Nos. 300/2	..	1·00	1·40

Stamps from No. **MS303** have the inscription in gold on a blue panel.

1979 (29 Nov). *Christmas. Paintings. T 66 and similar vert designs. Multicoloured. P 13.*

304	20 c. Type **66**	..	..	10	10
305	25 c. "Virgin with Milk" (R. di Mur)	15	15
306	30 c. "Virgin and Child" (S. di G. Sassetta)	20	20
307	50 c. "Virgin and Child" (J. Huguet) ..	25	25
304/7	..	..	*Set of 4*	60	60
MS308	95 × 113 mm. Nos. 304/7 ..	75	1·25

1979 (29 Nov). *Christmas. Children's Charity. Designs as Nos. 304/7 in separate miniature sheets, 49 × 84 mm, each with a face value of 85 c. + 5 c. P 13.*

MS309	As Nos. 304/7	..	*Set of 4 sheets*	1·50	2·00

HURRICANE RELIEF Plus 2c

(67)   **68** "Pietà" (Bellini)

1980 (25 Jan). *Hurricane Relief. Various stamps surch as T 67 in black (Nos. 310/19) or silver (320/30).*

(a) Nos. 284/93 (Death Centenary of Sir Rowland Hill)

310	20 c. + 2 c. Type **63**	..	..	20	25
311	20 c. + 2 c. Sir Rowland Hill and original Bath mail coach	20	25
312	30 c. + 2 c. Basel 1845 2½ r. stamp ..	30	35
313	30 c. + 2 c. Sir Rowland Hill and Alpine village coach	30	35
314	35 c. + 2 c. U.S.A. 1847 5 c. stamp ..	35	40

315	35 c. + 2 c. Sir Rowland Hill and first Trans-atlantic U.S.A. mail vessel	..	35	40
316	50 c. + 2 c. France 1849 20 c. stamp	..	50	55
317	50 c. + 2 c. Sir Rowland Hill and French Post Office railway van, 1849.	..	50	55
318	60 c. + 2 c. Bavaria 1849 1 k. stamp.	..	60	65
319	60 c. + 2 c. Sir Rowland Hill and Bavarian coach with mail	..	60	65

(b) Nos. 295/8 (Death Bicentenary of Captain Cook)

320	20 c. + 2 c. Type **64**	..	20	25
321	30 c. + 2 c. Cook's men during a landing on Erromanga	..	30	35
322	35 c. + 2 c. H.M.S. *Resolution* and H.M.S. *Discovery* in Queen Charlotte's Sound ..		35	40
323	75 c. + 2 c. Death of Captain Cook, Hawaii	..	75	80

(c) Nos. 300/2 (10th Anniv of Moon Landing)

324	30 c. + 2 c. Type **65**	..	30	35
325	35 c. + 2 c. Lunar module on Moon	..	35	40
326	60 c. + 2 c. Helicopter, recovery ship and command module after splashdown	..	60	65

(d) Nos. 304/7 (Christmas)

327	20 c. + 2 c. Type **66**	..	20	25
328	25 c. + 2 c. "Virgin with Milk" (R. de Mur)	..	25	30
329	30 c. + 2 c. "Virgin and Child" (S. di G. Sassetta)	..	30	35
330	50 c. + 2c. "Virgin and Child" (J. Huguet)	..	50	55
310/30		Set of 21	7·50	8·00

On Nos. 310/19 "HURRICANE RELIEF" covers the two designs of each value.

1980 (2 Apr). *Easter. Paintings.* T **68** *and similar horiz designs showing "Pietà" paintings by various artists. Multicoloured. P* 13½ × 13.

331	25 c. Type **68**	..	30	15
332	30 c. Botticelli	..	35	20
333	35 c. Antony van Dyck	..	35	20
331/3		Set of 3	90	50
MS334	75 × 104 mm. As Nos. 331/3, but each with additional premium of "+ 2 c."		55	90

The premiums on No. MS334 were used to support Hurricane Relief.

1980 (2 Apr). *Easter. Hurricane Relief. Designs as Nos. 331/3 in separate miniature sheets, 75 × 52 mm, each with a face value of 85 c. + 5 c. P* 13 × 14.

MS335	As Nos. 331/3	..	Set of 3 sheets	1·25	1·75

69 Ceremonial Stool, New Guinea

1980 (30 July). *South Pacific Festival of Arts, New Guinea.* T **69** *and similar vert designs. Multicoloured. P* 13.

336	20 c. Type **69**	..	20	20
337	20 c. Ku-Tagwa plaque, New Guinea..	..	20	20
338	20 c. Suspension hook, New Guinea	..	20	20
339	20 c. Ancestral board, New Guinea	..	20	20
340	25 c. Platform post, New Hebrides	..	25	25
341	25 c. Canoe ornament, New Ireland	..	25	25
342	25 c. Carved figure, Admiralty Islands	..	25	25
343	25 c. Female with child, Admiralty Islands	..	25	25
344	30 c. The God A'a, Rurutu (Austral Islands)	..	25	30
345	30 c. Statue of Tangaroa, Cook Islands	..	25	30
346	30 c. Ivory pendant, Tonga	..	25	30
347	30 c. Tapa (Hiapo) cloth, Niue.	..	25	30
348	35 c. Feather box (Waka), New Zealand	..	30	35
349	35 c. Hei-Tiki amulet, New Zealand	..	30	35
350	35 c. House post, New Zealand	..	30	35
351	35 c. Feather image of god Ku, Hawaii	..	30	35
336/51		Set of 16	3·75	4·00
MS352	Four sheets, each 86 × 124 mm. (a) Nos. 336, 340, 344, 348; (b) Nos. 337, 341, 345, 349; (c) Nos. 338, 342, 346, 350; (d) Nos. 339, 343, 347, 351. Each stamp with an additional premium of 2 c.		Set of 4 sheets	4·00	3·50

Nos. 336/9, 340/3, 344/7 and 348/51 were each printed together, *se-tenant*, in horizontal strips of 4 throughout the sheet.

NEW ZEALAND STAMP EXHIBITION

ZEAPEX '80 AUCKLAND

(70) (71)

1980 (22 Aug). *"Zeapex '80" International Stamp Exhibition, Auckland. Nos. 284, 286, 288, 290 and 292 optd with* T **70** *and Nos. 285, 287, 289, 291 and 293 optd with* T **71**, *both in black on silver background.*

353	20 c. Type **63**	..	20	20
354	20 c. Sir Rowland Hill and original Bath mail coach	..	20	20
355	30 c. Basel 1845 2½ r. stamp.	..	30	25
356	30 c. Sir Rowland Hill and Alpine village coach	..	30	25
357	35 c. U.S.A. 1847 5 c. stamp	..	35	25

358	35 c. Sir Rowland Hill and first Transatlantic U.S.A. mail vessel	..	35	25
359	50 c. France 1849 20 c. stamp.	..	45	30
360	50 c. Sir Rowland Hill and French Post Office railway van, 1849	..	45	30
361	60 c. Bavaria 1849 1 k. stamp.	..	55	35
362	60 c. Sir Rowland Hill and Bavarian coach with mail	..	55	35
353/62		Set of 10	3·50	2·50
MS363	143 × 149 mm. Nos. 353/62, each additionally surcharged "+ 2 c."		4·00	3·25

72 Queen Elizabeth the Queen Mother **73** 100 Metre Dash

1980 (15 Sept). *80th Birthday of Queen Elizabeth the Queen Mother. P* 13.

364	**72**	$1.10 multicoloured	..	1·25	1·50
MS365	55 × 80 mm. **72** $3 multicoloured	..		2·50	2·50

No. 364 was printed in small sheets of 6 including one *se-tenant* stamp-size label.

1980 (30 Oct). *Olympic Games, Moscow.* T **73** *and similar horiz designs. Multicoloured. P* 14 × 13½.

366	20 c. Type **73**		15	15
367	20 c. Allen Wells, Great Britain (winner of 100 metre dash)..		15	15
368	25 c. } 400 metre freestyle (winner, Ines Diers,		15	20
369	25 c. } D.D.R.)		15	20
370	30 c. } "Soling" Class Yachting (winner,		20	20
371	30 c. } Denmark)		20	20
372	35 c. } Football (winner, Czechoslovakia)		20	25
373	35 c. }		20	25
366/73		Set of 8	1·25	1·40
MS374	119 × 128 mm. Nos. 366/73, each stamp including premium of 2 c...		1·60	2·00

Nos. 366/7, 368/9, 370/1 and 372/3 were each printed together, *se-tenant*, in horizontal pairs throughout the sheet, forming composite designs. On the 25 c. and 35 c. stamps the face value is at right on the first design and at left on the second in each pair. For the 30 c. No. 370 has a yacht with a green sail at left and No. 371 a yacht with a red sail.

74 "The Virgin and Child" **75** *Phalaenopsis sp.*

1980 (28 Nov). *Christmas and 450th Death Anniv of Andrea del Sarto (painter).* T **74** *and similar vert designs showing different "The Virgin and Child" works. P* 13.

375	20 c. multicoloured	..	15	15
376	25 c. multicoloured	..	15	15
377	30 c. multicoloured	..	20	20
378	35 c. multicoloured	..	20	20
375/8		Set of 4	60	60
MS379	87 × 112 mm. Nos. 375/8	..	85	95

1980 (28 Nov). *Christmas. Children's Charity. Designs as Nos. 375/8 in separate miniature sheets 62 × 84 mm, each with a face value of 80 c. + 5 c. P* 13.

MS380	As Nos. 375/8	..	Set of 4 sheets	2·75	3·00

1981 (2 Apr)–**82**. *Flowers (1st series). Horiz designs as* T **75**. *Multicoloured. P* 13.

381	2 c. Type **75**	..	10	10
382	2 c. Moth Orchid	..	10	10
383	5 c. *Euphorbia pulcherrima*	..	10	10
384	5 c. Poinsettia	..	10	10
385	10 c. *Thunbergia alata*	..	10	10
386	10 c. Black-eyed Susan	..	10	10
387	15 c. *Cochlospermum hibiscoides*	..	15	15
388	15 c. Buttercup Tree	..	15	15
389	20 c. *Begonia sp.*	..	20	20
390	20 c. Begonia	..	20	20
391	25 c. *Plumeria sp.*	..	25	25
392	25 c. Frangipani	..	25	25
393	30 c. *Strelitzia reginae* (26 May)	..	30	30
394	30 c. Bird of Paradise (26 May)	..	30	30
395	30 c. *Hibiscus syriacus* (26 May)	..	30	30
396	30 c. Rose of Sharon (26 May)..	..	30	30
397	40 c. *Nymphaea sp.* (26 May)	..	35	35
398	40 c. Water Lily (26 May)	..	35	35
399	50 c. *Tibouchina sp.* (26 May)	..	45	45
400	50 c. Princess Flower (26 May)	..	45	45
401	60 c. *Nelumbo sp.* (26 May)	..	55	55
402	60 c. Lotus (26 May)	..	55	55
403	80 c. *Hybrid hibiscus* (26 May)	..	75	75
404	80 c. Yellow Hibiscus (26 May)	..	75	75

405	$1 Golden Shower Tree (*Cassia fistula*) (9.12.81)	..	1·00	1·00
406	$2 Orchid var. (9.12.81)	..	2·50	2·50
407	$3 Orchid sp. (9.12.81)	..	3·50	3·50
408	$4 *Euphorbia pulcherrima poinsettia* (15.1.82)	..	3·00	3·25
409	$6 Hybrid hibiscus (15.1.82)	..	4·50	4·75
410	$10 Scarlet Hibiscus (*Hibiscus rosasinensis*) (12.3.82)	..	7·50	7·75
381/410		Set of 30	26·00	26·00

The two designs of the 2 c. to 80 c. show different drawings of the same flower, one inscribed with its name in Latin, the other giving the common name. These were printed together, *se-tenant*, in horizontal and vertical pairs throughout the sheet.

Nos. 405/10 are larger, 47 × 33 mm.

See also Nos. 527/36.

76 "Jesus Defiled" (El Greco) **77** Prince Charles

1981 (10 Apr). *Easter. Details of Paintings.* T **76** *and similar horiz designs. P* 14.

425	35 c. Type **76**	..	30	30
426	50 c. "Pietà" (Fernando Gallego)	..	50	50
427	60 c. "The Supper of Emmaus" (Jacopo da Pontormo)	..	55	55
425/7		Set of 3	1·25	1·25
MS428	69 × 111 mm. As Nos. 425/7, but each with charity premium of 2 c. P 13½		1·40	1·60

1981 (10 Apr). *Easter. Children's Charity. Designs as Nos. 425/7 in separate miniature sheets 78 × 86 mm, each with a face value of 80 c. + 5 c. P* 13½ × 14.

MS429	As Nos. 425/7	..	Set of 3 sheets	2·00	2·00

1981 (26 June). *Royal Wedding.* T **77** *and similar vert designs. Multicoloured. P* 14.

430	75 c. Type **77**	..	70	60
431	95 c. Lady Diana Spencer	..	80	70
432	$1.20, Prince Charles and Lady Diana		90	80
430/2		Set of 3	2·25	1·90
MS433	78 × 85 mm. Nos. 430/2	..	3·00	3·25

Nos. 430/2 were each printed in small sheets of 6, including one *se-tenant* stamp-size label.

78 Footballer Silhouettes (79)

1981 (16 Oct). *World Cup Football Championship, Spain (1982).* T **78** *and similar horiz designs showing footballer silhouettes. P* 13.

434	30 c. blue-green, gold & new blue (Type **78**)		20	20
435	30 c. blue-green, gold and new blue (gold figure 3rd from left of stamp)		20	20
436	30 c. blue-green, gold and new blue (gold figure 4th from left)		20	20
437	35 c. new blue, gold and reddish orange (gold figure 3rd from left)		25	25
438	35 c. new blue, gold and reddish orange (gold figure 4th from left)		25	25
439	35 c. new blue, gold and reddish orange (gold figure 2nd from left)		25	25
440	40 c. reddish orange, gold and blue-green (gold figure 3rd from left, displaying close control)		25	25
441	40 c. reddish orange, gold and blue-green (gold figure 2nd from left)		25	25
442	40 c. reddish orange, gold and blue-green (gold figure 3rd from left, heading)		25	25
434/42		Set of 9	1·90	1·90
MS443	162 × 122 mm. 30 c. + 3 c., 35 c. + 3 c., 40 c. + 3 c. (each × 3). As Nos. 434/42 ..		2·00	2·50

The three designs of each value were printed together, *se-tenant*, in horizontal strips of 3 throughout the sheets.

1981 (3 Nov). *International Year for Disabled Persons. Nos. 430/3 surch as* T **79**.

444	75 c. + 5 c. Type **77**	..	1·75	1·25
445	95 c. + 5 c. Lady Diana Spencer	..	2·00	1·50
446	$1.20 + 5 c. Prince Charles and Lady Diana		3·00	1·75
444/6		Set of 3	6·00	4·00
MS447	78 × 85 mm. As Nos. 444/6, with each surcharged "+ 10 c."		5·00	5·00

Nos. 444/6 have a commemorative inscription overprinted on the sheet margins.

OMNIBUS ISSUES

Details, together with prices for complete sets, of the various Omnibus issues from the 1935 Silver Jubilee series to date are included in a special section following Zimbabwe at the end of Volume 2.

80 "The Holy
Family with Angels"
(detail)

81 Prince of Wales

1981 (11 Dec). *Christmas and 375th Birth Anniv of Rembrandt. T **80** and similar vert designs. Multicoloured. P 14 × 13.*
448	20 c. Type **80**		45	30
449	35 c. "Presentation in the Temple"		65	40
450	50 c. "Virgin and Child in Temple"		75	60
451	60 c. "The Holy Family"		90	75
448/51		*Set of 4*	2·50	1·90
MS452	79 × 112 mm. Nos. 448/51 .		2·50	2·25

1982 (22 Jan). *Christmas. Children's Charity. Designs as Nos. 448/51 in separate miniature sheets 66 × 80 mm, each with a face value of 80 c. + 5 c. P 14 × 13.*
MS453	As Nos. 448/51 .	*Set of 4 sheets*	2·00	2·50

1982 (1 July). *21st Birthday of Princess of Wales. T **81** and similar horiz designs. Multicoloured. P 14.*
454	50 c. Type **81**		55	55
455	$1.25, Prince and Princess of Wales		90	90
456	$2.50, Princess of Wales		1·60	1·60
454/6		*Set of 3*	2·75	2·75
MS457	81 × 101 mm. Nos. 454/6 .		3·75	3·50

Nos. 454/6 were each printed in small sheets of 6 including one *se-tenant* stamp-size label.
The stamps from No. **MS457** are without white borders.

(82)   83 Infant

1982 (23 July). *Birth of Prince William of Wales (1st issue). Nos. 430/3 optd as T **82**.*
458	75 c. Type **77** (optd with T **82**) .		2·25	1·75
	a. Pair. Nos. 458/9 .		4·50	3·50
459	75 c. Type **77** (optd "BIRTH OF PRINCE WILLIAM OF WALES 21 JUNE 1982")		2·25	1·75
460	95 c. Lady Diana Spencer (optd with T **82**)		3·25	2·25
	a. Pair. Nos. 460/1 .		6·50	4·50
461	95 c. Lady Diana Spencer (optd "BIRTH OF PRINCE WILLIAM OF WALES 21 JUNE 1982")		3·25	2·25
462	$1.20, Prince Charles and Lady Diana Spencer (optd with T **82**) .		4·25	2·75
	a. Pair. Nos. 462/3 .		8·50	5·50
463	$1.20, Prince Charles and Lady Diana Spencer (optd "BIRTH OF PRINCE WILLIAM OF WALES 21 JUNE 1982")		4·25	2·75
458/63		*Set of 6*	18·00	12·00
MS464	78 × 85 mm. Nos. 430/2 each optd "PRINCE WILLIAM OF WALES 21 JUNE 1982" .		8·50	6·00

Nos. 458/9, 460/1 and 462/3 were each printed *se-tenant* in small sheets of 6, containing three stamps overprinted with Type **82**, two with "BIRTH OF PRINCE WILLIAM OF WALES 21 JUNE 1982" and one stamp-size label.

1982 (10 Sept). *Birth of Prince William of Wales (2nd issue). Designs as Nos. 454/7 but with changed inscriptions. Multicoloured. P 14.*
465	50 c. Type **81**		55	55
466	$1.25, Prince and Princess of Wales		1·25	1·25
467	$2.50, Princess of Wales		2·00	2·00
465/7		*Set of 3*	3·50	3·50
MS468	81 × 101 mm. As Nos. 465/7 .		3·75	4·00

Nos. 465/7 were each printed in small sheets of 6 including one *se-tenant*, stamp-size, label.

1982 (3 Dec). *Christmas. Paintings of Infants by Bronzino, Murillo and Boucher. T **83** and similar horiz designs. P 13 × 14½.*
469	40 c. multicoloured		65	35
470	52 c. multicoloured		75	45
471	83 c. multicoloured		1·40	80
472	$1.05, multicoloured		1·50	95
469/72		*Set of 4*	4·00	2·25
MS473	110 × 76 mm. Designs as Nos. 469/72 (each 31 × 27 mm), but without portrait of Princess and Prince William. P 13½ .		2·50	2·75

MINIMUM PRICE

The minimum price quote is 10p which represents a handling charge rather than a basis for valuing common stamps. For further notes about prices see introductory pages.

---

84 Prince and Princess of Wales with Prince William

85 Prime Minister Robert Rex

1982 (3 Dec). *Christmas. Children's Charity. Sheet 72 × 58 mm. P 13 × 13½.*
MS474	**84** 80 c. + 5 c. multicoloured		1·00	1·00

No. MS474 occurs with four different designs in the sheet margin.

1983 (14 Mar). *Commonwealth Day. T **85** and similar horiz designs. Multicoloured. P 13.*
475	70 c. Type **85**		65	70
476	70 c. H.M.S. *Resolution* and H.M.S. *Adventure* off Niue, 1774		65	70
477	70 c. Passion flower		65	70
478	70 c. Limes		65	70
475/8		*Set of 4*	2·40	2·50

Nos. 475/8 were issued together, *se-tenant*, in blocks of four throughout the sheet.

86 Scouts signalling   (87)

1983 (28 Apr). *75th Anniv of Boy Scout Movement and 125th Birth Anniv of Lord Baden-Powell. T **86** and similar vert designs. Multicoloured. P 13.*
479	40 c. Type **86**		35	40
480	50 c. Planting sapling .		45	50
481	83 c. Map-reading		85	90
479/81		*Set of 3*	1·50	1·60
MS482	137 × 90 mm. As Nos. 479/81, but each with premium of 3 c. .		1·60	1·75

1983 (14 July). *15th World Scout Jamboree, Alberta, Canada. Nos. 479/82 optd with T **87**, in black on silver background.*
483	40 c. Type **86**		35	40
484	50 c. Planting sapling .		45	50
485	83 c. Map-reading		85	90
483/5		*Set of 3*	1·50	1·60
MS486	137 × 90 mm. As Nos. 483/5, but each with premium of 3 c. .		1·60	1·75

88 Black Right Whale

1983 (15 Aug). *Protect the Whales. T **88** and similar horiz designs. Multicoloured. P 13 × 14.*
487	12 c. Type **88**		65	55
488	25 c. Fin Whale		85	70
489	35 c. Sei Whale		1·25	1·00
490	40 c. Blue Whale		1·50	1·25
491	58 c. Bowhead Whale		1·60	1·40
492	70 c. Sperm Whale		2·00	1·60
493	83 c. Humpback Whale		2·25	2·00
494	$1.05, Minke Whale ("Lesser Rorqual")		2·75	2·25
495	$2.50, Grey Whale		4·00	3·75
487/95		*Set of 9*	15·00	13·00

89 Montgolfier Balloon, 1783

90 "The Garvagh Madonna"

1983 (14 Oct). *Bicentenary of Manned Flight. T **89** and similar horiz designs. Multicoloured. (a) Postage. P 13½.*
496	25 c. Type **89**		20	20
497	40 c. Wright Brothers' *Flyer*, 1903		35	40
498	58 c. *Graf Zeppelin*, 1928		50	50
499	70 c. Boeing "247", 1933		65	65
500	83 c. "Apollo 8", 1968		80	80
501	$1.05, Space shuttle *Columbia*, 1982		95	95
496/501		*Set of 6*	3·00	3·00

(b) Air. Inscr "AIRMAIL"
MS502	118 × 130 mm. Nos. 496/501. P 13		3·00	3·25

1983 (25 Nov). *Christmas. 500th Birth Anniv of Raphael. T **90** and similar vert designs. Multicoloured. P 14 × 13½.*
503	30 c. Type **90**		25	30
504	40 c. "Madonna of the Granduca"		30	35
505	58 c. "Madonna of the Goldfinch"		45	50
506	70 c. "The Holy Family of Francis I"		55	60
507	83 c. "The Holy Family with Saints" .		65	70
503/7		*Set of 5*	2·00	2·25
MS508	120 × 114 mm. As Nos. 503/7 but each with a premium of 3 c. .		2·25	2·50

83c

(90a)

1983 (30 Nov). *Various stamps surch as T **90a**.*

(a) Nos. 393/4, 399/404 and 407
509	52 c. on 30 c. *Strelitzia reginae*		40	45
510	52 c. on 30 c. Bird of Paradise .		40	45
511	58 c. on 50 c. *Tibouchina sp.*		50	55
512	58 c. on 50 c. Princess Flower .		50	55
513	70 c. on 60 c. *Nelumbo sp.*		55	60
514	70 c. on 60 c. Lotus		55	60
515	83 c. on 80 c. *Hybrid hibiscus* .		70	75
516	83 c. on 80 c. Yellow Hibiscus .		70	75
517	$3.70 on $3 *Orchid sp.*		3·00	3·25

(b) Nos. 431/2 and 455/6
518	$1.10 on 95 c. Lady Diana Spencer		3·00	2·25
	a. Error. Surch on No. 458		6·00	6·00
	ab. Pair. Nos. 518a/b		13·00	13·00
	b. Error. Surch on No. 459		7·00	7·00
519	$1.10 on $1.25, Prince and Princess of Wales (Gold on Blk.)		2·25	2·00
520	$2.60 on $1.20, Prince Charles and Lady Diana		5·50	3·50
	a. Error. Surch on No. 462		6·00	6·00
	ab. Pair. Nos. 520a/b		13·00	13·00
	b. Error. Surch on No. 463		7·00	7·00
521	$2.60 on $2.50, Princess of Wales (Gold on Blk.) .		3·50	3·25
509/21		*Set of 13*	19·00	17·00

1983 (29 Dec). *Christmas. 500th Birth Anniv of Raphael. Children's Charity. Designs as Nos. 503/7 in separate miniature sheets, 65 × 80 mm, each with face value of 85 c. + 5 c. P 13½.*
MS522	As Nos. 503/7 .	*Set of 5 sheets*	2·75	3·00

91 Morse Key Transmitter   92 *Phalaenopsis sp.*

1984 (23 Jan). *World Communications Year. T **91** and similar vert designs. Multicoloured. P 13 × 13½.*
523	40 c. Type **91**		30	35
524	52 c. Wall-mounted phone		40	45
525	83 c. Communications satellite		60	65
523/5		*Set of 3*	1·10	1·25
MS526	114 × 90 mm. Nos. 523/5 .		1·50	1·50

1984 (20 Feb–23 July). *Flowers (2nd series). Designs as Nos. 527 etc., but with gold frames and redrawn inscr as in T **92**. Multicoloured. P 13 (Nos. 537/42) or 13 × 13½ (others).*
527	12 c. Type **92**		10	10
528	25 c. *Euphorbia pulcherrima*		15	20
529	30 c. *Cochlospermum hibiscoides*		20	25
530	35 c. *Begonia sp.*		20	25
531	40 c. *Plumeria sp.*		25	30
532	52 c. *Strelitzia reginae* .		35	40
533	58 c. *Hibiscus syriacus*		40	45
534	70 c. *Tibouchina sp.*		55	50
535	83 c. *Nelumbo sp.*		55	60
536	$1.05, *Hybrid hibiscus*		70	75
537	$1.75, *Cassia fistula* (10.5)		1·10	1·25
538	$2.30, *Orchid var.* (10.5)		1·50	1·60
539	$3.90, *Orchid sp.* (10.5)		2·75	3·00
540	$5 *Euphorbia pulcherrima poinsettia* (18.6)		4·00	3·50
541	$6.60, *Hybrid hibiscus* (18.6)		4·25	4·50
542	$8.30, *Hibiscus rosasinensis* (23.7) .		5·50	5·75
527/42		*Set of 16*	20·00	20·00

Nos. 537/42 are larger, 39 × 31 mm.

93 Discus-throwing

94 Koala

1984 (15 Mar). *Olympic Games, Los Angeles.* T **93** *and similar multicoloured designs showing ancient Greek sports.* P 14.

547	30 c. Type **93** ..	..	25	30
548	35 c. Sprinting (*horiz*)	..	30	35
549	40 c. Horse racing (*horiz*)	..	35	40
550	58 c. Boxing (*horiz*) ..	..	50	55
551	70 c. Javelin-throwing	..	60	65
547/51		*Set of 5*	1·75	2·00

1984 (24 Aug). *"Ausipex" International Stamp Exhibition, Melbourne (1st issue).* P 14. (*a*) *Postage.* Vert designs as T **94** *showing Koala Bears.*

552	25 c. multicoloured	..	50	30
553	35 c. multicoloured	..	55	35
554	40 c. multicoloured	..	60	40
555	58 c. multicoloured	..	80	55
556	70 c. multicoloured	..	95	65

(*b*) *Air.* Vert designs showing Red Kangaroos

557	83 c. multicoloured	..	1·25	75
558	$1.05, multicoloured	..	1·50	95
559	$2.50, multicoloured	..	3·00	2·25
552/9		*Set of 8*	8·00	5·50
MS560	110 × 64 mm. $1.75, Wallaby; $1.75, Koala Bear. P 13½		3·25	3·75

See also Nos. MS566/7.

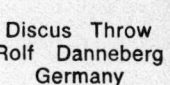

Discus Throw Rolf Danneberg Germany

(95)

96 Niue National Flag and Premier Sir Robert Rex

1984 (7 Sept). *Olympic Gold Medal Winners, Los Angeles.* Nos. 547/51 optd as T **95** in red (35 c.) or gold (*others*).

561	30 c. Type **93** (opt T **95**)		25	30
562	35 c. Sprinting (optd "1,500 Metres Sebastian Coe Great Britain")		30	35
563	40 c. Horse racing (optd "Equestrian Mark Todd New Zealand")		30	35
564	58 c. Boxing (optd "Boxing Tyrell Biggs United States")		45	50
565	70 c. Javelin-throwing (optd "Javelin Throw Arto Haerkoenen Finland")		55	60
561/5	.. .. ..	*Set of 5*	1·75	1·90

1984 (20 Sept). *"Ausipex" International Stamp Exhibition, Melbourne (2nd issue).* Designs as Nos. 552/60 in miniature sheets of six or four. Multicoloured. P 13½.

MS566	109 × 105 mm. Nos. 552/6 and $1.75, Koala Bear (as No. MS560)		3·00	3·50
MS567	80 × 105 mm. Nos. 557/9 and $1.75, Wallaby (as No. MS560) ..		4·50	4·75

1984 (19 Oct). *10th Anniv of Self-Government.* T **96** *and similar horiz designs.* Multicoloured. P 13.

568	40 c. Type **96** ..	..	30	35
569	58 c. Map of Niue and Premier Rex..		45	50
570	70 c. Premier Rex receiving proclamation of self-government..	..	55	60
568/70		*Set of 3*	1·10	1·25
MS571	110 × 83 mm. Nos. 568/70 ..		1·25	1·40
MS572	100 × 74 mm. $2.50, As 70 c. (50 × 30 mm)	..	1·75	1·90

$2 Prince Henry

15. 9. 84

(97)

98 "The Nativity" (A. Vaccaro)

1984 (22 Oct). *Birth of Prince Henry.* Nos. 430 and 454 optd as T **97**.

573	$2 on 50 c. Type **81** (Sil.)	..	2·50	1·75
574	$2 on 75 c. Type **77** (R.)	..	2·50	1·75

1984 (23 Nov). *Christmas.* T **98** *and similar vert designs.* Multicoloured. P 13 × 13½.

575	40 c. Type **98** ..	..	30	35
576	58 c. "Virgin with Fly" (anon, 16th-century)	..	45	50
577	70 c. "The Adoration of the Shepherds" (B. Murillo)	..	55	60
578	83 c. "Flight into Egypt" (B. Murillo)		65	70
575/8		*Set of 4*	1·75	1·90
MS579	115 × 111 mm. As Nos. 575/8 but each stamp with a 5 c. premium		2·00	2·25
MS580	Four sheets, each 66 × 98 mm. As Nos. 575/8, but each stamp 30 × 42 mm. with a face value of 95 c. + 10 c. P 13½	*Set of 4 sheets*	2·50	3·00

99 House Wren

1985 (15 Apr). *Birth Bicentenary of John J. Audubon (ornithologist).* T **99** *and similar horiz designs showing original paintings.* Multicoloured. P 14.

581	40 c. Type **99** ..	..	1·25	35
582	70 c. Veery ..	..	1·60	60
583	83 c. Grasshopper Sparrow	..	1·75	70
584	$1.05, Henslow's Sparrow ..		2·25	85
585	$2.50, Vesper Sparrow ..	..	3·00	2·00
581/5		*Set of 5*	9·00	4·00
MS586	Five sheets, each 54 × 60 mm. As Nos. 581/5 but each stamp 34 × 26 mm with a face value of $1.75 and without the commemorative inscription..	*Set of 5 sheets*	7·50	8·50

100 The Queen Mother in Garter Robes

1985 (14 June). *Life and Times of Queen Elizabeth the Queen Mother.* T **100** *and similar horiz designs.* Multicoloured. P 13.

587	70 c. Type **100**..	..	55	60
588	$1.15, In open carriage with the Queen ..		90	95
589	$1.50, With Prince Charles during 80th birthday celebrations ..	..	1·10	1·25
587/9		*Set of 3*	2·25	2·50
MS590	70 × 70 mm. $3 At her desk in Clarence House (38 × 35 mm)		2·25	2·50

Nos. 587/9 were each issued in sheetlets of five stamps and one stamp-size label at top left, showing the Queen Mother's arms.
For Nos. 587/9 in miniature sheet see No. MS627.

MINI SOUTH PACIFIC GAMES, RAROTONGA

(101)

52 c

1985 (26 July). *South Pacific Mini Games, Rarotonga.* Nos. 547/8 and 550/1 surch as T **101** in black and gold.

591	52 c. on 70 c. Javelin-throwing	..	40	45
592	83 c. on 58 c. Boxing ..	..	65	70
593	95 c. on 35 c. Sprinting	..	75	80
594	$2 on 30 c. Type **93**..	..	1·50	1·60
591/4		*Set of 4*	3·00	3·25

On Nos. 591/4 the new face values and inscriptions are surcharged in black on gold panels. The Games emblem is in gold only.

103 "R. Strozzi's Daughter" (Titian)

PACIFIC ISLANDS CONFERENCE, RAROTONGA

(102)

1985 (26 July). *Pacific Islands Conference, Rarotonga.* Nos. 475/8 optd with T **102** in black on silver.

595	70 c. Type **85** ..	..	55	60
596	70 c. *Resolution* and *Adventure* off Niue, 1774	..	55	60
597	70 c. Passion flower	..	55	60
598	70 c. Limes ..	..	55	60
595/8		*Set of 4*	2·00	2·25

No. 595 also shows an overprinted amendment to the caption which now reads "Premier Sir Robert Rex K.B.E.".

1985 (11 Oct). *International Youth Year.* T **103** *and similar vert designs.* Multicoloured. P 13.

599	58 c. Type **103**.	..	85	80
600	70 c. "The Fifer" (E. Manet) ..		1·00	90
601	$1.15, "Portrait of a Young Girl" (Renoir) ..	..	1·60	1·50
602	$1.50, "Portrait of M. Berard" (Renoir)	..	2·00	2·25
599/602		*Set of 4*	5·00	5·00
MS603	Four sheets, each 63 × 79 mm. As Nos. 599/602 but each with a face value of $1.75 + 10 c...	*Set of 4 sheets*	7·00	6·50

104 "Virgin and Child"

1985 (29 Nov). *Christmas. Details of Paintings by Correggio.* T **104** *and similar vert designs.* Multicoloured. P 13 × 13½.

604	58 c. Type **104**..	..	70	50
605	85 c. "Adoration of the Magi"	..	90	70
606	$1.05, "Virgin with Child and St. John" ..		1·25	85
607	$1.45, "Virgin and Child with St. Catherine" ..	..	1·75	1·25
604/7		*Set of 4*	4·25	3·00
MS608	83 × 123 mm. As Nos. 604/7, but each stamp with a face value of 60 c. + 10 c...		2·10	2·25
MS609	Four sheets, each 80 × 90 mm. 65 c. Type **104**; 95 c. As No. 605; $1.20, As No. 606; $1.75, As No. 607 (each stamp 49 × 59 mm). Imperf	*Set of 4 sheets*	3·50	4·00

105 "The Constellations" (detail)

106 Queen Elizabeth II and Prince Philip

1986 (24 Jan). *Appearance of Halley's Comet.* T **105** *and similar horiz designs showing details from ceiling painting "The Constellations" by Giovanni de Vecchi.* Nos. 611/13 show different spacecraft at top left. P 13½.

610	60 c. multicoloured	..	50	50
611	75 c. multicoloured (*Vega* spacecraft)	..	65	65
612	$1.10, multicoloured (*Planet A* spacecraft)		90	90
613	$1.50, multicoloured (*Giotto* spacecraft) ..		1·25	1·25
610/13		*Set of 4*	3·00	3·00
MS614	125 × 91 mm. As Nos. 610/13 but each stamp with a face value of 95 c...	..	3·00	3·25

Stamps from No. MS614 are without borders.

1986 (28 Apr). *60th Birthday of Queen Elizabeth II.* T **106** *and similar vert designs.* Multicoloured. P 14½ × 13.

615	$1.10, Type **106**	..	1·00	1·00
616	$1.50, Queen and Prince Philip at Balmoral	..	1·25	1·25
617	$2 Queen at Buckingham Palace	..	1·75	1·75
615/17		*Set of 3*	3·50	3·50
MS618	110 × 70 mm. As Nos. 615/17, but each stamp with a face value of 75 c...		2·75	2·75
MS619	58 × 89 mm. $3 Queen and Prince Philip at Windsor Castle..	..	3·75	3·75

107 U.S.A. 1847 Franklin 5 c. Stamp and Washington Sculpture, Mt. Rushmore, U.S.A.

108 "Statue under Construction, Paris, 1883" (Victor Dargaud)

1986 (22 May). "Ameripex '86" International Stamp Exhibition, Chicago. T **107** and similar vert design. Multicoloured. P 14.
620	$1 Type **107**	..	1·40	1·40
	a. Horiz pair. Nos. 620/1	..	2·75	2·75
621	$1 Flags of Niue and U.S.A. and Mt. Rushmore sculptures		1·40	1·40

Nos. 620/1 were printed together, se-tenant, in horizontal pairs, within sheetlets of 8 stamps, each pair forming a composite design.

1986 (4 July). Centenary of Statue of Liberty (1st issue). T **108** and similar vert design. Multicoloured. P 13 × 13½.
622	$1 Type **108**	..	1·75	1·75
623	$2.50, "Unveiling of the Statue of Liberty" (Edmund Morand).	..	2·50	2·50
MS624	107×73 mm. As Nos. 622/3, but each stamp with a face value of $1.25	..	2·50	3·00

See also No. MS648.

109 Prince Andrew, Miss Sarah Ferguson and Westminster Abbey

1986 (23 July). Royal Wedding. T **109** and similar horiz design. Multicoloured. P 13½×13.
625	$2.50, Type **109**	..	2·75	2·75
MS626	106×68 mm. $5 Prince Andrew and Miss Sarah Ferguson (43×30 mm)	..	6·00	6·00

1986 (4 Aug). 86th Birthday of Queen Elizabeth the Queen Mother. Nos. 587/9 in miniature sheet, 109×83 mm. P 13.
MS627	Nos. 587/9 ..	..	5·00	5·50

110 Great Egret   **111** "Virgin and Child" (Perugino)

1986 (4 Aug). "Stampex '86" Stamp Exhibition, Adelaide. Australian Birds. T **110** and similar multicoloured designs. P 13×13½ (40, 75 c., $1, $2.20) or 13½×13 (others).
628	40 c. Type **110**.	..	1·50	1·00
629	60 c. Painted Finch (horiz) ..	..	1·75	1·25
630	75 c. Australian King Parrot	..	2·00	1·40
631	80 c. Variegated Wren (horiz)	..	2·25	1·75
632	$1 Peregrine Falcon	..	2·75	2·00
633	$1.65, Azure Kingfisher (horiz)	..	3·50	2·75
634	$2.20, Budgerigars..	..	4·25	3·75
635	$4.25, Emu (horiz) ..	..	6·00	5·50
628/35		Set of 8	22·00	18·00

1986 (14 Nov). Christmas. Paintings from the Vatican Museum. T **111** and similar vert designs. Multicoloured. P 14.
636	80 c. Type **111**.	..	1·25	1·25
637	$1.15, "Virgin of St. N. dei Frari" (Titian)	..	1·50	1·50
638	$1.80, "Virgin with Milk" (Lorenzo di Credi)		2·40	2·40
639	$2.60, "Madonna of Foligno" (Raphael)	..	3·25	3·25
636/9		Set of 4	7·50	7·50
MS640	87×110 mm. As Nos. 636/9, but each stamp with a face value of $1.50. P 13½		4·00	4·50
MS641	70×100 mm. $7.50, As No. 639, but 27×43 mm. P 14½×13	..	6·50	7·50

(112)

1986 (21 Nov). Visit of Pope John Paul II to South Pacific. Nos. 636/41 surch as T **112** in black on silver.
642	80 c. + 10 c. Type **111**	..	1·60	1·60
643	$1.15 + 10 c. "Virgin of St. N. dei Frari" (Titian)	..	1·90	1·90
644	$1.80 + 10 c. "Virgin with Milk" (Lorenzo di Credi)..		3·00	3·00
645	$2.60 + 10 c. "Madonna of Foligno" (Raphael)	..	3·50	3·50
642/5		Set of 4	9·00	9·00
MS646	87×110 mm. As Nos. 642/5, but each stamp with a face value of $1.50 + 10 c...		7·00	7·50
MS647	70×100 mm. $7.50 + 50 c. As No. 645, but 27×43 mm	..	8·50	9·00

1987 (20 May). Centenary of Statue of Liberty (1986) (2nd issue). Two sheets, each 122×122 mm, containing multicoloured designs as T **63** of Cook Islands (Penrhyn). Litho. P 13½×14 (horiz) or 14×13½ (vert).
MS648	Two sheets (a) 75 c. Sailing ship under Brooklyn Bridge; 75 c. Restoring Statue's flame; 75 c. Steam-cleaning Statue's torch; 75 c. Esmerelda (Chilean cadet ship) off Manhattan; 75 c. Cadet barque at dusk. (b) 75 c. Statue of Liberty at night (vert); 75 c. Statue at night (side view) (vert); 75 c. Cleaning Statue's crown (vert); 75 c. Statue at night (rear view) (vert); 75 c. Cleaning a finial (vert) .. ..Set of 2 sheets		4·25	4·75

113 Boris Becker, Olympic Rings and Commemorative Coin

(Des G. Vasarhelyi. Litho Questa)

1987 (25 Sept). Olympic Games, Seoul (1988). Tennis (1st issue). T **113** and similar horiz designs showing Boris Becker in play. P 13½×14.
649	80 c. multicoloured ..	..	1·25	1·25
650	$1.15, multicoloured	..	1·50	1·50
651	$1.40, multicoloured	..	1·75	1·75
652	$1.80, multicoloured	..	2·00	2·00
649/52		Set of 4	6·00	6·00

(Des G. Vasarhelyi. Litho Questa)

1987 (20 Oct). Olympic Games, Seoul (1988). Tennis (2nd issue). Horiz designs as T **113**, but showing Steffi Graf. P 13½×14.
653	85 c. multicoloured	..	1·00	1·00
654	$1.05, multicoloured	..	1·25	1·25
655	$1.30, multicoloured	..	1·50	1·50
656	$1.75, multicoloured	..	1·75	1·75
653/6		Set of 4	5·00	5·00

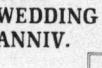

40TH WEDDING ANNIV.

4.85

(114)   **115** "The Nativity"

1987 (20 Nov). Royal Ruby Wedding. Nos. 616/17 optd with T **114**.
657	$4.85 on $1.50, Queen and Prince Philip at Balmoral	..	3·50	3·75
658	$4.85 on $2 Queen at Buckingham Palace ..	3·50	3·75

On Nos. 657/8 the original values are obliterated in gold.

1987 (4 Dec). Christmas. Religious Paintings by Dürer. T **115** and similar horiz designs. Multicoloured. P 13½.
659	80 c. Type **115**.	..	75	75
660	$1.05, "Adoration of the Magi"	..	1·00	1·00
661	$2.80, "Celebration of the Rosary"	..	2·50	2·50
659/61		Set of 3	3·75	3·75
MS662	100×140 mm. As Nos. 659/61, but each size 48×37 mm with a face value of $1.30		2·75	3·25
MS663	90×80 mm. $7.50, As No. 661, but size 51×33 mm	..	5·50	6·00

Nos. 659/61 each include a detail of an angel with lute as in T **115**. Stamps from the miniature sheets are without this feature.

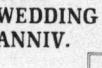

116 Franz Beckenbauer in Action

(Des G. Vasarhelyi. Litho Questa)

1988 (20 June). European Cup Football Championship, West Germany. T **116** and similar horiz designs. Multicoloured. P 13½ × 14.
664	20 c. Type **116**		40	40
665	40 c. German "All Star" team in action		65	65
666	60 c. Bayern Munich team with European Cup, 1974		75	75
667	80 c. World Cup match, England, 1966		95	95
668	$1.05, World Cup match, Mexico, 1970		1·25	1·25
669	$1.30, Beckenbauer with pennant, 1974		1·75	1·75
670	$1.80, Beckenbauer and European Cup, 1974	..	2·00	2·00
664/70		Set of 7	7·00	7·00

NEW INFORMATION

The editor is always interested to correspond with people who have new information that will improve or correct the Catalogue.

Australia 24 Jan 88
French Open 4 June 88

(117)   **118** Angels

1988 (14 Oct). Steffi Graf's Tennis Victories. Nos. 653/6 optd with T **117**.
671	85 c. multicoloured (optd with T **117**)		60	65
672	$1.05, mult (optd "Wimbledon 2 July 88 U S Open 10 Sept. 88")		75	80
673	$1.30, mult (optd "Women's Tennis Grand Slam: 10 September 88")		90	95
674	$1.75, multicoloured (optd "Seoul Olympic Games Gold Medal Winner")	..	1·25	1·40
671/4		Set of 4	3·25	3·50

1988 (28 Oct). Christmas. T **118** and similar vert designs showing details from "The Adoration of the Shepherds" by Rubens. Multicoloured. P 13½.
675	60 c. Type **118**	..	70	70
676	80 c. Shepherds	..	90	90
677	$1.05, Virgin Mary	..	1·50	1·50
678	$1.30, Holy Child	..	1·75	1·75
675/8		Set of 4	4·25	4·25
MS679	83 × 103 mm. $7.20, The Nativity (38 × 49 mm)	..	5·00	6·00

119 Astronaut and "Apollo 11" Emblem

(Des G. Vasarhelyi)

1989 (20 July). 20th Anniv of First Manned Landing on Moon. T **119** and similar horiz designs. Multicoloured. P 14.
680	$1.50, Type **119**	..	2·50	2·50
	a. Horiz strip of 3. Nos. 680/2		6·75	
681	$1.50, Earth and Moon	..	2·50	2·50
682	$1.50, Astronaut and "Apollo 1" emblem	..	2·50	2·50
680/2		Set of 3	6·75	6·75
MS683	160×64 mm. As Nos. 680/2, but each stamp with a face value of $1.15. P 13		3·00	3·50

Nos. 680/2 were printed together, se-tenant, in horizontal strips of 3 throughout the sheet.

120 Priests

1989 (22 Nov). Christmas. T **120** and similar multicoloured designs showing details from "Presentation in the Temple" by Rembrandt. P 13.
684	70 c. Type **120**	..	1·00	1·00
685	80 c. Virgin and Christ Child in Simeon's arms	..	1·10	1·10
686	$1.05, Joseph	..	1·40	1·40
687	$1.30, Simeon and Christ Child	..	1·75	1·75
684/7		Set of 4	4·75	4·75
MS688	84×110 mm. $7.20, "Presentation in the Temple" (39×49 mm). P 13½	..	8·00	8·50

121 Fritz Walter

1990 (5 Feb). World Cup Football Championship, Italy. German Footballers. T **121** and similar horiz designs. Multicoloured. P 13½×13.
689	80 c. Type **121**	..	1·75	1·75
690	$1.15, Franz Beckenbauer	..	2·00	2·00
691	$1.40, Uwe Seeler	..	2·25	2·25
692	$1.80, German team emblem and signatures of former captains	..	2·75	2·75
689/92		Set of 4	8·00	8·00

122 "Merchant Maarten Looten" (Rembrandt)

123 Queen Elizabeth the Queen Mother

1990 (2 May). *150th Anniv of the Penny Black. T* **122** *and similar vert designs showing Rembrandt paintings. Multicoloured. P* 13½.

693	80 c. Type **122**		1·25	1·25
694	$1.05, "Rembrandt's Son Titus with Pen in Hand"		1·50	1·50
695	$1.30, "The Shipbuilder and his Wife"		1·75	1·75
696	$1.80, "Bathsheba with King David's Letter"		2·25	2·25
693/6		*Set of 4*	6·00	6·00
MS697	82×143 mm. As Nos. 693/6, but each with a face value of $1.50		6·50	6·50

1990 (23 July). *90th Birthday of Queen Elizabeth the Queen Mother. P* 13×13½.

698	**123** $1.25, multicoloured		2·50	2·50
MS699	84×64 mm. **123** $7 multicoloured		8·50	8·50

124 "Adoration of the Magi" (Dirk Bouts)

(125)

(Litho Questa)

1990 (27 Nov). *Christmas. Religious Paintings. T* **124** *and similar vert designs. Multicoloured. P* 14.

700	70 c. Type **124**		75	75
701	80 c. "Holy Family" (Fra Bartolommeo)		90	90
702	$1.05, "Nativity" (Memling)		1·10	1·10
703	$1.30, "Adoration of the Kings" (Bruegel the Elder)		1·40	1·40
700/3		*Set of 4*	3·75	3·75
MS704	100×135 mm. $7.20, "Virgin and Child Enthoned" (detail, Cosimo Tura)		6·50	7·00

1990 (5 Dec). *"Birdpex '90" Stamp Exhibition, Christchurch, New Zealand. No.* 410 *optd with T* **125** *in silver.*

705	$10 Scarlet Hibiscus		8·00	8·50

SIXTY FIFTH BIRTHDAY QUEEN ELIZABETH II

(126)

1991 (22 Apr). *65th Birthday of Queen Elizabeth II. No.* 409 *optd with T* **126**.

706	$6 Hybrid hibiscus		5·50	6·00

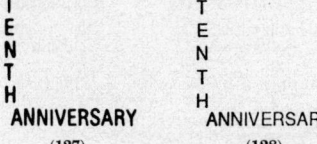

T E N T H ANNIVERSARY (127)

T E N T H ANNIVERSARY (128)

1991 (26 June). *10th Wedding Anniv of Prince and Princess of Wales. Nos.* 430/2 *optd. A. With T* **127** *in typography (75 c. in silver). B. With T* **128** *in lithography (75 c. in black).*

		A		B	
707	75 c. Type **77**	80	80	80	80
708	95 c. Lady Diana Spencer	1·10	1·10	1·10	1·10
709	$1.20, Prince Charles and Lady Diana	1·40	1·40	1·40	1·40
707/9	*Set of 3*	3·00	3·00	3·00	3·00

Nos. 707A/9A come from small sheets of 6, including one se-tenant stamp-size label, and Nos. 707B/9B from uncut sheets containing four such small sheets.

MINIMUM PRICE

The minimum price quote is 10p which represents a handling charge rather than a basis for valuing common stamps. For further notes about prices see introductory pages.

---

129 "The Virgin and Child with Sts Jerome and Dominic" (Lippi)

130 Banded Rail

(Des G. Vasarhelyi. Litho Questa)

1991 (11 Nov). *Christmas. Religious Paintings. T* **129** *and similar vert designs. Multicoloured. P* 14.

710	20 c. Type **129**		20	20
711	50 c. "The Isenheim Altarpiece" (M. Grunewald)		50	50
712	$1 "The Nativity" (G. Pittoni)		90	90
713	$2 "Adoration of the Kings" (J. Brueghel the Elder)		1·75	1·75
710/13		*Set of 4*	3·00	3·00
MS714	79×104 mm. $7 "Adoration of the Shepherds" (G. Reni)		5·00	5·50

(Litho B.D.T.)

1992 (19 Feb–15 May). *Birds. T* **130** *and similar vert designs. Multicoloured. P* 14.

718	20 c. Type **130**		10	10
719	50 c. Red-tailed Tropic Bird		35	40
720	70 c. Purple Swamphen		45	50
721	$1 Pacific Pigeon		65	70
722	$1.50, White-collared Kingfisher (20.3.92)		1·00	1·10
723	$2 Blue-crowned Lory (20.3.92)		1·25	1·40
724	$3 Purple-capped Fruit Dove (16.4.92)		2·00	2·10
726	$5 Barn Owl (15.5.92)		3·25	3·50
718/26		*Set of 8*	8·00	9·00

131 Columbus before King Ferdinand and Queen Isabella

(Des G. Vasarhelyi. Litho B.D.T.)

1992 (22 May). *500th Anniv of Discovery of America by Columbus. T* **131** *and similar horiz designs. Multicoloured. P* 13½×13.

731	$2 Type **131**		1·75	1·75
732	$3 Fleet of Columbus		2·50	2·50
733	$5 Claiming the New World for Spain		4·50	4·50
731/3		*Set of 3*	8·00	8·00

132 Tennis and $10 Commemorative Coin

(Des G. Vasarhelyi. Litho B.D.T.)

1992 (22 July). *Olympic Games, Barcelona. T* **132** *and similar horiz designs. Multicoloured. P* 13.

734	$2.50, Type **132**		2·00	2·00
	a. Horiz strip of 3. Nos. 734/6		5·50	
735	$2.50, Olympic flame and national flags		2·00	2·00
736	$2.50, Gymnastics and different $10 coin		2·00	2·00
734/6		*Set of 3*	5·50	5·50
MS737	152×87 mm. $5 Water polo		4·00	4·50

Nos. 734/6 were printed together, se-tenant, in horizontal strips of 3 throughout the sheet.

$1 = (133)

134 "St. Catherine's Mystic Marriage" (detail) (Memling)

1992 (30 Sept). *6th Festival of Pacific Arts, Rarotonga. Nos.* 336/51 *surch with T* **133**.

738	$1 on 20 c. Type **69**		90	90
739	$1 on 20 c. Ku-Tagwa plaque, New Guinea		90	90
740	$1 on 20 c. Suspension hook, New Guinea		90	90
741	$1 on 20 c. Ancestral board, New Guinea		90	90
742	$1 on 25 c. Platform post, New Hebrides		90	90
743	$1 on 25 c. Canoe ornament, New Ireland		90	90
744	$1 on 25 c. Carved figure, Admiralty Islands		90	90
745	$1 on 25 c. Female with child, Admiralty Islands		90	90
746	$1 on 30 c. The God A'a, Rurutu (Austral Islands)		90	90
747	$1 on 30 c. Statue of Tangaroa, Cook Islands		90	90
748	$1 on 30 c. Ivory pendant, Tonga		90	90
749	$1 on 30 c. Tapa (Hiapo) cloth, Niue		90	90
750	$1 on 35 c. Feather box (Waka), New Zealand		90	90
751	$1 on 35 c. Hei-Tiki amulet, New Zealand		90	90
752	$1 on 35 c. House post, New Zealand		90	90
753	$1 on 35 c. Feather image of god Ku, Hawaii		90	90
738/53		*Set of 16*	13·00	13·00

1992 (18 Nov). *Christmas. Different details from "St. Catherine's Mystic Marriage" by Hans Memling. T* **134** *and similar vert designs. Litho. P* 13½.

754	20 c. Type **134**		15	15
755	50 c. multicoloured		50	50
756	$1 multicoloured		90	90
757	$2 multicoloured		1·75	1·75
754/7		*Set of 4*	3·00	3·00
MS758	87×101 mm. $7 multicoloured (as 50 c., but larger (36×47 mm))		5·50	6·00

135 Queen on Official Visit

136 Rough-toothed Dolphin

(Litho B.D.T.)

1992 (7 Dec). *40th Anniv of Queen Elizabeth II's Accession. T* **135** *and similar vert designs. Multicoloured. P* 14.

759	70 c. Type **135**		65	65
760	$1 Queen in green evening dress		95	95
761	$1.50, Queen in white embroidered evening dress		1·25	1·25
762	$2 Queen with bouquet		1·90	1·90
759/62		*Set of 4*	4·25	4·25

(Des G. Drummond. Litho B.D.T.)

1993 (13 Jan). *Endangered Species. South Pacific Dolphins. T* **136** *and similar horiz designs. Multicoloured. P* 14.

763	20 c. Type **136**		15	15
764	50 c. Fraser's Dolphin		50	50
765	75 c. Pantropical Spotted Dolphin		75	75
766	$1 Risso's Dolphin		95	95
763/6		*Set of 4*	2·10	2·10

OFFICIAL STAMPS

O.H.M.S.   O.H.M.S.

(O 1)   (O 2)

1985 (1 July)–87. *Nos.* 408/10 *optd with Type O* **2** *in gold and Nos.* 527/42 *optd with Type O* **1** *in blue, all by foil embossing.*

O 1	12 c. Type **92**		10	10
O 2	25 c. Euphorbia pulcherrima		15	20
O 3	30 c. Cochlospermum hibiscoides		20	25
O 4	35 c. Begonia sp.		25	30
O 5	40 c. Plumeria sp.		25	30
O 6	52 c. Strelitzia reginae		35	40
O 7	58 c. Hibiscus syriacus		40	45
O 8	70 c. Tibouchina sp.		45	50
O 9	83 c. Nelumbo sp.		55	60
O10	$1.05, Hybrid hibiscus		70	75
O11	$1.75, Cassia fistula		1·10	1·25
O12	$2.30, Orchid var. (29.11.85)		1·50	1·60
O13	$3.90, Orchid sp. (29.11.85)		2·50	2·75
O14	$4 Euphorbia pulcherrima poinsettia (1.4.86)		2·75	3·00
O15	$5 Euphorbia pulcherrima poinsettia (1.4.86)		3·25	3·50
O16	$6 Hybrid hibiscus (29.4.87)		4·00	4·25
O17	$6.60, Hybrid hibiscus (15.9.86)		4·25	4·50
O18	$8.30, Hibiscus rosasinensis (15.9.86)		5·50	5·75
O19	$10 Scarlet Hibiscus (29.4.87)		6·50	6·75
O1/19		*Set of 19*	29·00	32·00

Norfolk Island

The stamps of TASMANIA were used on Norfolk Island from mid-1854 until May 1855, such use being identified by the "72" numeral cancellation. From 1877 the stamps of NEW SOUTH WALES were in regular use, being replaced by issues for AUSTRALIA from 1913 to 1947.

AUSTRALIAN ADMINISTRATION

PRINTERS. Nos. 1 to 42 were printed at the Note Printing Branch Reserve Bank of Australia (until 14 Jan 1960, known as the Note Printing Branch, Commonwealth Bank) by recess. See note at the beginning of Australia re imprints.

1 Ball Bay

1947 (10 June)–59. *Toned paper.* P 14.

1	1	½d. orange				35	50
		a. White paper (11.56)				1·50	4·00
2		1d. bright violet				50	50
		a. White paper (11.56)				7·50	16·00
3		1½d. emerald-green				50	50
		a. White paper (11.56)				13·00	23·00
4		2d. reddish violet				55	30
		a. White paper (11.56)				£130	£130
5		2½d. scarlet				80	30
6		3d. chestnut				70	55
6a		3d. emerald-green (*white paper*) (6.7.59)			15·00	3·75
7		4d. claret				70	40
8		5½d. indigo				70	30
9		6d. purple-brown				70	30
10		9d. magenta				1·25	40
11		1s. grey-green				70	40
12		2s. yellow-bistre				3·00	1·25
12a		2s. deep blue (*white paper*) (6.7.59)			24·00	5·00
1/12a					*Set of 14*	45·00	13·00

Stamps of T 1, perf 11, or in different colours, perf 11, are printer's waste which leaked from the Note Ptg Branch. They were never distributed to post offices for sale to the public.

2 Warder's Tower   3 Airfield

1953 (10 June). *T 2/3 and similar designs.* P 14½ × 15 (*vert*) or 15 × 14½ (*horiz*).

13		3½d. brown-lake				3·00	90
14		6½d. deep green				3·00	1·00
15		7½d. deep blue				4·00	3·00
16		8½d. chocolate				7·00	3·50
17		10d. reddish violet				5·00	75
18		5s. sepia				38·00	8·00
13/18					*Set of 6*	55·00	15·00

Designs: *Horiz* (*as T 3*)—7½d. Old Stores (Crankmill); 5s. Bloody Bridge. *Vert* (*as T 2*)—8½d. Barracks entrance; 10d. Salt House.

8 Norfolk Island Seal and Pitcairners Landing

Two types of 2s.:

Type I   Type II

Alternate stamps on each horizontal row are with or without a dot in bottom right corner.

1956 (8 June). *Centenary of Landing of Pitcairn Islanders on Norfolk Island.* P 15 × 14½.

19	8	3d. deep bluish green				1·25	30
20		2s. violet (I)				1·75	50
		a. Type II				1·75	50
		b. *Deep violet* (I)				2·75	1·75
		ba. Type II				2·75	1·75

(9)   (10)   (11)

1958 (1 July). *Nos. 15/16 surch with T 9/10.*

21	7d. on 7½d. deep blue				1·00	45
22	8d. on 8½d. chocolate				1·00	45

1959 (7 Dec). *150th Anniv of Australian Post Office. No. 331 of Australia surch with T 11.*

23	5d. on 4d. slate (R.)				35	30

12 Hibiscus insularis   14 White Tern

16 Red Hibiscus   17 Queen Elizabeth II and Cereus

21 Rose Apple   22 Red-tailed Tropic Bird

(Design recess; centre typo (T 21))

1960–62. *T 12, 14, 16/17, 21/2 and similar designs.* P 14½ or 14½ × 14 (10s.))

24		1d. bluish green (23.5.60)				15	10
25		2d. rose and myrtle-green (23.5.60)			20	10
26		3d. green (1.5.61)				70	15
27		5d. bright purple (20.6.60)				55	20
28		8d. red (20.6.60)				80	50
29		9d. ultramarine (23.5.60)				80	45
30		10d. brown and reddish violet (as No. 17) (27.2.61)		2·50	1·25
31		1s. 1d. carmine-red (16.10.61)			80	35
32		2s. sepia (1.5.61)				6·00	90
33		2s. 5d. deep violet (5.2.62)				1·00	40
34		2s. 8d. cinnamon and deep green (9.4.62)		2·00	55
35		5s. sepia and deep green (as No. 18) (27.2.61)		6·00	75
36		10s. emerald-green (14.8.61) (Optd S. £48)		60·00	26·00
24/36					*Set of 13*	70·00	28·00

Designs: *Vert* (*as T 12*)—2d. *Lagunaria patersonii*; 5d. Lantana. (*As T 21*); 1s. 1d. Fringed Hibiscus; 2s. 5d. Passion-flower. (*As T 14*)—2s. Solander's Petrel.

Nos. 30 and 35 are redrawn.

The Specimen overprint on No. 36 is from sets sold by the Australian Post Office.

2/8

≡ 1/1   2/5   ≡

(23)   (24)   (25)

1960. *As Nos. 13/15 but colours changed, surch with T 23/5.*

37		1s. 1d. on 3½d. deep ultramarine (26.9.60)		3·50	1·25
38		2s. 5d. on 6½d. bluish green (26.9.60)		3·50	1·25
39		2s. 8d. on 7½d. sepia (29.8.60)			8·00	2·25
37/9					*Set of 3*	13·50	4·25

26 Queen Elizabeth II and Map   27 Open Bible and Candle

1960 (24 Oct). *Introduction of Local Government.* P 14.

40	26	2s. 8d. reddish purple				15·00	6·00

(Des K. McKay. Adapted and eng B. Stewart. Recess)

1960 (21 Nov). *Christmas.* P 15×14½.

41	27	5d. bright purple				80	30

28 Open Prayer Book and Text   29 "Tweed Trousers" (*Atypichthys latus*)

(Des G. Lissenden. Eng P. Morriss. Recess)

1961 (20 Nov). *Christmas.* P 14½×14.

42	28	5d. slate-blue				30	30

PRINTERS. All the following issues to No. 233 were printed in photogravure by Harrison and Sons, Ltd, London, *except where otherwise stated.*

1962–63. *Fishes. Horiz designs as T 29.* P 14½×14.

43	6d. sepia, yellow & dp bluish green (16.7.62)	1·00	25
44	11d. red-orange, brown and blue (25.2.63)	2·50	80
45	1s. blue, pink and yellow-olive (17.9.62)	1·00	25
46	1s. 3d. blue, red-brown and green (15.7.63)	2·50	1·75
47	1s. 6d. sepia, violet and light blue (6.5.63)	3·00	80
48	2s. 3d. dp blue, red & greenish yell (23.9.63)	4·50	80
43/8	*Set of 6*	13·00	4·25

Designs:—11d. "Trumpeter"; 1s. "Po'ov"; 1s. 3d. "Dreamfish"; 1s. 6d. "Hapoéka"; 2s. 3d. "Ophie" (*carangidae*).

30 "Madonna and Child"   31 "Peace on Earth..."

(Des and eng G. Lissenden. Recess Note Ptg Branch, Reserve Bank of Australia)

1962 (19 Nov). *Christmas.* P 14½.

49	30	5d. ultramarine				35	20

(Des R. Warner. Eng B. Stewart. Recess Note Ptg Branch, Reserve Bank of Australia)

1963 (11 Nov). *Christmas.* P 14½.

50	31	5d. red				30	20

32 Overlooking Kingston   33 Norfolk Pine

1964 (24 Feb–28 Sept). *Views. Horiz designs as T 32.* *Multicoloured.* P 14½×14.

51		5d. Type 32				75	15
52		8d. Kingston				1·00	20
53		9d. The Arches (Bumboras) (11.5)			2·50	15
54		10d. Slaughter Bay (28.9)				3·00	25
51/4					*Set of 4*	6·50	65

(Photo Note Ptg Branch, Reserve Bank of Australia, Melbourne)

1964 (1 July). *50th Anniv of Norfolk Island as Australian Territory.* P 13½.

55	33	5d. black, red and orange				30	15
56		8d. black, red and grey-green				30	15

34 Child looking at Nativity Scene   35 Nativity Scene

(Des P. Morriss and J. Mason. Photo Note Ptg Branch, Reserve Bank of Australia)

1964 (9 Nov). *Christmas.* P 13½.

57	34	5d. green, blue, buff and violet				30	10

1965 (14 Apr). *50th Anniv of Gallipoli Landing. As T 22 of Nauru.* P 13½.

58		5d. sepia, black and emerald				10	10

(Des J. Mason. Photo Note Ptg Branch, Reserve Bank of Australia)

1965 (25 Oct). *Christmas. Helecon paper.* P 13½.

59	35	5d. multicoloured				10	10

ALTERED CATALOGUE NUMBERS

Any Catalogue numbers altered from the last edition are shown as a list in the introductory pages.

(New Currency. 100 cents = $1 Australian)

38 Hibiscus insularis   **39** Headstone Bridge

1966 (14 Feb). *Decimal currency. Various stamps surch in black on silver tablets, which vary slightly in size, obliterating old value as in T 38. Surch typo.*

60	38	1 c. on 1d. bluish green (*value tablet* 4×5 mm)		20	10
		a. Value tablet larger, 5½×5½ mm		40	30
61	—	2 c. on 2d. rose & myrtle-green (No. 25)		20	10
62	14	3 c. on 3d. green		50	10
		a. Silver tablet omitted		£250	
63	—	4 c. on 5d. bright purple (No. 27)		25	10
64	16	5 c. on 8d. red		30	10
65	—	10 c. on 10d. brown & reddish vio (No. 30)		40	15
66	—	15 c. on 1s. 1d. carmine-red (No. 31)		45	15
67	—	20 c. on 2s. sepia (No. 32)		3·50	1·75
68	—	25 c. on 2s. 5d. deep violet (No. 33)		1·50	40
69	21	30 c. on 2s. 8d. cinnamon and deep green		1·00	50
70	—	50 c. on 5s. sepia and deep green (No. 35)		4·50	75
71	22	$1 on 10s. emerald-green (*value tablet* 7×6½ mm)		3·50	1·75
		a. Value tablet smaller, 6½×4 mm		3·50	1·75
60/71			*Set of 12*	14·50	5·25

1966 (27 June). *Horiz designs as T 39. Multicoloured. P 14½ × 14.*

72		7 c. Type 39		40	15
73		9 c. Cemetery Road		40	15

41 St. Barnabas' Chapel (interior)   **42** St. Barnabas' Chapel (exterior)

1966 (23 Aug). *Centenary of Melanesian Mission. P 14 × 14½.*

74	41	4 c. multicoloured		10	10
75	42	25 c. multicoloured		20	10

43 Star over Philip Island   **44** H.M.S. *Resolution*, 1774

(Des B. G. W. McCoy)

1966 (24 Oct). *Christmas. P 14½.*

76	43	4 c. multicoloured		10	10

(Des Harrison)

1967 (17 Apr)–**68**. *T 44 and similar horiz designs showing ships. Multicoloured. P 14 × 14½.*

77		1 c. Type 44		10	10
78		2 c. La Boussole and L'Astrolabe, 1788		15	10
79		3 c. H.M.S. Supply, 1788		15	10
80		4 c. H.M.S. Sirius, 1790		15	10
81		5 c. Norfolk (cutter), 1798 (14.8.67)		20	10
82		7 c. H.M.S. Mermaid (survey cutter), 1825 (14.8.67)		20	10
83		9 c. Lady Franklin, 1853 (14.8.67)		20	10
84		10 c. Morayshire, 1856 (14.8.67)		20	20
85		15 c. Southern Cross, 1866 (18.3.68)		45	30
86		20 c. Pitcairn, 1891 (18.3.68)		60	40
87		25 c. Norfolk Island whaleboat, 1895 (18.3.68)		1·00	75
88		30 c. Iris (cable ship), 1907 (18.6.68)		2·00	1·75
89		50 c. Resolution, 1926 (18.6.68)		3·00	2·25
90		$1 Morinda, 1931 (18.6.68)		5·50	2·50
77/90			*Set of 14*	12·50	8·00

45 Lions Badge and 50 Stars   **46** Prayer of John Adams and Candle

(Des M. Ripper. Photo Note Ptg Branch, Reserve Bank of Australia)

1967 (7 June). *50th Anniv of Lions International. P 13½.*

91	45	4 c. black, bluish green and olive-yellow		10	10

(Des B. G. W. McCoy)

1967 (16 Oct). *Christmas. P 14.*

92	46	5 c. black, light yellow-olive and red		10	10

47 Queen Elizabeth II

(Photo Note Ptg Branch, Reserve Bank of Australia)

1968 (5 Aug)–**71**. *Coil stamps. P 15×imperf.*

93	47	3 c. black, light brown and vermilion		10	10
94		4 c. black, light brown and blue-green		10	10
95		5 c. black, light brown and deep violet		10	10
95a		6 c. black, lt brown & lake-brn (25.8.71)		30	35
93/5a			*Set of 4*	45	45

59 "Skymaster" and "Lancastrian" Aircraft   **60** Bethlehem Star and Flowers

(Des Harrison)

1968 (25 Sept). *21st Anniv of QANTAS Air Service, Sydney–Norfolk Island. P 14.*

96	59	5 c. bluish black, carmine-red & lt blue		10	10
97		7 c. blackish brown, carmine-red & turq		10	10

(Des Mrs. B. L. Laing)

1968 (24 Oct). *Christmas. P 14 × 14½.*

98	60	5 c. multicoloured		10	10

61 Captain Cook, Quadrant and Chart of Pacific Ocean   **62** Van Diemen's Land, Norfolk Island and Sailing Cutter

(Des V. Whiteley from sketch by J. G. Cowan)

1969 (3 June). *Captain Cook Bicentenary (1st issue). Observation of the transit of Venus across the Sun, from Tahiti. P 14.*

99	61	10 c. multicoloured		10	10

See also Nos. 118/19, 129, 152/5, 200/2 and 213/14.

(Des Mrs. A. Bathie and Mrs. M. J. McCoy)

1969 (29 Sept). *125th Anniv of the Annexation of Norfolk Island to Van Diemen's Land. P 14 × 14½.*

100	62	5 c. multicoloured		10	10
101		30 c. multicoloured		20	10

63 "The Nativity" (carved mother-of-pearl plaque)   **64** New Zealand Grey Flyeater

(Des J. G. Cowan)

1969 (27 Oct). *Christmas. P 14½ × 14.*

102	63	5 c. multicoloured		10	10

(Des G. Mathews)

1970–71. *Birds. T 64 and similar multicoloured designs. Chalk-surfaced paper. P 14.*

103		1 c. Scarlet Robins (22.7.70)		30	10
104		2 c. Golden Whistler (24.2.71)		30	20
105		3 c. Type 64 (25.2.70)		30	10
106		4 c. Long-tailed Koels (25.2.70)		60	10
107		5 c. Red-fronted Parakeet (24.2.71)		1·50	45
108		7 c. Long-tailed Triller (22.7.70)		45	10
109		9 c. Island Thrush (25.2.70)		70	10
110		10 c. Boobook Owl (22.7.70)		1·75	40
111		15 c. Norfolk Island Pigeon (24.2.71)		1·50	65
112		20 c. White-chested White Eye (16.6.71)		4·50	3·00
113		25 c. Norfolk Island Parrots (22.7.70)		2·50	40
		a. Error. Glazed, ordinary paper			
114		30 c. Collared Grey Fantail (16.6.71)		4·50	1·75
115		45 c. Norfolk Island Starlings (25.2.70)		3·50	80
116		50 c. Crimson Rosella (24.2.71)		4·00	1·75
117		$1 Sacred Kingfisher (16.6.71)		9·00	9·00
103/17			*Set of 15*	32·00	17·00

Nos. 105, 106, 109, 112, 114, 115 and 117 are horizontal, and the remainder vertical designs.

It is believed that only one sheet of No. 113a was issued.

65 Capt. Cook and Map of Australia   **66** First Christmas Service, 1788

(Des R. Bates)

1970 (29 Apr). *Captain Cook Bicentenary (2nd issue). Discovery of Australia's East Coast. T 65 and similar horiz design. Multicoloured. P 14.*

118		5 c. Type 65		15	10
119		10 c. H.M.S. Endeavour and aborigine		40	10

(Des R. Bates)

1970 (15 Oct). *Christmas. P 14.*

120	66	5 c. multicoloured		10	10

67 Bishop Patteson and Martyrdom of St. Stephen   **68** Rose Window, St. Barnabas Chapel, Kingston

(Des R. Bates)

1971 (20 Sept). *Death Centenary of Bishop Patteson. T 67 and similar horiz designs. Multicoloured. P 14 × 14½.*

121		6 c. Type 67		10	10
		a. Pair. Nos. 121/2		10	10
122		6 c. Bible, Martyrdom of St. Stephen and knotted palm-frond		10	10
123		10 c. Bishop Patteson and stained-glass		10	10
		a. Pair. Nos. 123/4		20	20
124		10 c. Cross and Bishop's Arms		10	10
121/4			*Set of 4*	30	30

Nos. 121/2 and 123/4 were printed in *se-tenant* pairs throughout the sheet.

(Des G. Hitch. Photo Heraclio Fournier, Spain)

1971 (25 Oct). *Christmas. P 14 × 13½.*

125	68	6 c. multicoloured		10	10

69 Map and Flag   **70** "St. Mark" (stained-glass window, All Saints, Norfolk Is)

(Des G. Hitch)

1972 (7 Feb). *25th Anniv of South Pacific Commission. P 14 × 14½.*

126	69	7 c. multicoloured		15	10

(Des Mrs. M. J. McCoy)

1972 (16 Oct). *Christmas. P 14.*

127	70	7 c. multicoloured		10	10

71 Cross and Pines. (stained-glass window, All Saints Church)   **72** H.M.S. *Resolution* in the Antarctic

(Des Harrison)

1972 (20 Nov). *Centenary of First Pitcairner-built Church. P 14.*

128	71	12 c. multicoloured		10	10
		a. Purple (background to dates) omitted			

No. 128a occurred on the top row of one sheet.

(Des G. Hitch)

1973 (17 Jan). *Captain Cook Bicentenary (3rd issue). Crossing of the Antarctic Circle. P* 14.

129	**72**	35 c. multicoloured		3·00	2·25

73 Child and Christmas Tree   **74** Protestant Clergyman's Quarters

(Des B. W. McCoy (T **73**), R. Westwood (35 c.))

1973 (22 Oct). *Christmas. T* **73** *and similar vert design. Multicoloured. P* 14.

130	7 c. Type **73**		20	10
131	12 c. Type **73**		25	10
132	35 c. Fir trees and star		70	80
130/2		Set of 3	1·00	90

(Des G. Hitch)

1973 (19 Nov)–**75**. *Historic Buildings. T* **74** *and similar horiz designs. Multicoloured. P* 14 × 14½.

133	1 c. Type **74**		10	10
134	2 c. Royal Engineers' Office (1.5.74)		10	10
135	3 c. Double Quarters for Free Overseers (19.2.75)		25	15
136	4 c. Guard House (12.7.74)		20	20
137	5 c. Entrance to Pentagonal Gaol		25	15
138	7 c. Pentagonal Gaol (1.5.74)		35	35
139	8 c. Prisoners' Barracks (19.2.75)	1·00	35
140	10 c. Officers' Quarters, New Military Barracks		50	45
141	12 c. New Military Barracks (1.5.74)		50	30
142	14 c. Beach Stores (12.7.74)		60	60
143	15 c. The Magazine (19.2.75)	1·50	50
144	20 c. Entrance, Old Military Barracks (12.7.74)	80	80
145	25 c. Old Military Barracks (19.2.75)	1·50	90
146	30 c. Old Stores (Crankmill) (1.5.74)	1·00	60
147	50 c. Commissariat Stores	1·25	1·75
148	$1 Government House (12.7.74)	2·25	3·75
133/48		Set of 16	11·00	10·00

75 Royal Couple and Map

(Des Harrison)

1974 (8 Feb). *Royal Visit. P* 14 × 14½.

149	**75**	7 c. multicoloured		40	15
150		35 c. multicoloured		1·25	75

76 Chichester's *Madame Elijah*

(Des B. McCoy. Litho State Bank Note Printing Works, Helsinki)

1974 (28 Mar). *First Aircraft Landing on Norfolk Island. P* 14.

151	**76**	14 c. multicoloured		1·00	70

77 "Captain Cook" (engraving by J. Basire)   **78** Nativity Scene (pearl-shell pew carving)

(Des C. I. Buffett. Litho Questa)

1974 (8 Oct). *Captain Cook Bicentenary (4th issue). Discovery of Norfolk Is. T* **77** *and similar vert designs. Multicoloured. P* 14.

152	7 c. Type **77**		1·50	75
153	10 c. "H.M.S. *Resolution*" (H. Roberts)	2·50	1·75
154	14 c. Norfolk Island Pine		2·75	2·25
155	25 c. "Norfolk Island flax" (G. Raper)	3·25	3·00
152/5		Set of 4	9·00	7·00

(Des G. Hitch)

1974 (18 Oct). *Christmas. P* 14½.

156	**78**	7 c. multicoloured	15	10
157		30 c. multicoloured	60	75

79 Norfolk Pine

(Manufactured by Walsall)

1974 (16 Dec). *Centenary of Universal Postal Union. T* **79** *and similar "island"-shaped designs. Multicoloured. Imperf (backing-paper roll 20). Self-adhesive.*

158	10 c. Type **79**		35	40
159	15 c. Offshore islands		40	45
160	35 c. Crimson Rosella and Sacred Kingfisher	70	75
161	40 c. Pacific map		75	90
158/61		Set of 4	2·00	2·25
MS162	106 × 101 mm. Map of Norfolk Is. cut-to-shape with reduced-size replicas of Nos. 158/61	23·00	27·00

80 H.M.S. *Mermaid* (survey cutter)

(Manufactured by Walsall)

1975 (18 Aug). *150th Anniv of Second Settlement. T* **80** *and similar "island"-shaped design. Multicoloured. Imperf (backing-paper roll 20). Self-adhesive.*

163	10 c. Type **80**		45	45
164	35 c. Kingston, 1835 (from painting by T. Seller)	80	80

81 Star on Norfolk Island Pine   **82** Memorial Cross

(Des Harrison)

1975 (6 Oct). *Christmas. P* 14.

165	**81**	10 c. multicoloured	15	10
166		15 c. multicoloured	20	10
167		35 c. multicoloured	30	35
165/7		Set of 3	60	45

(Des Harrison)

1975 (24 Nov). *Centenary of St. Barnabas Chapel. T* **82** *and similar horiz design. Multicoloured. P* 14.

168	30 c. Type **82**		20	15
169	60 c. Laying foundation stone and Chapel in 1975	40	40

83 Launching of *Resolution*   **84** Whaleship *Charles W. Morgan*

(Des Harrison)

1975 (1 Dec). *50th Anniv of Launching of Schooner "Resolution". T* **83** *and similar horiz design. Multicoloured. P* 14.

170	25 c. Type **83**		25	30
171	45 c. *Resolution* at sea		40	55

(Des Harrison)

1976 (5 July). *Bicentenary of American Revolution. T* **84** *and similar horiz designs. Multicoloured. P* 14.

172	18 c. Type **84**		30	15
173	25 c. Thanksgiving Service		40	20
174	40 c. "Flying Fortress" over Norfolk Is	75	45
175	45 c. California Quail		1·00	55
172/5		Set of 4	2·25	1·25

85 Swallow-tailed Tern and Sun   **86** *Vanessa ita*

(Des Harrison)

1976 (4 Oct). *Christmas. P* 14.

176	**85**	18 c. multicoloured	25	15
177		25 c. multicoloured	40	20
178		45 c. multicoloured	85	50
176/8		Set of 3	1·40	75

(Des B. Hargreaves)

1976 (17 Nov)–**77**. *Butterflies and Moths. T* **86** *and similar horiz designs. Multicoloured. P* 14.

179	1 c. Type **86**		10	40
180	2 c. *Utetheisa pulchelloides* (moth) (22.2.77)	10	40
181	3 c. *Agathia asterias* (moth) (5.7.77)	10	20
182	4 c. *Cynthia kershawi* (moth) (5.7.77)	10	25
183	5 c. *Leucania loreyimima* (moth)	15	30
184	10 c. *Hypolimnas bolina*		30	35
185	15 c. *Pyrrhorachis pyrrhogona* (moth) (22.2.77)	30	30
186	16 c. *Austrocarea iocephala* (moth)	30	30
187	17 c. *Pseudocoremia christiani* (moth) (10.5.77)	35	30
188	18 c. *Cleora idiocrossa* (moth)	35	30
189	19 c. *Simplicia caeneusalis* (moth) (10.5.77)	35	30
190	20 c. *Austrocidaria ralstonae* (moth) (10.5.77)	40	30
191	30 c. *Hippotion scrofa* (moth) (22.2.77)	50	40
192	40 c. *Papilio amynthor (ilioneus)* (10.5.77)	55	40
193	50 c. *Tiracola plagiata* (moth) (22.2.77)	70	60
194	$1 *Precis villida*		1·00	75
195	$2 *Cepora perimale* (5.7.77)	1·75	1·40
179/95		Set of 17	6·50	6·50

87 Queen's View, Kingston

(Des Harrison)

1977 (10 June). *Silver Jubilee. P* 14.

196	**87**	25 c. multicoloured		35	30

88 Hibiscus Flowers and Oil Lamp   **89** Captain Cook (from a portrait by Nathaniel Dance)

(Des Mrs. M. J. McCoy)

1977 (4 Oct). *Christmas. P* 14 × 14½.

197	**88**	18 c. multicoloured	15	10
198		25 c. multicoloured	15	10
199		45 c. multicoloured	30	35
197/9		Set of 3	55	50

(Des Harrison)

1978 (18 Jan). *Captain Cook Bicentenary (5th issue). Discovery of Hawaii. T* **89** *and similar horiz designs. Multicoloured. P* 14½.

200	18 c. Type **89**		30	20
201	25 c. Discovery of Northern Hawaiian islands	40	30
202	80 c. British flag against island background	90	70
200/2		Set of 3	1·40	1·10

90 Guide Flag and Globe

(Manufactured by Walsall)

1978 (22 Feb). *50th Anniv of Girl Guides. T* **90** *and similar "island"-shaped designs. Multicoloured. Imperf (backing paper roul 20). Self-adhesive.*

203	18 c. Type 90	30	15
204	25 c. Emblem and scarf badge	45	25
	a. Horiz roul omitted (vert pair)		
205	35 c. Emblem and Queen Elizabeth	60	35
	a. Horiz roul omitted (vert pair)		
206	45 c. Emblem and Lady Baden-Powell	75	45
203/6	Set of 4	1·90	1·10

Nos. 204a and 205a each come from sheets of 20 on which all the horizontal roulettes were omitted.

91 St. Edward's Crown

(Des Harrison)

1978 (29 June). *25th Anniv of Coronation. T* **91** *and similar horiz design. Multicoloured. P* 14½.

207	25 c. Type 91	15	15
208	70 c. Coronation regalia	40	45

92 View of Duncombe Bay with Scout at Camp Fire

(Des S. Jensen. Manufactured by Walsall)

1978 (22 Aug). *50th Anniv of Boy Scouts. T* **92** *and similar "island"-shaped designs. Multicoloured. Imperf (backing paper roul 20). Self-adhesive.*

209	20 c. Type 92	35	30
210	25 c. View from Kingston and emblem	85	75
211	35 c. View of Anson Bay and Link Badge	85	75
212	45 c. Sunset scene and Lord Baden-Powell	1·00	85
209/12	Set of 4	2·50	2·10

93 Chart showing Route of Arctic Voyage	**94** Poinsettia and Bible

(Des G. Hitch)

1978 (29 Aug). *Captain Cook Bicentenary (6th issue). Northernmost Voyages. T* **93** *and similar horiz design. Multicoloured. P* 14½.

213	25 c. Type 93	60	30
214	90 c. "H.M.S. *Resolution* and H.M.S. *Discovery* in Pack Ice" (painting by Webber)	1·50	80

(Des Mrs. M. J. McCoy)

1978 (3 Oct). *Christmas. T* **94** *and similar vert designs. Multicoloured. P* 14½ × 14.

215	20 c. Type 94	15	10
216	30 c. Native Oak and Bible	20	15
217	55 c. Hibiscus and Bible	30	30
215/17	Set of 3	60	50

95 Cook and Village of Staithes near Marton

(Des Harrison)

1978 (27 Oct). *250th Birth Anniv of Captain Cook. T* **95** *and similar horiz design. Multicoloured. P* 14½.

218	20 c. Type 95	35	25
219	80 c. Cook and Whitby Harbour	1·40	1·25

MINIMUM PRICE

The minimum price quote is 10p which represents a handling charge rather than a basis for valuing common stamps. For further notes about prices see introductory pages.

96 H.M.S. *Resolution*	**97** Assembly Building

(Des G. Hitch)

1979 (14 Feb). *Death Bicentenary of Captain Cook. T* **96** *and similar horiz designs. Multicoloured. P* 14.

220	20 c. Type 96	80	30
	a. Pair. Nos. 220/1	1·60	60
221	20 c. Cook (statue)	80	30
222	40 c. Cook's death	90	50
	a. Pair. Nos. 222/3	1·75	1·00
223	40 c. Cook's death (different)	90	50
220/23	Set of 4	3·00	1·60

The 20 c. designs depict the *Resolution* and Cook's statue on a map showing the last voyage. The 40 c. designs show Cook's death from an aquatint by John Clevely.

Nos. 220/1 and 222/3 were each printed together, *se-tenant*, in horizontal pairs throughout the sheets, forming composite designs.

1979 (10 Aug). *First Norfolk Island Legislative Assembly. P* 14½ × 14.

224	**97** $1 multicoloured	50	50

98 Tasmania 1853 1d. Stamp and Sir Rowland Hill

1979 (27 Aug). *Death Centenary of Sir Rowland Hill. T* **98** *and similar horiz designs showing stamps and Sir Rowland Hill. P* 14 × 14½.

225	20 c. new blue and sepia	20	10
226	30 c. brown-red and olive-grey	25	15
227	55 c. violet and indigo	40	30
225/7	Set of 3	75	50
MS228	142 × 91 mm. No. 227. P 14	55	1·00

Designs:—30 c. Penny Red; 55 c. 1d. "Ball Bay".

99 I.Y.C. Emblem and Map of Pacific showing Norfolk Island as Pine Tree

(Des Claire Walters. Litho Asher and Co, Melbourne)

1979 (25 Sept). *International Year of the Child. P* 15.

229	**99** 10 c. multicoloured	40	45

100 Emily Bay	**101** Lions International Emblem

1979 (5 Nov).* *Christmas. T* **100** *and similar horiz designs showing different aspects of Emily Bay. P* 12½ × 13.

230	15 c. multicoloured	15	15
	a. Horiz strip of 3. Nos. 230/2	40	
231	20 c. multicoloured	15	15
232	30 c. multicoloured	15	15
230/2	Set of 3	40	40
MS233	152 × 83 mm. Nos. 230/2. P 14 × 14½	1·00	1·25

Nos. 230/2 were printed together, *se-tenant*, in horizontal strips of 3 throughout the sheet, forming a composite design.

*Although released by the Crown Agents in London on 2 October the stamps were not released locally until 5 November.

(Des Norfolk Island Lions Club. Litho Asher and Co, Melbourne)

1980 (25 Jan). *Lions Convention. P* 15.

234	**101** 50 c. multicoloured	35	30

102 Rotary International Emblem

(Des E. Lenthall. Litho Asher and Co, Melbourne)

1980 (21 Feb). *75th Anniv of Rotary International. P* 15.

235	**102** 50 c. multicoloured	35	30
	a. Black (face value and "NORFOLK ISLAND") omitted		

103 "D.H. 60 (Gypsy Moth)" *Mme Elijah*

(Des G. Hitch. Litho Harrison)

1980 (25 Mar)–81. *Aeroplanes. Horiz designs as T* **103**. *Multicoloured. P* 14½ × 14.

236	1 c. Hawker Siddeley "H.S. 748" (3.3.81)	15	20
237	2 c. Type 103	15	20
238	3 c. Curtis "P-40 Kittyhawk"	15	20
239	4 c. Chance Vought "F4U-1 Corsair" (19.8.80)	15	20
240	5 c. Grumman "TBF-1c Avenger" (19.8.80)	15	20
241	15 c. Douglas "SBD-5 Dauntless" (19.8.80)	30	30
242	20 c. Cessna "172"	30	30
243	25 c. Lockheed "Hudson" (3.3.81)	30	35
244	30 c. Lockheed "PV-1 Ventura" (13.1.81)	40	50
245	40 c. Avro "York" (3.3.81)	50	45
246	50 c. Douglas "DC-3" (13.1.81)	65	55
247	60 c. Avro "691 Lancastrian" (13.1.81)	75	65
248	80 c. Douglas "DC-4" (13.1.81)	95	85
249	$1 Beechcraft "Super King Air" (3.3.81)	1·25	90
250	$2 Fokker "F-27 Friendship" (19.8.80)	2·50	90
251	$5 Lockheed "C-130 Hercules"	6·00	2·00
236/51	Set of 16	13·00	8·00

104 Queen Elizabeth the Queen Mother

(Des K. Williams. Litho Harrison)

1980 (4 Aug). *80th Birthday of Queen Elizabeth the Queen Mother. P* 14.

252	**104** 22 c. multicoloured	30	20
253	60 c. multicoloured	65	40

105 Red-tailed Tropic Birds

(Des K. Williams. Litho Harrison)

1980 (28 Oct). *Christmas. Birds. T* **105** *and similar horiz designs. Multicoloured. P* 14 × 14½.

254	15 c. Type 105	35	25
	a. Horiz strip of 3. Nos. 254/6	95	
255	22 c. White Terns	35	25
256	35 c. White-capped Noddys	35	25
257	60 c. White Terns (different)	60	45
254/7	Set of 4	1·50	1·10

Nos. 254/6 were printed together, *se-tenant*, in horizontal strips of 3 throughout the sheet.

106 *Morayshire* and View of Norfolk Island	**107** Wedding Bouquet from Norfolk Island

(Des Jennifer Toombs. Litho Harrison)

1981 (5 June). *125th Anniv of Pitcairn Islanders' Migration to Norfolk Island. T* **106** *and similar horiz designs. Multicoloured. P* 14½.

258	5 c. Type 106	15	15
259	35 c. Islanders arriving ashore	55	30
260	60 c. View of new settlement	85	45
258/60	Set of 3	1·40	80
MS261	183 × 127 mm. Nos. 258/60	2·00	1·75

(Des J.W. Litho Harrison)

1981 (22 July). *Royal Wedding. T* **107** *and similar vert designs. Multicoloured. P* 14.

262	35 c. Type 107	20	15
263	55 c. Prince Charles at horse trials	35	25
264	60 c. Prince Charles and Lady Diana Spencer	35	35
262/4	Set of 3	80	65

108 Uniting Church of Australia **109** Pair of White-chested White Eyes

(Des K. Williams. Litho Harrison)

1981 (15 Sept). *Christmas. Churches. T* **108** *and similar horiz designs. Multicoloured. P* 14½ × 14.

265	18 c. Type **108**		..	20	10
266	24 c. Seventh Day Adventist Church	..		25	15
267	30 c. Church of the Sacred Heart			30	20
268	$1 St. Barnabas Chapel	..		70	70
265/8	..		*Set of* 4	1·25	1·00

(Des P. Slater. Litho Questa)

1981 (10 Nov). *White-chested White Eye ("Silvereye"). T* **109** *and similar horiz designs. Multicoloured. P* 14 × 14½.

269	35 c. Type **109**		..	45	40
	a. Horiz strip of 5. Nos. 269/73			2·25	
270	35 c. Bird on nest	..		45	40
271	35 c. Bird with egg	..		45	40
272	35 c. Parents with chicks	..		45	40
273	35 c. Fledgelings	..		45	40
269/73			*Set of* 5	2·25	2·00

Nos. 269/73 were printed together, *se-tenant*, in horizontal strips of 5 throughout the sheet.

110 Aerial View of Philip Island

(Des local artist. Litho Harrison)

1982 (12 Jan). *Philip and Nepean Islands. T* **110** *and similar horiz designs. Multicoloured. P* 14 × 13½.

274	24 c. Type **110**	..	..	30	25
	a. Horiz strip of 5. Nos. 274/8			1·40	
275	24 c. Close-up view of Philip Island landscape			30	25
276	24 c. Gecko (*Phyllodactylus guentheri*), Philip Island			30	25
277	24 c. Sooty Tern (*Sterna fuscata*), Philip Island			30	25
278	24 c. Philip Island Hibiscus (*Hibiscus insularis*)	..		30	25
279	35 c. Aerial view of Nepean Island			40	35
	a. Horiz strip of 5. Nos. 279/83			1·75	
280	35 c. Close-up view of Nepean Island landscape			40	35
281	35 c. Gecko (*Phyllodactylus guentheri*), Nepean Island			40	35
282	35 c. Blue-faced Boobies (*Sula dactylatra*), Nepean Island			40	35
283	35 c. *Carpobrotus glaucescens* (flower), Nepean Island			40	35
274/83			*Set of* 10	3·00	2·50

The five designs of each value were printed together, *se-tenant*, in horizontal strips of 5 throughout the sheet.

111 Sperm Whale

(Des Jennifer Toombs. Litho Harrison)

1982 (23 Feb). *Whales. T* **111** *and similar horiz designs. P* 14½.

284	24 c. multicoloured	..		45	35
285	55 c. multicoloured	..		85	75
286	80 c. black, mauve and stone	..		1·10	1·00
284/6	..		*Set of* 3	2·25	1·90

Designs:—55 c. Black Right Whale; 80 c. Humpback Whale.

112 *Diocet*, Wrecked 20 April 1873

(Litho Harrison)

1982 (18 May–27 July). *Shipwrecks. T* **112** *and similar horiz designs. Multicoloured. P* 14½ × 14.

287	24 c. H.M.S. *Sirius*, wrecked 19 March 1790 (27 July)			50	50
288	27 c. Type **112**	..		50	50
289	35 c. *Friendship*, wrecked 17 May 1835 (27 July)			90	70
290	40 c. *Mary Hamilton*, wrecked 6 May 1873			90	80
291	55 c. *Fairlie*, wrecked 14 February 1840 (27 July)			1·25	95
292	65 c. *Warrigal*, wrecked 18 March 1918			1·25	1·25
287/92			*Set of* 6	4·75	4·25

C-KURITY PAPER. The following issues up to No. 342 were all printed on this type of security paper, *unless otherwise stated.* It shows a pattern of blue fluorescent markings, resembling rosettes, on the reverse beneath the gum.

113 R.N.Z.A.F. "Hudson" dropping Christmas Supplies, 1942 **114** 50th (Queen's Own) Regiment

(Des A. Theobald. Litho Walsall)

1982 (7 Sept). *Christmas. 40th Anniv of first Supply-plane Landings on Norfolk Island (Christmas Day 1942). T* **113** *and similar horiz designs. Multicoloured. P* 14.

293	27 c. Type **113**	..		30	35
294	40 c. "Hudson" landing Christmas supplies, 1942			45	65
295	75 c. Christmas, 1942	..		90	1·40
293/5	..		*Set of* 3	1·50	2·25

(Des W. Fenton. Litho Questa)

1982 (9 Nov). *Military Uniforms. T* **114** *and similar vert designs. Multicoloured. P* 14½ × 14.

296	27 c. Type **114**	..		30	35
297	40 c. 58th (Rutlandshire) Regiment	..		45	75
298	55 c. 80th (Staffordshire Volunteers) Battalion Company			65	95
299	65 c. 11th (North Devonshire) Regiment			80	1·25
296/9			*Set of* 4	2·00	3·00

115 *Panaeolus papilionaceus* **116** Beechcraft "18" Aircraft

(Des Jane Thatcher. Litho Enschedé)

1983 (29 Mar). *Fungi. T* **115** *and similar vert designs. Multicoloured. P* 13½ × 13.

300	27 c. Type **115**	..		45	35
301	40 c. *Coprinus domesticus*	..		70	50
302	55 c. *Marasmius niveus*	..		95	70
303	65 c. *Cymatoderma elegans* var *lamellatum*			1·25	85
300/3			*Set of* 4	3·00	2·25

(Des Walsall. Litho Format)

1983 (12 July). *Bicentenary of Manned Flight. T* **116** *and similar horiz designs. Multicoloured. P* 14½ × 14.

304	10 c. Type **116**	..		15	15
305	27 c. Fokker "F28 Fellowship"	..		30	35
306	45 c. French military "DC 4"	..		50	60
307	75 c. Sikorsky helicopter	..		90	95
304/7			*Set of* 4	1·60	1·90
MS308	105 × 100 mm. Nos. 304/7			2·00	2·50

117 St. Matthew **118** Cable Ship *Chantik*

(Des McCombie-Skinner Studio. Litho Format)

1983 (13 Sept). *Christmas. 150th Birth Anniv of Sir Edward Burne-Jones. T* **117** *and similar vert designs showing stained-glass windows from St. Barnabas Chapel, Norfolk Island. Multicoloured. P* 14.

309	5 c. Type **117**	..		10	10
310	24 c. St. Mark	..		30	30
311	30 c. Jesus Christ	..		40	40
312	45 c. St. Luke	..		55	55
313	85 c. St. John	..		1·10	1·10
309/13			*Set of* 5	2·25	2·25

(Des G. Drummond. Litho Format)

1983 (15 Nov). *World Communications Year. ANZCAN Cable. T* **118** *and similar horiz designs. Multicoloured. Ordinary paper. P* 14½ × 14.

314	30 c. Type **118**	..		40	40
315	45 c. *Chantik* during in-shore operations	..		55	55
316	75 c. Cable ship *Mercury*	..		95	95
317	85 c. Diagram of cable route	..		1·10	1·10
314/17			*Set of* 4	2·75	2·75

---

119 Popwood **120** *Cheilodactylidae*

(Des I. Loe. Litho B.D.T.)

1984 (10 Jan–27 Mar). *Flowers. T* **119** *and similar vert designs. Multicoloured. P* 14.

318	1 c. Type **119** (27.3)	..		20	20
319	2 c. Strand Morning Glory	..		30	20
320	3 c. Native Phreatia	..		35	20
321	4 c. Philip Island Wisteria (27.3)			35	20
322	5 c. Norfolk Island Palm (27.3)			35	20
323	10 c. Evergreen	..		40	20
324	15 c. Bastard Oak (27.3)			50	30
325	20 c. Devil's Guts	..		50	30
326	25 c. White Oak	..		60	35
327	30 c. Ti (27.3)	..		70	40
328	35 c. Philip Island Hibiscus (27.3)			70	40
329	40 c. Native Wisteria	..		80	45
330	50 c. Native Jasmine	..		1·25	50
331	$1 Norfolk Island Hibiscus (27.3)	..		1·25	1·00
332	$3 Native Oberonia (27.3)	..		3·00	2·75
333	$5 Norfolk Island Pine	..		4·50	4·00
318/33			*Set of* 16	14·00	10·50

(Des Marg Towt. Litho Cambec Press, Melbourne)

1984 (17 Apr). *Reef Fishes. T* **120** *and similar horiz designs. Multicoloured. Ordinary paper. P* 13½ × 14.

334	30 c. Type **120**	..		40	45
335	45 c. *Pseudopeneus signatus*	..		60	65
336	75 c. *Acanthuridae*	..		1·00	1·10
337	85 c. *Chaeton ancinetus*	..		1·25	1·40
334/7			*Set of* 4	2·75	3·25

121 Owl with Eggs **122** 1953 7½d. and 1974 Cook Bicent 10 c. Stamps

(Des P. Slater. Litho Questa)

1984 (17 July). *Boobook Owl. T* **121** *and similar vert designs. Multicoloured. P* 14.

338	30 c. Type **121**	..		65	50
	a. Horiz strip of 5. Nos. 338/42			3·00	
339	30 c. Fledgeling	..		65	50
340	30 c. Young owl on stump	..		65	50
341	30 c. Adult on branch	..		65	50
342	30 c. Owl in flight	..		65	50
338/42			*Set of* 5	3·00	2·25

Nos. 338/42 were printed together, *se-tenant*, in horizontal strips of 5 throughout the sheet.

(Des D. Miller. Litho Harrison)

1984 (18 Sept). *"Ausipex" International Stamp Exhibition, Melbourne. T* **122** *and similar horiz designs. Multicoloured. W w* 14 (*sideways*). *P* 14.

343	30 c. Type **122**	..		30	35
344	45 c. John Buffett commemorative postal stationery envelope			45	45
345	75 c. Design from Presentation Pack for 1982 Military Uniforms issue	..		90	1·75
343/5			*Set of* 3	1·50	2·50
MS346	151 × 93 mm. Nos. 343/5. P 14½	..		3·75	4·00

123 Font, Kingston Methodist Church **124** The Revd. Nobbs teaching Pitcairn Islanders

(Des R. Murphy. Litho Questa)

1984 (9 Oct). *Christmas. Centenary of Methodist Church on Norfolk Island. T* **123** *and similar vert designs. Multicoloured. W w* 14. *P* 14.

347	5 c. Type **123**	..		10	10
348	24 c. Church service in Old Barracks, Kingston, late 1800's			35	40
349	30 c. The Revd. & Mrs. A. H. Phelps and sailing ship			40	45
350	45 c. The Revd. A. H. Phelps and First Congregational Church, Chester, U.S.A.			60	65
351	85 c. Interior of Kingston Methodist Church	..		1·25	1·40
347/51			*Set of* 5	2·40	2·50

(Des D. Hopkins. Litho B.D.T.)

1984 (6 Nov). *Death Centenary of the Revd. George Hunn Nobbs (leader of Pitcairn community). T* **124** *and similar vert designs. Multicoloured. W w* **14**. *P* 14 × 15.

352	30 c. Type **124**	..	..	..	40	45
353	45 c. The Revd. Nobbs with sick islander				60	65
354	75 c. Baptising baby	..	..	..	1·00	1·10
355	85 c. Presented to Queen Victoria, 1852			1·25	1·40
352/5	..	..	..	*Set of* 4	3·00	3·25

125 *Fanny Fisher*   **126** The Queen Mother (from photo by Norman Parkinson)

(Des D. Hopkins. Litho Cambec Press, Melbourne)

1985 (19 Feb). *19th-Century Whaling Ships (1st series). T* **125** *and similar horiz designs. Multicoloured. P* 13½ × 14.

356	5 c. Type **125**	..	..	..	30	15
357	33 c. *Costa Rica Packet*	..	..	85	55
358	50 c. *Splendid*	..	..	..	1·25	1·00
359	90 c. *Onward*	..	..	..	1·75	1·75
356/9	..	..	..	*Set of* 4	3·75	3·00

See also Nos. 360/3.

(Des D. Hopkins. Litho Cambec Press, Melbourne)

1985 (30 Apr). *19th-Century Whaling Ships (2nd series). Horiz designs as T* **125**. *Multicoloured. P* 13½ × 14.

360	15 c. *Waterwitch*	..	..	..	50	50
361	20 c. *Canton*	..	..	..	60	60
362	60 c. *Aladdin*	..	..	..	1·25	1·40
363	80 c. *California*	..	..	..	1·60	1·90
360/3	..	..	..	*Set of* 4	3·50	4·00

(Des A. Theobald ($1), C. Abbott (others). Litho Questa)

1985 (6 June). *Life and Times of Queen Elizabeth the Queen Mother. T* **126** *and similar vert designs. Multicoloured. W w* **16**. *P* 14½ × 14.

364	5 c. The Queen Mother (from photo by Dorothy Wilding)				10	10
365	33 c. With Princess Anne at Trooping the Colour				35	40
366	50 c. Type **126**	..	..	..	50	55
367	90 c. With Prince Henry at his christening (from photo by Lord Snowdon)				95	1·00
364/7	..	..	..	*Set of* 4	1·75	1·90
MS368	91 × 73 mm. $1 With Princess Anne at Ascot Races. Wmk sideways				1·10	1·25

127 "Swimming"   **128** Prize-winning Cow and Owner

(Des from children's paintings. Litho Cambec Press, Melbourne)

1985 (9 July). *International Youth Year. T* **127** *and similar horiz design. Multicoloured. P* 13½ × 14.

369	33 c. Type **127**	..	..	..	75	40
370	50 c. "A Walk in the Country"	..	..	1·50	85

(Des Flett Henderson & Arnold. Litho Cambec Press, Melbourne)

1985 (10 Sept). *125th Anniv of Royal Norfolk Island Agricultural and Horticultural Show. T* **128** *and similar horiz design. Multicoloured. P* 13½ × 14.

371	80 c. Type **128**	..	..	..	75	80
372	90 c. Show exhibits	..	..	..	85	90
MS373	132 × 85 mm. Nos. 371/2	..	..	1·75	2·50

129 Shepherds with Flock   **130** Long-spined Sea Urchin

(Des R. Murphy. Litho Cambec Press, Melbourne)

1985 (3 Oct). *Christmas. T* **129** *and similar vert designs. Multicoloured. P* 13½.

374	27 c. Type **129**	..	..	..	60	30
375	33 c. Mary and Joseph with donkey	..	75	40
376	50 c. The Three Wise Men	..	..	1·40	65
377	90 c. The Nativity	..	..	..	1·75	1·25
374/7	..	..	..	*Set of* 4	4·00	2·25

(Des L. Curtis. Litho Cambec Press, Melbourne)

1986 (14 Jan). *Marine Life. T* **130** *and similar horiz designs. Multicoloured. P* 13½ × 14.

378	5 c. Type **130**	..	..	..	10	10
379	33 c. Blue Starfish	..	..	..	40	35
380	55 c. Eagle Ray	..	..	..	60	75
381	75 c. Moray Eel	..	..	..	85	1·00
378/81	..	..	..	*Set of* 4	1·75	2·00
MS382	100 × 95 mm. Nos. 378/81	..	..	3·00	3·50

131 *Giotto* Spacecraft   **132** Isaac Robinson (U.S. Consul 1887–1908)

(Des G. Revell. Litho Leigh-Mardon Ltd, Melbourne)

1986 (11 Mar). *Appearance of Halley's Comet. T* **131** *and similar vert design. Multicoloured. P* 14½ × 15.

383	$1 Type **131**	..	..	..	1·50	1·75
	a. Horiz pair. Nos. 383/4	..	..	3·00	3·50
384	$1 Halley's Comet	..	..	..	1·50	1·75

Nos. 383/4 were printed together, *se-tenant*, in horizontal pairs throughout the sheet, each pair forming a composite design.

(Des G. Revell. Litho Cambec Press, Melbourne)

1986 (22 May). *"Ameripex '86" International Stamp Exhibition, Chicago. T* **132** *and similar multicoloured designs. P* 13½.

385	33 c. Type **132**	..	..	..	60	35
386	50 c. Ford "Model T" (first vehicle on island) (horiz)				80	50
387	80 c. Statue of Liberty	..	..	1·10	80
385/7	..	..	..	*Set of* 3	2·25	1·50
MS388	125 × 100 mm. Nos. 385/7	..	..	2·50	2·50

No. 387 also commemorates the Centenary of the Statue of Liberty.

133 Princess Elizabeth and Dog   **134** Stylized Dove and Norfolk Island

(Des Allison Ryves. Litho Cambec Press, Melbourne)

1986 (12 June). *60th Birthday of Queen Elizabeth II. T* **133** *and similar vert designs. Multicoloured. P* 13½.

389	5 c. Type **133**	..	..	..	10	10
390	33 c. Queen Elizabeth II	..	..	50	35
391	80 c. Opening Norfolk Island Golf Club	..	1·25	1·40
392	90 c. With Duke of Edinburgh in carriage	..	1·50	1·60
389/92	..	..	..	*Set of* 4	3·00	3·00

(Des Lyn Studham. Litho Cambec Press, Melbourne)

1986 (23 Sept). *Christmas. P* 13½ × 14.

393	**134** 30 c. multicoloured	..	..	35	30
394	40 c. multicoloured	..	..	50	45
395	$1 multicoloured	..	..	..	1·40	1·50
393/5	..	..	..	*Set of* 3	2·00	2·00

135 British Convicts, 1787   **136** Stone Tools

(Des Josephine Martin. Litho Cambec Press, Melbourne)

1986 (14 Oct–16 Dec). *Bicentenary of Norfolk Island Settlement* (1988) *(1st issue). Governor Phillip's Commission. T* **135** *and similar vert designs. Multicoloured. P* 14 × 13½.

396	36 c. Type **135**.	..	..	..	75	35
397	55 c. Judge passing sentence of transportation				1·25	65
398	90 c. Governor Phillip meeting Home Secretary (inscr "Home Society")				2·25	1·50
399	90 c. As No. 398, but correctly inscr "Home Secretary" (16.12)				2·25	1·50
400	$1 Captain Arthur Phillip.	..	..	2·25	1·50
396/400	..	..	..	*Set of* 5	8·00	5·00

See also Nos. 401/4, 421/4, 433/5, 436/7 and 438/43.

(Des B. Clinton. Litho Cambec Press, Melbourne)

1986 (16 Dec). *Bicentenary of Norfolk Island Settlement* (1988) *(2nd issue). Pre-European Occupation. T* **136** *and similar horiz designs. Multicoloured. P* 13½.

401	36 c. Type **136**.	..	..	..	65	45
402	36 c. Bananas and taro	..	..	65	45
403	36 c. Polynesian outrigger canoe	..	65	45
404	36 c. Maori chief	..	..	..	65	45
401/4	..	..	..	*Set of* 4	2·40	1·60

137 Philip Island from Point Ross   **138** Male Red-fronted Parakeet

(Des C. Abbott. Litho CPE Australia Ltd, Melbourne)

1987 (17 Feb)–**88**. *Norfolk Island Scenes. T* **137** *and similar square designs. Multicoloured. P* 13½.

405	1 c. Cockpit Creek Bridge (17.5.88)	..	30	40
406	2 c. Cemetery Bay Beach (17.5.88)	..	30	40
407	3 c. Island guesthouse (17.5.88)	..	30	40
408	5 c. Type **137**.	..	..	20	30
409	15 c. Cattle in pasture (27.7.87)	..	40	45
410	30 c. Rock fishing (7.4.87)	..	..	30	40
411	37 c. Old Pitcairner-style house (27.7.87)	70	75
412	40 c. Shopping centre (7.4.87)	..	35	45
413	50 c. Emily Bay	..	..	45	55
414	60 c. Bloody Bridge (27.7.87)	..	90	90
415	80 c. Pitcairner-style shop (7.4.87)	..	1·25	1·25
416	90 c. Government House	..	..	1·00	1·40
417	$1 Melanesian Memorial Chapel	..	1·00	1·10
418	$2 Convict Settlement, Kingston (7.4.87)	1·75	2·00
419	$3 Ball Bay (27.7.87)	..	..	3·75	3·75
420	$5 Northern cliffs (17.5.88)	..	5·50	6·50
405/20	..	..	..	*Set of* 16	16·00	19·00

(Des Josephine Martin. Litho CPE Australia Ltd, Melbourne)

1987 (13 May). *Bicentenary of Norfolk Island Settlement* (1988) *(3rd issue). The First Fleet. Vert designs as T* **135**. *Multicoloured. P* 14 × 13½.

421	5 c. Loading supplies, Deptford	..	40	40
422	55 c. Fleet leaving Spithead	..	..	1·40	1·50
	a. Horiz pair. Nos. 422/3	..	..	2·75	3·00
423	55 c. H.M.S. *Sirius* leaving Spithead	..	1·40	1·50
424	$1 Female convicts below decks	..	2·25	2·25
421/4	..	..	..	*Set of* 4	4·75	5·00

Nos. 422/3 were printed together, *se-tenant*, in horizontal pairs throughout the sheet, forming a composite design.

(Des P. Slater. Litho CPE Australia Ltd, Melbourne)

1987 (16 Sept). *Red-fronted Parakeet ("Green Parrot"). T* **138** *and similar vert designs. Multicoloured. P* 14 × 13½.

425	5 c. Type **138**.	..	..	..	60	60
	a. Horiz strip of 4. Nos. 425/8	..	4·75	
426	15 c. Adult with fledgeling and egg	..	1·00	1·00
427	36 c. Young parakeets	..	..	1·75	1·75
428	55 c. Female parakeet	..	..	2·00	2·00
425/8	..	..	..	*Set of* 4	4·75	4·75

Nos. 425/8 were printed together, *se-tenant*, in horizontal strips of four throughout the sheet.

139 Christmas Tree and Restored Garrison Barracks   **140** Airliner, Container Ship and Sydney Harbour Bridge

(Des T. Bland and Alison Ryves. Litho CPE Australia Ltd, Melbourne)

1987 (13 Oct). *Christmas. T* **139** *and similar horiz designs. Multicoloured. P* 13½ × 14.

429	30 c. Type **139**.	..	..	..	30	30
430	42 c. Children opening presents	..	45	55
431	58 c. Father Christmas with children	..	60	65
432	63 c. Children's party	..	..	70	80
429/32	..	..	..	*Set of* 4	1·90	2·10

(Des Josephine Martin. Litho CPE Australia Ltd, Melbourne)

1987 (8 Dec). *Bicentenary of Norfolk Island Settlement* (1988) *(4th issue). Visit of La Perouse (navigator). Vert designs as T* **135**. *Multicoloured. P* 14 × 13½.

433	37 c. La Perouse with King Louis XVI	..	75	55
434	90 c. *L'Astrolabe* and *La Boussole* off Norfolk Island				1·75	2·00
435	$1 *L'Astrolabe* wrecked in Solomon Islands	2·00	2·25
433/5	..	..	..	*Set of* 3	4·25	4·50

(Des Josephine Martin. Litho CPE Australia Ltd, Melbourne)

1988 (25 Jan). *Bicentenary of Norfolk Island Settlement* (5th issue). *Arrival of First Fleet at Sydney. Vert designs as T* **135**. *Multicoloured. P* 14 × 13½.

436	37 c. Ship's cutter approaching Port Jackson	90	65
437	$1 Landing at Sydney Cove	..	2·10	2·10

(Des Josephine Martin. Litho CPE Australia Ltd, Melbourne)

1988 (4 Mar). *Bicentenary of Norfolk Island Settlement (6th issue). Foundation of First Settlement. Vert designs as T 135. Multicoloured. P 14 × 13½.*
438	5 c. Lt. Philip Gidley King	..	..	..	20	20
439	37 c. Raising the flag, March 1788	..	..	75	75
440	55 c. King exploring	..	..	..	1·25	1·25
441	70 c. Landing at Sydney Bay, Norfolk Island	1·50	1·50
442	90 c. H.M.S. *Supply* (brig)	..	..	1·75	1·75
443	$1 Sydney Bay settlement, 1788 ..	..	1·90	1·90
438/43			*Set of 6*	6·50	6·50

(Des Janet Boschen. Litho CPE Australia Ltd, Melbourne)

1988 (30 July). *"Sydpex '88" National Stamp Exhibition, Sydney. T 140 and similar multicoloured designs. P 14 × 13½ (vert) or 13½ × 14 (horiz).*
444	37 c. Type **140**	..	..	..	65	65
445	37 c. Exhibition label under magnifying glass *(horiz)*	..	..	65	65
446	37 c. Telephone and dish aerial	..	65	65
444/6			*Set of 3*	1·75	1·75
MS447	118×84 mm. Nos. 444/6	..	..	2·75	3·00

In No. **MS**447 the horizontal design is perforated 14 at foot and 13½ on the other three sides.

141 Flowers and Decorations

142 Pier Store and Boat Shed

(Des Sue Pearson. Litho CPE Australia Ltd, Melbourne)

1988 (27 Sept). *Christmas. T 141 and similar vert designs. Multicoloured. P 14 × 13½.*
448	30 c. Type **141**	..	..	..	40	40
449	42 c. Flowers	..	..	..	60	70
450	58 c. Fishes and beach	..	..	75	85
451	63 c. Norfolk Island	..	..	85	1·00
448/51			*Set of 4*	2·40	2·75

(Des R. Murphy. Litho CPE Australia Ltd, Melbourne)

1988 (6 Dec). *Restored Buildings from the Convict Era. T 142 and similar horiz designs. Multicoloured. P 13½ × 14.*
452	39 c. Type **142**	..	..	..	35	40
453	55 c. Royal Engineers Building	..	50	55
454	90 c. Old Military Barracks	..	85	90
455	$1 Commissariat Store and New Military Barracks	..	..	95	1·00
452/5			*Set of 4*	2·40	2·50

143 *Lamprima aenea*

144 H.M.S. *Bounty* off Tasmania

(Des T. Nolan. Litho CPE Australia Ltd, Melbourne)

1989 (14 Feb). *Endemic Insects. T 143 and similar horiz designs. Multicoloured. P 13½ × 14.*
456	39 c. Type **143**	..	..	..	45	40
457	55 c. *Insulascirtus nythos*	..	..	60	70
458	90 c. *Caedicia araucariae*	..	1·00	1·10
459	$1 *Thrincophora aridela*	..	1·10	1·25
456/9			*Set of 4*	2·75	3·00

(Des C. Abbott. Litho CPE Australia Ltd, Melbourne (Nos. 460/3), B.D.T. (No. **MS**464))

1989 (28 Apr). *Bicentenary of the Mutiny on the Bounty. T 144 and similar horiz designs. Multicoloured. P 13½.*
460	5 c. Type **144**	..	..	..	40	30
461	39 c. Mutineers and Polynesian women, Pitcairn Island	..	..	1·40	1·25
462	55 c. Lake Windermere, Cumbria (Christian's home county)	..	1·90	1·75
463	$1.10, "Mutineers casting Bligh adrift" (Robert Dodd)	..	..	2·75	2·50
460/3			*Set of 4*	5·75	5·25

MS464 110×85 mm. 39 c. No. 461; 90 c. Isle of Man 1989 Mutiny 35p., No. 414; $1 Pitcairn Islands 1989 Settlement Bicent 90 c., No. 345. P 14 .. .. .. 5·00 5·00

145 Norfolk Island Flag

146 Red Cross

(Des R. Fletcher. Litho CPE Australia Ltd, Melbourne)

1989 (10 Aug). *10th Anniv of Internal Self-Government. T 145 and similar vert designs. Multicoloured. P 14×13½.*
465	41 c. Type **145**	..	..	..	60	55
466	55 c. Old ballot box	..	..	70	65
467	$1 Norfolk Island Act, 1979	..	1·40	1·40
468	$1.10, Island crest	..	..	1·50	1·60
465/8			*Set of 4*	3·75	3·75

(Des E. Lenthall. Litho CPE Australia Ltd, Melbourne)

1989 (25 Sept). *75th Anniv of Red Cross on Norfolk Island. P 13½.*
469	146 $1 bright rose-red and ultramarine	..	2·50	2·00

147 "Gethsemane"

148 John Royle (first announcer)

(Des Sue Pearson. Litho CPE Australia Ltd, Melbourne)

1989 (9 Oct). *Christmas. T 147 and similar horiz designs showing opening lines of hymns and local scenes. Multicoloured. P 13½×14.*
470	36 c. Type **147**	..	..	80	40
471	60 c. "In the Sweet Bye and Bye"	..	1·40	1·40
472	75 c. "Let the Lower Lights Be Burning"	1·60	1·60
473	80 c. "The Beautiful Stream"	..	1·75	2·00
470/3			*Set of 4*	5·00	4·75

(Des Philatelic Studios. Litho Leigh-Mardon Ltd, Melbourne)

1989 (21 Nov). *50th Anniv of Radio Australia. T 148 and similar vert designs each showing Kingston buildings. Multicoloured. P 14×13½.*
474	41 c. Type **148**	..	..	80	55
475	65 c. Radio waves linking Australia and Norfolk Island	..	..	1·40	1·50
476	$1.10, Anniversary kookaburra logo	..	2·25	2·50
474/6			*Set of 3*	4·00	4·00

149 H.M.S. *Bounty* on fire, Pitcairn Island, 1790

150 H.M.S. *Sirius* striking Reef

(Des G. Hitch. Litho Leigh-Mardon Ltd, Melbourne)

1990 (23 Jan). *History of the Norfolk Islanders (1st series). Settlement on Pitcairn Island. T 149 and similar vert design. Multicoloured. P 14½.*
477	70 c. Type **149**	..	..	1·75	1·75
478	$1.10, Arms of Norfolk Island	..	2·25	2·25

See also Nos. 503/4 and 516/17.

(Des Maree Edmiston. Litho Leigh-Mardon Ltd, Melbourne)

1990 (19 Mar). *Bicentenary of Wreck of H.M.S. Sirius. T 150 and similar horiz designs. Multicoloured. P 13½.*
479	41 c. Type **150**	..	..	1·25	1·25
	a. Horiz pair. Nos. 479/80	..	2·50	2·50
480	41 c. H.M.S. *Sirius* failing to clear bay	1·25	1·25
481	65 c. Divers at work on wreck	..	1·75	1·75
482	$1 Recovered artifacts and chart of site	2·25	2·25
479/82			*Set of 4*	6·00	6·00

Nos. 479/80 were printed together, *se-tenant*, in horizontal pairs throughout the sheet, each pair forming a composite design.

151 Unloading Lighter, Kingston

152 *Ile de Lumiere* (freighter)

(Des Philatelic Studios. Litho Leigh-Mardon Ltd, Melbourne)

1990 (17 July)**-**91. *Ships. T 151 and horiz designs as T 152. P 14×14½ (5, 10 c.) or 14½ (others).*
483	151 5 c. purple-brown	..	..	10	10
484	10 c. ochre	..	..	10	10
485	— 45 c. multicoloured (19.2.91)	..	40	45
486	— 50 c. multicoloured (19.2.91)	..	45	50
487	— 65 c. multicoloured (19.2.91)	..	55	60
488	152 70 c. multicoloured	..	..	60	65
489	— 75 c. multicoloured (13.8.91)	..	65	70
490	— 80 c. multicoloured (13.8.91)	..	70	75
491	— 90 c. multicoloured (13.8.91)	..	75	80
492	— $1 multicoloured (13.8.91)	..	85	90
493	— $2 multicoloured	..	..	1·75	1·90
494	— $5 multicoloured (19.2.91)	..	4·25	4·50
483/94			*Set of 12*	10·00	11·00

Designs: *Horiz* (as T **152**)—45 c. *La Dunkerquoise* (French patrol vessel); 50 c. *Dmitri Mendeleev* (Soviet research vessel); 65 c. *Pacific Rover* (tanker); 75 c. *Norfolk Trader* (freighter); 80 c. *Roseville* (transport); 90 c. *Kalia* (container ship); $1 *Bounty* (replica); $2 H.M.A.S. *Success* (supply ship); $5 H.M.A.S. *Whyalla* (patrol vessel).

153 Santa on House Roof

154 William Charles Wentworth

(Des G. Hitch, adapted Philatelic Studios. Litho Leigh-Mardon Ltd, Melbourne)

1990 (25 Sept). *Christmas. T 153 and similar multicoloured designs. P 14½.*
499	38 c. Type **153**	..	..	65	45
500	43 c. Santa at Kingston Post Office	..	70	50
501	65 c. Santa over Sydney Bay, Kingston *(horiz)*	..	..	1·25	1·25
502	85 c. Santa on Officers' Quarters *(horiz)*	1·40	1·75
499/502			*Set of 4*	3·50	3·50

(Des G. Hitch. Litho Leigh-Mardon Ltd, Melbourne)

1990 (11 Oct). *History of the Norfolk Islanders (2nd series). The First Generation. T 154 and similar vert design. P 14½.*
503	70 c. reddish brown and pale cinnamon	..	85	85
504	$1.20, reddish brown and pale cinnamon	1·40	1·40

Designs:—$1.20, Thursday October Christian.

155 Adult Robin and Chicks in Nest

156 Map of Norfolk Island

(Des E. Monks. Litho Leigh-Mardon Ltd, Melbourne)

1990 (3 Dec). *"Birdpex '90" Stamp Exhibition, Christchurch, New Zealand. Scarlet Robin. T 155 and similar vert designs. Multicoloured. P 14½.*
505	65 c. Type **155**	..	..	75	75
506	$1 Hen on branch	..	..	1·25	1·25
507	$1.20, Cock on branch	..	..	1·40	1·40
505/7			*Set of 3*	3·00	3·00
MS508	70×90 mm. $1 Hen; $1 Cock and hen	..	2·75	3·00

(Des Philatelic Studios. Litho Leigh-Mardon Ltd, Melbourne)

1991 (9 Apr). *Ham Radio Network. T 156 and similar vert designs. Multicoloured. P 14½.*
509	43 c. Type **156**	..	..	75	50
510	$1 Globe showing Norfolk Island	..	1·75	2·00
511	$1.20, Map of South-west Pacific	..	2·00	2·25
509/11			*Set of 3*	4·00	4·25

157 Display in *Sirius* Museum

158 H.M.S. *Pandora* wrecked on Great Barrier Reef (1791)

(Des Philatelic Studios. Litho Leigh-Mardon Ltd, Melbourne)

1991 (16 May). *Norfolk Island Museums. T 157 and similar multicoloured designs. P 14½.*
512	43 c. Type **157**	..	..	70	50
513	70 c. 19th-century sitting room, House Museum *(horiz)*	..	..	1·25	1·25
514	$1 Carronade, *Sirius* Museum *(horiz)*	..	1·75	1·75
515	$1.20, Reconstructed jug and beaker, Archaeological Museum	..	..	1·75	2·00
512/15			*Set of 4*	4·75	5·00

(Des Philatelic Studios. Litho Leigh-Mardon, Melbourne)

1991 (2 July). *History of the Norfolk Islanders (3rd series). Search for the Bounty. T **158** and similar horiz design. Multicoloured. P* 13¹/₂×14.

| 516 | $1 Type **158** | .. | .. | 1·50 | 1·75 |
| 517 | $1.20, H.M.S. *Pandora* leaving bay | .. | 1·75 | 2·00 |

159 Hibiscus and Island Scene   **160** Tank and Soldier in Jungle

(Des Philatelic Studios. Litho Leigh-Mardon Ltd, Melbourne)

1991 (23 Sept). *Christmas. P* 14¹/₂.

518	**159**	38 c. multicoloured	..	..	..	70	40
519		43 c. multicoloured	..	..	..	80	55
520		65 c. multicoloured	..	..	..	1·00	1·25
521		85 c. multicoloured	..	..	..	1·10	1·40
518/21			..	..	*Set of 4*	3·25	3·25

(Des Philatelic Studios. Litho Leigh-Mardon Ltd, Melbourne)

1991 (9 Dec). *50th Anniv of Outbreak of Pacific War. T **160** and similar horiz designs. Multicoloured. P* 14¹/₂.

522	43 c. Type **160**	..	..	..	65	45
523	70 c. B17 Flying Fortress on jungle airstrip	1·25	1·25
524	$1 Warships	..	..	..	1·75	2·00
522/4			..	..	*Set of 3*	3·25	3·25

161 Coat of Arms   **162** Deployment Map

(Des Philatelic Studios. Litho Leigh-Mardon Ltd, Melbourne)

1992 (11 Feb). *500th Anniv of Discovery of America by Columbus. T **161** and similar vert designs. Multicoloured. P* 14¹/₂.

525	45 c. Type **161**	..	..	..	60	45
526	$1.05, *Santa Maria*	..	..	1·40	1·50
527	$1.20, Columbus and globe	..	1·90	2·00
525/7			..	..	*Set of 3*	3·50	3·50

(Des Philatelic Studios. Litho Leigh-Mardon Ltd, Melbourne)

1992 (4 May). *50th Anniv of Battle of the Coral Sea. T **162** and similar vert designs. Multicoloured. P* 14¹/₂.

528	45 c. Type **162**	..	..	..	60	45
529	70 c. H.M.A.S. *Australia* (cruiser)	..	1·00	1·10
530	$1.05, U.S.S. *Yorktown* (aircraft carrier)	1·60	1·75
528/30			..	..	*Set of 3*	3·00	3·00

(Des Philatelic Studios. Litho Leigh-Mardon Ltd, Melbourne)

1992 (4 May). *50th Anniv of Battle of Midway. Vert designs as T **162**. Multicoloured. P* 14¹/₂.

531	45 c. Battle area	..	..	..	60	45
532	70 c. Catalina PBY 5 flying boat over task force	..	..	..	1·00	1·10
533	$1.05, Douglas SBD 5 Dauntless dive bomber and burning Japanese aircraft carrier	..	..	1·60	1·75
531/3			..	..	*Set of 3*	3·00	3·00

(Des Philatelic Studios. Litho Leigh-Mardon Ltd, Melbourne)

1992 (6 Aug). *50th Anniv of Battle of Guadalcanal. Multicoloured designs as T **162**, but horiz. P* 14¹/₂.

534	45 c. American troops landing	..	50	45
535	70 c. Machine-gun crew	..	..	90	1·00
536	$1.05, Map of Pacific with Japanese and American flags	..	..	1·40	1·50
534/6			..	..	*Set of 3*	2·50	2·75

163 Norfolk Pines above Ball Bay   **164** Boat Shed and Flaghouses, Kingston

(Des Philatelic Studios. Litho Leigh-Mardon Ltd, Melbourne)

1992 (29 Oct). *Christmas. T **163** and similar vert designs. Multicoloured. P* 14¹/₂.

537	40 c. Type **163**	..	..	..	50	40
538	45 c. Headstone Creek	..	..	60	45
539	75 c. South side of Ball Bay	..	90	90
540	$1.20, Rocky Point Reserve	..	1·40	1·60
537/40			..	..	*Set of 4*	3·00	3·00

(Des Philatelic Studios. Litho Leigh-Mardon Ltd, Melbourne)

1993 (23 Feb). *Tourism. Historic Kingston. T **164** and similar horiz designs. Multicoloured. P* 14¹/₂.

541	45 c. Type **164**	..	..	40	45
	a. Horiz strip of 5. Nos. 541/5	..	1·75	
542	45 c. Old Military Barracks	..	40	45
543	45 c. All Saints Church	..	..	40	45
544	45 c. Officers' Quarters	..	..	40	45
545	45 c. Quality Row	..	..	40	45
541/5			..	*Set of 5*	1·75	2·00

Nos. 541/5 were printed together, *se-tenant*, in horizontal strips of 5 forming a composite design.

North Borneo
see Malaysia

Northern Nigeria
see Nigeria

Northern Rhodesia
see Zambia

North-West Pacific Islands
see Papua New Guinea

Nova Scotia
see Canada

Nyasaland Protectorate
see Malawi

Orange Free State
see South Africa

Pakistan

DOMINION

PAKISTAN	**PAKISTAN**
(1)	(2)

1947 (1 Oct). *Nos. 259/68 and 269a/77 (King George VI) of India optd by litho at Nasik, as T 1 (3 p. to 12 a.) or 2 (14 a. and rupee values).*

1	3 p. slate	..	..	10	10
2	½ a. purple	..	..	10	10
3	9 p. green	..	..	10	10
4	1 a. carmine	..	..	10	10
5	1½ a. dull violet	..	..	10	10
6	2 a. vermilion	..	..	10	10
7	3 a. bright violet	..	..	10	20
8	3½ a. bright blue	..	..	45	2·00
9	4 a. brown	..	..	10	10
10	6 a. turquoise-green	..	..	50	30
11	8 a. slate-violet	..	..	20	20
12	12 a. lake	..	..	1·00	15
13	14 a. purple	..	..	1·40	35
14	1 r. grey and red-brown	..	..	1·25	20
15	2 r. purple and brown	..	..	1·50	40
16	5 r. green and blue	..	..	3·25	1·50
17	10 r. purple and claret	..	..	4·00	90

18	15 r. brown and green	..	42·00	65·00
19	25 r. slate-violet and purple	..	45·00	35·00
1/19		*Set of* 19	90·00	95·00

Numerous provisional "PAKISTAN" overprints, both hand-stamped and machine-printed, in various sizes and colours, on Postage and Official stamps, also exist.

These were made under authority of Provincial Governments, District Head Postmasters or Local Postmasters and are of considerable philatelic interest.

The 1 a. 3 p. (India No. 269) exists only as a local issue (*price, Karachi opt, 70p. unused; £1.25 used*).

The 12 a., as No. 12 but overprinted at Karachi exists with overprint inverted (*Price £60 unused*).

The 1 r. value with local overprint exists with overprint inverted (*Price £150 unused*) or as a pair with one stamp without overprint (*Price £600 unused*).

3 Constituent Assembly Building, Karachi   6 Crescent and Stars

(Des A. R. Chughtai (1 r.). Recess D.L.R.)

1948 (9 July). *Independence. T 3, 6 and similar horiz designs. P 13½ × 14 or 11½ (1 r.).*

20	1½ a. ultramarine	..	30	30
21	2½ a. green	..	30	10
22	3 a. purple-brown	..	30	10
23	1 r. scarlet	..	45	20
	a. Perf 14 × 13½	..	3·50	10·00
20/3		*Set of* 4	1·25	60

Designs:—2½ a. Karachi Airport entrance; 3 a. Gateway to Lahore Fort.

7 Scales of Justice   8 Star and Crescent   9 Lloyds Barrage

10 Karachi Airport   13 Khyber Pass

(Des M. M. A. Suharwardi (T 8). Recess Pakistan Security Ptg Corp Ltd, Karachi (P 13 and 13½), D.L.R. (others))

1948 (14 Aug)–**56**? *T 7/10, 13 and similar designs.*

24	7	3 p. red (p 12½)	..	10	10
		a. Perf 13½ (1954?)	..	10	10
25		6 p. violet (p 12½)	..	30	10
		a. Perf 13½ (1954?)	..	75	40
26		9 p. green (p 12½)	..	30	10
		a. Perf 13½ (1954?)	..	20	10
27	8	1 a. blue (p 12½)	..	10	10
28		1½ a. grey-green (p 12½)	..	10	10
29		2 a. red (p 12½)	..	20	20
30	9	2½ a. green (p 14×13½)	..	1·25	3·00
31	10	3 a. green (p 14)	..	85	20
32	9	3½ a. bright blue (p 14×13½)	..	65	2·50
33		4 a. reddish brown (p 12½)	..	30	30
34	—	6 a. blue (p 14×13½)	..	30	50
35	—	8 a. black (p 12½)	..	30	30
36	10	10 a. scarlet (p 14)	..	80	3·00
37	—	12 a. scarlet (p 14×13½)	..	2·25	30
38	—	1 r. ultramarine (p 14)	..	3·00	10
		a. Perf 13½ (1954?)	..	8·00	1·25
39	—	2 r. chocolate (p 14)	..	18·00	30
		a. Perf 13½ (1954?)	..	18·00	75
40	—	5 r. carmine (p 14)	..	12·00	30
		a. Perf 13½ (7.53)	..	8·50	20
41	13	10 r. magenta (p 14)	..	6·50	8·00
		a. Perf 12	..	38·00	3·25
		b. Perf 13 (1951)	..	12·00	30
42		15 r. blue-green (p 12)	..	14·00	8·50
		a. Perf 14	..	12·00	24·00
		b. Perf 13 (1956?)	..	15·00	12·00
43		25 r. violet (p 14)	..	40·00	42·00
		a. Perf 12	..	22·00	27·00
		b. Perf 13 (1954)	..	28·00	15·00
24/43			*Set of* 20	70·00	30·00

Designs: *Vert (as T 7)*—6 a., 8 a., 12 a. Karachi Port Trust. (*As T 10*)—1 r., 2 r., 5 r. Salimullah Hostel, Dacca.

For 25 r. with W 98, see No. 210.

14 Star and Crescent   15 Karachi Airport

(Recess Pakistan Security Ptg Corp (P 13½), D.L.R. (others).

1949 (Feb)–**53**? *Redrawn. Crescent moon with points to left as T 14/15.*

44	14	1 a. blue (p 12½)	..	2·00	10
		a. Perf 13½ (1953?)	..	2·00	10
45		1½ a. grey-green (p 12½)	..	2·00	10
		a. Perf 13½ (1952?)	..	2·00	10
46		2 a. red (p 12½)	..	2·00	10
		a. Perf 13½ (1953?)	..	2·00	10
47	15	3 a. green (p 14)	..	1·75	65
48	—	6 a. blue (as No. 34) (p 14×13½)	..	5·50	15
49	—	8 a. black (as No. 35) (p 12½)	..	3·00	45
50	15	10 a. scarlet (p 14)	..	5·50	70
51	—	12 a. scarlet (as No. 37) (p 14×13½)	..	9·50	15
44/51			*Set of* 8	28·00	2·00

16

(Recess D.L.R.)

1949 (11 Sept). *First Death Anniv of Mohammed Ali Jinnah. T 16 and similar design. P 14.*

52	16	1½ a. brown	..	1·25	55
53		3 a. green	..	1·25	55
54	—	10 a. black	..	2·75	4·50
52/4			*Set of* 3	4·75	5·00

Design:—10 a. Similar inscription reading "QUAID-I-AZAM/MOHAMMAD ALI JINNAH" etc.

17 Pottery   18 Aeroplane and Hour-glass

Two Types of 3½ a.:

I   II

19 Saracenic Leaf Pattern   20 Archway and Lamp

(Des A. R. Chughtai. Recess D.L.R., later printings, Pakistan Security Ptg Corp)

1951 (14 Aug)–**56**. *Fourth Anniv of Independence. P 13.*

55	17	2½ a. carmine	..	70	35
56	18	3 a. purple	..	40	10
57	17	3½ a. blue (I)	..	60	1·00
57a		3½ a. blue (II) (12.56)	..	2·25	60
58	19	4 a. green	..	35	10
59		6 a. brown-orange	..	45	10
60	20	8 a. sepia	..	3·75	10
61		10 a. violet	..	80	10
62	18	12 a. slate	..	90	10
55/62			*Set of* 9	9·00	2·00

The above and the stamps issued on the 14 August 1954, 1955 and 1956, are basically definitive issues, although issued on the Anniversary date of Independence.

21 "Scinde Dawk" stamp and Ancient and Modern Transport

(Recess D.L.R.)

1952 (14 Aug). *Centenary of "Scinde Dawk" Issue of India. P 13.*

63	21	3 a. deep olive/yellow-olive	..	75	50
64		12 a. deep brown/salmon	..	1·00	15

PRINTERS. All issues up to No. 219 were recess-printed by the Pakistan Security Printing Corporation, *unless otherwise stated.*

22 Kaghan Valley

23 Mountains, Gilgit

24 Tea Plantation, East Pakistan

1954 (14 Aug). *Seventh Anniv of Independence. T 22/4 and similar designs. P 13½ (14 a., 1 r., 2 r.) or 13 (others).*

65	6 p. reddish violet		10	10
66	9 p. blue		1·75	80
67	1 a. carmine		10	10
68	1½ a. red		10	10
69	14 a. deep green		55	10
70	1 r. green		9·00	10
71	2 r. red-orange		2·00	10
65/71		Set of 7	12·00	90

Designs: *As T 22*—1½ a. Mausoleum of Emperor Jehangir, Lahore. *As T 23*—1 a. Badshahi Mosque, Lahore. *As T 24*—1 r. Cotton plants, West Pakistan; 2 r. Jute fields and river, East Pakistan.

29 View of K 2

1954 (25 Dec). *Conquest of K 2 (Mount Godwin-Austen). P 13.*

72	29	2 a. deep violet	30	15

30 Karnaphuli Paper Mill,
Type I (Arabic fraction on left) | Type II (Arabic fraction on right)

1955 (14 Aug)–56. *Eighth Anniv of Independence. T 30 and similar horiz designs. P 13.*

73	2½ a. scarlet (I)		30	30
73a	2½ a. scarlet (II) (12.56)		30	30
74	6 a. deep ultramarine		70	10
75	8 a. deep reddish violet		2·75	10
76	12 a. carmine and orange		2·50	10
73/6		Set of 5	6·00	55

Designs:—6 a. Textile mill, West Pakistan; 8 a. Jute mill, East Pakistan; 12 a. Main Sui gas plant.

**TENTH
ANNIVERSARY
UNITED NATIONS**

24.10.55.

(34)

35 Map of West Pakistan

**TENTH
ANNIVERSARY
UNITED NATIONS**

24.10.55.

"UNITED NATIONS"
shifted 1 mm to left
(1½ a. R. 7/10; 12 a.
R. 3/8, 5/8, 7/8, 9/8)

1955 (24 Oct). *Tenth Anniv of United Nations. Nos. 68 and 76 optd as T 34.*

77	1½ a. red (B.)		1·75	5·00
	a. "UNITED NATIONS" 1 mm to left	3·50	6·00
78	12 a. carmine and orange (B.)		75	4·50
	a. "UNITED NATIONS" 1 mm to left	3·50	6·00

Forgeries exist of the overprint on No. 77. These are in very uneven thin type and measure 20×18 mm instead of the genuine 19½×19 mm.

1955 (7 Dec). *West Pakistan Unity. P 13½.*

79	35	1½ a. myrtle-green	15	10
80		2 a. sepia	15	10
81		12 a. deep rose-red	55	15
79/81		Set of 3	75	30

REPUBLIC

36 Constituent Assembly Building, Karachi

(Litho D.L.R.)

1956 (23 Mar). *Republic Day. P 13.*

82	36	2 a. myrtle-green	45	10

37 | 38 Map of East Pakistan

1956 (14 Aug). *Ninth Anniv of Independence. P 13½.*

83	37	2 a. scarlet	30	10

1956 (15 Oct). *First Session of National Assembly of Pakistan at Dacca. P 13½.*

84	38	1½ a. myrtle-green	15	80
85		2 a. sepia	15	10
86		12 a. deep rose-red	20	30
84/6		Set of 3	45	1·10

39 Karnaphuli Paper Mill, East Bengal | 40 Pottery

41 Orange Tree

1957 (23 Mar). *First Anniv of Republic. P 13.*

87	39	2½ a. scarlet	20	10
88	40	3½ a. blue	30	10
89	41	10 r. myrtle-green and yellow-orange	80	20
87/9		Set of 3	1·10	30

The above and No. 95 are primarily definitive issues, although issued on the Anniversary of Republic Day.
For 10 r. with W 98, see No. 208.

42 Pakistani Flag | 43 Pakistani Industries

(Litho D.L.R.)

1957 (10 May). *Centenary of Struggle for Independence (Indian Mutiny). P 13.*

90	42	1½ a. bronze-green	30	10
91		12 a. light blue	60	10

(Litho D.L.R.)

1957 (14 Aug). *Tenth Anniv of Independence. P 14.*

92	43	1½ a. ultramarine	15	10
93		4 a. orange-red	25	30
94		12 a. mauve	30	40
92/4		Set of 3	65	70

44 Coconut Tree | 45

1958 (23 Mar). *Second Anniv of Republic. P 13.*

95	44	15 r. red and deep reddish purple	4·25	3·00

This is a definitive issue, see note below No. 89.
See No. 209 for this stamp with W 98.

(Photo Harrison)

1958 (21 Apr). *20th Death Anniv of Mohammed Iqbal (poet). P 14½ × 14.*

96	45	1½ a. yellow-olive and black	30	10
97		2 a. orange-brown and black	30	10
98		14 a. turquoise-blue and black	55	10
96/8		Set of 3	1·00	20

46 U.N. Charter and Globe

**PAKISTAN
BOY SCOUT
2nd NATIONAL
JAMBOREE**

CHITTAGONG
Dec. 58—Jan. 59

(47)

1958 (10 Dec). *Tenth Anniv of Declaration of Human Rights. P 13.*

99	46	1½ a. turquoise-blue	10	10
100		14 a. sepia	40	10

1958 (28 Dec). *Second Pakistan Boy Scouts National Jamboree, Chittagong. Nos. 65 and 75 optd with T 47.*

101	6 p. reddish violet		15	10
102	8 a. deep reddish violet		30	10

**REVOLUTION
DAY**
Oct. 27, 1959

(48)

49 "Centenary of An Idea"

1959 (27 Oct). *Revolution Day. No. 74 optd with T 48 in red.*

103	6 a. deep ultramarine		40	10

1959 (19 Nov). *Red Cross Commemoration. Recess; cross typo. P 13.*

104	49	2 a. red and green	15	10
105		10 a. red and deep blue	55	10

50 Armed Forces Badge | 51 Map of Pakistan

(Litho D.L.R.)

1960 (10 Jan). *Armed Forces Day. P 13½ × 13.*

106	50	2 a. red, ultramarine and blue-green	20	10
107		14 a. red and bright blue	65	10

1960 (23 Mar). *P 13 × 13½.*

108	51	6 p. deep purple	20	10
109		2 a. brown-red	40	10
110		8 a. deep green	70	10
111		1 r. blue	90	10
108/11		Set of 4	2·00	15

52 Uprooted Tree | 53 Punjab Agricultural College

1960 (7 Apr). *World Refugee Year. P 13.*

112	52	2 a. rose-carmine	10	10
113		10 a. green	20	10

1960 (10 Oct). *Golden Jubilee of Punjab Agricultural College, Lyallpur. T 53 and similar horiz design. P* 12½ × 14.

114		2 a. slate-blue and carmine-red			10	10
115		8 a. bluish green and reddish violet	. .		10	10

Design:—8 a. College arms.

55 "Land Reforms, Rehabilitation and Reconstruction" **56** Caduceus

(Des M. H. Hanjra. Photo D.L.R.)

1960 (27 Oct). *Revolution Day. P* 13 × 13½.

116	55	2 a. green, pink and brown	. .		10	10
		a. Green and pink omitted	. .		9·00	
		b. Pink omitted	. .		5·00	
117		14 a. green, yellow and ultramarine		20	20

(Photo D.L.R.)

1960 (16 Nov). *Centenary of King Edward Medical College, Lahore. P* 13.

118	56	2 a. yellow, black and blue	. .		40	10
119		14 a. emerald, black and carmine	. .		85	10

57 "Economic Co-operation" **58** Zam-Zama Gun, Lahore ("Kim's Gun," after Rudyard Kipling)

1960 (5 Dec). *International Chamber of Commerce C.A.F.E.A. Meeting, Karachi. P* 13.

120	57	14 a. orange-red	. .	. .	15	10

(Centre typo, background recess Pakistan Security Ptg Corp)

1960 (24 Dec). *Third Pakistan Boy Scouts National Jamboree, Lahore. P* 12½ × 14.

121	58	2 a. carmine, yellow & dp bluish green		40	10

(New Currency. 100 paisa=1 rupee)

꠱ PAISA

(59)

1961 (1 Jan–14 Feb). *Nos.* 24a, 67/8, 83 *and* 108/9, *surch as T* 59. *Nos.* 123/4 *and* 126 *surch by Pakistan Security Ptg Corp and others by the Times Press, Karachi.*

122		1 p. on 1½ a. red (10.1)	. .	. .	20	10
123		2 p. on 3 p. red		. .	10	10
124		3 p. on 6 p. deep purple		. .	10	10
		a. "PASIA" for "PAISA"	. .		2·50	
125		7 p. on 1 a. carmine (14.2)	. .		25	10
126		13 p. on 2 a. brown-red (14.2)	. .		25	10
		a. "PAIS" for "PAISA"	. .		2·50	
127		13 p. on 2 a. scarlet (14.2)	. .		15	10
122/7				*Set of* 6	85	30

No. 122. Two settings were used, the first with figure "1" 2½ mm tall and the second 3 mm.

On the 1 p. with tall "1" and the 13 p. (No. 127), the space between the figures of value and "P" of "PAISA" varies between 1½ mm and 3 mm.

See also Nos. 262/4.

ERRORS. In the above issue and the corresponding official stamps we have listed errors in the stamps surcharged by the Pakistan Security Printing Corp but have not included the very large number of errors which occurred in the stamps surcharged by the less experienced Times Press. This was a very hurried job and there was no time to carry out the usual checks. It is also known that some errors were not issued to the public but came on the market by other means.

NOTE. Stamps in the old currency were also *handstamped* with new currency equivalents and issued in various districts but these local issues are outside the scope of this catalogue.

60 Khyber Pass **61** Shalimar Gardens, Lahore

62 Chota Sona Masjid (gateway)

(a)	*(b)*	*(c)*

Types *(a)* and *(b)* show the first letter in the top right-hand inscription; *(a)* wrongly engraved, "SH" *(b)* corrected to "P".

On Nos. 131/2 and 134 the corrections were made individually on the plate, so that each stamp in the sheet may be slightly different. Type *(c)* refers to No. 133a only.

1961–63. *No wmk. P* 13 (*T* 62) *or* 14 (*others*).

(a) Inscribed "SHAKISTAN" in Bengali

128	60	1 p. violet (1.1.61)			60	10
129		2 p. rose-red (12.1.61)	. .		60	10
130		5 p. ultramarine (23.3.61)			50	10

(b) Inscribed "PAKISTAN" in Bengali

131	60	1 p. violet			30	10
132		2 p. rose-red			10	10
133		3 p. reddish purple (27.10.61)			30	10
		a. Re-engraved. First letter of Bengali inscription as Type (c) (1963)			1·50	2·00
134		5 p. ultramarine			80	10
135		7 p. emerald (23.3.61)			60	10
136	61	10 p. brown (14.8.61)			20	10
137		13 p. slate-violet (14.8.61)			10	10
138		25 p. deep blue (1.1.62)			3·75	10
139		40 p. deep purple (1.1.62)			40	10
140		50 p. deep bluish green (1.1.62)	. .		35	10
141		75 p. carmine-red (23.3.62)			40	10
142		90 p. yellow-green (1.1.62)			50	10
143	62	1 r. vermilion (7.1.63)			1·75	10
		a. Imperf (pair)			2·50	
144		1 r. 25, reddish violet (27.10.61)			75	10
144a		2 r. orange (7.1.63)			4·50	15
144b		5 r. green (7.1.63)			6·00	1·00
128/44b				*Set of* 19	20·00	1·90

See also Nos. 170/81 and 204/7.

(63) **64** Warsak Dam and Power Station

1961 (12 Feb). *Lahore Stamp Exhibition. No.* 110 *optd with T* 63.

145	51	8 a. deep green (R.)	. .	. .	50	80

1961 (1 July). *Completion of Warsak Hydro-Electric Project. P* 12½ × 14.

146	64	40 p. black and blue	. .		40	10

65 Narcissus **66** Ten Roses

1961 (2 Oct). *Child Welfare Week. P* 14.

147	65	13 p. turquoise-blue			15	10
148		90 p. bright purple			45	20

1961 (4 Nov). *Co-operative Day. P* 13.

149	66	13 p. rose-red and deep green	. .		30	10
150		90 p. rose-red and blue	. .		70	20

67 Police Crest and "Traffic Control" **68** Locomotive *Eagle* of 1861

(Photo D.L.R.)

1961 (30 Nov). *Police Centenary. P* 13.

151	67	13 p. silver, black and blue	. .		50	10
152		40 p. silver, black and red	. .		1·00	20

(Des M. Thoma. Photo D.L.R.)

1961 (31 Dec). *Railway Centenary. T* 68 *and similar horiz design. P* 14.

153		13 p. green, black and yellow	. .		50	10
154		50 p. yellow, black and green	. .		75	60

Design:—50 p. Diesel locomotive and tracks forming "1961".

(70) **71** *Anopheles* sp (mosquito)

1962 (6 Feb). *First Karachi–Dacca Jet Flight. No.* 87 *surch with T* 70.

155	39	13 p. on 2½ a. scarlet (R.)	. .		60	40

(Photo D.L.R.)

1962 (7 Apr). *Malaria Eradication. T* 71 *and similar horiz design. P* 14.

156		10 p. black, yellow and red			20	10
157		13 p. black, greenish yellow and red	. .		20	10

Design:—13 p. Mosquito pierced by blade.

73 Pakistan Map and Jasmine

(Photo Courvoisier)

1962 (8 June). *New Constitution. P* 12.

158	73	40 p. yellow-green, bluish green and grey		45	10

74 Football **78** Marble Fruit Dish and Bahawalpuri Clay Flask

1962 (14 Aug). *Sports. T* 74 *and similar horiz designs. P* 12½ × 14.

159		7 p. black and blue		. .	10	10
160		13 p. black and green			10	10
161		25 p. black and purple			10	10
162		40 p. black and orange-brown	. .		1·40	1·10
159/62				*Set of* 4	1·50	1·25

Designs:—13 p. Hockey; 25 p. Squash; 40 p. Cricket.

1962 (10 Nov). *Small Industries. T* 78 *and similar vert designs. P* 13.

163		7 p. brown-lake	. .		10	10
164		13 p. deep green	. .		2·00	75
165		25 p. reddish violet	. .		10	10
166		40 p. yellow-green	. .		10	10
167		50 p. deep red	. .		10	10
163/7				*Set of* 5	2·00	90

Designs:—13 p. Sports equipment; 25 p. Camel-skin lamp and brassware; 40 p. Wooden powderbowl and basket-work; 50 p. Inlaid cigarette-box and brassware.

83 "Child Welfare"

(Des M. Thoma. Photo D.L.R.)

1962 (11 Dec). *16th Anniv of U.N.I.C.E.F. P* 14.

168	83	13 p. black, light blue and maroon		15	10
169		40 p. black, yellow and turquoise-blue		15	10

Nos. 170, etc. Nos. 131/42

1962–70. *As T* 60/1 *but with redrawn Bengali inscription at top right. No wmk.*

170	60	1 p. violet (1963)	. .		10	10
171		2 p. rose-red (1964)		. .	65	10
		a. Imperf (pair)		. .	2·75	
172		3 p. reddish purple (1970)			2·50	1·25
173		5 p. ultramarine (1963)	. .		10	10
174		7 p. emerald (1964)		. .	3·50	1·25
175	61	10 p. brown (1963)		. .	10	10
176		13 p. slate-violet	. .		10	10
176a		15 p. bright purple (31.12.64)	. .		15	10
		ab. Imperf (pair)	. .		3·75	
176b		20 p. myrtle-green (26.1.70)	. .		30	10
		ba. Imperf (pair)	. .		2·75	
177		25 p. deep blue (1963)	. .		3·50	10
		a. Imperf (pair)	. .		5·00	
178		40 p. deep purple (1964)	. .		15	10
		a. Imperf (pair)			6·00	
179		50 p. deep bluish green (1964)	. .		15	10
180		75 p. carmine-red (1964)	. .		30	40
181		90 p. yellow-green (1964)	. .		30	60
170/81				*Set of* 14	10·50	3·50

Other values in this series and the high values (Nos. 204/10) are known imperforate but we are not satisfied as to their status.

(84)

97 Thermal Power Installations

1964 (21 Dec). *First Convocation of the West Pakistan University of Engineering and Technology, Lahore.* P 12½ × 14.
219 **107** 15 p. chestnut 10 10

U.N. FORCE W. IRIAN

85 "Dancing" Horse, Camel and Bull

1963 (15 Feb). *Pakistan U.N. Force in West Irian. No. 176 optd with T 84.*
182 **61** 13 p. slate-violet (R.) 10 10

(Des S. Jahangir. Photo Courvoisier)

1963 (13 Mar). *National Horse and Cattle Show.* P 11½.
183 **85** 13 p. blue, sepia and cerise .. 10 10

86 Wheat and Tractor

1963 (21 Mar). *Freedom from Hunger. T 86 and similar horiz design.* P 12½ × 14.
184 13 p. orange-brown 75 10
185 50 p. bistre-brown .. .. 1·75 40
Design:—50 p. Rice.

(88)

89 Centenary Emblem

1963 (23 Mar). *2nd International Stamp Exhibition, Dacca. No. 109 surch with T 88.*
186 **51** 13 p. on 2 a. brown-red 30 10

1963 (25 June). *Centenary of Red Cross. Recess; cross typo.* P 13.
187 **89** 40 p. red and deep olive .. .. 1·25 15

90 Paharpur (94)

1963 (16 Sept). *Archaeological Series. T 90 and similar designs.* P 14 × 12½ (13 p.) or 12½ × 15 (others).
188 7 p. ultramarine 20 10
189 13 p. sepia 25 10
190 40 p. carmine 35 10
191 50 p. deep reddish violet .. 45 10
188/91 .. .. *Set of* 4 1·10 30
Designs: *Vert*—13 p. Moenjodaro; *Horiz*—40 p. Taxila; 50 p. Mainamati.

1963 (7 Oct). *Centenary of Public Works Department. No. 133 surch with T 94 by typography.*
192 **60** 13 p. on 3 p. reddish purple .. 10 10
Forged surcharges applied in *lithography* exist.

95 Ataturk's Mausoleum

1963 (10 Nov). *25th Death Anniv of Kemal Atatürk.* P 13½.
193 **95** 50 p. red 35 10

96 Globe and U.N.E.S.C.O. Emblem

(Photo D.L.R.)

1963 (10 Dec). *15th Anniv of Declaration of Human Rights.* P 14.
194 **96** 50 p. brown, red and ultramarine .. 30 10

COVER PRICES

Cover factors are quoted at the beginning of each country for most issues to 1945. An explanation of the system can be found on page x. The factors quoted do not, however, apply to philatelic covers.

1963 (25 Dec). *Completion of Multan Thermal Power Station.* P 12½ × 14.
195 **97** 13 p. ultramarine 10 10

98 Multiple Star and Crescent

99 Temple of Thot, Queen Nefertari and Maids

1963–79. *As Nos. 43b, 89, 95 and 143/44b, but W* **98.**
204 **62** 1 r. vermilion 30 10
  b. Imperf (pair) .. .. 7·00
205 1 r. 25, reddish violet (1964) .. 1·00 10
  a. *Purple* (1975?) .. .. 1·00 10
  ab. Imperf (pair) .. .. 6·00
206 2 r. orange (1964) 55 15
  a. Imperf (pair) .. .. 8·00
207 5 r. green (1964) .. .. 3·50 40
  a. Imperf (pair) .. .. 14·00
208 **41** 10 r. myrtle-green & yellow-orge (1968) 4·00 3·50
  a. Imperf (pair) .. ..
  b. Wmk sideways .. 75 75
209 **44** 15 r. red and deep reddish purple (*wmk sideways*) (20.3.79) .. 80 1·00
  a. Imperf (pair) .. .. 18·00
210 **13** 25 r. violet (1968) .. 12·00 15·00
  a. Wmk sideways .. 2·00 2·50
  ab. Imperf (pair) .. .. 15·00
204/10a .. .. *Set of* 7 8·00 4·50

1964 (30 Mar). *Nubian Monuments Preservation. T* **99** *and similar horiz design.* P 13 × 13½.
211 13 p. turquoise-blue and red .. 30 10
212 50 p. bright purple and black .. 70 10
Design:—50 p. Temple of Abu Simbel.

101 "Unisphere" and Pakistan Pavilion

103 Shah Abdul Latif's Mausoleum

1964 (22 Apr). *New York World's Fair. T* **101** *and similar design.* P 12½ × 14 (13 p.) or 14 × 12½ (1 r. 25).
213 13 p. ultramarine 10 10
214 1 r. 25, ultramarine and red-orange.. 30 20
Design: *Vert*—1 r. 25, Pakistan Pavilion on "Unisphere".

1964 (25 June). *Death Bicentenary of Shah Abdul Latif of Bhit.* P 13½ × 13.
215 **103** 50 p. bright blue and carmine-lake .. 50 10

104 Mausoleum of Quaid-i-Azam

105 Mausoleum

1964 (11 Sept). *16th Death Anniv of Mohammed Ali Jinnah (Quaid-i-Azam).* P 13½ (15 p.) or 13 (50 p.).
216 **104** 15 p. emerald-green 20 10
217 **105** 50 p. bronze-green 65 10

106 Bengali and Urdu Alphabets

107 University Building

1964 (5 Oct). *Universal Children's Day.* P 13.
218 **106** 15 p. brown 10 10

PROCESS. All the following issues were lithographed by the Pakistan Security Printing Corporation, *unless otherwise stated.*

108 "Help the Blind"

109 "I.T.U. Emblem and Symbols

(Des A. Chughtai)

1965 (28 Feb). *Blind Welfare.* P 13.
220 **108** 15 p. ultramarine and yellow .. 10 10

1965 (17 May). *I.T.U. Centenary. Recess.* P 12½ × 14.
221 **109** 15 p. reddish purple .. .. 1·25 30

110 I.C.Y. Emblem

1965 (26 June). *International Co-operation Year.* P 13 × 13½.
222 **110** 15 p. black and light blue .. 50 15
223 50 p. green and yellow .. .. 1·00 40

111 "Co-operation"

112 Globe and Flags of Turkey, Iran and Pakistan

1965 (21 July). *First Anniv of Regional Development Co-operation Pact.* P 13½ × 13 (15 p.) or 13 (50 p.).
224 **111** 15 p. multicoloured 15 10
225 **112** 50 p. multicoloured 45 10

113 Soldier and Tanks

1965 (25 Dec). *Pakistan Armed Forces. T* **113** *and similar horiz designs. Multicoloured.* P 13½ × 13.
226 7 p. Type **113** 45 20
227 15 p. Naval officer and *Tughril* (destroyer).. 80 10
228 50 p. Pilot and "F-104" Starfighters 1·25 20
226/8 .. .. .. *Set of* 3 2·25 40

116 Army, Navy and Air Force Crests

117 Atomic Reactor, Islamabad

1966 (13 Feb). *Armed Forces Day.* P 13½ × 13.
229 **116** 15 p. royal blue, dull grn, brt blue & buff 10 10

1966 (30 Apr). *Inauguration of Pakistan's First Atomic Reactor. Recess.* P 13.
230 **117** 15 p. black 10 10

118 Bank Crest   **119** Children

1966 (25 Aug). *Silver Jubilee of Habib Bank.* P 12½ × 14.
231 **118** 15 p. blue-green, yellow-orange & sepia   10   10

1966 (3 Oct). *Universal Children's Day.* P 13½.
232 **119** 15 p. black, red and pale yellow 10   10

120 U.N.E.S.C.O. Emblem

1966 (24 Nov). *20th Anniv of U.N.E.S.C.O.* P 14.
233 **120** 15 p. multicoloured .. .. .. 1·75   30

121 Flag, Secretariat Building
and President Ayub

1966 (29 Nov). *Islamabad (new capital).* P 13.
234 **121** 15 p. deep bluish green, chestnut, light
     blue and bistre-brown   15   10
235   50 p. deep bluish green, chestnut, light
     blue and black 40   10

122 Avicenna   **123** Mohammed Ali Jinnah

1966 (3 Dec). *Foundation of Health and Tibbi Research Institute.*
P 13 × 13½.
236 **122** 15 p. dull green and salmon 15   10
     a. Imperf (pair) .. .. .. 55·00

1966 (25 Dec). *90th Birth Anniv of Mohammed Ali Jinnah.* T **123**
*and similar design bearing same portrait but in different frame.
Litho and recess.* P 13.
237 **123** 15 p. black, orange and greenish blue .. 10   10
238   –   50 p. black, purple and ultramarine .. 30   10

124 Tourist Year Emblem   **125** Emblem of
                                      Pakistan
                                   T.B. Association

1967 (1 Jan). *International Tourist Year.* P 13½ × 13.
239 **124** 15 p. black, light blue and yellow-brown   10   10

1967 (10 Jan). *Tuberculosis Eradication Campaign.* P 13½ × 13.
240 **125** 15 p. red, sepia and chestnut 10   10

126 Scout Salute and Badge   **127** "Justice"

1967 (29 Jan). *4th National Scout Jamboree.* Photo. P 12½ × 14.
241 **126** 15 p. light orange-brown and maroon .. 15   10

1967 (17 Feb). *Centenary of West Pakistan High Court.* P 13.
242 **127** 15 p. black, slate, light red and slate-blue   10   10

128 Dr. Mohammed Iqbal (philosopher)

1967 (21 Apr). *Iqbal Commemoration.* P 13.
243 **128** 15 p. sepia and light red ..   10   10
244   1 r. sepia and deep green ..   30   10

129 Hilal-i-Isteqlal Flag

1967 (15 May). *Award of Hilal-i-Isteqlal (for Valour) to Lahore,
Sialkot, and Sargodha.* P 13.
245 **129** 15 p. multicoloured 10   10

130 "20th Anniversary"

1967 (14 Aug). *20th Anniv of Independence.* Photo. P 13.
246 **130** 15 p. red and deep bluish green 10   10

131 "Rice Exports"   **132** Cotton Plant, Yarn
                                     and Textiles

1967 (26 Sept). *Pakistan Exports.* T **131/2** *and similar design.*
Photo. P 13 × 13½.
247   10 p. yellow, deep bluish green and deep blue   10   15
248   15 p. multicoloured 10   10
     a. Pale orange (top panel) omitted .. .. 10·00
249   50 p. multicoloured 20   15
247/9   *Set of* 3   30   30
Design: *Vert as* T **132**—50 p. Raw jute, bale and bags.

134 Clay Toys

1967 (2 Oct). *Universal Children's Day.* P 13.
250 **134** 15 p. multicoloured 10   10

135 Shah and Empress of Iran and
Gulistan Palace, Teheran

1967 (26 Oct). *Coronation of Shah Mohammed Riza Pahlavi and
Empress Farah of Iran. Recess and litho.* P 13.
251 **135** 50 p. purple, blue and light yellow-ochre   40   10

136 "Each For All–All For Each"

1967 (4 Nov). *Co-operative Day.* P 13.
252 **136** 15 p. multicoloured 10   10

137 Mangla Dam

1967 (23 Nov). *Indus Basin Project.* P 13.
253 **137** 15 p. multicoloured 10   10

138 Crab pierced by Sword   **139** Human Rights
                                       Emblem

1967 (26 Dec). *The Fight Against Cancer.* P 13.
254 **138** 15 p. red and black 50   10

1968 (31 Jan). *Human Rights Year.* Photo. P 14 × 13.
255 **139** 15 p. red and deep turquoise-blue .. 10   15
256   50 p. red, yellow and silver-grey .. 10   15

140 Agricultural University,   **141** W.H.O. Emblem
       Mymensingh

1968 (28 Mar). *First Convocation of East Pakistan Agricultural
University.* Photo. P 13½ × 13.
257 **140** 15 p. multicoloured 10   10

1968 (7 Apr). *20th Anniv of World Health Organization.* Photo.
P 14 × 13.
258 **141** 15 p. green and orange-red ..   10   15
     a. "PAIS" for "PAISA" (R.4/5) .. 1·00
259   50 p. red-orange and indigo 10   15

142 Kazi Nazrul Islam (poet, composer
and patriot)

1968 (25 June). *Nazrul Islam Commemoration. Recess and litho.*
P 13.
260 **142** 15 p. sepia and pale yellow 20   15
261   50 p. sepia and pale rose-red 40   15
     Nos. 260/1 with a two-line inscription giving the wrong date of
birth ("1889") were prepared but not issued. Some are known to
have been released in error.

4 PAISA
(143)

1968 (18 July–Aug). *Nos. 56, 74 and 61 surch as T* **143**.
262	4 p. on 3 a. purple	..	..	20	45
263	4 p. on 6 a. deep ultramarine (R.) (Aug)	..	50	55
264	60 p. on 10 a. violet (R.)	..	..	30	35
	a. Surch in black	..	..	30	55
	b. Surch triple	..	..	30·00	
262/4	..			Set of 3	90	1·25

144 Children running with Hoops

1968 (7 Oct). *Universal Children's Day. P* 13.
265	144	15 p. multicoloured	..	..	10	10

145 "National Assembly"

1968 (27 Oct). *"A Decade of Development". T* **145** *and similar horiz designs. P* 13.
266	10 p. multicoloured	..	..	..	10	10
267	15 p. multicoloured	..	..	15	10
268	50 p. multicoloured	..	..	55	15
269	60 p. light blue, dull purple and vermilion	..	55	25
266/9	..			Set of 4	1·25	55

Designs:—15 p. Industry and agriculture; 50 p. Army, Navy and Air Force; 60 p. Minaret and atomic reactor plant.

149 Chittagong Steel Mill

1969 (7 Jan). *Pakistan's First Steel Mill, Chittagong. P* 13.
270	149	15 p. grey, light blue & pale yellow-olive	10	10

150 "Family" 151 Olympic Gold Medal and Hockey Player

1969 (14 Jan). *Family Planning. P* 13½ × 13.
271	150	15 p. bright purple & pale greenish blue	10	10

1969 (30 Jan). *Olympic Hockey Champions. Photo. P* 13½.
272	151	15 p. black, gold, deep green & pale blue	65	50
273		1 r. black, gold, dp green & flesh-pink	..	1·75	75

152 Mirza Ghalib and Lines of Verse

1969 (15 Feb). *Death Centenary of Mirza Ghalib (poet). P* 13.
274	152	15 p. multicoloured	..	..	15	15
275		40 p. multicoloured	..	..	40	15

The lines of verse on No. 275 are different from those in T **152**.

153 Dacca Railway Station

1969 (27 Apr). *First Anniv of New Dacca Railway Station. P* 13.
276	153	15 p. multicoloured	..	..	30	10

154 I.L.O. Emblem and 155 Mughal Miniature
"1919–1969" (Pakistan)

1969 (15 May). *50th Anniv of International Labour Organisation. P* 13½.
277	154	15 p. buff and bluish green	..	..	10	10
278		50 p. cinnamon and cerise	..	..	30	10

1969 (21 July). *Fifth Anniv of Regional Co-operation for Development. T* **155** *and similar vert designs. Multicoloured. P* 13.
279	20 p. Type **155**	..			15	10
280	50 p. Safav miniature (Iran)	..		15	10
281	1 r. Ottoman miniature (Turkey)	..	20	10
279/81	..	..		Set of 3	45	30

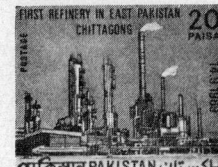

158 Eastern Refinery, Chittagong

1969 (14 Sept). *First Oil Refinery in East Pakistan. Photo. P* 13½ × 13.
282	158	20 p. multicoloured	..	..	10	10

159 Children playing Outside "School"

1969 (6 Oct). *Universal Children's Day. Photo. P* 13.
283	159	20 p. multicoloured	..	..	10	10

160 Japanese Doll and P.I.A. Air Routes

1969 (1 Nov). *Inauguration of P.I.A. Pearl Route, Dacca–Tokyo. P* 13½ × 13.
284	160	20 p. multicoloured	..	..	30	10
		a. Yellow and pink omitted	..	7·00	
285		50 p. multicoloured	..	..	40	40
		a. Yellow and pink omitted	..	7·00	

161 "Reflection of Light" Diagram

1969 (4 Nov). *Millenary Commemorative of Ibn-al-Haitham (physicist). Photo. P* 13.
286	161	20 p. black, lemon and light blue	..	10	10

162 Vickers "Vimy" and 163 Flags, Sun Tower and
Karachi Airport Expo Site Plan

1969 (2 Dec). *50th Anniv of First England–Australia Flight. Photo. P* 13½ × 13.
287	162	50 p. multicoloured	..	..	40	35

1970 (15 Mar). *World Fair, Osaka. P* 13.
288	163	50 p. multicoloured	..	..	15	30

164 New U.P.U. H.Q. Building

1970 (20 May). *New U.P.U. Headquarters Building. P* 13½ × 13.
289	164	20 p. multicoloured	..	..	10	10
290		50 p. multicoloured	..	..	20	25

The above, in a miniature sheet, additionally inscr "U.P.U. Day 9th Oct, 1971", were put on sale on that date in very limited numbers.

165 U.N. H.Q. Building

1970 (26 June). *25th Anniv of United Nations. T* **165** *and similar horiz design. Multicoloured. P* 13 × 13½.
291	20 p. Type **165**	..	..		15	10
292	50 p. U.N. emblem	..	..	15	20

167 I.E.Y. Emblem, Book and Pen

1970 (6 July). *International Education Year. P* 13.
293	167	20 p. multicoloured	..	..	10	10
294		50 p. multicoloured	..	..	20	20

168 Saiful Malook Lake (Pakistan)

1970 (21 July). *Sixth Anniv of Regional Co-operation for Development. T* **168** *and similar square designs. Multicoloured. P* 13.
295	20 p. Type **168**	..	..		15	10
296	50 p. Seeyo-Se-Pol Bridge, Esfahan (Iran)	..	20	10
297	1 r. View from Fethiye (Turkey)	..	20	15
295/7	..	..		Set of 3	50	30

171 Asian Productivity Symbol 172 Dr. Maria Montessori

1970 (18 Aug).   *Asian Productivity Year. Photo. P* 12½ × 14.
298   171   50 p. multicoloured   10   15

1970 (31 Aug).   *Birth Centenary of Dr. Maria Montessori
(educationist). P* 13.
299   172   20 p. multicoloured   10   10
300   50 p. multicoloured   10   20

173 Tractor and Fertilizer Factory

1970 (12 Sept).   *Tenth Near East F.A.O. Regional Conference,
Islamabad. P* 13.
301   173   20 p. bright green, and orange-brown   10   20

174 Children and   175 Pakistan Flag
Open Book   and Text

1970 (5 Oct).   *Universal Children's Day. Photo. P* 13.
302   174   20 p. multicoloured   10   10

1970 (7 Dec).   *General Elections for National Assembly.
P* 13½ × 13.
303   175   20 p. green and bluish violet   ..   10   10

1970 (17 Dec).   *General Elections for Provincial Assemblies. As
No. 303, but inscr* "PROVINCIAL ASSEMBLIES 17TH DEC.,
1970".
304   175   20 p. green and pale magenta   ..   10   10

176 Conference Crest and burning Al-Aqsa Mosque

1970 (26 Dec).   *Conference of Islamic Foreign Ministers. Karachi.
P* 13.
305   176   20 p. multicoloured   10   10

177 Coastal Embankments

1971 (25 Feb).   *Coastal Embankments in East Pakistan Project.
P* 13.
306   177   20 p. multicoloured   10   10

178 Emblem and United   180 Chaharbagh School (Iran)
Peoples of the World

179 Maple Leaf Cement Factory, Daudkhel

1971 (21 Mar).   *Racial Equality Year. P* 13.
307   178   20 p. multicoloured   10   15
308   50 p. multicoloured   20   25

1971 (1 July).   *20th Anniv of Colombo Plan. P* 13.
309   179   20 p. brown, black and reddish violet   ..   10   10

1971 (21 July).   *Seventh Anniv of Regional Co-operation for Development. T* **180** *and similar horiz designs. Multicoloured. P* 13.
310   10 p. Selimiye Mosque (Turkey)   ..   10   15
311   20 p. Badshahi Mosque (Lahore)   ..   20   25
312   50 p. Type **180**   30   35
310/12   ..   ..   Set of 3   55   65

181 Electric Locomotive and Boy with
Toy Train

1971 (4 Oct).   *Universal Children's Day. P* 13.
313   181   20 p. multicoloured   ..   ..   1·25   30

182 Horseman and Symbols

1971 (15 Oct).   *2500th Anniv of Persian Monarchy. P* 13.
314   182   10 p. multicoloured   25   30
315   20 p. multicoloured   35   40
316   50 p. multicoloured   45   50
314/16   ..   ..   ..   Set of 3   95   1·10
The above exist in a miniature sheet, but only a very limited
quantity was placed on sale.

183 Hockey-player and Trophy

1971 (24 Oct).   *World Cup Hockey Tournament, Barcelona. P* 13.
317   183   20 p. multicoloured   ..   ..   1·25   45

184 Great Bath, Moenjodaro

1971 (4 Nov).   *25th Anniv of U.N.E.S.C.O. and Campaign to save
the Moenjodaro Excavations. P* 13.
318   184   20 p. multicoloured   15   20

185 U.N.I.C.E.F. Symbol

1971 (11 Dec).   *25th Anniv of U.N.I.C.E.F. P* 13.
319   185   50 p. multicoloured   30   40

186 King Hussein and Jordanian Flag

1971 (25 Dec).   *50th Anniv of Hashemite Kingdom of Jordan. P* 13.
320   186   20 p. multicoloured   15   15

187 Badge of Hockey Federation   188 Reading Class
and Trophy

1971 (31 Dec).   *Hockey Championships Victory. P* 13.
321   187   20 p. multicoloured   ..   ..   1·50   90

1972 (15 Jan).   *International Book Year. P* 13½.
322   188   20 p. multicoloured   20   30

OUTSIDE THE COMMONWEALTH

On 30 January 1972 Pakistan left the Commonwealth.

189 View of Venice

1972 (7 Feb).   *U.N.E.S.C.O. Campaign to Save Venice. P* 13.
323   189   20 p. multicoloured   30   30

190 E.C.A.F.E. Emblem and Discs   191 Human Heart

1972 (28 Mar).   *25th Anniv of E.C.A.F.E. (Economic Commission
for Asia and the Far East). P* 13.
324   190   20 p. multicoloured   10   20

1972 (7 Apr).   *World Health Day. P* 13 × 13½.
325   191   20 p. multicoloured   20   30

192 "Only One Earth"   193 "Fisherman"
(Cevat Dereli)

1972 (5 June).   *U.N. Conference on the Human Environment,
Stockholm. P* 13 × 13½.
326   192   20 p. multicoloured   20   30

1972 (21 July).   *Eighth Anniv of Regional Co-operation for Development. T* **193** *and similar vert designs. Multicoloured. P* 13.
327   10 p. Type **193**   10   20
328   20 p. "Iranian Woman" (Behzad)   ..   15   25
329   50 p. "Will and Power" (A. R. Chughtai)   35   45
   a. Brown-ochre (border) omitted   ..   15·00
327/9   ..   ..   ..   Set of 3   55   80

194 Mohammed Ali Jinnah and Tower   195 Donating Blood

1972 (14 Aug). *25th Anniv of Independence. T* **194** *and similar horiz designs. Multicoloured. P* 13 (10 and 60 p.) or 14 × 12½ (20 p.).

330	10 p. Type **194** ..		10	10
331	20 p. "Land Reform" (74 × 23½ mm)..		15	20
	a. Horiz strip of 4. Nos. 331/4		55	
332	20 p. "Labour Reform" (74 × 23½ mm)		15	20
333	20 p. "Education Policy" (74 × 23½ mm)		15	20
334	20 p. "Health Policy" (74 × 23½ mm)		15	20
335	60 p. National Assembly Building (46 × 28 mm) ..		25	25
330/5		*Set of 6*	80	1·00

Nos. 331/4 were printed horizontally *se-tenant* throughout the sheet.

1972 (6 Sept). *National Blood Transfusion Service. P* 13½×12½.

336	**195**	20 p. multicoloured	15	30

196 People and Squares

1972 (16 Sept). *Centenary of Population Census. P* 13½.

337	**196**	20 p. multicoloured	15	20

197 Children from Slums

1972 (2 Oct). *Universal Children's Day. P* 13.

338	**197**	20 p. multicoloured	15	30

198 People and Open Book

1972 (23 Oct). *Education Week. P* 13.

339	**198**	20 p. multicoloured	20	20

199 Nuclear Power Plant

1972 (28 Nov). *Inauguration of Karachi Nuclear Power Plant. P* 13.

340	**199**	20 p. multicoloured	15	30

200 Copernicus in Observatory

1973 (19 Feb). *500th Birth Anniv of Nicholas Copernicus (astronomer). P* 13.

341	**200**	20 p. multicoloured	20	30

201 Moenjodaro Excavations   202 Elements of Meteorology

1973 (23 Feb). *50th Anniv of Moenjodaro Excavations. P* 13 × 13½.

342	**201**	20 p. multicoloured	20	30

1973 (23 Mar). *I.M.O./W.M.O. Centenary. P* 13.

343	**202**	20 p. multicoloured	20	30

203 Prisoners-of-war

1973 (18 Apr). *Prisoners-of-war in India. P* 13.

344	**203**	1 r. 25, multicoloured	1·50	1·50

204 National Assembly Building and Constitution Book

1973 (21 Apr). *Constitution Week. P* 12½ × 13½.

345	**204**	20 p. multicoloured	40	40

205 Badge and State Bank Building

1973 (1 July). *25th Anniv of Pakistan State Bank. P* 13.

346	**205**	20 p. multicoloured	15	30
347		1 r. multicoloured	30	50

206 Lut Desert Excavations (Iran)   207 Constitution Book and Flag

1973 (21 July). *9th Anniv of Regional Co-operation for Development. T* **206** *and similar vert designs. Multicoloured. P* 13 × 13½.

348	20 p. Type **206** ..		30	20
349	60 p. Main Street, Moenjodaro (Pakistan)		55	50
350	1 r. 25, Mausoleum of Antiochus I (Turkey)		75	1·25
348/50		*Set of 3*	1·40	1·75

1973 (14 Aug). *Independence Day and Enforcement of the Constitution. P* 13.

351	**207**	20 p. multicoloured	15	30

208 Mohammed Ali Jinnah (Quaid-i-Azam)   209 *Wallago attu*

1973 (11 Sept). *25th Death Anniv of Mohammed Ali Jinnah. P* 13.

352	**208**	20 p. light emerald, pale yellow and black	15	20

1973 (24 Sept). *Fishes. T* **209** *and similar horiz designs. Multicoloured. P* 13½.

353	10 p. Type **209** ..		80	80
	a. Horiz strip of 4. Nos. 353/6		3·50	
354	20 p. *Labeo rohita*		90	90
355	60 p. *Tilapia mossambica*		1·00	1·00
356	1 r. *Catla catla*		1·25	1·25
353/6		*Set of 4*	3·50	3·50

Nos. 353/6 were printed within one sheet, horizontally *se-tenant*.

210 Children's Education

1973 (1 Oct). *Universal Children's Day. P* 13.

357	**210**	20 p. multicoloured	15	30

211 Harvesting

1973 (15 Oct). *Tenth Anniv of World Food Programme. P* 13.

358	**211**	20 p. multicoloured	50	40

212 Ankara and Kemal Atatürk

1973 (29 Oct). *50th Anniv of Turkish Republic. P* 13.

359	**212**	50 p. multicoloured	45	35

213 Boy Scout   214 "Basic Necessities"

1973 (11 Nov). *National Silver Jubilee Scout Jamboree. P* 13.

360	**213**	20 p. multicoloured	80	50

1973 (16 Nov). *25th Anniv of Declaration of Human Rights. P* 13.

361	**214**	20 p. multicoloured	30	30

215 Al-Biruni and Nandana Hill   216 Dr. Hansen, Microscope and Bacillus

1973 (26 Nov). *Al-Biruni Millennium Congress. P* 13.

362	**215**	20 p. multicoloured	40	20
363		1 r. 25, multicoloured	85	75

1973 (29 Dec). *Centenary of Hansen's Discovery of Leprosy Bacillus. P* 13.

364	**216**	20 p. multicoloured	75	50

217 Family and Emblem   218 Conference Emblem

1974 (1 Jan). *World Population Year. P* 13.

365	**217**	20 p. multicoloured	10	10
366		1 r. 25, multicoloured	30	40

1974 (22 Feb). *Islamic Summit Conference, Lahore. T 218 and similar design. P 14 × 12½ (20 p.) or 13 (65 p.).*
367	20 p. Type 218	..		10	10
368	65 p. Emblem on "Sun" (42 × 30 mm)	..		25	45
MS369	102 × 102 mm. Nos. 367/8. Imperf			2·50	5·00

219 Units of Weight and Measurement   **220** "Chand Chauthai" Carpet, Pakistan

1974 (1 July). *Adoption of International Weights and Measures System. P 13.*
370	219	20 p. multicoloured	.. ..	15	25

1974 (21 July). *Tenth Anniv of Regional Co-operation for Development. Vert designs as T 220 showing carpets from member countries. Multicoloured. P 13.*
371	20 p. Type 220	.. .:		15	15
372	60 p. Persian carpet, 16th-century			45	50
373	1 r. 25, Anatolian carpet, 15th-century			65	1·00
371/3	..	.. ..	*Set of 3*	1·10	1·50

221 Hands protecting Sapling   **222** Torch and Map

1974 (9 Aug). *Tree Planting Day. P 13.*
374	221	20 p. multicoloured	.. ..	50	40

1974 (26 Aug). *Namibia Day. P 13.*
375	222	60 p. multicoloured	.. ..	35	60

223 Highway Map

1974 (23 Sept). *Shahrah-e-Pakistan (Pakistan Highway). P 13.*
376	223	20 p. multicoloured	.. ..	55	50

224 Boy at Desk   **225** U.P.U. Emblem

1974 (7 Oct). *Universal Children's Day. P 13.*
377	224	20 p. multicoloured	.. ..	30	30

1974 (9 Oct). *Centenary of Universal Postal Union. T 225 and similar vert design. Multicoloured. P 13 × 13½ (20 p.) or 13 (2 r. 25).*
378	20 p. Type 225	..		20	20
379	2 r. 25, U.P.U. emblem, aeroplane and mail-wagon (30 × 41 mm)	.. ..		55	1·40
MS380	100 × 101 mm. Nos. 378/9. Imperf			4·00	8·50

226 Liaquat Ali Khan   **227** Dr. Mohammed Iqbal (poet and philosopher)

1974 (16 Oct). *Liaquat Ali Khan (First Prime Minister of Pakistan). P 13 × 13½.*
381	226	20 p. black and light vermilion	..	30	30

1974 (9 Nov). *Birth Centenary of Dr. Iqbal (1977) (1st issue). P 13.*
382	227	20 p. multicoloured	..	30	30

See also Nos. 399, 433 and 445/9.

228 Dr. Schweitzer and River Scene

1975 (14 Jan). *Birth Centenary of Dr. Albert Schweitzer. P 13.*
383	228	2 r. 25, multicoloured	..	2·00	2·25

229 Tourism Year Symbol

1975 (15 Jan). *South East Asia Tourism Year. P 13.*
384	229	2 r. 25, multicoloured	..	55	80

230 Assembly Hall, Flags and Prime Minister Bhutto

(Des A. Salahuddin)

1975 (22 Feb). *First Anniv of Islamic Summit Conference, Lahore. P 13.*
385	230	20 p. multicoloured	.. ..	35	25
386		1 r. multicoloured	.. ..	90	1·25

231 "Scientific Research"   **232** "Globe" and Algebraic Symbol

(Des A. Salahuddin (20 p.), M. Ahmed (2 r. 25))

1975 (15 June). *International Women's Year. T 231 and similar horiz design. Multicoloured. P 13.*
387	20 p. Type 231	..		20	25
388	2 r. 25, Girl teaching woman ("Adult Education")	.. ..		1·10	1·75

1975 (14 July). *International Congress of Mathematical Sciences, Karachi. P 13.*
389	232	20 p. multicoloured	.. ..	50	40

233 Pakistani Camel-skin Vase   **234** Sapling and Dead Trees

---

(Des I. Gilani)

1975 (21 July). *Eleventh Anniv of Regional Co-operation for Development. T 233 and similar multicoloured designs. P 13.*
390	20 p. Type 233	..		25	30
391	60 p. Iranian tile (horiz)	..		50	70
392	1 r. 25, Turkish porcelain vase	..		75	1·25
390/2	..		*Set of 3*	1·40	2·00

1975 (6 Aug). *Tree Planting Day. P 13 × 13½.*
393	234	20 p. multicoloured	.. ..	35	30

235 Black Partridge   **236** "Today's Girls"

(Des A. Salahuddin)

1975 (30 Sept). *Wildlife Protection (1st series). P 13.*
394	235	20 p. multicoloured	..	1·00	35
395		2 r. 25, multicoloured	..	3·75	3·50

See also Nos. 400/1, 411/12, 417/18, 493/6, 560, 572/3, 581/2, 599, 600, 605, 621/2, 691, 702, 780/3 and 853.

1975 (6 Oct). *Universal Children's Day. P 13.*
396	236	20 p. multicoloured	.. ..	30	30

237 Hazrat Amir Khusrau, Sitar and Tabla

(Des A. Salahuddin)

1975 (24 Oct). *700th Birth Anniv of Hazrat Amir Khusrau (poet and musician). P 13½ × 12½.*
397	237	20 p. multicoloured	.. ..	20	45
398		2 r. 25, multicoloured	.. ..	75	1·60

238 Dr. Mohammed Iqbal   **239** Urial (wild sheep)

(Des A. Salahuddin)

1975 (9 Nov). *Birth Centenary of Dr. Iqbal (1977) (2nd issue). P 13.*
399	238	20 p. multicoloured	.. ..	30	30

(Des M. Ahmed)

1975 (31 Dec). *Wildlife Protection (2nd series). P 13.*
400	239	20 p. multicoloured	..	40	30
401		3 r. multicoloured	..	2·50	3·00

240 Moenjodaro Remains   **241** Dome and Minaret of Rauza-e-Mubarak

(Des A. Salahuddin)

1976 (29 Feb). *"Save Moenjodaro" (1st series). T 240 and similar vert designs. Multicoloured. P 13.*
402	10 p. Type 240	..		65	75
	a. Horiz strip of 5. Nos. 402/6	..		3·25	
403	20 p. Remains (different)	..		75	85
404	65 p. The Citadel	..		75	85
405	3 r. Well inside a house	..		75	85
406	4 r. The "Great Bath"	..		85	95
402/6	..		*Set of 5*	3·25	3·75

Nos. 402/6 were printed horizontally se-tenant within the sheet, the five stamps forming a composite design of the excavations.
See also Nos. 414 and 430.

(Des A. Ghani. Photo)

1976 (3 Mar). *International Congress on Seerat.* P 13 × 13½.
407 241 20 p. multicoloured 20 20
408 3 r. multicoloured 70 90

242 Alexander Graham Bell and Telephone Dial

(Des M. M. Saeed. Photo)

1976 (10 Mar). *Telephone Centenary.* P 13.
409 242 3 r. multicoloured .. .. .. 1·25 2·00

243 College Arms within "Sun"

(Des A. Salahuddin)

1976 (15 Mar). *Centenary of National College of Arts, Lahore.* P 13.
410 243 20 p. multicoloured 30 40

244 Common Peafowl

(Des A. Salahuddin)

1976 (31 Mar). *Wildlife Protection (3rd series).* P 13.
411 244 20 p. multicoloured 75 35
412 3 r. multicoloured .. .. 3·25 4·00

245 Human Eye

(Des M. M. Saeed)

1976 (7 Apr). *Prevention of Blindness.* P 13.
413 245 20 p. multicoloured 40 40

247 Jefferson Memorial   **248** Ibex

(Des I. Gilani (90 p.), A. Salahuddin (4 r.))

1976 (4 July). *Bicentenary of American Revolution.* T **247** and similar horiz design. Multicoloured. P 13 (90 p.) or 13½ (4 r.).
415 90 p. Type **247** .. .. 1·00 60
416 4 r. "Declaration of Independence" (47 × 36 mm) .. .. .. 3·75 4·50

(Des M. Ahmed)

1976 (12 July). *Wildlife Protection (4th series).* P 13.
417 248 20 p. multicoloured 30 35
418 3 r. multicoloured .. .. 1·75 2·50

249 Mohammed Ali Jinnah

(Des A. Salahuddin)

1976 (21 July). *Twelfth Anniv of Regional Co-operation for Development.* T **249** *and similar diamond-shaped designs. Multicoloured.* P 14.
419 20 p. Type **249** 50 50
   a. Vert strip of 3. Nos. 419/21 .. 1·40
420 65 p. Reza Shah the Great (Iran) 50 50
421 90 p. Kemal Atatürk (Turkey) 50 50
419/21 *Set of 3* 1·40 1·40
Nos. 419/21 were printed vertically *se-tenant* throughout the sheet.

250 Urdu Text   **251** Mohammed Ali Jinnah and Wazir Mansion

1976 (14 Aug). *Birth Centenary of Mohammed Ali Jinnah (1st issue).* P 13. (a) Type **250**.
422 5 p. black, new blue and yellow 20 25
   a. Block of 8. Nos. 422/9 .. .. 1·75
423 10 p. black, yellow and magenta 20 25
424 15 p. black and violet-blue 20 25
425 1 r. black, yellow and new blue 30 30

(b) *Multicoloured designs as* T **251**, *different buildings in the background*
426 20 p. Type **251** 20 25
427 40 p. Sind Madressah 20 25
428 50 p. Minar Qarardad-e-Pakistan 20 25
429 3 r. Mausoleum 45 50
422/9 *Set of 8* 1·75 2·10
Nos. 422/9 were printed in *se-tenant* blocks of 8 throughout the sheet.
See also No. 436.

252 Dancing-girl, Ruins and King Priest

(Des A. Salahuddin)

1976 (31 Aug). *"Save Moenjodaro" (3rd series).* P 14.
430 252 65 p. multicoloured 35 45

253 U.N. Racial Discrimination Emblem

(Des A. Salahuddin)

1976 (15 Sept). *U.N. Decade to Combat Racial Discrimination.* P 12½ × 13½.
431 253 65 p. multicoloured 30 40

254 Child in Maze and Basic Services

(Des M. Ahmed)

1976 (4 Oct). *Universal Children's Day.* P 13.
432 254 20 p. multicoloured 20 30

Stamps commemorating the visit of King Khalid of Saudi Arabia and showing the Islamabad Mosque were prepared for release on 11 October 1976, but withdrawn before issue. Some are known to have been released in error.

255 Verse from "Allama Iqbal"   **256** Mohammed Ali Jinnah giving Scout Salute

(Des M. A. Javed)

1976 (9 Nov). *Birth Centenary of Dr. Iqbal (1977) (3rd issue).* P 13.
433 255 20 p. multicoloured 15 30

(Des I. Gilani)

1976 (20 Nov). *Quaid-i-Azam Centenary Jamboree.* P 13½.
434 256 20 p. multicoloured 45 30

257 Children Reading   **258** Mohammed Ali Jinnah

(Des M. Ahmed)

1976 (15 Dec). *Children's Literature.* P 13.
435 257 20 p. multicoloured 20 30

(Litho and embossed Cartor S.A., France)

1976 (25 Dec). *Birth Centenary of Mohammed Ali Jinnah (2nd issue).* P 12½.
436 258 10 r. emerald and gold .. .. 2·50 3·50

259 Rural Family   **260** Turkish Vase, 1800 B.C.

(Des M. Ahmed)

1977 (14 Apr). *Social Welfare and Rural Development Year.* P 13.
437 259 20 p. multicoloured 15 10

(Des A. Salahuddin)

1977 (21 July). *13th Anniv of Regional Co-operation for Development.* T **260** *and similar horiz designs.* P 13.
438 20 p. red-orange, violet-blue and black .. 25 10
439 65 p. multicoloured .. 35 15
440 90 p. multicoloured .. 45 30
438/40 *Set of 3* 95 45
Designs:—60 p. Pakistani toy bullock cart, Moenjodaro; 90 p. Pitcher with spout, Sialk Hill, Iran.

261 Forest   **262** Desert Scene

(Des A. Ahmed)

1977 (9 Aug). *National Tree Plantation Campaign.* P 13.
441 261 20 p. multicoloured 10 10

(Des M. A. Javed)

1977 (5 Sept). *U.N. Conference on Desertification, Nairobi.* P 13.
442 262 65 p. multicoloured 30 20

263 "Water for the Children of the World"   **264** Aga Khan III

(Des A. Salahuddin)

1977 (3 Oct). *Universal Children's Day.* P 13½ × 12½.
443 263 50 p. multicoloured 40 20

(Des A. Rauf)

1977 (2 Nov). *Birth Centenary of Aga Khan III.* P 13.
444 264 2 r. multicoloured 55 85

265 Iqbal and Spirit of the Poet Roomi (from painting by Behzad)   **266** The Holy "Khana-Kaaba" (House of God, Mecca)

(Des A. Ahmed)

1977 (9 Nov). *Birth Centenary of Dr. Mohammed Iqbal (4th issue).* T **265** *and similar vert designs. Multicoloured.* P 13.
445 20 p. Type **265** 25 35
   a. Horiz strip of 5. Nos. 445/9 .. 1·40
446 65 p. Iqbal looking at Jamaluddin Afghani and
   Saeed Haleem Pasha at prayer (Behzad) 25 35
447 1 r. 25, Urdu verse 30 40
448 2 r. 25, Persian verse.. .. 35 45
449 3 r. Iqbal 40 50
445/9 .. .. *Set of 5* 1·40 1·90
  Nos. 445, 448/9, 447 and 446 (in that order) were issued in horizontal *se-tenant* strips of 5.

(Des I. Gilani)

1977 (21 Nov). *Haj (pilgrimage to Mecca).* P 14.
450 266 65 p. multicoloured 30 30

267 Rheumatic Patient and Healthy Man   **268** Woman in Costume of Rawalpindi-Islamabad

(Des T. Hameed)

1977 (19 Dec). *World Rheumatism Year.* P 13.
451 267 65 p. turquoise-blue, black and yellow .. 30 20

(Des A. Salahuddin)

1978 (5 Feb). *Indonesia–Pakistan Economic and Cultural Co-operation Organization.* P 12½ × 13½.
452 268 75 p. multicoloured 30 20

269 Human Body and Sphygmomanometer   **270** Henri Dunant

(Des A. Salahuddin)

1978 (20 Apr). *World Hypertension Month.* P 13.
453 269 20 p. multicoloured 15 10
454 2 r. multicoloured 60 60
  The 2 r. value is as T **269**, but has the words "Down with high blood pressure" instead of the Urdu inscription at bottom left.

(Des A. Salahuddin)

1978 (8 May). *150th Birth Anniv of Henri Dunant (founder of Red Cross).* P 14.
455 270 1 r. black, new blue and vermilion .. 55 20

271 Red Roses (Pakistan)   **272** "Pakistan, World Cup Hockey Champions"

(Des A. Salahuddin)

1978 (21 July). *14th Anniv of Regional Co-operation for Development.* T **271** *and similar vert designs. Multicoloured.* P 13½.
456 20 p. Type **271** 35 20
   a. Horiz strip of 3. Nos. 456/8 .. 1·40
457 90 p. Pink roses (Iran).. .. 50 20
458 2 r. Yellow rose (Turkey) 75 25
456/8 .. .. .. *Set of 3* 1·40 60
  Nos. 456/8 were printed together, *se-tenant,* in horizontal strips of 3 throughout the sheet.

(Des M. Munawar)

1978 (26 Aug). *"Riccione '78" International Stamp Fair.* T **272** *and similar vert design. Multicoloured.* P 13.
459 1 r. Type **272** .. .. 1·00 25
460 2 r. Fountain at Plazza Turismo .. 1·25 35

273 Cogwheels within Globe Symbol   **274** St. Patrick's Cathedral

(Des A. Salahuddin)

1978 (3 Sept). *U.N. Technical Co-operation amongst Developing Countries Conference.* P 13.
461 273 75 p. multicoloured 15 10

(Des A. Salahuddin)

1978 (29 Sept). *Centenary of St. Patrick's Cathedral, Karachi.* T **274** *and similar vert design. Multicoloured.* P 13.
462 1 r. Type **274** 10 10
463 2 r. Stained glass window 25 25

275 Minar-i-Qarardad-e-Pakistan   **276** Tractor

276a Mausoleum of Ibrahim Khan Makli, Thatta

Two Dies of 75 p. value:

Die I   Die II

Die I. Size of design 26½ × 21½ mm. Figures of value large; "p" small. Plough does not touch left-hand frame.
Die II. Size of design 25½ × 21 mm. Smaller figures; larger "p". Plough touches left-hand frame.

(Des A. Salahuddin. Litho (10, 25, 40, 50, 90 p.), recess (others))

1978 (7 Nov)–81. *No wmk (2 to 90 p.) or W 98 (1 to 5 r.).* P 14×13½ (2 to 5 p.), 13½×14 (10 to 90 p.) or 13 (1 to 5 r.).
464 275 2 p. deep grey-green 10 10
465 3 p. black 10 10
   a. Imperf (pair) .. .. 5·00
466 5 p. deep ultramarine 10 10
467 276 10 p. new blue & greenish bl (7.10.79) .. 10 10
468 20 p. deep yellow-green (25.3.79) .. 50 10
469 25 p. dp green & dull magenta (19.3.79) 60 10
470 40 p. new blue and magenta (16.12.78) 60 10
471 50 p. slate-lilac & turq-green (19.3.79) .. 30 10
472 60 p. black (16.12.78) 10 10
   a. Imperf (pair) .. .. 5·00
473 75 p. dull vermilion (I) (16.12.78) .. 60 10
   a. Imperf (pair) .. .. 16·00
   b. Die II (1980) 55 10
   ba. Imperf (pair) .. .. 7·00
474 90 p. magenta and new blue (16.12.78) 20 10
475 276a 1 r. bronze-green (2.8.80) .. 10 10
   a. Imperf (pair) .. .. 20·00
476 1 r. 50, red-orange (17.11.79) .. 10 10
   a. Imperf (pair) .. .. 6·00
477 2 r. carmine-red (17.11.79) .. 15 10
   a. Imperf (pair) .. .. 7·00
478 3 r. blue-black (4.6.80) .. 20 10
   a. Imperf (pair) .. .. 9·00
479 4 r. black (1.1.81) .. 30 10
   a. Imperf (pair) .. .. 9·00
480 5 r. sepia (1.1.81) .. 30 10
   a. Imperf (pair) .. .. 9·00
464/80 .. .. *Set of 17* 3·25 75
  The remaining values as Type **276** printed in recess, are from Die II.
  Postal forgeries exist of the 2 r. and 3 r. values. These are poorly printed with perforations which do not match those of the genuine stamps.

GUM. Later printings of the 10 p., 20 p., 25 p., 4 r. and 5 r. values (Nos. 467/9 and 479/80) occur with matt, almost invisible gum of a PVA type, instead of the gum arabic used previously.

277 Emblem and "United Races" Symbol   **278** Maulana Mohammad Ali Jauhar

(Des M. Munawar)

1978 (20 Nov). *International Anti-Apartheid Year.* P 13.
481 277 1 r. multicoloured 15 15

(Des A. Salahuddin)

1978 (10 Dec). *Birth Centenary of Maulana Mohammad Ali Jauhar (patriot).* P 13.
482 278 50 p. multicoloured 40 20

279 "Tornado", "Rapide" and Wright *Flyer*

(Des A. Salahuddin)

1978 (24 Dec). *75th Anniv of Powered Flight. T 279 and similar diamond-shaped designs. Multicoloured. P 13.*
483 65 p. Type 279 .. .. 75 85
  a. Block of 4. Nos. 483/6 .. .. 3·75
484 1 r. "Phantom F4F", "Tri-star" and Wright
    Flyer .. .. 90 1·00
485 2 r. "X15", Tu. "104" and Wright *Flyer* 1·10 1·25
486 2 r. 25, Mig "15", "Concorde" and Wright
    Flyer .. .. 1·50 1·75
483/6 .. .. *Set of* 4 3·75 4·25
  Nos. 483/6 were printed together, *se-tenant*, in blocks of 4 throughout the sheet.

280 "Holy Koran illumina-   **281** "Aspects of A.P.W.A."
ting Globe" and Raudha-e-
Mubarak (mausoleum)

(Des A. Salahuddin)

1979 (10 Feb). *"12th Rabi-ul-Awwal" (Prophet Mohammed's birthday). P 13.*
487 280 20 p. multicoloured 30 15

(Des M. Saeed)

1979 (25 Feb). *30th Anniv of A.P.W.A. (All Pakistan Women's Association). P 13.*
488 281 50 p. multicoloured 40 15

282 Tippu Sultan Shaheed of Mysore

(Des A. Rauf)

1979 (23 Mar). *Pioneers of Freedom (1st series). T 282 and similar diamond-shaped designs. Multicoloured. W 98. P 14.*
490 10 r. Type 282 .. .. .. 50 55
  a. Horiz strip of 3. Nos. 490/2 .. 2·25
491 15 r. Sir Syed Ahmad Khan 75 80
492 25 r. Altaf Hussain Hali .. .. 1·25 1·40
490/2 .. .. *Set of* 3 2·25 2·40
  Nos. 490/2 were printed together *se-tenant* in the same sheet: there being ten horizontal strips of 3 values and ten additional 10 r. stamps.
  See also Nos. 757, 801/27, 838/46 and 867/9.

283 Himalayan Monal Pheasant

(Des M. Ahmed)

1979 (17 June). *Wildlife Protection (5th series). Pheasants. T 283 and similar horiz designs. Multicoloured. P 13.*
493 20 p. Type 283 .. .. .. 95 50
494 25 p. Kalij 95 55
495 40 p. Koklass .. .. .. 1·25 1·00
496 1 r. Cheer .. .. 2·25 1·75
493/6 .. .. *Set of* 4 4·75 3·50

284 "Pakistan Village Scene" (Ustad Bakhsh)

(Des A. Rauf)

1979 (21 July). *15th Anniv of Regional Co-operation for Development. T 284 and similar horiz designs. Multicoloured. P 14 × 12½.*
497 40 p. Type 284 .. .. .. 20 25
  a. Vert strip of 3. Nos. 497/9 .. 60
498 75 p. "Iranian Goldsmith" (Kamal al Molk) .. 20 25
499 1 r. 60, "Turkish Harvest" (Namik Ismail) .. 25 30
497/9 .. .. *Set of* 3 60 70
  Nos. 497/9 were printed together, *se-tenant*, in vertical strips of 3 throughout the sheet.

285 Guj Embroidered Shirt (detail)

1979 (23 Aug). *Handicrafts (1st series). T 285 and similar horiz designs. Multicoloured. P 14 × 12½.*
500 40 p. Type 285 .. .. .. 20 20
  a. Block of 4. Nos. 500/3 .. 1·00
501 1 r. Enamel inlaid brass plate .. 25 25
502 1 r. 50, Baskets 30 30
503 2 r. Chain-stitch embroidered rug (detail) .. 40 40
500/3 .. .. *Set of* 4 1·00 1·00
  Nos. 500/3 were printed together, *se-tenant*, in blocks of 4 throughout the sheet.
  See also Nos. 578/9, 595/6 and 625/8.

286 Children playing on Climbing Frame

(Des A. Rauf)

1979 (10 Sept). *S.O.S. Children's Village, Lahore (orphanage). P 13.*
504 286 50 p. multicoloured 30 30

287 "Island" (Z. Maloof)

(Des A. Salahuddin)

1979 (22 Oct). *International Year of the Child. Children's Paintings. T 287 and similar horiz designs. Multicoloured. P 14 × 12½.*
505 40 p. Type 287 .. .. .. 15 15
  a. Block of 4. Nos. 505/8 .. 85
506 75 p. "Playground" (R. Akbar) .. 25 25
507 1 r. "Fairground" (M. Azam) .. 25 25
508 1 r. 50, "Hockey Match" (M. Tayyab) .. 30 30
505/8 .. .. *Set of* 4 85 85
MS509 79 × 64 mm. 2 r. "Child looking at Faces in
  the Sky" (M. Mumtaz) (*vert*). Imperf .. 2·75 3·25
  Nos. 505/8 were printed together, *se-tenant*, in blocks of 4 throughout the sheet.
  Examples of No. **MS**509 are known overprinted in gold for the "PHILEXFRANCE" International Stamp Exhibition in 1982. The Pakistan Post Office has declared such overprints to be bogus.

288 Warrior attacking Crab   **289** Pakistan Customs
                                         Emblem

(Des A. Salahuddin)

1979 (12 Nov). *Fight Against Cancer. P 14.*
510 288 40 p. black, greenish yellow and magenta 50 30

(Des A. Salahuddin)

1979 (10 Dec). *Centenary of Pakistan Customs Service. P 13 × 13½.*
511 289 1 r. multicoloured 30 30

---

290 Boeing "747 (Jumbo)" and   **291** Islamic Pattern
Douglas "DC-3" Airliners

(Des A. Salahuddin)

1980 (10 Jan). *25th Anniv of Pakistan International Air Lines. P 13.*
512 290 1 r. multicoloured 65 65

(Des and litho Secura, Singapore)

1980 (15 Jan–10 Mar). *Matt, almost invisible PVA gum. P 12.*
513 291 10 p. slate-green and orange-yellow 10 10
514 15 p. slate-green and bright yellow-green 10 10
515 25 p. violet and brown-red (10.3) 10 20
516 35 p. carmine & brt yellow-green (10.3) .. 10 20
517 — 40 p. rosine and olive-sepia .. 15 10
518 — 50 p. violet and dull yellow-green (10.3) 10 20
519 — 80 p. brt yellow-green & black (10.3) 15 30
513/19 .. .. *Set of* 7 70 1·00
  The 40 to 80 p. values also show different Islamic patterns, the 40 p. being horizontal and the remainder vertical.

292 Young Child   **293** Conference Emblem

(Des M. Saeed)

1980 (16 Feb). *5th Asian Congress of Paediatric Surgery, Karachi. P 13.*
530 292 50 p. multicoloured 50 50

(Des A. Salahuddin)

1980 (17 May). *11th Islamic Conference of Foreign Ministers, Islamabad. P 13.*
531 293 1 r. multicoloured 40 45

294 Karachi Port

(Des A. Salahuddin)

1980 (15 July). *Centenary of Karachi Port Authority. P 13 × 13½.*
532 294 1 r. multicoloured 70 70

RICCIONE 80
(295)   **296** College Emblem with
              Old and New Buildings

1980 (30 Aug). *"Riccione 80" International Stamp Exhibition. Nos. 505/8 optd with T 295 in red.*
533 40 p. Type 287 .. .. .. 25 25
534 75 p. "Playground" (R. Akbar) .. 30 30
535 1 r. "Fairground" (M. Azam) .. 35 35
536 1 r. 50, "Hockey Match" (M. Tayyab) .. 45 45
533/6 .. .. *Set of* 4 1·25 1·25

(Des M. Munawar)

1980 (18 Sept). *75th Anniv of Command and Staff College, Quetta. P 13.*
537 296 1 r. multicoloured 10 15

WORLD TOURISM CONFERENCE
MANILA 80
(297)

1980 (27 Sept). *World Tourism Conference, Manila. No. 496 optd with T 297.*
538 1 r. Cheer 30 15

298 Birth Centenary Emblem

(Des A. Salahuddin)

1980 (5 Oct). *Birth Centenary of Hafiz Mahmood Shairani. P* 13.
539 298 40 p. multicoloured 30 50

299 Shalimar Gardens, Lahore

(Des A. Salahuddin)

1980 (23 Oct). *Aga Khan Award for Architecture. P* 13.
540 299 2 r. multicoloured 30 60

300 Rising Sun   301 Money Order Form

(Des S. Ahmed (40 p.), J. Sultana (2 r.), A. Salahuddin (others))

1980 (10 Nov). *1400th Anniv of Hegira (1st issue). T* **300** *and similar multicoloured designs. P* 14 (2 r.) *or* 13 *(others)*.
541 40 p. Type **300** 10 10
542 2 r. Ka'aba and symbols of Moslem achieve-
       ment (34 × 34 *mm*) 25 40
543 3 r. Holy Koran illuminating World (31 × 54
       mm) 30 60
541/3 .. .. .. *Set of* 3 55 95
MS544 106 × 84 mm. 4 r. Candles. Imperf 45 1·00
  See also No. 549.

(Des A. Ahmed)

1980 (20 Dec). *Centenary of Money Order Service. P* 13.
545 301 40 p. multicoloured 15 40

302 Postcards   303 Heinrich von Stephan
encircling Globe   and U.P.U. Emblem

(Des A. Ahmed)

1980 (27 Dec). *Centenary of Postcard Service. P* 13.
546 302 40 p. multicoloured 15 40

(Des J. Sultana)

1981 (7 Jan). *150th Birth Anniv of Heinrich von Stephan (founder of U.P.U.). P* 13.
547 303 1 r. multicoloured 20 15

304 Aircraft and Airmail Letters

(Des J. Sultana)

1981 (15 Feb). *50th Anniv of Airmail Service. P* 13.
548 304 1 r. multicoloured 20 15

305 Mecca   306 Conference Emblem and
                           Afghan Refugees

1981 (7 Mar). *1400th Anniv of Hegira (2nd issue). P* 13.
549 305 40 p. multicoloured 15 40

(Des Z. Akhlaq (Nos. 550 and 552), A. Ahmed (Nos. 551 and 553),
M. Jafree (No. 554))

1981 (29 Mar). *Islamic Summit Conference (1st issue). T* **306** *and similar multicoloured designs. P* 13.
550 40 p. Type **306** 25 10
551 40 p. Conference emblem encircled by flags and
       Afghan refugees (28 × 58 *mm*) .. 25 10
552 1 r. Type **306** 40 10
553 1 r. As No. 551 .. .. .. 40 10
554 2 r. Conference emblem and map showing
       Afghanistan (48 × 32 *mm*) .. 55 50
550/4 .. .. .. *Set of* 5 1·75 75

307 Conference Emblem   308 Kemal Atatürk

(Des A. Salahuddin (Nos. 555, 557), A. Irani (Nos. 556, 558))

1981 (20 Apr). *Islamic Summit Conference (2nd issue). T* **307** *and similar multicoloured design. P* 13.
555 40 p. Type **307** 10 10
556 40 p. Conference emblem and flags (28 × 46
       mm) 10 10
557 85 p. Type **307** 20 15
558 85 p. As No. 556 .. .. .. 20 15
555/8 .. .. .. *Set of* 4 55 30

(Des A. Salahuddin)

1981 (19 May). *Birth Centenary of Kemal Atatürk (Turkish statesman). P* 13.
559 308 1 r. multicoloured 20 15

309 Green Turtle   310 Dome of the Rock

(Des Jamal. Litho Secura, Singapore)

1981 (20 June). *Wildlife Protection (6th series). Matt, almost invisible PVA gum. P* 12 × 11½.
560 309 40 p. multicoloured 65 20

(Des A. Salahuddin)

1981 (25 July). *Palestinian Welfare. P* 13.
561 310 2 r. multicoloured 35 35

311 Malubiting West

(Litho Secura, Singapore)

1981 (20 Aug). *Mountain Peaks (1st series). Karakoram Range. T* **311** *and similar multicoloured designs. Matt, almost invisible PVA gum. P* 14 × 13½.
562 40 p. Type **311** 40 40
       a. Horiz pair. Nos. 562/3 .. .. 80 80
563 40 p. Malubiting West (24 × 31 *mm*) .. 40 40
564 1 r. Haramosh 75 75
       a. Horiz pair. Nos. 564/5 .. 1·50 1·50
565 1 r. Haramosh (24 × 31 *mm*) .. 75 75
566 1 r. 50, K6 .. .. .. 90 90
       a. Horiz pair. Nos. 566/7 .. 1·75 1·75
567 1 r. 50, K6 (24 × 31 *mm*) .. 90 90
568 2 r. K2, Broad Peak, Gasherbrum 4 and
       Gasherbrum 2 .. .. 1·00 1·25
       a. Horiz pair. Nos. 568/9 .. 2·00 2·50
569 2 r. K2 (24 × 31 *mm*) .. 1·00 1·25
562/9 .. .. .. *Set of* 8 5·50 6·00
  The two designs of each value were printed together, se-tenant,
in horizontal pairs throughout the sheet.
  See also Nos. 674/5.

312 Pakistan Steel   313 Western Tragopan
"Furnace No. 1"

(Des A. Ahmed)

1981 (31 Aug). *First Firing of Pakistan Steel "Furnace No. 1", Karachi. P* 13.
570 312 40 p. multicoloured 20 10
571   2 r. multicoloured 40 30

(Litho Secura, Singapore)

1981 (15 Sept). *Wildlife Protection (7th series). Matt, almost invisible PVA gum. P* 14.
572 313 40 p. multicoloured .. .. 1·25 75
573   2 r. multicoloured .. .. 3·25 3·50
  The 2 r. value is as Type **313** but the background design shows a
winter view.

314 Disabled People and   315 World Hockey Cup below
I.Y.D.P. Emblem   flags of participating Countries

(Des M. Saeed)

1981 (12 Dec). *International Year for Disabled Persons. P* 13.
574 314 40 p. multicoloured 30 30
575   2 r. multicoloured .. .. 95 1·25

(Des A. Salahuddin)

1982 (31 Jan). *Pakistan—World Cup Hockey Champions. T* **315** *and similar vert design. Multicoloured. P* 13.
576 1 r. Type **315** .. .. .. 1·75 1·25
577 1 r. World Hockey Cup above flags of partici-
       pating countries .. .. 1·75 1·25

316 Camel Skin Lamp   317 Chest X-Ray of Infected
                           Person

(Des A. Salahuddin. Litho Secura, Singapore)

1982 (20 Feb). *Handicrafts (2nd series). T* **316** *and similar vert design. Multicoloured. P* 14.
578 1 r. Type **316** 40 40
579 1 r. Hala pottery 40 40
  See also Nos. 595/6.

(Des A. Ahmed)

1982 (24 Mar). *Centenary of Robert Koch's Discovery of Tubercle Bacillus.* P 13.
580   317   1 r. multicoloured   85   70

318 Indus Dolphin

(Des A. Salahuddin. Litho Secura, Singapore)

1982 (24 Apr). *Wildlife Protection* (8th series). P 12 × 11½.
581   318   40 p. multicoloured   ..   ..   1·50   1·00
582   —   1 r. multicoloured   ..   ..   2·75   2·25
The 1 r. value is as Type **318** but the design is reversed.

319 "Apollo–Soyuz" Link-up, 1975

(Des A. Salahuddin)

1982 (7 June). *Peaceful Uses of Outer Space.* P 13.
583   319   1 r. multicoloured   ..   ..   1·40   65

320 Sukkur Barrage

(Des A. Salahuddin)

1982 (17 July). *50th Anniv of Sukkur Barrage.* P 13.
584   320   1 r. multicoloured   30   20

321 Pakistan National Flag
and Stylised Sun

(322)

RICCIONE – 82 -

(Des A. Ahmed)

1982 (14 Aug). *Independence Day.* T **321** and similar vert design. Multicoloured. P 13.
585   40 p. Type **321**   10   30
586   85 p. Map of Pakistan and stylised torch   20   50

1982 (28 Aug). *"Riccione 82" International Stamp Exhibition. No. 584 optd with T* **322**.
587   320   1 r. multicoloured   15   15

323 Arabic Inscription and University Emblem

(Des Syed Tanwir Rizvi)

1982 (14 Oct). *Centenary of the Punjab University.* P 13½ × 13.
588   323   40 p. multicoloured   15   15

324 Scout Emblem and Tents   **325** Laying Pipeline

(Des M. Saeed)

1982 (23 Dec). *75th Anniv of Boy Scout Movement.* P 13.
589   324   2 r. multicoloured   30   30

(Des A. Salahuddin)

1983 (6 Jan). *Inauguration of Quetta Natural Gas Pipeline Project.* P 13.
590   325   1 r. multicoloured   15   20

326 Papilio polyctor

(Litho Secura, Singapore)

1983 (15 Feb). *Butterflies.* T **326** and similar horiz designs. Multicoloured. Matt, almost invisible PVA gum. P 13½.
591   40 p. Type **326**   90   20
592   50 p. Atrophaneura aristolochiae   ..   90   20
593   60 p. Danaus chrysippus   ..   ..   1·00   40
594   1 r. 50, Papilio demoleus   ..   ..   1·75   1·00
591/4   Set of 4   4·00   1·60

(Litho Secura, Singapore)

1983 (9 Mar). *Handicrafts* (3rd series). *Vert designs as T* **316**. Multicoloured. Matt, almost invisible PVA gum. P 14.
595   1 r. Five flower motif needlework, Sind   ..   15   15
596   1 r. Straw mats   15   15

327 School of Nursing and University Emblem

(Des A. Salahuddin)

1983 (16 Mar). *Presentation of Charter to Aga Khan University, Karachi.* P 13½ × 13.
597   327   2 r. multicoloured   30   30
No. 597 was issued in sheets of 8 (2 × 4), each horizontal pair being separated by a different *se-tenant* label showing views of the University.

328 Yak Caravan crossing
Zindiharam-Darkot Pass, Hindu Kush

(Des A. Salahuddin)

1983 (28 Apr). *Trekking in Pakistan.* P 13.
598   328   1 r. multicoloured   50   30

329 Marsh Crocodile

(Litho Secura, Singapore)

1983 (19 May). *Wildlife Protection* (9th series). *Matt, almost invisible PVA gum.* P 13½.
599   329   3 r. multicoloured   ..   ..   2·50   1·50

330 Goitred Gazelle   **331** Floral Design

(Litho Secura, Singapore)

1983 (20 June). *Wildlife Protection* (10th series). *Matt, almost invisible PVA gum.* P 14 × 13½.
600   330   1 r. multicoloured   ..   ..   1·75   1·25

(Des A. Ahmed)

1983 (14 Aug). *36th Anniv of Independence.* T **331** and similar vert design. Multicoloured. P 13.
601   60 p. Type **331**   10   10
602   4 r. Hand holding flaming torch   ..   40   45

332 Traditional Weaving, Pakistan

(Des A. Salahuddin)

1983 (19 Aug). *Indonesian–Pakistan Economic and Cultural Co-operation Organization, 1969–1983.* T **332** and similar horiz design. Multicoloured. P 13.
603   2 r. Type **332**   20   25
604   2 r. Traditional weaving, Indonesia   20   25

333 "Siberian Cranes" (Great White Cranes) (Sir Peter Scott)

1983 (8 Sept). *Wildlife Protection* (11th series). P 13.
605   333   3 r. multicoloured   ..   ..   2·25   1·25

334 W.C.Y. Emblem

1983 (9 Oct). *World Communications Year.* T **334** and similar multicoloured design. P 13 (2 r.) or 14 (3 r.).
606   2 r. Type **334**   20   25
607   3 r. W.C.Y. emblem (different) (33 × 33 mm)   30   35

335 Farm Animals   **336** Agricultural Produce
and Fertiliser Factory

(Des A. Salahuddin)

1983 (24 Oct). *World Food Day.* T **335** and similar horiz designs. Multicoloured. P 13.
608   3 r. Type **335** ..   ..   ..   1·25   1·25
   a. Horiz strip of 4. Nos. 608/11   ..   4·50
609   3 r. Fruit   ..   ..   ..   1·25   1·25
610   3 r. Crops   ..   ..   ..   1·25   1·25
611   3 r. Sea food   ..   ..   1·25   1·25
608/11   Set of 4   4·50   4·50
Nos. 608/11 were printed together, *se-tenant*, in horizontal strips of four throughout the sheet.

(Des J. Sultana)

1983 (24 Oct). *National Fertiliser Corporation.* P 13 × 13½.
612   336   60 p. multicoloured   15   30

337 Lahore, 1852   **338** Winner of
"Enterprise" Event

(Des A. Salahuddin)

1983 (13 Nov). *National Stamp Exhibition, Lahore. T 337 and similar vert designs showing panoramic view of Lahore in 1852. Multicoloured. P 13 × 13½.*

613	60 p. Musti Durwaza Dharmsala	25	25
	a. Horiz strip of 6. Nos. 613/18	1·40	
614	60 p. Khabgha	25	25
615	60 p. Type 337	25	25
616	60 p. Summan Burj Hazuri	25	25
617	60 p. Flower Garden, Samadhi Northern Gate	25	25
618	60 p. Budda Darya, Badshahi Masjid	25	25
613/18	*Set of 6*	1·40	1·40

Nos. 613/18 were printed together, *se-tenant* in sheets of twelve, containing two horizontal strips of six.

(Des J. Sultana)

1983 (31 Dec). *Yachting Champions, Asian Games, Delhi. T 338 and similar vert design. Multicoloured. P 13.*

619	60 p. Type 338	1·00	75
620	60 p. Winner of "OK" Dinghy event	1·00	75

339 Snow Leopard

(Litho Secura, Singapore)

1984 (21 Jan). *Wildlife Protection (12th series). Matt, almost invisible PVA gum. P 14.*

621	339	40 p. multicoloured	1·50	75
622		1 r. 60, multicoloured	3·25	4·00

340 Jahangir Khan (World Squash Champion)   **341** P.I.A. Airliner

1984 (17 Mar). *Squash. P 13.*

623	340	3 r. multicoloured	1·25	90

(Des A. Salahuddin)

1984 (29 Apr). *20th Anniv of Pakistan International Airways' Service to China. P 13.*

624	341	3 r. multicoloured	3·25	3·25

342 Glass-work   **343** Attock Fort

(Des A. Salahuddin. Litho Secura, Singapore)

1984 (31 May). *Handicrafts (4th series). T 342 and similar designs showing glass-work in Sheesh Mahal, Lahore Fort. P 13½.*

625	1 r. multicoloured (blue frame)	10	15
626	1 r. multicoloured (red frame)	10	15
627	1 r. multicoloured (green frame) (horiz)	10	15
628	1 r. multicoloured (violet frame) (horiz)	10	15
625/8	*Set of 4*	35	55

(Des J. Sultana)

1984 (16 June)–**86**. *Forts. T 343 and similar horiz designs. P 11.*

629	5 p. brownish black & brown-pur (1.11.84)	10	10
630	10 p. brownish black and rose-red (25.9.84)	10	10
631	15 p. reddish violet & bistre-brown (1.12.86)	10	10
632	20 p. black and bright reddish violet	10	10
	a. Black ptd double		
633	50 p. sepia and Venetian red (10.4.86)	10	10
634	60 p. blackish brown and light brown	10	10
635	70 p. greenish blue (3.8.86)	10	10
636	80 p. bistre-brown and dull scarlet (1.7.86)	10	10
629/36	*Set of 8*	40	40

Design:—5 p. Kot Diji Fort; 10 p. Rohtas Fort; 15 p. Bala Hisar Fort; 50 p. Hyderabad Fort; 60 p. Lahore Fort; 70 p. Sibi Fort; 80 p. Ranikot Fort.

No. 632a appears to have received two distinct impressions of the black plate rather than an offset from the litho "blanket".

---

344 Shah Rukn i Alam's Tomb, Multan

1984 (26 June). *Aga Khan Award for Architecture. P 13.*

647	344	60 p. multicoloured	85	85

345 Radio Mast and Map of World

1984 (1 July). *20th Anniv of Asia–Pacific Broadcasting Union. P 13.*

648	345	3 r. multicoloured	80	60

346 Wrestling

(Des A. Salahuddin)

1984 (31 July). *Olympic Games, Los Angeles. T 346 and similar horiz designs. Multicoloured. P 13.*

649	3 r. Type 346	95	55
650	3 r. Boxing	95	55
651	3 r. Athletics	95	55
652	3 r. Hockey	95	55
653	3 r. Yachting	95	55
649/53	*Set of 5*	4·25	2·50

347 Jasmine (National flower) and Inscription   **348** Gearwheel Emblem and Flags of Participating Nations

(Des M. Munawar)

1984 (14 Aug). *Independence Day. T 347 and similar horiz design. Multicoloured. P 13.*

654	60 p. Type 347	10	10
655	4 r. Symbolic torch	45	50

(Des A. Zafar)

1984 (1 Sept). *Pakistan International Trade Fair. P 13.*

656	348	60 p. multicoloured	40	30

349 Interior of Main Dome

1984 (5 Nov). *Tourism Convention. Shahjahan Mosque, Thatta. T 349 and similar horiz designs. Multicoloured. P 13½.*

657	1 r. Type 349	30	30
	a. Horiz strip of 5. Nos. 657/61	1·40	
658	1 r. Brick and glazed tile work	30	30
659	1 r. Gateway	30	30
660	1 r. Symmetrical archways	30	30
661	1 r. Interior of a dome	30	30
657/61	*Set of 5*	1·40	1·40

Nos. 657/61 were printed together, *se-tenant*, in horizontal strips of 5 throughout the sheet

---

350 Bank Emblem in Floral Pattern

(Des A. Zafar)

1984 (7 Nov). *25th Anniv of United Bank Ltd. P 13½.*

662	350	60 p. multicoloured	50	50

351 Conference Emblem   **352** Postal Life Insurance Emblem within Hands

(Des A. Salahuddin)

1984 (24 Dec). *20th United Nations Conference on Trade and Development. P 14.*

663	351	60 p. multicoloured	50	30

(Des A. Zafar and J. Sultana)

1984 (29 Dec). *Centenary of Postal Life Insurance. T 352 and similar vert design. Multicoloured. P 13½.*

664	60 p. Type 352	35	15
665	1 r. "100" and Postal Life Insurance emblem	45	15

353 Bull (Wall painting)   **354** International Youth Year Emblem and "75"

(Des A. Salahuddin and M. Munawar)

1984 (31 Dec). *U.N.E.S.C.O. Save Moenjadoro Campaign. T 353 and similar vert design. Multicoloured. P 13½.*

666	2 r. Type 353	90	90
	a. Horiz pair. Nos. 666/7	1·75	1·75
667	2 r. Bull (seal)	90	90

Nos. 666/7 were printed together, *se-tenant*, in horizontal pairs throughout the sheet.

(Des A. Salahuddin)

1985 (6 Jan). *75th Anniv of Girl Guide Movement. P 13½.*

668	354	60 p. multicoloured	1·25	40

355 Smelting Ore   **356** Map of Pakistan and Rays of Sun

1985 (15 Jan). *Inauguration of Pakistan Steel Corporation. T 355 and similar multicoloured design. P 13.*

669	60 p. Type 355	45	20
670	1 r. Pouring molten steel from ladle (28 × 46 mm)	55	20

(Des A. Salahuddin)

1985 (20 Mar). *Presidential Referendum of 19 December 1984. P 13.*

671	356	60 p. multicoloured	50	30

357 Ballot Box and
Voting Paper

(Des A. Salahuddin (No. 672), Sultana Shamim Haider
(No. 673))

1985 (23 Mar). *March Elections. T* **357** *and similar multicoloured design. P* 13.
672   1 r. Type **357**   40   15
673   1 r. Minar-e-Qarardad-e-Pakistan   Tower,
    and word "Democracy" (31×43 *mm*) ..   40   15

(Des and litho Secura, Singapore)

1985 (27 May). *Mountain Peaks (2nd series). Horiz designs as
T* **311.** *Multicoloured. Matt, almost invisible PVA gum.
P* 14×13½.
674   40 p. Rakaposhi (Karakoram Range)   ..   1·00   50
675   2 r. Nangaparbat (Western Himalayas) ..   2·25   2·50

358 Trophy and Medals from
Olympic Games 1984, Asia Cup
1985 and World Cup 1982

(Des A. Salahuddin)

1985 (5 July). *Pakistan Hockey Team "Grand Slam" Success.
P* 13.
676   **358**   1 r. multicoloured   ..   ..   ..   1·40   95

359 King Edward Medical College

(Des Sultana Shamim Haider)

1985 (28 July). *125th Anniv of King Edward Medical College,
Lahore. P* 13.
677   **359**   3 r. multicoloured   90   55

360 Illuminated Inscription
in Urdu

(Des A. Salahuddin)

1985 (14 Aug). *Independence Day. T* **360** *and similar horiz
design. Multicoloured. P* 13.
678   60 p. Type **360**   15   15
    a. Sheetlet. Nos. 678/9×2   ..   55
679   60 p. Illuminated   "XXXVIII" (inscr   in
    English)   15   15
  Nos. 678/9 were issued *se-tenant*, both horizontally and
vertically, in sheetlets of four stamps and four stamp-size labels
inscribed in Urdu.

361 Sind Madressah-tul-Islam, Karachi

(Des A. Salahuddin)

1985 (1 Sept). *Centenary of Sind Madressah-tul-Islam (theological college), Karachi. P* 13.
680   **361**   2 r. multicoloured   90   55

362 Jamia Masjid Mosque by Day

(Des A. Salahuddin)

1985 (14 Sept). *Inauguration of New Jamia Masjid Mosque,
Karachi. T* **362** *and similar horiz design. Multicoloured. P* 13.
681   1 r. Type **362**   65   35
682   1 r. Jamia Masjid illuminated at night   ..   65   35

363 Lawrence College, Murree

(Des A. Salahuddin)

1985 (21 Sept). *125th Anniv of Lawrence College, Murree. P* 13.
683   **363**   3 r. multicoloured   ..   ..   1·00   55

364 United Nations Building, New York

(Des A. Salahuddin)

1985 (24 Oct). *40th Anniv of United Nations Organization.
T* **364** *and similar diamond-shaped design. Multicoloured.
P* 14.
684   1 r. Type **364**   15   15
685   2 r. U.N. Building and emblem   25   25

365 Tents and Jamboree Emblem

(Des A. Salahuddin)

1985 (8 Nov). *10th National Scout Jamboree. P* 13.
686   **365**   60 p. multicoloured   ..   ..   1·25   90

366 Islamabad   **367** Map of S.A.A.R.C.
Countries and National
Flags

(Des H. Durrani)

1985 (30 Nov). *25th Anniv of Islamabad. P* 14½×14.
687   **366**   3 r. multicoloured   75   45

(Des A. Salahuddin)

1985 (8 Dec). *1st Summit Meeting of South Asian Association
for Regional Cooperation, Dhaka, Bangladesh. T* **367** *and
similar multicoloured design. P* 13½×13 (1 r.) or 13 (2 r.).
688   1 r. Type **367** ..   ..   ..   1·50   2·75
689   2 r. National flags (39×39 *mm*)   ..   1·00   1·00
  No. 688 is reported to have been withdrawn on 9 December
1985.

368 Globe and Peace Dove   **369** Peregrine Falcon

(Des A. Salahuddin)

1985 (14 Dec). *25th Anniv of U.N. General Assembly's Declaration on Independence for Colonial Territories. P* 13.
690   **368**   60 p. multicoloured   50   40

(Des and litho Secura, Singapore)

1986 (20 Jan). *Wildlife Protection (13th series). Peregrine
Falcon. Matt, almost invisible PVA gum. P* 13½.
691   **369**   1 r. 50, multicoloured ..   ..   2·50   2·25

370 A.D.B.P. Building,
Islamabad

(Des A. Salahuddin)

1986 (18 Feb). *25th Anniv of Agricultural Development Bank of
Pakistan. P* 13.
692   **370**   60 p. multicoloured   60   40

371 Government S.E. College   **372** Emblem and
Bar Graph

(Des Sultana Shamim Haider)

1986 (25 Apr). *Centenary of Government Sadiq Egerton College, Bahawalpur. P* 13.
693   **371**   1 r. multicoloured   70   30

(Des Sultana Shamim Haider)

1986 (11 May). *25th Anniv of Asian Productivity Organization.
P* 13½.
694   **372**   1 r. multicoloured   45   30

373 "1947 1986"   **374** Open Air Class

(Des A. Salahuddin (80 p.), M. Munawar (1 r.))

1986 (14 Aug). *39th Anniv of Independence. T* **373** *and similar
vert design. Multicoloured. P* 14.
695   80 p. Type **373**   15   15
696   1 r. Illuminated inscription in Urdu   ..   15   15

(Des Sultana Shamim Haider)

1986 (8 Sept). *International Literacy Day. P* 13.
697   **374**   1 r. multicoloured   30   20

375 Mother and Child   **376** Aitchison College

1986 (28 Oct). *U.N.I.C.E.F. Child Survival Campaign.* P 13½ × 13.
698 375 80 p. multicoloured 45 20

(Des A. Salahuddin)
1986 (3 Nov). *Centenary of Aitchison College, Lahore.* P 13½.
699 376 2 r. 50, multicoloured 30 30

377 Two Doves carrying   378 Table Tennis Players
Olive Branches

(Des Sultana Shamim Haider)
1986 (20 Nov). *International Peace Year.* P 13.
700 377 4 r. multicoloured 50 50

(Des A. Salahuddin)
1986 (25 Nov). *4th Asian Cup Table Tennis Tournament, Karachi.* P 14.
701 378 2 r. multicoloured 75 30

379 Argali

(Des M. Jamal. Litho Secura, Singapore)
1986 (4 Dec). *Wildlife Protection (14th series). Argali. Matt, almost invisible PVA gum.* P 14.
702 379 2 r. multicoloured .. .. .. 2·00 85

380 Selimiye Mosque,
Edirne, Turkey

(Des A. Salahuddin)
1986 (20 Dec). *"Ecophilex '86" International Stamp Exhibition, Islamabad.* T 380 and similar vert designs. Multicoloured. P 13.
703 3 r. Type 380 .. .. 85 85
  a. Horiz strip of 3. Nos. 703/5 .. .. 2·25
704 3 r. Gawhar Shad Mosque, Mashhad, Iran .. 85 85
705 3 r. Grand Mosque, Bhong, Pakistan .. 85 85
703/5 .. .. Set of 3 2·25 2·25
Nos. 703/5 were printed together, *se-tenant*, in horizontal strips of three, within sheetlets of 12.

381 St. Patrick's School

(Des A. Salahuddin)
1987 (29 Jan). *125th Anniv of St. Patrick's School, Karachi.* P 13.
706 381 5 r. multicoloured .. .. .. 1·00 90

MINIMUM PRICE

The minimum price quote is 10p which represents a handling charge rather than a basis for valuing common stamps. For further notes about prices see introductory pages.

382 Mistletoe Flowerpecker and
Defence Symbols

(Des A. Salahuddin)
1987 (21 Feb). *Post Office Savings Bank Week.* T 382 and similar vert designs, each showing a different bird. Multicoloured. P 13.
707 5 r. Type 382 .. .. 85 55
  a. Block of 4. Nos. 707/10 .. .. 3·00
708 5 r. Spotted Pardalote and laboratory apparatus 85 55
709 5 r. Black-throated Blue Warbler and agriculture symbols 85 55
710 5 r. Red-capped Manakin and industrial skyline 85 55
707/10 .. .. Set of 4 3·00 2·00
Nos. 707/10 were printed together, *se-tenant*, in blocks of four throughout the sheet of 32 which contained six blocks of four and eight labels in the left and right-hand vertical columns.

383 New Parliament House, Islamabad

(Des A. Salahuddin)
1987 (23 Mar). *Inauguration of New Parliament House, Islamabad.* P 13.
711 383 3 r. multicoloured 30 30

384 Opium Poppies and Flames

(Des A. Salahuddin)
1987 (30 June). *Campaign against Drug Abuse.* P 13.
712 384 1 r. multicoloured 45 20

385 Flag and National Anthem Score

(Des A. Salahuddin)
1987 (14 Aug). *40th Anniv of Independence.* T 385 and similar horiz design. Multicoloured. P 13.
713 80 p. Type 385 .. .. 10 10
714 3 r. Text of speech by Mohammed Ali Jinnah, Minar-e-Qardad-e-Pakistan Tower and arms 20 25

386 "Tempest II"

(Des M. Hussaini and A. Salahuddin)
1987 (7 Sept). *Air Force Day.* T 386 and similar horiz designs showing military aircraft. Multicoloured. P 13½.
715 3 r. Type 386 .. .. 60 60
  a. Sheetlet. Nos. 715/24 .. .. .. 5·50
716 3 r. Hawker "Fury" 60 60
717 3 r. Supermarine "Attacker" 60 60
718 3 r. "F86 Sabre" 60 60
719 3 r. "F104 Star Fighter" 60 60
720 3 r. "C130 Hercules" 60 60
721 3 r. "F6" 60 60
722 3 r. "Mirage III" 60 60
723 3 r. "A5" 60 60
724 3 r. "F16 Fighting Falcon" 60 60
715/24 .. .. Set of 10 5·50 5·50
Nos. 715/24 were printed together, *se-tenant*, in sheetlets of 10.

387 Pasu Glacier

(Des A. Salahuddin)
1987 (1 Oct). *Pakistan Tourism Convention.* T 387 and similar horiz designs showing views along Karakoram Highway. Multicoloured. P 13.
725 1 r. 50, Type 387 .. .. .. 30 30
  a. Block of 4. Nos. 725/8 .. .. 1·10
726 1 r. 50, Apricot trees 30 30
727 1 r. 50, Karakoram Highway 30 30
728 1 r. 50, View from Khunjerab Pass .. 30 30
725/8 .. .. Set of 4 1·10 1·10
Nos. 725/8 were printed together, *se-tenant*, in blocks of four throughout the sheet of 24.

388 Shah Abdul Latif Bhitai Mausoleum

(Des A. Salahuddin)
1987 (8 Oct). *Shah Abdul Latif Bhitai (poet) Commemoration.* P 13.
729 388 80 p. multicoloured 20 20

389 D. J. Sind Science College, Karachi

(Des Sultana Shamim Haider)
1987 (7 Nov). *Centenary of D. J. Sind Science College, Karachi.* P 13.
730 389 80 p. multicoloured 20 20

390 College Building   391 Homeless People,
Houses and Rising Sun

(Des Sultana Shamim Haider)
1987 (9 Dec). *25th Anniv of College of Physicians and Surgeons.* P 13.
731 390 1 r. multicoloured 20 20

(Des Sultana Shamim Haider)
1987 (15 Dec). *International Year of Shelter for the Homeless.* P 13.
732 391 3 r. multicoloured 30 30

392 Cathedral Church of the Resurrection, Lahore

(Des A. Salahuddin)

1987 (20 Dec). *Centenary of Cathedral Church of the Resurrection, Lahore. P* 13.
733 **392** 3 r. multicoloured 30 30

393 Honeycomb and Arms

(Des A. Salahuddin)

1987 (28 Dec). *40th Anniv of Pakistan Post Office. P* 13.
734 **393** 3 r. multicoloured 30 30

394 Corporation Emblem

(Des A. Salahuddin)

1987 (31 Dec). *Radio Pakistan's New Programme Schedules. P* 13.
735 **394** 80 p. multicoloured 15 15

395 Jamshed Nusserwanjee Mehta and Karachi Municipal Corporation Building

396 Leprosy Symbols within Flower

(Des A. Salahuddin)

1988 (7 Jan). *Birth Centenary (1986) of Jamshed Nusserwanjee Mehta (former President of Karachi Municipal Corporation). P* 13.
736 **395** 3 r. multicoloured 30 30

(Des Sultana Shamim Haider)

1988 (31 Jan). *World Leprosy Day. P* 13.
737 **396** 3 r. multicoloured 35 30

397 W.H.O. Building, Geneva

(Des A. Salahuddin)

1988 (7 Apr). *40th Anniv of World Health Organization. P* 13.
738 **397** 4 r. multicoloured 35 35

The new-issue supplement to this Catalogue appears each month in

GIBBONS STAMP MONTHLY

—from your newsagent or by postal subscription— sample copy and details on request.

398 Globe   **399** Crescent, Leaf Pattern and Archway

1988 (8 May). *125th Anniv of International Red Cross and Crescent. P* 13.
739 **398** 3 r. multicoloured 30 30

(Des A. Salahuddin)

1988 (14 Aug). *Independence Day. P* 13½.
740 **399** 80 p. multicoloured 10 10
741 4 r. multicoloured 25 30

400 Field Events

(Des A. Salahuddin)

1988 (17 Sept). *Olympic Games, Seoul. T* **400** *and similar horiz designs. Multicoloured. P* 13.
742 10 r. Type **400** 75 75
   a. Sheetlet. Nos. 742/51 .. .. 6·75
743 10 r. Track events 75 75
744 10 r. Jumping and pole vaulting .. 75 75
745 10 r. Gymnastics 75 75
746 10 r. Table tennis, tennis, hockey and base-ball 75 75
747 10 r. Volleyball, football, basketball and handball 75 75
748 10 r. Wrestling, judo, boxing and weight-lifting.. .. 75 75
749 10 r. Shooting, fencing and archery .. 75 75
750 10 r. Water sports 75 75
751 10 r. Equestrian events and cycling .. 75 75
742/51 *Set of* 10 6·75 6·75
Nos. 742/51 were issued, *se-tenant*, in sheetlets of ten stamps and thirty-six half stamp-size labels.

401 Markhor

(Litho Secura, Singapore)

1988 (29 Oct). *Wildlife Protection (15th series). Markhor. Matt, almost invisible PVA gum. P* 14.
752 **401** 2 r. multicoloured 30 30

402 Islamia College, Peshawar

(Des A. Salahuddin)

1988 (22 Dec). *75th Anniv of Islamia College, Peshawar. P* 13½.
753 **402** 3 r. multicoloured 30 30

403 Symbols of Agriculture, Industry and Education with National Flags

(Des Sultana Shamim Haider (25 r.), G. M. Shaikh (50 r.), A. Salahuddin (75 r.))

1988 (29 Dec). *South Asian Association for Regional Co-operation, 4th Summit Meeting, Islamabad. T* **403** *and similar multicoloured designs. P* 13 (25 r.), 14 (50 r.) *or* 13½×13 (75 r.).
754 25 r. Type **403** .. .. 1·40 1·50
755 50 r. National flags on globe and symbols of communications (33×33 *mm*) .. 3·00 3·25
756 75 r. Stamps from member countries (52×29 *mm*) .. .. 4·25 4·50
754/6 *Set of* 3 7·75 8·25
No. 755 was printed in sheets of eight stamps and one stamp-size label, showing the S.A.A.R.C. emblem, in the central position.

(Des A. Salahuddin)

1989 (23 Jan). *Pioneers of Freedom (2nd series). Diamond-shaped design as T* **282**. *Multicoloured. W* **98**. *P* 14.
757 3 r. Maulana Hasrat Mohani .. 15 20

404 Logo   **405** Zulfikar Ali Bhutto

(Des A. Salahuddin)

1989 (18 Feb). *"Adasia 89" 16th Asian Advertising Congress, Lahore. P* 13.
758 **404** 1 r. mult ("Pakistan" in yellow) .. 20 20
   a. Sheetlet. Nos. 758/60, each × 3 1·60
759 1 r. mult ("Pakistan" in turquoise-bl) 20 20
760 1 r. mult ("Pakistan" in white) .. 20 20
758/60 *Set of* 3 55 55
Nos. 758/60 were printed together, *se-tenant*, in horizontal and vertical strips of three within the sheetlets of nine.

(Des A. Munir (1 r.), A. Salahuddin (2 r.))

1989 (4 Apr). *10th Death Anniv of Zulfikar Ali Bhutto (statesman). T* **405** *and similar vert design. Multicoloured. P* 13.
761 1 r. Type **405** 15 10
762 2 r. Zulfikar Ali Bhutto (*different*) .. 20 20

406 "Daphne" Class Submarine

(Des A. Salahuddin)

1989 (1 June). *25 Years of Pakistan Navy Submarine Operations. T* **406** *and similar horiz designs. Multicoloured. P* 13½.
763 1 r. Type **406** 30 20
   a. Vert strip of 3. Nos. 763/5 .. 80
764 1 r. "Fleet Snorkel" class submarine .. 30 20
765 1 r. "Agosta" class submarine .. 30 20
763/5 *Set of* 3 80 55
Nos. 763/5 were printed together, *se-tenant*, in vertical strips of three throughout the sheet.

407 "The Oath of the Tennis Court" (David)

(Des A. Salahuddin)

1989 (24 June). *Bicentenary of French Revolution. P* 13½.
766 **407** 7 r. multicoloured 60 70

408 Pitcher, *c.* 2200 B.C.   **409** Satellites and Map of Asian Telecommuni-cations Network

(Des A. Salahuddin)

1989 (28 June). *Archaeological Artifacts. T* **408** *and similar square designs showing terracotta pottery from Baluchistan Province. Multicoloured. P* 14.

767	1 r. Type 408	..	..	..	15	15
	a. Block of 4. Nos. 767/70			..	55	
768	1 r. Jar, c. 2300 B.C.	..	..	..	15	15
769	1 r. Vase, c. 3600 B.C.	..	..	..	15	15
770	1 r. Jar, c. 2600 B.C.	..	..	..	15	15
767/70				Set of 4	55	55

Nos. 767/70 were printed together, *se-tenant*, in blocks of four throughout the sheet.

(Des G. Shaikh)

1989 (1 July). *10th Anniv of Asia-Pacific Telecommunity. P* 13½.

771	**409** 3 r. multicoloured	..	..	..	30	30

410 Container Ship at Wharf

411 Mohammed Ali Jinnah

(Des A. Salahuddin)

1989 (5 Aug). *Construction of Integrated Container Terminal, Port Qasim. P* 14.

772	**410** 6 r. multicoloured	..	..	..	1·25	1·50

(Des A. Salahuddin. Eng A. Munir. Recess and litho)

1989 (14 Aug). *W* **98**. *P* 13.

773	**411** 1 r. multicoloured	..	..	..	10	10
774	1 r. 50, multicoloured	..	..	10	10
775	2 r. multicoloured	..	..	..	10	15
776	3 r. multicoloured	..	..	..	15	20
777	4 r. multicoloured	..	..	..	20	25
778	5 r. multicoloured	..	..	..	25	30
773/8				Set of 6	70	90

Examples of Nos. 773/8 overprinted "NATIONAL SEMINAR ON PHILATELY MULTAN 1992" as a continuous pattern were available at this event on 15 and 16 April 1992.

Details of authorisation by the Pakistan Post Offices and of availability at Multan are disputed, but, even if officially sanctioned, these overprints do not fulfil the criteria for catalogue listing due to their limited availability. They were not available from any post office other than Multan and, it is reported, only forty-five sheets of each of the three higher values were overprinted.

412 Mausoleum of Shah Abdul Latif Bhitai

413 Asiatic Black Bear

(Des A. Salahuddin)

1989 (16 Sept). *300th Birth Anniv of Shah Abdul Latif Bhitai (poet). P* 13.

779	**412** 2 r. multicoloured	..	..	..	20	20

COMMONWEALTH MEMBER

Pakistan rejoined the Commonwealth on 1 October 1989.

(Des A. McCoy)

1989 (7 Oct). *Wildlife Protection* (15th series). *Asiatic Black Bear. T* **413** *and similar horiz designs. Multicoloured. P* 13½.

780	4 r. Type 413	..	..	..	55	55
	a. Block of 4. Nos. 780/3	..	..	2·00	
781	4 r. Bear among boulders	..	..	55	55
782	4 r. Standing on rock	..	..	55	55
783	4 r. Sitting by trees	..	..	55	55
780/3				Set of 4	2·00	2·00

Nos. 780/3 were printed together, *se-tenant*, in blocks of 4 throughout the sheet.

OMNIBUS ISSUES

Details, together with prices for complete sets, of the various Omnibus issues from the 1935 Silver Jubilee series to date are included in a special section following Zimbabwe at the end of Volume 2.

414 Ear of Wheat encircling Globe

415 Games Emblem and Flags of Member Countries

(Des A. Salahuddin)

1989 (16 Oct). *World Food Day. P* 14×12½.

784	**414** 1 r. multicoloured	..	..	..	35	35

(Des A. Salahuddin)

1989 (20 Oct). *4th South Asian Sports Federation Games, Islamabad. P* 13.

785	**415** 1 r. multicoloured	..	..	..	35	35

416 Patchwork Kamblee (cloth) entering Gate of Heaven

(Des Farah and Fareeda Batul)

1989 (20 Oct). *800th Birth Anniv of Baba Farid (Muslim spiritual leader). P* 13.

786	**416** 3 r. multicoloured	..	..	..	30	30

417 Pakistan Television Logo

418 Family of Drug Addicts in Poppy Bud

(Des A. Salahuddin)

1989 (26 Nov). *25th Anniv of Television Broadcasting in Pakistan. P* 13½.

787	**417** 3 r. multicoloured	..	..	..	30	30

(Des M. Munawar)

1989 (8 Dec). *South Asian Association for Regional Co-operation Anti-Drugs Campaign. P* 13.

788	**418** 7 r. multicoloured	..	..	..	55	60

419 Murray College, Sialkot

(Des A. Salahuddin)

1989 (18 Dec). *Centenary of Murray College, Sialkot. P* 14.

789	**419** 6 r. multicoloured	..	..	..	50	60

420 Government College, Lahore

(Des N. Sheikh)

1989 (21 Dec). *125th Anniv of Government College, Lahore. P* 13.

790	**420** 6 r. multicoloured	..	..	..	50	60

421 Fields, Electricity Pylons and Rural Buildings

(Des A. Salahuddin)

1989 (31 Dec). *10th Anniv of Centre for Asia and Pacific Integrated Rural Development. P* 13.

791	**421** 3 r. multicoloured	..	..	..	30	30

422 Emblem and Islamic Patterns

(Des A. Salahuddin)

1990 (9 Feb). *20th Anniv of Organization of the Islamic Conference. P* 13.

792	**422** 1 r. multicoloured	..	..	..	20	20

423 Hockey Match

(Des M. Khan)

1990 (12 Feb). *7th World Hockey Cup, Lahore. P* 13½.

793	**423** 2 r. multicoloured	..	..	..	90	90

424 Mohammed Iqbal addressing Crowd and Liaquat Ali Khan taking Oath

(Des A. Zafar (1 r.), A. Salahuddin (7 r.))

1990 (23 Mar). *50th Anniv of Passing of Pakistan Resolution. T* **424** *and similar multicoloured designs. P* 13 (1 r.) *or* 13½ (7 r.).

794	1 r. Type 424	..	..	30	30
	a. Horiz strip of 3. Nos. 794/6		80	
795	1 r. Maulana Mohammad Ali Jauhar and Mohammed Ali Jinnah with banner	..		30	30
796	1 r. Women with Pakistan flag, and Mohammed Ali Jinnah taking Governor-General's oath, 1947			30	30
797	7 r. Minar-i-Qarardad-e-Pakistan Monument and Resolution in Urdu and English (86×42 mm)			75	75
794/7			Set of 4	1·50	1·50

Nos. 794/6 were printed together, *se-tenant*, in horizontal strips of 3 throughout the sheet, each strip forming a composite design.

425 Pregnant Woman resting

(Des Family Planning Association of Pakistan)

1990 (24 Mar). *"Safe Motherhood" South Asia Conference, Lahore. P 13½.*
798 **425** 5 r. multicoloured 50 50

426 "Decorated Verse by Ghalib" (Shakir Ali)

(Des A. Salahuddin)

1990 (19 Apr). *Painters of Pakistan (1st series). Shakir Ali. P 13½×13.*
799 **426** 1 r. multicoloured 20 20
See also Nos. 856/7.

427 Satellite in Night Sky

(Des A. Salahuddin)

1990 (26 July). *Launch of 'Badr 1' Satellite. P 13.*
800 **427** 3 r. multicoloured 30 30

428 Allama Mohammed Iqbal

1990 (14 Aug). *Pioneers of Freedom (3rd series). T 428 and similar vert designs. Each brown and green. P 13.*
801 1 r. Type **428** 10 10
    a. Sheetlet. Nos. 801/9 75
802 1 r. Mohammed Ali Jinnah 10 10
803 1 r. Sir Syed Ahmad Khan 10 10
804 1 r. Nawab Salimullah 10 10
805 1 r. Mohtarma Fatima Jinnah .. 10 10
806 1 r. Aga Khan III 10 10
807 1 r. Nawab Mohammad Ismail Khan .. 10 10
808 1 r. Hussain Shaheed Suhrawardy .. 10 10.
809 1 r. Syed Ameer Ali 10 10
810 1 r. Nawab Bahadur Yar Jung .. 10 10
    a. Sheetlet. Nos. 810/18 75
811 1 r. Khawaja Nazimuddin 10 10
812 1 r. Maulana Obaidullah Sindhi .. 10 10
813 1 r. Sahibzada Abdul Qaiyum Khan .. 10 10
814 1 r. Begum Jahanara Shah Nawaz .. 10 10
815 1 r. Sir Ghulam Hussain Hidayatullah .. 10 10
816 1 r. Qazi Mohammad Isa 10 10
817 1 r. Sir M. Shahnawaz Khan Mamdot .. 10 10
818 1 r. Pir Sahib of Manki Sharif .. 10 10
819 1 r. Liaquat Ali Khan 10 10
    a. Sheetlet. Nos. 819/27 75
820 1 r. Maulvi A. K. Fazl-ul-Haq .. 10 10
821 1 r. Allama Shabbir Ahmad Usmani .. 10 10
822 1 r. Sadar Abdur Rab Nishtar .. 10 10
823 1 r. Bi Amma 10 10
824 1 r. Sir Abdullah Haroon 10 10
825 1 r. Chaudhry Rahmat Ali 10 10
826 1 r. Raja Sahib of Mahmudabad .. 10 10
827 1 r. Hassanally Effendi 10 10
801/27 *Set of 27* 2·00 2·00
Nos. 801/9, 810/18 and 819/27 were each printed together, *se-tenant*, in sheetlets of nine.
See also Nos. 838/46 and 870/2.

429 Cultural Aspects of Indonesia and Pakistan

(Des J. Engineer)

1990 (19 Aug). *Indonesia–Pakistan Economic and Cultural Cooperation Organization. P 13.*
828 **429** 7 r. multicoloured 50 50

430 Globe, Open Book and Pen

(Des S. Afar)

1990 (8 Sept). *International Literacy Year. P 13*
829 **430** 3 r. multicoloured 20 20

431 College Crests   432 Children and Globe

(Des I. Gilani)

1990 (22 Sept). *Joint Meeting between Royal College of Physicans, Edinburgh, and College of Physicians and Surgeons, Pakistan. P 13.*
830 **431** 2 r. multicoloured 15 20

(Des A. Salahuddin)

1990 (29 Sept). *U. N. World Summit for Children, New York. P 13.*
831 **432** 7 r. multicoloured 55 65

433 Girl within Members' Flags

(Des A. Salahuddin)

1990 (21 Nov). *South Asian Association for Regional Co-operation Year of Girl Child. P 13½.*
832 **433** 2 r. multicoloured 15 20

434 Paper passing over Rollers   435 Civil Defence Worker protecting Islamabad

(Des I. Jillani)

1990 (8 Dec). *25th Anniv of Security Papers Limited. P 13.*
833 **434** 3 r. multicoloured 20 30
    a. Red ("25 YEARS OF SECURITY PAPERS LTD") omitted .. .. 60·00

(Des I. Jillani)

1991 (1 Mar). *International Civil Defence Day. P 13.*
834 **435** 7 r. multicoloured 50 50

436 Logo and Flags of Member Countries

(Des A. Salahuddin)

1991 (12 Mar). *South and West Asia Postal Union Commemoration. P 13.*
835 **436** 5 r. multicoloured 45 45

437 Globe and Figures

(Des S. Afsar)

1991 (11 July). *World Population Day. P 13.*
836 **437** 10 r. multicoloured 70 75

438 Mentally Handicapped Athlete   439 Habib Bank Headquarters and Emblem

(Des A. Salahuddin)

1991 (19 July). *Pakistan Participation in Special Olympic Games. P 13.*
837 **438** 7 r. multicoloured 55 60

1991 (14 Aug). *Pioneers of Freedom (4th series). Vert designs as T 428. Each brown and green. P 13.*
838 1 r. Maulana Zafar Ali Khan 15 15
    a. Sheetlet. Nos. 838/46 .. 1·00
839 1 r. Maulana Mohamed Ali Jauhar .. 15 15
840 1 r. Chaudhry Khaliquzzaman .. 15 15
841 1 r. Hameed Nizami 15 15
842 1 r. Begum Ra'ana Liaquat Ali Khan .. 15 15
843 1 r. Mirza Abol Hassan Ispahani .. 15 15
844 1 r. Raja Ghazanfar Ali Khan .. 15 15
845 1 r. Malik Barkat Ali 15 15
846 1 r. Mir Jaffer Khan Jamali .. 15 15
838/46 *Set of 9* 1·00 1·00
Nos. 838/46 were printed together, *se-tenant*, as a sheetlet of nine.

(Des I. Jillani)

1991 (25 Aug). *50th Anniv of Habib Bank. P 13.*
847 **439** 1 r. multicoloured 10 10
848 5 r. multicoloured 35 40

440 St. Joseph's Convent School

(Des A. Salahuddin)

1991 (8 Sept). *130th Anniv (1992) of St. Joseph's Convent School, Karachi. P 13.*
849 **440** 5 r. multicoloured 45 45

441 Emperor Sher Shah Suri   442 Jinnah Antarctic Research Station

(Des S. Akhtar)

1991 (5 Oct). *Emperor Sher Shah Suri (founder of road network) Commemoration. Multicoloured. P 13.*
850 5 r. Type **441** 45 45
MS851 92×80 mm. 7 r. Emperor on horseback and portrait as Type 441. Imperf .. 65 75

(Des I. Jillani)

1991 (28 Oct). *Pakistan Scientific Expedition to Antarctica. P* 13.
852 442 7 r. multicoloured 80 80

443 Houbara Bustard   444 Mosque

1991 (4 Nov). *Wildlife Protection (16th series). P* 13.
853 443 7 r. multicoloured 75 75

1991 (22 Nov). *300th Death Anniv of Hazrat Sultan Bahoo. P* 13.
854 444 7 r. multicoloured 55 55

445 Development
Symbols and Map of
Asia

1991 (19 Dec). *25th Anniv of Asian Development Bank. P* 13.
855 445 7 r. multicoloured 55 55

1991 (24 Dec). *Painters of Pakistan (2nd series). Horiz designs as T* 426. *Multicoloured. P* 13½×13.
856 1 r. "Procession" (Haji Muhammad Sharif) 20 20
857 1 r. "Women harvesting" (Ustad Allah Bux) 20 20

446 American Express Travellers Cheques of 1891 and
1991

1991 (26 Dec). *Centenary of American Express Travellers Cheques. P* 13½.
858 446 7 r. multicoloured 55 55

447 Flag, Banknote and Banking
Equipment

1992 (8 Apr). *1st Anniv of Muslim Commercial Bank Privatisation. T* 447 *and similar horiz design. Multicoloured. P* 13.
859 1 r. Type 447 .. .. 10 10
860 7 r. Flag with industrial and commercial scenes 45 45

448 Imran Khan   449 "Rehber-1" Rocket and
(team captain) and   Satellite View of Earth
Trophy

(Des I. Jillani (2 r.), A. Salahuddin (5 r.), M. Ahmed (7 r.))

1992 (27 Apr). *Pakistan's Victory in World Cricket Championship. T* 448 *and similar multicoloured designs. P* 13.
861 2 r. Type 448 .. .. 20 20
862 5 r. Trophy and national flags (*horiz*) 50 50
863 7 r. Pakistani flag, trophy and symbolic cricket ball 70 70
861/3 Set of 3 1·25 1·25

(Des I. Jillani (1 r.), S. Afsar (2 r.))

1992 (7 June). *International Space Year. T* 449 *and similar horiz design. Multicoloured. P* 13.
864 1 r. Type 449 .. .. 15 10
865 2 r. Satellite orbiting Earth and logo 20 20

450 Surgical Instruments   451 Globe and Symbolic Family

(Des S. Afsar)

1992 (5 July). *Industries. T* 450 *and similar horiz designs. Multicoloured. P* 13½.
866 10 r. Type 450 .. .. 50 55
  a. Horiz strip of 3. Nos. 866/8 .. .. 2·25
867 15 r. Leather goods 75 80
868 25 r. Sports equipment .. .. 1·25 1·40
866/8 Set of 3 2·25 2·50
Nos. 866/8 were printed together, *se-tenant*, in horizontal strips of three throughout the sheet.

(Des S. Afsar)

1992 (25 July). *Population Day. P* 13.
869 451 6 r. multicoloured 40 45

(Des S. Akhtar)

1992 (14 Aug). *Pioneers of Freedom (5th series). Vert designs as T* 428. *Each brown and green. P* 13.
870 1 r. Syed Suleman Nadvi 15 15
  a. Horiz strip of 3. Nos. 870/2 40
871 1 r. Nawab Iftikhar Hussain Khan Mamdot 15 15
872 1 r. Maulana Muhammad Shibli Naumani 15 15
870/2 Set of 3 40 40
Nos. 870/2 were printed together, *se-tenant*, in horizontal strips of three throughout a sheetlet of nine.

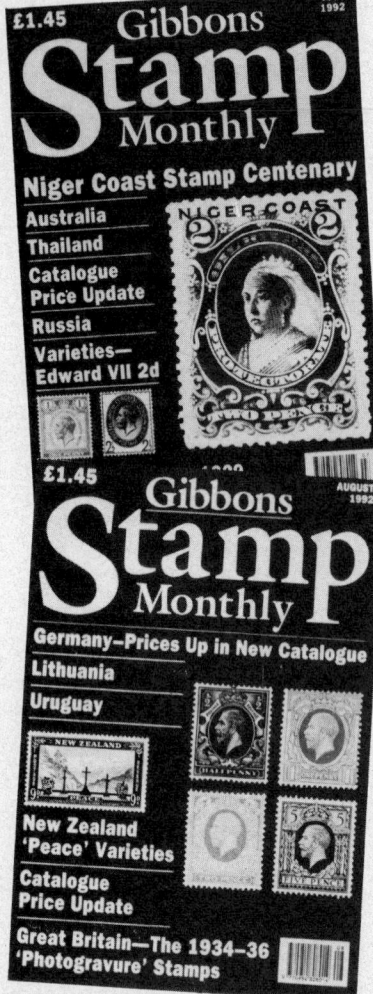

OFFICIAL STAMPS

PAKISTAN

(O 1)

1947. *Nos. O138/41 and O143/50 (King George VI) of India, optd as Type O 1 (Nos. O1/9) or as T 2 (Nos. O10/13) both in litho by Nasik.*

O 1		3 p. slate	..	40	10
O 2		½ a. purple	..	20	10
O 3		9 p. green	..	1·50	2·50
O 4		1 a. carmine	..	20	10
O 5		1½ a. dull violet	..	20	10
O 6		2 a. vermilion	..	30	10
O 7		2½ a. bright violet	..	2·25	3·00
O 8		4 a. brown	..	30	10
O 9		8 a. slate-violet	..	40	45
O10		1 r. grey and red-brown	..	80	60
O11		2 r. purple and brown	..	3·50	1·50
O12		5 r. green and blue	..	13·00	18·00
O13		10 r. purple and claret	..	28·00	55·00
O1/13			*Set of 13*	45·00	70·00

See note after No. 19. The 1 a. 3 p. (India No. O146a) exists only as a local issue (*Price, Karachi opt, £3 mint, £6 used*).

SERVICE   SERVICE   SERVICE

(O 2)   (O 3)   (O 4)

NOTE. Apart from a slight difference in size, Types O 2 and O 3 can easily be distinguished by the difference in the shape of the "c". Type O 4 is taller and thinner in appearance.

PRINTERS. Type O 2 was overprinted by De La Rue and Types O 3 and O 4 by the Pakistan Security Ptg Corp.

1948 (14 Aug)–54. *Optd with Type O 2.*

O14	7	3 p. red (No. 24) ..	..	10	10
O15		6 p. violet (No. 25) (R.) ..	..	10	10
O16		9 p. green (No. 26) (R.)	..	10	10
O17	8	1 a. blue (No. 27) (R.)	..	2·75	10
O18		1½ a. grey-green (No. 28) (R.)	..	2·25	10
O19		2 a. red (No. 29) ..	..	1·25	10
O20	10	3 a. green (No. 31)	..	8·50	1·75
O21	9	4 a. reddish brown (No. 33) ..	..	80	10
O22		8 a. black (No. 35) (R.)	..	80	2·75
O23	–	1 r. ultramarine (No. 38)	..	1·00	10
O24	–	2 r. chocolate (No. 39) ..	..	8·50	3·50
O25	–	5 r. carmine (No. 40)	..	9·00	4·25
O26	13	10 r. magenta (No. 41)	..	9·00	28·00
		a. Perf 12 (10.10.51)	..	11·00	25·00
		b. Perf 13 (1954?)	..	12·00	32·00
O14/26			*Set of 13*	40·00	35·00

1949. *Optd with Type O 2.*

O27		1 a. blue (No. 44) (R.)	..	75	10
O28		1½ a. grey-green (No. 45) (R.)	..	30	10
		a. Opt inverted	..	—	35·00
O29		2 a. red (No. 46) ..	..	90	10
		a. Opt omitted (in pair with normal)	..		£100
O30		3 a. green (No. 47) ..	..	6·50	2·25
O31		8 a. black (No. 49) (R.) ..	..	16·00	7·50
O27/31			*Set of 5*	22·00	9·00

1951 (14 Aug). *4th Anniv of Independence. As Nos. 56, 58 and 60, but inscr "SERVICE" instead of "PAKISTAN POSTAGE".*

O32	18	3 a. purple	..	1·75	3·25
O33	19	4 a. green	..	60	10
O34	20	8 a. sepia	..	3·00	85
O32/4			*Set of 3*	4·75	3·75

1953. *Optd with Type O 3.*

O35		3 p. red (No. 24a)	..	10	10
O36		6 p. violet (No. 25a) (R.)	..	10	10
O37		9 p. green (No. 26a) (R.)	..	10	10
O38		1 a. blue (No. 44a) (R.)	..	10	10
O39		1½ a. grey-green (No. 45a) (R.)	..	10	10
O40		2 a. red (No. 46a) (1953?)	..	15	10
O41		1 r. ultramarine (No. 38a)	..	3·25	90
O42		2 r. chocolate (No. 39a)	..	2·25	10
O43		5 r. carmine (No. 40a)	..	8·00	4·50
O44		10 r. magenta (No. 41b) (date?)	..	13·00	32·00
O35/44			*Set of 10*	24·00	35·00

1954 (14 Aug). *Seventh Anniv of Independence. Nos. 65/71 optd with Type O 3.*

O45		6 p. reddish violet (R.)	..	10	85
O46		9 p. blue (R.) ..	..	65	4·25
O47		1 a. carmine	..	15	70
O48		1½ a. red	..	15	70
O49		14 a. deep green (R.) ..	..	60	3·25
O50		1 r. green (R.)	..	75	10
O51		2 r. red-orange	..	1·25	15
O45/51			*Set of 7*	3·25	9·00

1955 (14 Aug). *Eighth Anniv of Independence. No. 75 optd with Type O 3.*

O52		8 a. deep reddish violet (R.)..	..	20	10

1957 (Jan)–59. *Nos. 65/71 optd with Type O 4.*

O53		6 p. reddish violet (R.)	..	10	10
		a. Opt inverted	..	†	—
O54		9 p. blue (R.) (1.59)	..	10	30
		a. Opt inverted	..		
O55		1 a. carmine	..	10	10
		a. Opt inverted	..		
O56		1½ a. red	..	10	10
		a. Opt double	..		
O57		14 a. deep green (R.) (2.59) ..	..	40	2·00
O58		1 r. green (R.) (4.58)..	..	40	10
O59		2 r. red-orange (4.58)	..	2·50	10
O53/9			*Set of 7*	3·25	2·25

1958 (Jan)–61. *Optd with Type O 4.*

O60	7	3 p. red (No. 24a)	..	10	10
O61	–	5 r. carmine (No. 40a) (7.59)	..	3·00	15
O62	41	10 r. myrtle-green and yellow-orange (No. 89) (R.) (1961) ..	..	6·00	6·00
		a. Opt inverted	..	12·00	
O60/2			*Set of 3*	8·00	6·00

1958 (Jan)–61. *Nos. 74/5 optd with Type O 4.*

O63		6 a. deep ultramarine (R.) (4.61)	..	10	10
O64		8 a. deep reddish violet (R.)	..	10	10

1959 (Aug). *No. 83 optd with Type O 4.*

O65	37	2 a. scarlet	..	10	10

1961 (Apr). *Nos. 110/11 optd with Type O 4.*

O66	51	8 a. deep green	..	10	10
O67		1 r. blue	..	10	10
		a. Opt inverted	..	6·50	

NEW CURRENCY. In addition to the local *handstamped* surcharges mentioned in the note above No. 122, the following *typographed* surcharges were made at the Treasury at Mastung and issued in the Baluchi province of Kalat: 6 p. on 1 a. (No. O55), 9 p. on 1½ a. (No. O56) and 13 p. on 2 a. (No. O65). They differ in that the surcharges are smaller and "PAISA" is expressed as "Paisa". Being locals they are outside the scope of this catalogue.

1961. *Optd with Type O 4.*

O68		1 p. on 1½ a. (No. 122)	..	10	10
		a. Optd with Type O 3	..	1·25	75
O69		2 p. on 3 p. (No. 123) (1.1.61)	..	10	10
		a. Surch double	..		
		b. Optd with Type O 3	..	2·25	2·25
O70		3 p. on 6 p. (No. 124) ..	..	10	10
O71		7 p. on 1 a. (No. 125).	..	10	10
		a. Optd with Type O 3	..	2·25	2·25
O72		13 p. on 2 a. (No. 126).	..	10	10
O73		13 p. on 2 a. (No. 127).	..	10	10
O68/73			*Set of 6*	30	30

No. O68 exists with small and large "1" (see note below Nos. 122/7, etc.).

ERRORS. See note after No. 127.

SERVICE   SERVICE

(O 5)   (O 6)

1961–63. *Nos. 128/44b optd with Type O 4 (rupee values) or O 5 (others). (a) Inscribed "SHAKISTAN".*

O74		1 p. violet (R.) (1.1.61)	..	10	10
O75		2 p. rose-red (R.) (12.1.61)	..	10	10
O76		5 p. ultramarine (R.) (23.3.61)	..	15	10

(b) Inscribed "PAKISTAN"

O77		1 p. violet (R.)	..	55	10
O78		2 p. rose-red (R.)	..	10	10
O79		3 p. reddish purple (R.) (27.10.61)	..	10	10
O80		5 p. ultramarine (R.)	..	1·75	10
O81		7 p. emerald (R.) (23.3.61)	..	10	10
O82		10 p. brown (R.)	..	10	10
		a. Opt inverted	..		
O83		13 p. slate-violet (R.) (14.2.61)	..	10	10
O85		40 p. deep purple (R.) (1.1.62)	..	10	10
O86		50 p. deep bluish green (R.) (1.1.62)	..	15	10
		a. Opt double	..	÷	
O87		75 p. carmine-red (R.) (23.3.62)	..	20	10
		a. Opt double	..		
O88		1 r. vermilion (7.1.63)	..	35	10
		a. Opt double	..	8·00	
		b. Opt as Type O 3 ..	..	6·00	6·00
		c. Opt inverted	..	6·00	
O89		2 r. orange (7.1.63)	..	1·25	20
O90		5 r. green (R.) (7.1.63)	..	4·00	4·50
O74/90			*Set of 16*	8·00	5·00

1963–78? *Nos. 170, etc., optd with Type O 5, in red.*

O 91		1 p. violet	..	10	10
O 92		2 p. rose-red (1965) ..	..	10	10
		a. Opt inverted	..	1·25	
		b. Albino opt	..		
		c. Opt double, one albino ..	..		
O 93		3 p. reddish purple (1967)	..	1·25	70
		a. Opt double	..	3·50	
		b. Opt inverted	..	1·25	
O 94		5 p. ultramarine	..	10	10
		a. Opt inverted	..	1·25	
		ab. Vert pair, top stamp without opt, lower with opt inverted	..		
O 95		7 p. emerald (date?)..	..	4·50	2·75
O 96		10 p. brown (1965)	..	10	10
		a. Opt inverted	..	1·50	
O 97		13 p. slate-violet	..	10	10
O 98		15 p. bright purple (31.12.64)	..	10	40
O 99		20 p. myrtle-green (26.1.70) ..	..	10	30
		a. Opt double	..	20·00	
O100		25 p. deep blue (1977)	..	3·25	85
O101		40 p. deep purple (1972?)	..	4·50	2·00
O102		50 p. deep bluish green (1965)	..	10	15
O103		75 p. carmine-red (date?)	..	4·00	4·00
O104		90 p. yellow-green (5.78?)	..	2·50	2·50
O91/104			*Set of 14*	18·00	12·00

1968–(?). *Nos. 204, 206 and 207 optd with Type O 4.*

O105	62	1 r. vermilion	..	80	30
		a. Opt inverted	..	6·00	
O107		2 r. orange (date?)	..	4·50	85
		a. Opt inverted	..	6·00	
O108		5 r. green (R.) (date?)	..	8·00	2·75
		a. Opt inverted	..	9·50	
O105/8			*Set of 3*	12·00	3·50

1979–85. *Nos. 464/72, 473b and 475/80 optd as Type O 5 in black (2 r.) or in red (reading vertically downwards on 2, 3 and 5 p.) (others).*

O109	275	2 p. deep grey-green	..	10	10
		a. Opt reading upwards ..			
		ab. Horiz pair, one with opt reading upwards, the other with opt omitted ..			
O110		3 p. black	..	10	10
		a. Opt reading upwards ..			
O111		5 p. deep ultramarine	..	10	10
		a. Opt reading upwards ..	..	1·50	1·50
		b. Vert pair, top stamp without opt	..	3·00	
O112	276	10 p. new blue and greenish blue	..	10	10
O113		20 p. deep yellow-green	..	10	10
O114	276	25 p. deep green and dull magenta	..	10	10
O115		40 p. new blue and magenta..	..	30	10
		a. Opt inverted	..		
		b. Albino opt	..	10·00	
O116		50 p. slate-lilac and turquoise-green	..	10	10
O117		60 p. black	..	1·00	10
O118		75 p. dull vermilion (Die II) (1980)	..	75	10
O119	276a	1 r. bronze-green (1979) ..	..	1·00	10
O120		1 r. 50, red-orange (1979) ..	..	10	10
O121		2 r. carmine-red (1979)	..	15	10
O122		3 r. blue-black (1980)	..	20	20
O123		4 r. black (1985)	..	30	25
O124		5 r. sepia (1985)	..	35	30
O109/24			*Set of 16*	3·75	1·50

(Des and litho Secura, Singapore)

1980 (15 Jan–10 Mar). *As Nos. 513/19 but inscr "SERVICE". P 12.*

O125	291	10 p. slate-green and orange-yellow ..		50	10
O126		15 p. slate-green & brt yellow-green ..		20	10
O127		25 p. violet and brown-red (10 Mar)..		10	10
O128		35 p. carmine & brt yell-grn (10 Mar)..		10	10
O129	–	40 p. rosine and olive-sepia	..	20	10
O130	–	50 p. violet & dull yell-green (10 Mar)	..	15	10
O131	–	80 p. brt yellow-green & blk (10 Mar)..		20	20
O125/31			*Set of 7*	1·10	45

1984 (25 Sept)–89. *Nos. 629/30 and 632/6 optd with Type O 6 in red.*

O132	–	5 p. brownish blk & brn-pur (1989?)	..	10	10
O133	–	10 p. brownish black and rose-red	..	10	10
O135	343	20 p. black and bright reddish violet (opt at right) (20.11.84)	..	10	10
		a. Opt at left	..	10	10
O136	–	50 p. sepia and Venetian red (1988?)	..	10	10
O137	–	60 p. lt brown & blackish brown (1985)	..	10	10
O138	–	70 p. greenish blue (1988?)	..	10	10
O139	–	80 p. bistre-brown & dull scar (1988)	..	10	10
O132/9			*Set of 7*	35	35

1989 (24 Dec). *No. 773 optd with Type O 5.*

O140	411	1 r. multicoloured	..	10	10

O 7 State Bank of
Pakistan Building,
Islamabad

1990 (12 Apr). *W 98 (sideways). P 13½.*

O141	O 7	1 r. carmine and dull green ..	..	10	10
O142		2 r. carmine and rose-carmine	..	10	15
O143		3 r. carmine and ultramarine	..	15	20
O144		4 r. carmine and red-brown ..	..	20	25
O145		5 r. carmine and reddish purple	..	25	30
O141/5			*Set of 5*	70	85

BAHAWALPUR

Bahawalpur, a former feudatory state situated to the west of the Punjab, was briefly independent following the partition of India on 15 August 1947 before acceding to Pakistan on 3 October of the same year.

East India Company and later Indian Empire post offices operated in Bahawalpur from 1854. By a postal agreement of 1879 internal mail from the state administration was carried unstamped, but this arrangement was superseded by the issue of Official stamps in 1945.

There had been a previous abortive attempt to introduce Bahawalpur postage stamps in 1933, but the scheme did not receive the approval of the Imperial Government. The proposed definitive stamps, 1, 2, 4, 8 a., 1 and 2 r., were very similar to those eventually used for the 1945 Official series, but were on unwatermarked paper. Residual stocks of the 1933 1 a., 8 a., 1 r. and 2 r. were used for the provisional Officials, Nos. O7 and O11/13.

In addition to the proposed definitives there was also a 1 a., showing the Bahawalpur coat of arms, to commemorate the centenary of the alliance with Great Britain. Although not officially issued an example of this stamp is known used on cover of 14 August 1933 from Deh Rawal to Sadiq Garh. Both this 1 a. and the same value from the proposed definitive set also exist with Official Arabic overprint in black. These also were not issued, although one used example of the latter has been recorded.

Stamps of India were overprinted in the interim period between 15 August and 3 October 1947. After the state joined Pakistan postage stamps were issued for internal use until 1952.

PRICES FOR STAMPS ON COVER

The postage and Official stamps of Bahawalpur are rare used on cover.

---

(1)

1947 (15 Aug). *Nos. 265/8, 269a/77 and 259/62* (*King George VI) of India optd locally with T 1.*

1	3 p. slate (R.)			7·00
2	½ a. purple			7·00
3	9 p. green (R.)			7·00
4	1 a. carmine			7·00
5	1½ a. dull violet (R.)			7·50
6	2 a. vermilion			7·50
7	3 a. bright violet (R.)			7·50
8	3½ a. bright blue (R.)			7·50
9	4 a. brown			8·00
10	6 a. turquoise-green (R.)			8·00
11	8 a. slate-violet (R.)			8·00
12	12 a. lake			8·00
13	14 a. purple			40·00
14	1 r. grey and red-brown			18·00
15	2 r. purple and brown (R.)			£425
16	5 r. green and blue (R.)			£450
17	10 r. purple and claret			£475
1/17			*Set of 17*	£1300

Nos. 1/17 were issued during the interim period, following the implementation of the Indian Independence Act, during which time Bahawalpur was part of neither of the two Dominions created. The Amir acceded to the Dominion of Pakistan on 3 October 1947 and these overprinted stamps of India were then withdrawn.

The stamps of Bahawalpur only had validity for use within the state. For external mail Pakistan stamps were used.

PRINTERS. All the following issues were recess-printed by De La Rue & Co, Ltd, London.

2 Amir Muhammad Bahawal Khan I Abbasi

3

1947 (1 Dec). *Bicentenary Commemoration.* W 3 (*sideways*). *P 12½ × 11½.*

18	2	½ a. black and carmine		30	1·25

---

4 H.H. the Amir of Bahawalpur

5 The Tombs of the Amirs

6 Mosque in Sadiq-Garh

7 Fort Derawar from the Lake

8 Nur-Mahal Palace

9 The Palace, Sadiq-Garh

10 H.H. the Amir of Bahawalpur

11 Three Generations of Rulers; H.H. the Amir in centre

1948 (1 Apr). W 3 (*sideways on vert designs*). P 12½ (*T 4*), 11½ × 12½ (*T 5, 7, 8 and 9*), 12½ × 11½ (*T 6 and 10*) or 13½ × 14 (*T 11*).

19	4	3 p. black and blue		20	8·00
20		½ a. black and claret		20	8·00
21		9 p. black and green		20	8·00
22		1 a. black and carmine		20	8·00
23		1½ a. black and violet		20	8·00
24	5	2 a. green and carmine		20	9·00
25	6	4 a. orange and brown		30	10·00
26	7	6 a. violet and blue		30	11·00
27	8	8 a. carmine and violet		30	11·00
28	9	12 a. green and carmine		35	12·00
29	10	1 r. violet and brown		3·75	18·00
30		2 r. green and claret		11·00	23·00
31		5 r. black and violet		14·00	35·00
32	11	10 r. scarlet and black		19·00	50·00
19/32				*Set of 14* 45·00	£200

12 H.H. The Amir of Bahawalpur and Mohammed Ali Jinnah

13 Soldiers of 1848 and 1948

1948 (3 Oct). *First Anniv of Union of Bahawalpur with Pakistan.* W 3. P 13.

33	12	1½ a. carmine and blue-green	10	1·00

1948 (15 Oct). *Multan Campaign Centenary.* W 3. P 11½.

34	13	1½ a. black and lake	20	5·50

1948. *As Nos. 29/32, but colours changed.*

35	10	1 r. deep green and orange	25	10·00
36		2 r. black and carmine	30	13·00
37		5 r. chocolate and ultramarine	30	22·00
38	11	10 r. red-brown and green	35	27·00
35/8			*Set of 4* 1·10	65·00

14 Irrigation

17 U.P.U. Monument, Berne

1949 (3 Mar). *Silver Jubilee of Accession of H.H. the Amir of Bahawalpur.* T 14 *and similar horiz designs.* W 3. P 14.

39	3 p. black and ultramarine		10	5·50
40	½ a. black and brown-orange		10	5·50
41	9 p. black and green		10	5·50
42	1 a. black and carmine		10	5·50
39/42			*Set of 4* 30	20·00

Designs:—½ a. Wheat; 9 p. Cotton; 1 a. Sahiwal bull.

1949 (10 Oct). *75th Anniv of Universal Postal Union.* W 3. P 13.

43	17	9 p. black and green	20	2·00
		a. Perf 17½ × 17	2·25	11·00
44		1 a. black and magenta	20	2·00
		a. Perf 17½ × 17	2·25	11·00
45		1½ a. black and orange	20	2·00
		a. Perf 17½ × 17	2·25	11·00
46		2½ a. black and blue	20	2·00
		a. Perf 17½ × 17	2·25	11·00
43/6			*Set of 4* 70	7·00
43a/6a			*Set of 4* 8·00	40·00

OFFICIAL STAMPS

O 1 Panjnad Weir

O 2 Dromedary and Calf

O 3 Blackbuck

O 4 Eastern White Pelicans

O 5 Juma Masjid Palace, Fort Derawar

O 6 Temple at Pattan Manara

1945 (1 Jan). *Various horizontal pictorial designs, with red Arabic opt.* W 3. P 14.

O1	O 1	½ a. black and green		1·25	4·50
O2	O 2	1 a. black and carmine		1·75	3·25
		a. Opt omitted		†	—
O3	O 3	2 a. black and violet		2·75	4·50
O4	O 4	4 a. black and olive-green		6·50	12·00
O5	O 5	8 a. black and brown		6·50	7·00
O6	O 6	1 r. black and orange		6·50	7·00
O1/6				*Set of 6* 23·00	35·00

O 7 Baggage Camels   (O 8)

1945 (10 Mar). *Previously unissued design with red Arabic opt. No wmk.* P 14.

O7	O 7	1 a. black and brown	22·00	42·00

1945 (Mar–June). *Surch as Type O 8* (*at Security Printing Press, Nasik) instead of red Arabic opt. No wmk.* P 14.

O11	O 5	½ a. on 8 a. black and purple	4·25	2·00
O12	O 6	1½ a. on 1 r. black and orange	16·00	3·75
O13	O 1	1½ a. on 2 r. black and blue (1 June)	65·00	4·25
O11/13			*Set of 3* 75·00	9·00

The stamps used as a basis for Nos. O7 and O11/13 were part of the postage series prepared in 1933, but not issued.

SERVICE

(O 9)

O 10 H.H. the Amir of Bahawalpur

1945. *Optd with Type O 9* (*by D.L.R.) instead of red Arabic opt. No wmk.* P 14.

O14	O 1	½ a. black and carmine	1·00	6·00
O15	O 2	1 a. black and carmine	1·50	7·00
O16	O 3	2 a. black and orange	2·75	19·00
O14/16			*Set of 3* 4·75	29·00

1945. *P* 14.
O17	O 10	3 p. black and blue	..	..	..	75	3·25
O18		1½ a. black and violet..				5·50	4·75

O 11 Allied Banners

(Des E. Meronti. Recess, background litho)

1946 (1 May). *Victory.* P 14.
O19	O 11	1½ a. green and grey	..	..	..	1·75	2·00

1948. Nos. 19, 22, 24/5 and 35/8 optd as Nos. O1/6.
O20	4	3 p. black and blue (R.)	..	..		15	5·50
O21		1 a. black and carmine (Blk.)	..		15	4·50
O22	5	2 a. green and carmine (Blk.)	..		15	6·00
O23	6	4 a. orange and brown (Blk.)	..		15	8·00
O24	10	1 r. deep green and orange (R.)		15	9·00
O25		2 r. black and carmine (R.)	..		15	11·00
O26		5 r. chocolate and ultramarine (R.)		20	19·00
O27	11	10 r. red-brown and green (R.)		30	24·00
O20/7				Set of 8	1·25	75·00

1949 (10 Oct). *75th Anniv of Universal Postal Union.* Nos. 43/6 optd as Nos. O1/6.
O28	17	9 p. black and green	..	..	..	15	4·50
		a. Perf 17½ × 17	..	..	2·40	17·00
O29		1 a. black and magenta..	..		15	4·50
		a. Perf 17½ × 17	..	..	2·40	17·00
O30		1½ a. black and orange	..		15	4·50
		a. Perf 17½ × 17	..	..	2·40	17·00
O31		2½ a. black and blue	..		15	4·50
		a. Perf 17½ × 17	..	..	2·40	17·00
O28/31			..	..	Set of 4	55	16·00
O28a/31a			..	..	Set of 4	8·50	60·00

Since 1949 only Pakistan stamps have been used in Bahawalpur for both internal and external mail.

Palestine

The stamps of TURKEY were used in Palestine from 1865. In addition various European Powers, and Egypt, maintained post offices at Jerusalem (Austria, France, Germany, Italy, Russia), Jaffa (Austria, Egypt, France, Germany, Russia) and Haifa (Austria, France) using their own stamps or issues specially prepared for Levant post offices. All foreign post offices had closed by the time of the British Occupation.

PRICES FOR STAMPS ON COVER TO 1945
No. 1	*from* × 6	
No. 2	*from* × 4	
Nos. 3/4	*from* × 5	
Nos. 5/15	*from* × 4	
Nos. 16/29	*from* × 3	
Nos. 30/42	*from* × 2	
No. 43		
Nos. 44/57	*from* × 2	
Nos. 58/9		
Nos. 60/8	*from* × 3	
Nos. 69/70		
Nos. 71/89	*from* × 3	
Nos. 90/103	*from* × 4	
Nos. 104/11	*from* × 8	
Nos. D1/5	*from* × 30	
Nos. D6/20	*from* × 10	

BRITISH MILITARY OCCUPATION

Nos. 1/15 were issued by the British military authorities for use by the civilian population in territories previously part of the Ottoman Empire. In addition to Palestine they were available from E.E.F. post offices in Syria (including what subsequently became Transjordan) from 23 September 1918 to 23 February 1922, Lebanon from 21 October 1918 to September 1920 and Cilicia from 2 September 1919 to 16 July 1920. Use in the following post offices outside Palestine is recorded in *British Empire Campaigns and Occupations in the Near East, 1914–1924* by John Firebrace:

Adana, Cilicia	Broumana, Lebanon
Akkari ("Akkar"), Syria	Damascus ("Damas"), Syria
Aleppo ("Alep, Halep"), Syria	Damour ("Damor"), Lebanon
Aleih ("Alie"), Lebanon	Der'a ("Deraa"), Syria
Alexandretta, Syria	Deurt-Yol, Syria
Antakie, Syria	Djey Han, Syria
Ba'abda, Lebanon	Djezzin ("Djezzine"), Lebanon
Baalbek, Lebanon	Djon, Lebanon
Bab, Syria	Djounie, Lebanon
Babitoma, Syria	Djubeil, Lebanon
Behamdoun, Lebanon	Douma, Syria
Beit ed Dine, Lebanon	Edleb, Syria
Bekaa, Lebanon	Feke, Turkey
Beyrouth, Lebanon	Habib Souk, Syria
Beit Mery, Beyrouth, Lebanon	Hajin ("Hadjin"), Cilicia
	Hama, Syria
Bouzanti, Syria	Hasbaya, Lebanon

Hasine, Cilicia	Racheya, Lebanon
Hommana, Lebanon	Safita, Syria
Homs, Syria	Savour, Tyre, Lebanon
Kozan, Cilicia	Selimie, Syria
Lattakia ("Laskie, Lattaquie"), Syria	Sidan ("Saida (Echelle)"), Lebanon
Massel el Chouf ("Moussalc"), Lebanon	Suweidiya ("Suvedie"), Syria
Merdjajoun, Lebanon	Talia, Syria
Mersina ("Mersine"), Cilicia	Tarsous, Cilicia
Mounboudje, Syria	Tartous, Turkey
Nabatti, Lebanon	Tibnin, Lebanon
Nebk ("Nebik"), Syria	Tripoli, Syria
Payass, Syria	Zahle, Lebanon
	Zebdani, Syria

This information is reproduced here by permission of the publishers, Robson Lowe Publications.

1	(2)	3

"E.E.F." = Egyptian Expeditionary Force

(Des G. Rowntree. Litho Typographical Dept, Survey of Egypt, Giza, Cairo)

1918 (10 Feb). *Wmk Royal Cypher in column* (*W* **100** *of Great Britain). Ungummed. Roul* 20.
1	1	1 p. indigo (Optd S. £375)	..	£200	£130
		a. Deep blue	..	£180	£120
		b. Blue	..	£180	£120

Control: A 18 (*Prices, corner block of* 4; No. 1 £850. No. 1*a*, £750. No. 1*b*, £850).

1918 (16 Feb). *As last (ungummed), surch with T* **2.**
2	1	5 m. on 1 p. cobalt-blue (Optd S. £375)	..	£120	£650
		a. "MILLILMES" (No. 10 in sheet)	..	£3250	£4000

Control: B 18 A. (*Corner block, £1000*).

1918 (5 Mar). *As No.* 1 *but colour changed. With gum.*
3	1	1 p. ultramarine	..	..	2·50	2·50

Control: C 18. (*Corner block, £70.*)

1918 (5 Mar and 13 May). *No.* 3 *surch with T* **2.**
4	1	5 m. on 1 p. ultramarine	..	5·00	4·00
		a. Arabic surch wholly or partly missing (No. 11 in sheet)	..	£400	£400

Controls: C 18 B (Mar). (*Corner block, £750.*)
D 18 C (May). (*Corner block, £175.*)

(Typo Stamping Dept, Board of Inland Revenue, Somerset House, London)

1918 (16 July–27 Dec). *Wmk Royal Cypher in column.* P 15 × 14.
5	3	1 m. sepia..	..	..	..	30	40
		a. Deep sepia	..	..	40	40
6		2 m. blue-green	..	..	30	35
		a. Deep green	..	..	50	40
7		3 m. yellow-brown (17 Dec)	..	35	35
		a. Chestnut	..	..	9·00	6·00
8		4 m. scarlet	..	..	35	40
9		5 m. yellow-orange (25 Sept)	..	35	30
		a. Orange	..	..	55	45
10		1 p. deep indigo (9 Nov)	..	35	25
11		2 p. pale olive	..	..	60	60
		a. Olive	..	..	1·25	1·10
12		5 p. purple	..	..	1·75	2·25
13		9 p. ochre (17 Dec)	..	2·25	4·00
14		10 p. ultramarine (17 Dec)	..	2·25	3·00
15		20 p. pale grey (27 Dec)	..	9·00	15·00
		a. Slate-grey	..	..	12·00	20·00
5/15			..	..	Set of 11	16·00	24·00

There are two sizes of the design of this issue:
19 × 23 mm. 1, 2, and 4 m., and 2 and 5 p.
18 × 21½ mm. 3 m., and 1, 9, 10 and 20 p.
There are numerous minor plate varieties in this issue, such as stops omitted in "E.E.F.", malformed Arabic characters, etc.

CIVIL ADMINISTRATION UNDER BRITISH HIGH COMMISSIONER

Palestine was placed under civil administration by a British High Commissioner on 1 July 1920.

فلـطين | فلسطين | فلسطين

PALESTINE | **PALESTINE** | PALESTINE

סלשתינה א״י | פלשתינה א״י | פלשתינה א״י

(4)	(5)	(6)

Differences:—
T **5.** 20 mm vert and 7 mm between English and Hebrew.
T **6.** 19 mm and 6 mm respectively.

(Optd at Greek Orthodox Convent, Jerusalem)

1920 (1 Sept). *Optd with T* **4** (*Arabic 8 mm long*). (a) P 15 × 14.
16	3	1 m. sepia..	..	..	1·40	1·40
17		2 m. blue-green	..	..	6·00	4·50
18		3 m. chestnut	..	..	3·50	4·50
		a. Opt inverted	..	£500	£550
19		4 m. scarlet	..	..	1·00	1·25
20		5 m. yellow-orange	..	8·00	4·00
21		1 p. deep indigo (Sil.)	..	1·00	80
22		2 p. deep olive	..	..	1·75	1·90

23	3	5 p. deep purple	..	..	..	7·50	13·00
24		9 p. ochre	..	..	..	7·50	18·00
25		10 p. ultramarine	..	..	9·00	16·00
26		20 p. pale grey	..	..	15·00	32·00

(b) P 14
27	3	2 m. blue-green	..	..	..	1·10	1·25
28		3 m. chestnut	..	..	35·00	35·00
29		5 m. orange	..	..	1·25	90
16/29			..	..	Set of 14	90·00	£110

Two settings of T 4 are known to specialists, the first, of 24, being used for all values perforated 15×14 (but only on one sheet of the 1 p.) and the second, of 12, for all values in both perforations.

Apart from minor varieties due to broken type, there are three major errors which are rare in some values. These are (*a*) two Hebrew characters at left transposed (all values of first setting only); (*b*) diamond-shaped dot over the Arabic "t" making the word read "Faleszin" for "Falestin" (2 p. to 20 p. of first setting and 1 m. and 3 m. perf 15 × 14, and 5 m. perf 14 of second setting); (*c*) "B" for final "E" of "PALESTINE" (2 p. to 20 p. of first setting and all values of second setting except 3 m. perf 14).

Faulty registration of the overprint in this issue has resulted in numerous misplaced overprints, either vertically or horizontally, which are not of great importance with the exception of Nos. 21 and 29 which exist with the overprint out of sequence, i.e. Hebrew/Arabic/English or English/Arabic/Hebrew or English/Hebrew only. Also all values are known with Arabic/English only.

1920 (22 Sept)–**21.** *Optd with T* **5*** (*Arabic 10 mm long*).
(a) P 15 × 14.
30	3	1 m. sepia (27.12.20)	..	..	75	1·00
		a. Opt inverted	..	..	£400	†
31		2 m. blue-green (27.12.20)	..	3·00	4·00
32		3 m. yellow-brown (27.12.20)	..	85	1·00
33		4 m. scarlet (27.12.20)	..	1·00	1·25
34		5 m. yellow-orange	..	..	2·00	1·00
35		1 p. deep indigo (Silver) (21.6.21)	..	£600	25·00
36		2 p. olive (21.6.21)	..	55·00	25·00
37		5 p. deep purple (21.6.21)	..	20·00	8·00

(b) P 14
38	3	1 m. sepia ..	..	..	£600	£700
39		2 m. blue-green	..	..	2·50	4·00
40		4 m. scarlet	..	..	60·00	80·00
41		5 m. orange	..	..	£120	10·00
		a. Yellow-orange	..	1·25	1·10
42		1 p. deep indigo (Silver)	..	25·00	1·25
43		5 p. purple	..	..	£225	£500

*In this setting the Arabic and Hebrew characters are badly worn and blunted, the Arabic "S" and "T" are joined (i.e. there is no break in the position indicated by the arrow in our illustration); the letters of "PALESTINE" are often irregular or broken; and the space between the two groups of Hebrew characters varies from 1 mm to over 1¾ mm. The " character in the left-hand Hebrew word extends above the remainder of the line (*For clear, sharp overprint, see Nos. 47/59.*)

The dates of issue given are irrespective of the perforations, i.e. one or both perfs could have been issued on the dates shown. Nos. 31 and 39 exist with any one line of the overprint partly missing.

1920 (6 Dec). *Optd with T* **6.** (a) *P* 15 × 14.
44	3	3 m. yellow-brown	..	..	30·00	35·00
44a		5 m. yellow-orange	..	£13000	£11000

(b) P 14
45	3	1 m. sepia	..	..	25·00	30·00
46		5 m. orange	..	..	£300	30·00

فلسطين | فلسطين | فلسطين

PALESTINE | **PALESTINE** | **PALESTINE**

פלשתינה א״י | פלשתינה א״י | פלשתינה א״י

(6a)	(7)	(8)

1921 (29 May–4 Aug). *Optd as T* **6a.** (a) *P* 15×14.
47	3	1 m. sepia (23.6)	..	..	4·50	3·50
48		2 m. blue-green (23.6)	..	7·50	5·00
49		3 m. yellow-brown (23.6)	..	20·00	2·50
		a. "PALESTINE" omitted	..	£2000	
50		4 m. scarlet (23.6)	..	16·00	3·00
51		5 m. yellow-orange	..	16·00	1·00
52		1 p. deep indigo (Silver) (July)	..	16·00	60
53		2 p. olive (4.8)	..	20·00	5·00
54		5 p. purple (4.8)	..	18·00	8·00
55		9 p. ochre (4.8)	..	30·00	90·00
56		10 p. ultramarine (4.8)	..	30·00	14·00
57		20 p. pale grey (4.8)	..	75·00	50·00
47/57			Set of 11	£225	£160

(b) P 14
58	3	1 m. sepia ..	..	..	—	£2500
59		20 p. pale grey	..	£12000	£3000

In this setting the Arabic and Hebrew characters are sharp and pointed and there is usually a break between the Arabic "S" and "T", though this is sometimes filled with ink. The space between the two groups of Hebrew characters is always 1¾ mm. The top of the " character in the Hebrew aligns with the remainder of the word.

1921 (Sept–Oct). *Optd with T* **7** ("PALESTINE" *in sans-serif letters*) *by Stamping Dept, Board of Inland Revenue, Somerset House, London. Wmk Royal Cypher in column. P* 15 × 14.
60	3	1 m. sepia ..	..	..	..	35	30
61		2 m. blue-green	..	..	..	35	30
62		3 m. yellow-brown	..	..	35	30
63		4 m. scarlet	..	..	..	50	50
64		5 m. yellow-orange	..	..	40	30
65		1 p. bright turquoise-blue	..	60	35
66		2 p. olive	..	..	..	70	40
67		5 p. deep purple	..	..	4·00	5·00
68		9 p. ochre	..	..	..	12·00	14·00
69		10 p. ultramarine	..	..	15·00	1500
70		20 p. pale grey	..	..	45·00	£1100
60/70			..	..	Set of 11	70·00	

(Printed and optd by Waterlow & Sons from new plates)

1922 (Sept–Nov). *T 3 (redrawn), optd with T 8. Wmk Mult Script CA. (a) P 14.*

71	3	1 m. sepia	..	..	30	30
		a. Deep brown..	..	..	40	30
		b. Opt inverted	..	..	—£11000	
		c. Opt double ..	..	..	£225	£375
72		2 m. yellow	..	..	35	30
		a. Orange-yellow	..	..	1·00	50
73		3 m. greenish blue	..	..	35	15
74		4 m. carmine-pink	..	..	30	20
75		5 m. orange	..	..	35	20
76		6 m. blue-green ..	..	..	65	30
77		7 m. yellow-brown	..	..	65	30
78		8 m. scarlet	..	..	65	30
79		1 p. grey..	..	..	65	30
80		13 m. ultramarine	..	..	50	15
81		2 p. olive	..	..	1·25	35
		a. Opt inverted	..	..	£350	£500
		b. Ochre	..	..	£110	5·50
82		5 p. deep purple..	..	..	4·50	1·25
82a		9 p. ochre	..	..	£1100	£225
83		10 p. light blue	..	..	22·00	7·50
		a. "E.F.F." for "E.E.F." in bottom panel		£600	£500
84		20 p. bright violet	..	..	£120	90·00

(b) P 15 × 14

86	3	5 p. deep purple	..	..	30·00	4·00
87		9 p. ochre	..	..	9·00	9·00
88		10 p. light blue	..	..	7·50	2·50
		a. "E.F.F." for "E.E.F." in bottom panel	£450	£325
89		20 p. bright violet	..	..	9·00	5·50
71/89 Optd "Specimen"		..	*Set of 15*	£400	

Most values can be found on thin paper.

In this issue the design of all denominations is the same size, 18 mm × 21½ mm. Varieties may be found with one or other of the stops between "E.E.F." missing.

BRITISH MANDATE TO THE LEAGUE OF NATIONS

The League of Nations granted a mandate to Great Britain for the administration of Palestine on 29 September 1923.

9 Rachel's Tomb   **10** Dome of the Rock

11 Citadel, Jerusalem   **12** Sea of Galilee

(Des F. Taylor. Typo Harrison)

1927 (1 June)–45. *Wmk Mult Script CA. P 13½ × 14½ (2 m. to 20 m.) or 14.*

90	9	2 m. greenish blue (14.8.27)	..	..	30	10
91		3 m. yellow-green	..	..	30	10
92	10	4 m. rose-pink (14.8.27)..	..	..	2·75	1·25
93	11	5 m. orange (14.8.27)	..	..	45	10
		a. From coils. Perf 14½×14 (1935)	13·00	18·00
		b. Yellow (12.44)	..	..	60	15
		c. Yellow. From coils. Perf 14½ × 14 (1945)	..	23·00	23·00
94	10	6 m. pale green (14.8.27)	..	2·25	1·50
		a. Deep green	..	..	50	20
95	11	7 m. scarlet (14.8.27)	..	..	4·00	1·00
96	10	8 m. yellow-brown (14.8.27)	..	11·00	5·00
97	9	10 m. slate (14.8.27)	..	..	40	10
		a. Grey. From coils. Perf 14½ × 14 (11.38)	..	22·00	23·00
		b. Grey (1944)..	..	..	40	10
98	10	13 m. ultramarine	..	..	3·75	30
99	11	20 m. dull olive-green (14.8.27)	..	1·40	15
		a. Bright olive-green (12.44)	..	1·40	15
100	12	50 m. deep dull purple (14.8.27)	..	1·00	25
		a. Bright purple (12.44)	..	1·00	20
101		90 m. bistre (14.8.27)	..	..	60·00	60·00
102		100 m. turquoise-blue (14.8.27)	..	2·00	50
103		200 m. deep violet (14.8.27)	..	8·00	4·50
		a. Bright violet (1928)	..	..	27·00	16·00
		b. Blackish violet (12.44)	..	5·50	3·00
90/103b			*Set of 14*	85·00	65·00
90/103 H/S "Specimen"			*Set of 14*	£325	

Three sets may be made of the above issue; one on thin paper, one on thicker paper with a ribbed appearance, and another on thick white paper without ribbing.

2 m. stamps in the grey colour of the 10 m., including an example postmarked in 1935, exist as do 50 m. stamps in blue, but it has not been established whether they were issued.

Nos. 90/1 and 93 exist in coils, constructed from normal sheets.

1932 (1 June)–44. *New values and colours. Wmk Mult Script CA. P 13½ × 14½ (4 m. to 15 m.) or 14.*

104	10	4 m. purple (1.11.32)	..	..	30	10
105	11	7 m. deep violet	..	..	45	10
106	10	8 m. scarlet	..	..	60	20
107		13 m. bistre (1.8.32)	..	..	40	10
108		15 m. ultramarine (1.8.32)	..	..	80	10
		a. Grey-blue (12.44)..	..	..	50	10
		b. Greenish blue	..	..	65	10
109	12	250 m. brown (15.1.42)	..	2·50	2·00
110		500 m. scarlet (15.1.42)	..	4·50	2·75
111		£P1 black (15.1.42)	..	..	5·00	3·25
104/11			*Set of 8*	13·00	7·50
104/11 Perf "Specimen"		*Set of 8*	£375	

No. 108 exists in coils, constructed from normal sheets.

POSTAL FISCALS

Type-set stamps inscribed "O.P.D.A." (= Ottoman Public Debt Administration) or "H.J.Z." (Hejaz Railway); British 1d. stamps of 1912–24 and Palestine stamps overprinted with one or other of the above groups of letters, or with the word "Devair", with or without surcharge of new value, are fiscal stamps. They are known used as postage stamps, alone, or with other stamps to make up the correct rates, and were passed by the postal authorities, although they were not definitely authorised for postal use.

POSTAGE DUE STAMPS

D 1   **D 2** (MILLIEME)   **D 3** (MIL)

(Typo Greek Orthodox Convent Press, Jerusalem)

1923 (1 Apr). *P 11.*

D1	D 1	1 m. yellow-brown	..	..	25·00	42·00
		a. Imperf (pair)	..	..	£250	
		b. Imperf between (horiz pair)	..	£1100	
D2		2 m. blue-green	..	..	22·00	32·00
		a. Imperf (pair)	..	..	£350	
D3		4 m. scarlet	..	..	22·00	38·00
D4		8 m. mauve	..	..	17·00	26·00
		a. Imperf (pair)	..	..	£120	
		b. Imperf between (horiz pair)	..	—£1800	
D5		13 m. steel blue	..	..	15·00	26·00
		a. Imperf between (horiz pair)	..	£850	
D1/5			*Set of 5*	90·00	£150

Perfectly centred and perforated stamps of this issue are worth considerably more than the above prices, which are for average specimens.

(Types D 2/3. Typo D.L.R.)

1924 (1 Dec). *Wmk Mult Script CA. P 14.*

D 6	D 2	1 m. deep brown	..	..	90	1·75
D 7		2 m. yellow	..	..	1·00	1·75
D 8		4 m. green	..	..	1·10	1·25
D 9		8 m. scarlet	..	..	2·50	90
D10		13 m. ultramarine	..	..	2·50	2·50
D11		5 p. violet	..	..	7·00	1·75
D6/11			*Set of 6*	13·50	9·00
D6/11 Optd "Specimen"		*Set of 6*	£275	

1928 (1 Feb)–45. *Wmk Mult Script CA. P 14.*

D12	D 3	1 m. brown	..	..	45	75
		a. Perf 15 × 14 (1944)	..	25·00	45·00
D13		2 m. yellow	..	..	55	60
D14		4 m. green	..	..	70	1·25
		a. Perf 15 × 14 (1945)	..	38·00	60·00
D15		6 m. orange-brown (10.33)	..	7·00	7·00
D16		8 m. carmine	..	..	1·50	70
D17		10 m. pale grey	..	..	1·25	60
D18		13 m. ultramarine	..	..	1·50	1·50
D19		20 m. pale olive-green	..	1·60	1·25
D20		50 m. violet	..	..	2·50	1·25
D12/20			*Set of 9*	15·00	13·50
D12/20 Perf (D15) or Optd (others) "Specimen"		*Set of 9*	£300	

The British Mandate terminated on 14 May 1948. Later issues of stamps and occupation issues will be found listed under Gaza, Israel and Jordan in Part 19 (*Middle East*) of this catalogue.

Papua New Guinea

NEW GUINEA

Stamps of Germany and later of GERMAN NEW GUINEA were used in New Guinea from 1888 until 1914.

During the interim period between the "G.R.I." surcharges and the "N.W. PACIFIC ISLANDS" overprints, stamps of AUSTRALIA perforated "OS" were utilised.

PRICES FOR STAMPS ON COVER

Nos. 1/30	*from* × 3
Nos. 31/2	—
Nos. 33/49	*from* × 3
Nos. 50/9	*from* × 2
Nos. 60/2	—
Nos. 63/4	*from* × 2
Nos. 64c/q	—
Nos. 65/81	*from* × 5
Nos. 83/5	—
Nos. 86/97	*from* × 5
No. 99	—
Nos. 100/16	*from* × 4
Nos. 117/18	—
Nos. 119/24	*from* × 4
Nos. 125/203	*from* × 2
Nos. 204/5	—
Nos. 206/11	*from* × 8
Nos. 212/25	*from* × 2
Nos. O1/33	*from* × 8

AUSTRALIAN OCCUPATION

Stamps of German New Guinea surcharged

G.R.I.   **G.R.I.**   **G.R.I.**
2d.   **1s.**   **1d.**
(1)   (2)   (3)

SETTINGS. The "G.R.I" issues of New Guinea were surcharged on a small hand press which could only accommodate one horizontal row of stamps at a time. In addition to complete sheets the surcharges were also applied to multiples and individual stamps which were first lightly affixed to plain paper backing sheets. Such backing sheets could contain a mixture of denominations, some of which required different surcharges.

Specialists recognise twelve settings of the low value surcharges (1d. to 8d.):

Setting 1 (Nos. 1/4, 7/11) shows the bottom of the "R" 6 mm from the top of the "d"

Setting 2 (Nos. 16/19, 22/6) shows the bottom of the "R" 5 mm from the top of the "d"

Setting 3 was used for the Official stamps (Nos. O1/2)

Setting 4, which included the 2½d. value for the first time, and Setting 5 showed individual stamps with either 6 mm or 5 mm spacing.

These five settings were for rows of ten stamps, but the remaining seven, used on odd stamps handed in for surcharging, were applied as strips of five only. One has, so far, not been reconstructed, but of the remainder three show the 6 mm spacing, two the 5 mm and one both.

On the shilling values the surcharges were applied as horizontal rows of four and the various settings divide into two groups, one with 3½ to 4½ mm between the bottom of the "R" and the top of numeral, and the second with 5½ mm between the "R" and numeral. The first group includes the very rare initial setting on which the space is 4 to 4½ mm.

G.R.I.   **G.R.I.**   **G.R.I.**
2d.   **1d.**   **1s.**

"1" for "I"   Short "1"   Large "S"
(Setting 1)   (Setting 1)   (Setting 1)

1914 (17 Oct)–15. *Stamps of 1901 surch.*

(a) As T 1. "G.R.I." and value 6 mm apart

1	1d. on 3 pf. brown	..	..	£250	£250
	a. "1" for "I"	..	..	£500	
	b. Short "1"	..	..	£500	
	c. "1" with straight top serif (Setting 6)	£500	
	d. "I" for "1" (Setting 12)	..	£700	
2	1d. on 5 pf. green	..	..	32·00	40·00
	a. "1" for "I"	..	..	£170	
	b. Short "1"	..	..	£170	
	c. "1" with straight top serif (Settings 6 and 9)	..	£225	
3	2d. on 10 pf. carmine	..	..	50·00	60·00
	a. "1" for "I"	..	..	£200	
4	2d. on 20 pf. ultramarine	..	35·00	42·00
	a. "1" for "I"	..	..	£170	
	e. Surch double, one "G.R.I." albino	£1800	
	f. Surch inverted	..	..	£3250	
5	2½d. on 10 pf. carmine (27.2.15)	..	65·00	£140
	a. Fraction bar omitted (Setting 9)	£1100	£1300
6	2½d. on 20 pf. ultramarine (27.2.15)	..	65·00	£140
	a. Fraction bar omitted (Setting 9)		
7	3d. on 25 pf. black and red/yellow	..	£160	£190
	a. "1" for "I"	..	..	£450	£500
8	3d. on 30 pf. black and orange/buff	..	£180	£225
	a. "1" for "I"	..	..	£475	
	e. Surch double	..	..	£3250	£3250
9	4d. on 40 pf. black and carmine	..	£225	£275
	a. "1" for "I"	..	..	£600	
	e. Surch double	..	..	£850	£1300
	f. Surch inverted	..	..	£3250	
10	5d. on 50 pf. black and purple/buff	..	£400	£550
	a. "1" for "I"	..	..	£850	£1000
	e. Surch double	..	..	£3250	
11	8d. on 80 pf. black and carmine/rose	..	£600	£750
	a. "1" for "I"	..	..	£1300	
	d. No stop after "d"	..	..	£1600	
	e. Error. Surch "G.R.I. 4d."	..	£2500	

(b) As T 2. "G.R.I." and value 3½ to 4 mm apart

12	1s. on 1 m. carmine	..	..	£1400	£1900
	a. Large "s"	..	..	£3500	£3500
13	2s. on 2 m. blue	..	..	£1500	£2250
	a. Large "s"	..	..	£3500	£4500
	c. Error. Surch "G.R.I. 5s."	..	£9000	
14	3s. on 3 m. violet-black	..	..	£3000	£3750
	a. Large "s"	..	..	£5000	
	b. No stop after "I" (Setting 3)	£6000	£6000
15	5s. on 5 m. carmine and black	..	£5000	£6000
	a. Large "s"	..	..	£7500	
	b. No stop after "I" (Setting 3) ..	£7500	£9500
	c. Error. Surch "G.R.I. 1s."	..	£14000	

G.R.I.   **G.R.I.**
3d.   **5d.**
Thick "3"   Thin "5"
(Setting 2)   (Setting 2)

1914 (16 Dec)–**15.** *Stamps of 1901 surch.*
(a) As T 1. *"G.R.I." and value 5 mm apart*

16	1d. on 3 pf. brown	40·00	50·00
	a. "I" for "1" (Setting 11)	£250	
	b. Short "1" (Setting 2)	£180	
	c. "1" with straight top serif (Settings 2 and 6)	70·00	85·00
	e. Surch double	£275	£400
	f. Surch double, one inverted	£1300	
	g. Surch inverted	£800	£1200
	h. Error. Surch "G.R.I. 4d."	£3500	
17	1d. on 5 pf. green	14·00	22·00
	b. Short "1" (Setting 2)	£110	£140
	c. "1" with straight top serif (Setting 2)	32·00	48·00
	e. "d" inverted	†	£800
	f. "1d" inverted	†	£2500
	g. "G.R.I." without stops or spaces	£2500	
	ga. "G.R.I." without stops, but with normal spaces	—	£2500
	h. "G.I.R." instead of "G.R.I."	£3250	£3500
	i. Surch double	£850	
18	2d. on 10 pf. carmine	18·00	26·00
	e. No stop after "d" (Setting 2)	90·00	£130
	f. Stop before, instead of after, "G" (Settings 4 and 5)	£2500	
	g. Surch double	£3750	£3750
	h. Surch double, one inverted	—	£2000
	i. In vert pair with No. 20	£8500	
	j. In horiz pair with No. 20	£8500	
	k. Error. Surch "G.R.I. 1d."	£2750	£2000
	l. Error. Surch "G.I.R. 3d."	£3500	
19	2d. on 20 pf. ultramarine	24·00	32·00
	e. No stop after "d" (Setting 2)	70·00	£100
	f. No. stop after "I" (Setting 11)	£500	
	g. "R" inverted (Settings 4 and 5)	—	£2000
	h. Surch double	£650	£1600
	i. Surch double, one inverted	£1100	£1600
	j. Surch inverted	£2000	£2750
	k. Albino surch (in horiz pair with normal)	£5500	
	l. In vert pair with No. 21	£5000	£6500
	m. Error. Surch "G.R.I. 1d."	£3500	£3500
20	2½d. on 10 pf. carmine (27.2.15)	£160	£275
21	2½d. on 20 pf. ultramarine (27.2.15)	£1200	£1500
22	3d. on 25 pf. black and red/*yellow*	80·00	£100
	e. Thick "3"	£450	
	f. Surch double	£2250	£3000
	g. Surch inverted	£2250	£3000
	h. Surch omitted (in horiz pair with normal)	£5500	
	i. Error. Surch "G.R.I. 1d."	£5500	
23	3d. on 30 pf. black and orange/*buff*	70·00	95·00
	e. No stop after "d" (Setting 2)	£425	
	f. Thick "3"	£400	
	g. Surch double	£850	£1300
	h. Surch double, one inverted	£1000	£1500
	i. Surch double, both inverted	£2250	£3000
	j. Surch inverted	£2000	
	k. Albino surch	£5500	
	l. Surch omitted (in vert pair with normal)	£3250	
	m. Error. Surch "G.R.I. 1d."	£2500	£3500
24	4d. on 40 pf. black and carmine	85·00	£110
	e. Surch double	£800	
	f. Surch double, one inverted	£1100	
	g. Surch double, both inverted	£3000	
	h. Surch inverted	£1600	
	i. Error. Surch "G.R.I. 1d."	£1600	
	ia. Surch "G.R.I. 1d." inverted	£2750	
	j. Error. Surch "G.R.I. 3d." double	£4500	
	k. No stop after "I" (Setting 11)	£1500	
25	5d. on 50 pf. black and purple/*buff*	£120	£150
	e. Thin "5"	£700	£1200
	f. Surch double	£800	
	g. Surch double, one inverted	£2000	£3250
	h. Surch double, both inverted	£2500	£3250
	i. Surch inverted	£1600	
	j. Error. Surch "G.I.R. 3d."	£5000	
26	8d. on 80 pf. black and carmine/*rose*	£300	£400
	e. Surch double	£1600	£1900
	f. Surch double, one inverted	£1500	£1900
	g. Surch triple	£1700	£2000
	h. Surch inverted	£2750	£3250
	i. Error. Surch "G.R.I. 3d."	£5500	

(b) As T 2. *"G.R.I." and value 5½ mm apart*

27	1s. on 1 m. carmine	£2000	£2750
	a. No stop after "I" (Setting 7)	£4000	
28	2s. on 2 m. blue	£2250	£3500
29	3s. on 3 m. violet-black	£3500	£4750
	a. "G.R.I." double	£10000	
30	5s. on 5 m. carmine and black	£9000	£11000

1915. *Nos.* 18 *and* 19 *further surch as in T* 3.

31	"1" on 2d. on 10 pf.	£9000	£9000
32	"1" on 2d. on 20 pf.	£9000	£6000

OFFICIAL STAMPS

O. S.
G.R.I.
1d.

(O 3*a*)

1915 (27 Feb). *Stamps of* 1901 *surch as Type O* 3*a.* *"G.R.I." and value* 3½ *mm apart.*

O1	1d. on 3 pf. brown	25·00	70·00
	a. "1" and "d" spaced	75·00	
	b. Surch double	£2000	
O2	1d. on 5 pf. green	75·00	£130
	a. "1" and "d" spaced	£150	

German New Guinea Registration Labels surcharged

4   4a

G.R.I.
3d.

Sans serif "G" and different "3"

1915 (Jan). *Registration Labels surch "G.R.I.* 3d." *in settings of five or ten and used for postage. Each black and red on buff. Inscr "(Deutsch Neuguinea)" spelt in various ways as indicated.* P 14 (No. 43) *or* 11½ (*others*).

I. *With name of town in sans-serif letters as T* 4

33	Rabaul "(Deutsch Neuguinea)"	£110	£150
	a. "G.R.I. 3d." double	£1200	£1400
	b. No bracket before "Deutsch"	£475	£650
	ba. No bracket and surch double	£3250	
	d. "(Deutsch-Neuguinea)"	£170	£225
	da. "G.R.I. 3d." double	£3250	£3250
	db. No stop after "I"	£550	
	dc. "G.R.I. 3d" inverted	£3000	
	dd. No bracket before "Deutsch"	£750	
	de. No bracket after "Neuguinea"	£750	
34	Deulon "(Deutsch Neuguinea)"	£5500	
35	Friedrich-Wilhelmshafen "(Deutsch Neuguinea)"	£120	£300
	a. No stop after "d"	£275	
	b. "G" omitted	£2000	
	c. Sans-serif "G"	£3250	
	d. Sans-serif "G" and different "3"	£2750	
	e. Surch inverted	†	£3000
	f. "(Deutsch-Neuguinea)"	£140	£300
	fa. No stop after "d"	£325	
36	Herbertshöhe "(Deutsch Neuguinea)"	£170	£350
	a. No stop after "d"	£375	
	b. No stop after "I"	£650	
	c. "G" omitted	£2500	
	d. Surch omitted (in horiz pair with normal)	£4250	
	e. "(Deutsch Neu-Guinea)"	£300	
37	Käwieng "(Deutsch-Neuguinea)"	£425	
	a. No bracket after "Neuguinea"	£1800	
	b. "Deutsch Neu-Guinea"	£150	£300
	ba. No stop after "d"	£325	
	bb. "G.R.I." double	£1600	
	bc. "3d." double	£1600	
	bd. "G" omitted	£3000	
38	Kieta "(Deutsch-Neuguinea)"	£300	£500
	a. No bracket before "Deutsch"	£950	£1300
	b. No stop after "d"	£650	
	c. Surch omitted (righthand stamp of horiz pair)	£3500	
	e. No stop after "I"	£900	
	f. "G" omitted	£2750	
39	Manus "(Deutsch Neuguinea)"	£180	£350
	a. "G.R.I. 3d." double	£1800	
	b. No bracket before "Deutsch"	£700	£900
40	Stephansort "(Deutsch Neu-Guinea)"	†	£1500
	a. No stop after "d"	†	£3000

II. *With name of town in letters with serifs as T* 4a

41	Friedrich Wilhelmshafen "(Deutsch-Neuguinea)"	£150	£300
	b. No stop after "d"	£325	£500
	c. No stop after "I"	£600	£900
	d. No bracket before "Deutsch"	£700	£1000
	e. No bracket after "Neuguinea"	£700	£1000
42	Käwieng "(Deutsch Neuguinea)"	£130	£275
	a. No stop after "d"	£275	
43	Manus "(Deutsch-Neuguinea)"	£1300	£1800
	a. No stop after "I"	£2250	£2250

Stamps of Marshall Islands surcharged

SETTINGS. The initial supply of Marshall Islands stamps, obtained from Nauru, was surcharged with Setting 2 (5 mm between "R" and "d") on the penny values and with the 3½ to 4 setting on the shilling stamps.

Small quantities subsequently handed in were surcharged, often on the same backing sheet as German New Guinea values, with Settings 6, 7 or 12 (all 6 mm between "R" and "d") for the penny values and with a 5½ mm setting for the shilling stamps.

1914 (16 Dec). *Stamps of* 1901 *surch.*
(a) As T 1. *"G.R.I." and value* 5 *mm apart*

50	1d. on 3 pf. brown	40·00	55·00
	c. "1" with straight top serif (Setting 2)	95·00	£130
	d. ".G.R.I." and "1" with straight top serif (Settings 4 and 5)	†	£3250
	e. Surch inverted	£1600	
51	1d. on 5 pf. green	42·00	50·00
	c. "1" with straight top serif (Settings 2 and 11)	£100	£120
	d. "I" for "1" (Setting 11)	£425	
	e. "1" and "d" spaced	£325	£350
	f. Surch double	£850	£1300
	g. Surch inverted	£1000	
52	2d. on 10 pf. carmine	14·00	22·00
	e. No stop after "G" (Setting 2)	£500	
	f. Surch double	£800	£1500
	g. Surch double, one inverted	£950	£1500
	h. Surch inverted	£1300	
	i. Surch sideways	£2500	
53	2d. on 20 pf. ultramarine	15·00	25·00
	e. No stop after "d" (Setting 2)	40·00	70·00
	f. Surch double	£900	£1600
	g. Surch double, one inverted	£1700	£2000
	i. Surch inverted	£2000	£2000

54	3d. on 25 pf. black and red/*yellow*	£250	£325
	e. No stop after "d" (Settings 2 and 11)	£500	£650
	f. Thick "3"	£700	
	g. Surch double	£1000	£1500
	h. Surch double, one inverted	£1000	
	i. Surch inverted	£1800	
55	3d. on 30 pf. black and orange/*buff*	£275	£350
	e. No stop after "d" (Setting 2)	£550	£650
	f. Thick "3"	£750	
	g. Surch inverted	£1600	£1800
	h. Surch double	£1500	
56	4d. on 40 pf. black and carmine	85·00	£120
	e. No stop after "d" (Setting 2)	£250	£350
	f. "d" omitted (Setting 2)	†	£2750
	g. Surch double	£1500	£1800
	h. Surch triple	£2750	
	i. Surch inverted	£1800	
	j. Error. Surch "G.R.I. 1d."	£4000	
	k. Error. Surch "G.R.I. 3d."	£4000	
57	5d. on 50 pf. black and purple/*buff*	£130	£170
	e. Thin "5"	£2250	
	f. "d" omitted (Setting 2)	£1000	
	g. Surch double	£2250	
	h. Surch inverted	£2750	
58	8d. on 80 pf. black and carmine/*rose*	£375	£475
	e. Surch double	£1800	
	f. Surch double, both inverted	£2500	£3000
	g. Surch triple	£3250	
	h. Surch inverted	£2250	£3000

(b) As T 2. *"G.R.I." and value* 3½-4 *mm apart*

59	1s. on 1 m. carmine	£1600	£2250
	b. No stop after "I"	£2750	
	e. Surch double	£7500	
60	2s. on 2 m. blue	£1100	£1600
	b. No stop after "I"	£2250	£3000
	e. Surch double	£7500	
	f. Surch double, one inverted	£6500	£6500
61	3s. on 3 m. violet-black	£2750	£3750
	b. No stop after "I"	£4000	
	e. Surch double	£7500	£9000
62	5s. on 5 m. carmine and black	£4750	£6000
	e. Surch double, one inverted	†	£12000

1915. *Nos.* 52 *and* 53 *further surch as in T* 3.

63	"1" on 2d. on 10 pf. carmine	£140	£170
	a. "1" double	£6000	
	b. "1" inverted	£6000	£6000
64	"1" on 2d. on 20 pf. ultramarine	£3000	£2000
	a. On No 53e	£5000	£2750
	b. "1" inverted	£7000	£7000

1915. *Stamps of* 1901 *surch.*
(a) As T 1. *"G.R.I." and value* 6 *mm apart*

64c	1d. on 3 pf. brown		£600
	cc. "1" with straight top serif (Setting 6)	†	£1600
	cd. "I" for "1" (Setting 12)	£900	
	ce. Surch inverted	£3000	
64d	1d. on 5 pf. green	£650	£1300
	dc. "1" with straight top serif (Setting 6)	£900	
	dd. "I" for "1" (Setting 12)	£900	
	de. Surch inverted	£3000	
	df. Surch double	£3000	
64e	2d. on 10 pf. carmine	£950	£1400
	ea. Surch sideways	£3500	
64f	2d. on 20 pf. ultramarine	£800	£1400
	fe. Surch inverted	£3000	
64g	2½d. on 10 pf. carmine	£4750	
64h	2½d. on 20 pf. ultramarine	£7500	
64i	3d. on 25 pf. black and red/*yellow*	£1100	£1600
64j	3d. on 30 pf. black and orange/*buff*	£1100	£1600
	je. Error. Surch "G.R.I. 3d."	£4000	
64k	4d. on 40 pf. black and carmine	£1100	£1600
	ke. Surch double	£3250	
	kf. Surch inverted	£3250	
64l	5d. on 50 pf. black and purple/*buff*	£950	£1600
	le. Surch double	£3250	
64m	8d. on 80 pf. black and carmine/*rose*	£1600	£2250
	me. Surch inverted	£3750	

(b) As T 2. *"G.R.I." and value* 5½ *mm apart*

64n	1s. on 1 m. carmine	£4750	
	na. Large "s" (Setting 5)	£6000	
	nb. No stop after "I" (Setting 7)	£6000	
64o	2s. on 2 m. blue	£3750	
	oe. Surch double, one inverted	£11000	
64p	3s. on 3 m. violet-black	£6500	
	pe. Surch inverted	£11000	
64q	5s. on 5 m. carmine and black	£9000	
	qa. Large "s" (Setting 5)	£11000	

Stamps of Australia overprinted

T 1 *of Australia*   *T* 5a *of Australia*

W 2 *of Australia*   *W* 5 *of Australia*

W 6 of Australia

N. W. PACIFIC ISLANDS. (a)	N. W. PACIFIC ISLANDS. (b)	N. W. PACIFIC ISLANDS. (c)

(6)

1915–16. *Stamps of Australia optd in black as T* **6** (*a*), (*b*) *or* (*c*).

(i) *T* **5a.** *W* **5** *of Australia. P* 14 (4 Jan–15 March 1915)

65	½d. green		..	1·25	5·50
66	½d. bright green	..	..	1·75	6·00
67	1d. pale rose (Die I) (4.1)		..	4·25	4·25
68	1d. dull red (Die I)		..	5·50	4·75
69	1d. carmine-red (Die I)	..	..	5·00	4·50
	a. Substituted cliché		..	—	£700
69b	1d. carmine-red (Die II)		..	£250	£200
	c. Substituted cliché		..		£1100
70	4d. yellow-orange		..	3·75	9·50
	a. Line through "FOUR PENCE"			£350	£550
	b. Pale orange-yellow		..	15·00	24·00
71	4d. chrome-yellow		..	£250	£275
72	5d. brown		..	3·25	15·00

(ii) *T* **1.** *W* **2** *of Australia. P* 12 (4 Jan 1915–March 1916)

73	2d. grey (Die I)		..	17·00	30·00
74	2½d. indigo (4.1.15)		..	2·75	15·00
76	3d. yellow-olive (Die I)		..	17·00	35·00
	a. Die II		..	£300	£350
	ab. In pair with Die I		..	£500	£550
77	3d. greenish olive (Die I)		..	£190	£250
	a. Die II		..		£1300
	ab. In pair with Die I		..		£2250
78	6d. ultramarine ..		..	26·00	50·00
	a. Retouched "E"		..		£5000
79	9d. violet		..	35·00	55·00
81	1s. green		..	38·00	55·00
83	5s. grey and yellow (3.16)		..	£750	£900
84	10s. grey and pink (12.15)		..	£110	£160
85	£1 brown and ultramarine (12.15)		..	£450	£650

(iii) *T* **1.** *W* **5** *of Australia. P* 12 (Oct 1915–July 1916)

86	2d. grey (Die I) ..		..	7·50	12·00
87	2½d. indigo (7.16)		..	£9500	£9000
88	6d. ultramarine		..	9·50	20·00
89	9d. violet (12.15)		..	13·00	15·00
90	1s. emerald (12.15)		..	9·00	23·00
91	2s. brown (12.15)		..	80·00	£100
92	5s. grey and yellow (12.15)		..	80·00	£100

(iv) *T* **1.** *W* **6** *of Australia. P* 12 (Dec 1915–Aug 1916)

94	2d. grey (Die I)		..	4·75	11·00
	a. In pair with Die IIA		..	£180	
96	3d. yellow-olive (Die I)		..	4·75	11·00
	a. Die II		..	75·00	£100
	ab. In pair with Die I		..	£140	
97	2s. brown (8.16) ..		..	27·00	45·00
99	£1 brown and ultramarine (8.16)		..	£300	£450

Dates for Nos. 67 and 74 are issue dates. All other dates are those of despatch. Nos. 65/6, 68/73, 76/81 were despatched on 15 March 1915.

For Die IIA of 2d. see note below Australia No. 45.

SETTINGS. Type **6** exists in three slightly different versions, illustrated above as (*a*), (*b*), *and* (*c*). These differ in the letters "S" of "ISLANDS" as follows:

(*a*) Both "SS" normal.
(*b*) First "S" with small head and large tail and second "S" normal.
(*c*) Both "SS" with small head and large tail.

Type **11**, which also shows the examples of "S" as the normal version, can be identified from Type **6**(*a*) by the relative position of the second and third lines of the overprint. On Type **6**a the "P" of "PACIFIC" is exactly over the first "S" of "ISLANDS". On Type **11** the "P" appears over the space between "I" and "S".

It has been established, by the study of minor variations, that there are actually six settings of the "N.W. PACIFIC ISLANDS" overprint, including that represented by T **11**, but the following are the different arrangements of Type **6**(*a*), (*b*), and (*c*) which occur.

A. Horizontal rows 1 and 2 all Type (*a*). Row 3 all Type (*b*). Rows 4 and 5 all Type (*c*).
B. (½d. green only). As A, except that the types in the bottom row run (*c*) (*c*) (*c*) (*b*) (*c*).
C. As A, but bottom row now shows types (*a*) (*c*) (*c*) (*c*) (*b*) (*c*).

Horizontal strips and pairs showing varieties (*a*) and (*c*), or (*b*) and (*c*) *se-tenant* are scarce.

The earliest printing of the 1d. and 2½d. values was made on sheets with margin attached on two sides, the later printings being on sheets from which the margins had been removed. In this printing the vertical distances between the overprints are less than in later printings, so that in the lower horizontal rows of the sheet the overprint is near the top of the stamp.

The settings used on King George stamps and on the Kangaroo type are similar, but the latter stamps being smaller the overprints are closer together in the vertical rows.

PURPLE OVERPRINTS. We no longer differentiate between purple and black overprints in the above series. In our opinion the two colours are nowadays insufficiently distinct to warrant separation.

PRICES. The prices quoted for Nos. 65 to 101 apply to stamps with opts Types **6** (*a*) or **6** (*c*). Stamps with opt Type **6** (*b*) are worth a 25 per cent premium. Vertical strips of three, showing (*a*), (*b*) and (*c*), are worth from four times the prices quoted for singles as Types **6** (*a*) or **6** (*c*).

N. W. PACIFIC ISLANDS.

One Penny	
(10)	(11)

1918 (23 May). *Nos.* 72 *and* 81 *surch locally with T* **10.**

100	1d. on 5d. brown		..	90·00	80·00
101	1d. on 1s. green	..	..	90·00	80·00
	Types **6** (*a*), (*b*), (*c*) occur on these stamps also.				

1918–23. *Stamps of Australia optd with T* **11** ("P" of "PACIFIC" *over space between* "I" *and* "S" *of* "ISLANDS").

(i) *T* **5a.** *W* **5** *of Australia. P* 14

102	½d. green		..	50	3·25
103	1d. carmine-red (Die I)		..	1·75	1·60
	a. Substituted cliché			£800	£500
	b. Rosine. Rough paper, locally gummed (perfd "OS")			£400	£120
103c	1d. carmine-red (Die II)		..	£120	48·00
	d. Substituted cliché			£800	£500
	e. Rosine. Rough paper, locally gummed (perfd "OS")			—	£400
104	4d. yellow-orange (1919)		..	3·25	16·00
	a. Line through "FOUR PENCE"			£1000	£1200
105	5d. brown (1919)		..	1·75	12·00

(ii) *T* **1.** *W* **6** *of Australia. P* 12

106	2d. grey (Die I) (1919)		..	2·50	16·00
	a. Die II		..	9·00	38·00
107	2½d. indigo (1919)		..	3·00	15·00
	a. "1" of "½" omitted			£5500	£5500
108	2½d. blue (1920)		..	6·50	24·00
109	3d. greenish olive (Die I) (1919)		..	16·00	21·00
	a. Die II			42·00	60·00
	ab. In pair with Die I			£300	
	b. Light olive (Die II) (1923)		..	12·00	19·00
110	6d. ultramarine (1919)		..	4·50	14·00
111	6d. greyish ultramarine (1922)		..	42·00	65·00
112	9d. violet (1919)		..	6·50	35·00
113	1s. emerald		..	6·50	28·00
114	1s. pale blue-green (1919)		..	13·00	28·00
115	2s. brown (1919)		..	28·00	38·00
116	5s. grey and yellow (1919)		..	60·00	60·00
117	10s. grey and bright pink (1919)		..	£150	£200
118	£1 brown and ultramarine (1922)..		..	£2750	

(iii) *T* **5a.** *W* **6**a *of Australia* (*Mult Crown A*). *P* 14

119	½d. green (1919)		..	40	3·50

(iv) *T* **5a.** *W* **5** *of Australia. Colour changes and new value*

120	1d. bright violet (1922)		..	1·00	5·50
121	2d. orange (1921)		..	2·75	4·50
122	2d. scarlet (1922)		..	4·50	8·00
123	4d. violet (1922)		..	27·00	45·00
	a. "FOUR PENCE" in thinner letters			£750	
124	4d. ultramarine (1922)		..	10·00	45·00
	a. "FOUR PENCE" in thinner letters			£750	
120/4			*Set of* 5	42·00	95·00

Type **11** differs from Type **6** (*a*) in the position of the "P" of "PACIFIC", which is further to the left in Type **11**.

MANDATED TERRITORY OF NEW GUINEA

PRINTERS. See note at the beginning of Australia.

12 Native Village	(13)

(Des R. Harrison. Eng T. Harrison. Recess Note Printing Branch, Treasury, Melbourne, from 1926 Note Ptg Branch, Commonwealth Bank of Australia, Melbourne).

1925–28. *P* 11.

125	12	½d. orange	..	2·00	3·75
126		1d. green	..	2·00	3·75
126a		1½d. orange-vermilion (1926)	..	2·25	2·25
127		2d. claret	..	2·00	4·50
128		3d. blue	..	4·25	4·00
129		4d. olive-green	..	11·00	15·00
130		6d. dull yellow-brown	..	19·00	42·00
		a. Olive-bistre (1927)	..	6·00	42·00
		b. Pale yellow-bistre (1928)	..	4·50	42·00
131		9d. dull purple (*to* violet)	..	13·00	40·00
132		1s. dull blue-green	..	15·00	22·00
133		2s. brown-lake	..	30·00	40·00
134		5s. olive-bistre	..	48·00	65·00
135		10s. dull rose	..	£110	£160
136		£1 dull olive-green	..	£200	£250
125/36			*Set of* 13	£400	£550

1931 (8 June). *Air. Optd with T* **13.** *P* 11.

137	12	½d. orange	..	75	3·25
138		1d. green	..	1·60	3·50
139		1½d. orange-vermilion	..	1·00	4·50
140		2d. claret	..	1·00	7·00
141		3d. blue	..	1·50	11·00
142		4d. olive-green	..	1·25	7·50
143		6d. pale yellow-bistre	..	1·75	13·00
144		9d. violet	..	3·00	16·00
145		1s. dull blue-green	..	7·00	30·00
146		2s. brown-lake	..	7·00	30·00
147		5s. olive-bistre	..	20·00	55·00
148		10s. bright pink	..	65·00	90·00
149		£1 olive-grey	..	£110	£150
137/49			*Set of* 13	£200	£350

NEW INFORMATION

The editor is always interested to correspond with people who have new information that will improve or correct the Catalogue.

---

14 Raggiana Bird of Paradise (Dates either side of value)	AIR MAIL (15)

(Recess John Ash, Melbourne)

1931 (2 Aug). *Tenth Anniv of Australian Administration. T* **14** (*with dates*). *P* 11.

150	14	1d. green	..	1·50	40
151		1½d. vermilion	..	4·00	8·50
152		2d. claret	..	3·00	2·00
153		3d. blue	..	3·00	4·00
154		4d. olive-green	..	5·00	12·00
155		5d. deep blue-green	..	3·50	14·00
156		6d. bistre-brown	..	3·00	14·00
157		9d. violet	..	5·50	14·00
158		1s. pale blue-green	..	5·00	15·00
159		2s. brown-lake	..	6·50	25·00
160		5s. olive-brown	..	35·00	48·00
161		10s. bright pink	..	75·00	£120
162		£1 olive-grey	..	£140	£200
150/62			*Set of* 13	£250	£425

1931 (2 Aug). *Air. Optd with T* **15.**

163	14	½d. orange	..	75	1·75
164		1d. green	..	1·75	2·75
165		1½d. vermilion	..	1·40	7·00
166		2d. claret	..	1·00	2·75
167		3d. blue	..	3·00	3·25
168		4d. olive-green	..	3·00	5·00
169		5d. deep blue-green	..	3·50	6·50
170		6d. bistre-brown	..	6·00	21·00
171		9d. violet	..	7·50	15·00
172		1s. pale blue-green	..	6·50	15·00
173		2s. dull lake	..	10·00	42·00
174		5s. olive-brown	..	32·00	60·00
175		10s. bright pink	..	60·00	£100
176		£1 olive-grey	..	£100	£170
163/76			*Set of* 14	£200	£350

1932 (30 June)–**1934.** *T* **14** (*redrawn without dates*). *P* 11.

177		1d. green	..	50	20
178		1½d. claret	..	60	7·50
179		2d. vermilion	..	55	20
179a		2½d. green (14.9.34)	..	4·00	9·00
180		3d. blue	..	90	80
180a		3½d. aniline carmine (14.9.34)	..	10·00	9·00
181		4d. olive-green	..	75	2·75
182		5d. deep blue-green	..	75	70
183		6d. bistre-brown	..	1·00	3·00
184		9d. violet	..	7·50	17·00
185		1s. blue-green	..	4·00	10·00
186		2s. dull lake..	..	4·00	16·00
187		5s. olive	..	27·00	45·00
188		10s. pink	..	60·00	80·00
189		£1 olive-grey	..	90·00	£100
177/89			*Set of* 15	£190	£250

1932 (30 June)–**34.** *Air. T* **14** (*redrawn without dates*), *optd with T* **15.** *P* 11.

190		½d. orange	..	40	1·50
191		1d. green	..	40	1·50
192		1½d. claret	..	60	4·50
193		2d. vermilion	..	60	30
193a		2½d. green (14.9.34)	..	3·50	2·25
194		3d. blue	..	1·10	1·60
194a		3½d. aniline carmine (14.9.34)	..	3·50	3·25
195		4d. olive-green	..	2·50	7·00
196		5d. deep blue-green	..	4·50	7·50
197		6d. bistre-brown	..	2·75	10·00
198		9d. violet	..	5·50	9·00
199		1s. pale blue-green	..	4·50	7·50
200		2s. dull lake..	..	5·50	30·00
201		5s. olive-brown	..	45·00	55·00
202		10s. pink	..	65·00	70·00
203		£1 olive-grey	..	75·00	55·00
190/203			*Set of* 16	£190	£200

The ½d. orange redrawn without dates exists without overprint, but it is believed that this was not issued (*Price* £125 *un*).

16 Bulolo Goldfields

(Recess John Ash, Melbourne)

1935 (1 May). *Air. P* 11.

204	16	£2 bright violet	..	£225	£130
205		£5 emerald-green	..	£600	£450

**HIS MAJESTY'S JUBILEE.
1910 — 1935**

(17)	18

1935 (27 June). *Silver Jubilee. As Nos.* 177 *and* 179, *but shiny paper. Optd with T* **17.**

206		1d. green	..	45	35
207		2d. vermilion..	..	80	35

(Recess John Ash, Melbourne)

1937 (18 May). *Coronation.* P 11.

208	18	2d. scarlet	.. ..	50	30
209		3d. blue	.. ..	70	30
210		5d. green	.. ..	50	35
		a. Red-entry (design completely duplicated) (Pl 2a R. 5/2)	..	65·00	80·00
211		1s. purple	.. ..	1·10	35
208/11	.. ..		*Set of* 4	2·50	1·10

(Recess John Ash, Melbourne)

1939 (1 Mar). *Air. Inscr* "AIR MAIL POSTAGE" *at foot.* P 11.

212	16	1d. orange	.. ..	80	4·00
213		1d. green	.. ..	2·50	3·00
214		1½d. claret	.. ..	80	5·50
215		2d. vermilion	.. ..	4·00	3·00
216		3d. blue	.. ..	5·00	11·00
217		4d. yellow-olive	..	3·00	7·50
218		5d. deep green	..	3·00	2·25
219		6d. bistre-brown	..	7·00	11·00
220		9d. violet	.. ..	7·00	16·00
221		1s. pale blue-green	..	8·50	16·00
222		2s. dull lake	.. ..	45·00	40·00
223		5s. olive-brown	..	90·00	85·00
224		10s. pink	.. ..	£250	£190
225		£1 olive-green	..	£100	£110
212/25	.. ..		*Set of* 14	£475	£450

OFFICIAL STAMPS

Australian stamps perforated "O S" exist with overprint Type **11** for use in New Guinea. We do not list such varieties.

(O 1) (O 2)

1925-31. *Optd with Type* O **1.** P 11.

O3	12	1d. green	.. ..	80	4·25
O4		1½d. orange-vermilion (1931)	..	5·50	17·00
O5		2d. claret	.. ..	1·60	3·75
O6		3d. blue ..	.. ..	2·00	5·50
O7		4d. olive-green ..	..	3·00	8·50
O8		6d. olive-bistre	..	17·00	40·00
		a. *Pale yellow-bistre* (1931)		7·00	40·00
O9		9d. violet ..	..	3·75	40·00
O10		1s. dull blue-green	..	5·00	40·00
O11		2s. brown-lake	..	27·00	75·00
O3/11			*Set of* 9	50·00	£200

1931 (2 Aug). *Optd with Type* O **2.** P 11.

O12	14	1d. green	.. ..	1·50	12·00
O13		1½d. vermilion	..	2·25	12·00
O14		2d. claret	.. ..	4·00	7·00
O15		3d. blue	.. ..	2·25	6·00
O16		4d. olive-green ..	..	2·25	8·50
O17		5d. deep blue-green ..		5·50	12·00
O18		6d. bistre-brown	..	8·50	17·00
O19		9d. violet ..	..	9·00	28·00
O20		1s. pale blue-green	..	12·00	28·00
O21		2s. brown-lake	..	35·00	75·00
O22		5s. olive-brown ..		£100	£160
O12/22			*Set of* 11	£160	£325

1932 (30 June)-**34.** *T* **14** (*redrawn without dates*), *optd with Type* O **2.** P 11.

O23		1d. green	.. ..	2·25	3·50
O24		1½d. claret	..	2·75	12·00
O25		2d. vermilion	..	2·75	2·75
O26		2½d. green (14.9.34)	..	2·75	7·50
O27		3d. blue	.. ..	5·50	15·00
O28		3½d. aniline carmine (14.9.34)		3·00	10·00
O29		4d. olive-green	..	4·50	14·00
O30		5d. deep blue-green ..		4·50	14·00
O31		6d. bistre-brown	..	6·00	28·00
O32		9d. violet	..	10·00	40·00
O33		1s. pale blue-green	..	15·00	28·00
O34		2s. dull lake	..	35·00	85·00
O35		5s. olive-brown	..	£120	£170
O23/35			*Set of* 13	£190	£375

Civil Administration in New Guinea was suspended in 1942, following the Japanese invasion.

Various New Guinea stamps exist overprinted with an anchor and three Japanese characters in a style similar to the Japanese Naval Control Area overprints found on the stamps of Netherlands Indies. These overprints on New Guinea are bogus and are believed to have originated in Japan during 1947.

On resumption, after the Japanese defeat in 1945, Australian stamps were used until the appearance of the issue for the combined territories of Papua & New Guinea.

PAPUA (BRITISH NEW GUINEA)

Stamps of QUEENSLAND were used in British New Guinea (Papua) from at least 1885 onwards. Post Offices were opened at Daru (1894), Kulumadau (Woodlarks) (1899), Nivani (1899), Port Moresby (1885), Samarai (1888), Sudest (1899) and Tamata (1899). Stamps were usually cancelled "N.G." (at Port Moresby from 1885) or "BNG" (without stops at Samarai or with stops at the other offices) from 1888. Queensland stamps were replaced in Papua by the issue of 1901.

PRICES FOR STAMPS ON COVER

Nos. 1/7	*from* × 15
No. 8	
Nos. 9/14a	*from* × 20
Nos. 14c/21	*from* × 5
No. 22	
Nos. 23/9a	*from* × 6
No. 29b	
Nos. 30/2	*from* × 9
Nos. 34/8b	*from* × 5
No. 38c	
Nos. 38d/71	*from* × 8
Nos. 72/4	
Nos. 75/92a	*from* × 8
Nos. 93/8	*from* × 10
Nos. 99/109	*from* × 6
Nos. 110/11	
Nos. 112/14	*from* × 6
No. 115	
Nos. 116/28	*from* × 5
Nos. 130/53	*from* × 4
Nos. 154/7	*from* × 12
Nos. 158/67	*from* × 4
No. 168	*from* × 3
Nos. O1/54	*from* × 10
Nos. O55/66a	*from* × 7

1 Lakatoi (trading canoe) with Hanuabada Village in Background

2 (Horizontal)

(Recess D.L.R.)

1901 (1 July)-**05.** *Wmk Mult Rosettes, W* **2.** P 14.

I. Thick paper. Wmk horizontal

1	1	½d. black and yellow-green	..	7·00	10·00
2		1d. black and carmine	..	5·00	7·00
3		2d. black and violet	..	7·00	7·00
4		2½d. black and ultramarine	..	13·00	10·00
5		4d. black and sepia	..	45·00	35·00
6		6d. black and myrtle-green	..	42·00	35·00
7		1s. black and orange	..	60·00	65·00
8		2s. 6d. black and brown (1905)		£600	£550

II. Thick paper. Wmk vertical

9	1	½d. black and yellow-green	..	3·00	3·75
10		1d. black and carmine	..	3·00	2·00
11		2d. black and violet	..	5·50	4·00
12		2½d. black and ultramarine	..	8·00	12·00
13		4d. black and sepia	..	32·00	48·00
14		6d. black and myrtle-green	..	48·00	70·00
14a		1s. black and orange	..	55·00	75·00
14b		2s. 6d. black and brown	..	£2500	£2000

III. Thin paper. Wmk horizontal

14c	1	½d. black and yellow-green	..	£170	£140
14d		2½d. black and ultramarine	..	£225	£160
14e		2½d. black and dull blue	..	£375	£250

IV. Thin paper. Wmk vertical

15	1	½d. black and yellow-green	..	8·00	15·00
16		1d. black and carmine	..		
17		2d. black and violet	..	42·00	16·00
18		2½d. black and ultramarine	..		
18a		2½d. black and dull blue ..			
19		4d. black and sepia	..	£190	£500
20		6d. black and myrtle-green		£550	£1000
21		1s. black and orange	..	£500	£1000
22		2s. 6d. black and brown	..	£550	£1000
1/22			*Set of* 8	£650	£650

The sheets of the ½d., 2d. and 2½d. show a variety known as "white leaves" on R. 4/5 while the 2d. and 2½d. (both R. 6/2) and the ½d. and 1s. (both R. 6/3) show what is known as the "unshaded leaves" variety.

Papua. **Papua.**

(3) (4)

1906-7. A. *Optd with T* **3** (*large opt*), *at Port Moresby* (8 Nov 1906).

I. Thick paper. Wmk horizontal

23	1	4d. black and sepia	..	£180	£150
24		6d. black and myrtle-green	..	38·00	40·00
25		1s. black and orange ..	..	20·00	38·00
26		2s. 6d. black and brown	..	£140	£150

II. Thick paper. Wmk vertical

27	1	2½d. black and ultramarine	..	3·75	13·00
28		4d. black and sepia	..	£160	£130
29		6d. black and myrtle-green	..	18·00	40·00
29a		1s. black and orange	..	£950	£800
29b		2s. 6d. black and brown	..	£5000	£3750

III. Thin paper. Wmk vertical

30	1	½d. black and yellow-green	..	4·50	18·00
31		1d. black and carmine	..	7·50	14·00
32		2d. black and violet	..	4·50	3·00
23/32 (*cheapest*)	.. ..		*Set of* 8	£325	£375

B. *Optd with T* **4** (*small opt*), *at Brisbane* (May-June 1907)

I. Thick paper. Wmk horizontal

34	1	½d. black and yellow-green	..	75·00	95·00
35		2½d. black and ultramarine	..	75·00	95·00
36		1s. black and orange	..	£110	£160
37		2s. black and brown	..	32·00	45·00
		a. Opt reading downwards	..	£3000	
		c. Opt double (horiz) ..	..	†£2500	
		d. Opt triple (horiz) ..	..	†£2000	

II. Thick paper. Wmk vertical

38	1	2½d. black and ultramarine	..	6·00	18·00
		a. Opt double			
38b		1s. black and orange	..	60·00	70·00
38c		2s. 6d. black and brown	..	£3500	£3500

III. Thin paper. Wmk horizontal

38d	1	½d. black and yellow-green	..	50·00	55·00
39		2½d. black and ultramarine	..	23·00	50·00
		a. Opt double			
39b		2½d. black and dull blue	..	£110	£110

IV. Thin paper. Wmk vertical

40	1	½d. black and yellow-green	..	3·50	5·50
		a. Opt double	..	£1600	
41		1d. black and carmine	..	3·75	6·00
		a. Opt reading upwards		£1200	£850
42		2d. black and violet	..	4·50	2·25
42a		2½d. black and ultramarine			
43		4d. black and sepia ..	..	25·00	45·00
44		6d. black and myrtle-green	..	21·00	35·00
		a. Opt double		£1900	£3500
45		1s. black and orange	..	27·00	40·00
		a. Opt double, one diagonal ..		£4000	£2500
46		2s. 6d. black and brown	..	38·00	48·00
34/46 (*cheapest*)	.. ..		*Set of* 8	£110	£180

In the setting of this overprint Nos. 10, 16, and 21 have the "p" of "Papua" with a defective foot or inverted "d" for "p", and in No. 17 the "pua" of "Papua" is a shade lower than the first "a".

No. 37a comes from a single sheet on which the overprints were sideways. Examples exist showing one, two or four complete or partial overprints.

PRINTERS. All the following issues were printed at Melbourne by the Stamp Ptg Branch (to 1928) or Note Ptg Branch.

5 Large "PAPUA" B C

Three types of the 2s. 6d.:—

A. Thin top to "2" and small ball. Thin "6" and small ball. Thick uneven stroke.

B. Thin top to "2" and large, well shaped ball. Thin "6" and large ball. Very thick uneven stroke.

C. Thick top to "2" and large, badly shaped ball. Thick "6" and uneven ball. Thin even line.

Type A is not illustrated as the stamp is distinguishable by perf and watermark.

The litho stones were prepared from the engraved plates of the 1901 issue, value for value except the 2s. 6d. for which the original plate was mislaid. No. 48 containing Type A was prepared from the original ½d. plate with the value inserted on the stone and later a fresh stone was prepared from the 1d. plate and this contained Type B. Finally, the original plate of the 2s. 6d. was found and a third stone was prepared from this, and issued in 1911. These stamps show Type C.

6 Small "PAPUA"

(Litho Stamp Ptg Branch, Melbourne, from transfers taken from original engraved plates)

1907-10. *Wmk Crown over A, W w* **11.**

A. *Large* "PAPUA". (a) *Wmk upright.* P 11

47	5	½d. black and yellow-green (11.07)	..	1·00	3·00

(b) *Wmk sideways.* P 11

48	5	2s. 6d. black and chocolate (A) (12.09)	..	48·00	60·00
		a. "POSTAGIE" at left (R. 1/5)	..	£425	

B. *Small* "PAPUA"

I. Wmk upright. (a) P 11 (1907-8)

49	6	1d. black and rose (6.08)	..	4·75	2·00
50		2d. black and purple (10.08)	..	4·00	4·50
51		2½d. black & bright ultramarine (7.08)		13·00	22·00
		a. *Black and pale ultramarine*		5·50	6·50
52		4d. black and sepia (20.1.07)	..	4·00	7·00
53		6d. black and myrtle-green (4.08)	..	11·00	15·00
54		1s. black and orange (10.08)	..	16·00	18·00

(b) P 12½ (1907-9)

55	6	2d. black and purple (10.08) ..		13·00	6·00
56		2½d. black and bright ultramarine (7.08)		70·00	85·00
		b. *Black and pale ultramarine*		40·00	60·00
57		4d. black and sepia (20.1.07) ..		7·50	8·00
58		1s. black and orange (1.09)	..	50·00	75·00

II. Wmk sideways. (a) P 11 (1909-10)

59	6	½d. black and yellow-green (12.09)	..	2·25	2·75
		a. *Black and deep green* (1910)	..	28·00	42·00
60		1d. black and carmine (1.10)	..	8·50	7·00
61		2d. black and purple (1.10)	..	4·50	2·75
62		2½d. black and dull blue (1.10)	..	4·25	17·00
63		4d. black and sepia (1.10)	..	3·50	6·50
64		6d. black and myrtle-green (11.09)	..	10·00	10·00
65		1s. black and orange (3.10)	..	40·00	48·00

(b) P 12½ (1909-10)

66	6	½d. black and yellow-green (12.09)	..	1·40	2·00
		a. *Black and deep green* (1910)	..	30·00	38·00
67		1d. black and carmine (12.09) ..		6·00	7·00
68		2d. black and purple (1.10)	..	3·00	2·50
69		2½d. black and dull blue (1.10)	..	7·50	26·00
70		6d. black and myrtle-green (11.09)	..	£2500	£3250
71		1s. black and orange (3.10)	..	12·00	25·00

| 72 | 6 | ½d. black and yellow-green | .. | .. | £1900 | £1900 |
| 73 | | 2d. black and purple | .. | .. | | £750 |

(d) Mixed perfs 11 and 12½

| 74 | 6 | 4d. black and sepia | .. | .. | .. | £3750 |

(Litho Stamp Ptg Branch, Melbourne, by J. B. Cooke, from new stones made by fresh transfers)

1910 (Sept)–11. *Large "PAPUA". W w 11 (upright). P 12½.*

75	5	½d. black and green (12.10)	..	3·50	9·00
76		1d. black and carmine	..	9·00	3·25
77		2d. black and dull purple (*shades*) (12.10)	..	4·00	4·25
		a. "C" for "O" in "POSTAGE" (R.4/3)		60·00	60·00
78		2½d. black and blue-violet (10.10)		4·50	17·00
79		4d. black and sepia (10.10)	..	2·75	10·00
80		6d. black and myrtle-green	..	5·50	7·50
81		1s. black and deep orange (12.10)		5·50	15·00
82		2s. 6d. black and brown (B)	..	42·00	60·00
83		2s. 6d. black and brown (C) (1911)		45·00	65·00
75/83			*Set of 8*	70·00	£110

A variety showing a white line or "rift" in clouds occurs on R. 5/3 in Nos. 49/74 and the "white leaves" variety mentioned below No. 22 occurs on the 2d. and 2½d. values in both issues. They are worth about four times the normal price.

ONE PENNY

8   (9)

(Typo J. B. Cooke)

1911–15. *Printed in one colour. W 8 (sideways).*

(a) P 12½ (1911–12)

84	6	½d. yellow-green	..	..	70	3·25
		a. Green			30	2·00
85		1d. rose-pink	..		70	40
86		2d. bright mauve	..		70	75
87		2½d. bright ultramarine	..	4·75	8·50
		a. Dull ultramarine		5·50	8·50
88		4d. pale olive-green	..	2·00	11·00
89		6d. orange-brown	..	3·75	5·00
90		1s. yellow	..	8·50	14·00
91		2s. 6d. rose-carmine	..	30·00	38·00
		a. Rose-red (aniline)			£150
84/91			*Set of 8*	45·00	70·00

No. 91a always shows the watermark Crown to right of A, *as seen from the back of the stamp.*

(b) P 14

| 92 | 6 | 1d. rose-pink (6.15) | .. | 20·00 | 5·00 |
| | | a. Pale scarlet | .. | 6·00 | 2·00 |

1917. *Above issue surch with T 9 at Port Moresby.*

93	6	1d. on ½d. yellow-green	..	..	90	1·40
		a. Green		..	50	1·00
94		1d. on 2d. bright mauve	..	..	12·00	14·00
95		1d. on 2½d. ultramarine	..	1·25	3·75
96		1d. on 4d. pale olive-green	..	1·00	4·50
97		1d. on 6d. orange-brown	..	8·00	13·00
98		1d. on 2s. 6d. rose-carmine	..	1·50	8·00
93/98			*Set of 6*	22·00	40·00

(Typo J. B. Cooke (1916–18), T. S. Harrison (1918–26), A. J. Mullett (No. 101a only) (1926–27), or John Ash (1927–31))

1916–31. *Printed in two colours. W 8 (sideways). P 14.*

99	6	½d. myrtle and apple green (Harrison and Ash) (1919)	..	80	80
		a. Myrtle and pale olive-green (1927)		1·00	1·00
100		1d. black and carmine-red (1916)	..	1·40	90
		a. Grey-black and red (1918)	..	1·60	30
		b. Intense black and red (Harrison) (1926)	..	1·90	1·90
101		1½d. pale grey-blue (*shades*) and brown (1925)	..	1·25	60
		a. Cobalt and light brown (Mullett) (1927)	..	6·00	3·25
		b. Bright blue and bright brown (1929)	..	1·75	1·60
		c. "POSTACE" at right (R. 1/1) (all ptgs)	*From*	35·00	38·00
102		2d. brown-purple and brown-lake (1919)	..	1·25	75
		a. Deep brown-purple and lake (1931)	23·00	1·25
		b. Brown-purple and claret (1931)	2·00	75
103		2½d. myrtle and ultramarine (1919)	..	4·25	10·00
104		3d. black and bright blue-green (1916)	..	1·25	1·75
		a. Error. Black and deep greenish Prussian blue*	..	£475	£475
		b. Sepia-black and bright blue-green (Harrison)	..	20·00	17·00
		c. Black and blue-green (1927)	..	4·25	7·00
105		4d. brown and orange (1919)	..	2·50	4·50
		a. Light brown and orange (1927)	..	5·00	13·00
106		5d. bluish slate and pale brown (1931)	4·25	15·00
107		6d. dull and pale purple (1919)	..	2·75	8·50
		a. Dull purple and red-purple (1927)	8·00	15·00
		b. "POSTACE" at left (R.6/2) (all ptgs)	*From*	65·00	95·00
108		1s. sepia and olive (1919)	..	3·50	6·00
		a. Brown and yellow-olive (1927)	6·00	12·00
109		2s. 6d. maroon and pale pink (1919)	18·00	38·00
		a. Maroon and bright pink (shades) (1927)	..	18·00	48·00
110		5s. black and deep green (1916)	..	40·00	45·00
111		10s. green and pale ultramarine (1925)	£140	£180
99/111			*Set of 13*	£200	£250

*Beware of similar shades produced by removal of yellow pigment. No. 104a is a colour trial, prepared by Cooke, of which, it is believed, five sheets were sold in error.

The printers of the various shades can be determined by their dates of issue. The Ash printings are on whiter paper. For 9d. and 1s 3d. values, see Nos. 127/8.

AIR MAIL

(10)   (11)

1929 (Oct)–30. *Air. Optd with T 10 by Govt Printer, Port Moresby.*

(a) Cooke printing. Yellowish paper

| 112 | 6 | 3d. black and bright blue-green | .. | 1·10 | 7·00 |
| | | a. Opt omitted in vert pair with normal | | £2250 | |

(b) Harrison printing. Yellowish paper

| 113 | 6 | 3d. sepia-black and bright blue-green | 50·00 | 60·00 |

(c) Ash printing. White paper

114	6	3d. black and blue-green	..	80	7·00
		a. Opt omitted in horiz pair with normal	..	£3250	
		b. Ditto, but vert pair	..	£2750	
		c. Opt vertical, on back	..	£2750	
		d. Opts tête-bêche (pair)	..	£2000	

1930 (15 Sept). *Air. Optd with T 11, in carmine by Govt Printer, Port Moresby. (a) Harrison printings. Yellowish paper.*

115	6	3d. sepia-black and bright blue-green	£1300	£2000
116		6d. dull and pale purple	..	3·00	16·00
		a. "POSTAGE" at left (R. 6/2)	65·00	£110
117		1s. sepia and olive	..	7·00	27·00
		a. Opt inverted	..	£3000	

(b) Ash printings. White paper

118	6	3d. black and blue-green	..	55	5·50
119		6d. dull purple and red-purple	..	7·00	10·00
		a. "POSTAGE" at left (R. 6/2)	70·00	£100
120		1s. brown and yellow-olive	..	4·00	15·00
118/20			*Set of 3*	10·50	27·00

The rare Harrison printing with this overprint, No. 115, should not be confused with examples of the Ash printing, No. 118, which have been climatically toned.

5d.

TWO PENCE   **FIVE PENCE**

(12)   (13)

1931 (1 Jan). *Surch with T 12 by Govt Printer, Port Moresby.*

(a) Mullett printing

| 121 | 6 | 2d. on 1½d. cobalt and light brown | .. | 14·00 | 32·00 |
| | | a. "POSTACE" at right (R. 1/1) | .. | £150 | £250 |

(b) Ash printing

| 122 | 6 | 2d. on 1½d. bright blue and bright brown | .. | 80 | 2·00 |
| | | a. "POSTACE" at right (R. 1/1) | .. | 32·00 | 48·00 |

1931. *Surch as T 13 by Govt Printer, Port Moresby.*

(a) Cooke printing

| 123 | 6 | 1s. 3d. on 5s. black and deep green | .. | 4·00 | 9·00 |

(b) Harrison printing. Yellowish paper

| 124 | 6 | 9d. on 2s. 6d. maroon and pale pink (Dec) | 5·50 | 17·00 |

(c) Ash printings. White paper

| 125 | 6 | 5d. on 1s. brown and yellow-olive (26.7) | 60 | 1·75 |
| 126 | | 9d. on 2s. 6d. maroon and bright pink | 5·00 | 8·50 |

(Typo J. Ash)

1932. *W 15 of Australia (Mult "C of A"). P 11.*

127	5	9d. lilac and violet	..	..	4·00	25·00
128		1s. 3d. lilac and pale greenish blue	..	7·00	30·00
127/8 Optd "Specimen"		..	..	*Set of 2*	£450

15 Motuan Girl

18 Raggiana Bird of Paradise

20 Native Mother and Child

22 Papuan Motherhood

(Des F. E. Williams (2s., £1 and frames of other values), E. White-house (2d., 4d., 6d., 1s., and 10s.); remaining centres from photos by Messrs F. E. Williams and Gibson. Recess J. Ash (all values) and W. C. G. McCracken (½d., 1d., 2d., 4d.))

1932 (14 Nov). *T 15, 18, 20, 22 and similar designs. No wmk. P 11.*

130		½d. black and orange	..	55	2·50
		a. Black and buff (McCracken)	..	12·00	20·00
131		1d. black and green	..	70	30
132		1½d. black and lake	..	60	5·00
133		2d. red	..	6·00	30
134		3d. black and blue	..	2·00	6·50
135		4d. olive-green	..	3·00	8·50
136		5d. black and slate-green	..	2·00	4·00
137		6d. bistre-brown	..	4·25	7·00
138		9d. black and violet	..	7·00	18·00
139		1s. dull blue-green	..	2·50	11·00
140		1s. 3d. black and dull purple	..	8·50	20·00
141		2s. black and slate-green	..	11·00	20·00
142		2s. 6d. black and rose-mauve	..	24·00	38·00
143		5s. black and olive-brown	..	55·00	60·00
144		10s. violet	..	75·00	75·00
145		£1 black and olive-grey	..	£170	£170
130/145			*Set of 16*	£325	£375

Designs: *Vert (as T 15)*—1d. A Chieftain's son; 1½d. Tree-houses; 3d. Papuan dandy; 5d. Masked dancer; 9d. Papuan shooting fish; 1s. 3d. Lakatoi; 2s. Papuan art; 2s. 6d. Pottery making; 5s. Native policeman; £1 Delta house. (*As T 18*)—1s. *Dubu*—or ceremonial platform. *Horiz (as T 20)*—10s. Lighting a fire.

31 Hoisting the Union Jack   32 Scene on H.M.S. *Nelson*

(Recess J. Ash)

1934 (6 Nov). *50th Anniv of Declaration of British Protectorate. P 11.*

146	31	1d. green	..	..	80	2·25
147	32	2d. scarlet	..	..	1·75	25
148	31	3d. blue	..	..	1·50	3·00
149	32	5d. purple	..	..	5·50	7·00
146/9	..		..	*Set of 4*	8·50	13·00

HIS MAJESTY'S JUBILEE.

1910	**1935**
(33)	

HIS MAJESTY'S JUBILEE. 1910 — 1935

(34)

MAJESTY'S   **MAJESTY'S**

Normal   "Accent" flaw (R. 5/4)

1935 (9 July). *Silver Jubilee. Nos. 131, 133/4 and 136 optd with T 33 or 34 (2d.).*

150		1d. black and green	..	55	80
		a. "Accent" flaw	..	24·00	35·00
151		2d. scarlet	..	1·25	60
152		3d. black and blue	..	1·25	2·50
		a. "Accent" flaw	..	42·00	65·00
153		5d. black and slate-green	..	2·75	2·75
		a. "Accent" flaw	..	60·00	75·00
150/3	..		*Set of 4*	5·25	6·00

35   36 Port Moresby

(Recess J. Ash)

1937 (14 May). *Coronation. P 11.*

154	35	1d. green	..	..	50	15
155		2d. scarlet	..	..	50	15
156		3d. blue	..	..	50	20
157		5d. purple	..	..	50	55
154/7	..		..	*Set of 4*	1·75	95

(Recess J. Ash)

1938 (6 Sept). *Air. 50th Anniv of Declaration of British Possession. P 11.*

158	36	2d. rose-red	..	..	3·75	2·25
159		3d. bright blue	..	..	3·75	25
160		5d. green	..	..	3·75	3·25
161		8d. brown-lake	..	..	9·00	11·00
162		1s. mauve	..	..	26·00	14·00
158/62			*Set of 5*	42·00	30·00

MINIMUM PRICE

The minimum price quote is 10p which represents a handling charge rather than a basis for valuing common stamps. For further notes about prices see introductory pages.

37 Natives poling Rafts

(Recess J. Ash)

1939 (6 Sept). *Air. P* 11.
163	37	2d. rose-red	..	..	6·00	3·00
164		3d. bright blue	..	..	6·00	4·50
165		5d. green	..	..	9·00	1·50
166		8d. brown-lake	..	..	10·00	2·50
167		1s. mauve	..	..	13·00	5·50

(Recess W. C. G. McCracken)

1941 (2 Jan). *Air. P* 11½.
168	37	1s. 6d. olive-green	45·00	32·00
163/168			*Set of* 6	80·00 45·00

OFFICIAL STAMPS

1908 (Oct). *Punctured* "OS".
O1	1	2s. 6d. black and brown (No. 37)..	..	— 40·00
O2		2s. 6d. black and brown (No. 38c)..	..	£1600 £1600
O3		2s. 6d. black and brown (No. 46)..		£600 £450

1909–10. *Nos. 49/71 punctured* "OS". I. *Wmk upright.* (a) *P* 11.
O4	6	1d. black and rose	..	8·50 3·00
O5		2d. black and purple	..	9·50 4·25
O6		2½d. black and bright ultramarine	..	20·00 14·00
		a. *Black and pale ultramarine*	..	8·50 4·25
O7		4d. black and sepia	..	9·00 4·50
O8		6d. black and myrtle-green	..	18·00 12·00
O9		1s. black and orange	..	21·00 14·00
O4/9			*Set of* 6	65·00 38·00

(b) *P* 12½
O10	6	2d. black and purple	..	12·00 4·75
O11		2½d. black and bright ultramarine	..	55·00 40·00
		b. *Black and pale ultramarine*	..	38·00 28·00
O12		4d. black and sepia	..	14·00 6·50
O13		1s. black and orange	..	60·00 38·00
O10/13			*Set of* 4	£110 70·00

II. *Wmk sideways.* (a) *P* 11
O14	6	½d. black and yellow-green	..	7·50 4·50
		a. *Black and deep green*	..	40·00 30·00
O15		1d. black and carmine..		16·00 5·50
O16		2d. black and purple	..	8·50 2·00
O17		2½d. black and dull blue	..	9·50 5·00
O18		4d. black and sepia	..	8·50 4·00
O19		6d. black and myrtle-green	..	21·00 5·00
O20		1s. black and orange	..	55·00 28·00
O14/20			*Set of* 7	£110 48·00

(b) *P* 12½
O21	6	½d. black and yellow-green	..	4·25 1·50
		a. *Black and deep green*	..	42·00 30·00
O22		1d. black and carmine..		11·00 4·00
O23		2d. black and purple	..	7·50 1·50
O24		2½d. black and dull blue	..	18·00 11·00
O25		6d. black and myrtle-green	..	— £700
O26		1s. black and orange	..	25·00 14·00

1910. *Nos. 47/8 punctured* "OS".
O27	5	½d. black & yellow-green (*wmk upright*)	6·00 6·00
O28		2s. 6d. black & chocolate(*wmk sideways*)	£100 80·00

1910–11. *Nos. 75/83 punctured* "OS".
O29	5	½d. black and green	..	6·50 3·00
O30		1d. black and carmine.	..	9·50 3·00
O31		2d. black and dull purple	..	7·50 3·00
		a. "C" for "O" in "POSTAGE"	..	85·00 55·00
O32		2½d. black and blue-violet	..	9·50 6·00
O33		4d. black and sepia	..	9·50 5·00
O34		6d. black and myrtle-green	..	9·50 6·00
O35		1s. black and deep orange	..	17·00 9·00
O36		2s. 6d. black and brown (B)	..	60·00 35·00
O37		2s. 6d. black and brown (C)	..	65·00 42·00
O29/37			*Set of* 8	£110 60·00

1911–12. *Nos. 84/91 punctured* "OS".
O38	6	½d. yellow-green	..	2·75 2·00
O39		1d. rose-pink	..	3·25 1·25
O40		2d. bright mauve	..	3·25 1·25
O41		2½d. bright ultramarine	..	7·50 6·00
O42		4d. pale olive-green	..	8·50 11·00
O43		6d. orange-brown	..	7·50 6·00
O44		1s. yellow	..	12·00 11·00
O45		2s. 6d. rose-carmine	..	38·00 45·00
O38/45			*Set of* 8	75·00 75·00

1930. *Nos. 99/102a and 104c/9 punctured* "OS".
O46	6	½d. myrtle and apple green	..	1·75 2·75
O47		1d. intense black and red	..	2·50 2·75
O48		1½d. bright blue and bright brown	..	2·25 2·75
		"POSTACE" at right	..	45·00 55·00
O49		2d. deep brown-purple and lake	..	12·00 12·00
O50		3d. black and blue-green	..	19·00 24·00
O51		4d. light brown and orange	..	8·50 13·00
O52		6d. dull purple and pale purple	..	7·00 8·50
		a. "POSTACE" at left	..	90·00 £110
O53		1s. brown and yellow-olive	..	9·50 14·00
O54		2s. 6d. maroon and pale pink..	..	38·00 48·00
O46/54			*Set of* 9	90·00 £110

(O 1)

(Typo T. S. Harrison (1d. and 2s. 6d.) and J. Ash)

1931 (29 July)–32. *Optd with Type O* 1. *W* 8 *or W* 15 *of Australia* (9d., 1s. 3d.). *P* 14 *or* 11 (9d., 1s. 3d.).
O55	6	½d. myrtle and apple-green	..	1·00	4·25
O56		1d. grey-black and red			
		a. *Intense black and red*	..	3·25	4·25
O57		1½d. bright blue and bright brown		1·40	9·50
		a. "POSTACE" at right	..	45·00	90·00
O58		2d. brown-purple and claret	..	2·25	8·00
O59		3d. black and blue-green	..	2·25	15·00
O60		4d. light brown and orange	..	2·25	13·00
O61		5d. bluish slate and pale brown	..	6·00	32·00
O62		6d. dull purple and red-purple	..	4·00	8·50
		a. "POSTACE" at left	..	80·00	£150
O63		9d. lilac and violet (1932)	..	35·00	50·00
O64		1s. brown and yellow-olive	..	8·00	24·00
O65		1s. 3d. lilac & pale greenish blue (1932)	35·00	55·00
O66		2s. 6d. maroon and pale pink (Harrison)	..	38·00	90·00
		a. *Maroon and bright pink* (Ash)	..	38·00	90·00
O55/66		..	..	*Set of* 12	£120 £275

Civil Administration, in Papua, was suspended in 1942; on resumption, after the Japanese defeat in 1945, Australian stamps were used until the appearance of the issue of the combined territories of Papua & New Guinea.

PAPUA NEW GUINEA

AUSTRALIAN TRUST TERRITORY

The name of the combined territory was changed from "Papua and New Guinea" to "Papua New Guinea" at the beginning of 1972.

SPECIMEN OVERPRINTS. These come from specimen sets in which the lower values were cancelled-to-order, but stamps above the value of 10s. were overprinted "Specimen". These overprints are listed as they could be purchased from the Post Office.

1 Matschie's Tree Kangaroo   2 Buka Head-dresses   3 Native Youth

14 Map of Papua and New Guinea   15 Papuan shooting Fish

(Recess Note Printing Branch, Commonwealth Bank, Melbourne)

1952 (30 Oct)–58. *T* 1/3, 14/15 *and similar designs. P* 14.
1		½d. emerald	30	10
2		1d. deep brown	20	10
3		2d. blue	35	10
4		2½d. orange	1·75	40
5		3d. deep green	1·25	10
6		3½d. carmine-red	60	10
6a		3½d. black (2.6.58)	11·00	4·25
7		6½d. dull purple	2·25	10
		a. *Maroon* (1956)	5·00	15
8		7½d. blue	8·00	3·50
9		9d. brown	6·00	60
10		1s. yellow-green	2·75	10
11		1s. 6d. deep green	12·00	80
12		2s. indigo	8·00	10
13		2s. 6d. brown-purple	7·50	40
14		10s. blue-black	50·00	8·00
15		£1 deep brown	60·00	10·00
1/15			*Set of* 16	£150 25·00
14/15 Optd "Specimen"			*Set of* 2	£120

Designs: *Vert* (*as T* 1/3)—2½d. Greater Bird of Paradise; 3d. Native policeman; 3½d. Papuan head-dress. (*As T* 15)—6½d. Kiriwina Chief House; 7½d. Kiriwina yam house; 1s. 6d. Rubber tapping; 2s. Sepik dancing masks. *Horiz* (*as T* 14)—9d. Copra making; 1s. Lakatoi; 2s. 6d. Native shepherd and flock.

(16)   (17)

1957 (29 Jan). *Nos. 4 and 10 surch with T* 16 *or T* 17.
16		4d. on 2½d. orange	30 10
17		7d. on 1s. yellow-green	20 10

18 Cacao Plant   19 Klinki Plymill

---

20 Cattle   21 Coffee Beans

(Recess Note Ptg Branch, Commonwealth Bank, Melbourne)

1958 (2 June)–60. *New values. P* 14.
18	18	4d. vermilion	..	1·50	10
19		5d. green (10.11.60)	..	2·25	10
20	19	7d. bronze-green	..	10·00	10
21		8d. deep ultramarine (10.11.60)	..	1·50	2·00
22	20	1s. 7d. red-brown	..	27·00	20·00
23		2s. 5d. vermilion (10.11.60)	..	4·75	3·25
24	21	5s. crimson and olive-green	..	13·00	1·50
18/24			*Set of* 7	55·00	24·00

(22)   23 Council Chamber, Port Moresby

1959 (1 Dec). *No. 1 surch with T* 22.
25	1	5d. on ½d. emerald	..	70 10

(Photo Harrison)

1961 (10 Apr). *Reconstitution of Legislative Council. P* 15 × 14.
26	23	5d. deep green and yellow	..	1·50	25
27		2s. 3d. deep green and light salmon	..	4·50	1·50

24 Female, Goroka, New Guinea   26 Female Dancer

28 Traffic Policeman

(Des Pamela M. Prescott, Recess Note Ptg Branch, Reserve Bank of Australia, Melbourne)

1961 (26 July)–62. *T* 24, 26, 28 *and similar designs. P* 14½ × 14 (1d., 3d., 3s.) *or* 14 × 14½ (*others*).
28		1d. lake	..	1·25	10
29		3d. indigo	..	30	10
30		1s. bronze-green	..	3·25	15
31		2s. maroon	..	45	15
32		3s. deep bluish green (5.9.62)	..	2·00	1·00
28/32			*Set of* 5	6·50	1·25

Designs:—*Vert* (*as T* 24)—3d. Tribal Elder, Tari, Papua. (*As T* 26)—2s. Male dancer.

29 Campaign Emblem   30 Map of South Pacific

(Recess Note Ptg Branch, Reserve Bank of Australia, Melbourne)

1962 (7 Apr). *Malaria Eradication. P* 14.
33	29	5d. carmine-red and light blue	..	45	15
34		1s. red and sepia	..	1·00	25
35		2s. black and yellow-green	..	1·40	70
33/5			*Set of* 3	2·50	1·00

(Des Pamela M. Prescott. Recess Note Ptg Branch, Reserve Bank of Australia, Melbourne)

1962 (9 July). *Fifth South Pacific Conference, Pago Pago. P* 14½ × 14.
36	30	5d. scarlet and light green	..	70	15
37		1s. deep violet and light yellow	..	2·00	60
38		2s. 6d. deep green and light blue	..	2·00	1·00
36/8			*Set of* 3	4·25	1·60

31 Throwing the Javelin   33 Runners

(Des G. Hamori. Photo Courvoisier)

1962 (24 Oct). *Seventh British Empire and Commonwealth Games, Perth. T* **31**, **33** *and similar design. P* 11½.
39   5d. brown and light blue   30   10
   a. Pair. Nos. 39/40   60   50
40   5d. brown and orange   30   10
41   2s. 3d. brown and light green   1·75   75
39/41   *Set of* 3   2·10   1·25
Design: (*As T* **31**)—5d. High jump.
Nos. 39/40 are arranged together *se-tenant* in sheets of 100.

34 Raggiana Bird of Paradise   35 Common Phalanger

36 Rabaul   37 Queen Elizabeth II

(Des S. T. Cham (10s.), A. Buckley (photo) (£1). Photo Harrison (£1), Courvoisier (others)).

1963. *P* 14½ (£1) *or* 11½ (*others*).
42   **34**   5d. yellow, chestnut and sepia (27 Mar)   1·75   10
43   **35**   6d. red, yellow-brown and grey (27 Mar)   1·00   90
44   **36**   10s. multicoloured (13 Feb)   19·00   7·00
45   **37**   £1 sepia, gold and blue-green (3 July)   12·00   2·50
   a. Gold ptd double
42/5   *Set of* 4   30·00   9·50
44/5 Optd "Specimen"   *Set of* 2   90·00

38 Centenary Emblem   39 Waterfront, Port Moresby

(Des G. Hamori. Photo Note Ptg Branch, Reserve Bank of Australia, Melbourne)

1963 (1 May). *Red Cross Centenary. P* 13½×13.
46   **38**   5d. red, grey-brown and bluish green   70   10

(Des J. McMahon (8d.), Pamela M. Prescott (2s. 3d.). Recess Note Ptg Branch, Reserve Bank of Australia, Melbourne)

1963 (8 May). *T* **39** *and similar horiz design. P* 14×13½.
47   **39**   8d. green   40   15
48   –   2s. 3d. ultramarine   30   20
Design:—2s. 3d. Piaggio "P-166" aircraft landing at Tapini.

40 Games Emblem   41 Watam Head

(Des Pamela M. Prescott. Recess Note Ptg Branch, Reserve Bank of Australia, Melbourne)

1963 (14 Aug). *First South Pacific Games, Suva. P* 13½ × 14½.
49   **40**   5d. bistre   10   10
50   1s. deep green   20   20

(Des Pamela M. Prescott. Photo Courvoisier)

1964 (5 Feb). *Native Artefacts. T* **41** *and similar vert designs. Multicoloured. P* 11½.
51   11d. Type **41**   1·00   10
52   2s. 5d. Watam Head (*different*)   1·00   75
53   2s. 6d. Bosmun Head   1·00   10
54   5s. Medina Head   1·25   15
51/4   *Set of* 4   3·75   90

45 Casting Vote   46 "Health Centres"

(Photo Courvoisier)

1964 (4 Mar). *Common Roll Elections. P* 11½.
55   **45**   5d. brown and drab   10   10
56   2s. 3d. brown and pale blue   20   25

(Recess Note Ptg Branch, Reserve Bank of Australia, Melbourne)

1964 (5 Aug). *Health Services. T* **46** *and similar vert designs. P* 14.
57   5d. violet   10   10
58   8d. bronze-green   10   10
59   1s. blue   10   10
60   1s. 2d. brown-red   15   30
57/60   *Set of* 4   40   40
Designs:—8d. "School health"; 1s. "Infant, child and maternal health"; 1s. 2d. "Medical training".

50 Striped Gardener Bowerbird   51 Emperor of Germany Bird of Paradise

(Photo Courvoisier)

1964 (28 Oct)—**65**. *Vert designs as T* **50** (1*d.* to 8*d.*) *or* **51** (*others*). *Multicoloured; background colours given. P* 11½ (1*d.* to 8*d.*) *or* 12 × 11½ (1*s.* to 10*s.*).
61   1d. pale olive-yellow (20.1.65)   40   10
62   3d. light grey (20.1.65)   50   10
63   5d. pale red (20.1.65)   55   10
64   6d. pale green   75   10
65   8d. lilac   1·25   20
66   1s. salmon   1·25   10
67   2s. light blue (20.1.65)   1·00   30
68   2s. 3d. light green (20.1.65)   1·00   85
69   3s. pale yellow (20.1.65)   1·25   1·25
70   5s. cobalt (20.1.65)   16·00   2·00
71   10s. pale drab (Optd S. £120)   11·00   4·00
61/71   *Set of* 11   32·00   8·00
Designs:—3d. Adelbert Bowerbird; 5d. Blue Bird of Paradise; 6d. Lawes's Parotia; 8d. Black-billed Sicklebill; 2s. Brown Sicklebill; 2s. 3d. Lesser Bird of Paradise; 3s. Magnificent Bird of Paradise; 5s. Twelve-wired Bird of Paradise; 10s. Magnificent Riflebird.

61 Canoe Prow

(Des Pamela M. Prescott. Photo Courvoisier)

1965 (24 Mar). *Sepik Canoe Prows in Port Moresby Museum. T* **61** *and similar horiz designs showing carved prows. P* 11½.
72   4d. multicoloured   40   10
73   1s. 2d. multicoloured   1·75   85
74   1s. 6d. multicoloured   50   10
75   4s. multicoloured   1·50   25
72/5   *Set of* 4   3·50   1·10

1965 (14 Apr). *50th Anniv of Gallipoli Landing. As T* **22** *of Nauru. P* 13½.
76   2s. 3d. sepia, black and emerald   20   10

65 Urban Plan and Native House

(Des G. Hamori. Photo Courvoisier)

1965 (7 July). *Sixth South Pacific Conference, Lae. T* **65** *and similar horiz design. P* 11½.
77   6d. multicoloured   10   10
78   1s. multicoloured   10   10
No. 78 is similar to T **65** but with the plan on the right and the house on the left. Also "URBANISATION" reads downwards.

66 Mother and Child   67 Globe and U.N. Emblem

(Photo Courvoisier)

1965 (13 Oct). *20th Anniv of U.N.O. T* **66/7** *and similar vert design. P* 11½.
79   6d. sepia, blue and pale turquoise-blue   10   10
80   1s. orange-brown, blue & dp reddish violet   10   10
81   2s. blue, blue-green and light yellow-olive   10   10
79/81   *Set of* 3   15   15
Design:—2s. U.N. Emblem and globes.

69 Papilio ulysses   71 Ornithoptera priamus

(Photo Courvoisier)

1966 (14 Feb–12 Oct). *Decimal Currency. Butterflies. Vert designs as T* **69** (1 to 5 c.), *or horiz as T* **71** (*others*). *Multicoloured. P* 11½.
82   1 c. Type **69**   40   40
83   3 c. Cyrestis acilia   40   50
84   4 c. Graphium weiskei   40   20
85   5 c. Terinos alurgis   40   10
86   10 c. Type **71**   50   30
86a   12 c. Euploea callithoe (12.10)   2·25   2·25
87   15 c. Papilio euchenor   4·25   80
88   20 c. Parthenos sylvia   2·50   25
89   25 c. Delias aruna   4·50   70
90   50 c. Apaturina erminea   12·00   1·25
91    $1 Doleschallia dascylus   3·50   1·25
92    $2 Ornithoptera paradisea   6·50   5·50
82/92   *Set of* 12   35·00   12·00

80 "Molala Harai"   84 Throwing the Discus

(Des Rev. H. A. Brown. Photo Courvoisier)

1966 (8 June). *Folklore. Elema Art* (1st series). *T* **80** *and similar vert designs. P* 11½.
93   2 c. black and carmine   10   10
94   7 c. black, light yellow and light blue   10   10
95   30 c. black, carmine and apple-green   15   10
96   60 c. black, carmine and yellow   40   20
93/6   *Set of* 4   65   35
Designs:—7 c. "Marai"; 30 c. "Meavea Kivovia"; 60 c. "Toivita Tapaivita".
Nos. 93/6 were supplementary values to the decimal currency definitive issue.
See also Nos. 152/5 and 342/5.

(Photo Courvoisier)

1966 (31 Aug). *South Pacific Games, Nouméa. T* **84** *and similar vert designs. Multicoloured. P* 11½.
97   5 c. Type **84**   10   10
98   10 c. Football   10   10
99   20 c. Tennis   15   10
97/9   *Set of* 3   30   15

87 Mucuna novoguineensis   91 "Fine Arts"

(Des Mrs. D. Pearce. Photo Courvoisier)

1966 (7 Dec). *Flowers. T* **87** *and similar vert designs. Multicoloured. P* 11½.

100	5 c. Type 87	..	15	10
101	10 c. *Tecomanthe dentrophila*	.. ..	15	10
102	20 c. *Rhododendron macgregoriae*		25	10
103	60 c. *Rhododendron konori*	.. ..	55	60
100/3	..	*Set of 4*	1·00	75

(Des G. Hamori. Photo Courvoisier)

1967 (8 Feb). *Higher Education. T* **91** *and similar horiz designs. Multicoloured. P* 12½ × 12.

104	1 c. Type 91	.. ..	10	10
105	3 c. "Surveying"	.. ..	10	10
106	4 c. "Civil Engineering"	..	10	10
107	5 c. "Science"	.. ..	10	10
108	20 c. "Law"	.. ..	10	10
104/8	..	*Set of 5*	20	20

96 *Sagra speciosa*

100 Laloki River

(Des Pamela M. Prescott. Photo Courvoisier)

1967 (12 Apr). *Fauna Conservation (Beetles). T* **96** *and similar vert designs. Multicoloured. P* 11½.

109	5 c. Type 96	.. ..	20	10
110	10 c. *Eupholus schoenherri*	.. ..	30	10
111	20 c. *Sphingnotus albertisi*	..	50	10
112	25 c. *Cyphogastra albertisi*	..	55	10
109/12	..	*Set of 4*	1·40	30

(Des G. Wade. Photo Courvoisier)

1967 (28 June). *Laloki River Hydro-Electric Scheme, and "New Industries". T* **100** *and similar vert designs. Multicoloured. P* 12½.

113	5 c. Type 100	.. ..	10	10
114	10 c. Pyrethrum	.. ..	10	10
115	20 c. Tea Plant..	.. ..	10	10
116	25 c. Type 100	.. ..	10	10
113/16	..	*Set of 4*	30	20

103 Air Attack at Milne Bay

107 Papuan Lory

(Des R. Hodgkinson (2 c.), F. Hodgkinson (5 c.), G. Wade (20 c., 50 c.). Photo Courvoisier)

1967 (30 Aug). *25th Anniv of the Pacific War. T* **103** *and similar multicoloured designs. P* 11½.

117	2 c. Type 103	.. ..	10	20
118	5 c. Kokoda Trail (*vert*)	.. ..	10	10
119	20 c. The Coast Watchers	.. ..	15	10
120	50 c. Battle of the Coral Sea	..	50	30
117/20	..	*Set of 4*	60	55

(Des T. Walcot. Photo Courvoisier)

1967 (29 Nov). *Christmas. Territory Parrots. T* **107** *and similar vert designs. Multicoloured. P* 12½.

121	5 c. Type 107	.. ..	20	10
122	7 c. Pesquet's Parrot	.. ..	25	15
123	20 c. Dusky Lory	.. ..	60	10
124	25 c. Edward's Fig Parrot	..	60	10
121/4	.. ..	*Set of 4*	1·50	30

111   Chimbu Head-dresses   **112**

(Des P. Jones. Photo Courvoisier)

1968 (21 Feb). *"National Heritage". T* **111/12** *and similar multicoloured designs. P* 12 × 12½ (5, 60 c.) *or* 12½ × 12 (10, 20 c.).

125	5 c. Type 111	.. ..	10	10
126	10 c. Southern Highlands Head-dress (*horiz*)	10	10
127	20 c. Western Highlands Head-dress (*horiz*)	15	10
128	60 c. Type 112	.. ..	40	20
125/8	..	*Set of 4*	60	40

---

115 *Hyla thesaurensis*

119 Human Rights Emblem and Papuan Head-dress (abstract)

(Des and photo Courvoisier)

1968 (24 Apr). *Fauna Conservation (Frogs). T* **115** *and similar horiz designs. Multicoloured. P* 11½.

129	5 c. Type 115	.. ..	15	15
130	10 c. *Hyla iris*	.. ..	15	10
131	15 c. *Ceratobatrachas guentheri*	..	15	10
132	20 c. *Nyctimystes narinosa*	..	20	10
129/32	..	*Set of 4*	60	30

(Des G. Hamori. Litho Enschedé)

1968 (26 June). *Human Rights Year. T* **119** *and similar horiz design. Multicoloured. P* 13½ × 12½.

133	5 c. Type 119	.. ..	10	10
134	10 c. Human Rights in the World (abstract) ..	10	10

121 Leadership (abstract)

123 Egg Cowry

(Des G. Hamori. Litho Enschedé)

1968 (26 June). *Universal Suffrage. T* **121** *and similar horiz design. Multicoloured. P* 13½ × 12½.

135	20 c. Type 121	.. ..	15	10
136	25 c. Leadership of the Community (abstract)	15	10

(Des P. Jones. Photo Courvoisier)

1968–69. *Seashells. Multicoloured designs as T* **123.** *P* 12 × 12½ ($2), 12½ × 12 (1 c. to 20 c.) *or* 11½ (*others*).

137	1 c. Type 125 (29.1.69)		10	10
138	3 c. Laciniated Conch (30.10.68)		30	30
139	4 c. Lithograph Cone (29.1.69)		20	30
140	5 c. Marbled Cone (28.8.68)		25	10
141	7 c. Episcopal Mitre (29.1.69)		35	10
142	10 c. Red Volute (30.10.68)		45	10
143	12 c. Areola Bonnet (29.1.69) ..		1·50	90
144	15 c. Scorpion Conch (30.10.68)		80	30
145	20 c. Fluted Clam (28.8.68)		90	10
146	25 c. Chocolate Flamed Venus Shell (28.8.68)	90	30
147	30 c. Giant Murex (28.8.68) ..		1·25	55
148	40 c. Chambered Nautilus (30.10.68)..		1·00	40
149	60 c. Pacific Triton (28.8.68)		1·25	20
150	$1 Emerald Snail (30.10.68)		3·00	50
151	$2 Glory of the Sea (*vert*) (29.1.69)		19·00	4·50
137/51	..	*Set of 15*	28·00	7·50

The 1, 5, 7, 15, 40, 60 c. and $1 exist with PVA gum as well as gum arabic.

138 Tito Myth   **140** Luvuapo Myth

139 Iko Myth   **141** Miro Myth

(Des from native motifs by Revd. H. A. Brown. Litho Enschedé)

1969 (9 Apr). *Folklore. Elema Art (2nd series). P* 12½ × 13½ × *Roul* 9 *between se-tenant pairs.*

152	138	5 c. black, yellow and red	.. ..	10	10
		a. Pair. Nos. 152/3	.. ..	20	20
153	139	5 c. black, yellow and red	.. ..	10	10
154	140	10 c. black, grey and red	.. ..	15	20
		a. Pair. Nos. 154/5	.. ..	30	40
155	141	10 c. black, grey and red	.. ..	15	20
152/5		..	*Set of 4*	50	60

Nos. 152/3 and 154/5 were issued in vertical *se-tenant* pairs, separated by a line of roulette.

OMNIBUS ISSUES

Details, together with prices for complete sets, of the various Omnibus issues from the 1935 Silver Jubilee series to date are included in a special section following Zimbabwe at the end of Volume 2.

---

142 "Fireball" Class Yacht

145 *Dendrobium ostinoglossum*

(Des J. Fallas. Recess Note Ptg Branch, Reserve Bank of Australia)

1969 (25 June). *Third South Pacific Games, Port Moresby. T* **142** *and similar designs. P* 14 × 14½ (5 c.) *or* 14½ × 14 (*others*).

156	5 c. black	.. ..	10	10
157	10 c. deep bluish violet	.. ..	10	10
158	20 c. myrtle-green	.. ..	10	10
156/8	..	*Set of 3*	30	30

Designs: Horiz—10 c. Swimming pool, Boroko; 20 c. Games arena, Konedobu.

(Des P. Jones. Photo Courvoisier)

1969 (27 Aug). *Flora Conservation (Orchids). T* **145** *and similar vert designs. Multicoloured. P* 11½.

159	5 c. Type 145	..	25	10
160	10 c. *Dendrobium lawesii*	..	35	40
161	20 c. *Dendrobium pseudofrigidum*	..	55	60
162	30 c. *Dendrobium conanthum*..	..	70	40
159/62	..	*Set of 4*	1·75	1·25

149 Bird of Paradise

150 Native Potter

(Des G. Hamori. Photo Note Ptg Branch, Reserve Bank of Australia)

1969 (24 Sept)–**71.** *Coil stamps. P* 15 × *imperf.*

162a	149	2 c. blue, black and red (1.4.71)	..	10	15
163		5 c. bright green, brown and red-orange	10	10

(Des G. Hamori. Photo Courvoisier)

1969 (24 Sept). *50th Anniv of International Labour Organization. P* 11½.

164	150	5 c. multicoloured	.. ..	10	10

151 Tareko

155 Prehistoric Ambun Stone

(Des G. Hamori. Photo Courvoisier)

1969 (29 Oct). *Musical Instruments. T* **151** *and similar horiz designs. P* 12½ × 12.

165	5 c. multicoloured	..	10	10
166	10 c. black, olive-green and pale yellow	10	10
167	25 c. black, yellow and brown..	..	15	10
168	30 c. multicoloured	..	25	10
165/8	..	*Set of 4*	55	30

Designs:—10 c. Garamut; 25 c. Iviliko; 30 c. Kundu.

(Des R. Bates. Photo Courvoisier)

1970 (11 Feb). *"National Heritage". T* **155** *and similar horiz designs. Multicoloured. P* 12½ × 12.

169	5 c. Type 155	.. ..	15	10
170	10 c. Masawa canoe of Kula Circuit	..	20	15
171	25 c. Torres' Map, 1606	..	45	15
172	30 c. H.M.S. *Basilisk* (paddle-sloop), 1873 ..	60	20
169/72	..	*Set of 4*	1·25	50

159 King of Saxony Bird of Paradise

(Des T. Walcot. Photo Courvoisier)

1970 (13 May). *Fauna Conservation (Birds of Paradise). T* **159** *and similar vert designs. Multicoloured. P* 12.

173	5 c. Type 159	.. ..	1·00	15
174	10 c. King Bird of Paradise	..	1·50	60
175	15 c. Raggiana Bird of Paradise	..	2·25	1·00
176	25 c. Sickle-crested Bird of Paradise	..	2·50	70
173/6	..	*Set of 4*	6·50	2·25

163 McDonnell Douglas "DC-6B" and Mt Wilhelm   **164** Lockheed "Electra" and Mt Yule

165 Boeing "727" and Mt Giluwe   **166** Fokker "Friendship" and Manam Island

(Des D. Gentleman. Photo Harrison)

1970 (8 July). *Australian and New Guinea Air Services. T 163/6 and similar horiz designs. Multicoloured. P 14½ × 14.*

177	5 c. Type 163	25	10
	a. Block of 4. Nos. 177/80	90	
178	5 c. Type 164	25	10
179	5 c. Type 165	25	10
180	5 c. Type 166	25	10
181	25 c. McDonnell Douglas "DC-3" and Matupi Volcano	60	40
182	30 c. Boeing "707" and Hombrom's Bluff	70	60
177/82	Set of 6	2·00	1·25

Nos. 177/80 were issued together, *se-tenant*, in blocks of 4 throughout the sheet.

169 N. Miklouho-Maclay (scientist) and Effigy   **170** Wogeo Island Food Bowl

(Des D. Gentleman. Photo Courvoisier)

1970 (19 Aug). *42nd ANZAAS (Australian-New Zealand Association for the Advancement of Science) Congress, Port Moresby. T 169 and similar horiz designs. P 11½.*

183	5 c. multicoloured	10	10
184	10 c. multicoloured	15	10
185	15 c. multicoloured	50	15
186	20 c. multicoloured	50	15
183/6	Set of 4	1·10	35

Designs:—10 c. B. Malinowski (anthropologist) and native hut; 15 c. T. Salvadori (ornithologist) and Double-wattled Cassowary; 20 c. F.R.R. Schlechter (botanist) and flower.

(Des P. Jones. Photo Courvoisier)

1970 (28 Oct). *Native Artefacts. T 170 and similar multicoloured designs. P 12½ × 12 (30 c.) or 12 × 12½ (others).*

187	5 c. Type 170	10	10
188	10 c. Lime Pot	20	10
189	15 c. Aibom Sago Storage Pot	20	10
190	30 c. Manus Island Bowl (horiz)	25	20
187/90	Set of 4	70	40

171 Eastern Highlands Dwelling   **172** Spotted Phalanger

(Des G. Wade. Photo Courvoisier)

1971 (27 Jan). *Native Dwellings. T 171 and similar vert designs showing dwellings from the places given. Multicoloured. P 11½.*

191	5 c. Type 171	15	10
192	7 c. Milne Bay	15	15
193	10 c. Purari Delta	15	10
194	40 c. Sepik	35	60
191/4	Set of 4	70	80

(Des R. Bates. Photo Courvoisier)

1971 (31 Mar). *Fauna Conservation. T 172 and similar multicoloured designs. P 11½.*

195	5 c. Type 172	30	10
196	10 c. Long-fingered Possum	60	15
197	15 c. Feather-tailed Possum	1·25	1·00
198	25 c. Long-nosed Echidna (horiz)	1·75	1·00
199	30 c. Ornate Tree Kangaroo (horiz)	1·75	70
195/9	Set of 5	5·00	2·50

173 "Basketball"   **174** Bartering Fish for Vegetables

(Des G. Hamori, Litho D.L.R.)

1971 (9 June). *Fourth South Pacific Games, Papeete, Tahiti. T 173 and similar horiz designs. Multicoloured. P 13½ × 14.*

200	7 c. Type 173	10	10
201	14 c. "Sailing"	15	20
202	21 c. "Boxing"	15	15
203	28 c. "Athletics"	15	35
200/3	Set of 4	50	75

(Des G. Wade. Photo Courvoisier)

1971 (18 Aug). *Primary Industries. T 174 and similar vert designs. Multicoloured. P 11½.*

204	7 c. Type 174	15	10
205	9 c. Man stacking yams	20	25
206	14 c. Vegetable market	30	10
207	30 c. Highlanders cultivating garden	50	50
204/7	Set of 4	1·00	80

175 Sia Dancer   **176** Papuan Flag over Australian Flag

(Des Bette Hays. Photo Courvoisier)

1971 (27 Oct). *Native Dancers. T 175 and similar multicoloured designs. P 11½.*

208	7 c. Type 175	20	10
209	9 c. Urasena dancer	30	20
210	20 c. Siassi Tubuan dancers (horiz)	80	90
211	28 c. Sia dancers (horiz)	1·00	1·10
208/11	Set of 4	2·10	2·00

(Des R. Bates. Photo Courvoisier)

1972 (26 Jan). *Constitutional Development. T 176 and similar horiz design. P 12½ × 12.*

212	**176** 7 c. multicoloured	30	10
	a. Pair. Nos. 212/13	60	90
213	— 7 c. multicoloured	30	10

Design:—No. 213, Crest of Papua New Guinea and Australian coat of arms.
Nos. 212/13 were printed vertically *se-tenant* within the sheet.

177 Map of Papua New Guinea and Flag of South Pacific Commission   **178** Turtle

(Des R. Bates. Photo Courvoisier)

1972 (26 Jan). *25th Anniv of South Pacific Commission. T 177 and similar horiz design. P 12½ × 12.*

214	**177** 15 c. multicoloured	65	55
	a. Pair. Nos. 214/15	1·25	2·00
215	— 15 c. multicoloured	65	55

Design:—No. 215, Man's face and flag of the Commission.
Nos. 214/15 were printed vertically *se-tenant* within the sheet.

(Des R. Bates. Photo Courvoisier)

1972 (17 Mar). *Fauna Conservation (Reptiles). T 178 and similar horiz designs. Multicoloured. P 11½.*

216	7 c. Type 178	40	10
217	14 c. Rainforest Dragon	1·00	1·25
218	21 c. Green Python	1·25	1·50
219	30 c. Salvador's Monitor	1·75	1·25
216/19	Set of 4	4·00	3·50

179 Curtiss "Seagull MF6" Aircraft and *Eureka* (schooner)   **180** New National Flag

(Des Major L. G. Halls. Photo Courvoisier)

1972 (7 June). *50th Anniv of Aviation. T 179 and similar horiz designs. Multicoloured. P 11½.*

220	7 c. Type 179	40	10
221	14 c. De Havilland "37" and native porters	1·00	1·25
222	20 c. Junkers "G-31" and gold dredger	1·10	1·25
223	25 c. Junkers "F-13" and mission church	1·10	1·25
220/3	Set of 4	3·25	3·50

(Des R. Bates. Photo Courvoisier)

1972 (16 Aug). *National Day. T 180 and similar vert designs. Multicoloured. P 11½.*

224	7 c. Type 180	30	10
225	10 c. Native drum	35	25
226	30 c. Blowing conch-shell	60	50
224/6	Set of 3	1·10	70

181 Rev. Copland King   **182** Mt Tomavatur Station

(Des G. Wade. Photo Courvoisier)

1972 (25 Oct). *Christmas (Missionaries). T 181 and similar horiz designs. Multicoloured. P 11½.*

227	7 c. Type 181	25	40
228	7 c. Rev. Dr. Flierl	25	40
229	7 c. Bishop Verjus	25	40
230	7 c. Pastor Ruatoka	25	40
227/30	Set of 4	90	1·40

(Des R. Bates. Photo Courvoisier)

1973 (24 Jan). *Completion of Telecommunications Project, 1968–72. T 182 and similar horiz designs. Multicoloured. P 12½ (Nos. 231/4) or 11½ (others).*

231	7 c. Type 182	45	20
	a. Block of 4. Nos. 231/4	1·60	
232	7 c. Mt Kerigomma Station	45	20
233	7 c. Sattelburg Station	45	20
234	7 c. Wideru Station	45	20
235	7 c. Teleprinter (36 × 26 mm)	45	55
236	30 c. Network Map (36 × 26 mm)	1·25	1·50
231/6	Set of 6	3·00	2·50

Nos. 231/4 were printed in *se-tenant* blocks of four within the sheet.

183 Queen Carola's Parotia   **184** Wood Carver

(Des W. Cooper. Photo Courvoisier)

1973 (30 Mar). *Birds of Paradise. T 183 and similar vert designs. Multicoloured. P 11½.*

237	7 c. Type 183	1·75	35
238	14 c. Goldie's Bird of Paradise	3·00	1·25
239	21 c. Ribbon-tailed Bird of Paradise (18 × 49 mm)	3·50	2·00
240	28 c. Princess Stephanie's Bird of Paradise (18 × 49 mm)	5·00	2·50
237/40	Set of 4	12·00	5·50

(Des R. Bates. Photo Courvoisier)

1973 (13 June)–74. *T 184 and similar horiz designs. Multicoloured. P 11½.*

241	1 c. Type 184	10	10
242	3 c. Wig-makers (23.1.74)	40	10
243	5 c. Mt Bagana (22.8.73)	55	10
244	6 c. Pig Exchange (7.8.74)	70	90
245	7 c. Coastal village	30	10
246	8 c. Arawe mother (23.1.74)	35	30
247	9 c. Fire dancers	30	20
248	10 c. Tifalmin hunter (23.1.74)	55	10
249	14 c. Crocodile hunters (22.8.73)	45	70
250	15 c. Mt Elimbari	50	30
251	20 c. Canoe-racing, Manus (23.1.74)	1·50	40
252	21 c. Making sago (22.8.73)	65	80
253	25 c. Council House	70	45
254	28 c. Menyamya bowmen (22.8.73)	80	75
255	30 c. Shark-snaring (22.8.73)	1·25	75
256	40 c. Fishing canoes, Madang	1·50	80
257	60 c. Tapa cloth-making (23.1.74)	3·50	1·00
258	$1 Asaro Mudmen (23.1.74)	5·00	3·25
259	$2 Enga "Sing Sing" (7.8.74)	10·00	8·50
241/59	Set of 19	26·00	18·00

ALTERED CATALOGUE NUMBERS

Any Catalogue numbers altered from the last edition are shown as a list in the introductory pages.

PAPUA NEW GUINEA

185 Stamps of German New Guinea, 1897

(Des R. Bates. Photo (1 c.), litho and recess (6 c.) or litho (7 c.) State Printing Works, Berlin. Photo and recess D.L.R. (9 c.). Recess and typo Reserve Bank of Australia (25 and 30 c.))

1973 (24 Oct). *75th Anniv of Papua New Guinea Stamps. T 185 and similar horiz designs. Chalky paper (25, 30 c.). P 13½ (1, 6, 7 c.), 14 × 13½ (9 c.) or 14 × 14½ (25, 30 c.).*

260	1 c. multicoloured				15	15
261	6 c. indigo, new blue and silver				25	35
262	7 c. multicoloured				30	35
263	9 c. multicoloured				35	45
264	25 c. orange and gold				60	1·00
265	30 c. plum and silver				75	1·25
260/65				Set of 6	2·25	3·25

Designs: As T 185—6 c. 2 mark stamp of German New Guinea, 1900; 7 c. Surcharged registration label of New Guinea, 1914. 46 × 35 mm.—9 c. Papua 1s. stamp, 1901. 45 × 38 mm—25 c. ½d. stamp of New Guinea, 1925; 30 c. Papua 10s. stamp, 1932.

SELF-GOVERNMENT

186 Native Carved Heads   187 Queen Elizabeth II (from photograph by Karsh)

(Des G. Wade. Photo Courvoisier)

1973 (5 Dec). *Self-Government. P 11½.*

266	186	7 c. multicoloured			30	15
267		10 c. multicoloured			50	65

(Des and photo Harrison)

1974 (22 Feb). *Royal Visit. P 14 × 14½.*

268	187	7 c. multicoloured			25	15
269		30 c. multicoloured			1·00	1·75

188 Blyth's Hornbill   189 Dendrobium bracteosum

(Des T. Nolan. Photo Courvoisier)

1974 (12 June). *Birds' Heads. T 188 and similar multicoloured designs. P 11½ (10 c.) or 12 (others).*

270	7 c. Type 188			2·00	70
271	10 c. Double-wattled Cassowary (33 × 49 mm)		3·00	3·25
272	30 c. New Guinea Harpy Eagle			7·00	8·50
270/2			Set of 3	11·00	11·00

(Des T. Nolan. Photo Courvoisier)

1974 (20 Nov). *Flora Conservation. T 189 and similar vert designs. Multicoloured. P 11½.*

273	7 c. Type 189			50	10
274	10 c. D. anosmum			1·00	50
275	20 c. D. smillieae			1·40	1·25
276	30 c. D. insigne			1·75	1·75
273/6			Set of 4	4·25	3·25

190 Motu Lakatoi   191 1-toea Coin

(Des G. Wade. Photo Courvoisier)

1975 (26 Feb). *National Heritage—Canoes. T 190 and similar horiz designs. Multicoloured. P 11½.*

277	7 c. Type 190			30	10
278	10 c. Tami two-master morobe		45	60
279	25 c. Aramia racing canoe			1·10	1·75
280	30 c. Buka Island canoe			1·10	1·25
277/80			Set of 4	2·75	3·25

(New Currency. 100 toea = 1 kina)

(Des G. Wade. Photo Courvoisier)

1975 (21 Apr). *New Coinage. T 191 and similar multicoloured designs. P 11½.*

281	1 t. Type 191			10	10
282	7 t. New 2 t. and 5 t. coins (45 × 26 mm)		40	10
283	10 t. New 10 t. coin			60	30
284	20 t. New 20 t. coin			1·00	80
285	1 k. New 1 k. coin (45 × 26 mm)		3·50	4·00
281/5			Set of 5	5·00	4·50

192 Ornithoptera alexandrae   193 Boxing

(Des R. Bates. Photo Courvoisier)

1975 (11 June). *Fauna Conservation (Birdwing Butterflies). T 192 and similar vert designs. Multicoloured. P 11½.*

286	7 t. Type 192			50	10
287	10 t. O. victoriae			80	65
288	30 t. O. allottei			1·75	2·00
289	40 t. O. chimaera			2·25	2·75
286/9			Set of 4	4·75	5·00

(Des R. Bates. Photo Courvoisier)

1975 (2 Aug). *Fifth South Pacific Games, Guam. T 193 and similar vert designs. Multicoloured. P 11½.*

290	7 t. Type 193			15	10
291	20 t. Running			25	30
292	25 t. Basketball			30	45
293	30 t. Swimming			35	50
290/3			Set of 4	95	1·10

INDEPENDENT

194 Map and National Flag

(Des and photo Courvoisier)

1975 (10 Sept). *Independence. T 194 and similar horiz design. Multicoloured. P 11½.*

294	7 t. Type 194			20	10
295	30 t. Map and National emblem		40	65
MS296	116 × 58 mm. Nos. 294/5		1·50	1·75

195 M.V. Bulolo   196 Rorovana Carvings

(Des R. Bates. Photo Courvoisier)

1976 (21 Jan). *Ships of the 1930s. T 195 and similar horiz designs. Multicoloured. P 11½.*

297	7 t. Type 195			30	10
298	15 t. M.V. Macdhui			45	30
299	25 t. M.V. Malaita			65	65
300	60 t. S.S. Montoro			1·75	2·50
297/300			Set of 4	2·75	3·25

(Des R. Bates. Photo Courvoisier)

1976 (17 Mar). *Bougainville Art. T 196 and similar horiz designs. Multicoloured. P 11½.*

301	7 t. Type 196			20	10
302	20 t. Upe hats			40	75
303	25 t. Kapkaps			50	85
304	30 t. Canoe paddles			55	90
301/4			Set of 4	1·50	2·25

NEW INFORMATION

The editor is always interested to correspond with people who have new information that will improve or correct the Catalogue.

197 Rabaul House   198 Landscouts

(Des G. Wade. Photo Courvoisier)

1976 (9 June). *Native Dwellings. T 197 and similar horiz designs. Multicoloured. P 11½.*

305	7 t. Type 197			20	10
306	15 t. Aramia house			35	30
307	30 t. Telefomin house			70	75
308	40 t. Tapini house			80	1·00
305/8			Set of 4	1·75	1·90

(Des R. Bates. Photo Courvoisier)

1976 (18 Aug). *50th Anniversaries of Survey Flight and Scouting in Papua New Guinea. T 198 and similar horiz designs. Multicoloured. P 11½.*

309	7 t. Type 198			30	10
310	10 t. D. H. floatplane			40	30
311	15 t. Seascouts			50	65
312	60 t. Floatplane on water			1·25	2·25
309/12			Set of 4	2·25	3·00

199 Father Ross and New Guinea Highlands

(Des R. Bates. Photo Courvoisier)

1976 (28 Oct). *William Ross Commemoration. P 11½.*

313	199	7 t. multicoloured			40	15

200 Clouded Rainbow Fish

(Des P. Jones. Photo Courvoisier)

1976 (28 Oct). *Fauna Conservation (Tropical Fish). T 200 and similar horiz designs. Multicoloured. P 11½.*

314	5 t. Type 200			30	10
315	15 t. Emperor or Imperial Angel Fish		60	45
316	30 t. Freckled Rock Cod			1·10	70
317	40 t. Threadfin Butterfly Fish		1·40	1·00
314/17			Set of 4	3·00	2·00

201 Man from Kundiawa   202 Headdress, Wasara Tribe

(Des R. Bates. Litho Questa (1, 2 k.) or photo Courvoisier (others))

1977 (12 Jan)–78. *T 201/2 and similar multicoloured designs showing headdresses. P 14 (1, 2 k.) or 11½ (others).*

318	1 t. Type 201 (29.3.78)			10	10
319	5 t. Masked dancer, Abelam area of Maprik (29.3.78)		10	10
320	10 t. Headdress from Koiari (7.6.78)		30	15
321	15 t. Woman with face paint, Hanuabada (29.3.78)		30	20
322	20 t. Orokaiva dancer (7.6.78)		50	30
323	25 t. Haus Tambaran dancer, Abelam area of Maprik (29.3.78)		40	30
324	30 t. Asaro Valley headdress (29.3.78)		45	35
325	35 t. Singsing costume, Garaina (7.6.68)		70	45
326	40 t. Waghi Valley headdress (29.3.78)		60	35
327	50 t. Trobriand Island dancer (7.6.78)		1·25	60
328	1 k. Type 202			1·50	1·50
329	2 k. Headdress, Mekeo tribe			3·00	3·00
318/29			Set of 12	8·00	6·50

Sizes:—1, 5, 20 t. 25 × 31 mm; 35, 40 t. 23 × 38 mm; 1 k. 28 × 35 mm; 2 k. 33 × 23 mm; others 26 × 26 mm.

203 National Flag and Queen Elizabeth II   204 White-breasted Ground Pigeon

(Des and photo Harrison)

1977 (16 Mar). *Silver Jubilee. Horiz designs showing Queen Elizabeth as T 203. Multicoloured. P 14½ × 14.*
330	7 t. Type 203	..	25	10
	a. Silver (face value and inscr) omitted		£450	
331	15 t. National emblem	..	35	35
332	35 t. Map of P.N.G.	..	65	70
330/2	.. ..	*Set of 3*	1·10	1·00

(Des W. Cooper. Photo Courvoisier)

1977 (8 June). *Fauna Conservation (Birds). T 204 and similar horiz designs. Multicoloured. P 11½.*
333	5 t. Type 204	..	35	10
334	7 t. Victoria Crowned Pigeon	..	35	10
335	15 t. Pheasant Pigeon	..	65	65
336	30 t. Orange-fronted Fruit Dove	..	1·00	1·00
337	50 t. Banded Imperial Pigeon	..	1·60	2·00
333/7	.. ..	*Set of 5*	3·50	3·50

205 Guides and Gold Badge   **206** Kari Marupi Myth

(Des R. Bates. Litho Questa)

1977 (10 Aug). *50th Anniv of Guiding in Papua New Guinea. Horiz designs showing badge as T 205. Multicoloured. P 14½.*
338	7 t. Type 205	..	20	10
339	15 t. Guides mapping	..	35	20
340	30 t. Guides washing	..	55	50
341	35 t. Guides cooking	..	60	60
338/41	.. ..	*Set of 4*	1·50	1·25

(Des Revd. H. A. Brown. Litho Enschedé)

1977 (19 Oct). *Folklore. Elema Art (3rd series). T 206 and similar vert designs. P 13½ × 13.*
342	7 t. multicoloured	..	20	10
343	20 t. multicoloured	..	45	35
344	30 t. orange-red, light blue and black	..	50	75
345	35 t. orange-red, yellow and black	..	50	75
342/5	.. ..	*Set of 4*	1·50	1·75

Designs:—20 t. Savoripi clan myth; 30 t. Oa-Laea myth; 35 t. Oa-Iriarapo myth.

207 Blue-tailed Skink   **208** Roboastra arika

(Des T. Nolan. Photo Courvoisier)

1978 (25 Jan). *Fauna Conservation (Skinks). T 207 and similar horiz designs. Multicoloured. P 11½.*
346	10 t. Type 207	..	30	10
347	15 t. Green Tree Skink	..	35	20
348	35 t. Crocodile Skink	..	55	55
349	40 t. New Guinea Blue-tongued Skink	..	75	70
346/9	.. ..	*Set of 4*	1·75	1·40

(Des B. Twigden. Photo Courvoisier)

1978 (29 Aug). *Sea Slugs. T 208 and similar horiz designs. Multicoloured. P 11½.*
350	10 t. Type 208	..	30	10
351	15 t. Chromodoris fidelis	..	35	30
352	35 t. Flabellina macassarana	..	70	90
353	40 t. Chromodoris trimarginata	..	75	1·25
350/3	.. ..	*Set of 4*	1·90	2·25

209 Present Day Royal Papua   **210** Ocarina
New Guinea Constabulary

(Des R. Bates. Photo Harrison)

1978 (26 Oct). *History of Royal Papua New Guinea Constabulary. T 209 and similar horiz designs showing uniformed police and constabulary badges. Multicoloured. P 14½.*
354	10 t. Type 209	..	30	10
355	15 t. Mandated New Guinea Constabulary, 1921–1941	..	40	15
356	20 t. British New Guinea Armed Constabulary, 1890–1906	..	45	40
357	25 t. German New Guinea Police, 1899–1914	..	50	45
358	30 t. Royal Papua and New Guinea Constabulary, 1906–1964	..	60	60
354/8	..	*Set of 5*	2·00	1·50

(Des R. Bates. Litho Questa)

1979 (24 Jan). *Musical Instruments. T 210 and similar multicoloured designs. P 14½ × 14 (7, 28 t.) or 14 × 14½ (others).*
359	7 t. Type 210	..	15	10
360	20 t. Musical bow (*horiz*)	..	25	20
361	28 t. Launut	..	30	30
362	35 t. Nose flute (*horiz*)	..	40	45
359/62	.. ..	*Set of 4*	1·00	90

211 East New Britain   **212** Katudababila (waist belt)
Canoe

(Des G. Wade. Litho Questa)

1979 (28 Mar). *Traditional Canoe Prows and Paddles. T 211 and similar vert designs. Multicoloured. P 14½.*
363	14 t. Type 211	..	15	15
364	21 t. Sepik war canoe	..	25	25
365	25 t. Trobriand Island canoe	..	25	30
366	40 t. Milne Bay canoe	..	40	60
363/6	..	*Set of 4*	95	1·10

(Des R. Bates. Photo Courvoisier)

1979 (6 June). *Traditional Currency. T 212 and similar horiz designs. Multicoloured. P 12½ × 12.*
367	7 t. Type 212	..	10	10
368	15 t. Doga (chest ornament)	..	20	30
369	25 t. Mwali (armshell)	..	35	55
370	35 t. Soulava (necklace)	..	45	75
367/70	..	*Set of 4*	1·00	1·50

213 Aenetus cyanochlora   **214** "The Right to Affection and Love"

(Des T. Nolan. Photo Courvoisier)

1979 (29 Aug). *Fauna Conservation. Moths. T 213 and similar multicoloured designs. P 11½.*
371	7 t. Type 213	..	20	10
372	15 t. Celerina vulgaris	..	30	35
373	20 t. Alcidis aurora (*vert*)	..	40	60
374	25 t. Phyllodes conspicillator	..	45	70
375	30 t. Lyssa patroclus (*vert*)	..	55	75
371/5		*Set of 5*	1·75	2·25

(Des G. Wade. Litho Enschedé)

1979 (24 Oct). *International Year of the Child. T 214 and similar vert designs. Multicoloured. P 13½ × 13.*
376	7 t. Type 214	..	10	10
377	15 t. "The right to adequate nutrition and medical care"	..	15	15
378	30 t. "The right to play"	..	20	20
379	60 t. "The right to a free education"	..	45	60
376/9	..	*Set of 4*	80	90

215 "Post Office Service"   **216** Detail from Betrothal
Ceremony Mural,
Minj District,
Western Highlands Province

(Des G. Wade. Litho Enschedé)

1980 (23 Jan). *Admission to U.P.U. (1979). T 215 and similar horiz designs. Multicoloured. P 13 × 13½.*
380	7 t. Type 215	..	10	10
381	25 t. "Wartime mail"	..	25	25
382	35 t. U.P.U. emblem	..	35	40
383	40 t. "Early postal services"	..	40	50
380/3	..	*Set of 4*	1·00	1·10

(Des W. Tubun. Photo Courvoisier)

1980 (26 Mar). *South Pacific Festival of Arts. T 216 and similar vert designs showing different details from mural of betrothal ceremony, Minj District, Western Highlands Province. P 11½.*
384	20 t. black, greenish yellow and pale orange	..	25	35
	a. Strip of 5. Nos. 384/8		1·10	
385	20 t. multicoloured (two figures—left-hand black and yellow; right-hand black, yellow and red)		25	35
386	20 t. multicoloured (two figures—left-hand black and orange; right-hand black)		25	35
387	20 t. multicoloured (two figures, one behind the other)		25	35
388	20 t. multicoloured (one figure)		25	35
384/8		*Set of 5*	1·10	1·60

Nos. 384/8 were printed together, *se-tenant*, in horizontal strips of 5 throughout the sheet.

217 Family being Interviewed

(Des R. Bates. Litho Questa)

1980 (4 June). *National Census. T 217 and similar horiz designs. Multicoloured. P 14 × 13½.*
389	7 t. Type 217	..	10	10
390	15 t. Population symbol	..	15	15
391	40 t. Figures and map of Papua New Guinea	30	40
392	50 t. Heads symbolising population growth	..	35	50
389/92	..	*Set of 4*	80	1·00

218 Donating Blood   **219** Dugong

(Des R. Bates. Litho Questa)

1980 (27 Aug). *Red Cross Blood Bank. T 218 and similar horiz designs. Multicoloured. P 14½.*
393	7 t. Type 218	..	15	10
394	15 t. Receiving transfusion	..	20	20
395	30 t. Map of Papua New Guinea showing blood transfusion centres		25	25
396	60 t. Blood and its components	..	40	60
393/6	..	*Set of 4*	90	1·00

(Des Dr. E. Lindgren (35 t.), T. Nolan (others). Photo Courvoisier)

1980 (29 Oct). *Mammals. T 219 and similar multicoloured designs. P 11½.*
397	7 t. Type 219	..	10	10
398	30 t. New Guinea Marsupial Cat (*vert*)	..	40	40
399	35 t. Tube-nosed Bat (*vert*)	..	40	40
400	45 t. Rufescent Bandicoot ("Mumut")	..	50	50
397/400		*Set of 4*	1·25	1·25

220 White-headed   **221** Native Mask
Kingfisher

(Des W. Peckover. Photo Courvoisier)

1981 (21 Jan). *Kingfishers. T 220 and similar multicoloured designs. P 11½.*
401	3 t. Type 220	..	15	20
402	7 t. Forest Kingfisher	..	15	10
403	20 t. Sacred Kingfisher	..	50	50
404	25 t. White-tailed Kingfisher (26 × 46 mm)	..	60	85
405	60 t. Blue-winged Kookaburra	..	1·40	2·00
401/5	..	*Set of 5*	2·50	3·25

(Des R. Bates. Photo Note Ptg Branch, Reserve Bank of Australia)

1981 (21 Jan). *Coil stamps. Vert designs as T 221. P 15 × imperf.*
406	2 t. reddish violet and orange	..	10	20
407	5 t. cerise and blue-green	..	10	20

Design:—5 t. Hibiscus flower.

---

222 Mortar Team   223 M.A.F. (Missionary Aviation Fellowship) Aeroplane

(Des T. Reilly (15 t.), R. Bates (others). Litho Enschedé)

1981 (25 Mar). *Defence Force. T **222** and similar horiz designs. Multicoloured. P 13 × 13½.*

408	7 t. Type **222** ..		15	10
409	15 t. Aeroplane and aircrew ..	..	30	25
410	40 t. *Aitape* (patrol boat) and seamen		70	65
411	50 t. Medical team examining children		75	75
408/11	.. ..	*Set of 4*	1·75	1·50

(Des G. Wade. Litho Questa)

1981 (17 June). *"Mission Aviation". T **223** and similar vert designs. Multicoloured. P 14.*

412	10 t. Type **223** ..		20	10
413	15 t. Catholic mission aeroplane		25	25
414	20 t. S.I.L. (Summer Institute of Linguistics) helicopter		35	35
415	30 t. Lutheran mission aeroplane		55	55
416	35 t. S.D.A. (Seventh Day Adventist Church) aeroplane		65	65
412/16	.. .. ..	*Set of 5*	1·75	1·75

224 Scoop Net Fishing   225 *Forcartia buhleri*

(Des G. Wade. Litho Questa)

1981 (26 Aug). *Fishing. T **224** and similar horiz designs. Multicoloured. P 14.*

417	10 t. Type **224** ..		15	10
418	15 t. Kite fishing ..		30	30
419	30 t. Rod fishing ..		50	50
420	60 t. Scissor net fishing		95	85
417/20	.. .. ..	*Set of 4*	1·75	1·60

(Des P. Jones. Photo Courvoisier)

1981 (28 Oct). *Land Snail Shells. T **225** and similar horiz designs. Multicoloured. P 11½ × 12.*

421	5 t. Type **225** ..		10	10
422	15 t. *Naninia citrina* ..		25	25
423	20 t. *Papuina adonis* and *papuina hermione* ..		35	35
424	30 t. *Papustyla hindei* and *papustyla novae-pommeraniae* ..		50	50
425	40 t. *Rhynchotrochus strabo*		70	80
421/5	.. ..	*Set of 5*	1·75	1·75

226 Lord Baden-Powell and Flag-raising Ceremony   227 Yangoru and Boiken Bowls, East Sepik

(Des G. Wade. Photo Courvoisier)

1982 (20 Jan). *75th Anniv of Boy Scout Movement. T **226** and similar horiz designs. Multicoloured. P 11½.*

426	15 t. Type **226** ..		40	25
427	25 t. Scout leader and camp		60	50
428	35 t. Scout, and hut building ..		75	65
429	50 t. Percy Chatterton, and Scouts administering first aid ..		90	85
426/9	.. ..	*Set of 4*	2·40	2·00

(Des R. Bates. Litho Questa)

1982 (24 Mar). *Native Pottery. T **227** and similar multicoloured designs. P 14 (10, 20 t.) or 14½ (others).*

430	10 t. Type **227** ..		15	10
431	20 t. Utu cooking pot and small Gumalu pot, Madang ..		30	30
432	40 t. Wanigela pots, Northern District (37 × 23 mm) ..		55	55
433	50 t. Ramu Valley pots, Madang (37 × 23 mm)		70	80
430/3	..	*Set of 4*	1·50	1·60

ALTERED CATALOGUE NUMBERS

Any Catalogue numbers altered from the last edition are shown as a list in the introductory pages.

---

228 "Eat Healthy Foods"   229 *Stylophora sp*

(Des G. Wade, Litho J.W.)

1982 (21 May). *Food and Nutrition. T **228** and similar horiz designs. Multicoloured. P 14½ × 14.*

434	10 t. Type **228** ..		15	10
435	15 t. Protein foods ..		30	30
436	30 t. Protective foods ..		55	55
437	40 t. Energy foods ..		65	70
434/7	.. ..	*Set of 4*	1·50	1·50

(Des Courvoisier or W. Peckover (5 k.). Photo Courvoisier)

1982 (21 July)—**85**. *Granite paper. (a) Corals. Multicoloured designs as T **229**. P 11½.*

438	1 t. Type **229** ..		10	20
439	3 t. *Dendrophyllia sp. (vert)* (12.1.83)	..	60	30
440	5 t. *Acropora humilis* ..		15	10
441	10 t. *Dendronephthya sp. (vert)* (12.1.83)		80	10
442	12 t. As 10 t. (29.5.85) ..		3·50	2·00
443	15 t. *Distichopora sp* ..		30	20
444	20 t. *Isis sp. (vert)* (9.11.83)		70	25
445	25 t. *Acropora sp. (vert)* (9.11.83)		40	30
446	30 t. *Dendronephthya sp. (diff) (vert)* (12.1.83)		1·50	60
447	35 t. *Stylaster elegans (vert)* (9.11.83)		80	50
448	40 t. *Antipathes sp. (vert)* (12.1.83)		2·00	50
449	45 t. *Turbinarea sp. (vert)* (9.11.83)		2·00	60
450	1 k. *Xenia sp* ..		1·25	1·25
451	3 k. *Distichopora sp. (vert)* (12.1.83)		3·75	3·50

(b) Bird of Paradise. Multicoloured square design, 33 × 33 mm

452	5 k. Raggiana Bird of Paradise (15.8.84)		6·00	6·50
438/52	.. .. ..	*Set of 15*	21·00	15·00

230 Missionaries landing on Beach   231 Athletics

(Des B. To Una. Photo Courvoisier)

1982 (15 Sept). *Centenary of Catholic Church in Papua New Guinea. Mural on wall of Nordup Catholic Church, East New Britain. T **230** and similar vert designs. Multicoloured. P 11½.*

457	10 t. Type **230** ..		25	20
	a. Horiz strip of 3. Nos. 457/9		65	
458	10 t. Missionaries talking to natives ..		25	20
459	10 t. Natives with slings and spears ready to attack ..		25	20
457/9	.. .. ..	*Set of 3*	65	55

Nos. 457/9 come in *se-tenant* strips of 3 horizontally throughout the sheet, each strip forming a composite design.

(Des R. Bates. Litho Questa)

1982 (6 Oct). *Commonwealth Games and "Anpex 82" Stamp Exhibition, Brisbane. T **231** and similar horiz designs. Multicoloured. P 14½.*

460	10 t. Type **231** ..		15	10
461	15 t. Boxing ..		25	25
462	45 t. Rifle-shooting ..		55	70
463	50 t. Bowls ..		65	75
460/3	.. ..	*Set of 4*	1·40	1·60

232 National Flag

(Des Walsall. Litho Harrison)

1983 (9 Mar). *Commonwealth Day. T **232** and similar horiz designs. Multicoloured. P 14.*

464	10 t. Type **232** ..		15	10
465	15 t. Basket-weaving and cabbage-picking ..		20	30
466	20 t. Crane hoisting roll of material ..		25	35
467	50 t. Lorries and ships. ..		60	75
464/7	..	*Set of 4*	1·10	1·40

233 Transport Communications   234 *Chelonia depressa*

(Des G. Wade. Litho J.W.)

1983 (7 Sept). *World Communications Year. T **233** and similar horiz designs. Multicoloured. P 14.*

468	10 t. Type **233** ..		30	10
469	25 t. "Postal service" ..		70	45
470	30 t. "Telephone service" ..		80	50
471	60 t. "Transport service" ..		1·50	90
468/71	..	*Set of 4*	3·00	1·75

(Des R. Bates. Photo Courvoisier)

1984 (8 Feb). *Turtles. T **234** and similar horiz designs. Multicoloured. P 11½.*

472	5 t. Type **234** ..		20	10
473	10 t. *Chelonia mydas* ..		35	10
474	15 t. *Eretmochelys imbricata* ..		50	30
475	20 t. *Lepidochelys olivacea* ..		65	35
476	25 t. *Caretta caretta* ..		70	50
477	40 t. *Dermochelys coriacea* ..		95	75
472/7	.. ..	*Set of 6*	3·00	1·75

235 Avro "X VH-UXX" *Faith in Australia*

(Des T. Reilly. Litho Format)

1984 (9 May). *50th Anniv of First Airmail Australia-Papua New Guinea. T **235** and similar horiz designs. Multicoloured. P 14½ × 14.*

478	20 t. Type **235** ..		40	30
479	25 t. "DH86B VH-UYU" *Carmania*		50	45
480	40 t. Westland "Widgeon VH-UGI"		90	80
481	60 t. Consolidated "Catalina NC777" *Guba* ..		1·40	1·25
478/81	..	*Set of 4*	3·00	2·50

236 Parliament House   237 Ceremonial Shield and Club, Central Province

(Des A. Brennan, adapted G. Vasarhelyi. Litho Harrison)

1984 (7 Aug). *Opening of New Parliament House. P 13½ × 14.*

482	**236**	10 t. multicoloured		30	30

(Des Revd. A. H. Brown. Photo Courvoisier)

1984 (21 Sept). *Ceremonial Shields. T **237** and similar vert designs. Multicoloured. Granite paper. P 11½.*

483	10 t. Type **237** ..		30	10
484	20 t. Ceremonial shield, West New Britain		50	50
485	30 t. Ceremonial shield, Madang Province		75	1·00
486	50 t. Ceremonial shield, East Sepik		1·25	1·75
483/6	..	*Set of 4*	2·50	3·00

238 H.M.S. *Nelson* at Port Moresby, 1884   239 Fergusson Island

(Des R. Bates, Litho Format)

1984 (6 Nov). *Centenary of Protectorate Proclamations for British New Guinea and German New Guinea. T **238** and similar horiz designs. Multicoloured. P 14½ × 14.*

487	10 t. Type **238** ..		35	45
	a. Horiz pair. Nos. 487/8 ..		70	90
488	10 t. Papua New Guinea flag and Port Moresby, 1984 ..		35	45
489	45 t. Papua New Guinea flag and Rabaul, 1984 ..		1·25	1·75
	a. Horiz pair. Nos. 489/90 ..		2·50	3·50
490	45 t. German warship *Elisabeth* at Rabaul, 1884 ..		1·25	1·75
487/90	.. ..	*Set of 4*	3·00	4·00

as horizontal pairs throughout the sheets, each pair forming a composite picture.

(Des R. Bates. Photo Courvoisier)

1985 (6 Feb). *Tourist Scenes. T **239** and similar multicoloured designs. Granite paper. P 11½.*

491	10 t. Type **239** ..		30	10
492	25 t. Sepik River ..		65	55
493	40 t. Chimbu Gorge (*horiz*) ..		95	80
494	60 t. Dali Beach, Vanimo (*horiz*) ..		1·40	1·40
491/4	..	*Set of 4*	3·00	2·50

12t
(240)

241 Dubu Platform,
Central Province

1985 (1 Apr). *No. 408 surch with T 240.*
495 12 t. on 7 t. Type 222 .. .. .. 50 60
  a. Surch omitted (in horiz pair with
    normal) £110
  b. Surch inverted .. .. .. † —
At least one sheet of No. 495 exists with the surcharge
completely omitted on five positions of the sheet and poorly
printed on the remainder.

(Des G. Wade. Photo Heraclio Fournier)

1985 (1 May). *Ceremonial Structures. T 241 and similar vert
designs. Multicoloured. P 13.*
496 15 t. Type 241.. .. .. .. 45 15
497 20 t. Tamuniai house, West New Britain .. 60 50
498 30 t. Traditional yam tower, Trobriand
  Island 85 80
499 60 t. Huli grave, Tari .. .. .. 1·25 1·75
496/9 .. .. *Set of 4* 2·75 3·00

242 Head of New Britain
Sparrow Hawk

243 National Flag and
Parliament House

(Des P. Slater. Litho Format)

1985 (26 Aug). *Birds of Prey. T 242 and similar vert designs,
Multicoloured. P 14 × 14½.*
500 12 t. Type 242.. .. .. .. 55 70
  a. Horiz pair. Nos. 500/1 .. .. 1·10 1·40
501 12 t. New Britain Sparrow Hawk in flight .. 55 70
502 30 t. Doria's Goshawk .. .. 80 1·00
  a. Horiz pair. Nos. 502/3 .. .. 1·60 2·00
503 30 t. Doria's Goshawk in flight .. 80 1·00
504 60 t. Long-tailed Honey Buzzard .. 1·50 1·75
  a. Horiz pair. Nos. 504/5 .. .. 3·00 3·50
505 60 t. Long-tailed Honey Buzzard in flight 1·50 1·75
500/5 .. .. *Set of 6* 5·25 6·25
Nos. 500/1, 502/3 and 504/5 were each printed together,
se-tenant, in horizontal pairs throughout the sheets.

(Des R. Bates. Litho B.D.T.)

1985 (11 Sept). *10th Anniv of Independence. P 14 × 15.*
506 243 12 t. multicoloured 60 50

244 Early Postcard,
Aerogramme, Inkwell
and Spectacles

245 Figure with
Eagle

(Des R. Bates. Litho Walsall)

1985 (9 Oct). *Centenary of the Papua New Guinea Post Office.
T 244 and similar horiz designs. Multicoloured. P 14½ × 14.*
507 12 t. Type 244.. .. .. .. 45 10
508 30 t. Queensland 1897 1d. die with proof and
  modern press printing stamps.. .. 95 80
509 40 t. Newspaper of 1885 announcing shipping service and loading mail into aircraft .. .. 1·25 95
510 60 t. Friedrich-Wilhelmshafen postmark of
  1892 and Port Moresby F.D.C. postmark of 9 Oct 1985. .. .. 1·75 2·00
507/10 .. .. *Set of 4* 4·00 3·50
MS511 90 × 79 mm. Nos. 507/10 .. .. 4·00 5·00

(Des R. Bates. Photo Courvoisier)

1985(13 Nov). *Nombowai Wood Carvings. T 245 and similar
vert designs. Multicoloured. Granite paper. P 11½.*
512 12 t. Type 245.. .. .. .. 50 10
513 30 t. Figure with clamshell .. .. 1·25 75
514 60 t. Figure with dolphin .. .. 2·00 2·00
515 80 t. Figure of woman with cockerel .. 2·50 2·75
512/15 .. .. *Set of 4* 5·75 5·00

246 *Cypraea valentia* **247** Rufous Fantail

(Des R. Bates. Photo Courvoisier)

1986 (12 Feb). *Seashells. T 246 and similar horiz designs.
Multicoloured. Granite paper. P 11½.*
516 15 t. Type 246.. .. .. .. 55 15
517 35 t. *Oliva buelowi* .. .. .. 1·25 1·25
518 45 t. *Oliva parkinsoni* .. .. 1·50 1·60
519 70 t. *Cypraea aurantium* .. .. 2·00 2·75
516/19 .. .. *Set of 4* 4·75 5·25

(Des A. Theobald. Litho Harrison)

1986 (21 Apr). *60th Birthday of Queen Elizabeth II. Vert
designs as T 110 of Ascension. Multicoloured. P 14½ × 14.*
520 15 t. Princess Elizabeth in A.T.S. uniform,
  1945 .. .. 20 15
521 35 t. Silver Wedding Anniversary photograph (by Patrick Lichfield), Balmoral,
  1972 .. .. 50 55
522 50 t. Queen inspecting guard of honour, Port
  Moresby, 1982 .. .. .. 70 75
523 60 t. On board Royal Yacht *Britannia*, Papua
  New Guinea, 1982 .. .. 85 90
524 70 t. At Crown Agents' Head Office, London,
  1983 .. .. 95 1·10
520/4 .. .. *Set of 5* 3·00 3·00

(Des W. Peckover. Photo Courvoisier)

1986 (22 May). *"Ameripex '86" International Stamp Exhibition, Chicago. Small Birds (1st series). T 247 and similar
multicoloured designs. Granite paper. P 12½.*
525 15 t. Type 247.. .. .. .. 70 15
526 35 t. Streaked Berrypecker .. .. 1·40 65
527 45 t. Red-breasted Pitta .. .. 1·50 80
528 70 t. Olive-yellow Robin (*vert*) .. 2·00 2·00
525/8 .. .. *Set of 4* 5·00 3·25
The scientific name on the 15 t. value refers to the 45 t. design,
and vice versa.
See also Nos. 597/601.

248 Martin Luther nailing
Theses to Cathedral Door,
Wittenberg, and Modern
Lutheran Pastor

249 *Dendrobium
vexillarius*

(Des local artist. Litho Questa)

1986 (3 July). *Centenary of Lutheran Church in Papua New
Guinea. T 248 and similar vert design. Multicoloured.
P 14 × 15.*
529 15 t. Type 248.. .. .. .. 75 15
530 70 t. Early church, Finschhafen, and modern
  Martin Luther Chapel, Lae Seminary.. 2·25 1·50

(Des Harrison. Litho B.D.T.)

1986 (4 Aug). *Orchids. T 249 and similar vert designs.
Multicoloured. P 13½.*
531 15 t. Type 249.. .. .. .. 75 15
532 35 t. *Dendrobium lineale* .. .. 1·50 75
533 45 t. *Dendrobium johnsoniae* .. 1·75 1·10
534 70 t. *Dendrobium cuthbertsonii* .. 2·50 1·75
531/4 .. .. *Set of 4* 6·00 3·25

250 Maprik Dancer **251** White Cap Anemonefish

(Des R. Bates. Litho B.D.T.)

1986 (12 Nov). *Papua New Guinea Dancers. T 250 and similar
vert designs. Multicoloured. P 14.*
535 15 t. Type 250.. .. .. .. 65 15
536 35 t. Kiriwina.. .. .. .. 1·40 75
537 45 t. Kundiawa .. .. .. 1·50 95
538 70 t. Fasu .. .. 2·40 2·25
535/8 .. .. *Set of 4* 5·50 3·75

(Des Harrison. Litho Format)

1987 (15 Apr). *Anemonefish. T 251 and similar horiz designs.
Multicoloured. P 15.*
539 17 t. Type 251.. .. .. .. 70 25
540 30 t. Black Anemonefish .. .. 1·40 80
541 35 t. Tomato Clownfish .. .. 1·50 90
542 70 t. Spine Cheek Anemonefish .. 2·50 2·50
539/42 .. .. *Set of 4* 5·50 4·00

252 *Roebuck* (Dampier), 1700 (253)

(Des R. Bates. Photo Courvoisier)

1987 (15 June)—**88**. *Ships. T 252 and similar square designs.
Multicoloured. Granite paper. P 11½.*
543 1 t. *Boudeuse* (De Bougainville), 1768
  (16.11.88) 10 10
544 5 t. Type 252.. .. .. .. 30 10
545 10 t. H.M.S. *Swallow* (Philip Carteret), 1767
  (16.11.88) 15 20
546 15 t. H.M.S. *Fly* (Blackwood), 1845 (17.2.88) 30 30
547 17 t. As 15 t. (16.3.88) 20 25
548 20 t. H.M.S. *Rattlesnake* (Owen Stanley),
  1849 (17.2.88) 40 40
549 30 t. *Vitiaz* (Maclay), 1871 (16.11.88) .. 40 45
550 35 t. *San Pedrico* (Torres) and zabra, 1606 .. 45 50
551 40 t. *L'Astrolabe* (d'Urville), 1827 (17.2.88) .. 60 65
552 45 t. *Neva* (D'Albertis), 1876 .. .. 65 70
553 60 t. Spanish galleon (Jorge de Meneses),
  1526 (17.2.88) 75 80
554 70 t. *Eendracht* (Schouten and Le Maire),
  1616 .. .. 90 95
555 1 k. H.M.S. *Blanche* (Simpson), 1872
  (16.3.88) .. .. 1·25 1·60
556 2 k. *Merrie England* (steamer), 1889 .. 3·00 2·75
557 3 k. *Samoa* (German colonial steamer),
  1884 (16.11.88) .. .. 4·00 4·25
543/57 .. .. *Set of 15* 12·00 12·50
A printing by lithography of a 45 t. (as issued 70 t.), 70 t. (as
45 t.), 80 t. (as 35 t.) and 2 k. was originally produced, but such
stamps were not issued for postal purposes. Examples in
circulation are from a small quantity sold by the U.S.A.
philatelic agent in error.

(Des Revd. A. H. Brown. Photo Courvoisier)

1987 (19 Aug). *War Shields. Vert designs as T 237. Multicoloured. Granite paper. P 11½.*
558 15 t. Gulf Province 20 25
559 35 t. East Sepik 45 50
560 45 t. Madang Province 55 60
561 70 t. Telefomin 85 90
558/61 .. .. *Set of 4* 1·90 2·00

1987 (23 Sept). *No. 442 surch with T 253.*
562 15 t. on 12 t. *Dendronephthya sp.* .. 55 55
For similar 20 t. surcharge see No. 602.

254 *Protoreaster nodosus* **255** Cessna "Stationair 6"
taking off, Rabaraba

(Des Harrison. Litho B.D.T.)

1987 (30 Sept). *Starfish. T 254 and similar horiz designs.
Multicoloured. P 13½.*
563 17 t. Type 254.. .. .. .. 40 25
564 35 t. *Gomophia egeriae* 75 50
565 45 t. *Choriaster granulatus* 85 70
566 70 t. *Neoferdina ocellata* .. .. 1·40 1·00
563/6 .. .. *Set of 4* 3·00 2·25

(Des A. Theobald. Litho Questa)

1987 (11 Nov). *Aircraft in Papua New Guinea. T 255 and
similar horiz designs. Multicoloured. P 14.*
567 15 t. Type 255.. .. .. .. 55 25
568 35 t. Britten-Norman "Islander" over Hom-
  brum Bluff .. .. .. 1·00 60
569 45 t. DHC "Twin Otter" over Highlands .. 1·25 80
570 70 t. Fokker "F28" over Madang .. 2·00 1·40
567/70 .. .. *Set of 4* 4·25 2·75

PRICES OF SETS

Set prices are given for many issues, generally
those containing three stamps or more. Definitive
sets include one of each value or major colour
change, but do not cover different perforations,
die types or minor shades. Where a choice is
possible the set prices are based on the cheapest
versions of the stamps included in the listings.

256 Pre-Independence
Policeman on Traffic
Duty and Present-
day Motorcycle Patrol

(Des R. Bates. Litho Questa)

1988 (15 June). *Centenary of Royal Papua New Guinea Constabulary. T* **256** *and similar vert designs. Multicoloured.* P 14 × 15.

571	17 t. Type **256**		30	25
572	35 t. British New Guinea Armed Constabulary, 1890, and Governor W. MacGregor		60	50
573	45 t. Police badges		75	65
574	70 t. German New Guinea Police, 1888, and Dr. A. Hahl (founder)		1·25	1·50
571/4		Set of 4	2·50	2·50

257 Lakatoi (canoe) and Sydney Opera House

(Des R. Bates. Litho Harrison)

1988 (30 July). *"Sydpex '88" National Stamp Exhibition, Sydney.* P 14.
575 **257** 35 t. multicoloured 80 50

258 Papua New Guinea
Flag on Globe and
Fireworks

259 Male and Female
Butterflies in Courtship

(Des R. Bates. Litho CPE Australia Ltd, Melbourne)

1988 (30 July). *Bicentenary of Australian Settlement. T* **258** *and similar horiz design. Multicoloured.* P 13½.

576	35 t. Type **258**		55	65
	a. Horiz pair. Nos. 576/7		1·10	1·25
577	35 t. Australian flag on globe and fireworks		55	65
MS578	90 × 50 mm. Nos. 576/7		1·10	1·25

Nos. 576/7 were printed together, *se-tenant*, in horizontal pairs throughout the sheet, each pair forming a composite design.

(Des M. Parsons, adapted D. Miller. Litho Walsall)

1989 (19 Sept). *Endangered Species. Ornithoptera alexandrae (Queen Alexandra's Birdwing butterfly). T* **259** *and similar multicoloured designs.* P 14½.

579	5 t. Type **259**		40	10
580	17 t. Female laying eggs and mature larva (vert)		80	30
581	25 t. Male emerging from pupa (vert)		1·10	75
582	35 t. Male feeding		1·40	1·50
579/82		Set of 4	3·25	2·40

260 Athletics

(Des G. Wade. Litho CPE Australia Ltd, Melbourne)

1988 (19 Sept). *Olympic Games, Seoul. T* **260** *and similar horiz design. Multicoloured.* P 13½.

583	17 t. Type **260**		20	25
584	45 t. Weightlifting		60	65

COVER PRICES

Cover factors are quoted at the beginning of each country for most issues to 1945. An explanation of the system can be found on page x. The factors quoted do not, however, apply to philatelic covers.

261 Rhododendron
zoelleri

263 Writing Letter

262

(Des N. Cruttwell and I. Loe. Litho Leigh-Mardon Ltd, Melbourne)

1989 (25 Jan). *Rhododendrons. T* **261** *and similar vert designs. Multicoloured.* W **262**. P 14½.

585	3 t. Type **261**		10	10
586	20 t. Rhododendron cruttwellii		35	30
587	60 t. Rhododendron superbum		1·00	1·00
588	70 t. Rhododendron christianae		1·10	1·10
585/8		Set of 4	2·25	2·25

(Des R. Bates. Litho Leigh-Mardon Ltd, Melbourne)

1989 (22 Mar). *International Letter Writing Week. T* **263** *and similar square designs. Multicoloured.* W **262**. P 14½.

589	20 t. Type **263**		30	30
590	35 t. Stamping letter		55	50
591	60 t. Posting letter		90	1·10
592	70 t. Reading letter		1·10	1·40
589/92		Set of 4	2·50	3·00

264 Village House, Buka
Island, North Solomons

265 Tit Berrypecker
(female)

(Des G. Wade. Litho Leigh-Mardon Ltd, Melbourne)

1989 (17 May). *Traditional Dwellings. T* **264** *and similar horiz designs. Multicoloured.* W **262**. P 15.

593	20 t. Type **264**		35	35
594	35 t. Koiari tree house, Central Province		60	60
595	60 t. Longhouse, Lauan, New Ireland		1·00	1·25
596	70 t. Decorated house, Basilaki, Milne Bay		1·25	1·50
593/6		Set of 4	3·00	3·25

(Des W. Peckover. Litho Questa)

1989 (12 July). *Small Birds (2nd issue). T* **265** *and similar vert designs. Multicoloured.* P 14½.

597	20 t. Type **265**		70	55
	a. Horiz pair. Nos. 597/8		1·40	1·10
598	20 t. Tit Berrypecker (male)		70	55
599	35 t. Blue-capped Babbler		90	75
600	45 t. Black-throated Robin		1·10	1·00
601	70 t. Large Mountain Sericornis		1·60	1·60
597/601		Set of 5	4·50	4·00

Nos. 597/8 were printed together, *se-tenant*, in horizontal pairs throughout the sheet.

1989 (12 July). *No.* 539 *surch as T* **253**.

602	20 t. on 17 t. Type **251**		60	60
	a. Surch double		†	—

266 Motu Motu
Dancer, Gulf Province

267 Hibiscus, People going
to Church and Gope Board

(Des G. Wade. Litho Leigh-Mardon Ltd, Melbourne)

1989 (6 Sept). *Traditional Dancers. T* **266** *and similar vert designs. Multicoloured.* W **262**. P 14×14½.

603	20 t. Type **266**		60	35
604	35 t. Baining, East New Britain		95	90
605	60 t. Vailala River, Gulf Province		1·75	2·00
606	70 t. Timbunke, East Sepik Province		1·90	2·25
603/6		Set of 4	4·75	5·00

(Des R. Bates. Litho Leigh-Mardon Ltd, Melbourne)

1989 (8 Nov). *Christmas. T* **267** *and similar horiz designs showing flowers and carved panels. Multicoloured.* P 14×14½.

607	20 t. Type **267**		40	35
608	35 t. Rhododendron, Virgin and Child and mask		60	60
609	60 t. D'Albertis Creeper, Christmas candle and warshield		1·25	1·50
610	70 t. Pacific Frangapani, peace dove and flute mask		1·40	1·75
607/10		Set of 4	3·25	3·75

268 Guni Falls

269 Boys and Census
Form

(Des A. Theobald. Litho Questa)

1990 (1 Feb). *Waterfalls. T* **268** *and similar vert designs. Multicoloured.* P 14.

611	20 t. Type **268**		50	35
612	35 t. Rouna Falls		75	75
613	60 t. Ambua Falls		1·25	1·50
614	70 t. Wawoi Falls		1·50	1·75
611/14		Set of 4	3·50	4·00

MACHINE LABELS. From 7 March 1990 gummed labels inscribed "PAPUA NEW GUINEA BOROKO" with values from 1 t. to 99 k. 99 were available from an automatic machine installed at Boroko Post Office. A second machine was operational at Rabaul Post Office from 8 February 1991. Labels from this machine do not carry an indication of its location.

(Des R. Bates. Litho Questa)

1990 (2 May). *National Census. T* **269** *and similar horiz design. Multicoloured.* P 14½×15.

615	20 t. Type **269**		40	30
616	70 t. Family and census form		1·50	1·60

270 Gwa Pupi Dance
Mask

271 Sepik and Maori
Kororu Masks

(Des G. Vasarhelyi. Litho Leigh-Mardon Ltd, Melbourne)

1990 (11 July). *Gogodala Dance Masks. T* **270** *and similar vert designs. Multicoloured.* P 13½.

617	20 t. Type **270**		60	30
618	35 t. Tauga paiyale		95	70
619	60 t. A: ga		1·60	1·75
620	70 t. Owala		1·90	2·25
617/20		Set of 4	4·50	4·50

(Des R. Bates. Litho Leigh-Mardon Ltd, Melbourne)

1990 (24 Aug). *"New Zealand 1990" International Stamp Exhibition, Auckland.* P 14½.
621 **271** 35 t. multicoloured 75 75

272 Dwarf Cassowary
and Great Spotted Kiwi

273 Whimbrel

(Des R. Bates. Litho Leigh-Mardon Ltd, Melbourne)

1990 (24 Aug). *150th Anniv of Treaty of Waitangi. T 272 and similar square design. Multicoloured. P 14½.*
622	20 t. Type 272	70	40
623	35 t. Double-wattled Cassowary and Brown Kiwi	1·10	1·25

(Des L. Curtis. Litho Questa)

1990 (26 Sept). *Migratory Birds. T 273 and similar horiz designs. Multicoloured. P 14½×13½.*
624	20 t. Type 273	55	30
625	35 t. Sharp-tailed Sandpiper	85	70
626	60 t. Turnstone	1·50	1·60
627	70 t. Terek Sandpiper	1·75	1·90
624/7	Set of 4	4·25	4·00

274 Jew's Harp   275 Rhynchotrochus weigmani

(Des R. Bates. Litho Leigh-Mardon Ltd, Melbourne)

1990 (31 Oct). *Musical Instruments. T 274 and similar square designs. Multicoloured. P 13.*
628	20 t. Type 274	35	30
629	35 t. Musical bow	60	50
630	60 t. Wantoat drum	1·00	1·10
631	70 t. Gogodala rattle	1·10	1·25
628/31	Set of 4	2·75	2·75

(Des P. Schouter. Litho Leigh-Mardon Ltd, Melbourne)

1991 (6 Mar). *Land Shells. T 275 and similar horiz designs. Multicoloured. P 14×14½.*
632	21 t. Type 275	35	30
633	40 t. Forcartia globula and Canefriula azonata	60	50
634	50 t. Planispira deaniana	90	70
635	80 t. Papuina chancel and Papuina xanthocheila	1·25	1·50
632/5	Set of 4	2·75	2·75

276 Magnificent Riflebird   277 Cricket

Two types of inscr on 21 t. and 45 t.:
Type I. Inscribed "1992 BIRD OF PARADISE" at foot
Type II. Inscribed "MAY 1992 BIRD OF PARADISE" at foot

(Des W. Peckover (10 k.), R. Bates (others). Litho Leigh-Mardon Ltd, Melbourne)

1991 (1 May)–93. *Birds of Paradise. T 276 and similar multicoloured designs. P 13 (10 k.) or 14½ (others).*
636	1 t. Type 276 (20.1.93)	10	10
637	5 t. Loria's Bird of Paradise (2.9.92)	10	10
638	10 t. Sickle Crested Bird of Paradise (20.1.93)	15	20
639	20 t. Wahnes' Parotia (20.1.93)	25	30
640	21 t. Crinkle-collared Manucode (I) (25.3.92)	25	30
	a. Type II (5.92)	—	30
641	30 t. Goldie's Bird of Paradise (20.1.93)	40	45
642	40 t. Yellow-breasted Bird of Paradise (2.9.92)	50	55
643	45 t. King Bird of Paradise (I) (25.3.92)	60	65
	a. Type II (5.92)	—	65
644	50 t. Short-tailed Paradigalla Bird of Paradise (2.9.92)	65	70
645	60 t. Queen Carola's Parotia (25.3.92)	80	85
646	90 t. Emperor of Germany Bird of Paradise (25.3.92)	1·10	1·25
647	1 k. Magnificent Bird of Paradise (2.9.92)	1·25	1·40
648	2 k. Superb Bird of Paradise (2.9.92)	2·50	2·75
649	5 k. Trumpet Bird (20.1.93)	6·50	6·75
650	10 k. Lesser Bird of Paradise (32×32 mm)	13·00	13·50
636/50	Set of 15	25·00	27·00

Examples of the 21, 45, 60 and 90 t. values with the currency shown as "T" were prepared, but not issued. The issued stamps show the currency as "t".

(Des D.D.S. Associates and T. Sipa. Litho Leigh-Mardon Ltd, Melbourne)

1991 (26 June). *9th South Pacific Games. T 277 and similar horiz designs. Multicoloured. P 13.*
651	21 t. Type 277	50	30
652	40 t. Athletics	80	70
653	50 t. Baseball	95	80
654	80 t. Rugby Union	1·60	1·75
651/4	Set of 4	3·50	3·25

278 Cathedral of St. Peter and St. Paul, Dogura   279 Rambusto Headdress, Manus Province

(Des G. Wade. Litho Questa)

1991 (7 Aug). *Centenary of Anglican Church in Papua New Guinea. T 278 and similar horiz designs. Multicoloured. P 14½.*
655	21 t. Type 278	45	30
656	40 t. Missionaries landing, 1891, and Kaieta shrine	80	80
657	80 t. First church and Modawa tree	1·60	1·75
655/7	Set of 3	2·50	2·50

(Des D.D.S. Associates and T. Sipa. Litho Leigh-Mardon Ltd, Melbourne)

1991 (16 Oct). *Tribal Headdresses. T 279 and similar vert designs. Multicoloured. P 13.*
658	21 t. Type 279	40	30
659	40 t. Marawaka, Eastern Highlands	75	75
660	50 t. Tufi, Oro Province	85	85
661	80 t. Sina Sina, Simbu Province	1·50	1·75
658/61	Set of 4	3·25	3·25

280 Nina   281 Canoe Prow Shield, Bamu

(Des G. Wade. Litho Leigh-Mardon Ltd, Melbourne)

1992 (15 Apr). *500th Anniv of Discovery of America by Columbus and "EXPO '92" World's Fair, Seville. T 280 and similar horiz designs. Multicoloured. P 14.*
662	21 t. Type 280	40	30
663	45 t. Pinta	90	80
664	60 t. Santa Maria	1·40	1·25
665	90 t. Christopher Columbus and ships	1·90	1·75
662/5	Set of 4	4·25	3·75

(Des G. Wade. Litho Leigh-Mardon Ltd, Melbourne)

1992 (22 May). *"World Columbian Stamp Expo '92", Chicago. Sheet, 110×80 mm, containing Nos. 664/5. P 14.*
MS666   60 t. *Santa Maria*; 90 t. *Christopher Columbus and ships (sold at 1 k. 70)* ... 2·40 2·75

(Des I. Giles. Litho Leigh-Mardon Ltd, Melbourne)

1992 (3 June). *Papuan Gulf Artifacts. T 281 and similar vert designs. Multicoloured. P 14.*
667	21 t. Type 281	35	30
668	45 t. Skull rack, Kerewa	75	75
669	60 t. Ancestral figure, Era River	1·10	1·10
670	90 t. Gope (spirit) board, Urama	1·40	1·50
667/70	Set of 4	3·25	3·25

282 Papuan Infantryman   283 Hibiscus tiliaceus

(Des G. Wade. Litho Leigh-Mardon Ltd, Melbourne)

1992 (22 July). *50th Anniv of Second World War Campaigns in Papua New Guinea. T 282 and similar vert designs. Multicoloured. P 14.*
671	21 t. Type 282	35	30
672	45 t. Australian militiaman	75	75
673	60 t. Japanese infantryman	1·10	1·10
674	90 t. American infantryman	1·40	1·50
671/4	Set of 4	3·25	3·25

(Des T. Sipa. Litho Leigh-Mardon Ltd, Melbourne)

1992 (28 Oct). *Flowering Trees. T 283 and similar vert designs. Multicoloured. P 14.*
675	21 t. Type 283	40	30
676	45 t. Castanospermum australe	85	85
677	60 t. Cordia subcordata	1·25	1·25
678	90 t. Acacia auriculiformis	1·75	1·75
675/8	Set of 4	3·75	3·75

POSTAGE DUE STAMPS

POSTAL CHARGES

6d.   **POSTAL CHARGES**

● IXIXIXIXIX   **3s.**

(D 1)   (D 2)

1960 (1 Mar). *Postage stamps surcharged. (a) No. 8 with Type D 1.*
D1	6d. on 7½d. blue (R.)		£750	£400
	a. Surch double		£3250	£1800

(b) Nos. 1, 4, 6a, 7/8 as Type D 2
D2	1d. on 6½d. maroon		14·00	7·00
D3	3d. on ½d. emerald (B.)		16·00	5·50
	a. Surch double		£475	
D4	6d. on 7½d. blue (R.)		32·00	13·00
	a. Surch double		£475	
D5	1s. 3d. on 3½d. black (O.)		24·00	13·00
D6	3s. on 2½d. orange		40·00	26·00
D2/6	Set of 5		£110	55·00

Of No. D1a, only a few copies are known from a sheet used at Goroka.

D 3

(Typo Note Ptg Branch, Reserve Bank of Australia, Melbourne)

1960 (2 June). *W 15 of Australia. P 14.*
D 7	D 3	1d. orange		65	60
D 8		3d. yellow-brown		70	65
D 9		6d. blue		75	40
D10		9d. deep red		75	1·60
D11		1s. light emerald		75	50
D12		1s. 3d. violet		1·40	1·75
D13		1s. 6d. pale blue		5·50	5·50
D14		3s. yellow		6·00	1·25
D7/14		Set of 8		15·00	11·00

The use of Postal Charge stamps was discontinued on 12 February 1966, but they remained on sale at the Philatelic Bureau until 31 August 1966.

Pitcairn Islands

CROWN COLONY

The settlement of Pitcairn Island by the *Bounty* mutineers in 1790 was not discovered until the American whaler *Topaz*, Capt. Mayhew Folger, called there in 1808. A visit by two Royal Navy frigates followed in 1814 and reports from their captains resulted in considerable interest being taken in the inhabitants' welfare by religious and philanthropic circles in Great Britain.

Due to overcrowding the population was resettled on Tahiti in 1831, but many soon returned to Pitcairn which was taken under British protection in 1838. The island was again evacuated in 1856, when the inhabitants were moved to Norfolk Island, but a number of families sailed back to their original home in 1859 and 1864.

The earliest surviving letter from the island is dated 1849. Before 1921 the mail service was irregular, as it depended on passing ships, and mail for the island was often sent via Tahiti. Some covers, purportedly sent from Pitcairn between 1883 and 1890 are known handstamped "Pitcairn Island" or "PITCAIRN ISLAND", but these are now believed to be forgeries.

In 1921 a regular mail service was introduced. As there were no stamps available letters were allowed free postage as long as they carried a cachet indicating their origin. The following illustrations are taken from *Pitcairn Islands Postal Markings 1883–1991*, published by the Pitcairn Islands Study Group, and are reproduced by permission of the author, Mr. Cy Kitching. Cachets I to XI are shown three-quarter size.

**POSTED IN PITCAIRN
NO STAMPS AVAILABLE**

Cachet I

Cat No.				Value on cover
C1	**1921.**	Cachet I (62×8 *mm*) (*violet*)	..	..£2500

**POSTED AT PITCAIRN ISLAND
NO STAMPS AVAILABLE.**

Cachet II

| C2 | **1921–25.** | Cachet II (*violet or red*) | .. | ..£2000 |

**POSTED AT PITCAIRN ISLAND
NO STAMPS AVAILABLE.**

Cachet III

| C3 | **1922–28.** | Cachet III (49×8½mm) (*vio, pur or blk*) | £1500 |

**POSTED IN PITCAIRN ISLAND
1923 NO STAMPS AVAILABLE**

Cachet IV

| C4 | **1923.** | Cachet IV (*black*) | .. | .. | ..£2250 |

**POSTED AT PITCAIRN ISLAND
NO STAMPS AVAILABLE**

Cachet V

| C5 | **1923–28** (Aug.) | Cachet V (47×9mm) (*red or black*) £1500 |

Cachet VI

C6	1923.	Cachet VI (*blue-green*)	..	..
C7	1923.	As Cachet V, but in three lines (*red*)	..
C8	1924.	As Cachet IV, but dated "1924" (*black*)	..

Cachet VII

| C9 | 1924. | Cachet VII (36×4 *mm*) (*violet*) |

**POSTED AT PITCAIRN ISLAND
NO STAMPS AVAILABLE.**

Cachet VIII

| C10 | **1924–27.** | Cachet VIII (*violet*) | .. | .. | ..£1500 |
| C11 | **1925** (Sept). | As Cachet IV, but dated "1925" (*blk*) £2000 |

**POSTED IN PITCAIRN
NO STAMPS AVAILABLE.**

Cachet IX

| C12 | **1925.** | Cachet IX (48×5 *mm*) | .. | .. | ..£1700 |

**POSTED IN PITCAIRN
NO STAMPS AVAILABLE.**

Cachet X

| C13 | **1926** (Jan). | Cachet X (64×8 *mm*) (*purple or black*) |

**POSTED AT PITCAIRN
NO STAMPS AVAILABLE**

Cachet XI

| C14 | **1926.** | Cachet XI (36×3¾ *mm*) | .. | .. |

In 1927 the New Zealand Post Office opened a postal agency on Pitcairn Island using New Zealand stamps cancelled with Type Z **1**. Some impressions of this postmark appear to show a double ring, but this is the result of heavy or uneven use of the handstamp. The postal agency operated from 7 June 1927 until 14 October 1940.

PRICES. Those quoted for Nos. Z1/17 are for examples showing a virtually complete strike of Type Z **1**. Due to the size of the cancellation such examples will usually be on piece.

Z **1**

Stamps of New Zealand cancelled with Type Z **1**.

1925–29.	*King George V (Nos. 446/8).*					
Z1	½d. green	..	..	..	..	15·00
Z2	1½d. orange-brown	..	..	..	30·00
Z3	2d. yellow	..	..	..	25·00

1926.	*King George V in Admiral's uniform (No. 468).*			
Z4	1d. rose-carmine	..	..	..	15·00

1935.	*Pictorials (Nos. 556/7).* W **43.**			
Z5	½d. bright green	..	..	40·00
Z6	1d. scarlet	..	..	..	25·00

1936.	*Pictorials (Nos. 577/8, 580).* W **98.**			
Z7	½d. bright green	..	..	30·00
Z8	1d. scarlet	..	..	..	10·00
Z9	2d. orange	..	..	..	40·00

1936.	*Congress of British Empire Chambers of Commerce (Nos. 593/5).*			
Z10	½d. emerald-green	..	..	25·00
Z11	1d. scarlet	..	..	..	25·00
Z12	2½d. blue	..	..	..	30·00

1937.	*Coronation (Nos. 599/601).*			
Z13	1d. carmine	..	..	..	20·00
Z14	2½d. Prussian blue	..	..	20·00
Z15	6d. red-orange	..	..	20·00

1938.	*King George VI (Nos. 603, 605).*			
Z16	½d. green	..	..	..	45·00
Z17	1d. scarlet	..	..	..	45·00

PRICES FOR STAMPS ON COVER TO 1945
Nos. 1/8   *from* × 10

1 Cluster of Oranges   **2** Christian on *Bounty* and Pitcairn Island

(Recess B.W. (1d., 3d., 4d., 8d. and 2s. 6d.), and Waterlow (others))

1940 (15 Oct)–51. *T* **1/2** *and similar horiz designs. Wmk Mult Script CA. P* 11½ × 11 (1d., 3d., 4d., 8d. and 2s. 6d.) or 12½ (*others*).

1	½d. orange and green	..	..	..	40	60
2	1d. mauve and magenta	..	..	55	70
3	1½d. grey and carmine	..	..	55	50

4	2d. green and brown	..	..	1·75	1·40
5	3d. yellow-green and blue	..	1·25	1·40
5a	4d. black and emerald-green (1.9.51)	..	13·00	7·00
6	6d. brown and grey-blue	..	5·00	2·25
6a	8d. olive-green and magenta (1.9.51)	..	13·00	7·00
7	1s. violet and grey	..	..	3·00	2·00
8	2s. 6d. green and brown	..	7·50	4·25
1/8		*Set of 10*	42·00	24·00
1/8 (ex. *a* Nos. Perf "Specimen"	..	*Set of 8* £750

Designs:—1½d. John Adams and his house; 2d. Lt. Bligh and H.M.S. *Bounty*; 3d. Pitcairn Islands and Pacific Ocean; 4d. *Bounty* Bible; 6d. H.M.S. *Bounty*; 8d. School, 1949; 1s. Fletcher Christian and Pitcairn Island; 2s. 6d. Christian on H.M.S. *Bounty* and Pitcairn Coast.

Flagstaff flaw
(R. 8/2)

1946 (2 Dec). *Victory. As Nos. 141/2 of Jamaica.*

9	2d. brown	..	..	..	30	15
10	3d. blue	..	..	..	30	15
	a. Flagstaff flaw	..	..	18·00	
9/10 Perf "Specimen"		*Set of 2* £140

1949 (1 Aug). *Royal Silver Wedding. As Nos. 143/4 of Jamaica.*

11	1½d. scarlet	..	..	..	2·00	1·00
12	10s. mauve	..	..	..	80·00	65·00

1949 (10 Oct). *75th Anniv of U.P.U. As Nos. 145/8 of Jamaica.*

13	2½d. red-brown	..	..	..	2·00	3·00
14	3d. deep blue	..	..	..	8·50	4·00
15	6d. deep blue-green	..	..	11·00	5·00
16	1s. purple	..	..	..	11·00	5·00
13/16	..	..	..	*Set of 4* 30·00	15·00

1953 (2 June). *Coronation. As No. 153 of Jamaica, but ptd by B.W.*

17	4d. black and deep bluish green	..	2·00	2·75

9 *Cordyline terminalis*   **10** Pitcairn Island Map

(Recess D.L.R.)

1957 (2 July)–63. *T* **9/10** *and similar designs. Wmk Mult Script CA. P* 13×12½ (*horiz*) *or* 12½×13 (*vert*).

18	½d. green and reddish lilac	..	80	75
	a. Green and reddish purple (9.3.63)	1·25	2·25
19	1d. black and olive-green	..	1·75	80
	a. Black and yellow-olive (19.2.59)	10·00	13·00
	b. Black and light olive-green (24.2.60)	5·50	3·75
20	2d. brown and greenish blue	..	75	60
21	2½d. deep brown and red-orange	..	50	40
22	3d. emerald and deep ultramarine	..	80	40
23	4d. scarlet and deep ultramarine (I)	..	90	40
23a	4d. carmine-red & dp ultram (II) (5.11.58)	5·00	1·50
24	6d. pale buff and indigo	..	1·25	55
25	8d. deep olive-green and carmine-lake	60	40
26	1s. black and yellowish brown	..	1·00	40
27	2s. green and red-orange	..	28·00	10·00
28	2s. 6d. ultramarine and lake	..	12·00	6·50
	a. Blue and deep lake (10.2.59)	18·00	10·00
18/28		*Set of 12* 48·00	20·00

Designs: Vert—2d. John Adams and *Bounty* Bible; 2s. Island wheelbarrow. *Horiz*—2½d. Handicrafts: Bird model; 3d. Bounty Bay; 4d. Pitcairn School; 6d. Pacific Ocean map; 8d. Inland scene; 1s. Handicrafts: Ship model; 2s. 6d. Launching new whaleboat.
Nos. 23/a. Type I is inscribed "PITCAIRN SCHOOL"; Type II "SCHOOLTEACHER'S HOUSE".
See also No. 33.

20 Pitcairn Island and Simon Young

(Des H. E. Maud. Photo Harrison)

1961 (15 Nov). *Centenary of Return of Pitcairn Islanders from Norfolk Island. T* **20** *and similar horiz designs. W w* **12**. *P* 14½ × 13½.

29	3d. black and yellow	..	..	20	15
30	6d. red-brown and blue	..	..	50	20
31	1s. red-orange and blue-green	..	60	50
29/31	..	..	..	*Set of 3* 1·10	75

Designs:—6d. Norfolk Island and Pitcairn Islands; 1s. Migrant brigantine *Mary Ann.*

1963 (4 June). *Freedom from Hunger. As No. 80 of Lesotho.*
32   2s. 6d. ultramarine ..   ..   ..   22·00   3·00

1963 (4 Dec). *As No. 18a, but wmk w 12.*
33   **9**   ½d. green and reddish purple ..   45   60

1963 (9 Dec). *Red Cross Centenary. As Nos. 203/4 of Jamaica.*
34   2d. red and black ..   ..   2·00   1·00
35   2s. 6d. red and blue ..   ..   11·00   5·50

23 Pitcairn Is Longboat   **24** Queen Elizabeth II (after Anthony Buckley)

(Des M. Farrar Bell. Photo Harrison)

1964 (5 Aug)–**65**. *T 23/4 and similar horiz designs. Multi-coloured. W w 12. P 14 × 14½.*
36   ½d. Type **23**   10   30
37   1d. H.M.S. *Bounty*   30   30
38   2d. "Out from Bounty Bay" ..   30   30
39   3d. Great Frigate Bird ..   30   30
40   4d. White Tern   30   30
41   6d. Pitcairn Warbler..   ..   30   30
42   8d. Red-footed Booby ..   30   30
   a. Pale blue (beak) omitted ..   £150
43   10d. Red-tailed Tropic Birds ..   30   30
44   1s. Henderson Island Crake..   30   30
45   1s. 6d. Stephen's Lory ..   5·50   1·25
46   2s. 6d. Murphy's Petrel ..   5·00   1·50
47   4s. Henderson Island Fruit Dove ..   7·00   1·75
48   8s. Type **24** (5.4.65) ..   2·50   1·75
36/48 ..   ..   ..   *Set of 13* 20·00   8·00

1965 (17 May). *I.T.U. Centenary. As Nos. 98/9 of Lesotho.*
49   1d. mauve and orange-brown ..   1·00   40
50   2s. 6d. turquoise-green and bright blue ..   15·00   3·50

1965 (25 Oct). *International Co-operation Year. As Nos. 100/1 of Lesotho.*
51   1d. reddish purple and turquoise-green ..   1·00   40
52   1s. 6d. deep bluish green and lavender ..   14·00   4·00

1966 (24 Jan). *Churchill Commemoration. As Nos. 102/5 of Lesotho.*
53   2d. new blue ..   ..   1·50   60
54   3d. deep green ..   ..   4·50   80
55   6d. brown ..   ..   6·00   1·50
56   1s. bluish violet ..   ..   8·00   2·00
53/6 ..   ..   ..   *Set of 4* 18·00   4·50

25 Footballer's Legs, Ball and Jules Rimet Cup

(Des V. Whiteley. Litho Harrison)

1966 (1 Aug). *World Cup Football Championships. W w 12 (sideways). P 14.*
57   **25**   4d. violet, yellow-green, lake & yellow-brn   2·00   1·00
58   2s. 6d. chocolate, blue-grn, lake & yell-brn   5·00   1·75

1966 (20 Sept). *Inauguration of W.H.O. Headquarters, Geneva. As Nos. 185/6 of Montserrat.*
59   8d. black, yellow-green and light blue ..   4·50   1·25
60   1s. 6d. black, light purple and yellow-brown   7·50   1·50

1966 (1 Dec). *20th Anniv of U.N.E.S.C.O. As Nos. 342/4 of Mauritius.*
61   ½d. slate-violet, red, yellow and orange ..   20   30
62   10d. orange-yellow, violet and deep olive ..   5·00   1·75
63   2s. black, bright purple and orange ..   11·00   2·25
61/3 ..   ..   ..   *Set of 3* 14·50   4·00

36 Mangarevan Canoe, *circa* 1325

(Des V. Whiteley. Photo Harrison)

1967 (1 Mar). *Bicentenary of Discovery of Pitcairn Islands. T 36 and similar horiz designs. Multicoloured. W w 12. P 14½.*
64   ½d. Type **36**   10   10
65   1d. P. F. de Quiros and *San Pedro y Pablo*, 1606 ..   15   10
66   8d. *San Pedro y Pablo* and *Los Tres Reyes*, 1606 ..   25   10
67   1s. Carteret and H.M.S. *Swallow*, 1767 ..   25   10
68   1s. 6d. *Hercules*, 1819 ..   30   10
64/8 ..   ..   ..   *Set of 5* 85   35

(New Currency. 100 cents = 1 New Zealand dollar)

½C

(**41** Bounty Anchor)

1967 (10 July). *Decimal currency. Nos. 36/48 surch in decimal currency by die-stamping in gold as T 41.*
69   ½ c. on ½d. multicoloured ..   10   10
   a. Deep brown omitted ..   £375
   b. Surch double, one albino ..   £110
70   1 c. on 1d. multicoloured ..   30   30
71   2 c. on 2d. multicoloured ..   25   30
72   2½ c. on 3d. multicoloured ..   25   30
73   3 c. on 4d. multicoloured ..   25   15
74   5 c. on 6d. multicoloured ..   30   30
75   10 c. on 8d. multicoloured ..   30   30
   a. "10 c." omitted ..   £300
   b. Pale blue (beak) omitted ..   £150
76   15 c. on 10d. multicoloured ..   70   40
77   20 c. on 1s. multicoloured ..   80   55
78   25 c. on 1s. 6d. multicoloured ..   2·50   1·25
79   30 c. on 2s. 6d. multicoloured ..   2·75   1·25
80   40 c. on 4s. multicoloured ..   4·25   1·25
81   45 c. on 8s. multicoloured ..   4·25   1·50
69/81 ..   ..   *Set of 13* 15·00   7·00
On No. 75a the anchor emblem is still present. Several examples of this variety have been identified as coming from R. 9/1.
The ½ c. and 1 c. exist with PVA gum as well as gum arabic.

42 Bligh and *Bounty*'s Launch

(Des Jennifer Toombs. Litho D.L.R.)

1967 (7 Dec). *150th Death Anniv of Admiral Bligh. T 42 and similar horiz designs. P 13½ × 13.*
82   1 c. turq-blue, black and royal blue (*shades*)   10   10
83   8 c. black, yellow and magenta ..   25   10
84   20 c. black, brown and pale buff ..   25   15
82/4 ..   ..   *Set of 3* 55   30
Designs:—8 c. Bligh and followers cast adrift; 20 c. Bligh's tomb.

45 Human Rights Emblem

(Des G. Hamori. Litho D.L.R.)

1968 (4 Mar). *Human Rights Year. P 13½ × 13.*
85   **45**   1 c. multicoloured ..   10   10
86   2 c. multicoloured ..   10   10
87   25 c. multicoloured ..   20   20
85/7 ..   ..   ..   *Set of 3* 30   30

46 Miro Wood and Flower

(Des Jennifer Toombs. Photo Harrison)

1968 (19 Aug). *Handicrafts (1st series). T 46 and similar designs. W w 12 (sideways on vert designs). P 14 × 13½ (5, 10 c.) or 13½ × 14 (others).*
88   5 c. multicoloured ..   15   10
89   10 c. bronze-green, brown and orange ..   20   20
90   15 c. deep bluish violet, chocolate and salmon   20   20
91   20 c. multicoloured ..   25   20
88/91 ..   ..   *Set of 4* 70   60
Designs: *Horiz*—10 c. Flying Fish model. *Vert*—15 c. "Hand" vases; 20 c. Woven baskets.
See also Nos. 207/10.

50 Microscope and Slides

(Des Jennifer Toombs. Litho D.L.R.)

1968 (25 Nov). *20th Anniv of World Health Organisation. T 50 and similar horiz design. W w 12 (sideways). P 14.*
92   2 c. black, turquoise-blue and ultramarine ..   10   10
93   20 c. black, orange and bright purple ..   25   20
Design:—20 c. Hypodermic syringe and jars of tablets.

52 Pitcairn Island   **62** "Flying Fox" Cable System

(Des Jennifer Toombs. Litho Questa (50 c., $1), D.L.R. (others))

1969 (17 Sept)–**75**. *T 52, 62 and similar designs. Chalk-surfaced paper. W w 12 (upright on 3 c., 25 c., sideways on $1 and horiz designs). P 14½ × 14 (50 c.), 14 ($1) or 13 (others).*
94   1 c. multicoloured ..   35   15
   a. Glazed, ordinary paper (9.8.71) ..   1·25   65
95   2 c. multicoloured ..   25   15
96   3 c. multicoloured ..   25   15
97   4 c. multicoloured ..   30   15
98   5 c. multicoloured ..   30   15
99   6 c. multicoloured ..   30   20
100   8 c. multicoloured ..   35   20
101   10 c. multicoloured ..   2·00   85
   a. Glazed, ordinary paper (9.8.71) ..   1·75   2·00
102   15 c. multicoloured ..   60   50
   a. Queen's head omitted ..   £475
103   20 c. multicoloured ..   60   40
104   25 c. multicoloured ..   70   40
105   30 c. multicoloured ..   55   45
106   40 c. multicoloured ..   75   60
106*a*   50 c. multicoloured (*glazed, ordinary paper*) (2.1.73) ..   11·00   10·00
106*b* $1 multicoloured (*glazed, ordinary paper*) (21.4.75) ..   16·00   15·00
94/106*b* ..   *Set of 15* 30·00   26·00
Designs: *Horiz*—2 c. Captain Bligh and *Bounty* chronometer; 4 c. Plans and drawing of *Bounty*; 5 c. Breadfruit containers and plant; 6 c. Bounty Bay; 8 c. Pitcairn longboat; 10 c. Ship landing point; 15 c. Fletcher Christian's Cave; 20 c. Thursday October Christian's House; 30 c. Radio Station, Taro Ground; 40 c. *Bounty* Bible; 50 c. Pitcairn Coat of Arms. *Vert*—3 c. *Bounty* anchor; $1 Queen Elizabeth II.
See also No. 133.

65 Lantana   **69** Auntie and Ann (grouper)

(Des Jennifer Toombs. Litho D.L.R.)

1970 (23 Mar). *Flowers. T 65 and similar vert designs. Multi-coloured. W w 12. P 14.*
107   1 c. Type **65**   20   20
108   2 c. "Indian Shot"   45   25
109   5 c. Pulau   85   40
110   25 c. Wild Gladiolus ..   2·00   1·10
107/10 ..   ..   *Set of 4* 3·25   1·75

(Des Jennifer Toombs. Photo Harrison)

1970 (12 Oct). *Fishes. T 69 and similar horiz designs. Multi-coloured. W w 12. P 14.*
111   5 c. Type **69** ..   ..   2·75   70
112   10 c. Dream Fish (rudder fish) ..   2·75   85
113   15 c. Elwyn's Trousers (wrasse) ..   3·25   1·00
114   20 c. Whistling Daughter (wrasse) ..   3·50   1·25
111/14 ..   ..   *Set of 4* 11·00   3·50

ROYAL VISIT 1971

(**70**)   **71** Polynesian Rock Carvings

1971 (22 Feb). *Royal Visit. No. 101 optd with T 70, in silver.*
115   10 c. multicoloured ..   ..   2·25   3·00

(Des Jennifer Toombs. Litho A & M)

1971 (3 May). *Polynesian Pitcairn. T* **71** *and similar multi-coloured designs. W* w **12** *(sideways on 10 and 15 c.). P* 13½.
116	5 c. Type **71**			1·75	1·00
117	10 c. Polynesian artefacts (*horiz*)			2·25	1·25
118	15 c. Polynesian stone fish-hook (*horiz*)			2·50	1·25
119	20 c. Polynesian stone deity			2·50	1·50
116/19			Set of 4	8·00	4·50

72 Commission Flag

73 Red-tailed Tropic Birds and Longboat

(Des Jennifer Toombs. Litho Questa)

1972 (4 Apr). *25th Anniv of South Pacific Commission. T* **72** *and similar horiz designs. Multicoloured (except 4 c.). W* w **12** *(sideways on 4 c.). P* 14.
120	4 c. dp blue, blue-violet & brt yellow (T **72**)		1·00	1·00
121	8 c. Young and Elderly (Health)			1·00	1·00
122	18 c. Junior School (Education)			1·50	1·50
123	20 c. Goods store (Economy)			2·00	2·00
120/3			Set of 4	5·00	5·00

(Des (from photographs by D. Groves) and photo Harrison)

1972 (20 Nov). *Royal Silver Wedding. Multicoloured; background colour given. W* w **12**. *P* 14 × 14½.
124	**73**	4 c. slate-green		40	60
125		20 c. bright blue		60	90

74 Rose-apple

75 Horn-shell and Mitres

(Des Jennifer Toombs. Litho J.W.)

1973 (25 June). *Flowers. T* **74** *and similar vert designs. Multi-coloured. W* w **12** *(sideways). P* 14.
126	4 c. Type **74**			1·25	55
127	8 c. Mountain-apple			1·75	75
128	15 c. "Lata"			3·00	1·00
129	20 c. "Dorcas-flower"			3·25	1·25
130	35 c. Guava			4·00	1·75
126/30			Set of 5	12·00	4·75

1973 (14 Nov). *Royal Wedding. As Nos. 322/3 of Montserrat. Centre multicoloured. W* w **12** *(sideways). P* 13½.
131	10 c. bright mauve			30	15
132	25 c. emerald			35	30

1974 (4 Feb). *As No. 94a, but wmk upright. Glazed, ordinary paper.*
133	**52**	1 c. multicoloured	3·75	4·50

134/46 Catalogue numbers vacant.

(Des Jennifer Toombs. Litho Questa)

1974 (15 Apr). *Shells. T* **75** *and similar horiz designs. Multi-coloured. W* w **12**. *P* 14.
147	4 c. Type **75**			1·50	60
148	10 c. Dove-shell			1·75	80
149	18 c. Limpet and False Limpet			2·00	1·00
150	50 c. Lucine shell			2·75	1·25
147/50			Set of 4	7·00	3·25
MS151	130 × 121 mm. Nos. 147/50		8·00	13·00

76 Island Post Office

(Des Jennifer Toombs. Litho Questa)

1974 (22 July). *Centenary of Universal Postal Union. T* **76** *and similar horiz designs. W* w **12** *(sideways). P* 14.
152	4 c. multicoloured			25	30
153	20 c. bright purple, light cinnamon and black	40	50
154	35 c. multicoloured			50	60
152/4			Set of 3	1·00	1·25

Designs:—20 c. Pre-stamp letter, 1922; 35 c. Mailship and Pitcairn longboat.

77 Churchill and Text "Lift up your Hearts . . ."

(Des Jennifer Toombs. Litho Questa)

1974 (30 Nov). *Birth Centenary of Sir Winston Churchill. T* **77** *and similar horiz design. W* w **14** *(sideways). P* 14½.
155	20 c. blackish olive, apple-green & dp slate	50	85
156	35 c. sepia, greenish yellow and deep slate	75	90

Design:—35 c. Text "Give us the tools . . .".

78 H.M.S. *Seringapatam*, 1830

(Des Jennifer Toombs. Litho Walsall)

1975 (22 July). *Mailboats. T* **78** *and similar horiz designs. Multi-coloured. W* w **14** *(sideways). P* 14.
157	4 c. Type **78**			65	60
158	10 c. *Pitcairn* (missionary schooner), 1890	70	85
159	18 c. R.M.S. *Athenic*, 1904		80	1·40
160	50 c. S.S. *Gothic*, 1948		2·00	2·75
157/60			Set of 4	3·50	5·00
MS161	145 × 110 mm. Nos. 157/60		10·00	15·00

79 *Polistes jadwigae* (wasp)   **80** Fletcher Christian

(Des Jennifer Toombs. Litho Questa)

1975 (9 Nov). *Pitcairn Insects. T* **79** *and similar horiz designs. Multicoloured. W* w **12** *(sideways). P* 14.
162	4 c. Type **79**			50	45
163	6 c. *Euconocephalus* sp (grasshopper)	70	55
164	10 c. *Anomis flavia* and *Chasmina tibialis* (moths)		80	70
165	15 c. *Pantala flavescens* (skimmer)	1·25	1·25
166	20 c. *Gnathothlibus erotus* (Banana moth)	1·50	1·50
162/6			Set of 5	4·25	4·00

(Des Jennifer Toombs. Litho J.W.)

1976 (4 July). *Bicentenary of American Revolution. T* **80** *and similar vert designs. Multicoloured. W* w **14**. *P* 13½.
167	5 c. Type **80**			40	65
	a. Horiz pair. Nos. 167 and 169	1·10	1·60
168	10 c. H.M.S. *Bounty*			50	80
	a. Horiz pair. Nos. 168 and 170	1·50	2·25
169	30 c. George Washington		75	95
170	50 c. *Mayflower*, 1620		1·00	1·50
167/70			Set of 4	2·50	3·50

The 5 and 30 c. and 10 and 50 c. values were each printed together, *se-tenant*, in horizontal pairs throughout the sheets.

81 Chair of Homage   **82** The Island's Bell

(Des Jennifer Toombs. Litho J.W.)

1977 (6 Feb). *Silver Jubilee. T* **81** *and similar vert designs. Multi-coloured. W* w **14**. *P* 13.
171	8 c. Prince Philip's visit, 1971		20	20
172	20 c. Type **81**			30	30
173	50 c. Enthronement			50	50
171/3			Set of 3	90	90

(Des Jennifer Toombs. Litho Walsall)

1977 (12 Sept)–**81**. *Various multicoloured designs as T* **82**. *W* w **14** *(upright on 1 c., 9 c., 70 c. and $2; sideways on others). P* 14.
174	1 c. Type **82**			30	50
175	2 c. Building a longboat		30	50
176	5 c. Landing cargo			35	50
177	6 c. Sorting supplies			30	50

178	9 c. Cleaning wahoo (fish)			30	50
179	10 c. Cultivation			30	50
179a	15 c. Sugar Mill (1.10.81)		1·25	1·00
180	20 c. Grating coconut and bananas	30	50
181	35 c. The Island church		35	70
182	50 c. Fetching miro logs, Henderson Is.	45	80
182a	70 c. Burning obsolete stamp issues (1.10.81)	1·25	1·25
183	$1 Prince Philip, Bounty Bay and Royal Yacht *Britannia*		65	1·10
184	$2 Queen Elizabeth II (photograph by Reginald Davis)		1·25	1·75
174/84			Set of 13	6·50	9·00

The 1 c., 9 c., 70 c. and $2 are vertical designs, the remainder horizontal.

83 Building a *Bounty* Model   **84** Coronation Ceremony

(Des E. W. Roberts. Litho Questa)

1978 (9 Jan). *"Bounty Day". T* **83** *and similar horiz designs. Multicoloured. W* w **14** *(sideways). P* 14½.
185	6 c. Type **83**			40	35
186	20 c. The model at sea		70	60
187	35 c. Burning the model		85	70
185/7			Set of 3	1·75	1·50
MS188	166 × 122 mm. Nos. 185/7		7·50	9·00

(Des Jennifer Toombs. Litho Cartor S.A., France)

1978 (9 Oct). *25th Anniv of Coronation. Sheet* 94 × 78 mm. *W* w **14**. *P* 12.
MS189	**84**	$1.20, multicoloured	1·75	2·25

85 Harbour before Development

(Des J.W. Litho Bruder Rosenbaum, Vienna)

1978 (18 Dec). *"Operation Pallium" (Harbour Development Project). T* **85** *and similar horiz designs. Multicoloured. W* w **14** *(sideways). P* 13½.
190	15 c. Type **85**			30	40
191	20 c. Unloading R.F.A. *Sir Geraint*	40	50
192	30 c. Work on the jetty		45	55
193	35 c. Harbour after development		50	60
190/3			Set of 4	1·50	1·90

86 John Adams and Diary Extract

(Des Jennifer Toombs. Litho Questa)

1979 (5 Mar). *150th Death Anniv of John Adams (mutineer from the "Bounty"). T* **86** *and similar horiz design. Multicoloured. W* w **14** *(sideways). P* 14.
194	35 c. Type **86**			40	70
195	70 c. John Adams' grave and diary extract	60	90

87 Pitcairn's Island sketched from H.M.S. *Amphitrite*

(Des Jennifer Toombs. Litho Questa)

1979 (12 Sept). *19th-century Engravings. T* **87** *and similar horiz designs. W* w **14** *(sideways). P* 14.
196	6 c. black, brown-ochre and stone	15	20
197	9 c. black, violet and pale violet	15	25
198	20 c. black, brt green & pale yellowish green	15	40
199	70 c. black, scarlet and pale rose	50	1·00
196/9			Set of 4	85	1·75

Designs:—9 c. Bounty Bay and Village of Pitcairn; 20 c. Lookout Ridge; 70 c. Church and School House.

88 Taking Presents to the Square

(Des and litho J.W.)

1979 (28 Nov). *Christmas and International Year of the Child. T **88** and similar horiz designs. Multicoloured. W w **14** (sideways). P 13.*

200	6 c. Type **88**			15	20
201	9 c. Decorating trees with the presents			15	20
202	20 c. Chosen men distribute the gifts			25	35
203	35 c. Carrying presents home			30	40
200/3			Set of 4	75	1·00
MS204	198×73 mm. Nos. 200/3. P 13½×14			2·00	2·00

89 Loading Mail from Supply
Ship to Longboats

(Des Jennifer Toombs. Litho Format)

1980 (6 May). *"London 1980" International Stamp Exhibition. Sheet 120 × 135 mm containing T **89** and similar horiz designs. Multicoloured. W w **14** (sideways). P 14½.*
MS205 35 c. Type **89**; 35 c. Mail being conveyed by "Flying Fox" (hoisting mechanism) to the Edge; 35 c. Tractor transporting mail from the Edge to Adamstown; 35 c. Mail being off-loaded at Post Office .. 1·00 1·50

90 Queen Elizabeth the
Queen Mother at Henley
Regatta

(Des Harrison. Litho Questa)

1980 (4 Aug). *80th Birthday of Queen Elizabeth the Queen Mother. W w **14** (sideways). P 14.*
206 **90** 50 c. multicoloured 50 70

(Des Jennifer Toombs. Litho Questa)

1980 (29 Sept). *Handicrafts (2nd series). Multicoloured designs as T **46**. W w **14** (sideways on 9 and 20 c.). P 14.*

207	9 c. Turtles (wood carvings)			10	10
208	20 c. Pitcairn wheelbarrow (wood carving)			10	15
209	35 c. Gannet (wood carving) (*vert*)			15	25
210	40 c. Woven bonnet and fan (*vert*)			15	25
207/10			Set of 4	40	65

91 Part of Adamstown

(Des BG Studio. Litho Rosenbaum Bros, Vienna)

1981 (22 Jan). *Landscapes. T **91** and similar horiz designs. Multicoloured. W w **14** (sideways). P 13½.*

211	6 c. Type **91**			10	10
212	9 c. Big George			10	15
213	20 c. Christian's Cave, Gannets Ridge			15	20
214	35 c. Radio Station from Pawala Valley Ridge			20	30
215	70 c. Tatrimoa			30	45
211/15			Set of 5	75	1·10

92 Islanders preparing for
Departure

93 Prince Charles as
Colonel-in-Chief,
Cheshire Regiment

(Des Jennifer Toombs. Litho Heraclio Fournier)

1981 (3 May). *125th Anniv of Pitcairn Islanders' Migration to Norfolk Island. T **92** and similar horiz designs. Multicoloured. P 13 × 14.*

216	9 c. Type **92**			15	20
217	35 c. View of Pitcairn Island from *Morayshire*			30	45
218	70 c. *Morayshire*			45	65
216/18			Set of 3	80	1·10

(Des J.W. Litho Format)

1981 (22 July). *Royal Wedding. T **93** and similar vert designs. Multicoloured. W w **14**. P 14.*

219	20 c. Wedding bouquet from Pitcairn Islands			25	25
220	35 c. Type **93**			40	40
221	$1.20, Prince Charles and Lady Diana Spencer			75	85
219/21			Set of 3	1·25	1·40

94 Lemon

95 Pitcairn Islands
Coat of Arms

(Des Daphne Padden. Litho Harrison)

1982 (23 Feb). *Fruit. T **94** and similar horiz designs. Multicoloured. W w **14** (sideways). P 14½.*

222	9 c. Type **94**			10	10
223	20 c. Pomegranate			15	20
224	35 c. Avocado			25	30
225	70 c. Pawpaw			50	65
222/5			Set of 4	90	1·10

(Des Jennifer Toombs. Litho Harrison)

1982 (1 July). *21st Birthday of Princess of Wales. T **95** and similar vert designs. Multicoloured. W w **14**. P 14½ × 14.*

226	6 c. Type **95**			10	20
227	9 c. Princess at Royal Opera House, Covent Garden, December 1981			10	20
228	70 c. Balcony Kiss			50	75
229	$1.20, Formal portrait			80	1·10
226/9			Set of 4	1·25	2·00

96 Raphael's Angels

(Des Leslie McCombie. Litho Walsall)

1982 (19 Oct). *Christmas. T **96** and similar designs showing Raphael's Angels. W w **14** (sideways on 15 c. and 20 c.). P 13½ × 14 (15 c., 20 c.) or 14 × 13½ (others).*

230	15 c. black, silver and pink			15	15
231	20 c. black, silver and pale lemon			20	20
232	50 c. yellow-brown, silver and stone			45	45
233	$1 black, silver and cobalt			85	85
230/3			Set of 4	1·50	1·50

The 50 c. and $1 are vertical designs.

97 Radio Operator

(Des Jennifer Toombs. Litho Harrison)

1983 (14 Mar). *Commonwealth Day. T **97** and similar horiz designs. Multicoloured. W w **14** (sideways). P 13½.*

234	6 c. Type **97**			10	10
235	9 c. Postal clerk			10	10
236	70 c. Fisherman			50	65
237	$1.20, Artist			80	1·10
234/7			Set of 4	1·25	1·60

98 *Topaz* sights Smoke on Pitcairn

(Des Jennifer Toombs. Litho B.D.T.)

1983 (14 June). *175th Anniv of Folger's Discovery of the Settlers. T **98** and similar horiz designs. Multicoloured. W w **14** (sideways). P 14.*

238	6 c. Type **98**			20	15
239	20 c. Three islanders approach the *Topaz*			30	30
240	70 c. Capt. Mayhew Folger welcomed by John Adams			75	75
241	$1.20, Folger presented with *Bounty* chronometer			1·10	1·10
238/41			Set of 4	2·10	2·10

99 Hattie-Tree

(Des Jennifer Toombs. Litho B.D.T.)

1983 (6 Oct). *Trees of Pitcairn Islands (1st series). T **99** and similar horiz designs. Multicoloured. W w **14** (sideways). P 13½.*

242	35 c. Type **99**			30	55
	a. Pair. Nos. 242/3			60	1·10
243	35 c. Leaves from Hattie-Tree			30	55
244	70 c. Pandanus			65	90
	a. Pair. Nos. 244/5			1·25	1·75
245	70 c. Pandanus and basket weaving			65	90
242/5			Set of 4	1·75	2·50

The two designs of each value were printed together, *se-tenant*, in horizontal and vertical pairs throughout the sheet.
See also Nos. 304/7.

100 *Pseudojuloides atavai*

(Des C. Abbott. Litho Format)

1984 (11 Jan). *Fishes (1st series). T **100** and similar horiz designs. Multicoloured. W w **14** (sideways). P 14½.*

246	1 c. Type **100**			20	30
247	4 c. *Halichoeres melasmapomus*			30	35
248	6 c. *Scarus longipinnis*			30	35
249	9 c. *Variola louti*			30	35
250	10 c. *Centropyge hotumatua*			30	40
251	15 c. *Stegastes emeryi*			30	40
252	20 c. *Chaetodon smithi*			40	50
253	35 c. *Xanthichthys mento*			50	60
254	50 c. *Chrysiptera galba*			50	75
255	70 c. *Genicanthus spinus*			70	95
256	$1 *Myripristis tiki*			90	1·25
257	$1.20, *Anthias ventralis*			1·75	2·00
258	$2 *Pseudocaranx dentex*			2·25	2·50
246/58			Set of 13	8·00	9·50

For 90 c. and $3 values see Nos. 312/13.

101 "Southern Cross"

(Des J. Cooter. Litho Walsall)

1984 (14 May). *Night Sky. T **101** and similar horiz designs. W w **14** (sideways). P 14.*

259	15 c. deep violet-blue, pale rose-lilac and gold			20	20
260	20 c. deep violet-blue, bright yell-grn & gold			30	30
261	70 c. deep violet-blue, yellow-ochre and gold			75	75
262	$1 deep violet-blue, pale blue and gold			1·00	1·00
259/62			Set of 4	2·00	2·00

Constellations:—20 c. "Southern Fish"; 70 c. "Lesser Dogs"; $1 "The Virgin".

102 Aluminium Longboat

103 "H.M.S. *Portland* standing
off Bounty Bay"
(J. Linton Palmer)

(Des C. Abbott. Litho Enschedé)

1984 (21 Sept). *"Ausipex" International Stamp Exhibition, Melbourne. Sheet 134 × 86 mm containing T **102** and similar horiz design. Multicoloured. W w **14** (sideways). P 13½ × 14.*
MS263 50 c. Type **102**; $2 Traditional-style wooden longboat .. .. 2·00 2·25

(Des Jennifer Toombs. Litho Questa)

1985 (16 Jan). *19th-Century Paintings (1st series). T **103** and similar horiz designs. Multicoloured. W w **14** (sideways). P* 13½ × 14 ($2) or 14 (others).
264	6 c. Type **103** ..	30	20
265	9 c. "Christian's Look Out" (J. Linton Palmer)	30	20
266	35 c. "The Golden Age" (J. Linton Palmer)	70	50
267	$2 "A View of the Village, 1825" (William Smyth) (48 × 31 *mm*)	2·00	1·60
264/7	*Set of* 4	3·00	2·25

The original printing of No. 267 was incorrectly dated "1835". The mistake was, however, spotted before issue and a replacement printing, correctly dated "1825", was provided. Those stamps dated "1835" were never issued for postal purposes, although isolated examples exist which may have been supplied by various philatelic agents in error.

See also Nos. 308/11.

104 The Queen Mother with the Queen and Princess Margaret, 1980   105 *Act 6* (container ship)

(Des A. Theobald ($2), C. Abbott (others). Litho Questa)

1985 (7 June). *Life and Times of Queen Elizabeth the Queen Mother. T **104** and similar vert designs. Multicoloured. W w **16**. P* 14½ × 14.
268	6 c. Receiving the Freedom of Dundee, 1964 ..	10	20
269	35 c. Type **104** ..	40	55
270	70 c. The Queen Mother in 1983 ..	70	90
271	$1.20, With Prince Henry at his christening (from photo by Lord Snowdon)	1·10	1·40
268/71	*Set of* 4	2·10	2·75
MS272	91 × 73 mm. $2 In coach at Ascot Races. Wmk sideways	2·00	2·00

(Des E. Nisbet. Litho Format)

1985 (28 Aug). *Ships (1st series). T **105** and similar multicoloured designs. W w **14** (sideways). P* 14 (Nos. 273/4) or 14 × 13½ (others).
273	50 c. Type **105**..	1·00	1·25
274	50 c. *Columbus Louisiana* (container ship) ..	1·00	1·25
275	50 c. *Essi Gina* (tanker) (48 × 35 *mm*)	1·00	1·25
276	50 c. *Stolt Spirit* (tanker) (48 × 35 *mm*)	1·00	1·25
273/6	*Set of* 4	3·50	4·50

See also Nos. 296/9.

106 "Madonna and Child" (Raphael)   107 Green Turtle

(Des Jennifer Toombs. Litho Walsall)

1985 (26 Nov). *Christmas. T **106** and similar vert designs showing "Madonna and Child" paintings. Multicoloured. W w **16**. P* 14 × 13½.
277	6 c. Type **106**..	30	20
278	9 c. Krause (after Raphael)..	30	20
279	35 c. Andreas Mayer ..	65	50
280	$2 Unknown Austrian master	2·25	2·50
277/80	*Set of* 4	3·25	3·00

(Des J. Thatcher. Litho Questa)

1986 (12 Feb). *Turtles. T **107** and similar horiz designs. Multicoloured. W w **16** (sideways). P* 14½.
281	9 c. Type **107**..	75	75
282	20 c. Green Turtle and Pitcairn Island	1·25	1·25
283	70 c. Hawksbill Turtle	2·50	2·50
284	$1.20, Hawksbill Turtle and Pitcairn Island	3·25	3·25
281/4	*Set of* 4	7·00	7·00

(Des A. Theobald. Litho Questa)

1986 (21 Apr). *60th Birthday of Queen Elizabeth II. Vert designs as T **230**a of Jamaica. Multicoloured. W w **16**. P* 14½ × 14.
285	6 c. Princess Elizabeth at Royal Lodge, Windsor, 1946	15	15
286	9 c. Wedding of Princess Anne, 1973	15	15
287	20 c. At Order of St. Michael and St. George service, St. Paul's Cathedral, 1961	30	30
288	$1.20, At Electrical Engineering Concert, Royal Festival Hall, 1971	1·10	1·25
289	$2 At Crown Agents Head Office, London, 1983	1·75	2·00
285/9	*Set of* 5	3·00	3·50

(Des D. Miller. Litho Questa)

1986 (23 July). *Royal Wedding. Square designs as T **231**a of Jamaica. Multicoloured. W w **16**. P* 14.
290	20 c. Prince Andrew and Miss Sarah Ferguson	50	50
291	$1.20, Prince Andrew aboard *Bluenose II* off Halifax, Canada, 1985	1·75	1·75

108 John I. Tay (pioneer missionary) and First Church   109 Pitcairn Island Home

(Des A. Theobald. Litho Walsall)

1986 (18 Oct). *Centenary of Seventh-Day Adventist Church on Pitcairn. T **108** and similar vert designs. Multicoloured. W w **16**. P* 14.
292	6 c. Type **108**..	40	40
293	20 c. *Pitcairn* (mission schooner) and second church (1907)	1·00	1·00
294	35 c. Baptism at Down Isaac and third church (1945)	1·50	1·50
295	$2 Islanders singing farewell hymn and present church (1954)	3·25	3·25
292/5 ..	*Set of* 4	5·50	5·50

(Des E. Nisbet. Litho Format)

1987 (20 Jan). *Ships (2nd series). Multicoloured designs as T **105**. W w **16** (sideways on Nos. 298/9). P* 14 (Nos. 296/7) or 14 × 13½ (others).
296	50 c. *Samoan Reefer* (freighter)	1·25	1·50
297	50 c. *Brussel* (container ship)	1·25	1·50
298	50 c. *Australian Exporter* (container ship) (48 × 35 *mm*)	1·25	1·50
299	50 c. *Taupo* (cargo liner) (48 × 35 *mm*)	1·25	1·50
296/9 ..	*Set of* 4	4·50	5·50

(Des E. Roberts and D. Robertson. Litho Format)

1987 (21 Apr). *Pitcairn Island Homes. T **109** and similar horiz designs showing different houses. W w **14** (sideways). P* 13½ × 14.
300	109 70 c. black, brt reddish violet & brt violet	75	60
301	— 70 c. black, pale orange-yell & brn-ochre	75	60
302	— 70 c. black, dull blue and ultramarine ..	75	60
303	— 70 c. black, blue-green & deep blue-green	75	60
300/3 ..	*Set of* 4	2·75	2·25

(Des Jennifer Toombs. Litho Format)

1987 (10 Aug). *Trees of Pitcairn Islands (2nd series). Horiz designs as T **99**. Multicoloured. W w **16** (sideways). P* 14½.
304	40 c. Leaves and flowers from *Erythrina variegata*	70	70
	a. Pair. Nos. 304/5..	1·40	1·40
305	40 c. *Erythrina variegata* tree	70	70
306	$1.80, Leaves from *Aleurites moluccana* and nut torch	2·00	2·00
	a. Pair. Nos. 306/7..	4·00	4·00
307	$1.80, *Aleurites moluccana* tree ..	2·00	2·00
304/7 ..	*Set of* 4	5·00	5·00

The two designs of each value were printed together, *se-tenant*, in horizontal and vertical pairs throughout the sheet.

(Des Jennifer Toombs. Litho Questa)

1987 (7 Dec). *19th-Century Paintings (2nd series). Horiz designs as T **103** showing paintings by Lt. Conway Shipley in 1848. Multicoloured. W w **16** (sideways). P* 13½ × 14 ($1.80) or 14 (others).
308	20 c. "House and Tomb of John Adams"	45	45
309	40 c. "Bounty Bay"	70	70
310	90 c. "School House and Chapel"	1·25	1·25
311	$1.80, "Pitcairn Island" (48 × 31 *mm*)	2·00	2·00
308/11	*Set of* 4	4·00	4·00

(Des C. Abbott. Litho Format)

1988 (14 Jan). *Fishes (2nd series). Horiz designs as T **100**. Multicoloured. W w **16** (sideways). P* 14½.
312	90 c. As No. 249	1·75	1·75
313	$3 *Gymnothorax eurostus* ..	4·25	4·25

110 *Bounty* (replica)   111 H.M.S. *Swallow* (survey ship), 1767

(Des M. Bradbery. Litho Questa)

1988 (9 May). *Bicentenary of Australian Settlement. Sheet* 112 × 76 *mm. W w **16**. P* 14 × 13½.
MS314	110 $3 multicoloured ..	2·10	2·25

(Des E. Nisbet. Litho B.D.T.)

1988 (14 Aug). *Ships. T **111** and similar horiz designs. Multicoloured. W w **14** (sideways). P* 13½.
315	5 c. Type **111**	10	10
316	10 c. H.M.S. *Pandora* (frigate), 1791	10	10
317	15 c. H.M.S. *Briton* and H.M.S. *Tagus* (frigates), 1814	10	15
318	20 c. H.M.S. *Blossom* (survey ship), 1825 ..	10	15
319	30 c. *Lucy Anne* (barque), 1831	20	25
320	35 c. *Charles Doggett* (whaling ship), 1831	20	25
321	40 c. H.M.S. *Fly* (sloop), 1838	25	30
322	60 c. *Camden* (missionary brig), 1840	40	45
323	90 c. H.M.S. *Virago* (paddle-sloop), 1853	60	65
324	$1.20, *Rakaia* (screw-steamer), 1867	80	85
325	$1.80, H.M.S. *Sappho* (screw-sloop), 1882	1·25	1·40
326	$5 H.M.S. *Champion* (corvette), 1893	3·25	3·50
315/26	*Set of* 12	6·50	7·25

For 20 c. and 90 c. values as above, but watermarked w **16** (sideways), see Nos. 369 and 374.

112 Raising the Union Jack, 1838   113 Angel

(Des Jennifer Toombs. Litho Walsall)

1988 (30 Nov). *150th Anniv of Pitcairn Island Constitution. T **112** and similar vert designs, each showing different extract from original Constitution. Multicoloured. W w **14**. P* 14.
327	20 c. Type **112**	15	20
328	40 c. Signing Constitution on board H.M.S. *Fly*, 1838	30	35
329	$1.05, Voters at modern polling station ..	75	80
330	$1.80, Modern classroom ..	1·25	1·40
327/30 ..	*Set of* 4	2·25	2·50

(Des M. Grimsdale. Litho Questa)

1988 (30 Nov). *Christmas. T **113** and similar vert designs. Multicoloured. W w **16**. P* 14 × 13½.
331	90 c. Type **113** ..	65	70
	a. Horiz strip of 4. Nos. 331/4	2·40	
332	90 c. Holy Family	65	70
333	90 c. Two Polynesian Wise Men	65	70
334	90 c. Polynesian Wise Man and shepherd	65	70
331/4	*Set of* 4	2·40	2·50

Nos. 331/4 were printed together, *se-tenant*, in horizontal strips of four throughout the sheet.

114 Loading Stores, Deptford   115 R.N.Z.A.F. "Orion" making Mail Drop, 1985

(Des C. Abbott. Litho Questa)

1989 (22 Feb). *Bicentary of Pitcairn Island Settlement (1st issue). T **114** and similar horiz designs. Multicoloured. W w **14** (sideways). P* 14.
335	20 c. Type **114** ..	40	30
	a. Sheetlet. Nos. 335/40 ..	2·25	
336	20 c. H.M.S. *Bounty* leaving Spithead	40	30
337	20 c. H.M.S. *Bounty* at Cape Horn	40	30
338	20 c. Anchored in Adventure Bay, Tasmania	40	30
339	20 c. Crew collecting breadfruit	40	30
340	20 c. Breadfruit in cabin	40	30
335/40	*Set of* 6	2·25	1·60

Nos. 335/40 were printed together, *se-tenant* in sheetlets of six, as two horizontal rows of three separated by a central gutter.

See also Nos. 341/7, 356/61 and 389/94.

(Des C. Abbott. Litho Questa (Nos. 341/6), B.D.T. (No. **MS**347))

1989 (28 Apr). *Bicentenary of Pitcairn Island Settlement (2nd issue). Horiz designs as T **114**. Multicoloured. W w **14** (sideways). P* 14.
341	90 c. H.M.S. *Bounty* leaving Tahiti	1·40	1·10
	a. Sheetlet. Nos. 341/6	7·50	
342	90 c. Bligh awoken by mutineers	1·40	1·10
343	90 c. Bligh before Fletcher Christian	1·40	1·10
344	90 c. Provisioning Bounty's launch	1·40	1·10
345	90 c. "Mutineers casting Bligh adrift" (Robert Dodd)	1·40	1·10
346	90 c. Mutineers discarding breadfruit plants	1·40	1·10
341/6	*Set of* 6	7·50	6·00
MS347	110 × 85 mm. 90 c. No. 345; 90 c. Isle of Man 1989 35p. Mutiny stamp; 90 c. Norfolk Island 39 c. Mutiny stamp. W w **16** (sideways)	3·50	4·00

Nos. 341/6 were printed in the same sheet format as Nos. 335/40.

(Des A. Theobald. Litho Questa)

1989 (25 July). *Aircraft. T* **115** *and similar horiz designs. Multicoloured. W* w **16** (*sideways*). *P* 14×14½.
348	20 c. Type **115**		25	25
349	80 c. Beechcraft "Queen Air" on photomission, 1983		80	80
350	$1.05, Helicopter landing diesel fuel from U.S.S. *Breton*, 1969		1·10	1·10
351	$1.30, R.N.Z.A.F. "Hercules" dropping bulldozer, 1983		1·25	1·25
348/51		*Set of 4*	3·00	3·00

116 Ducie Island

(Des A. Theobald. Litho Walsall)

1989 (23 Oct). *Islands of Pitcairn Group. T* **116** *and similar horiz designs. Multicoloured. W* w **14** (*sideways*). *P* 14.
352	15 c. Type **116**		15	15
353	90 c. Henderson Island		90	90
354	$1.05, Oeno Island		1·00	1·00
355	$1.30, Pitcairn Island		1·25	1·25
352/5		*Set of 4*	3·00	3·00

(Des C. Abbott. Litho Questa)

1990 (15 Jan). *Bicentenary of Pitcairn Island Settlement* (3*rd issue*). *Horiz designs as T* **114**. *Multicoloured. W* w **16** (*sideways*). *P* 14.
356	40 c. Mutineers sighting Pitcairn Island		50	40
	a. Sheetlet. Nos. 356/61		2·75	
357	40 c. Ship's boat approaching landing		50	40
358	40 c. Exploring island		50	40
359	40 c. Ferrying goods ashore		50	40
360	40 c. Burning of H.M.S. *Bounty*		50	40
361	40 c. Pitcairn Island village		50	40
356/61		*Set of 6*	2·75	2·25

Nos. 356/61 were printed in the same sheet format as Nos. 335/40.

117 Ennerdale, Cumbria, and Peter Heywood

(Des D. Ashby. Litho Questa)

1990 (3 May). *"Stamp World London 90" International Stamp Exhibition, London. T* **117** *and similar horiz designs showing English landmarks and Bounty crew members. Multicoloured. W* w **14** (*sideways*). *P* 14.
362	80 c. Type **117**		75	80
363	90 c. St. Augustine's Tower, Hackney, and John Adams		85	90
364	$1.05, Citadel Gateway, Plymouth, and William Bligh		1·00	1·25
365	$1.30, Moorland Close, Cockermouth, and Fletcher Christian		1·25	1·40
362/5		*Set of 4*	3·50	4·00

(Des E. Nisbet. Litho B.D.T.)

1990 (3 May). *As Nos.* 318 *and* 323, *but W* w **16** (*sideways*). *P* 13½.
369	20 c. H.M.S. *Blossom* (survey ship), 1825		10	15
	a. Booklet pane. No. 369×4 with margins all round		40	
374	90 c. H.M.S. *Virago* (paddle-sloop), 1853		60	65
	a. Booklet pane. No. 374×4 with margins all round		2·40	

Nos. 369 and 374 only exist from $4.40 stamp booklets.

(Des D. Miller. Litho Questa)

1990 (4 Aug). *90th Birthday of Queen Elizabeth the Queen Mother. Vert designs as T* **107** (40 c.) *or* **108** ($3) *of Kenya. Multicoloured. W* w **16**. *P* 14×15 (40 c.) *or* 14½ ($3).
378	40 c. multicoloured		50	50
379	$3 black and dull scarlet		2·50	2·50

Designs:—40 c. Queen Elizabeth, 1937; $3 King George VI and Queen Elizabeth on way to Silver Wedding Service, 1948.

118 *Bounty* Chronometer and 1940 1d. Definitive

119 Stephen's Lory ("Redbreast")

(Des D. Miller. Litho Walsall)

1990 (15 Oct). *50th Anniv of Pitcairn Islands Stamps. T* **118** *and similar horiz designs. Multicoloured. W* w **14** (*sideways*). *P* 13½×14.
380	20 c. Type **118**		30	30
381	80 c. *Bounty* Bible and 1958 4d. definitive		80	80
382	90 c. *Bounty* Bell and 1969 30 c. definitive		90	90
383	$1.05, Mutiny on the *Bounty* and 1977 $1 definitive		1·00	1·00
384	$1.30, Penny Black and 1988 15 c. ship definitive		1·40	1·40
380/4		*Set of 5*	4·00	4·00

(Des N. Harvey from paintings by Byatt. Litho Questa)

1990 (6 Dec). *"Birdpex '90" Stamp Exhibition, Christchurch, New Zealand. T* **119** *and similar vert designs. Multicoloured. W* w **14**. *P* 14.
385	20 c. Type **119**		30	30
386	90 c. Henderson Island Fruit Dove ("Wood Pigeon")		1·10	1·10
387	$1.30, Pitcairn Warbler ("Sparrow")		1·40	1·40
388	$1.80, Henderson Island Crake ("Chicken Bird")		1·60	1·60
385/8		*Set of 4*	4·00	4·00

Nos. 385/8 carry the "Birdpex '90" logo and inscription in the gutter between the two panes.

(Des N. Shewring. Litho Leigh-Mardon Ltd, Melbourne)

1991 (24 Mar). *Bicentenary of Pitcairn Islands Settlement* (4*th issue*). *Celebrations. Horiz designs as T* **114**. *Multicoloured. W* w **16**. *P* 14½.
389	80 c. Re-enacting landing of mutineers		1·00	1·10
	a. Sheetlet. Nos. 389/94		5·50	
390	80 c. Commemorative plaque		1·00	1·10
391	80 c. Memorial church service		1·00	1·10
392	80 c. Cricket match		1·00	1·10
393	80 c. Burning model of *Bounty*		1·00	1·10
394	80 c. Firework display		1·00	1·10
389/94		*Set of 6*	5·50	6·00

Nos. 389/94 were printed in the same sheet format as Nos. 335/40.

120 *Europa*   121 Bulldozer

(Des E. Nisbet. Litho Leigh-Mardon Ltd, Melbourne)

1991 (17 June). *Cruise Liners. T* **120** *and similar horiz designs. Multicoloured. W* w **16**. *P* 14½.
395	15 c. Type **120**		20	20
396	80 c. *Royal Viking Star*		85	85
397	$1.30, *World Discoverer*		1·25	1·25
398	$1.80, *Sagafjord*		1·90	1·90
395/8		*Set of 4*	3·75	3·75

(Des D. Miller. Litho Questa)

1991 (12 July). *65th Birthday of Queen Elizabeth II and 70th Birthday of Prince Philip. Vert designs as T* **58** *of Kiribati. Multicoloured. W* w **16** (*sideways*). *P* 14½×14.
399	20 c. Prince Philip		40	30
	a. Horiz pair. Nos. 399/400 separated by label		2·00	1·50
400	$1.30, Queen in robes of Order of St. Michael and St. George		1·60	1·25

Nos. 399/400 were printed in a similar sheet format to Nos. 366/7 of Kiribati.

(Des O. Bell. Litho Questa)

1991 (25 Sept). *Island Transport. T* **121** *and similar diamond-shaped designs. Multicoloured. W* w **14**. *P* 14.
401	20 c. Type **121**		20	20
402	80 c. Two-wheeled motorcycle		75	75
403	$1.30, Tractor		1·25	1·25
404	$1.80, Three-wheeled motorcycle		1·90	1·90
401/4		*Set of 4*	3·75	3·75

122 The Annunciation   123 *Carcharhinus galapagensis*

(Des Jennifer Toombs. Litho Questa)

1991 (18 Nov). *Christmas. T* **122** *and similar vert designs. Multicoloured. W* w **14**. *P* 14.
405	20 c. Type **122**		20	20
406	80 c. Shepherds and lamb		75	75
407	$1.30, Holy Family		1·10	1·10
408	$1.80, Three Wise Men		1·75	1·75
405/8		*Set of 4*	3·50	3·50

(Des D. Miller. Litho Questa ($1.80), Leigh-Mardon Ltd, Melbourne (others))

1992 (6 Feb). *40th Anniv of Queen Elizabeth II's Accession. Horiz designs as T* **113** *of Kenya. Multicoloured. W* w **14** (*sideways*) ($1.80) *or* w **16** (*sideways*) (*others*). *P* 14.
409	20 c. Bounty Bay		15	15
410	60 c. Sunset over Pitcairn		60	60
411	90 c. Pitcairn coastline		85	85
412	$1 Three portraits of Queen Elizabeth		90	90
413	$1.80, Queen Elizabeth II		1·60	1·60
409/13		*Set of 5*	3·75	3·75

(Des Jane Thatcher. Litho Leigh-Mardon Ltd, Melbourne)

1992 (30 June). *Sharks. T* **123** *and similar horiz designs. W* w **14** (*sideways*). *P* 15×14½.
414	20 c. Type **123**		15	15
415	$1 *Eugomphodus taurus*		85	85
416	$1.50, *Carcharhinus melanopterus*		1·40	1·40
417	$1.80, *Carcharhinus amblyrhynchos*		1·60	1·60
414/17		*Set of 4*	3·50	3·50

124 *Montastrea* sp. and *Acropora* spp. (corals)

(Des I. Loe. Litho Enschedé)

1992 (11 Sept). *The Sir Peter Scott Memorial Expedition to Henderson Island. T* **124** *and similar horiz designs. W* w **14** (*sideways*). *P* 14×14½.
418	20 c. Type **124**		15	15
419	$1 Henderson Sandalwood		85	85
420	$1.50, Murphy's Petrel		1·40	1·40
421	$1.80, Henderson Hawkmoth		1·60	1·60
418/21		*Set of 4*	3·50	3·50

125 Bligh's Birthplace at St. Tudy, Cornwall

(Des Jennifer Toombs. Litho Leigh-Mardon Ltd, Melbourne)

1992 (7 Dec). *175th Death Anniv of William Bligh. T* **125** *and similar horiz design. Multicoloured. W* w **14**. *P* 14½.
422	20 c. Type **125**		15	15
423	$1 Bligh on *Bounty*		85	85
424	$1.50, Voyage in *Bounty*'s launch		1·40	1·40
425	$1.80, "William Bligh" (R. Combe) and epitaph		1·60	1·60
422/5		*Set of 4*	3·50	3·50

126 H.M.S. *Chichester* (frigate)

(Des A. Theobald. Litho Questa)

1993 (10 Mar). *Modern Royal Navy Vessels. T* **126** *and similar horiz designs. Multicoloured. W* w **16** (*sideways*). *P* 14.
426	15 c. Type **126**		10	10
427	20 c. H.M.S. *Jaguar* (frigate)		10	10
428	$1.80, H.M.S. *Andrew* (submarine)		1·25	1·40
429	$3 H.M.S. *Warrior* (aircraft carrier) and helicopter		2·00	2·10
426/9		*Set of 4*	3·00	3·25

Prince Edward Island
see Canada

Qatar

An independent Arab Shaikhdom, with a British postal administration until 23 May 1963.

There was no postal service from Qatar until 18 May 1950. Prior to this date the few foreign residents made their own arrangements for their mail to be carried to Bahrain for onward transmission through the postal services.

The first organised post from the capital, Doha, was an extension of the work in the state by the British Political Officer. From 18 May 1950 British residents were able to send mail via his office. The first three sendings had the Bahrain or British Postal Agencies in Eastern Arabia stamps cancelled by a circular office stamp, but later batches, up to the introduction of the first Doha postmark in July 1950, had the stamps cancelled on arrival at Bahrain.

July 1950 Cancellation   1956 Cancellation

The Post Office became a separate entity in August 1950 when its services were made available to the general public. After initially using the Bahrain surcharges on Great Britain the supply of stamps for the Qatar office was switched to the British Postal Agencies in Eastern Arabia surcharges.

The circular cancellation, dating from July 1950, continued to be used until replaced by a slightly smaller version in early 1956.

A further post office was opened on 1 February 1956 at the Umm Said oil terminal, using its own cancellation.

Both offices were issued with standard oval Registered handstamps, Doha in 1950 and Umm Said in 1956.

1956 Umm Said Cancellation

All stamps to 1960 surcharged on Queen Elizabeth II issues of Great Britain

QATAR	QATAR	QATAR
NP 1 NP	**3 NP NP**	**75 NP**
(1)	(2)	(3)

1957 (1 Apr)–**59.** *Nos. 540/2, 543b/8, 551 and 555/6 (St. Edward's Crown wmk), surch as T 1 to 3.*

1	1	1 n.p. on 5d. brown	10	10
2	2	3 n.p. on ½d. orange-red	15	15
3		6 n.p. on 1d. ultramarine	15	15
4		9 n.p. on 1½d. green	15	10
5		12 n.p. on 2d. light red-brown	20	30
6	1	15 n.p. on 2½d. carmine-red (I)	15	10
7	2	20 n.p. on 3d. deep lilac (B.)	15	10
8	1	25 n.p. on 4d. ultramarine	40	40
9		40 n.p. on 6d. reddish purple	15	10
		a. Deep claret (21.7.59)	30	10
10		50 n.p. on 9d. bronze-green	40	15
11	3	75 n.p. on 1s. 3d. green	50	50
12		1 r. on 1s. 6d. grey-blue	5·50	50
1/12		*Set of 12*	7·00	1·75

QATAR 2 RUPEES
 I

QATAR 2 RUPEES
II
(4)

QATAR 5 RUPEES
 I

QATAR 5 RUPEES
II
(5)

QATAR 10 RUPEES
 I

QATAR 10 RUPEES
 II
(6)

Type I (4/6). Type-set overprints. Bold thick letters with sharp corners and straight edges. Bars close together and usually slightly longer than in Type II.
Type II (4/6). Plate-printed overprints. Thinner letters, rounded corners and rough edges. Bars wider apart.

(b) *Nos. 536/8 (St. Edward's Crown wmk) surcharged with T 4/6*

			I (1.4.57)		II (18.9.57)	
13	2 r. on 2s. 6d. black-brown		4·00	1·00	9·00	6·00
14	5 r. on 5s. rose-red		7·00	2·75	9·00	16·00
15	10 r. on 10s. ultramarine		8·50	8·50	45·00	£110
13/15	*Set of 3*		18·00	11·00	55·00	£120

QATAR
15 NP

(7)

1957 (1 Aug). *World Scout Jubilee Jamboree. Nos. 557/9 surch in two lines as T 7* (15 *n.p.*) *or in three lines (others).*

16	15 n.p. on 2½d. carmine-red		25	35
17	25 n.p. on 4d. ultramarine		25	35
18	75 n.p. on 1s. 3d. green		30	35
16/18	*Set of 3*		70	95

1960 (26 Apr–28 Sept). *Nos. 570/5 and 579 (Mult Crown wmk) surcharged as T 1 or 2.*

20	2	3 n.p. on ½d. orange-red (28.9)	70	1·75
21		6 n.p. on 1d. ultramarine (21.6)	1·25	2·75
22		9 n.p. on 1½d. green (28.9)	75	1·50
23		12 n.p. on 2d. light red-brown (28.9)	3·75	6·50
24	1	15 n.p. on 2½d. carmine-red (II)	35	10
25	2	20 n.p. on 3d. deep lilac (B.) (28.9)	35	10
26	1	40 n.p. on 6d. deep claret (21.6)	60	30
20/6		*Set of 7*	7·00	11·50

8 Shaikh Ahmad bin   9 Peregrine   10 Dhow
Ali al Thani   Falcon

11 Oil Derrick   12 Mosque

(Des O. C. Meronti (T 8), M. Goaman (T 9), M. Farrar Bell (T 10), J. Constable and O. C. Meronti (T 11/12). Photo Harrison, (T 8/10). Recess D.L.R. (T 11/12))

1961 (2 Sept). *P 14½ (5 n.p. to 75 n.p.) or 13 (1 r. to 10 r.).*

27	8	5 n.p. carmine	10	10
28		15 n.p. black	10	10
29		20 n.p. reddish purple	10	10
30		30 n.p. deep green	10	10
31	9	40 n.p. red	85	10
32		50 n.p. sepia	1·25	10
33	10	75 n.p. ultramarine	60	60
34	11	1 r. scarlet	70	10
35		2 r. ultramarine	2·00	25
36	12	5 r. bronze-green	9·00	80
37		10 r. black	24·00	2·25
27/37		*Set of 11*	35·00	3·75

The Qatar Post Department took over the postal services on 23 May 1963. Later stamp issues will be found listed in Part 19 (*Middle East*) of this catalogue.

Queensland
see Australia

Rhodesia

Stamps of BECHUANALAND (see BOTSWANA) were used in Matabeleland on the runner post between Gubulawayo and Mafeking (Bechuanaland) from 21 August 1888 until 5 May 1894. Such stamps were cancelled "GUBULAWAYO" or by the barrel oval "678" obliteration.

Between 27 June 1890 and 13 May 1892 external mail from Mashonaland sent via Bechuanaland was franked with that territory's stamps. A similar arrangement, using the stamps of MOZAMBIQUE existed for the route via Beira inaugurated on 29 August 1891. In both instances the stamps were cancelled by the post offices receiving the mail from Mashonaland. From 14 May until 31 July 1892 letters via Bechuanaland were franked with a combination of B.S.A Company and Bechuanaland issues.

Rhodesia joined the South African Postal Union on 1 August 1892 when its stamps became valid for international mail. Combination frankings with Mozambique stamps continued to be required until April 1894.

For the use of British Central Africa overprints in Northeastern Rhodesia from 1893 to 1899 see MALAWI (NYASALAND).

PRICES FOR STAMPS ON COVER TO 1945	
Nos. 1/7	*from* × 5
Nos. 8/13	—
Nos. 14/17	*from* × 2
Nos. 18/24	*from* × 10
Nos. 25/6	—
Nos. 27/8	*from* × 7
Nos. 29/35	*from* × 10
Nos. 36/7	—
Nos. 41/6	*from* × 6
Nos. 47/50	—
Nos. 51/3	*from* × 2
Nos. 58/64	*from* × 3
Nos. 66/72	*from* × 8
Nos. 73/4	—
Nos. 75/87	*from* × 6
Nos. 88/93a	—
Nos. 94/9	*from* × 3
Nos. 100/10	*from* × 5
Nos. 111/13e	—
Nos. 114/18	*from* × 7
Nos. 119/60a	*from* × 2
Nos. 160b/6b	—
Nos. 167/78	*from* × 2
Nos. 179/81a	—
Nos. 182/5a	*from* × 2
Nos. 186/208	*from* × 3
Nos. 209/41	*from* × 2
Nos. 242/54a	—
Nos. 255/77	*from* × 2
Nos. 278/9c	—
Nos. 280/1	*from* × 7
Nos. 282/310	*from* × 2
Nos. 311/22	—

A. ISSUES FOR THE BRITISH SOUTH AFRICA COMPANY TERRITORY

1   2   **½d.**
(3)

(Recess B.W.)

1892 (2 Jan)*–**93.** *Thin wove paper. P 14, 14½.*

1	1	1d. black	9·00	1·25
2		6d. ultramarine	48·00	20·00
3		6d. deep blue (1893)	22·00	2·50
4		1s. grey-brown	28·00	7·50
5		2s. vermilion	40·00	25·00
6		2s. 6d. grey-purple	24·00	25·00
7		2s. 6d. lilac (1893)	28·00	28·00
8		5s. orange-yellow	42·00	48·00
9		10s. deep green	60·00	90·00
10	2	£1 deep blue	£160	£130
11		£2 rose-red**	£375	£150
12		£5 sage-green	£1500	£450
13		£10 brown	£2750	£700
1/10		*Set of 10*	£350	£350

Great caution is needed in buying the high values in either used or unused condition, many stamps offered being revenue stamps cleaned and re-gummed or with forged postmarks.

*Printing of Nos. 1/28 commenced in 1890, although none were used for postal purposes before 2 January 1892 when the route to the East Coast was inaugurated.

**For later printings of the £2 see No. 74.

The following sheet watermarks are known on Nos. 1/26: (1) William Collins, Sons & Co's paper watermarked with the firm's monogram, and "PURE LINEN WOVE BANK" in double-lined capitals (1890 and 1891 ptgs). (2) As with "EXTRA STRONG" and "139" added (1892 ptgs). (3) Paper by Wiggins, Teape & Co, watermarked "W T & Co" in script letters in double-lined wavy border (1893 ptgs). (4) The same firm's paper, watermarked "1011" in double-lined figures (1894 ptgs except ½d.). (5) "WIGGINS TEAPE & CO LONDON" in double-lined block capitals (1894 ptg of No. 18). Many values can also be found on a slightly thicker paper without wmk, but single specimens are not easily distinguishable.

1892 (2 Jan). *Nos. 2 and 4 surch as T 3.*

14	1	½d. on 6d. ultramarine	..	65·00	£110
15		2d. on 6d. ultramarine	..	60·00	£140
16		4d. on 6d. ultramarine	..	80·00	£180
17		8d. on 1s. grey-brown	..	90·00	£250

Caution is needed in buying these surcharges as both forged surcharges and forged postmarks exist.

4   5 (ends of scrolls behind legs of springboks)

(T **4**. Centre recess; value B.W.)

1892 (2 Jan)–94. *Thin wove paper (wmks as note after No. 13).* P 14, 14½.

18	4	½d. dull blue and vermilion	..	2·50	1·00
19		½d. deep blue and vermilion (1893)	..	2·50	2·75
20		2d. sea-green and vermilion	..	8·50	1·75
21		3d. grey-black and green (8.92)	..	8·00	1·75
22		4d. chestnut and black	..	8·50	1·75
23		8d. rose-lake and ultramarine	..	10·00	5·50
24		8d. red and ultramarine (1892)	..	10·00	5·50
25		3s. brown and green (1894)	..	95·00	65·00
26		4s. grey-black and vermilion (1893)	..	30·00	40·00
18/26			Set of 7	£150	£100

(Recess P.B. from the Bradbury, Wilkinson plates)

1895. *Thick soft wove paper.* P 12½.

27	4	2d. green and red	..	20·00	5·00
28		4d. yellow-brown and black	..	22·00	9·00
		a. Imperf (pair)	..	£1500	

(Centre recess; value typo P.B.)

1896–97. *Wove paper.* P 14.

(a) *Die I. Plates 1 and 2.*

Small dot to the right of the tail of the right-hand supporter in the coat of arms. Body of lion only partly shaded.

29	5	1d. scarlet and emerald	..	10·00	3·25
		a. Carmine-red and emerald	..		
30		2d. brown and mauve	..	13·00	1·00
31		3d. chocolate and ultramarine	..	2·25	90
32		4d. ultramarine and mauve	..	30·00	
		a. Imperf between (pair)	..		
		b. Blue and mauve	..	11·00	9·00
33		6d. mauve and pink	..	60·00	8·00
34		8d. green and mauve/buff	..	4·50	45
		a. Imperf between (pair)	..		
		b. Imperf (pair)	..	£1500	
35		1s. green and blue	..	15·00	2·25
36		3s. green and mauve/blue	..	48·00	29·00
		a. Imperf (pair)	..	£3000	
37		4s. orange-red and blue/green	..	40·00	2·00
29/37			Set of 9	£180	50·00

(b) *Die II. Plates 3 and 4.*

No dot. Body of lion heavily shaded all over.

41	5	½d. slate and violet	..	1·00	1·50
42		1d. scarlet and emerald	..	1·50	2·25
43		2d. brown and mauve	..	4·25	3·50
44		4d. ultramarine and mauve	..	55·00	9·00
		a. Blue and mauve	..	6·00	40
46		6d. mauve and rose	..	4·50	45
47		2s. indigo and green/buff	..	20·00	3·50
48		2s. 6d. brown and purple/yellow	..	55·00	38·00
49		5s. chestnut and emerald	..	35·00	9·00
50		10s. slate and vermilion/rose	..	80·00	60·00
41/50			Set of 9	£180	£110

One Penny   THREE PENCE.

(6)   (7)

(Surchd by *Bulawayo Chronicle*)

1896 (April). *Matabele Rebellion provisionals. Surch with T 6 and 7.*

51	6	1d. on 3d. (No. 21)	..	£350	£375
		a. "P" in "Penny" inverted	..	£12000	
		b. "y" in "Penny" inverted	..		
		c. Surch double	..		
52		1d. on 4s. (No. 26)	..	£250	£225
		a. "P" in "Penny" inverted	..	£11000	
		b. "y" in "Penny" inverted	..	£11000	
		c. Single bar through original value		£800	£1000
53	7	3d. on 5s. (No. 8)	..	£150	£200
		a. "R" in "THREE" inverted	..	£12000	
		b. "T" in "THREE" inverted	..	£15000	

Nos. 51 and 52 occur in two settings, one with 9¾ mm between value and upper bar, the other with 11 mm between value and upper bar.

BRITISH SOUTH AFRICA COMPANY.

(8)   9 (Ends of scrolls between legs of springboks)

1896 (22 May–Aug). *Cape of Good Hope stamps optd by Argus Printing Co, Cape Town, with T 8. Wmk Anchor (3d. wmk Crown CA). P 14.*

58	6	½d. grey-black (No. 48a)	..	6·00	11·00
59	17	1d. rose-red (No. 58)	..	9·50	13·00
60	6	2d. deep bistre (No. 50a)	..	10·00	7·00
61		3d. pale claret (No. 40)	..	45·00	55·00
62		4d. blue (No. 51)	..	12·00	12·00
		a. "COMPANY," omitted	..	£7000	
63	4	6d. deep purple (No. 52a)	..	45·00	60·00
64	6	1s. yellow-ochre (No. 65) (Aug)	..	80·00	£110
58/64			Set of 7	£170	£225

(Eng J. A. C. Harrison (vignette), Bain or Rapkin (£1) (frames). Recess Waterlow)

1897. P 13½ to 16.

66	9	½d. grey-black and purple	..	1·60	3·00
67		1d. scarlet and emerald	..	3·00	3·75
68		2d. brown and mauve	..	3·50	60
69		3d. brown-red and slate-blue	..	2·50	30
		a. Imperf between (vert pair)	..	£1500	
70		4d. ultramarine and claret	..	5·00	1·25
		a. Imperf between (horiz pair)	..	£4250	£4250
71		6d. dull purple and pink	..	5·50	3·50
72		8d. green and mauve/buff	..	8·50	40
		a. Imperf between (vert pair)	..	—£1000	
73		£1 black and red-brown/green	..	£400	£225

(Recess Waterlow, from the Bradbury plate)

1897 (Jan). P 15.

74	2	£2 rosy red	..	£1600	£400

10   11   12

(Recess Waterlow)

1898–1908. P 13½ to 15½.

75	10	½d. dull bluish green	..	90	30
		a. Yellow-green (1904)	..	85	30
		aa. Imperf vert (horiz pair)	..	£650	
		ab. Imperf (pair)	..	£600	
76		½d. deep green (shades) (1908)	..	23·00	80
77		1d. rose (shades)	..	1·00	15
		a. Imperf (pair)	..	£550	£550
		b. Imperf between (vert pair)	..	£500	£500
78		1d. red (shades) (1905)	..	2·50	30
		a. Imperf vert (horiz pair)	..	£350	£375
		ab. Imperf horiz (vert pair)	..	£400	
		b. Imperf (pair)	..	£500	£500
79		2d. brown	..	1·25	15
80		2½d. dull blue (shades)	..	3·75	30
		a. Imperf vert (horiz pair)	..	£800	£800
		b. Grey-blue (shades) (1903)	..	8·50	80
81		3d. claret	..	3·75	40
		a. Imperf between (vert pair)	..	£700	
82		4d. olive	..	3·75	15
		a. Imperf between (vert pair)	..	£700	
83		6d. reddish purple	..	6·50	1·75
		a. Reddish mauve (1902)	..	12·00	5·00
84	11	1s. bistre	..	7·50	1·25
		a. Imperf between (vert pair)	..	£2250	
		ab. Imperf between (horiz pair)	..	£2250	
		b. Deep olive-bistre (1907)	..	£275	
		bc. Imperf (pair)	..	£2250	
		bd. Imperf between (horiz pair)	..	£2500	
		c. Bistre-brown (1908)	..	45·00	10·00
		d. Brownish yellow (1908)	..	14·00	4·25
85		2s. 6d. bluish grey (11.06)	..	30·00	55
		a. Imperf between (vert pair)	..	£900	£600
		b. Imperf (vert pair)	..	—£5000	
86		3s. deep violet (1902)	..	9·00	50
		a. Deep bluish violet (1908)	..	45·00	9·50
87		5s. brown-orange	..	24·00	8·50
88		7s. 6d. black (11.01)	..	45·00	14·00
89		10s. grey-green	..	15·00	1·50
90	12	£1 greyish red-purple (p 15½) (7.01)	..	£150	60·00
		a. Perf 14. Blackish purple (1902)	..	£200	60·00
91		£2 brown (5.08)	..	65·00	6·50
92		£5 deep blue (7.01)	..	£3000	£2250
93		£10 lilac (7.01)	..	£3000	£2250
93a		£20 yellow-bistre (1901?)	..	£8500	
75/90			Set of 14	£250	80·00
80/1, 85/6, 88/93 Perf "Specimen"				£900	

A £100 cherry-red, perf 13½, was ordered in June 1901, a number of mint, together with three examples showing fiscal cancellations, being known.

13 Victoria Falls   (14)

1P   VICTORIA FALLS   1P   RHODESIA.

(Recess Waterlow)

1905 (13 July). *Visit of British Association and Opening of Victoria Falls Bridge.* P 13½ to 15.

94	13	1d. red	..	2·75	3·25
95		2½d. deep blue	..	7·50	3·75
96		5d. claret (Optd S. £100)	..	18·00	42·00
97		1s. blue-green	..	18·00	23·00
		a. Imperf (pair)	..	£8000	
		b. Imperf between (horiz pair)	..	£11000	
		c. Imperf between (vert pair)	..	£11000	
		d. Imperf vert (horiz pair)	..	£8500	
98		2s. 6d. black	..	£100	£150
99		5s. violet	..	85·00	40·00
94/9			Set of 6	£200	£225
94/9 Perf (5d.) or Optd (others) "Specimen"			Set of 6	£250	

1909 (15 Apr)–12. *Optd as T 14. P 13½ to 15.*

100	10	½d. green to deep green	..	1·25	30
		a. No stop	..	42·00	27·00
		b. Yellow-green (1911)	..	35·00	27·00
101		1d. carmine-rose	..	1·25	30
		a. No stop	..	60·00	25·00
		b. Imperf between (horiz pair)	..	£300	
		c. Deep carmine-rose	..	1·25	30
		cd. Imperf between (horiz pair)	..	£350	
102		2d. brown	..	1·60	2·25
		a. No stop	..	75·00	50·00
103		2½d. pale dull blue	..	1·00	20
		a. No stop	..	30·00	22·00
104		3d. claret	..	1·60	20
		a. No stop	..	90·00	55·00
105		4d. olive	..	2·75	35
		a. No stop	..	60·00	55·00
106		6d. reddish purple	..	5·00	1·50
		a. No stop	..		
		b. Reddish mauve	..		
		c. Dull purple	..	12·00	2·50
		ca. No stop	..	70·00	45·00
107	11	1s. bistre	..		
		a. No stop	..		
		b. Bistre-brown	..		
		ba. No stop	..		
		c. Deep brownish bistre	..	8·50	1·25
		ca. No stop	..	75·00	32·00
108		2s. 6d. bluish grey	..	15·00	4·25
		a. No stop	..	75·00	55·00
109		3s. deep violet	..	15·00	4·25
110		5s. orange	..	25·00	14·00
		a. No stop	..	75·00	60·00
111		7s. 6d. black	..	60·00	11·00
112		10s. dull green	..	26·00	8·50
		a. No stop	..	£200	£180
113	12	£1 grey-purple	..	£100	60·00
		a. Vert pair, one without opt	..	£12000	
		b. Opt in violet	..	£275	£225
113c		£2 brown	..	£3250	£325
113d		£2 rosy brown (bluish paper) (p 14½×15) (1912)	..	£3000	£300
113e		£5 deep blue (bluish paper)	..	£5000	£2250
100/13			Set of 14	£225	85·00
100/13 Perf "Specimen"			Set of 14	£300	

In some values the no stop variety occurs in every stamp in a vertical row of a sheet, in other values only once in a sheet. Other varieties, such as no serif to the right of apex of "A", no serif to top of "E", etc., exist in some values.

RHODESIA. 5d   RHODESIA. TWO SHILLINGS.

(15)   (16)

1909 (April)–11. *Surch as T 15 and 16 (2s.), in black.*

114	10	5d. on 6d. reddish purple	..	6·50	7·00
		a. Surcharge in violet	..	75·00	
		b. Reddish mauve	..		
		c. Dull purple	..	9·50	7·00
116	11	7½d. on 2s. 6d. bluish grey	..	3·50	2·25
		a. Surcharge in violet	..	16·00	4·50
		ab. Surch double	..	†£6500	
117		10d. on 3s. deep violet	..	13·00	14·00
		a. Surcharge in violet	..	4·00	3·25
118		2s. on 5s. orange	..	12·00	7·00
114/18 Perf "Specimen"			Set of 4	£180	

In the 7½d. and 10d. surcharges the bars are spaced as in T 16.

17   18

(Recess Waterlow)

1910 (11 Nov)–13. (a) P 14.

119	17	½d. yellow-green	..	7·00	1·00
120		½d. bluish green	..	12·00	1·00
		a. Imperf (pair)	..	£7000	£4000
121		½d. olive-green	..	24·00	1·50
122		½d. dull green	..	60·00	50·00
123		1d. bright carmine	..	10·00	50
		a. Imperf between (vert pair)	..	£15000	£10000
124		1d. carmine-lake	..	26·00	70
125		1d. rose-red	..	12·00	50
126		2d. black and grey	..	29·00	5·50
127		2d. black-purple and slate-grey	..	£160	
128		2d. black and slate-grey	..	32·00	4·50
129		2d. black and slate	..	32·00	5·00
130		2d. black and grey-black	..	35·00	8·00

131	17	2½d. ultramarine	15·00	5·00
131a		2½d. bright ultramarine	13·00	5·00
132		2½d. dull blue	15·00	5·00
133		2½d. chalky blue	15·00	9·00
134		3d. purple and ochre	20·00	20·00
135		3d. purple and yellow-ochre	22·00	6·00
136		3d. magenta and yellow-ochre	60·00	45·00
137		3d. violet and ochre	70·00	70·00
138		4d. greenish black and orange	75·00	70·00
139		4d. brown-purple and orange	55·00	35·00
140		4d. black and orange	24·00	10·00
141		5d. purple-brown and olive-green	20·00	32·00
141a		5d. purple-brown and olive-yellow	18·00	38·00
		ab. Error. Purple-brown and ochre	£550	£150
143		5d. lake-brown and olive	£190	60·00
143a		5d. lake-brown and green	£18000	£1500
144		6d. red-brown and mauve	19·00	19·00
145		6d. brown and purple	19·00	8·00
145a		6d. bright chestnut and mauve	£650	60·00
146		8d. black and purple	£3500	
147		8d. dull purple and purple	£100	65·00
148		8d. greenish black and purple	£110	55·00
149		10d. scarlet and reddish mauve	26·00	48·00
150		10d. carmine and deep purple	£500	70·00
151		1s. grey-black and deep blue-green	26·00	15·00
151a		1s. black and deep blue-green	75·00	22·00
152		1s. black and pale blue-green	27·00	9·00
152a		1s. purple-black and blue-green	£200	38·00
153		2s. black and ultramarine	55·00	50·00
154		2s. black and dull blue	£600	55·00
154a		2s. purple-black and ultramarine	£2500	£200
155		2s. 6d. black and lake	£300	£275
155a		2s. 6d. black and crimson	£300	£275
156		2s. 6d. sepia and deep crimson	£375	£325
156a		2s. 6d. bistre-brown and crimson	£750	£500
157		2s. 6d. black and rose-carmine	£275	£275
158		3s. green and violet (shades)	£130	£130
158a		3s. bright green and magenta	£950	£550
159		5s. vermilion and deep green	£225	£200
160		5s. scarlet and pale yellow-green	£275	£200
160a		5s. crimson and yellow-green	£225	£200
160b		7s. 6d. carmine and pale blue	£600	£500
161		7s. 6d. carmine and light blue	£650	£550
162		7s. 6d. carmine and bright blue	£1300	£700
163		10s. deep myrtle and orange	£500	£250
164		10s. blue-green and orange	£375	£250
165		£1 carmine-red and bluish black	£900	£375
166		£1 rose-scarlet and bluish black	£1000	£375
166a		£1 crimson and slate-black	£1100	£600
		b. Error. Scarlet and reddish mauve	£8500	

(b) P 15

167	17	½d. blue-green	£250	13·00
168		½d. yellow-green	£250	11·00
169		½d. apple-green	£500	24·00
170		1d. carmine	£250	7·00
170a		1d. carmine-lake	£400	12·00
170b		1d. rose-carmine	£250	9·00
171		2d. black and grey-black	£600	26·00
171a		2d. black and grey	£600	26·00
171b		2d. black and slate	£600	26·00
172		2½d. ultramarine (shades)	70·00	35·00
173		3d. purple and yellow-ochre	£2500	50·00
173a		3d. claret and pale yellow-ochre	£1600	50·00
174		4d. black and orange (shades)	38·00	60·00
175		5d. lake-brown and olive-green	£750	75·00
176		6d. brown and mauve	£800	60·00
177		1s. black and blue-green (shades)	£750	55·00
178		2s. black and dull blue	£1400	£325
179		£1 red and black	£11000	£3500

(c) P 15 × 14 or 14 × 15

179a	17	½d. yellow-green	†	£2000
179b		1d. carmine	†	£3000
180		3d. purple and ochre	£3000	£200
181		4d. black and orange	£425	
181a		1s. black and blue-green	£16000	£3000

(d) P 13½

182	17	½d. yellow-green	£250	40·00
182a		½d. green	£250	40·00
183		1d. bright carmine	£1500	48·00
184		2½d. ultramarine (shades)	35·00	55·00
185		8d. black and purple (shades)	60·00	£200
185a		8d. grey-purple and dull purple	£350	£350

119/185 Optd "Specimen" perf 14 except 2½d. and
8d. perf 13½ ...... Set of 18 £2750

Plate varieties in T 17 are:—½d., double dot below "D" in right-hand value tablet (*from* £500 *un.* £350 used); 2d. to £1 excluding 2½d., straight stroke in Queen's right ear known as the "gash in ear" variety (*from* 3 *to* 8 *times normal*).

Stamps from the above and the next issue are known compound perf with 14 or 15 on one side only or on adjoining sides but we no longer list them.

(Recess Waterlow)

1913 (1 Sept)–**22**. *No wmk.* (i) *From single working plates.*

(a) P 14.

186	18	½d. blue-green	4·25	65
187		½d. deep green	2·25	65
		a. Imperf horiz (vert pair)	£500	
188		½d. yellow-green	4·50	65
188b		½d. dull green	3·25	65
		ba. Imperf vert (horiz pair)	£600	£600
189		½d. bright green	6·50	65
		a. Imperf between (vert pair)	£900	
190		1d. rose-carmine	3·50	55
		a. Imperf between (horiz pair)	£425	£400
191		1d. carmine-red (shades)	5·50	55
		a. Imperf between (pair)	£800	
192		1d. brown-red	2·75	40
193		1d. red	3·00	40
		a. Imperf between (horiz pair)	£600	
194		1d. scarlet	9·00	65
		a. Imperf between (horiz pair)	£700	
195		1d. rose-red	4·75	40
		a. Imperf between (horiz pair)	£425	
		b. Imperf between (vert pair)	£1300	
196		1d. rosine	£500	19·00
197		1½d. brown-ochre (1919)	2·25	60
		a. Imperf between (horiz pair)	£400	£400
198		1½d. bistre-brown (1917)	2·25	60
		a. Imperf between (horiz pair)	£425	£400

199	18	1½d. drab-brown (1917)	2·25	60
		a. Imperf between (horiz pair)	£400	
		b. Imperf between (vert pair)	£1200	
200		2½d. deep blue	3·00	12·00
201		2½d. bright blue	3·00	12·00

(b) P 15

202	18	½d. blue-green	8·50	7·00
203		½d. green	12·00	7·00
204		1d. rose-red	£500	75·00
		a. Imperf between (horiz pair)	£8000	
205		1d. brown-red	2·25	3·75
206		1½d. bistre-brown (1919)	17·00	7·00
206a		1½d. brown-ochre (1917)	28·00	8·00
207		2½d. deep blue	17·00	24·00
208		2½d. bright blue	15·00	23·00

(c) P 14 × 15

208a	18	½d. green	£2250	£150

(d) P 15 × 14

208b	18	½d. green	£2250	£190

(e) P 13½

208d	18	1d. red (shades)	—	£500

Die I   Die II   Die III

The remaining values were printed from double, i.e. head and duty, plates. There are at least four different head plates made from three different dies, which may be distinguished as follows:—

Die I. The King's left ear is neither shaded nor outlined; no outline to top of cap. Shank of anchor in cap badge is complete.

Die II. The ear is shaded all over, but has no outline. The top of the cap has a faint outline. Anchor as Die I.

Die III. The ear is shaded and outlined; a heavy continuous outline round the cap. Shank of anchor is broken just below the lowest line which crosses it.

(ii) Printed from double plates. Head Die I. (a) P 14.

209	18	2d. black and grey	5·50	3·75
210		3d. black and yellow	55·00	4·00
211		4d. black and orange-red	4·25	17·00
212		5d. black and green	3·50	5·00
213		6d. black and mauve	£130	23·00
213a		8d. violet and green	£4000	
214		2s. black and brown	60·00	55·00

(b) P 15

215	18	3d. black and yellow	4·00	9·50
216		4d. black and orange-red	90·00	11·00
217		6d. black and mauve	3·25	3·25
217a		8d. violet and green	£13000	
218		2s. black and brown	10·00	23·00

(iii) Head Die II. (a) P 14

219	18	2d. black and grey	8·00	1·25
220		2d. black and brownish grey	20·00	2·75
221		3d. black and deep yellow	18·00	2·75
222		3d. black and yellow	35·00	2·50
223		3d. black and buff	5·00	2·50
224		4d. black and orange-red	10·00	3·25
225		4d. black and deep orange-red	6·00	3·25
226		5d. black and grey-green	9·50	17·00
227		5d. black and bright green	7·50	17·00
228		6d. black and mauve	16·00	1·50
229		6d. black and purple	38·00	2·50
230		8d. violet and green	9·50	27·00
231		10d. blue and carmine-red	11·00	17·00
232		1s. black and greenish blue	17·00	18·00
233		1s. black and turquoise-blue	6·00	6·00
234		2s. black and brown	45·00	6·50
235		2s. black and yellow-brown	£150	17·00
236		2s. 6d. indigo and grey-brown	35·00	16·00
236a		2s. 6d. pale blue and brown	75·00	24·00
236b		2s. brown and blue	60·00	80·00
237		3s. chestnut and bright blue	60·00	85·00
238		5s. blue and yellow-green	90·00	48·00
239		5s. blue and blue-green	42·00	48·00
240		7s. 6d. blackish purple and slate-black	£170	£170
241		10s. crimson and yellow-green	£150	£180
242		£1 black and purple	£400	£450
243		£1 black and violet	£450	£550

(b) P 15

244	18	2d. black and grey	3·75	3·75
245		4d. black and deep orange-vermilion	£850	£225
246		8d. violet and green	£170	£130
247		10d. blue and red	4·25	17·00
248		1s. black and greenish blue	23·00	5·50
249		2s. 6d. indigo and grey-brown	30·00	65·00
250		3s. chocolate and blue	£700	£250
251		5s. blue and yellow-green	95·00	95·00
251a		5s. blue and blue-green	£1300	
252		7s. 6d. blackish purple and slate-black	75·00	£130
253		10s. red and green	£140	£250
254		£1 black and purple	£1000	£1000
254a		£1 black and deep purple	£2000	£2000
186/254a		Optd "Specimen" (various Dies and Perfs) ... Set of 19	£1900	

(iv) Head Die III. Toned paper, yellowish gum. (a) P 14

255	18	2d. black and brownish grey	7·50	3·00
256		2d. black and grey-black	4·00	1·40
		a. Imperf between (horiz pair)	£3750	
		b. Imperf between (horiz strip of 3)	£5500	
		c. Imperf vert (horiz pair)	£3250	£3250
257		2d. black and grey	4·50	1·90
258		2d. black and sepia	18·00	3·50
259		3d. black and yellow	4·00	1·40
260		3d. black and green	4·00	1·40
261		4d. black and orange-red	8·50	3·25
262		4d. black and dull red	7·50	3·75
263		5d. black and pale green	6·00	14·00
		a. Imperf between (horiz strip of 3)	£9000	

264	18	5d. black and green	6·00	14·00
265		6d. black and reddish mauve	3·50	2·25
		a. Imperf between (horiz pair)	£7500	
266		6d. black and dull mauve	3·50	2·25
267		8d. mauve and dull blue-green	15·00	35·00
268		8d. mauve and greenish blue	15·00	35·00
		a. Imperf vert (horiz pair)	£7000	
269		10d. indigo and carmine	9·50	27·00
270		10d. blue and red	8·50	27·00
271		1s. black and greenish blue	5·50	3·00
272		1s. black and pale blue-green	5·50	3·00
272a		1s. black and light blue	9·50	5·50
272b		1s. black and green	45·00	19·00
273		2s. black and brown	12·00	14·00
		aa. Imperf between (vert pair)	£15000	
273a		2s. black and yellow-brown	£1300	85·00
274		2s. 6d. dp ultramarine & grey-brn	25·00	29·00
274a		2s. 6d. pale blue and pale bistre-brown (shades)	65·00	38·00
274b		3s. chestnut and light blue	£160	75·00
275		5s. deep blue and blue-green (shades)	60·00	48·00
276		5s. blue & pale yell-grn (shades)	60·00	48·00
276a		7s. 6d. maroon and slate-black	£700	£850
277		10s. carmine-lake and yellow-green	£300	£160
278		£1 black and bright purple	£500	£500
279		£1 black and deep purple	£500	£500
279a		£1 black and violet-indigo	£500	£500
279b		£1 black and deep violet	£500	£500

(b) P 15

279c	18	2d. black and brownish grey	£5000	£550

Half   **Half-**

Penny   **Penny.**

(19)   (20)

1917 (15 Aug). *No. 190 surch at the Northern Rhodesian Administrative Press, Livingstone, with T* 19, *in violet or violet-black.*

280	18	½d. on 1d. rose-carmine (shades)	2·50	5·00
		a. Surch inverted	£1400	£1400
		b. Letters "n n" spaced wider	11·00	19·00
		c. Letters "n y" spaced wider	7·50	14·00

The setting was in two rows of 10 repeated three times in the sheet.
The two colours of the surcharge occur on the same sheet.

1917 (22 Sept). *No. 190 surch as T* 20 *(new setting with hyphen, and full stop after "Penny"), in deep violet.*

281	18	½d. on 1d. rose-carmine (shades)	1·40	3·75

1922–24. *New printings on white paper with clear white gum.*

(i) Single working plates. (a) P 14

282	18	½d. dull green (1922)	5·50	1·25
		a. Imperf between (vert pair)	£1400	£1000
283		½d. deep blue-green (1922)	4·75	1·75
284		1d. bright rose (1922)	4·75	2·75
285		1d. bright rose-scarlet (1923)	4·75	2·50
		a. Imperf between (horiz pair)	£1200	
286		1d. aniline red (8.24)	20·00	3·50
287		1½d. brown-ochre (1923)	6·50	2·00
		a. Imperf between (vert pair)	£1600	£1000

(b) P 15

288	18	½d. dull green (1923)	30·00	30·00
289		1d. bright rose-scarlet (1923)	40·00	40·00
290		1½d. brown-ochre (1923)	38·00	38·00

(ii) Double plates. Head Die III. (a) P 14

291	18	2d. black and grey-purple (1922)	2·25	1·25
292		2d. black and slate-purple (1923)	2·75	2·25
293		3d. black and yellow (1922)	10·00	12·00
294		4d. black & orange-vermilion (1922–3)	8·00	15·00
295		6d. jet-black and lilac (1922–3)	4·75	3·75
296		8d. mauve and pale blue-green (1922)	29·00	55·00
297		8d. violet and grey-green (1923)	29·00	55·00
298		10d. bright ultramarine and red (1922)	10·00	30·00
299		10d. brt ultramarine & carm-red (1923)	11·00	30·00
300		1s. black and dull blue (1922–3)	2·75	3·50
		a. Imperf between (horiz pair)	£6000	
		b. Imperf between (vert pair)	£8000	
301		2s. black and brown (1922–3)	19·00	23·00
302		2s. 6d. ultramarine and sepia (1922)	38·00	55·00
303		2s. 6d. violet-blue & grey-brown (1923)	38·00	55·00
304		3s. red-brown & turquoise-bl (1922)	50·00	80·00
305		3s. red-brown and grey-blue (1923)	80·00	£100
306		5s. brt ultramarine and emerald (1922)	75·00	90·00
307		5s. deep blue and bright green (1923)	75·00	90·00
308		7s. 6d. brown-purple and slate (1922)	£150	£200
309		10s. crimson and brt yellow-green (1922)	£140	£170
310		10s. carmine and yellow-green (1923)	£140	£190
311		£1 black and deep magenta (1922)	£475	£500
311a		£1 black and magenta (1923)	£475	£550

(b) P 15 (1923)

312	18	2d. black and slate-purple	35·00	
313		4d. black and orange-vermilion	38·00	
314		6d. jet-black and lilac	45·00	
315		8d. violet and grey-green	45·00	
316		10d. bright ultramarine & carmine-red	50·00	
317		1s. black and dull blue	50·00	
318		2s. black and brown	90·00	
319		2s. 6d. violet-blue and grey-brown	£100	
320		3s. red-brown and grey-blue	£130	
321		5s. deep blue and bright green	£150	
322		£1 black and magenta	£600	

The 1922 printing shows the mesh of the paper very clearly through the gum. In the 1923 printing the gum is very smooth and the mesh of the paper is not so clearly seen. Where date is given as "(1922–23)" two printings were made, which do not differ sufficiently in colour to be listed separately.

Nos. 312/22 were never sent out to Rhodesia but only issued in London. Any used copies could, therefore, only have been obtained by favour.

In 1924 Rhodesia was divided into NORTHERN and SOUTHERN RHODESIA (see ZAMBIA and ZIMBABWE), and between 1954 and 1964 these were merged in the Central African Federation (see RHODESIA AND NYASALAND). In 1964 there were again separate issues for Northern and Southern Rhodesia, but after the former became independent as Zambia, Southern Rhodesia was renamed Rhodesia in October 1964.

For issues inscribed "RHODESIA" between 1965 and 1978 see ZIMBABWE.

Rhodesia & Nyasaland

Stamps for the Central African Federation of Northern and Southern Rhodesia and Nyasaland Protectorate.

1   2

3 Queen Elizabeth II

(Recess Waterlow)

1954 (1 July)–**56**. P 13½×14 (*T* 1), 13½×13 (*T* 2) or 14½×13½ (*T* 3).

1	1	½d. red-orange	..	15	10
		a. Coil stamp. Perf 12½×14 (6.2.56)		25	1·50
2		1d. ultramarine	..	15	10
		a. Coil stamp. Perf 12½×14. *Deep blue* (9.55)		75	5·50
		ab. *Ultramarine* (1.10.55)	..	75	5·50
3		2d. bright green	..	15	10
3a		2½d. ochre (15.2.56)	..	2·00	10
4		3d. carmine-red	..	20	10
5		4d. red-brown	..	60	15
6		4½d. blue-green	..	15	10
7		6d. bright reddish purple	..	75	10
		a. *Bright purple* (5.5.56)	..	1·00	10
8		9d. violet	..	65	70
9		1s. grey-black	..	1·00	10
10	2	1s. 3d. red-orange and ultramarine	..	2·25	10
11		2s. deep blue and yellow-brown	..	5·00	65
12		2s. 6d. black and rose-red	..	5·50	65
13		5s. violet and olive-green	..	11·00	2·00
14	3	10s. dull blue-green and orange	..	13·00	7·00
15		£1 olive-green and lake	..	22·00	22·00
1/15			*Set of 16*	55·00	30·00

Nos. 1a and 2a printed on rotary machines by subsidiary company, Imprimerie Belge de Sécurité, in Belgium.

4 Aeroplane over Victoria Falls   5 Livingstone and Victoria Falls

(Des J. E. Hughes (3d.), V. E. Horne (1s.). Recess Waterlow)

1955 (15 June). *Centenary of Discovery of Victoria Falls.* P 13½ (3d.) or 13 (1s.).

16	4	3d. ultramarine & dp turquoise-grn	35	20
17	5	1s. purple and deep blue	45	30

6 Tea Picking   10 Rhodes's Grave   11 Lake Bangweulu

12a Rhodesian Railway Trains   19 Federal Coat of Arms

(Des M. Kinsella (9d.). Recess Waterlow (½d., 1d., 2d., 1s.) until 1962, then D.L.R., D.L.R. (2½d., 4d., 6d., 9d., 2s., 2s. 6d.) and B.W. (others))

1959 (12 Aug)–**62**. *T* 6, 10/11, 12a, 19 *and similar designs.* P 13½ × 14 (½d., 1d., 2d.), 14½ (2½d., 4d., 6d., 9d., 2s., 2s. 6d.), 14 × 13½ (3d.), 13½ × 13 (1s.), 14 (1s. 3d.) or 11 (*others*).

18		½d. black and light emerald	..	50	30
		a. Coil stamp. Perf 12½×14		1·75	3·50
19		1d. carmine-red and black	..	15	10
		a. Coil stamp. Perf 12½×14		1·75	3·50
		ab. *Carmine-red and grey-black*		1·75	3·50
		ac. Carmine-red (centre) omitted		£250	
20		2d. violet and yellow-brown	..	60	30
21		2½d. purple and grey-blue	..	40	40
22		3d. black and blue	..	15	10
		a. Centre omitted	..	£5000	
23		4d. maroon and olive	..	90	10
24		6d. ultramarine and deep myrtle-green	..	35	10
24a		9d. orge-brown & reddish violet (15.5.62)		5·00	2·00
25		1s. light green and ultramarine	..	60	10
26		1s. 3d. emerald and deep chocolate	..	1·75	10
27		2s. grey-green and carmine	..	3·25	45
28		2s. 6d. light blue and yellow-brown	..	3·75	30
29		5s. deep chocolate and yellow-green	..	5·50	2·25
30		10s. olive-brown and rose-red	..	23·00	12·00
31		£1 black and deep violet	..	35·00	25·00
18/31			*Set of 15*	70·00	38·00

Designs: *Vert* (as *T* 6)—1d. V.H.F. mast; 2d. Copper mining; 2½d. Fairbridge Memorial. (As *T* 11)—6d. Eastern Cataract, Victoria Falls. *Horiz* (as *T* 12a)—1s. Tobacco; 1s. 3d. Lake Nyasa; 2s. Chirundu Bridge; 2s. 6d. Salisbury Airport. (As *T* 19)—5s. Rhodes Statue; 10s. Mlanje.

Only three examples, all unused, are believed to exist of No. 22a, although further stamps from the same sheet can be found with the centre partially omitted.

20 Kariba Gorge, 1955

(Photo Harrison (3d., 6d.), D.L.R. (others))

1960 (17 May). *Opening of Kariba Hydro-Electric Scheme. T* 20 *and similar horiz designs.* P 14½ × 14 (3d., 6d.) or 14 (*others*).

32		3d. blackish green and red-orange		35	10
		a. Red-orange omitted	..	£1200	
33		6d. brown and yellow-brown	..	70	20
34		1s. slate-blue and green	..	1·75	1·50
35		1s. 3d. light blue and orange-brown		2·50	1·25
		a. *Blue and deep orange-brown*		5·00	5·00
36		2s. 6d. deep slate-purple and orange-red		3·25	7·00
37		5s. reddish violet and turquoise-blue		6·50	11·00
32/7			*Set of 6*	13·50	19·00

Designs:—3d. 330 kV power lines; 1s. Barrage wall; 1s. 3d. Barrage and lake; 2s. 6d. Interior of power station; 5s. Barrage wall and Queen Mother (top left).

26 Miner Drilling

(Des V. Whiteley. Photo Harrison)

1961 (8 May). *Seventh Commonwealth Mining and Metallurgical Congress. T* 26 *and similar horiz design.* P 15 × 14.

38		6d. olive-green and orange-brown	..	30	15
39		1s. 3d. black and light blue	..	40	60

Design:—1s. 3d. Surface installations, Nchanga Mine.

28 D.H. "Hercules" on Rhodesian Airstrip   31 Tobacco Plant

1962 (6 Feb). *30th Anniv of First London-Rhodesia Airmail Service. T* 28 *and similar horiz designs.* P 14½ × 14.

40		6d. bronze-green and vermilion	..	35	25
41		1s. 3d. light blue, black and yellow	..	1·00	50
42		2s. 6d. rose-red and deep violet	..	6·00	4·25
40/2			*Set of 3*	6·50	4·50

Designs:—1s. 3d. Empire "C" class flying-boat taking off from Zambesi; 2s. 6d. "Comet" at Salisbury airport.

(Des V. Whiteley. Photo Harrison)

1963 (18 Feb). *World Tobacco Congress, Salisbury. T* 31 *and similar vert designs.* P 14 × 14½.

43		3d. green and olive-brown	..	15	10
44		6d. green, brown and blue	..	20	35
45		1s. 3d. chestnut and indigo	..	30	45
46		2s. 6d. yellow and brown	..	75	2·50
43/6			*Set of 3*	1·25	3·00

Designs:—6d. Tobacco field; 1s. 3d. Auction floor; 2s. 6d. Cured tobacco.

35 Red Cross Emblem

(Photo Harrison)

1963 (6 Aug). *Red Cross Centenary.* P 14½ × 14.

47	35	3d. red	.. .. ..	45	10

36 African "Round Table" Emblem

(Des V. Whiteley. Photo Harrison)

1963 (11 Sept). *World Council of Young Men's Service Clubs, Salisbury.* P 14½ × 14.

48	36	6d. black, gold and yellow-green	..	30	75
49		1s. 3d. black, gold, yell-grn & lilac	..	30	50

POSTAGE DUE STAMPS

The 1d. and 2d. (Nos. 2/3) exist with a rubber-stamped "POSTAGE DUE" cancellation. In the absence of proper labels these values were used as postage dues at the Salisbury G.P.O. but according to the G.P.O. the handstamp was intended as a cancellation and not as an overprint (although "unused" examples of the 1d. are known). Its use was discontinued at the end of August 1959.

D 1

(Typo Federal Printing and Stationery Dept, Salisbury)

1961 (19 Apr). P 12½.

D1	D 1	1d. vermilion	..	1·25	3·00
		a. Imperf between (horiz pair)		£300	£350
D2		2d. deep violet-blue	..	1·75	3·00
D3		4d. green	..	1·75	8·00
D4		6d. purple	..	3·00	7·00
		a. Imperf between (horiz pair)		£550	
D1/4			*Set of 4*	7·00	19·00

The 2d. has a stop below the "D".

The stamps of the Federation were withdrawn on 19 February 1964 when all three constituent territories had resumed issuing their own stamps.

Sabah
see Malaysia

St. Helena

CROWN COLONY

PRICES FOR STAMPS ON COVER TO 1945

Nos. 1/5	*from* × 12
Nos. 6/45	*from* × 10
Nos. 46/52	*from* × 4
Nos. 53/67	*from* × 3
No. 71	—
Nos. 72/86	*from* × 3
Nos. 87/8	*from* × 10
Nos. 89/95	*from* × 3
No. 96	—
Nos. 97/110	*from* × 3
Nos. 111/13	—
Nos. 114/40	*from* × 2

ONE PENNY   FOUR PENCE

SIX PENCE

1   (2)   (3)

(Recess P.B.)

Wmk Large Star, W w 1

1856 (1 Jan). *Imperf.*
1	1	6d. blue	£500	£180

1861 (April (?)). (a) *Clean-cut perf 14 to 16.*
2	1	6d. blue	£1300	£250

(b) *Rough perf 14 to 16.*
2a	1	6d. blue	£400	£130

NOTE: The issues which follow consist of 6d. stamps, T 1, printed in various colours and (except in the case of the 6d. values) surcharged with a new value, as T 2 to 10, e.g. stamps described as "1d." are, in fact, 1d. on 6d stamps, and so on.
The numbers in the Type column below refer to the *types of the lettering of the surcharged value.*

(Printed by D.L.R. from P.B. plate)

Two Types of Bar on 1d. value:
A. Bar 16–17 mm long.
B. Bar 18½–19 mm long.

1863 (July). *Wmk Crown CC. Surch as T 2/3 with thin bar approximately the same length as the words. Imperf.*
3	2	1d. lake (Type A)	£110	£150
		a. Surch double	£4000	£2500
		b. Surch omitted	£11000	
4		1d. lake (Type B)	£110	£150
		a. Vert pair. Nos. 3/4	£4500	
5	3	4d. carmine (bar 15½–16½ mm)	£500	£250
		a. Surch double	£8000	£7500

ONE PENNY **ONE PENNY** **ONE PENNY**
(4 (A)) (4 (B)) (4 (C))

TWO PENCE **THREE PENCE** **FOUR PENCE**
(5) (6) (7)

ONE SHILLING **FIVE SHILLINGS**
(8) (9)

Three Types of Bar:
A. Thin bar (16½ to 17 mm) nearly the same length as the words.
B. Thick bar (14 to 14½ mm) much shorter than the words, except on the 2d. (Nos. 9, 22, 28) where it is nearly the same length.
C. Long bar (17 to 18 mm) same length as the words.

1864–80. *Wmk Crown CC. 6d. as T 1, without surcharge.*

(a) *P 12½ (1864–73)*
6	4	1d. lake (Type A) (1864)	28·00	24·00
		a. Surch double	£4750	
7		1d. lake (Type B) (1868)	85·00	50·00
		a. Surch double	£2000	
		b. Imperf	£2000	
8		1d. lake (Type C) (1871)	45·00	16·00
		a. Surch in blue-black	£850	£550
9	5	2d. yellow (Type B) (1868)	£100	60·00
		a. Imperf	£8500	
10		2d. yellow (Type C) (1873)	70·00	38·00
		a. Surch in blue-black	£4500	£2750
		b. Surch double, one albino		
11	6	3d. deep dull purple (Type B) (1868)	60·00	48·00
		a. Surch double	—	£6000
		b. Imperf	£750	
		c. Light purple	£2750	£750
12		3d. deep dull purple (Type A) (1873)	75·00	48·00
13	7	4d. carmine (Type A) (1864)	90·00	40·00
		a. Surch double	†	£5500
14		4d. carmine (Type B) (words 18 mm long) (1868)	75·00	48·00
		a. Surch double	†	£4500
		b. Surch double (18 + 19 mm widths)	£12000	£9000
		c. Imperf	£8000	
15		4d. carmine-rose (Type B) (words 19 mm long) (1868)	£190	£120
		a. Surch omitted	†	—
16	—	6d. dull blue (1871)	£550	£100
		a. Ultramarine (1873)	£275	80·00
17	8	1s. deep yellow-green (Type A) (1864)	£120	£120
		a. Surch double		†£18000
18		1s. deep yellow-green (Type B) (1868)	£325	£120
		a. Surch double	£10000	
		b. Imperf	£12000	
		c. Surch omitted*	£10000	
19		1s. deep green (Type C) (1871)	£200	16·00
		a. Surch in blue-black		
20	9	5s. orange (Type B) (1868)	35·00	48·00
		a. Yellow	£325	£275

(b) *P 14 × 12½ (1876)*
21	4	1d. lake (Type B)	48·00	15·00
22	5	2d. yellow (Type B)	60·00	60·00
23	6	3d. purple (Type B)	£170	70·00
24		4d. carmine (Type B) (words 16½ mm long)	80·00	60·00
25	—	6d. milky blue	£250	32·00
26	8	1s. deep green (Type C)	£275	20·00

(c) *P 14 (1880)*
27	4	1d. lake (Type B)	55·00	16·00
28	5	2d. yellow (Type B)	75·00	18·00
29	—	6d. milky blue	£275	42·00
30	8	1s. yellow-green (Type B)	20·00	12·00

The only known copy of No. 15a is in the Royal Collection, although a second badly damaged example may exist.
*No. 18c is from a sheet of the 1s. with surcharge misplaced, the fifth row of 12 stamps being thus doubly surcharged and the tenth row without surcharge.

2½d

(10) 11 12

1884–94. *Wmk Crown CA. T 1 surch. Bars similar to Type B above (except 2½d., T 10, and the 1s., in which the bar is nearly the same length as the words). The 6d. as before without surcharge. P 14.*
34	—	½d. green (words 17 mm) (1884)	3·25	6·00
		a. "N" and "Y" spaced	£350	
35	—	½d. emerald (words 17 mm) (1885)	6·50	7·50
		a. "N" and "Y" spaced	£700	
		b. Surch double	£1000	
		ba. Ditto. "N" and "Y" spaced*	£10000	
36	—	½d. deep green (words 14½ mm) (1893)	90	1·10
37	4	1d. red (1887)	2·75	2·00
38		1d. pale red (1890)	3·00	2·00
39	5	2d. yellow (1894)	1·25	3·50
40	10	2½d. ultramarine (1893)	2·00	5·00
		a. Surch double	£11000	
		b. Stamp doubly printed	£5500	
41	6	3d. deep mauve (1887)	2·00	2·75
		a. Surch double	—	£9000
42		3d. deep reddish lilac (1887)	4·50	7·00
		a. Surch double	£7000	£6000
43	7	4d. pale brown (words 16½ mm) (1890)	9·50	16·00
		a. Additional thin bar in surch (R. 7/4)	£450	
43b		4d. sepia (words 17 mm) (1894)	14·00	8·00
44	—	6d. grey (1887)	10·00	3·50
45	8	1s. yellow-green (1894)	24·00	15·00
		a. Surch double	£4250	
40/1, 43, 44 Optd "Specimen"			Set of 4	£180

Examples of the above are sometimes found showing no watermark; these are from the bottom row of the sheet, which had escaped the watermark, the paper being intended for stamps of a different size to Type 1.
Some are found without bar and others with bar at top of stamp, due to careless overprinting.
Of the 2½d. with double surcharge only six copies exist, and of the 2½d. double printed, one row of 12 stamps existed on one sheet only.
*No. 35ba. No. 35a occurs on stamp No. 216 in the sheet. In No. 35ba only one of the two surcharges shows the variety.

CANCELLATIONS. Nos. 36/45 and No. 20, have been sold cancelled with a violet diamond-shaped grill with four interior bars extending over two stamps. These cannot be considered as *used* stamps, and they are consequently not priced in the list.
This violet obliteration is easily removed and many of these remainders have been cleaned and offered as unused; some are repostmarked with a date and name in thin type rather larger than the original, a usual date being "Ap. 4.01."

(Typo D.L.R.)

1890–97. *Wmk Crown CA. Plate I for the 1½d. Plate II for the other values (for differences see Seychelles). P 14.*
46	11	½d. green (1897)	2·75	4·50
47		1d. carmine (1896)	7·50	1·00
48		1½d. red-brown and green (1890)	4·50	6·50
49		2d. orange-yellow (1896)	4·25	8·50
50		2½d. ultramarine (1896)	5·50	9·50
51		5d. mauve (1896)	11·00	23·00
52		10d. brown (1896)	16·00	45·00
46/52			Set of 7	45·00	90·00
46/52 Optd "Specimen"			Set of 7	£275

The note below No. 45a re violet diamond-shaped grill cancellation also applies to Nos. 46/52.

1902. *Wmk Crown CA. P 14.*
53	12	½d. green (Mar)	1·50	90
54		1d. carmine (24 Feb)	3·75	70
53/4 Optd "Specimen"			Set of 2	70·00

13 Government House 14 The Wharf

(Typo D.L.R.)

1903 (May). *Wmk Crown CC. P 14.*
55	13	½d. brown and grey-green	2·00	2·25
56	14	1d. black and carmine	1·50	35
57	13	2d. black and sage-green	6·00	1·25
58	14	8d. black and brown	14·00	32·00
59	13	1s. brown and brown-orange	14·00	28·00
60	14	2s. black and violet	45·00	75·00
55/60			Set of 6	75·00	£120
55/60 Optd "Specimen"			Set of 6	£200

A printing of the 1d. value in Type 14 in red only on Mult Crown CA paper was made in 1911, but not sold to the public. Examples are known overprinted "SPECIMEN" (Price £300).

MINIMUM PRICE

The minimum price quote is 10p which represents a handling charge rather than a basis for valuing common stamps. For further notes about prices see introductory pages.

15

(Typo D.L.R.)

1908 (May)–11. *P 14. (a) Wmk Mult Crown CA. Ordinary paper (2½d.) or chalk-surfaced paper (4d., 6d.).*
64	15	2½d. blue	1·00	1·40
66		4d. black and red/yellow	3·00	7·50
		a. Ordinary paper (1911)	1·25	4·75
67		6d. dull and deep purple	5·50	15·00
		a. Ordinary paper (1911)	2·75	9·50

(b) *Wmk Crown CA. Chalk-surfaced paper.*
71	15	10s. green and red/green	£180	£225
64/71			Set of 4	£180	£225
64/71 Optd "Specimen"			Set of 4	£225

16 17

(Typo D.L.R.)

1912–16. *Wmk Mult Crown CA. P 14.*
72	16	½d. black and green	1·25	6·00
73	17	1d. black and carmine-red	1·25	1·25
		a. Black and scarlet (1916)	24·00	27·00
74		1½d. black and dull orange (1913)	2·00	4·25
75	16	2d. black and greyish slate	2·00	1·75
76	17	2½d. black and bright blue	1·75	5·00
77	16	3d. black and purple/yellow (1913)	2·00	5·00
78	17	8d. black and dull purple	5·50	40·00
79	16	1s. black and black/green	8·00	20·00
80	17	2s. black and blue/blue.	27·00	60·00
81		3s. black and violet (1913)	48·00	90·00
72/81			Set of 10	90·00	£200
72/81 Optd "Specimen"			Set of 10	£250

No. 73a is on thicker paper than 73.

18 19

Split "A"

(Typo D.L.R.)

1912. *Wmk Mult Crown CA. Chalk-surfaced paper. P 14.*
83	18	4d. black and red/yellow	4·50	14·00
84		6d. dull and deep purple	2·50	5·00
83/4 Optd "Specimen"			Set of 2	60·00

1913. *Wmk Mult Crown CA. P 14.*
85	19	4d. black and red/yellow	5·50	3·50
		a. Split "A"	95·00	
86		6d. dull and deep purple	10·00	20·00
		a. Split "A"	£160	
85/6 Optd "Specimen"			Set of 2	70·00

WAR **TAX**
WAR **TAX**

ONE PENNY **1d.**
(20) (21)

1916 (Sept). *As No. 73a, on thin paper, surch with T 20.*
87	17	1d. + 1d. black and scarlet (Optd S. £50)	85	2·75
		a. Surch double	—	£6000

1919. *No. 73 on thicker paper, surch with T 21.*
88	17	1d. + 1d. black and carmine-red (shades)		
		(Optd S. £50)	40	3·00

1922 (Jan). *Printed in one colour. Wmk Mult Script CA. P 14.*
89	17	1d. green	50	17·00
90		1½d. rose-scarlet	6·00	25·00
91	16	3d. bright blue	12·00	18·00
89/91			Set of 3	17·00	70·00
89/91 Optd "Specimen"			Set of 3	75·00

22 Badge of St. Helena

PLATE FLAWS ON THE 1922–37 ISSUE. Many constant plate varieties exist on both the vignette and duty plates of this issue.

The three major varieties are illustrated and listed below with prices for mint examples. Fine used stamps showing these flaws are worth a considerable premium over the mint prices quoted.

a. Broken mainmast. Occurs on R.2/1 of all sheets from the second printing onwards. It does not appear on Nos. 93/6 and 112/13 as these stamps only exist from the initial printing invoiced in May 1922.

b. Torn flag. Occurs on R.4/6 of all sheets from printings up to and including that invoiced in December 1922. The flaw was retouched for the printing invoiced in December 1926 and so does not occur on Nos. 99e, 103 and 107/10.

c. Cleft rock. Occurs on R.5/1 of all sheets from the second printing onwards. It does not appear on Nos. 93/6 and 112/13 as these stamps only exist from the initial printing invoiced in May 1922.

(Des T. Bruce. Typo D.L.R.)

1922 (June)**–37.** P 14 (a) Wmk Mult Crown CA. Chalk-surfaced paper.

92	22	4d. grey and black/*yellow* (2.23)	..	6·00	7·50
		a. Broken mainmast ..	..	95·00	
		b. Torn flag	..	95·00	
		c. Cleft rock	..	85·00	
93		1s. 6d. grey and green/*blue-green*	..	22·00	48·00
		b. Torn flag	..	£350	
94		2s. 6d. grey and red/*yellow*	..	24·00	48·00
		b. Torn flag	..	£400	
95		5s. grey and green/*yellow*	..	38·00	75·00
		b. Torn flag	..	£475	
96		£1 grey and purple/*red*	..	£400	£450
		b. Torn flag	..	£1500	
92/6		Optd "Specimen"	*Set of 5*	£500	

The paper of No. 93 is bluish on the surface with a full green back.

(b) Wmk Mult Script CA. Ordinary paper (1s. 6d., 2s. 6d., 5s.) or chalk-surfaced paper (others).

97	22	½d. grey and black (2.23)	..	1·00	1·50
		a. Broken mainmast ..	..	35·00	
		b. Torn flag	..	60·00	
		c. Cleft rock	..	30·00	
98		1d. grey and green	..	1·75	1·00
		a. Broken mainmast ..	..	40·00	
		b. Torn flag	..	50·00	
		c. Cleft rock	..	35·00	
99		1½d. rose-red (2.23)	..	2·75	7·50
		a. Broken mainmast	..	85·00	
		b. Torn flag	..	85·00	
		c. Cleft rock ..	..	80·00	
		d. Carmine-rose	..	21·00	22·00
		da. Broken mainmast	..	£200	
		db. Torn flag	..	£200	
		dc. Cleft rock ..	..	£200	
		e. Deep carmine-red (1937)	..	80·00	£100
		ea. Broken mainmast	..	£500	
		ec. Cleft rock	..	£500	
100		2d. grey and slate (2.23)	..	1·75	2·00
		a. Broken mainmast ..	..	65·00	
		b. Torn flag ..	..	70·00	
		c. Cleft rock	..	55·00	
101		3d. bright blue (2.23)	..	2·00	4·00
		a. Broken mainmast	..	65·00	
		b. Torn flag ..	..	65·00	
		c. Cleft rock	..	55·00	

103	22	5d. green and carmine/*green* (1927)	..	2·75	5·50
		a. Broken mainmast	..	£120	
		c. Cleft rock	..	£110	
104		6d. grey and bright purple	..	3·50	8·00
		a. Broken mainmast	..	£130	
		b. Torn flag	..	£120	
		c. Cleft rock	..	£110	
105		8d. grey and bright violet (2.23)	..	3·25	6·50
		a. Broken mainmast ..	..	£150	
		b. Torn flag	..	£150	
		c. Cleft rock	..	£130	
106		1s. grey and brown	..	6·00	8·50
		a. Broken mainmast ..	..	£170	
		b. Torn flag ..	..	£140	
		c. Cleft rock	..	£120	
107		1s. 6d. grey and green/*green* (1927)	..	12·00	38·00
		a. Broken mainmast ..	..	£200	
		c. Cleft rock	..	£200	
108		2s. purple and blue/*blue* (1927)	..	12·00	32·00
		a. Broken mainmast ..	..	£200	
		c. Cleft rock	..	£200	
109		2s. 6d. grey and red/*yellow* (1927)	..	12·00	45·00
		a. Broken mainmast ..	..	£200	
		c. Cleft rock	..	£200	
110		5s. grey and green/*yellow* (1927)	..	32·00	65·00
		a. Broken mainmast ..	..	£350	
		c. Cleft rock	..	£350	
111		7s. 6d. grey and yellow-orange	..	75·00	£120
		a. Broken mainmast ..	..	£700	
		b. Torn flag	..	£550	
		c. Cleft rock	..	£700	
112		10s. grey and olive-green	..	£110	£160
		b. Torn flag	..	£750	
113		15s. grey and purple/*blue*	..	£850	£1400
		b. Torn flag	..	£2750	
97/112			*Set of 15*	£250	£350
97/113		Optd "Specimen"	*Set of 16*	£1000	

23 Lot and Lot's Wife   **24** The "Plantation"

30 St. Helena   **32** Badge of St. Helena

(Recess B.W.)

1934 (23 April). *Centenary of British Colonisation. T 23/4, 30, 32 and similar horiz designs. Wmk Mult Script CA. P 12.*

114		½d. black and purple	..	55	80
115		1d. black and green	..	55	85
116		1½d. black and scarlet	..	2·00	2·75
117		2d. black and orange	..	1·75	1·25
118		3d. black and blue	..	1·40	4·50
119		6d. black and light blue	..	3·25	3·00
120		1s. black and chocolate	..	6·00	18·00
121		2s. 6d. black and lake	..	35·00	48·00
122		5s. black and chocolate	..	75·00	85·00
123		10s. black and purple	..	£200	£250
114/123			*Set of 10*	£275	£350
114/23		Perf "Specimen"	*Set of 10*	£350	

Design:—1½d. Map of St. Helena; 2d. Quay at Jamestown; 3d. James Valley; 6d. Jamestown; 1s. Munden's Promontory; 5s. High Knoll.

1935 (6 May). *Silver Jubilee. As Nos. 114/17 of Jamaica, but ptd by D.L.R. P 13½×14.*

124		1½d. deep blue and carmine	..	75	2·50
		f. Diagonal line by turret	..	48·00	
125		2d. ultramarine and grey	..	1·25	90
		f. Diagonal line by turret	..	60·00	
126		6d. green and indigo	..	6·50	2·00
		f. Diagonal line by turret	..	£110	
		h. Dot by flagstaff	..	£120	
127		1s. slate and purple	..	7·50	11·00
		h. Dot flagstaff	..	£130	
124/7			*Set of 4*	14·50	15·00
124/7		Perf "Specimen"	*Set of 4*	95·00	

For illustrations of plate varieties see Omnibus section following Zimbabwe.

1937 (19 May). *Coronation. As Nos. 118/20 of Jamaica.*

128		1d. green	..	40	30
129		2d. orange	..	75	30
130		3d. bright blue	..	1·25	30
128/30			*Set of 3*	2·25	80
128/30		Perf "Specimen"	*Set of 3*	55·00	

The new-issue supplement to this Catalogue appears each month in

GIBBONS
STAMP MONTHLY

—from your newsagent or by postal subscription—
sample copy and details on request.

33 Badge of St. Helena

(Recess Waterlow)

1938 (12 May)**–44.** *Wmk Mult Script CA. P 12½.*

131	33	½d. violet	..	10	40
132		1d. green	..	20·00	4·00
132a		1d. yellow-orange (8.7.40)	..	20	30
133		1½d. scarlet	..	20	40
134		2d. red-orange	..	20	15
135		3d. ultramarine	..	90·00	30·00
135a		3d. grey (8.7.40)	..	30	30
135b		4d. ultramarine (8.7.40)	..	1·25	30
136		6d. light blue	..	1·25	30
136a		8d. sage-green (8.7.40)	..	2·50	90
		b. Olive-green (24.5.44)	..	4·50	3·00
137		1s. sepia	..	50	30
138		2s. 6d. maroon	..	9·00	3·50
139		5s. chocolate	..	12·00	7·50
140		10s. purple	..	12·00	15·00
131/140			*Set of 14*	£130	55·00
131/40		Perf "Specimen"	*Set of 14*	£300	
		See also Nos. 149/51.			

1946 (21 Oct). *Victory. As Nos. 141/2 of Jamaica.*

141		2d. red-orange	..	10	10
142		4d. blue	..	10	10
141/2		Perf "Specimen"	*Set of 2*	60·00	

1948 (20 Oct). *Royal Silver Wedding. As Nos. 143/4 of Jamaica.*

143		3d. black	..	30	20
144		10s. violet-blue	..	18·00	25·00

1949 (10 Oct). *75th Anniv of U.P.U. As Nos. 145/8 of Jamaica.*

145		3d. carmine	..	75	30
146		4d. deep blue	..	1·50	90
147		6d. olive	..	1·75	90
148		1s. blue-black	..	1·75	1·10
145/8			*Set of 4*	5·25	3·00

1949 (1 Nov). *Wmk Mult Script CA. P 12½.*

149	33	1d. black and green	..	50	80
150		1½d. black and carmine	..	50	80
151		2d. black and scarlet	..	50	80
149/51			*Set of 3*	1·40	2·25

1953 (2 June). *Coronation. As No. 153 of Jamaica.*

152		3d. black and deep reddish violet	..	80	65

34 Badge of St. Helena   **35** Heart-shaped Waterfall

(Recess D.L.R.)

1953 (4 Aug)**–59.** *Horiz designs as T 34, and T 35. Wmk Mult Script CA. P 14.*

153		½d. black and bright green	..	30	30
154		1d. black and deep green	..	15	20
155		1½d. black and reddish purple	..	1·50	70
		a. Black & deep reddish purple (14.1.59)	3·50	2·25
156		2d. black and claret	..	50	30
157		2½d. black and red	..	40	30
158		3d. black and brown	..	3·25	30
159		4d. black and deep blue	..	40	40
160		6d. black and deep lilac	..	40	30
161		7d. black and grey-black	..	65	1·25
162		1s. black and carmine	..	40	40
163		2s. 6d. black and violet	..	10·00	6·50
164		5s. black and deep brown	..	15·00	9·00
165		10s. black and yellow-orange	..	40·00	20·00
153/65			*Set of 13*	65·00	35·00

Designs:—1d. Flax plantation; 2d. Lace-making; 2½d. Drying flax; 3d. St. Helena Sand Plover; 4d. Flagstaff and The Barn; 6d. Donkeys carrying flax; 7d. Island map; 1s. The Castle; 2s. 6d. Cutting flax; 5s. Jamestown; 10s. Longwood House.

45 Stamp of 1856

(Recess D.L.R.)

1956 (3 Jan). *St. Helena Stamp Centenary. Wmk Mult Script CA. P 11½.*

166	45	3d. Prussian blue and carmine	..	10	10
167		4d. Prussian blue and reddish brown	..	10	10
168		6d. Prussian blue & dp reddish purple	..	15	15
166/8			*Set of 3*	30	30

46 Arms of East India Company

(Recess Waterlow)

1959 (5 May). *Tercentenary of Settlement. T 46 and similar horiz designs. W w 12. P 12½ × 13.*

169	3d. black and scarlet		10	10
170	6d. light emerald and slate-blue		30	35
171	1s. black and orange		30	35
169/71		*Set of 3*	65	70

Designs:—6d. East Indiaman *London* off James Bay; 1s. Commemoration Stone.

ST. HELENA
Tristan Relief
9d +
(49)

1961 (12 Oct). *Tristan Relief Fund. Nos. 46 and 49/51 of Tristan da Cunha surch as T 49 by Govt Printer, Jamestown.*

172	2½ c. + 3d. black and brown-red		—	£400
173	5 c. + 6d. black and blue		—	£400
174	7½ c. + 9d. black and rose-carmine		—	£475
175	10 c. + 1s. black and light brown		—	£550
172/5		*Set of 4*	£4000	£1600

The above stamps were withdrawn from sale on 19 October, 434 complete sets having been sold.

50 Cunning Fish   51 Yellow Canary

53 Queen Elizabeth II   63 Queen Elizabeth II with Prince Andrew (after Cecil Beaton)

(Des V. Whiteley. Photo Harrison)

1961 (12 Dec)–**65**. *T 50/1, 53, 63 and similar designs. W w 12. P 11½ × 12 (horiz), 12 × 11½ (vert) or 14½ × 14 (£1).*

176	1d. brt blue, dull violet, yellow & carmine		10	10
	a. Chalk-surfaced paper (4.5.65)		1·75	30
177	1½d. yellow, green, black and light drab		30	10
178	2d. scarlet and grey		15	10
179	3d. light blue, black, pink and deep blue		50	20
	a. Chalk-surfaced paper (30.11.65)		1·25	30
180	4½d. yellow-green, green, brown and grey		60	10
181	6d. red, sepia and light yellow-olive		3·25	35
	a. Chalk-surfaced paper (30.11.65)		4·25	35
182	7d. red-brown, black and violet		35	50
183	10d. brown-purple and light blue		35	40
184	1s. greenish yellow, bluish green & brown		35	40
185	1s. grey, black and slate-blue		8·50	3·00
186	2s. 6d. red, pale yellow and turquoise (chalk-surfaced paper)		2·50	1·50
187	5s. yellow, brown and green		10·00	2·75
188	10s. orange-red, black and blue		17·00	8·50
189	£1 chocolate and light blue		22·00	17·00
	a. Chalk-surfaced paper (30.11.65)		30·00	32·00
176/89 (*cheapest*)		*Set of 14*	60·00	32·00

Designs: *Horiz* (as T 50)—2d. Brittle Starfish; 7d. Trumpet Fish; 10d. Feather Starfish; 2s. 6d. Orange Starfish; 10s. Deep-water Bull's-eye. *Vert* (as T 51)—4½d. Red-wood Flower; 6d. Madagascar Red Fody; 1s. Gum-wood Flower; 1s. 6d. White Tern; 5s. Night-blooming Cereus.

1963 (4 June). *Freedom from Hunger. As No. 80 of Lesotho.*

190	1s. 6d. ultramarine		2·50	40

1963 (2 Sept). *Red Cross Centenary. As Nos. 203/4 of Jamaica.*

191	3d. red and black		75	25
192	1s. 6d. red and blue		3·00	75

COVER PRICES

Cover factors are quoted at the beginning of each country for most issues to 1945. An explanation of the system can be found on page x. The factors quoted do not, however, apply to philatelic covers.

**FIRST LOCAL POST
4th JANUARY 1965**
(64)

65 Badge of St. Helena

1965 (4 Jan). *First Local Post. Nos. 176, 179, 181 and 185 optd with T 64.*

193	1d. bright blue, dull violet, yellow & carmine	10	10
194	3d. light blue, black, pink and deep blue	10	10
195	6d. red, sepia and light yellow-olive	30	10
196	1s. 6d. grey, black and slate-blue	35	15
193/6		*Set of 4*	70	30

1965 (17 May). *I.T.U. Centenary. As Nos. 98/9 of Lesotho.*

197	3d. blue and grey-brown	35	15
198	6d. bright purple and bluish green	55	15

1965 (15 Oct). *International Co-operation Year. As Nos. 100/1 of Lesotho.*

199	1d. reddish purple and turquoise-green	20	15
200	6d. deep bluish green and lavender	55	15

1966 (24 Jan). *Churchill Commemoration. As Nos. 102/5 of Lesotho.*

201	1d. new blue	15	10
202	3d. deep green	35	10
203	6d. brown	50	10
204	1s. 6d. bluish violet	70	30
201/4		*Set of 4*	1·50	55

1966 (1 July). *World Cup Football Championships. As Nos. 57/8 of Pitcairn Islands.*

205	3d. violet, yellow-green, lake & yellow-brn	50	15
206	6d. chocolate, blue-green, lake & yellow-brn	75	15

1966 (20 Sept). *Inauguration of W.H.O. Headquarters, Geneva. As Nos. 185/6 of Montserrat.*

207	3d. black, yellow-green and light blue	50	15
208	1s. 6d. black, light purple and yellow-brown	2·75	15

1966 (1 Dec). *20th Anniversary of U.N.E.S.C.O. As Nos. 342/4 of Mauritius.*

209	3d. slate-violet, red, yellow and orange	1·50	20
210	6d. orange-yellow, violet and deep olive	2·50	30
211	1s. 6d. black, bright purple and orange	4·00	1·00
209/11		*Set of 3*	7·00	1·40

(Des W. H. Brown. Photo Harrison)

1967 (5 May). *New Constitution. W w 12 (sideways). P 14½ × 14.*

212	65	1s. multicoloured	10	10
213		2s. 6d. multicoloured	20	20
		a. Red (ribbon, etc.) omitted	£375	

66 Fire of London

(Des M. Goaman. Recess D.L.R.)

1967 (4 Sept). *300th Anniv of Arrival of Settlers after Great Fire of London. T 66 and similar horiz designs. W w 12. P 13.*

214	1d. carmine-red and black	10	10
	a. Carmine and black	40	40
215	3d. ultramarine and black	15	10
216	6d. slate-violet and black	15	10
217	1s 6d. olive-green and black	15	10
214/17		*Set of 4*	50	30

Designs:—3d. East Indiaman *Charles*; 6d. Settlers landing at Jamestown; 1s. 6d. Settlers clearing scrub.

70 Interlocking Maps of Tristan and St. Helena

(Des Jennifer Toombs. Photo Harrison)

1968 (4 June). *30th Anniv of Tristan da Cunha as a Dependency of St. Helena. T 70 and similar horiz design. W w 12. P 14 × 14½.*

218	70	4d. purple and chocolate	10	10
219	–	8d. olive and brown	10	10
220	70	1s. 9d. ultramarine and chocolate	10	20
221	–	2s. 3d. greenish blue and brown	15	20
218/21		*Set of 4*	35	45

Design:—8d., 2s. 3d. Interlocking maps of St. Helena and Tristan.

72 Queen Elizabeth and Sir Hudson Lowe

(Des M. Farrar Bell. Litho D.L.R.)

1968 (4 Sept). *150th Anniv of the Abolition of Slavery in St. Helena. T 72 and similar horiz design. Multicoloured. W w 12 (sideways). P 13 × 12½.*

222	3d. Type 72		10	10
223	9d. Type 72		10	10
224	1s. 6d. Queen Elizabeth and Sir George Bingham		15	15
225	2s. 6d. As 1s. 6d.		25	15
222/5		*Set of 4*	55	35

74 Blue Gum Eucalyptus and Road Construction

(Des Sylvia Goaman. Litho P.B.)

1968 (4 Nov). *Horiz designs as T 74. Multicoloured. W w 12 (sideways). P 13½.*

226	½d. Type 74		10	10
227	1d. Cabbage-tree and electricity development		10	10
228	1½d. St. Helena Redwood and dental unit		15	10
229	2d. Scrubweed and pest control		15	10
230	3d. Tree-fern and flats in Jamestown		30	10
231	4d. Blue gum Eucalyptus, pasture and livestock improvement		20	10
232	6d. Cabbage-tree and schools broadcasting		40	10
233	8d. St. Helena Redwood and country cottages		30	10
234	10d. Scrubweed and new school buildings		30	10
235	1s. Tree-fern and reafforestation		20	10
236	1s. 6d. Blue gum Eucalyptus and heavy lift crane		70	1·25
237	2s. 6d. Cabbage-tree and Lady Field Children's Home		80	1·40
238	5s. St. Helena Redwood and agricultural training		90	1·75
239	10s. Scrubweed and New General Hospital		2·25	3·00
240	£1 Tree-fern and lifeboat *John Dutton*		10·00	15·00
226/40		*Set of 15*	15·00	21·00

See also No. 274 for distinct shade of £1 value.

89 Brig *Perseverance*   93 W.O. and Drummer of the 53rd Foot, 1815

(Des J.W. Litho P.B.)

1969 (19 Apr). *Mail Communications. T 89 and similar horiz designs. Multicoloured. W w 12 (sideways). P 13½.*

241	4d. Type 89		20	20
242	8d. R.M.S. *Dane*		30	20
243	1s. 9d. S.S. *Llandovery Castle*		40	35
244	2s. 3d. R.M.S. *Good Hope Castle*		45	40
241/4		*Set of 4*	1·25	1·00

(Des R. North. Litho Format)

1969 (3 Sept). *Military Uniforms. T 93 and similar vert designs. Multicoloured. W w 12. P 14.*

245	8d. Type 93		30	15
246	8d. Officer and Surgeon, 20th Foot, 1816		40	15
247	1s. 6d. Drum Major, 66th Foot, 1816, and Royal Artillery Officer, 1820		50	15
248	2s. 6d. Private, 91st Foot, and 2nd Corporal, Royal Sappers and Miners, 1832		60	20
245/8		*Set of 4*	1·50	60

97 Dickens, Mr. Pickwick and Job Trotter (*Pickwick Papers*)

(Des Jennifer Toombs. Litho P.B.)

1970 (9 June). *Death Centenary of Charles Dickens. T 97 and similar horiz designs each incorporating a portrait of Dickens. Multicoloured. Chalk-surfaced paper. W w 12 (sideways). P 13½ × 13.*

249	4d. Type 97		25	10
	a. Shiny unsurfaced paper		25	80
	b. Yellow omitted		£225	
250	8d. Mr. Bumble and Oliver (*Oliver Twist*)		30	10
	a. Shiny unsurfaced paper		30	1·10
251	1s. 6d. Sairey Gamp and Mark Tapley (*Martin Chuzzlewit*)		45	15
	a. Shiny unsurfaced paper		45	1·50

252	2s. 6d. Jo and Mr. Turveydrop (*Bleak House*)	60	30
	a. Shiny unsurfaced paper ..	60	2·00
249/52	.. ..	*Set of 4*	1·40	60
249a/52a	.. .. ..	*Set of 4*	1·40	4·75

Supplies sent to St. Helena were on paper with a dull surface which reacts to the chalky test and with PVA gum. Crown Agents supplies were from a later printing on shiny paper which does not respond to the chalky test and with gum arabic.

98 "Kiss of Life"

99 Officer's Shako Plate (20th Foot)

(Des Jennifer Toombs. Litho J.W.)

1970 (15 Sept). *Centenary of British Red Cross. T* **98** *and similar horiz designs. W* w **12** (*sideways*). *P* 14.

253	6d. bistre, vermilion and black	10	10
254	9d. turquoise-green, vermilion and black	15	10
255	1s. 9d. pale grey, vermilion and black	20	10
256	2s. 3d. pale lavender, vermilion and black	25	20
253/6	.. ..	*Set of 4*	60	45

Designs:—9d. Nurse with girl in wheelchair; 1s. 9d. Nurse bandaging child's knee; 2s. 3d. Red Cross emblem.

(Des J.W. Litho Questa)

1970 (2 Nov). *Military Equipment* (1st *issue*). *T* **99** *and similar vert designs. Multicoloured. W* w **12**. *P* 12.

257	4d. Type **99** ..	80	20
258	9d. Officer's Breast-plate (66th Foot)	1·25	30
259	1s. 3d. Officer's Full Dress Shako (91st Foot)	1·50	40
260	2s. 11d. Ensign's Shako (53rd Foot)..	2·00	60
257/60	..	*Set of 4*	5·00	1·40

See also Nos. 281/4, 285/8 and 291/4.

100 Electricity Development

101 St. Helena holding the "True Cross"

(Litho P.B.)

1971 (15 Feb). *Decimal Currency. Designs as Nos.* 227/40, *but with values inscr in decimal currency as in T* **100**. *W* w **12** (*sideways*). *P* 13½.

261	½p. multicoloured ..	10	10
262	1p. multicoloured (as 1½d.)	10	10
263	1½p. multicoloured (as 2d.)	10	10
264	2p. multicoloured (as 3d.)	1·75	90
265	2½p. multicoloured (as 4d.)	10	10
266	3p. multicoloured (as 6d.)	15	10
267	4½p. multicoloured (as 8d.)	10	10
268	5p. multicoloured (as 10d.)..	10	10
269	7½p. multicoloured (as 1s.)..	30	35
270	10p. multicoloured (as 1s. 6d.)	30	35
271	12½p. multicoloured (as 2s. 6d.)	30	50
272	25p. multicoloured (as 5s.)..	60	1·25
273	50p. multicoloured (as 10s.)..	1·25	1·00
274	£1 multicoloured† ..	21·00	18·00
261/74	.. ..	*Set of 14*	23·00	22·00

†Although the design of No. 274 in no way differs from that of No. 240, it was reprinted specially for decimalisation, and differs considerably in shade from No. 240, as do others from their counterparts in the 1968 set.

The main differences in No. 274 are in the mountain which is blue rather than pinkish blue and in the sea which is light blue instead of greenish blue.

See also No. 309.

(Des R. Granger Barrett. Litho Questa)

1971 (5 Apr). *Easter. W* w **12**. *P* 14 × 14½.

275	**101** 2p. multicoloured ..	10	10
276	5p. multicoloured ..	15	15
277	7½p. multicoloured ..	25	20
278	12½p. multicoloured ..	30	25
275/8 ..	.. ..	*Set of 4*	70	60

PRICES OF SETS

Set prices are given for many issues, generally those containing three stamps or more. Definitive sets include one of each value or major colour change, but do not cover different perforations, die types or minor shades. Where a choice is possible the set prices are based on the cheapest versions of the stamps included in the listings.

102 Napoleon (after painting by J.-L. David) and Tomb on St. Helena

(Des J.W. Litho Questa)

1971 (5 May). *150th Death Anniv of Napoleon, T* **102** *and similar vert design. Multicoloured. W* w **12**. *P* 13½.

279	2p. Type **102** ..	50	40
280	34p. "Napoleon at St. Helena" (H. Delaroche)	2·00	85

(Des J.W. Litho Questa)

1971 (10 Nov). *Military Equipment* (2nd *issue*). *Multicoloured designs as T* **99**. *W* w **12**. *P* 14.

281	1½p. Artillery Private's hanger ..	1·00	30
282	4p. Baker rifle and socket bayonet	1·50	60
283	6p. Infantry Officer's sword ..	1·50	80
284	22½p. Baker rifle and sword bayonet..	2·00	1·25
281/4	.. ..	*Set of 4*	5·50	2·75

(Des and litho J.W.)

1972 (19 June). *Military Equipment* (3rd *issue*). *Multicoloured designs as T* **99**. *W* w **12**. *P* 14.

285	2p. multicoloured ..	50	20
286	5p. reddish lilac, new blue and black	90	50
287	7½p. multicoloured ..	1·10	60
288	12½p. pale olive-sepia, brown and black	1·50	75
285/8	..	*Set of 4*	3·50	1·90

Designs:—2p. Royal Sappers and Miners breast-plate, post 1823; 5p. Infantry sergeant's spoonton, *circa* 1830; 7½p. Royal Artillery officer's breast-plate, *circa* 1830; 12½p. English military pistol, *circa* 1800.

103 St. Helena Sand Plover and White Tern

(Des (from photograph by D. Groves) and photo Harrison)

1972 (20 Nov). *Royal Silver Wedding. Multicoloured; background colour given. W* w **12**. *P* 14 × 14½.

289	**103** 2p. slate-green ..	25	35
290	16p. lake-brown ..	50	65

(Des J.W. Litho Questa)

1973 (20 Sept). *Military Equipment* (4th *issue*). *Multicoloured designs as T* **99**. *W* w **12** (*sideways*). *P* 14.

291	2p. Other Rank's shako, 53rd Foot, 1815 ..	1·00	55
292	5p. Band and Drums sword, 1830 ..	1·75	1·00
293	7½p. Royal Sappers and Miners Officer's hat, 1830	2·00	1·25
294	12½p. General's sword, 1831 ..	3·00	1·50
291/4 ..	..	*Set of 4*	7·00	4·00

1973 (14 Nov). *Royal Wedding. As Nos.* 322/3 *of Montserrat*.

295	2p. violet-blue ..	15	10
296	18p. light emerald ..	25	20

104 *Westminster* and *Claudine* beached, 1849

(Des J.W. Litho Questa)

1973 (17 Dec). *Tercentenary of East India Company Charter. T* **104** *and similar horiz designs. Multicoloured. W* w **12**. *P* 14.

297	1½p. Type **104**	50	35
298	4p. *True Briton*, 1790 ..	60	65
299	6p. *General Goddard* in action, 1795	60	65
300	22½p. *Kent* burning in the Bay of Biscay, 1825	1·50	2·00
297/300	.. ..	*Set of 4*	3·00	3·25

105 U.P.U. Emblem and Ships

(Des J.W. Litho Questa)

1974 (15 Oct). *Centenary of Universal Postal Union. T* **105** *and similar horiz design. Multicoloured. W* w **12** (*sideways on* MS303).

301	5p. Type **105** ..	25	25
302	25p. U.P.U. emblem and letters ..	55	55
MS303	89 × 84 mm. Nos. 301/2 ..	1·00	1·50

106 Churchill in Sailor Suit, and Blenheim Palace

107 Capt. Cook and H.M.S. *Resolution*

(Des Jennifer Toombs. Litho Questa)

1974 (30 Nov). *Birth Centenary of Sir Winston Churchill. T* **106** *and similar horiz design. W* w **14** *sideways* (*Nos.* 304/5) *or W* w **12** *sideways* (MS306). *P* 14.

304	5p. multicoloured ..	25	25
305	25p. black, flesh and reddish purple ..	55	75
MS306	108 × 93 mm. Nos. 304/5 ..	1·00	2·00

Design:—25p. Churchill and River Thames.

(Des J. Cooter. Litho Questa)

1975 (14 July). *Bicentenary of Capt. Cook's Return to St. Helena. T* **107** *and similar horiz design. Multicoloured. W* w **14** (*sideways on* 25p.). *P* 13½.

307	5p. Type **107** ..	50	50
308	25p. Capt. Cook and Jamestown ..	1·00	1·50

(Litho Questa)

1975 (13 Aug). *As No.* 264 *but whiter paper. P* 14.

309	2p. multicoloured ..	90	4·50

108 *Mellissia begonifolia* (tree)

109 £1 Note

(Des Jennifer Toombs. Litho J.W.)

1975 (20 Oct). *Centenary of Publication of "St. Helena" by J. C. Melliss. T* **108** *and similar multicoloured designs. W* w **14** (*sideways on* 12 *and* 25p.). *P* 13.

310	2p. Type **108** ..	25	40
311	5p. *Mellissius adumbratus* (beetle) ..	35	60
312	12p. St. Helena Sand Plover (*horiz*) ..	90	1·50
313	25p. *Scorpaenia mellissii* (fish) (*horiz*)	1·00	1·75
310/13	.. ..	*Set of 4*	2·25	3·75

(Des V. Whiteley Studio. Litho J.W.)

1976 (15 Mar). *First Issue of Currency Notes. T* **109** *and similar horiz design. Multicoloured. W* w **12** (*sideways*). *P* 13½.

314	8p. Type **109** ..	40	35
315	33p. £5 Note ..	85	1·25

110 1d. Stamp of 1863

(Des C. Abbott. Litho J.W.)

1976 (4 May). *Festival of Stamps, London. T* **110** *and similar designs. W* w **14** (*sideways on* 5 *and* 25p.). *P* 13½.

316	5p. light red-brown, black and light flesh	15	15
317	8p. black, green and pale dull green	25	30
318	25p. multicoloured ..	40	45
316/18	..	*Set of 3*	70	80

Designs: *Vert*—8p. 1d. stamp of 1922. *Horiz*—25p. Mail carrier *Good Hope Castle*.

For miniature sheet containing No. 318 see Ascension No. MS218.

111 "High Knoll, 1806"
(Capt. Barnett)

(Des C. Abbott. Litho Questa)

1976 (14 Sept)–**82.** *Aquatints and Lithographs of St. Helena. T 111 and similar horiz designs. Multicoloured. W w 14 (sideways). P 13½ (£1, £2) or 14 (others).*

A. On white paper. Without imprint date.

319A	1p. Type 111	..	40	40
	a. Cream paper (13.6.80)		40	40
320A	3p. "The Friar Rock, 1815" (G. Bellasis)		40	40
	a. Cream paper (13.6.80)		40	40
321A	5p. "The Column Lot, 1815" (G. Bellasis)		30	40
322A	6p. "Sandy Bay Valley, 1809" (H. Salt) (23.11.76)		30	40
323A	8p. "Scene from Castle Terrace, 1815" (G. Bellasis)		40	45
324A	9p. "The Briars, 1815" (23.11.76)		40	50
325A	10p. "Plantation House, 1821" (J. Wathen)		50	60
326A	15p. "Longwood House, 1821" (J. Wathen) (23.11.76)		45	45
327A	18p. "St. Paul's Church" (V. Brooks)		45	65
328A	26p. "St. James's Valley, 1815" (Capt. Hastings)		45	65
329A	40p. "St. Matthew's Church, 1860" (V. Brooks)		70	1·25
330A	£1 "St. Helena, 1815" (G. Bellasis)		1·50	3·00
	a. Gold omitted		£750	
331A	£2 "Sugar Loaf Hill, 1821" (J. Wathen) (23.11.76)		3·50	5·50
319A/31A		Set of 13	8·75	13·00

B. On cream paper with imprint date ("1982") (10.5.82).

319B	1p. Type 111		20	30
325B	10p. "Plantation House, 1821" (J. Wathen)		50	1·00
331B	£2 "Sugar Loaf Hill, 1821" (J. Wathen)		3·75	5·00
319B/31B		Set of 3	4·00	5·75

The £1 and £2 are larger, 47×34 mm.

112 Duke of Edinburgh paying Homage

(Des M. Shamir. Litho J.W.)

1977 (7 Feb). *Silver Jubilee. T 112 and similar horiz designs. Multicoloured. W w 14 (sideways). P 13.*

332	8p. Royal visit, 1947		20	35
333	15p. Queen's sceptre with dove		25	45
334	26p. Type 112		35	50
332/4		Set of 3	70	1·10

113 Halley's Comet (from Bayeux Tapestry) **114** Sea Lion

(Des C. Abbott. Litho Questa)

1977 (23 Aug). *Tercentenary of Halley's Visit. T 113 and similar horiz designs. Multicoloured. W w 14 (sideways). P 14.*

335	5p. Type 113		35	20
336	8p. Late 17th-century sextant		50	20
337	27p. Halley and Halley's Mount, St. Helena		1·00	60
335/7		Set of 3	1·75	90

(Des Jennifer Toombs. Litho Questa)

1978 (2 June). *25th Anniv of Coronation. T 114 and similar vert designs. P 15.*

338	25p. agate, cerise and silver		40	50
	a. Sheetlet. Nos. 338/40 × 2		2·00	
339	25p. multicoloured		40	50
340	25p. agate, cerise and silver		40	50
338/40		Set of 3	1·10	1·40

Designs:—No. 338, Black Dragon of Ulster; No. 339, Queen Elizabeth II; No. 340, Type 114.

Nos. 338/40 were printed together in small sheets of 6, containing two se-tenant strips of 3, with horizontal gutter margin between.

115 Period Engraving of St. Helena

116 H.M.S. *Discovery* **117** Sir Rowland Hill

(Des J.W. Litho Questa)

1978 (14 Aug). *Wreck of the "Witte Leeuw". T 115 and similar horiz designs. Multicoloured. W w 14 (sideways). P 14½.*

341	3p. Type 115		15	15
342	5p. Chinese porcelain		20	20
343	8p. Bronze cannon		25	30
344	9p. Chinese porcelain (different)		30	35
345	15p. Pewter mug and ceramic flasks		50	55
346	20p. Dutch East Indiaman		60	70
341/6		Set of 6	1·75	2·00

(Des and litho (25p. also embossed) Walsall)

1979 (19 Feb). *Bicentenary of Captain Cook's Voyages, 1768–79. T 116 and similar vert designs. Multicoloured. P 11.*

347	3p. Type 116		20	15
348	8p. Cook's portable observatory		30	25
349	12p. Pharnaceum acidum (based on sketch by Joseph Banks)		35	35
350	25p. Flaxman/Wedgwood medallion of Captain Cook		55	90
347/50		Set of 4	1·25	1·50

118 R. F. Seal's Chart of 1823 showing the Elevation of the Coastline

(Des G. Vasarhelyi. Litho Questa)

1979 (10 Dec). *150th Anniv of the Inclined Plane. T 118 and similar designs. W w 14 (sideways on 5 and 8p.). P 14.*

355	5p. black, brownish grey and stone		20	15
356	8p. black, brownish grey and stone		20	20
357	50p. multicoloured		70	75
355/7		Set of 3	1·00	1·00

Designs: Horiz—8p. The Inclined Plane in 1829. Vert—50p. The Inclined Plane in 1979.

(Des J.W. Litho Questa)

1979 (20 Aug). *Death Centenary of Sir Rowland Hill. T 117 and similar designs. W w 14 (sideways on 8 to 32p.). P 14.*

351	5p. multicoloured		15	15
352	8p. multicoloured		20	20
353	20p. multicoloured		40	40
354	32p. black, magenta and deep mauve		55	55
351/4		Set of 4	1·10	1·10

Designs: Horiz—8p. 1965 1d. 1st Local Post stamp; 20p. 1863 1d. on 6d. stamp; 32p. 1902 1d. stamp.

119 Napoleon's Tomb, 1848 **120** East Indiaman

(Des J.W. Litho Questa)

1980 (23 Feb). *Centenary of Empress Eugenie's Visit. T 119 and similar horiz designs. W w 14 (sideways). P 14.*

358	5p. gold, reddish brown and pale red-brown		20	20
359	8p. gold, reddish brown and pale bistre		25	25
360	62p. gold, reddish brown & pale orange-brn		95	1·10
358/60		Set of 3	1·25	1·40
MS361	180 × 110 mm. Nos. 358/60		1·50	2·00

Designs:—8p. Landing at St. Helena; 62p. At the tomb of Napoleon.

(Des C. Abbott. Litho Format)

1980 (6 May). *"London 1980" International Stamp Exhibition. T 120 and similar vert designs. Multicoloured. W w 14. P 14½.*

362	5p. Type 120		15	15
363	8p. Dolphin postal stone		15	20
364	47p. Postal stone outside Castle entrance, Jamestown		60	80
362/4		Set of 3	80	1·00
MS365	111 × 120 mm. Nos. 362/4		85	1·50

121 Queen Elizabeth the Queen Mother in 1974

(Des and litho Harrison)

1980 (18 Aug*). *80th Birthday of Queen Elizabeth the Queen Mother. W w 14 (sideways). P 14.*

366	121	24p. multicoloured	50	50

*This is the local date of issue; the Crown Agents released the stamp on 4 August.

122 The Briars, 1815

(Des C. Abbott. Litho Questa)

1980 (17 Nov). *175th Anniv of Wellington's Visit. T 122 and similar multicoloured design. W w 14 (sideways on 9p.). P 14.*

367	9p. Type 122		15	15
368	30p. "Wellington" (Goya) (vert)		45	45

Nos. 367/8 were each printed in small sheets of 10 stamps.

123 Redwood **124** Detail from Reinel Portolan Chart, circa 1530

(Des Daphne Padden. Litho Enschedé)

1981 (5 Jan). *Endemic Plants. T 123 and similar horiz designs. Multicoloured. W w 14 (sideways). P 13½.*

369	5p. Type 123		15	15
370	8p. Old Father Live Forever		20	20
371	15p. Gumwood		25	25
372	27p. Black Cabbage		45	45
369/72		Set of 4	95	95

(Des Harrison. Litho Walsall)

1981 (22 May). *Early Maps. T 124 and similar horiz designs. W w 14 (sideways). P 14 × 14½.*

373	5p. multicoloured		25	15
374	8p. black, brown-lake and grey		30	20
375	20p. multicoloured		50	35
376	30p. multicoloured		55	50
373/6		Set of 4	1·40	1·10
MS377	114 × 83 mm. 24p. black and grey		40	65

Designs:—8p. John Thornton's Map of St. Helena, circa 1700; 20p. Map of St. Helena, 1815; 30p. Map of St. Helena, 1817; miniature sheet, Part of Gastaldi's map of Africa, 16th-century.

125 Prince Charles as Royal Navy Commander **126** Charonia Variegata

(Des J.W. Litho Questa)

1981 (22 July). *Royal Wedding. T 125 and similar vert designs. Multicoloured. W w 14. P 14.*

378	14p. Wedding bouquet from St. Helena		25	25
379	29p. Type 125		35	35
380	32p. Prince Charles and Lady Diana Spencer		50	50
378/80		Set of 3	1·00	1·00

(Des J.W. Litho Walsall)

1981 (10 Sept). *Seashells. T 126 and similar vert designs. Multicoloured. W w 14. P 14.*

381	7p. Type 126		35	20
382	10p. Cypraea spurca sanctaehelenae		40	25
383	25p. Janthina janthina		70	60
384	53p. Pinna rudis		1·25	1·25
381/4		Set of 4	2·40	2·10

127 Traffic Duty

128 *Sympetrum dilatatum*
(dragonfly)

(Des BG Studio. Litho Questa)

1981 (5 Nov). *25th Anniv of Duke of Edinburgh Award Scheme.*
T **127** *and similar vert designs. Multicoloured. W w* **14.** *P* 14.
385	7p. Type **127**		15	15
386	11p. Signposting		15	15
387	25p. Animal care		35	35
388	50p. Duke of Edinburgh, in Guards' uniform, on horse-back		70	70
385/8		*Set of* 4	1·25	1·25

(Des C. Abbott. Litho Questa)

1982 (4 Jan). *Insects (1st series). T* **128** *and similar horiz designs.*
Multicoloured. W w **14** *(sideways on 7, 10 and 25p., inverted on*
32p.). P 14½.
389	7p. Type **128**		30	25
390	10p. *Aplothorax burchelli* (beetle)		40	35
391	25p. *Ampulex compressa* (wasp)		70	60
392	32p. *Labidura herculeana* (earwig)		80	75
389/92		*Set of* 4	2·00	1·75
The 32p. is larger, 45×27 mm.
See also Nos. 411/14.

129 Charles Darwin

130 Prince and Princess of
Wales at Balmoral,
Autumn 1981

(Des L. Curtis. Litho Questa)

1982 (19 Apr). *150th Anniv of Charles Darwin's Voyage. T* **129**
and similar horiz designs. Multicoloured. W w **14** *(sideways).*
P 14.
393	7p. Type **129**		30	30
394	14p. Flagstaff Hill and Darwin's hammer		45	60
395	25p. Ring-necked Pheasant and Chukar Partridge		75	1·00
396	29p. H.M.S. *Beagle* off St. Helena		95	1·25
393/6		*Set of* 4	2·25	2·75

(Des C. Abbott. Litho Format)

1982 (1 July). *21st Birthday of Princess of Wales. T* **130** *and*
similar multicoloured designs. W w **14.** *P* 13½ × 14 (7, 55p.)
or 13½ (*others*).
397	7p. St. Helena coat of arms		15	20
398	11p. Type **130**		25	30
399	29p. Bride on Palace Balcony		55	80
	a. Perf 13½ × 14		30·00	14·00
	b. Imperf (pair)		£500	
400	55p. Formal portrait		1·00	1·50
397/400		*Set of* 4	1·75	2·50

1st PARTICIPATION
COMMONWEALTH GAMES 1982

(131)

132 Lord Baden-Powell

1982 (25 Oct). *Commonwealth Games, Brisbane. Nos. 326 and*
328 optd with T **131**.
401	15p. "Longwood House, 1821" (G. Wathen)	25	25
402	26p. "St. James's Valley, 1815" (Capt. Hastings)	45	45

(Des L. McCombie. Litho Walsall)

1982 (29 Nov). *75th Anniv of Boy Scout Movement. T* **132** *and*
similar designs. W w **14** *(inverted on 3p., 29p.; sideways on 11p.,*
59p.). P 14.
403	3p. lake-brown, grey and orange-yellow	15	15
404	11p. lake-brown, grey & bright yellow-green	35	25
405	29p. lake-brown, grey and reddish orange	70	60
406	59p. lake-brown, grey & bright yellow-green	1·25	1·25
403/6		*Set of* 4	2·25	2·00
Designs: *Horiz*—11p. Boy Scout (drawing by Lord Baden-
Powell); 59p. Camping at Thompsons Wood. *Vert*—29p. Canon
Walcott.

133 King and Queen Rocks

134 *Coriolus versicolor*

(Des C. Abbott. Litho B.D.T.)

1983 (14 Jan). *Views of St. Helena by Roland Svensson. T* **133** *and*
similar multicoloured designs. W w **14** *(sideways on 29p., 59p.).*
P 14.
407	7p. Type **133**		20	20
408	11p. Turk's Cap		25	25
409	29p. Coastline from Jamestown (*horiz*)		65	65
410	59p. Mundens Point (*horiz*)		1·40	1·40
407/10		*Set of* 4	2·25	2·25

(Des C. Abbott. Litho Questa)

1983 (22 Apr). *Insects (2nd series). Horiz designs as T* **128**. *Multi-*
coloured. W w **14** *(sideways). P* 14½.
411	11p. *Acherontia atropos* (hawk moth)		35	30
412	15p. *Helenasaldula aberrans* (shore-bug)		40	35
413	29p. *Anchastus compositarum* (click beetle)		65	55
414	59p. *Lamprochrus cossonoides* (weevil)		1·40	1·25
411/14		*Set of* 4	2·50	2·25

(Des Garden Studio. Litho Format)

1983 (16 June). *Fungi. T* **134** *and similar multicoloured designs.*
W w **14** *(sideways on 29p.). P* 14.
415	11p. Type **134**		20	20
416	15p. *Pluteus brunneisucus*		30	35
417	29p. *Polyporus induratus* (*horiz*)		55	70
418	59p. *Coprinus angulatus*		1·25	1·40
415/18		*Set of* 4	2·10	2·40

135 Java Sparrow

136 Birth of St. Helena

(Des J.W. Litho Questa)

1983 (12 Sept). *Birds. T* **135** *and similar vert designs. Multi-*
coloured. W w **14.** *P* 14.
419	7p. Type **135**		30	20
420	15p. Madagascar Red Fody		45	35
421	33p. Common Waxbill		80	70
422	59p. Yellow Canary		1·50	1·40
419/22		*Set of* 4	2·75	2·50

(Des Jennifer Toombs. Litho Questa)

1983 (17 Oct). *Christmas. Life of St. Helena (1st series). T* **136** *and*
similar vert design. Multicoloured. W w **14.** *P* 14 × 13½.
423	10p. Type **136**		25	35
	a. Sheetlet Nos. 423/4, each ×5		3·00	
424	15p. St. Helena being taken to convent		30	35
Nos. 423/4 were printed together in small sheets of 10, containing
horizontal strips of 5 for each value separated by a horizontal gutter
margin.
See also Nos. 450/3 and 468/71.

137 1934 ½d. Stamp

138 Prince Andrew and
H.M.S. *Invincible*
(aircraft carrier)

(Des C. Abbott. Litho Questa)

1984 (3 Jan). *150th Anniv of St. Helena as a British Colony. T* **137**
and similar square designs showing values of the 1934 Centenary
of British Colonisation issue or Colony Arms. Multicoloured.
W w **14** *(sideways). P* 13½.
425	1p. Type **137**		10	20
426	3p. 1934 1d. stamp		10	20
427	6p. 1934 1½d. stamp		10	30
428	7p. 1934 2d. stamp		15	30
429	11p. 1934 3d. stamp		20	40
430	15p. 1934 6d. stamp		25	45
431	29p. 1934 1s. stamp		50	95
432	33p. 1934 5s. stamp		55	1·25
433	59p. 1934 10s. stamp		1·10	2·00
434	£1 1934 2s. 6d. stamp		2·75	3·25
435	£2 St. Helena Coat of Arms		3·50	5·00
425/35		*Set of* 11	7·50	13·00

(Des D. Bowen. Litho Format)

1984 (4 Apr). *Visit of Prince Andrew. T* **138** *and similar horiz*
design. Multicoloured. W w **14** *(sideways). P* 14.
436	11p. Type **138**		25	25
437	60p. Prince Andrew and H.M.S. *Herald* (survey ship)		1·25	1·40

139 *St. Helena*
(schooner)
140 Twopenny Coin and Donkey

(Des A. Theobald. Litho Questa)

1984 (14 May). *250th Anniv of "Lloyd's List" (newspaper). T* **139**
and similar vert designs. Multicoloured. W w **14.** *P* 14½ × 14.
438	10p. Type **139**		20	20
439	18p. Solomons Facade (local agent)		35	35
440	25p. Lloyd's Coffee House, London		50	55
441	50p. *Papanui* (freighter)		1·00	1·00
438/41		*Set of* 4	1·90	1·90

(Des G. Drummond. Litho Format)

1984 (23 July). *New Coinage. T* **140** *and similar horiz designs.*
Multicoloured. W w **14** *(sideways). P* 14.
442	10p. Type **140**		35	35
443	15p. Five pence coin and St. Helena Sand Plover		45	45
444	29p. Penny coin and Yellowfin Tuna		75	75
445	50p. Ten pence coin and Arum Lily		1·25	1·25
442/5		*Set of* 4	2·50	2·50

141 Mrs. Rebecca Fuller
(former Corps Secretary)

142 Queen Elizabeth the
Queen Mother aged Two

(Des L. Curtis. Litho Walsall)

1984 (12 Oct). *Centenary of Salvation Army on St. Helena. T* **141**
and similar multicoloured designs. W w **14** *(sideways on 11p.,*
25p.). P 14.
446	7p. Type **141**		35	35
447	11p. Meals-on-wheels service (*horiz*)		45	50
448	25p. Salvation Army Citadel, Jamestown (*horiz*)		80	90
449	60p. Salvation Army band at Jamestown Clock Tower		1·75	2·00
446/9		*Set of* 4	3·00	3·25

(Des Jennifer Toombs. Litho Questa)

1984 (9 Nov). *Christmas. Life of St. Helena (2nd series). Vert*
designs as T **136**. *Multicoloured. W w* **14.** *P* 14.
450	6p. St. Helena visits prisoners		20	20
451	10p. Betrothal of St. Helena		30	30
452	15p. Marriage of St. Helena to Constantius		40	40
453	33p. Birth of Constantine		70	70
450/3		*Set of* 4	1·40	1·40

(Des A. Theobald (70p.), C. Abbott (others). Litho Questa)

1985 (7 June). *Life and Times of Queen Elizabeth the Queen*
Mother. T **142** *and similar vert designs. Multicoloured. W w* **16**.
P 14½ × 14.
454	11p. Type **142**		20	25
455	15p. At Ascot with the Queen		30	35
456	29p. Attending Gala Ballet at Covent Garden		60	65
457	55p. With Prince Henry at his christening		1·10	1·25
454/7		*Set of* 4	2·00	2·25
MS458	91 × 73 mm. 70p. The Queen Mother with Ford "V8 Pilot". Wmk sideways		1·40	1·60

143 Rock Bullseye

144 John J. Audubon

(Des L. Curtis. Litho Walsall)

1985 (12 July). *Marine Life.* T *143 and similar horiz designs. Multicoloured.* W w 14 *(sideways).* P 13 × 13½.

459	7p. Type **143**	..	..	25	25
460	11p. Mackerel..	..	..	30	30
461	15p. Skipjack Tuna	..	..	40	40
462	33p. Yellowfin Tuna	..	..	75	75
463	50p. Stump	..	..	1·25	1·25
459/63	..	..	*Set of 5*	2·75	2·75

(Des Josephine Martin (11p.). Litho Format)

1985 (2 Sept). *Birth Bicentenary of John J. Audubon (ornithologist).* T *144 and similar designs.* W w 14 *(inverted on 11p., sideways on others).* P 14.

464	11p. black and blackish brown	..	..	45	25
465	15p. multicoloured	..	..	55	35
466	25p. multicoloured	..	..	75	55
467	60p. multicoloured	..	..	1·40	1·40
464/7	..	..	*Set of 4*	2·75	2·25

Designs: *Horiz (from original Audubon paintings)*—15p. Moorhen ("Common Gallinule"); 25p. White-tailed Tropic Bird; 60p. Common Noddy.

(Des Jennifer Toombs. Litho Questa)

1985 (14 Oct). *Christmas. Life of St. Helena (3rd series). Vert designs as* T *136. Multicoloured.* W w 14. P 14 × 13½.

468	7p. St. Helena journeys to the Holy Land	..		25	25
469	10p. Zambres slays the bull	..		30	30
470	15p. The bull restored to life: conversion of St. Helena	..		40	40
471	60p. Resurrection of the corpse: the true Cross identified	..		1·50	1·50
468/71	..	..	*Set of 4*	2·25	2·25

145 Church Provident Society for Women Banner

146 Plaque at Site of Halley's Observatory on St. Helena

(Des A. Theobald. Litho J.W.)

1986 (7 Jan). *Friendly Societies' Banners.* T *145 and similar horiz designs. Multicoloured.* W w 16 *(sideways).* P 13 × 13½.

472	10p. Type **145**	..	..	25	25
473	11p. Working Men's Christian Association..			25	25
474	25p. Church Benefit Society for Children			55	55
475	29p. Mechanics and Friendly Benefit Society			65	65
476	33p. Ancient Order of Foresters			70	70
472/6	..	..	*Set of 5*	2·10	2·10

(Des A. Theobald. Litho Questa)

1986 (21 Apr). *60th Birthday of Queen Elizabeth II. Vert designs as* T *230a of Jamaica. Multicoloured.* W w 16. P 14½ × 14.

477	10p. Princess Elizabeth making 21st birthday broadcast, South Africa, 1947	..		20	25
478	15p. Silver Jubilee photograph, 1977	..		30	35
479	20p. Princess Elizabeth on board H.M.S. *Implacable*, 1947	..		40	45
480	50p. In the U.S.A., 1976	..		1·00	1·10
481	65p. At Crown Agents Head Office, London, 1983	..		1·25	1·40
477/81	..	..	*Set of 5*	2·75	3·25

(Des L. Curtis. Litho Walsall)

1986 (15 May). *Appearance of Halley's Comet.* T *146 and similar vert designs. Multicoloured.* W w 14. P 14½ × 14.

482	9p. Type **146**	..	..	25	25
483	12p. Edmond Halley	..	..	30	30
484	20p. Halley's planisphere of the southern stars	..		45	45
485	65p. *Unity* on passage to St. Helena, 1676	..		1·40	1·40
482/5	..	..	*Set of 4*	2·10	2·10

(Des D. Miller. Litho Questa)

1986 (23 July). *Royal Wedding. Square designs as* T *231a of Jamaica. Multicoloured.* W w 16. P 14.

486	10p. Prince Andrew and Miss Sarah Ferguson	..		20	25
487	40p. Prince Andrew with Governor J. Massingham on St. Helena	..		80	85

147 James Ross and H.M.S. *Erebus*

(Des C. Abbott. Litho Questa)

1986 (22 Sept). *Explorers.* T *147 and similar horiz designs.* W w 16 *(sideways).* P 14½.

488	1p. deep brown and pink	..	..	10	10
489	3p. royal blue and grey-blue	..	..	10	10
490	5p. bronze-green and deep yellow-green	..		10	15
491	9p. purple-brown and claret	..	..	20	25
492	10p. deep brown and light brown	..	..	20	25

493	12p. myrtle-green and light green	..		25	30
494	15p. red-brown and brown-rose	..		30	35
495	20p. deep dull blue and light blue	..		40	45
496	25p. sepia and salmon-pink	..		50	55
497	40p. bottle-green and dull blue-green	..		80	85
498	60p. reddish brown and pale orange-brown	..		1·25	1·40
499	£1 deep turquoise-blue and turquoise-blue			2·00	2·10
500	£2 deep lilac and reddish lilac	..		4·00	4·25
488/500	..	..	*Set of 13*	9·00	10·00

Designs:—3p. Robert FitzRoy and H.M.S. *Beagle*; 5p. Adam Johann von Krusenstern and *Nadezhda*; 9p. William Bligh and H.M.S. *Resolution*; 10p. Otto von Kotzebue and *Rurik*; 12p. Philip Carteret and H.M.S. *Swallow*; 15p. Thomas Cavendish and *Desire*; 20p. Louis-Antoine de Bougainville and *La Boudeuse*; 25p. Fyedor Petrovich Lütke and *Senyavin*; 40p. Louis Isidore Duperrey and *La Coquille*; 60p. John Byron and H.M.S. *Dolphin*; £1 James Cook and H.M.S. *Endeavour*; £2 Jules Dumont d'Urville and *L'Astrolabe*.

148 Prince Edward and H.M.S. *Repulse* (battle cruiser), 1925

149 St. Helena Tea Plant

(Des E. Nisbet. Litho Questa)

1987 (16 Feb). *Royal Visits to St. Helena.* T *148 and similar horiz designs. Multicoloured.* W w 16 *(sideways).* P 14.

501	9p. Type **148**	..	..	50	40
502	13p. King George VI and H.M.S. *Vanguard* (battleship), 1947	..		70	60
503	38p. Prince Philip and Royal Yacht *Britannia*, 1957..	..		1·40	1·50
504	45p. Prince Andrew and H.M.S. *Herald* (survey ship), 1984	..		1·60	1·75
501/4	..		*Set of 4*	3·75	3·75

(Des Annette Robinson. Litho Questa)

1987 (3 Aug). *Rare Plants (1st series).* T *149 and similar vert designs. Multicoloured.* W w 16. P 14½ × 14.

505	9p. Type **149**	..	..	65	40
506	13p. Baby's Toes	..	..	80	50
507	38p. Salad Plant	..	..	1·50	1·10
508	45p. Scrubwood	..	..	1·75	1·40
505/8	..	..	*Set of 4*	4·25	3·00

See also Nos. 531/4.

150 Lesser Rorqual

151 *Defence* and Dampier's Signature, 1691

(Des A. Riley. Litho Questa)

1987 (24 Oct). *Marine Mammals.* T *150 and similar horiz designs. Multicoloured.* W w 16 *(sideways).* P 14.

509	9p. Type **150**..	..	..	80	35
510	13p. Risso's Dolphin	..		85	50
511	45p. Sperm Whale	..		2·00	1·40
512	60p. Euphrosyne Dolphin	..		2·00	1·60
509/12	..	..	*Set of 4*	5·00	3·50
MS513	102 × 72 mm. 75p. Humpback Whale (48 × 31 mm). P 13½ × 14			2·00	2·00

1987 (9 Dec). *Royal Ruby Wedding. Nos. 477/81 optd with* T *45a of Kiribati in silver.*

514	10p. Princess Elizabeth making 21st birthday broadcast, South Africa, 1947	..		20	25
515	15p. Silver Jubilee photograph, 1977	..		30	35
	a. Opt omitted (vert pair with normal)	..		£150	
516	20p. Princess Elizabeth on board H.M.S. *Implacable*, 1947	..		40	45
517	50p. In the U.S.A., 1976	..		1·00	1·10
518	65p. At Crown Agents Head Office, London, 1983	..		1·25	1·40
514/18	..	..	*Set of 5*	2·75	3·25

No. 515a occurred on the top row of several sheets.

(Des A. Theobald. Litho Walsall)

1988 (1 Mar). *Bicentenary of Australian Settlement.* T *151 and similar horiz designs showing ships and signatures. Multicoloured.* W w 16 *(sideways).* P 14 × 14½.

519	9p. Type **151**	..	..	1·25	90
520	13p. H.M.S. *Resolution* (Cook), 1775	..		1·75	1·40
521	45p. H.M.S. *Providence* (Bligh), 1792	..		3·00	2·75
522	60p. H.M.S. *Beagle* (Darwin), 1836	..		3·75	3·25
519/22	..	..	*Set of 4*	9·00	7·50

ALTERED CATALOGUE NUMBERS

Any Catalogue numbers altered from the last edition are shown as a list in the introductory pages.

152 "The Holy Virgin with the Child"

153 Ebony

(Des N. Harvey. Litho Questa)

1988 (11 Oct). *Christmas.* T *152 and similar vert designs showing religious paintings. Multicoloured.* W w 14. P 14.

523	5p. Type **152**	..	..	10	15
524	20p. "Madonna"	..	..	40	45
525	38p. "The Holy Family with St. John"	..		75	80
526	60p. "The Holy Virgin with the Child"	..		1·25	1·40
523/6	..	..	*Set of 4*	2·25	2·50

(Des D. Miller (8p.), E. Nisbet and D. Miller (others). Litho Questa)

1988 (1 Nov). *300th Anniv of Lloyd's of London. Designs as* T *167a of Malawi.* W w 16 *(sideways on 20, 45p.).* P 14.

527	9p. agate and brown	..	..	20	25
528	20p. multicoloured	..	..	40	45
529	45p. multicoloured	..	..	90	95
530	60p. multicoloured	..	..	1·25	1·40
527/30	..	..	*Set of 4*	2·50	2·75

Designs: *Vert*—9p. Lloyd's Underwriting Room, 1886; 60p. *Spangereid* (full-rigged ship) on fire, St. Helena, 1920. *Horiz*—20p. *Edinburgh Castle* (liner); 45p. Bosun Bird (freighter).

(Des L. Ninnes. Litho Questa)

1989 (6 Jan). *Rare Plants (2nd series).* T *153 and similar vert designs. Multicoloured.* W w 16. P 14.

531	9p. Type **153**	..	..	30	30
532	20p. St. Helena Lobelia	..		55	55
533	45p. Large Bellflower	..		1·10	1·10
534	60p. She Cabbage Tree	..		1·40	1·40
531/4	..	..	*Set of 4*	3·00	3·00

154 Private, 53rd Foot

(155)

(Des C. Collins. Litho Format)

1989 (5 June). *Military Uniforms of 1815.* T *154 and similar vert designs. Multicoloured.* W w 16. P 14.

535	9p. Type **154**	..	..	35	35
	a. Horiz strip of 5. Nos. 535/9	..		3·50	
536	13p. Officer, 53rd Foot	..	..	40	40
537	20p. Royal Marine	..	..	55	55
538	45p. Officer, 66th Foot	..	..	1·25	1·25
539	60p. Private, 66th Foot	..	..	1·50	1·50
535/9	..	..	*Set of 5*	3·50	3·50

Nos. 535/9 were printed together, *se-tenant*, in horizontal strips of five throughout the sheet.

1989 (7 July). *"Philexfrance 89" International Stamp Exhibition, Paris. Nos. 535/9 optd with* T *155.*

540	9p. Type **154**	..	..	35	35
	a. Horiz strip of 5. Nos. 540/4	..		3·50	
541	13p. Officer, 53rd Foot	..	..	40	40
542	20p. Royal Marine	..	..	55	55
543	45p. Officer, 66th Foot	..	..	1·25	1·25
544	60p. Private, 66th Foot	..	..	1·50	1·50
540/4	..	..	*Set of 5*	3·50	3·50

156 Agricultural Studies

157 "The Madonna with the Pear" (Dürer)

(Des A. Edmonston. Litho Questa)

1989 (24 Aug). *New Prince Andrew Central School.* T *156 and similar horiz designs. Multicoloured.* W w 16 *(sideways).* P 14 × 14½.

545	13p. Type **156**	..	..	35	35
546	20p. Geography lesson	..	..	55	55
547	25p. Walkway and classroom block	..		65	65
548	60p. Aerial view of School	..	..	1·50	1·50
545/8	..	..	*Set of 4*	2·75	2·75

(Des D. Miller. Litho Questa)

1989 (23 Oct). *Christmas. Religious Paintings. T* **157** *and similar vert designs. Multicoloured. W* w **14**. *P* 14.

549	10p. Type **157**			40	30
550	20p. "The Holy Family under the Appletree" (Rubens)			65	65
551	45p. "The Virgin in the Meadow" (Raphael)			1·40	1·25
552	60p. "The Holy Family with St. John" (Raphael)			1·75	1·60
549/52			*Set of 4*	3·75	3·25

158 Chevrolet "6" 30 cwt Lorry, 1930

159 Sheep

(Des E. Nesbit. Litho Questa)

1989 (1 Dec). *Early Vehicles. T* **158** *and similar horiz designs. Multicoloured. W* w **16** *(sideways). P* 14½.

553	9p. Type **158**			40	40
554	20p. Austin "Seven", 1929			60	60
555	45p. Morris "Cowley" 11.9 h.p., 1929			1·25	1·25
556	60p. Sunbeam 25 h.p., 1932			1·60	1·60
553/6			*Set of 4*	3·50	3·50
MS557	93×74 mm. £1 Ford "Model A Fordor"			2·25	3·00

(Des Doreen McGuiness. Litho Questa)

1990 (1 Feb). *Farm Animals. T* **159** *and similar vert designs. Multicoloured. W* w **16**. *P* 14.

558	9p. Type **159**			30	30
559	13p. Pigs			35	35
560	45p. Cow and calf			1·00	1·25
561	60p. Geese			1·40	1·60
558/61			*Set of 4*	2·75	3·25

160 1840 Twopence Blue

161 Satellite Dish

(Des D. Miller. Litho Walsall)

1990 (3 May). *"Stamp World London 90" International Stamp Exhibition, London. T* **160** *and similar horiz designs. W* w **14** *(sideways). P* 14.

562	13p. black and cobalt			40	40
563	20p. multicoloured			65	65
564	38p. multicoloured			1·10	1·10
565	45p. multicoloured			1·40	1·40
562/5			*Set of 4*	3·25	3·25

Designs:—20p. 1840 Penny Black and 19th-century St. Helena postmark; 38p. Delivering mail to sub-post office; 45p. Mail van and Post Office, Jamestown.

(Des N. Shewring. Litho B.D.T.)

1990 (28 July). *Modern Telecommunications Links. T* **161** *and similar vert designs. Multicoloured. W* w **14**. *P* 13½.

566	20p. Type **161**			60	60
	a. Block of 4. Nos. 566/9			2·25	
567	20p. Digital telephone exchange			60	60
568	20p. Public card phone			60	60
569	20p. Facsimile machine			60	60
566/9			*Set of 4*	2·25	2·25

Nos. 566/9 were printed together, *se-tenant*, in blocks of 4 throughout the sheet of 16.

(Des D. Miller. Litho Questa)

1990 (4 Aug). *90th Birthday of Queen Elizabeth the Queen Mother. Vert designs as T* **107** (25p.) *or* **108** (£1) *of Kenya. W* w **16**. *P* 14×15 (25p.) *or* 14½ (£1).

570	25p. multicoloured			75	75
571	£1 black and purple-brown			2·50	2·75

Designs:—25p. Lady Elizabeth Bowes-Lyon, April 1923; £1 Queen Elizabeth visiting communal kitchen, 1940.

162 *Dane* (mail ship), 1857

163 Baptist Chapel, Sandy Bay

(Des L. Curtis. Litho Walsall)

1990 (13 Sept). *Maiden Voyage of St. Helena II. T* **162** *and similar horiz designs. Multicoloured. W* w **14** *(sideways). P* 14×14½.

572	13p. Type **162**			40	40
573	20p. *St. Helena I* offloading at St. Helena			65	65
574	38p. Launch of *St. Helena II*			1·10	1·10
575	45p. The Duke of York launching *St. Helena II*			1·25	1·40
572/5			*Set of 4*	3·00	3·25
MS576	100×100 mm. £1 *St. Helena II* and outline map of St. Helena			3·00	3·50

No. **MS576** also contains two imperforate designs of similar stamps from Ascension and Tristan da Cunha without face values.

(Des G. Vasarhelyi. Litho Questa)

1990 (18 Oct). *Christmas. Local Churches. T* **163** *and similar horiz designs. Multicoloured. W* w **14** *(sideways). P* 14.

577	10p. Type **163**			30	30
578	13p. St. Martin in the Hills Church			35	35
579	20p. St. Helena and the Cross Church			55	55
580	38p. St. James Church			1·00	1·00
581	45p. St. Paul's Cathedral			1·25	1·25
577/81			*Set of 5*	3·25	3·25

164 "Funeral Cortège, Jamestown Wharf" (detail, V. Adam)

165 Officer, Leicestershire Regiment

(Des N. Harvey. Litho Questa)

1990 (15 Dec). *150th Anniv of Removal of Napoleon's Body. T* **164** *and similar horiz designs. W* w **14** *(sideways). P* 13½×14.

582	13p. black, sepia and blue-green			40	40
583	20p. black, sepia and ultramarine			70	70
584	38p. black, sepia and deep magenta			1·25	1·25
585	45p. multicoloured			1·50	1·50
582/5			*Set of 4*	3·50	3·50

Designs:—20p. "Coffin being conveyed to the *Belle Poule*" (detail, V. Adam); 38p. "Transfer of the Coffin to the *Normandie*, Cherbourg" (detail, V. Adam); 45p. "Napoleon's Tomb, St. Helena" (T. Sutherland).

(Des C. Collins. Litho Questa)

1991 (2 May). *Military Uniforms of 1897. T* **165** *and similar vert designs. Multicoloured. W* w **14**. *P* 14.

586	13p. Type **165**			40	40
587	15p. Officer, York & Lancaster Regiment			45	45
588	20p. Colour-sergeant, Leicestershire Regt			65	65
589	38p. Bandsman, York & Lancaster Regt			1·25	1·25
590	45p. Lance-corporal, York & Lancaster Regt			1·50	1·50
586/90			*Set of 5*	3·75	3·75

(Des D. Miller. Litho Questa)

1991 (1 July). *65th Birthday of Queen Elizabeth II and 70th Birthday of Prince Philip. Vert designs as T* **58** *of Kiribati. Multicoloured. W* w **16** *(sideways). P* 14½×14.

591	25p. Queen Elizabeth II			80	90
	a. Horiz pair. Nos. 591/2 separated by label			1·60	1·75
592	25p. Prince Philip in naval uniform			80	90

Nos. 591/2 were printed in similar sheet format to Nos. 366/7 of Kiribati.

166 "Madonna and Child" (T. Vecellio)

167 Matchless (346cc) Motorcycle, 1947

(Des G. Vasarhelyi. Litho Walsall)

1991 (2 Nov). *Christmas. Religious Paintings. T* **166** *and similar vert designs. Multicoloured. W* w **14**. *P* 14.

593	10p. Type **166**			35	35
594	13p. "The Holy Family" (A. Mengs)			45	45
595	20p. "Madonna and Child" (W. Dyce)			65	65
596	38p. "The Two Trinities" (B. Murillo)			1·10	1·10
597	45p. "The Virgin and Child" (G. Bellini)			1·60	1·60
593/7			*Set of 5*	3·75	3·75

(Des N. Shewring. Litho Questa)

1991 (16 Nov). *"Phila Nippon '91" International Stamp Exhibition, Tokyo. Motorcycles. T* **167** *and similar horiz designs. W* w **16** *(sideways). P* 14½×14½.

598	13p. Type **167**			35	35
599	20p. Triumph "Tiger 100" (500cc), 1950			55	55
600	38p. Honda "CD" (175cc), 1967			95	95
601	45p. Yamaha "DTE 400", 1976			1·40	1·40
598/601			*Set of 4*	3·00	3·00
MS602	72×49 mm. 65p. Suzuki "RM" (250cc), 1984			1·75	2·00

168 *Eye of the Wind* (cadet ship) and Compass Rose

(Des R. Watton. Litho Walsall)

1992 (24 Jan). *500th Anniv of Discovery of America by Columbus and Re-enactment Voyages. T* **168** *and similar horiz designs. Multicoloured. W* w **14** *(sideways). P* 13½×14.

603	15p. Type **168**			50	50
604	25p. *Soren Larsen* (cadet ship) and map of Re-enactment Voyages			80	80
605	35p. *Santa Maria, Nina* and *Pinta*			1·25	1·25
606	50p. Columbus and *Santa Maria*			1·60	1·60
603/6			*Set of 4*	3·75	3·75

(Des D. Miller. Litho Questa (50p.), Walsall (others))

1992 (6 Feb). *40th Anniv of Queen Elizabeth II's Accession. Horiz designs as T* **113** *of Kenya. Multicoloured. W* w **14** *(sideways). P* 14.

607	11p. Prince Andrew Central School			35	35
608	15p. Plantation House			50	50
609	25p. Jamestown			75	75
610	35p. Three portraits of Queen Elizabeth			95	95
611	50p. Queen Elizabeth II			1·25	1·25
607/11			*Set of 5*	3·50	3·50

169 H.M.S. *Ledbury* (minesweeper)

170 Shepherds and Angel Gabriel

(Des N. Shewring. Litho Questa)

1992 (12 June). *10th Anniv of Liberation of Falkland Islands. Ships. T* **169** *and similar square designs. Multicoloured. W* w **14** *(sideways). P* 14.

612	13p. Type **169**			40	40
613	20p. H.M.S. *Brecon* (minesweeper)			60	60
614	38p. *St. Helena* (mail ship) off South Georgia			1·00	1·00
615	45p. Launch collecting first mail drop, 1982			1·25	1·25
612/15			*Set of 4*	3·00	3·00
MS616	116×116 mm. 13p.+3p. Type **169**; 20p.+4p. As No. 613; 38p.+8p. As No. 614; 45p.+9p. As No. 615			3·50	4·00

The premiums on No. **MS616** were for the S.S.A.F.A.

(Des G. Vasarhelyi. Litho Questa)

1992 (12 Oct). *Christmas. Children's Nativity Plays. T* **170** *and similar horiz designs. W* w **16** *(sideways). P* 13½×14.

617	13p. Type **170**			35	35
618	15p. Shepherds and Three Kings			45	45
619	20p. Mary and Joseph			60	60
620	45p. Nativity scene			1·25	1·25
617/20			*Set of 4*	2·40	2·40

171 Disc Jockey, Radio St. Helena (25th anniv)

172 Moses in the Bulrush

(Des D. Miller. Litho Questa)

1992 (4 Dec). *Local Anniversaries. T* **171** *and similar horiz designs. Multicoloured. W* w **14** *(sideways). P* 14×14½.

621	13p. Type **171**			40	40
622	20p. Scout parade (75th anniv of Scouting on St. Helena)			60	60
623	38p. H.M.S. *Providence* and breadfruit (bicent of Capt. Bligh's visit)			1·00	1·00
624	45p. Governor Brooke and Plantation House (bicent)			1·25	1·25
621/4			*Set of 4*	3·00	3·00

(Des M. Martineau. Litho Questa)

1993 (19 Mar). *Flowers. T* **172** *and similar vert designs. Multicoloured. W* w **16**. *P* 14½.

625	9p. Type **172**			20	25
626	13p. Periwinkle			25	30
627	20p. Everlasting Flower			40	45
628	38p. Cigar Plant			75	80
629	45p. Lobelia erinus			90	95
625/9			*Set of 5*	2·25	2·50

POSTAGE DUE STAMPS

D 1 Outline Map of St. Helena

(Des L. Curtis. Litho Questa)

1986 (9 June). *W* w **16**. *P* 14½×14.

D1	D 1	1p. deep brown and cinnamon ..	..	10	10
D2		2p. deep brown and bright orange		10	10
D3		5p. deep brown and orange-vermilion ..		10	15
D4		7p. black and bright reddish violet	..	15	20
D5		10p. black and violet-blue	..	20	25
D6		25p. black and pale emerald	..	50	55
D1/6	..	.. ..	Set of 6	95	1·10

St. Kitts-Nevis

ST. CHRISTOPHER

From 1760 the postal service for St. Christopher was organised by the Deputy Postmaster General on Antigua. It was not until May 1779 that the first postmaster was appointed to the island and the use of postmarks on outgoing mail commenced.

Stamps of Great Britain were used between May 1858 and the end of March 1860 when control of the postal services passed to the local authorities. In the years which followed, prior to the introduction of St. Christopher stamps in April 1870, a circular "PAID" handstamp was used on overseas mail.

BASSETERRE

Stamps of GREAT BRITAIN cancelled "A 12" as Type Z 1 of Jamaica.

1858 to 1860.

Z1	1d. rose-red (1857), perf 14	..	..	£500
Z2	2d. blue (1858) (Plate No. 7)	..	..	£900
Z3	4d. rose (1857) ..	..	..	£300
Z4	6d. lilac (1856)	..	..	£180
Z5	1s. green (1856)	..	..	£900

PRICES FOR STAMPS ON COVER

Nos. 1/5	from × 10
Nos. 6/8	from × 7
Nos. 9/10	from × 7
Nos. 11/21	from × 6
Nos. 22/3	from × 8
Nos. 24/8	—
Nos. R1/6	—

FOUR PENCE
(2)

Halfpenny
(3)

1870 (1 Apr)–79. *Wmk Crown CC.* (a) *P 12½.*

1	1	1d. dull rose	..	..	55·00	40·00
		a. Wmk sideways	..	..	£225	£180
2		1d. magenta (*shades*) (1871)	..	38·00	26·00
4		6d. yellow-green	..	..	85·00	17·00
5		6d. green (1871)	..	..	85·00	7·50

(b) *P 14*

6	1	1d. magenta (*shades*) (1875)	..	55·00	7·00
		a. Bisected diag or vert (½d.) (on cover) (3.82)	..		† £1100
7		2½d. red-brown (11.79)	..	£170	£225
8		4d. blue (11.79)	..	..	£150	15·00
		a. Wmk sideways	..	..	£500	£100
9		6d. green (1876)	..	..	50·00	5·00
		a. Imperf between (pair) ..			
		b. Wmk sideways	..	..	£300	90·00

The magenta used for the 1d. was a fugitive colour which reacts to both light and water.

No. 6a was authorised for use between March and June 1882 to make up the 2½d. letter rate and for ½d. book post.

1882 (June)–90. *Wmk Crown CA. P 14.*

11	1	½d. dull green	..	..	50	80
		a. Wmk sideways	..	..	£250	
12		1d. dull magenta	..	..	£475	60·00
		a. Bisected diagonally (½d.) (on cover)			
13		1d. carmine-rose (2.84)	..	..	60	70
		a. Bisected (½d.) (on cover)			
14		2½d. pale red-brown	..	..	£170	55·00
15		2½d. deep red-brown	..	..	£180	60·00
16		2½d. ultramarine (2.84)	..	..	1·50	1·50
17		4d. blue	..	..	£400	20·00
18		4d. grey (10.84)	..	..	1·25	80
19		6d. olive-brown ((3.90)	..	..	80·00	£225
20		1s. mauve (6.86)	..	..	90·00	65·00
21		1s. bright mauve (1890)	..	..	80·00	£110
19/20	Optd "Specimen"		*Set of 2*	£120	

1884 (Dec). No. 9 surch with T 2 by The Advertiser Press.

22	1	4d. on 6d. green	..	..	48·00	48·00
		a. Full stop after "PENCE"	..	48·00	48·00
		b. Surch double	..	..	£1600	

No. 22a occurred on alternate stamps.

1885 (March). No. 13 bisected and each half diagonally surch with T 3.

23	1	½d. on half of 1d. carmine-rose	..	24·00	35·00
		a. Unsevered pair	..	..	£100	£110
		ab. Ditto, one surch inverted	..	£350	£250
		b. Surch inverted	..	..	£250	£160
		c. Surch double ..			

ONE PENNY.
(4)

4d.
(5)

1886 (June). No. 9 surch with T 4 or 5 each showing a manuscript line through the original value.

24	1	1d. on 6d. green	..	..	16·00	28·00
		a. Surch inverted	..	..	£5000	
		b. Surch double	..	..	—	£1300
25		4d. on 6d. green.	..	..	48·00	90·00
		a. No stop after "d"	..	..	£180	£200
		b. Surch double	..	..	£1400	£1600

No. 24b is only known penmarked with dates between 21 July and 3 August 1886, or with violet handstamp.

1887 (May). No. 11 surch with T 4 showing a manuscript line through the original value.

26	1	1d. on ½d. dull green	..	..	28·00	38·00

ONE PENNY.
(7)

1888 (May). No. 16 surch.

(a) With T 4. Original value unobliterated

27	1	1d. on 2½d. ultramarine	..	£10000	£8500

(b) With T 7 showing a manuscript line through the original value

28	1	1d. on 2½d. ultramarine	..	38·00	42·00
		a. Surch inverted	..	..	£7000	£4750

The 1d. of Antigua was used provisionally in St. Christopher between February and March 1890 during a shortage of 1d. stamps. Such use can be distinguished by the postmark, which is "A 12" in place of "A02" (price from £160 used).

REVENUE STAMPS USED FOR POSTAGE

Saint Christopher
(R 1)

SAINT KITTS NEVIS REVENUE
(R 2)

1883. Nos. F6 and F8 of Nevis optd with Type R 1, in violet. Wmk Crown CA. P 14.

R1		1d. lilac-mauve	..	..	£225
R2		6d. green	..	60·00	90·00

1885. Optd with Type R 2. Wmk Crown CA. P 14.

R3	1	1d. rose	..	1·25	7·50
R4		3d. mauve	..	9·50	50·00
R5		6d. orange-brown	..	4·00	35·00
R6		1s. olive	..	1·50	35·00

Other fiscal stamps with overprints as above also exist, but none of these was ever available for postal purposes.

The stamps for St. Christopher was superseded by the general issue for Leeward Islands on 31 October 1890.

Stamps for St. Kitts, issued from 1980 onwards will be found listed after those for the combined colony.

NEVIS

Little is known concerning the early postal affairs of Nevis, but it is recorded that the British G.P.O. was to establish a branch office on the island under an Act of Parliament, passed in 1710, although arrangements may not have been finalised for a number of years afterwards. Nevis appears as "a new office" in the P.O. Accounts of 1787.

Stamps of Great Britain were used on the island from May 1858 until the colonial authorities assumed control of the postal service on 1 May 1860. Between this date and the introduction of Nevis stamps in 1861 No. CC1 was again used on overseas mail.

CHARLESTOWN

CROWNED-CIRCLE HANDSTAMPS

CC 1

CC1	CC 1	NEVIS (R.) (9.1852)..	Price on cover	£2000

No. CC1, but struck in black, was later used on several occasions up to 1886 where there were shortages of adhesive stamps.

Stamps of GREAT BRITAIN cancelled "A 09" as Type Z 1 of Jamaica.

1858 to 1860.

Z1	1d. rose-red (1857), perf 14	..	..	£375
Z2	2d. blue (1858) (Plate Nos. 7, 8)	..	..	
Z3	4d. rose (1857) ..	..	..	£300
Z4	6d. lilac (1856) ..	..	..	£300
Z5	1s. green (1856)	..	..	£275

PRICES FOR STAMPS ON COVER

Nos. 5/22	from × 8
Nos. 23/4	from × 4
Nos. 25/34	from × 6
Nos. 35/6	from × 7
Nos. F1/8	from × 12

1

2

3

4

The designs on the stamps refer to a medicinal spring on the island.

(Recess Nissen & Parker, London)

1861. Greyish paper. P 13.

5	1	1d. dull lake	..	..	45·00	35·00
		a. On blued paper ..	..	£180	95·00
6	2	4d. rose	..	..	75·00	55·00
		a. On blued paper ..	..	£650	£140
7	3	6d. grey-lilac	..	..	70·00	40·00
		a. On blued paper ..	..	£500	£180
8	4	1s. green	..	..	£150	50·00
		a. On blued paper ..	..	£750	£160

1866–76. White paper. P 15.

9	1	1d. pale red	..	..	30·00	25·00
10		1d. deep red	..	..	30·00	25·00
11	2	4d. orange	..	..	95·00	19·00
12		4d. deep orange	..	..	95·00	19·00
13	4	1s. blue-green	..	..	£150	26·00
14		1s. yellow-green (1876)	..	£800	£100
		a. Vertically laid paper	..	£10000	£3500
		b. No. 9 on sheet with crossed lines on hill £3500 £500
		c. Ditto. On laid paper	..		† £6500

Examples of the 4d. exist showing part of a papermakers watermark reading "A. COWAN & SONS EXTRA SUPERFINE".

(Lithographed by transfer from the engraved plates Nissen and Parker, London)

1876–78. P 15.

15	1	1d. pale rose-red	..	..	15·00	13·00
		a. Imperf (pair)	..	..	£225	
16		1d. deep rose-red	..	..	22·00	18·00
17		1d. vermilion-red (1878)	..	20·00	18·00
		a. Bisected (½d.) (on cover)	..		† £1100
18	2	4d. orange-yellow ..	..	£140	27·00
		a. Imperf between (vert pair)	..	£3000	
19	3	6d. grey (1878)	..	..	£190	£170
20	4	1s. pale green (1878)	..	55·00	80·00
		a. Imperf..			
		b. Imperf between (horiz strip of three) £3500
		c. No. 9 on sheet with crossed lines on hill £225
21		1s. deep green	..	..	60·00	90·00
		c. No. 9 on sheet with crossed lines on hill

No. 21c occurs on a small part of the deep green printing only.

RETOUCHES. 1d. Lithograph.

i.	No. 1 on sheet. Top of hill over kneeling figure redrawn by five thick lines and eight small slanting lines	£140 £150
ii.	No. 1 on sheet. Another retouch. Three series of short vertical strokes behind the kneeling figure..	£140 £150
iii.	No. 3 on sheet. Right upper corner star and border below star retouched	£140 £150
iv.	No. 9 on sheet. Retouch in same position as on No. 3 but differing in detail	£160 £170
v.	No. 12 on sheet. Dress of standing figure retouched by a number of horizontal and vertical lines ..	£140 £150

1878. Litho. P 11½.

22	1	1d. vermilion-red	..	..	38·00	48·00
		a. Bisected (½d.) (on cover)	..		† £1100
		b. Imperf (pair)..	..	£200	
		c. Imperf between (horiz pair)			

5 (Die I)

(6)

(Typo D.L.R.)

1879–80. Wmk Crown CC. P 14.

23	5	1d. lilac-mauve (1880) ..	..	35·00	26·00
		a. Bisected (½d.) (on cover)	..	†	£800
24		2½d. red-brown	..	..	85·00	75·00

1882–90. *Wmk Crown CA. P* 14.
25	5	½d. dull green (11.83)			2·50	5·00
26		1d. lilac-mauve			80·00	20·00
		a. Bisected (½d.) on cover (1883)			†	£700
27		1d. dull rose (11.83)			14·00	10·00
		a. Carmine (1884)			3·25	3·25
28		2½d. red-brown			90·00	45·00
29		2½d. ultramarine (11.83)			10·00	6·00
30		4d. blue			£275	45·00
31		4d. grey (1884)			3·75	2·50
32		6d. green (11.83)			£350	£350
33		6d. chestnut (10.88)			17·00	40·00
34		1s. violet (3.90)			85·00	£150
33/4	Optd "Specimen"			Set of 2	£110	

1883. *No. 26 bisected vertically and surch with T* **6,** *reading upwards or downwards.*
35	½d. on half 1d. lilac-mauve (V.)			£400	27·00
	a. Surch double			—	£275
	b. Surch on half "REVENUE" stamp No. F6			—	£500
36	½d. on half 1d. lilac-mauve			£400	25·00
	a. Surch double			—	£275
	b. Unsevered pair			£1000	£200
	ba. Surch on right half only			—	—
	c. Surch on half "REVENUE" stamp No. F6			—	£500

FISCALS USED FOR POSTAGE

Revenue   **REVENUE**
(F 1)   (F 2)

1882. (a) *Stamps of 1876 optd with Type* F **1.**
F1	1	1d. bright red			29·00	
F2	2	1d. rose			29·00	13·00
F3		4d. orange			55·00	
F4	3	6d. grey			90·00	
F5	4	1s. green			£100	
		a. No. 9 on sheet with crossed lines on hill				

(b) *Nos. 26, 30 and 32 optd with Type* F **2**
F6	5	1d. lilac-mauve			27·00	30·00
		a. Bisected (½d.) (on cover)				
F7		4d. blue			14·00	35·00
F8		6d. green			11·00	38·00

Nos. F1/5 were produced from fresh transfers. Similar "REVENUE" handstamps, both with and without stop, were also applied to postage issues.

The stamps of Nevis were superseded by the general issue for Leeward Islands on 31 October 1890. Stamps for Nevis were again issued in 1980 and will be found listed after those for the combined colony.

ST. KITTS-NEVIS

CROWN COLONY

Stamps for the combined colony were introduced in 1903, and were used concurrently with the general issues of Leeward Islands until the latter were withdrawn on 1 July 1956.

PRICES FOR STAMPS ON COVER TO 1945		
Nos. 1/9	*from* × 3	
No. 10	—	
Nos. 11/20	*from* × 3	
No. 21	—	
Nos. 22/3	*from* × 15	
Nos. 24/34	*from* × 3	
Nos. 35/6	—	
Nos. 37/47	*from* × 2	
Nos. 47a/b	—	
Nos. 48/57	*from* × 2	
Nos. 58/60	—	
Nos. 61/4	*from* × 5	
Nos. 65/7	*from* × 5	
Nos. 68/77	*from* × 2	

1 Christopher Columbus

2 Medicinal Spring

(Typo D.L.R.)

1903. *Wmk Crown CA. P* 14.
1	1	½d. dull purple and deep green			1·50	70
2	2	1d. grey-black and carmine			2·50	20
3	1	2d. dull purple and brown			2·25	8·00
4		2½d. grey-black and blue			9·50	3·50
5	2	3d. deep green and orange			3·50	15·00
6	1	6d. grey-black and bright purple			3·25	17·00
7		1s. grey-green and orange			6·00	11·00
8	2	2s. deep green and grey-black			11·00	15·00
9	1	2s. 6d. grey-black and violet			17·00	32·00
10	2	5s. dull green and sage-green			35·00	55·00
1/10				Set of 10	80·00	£140
1/10	Optd "Specimen"			Set of 10	£130	

1905–18. *Wmk Mult Crown CA. Chalk-surfaced paper* (1d. (No. 13), 5s.) *or ordinary paper* (others). *P* 14.
11	1	½d. dull purple and deep green			4·00	5·50
12		½d. grey-green (1907)			30	35
		a. Dull blue-green (1916)			30	1·25
13	2	1d. grey-black and carmine (1906)			1·00	25
14		1d. carmine (1907)			90	15
		a. Scarlet (1916)			35	20
15	1	2d. dull purple and brown			1·75	1·75
		a. Chalk-surfaced paper (1906)			90	2·00
16		2½d. grey-black and blue (1907)			14·00	2·75
17		2½d. bright blue (1907)			80	40
18	2	3d. deep green and orange			1·75	3·25
		a. Chalk-surfaced paper (1906)			80	2·00

19	1	6d. grey-black and deep violet			9·00	27·00
		a. Chalk-surfaced paper. *Grey-black and deep purple* (1908)			8·00	17·00
		ab. *Grey-black and bright purple* (1916)			4·25	15·00
20		1s. grey-green and orange (1909)			6·00	14·00
		a. Chalk-surfaced paper			2·00	18·00
21	2	5s. dull purple and sage-green (11.18)			27·00	60·00
11/21				Set of 11	50·00	90·00
12, 14, 17	Optd "Specimen"			Set of 3	60·00	

WAR TAX   WAR STAMP
(3)   (3a)

1916 (Oct). *Optd with T* **3.** *Wmk Mult Crown CA. P* 14.
| 22 | 1 | ½d. dull blue-green (No. 12a) (Optd S. £40) | | | 15 | 30 |
| | | a. Deep green | | | 10 | 30 |

No. 22a was a special printing produced for this overprint.

1918 (Aug). *Optd with T* **3a.** *Wmk Mult Crown CA. P* 14.
| 23 | 1 | 1½d. orange (Optd S. £45) | | | 15 | 30 |

No. 23 was a special printing produced for this overprint.

4

5

(Typo D.L.R.)

1920–22. *Wmk Mult Crown CA* (*sideways*). *Ordinary paper* (½d. to 2½d.) *or chalk-surfaced paper* (others). *P* 14.
24	4	½d. blue-green			3·00	3·50
25	5	1d. carmine			2·00	2·25
26	4	1½d. orange-yellow			1·25	80
27	5	2d. slate-grey			2·25	3·00
28	4	2½d. ultramarine			1·25	5·00
29	5	3d. purple/*yellow*			1·25	7·00
30	4	6d. dull purple and bright mauve			2·50	9·00
31	5	1s. grey and black/*green*			1·50	3·00
32	4	2s. dull purple and blue/*blue*			7·50	15·00
33	5	2s. 6d. grey and red/*blue*			5·00	25·00
34	4	5s. green and red/*pale yellow*			5·00	15·00
35	5	10s. green and red/*green*			12·00	45·00
36	4	£1 purple and black/*red* (1922)			£200	£275
24/36				Set of 13	£225	£375
24/36	Optd "Specimen"			Set of 13	£275	

1921–9. *Wmk Mult Script CA* (*sideways*). *Chalk-surfaced paper* (2½d.) (No. 44), 3d. (No. 45a) *and* 6d. *to* 5s.) *or ordinary paper* (others). *P* 14.
37	4	½d. blue-green			55	65
		a. Yellow-green (1922)			1·00	70
38	5	1d. rose-carmine			20	15
39		1d. deep violet (1922)			1·50	35
		a. Pale violet (1929)			2·25	85
40	4	1½d. red (1925)			1·00	2·50
40a		1½d. red-brown (1929)			30	15
41	5	2d. slate-grey (1922)			30	60
42	4	2½d. pale bright blue (1922)			2·50	2·25
43		2½d. brown (1922)			85	4·75
44		2½d. ultramarine (1927)			1·50	3·50
45	5	3d. dull ultramarine (1922)			40	2·50
45a		3d. purple/*yellow* (1927)			50	2·50
46	4	6d. dull and bright purple (1924)			2·00	4·50
46a	5	1s. black/*green* (1929)			3·75	6·00
47	4	2s. purple and blue/*blue* (1922)			3·50	13·00
47a	5	2s. 6d. black and red/*blue* (1927)			12·00	24·00
47b	4	5s. green and red/*yellow* (1929)			26·00	42·00
37/47b				Set of 16	50·00	£100
37/47b	Optd/Perf "Specimen"			Set of 16	£325	

In the Specimen set above No. 38 is overprinted. A later printing exists perforated "Specimen" (*Price* £70).

6 Old Road Bay and Mount Misery

(Typo D.L.R.)

1923. *Tercentenary of Colony. Chalk-surfaced paper. P* 14.
(a) *Wmk Mult Script CA* (*sideways*)
48	6	½d. black and green			2·00	6·00
49		1d. black and bright violet			2·00	1·50
50		1½d. black and scarlet			4·00	7·50
51		2d. black and slate-grey			1·75	1·50
52		2½d. black and brown			3·50	20·00
53		3d. black and ultramarine			3·25	12·00
54		6d. black and bright purple			8·00	23·00
55		1s. black and sage-green			27·00	27·00
56		2s. black and blue/*blue*			27·00	48·00
57		2s. 6d. black and red/*blue*			38·00	65·00
58		10s. black and red/*emerald*			£225	£325
		(b) *Wmk Mult Crown CA* (*sideways*)				
59	6	5s. black and red/*pale yellow*			60·00	£150
60		£1 black and purple/*red*			£750	£1200
48/60				Set of 13	£1000	£1700
48/60	Optd "Specimen"			Set of 13	£700	

1935 (6 May). *Silver Jubilee. As Nos. 114/17 of Jamaica, but ptd by Waterlow. P* 11×12.
61		1d. deep blue and scarlet			1·00	40
		j. Kite and vertical log			28·00	
		k. Kite and horizontal log			45·00	
62		1½d. ultramarine and grey			75	75
		j. Kite and vertical log			32·00	
63		2½d. brown and deep blue			1·00	80
64		1s. slate and purple			5·50	11·00
		j. Kite and vertical log			85·00	
		k. Kite and horizontal log			90·00	
61/4				Set of 4	7·50	11·50
61/4	Perf "Specimen"			Set of 4	75·00	

For illustrations of plate varieties see Omnibus section following Zimbabwe.

1937 (12 May). *Coronation. As Nos. 118/20 of Jamaica.*
65		1d. scarlet			30	15
66		1½d. buff			35	10
67		2½d. bright blue			40	35
65/7				Set of 3	95	55
65/7	Perf "Specimen"			Set of 3	50·00	

Nos. 61/7 are inscribed "ST. CHRISTOPHER AND NEVIS".

7 King George VI

8 King George VI and Medicinal Spring

9 King George VI and Christopher Columbus

10 King George VI and Anguilla Island

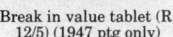
Break in value tablet (R. 12/5) (1947 ptg only)

Break in oval (R. 12/1) (1938 ptg only)

Break in value tablet frame (R.3/2)

Break in value tablet frame (R.12/3) (ptgs between 1941 and 1945 only)

Break in frame above ornament (R. 2/4) (ptgs between 1941 and 1944)

Break in oval at foot (R. 12/5) (ptgs between 1941 and 1945 only). Sometimes touched-in by hand painting)

Break in oval at left (R. 7/1) (1943 and 1944 ptgs only)

(Typo; centre litho (T 10). D.L.R.)

1938 (15 Aug)–**50**. *Wmk Mult Script CA* (sideways on T 8 and 9). *Chalk-surfaced paper* (10s., £1). *P* 14 (*T* 7 *and* 10) *or* 13×12 (*T* 8/9).

68	7	½d. green	..	2·00	10
		a. Blue-green (5.4.43)	..	10	10
69		1d. scarlet	..	2·75	60
		a. Carmine (5.43)	..	30	30
		b. Rose-red (1947)	..	40	30
70		1½d. orange	..	15	20
71	8	2d. scarlet and grey	..	13·00	2·25
		a. Chalk-surfaced paper. Carmine and deep grey (1940)	..	40·00	9·00
		b. Perf 14. Scarlet and pale grey (1941)	70	90
		ba. Scarlet and deep grey (5.43)	..	17·00	5·00
		c. Perf 14. Chalk-surfaced paper. Scarlet and pale grey (8.49)	..	1·25	1·00
72	7	2½d. ultramarine	..	2·50	30
		a. Bright ultramarine (5.4.43)	..	15	20
73	8	3d. dull reddish purple and scarlet	..	9·00	1·40
		a. Chalk-surfaced paper. Brown-purple & carmine-vermilion (1940)	12·00	2·75
		b. Perf 14. Chalk-surfaced paper. Deep reddish purple and scarlet (1942) ..	15·00	2·00
		c. Perf 14. Ordinary paper. Reddish lilac and scarlet (5.43)	..	1·25	10·00
		d. Perf 14. Ordinary paper. Purple and bright scarlet (1945, 1947)	..	2·00	2·00
		da. Break in value tablet			
		e. Perf 14. Chalk-surfaced paper. Reddish purple and scarlet (1946)	50·00	18·00
		f. Perf 14. Ordinary paper. Rose-lilac and bright scarlet (1948)	..	2·50	3·00
		g. Perf 14. Chalk-surfaced paper. Deep reddish purple & brt scarlet (1950)	1·25	1·75
74	9	6d. green and bright purple	..	6·00	1·50
		a. Break in oval	..	60·00	
		b. Perf 14. Chalk-surfaced paper. Green and deep claret (1942) ..	35·00	10·00
		c. Perf 14. Ordinary paper. Green and purple (5.43)	..	2·75	1·25
		d. Perf 14. Chalk-surfaced paper. Green and purple (10.48)	..	1·50	1·50
75	8	1s. black and green	..	11·00	1·25
		a. Break in value tablet frame	..	75·00	
		b. Perf 14 (1943)	..	2·25	75
		ba. Break in value tablet frame	..	42·00	
		c. Perf 14. Chalk-surfaced paper (28.7.49)	..	75	1·00
		ca. Break in value tablet frame	..	30·00	
76		2s. 6d. black and scarlet	..	20·00	9·00
		a. Perf 14. Chalk-surfaced paper (1942)	..	7·50	3·50
		ab. Ordinary paper (5.43)	..	7·00	3·50
77	9	5s. green and scarlet ..	..	60·00	10·00
		a. Perf 14. Chalk-surfaced paper (1941)	..	19·00	9·00
		ab. Break in value tablet frame	£130	
		ac. Break in frame above ornament	£130	
		ad. Break in oval at foot	£130	
		ae. Break in oval at left	£130	
		b. Perf 14. Ordinary paper (5.43)	..	17·00	7·00
		ba. Break in value tablet frame	£110	
		bb. Break in frame above ornament	£120	
		bc. Break in oval at foot	£100	
		bd. Break in oval at left	£110	
77c	10	10s. black and ultramarine (1.9.48)	12·00	18·00
77d		£1 black and brown (1.9.48)	..	15·00	22·00
68/77d			Set of 12	50·00	50·00
68/77 Perf "Specimen"			Set of 10	£180	

1946 (1 Nov). *Victory. As Nos. 141/2 of Jamaica.*

78		1½d. red-orange	..	10	10
79		3d. carmine	..	10	10
78/9 Perf "Specimen"		Set of 2	60·00	

1949 (3 Jan). *Royal Silver Wedding. As Nos. 143/4 of Jamaica.*

80		2½d. ultramarine	..	10	10
81		5s. carmine	..	4·00	2·50

1949 (10 Oct). *75th Anniv of U.P.U. As Nos. 145/8 of Jamaica.*

82		2½d. ultramarine	..	35	10
83		3d. carmine-red	..	40	30
84		6d. magenta	..	40	30
85		1s. blue-green	..	40	30
82/5			Set of 4	1·40	90

ANGUILLA

ANGUILLA

TERCENTENARY 1650-1950 (11)

TERCENTENARY 1650—1950 (12)

1950 (10 Nov). *Tercentenary of British Settlement in Anguilla. Nos. 69b, 70 and 72a (perf 14) optd as T* 11 *and new ptgs of T* 8/9 *on chalk-surfaced paper perf* 13×12½ *optd as T* 12.

86	7	1d. rose-red	..	10	10
87		1½d. orange	..	10	10
		a. Error. Crown missing, W 9a	..	£1000	
		b. Error. St. Edward's Crown, W 9b	..	£650	
88		2½d. bright ultramarine	..	10	10
89	8	3d. dull purple and scarlet	..	10	10
90	9	6d. green and bright purple	..	10	10
91	8	1s. black and green (R.)	..	10	10
		a. Break in value tablet frame	..	8·00	
86/91			Set of 6	40	40

Nos. 87a/b occur on a row in the watermark, in which the crowns and letters "CA" alternate.

(New Currency. 100 cents = 1 West Indian dollar)

1951 (16 Feb). *Inauguration of B.W.I. University College. As Nos.* 149/50 *of Jamaica.*

92		3c. black and yellow-orange	..	20	10
93		12c. turquoise-green and magenta	..	20	20

ST. CHRISTOPHER, NEVIS AND ANGUILLA
LEGISLATIVE COUNCIL

13 Bath House and Spa, Nevis

14 Map of the Islands

1952 (14 June). *Vert designs as T* 14 (3, 12 *c.*) *or horiz as* 13 (*others*). *Wmk Mult Script CA. P* 12½.

94		1 c. deep green and ochre	..	15	35
95		2 c. green	..	20	30
96		3 c. carmine-red and violet	..	30	40
97		4 c. scarlet	..	20	20
98		5 c. bright blue and grey	..	20	10
99		6 c. ultramarine	..	20	15
100		12 c. deep blue and reddish brown	..	20	10
101		24 c. black and carmine-red	..	20	10
102		48 c. olive and chocolate	..	1·50	1·50
103		60 c. ochre and deep green	..	1·50	1·50
104		$1.20, deep green and ultramarine	..	4·50	1·75
105		$4.80, green and carmine	..	11·00	17·00
94/105			Set of 12	18·00	21·00

Designs:—2 c. Warner Park; 4 c. Brimstone Hill; 5 c. Nevis from the sea, North; 6 c. Pinney's Beach, Nevis; 12 c. Sir Thomas Warner's Tomb; 24 c. Old Road Bay; 48 c. Sea Island cotton, Nevis; 60 c. The Treasury; $1.20, Salt pond, Anguilla; $4.80, Sugar factory.

1953 (2 June). *Coronation. As No.* 153 *of Jamaica.*

106		2 c. black and bright green	..	10	10

25 Sombrero Lighthouse

26 Map of Anguilla and Dependencies

(Recess Waterlow (until 1961), then D.L.R.)

1954 (1 Mar)–**63**. *Designs previously used for King George VI issue, but with portrait of Queen Elizabeth II as in T* 25/6 *or new values and designs* (½ *c.,* 8 *c.,* $2.40). *Wmk Mult Script CA. P* 12½.

106a		½ c. deep olive (3.7.56)	..	30	10
107		1 c. deep green and ochre	..	20	10
		a. Deep green and orange-ochre (13.2.62)	1·00	1·25
		b. Imperf vert (horiz strip of three)	† £1600	
108		2 c. green	..	45	10
		a. Yellow-green (31.7.63)	..	3·50	3·50
109		3 c. carmine-red and violet	..	65	10
		a. Carmine and deep violet (31.7.63)	3·50	4·00
110		4 c. scarlet	..	15	10
111		5 c. bright blue and grey	..	15	10
112		6 c. ultramarine	..	30	10
		a. Blue (19.2.63)	..	1·00	30
112b		8 c. grey-black (1.2.57)	..	4·00	10
113		12 c. deep blue and red-brown	..	15	10
114		24 c. black and carmine-red (1.12.54)	15	10
115		48 c. olive-bistre and chocolate (1.12.54)	60	50
116		60 c. ochre and deep green (1.12.54)	..	2·25	85
117		$1.20, dp green & ultramarine (1.12.54)	9·00	90
		a. Deep green and violet-blue (19.2.63)	16·00	4·00
117b		$2.40, black and red-orange (1.2.57)	8·00	11·00
118		$4.80, green and carmine (1.12.54)	12·00	11·00
106a/18			Set of 15	35·00	22·00

Design: *Horiz*—½ c., $1.20 Salt Pond; 1 c. Bath House and Spa; 2 c. Warner Park; 4 c. Brimstone Hill; 5 c. Nevis from the sea, North; 6 c. Pinney's Beach; 24 c. Old Road Bay; 48 c. Sea Island cotton; 60 c. The Treasury; $4.80, Sugar factory. *Vert*—3 c. Map of the islands; 12 c. Sir Thomas Warner's Tomb.

Stamps of St. Christopher, Nevis and Anguilla were in concurrent use with the stamps inscribed "LEEWARD ISLANDS" until 1 July 1956, when the general Leeward Islands stamps were withdrawn.

27 Alexander Hamilton and View of Nevis

(Des Eva Wilkin. Recess Waterlow)

1957 (11 Jan). *Birth Bicentenary of Alexander Hamilton. Wmk Mult Script CA. P* 12½.

119	27	24 c. green and deep blue	..	20	10

1958 (22 Apr). *Inauguration of British Caribbean Federation. As Nos.* 175/7 *of Jamaica.*

120		3 c. deep green	..	45	10
121		6 c. blue	..	80	1·00
122		12 c. scarlet	..	1·25	25
120/2			Set of 3	2·25	1·25

MINISTERIAL GOVERNMENT

28 One Penny Stamp of 1861

(Recess Waterlow)

1961 (15 July). *Nevis Stamp Centenary. T* 28 *and similar horiz designs. W w* 12. *P* 14.

123		2 c. red-brown and green	..	15	20
124		8 c. red-brown and deep blue..	20	10
125		12 c. black and carmine-red	..	25	15
126		24 c. deep bluish green and red-orange	30	15
123/6			Set of 4	80	50

Designs:—8 c. Fourpence stamp of 1861; 12 c. Sixpence stamp of 1861; 24 c. One shilling stamp of 1861.

1963 (2 Sept). *Red Cross Centenary. As Nos. 203/4 of Jamaica.*

127		3 c. red and black	..	10	10
128		12 c. red and blue	..	20	40

32 New Lighthouse, Sombrero   33 Loading Sugar Cane, St. Kitts

(Des V. Whiteley. Photo Harrison)

1963 (20 Nov)–**65**. *Vert designs as T* 32 (2, 3, 15, 25, 60 *c.,* $1, $5) *or horiz as* 33 (*others*) *in sepia and light blue* (½ *c.*), *greenish yellow and blue* ($1) *or multicoloured* (*others*). *W w* 12 (*upright*). *P* 14.

129		½ c. Type 32	..	10	10
130		1 c. Type 33	..	10	10
131		2 c. Pall Mall Square, Basseterre ..	10	10
		a. White fountain and Church	..	90·00	
132		3 c. Gateway, Brimstone Hill Fort, St. Kitts	10	10
133		4 c. Nelson's Spring, Nevis	..	10	10
134		5 c. Grammar School, St. Kitts	..	30	10
135		6 c. Crater, Mt Misery, St. Kitts	..	10	10
136		10 c. Hibiscus	..	15	10
137		15 c. Sea Island cotton, Nevis	..	35	10
138		20 c. Boat building, Anguilla	..	20	10
139		25 c. White-crowned Pigeon (turquoise-blue background)	..	65	10
		a. Turquoise-green background (13.4.65)	2·75	85
140		50 c. St. George's Church Tower, Basseterre	40	25
141		60 c. Alexander Hamilton	..	1·00	25
142		$1 Map of St. Kitts-Nevis	..	2·25	40
143		$2.50, Map of Anguilla	..	2·25	2·00
144		$5 Arms of St. Christopher, Nevis and Anguilla	..	3·50	3·00
129/44			Set of 16	10·00	6·00

The 1, 4, 5, 6, 10 and 20 c. values exist with PVA gum as well as gum arabic.

See also Nos. 166/71.

ARTS FESTIVAL ST KITTS 1964 (48)

49 Festival Emblem

1964 (14 Sept). *Arts Festival. Nos.* 132 *and* 139 *optd as T* 48.

145		3 c. Gateway, Brimstone Hill Fort, St. Kitts	10	10
		a. Opt double	..	£150	
146		25 c. White-crowned Pigeon	..	20	10
		a. "FESTIVAI" (R. 1/10)	..	55·00	

1965 (17 May). *I.T.U. Centenary. As Nos.* 98/9 *of Lesotho.*

147		2 c. bistre-yellow and rose-carmine	..	10	10
148		50 c. turquoise-blue and yellow-olive ..	40	35

1965 (15 Oct). *International Co-operation Year. As Nos.* 100/1 *of Lesotho.*

149		2 c. reddish purple and turquoise-green	10	20
150		25 c. deep bluish green and lavender	..	20	10

1966 (24 Jan). *Churchill Commemoration. As Nos.* 102/5 *of Lesotho.*

151		½ c. new blue	..	10	15
		a. Value omitted	..	£130	
		b. Value at left instead of right ..	50·00	
152		3 c. deep green	..	15	10
153		15 c. brown	..	30	20
154		25 c. bluish violet	..	35	20
151/4			Set of 4	75	55

1966 (4 Feb). *Royal Visit. As Nos. 183/4 of Montserrat.*
155   3 c. black and ultramarine   10   15
156   25 c. black and magenta   ..   30   15

1966 (1 July). *World Cup Football Championships. As Nos. 57/8 of Pitcairn Islands.*
157   6 c. violet, yellow-green, lake & yellow-brn ..   15   20
158   25 c. chocolate, blue-green, lake & yell-brn ..   35   10

(Photo Harrison)

1966 (15 Aug). *Arts Festival. P 14 × 14½.*
159   **49**   3 c. black, buff, emerald-green and gold   10   10
160   25 c. black, buff, emerald-green and silver   20   10

1966 (20 Sept). *Inauguration of W.H.O. Headquarters, Geneva. As Nos. 185/6 of Montserrat.*
161   3 c. black, yellow-green, and light blue   ..   10   10
162   40 c. black, light purple, and yellow-brown   ..   20   20

1966 (1 Dec). *20th Anniv of U.N.E.S.C.O. As Nos. 342/4 of Mauritius.*
163   3 c. slate-violet, red, yellow and orange   ..   10   10
164   6 c. orange-yellow, violet and deep olive   ..   10   10
165   40 c. black, bright purple and orange   ..   30   35
163/5   ..   ..   *Set of 3*   40   45

ASSOCIATED STATEHOOD

1967–69. *As Nos. 129, 131/2, 137, 139 and 142 but wmk sideways.*
166   **20**   ½ c. sepia and light blue (9.1.69)   ..   15   80
167   —   2 c. multicoloured (27.6.67)   ..   1·25   10
168   —   3 c. multicoloured (16.7.68)   ..   15   10
169   —   15 c. multicoloured (16.7.68)   ..   70   30
170   —   25 c. multicoloured (16.7.68)   ..   2·50   20
171   — $1 greenish yellow and blue (16.7.68)   5·00   4·00
   a. Greenish yellow & ultramarine-blue
   (19.12.69)   ..   ..   9·50   5·00
166/71   ..   ..   ..   *Set of 6*   8·75   5·00
The 2 c. and $1 values exist with PVA gum as well as gum arabic. Nos. 172/81 vacant.

50 Government Headquarters, Basseterre   53 John Wesley and Cross

(Des V. Whiteley. Photo Harrison)

1967 (1 July). *Statehood. T 50 and similar horiz designs. Multicoloured. W w 12. P 14½ × 14.*
182   3 c. Type **50**   10   10
183   10 c. National Flag   10   10
184   25 c. Coat of Arms   15   10
182/4 ..   ..   *Set of 3*   30   20

(Litho D.L.R.)

1967 (1 Dec). *West Indies Methodist Conference. T 53 and similar vert designs. P 13 × 13½.*
185   3 c. black, cerise and reddish violet   ..   10   10
186   25 c. black, light greenish blue and blue   ..   15   10
187   40 c. black, yellow and orange   15   10
185/7 ..   ..   *Set of 3*   30   20
Designs:—25 c. Charles Wesley and Cross; 40 c. Thomas Coke and Cross.

56 "Herald" Aircraft over *Jamaica Producer* (freighter)   57 Dr. Martin Luther King

(Des and litho D.L.R.)

1968 (30 July). *Caribbean Free Trade Area. W w 12 (sideways). P 13.*
188   **56**   25 c. multicoloured   15   10
189   50 c. multicoloured   15   10

(Des G. Vasarhelyi. Litho Enschedé)

1968 (30 Sept). *Martin Luther King Commemoration. W w 12. P 12 × 12½.*
190   **57**   50 c. multicoloured   10   10

58 "Mystic Nativity" (Botticelli)   60 Tarpon

(Des and photo Harrison)

1968 (27 Nov). *Christmas. Paintings. T 58 and similar vert design. Multicoloured. W w 12 (sideways). P 14½ × 14.*
191   12 c. Type **58**   10   10
192   25 c. "The Adoration of the Magi" (Rubens)   ..   10   10
193   40 c. Type **58**   10   10
194   50 c. As 25 c.   10   10
191/4 ..   ..   *Set of 4*   30   30

(Des G. Drummond. Photo Harrison)

1969 (25 Feb). *Fishes. T 60 and similar horiz designs. W w 12. P 14 × 14½.*
195   6 c. multicoloured   10   10
196   12 c. black, turquoise-green & greenish blue   15   10
197   40 c. multicoloured   20   10
198   50 c. multicoloured   25   15
195/8 ..   ..   *Set of 4*   60   30
Designs:—12 c. Garfish; 40 c. Horse-eye Jack; 50 c. Redsnapper.

64 The Warner Badge and Islands   67 "The Adoration of the Kings" (Mostaert)

(Des V. Whiteley. Litho Format)

1969 (1 Sept). *Sir Thomas Warner Commemoration. T 64 and similar horiz designs. Multicoloured. W w 12 (sideways). P 13½ × 14.*
199   20 c. Type **64**   10   10
200   25 c. Sir Thomas Warner's tomb   ..   10   10
201   40 c. Charles I's commission   15   15
199/201   ..   ..   ..   *Set of 3*   30   30

(Des Enschedé. Litho B.W.)

1969 (17 Nov). *Christmas. Paintings. T 67 and similar vert design. Multicoloured. W w 12 (sideways). P 13½.*
202   10 c. Type **67**   10   10
203   25 c. Type **67**   10   10
204   40 c. "The Adoration of the Kings" (Geertgen)   10   10
205   50 c. As 40 c.   10   10
202/5 ..   ..   *Set of 4*   30   30

73 Portuguese Caravels (16th-cent)

(Des and litho J.W.)

1970 (2 Feb–8 Sept). *Designs as T 73 in black, pale orange and emerald (½ c.) or multicoloured (others). W w 12 (upright on vert designs, sideways on horiz designs). P 14.*
206   ½ c. Pirates and treasure at Frigate Bay (*vert*)   10   10
207   1 c. English two-decker warship, 1650 (*vert*)   30   10
208   2 c. Naval flags of colonizing nations (*vert*) ..   15   10
209   3 c. Rapier hilt (17th-century) (*vert*)..   15   10
210   4 c. Type **73**   20   10
211   5 c. Sir Henry Morgan and fireships, 1669 ..   30   10
212   6 c. L'Ollonois and pirate carrack (16th-
   century)   30   10
213   10 c. 17th-century smugglers' ship   ..   30   10
214   15 c. "Piece-of-eight" (*vert*) (I)   ..   1·75   40
214a   15 c. "Piece-of-eight" (*vert*) (II) (8.9.70)   50   10
215   20 c. Cannon (17th-century)   ..   35   10
216   25 c. Humphrey Cole's Astrolabe, 1574 (*vert*)   40   10
217   50 c. Flintlock pistol (17th-century)   ..   85   80
218   60 c. Dutch flute (17th-century) (*vert*)..   2·25   70
219   $1 Captain Bartholomew Roberts and his
   crew's death warrant (*vert*)   ..   2·50   75
220   $2.50, Railing piece (16th-century)..   2·00   3·00
221   $5 Drake, Hawkins and sea battle ..   2·50   4·25
206/221   ..   ..   *Set of 17*   13·50   9·00
Nos. 214/a. Type I, coin inscribed "HISPANIANUM"; Type II, corrected to "HISPANIARUM". No. 214a also differs considerably in shade from No. 214.
See also Nos. 269/80 and 322/31.

85 Graveyard Scene (*Great Expectations*)

(Des Jennifer Toombs. Litho B.W.)

1970 (1 May). *Death Centenary of Charles Dickens. T 85 and similar designs. W w 12 (sideways on horiz designs). P 13.*
222   4 c. bistre-brown, gold and deep blue-green ..   10   10
223   20 c. bistre-brown, gold and reddish purple   ..   10   10
224   25 c. bistre-brown, gold and olive-green   ..   10   10
225   40 c. bistre-brown, gold and ultramarine   ..   10   15
222/5 ..   ..   ..   *Set of 4*   30   30
Designs: *Horiz*—20 c. Miss Havisham and Pip (*Great Expectations*). *Vert*—25 c. Dickens's Birthplace; 40 c. Charles Dickens.

86 Local Steel Band

(Des V. Whiteley. Litho Enschedé)

1970 (1 Aug). *Festival of Arts. T 86 and similar horiz designs. Multicoloured. W w 12 (sideways). P 13½.*
226   20 c. Type **86**   10   10
227   25 c. Local String Band   10   10
228   40 c. Scene from *A Midsummer Night's Dream*   15   15
226/8 ..   ..   ..   *Set of 3*   30   30

87 1d. Stamp of 1870 and Post Office, 1970   88 "Adoration of the Shepherds" (detail) (Frans van Floris)

(Des J. Cooter. Litho J.W.)

1970 (14 Sept). *Stamp Centenary. T 87 and similar horiz designs. W w 12 (sideways). P 14½.*
229   ½ c. green and rose   10   10
230   20 c. deep blue, green and rose   ..   10   10
231   25 c. brown-purple, green and rose   ..   10   10
232   50 c. scarlet, green and black   30   45
229/32 ..   ..   ..   *Set of 4*   50   50
Designs:—20 c., 25 c. 1d. and 6d. Stamps of 1870; 50 c. 6d. Stamp of 1870 and early postmark.

(Des Enschedé. Litho Format)

1970 (16 Nov). *Christmas. T 88 and similar vert design. Multicoloured. W w 12. P 14.*
233   3 c. Type **88**   10   10
234   20 c. "The Holy Family" (Van Dyck) ..   10   10
235   25 c. As 20 c.   10   10
236   40 c. Type **88**   15   20
233/6 ..   ..   ..   *Set of 4*   30   40

89 Monkey Fiddle

(Des Sylvia Goaman. Litho Format)

1971 (1 Mar). *Flowers. T 89 and similar horiz designs. Multicoloured. W w 12 (sideways). P 14½.*
237   5 c. Type **89**   10   10
238   20 c. Tropical Mountain Violet   ..   20   10
239   30 c. Trailing Morning Glory   20   10
240   50 c. Fringed Epidendrum   ..   40   50
237/40 ..   ..   ..   *Set of 4*   75   65

90 Royal Poinciana

(Des Enschedé. Litho J.W.)

1971 (1 June). *Phillipe de Poincy Commemoration.* T **90** *and similar multicoloured designs.* W w **12** (*sideways on* 20 *and* 30 c.). P 13½.

241	20 c. Type **90**	..	10	10
242	30 c. Château de Poincy	..	10	10
243	50 c. De Poincy's badge (*vert*) ..		20	15
241/3	..	Set of 3	35	30

91 The East Yorks   **92** "Crucifixion" (Massys)

(Des V. Whiteley. Litho Walsall)

1971 (1 Sept). *Siege of Brimstone Hill, 1782.* T **91** *and similar horiz designs. Multicoloured.* W w **12** (*sideways*). P 14½.

244	½ c. Type **91**	..	10	10
245	20 c. Royal Artillery	..	45	10
246	30 c. French infantry	..	55	10
247	50 c. The Royal Scots	..	75	20
244/7	..	Set of 4	1·60	35

(Des J. Cooter. Litho J.W.)

1972 (1 Apr). *Easter.* W w **12**. P 14 × 13½.

248	**92**	4 c. multicoloured	10	10
249		20 c. multicoloured	10	10
250		30 c. multicoloured	10	10
251		40 c. multicoloured	10	10
248/51		Set of 4	30	30

93 "Virgin and Child"   **94** Brown Pelicans
(Borgognone)

(Des J. Cooter. Litho J.W.)

1972 (2 Oct). *Christmas.* T **93** *and similar multicoloured designs.* W w **12** (*sideways on vert designs*). P 14.

252	3 c. Type **93**		10	10
253	20 c. "Adoration of the Kings" (J. Bassano) (*horiz*)		15	10
254	25 c. "Adoration of the Shepherds" (Domenichino)		15	10
255	40 c. "Virgin and Child" (Fiorenzo di Lorenzo)		20	10
252/5	..	Set of 4	45	30

(Des from photograph by D. Groves) and photo Harrison)

1972 (20 Nov). *Royal Silver Wedding. Multicoloured; background colour given.* W w **12**. P 14 × 14½.

256	**94**	20 c. carmine	15	15
257		25 c. bright blue ..	15	15

95 Landing on St. Christopher, 1623   **96** "The Last Supper" (Titian)

(Des J.W. Litho Questa)

1973 (28 Jan). *350th Anniv of Sir Thomas Warner's landing on St. Christopher.* T **95** *and similar horiz designs. Multicoloured.* W w **12**. P 13½.

258	4 c. Type **95**		15	10
259	25 c. Growing tobacco		15	10
260	40 c. Building fort at Old Road		20	10
261	$2.50, Concepcion		80	1·10
258/61		Set of 4	1·10	1·25

(Des J. Cooter. Litho Walsall)

1973 (16 Apr). *Easter.* T **96** *and similar multicoloured designs showing paintings of "The Last Supper" by the artists listed.* W w **12** (*sideways on* $2.50). P 13½ × 14 ($2.50) *or* 14 × 13½ (*others*).

262	4 c. Type **96**		10	10
263	25 c. Ascr to Roberti		10	10
264	$2.50, Juan de Juanes (*horiz*)		70	60
262/4	..	Set of 3	75	60

VISIT OF
H. R. H. THE PRINCE OF WALES 1973
(97)

1973 (31 May). *Royal Visit. Nos.* 258/61 *optd with* T **97** *by Questa.*

265	4 c. Type **95**		10	15
266	25 c. Growing tobacco		10	15
267	40 c. Building fort at Old Road		15	15
268	$2.50 Concepcion		45	50
265/8	..	Set of 4	65	85

(Des J.W. Litho Harrison ($10), J.W. (others))

1973 (12 Sept)–74. *As Nos.* 206, 208/9, 211/13, 214a/17, 219 *and new horiz design* ($10), *but* W w **12** (*sideways on vert designs, upright on horiz designs*).

269	½ c. Pirates and treasure at Frigate Bay	..	10	40
270	2 c. Naval flags of colonizing nations		20	45
271	3 c. Rapier hilt		20	45
272	5 c. Sir Henry Morgan and fireships, 1669 ..		35	45
273	6 c. L'Ollonois and pirate carrack (16th-century)		35	40
274	10 c. 17th-century smugglers' ship	..	40	60
275	15 c. "Piece-of-eight" (II)		65	85
276	20 c. Cannon (17th-century)		75	95
277	25 c. Humphrey Cole's Astrolabe, 1574		80	1·75
278	50 c. Flintlock pistol (17th-century)	..	1·10	1·50
279	$1 Captain Bartholomew Roberts and his crew's death warrant	..	2·75	3·50
280	$10 "The Apprehension of Blackbeard" (Edward Teach) (16.11.74)		20·00	13·00
269/80		Set of 12	25·00	22·00

Nos. 281/4 vacant.

99 Harbour Scene and 2d. Stamp of 1903

(Des V. Whiteley Studio. Litho Enschedé)

1973 (1 Oct). *70th Anniv of First St. Kitts-Nevis Stamps.* T **99** *and similar horiz designs. Multicoloured.* W w **12** (*sideways*). P 13 × 13½.

285	4 c. Type **99**		10	10
286	25 c. Sugar-mill and 1d. stamp of 1903		15	10
287	40 c. Unloading boat and ½d. stamp of 1903		35	10
288	$2.50, Rock-carvings and 3d. stamp of 1903		2·00	1·00
285/8		Set of 4	2·25	1·10
MS289	144 × 95 mm. Nos. 285/8 ..	..	2·75	5·50

1973 (14 Nov). *Royal Wedding. As Nos.* 322/3 *of Montserrat.*

290	25 c. light emerald		15	10
291	40 c. brown-ochre	..	15	10

100 "Madonna and Child"   **101** "Christ carrying the
(Murillo)   Cross" (S. del Piombo)

(Des J. Cooter. Litho Format)

1973 (1 Dec). *Christmas.* T **100** *and similar multicoloured designs showing "The Holy Family" by the artists listed.* W w **12** (*sideways on* $1). P 13½.

292	4 c. Type **100**		10	10
293	40 c. Mengs		20	10
294	60 c. Sassoferrato		25	15
295	$1 Filippino Lippi (*horiz*)		35	30
292/5	..	Set of 4	75	50

(Des J. Cooter. Litho D.L.R.)

1974 (8 Apr). *Easter.* T **101** *and similar multicoloured designs.* W w **12** (*sideways on* $2.50). P 13½.

296	4 c. Type **101**		10	10
297	25 c. "The Crucifixion" (Goya)		15	10
298	40 c. "The Trinity" (Ribera)		15	10
299	$2.50, "The Deposition" (Fra Bartolomeo) (*horiz*)		1·00	75
296/9	..	Set of 4	1·25	75

102 University Centre, St. Kitts   **103** Hands reaching for Globe

(Des G. Drummond. Litho Questa)

1974 (1 June). *25th Anniv of University of West Indies.* T **102** *and similar horiz design. Multicoloured.* W w **12** (*sideways*). P 13½.

300	10 c. Type **102**		10	10
301	$1 As Type **102** but showing different buildings		20	25
MS302	99 × 95 mm. Nos. 300/1 ..	..	35	65

(Des Jennifer Toombs. Litho Questa)

1974 (5 Aug). *Family Planning.* T **103** *and similar designs.* W w **12** (*sideways on* 25 c. *and* $2.50). P 14.

303	4 c. orange-brown, new blue and black		10	10
304	25 c. multicoloured		10	10
305	40 c. multicoloured		10	10
306	$2.50, multicoloured		35	55
303/6	..	Set of 4	50	65

Designs: *Horiz*—25 c. Instruction by nurse; $2.50, Emblem and globe on scales. *Vert*—40 c. Family group.

104 Churchill as Army   **105** Aeroplane and Map
Lieutenant

(Des PAD Studio. Litho Questa)

1974 (30 Nov). *Birth Centenary of Sir Winston Churchill.* T **104** *and similar vert designs. Multicoloured.* W w **12**. P 13½.

307	4 c. Type **104**		10	10
308	25 c. Churchill as Prime Minister		15	10
309	40 c. Churchill as Knight of the Garter		25	10
310	60 c. Churchill's statue, London		35	10
307/10		Set of 4	70	30
MS311	99 × 148 mm. Nos. 307/10		1·00	1·50

(Des J.W. Litho Questa)

1974 (16 Dec). *Opening of Golden Rock Airport, St. Kitts. Sheets* 98 × 148 *mm.* W w **12**. P 13½.

MS312	**105**	40 c. multicoloured ..	20	40
MS313		45 c. multicoloured ..	20	40

106 "The Last Supper"   **107** E.C.C.A. H.Q. Buildings,
(Doré)   Basseterre

(Des PAD Studio. Litho Questa)

1975 (24 Mar). *Easter.* T **106** *and similar vert designs showing paintings by Doré. Multicoloured.* W w **12**. P 14½.

314	4 c. Type **106**		10	10
315	25 c. "Christ Mocked"		10	10
316	40 c. "Jesus falling beneath the Cross"		10	10
317	$1 "The Erection of the Cross"		25	30
314/17	..	Set of 4	40	40

(Des J. Cooter. Litho Enschedé)

1975 (2 June*). *Opening of East Caribbean Currency Authority's Headquarters.* T **107** *and similar horiz designs.* W w **14** (*sideways*). P 13 × 13½.

318	12 c. multicoloured		10	10
319	25 c. multicoloured		10	10
320	40 c. light vermilion, silver and grey-black ..		15	10
321	45 c. multicoloured		15	15
	a. Silver omitted† ..		85·00	
318/21	..	Set of 4	30	30

Designs:—25 c. Specimen one-dollar banknote; 40 c. Half-dollar of 1801 and current 4-dollar coin; 45 c. Coins of 1801 and 1960.

*This is the local date of issue; the Crown Agents released the stamps on 28 April.

†This affects the dull silver coin on the left which on No. 321a appears in tones of the black plate.

1975–77. *As Nos. 207, 209/13, 214a/15 and 218/19 but W w 14 (sideways on 4, 5, 6, 10, 20 and 60 c.).*
A. *White, ordinary paper.*
B. *Cream, chalk-surfaced paper.*

		A		B	
322	1 c. English two-decker warship, 1650		†	30	30
323	3 c. Rapier hilt (17th-century)	20	10	1·75	2·00
324	4 c. Type **73**	20	10	1·75	2·00
325	5 c. Sir Henry Morgan and fireships, 1669	30	40	4·50	4·50
326	6 c. L'Ollonois and pirate carrack (16th-century)	80	10	1·00	2·00
327	10 c. 17th-century smugglers' ship	45	15	1·00	2·00
328	15 c. "Piece-of-eight" (II)	55	15	5·00	5·00
329	20 c. Cannon (17th-century)	1·40	2·75	1·75	5·00
330	60 c. Dutch flute (17th-century)	6·00	1·75		†
331	$1 Captain Bartholomew Roberts and his crew's death warrant		†	9·00	3·00
323A/30A	*Set of 8*	9·00	5·00		
322B/31B	*Set of 9*			23·00	23·00

Dates of issue: Ordinary paper—5, 6 and 20 c. 11.6.75; others 11.6.76. Chalk-surfaced paper—5, 15 c. and $1 16.8.77; others 17.5.77
Nos. 332/7 vacant.

108 Evangeline Booth
(Salvation Army General)

109 Golfer

(Des Jennifer Toombs. Litho Questa)

1975 (15 Sept). *International Women's Year. T* **108** *and similar vert designs. Multicoloured. W w 12. P 14.*

338	4 c. Type **108**	10	10
339	25 c. Sylvia Pankhurst	25	10
340	40 c. Marie Curie	50	30
341	$2.50, Lady Annie Allen (teacher and guider)	2·00	2·75
338/41	*Set of 4*	2·50	3·00

(Des Sue Lawes. Litho Questa)

1975 (1 Nov). *Opening of Frigate Bay Golf Course. W w 14 (sideways). P 13½.*

342	**109** 4 c. black and rose-red	25	10
343	25 c. black and greenish yellow	45	10
344	40 c. black and light emerald	55	10
345	$1 black and new blue	1·00	70
342/5	*Set of 4*	2·00	75

110 "St. Paul" (Pier
Francesco Sacchi)

111 "Crucifixion"
(detail)

(Des J.W. Litho Questa)

1975 (1 Dec). *Christmas. T* **110** *and similar vert designs showing details from paintings in the National Gallery, London. Multicoloured. W w 14. P 13½.*

346	25 c. Type **110**	20	10
347	40 c. "St James" (Bonifazio di Pitati)	35	10
348	45 c. "St. John the Baptist" (Mola)	35	10
349	$1 "St. Mary" (Raphael)	70	60
346/9	*Set of 4*	1·40	70

(Des J. Cooter. Litho Questa)

1976 (14 Apr). *Easter. Stained-glass Windows. T* **111** *and similar vert designs. Multicoloured. W w 14. P 14 × 13½ (4 c.) or 14 (others).*

350	4 c. Type **111**	10	10
	a. Strip of 3. Nos. 350/2	20	
351	4 c. } "Crucifixion"	10	10
352	4 c. }	10	10
353	25 c. "Last Supper"	30	10
354	40 c. "Last Supper" (different)	35	10
355	$1 "Baptism of Christ"	60	55
350/5	*Set of 6*	1·25	80

Nos. 350/2 were printed horizontally *se-tenant*, together forming a composite design, No. 350 being the left-hand stamp.
Nos. 353/5 are smaller, 27 × 35 mm.

1976 (8 July). *West Indian Victory in World Cricket Cup. As Nos. 419/20 of Jamaica.*

356	12 c. Map of the Caribbean	60	20
357	40 c. Prudential Cup	1·40	50
MS358	95 × 80 mm. Nos. 356/7	4·00	3·75

112 Crispus Attucks and the Boston
Massacre

113 "The Nativity"
(Sforza Book of Hours)

(Des J.W. Litho Questa)

1976 (26 July). *Bicentenary of American Revolution. T* **112** *and similar horiz designs. Multicoloured. W w 14 (sideways). P 13½.*

359	20 c. Type **112**	15	10
360	40 c. Alexander Hamilton and Battle of Yorktown	30	10
361	45 c. Jefferson and Declaration of Independence	30	10
362	$1 Washington and the Crossing of the Delaware	60	80
359/62	*Set of 4*	1·25	95

(Des Jennifer Toombs. Litho Questa)

1976 (1 Nov). *Christmas. T* **113** *and similar vert designs. Multicoloured. W w 14. P 14.*

363	20 c. Type **113**	10	10
364	40 c. "Virgin and Child with St. John" (Pintoricchio)	15	10
365	45 c. "Our Lady of Good Children" (Ford Maddox-Brown)	15	10
366	$1 "Little Hands Outstretched to Bless" (Margaret Tarrant)	35	50
363/6	*Set of 4*	65	60

114 Royal Visit, 1966

115 "Christ on the Cross"
(Niccolo di Liberatore)

(Des J.W. Litho Questa)

1977 (7 Feb). *Silver Jubilee. T* **114** *and similar vert designs. Multicoloured. W w 14. P 13½.*

367	50 c. Type **114**	15	10
368	55 c. The Sceptre	15	10
369	$1.50, Bishops paying homage	30	50
367/9	*Set of 3*	55	60

(Des G. Hutchins. Litho Questa)

1977 (14 Apr*). *Easter. T* **115** *and similar designs showing paintings from the National Gallery, London. Multicoloured. W w 14 (sideways on 50 c.). P 14.*

370	25 c. Type **115**	10	10
371	30 c. "The Resurrection" (imitator of Mantegna)	10	10
372	50 c. "The Resurrection" (Ugolino da Siena) (horiz)	15	10
373	$1 "Christ Rising from the Tomb" (Gaudenzio Ferrari)	25	30
370/3	*Set of 4*	55	45

*This is the local release date; the Crown Agents released the stamps ten days earlier.

116 Estridge Mission

117 Laboratory Instruments

(Des Jennifer Toombs. Litho Cartor S.A., France)

1977 (27 June). *Bicentenary of Moravian Mission. T* **116** *and similar horiz designs. W w 14 (sideways). P 12½.*

374	4 c. black, greenish blue and new blue	10	10
375	20 c. black, brt mauve & brt reddish violet	10	10
376	40 c. black, yellow and yellow-orange	15	15
374/6	*Set of 3*	30	30

Designs:—20 c. Mission symbol; 40 c. Basseterre Mission.

(Des G. Hutchins. Litho Questa)

1977 (11 Oct). *75th Anniv of Pan-American Health Organization. T* **117** *and similar vert designs. W w 14. P 14.*

377	3 c. multicoloured	10	10
378	12 c. multicoloured	15	10
379	20 c. multicoloured	20	10
380	$1 red-brown, bright orange and black	70	40
377/80	*Set of 4*	1·00	50

Designs:—12 c. Fat cells, blood cells and nerve cells; 20 c. "Community participation in health"; $1 Inoculation.

118 "Nativity"
(West Window)

119 Savanna Monkey
with Vervet

(Des Jennifer Toombs. Litho Rosenbaum Bros, Vienna)

1977 (15 Nov). *Christmas. Vert designs as T* **118** *showing stained-glass windows from Chartres Cathedral. Multicoloured. W w 14 (inverted). P 13½.*

381	4 c. Type **118**	10	10
382	6 c. "Three Magi" (West window)	10	10
383	40 c. "La Belle Verriere"	35	10
384	$1 "Virgin and Child" (Rose window)	75	45
381/4	*Set of 4*	1·10	55

(Des BG Studio. Litho Questa)

1978 (15 Apr). *The Savanna ("Green") Monkey. T* **119** *and similar vert design. W w 14. P 14½.*

385	**119** 4 c. yellow-brown, rosine and black	10	10
386	– 5 c. multicoloured	10	10
387	**119** 55 c. yellow-brown, apple-green & black	30	10
388	– $1.50, multicoloured	75	60
385/8	*Set of 4*	1·10	65

Design:—5 c., $1.50 Savanna Monkeys on branch.

120 Falcon of
Edward III

121 Tomatoes

(Des C. Abbott. Litho Questa)

1978 (2 June). *25th Anniv of Coronation. T* **120** *and similar vert designs. P 14.*

389	$1 olive-brown and vermilion	20	20
	a. Sheetlet. Nos. 389/91 × 2	1·10	
390	$1 multicoloured	20	20
391	$1 olive-brown and vermilion	20	20
389/91	*Set of 3*	55	55

Designs:—No. 389, Type **120**; No. 390, Queen Elizabeth II; No. 391, Brown Pelican.

(Des BG Studio. Litho D.L.R.)

1978 (8 Sept). *Horiz designs as T* **121**. *Multicoloured. W w 14 (sideways). P 14½ × 14.*

392	1 c. Type **121**	10	15
393	2 c. Defence Force band	10	15
394	5 c. Radio and T.V. station	10	10
395	10 c. Technical college	10	10
396	12 c. T.V. assembly plant	10	15
397	15 c. Sugar cane harvesting	15	10
398	25 c. Crafthouse (craft centre)	15	10
399	30 c. *Europa* (liner)	60	45
400	40 c. Lobster and sea crab	30	10
401	45 c. Royal St. Kitts Hotel and golf course	1·25	45
402	50 c. Pinney's Beach, Nevis	30	10
403	55 c. New runway at Golden Rock	30	10
404	$1 Cotton picking	35	30
405	$5 Brewery	1·00	1·25
406	$10 Pineapples and peanuts	2·25	2·50
392/406	*Set of 15*	6·00	5·00

122 Investiture

123 Wise Man with Gift
of Gold

(Des L. Curtis. Litho Rosenbaum Bros, Vienna)

1978 (9 Oct). *50th Anniv of Boy Scout Movement on St. Kitts and Nevis. T* **122** *and similar vert designs. Multicoloured. W w* **14**. *P* 13½.

407	5 c. Type **122**		..	10	10
408	10 c. Map reading		..	10	10
409	25 c. Pitching tent		..	20	15
410	40 c. Cooking		..	35	25
411	50 c. First aid		..	40	35
412	55 c. Rev. W. A. Beckett (founder of scouting in St. Kitts)		..	45	45
407/12			Set of 6	1·40	1·10

(Des Jennifer Toombs. Litho Walsall)

1978 (1 Dec). *Christmas. T* **123** *and similar vert designs. Multicoloured. W w* **14**. *P* 13½.

413	5 c. Type **123**		..	10	10
414	15 c. Wise Man with gift of Frankincense		..	10	10
415	30 c. Wise Man with gift of Myrrh		..	10	10
416	$2.25, Wise Men paying homage to the infant Jesus		..	35	50
413/16			Set of 4	50	55

124 *Canna coccinea*

125 St. Christopher 1870–76 1d. Stamp and Sir Rowland Hill

(Des Daphne Padden. Litho Questa)

1979 (19 Mar). *Flowers* (1st series). *T* **124** *and similar vert designs. Multicoloured. W w* **14**. *P* 14.

417	5 c. Type **124**		..	10	10
418	30 c. *Heliconia bihai*		..	30	20
419	55 c. *Ruellia tuberosa*		..	50	30
420	$1.50, *Gesneria ventricosa*		..	1·10	1·40
417/20			Set of 4	1·75	1·75

See also Nos. 430/3.

(Des J.W. Litho Walsall)

1979 (2 July). *Death Centenary of Sir Rowland Hill. T* **125** *and similar horiz designs showing stamps and portrait. Multicoloured. W w* **14** *(sideways). P* 14½ × 14.

421	5 c. Type **125**		..	10	10
422	15 c. 1970 Stamp Centenary 50 c. commemorative		..	10	10
423	50 c. Great Britain 1841 2d.		..	35	35
424	$2.50, St. Kitts-Nevis 1923 300th Anniversary of Colony £1 commemorative		..	90	1·10
421/4			Set of 4	1·25	1·40

126 "The Woodman's Daughter"

127 Nevis Lagoon

(Des BG Studio. Litho Format)

1979 (12 Nov). *Christmas and International Year of the Child. Paintings by Sir John Millais. T* **126** *and similar vert designs. Multicoloured. W w* **14**. *P* 13½.

425	5 c. Type **126**		..	10	10
426	25 c. "Cherry Ripe"		..	25	20
427	30 c. "The Rescue"		..	25	20
428	55 c. "Bubbles"		..	30	25
425/8			Set of 4	75	65
MS429	100 × 68 mm. $1 "Christ in the House of His Parents"		..	70	55

(Des J. Cooter. Litho Questa)

1980 (4 Feb). *Flowers* (2nd series). *Vert designs as T* **124**. *Multicoloured. W w* **14** *(inverted). P* 14.

430	4 c. *Clerodendrum aculeatum*		..	30	10
431	55 c. *Inga laurina*		..	40	20
432	$1.50, *Epidendrum difforme*		..	1·00	90
433	$2 *Salvia serotina*		..	1·10	90
430/3			Set of 4	2·50	1·50

(Des and litho Secura, Singapore)

1980 (6 May). *"London 1980" International Stamp Exhibition. T* **127** *and similar multicoloured designs. W w* **14** *(sideways, on 5 and 55 c., inverted on 30 c.). P* 13.

434	5 c. Type **127**		..	10	10
435	30 c. Fig Tree Church (*vert*)		..	20	10
436	55 c. Nisbet Plantation		..	45	25
437	$3 "Nelson" (Fuger) (*vert*)		..	1·00	1·00
434/7			Set of 4	1·60	1·25
MS438	107 × 77 mm. 75 c. Detail of "Nelson Falling" (D. Dighton). *P* 13½ × 13		..	85	70
	a. Wmk sideways		..	40·00	

OFFICIAL

(O 1)

1980 (3 Mar). *Nos. 396, 398 and 400/6 optd with Type* O **1**.

O1	12 c. T.V. assembly plant		..	1·25	1·00
O2	25 c. Crafthouse (craft centre)		..	15	20
O3	40 c. Lobster and sea crab		..	50	50
O4	45 c. Royal St. Kitts Hotel and golf course		..	45	45
O5	50 c. Pinney's Beach, Nevis		..	30	40
O6	55 c. New runway at Golden Rock		..	30	40
O7	$1 Cotton picking		..	1·25	2·25
O8	$5 Brewery		..	1·00	2·50
O9	$10 Pineapples and Peanuts		..	2·50	3·50
O1/9			Set of 9	7·00	10·00

From 23 June 1980 St. Kitts and Nevis had separate postal authorities, each with their own issues.

ST. KITTS

St. Kitts

(8)

1980 (23 June). *As Nos. 394/406 of St. Christopher, Nevis and Anguilla optd with T* **8**. A. *W w* **14** *(sideways)*. B. *No wmk*.

				A		B	
29	5 c. Radio and T.V. station		15	15	10	10
30	10 c. Technical college		15	15	10	10
31	12 c. T.V. assembly plant		80	80	†	
32	15 c. Sugar cane harvesting		15	15	10	10
33	25 c. Crafthouse (craft centre)		15	15	10	10
34	30 c. *Europa* (liner)		15	15	10	10
35	40 c. Lobster and sea crab		20	20	10	15
36	45 c. Royal St. Kitts Hotel and golf course		15	15	†	
37	50 c. Pinney's Beach, Nevis		15	15	†	
38	55 c. New runway at Golden Rock		15	15	15	15
39	$1 Cotton picking		25	25	25	25
40	$5 Brewery		1·00	1·00	1·25	1·50
41	$10 Pineapples and peanuts		1·75	1·75	2·00	2·50
29A/41A		Set of 13	4·75	4·75		
29B/41B		Set of 10			3·75	4·50

9 H.M.S. *Vanguard*, 1762

10 Queen Elizabeth the Queen Mother at Royal Variety Performance, 1978

(Litho Secura, Singapore)

1980 (8 Aug). *Ships. T* **9** *and similar horiz designs. Multicoloured. W w* **14** *(sideways). P* 13 × 13½.

42	4 c. Type **9**		..	10	10
	a. Opt omitted		..	60·00	
	c. No stop after "ST"		..	1·00	
43	10 c. H.M.S. *Boreas*, 1787		..	10	10
	a. Opt omitted		..	£100	
	c. No stop after "ST"		..	1·00	
44	30 c. H.M.S. *Druid*, 1827		..	15	10
	a. Opt omitted		..	£100	
	c. No stop after "ST"		..	1·25	
45	55 c. H.M.S. *Winchester*, 1831		..	20	15
	a. Opt inverted		..	£120	
	b. Opt omitted		..	£100	
	c. No stop after "ST"		..	1·50	
46	$1.50, Harrison Line *Philosopher*, 1857		..	40	30
	a. Opt omitted		..	£100	
	c. No stop after "ST"		..	2·00	
47	$2 Harrison Line *Contractor*, 1930		..	50	40
	a. Opt double		..	£100	
	b. Opt omitted		..	£150	
	c. No stop after "ST"		..	2·00	
42/7			Set of 6	1·25	90

Nos. 42/7 are overprinted "ST. KITTS" and have the previous combined inscription obliterated.

The "no stop" variety occurs on R.3/4 of the lower pane.

(Des and litho Format)

1980 (4 Sept). *80th Birthday of Queen Elizabeth the Queen Mother. W w* **14**. *P* 13½.

48	**10** $2 multicoloured		..	60	60

No. 48 was printed in sheets containing two *se-tenant* stamp-size labels.

11 The Three Wise Men

(Des Walsall. Litho Questa)

1980 (10 Nov). *Christmas. T* **11** *and similar horiz designs. Multicoloured. W w* **14** *(sideways). P* 14½ × 14.

49	5 c. Type **11**		..	10	10
50	15 c. The Shepherds		..	10	10
51	30 c. Bethlehem		..	10	10
52	$4 Nativity scene		..	60	60
49/52			Set of 4	70	65

12 Purple-throated Carib

13 Bananaquit

(Des Jennifer Toombs. Litho Questa)

1981 (5 Feb)**–82**. *Birds. Vert designs as T* **12** *(1 to 10 c.) or horiz as T* **13** *(15 c. to $10). Multicoloured. W w* **14** *(sideways on 1 to 10 c.). P* 13½ × 14 *(1 to 10 c.) or* 14 *(15 c. to $10).*
A. *Without imprint date.*
B. *With imprint date at foot of design.*

			A		B	
				A		B
53	1 c. Magnificent Frigate Bird	..	15	15	45	35
54	4 c. Wied's Crested Flycatcher		25	15	45	30
55	5 c. Type **12**		25	15	55	30
56	6 c. Burrowing Owl		35	25	65	40
57	8 c. Caribbean Martin		30	25	70	30
58	10 c. Yellow-crowned Night Heron		25	15	70	30
59	15 c. Type **13**		25	15	75	30
60	20 c. Scaly-breasted Thrasher		30	15	80	30
61	25 c. Grey Kingbird		30	15	80	30
62	30 c. Green-throated Carib		30	15	80	35
63	40 c. Turnstone		35	20	90	40
64	45 c. Black-faced Grassquit		35	25	1·00	45
65	50 c. Cattle Egret		40	30	1·10	50
66	55 c. Brown Pelican		40	30	1·25	50
67	$1 Lesser Antillean Bullfinch		60	50	2·00	80
68	$2.50, Zenaida Dove		1·25	1·25	3·25	2·25
69	$5 American Kestrel		2·25	2·50	5·00	4·50
70	$10 Antillean Crested Hummingbird		4·50	4·75	8·00	8·50
53/70		Set of 18	11·50	10·50	26·00	19·00

Dates of issue: Without imprint—5.2.81, 5 c. and 10 c. to $10; 30.5.81, 1, 4, 6, 8 c. With imprint—8.6.82, 1 c. to $10.

Nos. 59B/64B and 67B/8B exist with different imprint dates.

14 Battalion Company Sergeant, 3rd Regt of Foot ("The Buffs"), *circa* 1801

15 Miriam Pickard (first Guide Commissioner)

(Des G. Vasarhelyi. Litho Format)

1981 (5 Mar). *Military Uniforms* (1st series). *T* **14** *and similar vert designs. Multicoloured. W w* **14**. *P* 14½.

71	5 c. Type **14**		..	10	10
72	30 c. Battalion Company Officer, 45th Regt of Foot, 1796–97		..	20	10
73	55 c. Battalion Company Officer, 9th Regt of Foot, 1790		..	30	10
74	$2.50, Grenadier, 38th Regt of Foot, 1751		..	90	35
71/4			Set of 4	1·25	45

See also Nos. 110/13 and 220/6.

(Des D. Shults. Litho Questa)

1981 (23 June–14 Dec). *Royal Wedding. Horiz designs as T* **26/27** *of Kiribati. Multicoloured.* (a) *W w* **14**. *P* 14.

75	55 c. Saudadoes		..	15	15
	a. Sheetlet. No 75 × 6 and No. 76		..	1·10	
76	55 c. Prince Charles and Lady Diana Spencer		..	40	40
77	$2.50, *Royal George*		..	35	35
	a. Sheetlet No. 77 × 6 and No. 78		..	2·75	
78	$2.50, As No. 76		..	70	70
79	$4 *Britannia*		..	50	50
	a. Sheetlet. No 79 × 6 and No. 80		..	3·50	
80	$4 As No. 76		..	1·00	1·00
75/80			Set of 6	2·75	2·75
MS81	120 × 109 mm. $5 As No. 76. Wmk sideways				
	P 12 (14 Dec)		..	2·50	1·50

(b) *Booklet stamps. No wmk. P* 12 (19 Nov)

82	55 c. As No. 76		..	30	30
	a. Booklet pane. No. 82 × 4		..	1·00	
83	$2.50, As No. 78		..	1·10	1·25
	a. Booklet pane. No. 83 × 2		..	2·25	

Nos. 75/80 were printed in sheetlets of seven stamps of the same face value, each containing six of the "Royal Yacht" design and one of the larger design showing Prince Charles and Lady Diana.
Nos. 82/3 come from $9.40 stamp booklets.

(Des Jennifer Toombs. Litho Walsall)

1981 (21 Sept). *50th Anniv of St. Kitts Girl Guide Movement. T* **15** *and similar vert designs. Multicoloured. W w* **14**. *P* 14.

84	5 c. Type **15**		..	10	10
85	30 c. Lady Baden-Powell's visit, 1964		..	15	10
86	55 c. Visit of Princess Alice, 1960		..	30	10
87	$2 Thinking-Day parade, 1980's		..	60	35
84/7			Set of 4	1·00	45

16 Stained-glass Windows   17 Admiral Samuel Hood

(Des Jennifer Toombs. Litho Format)

1981 (30 Nov). *Christmas. T* **16** *and similar vert designs showing stained-glass windows. W* w **14**. *P* 13 × 14.

88	5 c. multicoloured		10	10
89	30 c. multicoloured		20	10
90	55 c. multicoloured		30	10
91	$3 multicoloured		1·00	50
88/91		*Set of* 4	1·40	60

(Des D. Shults. Litho Format)

1982 (15 Mar). *Bicentenary of Brimstone Hill Siege. T* **17** *and similar horiz designs. W* w **14** (*sideways*). *P* 14.

92	15 c. multicoloured		10	10
93	55 c. multicoloured		20	10
MS94	96 × 71 mm. $5 black, red-orange & yell-brn		2·50	1·50

Designs:—55 c. Marquis De Bouillé; $5 Battle scene.

ROYAL BABY

18 Alexandra, Princess   (19)
of Wales, 1863

(Des D. Shults and J. Cooter. Litho Format)

1982 (22 June). *21st Birthday of Princess of Wales. T* **18** *and similar designs. Multicoloured. W* w **14**. *P* 13½ × 14.

95	15 c. Type **18**		10	10
96	55 c. Coat of arms of Alexandra of Denmark		40	35
97	$6 Diana, Princess of Wales		1·25	1·25
95/7		*Set of* 3	1·50	1·50

1982 (12 July). *Birth of Prince William of Wales. Nos.* 95/7 *optd with T* **19**.

98	15 c. Type **18**		10	10
	a. Opt inverted		20·00	
99	55 c. Coat of arms of Alexandra of Denmark		40	35
100	$6 Diana, Princess of Wales		1·25	1·25
98/100		*Set of* 3	1·50	1·50

20 Naturalist Badge   21 Santa with Christmas Tree and Gifts

(Des Philatelists (1980) Ltd. Litho Questa)

1982 (18 Aug). *75th Anniv of Boy Scout Movement. T* **20** *and similar vert designs. Multicoloured. W* w **14**. *P* 14 × 13½.

101	5 c. Type **20**		10	10
102	55 c. Rescuer badge		40	15
103	$2 First Aid badge		1·10	80
101/3		*Set of* 3	1·40	90

(Des Marcel Frazer (5 c.), Sinclair Herbert (55 c.), Marijka Grey ($1.10), Gary Bowrin ($3). Litho Format)

1982 (20 Oct). *Christmas. Children's Paintings. T* **21** *and similar horiz designs. Multicoloured. W* w **14** (*sideways*). *P* 14 × 13½.

104	5 c. Type **21**		10	10
105	55 c. The Inn		15	10
106	$1.10, Three Kings		30	15
107	$3 Annunciation		80	40
104/7		*Set of* 4	1·25	60

22 Cruise Ship *Stella Oceanis*   23 Sir William Smith
at Basseterre   (founder)

(Des G. Drummond. Litho Format)

1983 (14 Mar). *Commonwealth Day. T* **22** *and similar horiz design. Multicoloured. W* w **14** (*sideways*). *P* 14.

108	55 c. Type **22**		20	10
109	$2 *Queen Elizabeth 2* at Basseterre		50	40

(Des G. Vasarhelyi. Litho Format)

1983 (25 May). *Military Uniforms (2nd series). Vert designs as T* **14**. *Multicoloured. W* w **14**. *P* 14½.

110	15 c. Light Company Private, 15th Regt of Foot, *circa* 1814		20	10
111	30 c. Battalion Company Officer, 15th Regt of Foot, *circa* 1780		35	15
112	55 c. Light Company Officer, 5th Regt of Foot, *circa* 1822		55	20
113	$2.50, Battalion Company Officer, 11th Regt of Foot, *circa* 1804		1·40	1·60
110/13		*Set of* 4	2·25	1·75

(Des J. Cooter. Litho Format)

1983 (27 July). *Centenary of the Boys' Brigade. T* **23** *and similar vert designs. Multicoloured. W* w **14**. *P* 13½.

114	10 c. Type **23**		25	10
115	45 c. B.B. members on steps of Sandy Point Methodist Church		55	20
116	50 c. Brigade drummers		65	25
117	$3 Boys' Brigade badge		2·50	3·25
114/17		*Set of* 4	3·50	3·50

(24)   (24a)   25 Montgolfier Balloon, 1783

1983 (19 Sept). *Nos.* 55, 59/63 *and* 66/70 *optd as T* **24** (*horiz 20 mm long on Nos.* 119/28)
A. *No imprint date*
B. *With imprint date*

			A		B	
118	5 c. Type **12**		15	10	15	10
	a. Opt inverted		†	48·00	—	
	b. Pair one without opt		†	80·00	—	
	c. Opt with T **24a** (local opt)	12·00	12·00	2·25	2·00	
	ca. Opt inverted (reading upwards)	35·00	—	11·00	—	
119	15 c. Type **13**		1·00	1·00	20	10
	a. Opt double		†	12·00		
120	20 c. Scaly-breasted Thrasher		†	25	10	
121	25 c. Grey Kingbird		†	30	10	
	a. Opt inverted		†	14·00	—	
122	30 c. Green-throated Carib	20·00	20·00	35	15	
123	40 c. Turnstone		†	40	20	
124	55 c. Brown Pelican	50	50	45	30	
	a. Opt inverted		†	11·00		
125	$1 Lesser Antillean Bullfinch	7·50	7·50	80	50	
126	$2.50, Zenaida Dove	2·00	2·00	1·50	1·25	
127	$5 American Kestrel	2·75	2·75	2·50	2·50	
128	$10 Antillean Crested Hummingbird	6·00	6·00	5·00	5·00	
118A/28A	*Set of* 8	35·00	35·00			
118B/28B	*Set of* 11			11·00	9·00	

(Des A. Theobald. Litho Format)

1983 (28 Sept). *Bicentenary of Manned Flight. T* **25** *and similar multicoloured designs. W* w **15** (*sideways on Nos.* 130/3). *P* 14.

129	10 c. Type **25**		10	10
130	45 c. Sikorsky *Russian Knight* biplane (*horiz*)		15	10
131	50 c. Lockheed "Tristar" (*horiz*)		20	15
132	$2.50, Bell "XS-1" (*horiz*)		60	75
129/32		*Set of* 4	90	95
MS133	108 × 145 mm. Nos. 129/32		95	1·25

26 Star over West Indian Town   27 Parrot in Tree

(Des Jennifer Toombs. Litho Format)

1983 (7 Nov). *Christmas. T* **26** *and similar horiz designs. Multicoloured. W* w **15** (*sideways*). *P* 14.

134	15 c. Type **26**		10	10
135	30 c. Shepherds watching Star		10	10
136	55 c. Mary and Joseph		15	10
137	$2.50, The Nativity		40	40
134/7		*Set of* 4	60	55
MS138	130 × 130 mm. Nos. 134/7. Wmk upright		75	1·10

(Des Court House Studio. Litho Format)

1984 (30 Jan). *Batik Designs (1st series). T* **27** *and similar vert designs. W* w **15**. *P* 14 × 13½.

139	45 c. multicoloured		20	10
140	50 c. multicoloured		20	10
141	$1.50, new blue, bistre-yellow & brt mag		55	60
142	$3 multicoloured		85	1·25
139/42		*Set of* 4	1·60	1·75

Designs:—50 c. Man under coconut tree; $1.50, Women with fruit; $3 Butterflies.
See also Nos. 169/72.

28 Cushion Star

(Des G. Drummond. Litho J.W.)

1984 (4 July). *Marine Wildlife. T* **28** *and similar multicoloured designs. W* w **15** (*sideways on 5 c. to 75 c.*). *P* 14.

143	5 c. Type **28**		30	20
144	10 c. Rough File Shell		35	20
145	15 c. Red-lined Cleaning Shrimp		35	15
146	20 c. Bristleworm		35	15
147	25 c. Flamingo Tongue		40	15
148	30 c. Christmas Tree Worm		40	20
149	40 c. Pink-tipped Anemone		55	25
150	50 c. Smallmouth Grunt		55	30
151	60 c. Glasseye Snapper		1·25	60
152	75 c. Reef Squirrelfish		90	55
153	$1 Sea Fans and Flamefish (*vert*)		1·00	60
154	$2.50, Reef Butterflyfish (*vert*)		2·25	2·75
155	$5 Blackbar Soldierfish (*vert*)		5·50	7·00
156	$10 Cocoa Damselfish (*vert*)		9·00	11·00
143/56		*Set of* 14	21·00	21·00

For 10 c., 60 c., $5 and $10 with watermark w **16** see Nos. 194/206.

29 Agriculture

(Des G. Vasarhelyi. Litho Questa)

1984 (15 Aug). *25th Anniv of 4-H Organisation. T* **29** *and similar horiz designs. Multicoloured. W* w **15** (*sideways*). *P* 14.

157	30 c. Type **29**		30	10
158	55 c. Animal husbandry		40	15
159	$1.10, The 4-H Pledge		70	60
160	$3 On parade		1·25	1·25
157/60		*Set of* 4	2·40	1·90

30 Construction of Royal St. Kitts Hotel

(Des K. Tatem (15 c.), Tessa Wattley (30 c.), Myrna Elcock and L. Freeman ($1.10), A. Williams ($3), adapted Jennifer Toombs. Litho Format)

1984 (18 Sept). *First Anniv of Independence of St. Kitts-Nevis. T* **30** *and similar multicoloured designs. W* w **15** (*sideways on 15, 30 c.*). *P* 14.

161	15 c. Type **30**		20	10
162	30 c. Independence celebrations		30	15
163	$1.10, National Anthem and aerial view (*vert*)		70	60
164	$3 "Dawn of a New Day" (*vert*)		1·60	1·40
161/4		*Set of* 4	2·50	2·00

31 Opening Presents

(Des Jennifer Toombs. Litho Questa)

1984 (1 Nov). *Christmas. T* **31** *and similar horiz designs. Multicoloured. W* w **15** (*sideways*). *P* 14.

165	15 c. Type **31**		15	10
166	60 c. Singing carols		45	35
167	$1 Nativity play		75	60
168	$2 Leaving church on Christmas Day		1·40	1·10
165/8		*Set of* 4	2·50	1·90

IMPERFORATES. Issues between Nos. 169 and 184 exist imperforate. Such items are not listed as there is no evidence that they fulfil the criteria outlined on page xi of this catalogue.

(Des Court House Studio. Litho Format)

1985 (6 Feb). *Batik Designs (2nd series). Horiz designs as T* **27**. *W w* **15** *(sideways). P* 13½ × 14.

169	15 c. black, bright green and light green	..	15	10
170	40 c. black, bright greenish blue and bright new blue	..	30	15
171	60 c. black, orange-vermilion and vermilion	..	45	20
172	$3 black, lake-brown and orange-brown	..	1·75	2·00
169/72		*Set of 4*	2·40	2·25

Designs:—15 c. Country bus; 40 c. Donkey cart; 60 c. Rum shop, and man on bicycle; $3 S.V. *Polynesia* (tourist yacht).

32 Container Ship *Tropic Jade*

33 James Derrick Cardin (leading Freemason)

(Des J. Cooter. Litho Format)

1985 (27 Mar). *Ships. T* **32** *and similar horiz designs. Multicoloured. W w* **15** *(sideways). P* 13½ × 14.

173	40 c. Type **32**	..	75	30
174	$1.20, *Atlantic Clipper* (schooner)	..	1·50	1·25
175	$2 *Mandalay* (schooner)	..	2·25	2·25
176	$2 *Cunard Countess* (liner)	..	2·25	2·25
173/6	..	*Set of 4*	6·00	5·50

(Des G. Vasarhelyi. Litho Format)

1985 (9 Nov). *150th Anniv of Mount Olive S.C. Masonic Lodge. T* **33** *and similar multicoloured designs. W w* **15** *(sideways on 15, 75 c., and $3). P* 15.

177	15 c. Type **33**	..	50	20
178	75 c. Banner of Mount Olive Lodge	..	1·50	1·10
179	$1.20, Masonic symbols (*horiz*)	..	2·25	2·25
180	$3 Lodge Charter (1835)	..	3·75	3·75
177/80		*Set of 4*	7·25	6·50

34 Map of St. Kitts

35 Queen Elizabeth and Prince Philip on St. Kitts

(Des J. Cooter. Litho Format)

1985 (27 Nov). *Christmas. 400th Anniv of Sir Francis Drake's Visit. T* **34** *and similar vert designs. Multicoloured. P* 15.

181	10 c. Type **34**	..	30	15
182	40 c. *Golden Hind*	..	75	35
183	60 c. Sir Francis Drake	..	85	50
184	$3 Drake's heraldic shield	..	2·50	2·25
181/4	..	*Set of 4*	4·00	3·00

(Des D. Miller. Litho B.D.T.)

1986 (9 July). *60th Birthday of Queen Elizabeth II. T* **35** *and similar vert designs. Multicoloured. P* 13½.

185	10 c. Type **35**	..	15	10
186	20 c. Queen Elizabeth on St. Kitts	..	25	15
187	40 c. At Trooping the Colour	..	50	30
188	$3 In Sweden	..	2·00	2·25
185/8	..	*Set of 4*	2·50	2·50

(Des D. Miller. Litho Walsall)

1986 (23 July). *Royal Wedding. Square designs as T* **231***a of Jamaica. Multicoloured. W w* **16**. *P* 14½×14.

189	15 c. Prince Andrew and Miss Sarah Ferguson	..	15	10
190	$2.50, Prince Andrew	..	1·50	2·00

36 Family on Smallholding

(37)

40th ANNIVERSARY U.N. WEEK 19-26 OCT.

(Des K. Tatem (15 c.), A. Williams ($1.20), adapted G. Vasarhelyi. Litho Questa)

1986 (18 Sept). *Agriculture Exhibition. T* **36** *and similar horiz design. Multicoloured. W w* **16** *(sideways). P* 13½×14.

191	15 c. Type **36**	..	20	10
192	$1.20, Hands holding people, computers and crops	..	1·25	1·40

(Litho Questa)

1986 (5 Nov)–**88**. *As Nos.* 144, 151 *and* 155/6 *but W w* **16** *(sideways on* 10, 60 c.*). With imprint date. P* 14.

194	10 c. Rough File Shell	..	65	55
201	60 c. Glasseye Snapper (17.8.88)	..	1·75	1·40
205	$5 Blackbar Soldierfish (*vert*) (17.8.88)	..	6·00	7·00
206	$10 Cocoa Damselfish (*vert*) (17.8.88)	..	11·00	12·00
194/206		*Set of 4*	18·00	19·00

No. 194 exists with different imprint dates below the design.

1986 (12 Nov). *40th Anniv of United Nations Week. Nos.* 185/8 *optd with T* **37** *in gold.*

207	10 c. Type **35**	..	20	15
208	20 c. Queen Elizabeth on St. Kitts	..	30	20
209	40 c. At Trooping the Colour	..	40	30
210	$3 In Sweden	..	2·25	2·75
	a. Opt triple	..	75·00	
207/10		*Set of 4*	2·75	3·00

38 Adult Green Monkey with Young

39 Frederic Bartholdi (sculptor)

(Des Doreen McGuinness. Litho Walsall)

1986 (1 Dec). *Green Monkeys on St. Kitts. T* **38** *and similar vert designs. Multicoloured. W w* **16**. *P* 14 × 13½.

211	15 c. Type **38**	..	35	15
212	20 c. Adult on ground	..	40	20
213	60 c. Young monkey in tree	..	1·10	80
214	$1 Adult grooming young monkey	..	1·75	2·00
211/14		*Set of 4*	3·25	2·75

(Des D. Miller. Litho Format)

1986 (17 Dec). *Centenary of Statue of Liberty. T* **39** *and similar multicoloured designs. W w* **16** *(sideways on* 60 c., $1.50*). P* 14.

215	40 c. Type **39**	..	40	30
216	60 c. Torch (1876) and head (1878) on exhibition (*horiz*)	..	65	50
217	$1.50, French ship *Isere* carrying Statue (*horiz*)	..	1·50	1·50
218	$3 Statue of Liberty, Paris, 1884	..	2·40	2·50
215/18		*Set of 4*	4·50	4·25
MS219	70 × 85 mm. $3.50, Head of Statue of Liberty	..	2·25	2·50

40 Officer, 9th Regt (East Norfolk), 1792

41 Sugar Cane Warehouse

(Des C. Collins. Litho Format)

1987 (25 Feb). *Military Uniforms (3rd series). T* **40** *and similar vert designs. Multicoloured. W w* **16**. *P* 14½.

220	15 c. Type **40**	..	40	30
221	15 c. Officer, Regt de Neustrie, 1779	..	40	30
222	40 c. Sergeant, 3rd Regt ("The Buffs"), 1801	..	75	45
223	40 c. Officer, French Artillery, 1812	..	75	45
224	$2 Light Company Private, 5th Regt, 1778	..	2·25	2·50
225	$2 Grenadier of the Line, 1796	..	2·25	2·50
220/5		*Set of 6*	6·25	6·00
MS226	121 × 145 mm. Nos. 220/5	..	6·25	6·50

The two designs for each value were printed in sheets of 50 containing two panes 5 × 5 with the British uniform depicted on the left-hand pane and the French on the right.

(Des G. Vasarhelyi. Litho Format)

1987 (15 Apr). *Sugar Cane Industry. T* **41** *and similar vert designs. Multicoloured (colour of panel behind "ST. KITTS" given). W w* **16**. *P* 14.

227	15 c. greenish yellow (Type 41)	..	20	20
	a. Horiz strip of 5. Nos. 227/31	..	90	
228	15 c. cinnamon	..	20	20
229	15 c. lilac	..	20	20
230	15 c. azure	..	20	20
231	15 c. pale greenish blue	..	20	20
232	75 c. bright green	..	75	75
	a. Horiz strip of 5. Nos. 232/6	..	3·25	
233	75 c. lilac	..	75	75
234	75 c. dull green	..	75	75
235	75 c. orange-yellow	..	75	75
236	75 c. greenish blue	..	75	75
227/36		*Set of 10*	4·25	4·25

Designs:—Nos. 227/31, Sugar cane factory; Nos. 232/6, Loading sugar train.

Nos. 227/31 and 232/6 were each printed together, *se-tenant*, in horizontal strips of five throughout the sheets, each strip forming a composite design.

42 B.W.I.A. "L-1011-500 TriStar"

43 *Hygrocybe occidentalis*

(Des T. Hadler. Litho Format)

1987 (24 June). *Aircraft visiting St. Kitts. T* **42** *and similar horiz designs. Multicoloured. W w* **14** *(sideways). P* 14.

237	40 c. Type **42**	..	65	30
238	60 c. L.I.A.T. BAe "Super 748"	..	85	60
239	$1.20, W.I.A. "DHC-6 Twin Otter"	..	1·50	1·50
240	$3 American Eagle Aérospatiale "ATR-42"	..	2·75	3·25
237/40		*Set of 4*	5·25	5·00

(Des I. Loe. Litho Questa)

1987 (26 Aug). *Fungi. T* **43** *and similar vert designs. Multicoloured. W w* **16**. *P* 14.

241	15 c. Type **43**	..	55	20
242	40 c. *Marasmius haematocephalus*	..	85	40
243	$1.20, *Psilocybe cubensis*	..	1·75	1·50
244	$2 *Hygrocybe acutoconica*	..	2·50	2·25
245	$3 *Boletellus cubensis*	..	2·75	3·00
241/5		*Set of 5*	7·50	6·50

44 Carnival Clown

45 Ixora

(Des Rose Cameron-Smith. Litho Format)

1987 (28 Oct). *Christmas. T* **44** *and similar square designs showing different clowns. Multicoloured. W w* **16** *(sideways). P* 14½.

246	15 c. multicoloured	..	25	15
247	40 c. multicoloured	..	55	30
248	$1 multicoloured	..	1·25	80
249	$3 multicoloured	..	2·50	3·00
246/9		*Set of 4*	4·00	3·75

See also Nos. 266/9.

(Des Josephine Martin. Litho Questa)

1988 (20 Jan). *Flowers. T* **45** *and similar vert designs. Multicoloured. W w* **16**. *P* 14½×14.

250	15 c. Type **45**	..	30	15
251	40 c. Shrimp Plant	..	55	30
252	$1 Poinsettia	..	1·00	75
253	$3 Honolulu Rose	..	2·50	3·00
250/3		*Set of 4*	4·00	3·75

46 Fort Thomas Hotel

47 Ball, Wicket and Leeward Islands Cricket Association Emblem

(Des L. Curtis. Litho Walsall)

1988 (20 Apr). *Tourism (1st series). Hotels. T* **46** *and similar horiz designs. Multicoloured. W w* **14** *(sideways). P* 14 × 14½.

254	60 c. Type **46**	..	40	40
255	60 c. Fairview Inn	..	40	40
256	60 c. Frigate Bay Beach Hotel	..	40	40
257	60 c. Ocean Terrace Inn	..	40	40
258	$3 The Golden Lemon	..	1·75	2·00
259	$3 Royal St. Kitts Casino and Jack Tar Village	..	1·75	2·00
260	$3 Rawlins Plantation Hotel and Restaurant	..	1·75	2·00
254/60		*Set of 7*	6·25	7·00

See also Nos. 270/5.

(Des Joan Thompson. Litho Walsall)

1988 (13 July). *75th Anniv of Leeward Islands Cricket Tournament. T* **47** *and similar vert design. Multicoloured. W w* **14**. *P* 13 × 13½.

261	40 c. Type **47**	..	75	30
262	$3 Cricket match at Warner Park	..	3·25	3·75

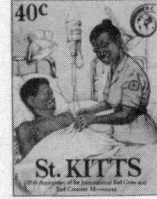

48 Flag of St. Kitts-Nevis

49 Red Cross Nurse with Hospital Patient

(Des L. Curtis. Litho Questa)

1988 (19 Sept). *5th Anniv of Independence. T **48** and similar vert designs. Multicoloured. W w **16**. P 14½ × 14.*

263	15 c. Type **48**			15	10
264	60 c. Arms of St. Kitts			50	50

MS265 61 × 53 mm. $5 Princess Margaret presenting Constitutional Instrument to Prime Minister Kennedy Simmonds, 1983. W w 14 .. 2·75 3·00

(Des Rose Cameron-Smith. Litho Format)

1988 (2 Nov). *Christmas. Square designs as T **44** showing carnival masqueraders. W w **14** (sideways). P 14½.*

266	15 c. multicoloured			10	10
267	40 c. multicoloured	..	..	20	25
268	80 c. multicoloured			40	45
269	$3 multicoloured	..	..	1·25	1·75
266/9			Set of 4	1·75	2·25

(Des L. Curtis. Litho Format)

1989 (25 Jan). *Tourism (2nd series). Colonial Architecture. Horiz designs as T **46**. Multicoloured. W w **16** (sideways). P 14.*

270	20 c. Georgian house		..	20	15
271	20 c. Colonial-style house	..		20	15
272	$1 Romney Manor	..		70	75
273	$1 Lavington Great House			70	75
274	$2 Government House	..		1·25	1·40
275	$2 Treasury Building	..		1·25	1·40
270/5	..		Set of 6	3·75	4·25

(Des C. Collins. Litho Format)

1989 (8 May). *125th Anniv of International Red Cross. T **49** and similar vert designs. W w **16**. P 14×14½.*

276	40 c. multicoloured			30	30
277	$1 multicoloured			65	65
278	$3 orange-vermilion and black	..		1·75	2·00
276/8			Set of 3	2·40	2·75

Designs:—$1 Loading patient into ambulance; $3 125th anniversary logo.

50 Battle on the Champ-de-Mars

51 Outline Map of St. Kitts

(Des D. Miller. Litho B.D.T.)

1989 (7 July). *"Philexfrance 89" International Stamp Exhibition, Paris. Sheet 115×99 mm. W w **16**. P 14.*

MS279 50 $5 multicoloured .. .. 3·25 3·50

(Des A. Theobald ($5), D. Miller (others). Litho Questa)

1989 (20 July). *20th Anniv of First Manned Landing on Moon. Multicoloured designs as T **51**a of Kiribati. W w **16** (sideways on 20 c., $1). P 14×13½ (10 c., $2) or 14 (others).*

280	10 c. Lunar rover on Moon	..		10	10
281	20 c. Crew of "Apollo 13" (30×30 mm)	..		10	10
282	$1 "Apollo 13" emblem (30×30 mm)	..		45	60
283	$2 "Apollo 13" splashdown, South Pacific		95	1·25
280/3			Set of 4	1·40	1·75

MS284 100×83 mm. $5 Aldrin leaving "Apollo 11" lunar module. Wmk inverted. P 14×13½ .. 3·50 4·00

(Des D. Miller. Litho B.D.T.)

1989 (25 Oct). *W w **16**. P 15×14.*

285	**51** 10 c. deep mauve and black	..	..	10	10
286	15 c. bright carmine and black	..		10	10
287	20 c. yellow-orange and black	..		15	10
288	40 c. yellow and black	..		20	20
289	60 c. bright blue and black	..		30	30
290	$1 yellow-green and black	..		50	60
285/90	..	..	Set of 6	1·10	1·10

52 *Santa Mariagalante* passing St. Kitts, 1493

(Des L. Curtis. Litho Questa)

1989 (8 Nov). *500th Anniv of Discovery of America (1992) by Columbus. T **52** and similar horiz designs. Multicoloured. W w **16** (sideways). P 14.*

291	15 c. Type **52**			45	20
292	80 c. Arms of Columbus and map of fourth voyage, 1502-04			1·25	1·25
293	$1 Navigation instruments, c. 1500		1·50	1·50
294	$5 Columbus and map of second voyage, 1493-96			4·50	5·00
291/4	..	..	Set of 4	7·00	7·00

53 Poinciana Tree

54 *Junonia evarete*

(Des G. Vasarhelyi. Litho Walsall)

1989 (17 Nov). *"World Stamp Expo '89" International Stamp Exhibition, Washington. T **53** and similar horiz designs. Multicoloured. W w **14** (sideways). P 14.*

295	15 c. Type **53**			25	10
296	40 c. Fort George Citadel, Brimstone Hill	..	55	30
297	$1 Private, Light Company, 5th Foot, 1778	..		1·10	80
298	$3 St. George's Anglican Church	..		2·75	3·25
295/8			Set of 4	4·25	4·00

(Des I. Loe. Litho B.D.T.)

1990 (6 June). *Butterflies. T **54** and similar horiz designs. Multicoloured. W w **14** (sideways). P 13½×14.*

299	15 c. Type **54**			25	15
300	40 c. *Anartia jatrophae*			45	25
301	60 c. *Heliconius charitonia*			65	45
302	$3 *Biblis hyperia*			2·25	2·75
299/302			Set of 4	3·25	3·25

(55)

56 Brimstone Hill

1990 (6 June). *"EXPO 90" International Garden and Greenery Exhibition, Osaka. Nos. 299/302 optd with T **55**.*

303	15 c. Type **54**			25	15
304	40 c. *Anartia jatrophae*	..		45	25
305	60 c. *Heliconius charitonia*			65	45
306	$3 *Biblis hyperia*			2·25	2·75
303/6			Set of 4	3·25	3·25

(Des D. Miller. Litho Questa)

1990 (30 June). *300th Anniv of English Bombardment of Brimstone Hill. T **56** and similar horiz designs. Multicoloured. W w **16** (sideways). P 14.*

307	15 c. Type **56**			20	10
308	40 c. Restored Brimstone Hill fortifications		35	25
309	60 c. 17th-century English marine and Fort Charles under attack ..			50	50
	a. Horiz pair. Nos. 309/10			2·75	2·75
310	$3 English sailors firing cannon	..	..	2·25	2·25
307/10			Set of 4	3·00	2·75

Nos. 307/9 were printed in complete sheets, each containing one value. No. 309 also exists *se-tenant*, as a horizontal pair, with No. 310. Each pair shows a composite design across the two stamps with no margin at the left of the 60 c. or at the right of the $3.

57 Spitfire Mk Vb *St. Kitts Nevis I*, 71 Squadron

(Des A. Theobald. Litho B.D.T.)

1990 (15 Sept). *50th Anniv of Battle of Britain. Sheet 103×76 mm. containing T **57** and similar horiz design. Multicoloured. W w **16** (sideways). P 14.*

MS311 $3 Type **57**; $3 Spitfire Mk Vb *St. Kitts Nevis II*, 345 Squadron .. .. 4·50 4·75

58 *Romney* (freighter)

(Des S. Williams. Litho B.D.T.)

1990 (10 Oct). *Ships. T **58** and similar horiz designs. Multicoloured. W w **14** (sideways). P 14.*

312	10 c. Type **58**			10	10
313	15 c. *Baralt* (freighter)	..		10	10
314	20 c. *Wear* (mail steamer)	..		10	10
315	25 c. *Sunmount* (freighter)			10	15
316	40 c. *Inanda* (cargo liner)	..		15	20
317	50 c. *Alcoa Partner* (freighter)			20	25
318	60 c. *Dominica* (freighter)			25	30
319	80 c. *C.G.M Provence* (container ship)		35	40
320	$1 *Director* (freighter)	..		45	50
321	$1.20, *Sailing barque*			55	60
322	$2 *Chigneco* (mail steamer)	..		85	90
323	$3 *Berbice* (mail steamer)			1·25	1·40
324	$5 *Vamos* (freighter)	..		2·25	2·40
325	$10 *Federal Maple* (freighter)			4·25	4·50
312/25	..	..	Set of 14	9·75	11·00

59 Single Fork Game

(Des G. Vasarhelyi. Litho Questa)

1990 (14 Nov). *Christmas. Traditional Games. T **59** and similar horiz designs. Multicoloured. W w **16** (sideways). P 14.*

326	10 c. Type **59**			15	10
327	15 c. Boulder breaking	..		15	10
328	40 c. Double fork	..		30	30
329	$3 The run up	..		1·75	1·75
326/9			Set of 4	2·10	2·00

60 White Periwinkle

61 Census Logo

(Des Annette Robinson. Litho Cartor, France)

1991 (8 May). *Flowers. T **60** and similar multicoloured designs. W w **14** (sideways on 10, 40 c.). P 14×13½ (10, 40 c.) or 13½×14 (others).*

330	10 c. Type **60**	..		20	10
331	40 c. Pink Oleander	..		30	25
332	60 c. Pink Periwinkle (*vert*)	..		55	40
333	$2 White Oleander (*vert*)			1·25	1·50
330/3			Set of 4	2·10	2·00

(Des G. Vasarhelyi, Litho B.D.T)

1991 (13 May). *National Census. W w **16**. P 14.*

334	**61** 15 c. multicoloured			15	10
335	$2.40, multicoloured			1·60	1·60

The $2.40 differs from Type **61** by showing "ST. KITTS" in a curved panel.

(Des D. Miller. Litho Questa)

1991 (17 June). *65th Birthday of Queen Elizabeth II and 70th Birthday of Prince Philip. Vert designs as T **58** of Kiribati. W w **16** (sideways). P 14½×14.*

336	$1.20, Prince Philip		75	75
	a. Horiz pair. Nos. 336/7 separated by label		1·75	1·75
337	$1.80, Queen holding bouquet of flowers	1·00	1·00

Nos. 336/7 were printed together in a similar sheet format to Nos. 366/7 of Kiribati.

62 Nassau Grouper

(Des G. Drummond. Litho Questa)

1991 (28 Aug). *Fishes. T **62** and similar horiz designs. Multicoloured. W w **14** (sideways). P 14.*

338	10 c. Type **62**			20	10
339	60 c. Hogfish	..		50	45
340	$1 Red Hind	..		80	80
341	$3 Porkfish	..		2·00	2·25
338/41			Set of 4	3·25	3·25

63 School of Continuing Studies, St. Kitts, and Chancellor Sir Shridath Ramphal

(Des G. Vasarhelyi. Litho Questa)

1991 (28 Sept). *40th Anniv of University of West Indies.* T **63** *and similar horiz designs. Multicoloured.* W w **16** (*sideways*). P 14.

342	15 c. Type **63**		20	10
343	50 c. Administration Building, Barbados		45	35
344	$1 Engineering Building, Trinidad and Tobago		80	75
345	$3 Mona Campus, Jamaica, and Sir Shridath Ramphal		2·25	2·50
342/5		*Set of 4*	3·25	3·25

64 Whipping The Bull

(Des Marijka Grey and G. Vasarhelyi. Litho Walsall)

1991 (6 Nov). *Christmas. "The Bull" (Carnival play).* T **64** *and similar horiz designs. Multicoloured.* W w **14** (*sideways*). P 14.

346	10 c. Type **64**		15	10
347	15 c. Death of The Bull		15	10
348	60 c. Cast of characters and musicians		45	45
349	$3 The Bull in procession		1·60	1·60
346/9		*Set of 4*	2·10	2·00

(Des D. Miller. Litho Questa ($3), Leigh-Mardon Ltd, Melbourne (others))

1992 (6 Feb). *40th Anniv of Queen Elizabeth II's Accession. Horiz designs as* T **113** *of Kenya. Multicoloured.* W w **14** (*sideways*) ($3) *or* w **16** (*sideways*) (*others*). P 14.

350	10 c. St. Kitts coastline		20	10
351	40 c. Warner Park Pavilion		35	25
352	60 c. Brimstone Hill		50	40
353	$1 Three portraits of Queen Elizabeth		75	75
354	$3 Queen Elizabeth II		1·90	2·25
350/4		*Set of 5*	3·25	3·25

65 Map of St. Kitts–Nevis   **66** Columbus meeting Amerindians

(Des L. Curtis. Litho Enschedé)

1992 (8 May). *50th Anniv of St. Kitts-Nevis Red Cross Society.* T **65** *and similar horiz designs. Multicoloured.* W w **14** (*sideways*). P 13½×14.

355	10 c. Type **65**		20	20
356	20 c. St. Kitts–Nevis flag		25	20
357	50 c. Red Cross House, St. Kitts		45	35
358	$2.40, Henri Dunant		1·50	1·75
355/8		*Set of 4*	2·25	2·25

(Adapted G. Vasarhelyi. Litho Cartor)

1992 (6 July). *Organization of East Caribbean States. 500th Anniv of Discovery of America by Columbus.* T **66** *and similar vert design. Multicoloured.* W w **14**. P 13.

359	$1 Type **66**		75	60
360	$2 Ships approaching island		1·25	1·40

67 Fountain, Independence Square   **68** Joseph and Mary travelling to Bethlehem

(Des D. Miller. Litho Enschedé)

1992 (19 Aug). *Local Monuments.* T **67** *and similar vert designs. Multicoloured.* W w **14**. P 12½×13.

361	25 c. Type **67**		25	20
362	50 c. Berkeley Memorial drinking fountain		35	35
363	80 c. Sir Thomas Warner's tomb		55	55
364	$2 War memorial		1·10	1·25
361/4		*Set of 4*	2·00	2·10

(Des L. Curtis. Litho Questa)

1992 (28 Oct). *Christmas.* T **68** *and similar vert designs. Multicoloured.* W w **16**. P 14½.

365	20 c. Type **68**		25	20
366	25 c. Shepherds and star		25	20
367	80 c. Wise Men with gifts		55	55
368	$3 Mary, Joseph and Holy Child		1·60	1·75
365/8		*Set of 4*	2·40	2·40

69 Short Singapore III

(Des A. Theobald. Litho Questa)

1993 (1 Apr). *75th Anniv of Royal Air Force. Aircraft.* T **69** *and similar horiz designs. Multicoloured.* W w **14** (*sideways*). P 14.

369	25 c. Type **69**		10	10
370	50 c. Bristol Beaufort		20	25
371	80 c. Westland Whirlwind helicopter		35	40
372	$1.60, English Electric Canberra		70	75
369/72		*Set of 4*	1·25	1·40
MS373	110×78 mm. $2 Handley Page 0/400; $2 Fairey Long-Range Monoplane; $2 Vickers Wellesley; $2 Sepecat Jaguar		3·25	3·50

OFFICIAL STAMPS

1980 (23 June). *Nos. 32/41 additionally optd with Type* O **1** *of St. Christopher, Nevis and Anguilla.* A. W w **14** (*sideways*). B. No wmk.

			A		B	
O 1	15 c. Sugar cane harvesting		10	10	†	
O 2	25 c. Crafthouse (craft centre)		10	10	10	10
O 3	30 c. *Europa* (liner)		10	10	15	15
O 4	40 c. Lobster and sea crab		10	15	15·00	27·00
O 5	45 c. Royal St. Kitts Hotel and golf course		15	15	†	
O 6	50 c. Pinney's Beach, Nevis		15	15	†	
O 7	55 c. New runway at Golden Rock		15	15	30	35
	a. Opt inverted		42·00	—	†	
O 8	$1 Cotton picking		25	25	40	50
O 9	$5 Brewery		1·00	1·50	2·25	3·50
O10	$10 Pineapples and peanuts		1·75	2·50	4·50	6·50
	a. Opt inverted		£100	—	†	
O1/10		*Set of 10*	3·50	4·50		
O2/10		*Set of 7*			20·00	35·00

OFFICIAL

(O 1)

1981 (5 Feb). *Nos. 59A/70A optd with Type* O **1**.

O11	15 c. Type **13**		20	10
O12	20 c. Scaly-breasted Thrasher		20	10
O13	25 c. Grey Kingbird		25	10
O14	30 c. Green-throated Carib		25	10
O15	40 c. Turnstone		35	15
O16	45 c. Black-faced Grassquit		40	20
O17	50 c. Cattle Egret		40	20
O18	55 c. Brown Pelican		50	25
O19	$1 Lesser Antillean Bullfinch		75	45
O20	$2.50, Zenaida Dove		1·60	1·00
O21	$5 American Kestrel		2·75	2·00
O22	$10 Antillean Crested Hummingbird		5·00	4·25
O11/22		*Set of 12*	11·50	8·00

1983 (2 Feb). *Nos. 75/80 optd with Type* O **1** (55 c.) *or surch also* (*others*).

O23	45 c. on $2.50, *Royal George* (New Blue)		25	25
	a. Sheetlet No. O23 × 6 and No. O24		1·40	
	b. Surch double		18·00	
	c. Albino surch		10·00	
	f. Deep ultramarine surch		50	
	fd. Surch inverted		7·50	
	fe. Surch inverted (horiz pair)		25·00	
	g. Black opt			
O24	45 c. on $2.50, Prince Charles and Lady Diana Spencer (New Blue)		25	25
	b. Surch double		60·00	
	c. Albino surch		30·00	
	f. Deep ultramarine surch		75	
	fd. Surch inverted		30·00	
	g. Black opt			
O25	55 c. *Saudadoes* (New Blue)		30	30
	a. Sheetlet No. O25 × 6 and No. O26		1·75	
	b. Opt double		22·00	
	c. Albino opt		12·00	
	d. Opt inverted		8·00	
	e. Opt inverted (horiz pair)		22·00	
	f. Deep ultramarine opt		60	
	fd. Opt inverted		7·00	
	fe. Opt inverted (horiz pair)		26·00	
O26	55 c. Prince Charles and Lady Diana Spencer (New Blue)		30	30
	b. Opt double		60·00	
	c. Albino opt		35·00	
	d. Opt inverted		27·00	
	f. Deep ultramarine opt		90	
	fd. Opt inverted		27·00	
O27	$1.10 on $4 *Britannia* (Blk.)		60	70
	a. Sheetlet. No. O27 × 6 and No. O28		3·50	
	b. Surch double		17·00	
	f. Deep ultramarine surch		4·00	
O28	$1.10 on $4 Prince Charles and Lady Diana Spencer (Blk.)		60	70
	b. Surch double		45·00	
	f. Deep ultramarine surch		30·00	
O23/8		*Set of 6*	2·10	2·25

Nos. O23fe, O25e and O25fe show the surcharge or overprint intended for the large design, inverted and struck across a horizontal pair of the smaller. Nos. O24fd, O26d and O26fd each show two inverted surcharges or overprints intended for a horizontal pair of the smaller design.

1984 (4 July). *Nos. 145/56 optd with Type* O **1**.

O29	15 c. Red-lined Cleaning Shrimp		25	25
O30	20 c. Bristleworm		30	30
O31	25 c. Flamingo Tongue		35	35
O32	30 c. Christmas Tree Worm		40	40
O33	40 c. Pink-tipped Anemone		50	50
O34	50 c. Smallmouth Grunt		60	60
O35	60 c. Glasseye Snapper		70	70
O36	75 c. Reef Squirrelfish		80	80
O37	$1 Sea Fans and Flamefish (*vert*)		1·00	1·00
O38	$2.50, Reef Butterflyfish (*vert*)		2·25	2·75
O39	$5 Blackbar Soldierfish (*vert*)		4·00	5·00
O40	$10 Cocoa Damselfish (*vert*)		7·50	9·50
O29/40		*Set of 12*	17·00	20·00

NEVIS

(7)   8 Nevis Lighter

1980 (23 June). *Nos. 394/406 of St. Christopher, Nevis and Anguilla optd with T 7.*
37	5 c. Radio and T.V. Station	10	10
38	10 c. Technical college	10	10
39	12 c. T.V. assembly plant	40	40
40	15 c. Sugar cane harvesting	10	10
41	25 c. Crafthouse (craft centre)..	15	10
	a. No wmk	1·75	3·00
42	30 c. *Europa* (liner)	20	15
43	40 c. Lobster and sea crab	70	70
44	45 c. Royal St. Kitts Hotel and golf course	70	70
45	50 c. Pinney's Beach, Nevis	50	50
46	55 c. New runway at Golden Rock	15	15
47	$1 Picking cotton	45	45
	a. No wmk	6·00	10·00
48	$5 Brewery	75	75
49	$10 Pineapples and peanuts	1·25	1·25
37/49	*Set of 13*	4·25	4·25

1980 (4 Sept). *80th Birthday of Queen Elizabeth the Queen Mother. As T 10 of St. Kitts, but inscr "NEVIS".*
50	$2 multicoloured	50	50

No. 50 was printed in sheets including two *se-tenant* stamp-size labels.

(Des Jennifer Toombs. Litho Questa)

1980 (8 Oct). *Boats. T 8 and similar multicoloured designs. W w 14 (sideways on 5, 30 and 55 c.). P 14.*
51	5 c. Type 8	10	10
52	30 c. Local fishing boat	15	10
53	55 c. *Caona* (catamaran)	20	10
54	$3 *Polynesia* (cruise schooner) (39 × 53 *mm*)	65	55
	a. Perf 12 (booklets)	65	1·10
	ab. Booklet pane of 3..	1·90	
51/4	*Set of 4*	90	70

No. 54a comes from $12.30 stamp booklets containing No. 53 × 6 and one pane as No. 54ab. In this pane each stamp is surrounded by white margins, the pane being divided in three by vertical roulettes.

9 Virgin and Child

(Des Jennifer Toombs. Litho Format)

1980 (20 Nov). *Christmas. T 9 and similar vert designs. Multicoloured. W w 14. P 14.*
55	5 c. Type 9	10	10
56	30 c. Angel	10	10
57	$2.50, The Three Wise Men..	30	30
55/7	*Set of 3*	35	35

10 Charlestown Pier   11 New River Mill

(Des Jennifer Toombs. Litho Questa)

1981 (5 Feb)–82. *Horiz designs as T 10 (5, 10 c.) or T 11 (15 c. to $10). Multicoloured. W w 14. P 14 × 13½ (5, 10 c.) or 14 (others).*
A. *No imprint date*
B. *With imprint date at foot of design (9.6.82.)*

		A		B	
58	5 c. Type 10	10	10	10	10
59	10 c. Court House and Library ..	10	10	10	10
60	15 c. Type 11	10	10	10	10
61	20 c. Nelson Museum	10	10	10	10
62	25 c. St. James' Parish Church ..	15	15	15	15
63	30 c. Nevis Lane	15	15	15	15
64	40 c. Zetland Plantation	20	20	20	20
65	45 c. Nisbet Plantation ..	20	20	20	25
66	50 c. Pinney's Beach	25	25	25	25
67	55 c. Eva Wilkin's Studio	25	30	25	30
68	$1 Nevis at dawn	50	45	50	45
69	$2.50, Ruins of Fort Charles ..	90	1·10	90	1·10
70	$5 Old Bath House	1·50	1·75	1·50	1·75
71	$10 Beach at Nisbet's	2·75	3·50	2·75	3·50
58/71	*Set of 14*	6·00	7·50	6·00	7·50

Nos. 61B/7B and 69B exist with different imprint dates.

(Des D. Shults. Litho Questa)

1981 (23 June–14 Dec). *Royal Wedding. Horiz designs as T 26/27 of Kiribati. Multicoloured. (a) W w 14. P 14.*
72	55 c. *Royal Caroline*	20	20
	a. Sheetlet. No. 72 × 6 and No. 73..	1·60	
73	55 c. Prince Charles and Lady Diana Spencer	40	40

74	$2 *Royal Sovereign* ..	40	40
	a. Sheetlet No. 74 × 6 and No. 75 ..	2·75	
75	$2 As No. 73..	80	80
76	$5 *Britannia* ..	80	80
	a. Sheetlet. No. 76 × 6 and No. 77..	5·75	
77	$5 As No. 73..	1·50	1·50
72/7	*Set of 6*	3·75	3·75
MS78	120 × 109 mm. $4.50, As No. 73, Wmk sideways. P 12 (14 Dec).	2·50	1·50

(b) Booklet stamps. No wmk. P 12 (19 Nov).
79	55 c. As No. 72..	25	30
	a. Booklet pane. No. 79 × 4 ..	1·00	
80	$2 As No. 75..	1·00	1·25
	a. Booklet pane. No. 80 × 2 ..	2·00	

Nos. 72/7 were printed in sheetlets of seven stamps of the same face value, each containing six of the "Royal Yacht" design and one of the larger design showing Prince Charles and Lady Diana.
Nos. 79/80 come from $8.40 stamp booklets.

12 *Heliconius charithonia*   13 Caroline of Brunswick, Princess of Wales, 1793

(Des Jennifer Toombs. Litho Questa)

1982 (16 Feb). *Butterflies (1st series). T 12 and similar horiz designs. Multicoloured. W w 14 (sideways). P 14.*
81	5 c. Type 12	10	10
82	30 c. *Siproeta stelenes*	15	10
83	55 c. *Marpesia petreus*	20	15
84	$2 *Phoebis agarithe*	60	70
81/4	*Set of 4*	90	90

See also Nos. 105/8.

(Des D. Shults and J. Cooter. Litho Format)

1982 (22 June). *21st Birthday of Princess of Wales. T 13 and similar vert designs. Multicoloured. W w 14. P 13½ × 14.*
85	30 c. Type 13	25	20
86	55 c. Coat of arms of Caroline of Brunswick ..	35	30
87	$5 Diana, Princess of Wales	1·25	1·40
85/7	*Set of 3*	1·75	1·75

1982 (12 July). *Birth of Prince William of Wales. Nos. 85/7 optd with T 19 of St. Kitts.*
88	30 c. Type 13	25	20
89	55 c. Coat of arms of Caroline of Brunswick ..	35	30
	a. Opt triple		35·00
90	$5 Diana, Princess of Wales	1·25	1·40
88/90	*Set of 3*	1·75	1·75

14 Cyclist

(Des Philatelists (1980) Ltd. Litho Questa)

1982 (18 Aug). *75th Anniv of Boy Scout Movement. T 14 and similar horiz designs. Multicoloured. W w 14 (sideways). P 13½ × 14.*
91	5 c. Type 14	20	10
92	30 c. Athlete	50	10
93	$2.50, Camp cook	1·25	80
91/3	*Set of 3*	1·75	85

15 Santa Claus   16 Tube Sponge

(Des Eugene Seabrookes (15 c.), Kharenzabeth Glasgow (30 c.), Davia Grant (£1.50), Leonard Huggins ($2.50); adapted Jennifer Toombs. Litho Format)

1982 (20 Oct). *Christmas. Children's Paintings. T 15 and similar multicoloured designs. W w 14 (sideways on $1.50 and $2.50). P 13½ × 14 (15 c., 30 c.) or 14 × 13½ (others).*
94	15 c. Type 15	10	10
95	30 c. Carollers	10	10
96	$1.50, Decorated house and local band (*horiz*)	25	25
97	$2.50, Adoration of the Shepherds (*horiz*) ..	50	50
94/7	*Set of 4*	75	75

(Des G. Drummond. Litho Format)

1983 (12 Jan). *Corals (1st series). T 16 and similar vert designs. Multicoloured. W w 14. P 14.*
98	15 c. Type 16	10	10
99	30 c. Stinging coral	15	10
100	55 c. Flower coral	25	10
101	$3 Sea Rod and Red Fire Sponge	70	80
98/101	*Set of 4*	90	90
MS102	82 × 115 mm. Nos. 98/101	1·10	1·60

See also Nos. 423/6.

17 H.M.S. *Boreas* off Nevis

(Des G. Drummond. Litho Format)

1983 (14 Mar). *Commonwealth Day. T 17 and similar horiz design. Multicoloured. W w 14 (sideways). P 14.*
103	55 c. Type 17	20	10
104	$2 Capt. Horatio Nelson and H.M.S. *Boreas* at anchor ..	65	75

(Des Jennifer Toombs. Litho Format)

1983 (8 June). *Butterflies (2nd series). Multicoloured designs as T 12. W w 14 (sideways on 30 c. and $2). P 14.*
105	30 c. *Pyrgus oileus*	20	15
106	55 c. *Junonia evarete*	25	20
107	$1.10, *Urbanus proteus*	50	55
108	$2 *Hypolimnas misippus*	95	1·00
105/8	*Set of 4*	1·75	1·75

INDEPENDENCE 1983   INDEPENDENCE 1983   NEVIS 10c

(18)   (18a)   19 Montgolfier Balloon, 1783

1983 (19 Sept). *Nos. 58 and 60/71 optd as T 18 (20 mm long on Nos. 110/21).*
A. *No imprint date*
B. *With imprint date.*

		A	B		
109	5 c. Type 10	†		10	10
	a. Vert pair, lower stamp without opt.	†		65·00	—
	b. Optd with T 18a (local opt)	13·00	11·00	2·50	2·00
	ba. Opt T 18a inverted	†		45·00	—
110	15 c. Type 11	35·00	35·00	10	10
111	20 c. Nelson Museum	5·00	5·00	10	10
112	25 c. St. James' Parish Church	5·00	5·00	10	15
113	30 c. Nevis Lane	90	90	15	15
	a. Opt inverted	†		11·00	—
114	40 c. Zetland Plantation	75	75	15	20
115	45 c. Nisbet Plantation ..	†		20	25
116	50 c. Pinney's Beach	†		20	25
117	55 c. Eva Wilkin's Studio	75	75	25	30
	a. Opt double..	†		12·00	
118	$1 Nevis at dawn	75	75	40	45
119	$2.50, Ruins of Fort Charles ..	1·10	1·10	90	1·10
120	$5 Old Bath House	1·90	2·25	1·50	1·75
121	$10 Beach at Nisbet's ..	3·50	4·25	2·75	3·00
	a. Opt inverted	60·00		†	
109bA/121A	*Set of 11*	60·00	60·00		
109B/121B	*Set of 13*			6·00	7·00

(Des A. Theobald. Litho Format)

1983 (28 Sept). *Bicentenary of Manned Flight. T 19 and similar multicoloured designs. W w 15 (sideways on 45 c. to $2.50). P 14.*
122	10 c. Type 19	10	10
123	45 c. Sikorsky "S-38", flying boat (*horiz*) ..	15	10
124	50 c. Beechcraft "Twin Bonanza" (*horiz*) ..	15	10
125	$2.50, B. Ae. "Sea Harrier" (*horiz*) ..	50	60
122/5	*Set of 4*	70	70
MS126	118×145 mm. Nos. 122/5. Wmk sideways	1·00	1·00

20 Mary praying over Holy Child

(Des Jennifer Toombs. Litho Format)

1983 (7 Nov). *Christmas. T 20 and similar horiz designs. Multicoloured. W w 15 (sideways). P 14.*
127	5 c. Type 20	10	10
128	30 c. Shepherds with flock	10	10
129	55 c. Three Angels	15	10
130	$3 Boy with two girls	55	60
127/30	*Set of 4*	70	70
MS131	135 × 149 mm. Nos. 127/30	1·00	1·25

21 *County of Oxford* (1945)   **22** *Boer War*

(Des J. W. Litho Format)

1983 (10 Nov). *Leaders of the World. Railway Locomotives (1st series). T* **21** *and similar horiz designs, the first in each pair showing technical drawings and the second the locomotive at work. P* 12½.

132	55 c. multicoloured		15	20
	a. Vert pair. Nos. 132/3		30	40
133	55 c. multicoloured		15	20
134	$1 bright crimson, new blue and black		20	25
	a. Vert pair. Nos. 134/5		40	50
135	$1 multicoloured		20	25
136	$1 magenta, new blue and black		20	25
	a. Vert pair. Nos. 136/7		40	50
137	$1 multicoloured		20	25
138	$1 bright crimson, black and greenish yellow		20	25
	a. Vert pair. Nos. 138/9		40	50
139	$1 multicoloured		20	25
140	$1 multicoloured		20	25
	a. Vert pair. Nos. 140/1		40	50
141	$1 multicoloured		20	25
142	$1 greenish yellow, black and new blue		20	25
	a. Vert pair. Nos. 142/3		40	50
143	$1 multicoloured		20	25
144	$1 greenish yellow, black & brt magenta		20	25
	a. Vert pair. Nos. 144/5		40	50
145	$1 multicoloured		20	25
146	$1 multicoloured		20	25
	a. Vert pair. Nos. 146/7		40	50
147	$1 multicoloured		20	25
132/47		*Set of* 16	2·75	3·50

Designs:—Nos. 132/3, *County of Oxford*, Great Britain (1945), 134/5, *Evening Star*, Great Britain (1960); 136/7, Stanier "Class 5", Great Britain (1934); 138/9, *Pendennis Castle*, Great Britain (1924); 140/1, *Winston Churchill*, Great Britain (1946); 142/3, *Mallard*, Great Britain (1935); 144/5, *Britannia*, Great Britain (1951); 146/7, *King George V*, Great Britain (1927).

Nos. 132/3, 134/5, 136/7, 138/9, 140/1, 142/3, 144/5 and 146/7 were printed together, *se-tenant* in vertical pairs throughout the sheets.

See also Nos. 219/26, 277/84, 297/308, 352/9 and 427/42.

(Des Court House Studio. Litho Format)

1984 (11 Apr). *Leaders of the World. British Monarchs (1st series). T* **22** *and similar vert designs. Multicoloured. P* 12½.

148	5 c. Type **22**		10	10
	a. Horiz pair. Nos. 148/9		10	10
149	5 c. Queen Victoria		10	10
150	50 c. Queen Victoria at Osborne House		30	30
	a. Horiz pair. Nos. 150/1		60	60
151	50 c. Osborne House		30	30
152	60 c. Battle of Dettingen		30	30
	a. Horiz pair. Nos. 152/3		60	60
153	60 c. George II		30	30
154	75 c. George II at the Bank of England		30	30
	a. Horiz pair. Nos. 154/5		60	60
155	75 c. Bank of England		30	30
156	$1 Coat of Arms of George II		35	35
	a. Horiz pair. Nos. 156/7		70	70
157	$1 George II (*different*)		35	35
158	$3 Coat of Arms of Queen Victoria		80	80
	a. Horiz pair. Nos. 158/9		1·60	1·60
159	$3 Queen Victoria (*different*)		80	80
148/59		*Set of* 12	3·75	3·75

Nos. 148/9, 150/1, 152/3, 154/5, 156/7 and 158/9 were printed together, *se-tenant* in horizontal pairs throughout the sheet.

See also Nos. 231/6.

23 *Golden Rock Inn*

(Des Jennifer Toombs. Litho J.W.)

1984 (16 May). *Tourism. (1st series). T* **23** *and similar horiz designs. Multicoloured. W w* **15** (*sideways*). *P* 14.

160	55 c. Type **23**		35	20
161	55 c. Rest Haven Inn		35	20
162	55 c. Cliffdwellers Hotel		35	20
163	55 c. Pinney's Beach Hotel		35	20
160/3		*Set of* 4	1·25	70

See also Nos. 245/8.

24 *Early Seal of Colony*

(Des G. Drummond. Litho Format)

1984 (8 June). *W w* **15** (*sideways*). *P* 14.

164	**24** $15 dull scarlet		4·50	5·50

IMPERFORATES AND MISSING COLOURS. Various issues between Nos. 165 and 410 exist either imperforate or with colours omitted. Such items are not listed as there is no evidence that they fulfil the criteria outlined on page xi of this catalogue.

25 *Cadillac*

(Des J. W. Litho Format)

1984 (25 July). *Leaders of the World. Automobiles (1st series). T* **25** *and similar horiz designs, the first in each pair showing technical drawings and the second paintings. P* 12½.

165	1 c. greenish yellow, black and magenta		10	10
	a. Vert pair. Nos. 165/6		10	10
166	1 c. multicoloured		10	10
167	5 c. new blue, magenta and black		10	10
	a. Vert pair. Nos. 167/8		10	10
168	5 c. multicoloured		10	10
169	15 c. multicoloured		15	15
	a. Vert pair. Nos. 169/70		30	30
170	15 c. multicoloured		15	15
171	35 c. magenta, greenish yellow and black		25	25
	a. Vert pair. Nos. 171/2		50	50
172	35 c. multicoloured		25	25
173	45 c. new blue, magenta and black		25	25
	a. Vert pair. Nos. 173/4		50	50
174	45 c. multicoloured		25	25
175	55 c. multicoloured		25	25
	a. Vert pair. Nos. 175/6		50	50
176	55 c. multicoloured		25	25
177	$2.50, magenta, black and greenish yellow		60	60
	a. Vert pair. Nos. 177/8		1·10	1·10
178	$2.50, multicoloured		60	60
179	$3 new blue, greenish yellow and black		70	70
	a. Vert pair. Nos. 179/80		1·40	1·40
180	$3 multicoloured		70	70
165/80		*Set of* 16	4·00	4·00

Designs:—Nos. 165/6, Cadillac "V16 Fleetwood Convertible" (1932); 167/8, Packard "Twin Six Touring Car" (1916); 169/70, Daimler, "2 Cylinder" (1886); 171/2, Porsche "911 S Targa" (1970); 173/4, Benz "Three Wheeler" (1885); 175/6, M.G. "TC" (1947); 177/8, Cobra "Roadster 289" (1966), 179/80, Aston Martin "DB6 Hardtop" (1966).

Nos. 165/6, 167/8, 169/70, 171/2, 173/4, 175/6, 177/8 and 179/80 were printed together, *se-tenant* in vertical pairs throughout the sheet.

See also Nos. 203/10, 249/64, 326/37, 360/71 and 411/22.

26 *Carpentry*   **27** *Yellow Bell*

(Des Jennifer Toombs. Litho Questa)

1984 (1 Aug). *10th Anniv of Culturama Celebrations. T* **26** *and similar horiz designs. Multicoloured. W w* **15** (*sideways*). *P* 14.

181	30 c. Type **26**		10	10
182	55 c. Grass mat and basket-making		15	10
183	$1 Pottery-firing		25	25
184	$3 Culturama Queen and dancers		55	55
181/4		*Set of* 4	95	85

(Des Jennifer Toombs. Litho Format)

1984 (8 Aug)–86. *Flowers. T* **27** *and similar vert designs. Multicoloured. W w* **15**. *P* 14. **A**. *Without imprint date.* **B**. *With imprint date at foot of design* (23.7.86).

			A		B	
185	5 c. Type **27**		10	10	†	
186	10 c. Plumbago		10	10	†	
187	15 c. Flamboyant		10	10	†	
188	20 c. Eyelash Orchid		60	15	20	20
189	30 c. Bougainvillea		10	15	†	
190	40 c. Hibiscus *sp.*		70	25	30	30
191	50 c. Night-blooming Cereus		15	20	†	
192	55 c. Yellow Mahoe		20	25	†	
193	60 c. Spider-lily		20	25	†	
194	75 c. Scarlet Cordia		25	30	†	
195	$1 Shell-ginger		35	40	†	
196	$3 Blue Petrea		1·00	1·10	†	
197	$5 Coral Hibiscus		1·75	2·00	†	
198	$10 Passion Flower		3·25	3·50	†	
185/98		*Set of* 14	7·75	7·75	†	

28 *Cotton-picking and Map*   **29** *C.P. Mead*

(Des A. Grant (15 c.), Tracy Watkins (55 c.), C. Manners ($1.10), D. Grant ($3), adapted Court House Advertising. Litho Format)

1984 (18 Sept). *First Anniv of Independence of St. Kitts-Nevis. T* **28** *and similar horiz designs. Multicoloured. W w* **15** (*sideways*). *P* 14.

199	15 c. Type **28**		15	10
200	55 c. Alexander Hamilton's birthplace		20	10
201	$1.10, Local agricultural produce		35	40
202	$3 Nevis Peak and Pinneys Beach		75	1·00
199/202		*Set of* 4	1·25	1·40

(Des J. W. Litho Format)

1984 (23 Oct). *Leaders of the World. Automobiles (2nd series). Horiz designs as T* **25**, *the first in each pair showing technical drawings and the second paintings. P* 12½.

203	5 c. black, pale new blue and yellow-brown		10	10
	a. Vert pair. Nos. 203/4		10	10
204	5 c. multicoloured		10	10
205	30 c. black, pale turquoise-green & lake-brn		15	15
	a. Vert pair. Nos. 205/6		30	30
206	30 c. multicoloured		15	15
207	50 c. black, pale drab and red-brown		15	15
	a. Vert pair. Nos. 207/8		30	30
208	50 c. multicoloured		15	15
209	$3 black, grey-brown and dull green		45	45
	a. Vert pair. Nos. 209/10		90	90
210	$3 multicoloured		45	45
203/10		*Set of* 8	1·40	1·40

Designs:—Nos. 203/4, Lagonda "Speed Model" touring car (1929); 205/6, Jaguar "E-Type" 4.2 litre (1967); 207/8, Volkswagen "Beetle" (1947); 209/10, Pierce Arrow "V12" (1932).

Nos. 203/10 were issued in a similar sheet format to Nos. 165/80.

(Des Court House Studio. Litho Format)

1984 (23 Oct). *Leaders of the World. Cricketers (1st series). T* **29** *and similar vert designs, the first in each pair showing a head portrait and the second the cricketer in action. P* 12½.

211	5 c. multicoloured		10	10
	a. Horiz pair. Nos. 211/12		15	15
212	5 c. multicoloured		10	10
213	25 c. multicoloured		30	30
	a. Horiz pair. Nos. 213/14		60	60
214	25 c. multicoloured		30	30
215	55 c. multicoloured		40	40
	a. Horiz pair. Nos. 215/16		80	80
216	55 c. multicoloured		40	40
217	$2.50, multicoloured		1·25	1·25
	a. Horiz pair. Nos. 217/18		2·50	2·50
218	$2.50 multicoloured		1·25	1·25
211/18		*Set of* 8	3·50	3·50

Designs:—Nos. 211/12, C. P. Mead; 213/14, J. B. Statham; 215/16, Sir Learie Constantine; 217/18, Sir Leonard Hutton.

Nos. 211/12, 213/14, 215/16 and 217/18 were printed together, *se-tenant*, in horizontal pairs throughout the sheets.

See also Nos. 237/44.

(Des J. W. Litho Format)

1984 (29 Oct). *Leaders of the World. Railway Locomotives (2nd series). Horiz designs as T* **21** *the first in each pair showing technical drawings and the second paintings. P* 12½.

219	5 c. multicoloured		10	10
	a. Vert pair. Nos. 219/20		10	10
220	5 c. multicoloured		10	10
221	10 c. multicoloured		15	15
	a. Vert pair. Nos. 221/2		15	15
222	10 c. multicoloured		10	10
223	60 c. multicoloured		25	25
	a. Vert pair. Nos. 223/4		50	50
224	60 c. multicoloured		25	25
225	$2.50, multicoloured		70	70
	a. Vert pair. Nos. 225/6		1·40	1·40
226	$2.50 multicoloured		70	70
219/26		*Set of* 8	1·75	1·75

Designs:—Nos. 219/20, Class "EF81", Japan (1968); 221/2, Class "5500", France (1927); 223/4, Class "240P", France (1940); 225/6, Shinkansen train, Japan (1964).

Nos. 219/26 were issued in a similar sheet format to Nos. 132/47.

30 *Fifer and Drummer from Honeybees Band*

(Des Jennifer Toombs. Litho Questa)

1984 (2 Nov). *Christmas. Local Music. T* **30** *and similar horiz designs. Multicoloured. W w* **15** (*sideways*). *P* 14.

227	15 c. Type **30**		15	10
228	40 c. Guitar and "barhow" players from Canary Birds Band		25	10
229	60 c. Shell All Stars steel band		30	10
230	$3 Organ and choir, St. John's Church, Fig Tree		1·25	1·00
227/30		*Set of* 4	1·75	1·10

(Des Court House Studio. Litho Format)

1984 (20 Nov). *Leaders of the World. British Monarchs (2nd series). Vert designs as T* **22**. *Multicoloured. P* 12½.

231	5 c. King John and Magna Carta		10	10
	a. Horiz pair. Nos. 231/2		10	10
232	5 c. Barons and King John		10	10
233	55 c. King John		20	20
	a. Horiz pair Nos. 233/4		40	40
234	55 c. Newark Castle		20	20
235	$2 Coat of arms		55	55
	a. Horiz pair. Nos. 235/6		1·10	1·10
236	$2 King John (*different*)		55	55
231/6		*Set of* 6	1·40	1·40

Nos. 231/6 were issued in a similar sheet format to Nos. 148/59.

(Des Court House Studio. Litho Format)

1984 (20 Nov). *Leaders of the World. Cricketers (2nd series). Vert designs as T 29, the first in each pair listed showing a head portrait and the second the cricketer in action.* P 12½.

237	5 c. multicoloured	..	10	10
	a. Horiz pair. Nos. 237/8	..	15	15
238	5 c. multicoloured	..	10	10
239	15 c. multicoloured	..	15	15
	a. Horiz pair. Nos. 239/40	..	30	30
240	15 c. multicoloured	..	15	15
241	55 c. multicoloured	..	20	20
	a. Horiz pair. Nos. 241/2	..	40	40
242	55 c. multicoloured	..	20	20
243	$2,50, multicoloured	..	75	60
	a. Horiz pair. Nos. 243/4	..	1·50	1·10
244	$2.50, multicoloured	..	75	60
237/44		*Set of 8*	2·10	1·75

Designs:—Nos. 237/8, J. D. Love; 239/40, S. J. Dennis; 241/2, B. W. Luckhurst; 243/4, B. L. D'Oliveira.
Nos. 237/44 were issued in a similar sheet format to Nos. 211/18.

(Des Jennifer Toombs. Litho Format)

1985 (12 Feb). *Tourism (2nd series). Horiz designs as T 23. Multicoloured. W w 15 (sideways). P 14.*

245	$1.20, Croney's Old Manor Hotel	..	45	45
246	$1.20, Montpelier Plantation Inn	..	45	45
247	$1.20, Nisbet's Plantation Inn	..	45	45
248	$1.20, Zetland Plantation Inn	..	45	45
245/8		*Set of 4*	1·60	1·60

(Des G. Turner (10 c.), J.W. (others). Litho Format)

1985 (20 Feb). *Leaders of the World. Automobiles (3rd series). Horiz designs as T 25, the first in each pair showing technical drawings and the second paintings.* P 12½.

249	1 c. black, light green and pale green	..	10	10
	a. Vert pair. Nos. 249/50	..	10	10
250	1 c. multicoloured	..	10	10
251	5 c. black, cobalt and pale violet-blue	..	10	10
	a. Vert pair. Nos. 251/2	..	10	10
252	5 c. multicoloured	..	10	10
253	10 c. black, grey-olive and pale green	..	10	10
	a. Vert pair. Nos. 253/4	..	10	10
254	10 c. multicoloured	..	10	10
255	50 c. black, sage-green and pale cinnamon	..	15	15
	a. Vert pair. Nos. 255/6	..	30	30
256	50 c. multicoloured	..	15	15
257	60 c. black, dull yellowish green and pale blue	..	15	15
	a. Vert pair. Nos. 257/8	..	30	30
258	60 c. multicoloured	..	15	15
259	75 c. black, dull vermilion and pale orange	..	15	15
	a. Vert pair. Nos. 259/60	..	30	30
260	75 c. multicoloured	..	15	15
261	$2.50, black, light green and azure	..	30	30
	a. Vert pair. Nos. 261/2	..	60	60
262	$2.50, multicoloured	..	30	30
263	$3 black, bright yellow-green and pale green	..	30	30
	a. Vert pair. Nos. 263/4	..	60	60
264	$3 multicoloured	..	30	30
249/64		*Set of 16*	2·25	2·25

Designs:—Nos. 249/50, Delahaye "Type 35 Cabriolet" (1935); 251/2, Ferrari "Testa Rossa" (1958); 253/4, Voisin "Aerodyne" (1934); 255/6, Buick "Riviera" (1963); 257/8, Cooper "Climax" (1960); 259/60, Ford "999" (1904); 261/2, MG "M-Type Midget" (1930); 263/4, Rolls-Royce "Corniche" (1971).
Nos. 249/64 were issued in a similar sheet format to Nos. 165/80.

31 Broad-winged Hawk   32 Eastern Bluebird

(Des Jennifer Toombs. Litho Format)

1985 (19 Mar). *Local Hawks and Herons. T 31 and similar horiz designs. Multicoloured. W w 15 (sideways). P 14.*

265	20 c. Type 31	..	75	20
266	40 c. Red-tailed Hawk	..	1·00	30
267	60 c. Little Blue Heron	..	1·25	40
268	$3 Great Blue Heron (white phase)	..	2·50	1·90
265/8		*Set of 4*	5·00	2·50

No. 268 was re-issued on 24 May 1990 overprinted "40th Anniversary C.S.S." to mark the fortieth anniversary of Charlestown Secondary School. This overprint was only available on First Day Covers.

(Des R. Vigurs. Litho Format)

1985 (25 Mar). *Leaders of the World. Birth Bicentenary of John J. Audubon (ornithologist) (1st issue). T 32 and similar vert designs. Multicoloured.* P 12½.

269	5 c. Type 32	..	15	10
	a. Horiz pair. Nos. 269/70	..	30	20
270	5 c. multicoloured	..	15	10
271	55 c. Belted Kingfisher	..	65	65
	a. Horiz pair. Nos. 271/2	..	1·25	1·25
272	55 c. Mangrove Cuckoo	..	65	65
273	60 c. Yellow Warbler	..	65	65
	a. Horiz pair. Nos. 273/4	..	1·25	1·25
274	60 c. Cerulean Warbler	..	65	65
275	$2 Burrowing Owl	..	1·75	1·75
	a. Horiz pair. Nos. 275/6	..	3·50	3·50
276	$2 Long-eared Owl	..	1·75	1·75
269/76		*Set of 8*	5·75	5·75

Nos. 269/70, 271/2, 273/4 and 275/6 were printed together, *se-tenant*, in horizontal pairs throughout the sheets.
See also Nos. 285/92.

(Des J.W. Litho Format)

1985 (26 Apr). *Leaders of the World. Railway Locomotives (3rd series). Horiz designs as T 21, the first in each pair showing technical drawings and the second the locomotive at work.* P 12½.

277	1 c. multicoloured	..	10	10
	a. Vert pair. Nos. 277/8	..	10	10
278	1 c. multicoloured	..	10	10
279	60 c. multicoloured	..	20	20
	a. Vert pair. Nos. 279/80	..	40	40
280	60 c. multicoloured	..	20	20
281	90 c. multicoloured	..	25	25
	a. Vert pair. Nos. 281/2	..	50	50
282	90 c. multicoloured	..	25	25
283	$2 multicoloured	..	60	60
	a. Vert pair. Nos. 283/4	..	1·10	1·10
284	$2 multicoloured	..	60	60
277/84		*Set of 8*	1·75	1·75

Designs:—Nos. 277/8, Class "Wee Bogie", Great Britain (1882); 279/80, *Comet*, Great Britain (1851); 281/2, Class "8H", Great Britain (1908); 283/4, Class "A" No. 23, Great Britain (1866).
Nos. 277/84 were issued in a similar sheet format to Nos. 132/47.

(Des R. Vigurs. Litho Format)

1985 (3 June). *Leaders of the World. Birth Bicentenary of John J. Audubon (ornithologist) (2nd issue). Vert designs as T 32 showing original paintings. Multicoloured.* P 12½.

285	1 c. Painted Bunting	..	10	10
	a. Horiz pair. Nos. 285/6	..	10	10
286	1 c. Golden-crowned Kinglet	..	10	10
287	40 c. Common Flicker	..	40	40
	a. Horiz pair. Nos. 287/8	..	80	80
288	40 c. Western Tanager	..	40	40
289	60 c. Varied Thrush ("Sage Thrasher")	..	45	45
	a. Horiz pair. Nos. 289/90	..	90	90
290	60 c. Evening Grosbeak	..	45	45
291	$2.50, Blackburnian Warbler	..	1·00	1·00
	a. Vert pair. Nos. 291/2	..	2·00	2·00
292	$2.50, Northern Oriole	..	1·00	1·00
285/92		*Set of 8*	3·50	3·50

Nos. 285/92 were issued in a similar sheet format to Nos. 269/76.
Nos. 285/92 exist with yellow omitted from stock dispersed by the liquidator of Format International Security Printers Ltd.

33 Guides and Guide   34 The Queen Mother
Headquarters   at Garter Ceremony

(Des G. Vasarhelyi. Litho Format)

1985 (17 June). *75th Anniv of Girl Guide Movement. T 33 and similar multicoloured designs. W w 15 (inverted on 60 c., sideways on 15 c.).* P 14.

293	15 c. Type 33	..	10	10
294	60 c. Girl Guide uniforms of 1910 and 1985 (vert)	..	20	25
295	$1 Lord and Lady Baden-Powell (vert)	..	35	40
296	$3 Princess Margaret in Guide uniform (vert)	..	90	1·25
293/6		*Set of 4*	1·40	1·75

(Des T. Hadler (75 c., $1, $2.50), J.W. (others). Litho Format)

1985 (26 July). *Leaders of the World. Railway Locomotives (4th series). Horiz designs as T 21, the first in each pair showing technical drawings and the second the locomotive at work.* P 12½.

297	5 c. multicoloured	..	10	10
	a. Vert pair. Nos. 297/8	..	10	10
298	5 c. multicoloured	..	10	10
299	30 c. multicoloured	..	15	15
	a. Vert pair. Nos. 299/300	..	30	30
300	30 c. multicoloured	..	15	15
301	60 c. multicoloured	..	20	20
	a. Vert pair. Nos. 301/2	..	40	40
302	60 c. multicoloured	..	20	20
303	75 c. multicoloured	..	25	25
	a. Vert pair. Nos. 303/4	..	50	50
304	75 c. multicoloured	..	25	25
305	$1 multicoloured	..	25	25
	a. Vert pair. Nos. 305/6	..	50	50
306	$1 multicoloured	..	25	25
307	$2.50, multicoloured	..	60	60
	a. Vert pair. Nos. 307/8	..	1·10	1·10
308	$2.50, multicoloured	..	60	60
297/308		*Set of 12*	2·50	2·50

Designs:—Nos. 297/8, Snowdon Ranger, Great Britain (1878); 299/300, Large Belpaire passenger locomotive, Great Britain (1904); 301/2, Great Western Railway "County" Class, Great Britain (1904); 303/4, *Nord L'Outrance*, France (1877); 305/6, Q.R. "Class PB-15", Australia (1899); 307/8, D.R.G. "Class 64", Germany (1928).
Nos. 297/308 were issued in a similar sheet format to Nos. 132/47.

(Des Court House Studio. Litho Format)

1985 (31 July). *Leaders of the World. Life and Times of Queen Elizabeth the Queen Mother. Various vertical portraits as T 34.* P 12½.

309	45 c. multicoloured	..	15	15
	a. Horiz pair. Nos. 309/10	..	30	30
310	45 c. multicoloured	..	15	15
311	75 c. multicoloured	..	20	20
	a. Horiz pair. Nos. 311/12	..	40	40

312	75 c. multicoloured	..	20	20
313	$1.20, multicoloured	..	35	35
	a. Horiz pair. Nos. 313/14	..	70	70
314	$1.20, multicoloured	..	35	35
315	$1.50, multicoloured	..	40	40
	a. Horiz pair. Nos. 315/16	..	80	80
316	$1.50, multicoloured	..	40	40
309/16		*Set of 8*	2·00	2·00
MS317	85×114 mm. $2 multicoloured; $2 multicoloured		90	1·40

The two designs of each value were issued, *se-tenant*, in horizontal pairs within the sheets.
Each *se-tenant* pair shows a floral pattern across the bottom of the portraits which stops short of the left-hand edge on the left-hand stamp and of the right-hand edge on the right-hand stamp.
Nos. 309/16 exist in unissued miniature sheets, one for each value, from stock dispersed by the liquidator of Format International Security Printers Ltd.
Designs as Nos. 309/10 and 315/16, but with face values of $3.50 × 2 and $6 × 2, also exist in additional miniature sheets from a restricted printing issued 27 December 1985.

35 Isambard Kingdom   36 St. Pauls Anglican
Brunel   Church, Charlestown

(Des Tudor Art Agency. Litho Format)

1985 (31 Aug). *150th Anniv of the Great Western Railway. T 35 and similar vert designs showing railway engineers and their achievements. Multicoloured.* P 12½.

318	25 c. Type 35	..	35	35
	a. Horiz pair. Nos. 318/19	..	70	70
319	25 c. Royal Albert Bridge, 1859	..	35	35
320	50 c. William Dean	..	45	45
	a. Horiz pair. Nos. 320/1	..	90	90
321	50 c. Locomotive *Lord of the Isles*, 1895	..	45	45
322	$1 Locomotive *Lode Star*, 1907	..	80	80
	a. Horiz pair. Nos. 322/3	..	1·60	1·60
323	$1 G. J. Churchward	..	80	80
324	$2.50, Locomotive *Pendennis Castle*, 1924	..	1·25	1·25
	a. Horiz pair. Nos. 324/5	..	2·50	2·50
325	$2.50, C. B. Collett	..	1·25	1·25
318/25		*Set of 8*	5·25	5·25

Nos. 318/19, 320/1, 322/3 and 324/5 were printed together, *se-tenant*, in horizontal pairs throughout the sheets, each pair forming a composite design.

(Des J.W. Litho Format)

1985 (4 Oct). *Leaders of the World. Automobiles (4th series). Horiz designs as T 25, the first in each pair showing technical drawings and the second paintings.* P 12½.

326	10 c. black, azure and brown-red	..	10	10
	a. Vert pair. Nos. 326/7	..	10	15
327	10 c. multicoloured	..	10	10
328	35 c. black, pale turquoise-grn & greenish bl	..	20	25
	a. Vert pair. Nos. 328/9	..	40	50
329	35 c. multicoloured	..	20	25
330	75 c. black, bright green & lt purple-brown	..	35	40
	a. Vert pair. Nos. 330/1	..	70	80
331	75 c. multicoloured	..	35	40
332	$1.15, black, pale cinnamon & olive-green	..	50	60
	a. Vert pair. Nos. 332/3	..	1·00	1·10
333	$1.15, multicoloured	..	50	60
334	$1.50, black, pale blue and carmine	..	60	70
	a. Vert pair. Nos. 334/5	..	1·10	1·40
335	$1.50, multicoloured	..	60	70
336	$2 black, rose-lilac and reddish violet	..	75	1·00
	a. Vert pair. Nos. 336/7	..	1·50	2·00
337	$2 multicoloured	..	75	1·00
326/37		*Set of 12*	4·00	5·50

Designs:—Nos. 326/7, Sunbeam "Coupe de l'Auto" (1912); 328/9, Cisitalia "Pininfarina Coupe" (1948); 330/1, Porsche "928 S" (1980); 332/3, MG "K3 Magnette" (1933); 334/5, Lincoln "Zephyr" (1937); 336/7, Pontiac 2 Door (1926).
Nos. 326/37 were issued in a similar sheet format to Nos. 165/80.

1985 (23 Oct). *Royal Visit. Nos. 76/7, 83, 86, 92/3, 98/9 and 309/10 optd as T 114 of Montserrat or surch also.*

338	16	15 c. multicoloured	1·00	1·00
339	—	30 c. multicoloured (No. 92)	2·00	1·50
340	—	30 c. multicoloured (No. 99)	1·00	1·00
341	—	40 c. on 55 c. multicoloured (No. 86)	2·00	1·75
342	34	45 c. multicoloured	2·25	2·00
		a. Horiz pair. Nos. 342/3	4·50	4·00
343	—	45 c. multicoloured (No. 310)	2·25	2·00
344	—	55 c. multicoloured (No. 83)	1·25	1·25
345	—	$1.50 on $5 multicoloured (No. 76)	2·25	2·25
		a. Sheetlet. No. 345 × 6 and No. 346	20·00	
		b. Error. Surch $1.60	2·75	2·75
		ba. Sheetlet. No. 345b × 6 and No. 346b	18·00	
346	—	$1.50 on $5 multicoloured (No. 77)	4·50	4·50
		b. Error. Surch $1.60	4·75	4·75
347	—	$2.50, multicoloured (No. 93)	2·75	2·50
338/47		*Set of 10*	18·00	17·00

Nos. 345b/ba and 346b had the surcharge intended for similar St. Vincent sheetlets applied by mistake.

(Des G. Drummond. Litho Format)

1985 (5 Nov). *Christmas. Churches of Nevis (1st series). T* **36** *and similar horiz designs. Multicoloured.* W **15**. P 15.

348	10 c. Type **36**			15	10
349	40 c. St. Theresa Catholic Church, Charles-				
	town			30	30
350	60 c. Methodist Church, Gingerland			45	50
351	$3 St. Thomas Anglican Church, Lowland			2·00	2·25
348/51			*Set of 4*	2·50	2·75

See also Nos. 462/5.

(Des T. Hadler. Litho Format)

1986 (30 Jan). *Leaders of the World. Railway Locomotives (5th series). Horiz designs as T* **21**, *the first in each pair showing technical drawings and the second the locomotive at work.* P 12½.

352	30 c. multicoloured			25	25
	a. Vert pair. Nos. 352/3			50	50
353	30 c. multicoloured			25	25
354	75 c. multicoloured			50	50
	a. Vert pair. Nos. 354/5			1·00	1·00
355	75 c. multicoloured			50	50
356	$1.50, multicoloured			80	80
	a. Vert pair. Nos. 356/7			1·60	1·60
357	$1.50, multicoloured			80	80
358	$2 multicoloured			1·10	1·10
	a. Vert pair. Nos. 358/9			2·10	2·10
359	$2 multicoloured			1·10	1·10
352/9			*Set of 8*	4·75	4·75

Designs:—Nos. 342/3, *Stourbridge Lion*, U.S.A. (1829); 354/5, "EP-2 Bi-Polar", U.S.A. (1919); 356/7, U.P. "BO × 4" gas turbine, U.S.A. (1953); 358/9, N.Y., N.H. and H.R. "FL9", U.S.A (1955). Nos. 352/9 were issued in a similar sheet format to Nos. 132/47.

(Des G. Turner (60 c.), J.W. (others). Litho Format)

1986 (30 Jan). *Leaders of the World. Automobiles (5th series). Horiz designs as T* **25**, *the first in each pair showing technical drawings and the second paintings.* P 12½.

360	10 c. black, pale cinnamon and yellow-olive.			10	10
	a. Vert pair. Nos. 360/1			10	20
361	10 c. multicoloured			10	10
362	60 c. black, salmon and bright scarlet			20	25
	a. Vert pair. Nos. 362/3			40	50
363	60 c. multicoloured			20	25
364	75 c. black, pale cinnamon and cinnamon			20	25
	a. Vert pair. Nos. 364/5			40	50
365	75 c. multicoloured			20	25
366	$1 black, lavender-grey and violet-grey			20	30
	a. Vert pair. Nos. 366/7			40	60
367	$1 multicoloured			20	30
368	$1.50, black, pale olive-yellow & olive-grn			30	45
	a. Vert pair. Nos. 368/9			60	90
369	$1.50, multicoloured			30	45
370	$3 black, azure and cobalt.			60	80
	a. Vert pair. Nos. 370/1			1·10	1·60
371	$3 multicoloured			60	80
360/71			*Set of 12*	2·75	3·75

Designs:—No. 360/1, Adler "Trumpf" (1936); 362/3, Maserati "Tipo 250F" (1957); 364/5, Oldsmobile "Limited" (1910); 366/7, Jaguar "C-Type" (1951); 368/9, ERA "1.5L B Type" (1937); 370/1 Chevrolet "Corvette" (1953). Nos. 360/71 were issued in a similar sheet format to Nos. 165/80.

37 "Spitfire" Prototype "K.5054", 1936

(Des J. Batchelor. Litho Format)

1986 (5 Mar). *50th Anniv of the "Spitfire" (fighter aircraft). T* **37** *and similar horiz designs. Multicoloured.* P 12½.

372	$1 Type **37**			1·00	85
373	$2.50, Mark "1A" in Battle of Britain, 1940			1·75	2·00
374	$3 Mark "XII" over convoy, 1944			2·00	2·25
375	$4 Mark "XXIV", 1948			2·25	2·75
372/5			*Set of 4*	6·25	7·00
MS376	114 × 86 mm. $6 "Seafire" Mark "III" on				
	escort carrier H.M.S. *Hunter*			4·00	4·50

Nos. 372/6 exist with red omitted and No. **MS**376 with black omitted from stock dispersed by the liquidator of Format International Security Printers Ltd.

38 Head of Amerindian   39 Brazilian Player

(Litho Format)

1986 (11 Apr). *500th Anniv of Discovery of America (1992) (1st issue). T* **38** *and similar vert designs. Multicoloured.* P 12½.

377	75 c. Type **38**			55	55
	a. Horiz pair. Nos. 377/8			1·10	1·10
378	75 c. Exchanging gifts for food from Amer-				
	indians			55	55

379	$1.75, Columbus's coat of arms			1·40	1·40
	a. Horiz pair. Nos. 379/80.			2·75	2·75
380	$1.75, Breadfruit plant			1·40	1·40
381	$2.50, Columbus's fleet			1·75	1·75
	a. Horiz pair. Nos. 381/2			3·50	3·50
382	$2.50, Christopher Columbus			1·75	1·75
377/82			*Set of 6*	6·50	6·50
MS383	95 × 84 mm. $6 Christopher Columbus				
	(*different*)			6·50	7·00

The two designs of each value were printed together, *se-tenant*, in horizontal pairs throughout the sheets. Each pair forms a composite design showing charts of Columbus's route in the background.

Miniature sheets, each containing $2 × 2 stamps in the above designs, also exist from a restricted printing and from stock dispersed by the liquidator of Format International Security Printers Ltd.

See also Nos. 546/54, 592/600 and 678/84.

(Des Court House Studio. Litho Format)

1986 (21 Apr). *60th Birthday of Queen Elizabeth II. Multicoloured designs as T* **117**a *of Montserrat.* P 12½.

384	5 c. Queen Elizabeth in 1976			10	10
385	75 c. Queen Elizabeth in 1953			20	25
386	$2 In Australia			50	60
387	$8 In Canberra, 1982 (*vert*)			2·00	2·50
384/7			*Set of 4*	2·50	3·00
MS388	85 × 115 mm. $10 Queen Elizabeth II			6·00	6·00

The 5 c., 75 c. and $2 values exist with PVA gum as well as gum arabic.

No. 387 also exists watermarked w **15** (inverted), but no examples have been reported used from Nevis.

Nos. 384/7 exist in separate miniature sheets from unissued stock dispersed by the liquidator of Format International Security Printers Ltd.

(Des Court House Studio. Litho Format)

1986 (16 May). *World Cup Football Championship, Mexico. T* **39** *and similar multicoloured designs.* P 12½ (75 c., $1, $1.75, $6) *or* 15 (*others*).

389	1 c. Official World Cup mascot (*horiz*)			10	10
390	2 c. Type **39**			10	10
391	5 c. Danish player			10	10
392	10 c. Brazilian player (*different*)			10	10
393	20 c. Denmark v Spain			20	20
394	30 c. Paraguay v Chile			30	30
395	60 c. Italy v West Germany			55	55
396	75 c. Danish team (56 × 36 *mm*)			65	65
397	$1 Paraguayan team (56 × 36 *mm*)			80	80
398	$1.75, Brazilian team (56 × 36 *mm*)			1·40	1·40
399	$3 Italy v England			2·00	2·00
400	$6 Italian team (56 × 36 *mm*)			3·50	3·50
389/400			*Set of 12*	8·75	8·75
MS401	Five sheets, each 85 × 115 mm. (a) $1.50,				
	As No. 398. (b) $2 As No. 393. (c) $2 As				
	No. 400. (d) $2.50, As No. 395. (e) $4				
	As No. 394.		*Set of 5 sheets*	9·50	9·00

40 Clothing Machinist   41 Gorgonia

(Des G. Vasarhelyi. Litho Questa)

1986 (18 July). *Local Industries. T* **40** *and similar horiz designs. Multicoloured.* W **15**. P 14.

402	15 c. Type **40**			20	15
403	40 c. Carpentry/joinery workshop			45	30
404	$1.20, Agricultural produce market			1·25	1·25
405	$3 Fishing boats landing catch			2·50	2·75
402/5			*Set of 4*	4·00	4·00

(Des Court House Studio. Litho Format)

1986 (23 July–15 Oct). *Royal Wedding (1st issue). Multicoloured designs as T* **118**a *of Montserrat.* P 12½.

406	60 c. Prince Andrew in midshipman's uni-				
	form			20	25
	a. Pair. Nos. 406/7.			40	50
407	60 c. Miss Sarah Ferguson			20	25
408	$2 Prince Andrew on safari in Africa				
	(*horiz*)			55	70
	a. Pair. Nos. 408/9.			1·10	1·40
409	$2 Prince Andrew at the races (*horiz*)			55	70
406/9			*Set of 4*	1·40	1·75
MS410	115 × 85 mm. $10 Duke and Duchess of				
	York on Palace balcony after wedding (*horiz*)				
	(15.10.86)			3·50	4·50

Nos. 406/7 and 408/9 were each printed together, *se-tenant*, in horizontal and vertical pairs throughout the sheets.

Nos. 408/9 exist in *tête-bêche* pairs from unissued stock dispersed by the liquidator of Format International Security Printers Ltd.

See also Nos. 454/7.

(Litho Format)

1986 (15 Aug). *Automobiles (6th series). Horiz designs as T* **25**, *the first in each pair showing technical drawings and the second paintings.* P 12½.

411	15 c. multicoloured			10	10
	a. Vert pair. Nos. 411/12			20	20
412	15 c. multicoloured			10	10
413	45 c. black, light blue and grey-blue			25	25
	a. Vert pair. Nos. 413/14			50	50
414	45 c. multicoloured			25	25

415	60 c. multicoloured			30	30
	a. Vert pair. Nos. 415/16			60	60
416	60 c. multicoloured			30	30
417	$1 black, yellow-green and dull green			40	40
	a. Vert pair. Nos. 417/18			80	80
418	$1 multicoloured			40	40
419	$1.75, black, pale reddish lilac & deep lilac			60	60
	a. Vert pair. Nos. 419/20			1·10	1·10
420	$1.75, multicoloured			60	60
421	$3 multicoloured			1·10	1·10
	a. Vert pair. Nos. 421/2			2·10	2·10
422	$3 multicoloured			1·10	1·10
411/22			*Set of 12*	4·75	4·75

Designs:—Nos. 411/12, Riley "Brooklands Nine" (1930); 413/14, Alfa Romeo "GTA" (1966); 415/16, Pierce Arrow "Type 66" (1913); 417/18, Willys-Knight "66 A" (1928); 419/20, Stude-baker "Starliner" (1953); 421/2, Cunningham "V-8" (1919).

Nos. 411/22 were issued in a similar sheet format to Nos. 165/80.

(Des G. Drummond. Litho Format)

1986 (8 Sept). *Corals (2nd series). T* **41** *and similar vert designs. Multicoloured.* W **15** (*sideways*). P 15.

423	15 c. Type **41**			50	20
424	60 c. Fire Coral			1·25	65
425	$2 Elkhorn Coral			2·50	2·50
426	$3 Vase Sponge and Feather Star			3·50	3·50
423/6			*Set of 4*	7·00	7·00

(Des Court House Studio. Litho Format)

1986 (1 Oct). *Railway Locomotives (6th series). Horiz designs as T* **21**, *the first in each pair showing technical drawings and the second the locomotive at work.* P 12½.

427	15 c. multicoloured			10	10
	a. Vert pair. Nos. 427/8			20	20
428	15 c. multicoloured			10	10
429	45 c. multicoloured			25	25
	a. Vert pair. Nos. 429/30			50	50
430	45 c. multicoloured			25	25
431	60 c. multicoloured			30	30
	a. Vert pair. Nos. 431/2			60	60
432	60 c. multicoloured			30	30
433	75 c. multicoloured			40	40
	a. Vert pair. Nos. 433/4			80	80
434	75 c. multicoloured			40	40
435	$1 multicoloured			45	50
	a. Vert pair. Nos. 435/6			90	1·00
436	$1 multicoloured			45	50
437	$1.50, multicoloured			60	70
	a. Vert pair. Nos. 437/8			1·10	1·40
438	$1.50, multicoloured			60	70
439	$2 multicoloured			70	80
	a. Vert pair. Nos. 439/40			1·40	1·60
440	$2 multicoloured			70	80
441	$3 multicoloured			90	1·10
	a. Vert pair. Nos. 441/2			1·75	2·10
442	$3 multicoloured			90	1·10
427/42			*Set of 16*	6·50	7·50

Designs:—Nos. 427/8, Connor Single Class, Great Britain (1859); 429/30, Class "P2" *Cock o' the North*, Great Britain (1934); 431/2, Class "7000", Japan (1926); 433/4, Palatinate Railway Class "P3", Germany (1897); 435/6, *Dorchester*, Canada (1836); 437/8, "Centennial" Class diesel, U.S.A. (1969); 439/40, *Lafayette*, U.S.A. (1837); 441/2, Class "C-16", U.S.A. (1882).

Nos. 427/42 were issued in a similar sheet format to Nos. 132/47.

(Des Court House Studio. Litho Format)

1986 (28 Oct). *Centenary of Statue of Liberty. Multicoloured designs as T* **121**a *of Montserrat.* P 13½×14 ($1, $2) *or* 14×13½ (*others*).

443	15 c. Statue of Liberty and World Trade				
	Centre, Manhattan			10	10
444	25 c. Sailing ship passing Statue			15	15
445	40 c. Statue in scaffolding			20	20
446	60 c. Statue (side view) and scaffolding			25	25
447	75 c. Statue and regatta			30	30
448	$1 Tall Ships parade passing Statue				
	(*horiz*)			35	35
449	$1.50, Head and arm of Statue above				
	scaffolding			50	50
450	$2 Ships with souvenir flags (*horiz*)			70	70
451	$2.50, Statue and New York waterfront			80	80
452	$3 Restoring Statue			1·10	1·10
443/52			*Set of 10*	4·00	4·00
MS453	Four sheets, each 85 × 115 mm. (a) $3.50,				
	Statue at dusk. (b) $4 Head of Statue. (c) $4.50,				
	Statue and lightning. (d) $5 Head and torch at				
	sunset		*Set of 4 sheets*	8·50	9·50

1986 (17 Nov). *Royal Wedding (2nd issue). Nos. 406/9 optd as T* **121** *of Montserrat in silver.*

454	60 c. Prince Andrew in midshipman's uni-				
	form			35	35
	a. Pair. Nos. 454/5.			70	70
455	60 c. Miss Sarah Ferguson			35	35
456	$2 Prince Andrew on safari in Africa (*horiz*)			1·10	1·10
	a. Pair. Nos. 456/7.			2·10	2·10
457	$2 Prince Andrew at the races (*horiz*)			1·10	1·10
454/7			*Set of 4*	2·50	2·50

42 Dinghy sailing

(Des G. Vasarhelyi. Litho Questa)

1986 (21 Nov). *Sports. T* **42** *and similar horiz designs. Multicoloured.* P 14.

458	10 c. Type **42**			10	10
459	25 c. Netball			30	15
460	$2 Cricket			1·75	1·75
461	$3 Basketball			2·00	2·00
458/61			*Set of 4*	3·75	3·75

43 St. George's
Anglican Church,
Gingerland

44 Constitution
Document, Quill and
Inkwell

(Des J. Cooter. Litho Questa)

1986 (8 Dec). *Christmas. Churches of Nevis (2nd series).* T **43** *and similar horiz designs. Multicoloured.* P 14.

462	10 c. Type **43**			10	10
463	40 c. Trinity Methodist Church, Fountain			20	25
464	$1 Charlestown Methodist Church			45	55
465	$5 Wesleyan Holiness Church, Brown Hill			2·25	2·75
462/5			*Set of 4*	2·75	3·25

(Des Maxine Marsh. Litho Questa)

1987 (11 Jan). *Bicentenary of U.S. Constitution and 230th Birth Anniv of Alexander Hamilton (U.S. statesman).* T **44** *and similar vert designs. Multicoloured.* P 14.

466	15 c. Type **44**			10	10
467	40 c. Alexander Hamilton and Hamilton House			20	25
468	60 c. Alexander Hamilton			25	35
469	$2 Washington and his Cabinet			90	1·25
466/9			*Set of 4*	1·25	1·75
MS470	70×82 mm. $5 Model ship *Hamilton* on float, 1788			6·50	6·50

America's Cup 1987 Winners 'Stars & Stripes'

(45)

1987 (20 Feb). *Victory of Stars and Stripes in America's Cup Yachting Championship. No.* **54** *optd with* T **45**.

471	$3 Windjammer's S.V. *Polynesia*		1·40	1·75

46 Fig Tree Church

(Des Maxine Marsh. Litho Questa)

1987 (11 Mar). *Bicentenary of Marriage of Horatio Nelson and Frances Nisbet:* T **46** *and similar horiz designs. Multicoloured.* W w 15. P 14.

472	15 c. Type **46**			10	10
473	60 c. Frances Nisbet			30	30
474	$1 H.M.S. *Boreas*			80	80
475	$3 Captain Horatio Nelson			2·25	2·50
472/5			*Set of 4*	3·00	3·25
MS476	102×82 mm. $3 As No. 473; $3 No. 475			5·00	5·50

47 Queen Angelfish

(Des C. Abbott. Litho Format)

1987 (6 July). *Coral Reef Fishes.* T **47** *and similar triangular designs. Multicoloured.* P 14½.

477	60 c. Type **47**			70	70
	a. Vert pair. Nos. 477/8			1·40	1·40
478	60 c. Blue Angelfish			70	70
479	$1 Stoplight Parrotfish (male)			90	90
	a. Vert pair. Nos. 479/80			1·75	1·75
480	$1 Stoplight Parrotfish (female)			90	90
481	$1.50, Red Hind			1·40	1·40
	a. Vert pair. Nos. 481/2			2·75	2·75
482	$1.50, Rock Hind			1·40	1·40
483	$2.50, Coney (bicoloured phase)			2·25	2·25
	a. Vert pair. Nos. 483/4			4·50	4·50
484	$2.50, Coney (red-brown phase)			2·25	2·25
477/84			*Set of 8*	9·25	9·25

Nos. 477/8, 479/80, 481/2 and 483/4 were each printed together, *se-tenant,* in pairs throughout the sheets. The second design for each value is in the form of an inverted triangle.

Nos. 477/84 exist imperforate from stock dispersed by the liquidator of Format International Security Printers Ltd.

48 *Panaeolus antillarum*

49 Rag Doll

(Des J. Cooter. Litho Format)

1987 (16 Oct). *Fungi (1st series).* T **48** *and similar vert designs. Multicoloured.* W w **16**. P 14.

485	15 c. Type **48**			30	20
486	50 c. *Pycnoporus sanguineus*			75	50
487	$2 *Gymnopilus chrysopellus*			2·25	2·00
488	$3 *Cantharellus cinnabarinus*			2·75	2·75
485/8			*Set of 4*	5·50	5·00

See also Nos. 646/54.

(Des J.W. Litho Walsall)

1987 (4 Dec). *Christmas. Toys.* T **49** *and similar horiz designs. Multicoloured.* W w **16** *(sideways).* P 14½.

489	10 c. Type **49**			10	10
490	40 c. Coconut boat			20	25
491	$1.20, Sandbox cart			55	60
492	$5 Two-wheeled cart			2·25	2·75
489/92			*Set of 4*	2·75	3·25

50 Hawk-wing Conch

51 Visiting Pensioners at Christmas

(Des Josephine Martin. Litho Questa)

1988 (15 Feb). *Seashells and Pearls.* T **50** *and similar vert designs. Multicoloured.* W w **16**. P 14½×14.

493	15 c. Type **50**			20	15
494	40 c. Roostertail Conch			30	20
495	60 c. Emperor Helmet			50	40
496	$2 Queen Conch			1·60	1·75
497	$3 King Helmet			1·75	1·90
493/7			*Set of 5*	4·00	4·00

(Des L. Curtis. Litho Walsall)

1988 (20 June). *125th Anniv of International Red Cross.* T **51** *and similar horiz designs. Multicoloured.* W w **16** *(sideways).* P 14 × 14½.

498	15 c. Type **51**			10	10
499	40 c. Teaching children first aid			15	20
500	60 c. Providing wheelchairs for the disabled			25	30
501	$5 Helping cyclone victim			2·10	2·50
498/501			*Set of 4*	2·25	2·75

52 Athlete on
Starting Blocks

53 Outline Map and
Arms of St. Kitts–
Nevis

(Des G. Vasarhelyi. Litho Format)

1988 (26 Aug). *Olympic Games, Seoul.* T **52** *and similar vert designs. Multicoloured.* W w **16**. P 14.

502	10 c. Type **52**			10	10
	a. Horiz strip of 4. Nos. 502/5			2·40	
503	$1.20, At start			50	55
504	$2 During race			85	90
505	$3 At finish			1·25	1·40
502/5			*Set of 4*	2·40	2·50
MS506	137 × 80 mm. As Nos. 502/5, but each size 24 × 36 mm. Wmk sideways			2·75	3·00

Nos. 502/5 were printed together, *se-tenant,* in horizontal strips of 4 throughout the sheet, each strip forming a composite design showing an athlete from start to finish of race.

(Des L. Curtis. Litho Questa)

1988 (19 Sept). *5th Anniv of Independence.* W w 14. P 14½ × 14.

507	**53** $5 multicoloured		2·10	2·25

(Des D. Miller (15 c., $2.50), E. Nisbet and D. Miller (60 c., $3). Litho Questa)

1988 (31 Oct). *300th Anniversary of Lloyd's of London. Multicoloured designs as* T **167a** *of Malawi.* W w **16** *(sideways on 60 c., $2.50).* P 14.

508	15 c. House of Commons passing Lloyd's Bill, 1871			15	10
509	60 c. *Cunard Countess* (liner) *(horiz)*			45	40
510	$2.50, Space shuttle deploying satellite *(horiz)*			1·60	1·75
511	$3 *Viking Princess* on fire, 1966			1·60	1·75
508/11			*Set of 4*	3·50	3·50

54 Poinsettia

55 British Fleet off St. Kitts

(Des I. Loe. Litho Questa)

1988 (7 Nov). *Christmas. Flowers.* T **54** *and similar vert designs. Multicoloured.* W w **16**. P 14½ × 14.

512	15 c. Type **54**			10	10
513	40 c. Tiger Claws			15	20
514	60 c. Sorrel Flower			25	30
515	$1 Christmas Candle			40	45
516	$5 Snow Bush			2·10	2·25
512/16			*Set of 5*	2·75	3·00

(Des Jane Hartley. Litho Format)

1989 (17 Apr). *"Philexfrance 89" International Stamp Exhibition, Paris. Battle of Frigate Bay, 1782.* T **55** *and similar vert designs. Multicoloured.* W w **16**. P 13½×14 ($3) or 14 *(others).*

517	50 c. Type **55**			20	25
	a. Horiz strip of 3. Nos. 517/19			1·50	
518	$1.20, Battle off Nevis			50	55
519	$2 British and French fleets exchanging broadsides			85	90
520	$3 French map of Nevis, 1764			1·25	1·40
517/20			*Set of 4*	2·50	2·75

Nos. 517/19 were printed together, *se-tenant,* in horizontal strips of 3 throughout the sheet, each strip forming a composite design.

56 Cicada

57 Queen Conch feeding

(Des I. Loe. Litho Questa)

1989 (15 May). *"Sounds of the Night".* T **56** *and similar vert designs. Multicoloured.* W w **16**. P 14.

521	10 c. Type **56**			15	15
522	40 c. Grasshopper			30	30
523	60 c. Cricket			45	45
524	$5 Tree frog			3·50	3·75
521/4			*Set of 4*	4·00	4·25
MS525	135×81 mm. Nos. 521/4			4·00	4·50

(Des A. Theobald ($6), D. Miller (others). Litho Questa)

1989 (20 July). *20th Anniv of First Manned Landing on Moon. Multicoloured designs as* T **51a** *of Kiribati.* W w **16** *(sideways on 40 c., $2).* P 14×13½ (15 c., $3) or 14 *(others).*

526	15 c. Vehicle Assembly Building, Kennedy Space Centre			10	10
527	40 c. Crew of "Apollo 12" (30×30 *mm*)			15	20
528	$2 "Apollo 12" emblem (30×30 *mm*)			85	90
529	$3 "Apollo 12" astronaut on Moon			1·25	1·40
526/9			*Set of 4*	2·00	2·25
MS530	100×83 mm. $6 Aldrin undertaking lunar seismic experiment. P 14×13½			2·50	2·75

(Des Deborah Dudley Max. Litho Questa)

1990 (31 Jan). *Queen Conch.* T **57** *and similar horiz designs. Multicoloured.*

531	10 c. Type **57**			10	10
532	40 c. Queen Conch from front			15	20
533	60 c. Side view of shell			25	30
534	$1 Back and flare			45	50
531/4			*Set of 4*	85	90
MS535	72×103 mm. $5 Underwater habitat			2·25	2·40

NEW INFORMATION

The editor is always interested to correspond with people who have new information that will improve or correct the Catalogue.

| 58 | Wyon Medal Portrait | 59 |

(Des M. Pollard. Litho B.D.T.)

1990 (3 May). *150th Anniv of the Penny Black. T **58** and similar vert designs. P 14×15.*
536	15 c. black and brown	..	..	10	10
537	40 c. black and deep blue-green	..	15	20
538	60 c. black ..	..	..	25	30
539	$4 black and ultramarine	..	1·75	1·90
536/9			*Set of 4*	2·00	2·25
MS540	114×84 mm. $5 blk, brn-lake & pale buff	2·25	2·40

Designs:—40 c. Engine-turned background; 60 c. Heath's engraving of portrait; $4 Essay with inscriptions; $5 Penny Black.
No. MS540 also commemorates "Stamp World London 90" International Stamp Exhibition.

(Des S. Pollard. Litho B.D.T.)

1990 (3 May). *500th Anniv of Regular European Postal Services. T **59** and similar square designs with different corner emblems. P 13½.*
541	15 c. brown	..	..	10	10
542	40 c. deep dull green	..	15	20
543	60 c. bright reddish violet	..	25	30
544	$4 ultramarine	..	..	1·75	1·90
541/4			*Set of 4*	2·00	2·25
MS545	110×82 mm. $5 brown-lake, pale buff and pale grey			2·25	2·40

Nos. 541/5 commemorate the Thurn and Taxis postal service and the designs are loosely based on those of the initial 1852–58 series.

60 Sand Fiddler Crab

(Des Mary Walters. Litho Questa)

1990 (25 June). *500th Anniv of Discovery of America by Columbus (1992) (2nd issue). New World Natural History – Crabs. T **60** and similar horiz designs. Multicoloured. P 14.*
546	5 c. Type **60**	..	..	10	10
547	15 c. Great Land Crab	..	10	10
548	20 c. Blue Crab	..	..	10	10
549	40 c. Stone Crab	..	..	15	20
550	60 c. Mountain Crab	..	25	30
551	$2 Sargassum Crab	..	85	90
552	$3 Yellow Box Crab	..	1·25	1·40
553	$4 Spiny Spider Crab	..	1·75	1·90
546/53			*Set of 8*	4·00	4·25
MS554	Two sheets, each 101×70 mm. (a) $5 Sally Lightfoot. (b) $5 Wharf Crab	*Set of 2 sheets*	4·25	4·50

(Des Young Phillips Studio. Litho Questa)

1990 (5 July). *90th Birthday of Queen Elizabeth the Queen Mother. Vert designs as T **198a** of Lesotho showing portraits, 1930–39. P 14.*
555	$2 brownish black, magenta and pale buff	85	90
	a. Strip of 3. Nos. 555/7	..	2·25	
556	$2 brownish black, magenta and pale buff	85	90
557	$2 brownish black, magenta and pale buff	85	90
555/7			*Set of 3*	2·25	2·40
MS558	90×75 mm. $6 chestnut, magenta & blk	2·50	2·75

Designs:—No. 555, Duchess of York with corgi; No. 556, Queen Elizabeth in Coronation robes, 1937; No. 557, Duchess of York in garden; No. MS558, Queen Elizabeth in Coronation robes, 1937 (*different*).
Nos. 555/7 were printed together, horizontally and vertically *se-tenant*, in sheetlets of 9 (3×3).

| 61 | MaKanaky, Cameroons | 62 | Cattleya deckeri |

(Des Young Phillips Studio. Litho Questa)

1990 (1 Oct). *World Cup Football Championship, Italy. Star Players. T **61** and similar vert designs. Multicoloured. P 14.*
559	10 c. Type **61**	..	..	10	10
560	25 c. Chovanec, Czechoslovakia	..	10	15
561	$2.50 Robson, England	..	1·10	1·10
562	$5 Voller, West Germany	..	2·25	2·40
559/62			*Set of 4*	3·25	3·50
MS563	Two sheets, each 90×75 mm. (a) $5 Maradona, Argentina (b) $5 Gordillo, Spain			
		Set of 2 sheets		4·25	4·50

(Des Mary Walters. Litho B.D.T.)

1990 (19 Nov). *Christmas. Native Orchids. T **62** and similar vert designs. Multicoloured. P 14.*
564	10 c. Type **62**	..	..	10	10
565	15 c. Epidendrum ciliare	..	10	10
566	20 c. Epidendrum fragrans	..	10	10
567	40 c. Epidendrum ibaguense	..	15	20
568	60 c. Epidendrum latifolium	..	25	30
569	$1.20, Maxillaria conferta	..	50	55
570	$2 Epidendrum strobiliferum	..	85	90
571	$3 Brassavola cucullata	..	1·25	1·40
564/71			*Set of 8*	3·00	3·25
MS572	102×71 mm. $5 Rodriguezia lanceolata	2·25	2·40

(Des T. Agans. Litho Questa)

1991 (14 Jan). *350th Death Anniv of Rubens. Multicoloured designs as T **250** of Maldive Islands, showing details from "The Feast of Achelous". P 13½×14.*
573	10 c. Two jugs (*vert*)	..	..	10	10
574	40 c. Woman at table (*vert*)	..	15	20
575	60 c. Two servants with fruit (*vert*)	25	30
576	$4 Achelous (*vert*)	..	1·75	1·90
573/6			*Set of 4*	2·00	2·25
MS577	101×71 mm. $5 "The Feast of Achelous". P 14×13½		2·25	2·40

63 *Agraulis vanillae*

(Des L. Nelson. Litho Questa)

1991 (1 Mar). *Butterflies. T **63** and similar horiz designs. Multicoloured. P 14.*
578	5 c. Type **63**	..	..	10	10
579	10 c. Historis odius	..	10	10
580	15 c. Marpesia corinna	..	10	10
581	20 c. Anartia amathea	..	10	10
582	25 c. Junonia evarete	..	10	15
583	40 c. Heliconius charithonia	..	15	20
584	50 c. Marpesia petreus	..	20	25
585	60 c. Dione juno	..	25	30
586	75 c. Heliconius doris	..	35	40
587	$1 Hypolimnas misippus	..	45	50
588	$3 Danaus plexippus	..	1·25	1·40
589	$5 Heliconius sara	..	2·25	2·40
590	$10 Tithorea harmonia	..	4·25	4·50
591	$20 Dryas julia	..	8·75	9·00
578/91	..	..	*Set of 14*	16·00	17·00

64 "Viking Mars Lander", 1976

(Des T. Agans. Litho Questa)

1991 (23 Apr). *500th Anniv of Discovery of America by Columbus (1992) (3rd series). History of Exploration. T **64** and similar multicoloured designs. P 14.*
592	15 c. Type **64**	..	..	10	10
593	40 c. "Apollo 11", 1969	..	15	20
594	60 c. "Skylab", 1973	..	25	30
595	75 c. "Salyut 6", 1977	..	35	40
596	$1 "Voyager 1", 1977	..	45	50
597	$2 "Venera 7", 1970	..	85	90
598	$4 "Gemini 4", 1965	..	1·75	1·90
599	$5 "Luna 3", 1959	..	2·25	2·40
592/9			*Set of 8*	5·50	6·00
MS600	Two sheets each 105×76 mm. (a) $6 Bow of *Santa Maria* (*vert*). (b) $6 Christopher Columbus (*vert*)	*Set of 2 sheets*	5·25	5·50

| 65 | Magnificent Frigate Bird | 66 | Marasmius haemtocephalus |

(Des Jennifer Toombs. Litho Questa)

1991 (28 May). *Island Birds. T **65** and similar horiz designs. Multicoloured. P 14.*
601	40 c. Type **65**	..	..	15	20
	a. Sheetlet. Nos. 601/20	..	2·75	
602	40 c. Roseate Tern	..	15	20
603	40 c. Red-tailed Hawk	..	15	20
604	40 c. Zenaida Dove	..	15	20
605	40 c. Bananaquit	..	15	20
606	40 c. American Kestrel	..	15	20

607	40 c. Grey Kingbird	..	..	15	20
608	40 c. Prothonotary Warbler	..	15	20
609	40 c. Blue-hooded Euphonia	..	15	20
610	40 c. Antillean Crested Hummingbird	..	15	20
611	40 c. White-tailed Tropic Bird	..	15	20
612	40 c. Yellow-bellied Sapsucker	..	15	20
613	40 c. Green-throated Carib	..	15	20
614	40 c. Purple-throated Carib	..	15	20
615	40 c. Red-billed Whistling Duck ("Black-bellied Tree-duck")	..	15	20
616	40 c. Ringed Kingfisher	..	15	20
617	40 c. Burrowing Owl	..	15	20
618	40 c. Turnstone	..	15	20
619	40 c. Great Blue Heron	..	15	20
620	40 c. Yellow-crowned Night-heron	..	15	20
601/20			*Set of 20*	2·75	3·50
MS621	76×59 mm. $6 Great Egret	..	2·50	2·75

Nos. 601/20 were printed together, *se-tenant*, in sheetlets of 20, forming a composite design.

(Des D. Miller. Litho Walsall)

1991 (5 July). *65th Birthday of Queen Elizabeth II. Horiz designs as T **210** of Lesotho. Multicoloured. P 14.*
622	15 c. Queen Elizabeth at polo match with Prince Charles	10	10
623	40 c. Queen and Prince Philip on Buckingham Palace balcony	15	20
624	$2 In carriage at Ascot, 1986	..	85	90
625	$4 Queen Elizabeth II at Windsor polo match, 1989	..	1·75	1·90
622/5			*Set of 4*	2·50	2·75
MS626	68×90 mm. $5 Queen Elizabeth and Prince Philip	..	2·25	2·40

(Des D. Miller. Litho Walsall)

1991 (5 July). *10th Wedding Anniv of Prince and Princess of Wales. Horiz designs as T **210** of Lesotho. Multicoloured. P 14.*
627	10 c. Prince Charles and Princess Diana	10	10
628	50 c. Prince of Wales and family	..	20	25
629	$1 Prince William and Prince Harry	..	45	50
630	$5 Prince and Princess of Wales	..	2·25	2·40
627/30			*Set of 4*	2·75	3·00
MS631	68×90 mm. $5 Prince and Princess of Wales in Hungary, and young princes at Christmas	..	2·25	2·40

(Litho Questa)

1991 (12 Aug). *"Phila Nippon '91" International Stamp Exhibition, Tokyo. Japanese Railway Locomotives. Multicoloured designs as T **257** of Maldive Islands. P 14.*
632	10 c. Class "C62" steam locomotive	..	10	10
633	15 c. Class "C56" steam locomotive (*horiz*)	10	10
634	40 c. Class "C-55" streamlined steam locomotive (*horiz*)	15	20
635	60 c. Class "1400" steam locomotive (*horiz*)	25	30
636	$1 Class "485 Bonnet" diesel rail car	45	50
637	$2 Class "C61" steam locomotive	..	85	90
638	$3 Class "485" express train (*horiz*)	1·25	1·40
639	$4 Class "7000" electric train (*horiz*)	1·75	1·90
632/9			*Set of 8*	4·25	4·75
MS640	Two sheets, each, 108×72 mm. (a) $5 Class "D51" steam locomotive (*horiz*). (b) $5 Hikari Bullet Train (*horiz*)	*Set of 2 sheets*	4·25	4·50

(Litho B.D.T.)

1991 (20 Dec). *Christmas. Drawings by Albrecht Dürer. Vert designs as T **211** of Lesotho. P 13.*
641	10 c. black and apple-green	..	10	10
642	40 c. black and yellow-orange	..	15	20
643	60 c. black and new blue	..	25	30
644	$3 black and bright mauve	..	1·25	1·40
641/4			*Set of 4*	1·60	1·75
MS645	Two sheets, each 96×124 mm. (a) $6 black. (b) $6 black	*Set of 2 sheets*	5·25	5·50

Designs:—10 c. "Mary being Crowned by an Angel"; 40 c. "Mary with the Pear"; 60 c. "Mary in a Halo"; $3 "Mary with Crown of Stars and Sceptre"; $6 (No. MS645a) "The Holy Family" (detail); $6 (No. MS645b) "Mary at the Yard Gate" (detail).

(Des D. Miller. Litho B.D.T.)

1991 (20 Dec). *Fungi (2nd series). T **66** and similar multicoloured designs. P 14.*
646	15 c. Type **66**	..	..	15	20
647	40 c. Psilocybe cubensis	..	15	20
648	60 c. Hygrocybe acutoconica	..	25	30
649	75 c. Hygrocybe occidentalis	..	35	40
650	$1 Boletellus cubensis	..	45	50
651	$2 Gymnopilus chrysopellus	..	85	90
652	$4 Cantharellus cinnabarinus	..	1·75	1·90
653	$5 Chlorophyllum molybdites	..	2·25	2·40
646/53			*Set of 8*	5·50	6·00
MS654	Two sheets, each 70×58 mm. (a) $6 Psilocybe cubensis, Hygrocybe acutoconica and Boletellus cubensis (*horiz*). (b) $6 Hygrocybe occidentalis, Marasmius haematocephalus and Gymnopilus chrysopellus (*horiz*) *Set of 2 sheets*	5·25	5·50

(Des D. Miller. Litho Questa)

1992 (26 Feb). *40th Anniv of Queen Elizabeth II's Accession. Horiz designs as T **214** of Lesotho. Multicoloured. P 14.*
655	10 c. Charlestown from the sea	..	15	20
656	40 c. Charlestown square	..	15	20
657	$1 Mountain scenery	..	45	50
658	$5 Early cottage	..	2·25	2·40
655/8			*Set of 4*	2·75	3·00
MS659	Two sheets, each 74×97 mm. (a) $6 Queen Conch on beach. (b) $6 Nevis sunset	*Set of 2 sheets*	5·25	5·50

67 Monique Knol
(cycling), France

(Des R. Sauber. Litho B.D.T.)

1992 (7 May). *Olympic Games, Barcelona. Gold Medal Winners of 1988. T* **67** *and similar vert designs. Multicoloured. P* 14.

660	20 c. Type **67**	..	15	20
661	25 c. Roger Kingdom (hurdles), U.S.A.		15	20
662	50 c. Yugoslavia (men's waterpolo)		20	25
663	80 c. Anja Fichtel (foil), West Germany		35	40
664	$1 Said Aouita, (mid-distance running), Morocco		45	50
665	$1.50, Yuri Sedykh (hammer throw), U.S.S.R.		65	70
666	$3 Shushunova (women's gymnastics), U.S.S.R.		1·25	1·40
667	$5 Valimir Artemov (men's gymnastics), U.S.S.R.		2·25	2·40
660/7		*Set of* 8	4·75	5·00

MS668 Two sheets, each 103×73 mm. (a) $6 Niam Suleymanoglu (weightlifting), Turkey. (b) $6 Florence Griffith-Joyner (women's 100 metres), U.S.A. .. .. *Set of* 2 *sheets* 5·25 5·50

69 Early Compass
and Ship

(Des L. Fried. Litho Questa)

1992 (6 July). *500th Anniv of Discovery of America by Columbus and "World Columbian Stamp Expo '92", Chicago. T* **69** *and similar multicoloured designs. P* 14.

678	20 c. Type **69**	..	15	20
679	50 c. Manatee and fleet	..	20	25
680	80 c. Green Turtle and *Santa Maria*	..	35	40
681	$1.50, *Santa Maria* and arms	..	65	70
682	$3 Queen Isabella of Spain and commission	..	1·25	1·40
683	$5 Pineapple and colonists	..	2·25	2·40
678/83		*Set of* 6	4·50	4·75

MS684 Two sheets, each 101×70 mm. (a) $6 Storm Petrel and town (*horiz*). (b) $6 Peppers and Carib canoe (*horiz*) .. *Set of* 2 *sheets* 5·25 5·50

OFFICIAL STAMPS

1980 (4 July*). *Nos.* 40/9 *additionally optd with Type* O 1 *of St. Christopher, Nevis and Anguilla.*

O 1	15 c. Sugar cane harvesting	..	10	10
O 2	25 c. Crafthouse (craft centre)	..	10	10
	a. "OFFICIAL" opt double	..	55·00	
	b. "OFFICIAL" opt omitted (in horiz pair with normal)	..	85·00	
	c. Optd on No. 41a	..	5·50	8·00
O 3	30 c. *Europa* (liner)	..	10	10
O 4	40 c. Lobster and sea crab	..	15	15
O 5	45 c. Royal St. Kitts Hotel and golf course	..	20	25
	a. Opt inverted	..	13·00	
O 6	50 c. Pinney's Beach, Nevis	..	20	25
	a. Opt inverted	..	75·00	
O 7	55 c. New runway at Golden Rock	..	20	25
	a. Opt double	..	15·00	
O 8	$1 Picking cotton	..	30	35
O 9	$5 Brewery	..	1·00	1·00
	a. Opt inverted	..	80·00	
O10	$10 Pineapples and peanuts	..	2·25	2·25
O1/10		*Set of* 10	4·00	4·50

*Earliest known date of use.

1981 (Mar). *Nos.* 60A/71A *optd with Type* O 1 *of St. Kitts.*

O11	15 c. New River Mill	..	10	10
O12	20 c. Nelson Museum	..	10	10
O13	25 c. St. James' Parish Church	..	10	15
O14	30 c. Nevis Lane	..	15	15
O15	40 c. Zetland Plantation	..	15	20
O16	45 c. Nisbet Plantation	..	20	25
O17	50 c. Pinney's Beach	..	20	25
O18	55 c. Eva Wilkin's Studio	..	25	30
O19	$1 Nevis at dawn	..	40	45
O20	$2.50, Ruins of Fort Charles	..	85	90
O21	$5 Old Bath House	..	1·25	1·75
O22	$10 Beach at Nisbet's	..	2·25	2·75
O11/22		*Set of* 12	5·00	6·50

1983 (2 Feb). *Nos.* 72/7 *optd with Type* O 1 *of St. Kitts* (55 c.) *or surch also* (*others*).

O23	45 c. on $2 *Royal Sovereign* (New Blue)	..	20	25
	a. Sheetlet. No. O23 × 6 and No. O24	..	1·40	
	b. Surch inverted	..	10·00	
	c. Surch inverted (horiz pair)	..	38·00	
	d. Albino surch	..	9·00	
	da. Albino surch inverted			
	e. Horiz pair, one without surch	..		
	f. Deep ultramarine surch	..	40	50
	fb. Surch inverted	..	7·00	
	fc. Surch inverted (horiz pair)	..	18·00	
	g. Black surch	..	60·00	
O24	45 c. on $2 Prince Charles and Lady Diana Spencer (New Blue)	..	20	25
	b. Surch inverted	..	30·00	
	d. Albino surch	..	23·00	
	f. Deep ultramarine surch	..	40	50
	fb. Surch inverted	..	18·00	
	g. Black surch	..	£150	
O25	55 c. *Royal Caroline* (New Blue)	..	20	25
	a. Sheetlet No. O25 × 6 and No. O26	..	1·40	
	d. Albino opt	..	9·00	
	db. Albino opt inverted	..	11·00	
	dc. Albino opt inverted (horiz pair)	..	13·00	
	f. Deep ultramarine opt	..	75	
	fb. Opt inverted	..	7·00	
	fc. Opt inverted (horiz pair)	..	25·00	
	ff. Opt double	..	16·00	
	g. Black opt	..	60·00	
O26	55 c. Prince Charles and Lady Diana Spencer (New Blue)	..	25	25
	d. Albino opt	..	20·00	
	db. Albino opt inverted	..	25·00	
	f. Deep ultramarine opt	..	1·00	
	fb. Opt inverted	..	25·00	
	ff. Opt double	..	32·00	
	g. Black opt	..	£150	
O27	$1.10 on $5 *Britannia* (Blk.)	..	45	50
	a. Sheetlet. No. O27 × 6 and No. O28	..	3·00	
	d. Albino surch	..	9·00	
	f. Deep ultramarine surch.	..	6·00	
	fb. Surch inverted	..	8·00	
	fc. Surch inverted (horiz pair)	..	32·00	
O28	$1.10 on $5 Prince Charles and Lady Diana Spencer (Blk.)	..	55	60
	d. Albino surch	..	27·00	
	f. Deep ultramarine surch	..	40·00	
	fb. Surch inverted	..	50·00	
O23/28		*Set of* 6	1·75	1·75

Nos. O23c, O23fc, O25dc, O25fc and O27fc show the surcharge or overprint intended for the large design inverted and struck across a horizontal pair of the smaller. Nos. O24b, O24fb, O26db, O26fb and O28fb each show two inverted surcharges intended for a horizontal pair of the smaller design.

1985 (2 Jan). *Nos.* 187/98 *optd with Type* O 1 *of St. Kitts.*

O29	15 c. Flamboyant	..	10	10
O30	20 c. Eyelash Orchid	..	10	10
O31	30 c. Bougainvillea	..	10	15
O32	40 c. Hibiscus sp.	..	15	20
O33	50 c. Night-blooming Cereus	..	20	25
O34	55 c. Yellow Mahoe	..	25	30
O35	60 c. Spider-lily	..	25	30
O36	75 c. Scarlet Cordia	..	30	35
O37	$1 Shell-ginger	..	40	45
O38	$3 Blue Petrea	..	1·25	1·40
O39	$5 Coral Hibiscus	..	2·10	2·25
O40	$10 Passion Flower	..	4·25	4·50
O29/40		*Set of* 12	8·50	9·25

St. Lucia

Although a branch office of the British G.P.O. was not opened at Castries, the island capital, until 1844 some form of postal arrangements for overseas mails existed from at least 1841 when the issue of a Ship Letter handstamp is recorded.

The stamps of Great Britain were used on the island from May 1858 until the end of April 1860 when the local authorities assumed responsibility for the postal service. No. CC1 was again used on overseas mail between 1 May and the introduction of St. Lucia stamps in December 1860.

CASTRIES
CROWN-CIRCLE HANDSTAMPS

CC1

CC1 CC1 ST. LUCIA (R). (1.5.1844)   *Price on cover* £750
No. CC1 was utilised, struck in black, during a shortage of 1d. stamps in 1904. *Price on cover* £275.

Stamps of GREAT BRITAIN *cancelled* "A 11" *as Type Z* **1** *of Jamaica.*

1858 *to* **1860**
Z1	1d. rose-red (1857), *perf* 14	..	..	..	..	£1100
Z2	2d. blue (1855)	..	..	..	..	
Z3	4d. rose (1857)	..	..	..	..	£325
Z4	6d. lilac (1856)	..	..	..	..	£200
Z5	1s. green (1856)	..	..	..	..	£800

PRICES FOR STAMPS ON COVER TO 1945

Nos. 1/3	*from* × 20
Nos. 5/8	*from* × 10
Nos. 9/10	†
Nos. 11/24	*from* × 8
Nos. 25/30	*from* × 6
Nos. 31/6	*from* × 3
Nos. 39/42	*from* × 6
Nos. 43/50	*from* × 8
Nos. 51/2	—
Nos. 53/62	*from* × 4
No. 63	*from* × 10
Nos. 64/75	*from* × 4
Nos. 76/7	—
Nos. 78/88	*from* × 3
No. 89	*from* × 4
No. 90	*from* × 20
Nos. 91/112	*from* × 3
Nos. 113/24	*from* × 2
Nos. 125/7	*from* × 10
Nos. 128/41	*from* × 2
Nos. D1/6	*from* × 20
Nos. F1/28	—

CROWN COLONY

1   Half penny (2)

(Recess P.B.)

1860 (18 Dec). *Wmk Small Star, W w* **2**. *P* 14 *to* 16.
1	1	(1d.) rose-red	..	..	..	£100	75·00
		a. Imperf vert (horiz pair)	..	..		
		b. Double impression	..	..	£1300	
2		(4d.) blue	..	..	..	£250	£180
		a. Deep blue	..	..		
		b. Imperf vert (horiz pair)	..	..		
3		(6d.) green	..	..	..	£300	£250
		a. Imperf vert (horiz pair)	..	..		
		b. Deep green	..	..	..	£300	£250

(Recess D.L.R.)

1863. *Wmk Crown CC. P* 12½.
5	1	(1d.) lake	..	..	..	55·00	80·00
		b. Brownish lake	..	..	..	75·00	75·00
7		(4d.) indigo	..	..	..	£100	£100
8		(6d.) emerald-green	..	..	£200	£200

Prepared for use, but not issued. Surch as T **2**
9	1	½d. on (6d.) emerald-green	..		42·00	
10		6d. on (4d.) indigo	..	..	£1000	

1864 (19 Nov)–**76.** *Wmk Crown CC.* (a) *P* 12½.
11	1	(1d.) black	..	..	..	16·00	12·00
		a. Intense black	..	..	..	15·00	11·00
12		(4d.) yellow	..	..	..	£120	30·00
		b. Lemon-yellow	..	..	..	£1500	
		c. Chrome-yellow	..	..	£130	30·00
		d. Olive-yellow	..	..	£250	70·00

13	1	(6d.) violet	..	..	..	70·00	28·00
		a. Mauve	..	..	..	£150	28·00
		b. Deep lilac	..	..	..	90·00	32·00
14		(1s.) brown-orange	..	..	£275	25·00
		b. Orange	..	..	..	£200	25·00
		c. Pale orange	..	..	£150	25·00
		ca. Imperf between (horiz pair)	..		

(b) *P* 14
15	1	(1d.) black (6.76)	..	..	16·00	15·00
		a. Imperf between (horiz pair)	..		
16		(4d.) yellow (6.76)	..	..	60·00	18·00
		a. Olive-yellow	..	..	£150	80·00
17		(6d.) mauve (6.76)	..	..	60·00	30·00
		a. Pale lilac	..	..	..	60·00	18·00
		b. Violet	..	..	..	£170	60·00
18		(1s.) orange (10.76)	..	..	£200	22·00
		a. Deep orange	..	..	£150	16·00

HALFPENNY   **2½ PENCE**
(3)   (4)   5

1881 (Sept). *Surch with T* **3** *or* **4**. *Wmk Crown CC. P* 14
23	1	½d. green	..	..	..	50·00	65·00
24		2½d. brown-red	..	..	20·00	18·00

The 1d. black is known surcharged "1d." in violet ink by hand, but there is no evidence that this was done officially.

1882–84. *Surch as T* **3**. *Wmk Crown CA.* (a) *P* 14
25	1	½d. green (1882)	..	..	12·00	22·00
26		1d. black (C.)	..	..	18·00	8·00
		a. Bisected (on cover)	..	..	†	
27		4d. yellow	..	..	..	£170	17·00
28		6d. violet	..	..	..	22·00	25·00
29		1s. orange	..	..	..	£250	£160

(b) *P* 12
30	1	4d. yellow	..	..	..	£250	28·00

Deep blue stamps, wmk Crown CA, perf 14 or 12, are fiscals from which the overprint "THREE PENCE—REVENUE", or "REVENUE", has been fraudulently removed.

(Typo D.L.R.)

1883 (6 July)–**86.** *Wmk Crown CA. Die* 1. *P* 14.
31	5	½d. dull green	..	..	3·00	3·00
32		1d. carmine-rose	..	..	24·00	7·50
33		2½d. blue	..	..	..	16·00	1·25
34		4d. brown (1885)	..	..	17·00	70
35		6d. lilac (1886)	..	..	£250	£200
36		1s. orange-brown (1885)	..	£350	£140

We no longer list imperforate examples of stamps appearing between 1863 and 1887 as there is no evidence that these were ever issued.

1886–87. *Wmk Crown CA. Die* I. *P* 14.
39	5	1d. dull mauve	..	..	2·50	5·00
40		3d. dull mauve and green	..	65·00	12·00
41		6d. dull mauve and blue (1887)	..	3·25	7·00
42		1s. dull mauve and red (1887)	..	65·00	15·00
39/42			..	..	*Set of* 4	£120	35·00
39/42 Optd "Specimen"			..	*Set of* 4	£160	

1891–98. *Wmk Crown CA. Die* II. *P* 14.
43	5	½d. dull green	..	..	50	30
44		1d. dull mauve	..	..	90	15
45		2d. ultramarine and orange (1898)	..	70	1·00
46		2½d. ultramarine	..	..	1·75	30
47		3d. dull mauve and green	..	3·25	5·50
48		4d. brown	..	..	1·40	2·25
49		6d. dull mauve and blue	..	14·00	14·00
50		1s. dull mauve and red	..	2·75	5·00
51		5s. dull mauve and orange	..	28·00	75·00
52		10s. dull mauve and black	..	55·00	75·00
43/52			..	*Set of* 10	95·00	£160
45, 51, 52 Optd "Specimen"		*Set of* 3	£120	

For description and illustration of differences between Die I and Die II see Introduction.

ONE $\frac{1}{2}d$ **ONE**
HALF   **PENNY**
PENNY
(6)   (7)   (8)

N   N
Normal "N"   Thick "N"

Three types of T **8**

I. All letters "N" normal.
II. Thick diagonal stroke in first "N".
III. Thick diagonal stroke in second "N".

1891–92 (a) *Stamps of Die* I *surch.*
53	6	½d. on 3d. dull mauve and green	..	60·00	65·00
		a. Small "A" in "HALF"	..	90·00	90·00
		b. Small "O" in "ONE"	..	90·00	90·00
54	7	½d. on half 6d. dull mauve and blue	..	14·00	3·25
		a. No fraction bar	..	£170	£120
		b. Surch sideways	..	£400	
		c. Surch double	..	£375	£400
		d. "2" in fraction omitted	..	£325	£450
		e. Thick "1" with sloping serif	£160	£110
		f. Surch triple	..	£550	
		g. Figure "1" used as fraction bar	£375	£225

55	8	1d. on 4d. brown (I) (12.91)	..	3·00	3·00
		a. Surch double	..	..	£160	
		b. Surch inverted	..	..	£700	£600
		c. Type II	..	..	..	18·00	18·00
		ca. Surch double	..	..	£225	
		cb. Surch inverted	..	..	—	£600
		d. Type III	..	..	..	18·00	18·00

(b) *Stamp of Die* II *surch*
56	6	½d. on 3d. dull mauve and green	32·00	14·00
		a. Surch double	..	..	£650	£600
		b. Surch inverted	..	..	£1600	£600
		c. Small "O" in "ONE"	..	£130	90·00
		d. Small "A" in "HALF"	..	£130	90·00
		e. "ONE" misplaced ("O" over "H")	£130	90·00

9   10

(Typo D.L.R.)

1902–3. *Wmk Crown CA. P* 14.
58	9	½d. dull purple and green	..	..	2·00	80
59		1d. dull purple and carmine	..	2·50	45
60		2½d. dull purple and ultramarine	..	9·50	5·50
61	10	3d. dull purple and yellow	..	4·00	8·50
62		1s. green and black	..	..	9·00	13·00
58/62			..	..	*Set of* 5	24·00	25·00
58/62 Optd "Specimen"			*Set of* 5	£100	

11 The Pitons

(Recess D.L.R.)

1902 (15 Dec). *400th Anniv of Discovery by Columbus. Wmk Crown CC, sideways. P* 14
63	11	2d. green and brown	..	..	6·50	1·75
63 Optd "Specimen"			..	..	60·00	

This stamp was formerly thought to have been issued on 16 December but it has been seen on a postcard clearly postmarked 15 December.

1904–10. *Wmk Mult Crown CA. Chalk-surfaced paper (Nos. 71, 73/5 and 77) or ordinary paper (others). P* 14.
64	9	½d. dull purple and green	..	1·50	20
		a. Chalk-surfaced paper	..	1·50	50
65		½d. green (1907)	..	..	1·25	45
66		1d. dull purple and carmine	..	2·00	30
		a. Chalk-surfaced paper	..	1·75	30
67		1d. carmine (1907)	..	..	1·50	20
68		2½d. dull purple and ultramarine	..	4·50	1·25
		a. Chalk-surfaced paper	..	3·00	2·25
69		2½d. blue (1907)	..	..	3·25	1·25
70	10	3d. dull purple and yellow	..	3·50	3·00
71		3d. purple/yellow (1909)	..	1·75	7·50
72		6d. dull purple and violet (1905)	..	6·50	5·50
		a. Chalk-surfaced paper	..	6·50	7·50
		ab. Dull purple and bright purple (1907)	4·50	12·00
73		6d. dull purple (1910)	..	15·00	25·00
74		1s. green and black (1905)	..	18·00	11·00
75		1s. black/green (1909)	..	2·75	4·50
76		5s. green and carmine (1905)	..	35·00	80·00
77		5s. green and red/yellow (1907)	..	40·00	48·00
64/77			..	..	*Set of* 14	£110	£170
65, 67, 69, 71/2, 72ab and 75/7 Optd "Specimen"			*Set of* 9	£170	

12   13   14

15   16

(Typo D.L.R.)

1912–20. *Wmk Mult Crown CA. Chalk-surfaced paper (3d. to 5s.) P* 14.
78	12	½d. deep green	..	..	60	40
		a. Yellow-green (1916)	..	55	30
79		1d. carmine-red	..	..	1·90	10
		a. Scarlet (1916)	..	..	3·00	10
		b. Rose-red	..	..	..	3·00	40
80	13	2d. grey	..	..	..	1·50	4·00
		a. Slate-grey (1916)	..	..	9·50	10·00
81	12	2½d. ultramarine	..	..	2·50	2·75
		a. Bright blue (1918)	..	1·75	2·75
		b. Deep bright blue	..	7·50	8·00

82	15	3d. purple/yellow			60	2·00
		a. On pale yellow (Die I)			5·00	9·00
		b. On pale yellow (Die II)			5·50	18·00
83	14	4d. black and red/yellow			90	1·75
		a. Opt double (Optd S. £25)			60	1·50
84	15	6d. dull and bright purple			2·00	6·50
		a. Grey-purple and purple (1918)			12·00	15·00
85		1s. black/green			2·50	4·25
		a. On blue-green, olive back			3·75	6·00
86		1s. orange-brown (1920)			4·25	25·00
87	16	2s. 6d. black and red/blue			15·00	20·00
88	15	5s. green and red/yellow			18·00	55·00
78/88			Set of 11		42·00	£110
78/88 Optd "Specimen"			Set of 11		£170	

WAR TAX (17) **WAR TAX** (18)

1916 (June). *No. 79a optd locally with T 17.*

89	12	1d. scarlet			3·50	3·25
		a. Opt double			£350	£375
		b. Carmine			30·00	25·00

For the overprinting with Type **17** the top margin of the sheet was folded beneath the top row of stamps so that marginal examples from this row show an inverted albino impression of the overprint in the top margin.

1916 (Sept). *No. 79a optd in London with T 18.*

90	12	1d. scarlet (Optd S. £40)			15	15

1921–26. *Wmk Mult Script CA. Chalk-surfaced paper (3d. (No. 100) to 5s.) P 14.*

91	12	½d. green			30	15
92		1d. rose-carmine			3·00	9·00
93		1d. deep brown (1922)			30	15
94	14	1½d. dull carmine (1922)			40	1·25
95	13	2d. slate-grey			30	15
96	12	2½d. bright blue			1·75	2·00
97		2½d. orange (1925)			5·50	28·00
98		2½d. dull blue (1926)			1·10	2·50
99	15	3d. bright blue (1922)			3·75	13·00
		a. Dull blue (1926)			1·00	10·00
100		3d. purple/yellow (1926)			55	4·50
		a. Deep purple/yellow			4·50	12·00
101	14	4d. black and red/yellow (1924)			80	2·50
102	15	6d. grey-purple and purple			1·25	4·75
103		1s. orange-brown			1·75	4·00
104	16	2s. 6d. black and red/blue (1924)			16·00	25·00
105	15	5s. green and red/pale yellow (1923)			28·00	55·00
91/105			Set of 15		50·00	£130
91/105 Optd "Specimen"			Set of 15		£200	

1935 (6 May). *Silver Jubilee. As Nos. 114/17 of Jamaica, but ptd by D.L.R. P 13½×14.*

109		½d. black and green			15	25
		f. Diagonal line by turret			18·00	
110		2d. ultramarine and grey			45	25
111		2½d. brown and deep blue			90	65
		f. Diagonal line by turret			40·00	
		g. Dot to left of chapel			45·00	
112		1s. slate and purple			3·50	3·75
		h. Dot by flagstaff			85·00	
109/12			Set of 4		4·50	4·50
109/12 Perf "Specimen"			Set of 4		75·00	

For illustrations of plate varieties see Omnibus section following Zimbabwe.

19 Port Castries

20 Columbus Square, Castries

21 Ventine Falls

25 The Badge of the Colony

(Recess D.L.R.)

1936 (1 Mar–Apr). *T 19/21, 25 and similar designs. Wmk Mult Script CA. P 14 or 13 × 12 (1s. and 10s.).*

113	19	½d. black and bright green			25	45
		a. Perf 13 × 12 (8.4.36)			50	3·50
114	20	1d. black and brown			30	10
		a. Perf 13 × 12 (8.4.36)			1·40	2·50
115	21	1½d. black and scarlet			55	30
		a. Perf 12 × 13			5·00	1·75
116	19	2d. black and grey			30	15
117	20	2½d. black and blue			30	15
118	21	3d. black and dull green			1·25	70
119	19	4d. black and red-brown			30	1·00
120	20	6d. black and orange			75	1·00
121	–	1s. black and light blue			90	2·00
122	–	2s. 6d. black and ultramarine			4·50	14·00
123	–	5s. black and violet			8·00	20·00
124	25	10s. black and carmine			42·00	50·00
113/124			Set of 12		55·00	80·00
113/24 Perf "Specimen"			Set of 12		£180	

Designs: *Vert (as T 21)* 2s. 6d. Inniskilling monument. *Horiz (as T 19)* 1s. Fort Rodney, Pigeon Island; 5s. Government House.

1937 (12 May). *Coronation. As Nos. 118/20 of Jamaica, but ptd by B.W. P 11×11½.*

125		1d. violet			30	15
126		1½d. carmine			40	20
127		2½d. blue			40	30
125/7			Set of 3		1·00	60
125/7 Perf "Specimen"			Set of 3		55·00	

26 King George VI

27 Columbus Square

28 Government House

31 Device of St. Lucia

(Des E. Crafer (T **26**), H. Fleury (5s.). Recess Waterlow (½d. to 3½d., 8d., 3s., 5s., £1), D.L.R. (6d., 1s.) and B.W. (2s., 10s.))

1938 (22 Sept)–48. *T 26/8, 31 and similar designs. Wmk Mult Script CA (sideways on 2s.).*

128	26	½d. green (p 14½ × 14)			55	10
		a. Perf 12½ (1943)			10	10
129		1d. violet (p 14½ × 14)			90	30
		a. Perf 12½ (1938)			10	15
129b		1d. scarlet (p 12½) (1947)			10	10
		c. Perf 14½ × 14 (1948)			10	10
130		1½d. scarlet (p 14½ × 14)			90	20
		a. Perf 12½ (1943)			15	35
131		2d. grey (p 14½ × 14)			20	40
		a. Perf 12½ (1943)			10	10
132		2½d. ultramarine (p 14½ × 14)			80	10
		a. Perf 12½ (1943)			10	10
132b		2½d. violet (p 12½) (1947)			10	10
133		3d. orange (p 14½ × 14)			10	10
		a. Perf 12½ (1943)			10	10
133b		3½d. ultramarine (p 12½) (1947)			30	15
134	27	6d. claret (p 13½)			55	40
		a. Carmine-lake (p 13½) (1945)			1·75	35
		b. Perf 12. Claret (1948)			50	45
134c	26	8d. brown (p 12½) (1946)			1·50	30
135	28	1s. brown (p 13½)			30	30
		a. Perf 12 (1948)			30	20
136	–	2s. blue and purple (p 12)			3·25	1·25
136a	26	3s. bright purple (p 12½) (1946)			8·00	2·75
137	–	5s. black and mauve (p 12½)			11·00	5·00
138	31	10s. black/yellow (p 12)			3·50	9·00
141	26	£1 sepia (p 12½) (1946)			11·00	8·00
128a/141			Set of 17		35·00	25·00
128/41 Perf "Specimen"			Set of 17		£300	

Designs: *Horiz (as T 28)*: 2s. The Pitons; 5s. Loading bananas.

1946 (8 Oct). *Victory. As Nos. 141/2 of Jamaica.*

142		1d. lilac			10	10
143		3½d. blue			10	10
142/3 Perf "Specimen"			Set of 2		50·00	

1948 (26 Nov). *Royal Silver Wedding. As Nos. 143/4 of Jamaica.*

144		1d. scarlet			15	10
145		£1 purple-brown			11·00	35·00

(New Currency. 100 cents=1 West Indian dollar)

32 King George VI   **33** Device of St. Lucia

(Recess Waterlow (**32**), B.W. (**33**))

1949 (1 Oct)–50. *Value in cents or dollars. Wmk Mult Script CA. P 12½ (1 c. to 16 c.), 11 × 11½ (others).*

146	32	1 c. green			10	10
		a. Perf 14 (1949)			75	40
147		2 c. magenta			10	10
		a. Perf 14½ × 14 (1949)			1·50	1·00
148		3 c. scarlet			10	20
149		4 c. grey			10	10
		a. Perf 14½ × 14			†	£5000
150		5 c. violet			10	10
151		6 c. orange			15	20
152		7 c. ultramarine			60	40
153		12 c. claret			10	20
		a. Perf 14½ × 14 (1950)			£325	£200
154		16 c. brown			1·00	20
155	33	24 c. light blue			30	10
156		48 c. olive-green			1·50	65
157		$1.20, purple			2·25	4·00
158		$2.40, blue-green			3·00	15·00
159		$4.80, rose-carmine			7·00	18·00
146/159			Set of 14		16·00	35·00

1949 (10 Oct). *75th Anniv of U.P.U. As Nos. 145/8 of Jamaica.*

160		5 c. violet			15	15
161		6 c. orange			35	25
162		12 c. magenta			25	20
163		24 c. blue-green			50	20
160/3			Set of 4		1·10	70

1951 (16 Feb). *Inauguration of B.W.I. University College. As Nos. 149/50 of Jamaica.*

164		3 c. black and scarlet			35	10
165		12 c. black and deep carmine			35	10

34 Phoenix rising from Burning Buildings

N E W   C O N S T I T U T I O N (35) 1951

(Flames typo, rest recess B.W.)

1951 (19 June). *Reconstruction of Castries. Wmk Mult Script CA. P 13½ × 13.*

166	34	12 c. red and blue			15	30

1951 (25 Sept). *New Constitution. Nos. 147, 149/50 and 153 optd with T 35 by Waterlow. P 12½.*

167	32	2 c. magenta			10	15
168		4 c. grey			10	15
169		5 c. violet			10	15
170		12 c. claret			10	25
167/70			Set of 4		30	60

1953 (2 June). *Coronation. As No. 153 of Jamaica.*

171		3 c. black and scarlet			30	10

36 Queen Elizabeth II   **37** Device of St. Lucia

(Recess Waterlow (T **36**), until 1960, then D.L.R. B.W. (T **37**))

1953 (28 Oct)–63. *Wmk Mult Script CA. P 14½×14 (T 36) or 11×11½ (T 37).*

172	36	1 c. green (1.4.54)			10	10
173		2 c. magenta			10	10
174		3 c. red (2.9.54)			10	10
175		4 c. slate (7.1.54)			10	10
176		5 c. violet (1.4.54)			10	10
		a. Slate-violet (19.2.63)			2·50	60
177		6 c. orange (2.9.54)			15	10
		a. Brown-orange (26.9.61)			1·75	10
178		8 c. lake (2.9.54)			10	10
179		10 c. ultramarine (2.9.54)			10	10
		a. Blue (14.8.62)			30	10
180		15 c. red-brown (2.9.54)			30	10
		a. Brown (30.10.57)			30	10
181	37	25 c. deep turquoise-blue (2.9.54)			30	10
182		50 c. deep olive-green (2.9.54)			4·00	50
183		$1 bluish green (2.9.54)			3·50	85
184		$2.50, carmine (2.9.54)			4·50	3·00
172/84			Set of 13		12·00	4·25

1958 (22 Apr). *Inauguration of British Caribbean Federation. As Nos. 175/7 of Jamaica.*

185		3 c. deep green			40	15
186		6 c. blue			70	80
187		12 c. scarlet			85	60
185/7			Set of 3		1·75	1·40

MINISTERIAL GOVERNMENT

38 Columbus's *Santa Maria* off the Pitons

39 Stamp of 1860

(Recess Waterlow)

1960 (1 Jan). *New Constitution for the Windward and Leeward Islands. W w 12. P 13.*

188	38	8 c. carmine-red			25	20
189		10 c. red-orange			25	20
190		25 c. deep blue			35	25
188/90			Set of 3		75	60

(Eng H. Bard. Recess Waterlow)

1960 (18 Dec). *Stamp Centenary.* W w **12**. P 13½.
191	**39**	5 c. rose-red and ultramarine				10	10
192		16 c. deep blue and yellow-green..				20	30
193		25 c. green and carmine-red				20	15
191/3 ..		..		*Set of 3*		45	50

1963 (4 June). *Freedom from Hunger. As No. 80 of Lesotho.*
194	25 c. bluish green	..	..	30	10

1963 (2 Sept). *Red Cross Centenary. As Nos. 203/4 of Jamaica.*
195	4 c. red and black	..	..	15	10
196	25 c. red and blue	..	..	40	80

40 Queen Elizabeth II **41**
(after A. C. Davidson-Houston)

42 Fishing Boats   **43** Castries Harbour

44 Vigie Beach   **45** Queen Elizabeth II

(Des V. Whiteley. Photo Harrison)

1964 (1 Mar)–**69**. *Designs as T* **40/5**. W w **12**. P 14½ (T **40**, *others* 14½×14 (*vert*) *or* 14×14½ (*horiz*).
197	1 c. crimson		..	..		10	10
198	2 c. bluish violet		..	..		30	10
199	4 c. turquoise-green		..	..		35	10
	a. Deep turquoise (5.8.69)		..	..		50	50
200	5 c. Prussian blue		..	..		30	10
201	6 c. yellow-brown ..		..	..		45	10
202	8 c. multicoloured		..	..		10	10
203	10 c. multicoloured		..	..		40	10
204	12 c. multicoloured		..	..		15	10
205	15 c. multicoloured		..	..		20	10
206	25 c. multicoloured		..	..		20	10
207	35 c. blue and buff		..	..		1·25	10
208	50 c. multicoloured		..	..		1·10	10
209	$1 multicoloured		..	..		1·25	25
210	$2.50, multicoloured		..	..		2·00	1·50
197/210			..	*Set of 14*		7·00	2·00

Designs:—1 to 6 c. Type **40**; 8, 10 c. Type **41**. Horiz as T **42/3**—15 c. Pigeon Island; 25 c. Reduit Beach; 50 c. The Pitons.
See also No. 249.

1964 (23 Apr). *400th Birth Anniv of William Shakespeare. As No. 156 of Montserrat.*
211	10 c. blue-green	..	..	10	10

1965 (17 May). *I.T.U. Centenary. As Nos. 98/9 of Lesotho.*
212	2 c. mauve and magenta	..	..	10	10
213	50 c. lilac and light olive-green	..		90	35

1965 (25 Oct). *International Co-operation Year. As Nos. 100/1 of Lesotho.*
214	1 c. reddish purple and turquoise-green			10	10
215	25 c. deep bluish green and lavender ..		..	20	20

1966 (24 Jan). *Churchill Commemoration. As Nos. 102/5 of Lesotho.*
216	4 c. new blue ..	..	..	10	10
217	6 c. deep green	..	..	15	20
218	25 c. brown	..	..	20	15
219	35 c. bluish violet	..	..	30	20
216/19	..	..	*Set of 4*	65	55

1966 (4 Feb). *Royal Visit. As Nos. 183/4 of Montserrat.*
220	4 c. black and ultramarine ..		..	10	10
221	25 c. black and magenta	..	..	40	35

1966 (1 July). *World Cup Football Championship, England. As Nos. 57/8 of Pitcairn Islands.*
222	4 c. violet, yellow-green, lake & yellow-brn ..		10	10
223	25 c. chocolate, blue-green, lake & yellow-brn		30	20

1966 (20 Sept). *Inauguration of W.H.O. Headquarters, Geneva. As Nos. 185/6 of Montserrat.*
224	4 c. black, yellow-green and light blue		10	10
225	25 c. black, light purple and yellow-brown		25	20

1966 (1 Dec). *20th Anniv of U.N.E.S.C.O. As Nos. 342/4 of Mauritius.*
226	4 c. slate-violet, red, yellow and orange		10	10
227	12 c. orange-yellow, violet and deep olive		20	20
228	25 c. black, bright purple and orange..		35	35
226/8 ..			*Set of 3*	60	55

ASSOCIATED STATEHOOD

STATEHOOD	STATEHOOD
1st MARCH 1967	1st MARCH 1967
(49)	(50)

51 Map of St. Lucia

(Optd by Art Printery, Castries from dies supplied by Harrison. Photo Harrison (No. 240))

1967 (7 Mar). *Statehood.* (*a*) *Postage. Nos.* **198** *and* **200/9** *optd with T* **49** (2, 5, 6 c.) *or* T **50** (*others*) *in red.*
229	2 c. bluish violet		..	..		20	15
	a. Horiz pair, one without opt						
230	5 c. Prussian blue		..	..		10	10
	a. Opt inverted		..	..		45·00	
231	6 c. yellow-brown		..	..		10	10
232	8 c. multicoloured		..	..		20	10
233	10 c. multicoloured		..	..		25	10
234	12 c. multicoloured		..	..		20	10
235	15 c. multicoloured		..	..		25	30
236	25 c. multicoloured		..	..		30	30
237	35 c. blue and buff		..	..		50	35
238	50 c. multicoloured		..	..		50	55
239	$1 multicoloured		..	..		50	55
229/39		..		*Set of 11*		2·75	2·25

(*b*) *Air.* P 14½ × 14.
240	**51**	15 c. new blue	..	..		10	10

Overprinted 1 c. and $2.50 stamps were prepared for issue but were not put on sale over the post office counter. Later, however, they were accepted for franking (*Price for set of 2 £4·50 mint, £10 used*).

52 "Madonna and Child   **53** Batsman and Sir Frederick
with the Infant Baptist"   Clarke (Governor)
(Raphael)

(Des and photo Harrison)

1967 (16 Oct). *Christmas.* W w **12** (*sideways*). P 14½.
241	**52**	4 c. multicoloured		..	..	10	10
242		25 c. multicoloured		..	..	20	10

(Des V. Whiteley. Photo Harrison)

1968 (8 Mar). *M.C.C.'s West Indies Tour.* W w **12** (*sideways*). P 14½ × 14.
243	**53**	10 c. multicoloured		..	..	20	15
244		35 c. multicoloured		..	..	45	40

54 "The Crucified Christ   **55** "Noli me tangere"
with the Virgin Mary,   (detail by Titian)
Saints and Angels"
(Raphael)

(Des and photo Harrison)

1968 (25 Mar). *Easter.* W w **12** (*sideways*). P 14 × 14½.
245	**54**	10 c. multicoloured		..	..	10	10
246	**55**	15 c. multicoloured		..	..	10	10
247	**54**	25 c. multicoloured		..	..	15	10
248	**55**	35 c. multicoloured		..	..	15	10
	a. Yellow (sunset) omitted		..	..		£140	
245/8 ..		..		*Set of 4*		40	20

1968 (14 May)*. *As No. 205 but* W w **12** (*sideways*).
249	15 c. multicoloured		..	..		15	15

*This is the London release date. Stamps from this printing were available some months earlier on St. Lucia.

56 Dr. Martin Luther   **57** "Virgin and Child
King   in Glory" (Murillo)

(Des V. Whiteley. Litho D.L.R.)

1968 (4 July). *Martin Luther King Commemoration.* W w **12**. P 13½ × 14.
250	**56**	25 c. blue, black and flesh		..	..	10	10
251		35 c. violet-black, black and flesh		..		10	10

(Des and photo Harrison)

1968 (17 Oct). *Christmas. Paintings. T* **57** *and similar vert design. Multicoloured.* W w **12** (*sideways*). P 14½ × 14.
252	5 c. Type **57**			..	..	10	10
253	10 c. "Madonna with Child" (Murillo)				10	10
254	25 c. Type **57**			..	..	10	10
255	35 c. As 10 c.			..	..	15	10
252/5				*Set of 4*		30	30

59 Purple-throated Carib

(Des V. Whiteley. Litho Format)

1969 (10 Jan). *Birds. T* **59** *and similar horiz design. Multicoloured.* W w **12** (*sideways*). P 14.
256	10 c. Type **59**			..	..	55	25
257	15 c. St. Lucia Amazon			..	..	70	30
258	25 c. Type **59**			..	..	90	35
259	35 c. As 15 c.			..	..	1·25	45
256/9				*Set of 4*		3·00	1·25

61 "Head of Christ   **62** "Resurrection of
Crowned with Thorns"   Christ" (Sodoma)
(Reni)

(Des and photo Harrison)

1969 (20 Mar). *Easter.* W w **12** (*sideways*). P 14½ × 14.
260	**61**	10 c. multicoloured		..	..	10	10
261	**62**	15 c. multicoloured		..	..	10	10
262	**61**	25 c. multicoloured		..	..	10	10
263	**62**	35 c. multicoloured		..	..	10	10
260/3 ..				*Set of 4*		30	30

63 Map showing "CARIFTA" Countries

(Des J. Cooter. Photo Harrison)

1969 (29 May). *First Anniv of CARIFTA (Caribbean Free Trade Area). T* **63** *and similar horiz designs. Multicoloured.* W w **12**. P 14.
264	5 c. Type **63**			..	..	10	10
265	10 c. Type **63**			..	..	10	10
266	25 c. Handclasp and names of CARIFTA countries			..		10	10
267	35 c. As 25 c.			..	..	10	10
264/7 ..				*Set of 4*		30	30

65 Emperor Napoleon and Empress Josephine   **66** "Virgin and Child" (P. Delaroche)

(Des and litho Enschedé)

1969 (22 Sept). *Birth Bicentenary of Napoleon Bonaparte. P 14 × 13.*

268	**65**	15 c. multicoloured	..	10	10
269		25 c. multicoloured	..	10	10
270		35 c. multicoloured	..	10	10
271		50 c. multicoloured	..	15	25
268/71			*Set of 4*	30	45

(Des J. W. Photo Harrison)

1969 (27 Oct). *Christmas. Paintings. T 66 and similar vert design. Multicoloured. W w 12 (sideways). P 14½ × 14.*

272	5 c.	Type **66**	..	10	10
273	10 c.	"Holy Family" (Rubens)	..	10	10
274	25 c.	Type **66**	..	15	10
275	35 c.	As 10 c.	..	15	10
272/5			*Set of 4*	40	30

68 House of Assembly   **69** "The Sealing of the Tomb" (Hogarth)

(Des J. Cooter ($10), Sylvia and M. Goaman (others). Litho Questa ($10), Format (others))

1970 (2 Feb)–**73**. *T 68 and similar designs. Multicoloured. W w 12 (sideways on 1 c. to 35 c. and $10). P 14.*

276	1 c.	Type **68**	..	10	10
277	2 c.	Roman Catholic Cathedral	..	10	10
278	4 c.	The Boulevard, Castries	..	15	10
279	5 c.	Castries Harbour	..	15	10
280	6 c.	Sulphur springs	..	15	10
281	10 c.	Vigie Airport	..	20	10
282	12 c.	Reduit Beach	..	20	10
283	15 c.	Pigeon Island	..	25	10
284	25 c.	The Pitons and yacht	..	40	10
285	35 c.	Marigot Bay	..	40	10
286	50 c.	Diamond Waterfall (*vert*)	..	70	60
287	$1	Flag of St. Lucia (*vert*)	..	75	70
288	$2.50,	St. Lucia Coat of Arms (*vert*)	..	1·50	1·75
289	$5	Queen Elizabeth II (*vert*)	..	3·25	4·75
289a	$10	Map of St. Lucia (*vert*) (3.12.73)	..	9·00	11·00
276/89a			*Set of 15*	15·00	17·00

See also Nos. 367/8 and 395/8.

(Des V. Whiteley. Litho Enschedé)

1970 (7 Mar). *Easter. Triptych by Hogarth. T 69 and similar multicoloured designs. W w 12 (sideways). Roul. 9 × P 12½.*

290	25 c.	Type **69**	..	15	20
		a. Strip of 3. Nos. 290/2		55	
291	35 c.	"The Three Marys at the Tomb"	..	15	20
292	$1	"The Ascension" (39 × 55 *mm*)	..	30	40
290/2			*Set of 3*	55	70

Nos. 290/2 were issued in sheets of 30 (6 × 5) containing the Hogarth Triptych spread over all three values of the set. This necessitated a peculiar arrangement with the $1 value (which depicts the centre portion of the triptych) 10 mm higher than the other values in the se-tenant strip.

72 Charles Dickens and Dickensian Characters

(Des V. Whiteley. Litho B.W.)

1970 (8 June). *Death Centenary of Charles Dickens. W w 12 (sideways). P 14.*

293	**72**	1 c. multicoloured	..	10	10
294		25 c. multicoloured	..	15	10
295		35 c. multicoloured	..	20	10
296		50 c. multicoloured	..	25	30
293/6			*Set of 4*	55	40

73 Nurse and Emblem

(Des R. Granger Barrett. Litho J.W.)

1970 (18 Aug). *Centenary of British Red Cross. T 73 and similar horiz design. Multicoloured. W w 12 (sideways). P 14.*

297	10 c.	Type **73**	..	10	10
298	15 c.	Flags of Great Britain, Red Cross and St. Lucia		20	10
299	25 c.	Type **73**	..	30	10
300	35 c.	As 15 c.	..	35	10
297/300			*Set of 4*	80	30

74 "Madonna with the Lilies" (Luca della Robbia)   **75** "Christ on the Cross" (Rubens)

(Des P. B. Litho and embossed Walsall)

1970 (16 Nov). *Christmas. P 11.*

301	**74**	5 c. multicoloured	..	10	10
302		10 c. multicoloured	..	10	10
303		35 c. multicoloured	..	25	10
304		40 c. multicoloured	..	25	15
301/4			*Set of 4*	55	30

(Des and litho Enschedé)

1971 (29 Mar). *Easter. T 75 and similar vert design. Multicoloured. W w 12. P 13½ × 13.*

305	10 c.	Type **75**	..	10	10
306	15 c.	"Descent from the Cross" (Rubens)	..	10	10
307	35 c.	Type **75**	..	25	10
308	40 c.	As 15 c.	..	25	15
305/8			*Set of 4*	55	30

76 Moule à Chique Lighthouse

(Des J. W. Litho Questa)

1971 (1 May). *Opening of Beane Field Airport. T 76 and similar horiz design. Multicoloured. W w 12 (sideways). P 14½ × 14.*

309	5 c.	Type **76**	..	30	15
310	25 c.	Aircraft landing at Beane Field	..	45	15

77 Morne Fortune

78 Morne Fortune, Modern View

(Des V. Whiteley. Litho Questa)

1971 (10 Aug.). *Old and New Views of St. Lucia. T 77/8 and similar horiz designs. Multicoloured. W w 12 (sideways). P 13½ × 13.*

311	5 c.	Type **77**	..	10	10
312	5 c.	Type **78**	..	10	10
313	10 c.	} Castries city	..	10	10
314	10 c.		..	10	10

315	25 c.	} Pigeon Island	20	20
316	25 c.		20	20
317	50 c.	} View from grounds of Govt House	40	40
318	50 c.		40	40
311/18			*Set of 8*	1·25	1·25

Each value of this issue was printed horizontally and vertically se-tenant in two designs showing respectively old and new views of St. Lucia.

The old views are taken from paintings by J. H. Caddy.

79 "Virgin and Child with Two Angels" (Verrocchio)   **80** "St. Lucia" (Dolci School) and Coat of Arms

(Des J. Cooter. Litho J.W.)

1971 (15 Oct). *Christmas. T 79 and similar vert designs. Multicoloured. W w 12. P 14.*

319	5 c.	Type **79**	..	10	10
320	10 c.	"Virgin and Child, St. John the Baptist and an Angel" (Morando)	..	10	10
321	35 c.	"Madonna and Child" (Battista)	..	15	10
322	40 c.	Type **79**	..	20	25
319/22			*Set of 4*	40	40

(Des and litho Harrison)

1971 (13 Dec). *National Day. W w 12. P 14 × 14½.*

323	**80**	5 c. multicoloured	..	10	10
324		10 c. multicoloured	..	10	10
325		25 c. multicoloured	..	20	10
326		50 c. multicoloured	..	40	30
323/6			*Set of 4*	60	40

81 "The Dead Christ Mourned" (Carracci)

(Des G. Drummond. Litho Questa)

1972 (15 Feb). *Easter. T 81 and similar horiz design. Multicoloured. W w 12. P 14.*

327	10 c.	Type **81**	..	10	10
328	25 c.	"Angels weeping over the dead Christ" (Guercino)	..	20	10
329	35 c.	Type **81**	..	30	10
330	50 c.	As 25 c.	..	40	40
327/30			*Set of 4*	85	45

82 Science Block and Teachers' College

(Des P. Powell. Litho Questa)

1972 (18 Apr). *Morne Educational Complex. T 82 and similar horiz designs. Multicoloured. W w 12. P 14.*

331	5 c.	Type **82**	..	10	10
332	15 c.	University Centre	..	10	10
333	25 c.	Secondary School	..	10	10
334	35 c.	Technical College	..	15	10
331/4			*Set of 4*	30	30

83 Steamship Stamp and Map

(Des J. Cooter. Litho Questa)

1972 (22 June). *Centenary of First Postal Service by St. Lucia Steam Conveyance Co Ltd. T 83 and similar horiz designs. W w 12. P 14.*

335	5 c.	multicoloured	..	15	10
336	10 c.	ultramarine, mauve and black	..	20	10
337	35 c.	light rose-carmine, pale greenish blue and black	..	45	10
338	50 c.	multicoloured	..	1·00	1·00
335/8			*Set of 4*	1·60	1·00

Designs:—10 c. Steamship stamp and Castries Harbour; 35 c. Steamship stamp and Soufrière; 50 c. Steamship stamps.

84 "The Holy Family" (Sebastiano Ricci)

(Des J. Cooter. Litho J.W.)

1972 (18 Oct). *Christmas. W w* **12** (*sideways*). *P* 14½.
339	84	5 c. multicoloured	..	10	10
340		10 c. multicoloured	..	10	10
341		35 c. multicoloured	..	20	10
342		40 c. multicoloured	..	25	15
339/42			*Set of 4*	50	30

85 Arms and St. Lucia Amazon   86 Week-day Headdress

(Des (from photograph by D. Groves) and photo Harrison)

1972 (20 Nov). *Royal Silver Wedding. Multicoloured; background colour given. W w* **12**. *P* 14 × 14½.
343	85	15 c. carmine	..	20	10
344		35 c. yellow-olive	..	20	10

(Des Sylvia Goaman. Litho A. & M.)

1973 (1 Feb). *Local Headdresses. T* **86** *and similar vert designs. Multicoloured. W w* **12**. *P* 13.
345	c. Type **86**	..		10	10
346	10 c. Formal style	..		10	10
347	25 c. Unmarried girl's style	..		15	10
348	50 c. Ceremonial style	..		25	30
345/8			*Set of 4*	45	40

87 Coat of Arms   88 H.M.S. *St. Lucia*, 1803

(Des and litho Harrison)

1973–76. *Coil Stamps. P* 14½ × 14.
A. *W w* **12** *upright* (19.4.73). B. *W w* **12** *sideways* (1976).
				A		B
349	87	5 c. olive-green	..	10	25	40	70
350		10 c. new blue	..	15	25	40	70
351		25 c. lake-brown	..	15	25	†
349/51			*Set of 3*	35	65	

For 10 c. value watermarked w **16** see No. 953.

(Des R. Granger Barrett. Litho Questa)

1973 (24 May). *Historic Ships. T* **88** *and similar horiz designs. Multicoloured. W w* **12**. *P* 13½ × 14.
352	15 c. Type **88**	..		15	10
353	35 c. H.M.S. *Prince of Wales*, 1765	..	20	10
354	50 c. *Oliph Blossom*, 1605	..	30	15
355	$1 H.M.S. *Rose*, 1757	..	45	55
352/5			*Set of 4*	1·00	70
MS356	122 × 74 mm. Nos. 352/5	..	1·00	2·75

89 Plantation and Flower   90 "The Virgin with Child" (Maratta)

(Des PAD Studio. Litho Walsall)

1973 (26 July). *Banana Industry. T* **89** *and similar horiz designs. Multicoloured. W w* **12**. *P* 14.
357	5 c. Type **89**	..		10	10
358	15 c. Aerial spraying	..		15	10
359	35 c. Boxing plant	..		20	10
360	50 c. Loading a boat	..		40	40
357/60			*Set of 4*	75	45

(Des J. Cooter. Litho Walsall)

1973 (17 Oct). *Christmas. T* **90** *and similar vert designs. Multicoloured. W w* **12** (*sideways*). *P* 13½.
361	5 c. Type 90	..		10	10
362	15 c. "Madonna in the Meadow" (Raphael)	..	10	10
363	35 c. "The Holy Family" (Bronzino)	..	15	10
364	50 c. "Madonna of the Pear" (Dürer)	..	20	25
361/4			*Set of 4*	45	30

1973 (14 Nov). *Royal Wedding. As Nos.* 322/3 *of Montserrat.*
365	40 c. grey-green	..		10	10
366	50 c. rosy lilac	..		10	10

1974 (15 Mar). *As Nos.* 277/8 *but wmk upright.*
367	2 c. Roman Catholic Cathedral	..	60	70
368	4 c. The Boulevard, Castries	..	80	90

91 "The Betrayal"   92 3-Escalins Coins, 1798

(Des J. Cooter. Litho D.L.R.)

1974 (1 Apr). *Easter. T* **91** *and similar horiz designs showing paintings by Ugolino da Siena. Multicoloured. W w* **12** (*sideways on Nos.* 369/72, *upright on* MS373). *P* 13.
369	5 c. Type 91	..		10	10
370	15 c. "The Way to Calvary"	..	15	10
371	80 c. "The Deposition"	..	15	15
372	$1 "The Resurrection"	..	20	25
369/72			*Set of 4*	50	40
MS373	180 × 140 mm. Nos. 369/72	..	1·25	2·00

(Des J. Cooter. Litho Format)

1974 (20 May). *Coins of Old St. Lucie. T* **92** *and similar vert designs. Multicoloured. W w* **12** (*sideways*). *P* 14 × 13½.
374	15 c. Type 92	..		15	10
375	35 c. 6-escalins coins, 1798	..	20	10
376	40 c. 2-livres 5-sols coins, 1813	..	20	10
377	$1 6-livres 15-sols coins, 1813	..	55	65
374/7			*Set of 4*	1·00	75
MS378	151 × 115 mm. Nos. 374/7	..	1·60	2·50

93 Baron de Laborie   94 "Virgin and Child" (Andrea del Verrocchio)

(Des J. W. Litho Questa)

1974 (29 Aug). *Past Governors of St. Lucia. T* **93** *and similar vert designs. Multicoloured. W w* **12** (*sideways on Nos.* 379/82, *upright on* MS383). *P* 14.
379	5 c. Type 93	..		10	10
380	35 c. Sir John Moore	..		10	10
381	80 c. Sir Dudley Hill	..		15	10
382	$1 Sir Frederick Clarke	..		25	35
379/82			*Set of 4*	50	50
MS383	153 × 117 mm. Nos. 379/82	..	50	2·00

(Des PAD Studio. Litho D.L.R.)

1974 (18 Nov). *Christmas. T* **94** *and similar vert designs. Multicoloured. W w* **12**. *P* 13 × 13½.
384	5 c. Type 94	..		10	10
385	35 c. "Virgin and Child" (Andrea della Robbia)	10	10
386	80 c. "Madonna and Child" (Luca della Robbia)	15	15
387	$1 "Virgin and Child" (Rossellino)	..	20	25
384/7			*Set of 4*	40	40
MS388	92 × 140 mm. Nos. 384/7	..	90	1·75

95 Churchill and Montgomery   96 "Christ on the Cross" (School of Van der Weyden)

(Des PAD Studio. Litho Format)

1974 (30 Nov). *Birth Centenary of Sir Winston Churchill. T* **95** *and similar horiz design. Multicoloured. W w* **12** (*sideways*). *P* 14.
389	5 c. Type 95	..		10	10
390	$1 Churchill and Truman	..		30	35

(Des J. Cooter. Litho Questa)

1975 (27 Mar). *Easter. T* **96** *and similar vert designs. Multicoloured. W w* **12**. *P* 13½.
391	5 c. Type 96	..		10	10
392	35 c. "Noli me tangere" (Romano)	..	10	10
393	80 c. "Calvary" (Gallego)	..	15	15
394	$1 "Noli me tangere" (Correggio)	..	20	25
391/4			*Set of 4*	40	40

1975 (28 July). *As Nos.* 278 *etc. but W w* **14** (*sideways*).
395	4 c. The Boulevard, Castries	..	1·10	1·10
396	5 c. Castries Harbour	..	1·10	1·10
397	10 c. Vigie Airport	..	1·40	1·40
398	15 c. Pigeon Island	..	2·25	2·00
395/8			*Set of 4*	5·25	5·00

97 "Nativity" (French Book of Hours)   98 American Schooner *Hanna*

1975 (12 Dec). *Christmas. T* **97** *and similar vert designs. Multicoloured. W w* **12**. *P* 14½.
399	5 c. Type 97	..		10	10
400	10 c. ⎫ Epiphany scene		10	10
401	10 c. ⎬ (stained-glass window)		10	10
402	10 c. ⎭		10	10
403	40 c. "Nativity" (Hastings Book of Hours)	30	20
404	$1 "Virgin and Child with Saints" (Borgognone)	70	50
399/404			*Set of 6*	1·25	90
MS405	105 × 109 mm. Nos. 399 and 403/4	75	1·00

Nos. 400/2 were printed horizontally *se-tenant* within the sheet to form the composite design listed.

(Des J. W. Litho Format)

1976 (26 Jan). *Bicentenary of American Revolution. T* **98** *and similar horiz designs showing ships. Multicoloured. P* 14½.
406	½ c. Type 98	..		10	10
407	1 c. Mail Packet *Prince of Orange*	..	10	10
408	2 c. H.M.S. *Edward*	..		10	10
409	5 c. Merchantman *Millern*	..	30	10
410	15 c. American lugger *Surprise*	..	60	10
411	35 c. H.M.S. *Serapis*	..	1·10	20
412	50 c. American frigate *Randolph*	..	1·25	40
413	$1 American frigate *Alliance*	..	2·25	1·00
406/13			*Set of 8*	5·00	1·75
MS414	142 × 116 mm. Nos. 410/13. P 13	..	3·50	4·50

99 Laughing Gull   100 H.M.S. *Ceres*

(Des J.W. Litho Questa)

1976 (17 May)–**79.** *Birds. T* **99** *and similar vert designs. Multicoloured. Ordinary paper. W w* **12** (1 c.) *or w* **14** (*others*). *P* 14.
415	1 c. Type 99	..		30	50
416	2 c. Little Blue Heron	..		30	50
417	4 c. Belted Kingfisher	..		35	50
418	5 c. St. Lucia Amazon	..		1·25	50
419	6 c. St. Lucia Oriole	..		1·25	60
420	8 c. Brown Trembler	..		1·25	60
421	10 c. American Kestrel	..		1·25	35
422	12 c. Red-billed Tropic Bird	..		1·25	50
423	15 c. Moorhen	..		1·25	15
424	25 c. Common Noddy	..		1·50	45
	a. Chalk-surfaced paper (7.79)	..	1·00	30
425	35 c. Sooty Tern	..		1·75	55
	a. Chalk-surfaced paper (1979)	..	3·00	3·00
426	50 c. Osprey	..		3·75	1·25
427	$1 White-breasted Trembler	..	3·25	1·40
428	$2.50, St. Lucia Black Finch	..	4·00	3·75
429	$5 Red-necked Pigeon	..		4·75	3·50
430	$10 Caribbean Elaenia	..		7·00	8·00
	a. Chalk-surfaced paper (7.79)	..	6·00	7·50
415/30a			*Set of 16*	30·00	20·00

1976 (19 July). *West Indian Victory in World Cricket Cup. As Nos.* 419/20 *of Jamaica.*
431	50 c. Caribbean map	..		1·00	1·00
432	$1 Prudential Cup	..		1·50	2·25
MS433	92 × 79 mm. Nos. 431/2	..	3·25	4·25

(Des J. Cooter. Litho Walsall)

1976 (4 Sept). *Royal Navy Crests. T 100 and similar vert designs. Multicoloured. W w 14 (inverted). P 14.*

434	10 c. Type 100			30	10
435	20 c. H.M.S. *Pelican*			50	10
436	40 c. H.M.S. *Ganges*			75	10
437	$2 H.M.S. *Ariadne*			1·75	2·00
434/7			*Set of 4*	3·00	2·00

101 "Madonna and Child" (Murillo)   **102** Queen Elizabeth II

(Des J. Cooter. Litho Questa)

1976 (15 Nov). *Christmas. T 101 and similar vert designs. Multicoloured. W w 14. P 13½.*

438	10 c. Type 101			10	10
439	20 c. "Madonna and Child with Angels" (Costa)			10	10
440	50 c. "Madonna and Child Enthroned" (Isenbrandt)			15	10
441	$2 "Madonna and Child with St. John" (Murillo)			50	65
438/41			*Set of 4*	70	75
MS442	105 × 93 mm. $2.50, As Type 101			70	1·25

(Des Daphne Padden. Litho Questa)

1977 (7 Feb). *Silver Jubilee. W w 14 (sideways). P 14.*

443	**102** 10 c. multicoloured			10	10
444	20 c. multicoloured			15	15
445	40 c. multicoloured			20	25
446	$2 multicoloured			60	90
443/6			*Set of 4*	95	1·25
MS447	128 × 95 mm. **102** $2.50 multicoloured			60	1·00

Nos. 443/6 were each issued in sheets of five stamps and one label.

103 Scouts from Tapion School   **104** "Nativity" (Giotto)

(Des J. W. Litho Format)

1977 (17 Oct). *Caribbean Boy Scout Jamboree. T 103 and similar vert designs. Multicoloured. P 14½.*

448	½ c. Type 103			10	10
449	1 c. Sea scouts			10	10
450	2 c. Scout from Micoud			10	10
451	10 c. Two scouts from Tapion School			15	10
452	20 c. Venture scouts			20	15
453	50 c. Scout from Gros Islet			45	45
454	$1 Sea scouts in motor boat			75	1·10
448/54			*Set of 7*	1·50	1·75
MS455	75 × 85 mm. $2.50, As $1			1·50	2·50

(Des J. W. Litho Questa)

1977 (31 Oct). *Christmas. T 104 and similar vert designs. Multicoloured. P 14.*

456	½ c. Type 104			10	10
457	1 c. "Perugia triptych" (Fra Angelico)			10	10
458	2 c. "Virgin and Child" (El Greco)			10	10
459	20 c. "Madonna of the Rosary" (Caravaggio)			10	10
460	50 c. "Adoration of the Magi" (Velazquez)			20	10
461	$1 "Madonna of Carmel" (Tiepolo)			30	40
462	$2.50, "Adoration of the Magi" (Tiepolo)			55	80
456/62			*Set of 7*	1·10	1·25

105 "Susan Lunden"   **106** Yeoman of the Guard and Life Guard

---

(Des C. Abbott. Litho Harrison)

1977 (28 Nov). *400th Birth Anniv of Rubens. T 105 and similar vert designs. Multicoloured. W w 14 (sideways). P 14 × 15.*

463	10 c. Type 105			10	10
464	35 c. "The Rape of the Sabine Women" (detail)			15	10
465	50 c. "Ludovicus Nonnius"			25	10
466	$2.50, "Minerva protects Pax from Mars" (detail)			65	80
463/6			*Set of 4*	1·00	90
MS467	145 × 120 mm. Nos. 463/6			1·00	1·75

(Des J. W. Litho Questa)

1978 (2 June). *25th Anniv of Coronation. T 106 and similar horiz designs. Multicoloured. P 14.*

468	15 c. Type 106			10	10
469	20 c. Groom and postillion			10	10
470	50 c. Footman and coachman			15	10
471	$3 State trumpeter and herald			60	80
468/71			*Set of 4*	85	90
MS472	114 × 88 mm. $5 Master of the Horse and Gentleman-at-Arms			1·00	1·25

Nos. 468/71 also exist perf 12 (*Price for set of 4 95p mint or used*) from additional sheetlets of 3 stamps and one label. Stamps perforated 14 are from normal sheets of 50.

107 Queen Angelfish

(Des G. Vasarhelyi. Litho Format)

1978 (19 June). *Fishes. T 107 and similar horiz designs. Multicoloured. P 15.*

473	10 c. Type 107			10	10
474	20 c. Foureye Butterflyfish			20	10
475	50 c. French Angelfish			40	20
476	$2 Yellowtail Damselfish			1·00	1·25
473/6			*Set of 4*	1·40	1·40
MS477	155 × 89 mm. $2.50, Rock Beauty			1·60	1·90

Nos. 473/6 exist imperforate from stock dispersed by the liquidator of Format International Security Printers Ltd.

108 French Grenadier and Map of the Battle   **109** The Annunciation

(Des J. W. Litho Questa)

1978 (29 Nov). *Bicentenary of Battle of Cul-de-Sac. T 108 and similar horiz designs. Multicoloured. P 14*

478	10 c. Type 108			15	10
479	30 c. British Grenadier officer and map of St. Lucia (Bellin), 1762			30	10
480	50 c. Coastline from Gros Islet to Cul-de-Sac and British fleet opposing French landings			40	15
481	$2.50, General James Grant, 1798, and Light Infantrymen of 46th Regiment			1·50	1·25
478/81			*Set of 4*	2·10	1·40

(Des Jennifer Toombs. Litho Questa)

1978 (4 Dec). *Christmas. T 109 and similar horiz design. Multicoloured. W w 14. P 14.*

482	30 c. Type 109			10	10
483	50 c. Type 109			15	10
484	55 c. The Nativity			15	10
485	80 c. As 55 c.			20	20
482/5			*Set of 4*	55	40

INDEPENDENT

110 Hewanorra International Air Terminal

(Des J. W. Litho Questa)

1979 (22 Feb). *Independence. T 110 and similar horiz designs. Multicoloured. W w 14 (sideways). P 14.*

486	10 c. Type 110			10	10
487	30 c. New coat of arms.			10	10
488	50 c. Government House and Sir Allen Lewis (first Governor-General)			15	10
489	$2 French, St. Lucia and Union flags on map of St. Lucia			30	45
486/9			*Set of 4*	50	55
MS490	127 × 80 mm. Nos. 486/9			50	1·00

---

111 Popes Paul VI and John Paul I

(Des J.W. Litho Harrison)

1979 (28 May). *Pope Paul VI Commemoration. T 111 and similar horiz designs. Multicoloured. W w 14 (sideways). P 14½ × 14.*

491	10 c. Type 111			10	10
492	30 c. President Sadat of Egypt with Pope Paul			20	10
493	50 c. Pope Paul with Secretary-General U Thant			35	20
494	55 c. Pope Paul and Prime Minister Golda Meir of Israel			40	25
495	$2 Martin Luther King received in audience by Pope Paul			1·00	80
491/5			*Set of 5*	1·75	1·25

112 Dairy Farming

(Des G. Drummond. Litho Format)

1979 (2 July). *Agriculture Diversification. T 112 and similar horiz designs. Multicoloured. W w 14 (sideways). P 14.*

496	10 c. Type 112			10	10
497	35 c. Fruit and vegetables			10	10
498	50 c. Water conservation			10	10
499	$3 Copra industry			35	50
496/9			*Set of 4*	50	60

113 Lindbergh and Flying-boat   **114** "A Prince of Saxony" (Cranach the Elder)

(Des L. Curtis. Litho Walsall)

1979 (2 Oct). *50th Anniv of Lindbergh's Inaugural Airmail Flight via St. Lucia. T 113 and similar horiz designs. W w 14 (sideways). P 14.*

500	10 c. black, Indian red and pale orange			10	10
501	30 c. multicoloured			10	10
502	50 c. multicoloured			10	10
503	$2 multicoloured			30	40
500/3			*Set of 4*	50	50

Designs:—30 c. Flying boat and route map; 50 c. Arrival at La Toc, September, 1929; $2 Letters on first flight.

(Litho Questa)

1979 (6 Dec). *International Year of the Child. Paintings. T 114 and similar vert designs. Multicoloured. P. 14.*

504	10 c. Type 114			10	10
505	50 c. "The Infanta Margarita" (Velazquez)			15	10
506	$2 "Girl playing Badminton" (Chardin)			30	40
507	$2.50, "Mary and Francis Wilcox" (Stock)			35	45
504/7			*Set of 4*	70	80
MS508	113 × 94 mm. $5 "Two Children" (Picasso)			1·10	1·60

115 Notice of Introduction of Penny Post   **116** "Madonna and Child" (Bernardino Fungai)

(Des J.W. Litho Questa)

1979 (10 Dec). *Death Centenary of Sir Rowland Hill. T 115 and similar vert designs. Multicoloured. P 14.*

509	10 c. Type 115			10	10
510	50 c. Original stamp sketch			20	10
511	$2 1860 1d. stamp			45	50
512	$2.50, Penny Black stamp			55	60
509/12			*Set of 4*	1·10	1·10
MS513	111 × 85 mm. $5 Sir Rowland Hill			90	1·10

Nos. 509/12 also exist perf 12 (*Price for set of 4 £1·10 mint or used*) from additional sheetlets of 5 stamps and one label. Stamps perforated 14 are from normal sheets of 40.

(Des R. Vigurs. Litho Walsall)

1980 (14 Jan). *Christmas (1979) and International Year of the Child. T* **116** *and similar vert designs showing "Madonna and Child" paintings by various artists. Multicoloured. W w* **14**. *P* 14.
514	10 c. Type **116**	..	..	10	10
515	50 c. Carlo Dolci	..	..	25	10
516	$2 Titian	..	..	70	40
517	$2.50, Giovanni Bellini	..	..	75	50
514/17			*Set of 4*	1·60	95
MS518	94 × 120 mm. Nos. 514/17.	..		1·60	1·60

117 St. Lucia Steam Conveyance Company Cover, 1873
118 Mickey Mouse astride Rocket

(Des G. Drummond. Litho Questa)

1980 (6 May). *"London 1980" International Stamp Exhibition. T* **117** *and similar horiz designs. Multicoloured. W w* **14** *(sideways). P* 14.
519	10 c. Type **117**	..	..	10	10
520	30 c. S.S. *Assistance* 1d. postmark of 1879	..	10	10
521	50 c. Postage due handstamp of 1929	..	15	10
522	$2 Crowned-circle paid stamp of 1844	..	40	55
519/22			*Set of 4*	60	65
MS523	85 × 76 mm. Nos. 519/22	..		65	90

(Litho Format)

1980 (29 May). *10th Anniv of Moon Landing (1979). Walt Disney Cartoon Characters. T* **118** *and similar multicoloured designs showing characters in space scenes. P* 11.
524	½ c. Type **118**	..	..	10	10
525	1 c. Donald Duck being towed by rocket				
	(*horiz*)	..	..	10	10
526	2 c. Minnie Mouse on Moon	..	..	10	10
527	3 c. Goofy hitching lift to Mars	..	10	10
528	4 c. Goofy and moondog (*horiz*)	..	10	10
529	5 c. Pluto burying bone on Moon (*horiz*)	..	10	10
530	10 c. Donald Duck and love-sick martian				
	(*horiz*)	..	..	10	10
531	$2 Donald Duck paddling spaceship (*horiz*)	1·75	1·00
532	$2.50, Mickey Mouse driving moonbuggy				
	(*horiz*)	..	..	2·00	1·10
524/32			*Set of 9*	3·75	2·00
MS533	102 × 127 mm. $5 Goofy leaping from				
	space-ship on to Moon. P 13½			3·00	2·25

119 Queen Elizabeth the Queen Mother

(Litho Questa)

1980 (4 Aug). *80th Birthday of Queen Elizabeth the Queen Mother. P* 14.
534	**119**	10 c. multicoloured	..	..	20	10
535		$2.50, multicoloured	..	..	1·40	1·50
MS536		85 × 65 mm. **119** $3 multicoloured		1·50	2·10

120 Hawker Siddeley "HS 748"

(Des A. Theobald. Litho Harrison)

1980 (11 Aug). *Transport. Horiz designs as T* **120**. *Multicoloured. W w* **14** *(sideways on 5 c. to $1). P* 14½ × 14.
537	5 c. Type **120**	..	..	25	10
538	10 c. McDonnell Douglas "DC-10" airliner	..	35	10
539	15 c. Local bus	..	..	35	10
540	20 c. Refrigerated freighter	..	..	35	10
541	25 c. "Islander" aeroplane	..	..	50	10
542	30 c. Pilot boat	..	..	40	20
543	50 c. Boeing "727" airliner	..	..	65	40
544	75 c. *Cunard Countess* (liner)	..	65	75
545	$1 Lockheed "Tristar" airliner	..	85	85
546	$2 Cargo liner	..	..	1·25	1·50
547	$5 Boeing "707" airliner	..	..	4·50	4·50
548	$10 *Queen Elizabeth 2* (liner)	..	5·50	6·50
537/48			*Set of 12*	14·00	13·50
For stamps with watermark W w **15** see Nos. 690/8.

121 Shot-putting
122 Coastal Landscape within Cogwheel

(Des M. Diamond. Litho Questa)

1980 (22 Sept). *Olympic Games, Moscow. T* **121** *and similar horiz designs. Multicoloured. P* 14.
549	10 c. Type **121**	..	..	10	10
550	50 c. Swimming	..	..	15	10
551	$2 Gymnastics	..	..	60	50
552	$2.50, Weight-lifting	..	..	70	60
549/52			*Set of 4*	1·40	1·10
MS553	108 × 83 mm. $5 Athletes with Olympic				
	Torch	..	..	1·25	1·40

(Des BG Studio. Litho Questa)

1980 (30 Sept). *75th Anniv of Rotary International. T* **122** *and similar vert designs showing different coastal landscapes within cogwheels. P* 14.
554	10 c. multicoloured	..	..	10	10
555	50 c. multicoloured	..	..	15	10
556	$2 greenish black, carmine & greenish yell	40	40
557	$2.50, multicoloured	..	..	50	55
554/7			*Set of 4*	1·00	1·00
MS558	103 × 106 mm. $5 multicoloured	..	1·50	1·75

123 Sir Arthur Lewis

(Des J. W. Litho Questa)

1980 (23 Oct). *Nobel Prize Winners. T* **123** *and similar vert designs. Multicoloured. P* 14.
559	10 c. Type **123**	..	..	10	10
560	50 c. Martin Luther King Jnr.	..	20	15
561	$2 Ralph Bunche	..	..	50	60
562	$2.50, Albert Schweitzer	..	..	70	80
559/62			*Set of 4*	1·25	1·40
MS563	115 × 91 mm. $5 Albert Einstein	..	1·75	2·00

1980
HURRICANE

$1.50 RELIEF

(124)

1980 (3 Nov). *Hurricane Relief. Nos.* 539/40 *and* 543 *surch with T* **124**.
564	$1.50 on 15 c. Local bus	..	30	40
565	$1.50 on 20 c. Refrigerated freighter	..	30	40
566	$1.50 on 50 c. Boeing "727" airliner	..	30	40
564/6			*Set of 3*	80	1·10

125 "The Nativity" (Giovanni Battista)
126 Brazilian Agouti

(Des J. Cooter. Litho Questa)

1980 (1 Dec). *Christmas. Paintings. T* **125** *and similar vert designs. Multicoloured. W w* **14**. *P* 14 × 13½.
567	10 c. Type **125**	..	..	10	10
568	30 c. "Adoration of the Kings" (Pieter the				
	Elder)	..	..	10	10
569	$2 "Adoration of the Shepherds" (ascribed to				
	Murillo)	..	..	40	60
567/9			*Set of 3*	50	60
MS570	102 × 88 mm. $1 × 3, Angel with people of				
	St. Lucia (*composite design*) (*each* 30 × 75 mm).			
	P 14½ × 14			65	90

(Des G. Drummond. Litho Questa)

1981 (19 Jan). *Wildlife. T* **126** *and similar vert designs. Multicoloured. P* 14.
571	10 c. Type **126**	..	..	15	10
572	50 c. St. Lucia Amazon	..	..	75	10
573	$2 Purple-throated Carib	..	..	1·25	80
574	$2.50, Fiddler Crab	..	..	1·25	1·00
571/4			*Set of 4*	3·00	1·75
MS575	103×87 mm. $5 *Danaus plexippus*				
	(butterfly)	..	..	2·40	2·50

127 Prince Charles at Balmoral
128 Lady Diana Spencer

(Des J. W. Litho Questa)

1981 (23 June). *Royal Wedding. T* **127** *and similar vert designs. Multicoloured. P* 14.
576	25 c. Prince Charles and Lady Diana Spencer	15	10
577	50 c. Clarence House	..	..	20	10
578	$4 Type **127**	..	..	75	80
576/8			*Set of 3*	1·00	90
MS579	96 × 82 mm. $5 Glass Coach and coachman	1·25	1·00
Nos. 576/8 also exist perforated 12 (*price for set of 3 £1 mint or used*) from additional sheetlets of five stamps and one label. These stamps have changed background colours.

(Manufactured by Walsall)

1981 (23 June). *Royal Wedding. Booklet stamps. T* **128** *and similar vert designs. Multicoloured. Roul* 5 × *imperf* Self-adhesive.*
580	50 c. Type **128**	..	..	15	30
	a. Booklet pane. Nos. 580/1 each × 3			1·75	
581	$2 Prince Charles	..	..	50	80
582	$5 Prince Charles and Lady Diana Spencer	1·75	2·50
	a. Booklet pane of 1.	..	..	1·75	
580/2			*Set of 3*	2·25	3·25
*The 50 c. and $2 values were each separated by various combinations of rotary knife (giving a straight edge) and roulette. The $5 value exists only with straight edges.

129 "The Cock"
130 "Industry"

(Des J.W. Litho Questa)

1981 (20 July). *Birth Centenary of Picasso. T* **129** *and similar vert designs. Multicoloured. P* 13½ × 14.
583	30 c. Type **129**	..	..	25	10
584	50 c. "Man with an Ice-Cream"	..	35	10
585	55 c. "Woman dressing her Hair"	..	35	10
586	$3 "Seated Woman"	..	..	95	85
583/6			*Set of 4*	1·75	1·00
MS587	128 × 102 mm. $5 "Night Fishing at				
	Antibes"	..	..	2·00	2·50

(Des Walsall. Litho Format)

1981 (28 Sept). *25th Anniv of Duke of Edinburgh Award Scheme. T* **130** *and similar vert designs. Multicoloured. W w* **14**. *P* 14½.
588	10 c. Type **130**	..	..	10	10
589	35 c. "Community service"	..	..	15	10
590	50 c. "Physical recreation"	..	..	20	10
591	$2.50, Duke of Edinburgh speaking at				
	Caribbean Conference, 1975	..	70	70
588/91			*Set of 4*	1·00	75

131 Louis Braille
132 "Portrait of Fanny Travis Cochran" (Cecilia Beaux)

(Des J.W. Litho Questa)

1981 (10 Nov). *International Year for Disabled Persons. Famous Disabled People. T* **131** *and similar horiz designs. Multicoloured.* *P* 14.

592	10 c. Type **131**	15	10
593	50 c. Sarah Bernhardt	40	15
594	$2 Joseph Pulitzer	1·10	90
595	$2.50, Henri de Toulouse-Lautrec	1·25	1·00
592/5	*Set of 4*	2·50	1·90
MS596	115 × 90 mm. $5 Franklin Delano Roosevelt	2·50	2·25

(Des BG Studio. Litho Questa)

1981 (1 Dec). *Decade for Women. Paintings. T* **132** *and similar vert designs. Multicoloured. P* 14.

597	10 c. Type **132**	10	10
598	50 c. "Women with Dove" (Marie Laurencin)	40	15
599	$2 "Portrait of a Young Pupil of David" (Aimee Duvivier)	1·10	90
600	$2.50, "Self-portrait" (Rosalba Carriera)	1·25	1·00
597/600	*Set of 4*	2·50	1·90
MS601	104 × 78 mm. $5 "Self-portrait" (Elizabeth Vigee-le-Brun)	3·00	2·50

133 "The Adoration of the Magi" (Sfoza)   134 1860 1d. Stamp

(Des BG Studio. Litho Format)

1981 (15 Dec). *Christmas Paintings. T* **133** *and similar vert designs. Multicoloured. W* w **14**. *P* 14.

602	10 c. Type **133**	15	10
603	30 c. "The Adoration of the Kings" (Orcanga)	30	10
604	$1.50, "The Adoration of the Kings" (Gerard)	1·10	60
605	$2.50, "The Adoration of the Kings" (Foppa)	1·75	1·25
602/5	*Set of 4*	3·00	1·75

(Des J.W. Litho Questa)

1981 (29 Dec). *First Anniv of U.P.U. Membership. T* **134** *and similar horiz designs. Multicoloured. P* 14.

606	10 c. Type **134**	20	10
607	30 c. 1969 First anniversary of Caribbean Free Trade Area 25 c. commemorative	45	15
608	50 c. 1979 Independence $2 commemorative	65	50
609	$2 U.P.U. emblem with U.P.U. and St. Lucia flags	1·90	2·50
606/9	*Set of 4*	3·00	3·00
MS610	128 × 109 mm. $5 U.P.U. Headquarters, Berne, and G.P.O. Building, Castries	3·25	2·75

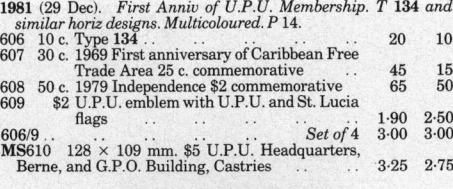

135 Scene from Football Match

(Des Clover Mill. Litho Format)

1982 (15 Feb). *World Cup Football Championship, Spain. T* **135** *and similar horiz designs showing scenes from different matches.* *P* 15.

611	10 c. multicoloured	20	10
612	50 c. multicoloured	70	15
613	$2 multicoloured	1·75	90
614	$2.50, multicoloured	2·00	1·00
611/14	*Set of 4*	4·25	1·90
MS615	104 × 84 mm. $5 multicoloured	3·00	2·25

136 Pigeon Island National Park   137 Map-reading

(Des J. Cooter. Litho Format)

1982 (13 Apr). *Bicentenary of Battle of the Saints. T* **136** *and similar horiz designs. Multicoloured. W* w **14**. *P* 14.

616	10 c. Type **136**	25	15
617	35 c. Battle scene	80	15
618	50 c. Rodney (English admiral) and De Grasse (French admiral)	1·10	45
619	$2.50, Map of the Saints, Martinique and St. Lucia	3·25	3·75
616/19	*Set of 4*	5·00	4·00
MS620	125 × 75 mm. Nos. 616/19	5·50	6·00

(Litho Questa)

1982 (4 Aug). *75th Anniv of Boy Scout Movement. T* **137** *and similar vert designs. Multicoloured. W* w **14**. *P* 14.

621	10 c. Type **137**	10	10
622	50 c. First Aid practice	30	15
623	$1.50, Camping	75	80
624	$2.50, Campfire singsong	1·25	1·50
621/4	*Set of 4*	2·25	2·25

138 Leeds Castle   139 "Adoration of the Kings" (detail, Jan Brueghel)

(Des PAD Studio. Litho Questa)

1982 (1 Sept). *21st Birthday of Princess of Wales. T* **138** *and similar vert designs. Multicoloured. P* 14½ × 14.

625	50 c. Type **138**	30	20
626	$2 Princess Diana boarding aircraft	90	75
627	$4 Wedding	1·60	1·40
625/7	*Set of 3*	2·50	2·10
MS628	102 × 75 mm. $5 Princess of Wales	2·00	2·00

(Des PAD Studio. Litho Harrison)

1982 (10 Nov). *Christmas. T* **139** *and similar vert designs depicting details from paintings. Multicoloured. W* w **14**. *P* 14.

629	10 c. Type **139**	10	10
630	30 c. "Nativity" (Lorenzo Costa)	15	10
631	50 c. "Virgin and Child" (Fra Filippo Lippi)	25	15
632	80 c. "Adoration of the Shepherds" (Nicolas Poussin)	40	55
629/32	*Set of 4*	75	75

140 The Pitons   141 Crown Agents Headquarters, Millbank, London

(Des D. Bowen. Litho Questa)

1983 (14 Mar). *Commonwealth Day. T* **140** *and similar horiz designs. Multicoloured. W* w **14** (*sideways*). *P* 14.

633	10 c. Type **140**	10	10
634	30 c. Tourist beach	15	10
635	50 c. Banana harvesting	20	15
636	$2 Flag of St. Lucia	60	1·00
633/6	*Set of 4*	85	1·10

(Des L. Curtis. Litho Questa)

1983 (1 Apr). *150th Anniv of Crown Agents. T* **141** *and similar vert designs. Multicoloured. W* w **14**. *P* 14.

637	10 c. Type **141**	10	10
638	15 c. Road construction	10	10
639	50 c. Road network map	20	25
640	$2 First St. Lucia stamp	60	1·00
637/40	*Set of 4*	80	1·25

142 Communications at Sea

(Des J.W. Litho Format)

1983 (12 July). *World Communications Year. T* **142** *and similar horiz designs. Multicoloured. P* 14½.

641	10 c. Type **142**	15	10
642	50 c. Communications in the air	40	15
643	$1.50, T.V. transmission via satellite	90	75
644	$2.50, Computer communications	1·40	1·25
641/4	*Set of 4*	2·50	2·00
MS645	107 × 88 mm. $5 Weather satellite	2·50	2·75

143 Longspine Squirrelfish

(Des G. Drummond. Litho Format)

1983 (23 Aug). *Coral Reef Fishes. T* **143** *and similar horiz designs. Multicoloured. P* 14½.

646	10 c. Type **143**	10	10
647	50 c. Banded Butterflyfish	20	15
648	$1.50, Blackbar Soldierfish	70	75
649	$2.50, Yellowtail Snapper	1·10	1·25
646/9	*Set of 4*	1·90	2·00
MS650	122 × 97 mm. $5 Red Hind	2·50	3·00

144 Duke of Sutherland (1930)   145 "The Niccolini-Cowper Madonna"

(Des J.W. Litho Format)

1983 (14 Oct). *Leaders of the World. Railway Locomotives* (1st series). *T* **144** *and similar horiz designs, the first in each pair showing technical drawings and the second the locomotive at work. P* 12½.

651	35 c. multicoloured	25	20
	a. Vert pair. Nos. 651/2	50	40
652	35 c. multicoloured	25	20
653	35 c. multicoloured	25	20
	a. Vert pair. Nos. 653/4	50	40
654	35 c. multicoloured	25	20
655	50 c. multicoloured	35	30
	a. Vert pair. Nos. 655/6	70	60
656	50 c. multicoloured	35	30
657	50 c. multicoloured	35	30
	a. Vert pair. Nos. 657/8	70	60
658	50 c. multicoloured	35	30
659	$1 multicoloured	50	50
	a. Vert pair. Nos. 659/60	1·00	1·00
660	$1 multicoloured	50	50
661	$1 multicoloured	50	50
	a. Vert pair. Nos. 661/2	1·00	1·00
662	$1 multicoloured	50	50
663	$2 multicoloured	70	70
	a. Vert pair. Nos. 663/4	1·40	1·40
664	$2 multicoloured	70	70
665	$2 multicoloured	70	70
	a. Vert pair. Nos. 665/6	1·40	1·40
666	$2 multicoloured	70	70
651/66	*Set of 16*	6·50	6·50

Designs:—Nos. 651/2, *Duke of Sutherland*, Great Britain (1930); 653/4, *City of Glasgow*, Great Britain (1940); 655/6, *Lord Nelson*, Great Britain (1926); 657/8, *Leeds United*, Great Britain (1928); 659/60, *Bodmin*, Great Britain (1945); 661/2, *Eton*, Great Britain (1930); 663/4, *Flying Scotsman*, Great Britain (1923); 665/6, *Rocket*, Great Britain (1829).

Nos. 651/2, 653/4, 655/6, 657/8, 659/60, 661/2, 663/4 and 665/6 were printed together, *se-tenant*, in vertical pairs throughout the sheets.

See also Nos. 715/26, 761/76, 824/31 and 858/73.

(Litho Format)

1983 (21 Nov). *Christmas. 500th Birth Anniv of Raphael. T* **145** *and similar vert designs showing details of Raphael paintings. Multicoloured. W* w **14**. *P* 14.

667	10 c. Type **145**	10	10
668	30 c. "The Holy Family with a Palm Tree"	20	10
669	50 c. "The Sistine Madonna"	35	20
670	$5 "The Alba Madonna"	2·50	2·25
667/70	*Set of 4*	2·75	2·25

146 George III   147 Clarke & Co's Drug Store

(Des Court House Studio. Litho Format)

1984 (13 Mar). *Leaders of the World. British Monarchs. T* **146** *and similar vert designs. Multicoloured. P* 12½.

671	5 c. Battle of Waterloo	10	10
	a. Horiz pair. Nos. 671/2	10	10
672	5 c. Type **146**	10	10
673	10 c. George III at Kew	10	10
	a. Horiz pair. Nos. 673/4	15	15
674	10 c. Kew Palace	10	10
675	35 c. Coat of Arms of Elizabeth I	20	20
	a. Horiz pair. Nos. 675/6	40	40
676	35 c. Elizabeth I	20	20
677	60 c. Coat of Arms of George III	30	30
	a. Horiz pair. Nos. 677/8	60	60
678	60 c. George III (*different*)	30	30
679	$1 Elizabeth I at Hatfield	40	40
	a. Horiz pair. Nos. 679/80	80	80

680	$1 Hatfield Palace	..	..	..	..	40	40
681	$2.50, Spanish Armada	..	..	..	..	75	75
	a. Horiz pair. Nos. 681/2	..	..	..		1·50	1·50
682	$2.50, Elizabeth I (different)..	..		..	75	75
671/82					Set of 12	3·00	3·00

Nos. 671/2, 673/4, 675/6, 677/8, 679/80 and 681/2 were printed together in se-tenant horizontal pairs throughout the sheets.

Unissued 30, 50 c., $1, $2.50 and $5 values, showing Alfred the Great or Richard I, exist from stock dispersed by the liquidator of Format International Security Printers Ltd.

(Des J. Cooter. Litho Questa)

1984 (6 Apr). *Historic Buildings. T* **147** *and similar multicoloured designs. W w* **15** *(sideways on 45 c. to $2.50). P* 14 × 13½ (10 c.) *or* 13½ × 14 *(others).*

683	10 c. Type **147**	..	..	..	..	10	10
684	45 c. Colonial architecture (*horiz*)		..		30	25
685	65 c. Colonial "chattel" house (*horiz*)		..	45	35
686	$2.50, Treasury after 1906 earthquake (*horiz*)		1·75	1·60
683/6					Set of 4	2·40	2·00

1984 (15 May). *As Nos. 540/42, 545/6 and 548, but W w* **15** *(sideways on 20 c. to $1). P* 14½ × 14.

690	20 c. Refrigerator ship..	..	..	..	80	20
691	25 c. "Islander" aeroplane	..	..	..	90	25
692	30 c. Pilot boat ..	..	..	..	..	1·25	30
695	$1 Lockheed "Tristar" airliner	..	..	2·50	90
696	$2 Cargo liner	..	..	..	..	4·25	2·75
698	$10 *Queen Elizabeth 2* (liner)	..	..	9·50	12·00
690/8	..	..	..	..	Set of 6	17·00	15·00

148 Logwood

(Des J. Cooter. Litho Format)

1984 (12 June). *Forestry Resources. T* **148** *and similar multicoloured designs. W w* **15** *(inverted on 65 c., sideways on others). P* 14 × 13½ (65 c.) *or* 13½ × 14 *(others).*

699	10 c. Type **148**	..	..	..	..	15	10
700	45 c. Calabash	..	..	..	..	60	30
701	65 c. Gommier (*vert*)	..	..	..	80	55
702	$2.50, Raintree	..	..	..	..	2·25	2·75
699/702					Set of 4	3·50	3·25

IMPERFORATES AND MISSING COLOURS.

Various issues between Nos. 703 and 893 exist either imperforate or with colours omitted. Such items are not listed as there is no evidence that they fulfil the criteria outlined on page xi of this catalogue.

149 Bugatti Type "57SC Atlantic Coupe"

(Des J.W. Litho Format)

1984 (25 June). *Leaders of the World. Automobiles (1st series). T* **149** *and similar horiz designs, the first in each pair showing technical drawings and the second paintings. P* 12½.

703	5 c. black, reddish lavender and lemon		..	10	10
	a. Vert pair. Nos. 703/4	..	..		10	10
704	5 c. multicoloured	..	..	..	..	10	10
705	10 c. black, azure and rose-carmine		..	10	10
	a. Vert pair. Nos. 705/6	..	..		10	10
706	10 c. multicoloured	..	..	..		10	10
707	$1 black, pale green and orange-brown		25	25
	a. Vert pair. Nos. 707/8	..	..		50	50
708	$1 multicoloured	..	..	..		25	25
709	$2.50, black, pale flesh and slate-blue		40	40
	a. Vert pair. Nos. 709/10	..	..		80	80
710	$2.50, multicoloured	..	..	..	40	40
703/10					Set of 8	1·25	1·25

Designs:—Nos. 703/4, Bugatti Type "57SC Atlantic Coupe"; 705/6, Chevrolet "Bel Air Convertible"; 707/8, Alfa Romeo "1750 GS (Zagato)"; 709/10, Duesenberg "S J Roadster".

Nos. 703/4, 705/6, 707/8 and 709/10 were printed together, se-tenant, in vertical pairs throughout the sheets.

See also Nos. 745/60, 789/96 and 902/13.

150 Pygmy Gecko   **151** Men's Volleyball

(Des Jennifer Toombs. Litho Format)

1984 (8 Aug). *Endangered Wildlife. T* **150** *and similar horiz designs. Multicoloured. W w* **15** *(sideways). P* 14.

711	10 c. Type **150**	..	..	..	..	40	10
712	45 c. Maria Island Ground Lizard	..	..	1·00	50
713	65 c. Green Iguana	..	..	..		1·25	85
714	$2.50, Couresse Snake	..	..	..	3·50	
711/14					Set of 4	5·00	4·50

(Des J.W. Litho Format)

1984 (21 Sept). *Leaders of the World. Railway Locomotives (2nd series). Horiz designs as T* **144**, *the first in each pair showing technical drawings and the second the locomotive at work. P* 12½.

715	1 c. multicoloured	..	..	..	..	10	10
	a. Vert pair. Nos. 715/16	..	..		10	10
716	1 c. multicoloured	..	..	..	..	10	10
717	15 c. multicoloured	..	..	..		15	15
	a. Vert pair. Nos. 717/18	..	..		30	30
718	15 c. multicoloured	..	..	..		15	15
719	50 c. multicoloured	..	..	..		20	20
	a. Vert pair. Nos. 719/20	..	..		40	40
720	50 c. multicoloured	..	..	..		20	20
721	75 c. multicoloured	..	..	..		25	25
	a. Vert pair. Nos. 721/2	..	..		50	50
722	75 c. multicoloured	..	..	..		25	25
723	$1 multicoloured	..	..	..		30	30
	a. Vert pair. Nos. 723/4	..	..		60	60
724	$1 multicoloured	..	..	..		30	30
725	$2 multicoloured	..	..	..		50	50
	a. Vert pair. Nos. 725/6	..	..		1·00	1·00
726	$2 multicoloured	..	..	..		50	50
715/26					Set of 12	2·50	2·50

Designs:—Nos. 715/16, *Taw*, Great Britain (1897); 717/18, "Crocodile 1.C.C.1." type, Switzerland (1920); 719/20, *The Countess*, Great Britain (1903); 721/2, Class "GE6/6 C.C.", Switzerland (1921); 723/4, Class "P8", Germany (1906); 725/6, *Der Adler*, Germany (1835).

Nos. 715/26 were issued in a similar sheet format to Nos. 651/66.

Nos. 715/26 exist imperforate from stock dispersed by the liquidator of Format International Security Printers Ltd.

(Des Court House Studio. Litho Format)

1984 (21 Sept). *Leaders of the World. Olympic Games, Los Angeles. T* **151** *and similar vert designs. Multicoloured. P* 12½.

727	5 c. Type **151**	..	..	..	..	10	10
	a. Horiz pair. Nos. 727/8	..	..		10	10
728	5 c. Women's volleyball	..	..		10	10
729	10 c. Women's hurdles..	..	..		10	10
	a. Horiz pair. Nos. 729/30	..	..		10	10
730	10 c. Men's hurdles	..	..	..		10	10
731	65 c. Show jumping	..	..	..		15	15
	a. Horiz pair. Nos. 731/2	..	..		30	30
732	65 c. Dressage	..	..	..		15	15
733	$2.50, Women's gymnastics..	..		40	40
	a. Horiz pair. Nos. 733/4	..	..		80	80
734	$2.50, Men's gymnastics	..	..		40	40
727/34					Set of 8	1·10	1·10

Nos. 727/8, 729/30, 731/2, 733/4 were printed together, se-tenant, in horizontal pairs throughout the sheets.

Examples of No. 537 exist overprinted "RUMBRIDGE PACK R.F.C./1984 TOUR". This was a private souvenir, connected with a tour to St. Lucia by an English rugby club in October 1984. It was not sold by the St. Lucia Post Office or Philatelic Bureau.

152 Glass of Wine and Flowers   **153** Slaves preparing Manioc

(Des G. Vasarhelyi. Litho Format)

1984 (31 Oct). *Christmas. T* **152** *and similar vert designs. Multicoloured. W w* **15**. *P* 14.

735	10 c. Type **152**	..	..	..	..	10	10
736	35 c. Priest and decorated altar	..		20	15
737	60 c. Nativity scene	..	..	..		35	35
738	$3 Holy Family	..	..	..		1·50	1·60
735/8	..	..	..	..	Set of 4	1·90	1·90
MS739	147 × 77 mm. Nos. 735/8	..	..	2·75	3·25

(Des J. Cooter. Litho Format)

1984 (12 Dec). *150th Anniv of Abolition of Slavery. T* **153** *and similar vert designs. Each black and yellow-ochre. W w* **15**. *P* 14 × 13½.

740	10 c. Type **153**	..	..	..	..	10	10
741	35 c. Sifting and cooking cassava flour		15	20
742	55 c. Cooking pot, and preparing tobacco	25	30
743	$5 Stripping tobacco leaves for twist tobacco	2·25	2·50
740/3	..	..	..	..	Set of 4	2·40	2·75
MS744	154 × 110 mm. As Nos. 740/3, but without dates and side inscription and with the face values in different positions	..	..	3·25	4·50

(Des Artists International (65 c.), J.W. (others). Litho Format)

1984 (19 Dec). *Leaders of the World. Automobiles (2nd series). Horiz designs as T* **149**, *the first in each pair showing technical drawings and the second paintings. P* 12½.

745	10 c. black, pale green and lake-brown		10	10
	a. Vert pair. Nos. 745/6	..	..		15	15
746	10 c. multicoloured	..	..	..		10	10
747	30 c. black, azure and bright yellow-green	15	15
	a. Vert pair. Nos. 747/8	..	..		30	30
748	30 c. multicoloured	..	..	..		15	15
749	55 c. black, greenish yellow and orange-brown	30	30
	a. Vert pair. Nos. 749/50	..	..		60	60
750	55 c. multicoloured	..	..	..		30	30
751	65 c. black, grey and brown-lilac	..		35	35
	a. Vert pair. Nos. 751/2	..	..		70	70
752	65 c. multicoloured	..	..	..		35	35
753	75 c. black, pale cinnamon, & orange-verm	35	35
	a. Vert pair. Nos. 753/4	..	..		70	70
754	75 c. multicoloured	..	..	..		35	35
755	$1 black, pale cinnamon and dull violet-blue	40	40
	a. Vert pair. Nos. 755/6	..	..		80	80

756	$1 multicoloured	..	..	..		40	40
757	$2 black, pale green and orange-red		50	50
	a. Vert pair. Nos. 757/8	..	..		1·00	1·00
758	$2 multicoloured	..	..	..		50	50
759	$3 black, pale cinnamon & orange-verm	60	60
	a. Vert pair. Nos. 759/60	..	..		1·10	1·10
760	$3 multicoloured	..	..	..		60	60
745/60					Set of 16	4·75	4·75

Designs:—Nos. 745/6, Panhard and Levassor; 747/8, N.S.U. "RO-80" Saloon; 749/50, Abarth "Bialbero"; 751/2, TVR "Vixen 2500M"; 753/4, Ford "Mustang" Convertible; 755/6, Ford "Model T"; 757/8, Aston Martin" DB3S"; 759/60, Chrysler "Imperial CG Dual Cowl" Phaeton.

Nos. 745/60 were issued in a similar sheet format to Nos. 703/10.

(Des T. Hadler (5, 15, 35 c.), J.W. (others). Litho Format)

1985 (4 Feb). *Leaders of the World. Railway Locomotives (3rd series). Horiz designs as T* **144**, *the first in each pair showing technical drawings and the second the locomotive at work. P* 12½.

761	5 c. multicoloured	..	..	..		10	10
762	5 c. multicoloured	..	..	..		10	10
	a. Vert pair. Nos. 761/2	..	..		10	10
763	15 c. multicoloured	..	..	..		15	15
	a. Vert pair. Nos. 763/4	..	..		30	30
764	15 c. multicoloured	..	..	..		15	15
765	35 c. multicoloured	..	..	..		15	15
	a. Vert pair. Nos. 765/6	..	..		30	30
766	35 c. multicoloured	..	..	..		15	15
767	60 c. multicoloured	..	..	..		15	15
	a. Vert pair. Nos. 767/8	..	..		30	30
768	60 c. multicoloured	..	..	..		15	15
769	75 c. multicoloured	..	..	..		20	20
	a. Vert pair. Nos. 769/70	..	..		40	40
770	75 c. multicoloured	..	..	..		20	20
771	$1 multicoloured	..	..	..		20	20
	a. Vert pair. Nos. 771/2	..	..		40	40
772	$1 multicoloured	..	..	..		20	20
773	$2 multicoloured	..	..	..		40	40
	a. Vert pair. Nos. 773/4	..	..		80	80
774	$2 multicoloured	..	..	..		40	40
775	$2.50, multicoloured	..	..	..	55	55
	a. Vert pair. Nos. 775/6	..	..		1·10	1·10
776	$2.50, multicoloured	..	..	..	55	55
761/76					Set of 16	3·25	3·25

Designs:—Nos. 761/2, Class "C53", Japan (1928); 763/4, Class "Heavy L", India (1885); 765/6, Class "B18¼", Australia (1926); 767/8, *Owain Glyndwr*, Great Britain (1923); 769/70, *Lion*, Great Britain (1838); 771/2, Coal type locomotive, Great Britain (1873); 773/4, No. 2238, Class "Q6", Great Britain (1921); 775/6, Class "H", Great Britain (1920).

Nos. 761/76 were issued in a similar sheet format to Nos. 651/66.

154 Girl Guide Badge in Shield and Crest of St. Lucia   **155** *Clossiana selene*

(Des Court House Studio. Litho Questa)

1985 (21 Feb). *75th Anniv of Girl Guide Movement and 60th Anniv of Guiding in St. Lucia. W w* **15**. *P* 14.

777	**154** 10 c. multicoloured	..	..		20	10
778	35 c. multicoloured	..	..	..		70	15
779	65 c. multicoloured	..	..	..		1·10	35
780	$3 multicoloured	..	..	..		3·00	1·90
777/80					Set of 4	4·50	2·25

(Des Jennifer Toombs. Litho Format)

1985 (28 Feb). *Leaders of the World. Butterflies. T* **155** *and similar vert designs. Multicoloured. P* 12½.

781	15 c. Type **155**	..	..	..		10	10
	a. Horiz pair. Nos. 781/2	..	..		15	15
782	15 c. *Inachis io*	..	..	..		10	10
783	40 c. *Philaethria dido* (s sp *werneckei*)	15	15
	a. Horiz pair. Nos. 783/4	..	..		30	30
784	40 c. *Callicore sorana*	..	..		15	15
785	60 c. *Kallima inachus*	..	..		15	15
	a. Horiz pair. Nos. 785/6	..	..		30	30
786	60 c. *Hypanartia paullus*	..	..		15	15
787	$2.25, *Morpho helena*	..	..		50	50
	a. Horiz pair. Nos. 787/8	..	..		1·00	1·00
788	$2.25, *Ornithoptera meridionalis*	..	50	50
781/8					Set of 8	1·60	1·60

Nos. 781/2, 783/4, 785/6 and 787/8 were printed together, se-tenant, in horizontal pairs throughout the sheets.

(Des J.W. Litho Format)

1985 (29 Mar). *Leaders of the World. Automobiles (3rd series). Horiz designs as T* **149**, *the first in each pair showing technical drawings and the second paintings. P* 12½.

789	15 c. black, cobalt and Indian red	..	10	10
	a. Vert pair. Nos. 789/90	..	..		15	15
790	15 c. multicoloured	..	..	..		10	10
791	50 c. black, pale orange and deep rose-red ..	15	15
	a. Vert pair. Nos. 791/2	..	..		30	30
792	50 c. multicoloured	..	..	..		15	15
793	$1 black, pale green and reddish orange ..	20	20
	a. Vert pair. Nos. 793/4	..	..		40	40
794	$1 multicoloured	..	..	..		20	20
795	$1.50, black, pale green & pale red-brown	30	30
	a. Vert pair. Nos. 795/6	..	..		60	60
796	$1.50, multicoloured	..	..	..	30	30
789/96					Set of 8	1·25	1·25

Designs:—Nos. 789/90, Hudson "Eight" (1940); 791/2, KdF (1937); 793/4, Kissel "Goldbug" (1925); 795/6, Ferrari "246 GTS" (1973).

Nos. 789/96 were issued in a similar sheet format to Nos. 703/10.

156 Grenadier, 70th Regiment, c 1775   **157** Messerschmitt "109-E"

(Des J. Cooter. Litho Format)

1985 (7 May). *Military Uniforms. T* **156** *and similar vert designs. Multicoloured. W w* **15** (*sideways*). *P* 15.

797	5 c. Type **156**.	25	15
798	10 c. Officer, Grenadier Company, 14th Regiment, 1780 ..	25	15
799	20 c. Officer, Battalion Company, 46th Regiment, 1781	40	15
800	25 c. Officer, Royal Artillery, c. 1782	40	15
801	30 c. Officer, Royal Engineers, 1782 ..	60	15
802	35 c. Officer, Battalion Company, 54th Regiment, 1782	50	20
803	45 c. Private, Grenadier Company, 14th Regiment, 1782..	80	40
804	50 c. Gunner, Royal Artillery, 1796..	80	40
805	65 c. Private, Battalion Company, 85th Regiment, c. 1796	70	50
806	75 c. Private, Battalion Company, 76th Regiment, 1796	75	55
807	90 c. Private, Battalion Company, 81st Regiment, c. 1796	85	60
808	$1 Sergeant, 74th (Highland) Regiment, 1796	90	60
809	$2.50, Private, Light Company, 93rd Regiment, 1803	3·50	3·75
810	$5 Private, Battalion Company, 1st West India Regiment, 1803	6·50	7·50
811	$15 Officer, Royal Artillery, 1850 ..	11·00	13·00
797/811	*Set of 15*	25·00	25·00

The 25 c. exists with different imprint dates below the design.

Examples of the 5, 10, 15, 20, 25, 40, 50 c. and $20 with "1986" imprint date, and in some cases imperforate, come from stock dispersed by the liquidator of Format International Security Printers Ltd.

For 5, 10, 30, 45, 50 c., $2.50, $5, and additional values, all without watermark see Nos. 928/46.

For 5, 10, 20, 25 c. and additional values, all watermarked w **16** (sideways) see Nos. 993/1003.

(Des J.W. Litho Format)

1985 (30 May). *Leaders of the World. Military Aircraft. T* **157** *and similar horiz designs, the first in each pair showing paintings and the second technical drawings. P* 12½.

812	5 c. multicoloured	10	10
	a. Vert pair. Nos. 812/13 ..	10	10
813	5 c. black, pale new blue and pale yellow ..	10	10
814	55 c. multicoloured	40	35
	a. Vert pair. Nos. 814/15 ..	80	70
815	55 c. black, pale new blue and pale yellow ..	40	35
816	60 c. multicoloured	40	40
	a. Vert pair. Nos. 816/17 ..	80	80
817	60 c. black, pale new blue and pale yellow ..	40	40
818	$2 multicoloured	80	80
	a. Vert pair. Nos. 818/19 ..	1·60	1·60
819	$2 black, pale new blue and pale yellow ..	80	80
812/19	*Set of 8*	3·00	3·00

Designs:—Nos. 812/13, Messerschmitt "109-E"; 814/15, Avro "683 Lancaster Mark I"; 816/17, North American "P.51-D Mustang"; 818/19, Supermarine "Spitfire Mark II".

Nos. 812/13, 814/15, 816/17 and 818/19 were printed together, *se-tenant*, in vertical pairs throughout the sheets.

158 Magnificent Frigate Birds, Frigate Island Bird Sanctuary   **159** Queen Elizabeth the Queen Mother

(Des G. Drummond. Litho Format)

1985 (20 June). *Nature Reserves. T* **158** *and similar horiz designs. Multicoloured. W w* **15**. *P* 15.

820	10 c. Type **158**.	45	20
821	35 c. Mangrove Cuckoo, Scorpion Island, Savannes Bay	1·40	45
822	65 c. Lesser Yellowlegs, Maria Island Reserve ..	2·00	85
823	$3 Audubon's Shearwaters, Lapins Island Reserve ..	4·00	5·00
820/3	*Set of 4*	7·00	6·00

(Des Tudor Art Agency ($2.50), J.W. (others). Litho Format)

1985 (26 June). *Leaders of the World. Railway Locomotives (4th series). Horiz designs as T* **144**, *the first in each pair showing technical drawings and second the locomotive at work. P* 12½.

824	10 c. multicoloured	10	10
	a. Vert pair. Nos. 824/5 ..	20	20
825	10 c. multicoloured	10	10
826	30 c. multicoloured	15	15
	a. Vert pair. Nos. 826/7 ..	30	30
827	30 c. multicoloured	15	15

828	75 c. multicoloured	20	20
	a. Vert pair. Nos. 828/9 ..	40	40
829	75 c. multicoloured	20	20
830	$2.50, multicoloured	55	55
	a. Vert pair. Nos. 830/1 ..	1·10	1·10
831	$2.50 multicoloured	55	55
824/31	*Set of 8*	1·75	1·75

Designs:—Nos. 824/5, No. 28 tank locomotive, Great Britain (1897); 826/7, No. 1621 Class "M", Great Britain (1893); 828/9, Class "Dunalastair", Great Britain (1896); 830/1, No. 2290 "Big Bertha" type, Great Britain (1919).

Nos. 824/31 were issued in a similar sheet format to Nos. 651/66.

(Des Court House Studio. Litho Format)

1985 (16 Aug). *Leaders of the World. Life and Times of Queen Elizabeth the Queen Mother. Various vertical portraits as T* **159**. *P* 12.

832	40 c. multicoloured	15	20
	a. Horiz pair. Nos. 832/3 ..	30	40
833	40 c. multicoloured	15	20
834	75 c. multicoloured	15	25
	a. Horiz pair. Nos. 834/5 ..	30	50
835	75 c. multicoloured	15	25
836	$1.10, multicoloured	25	35
	a. Horiz pair. Nos. 836/7 ..	50	70
837	$1.10, multicoloured	25	35
838	$1.75, multicoloured	40	55
	a. Horiz pair. Nos. 838/9 ..	80	1·10
839	$1.75, multicoloured	40	55
832/9	*Set of 8*	1·60	2·50
MS840	84 × 114 mm. 42 multicoloured; $2 multicoloured	90	1·40

The two designs of each value were issued, *se-tenant*, in horizontal pairs within the sheets.

Each *se-tenant* pair shows a floral pattern across the bottom of the portraits which stops short of the left-hand edge on the left-hand stamp and of the right-hand edge on the right-hand stamp.

Nos. 832/9, together with two unissued 25 c. designs, exist in miniature sheets, one for each value, from stock dispersed by the liquidator of Format International Security Printers Ltd.

Designs as Nos. 832/3 and 836/7, but with face values of $3 × 2 and $6 × 2, also exist in additional miniature sheets from a restricted printing issued 31 December 1985.

160 "Youth playing Banjo" (Wayne Whitfield)   **161** "Papa Jab"

(Litho Format)

1985 (5 Sept). *International Youth Year. Paintings by Young St. Lucians. T* **160** *and similar designs. W w* **15** (*sideways*). *P* 15.

841	10 c. black, new blue and bright magenta ..	10	10
842	45 c. multicoloured	30	25
843	75 c. multicoloured	50	40
844	$3.50, multicoloured	2·00	1·75
841/4	*Set of 4*	2·50	2·25
MS845	123 × 86 mm. $5 multicoloured	2·25	2·75

Designs: *Vert* (as T **160**)—45 c. "Motorcyclist" (Mark Maragh); 75 c. "Boy and Girl at Pitons" (Bartholomew Eugene); $3.50, "Abstract" (Lyndon Samuel). *Horiz* (80 × 55 *mm*)—$5 Young people and St. Lucia landscapes.

1985 (26 Oct). *Royal Visit. Nos.* 649, 685/6, 702, 713, 778 *and* 836/7 *optd as T* **114** *of Montserrat*.

846	**154**	35 c. multicoloured	3·50	2·50
847	—	65 c. multicoloured (No. 685)	3·00	3·00
848	—	65 c. multicoloured (No. 713) ..	3·00	3·00
849	—	$1.10, multicoloured (No. 836)	4·00	4·00
		a. Horiz pair. Nos. 849/50 ..	8·00	8·00
850	—	$1.10, multicoloured (No. 837) ..	4·00	4·00
851	—	$2.50, multicoloured (No. 649) ..	4·00	4·00
852	—	$2.50, multicoloured (No. 686) ..	3·50	3·50
853	—	$2.50, multicoloured (No. 702) ..	3·50	3·50
846/53			*Set of 8* 26·00	25·00

(Litho Format)

1985 (24 Dec). *Christmas. Masqueraders. T* **161** *and similar vert designs. Multicoloured. P* 15.

854	10 c. Type **161**..	10	10
855	45 c. "Paille Bananne"	20	25
856	75 c. "Cheval Bois"	30	35
854/6	*Set of 3*	50	60
MS857	70 × 83 mm. $4 "Madonna and Child" (Dunstan St. Omer)	1·75	1·90

(Des T. Hadler. Litho Format)

1986 (27 Jan). *Leaders of the World. Railway Locomotives (5th series). Horiz designs as T* **144**, *the first in each pair showing technical drawings and the second the locomotive at work. P* 12½.

858	5 c. multicoloured	15	15
	a. Vert pair. Nos. 858/9 ..	30	30
859	5 c. multicoloured	15	15
860	15 c. multicoloured	15	15
	a. Vert pair. Nos. 860/1 ..	30	30
861	15 c. multicoloured	15	15
862	30 c. multicoloured	30	30
	a. Vert pair. Nos. 862/3 ..	60	60

863	30 c. multicoloured	30	30
864	60 c. multicoloured	45	45
	a. Vert pair. Nos. 864/5 ..	90	90
865	60 c. multicoloured	45	45
866	75 c. multicoloured	50	50
	a. Vert pair. Nos. 866/7 ..	1·00	1·00
867	75 c. multicoloured	50	50
868	$1 multicoloured	65	65
	a. Vert pair. Nos. 868/9 ..	1·25	1·25
869	$1 multicoloured	65	65
870	$2.25, multicoloured	1·25	1·25
	a. Vert pair. Nos. 870/1 ..	2·50	2·50
871	$2.25, multicoloured	1·25	1·25
872	$3 multicoloured	1·60	1·60
	a. Vert pair. Nos. 872/3 ..	3·00	3·00
873	$3 multicoloured	1·60	1·60
858/73	*Set of 16*	9·00	9·00

Designs:—Nos. 858/9, Rack loco *Tip Top*, U.S.A (1983); 860/1, *Stephenson*, Great Britain (1975); 862/3, No. 737 Class "D", Great Britain (1901); 864/5, No. 13 Class "2-CO-2", Great Britain (1922); 866/7, *Electra*, Great Britain (1954); 868/9, *City of Newcastle*, Great Britain (1922); 870/1, Von Kruckenburg propeller-driven rail car, Germany (1930); 872/3, No. 860, Japan (1893).

Nos. 858/73 were issued in a similar sheet format to Nos. 651/66.

162 Campfire Cooking Utensils

(Des Court House Studio. Litho Format)

1986 (3 Mar). *75th Anniv of Girl Guide Movement and Boy Scouts of America. Two sheets, each* 85 × 113 *mm, containing vert designs as T* **162**. *Multicoloured. P* 12½.

MS874	$4 Type **162**: $4 Scout salute	3·00	3·50
MS875	$6 Wickerwork: $6 Lady Baden-Powell ..	4·00	5·00

The two stamps in each sheet were printed together, *se-tenant*, in horizontal pairs, each forming a composite design.

Nos. **MS**874/5 exist with plain or decorative margins.

Overprints on these miniature sheets commemorating "Capex '87" International Stamp Exhibition, Toronto, were not authorised by the St. Lucia administration.

(Des Court House Studio. Litho Format)

1986 (21 Apr). *60th Birthday of Queen Elizabeth II* (1st issue). *Multicoloured designs as T* **117**a *of Montserrat. P* 12½.

876	5 c. Queen Elizabeth II	10	10
877	$1 Princess Elizabeth	30	30
878	$3.50, Queen Elizabeth II (*different*)	75	1·10
879	$6 In Canberra, 1982 (*vert*)..	1·25	1·75
876/9	*Set of 4*	2·25	2·75
MS880	85 × 115 mm. $8 Queen Elizabeth II (*different*)	5·50	6·00

Nos. 876/9 exist in separate miniature sheets from stock dispersed by the liquidator of Format International Security Printers Ltd.

163 Queen Elizabeth and Marian Home

(Des Court House Studio. Litho Questa)

1986 (14 June). *60th Birthday of Queen Elizabeth II* (2nd issue). *T* **163** *and similar horiz designs. Multicoloured. W w* **15** (*sideways*). *P* 14 × 15.

881	10 c. Type **163**.	15	15
882	45 c. Queen addressing rally, Mindoo Phillip Park, 1985	35	35
883	50 c. Queen opening Leon Hess Comprehensive School, 1985	40	40
884	$5 Queen Elizabeth and Government House, Castries ..	2·50	2·75
881/4	*Set of 4*	3·00	3·25
MS885	121 × 85 mm. $7 Queen Elizabeth and Royal Yacht *Britannia*, Castries..	4·00	4·50

164 Pope John Paul II kissing Ground, Castries Airport

(Des Court House Studio. Litho Questa)

1986 (7 July). *Visit of Pope John Paul II. T* **164** *and similar multicoloured designs. W w* **15** *(sideways on* 55, 60 *c.). P* 14½×14 (80 *c.) or* 14×14½ *(others).*
886	55 c. Type **164**..				70	60
887	60 c. Pope and St. Joseph's Convent				70	60
888	80 c. Pope and Castries Catholic Cathedral *(vert)*				1·10	95
886/8 ..				*Set of 3*	2·25	2·00
MS889	85×123 mm. $6 Pope John Paul II *(vert)*. P 14½×14				5·00	5·50

(Litho Format)

1986 (12 Aug). *Royal Wedding* (1st issue). *Multicoloured designs as T* 118a *of Montserrat. P* 12½.
890	80 c. Miss Sarah Ferguson				45	50
	a. Pair. Nos. 890/1..				90	1·00
891	80 c. Prince Andrew ..				45	50
892	$2 Prince Andrew and Miss Sarah Ferguson *(horiz)*				1·25	1·40
	a. Pair. Nos. 892/3..				2·50	2·75
893	$2 Prince Andrew with Mrs Nancy Reagan *(horiz)*				1·25	1·40
890/3 ..				*Set of 4*	3·00	3·25

Nos. 890/1 and 892/3 were each printed together, *se-tenant*, in horizontal and vertical pairs throughout the sheets.

165 Peace Corps Teacher with Students

166 Prince Andrew in Carriage

(Des J. Cooter. Litho Questa)

1986 (25 Sept). *25th Anniv of United States Peace Corps. T* **165** *and similar multicoloured designs. W w* **15** *(sideways on* $2). *P* 14.
894	80 c. Type **165**..				35	40
895	$2 President John Kennedy *(vert)*				1·10	1·25
896	$3.50. Peace Corps emblem between arms of St. Lucia and U.S.A...				1·60	2·00
894/6 ..				*Set of 3*	2·75	3·25

(Des Court House Studio. Litho Format)

1986 (15 Oct). *Royal Wedding* (2nd issue). *T* **166** *and similar vert designs. Multicoloured. P* 15.
897	50 c. Type **166**..				30	30
898	80 c. Miss Sarah Ferguson in coach..				40	40
899	$1 Duke and Duchess of York at altar				45	50
900	$3 Duke and Duchess of York in carriage..				1·25	1·75
897/900 ..				*Set of 4*	2·25	2·75
MS901	115×85 mm. $7 Duke and Duchess of York on Palace balcony after wedding *(horiz)*				3·50	4·25

Examples of an unissued $10 miniature sheet exist from stock dispersed by the liquidator of Format International Security Printers Ltd.

(Des Court House Studio. Litho Format)

1986 (23 Oct). *Automobiles* (4th series). *Horiz designs as T* **149**, *the first in each pair showing technical drawings and the second paintings. P* 12½.
902	20 c. multicoloured ..				10	10
	a. Vert pair. Nos. 902/3				15	15
903	20 c. multicoloured ..				10	10
904	50 c. multicoloured ..				15	15
	a. Vert pair. Nos. 904/5				30	30
905	50 c. multicoloured ..				15	15
906	60 c. multicoloured ..				15	15
	a. Vert pair. Nos. 906/7				30	30
907	60 c. multicoloured ..				15	15
908	$1 multicoloured ..				15	15
	a. Vert pair. Nos. 908/9				30	30
909	$1 multicoloured ..				15	15
910	$1.50, multicoloured ..				20	20
	a. Vert pair. Nos. 910/11				40	40
911	$1.50, multicoloured ..				20	20
912	$3 multicoloured ..				45	45
	a. Vert pair. Nos. 912/13				90	90
913	$3 multicoloured ..				45	45
902/13 ..				*Set of 12*	2·10	2·10

Designs:—Nos. 902/3, AMC "AMX" (1969); 904/5, Russo-Baltique (1912); 906/7, Lincoln "K.B." (1932); 908/9, Rolls Royce "Phantom II Continental" (1933); 910/11, Buick "Century" (1939); 912/13, Chrysler "300 C" (1957).
Nos. 902/13 were issued in similar sheet format to Nos. 703/10.

167 Chak-Chak Band

(Des Jennifer Toombs. Litho Format)

1986 (7 Nov). *Tourism* (1st series). *T* **167** *and similar horiz designs. Multicoloured. W w* **15**. *P* 15.
914	15 c. Type **167**..				15	10
915	45 c. Folk dancing ..				35	30
916	80 c. Steel band				70	60
917	$5 Limbo dancing ..				2·75	3·00
914/17 ..				*Set of 4*	3·50	3·50
MS918	157×109 mm. $10 Fire-eating. Wmk sideways				6·00	7·00

See also Nos. 988/92.

168 St. Ann Catholic Church, Mon Repos

169 Outline Map of St. Lucia

(Litho Format)

1986 (3 Dec). *Christmas. T* **168** *and similar multicoloured designs. P* 15.
919	10 c. Type **168**..				10	10
920	40 c. St. Joseph the Worker Catholic Church, Gros Islet				35	25
921	80 c. Holy Trinity Anglican Church, Castries				60	45
922	$4 Our Lady of the Assumption Catholic Church, Soufriere *(vert)*				2·25	2·75
919/22 ..				*Set of 4*	3·00	3·25
MS923	120×101 mm $7 St. Lucy Catholic Church, Micoud				4·00	5·00

(Des L. Curtis. Litho Walsall)

1987 (24 Feb)–89. *W w* 14 *(sideways). P* 14. A. *No imprint at foot.* B. *With imprint date.*
			A		B	
924	**169**	5 c. black and cinnamon ..	15	15	20	20
925		10 c. black and pale emerald	15	15	20	20
926		45 c. black & bright orange	45	45	†	
927		50 c. black and violet-blue	45	45	50	50
927c		$1 black and bright rose	65	65	†	
924/7c	..		*Set of 5*	1·75	1·75	†

Dates of issue:—24.2.87, Nos. 924A/7A; 9.88, Nos. 924B/5B; 17.3.89, Nos. 927B, 927cA.
For 5 c. and 10 c. watermarked w **16** (sideways) see Nos. 1018/19.

(Des J. Cooter. Litho Format)

1987 (16 Mar). *As Nos.* 797/8, 801, 803/4, 809/10 *and new values* (15, 60, 80 *c. and* $20), *all without wmk. P* 15.
928	5 c. Type **156**..				20	20
929	10 c. Officer, Grenadier Company, 14th Regiment, 1780				25	25
930	15 c. Private, Battalion Company, 2nd West India Regiment, 1803				35	35
933	30 c. Officer, Royal Engineers, 1782				45	45
935	45 c. Private, Grenadier Company, 14th Regiment, 1782				50	50
936	50 c. Gunner, Royal Artillery, 1796..				60	60
937	60 c. Officer, Battalion Company, 5th Regiment, 1778				70	70
940	80 c. Officer, Battalion Company, 27th Regiment, c. 1780				90	90
943	$2.50, Private, Light Company, 93rd Regiment, 1803				3·00	3·25
944	$5 Private, Battalion Company, 1st West India Regiment, 1803				5·50	6·00
946	$20 Private, Grenadier Company, 46th Regiment, 1778..				17·00	21·00
928/46	..			*Set of 11*	26·00	30·00

For various values watermarked w **16** (sideways) see Nos. 993/1003.

170 Statue of Liberty and Flags of France and U.S.A.

171 First Cadastral Survey Map and Surveying Instruments, 1775

(Des A. Theobald. Litho Format)

1987 (29 Apr). *Centenary of Statue of Liberty* (1986). *T* **170** *and similar vert designs. Multicoloured. W w* **16**. *P* 14½.
947	15 c. Type **170**..				15	10
948	80 c. Statue and *Mauretania* (liner)..				75	55
949	$1 Statue and "Concorde"..				1·10	75
950	$5 Statue and flying boat at sunset				3·00	3·50
947/50	..			*Set of 4*	4·50	4·50
MS951	107×88 mm. $6 Statue and Manhattan at night. Wmk sideways				3·50	4·00

Unissued $3.50, $4 and $5 miniature sheets exist from stock dispersed by the liquidator of Format International Security Printers Ltd.

1987 (July). *Coil stamp. As No.* 350, *but W w* **16**. *P* 14½×14.
953	87	10 c. turquoise-green ..			30	30

(Des N. Shewring. Litho Walsall)

1987 (31 Aug). *New Cadastral Survey of St. Lucia. T* **171** *and similar vert designs. Multicoloured. W w* **16**. *P* 14.
955	15 c. Type **171**..				30	15
956	60 c. Map and surveying instruments, 1814				70	55
957	$1 Map and surveying instruments, 1888				90	90
958	$2.50, Cadastral survey map and surveying instruments, 1987 ..				2·25	2·50
955/8 ..				*Set of 4*	3·75	3·75

172 Ambulance and Nurse, 1987

173 "The Holy Family"

(Des C. Abbott. Litho Questa)

1987 (4 Nov). *Centenary of Victoria Hospital, Castries. T* **172** *and similar horiz designs. Multicoloured. W w* **16** *(sideways). P* 14×14½.
959	**172**	$1 multicoloured ..			1·00	1·00
		a. Pair. Nos. 959/60			2·00	2·00
960	–	$1 indigo ..			1·00	1·00
961	–	$2 multicoloured ..			1·50	1·50
		a. Pair. Nos. 961/2			3·00	3·00
962	–	$2 indigo ..			1·50	1·50
959/62				*Set of 4*	4·50	4·50
MS963		86×68 mm. $4.50, multicoloured			6·00	7·00

Designs:—No. 960, Nurse and carrying hammock, 1913; No. 961, $2 Victoria Hospital, 1987; No. 962, Victoria Hospital, 1887; No. MS963, Hospital gates, 1987.
Nos. 959/60 and 961/2 were each printed together, *se-tenant*, in horizontal and vertical pairs throughout the sheets.

(Des D. Miller. Litho Format)

1987 (30 Nov). *Christmas. T* **173** *and similar square designs showing paintings. Multicoloured. W w* **16** *(sideways). P* 14½.
964	15 c. Type **173**..				30	10
965	50 c. "Adoration of the Shepherds"..				60	30
966	70 c. "Adoration of the Magi"				70	55
967	90 c. "Madonna and Child"..				1·25	1·50
964/7 ..				*Set of 4*	2·50	2·25
MS968	82×67 mm. $6 Type **173**				3·50	4·00

174 St Lucia Amazon perched on Branch

175 Carib Clay Zemi

(Des W. Oliver. Litho Walsall)

1987 (18 Dec). *St. Lucia Amazon. T* **174** *and similar vert designs. Multicoloured. W w* **16**. *P* 14.
969	15 c. Type **174**..				45	20
970	35 c. Pair in flight ..				1·00	35
971	50 c. Perched on branch (rear view)..				1·40	1·00
972	$1 Emerging from tree ..				2·50	3·00
969/72 ..				*Set of 4*	4·75	4·00

(Des C. Collins. Litho Walsall)

1988 (24 Feb). *Amerindian Artifacts. T* **175** *and similar vert designs. Multicoloured. W w* **16**. *P* 14½×14.
973	25 c. Type **175**..				15	10
974	30 c. Troumassee cylinder ..				20	15
975	80 c. Three pointer stone ..				55	45
976	$3.50, Dauphine petroglyph ..				2·25	2·50
973/6 ..				*Set of 4*	2·75	2·75

176 East Caribbean Currency

177 Rural Telephone Exchange

(Des D. Miller (10 c.), S. Conlin (others). Litho B.D.T.)

1988 (29 Apr). *50th Anniv of St. Lucia Co-operative Bank. T* **176** *and similar horiz designs. Multicoloured. W w* 14 *(sideways). P* 15 × 14.
977	10 c. Type **176**				20	10
978	45 c. Castries branch				55	35
979	60 c. As 45 c.				45	45
980	80 c. Vieux Fort branch				1·25	1·50
977/80 ..				*Set of 4*	2·50	2·50

(Des A. Theobald. Litho Walsall)

1988 (10 June). *50th Anniv of Cable and Wireless (West Indies) Ltd. T* **177** *and similar horiz designs. Multicoloured.* W w **16** *(sideways). P* 14.

981	15 c. Type 177		10	10
982	25 c. Early and modern telephones		15	15
983	80 c. St. Lucia Teleport dish aerial		40	45
984	$2.50, Map showing Eastern Caribbean Microwave System		1·00	1·10
981/4		Set of 4	1·40	1·60

178 Stained Glass Window   **179** Garnished Lobsters

(Des O. Bell. Litho Format)

1988 (15 Aug). *Centenary of Methodist Church in St. Lucia. T* **178** *and similar diamond-shaped designs. Multicoloured.* W w **16** *(sideways). P* 14½.

985	15 c. Type 178		10	10
986	80 c. Church interior		40	45
987	$3.50, Methodist Church, Castries		1·50	1·60
985/7		Set of 3	1·75	1·90

(Des D. Miller. Litho Harrison)

1988 (15 Sept). *Tourism (2nd series). T* **179** *and similar vert designs showing local delicacies. Multicoloured.* W w **16**. *P* 14 × 13½.

988	10 c. Type 179		30	30
	a. Horiz strip of 4. Nos. 988/91		3·00	
989	30 c. Cocktail and tourists at buffet		45	45
990	80 c. Fresh fruits and roasted breadfruit		80	80
991	$2.50, Barbecued Red Snappers (fish)		1·75	1·75
988/91		Set of 4	3·00	3·00
MS992	88 × 104 mm. $5.50, Fruit stall, Castries market. P 14½ × 14		2·25	2·75

Nos. 988/91 were printed together, *se-tenant*, in horizontal strips of four throughout the sheet, forming a composite design of tourists at beach barbecue.

(Des J. Cooter. Litho Format)

1988 (Sept)–**89**. *As Nos.* 797/800, 930, 937, 940 *and* 946, *but* W w **16** *(sideways). P* 15.

993	5 c. Type 156 (6.89)		25	25
994	10 c. Officer, Grenadier Company, 14th Regiment, 1780 (6.89)		30	30
995	15 c. Private, Battalion Company, 2nd West India Regiment, 1803		40	40
996	20 c. Officer, Battalion Company, 46th Regiment, 1781 (6.89)		45	45
997	25 c. Officer, Royal Artillery, c. 1782		45	45
999	60 c. Officer, Battalion Company, 5th Regiment, 1778		80	80
1000	80 c. Officer, Battalion Company, 27th Regiment, c. 1780		1·00	1·00
1003	$20 Private, Grenadier Company, 46th Regiment, 1778 (6.89)		16·00	18·00
993/1003		Set of 8	18·00	19·00

The 15 c. and 25 c. exist with different imprint dates below the designs.

(Des D. Miller (10 c.), L. Curtis and D. Miller (60 c.), E. Nisbet and D. Miller (80 c.), S. Noon and D. Miller ($2.50). Litho Questa)

1988 (17 Oct). *300th Anniv of Lloyd's of London. Designs as T* **167***a of Malawi.* W w **14** *(sideways on 60, 80 c.) P* 14.

1004	10 c. black, grey-lilac and brown		30	10
1005	60 c. multicoloured		80	55
1006	80 c. multicoloured		1·10	90
1007	$2.50, multicoloured		2·50	3·00
1004/7		Set of 4	4·25	4·00

Designs: *Vert*—10 c. San Francisco earthquake, 1906; $2.50, Castries fire, 1948. *Horiz*—60 c. Castries Harbour; 80 c. *Lady Nelson* (liner) 1942.

180 Snow on the Mountain   **181** Princess Alexandra presenting Constitution

(Des R. Gorringe. Litho Format)

1988 (22 Nov). *Christmas. Flowers. T* **180** *and similar vert designs. Multicoloured.* W w **16**. *P* 14.

1008	15 c. Type 180		30	10
1009	45 c. Christmas Candle		55	40
1010	60 c. Balisier		70	70
1011	80 c. Poinsettia		1·00	1·25
1008/11		Set of 4	2·25	2·25
MS1012	79 × 75 mm. $5.50, Christmas flower arrangement. Wmk sideways		2·50	3·25

(Des S. Noon. Litho Walsall)

1989 (22 Feb). *10th Anniv of Independence. T* **181** *and similar vert designs. Multicoloured.* W w **14**. *P* 13½ × 13.

1013	15 c. Type 181		10	10
1014	80 c. Geothermal well		40	45
1015	$1 Sir Arthur Lewis Community College		45	50
1016	$2.50, Pointe Seraphine shopping centre		1·00	1·10
1013/16		Set of 4	1·75	1·90
MS1017	47 × 62 mm. $5 Man with national flag. W w 16.		2·25	2·50

1989 (12 Apr). *As Nos.* 924B/5B, *but* W w **16** *(sideways). With imprint date. P* 14.

1018	169	5 c. black and cinnamon	20	20
1019		10 c. black and pale emerald	30	30

182 *Gerronema citrinum*   **183** Local Revolutionary Declaration, 1789 and View of St. Lucia

(Des Josephine Martin. Litho Questa)

1989 (31 May). *Fungi. T* **182** *and similar vert designs. Multicoloured.* W w **16**. *P* 14½×14.

1022	15 c. Type 182		45	15
1023	25 c. *Lepiota spiculata*		60	15
1024	50 c. *Calocybe cyanocephala*		1·10	75
1025	$5 *Russula puiggarii*		5·00	5·50
1022/5		Set of 4	6·50	6·00

(Litho Questa)

1989 (14 July). *Bicentenary of the French Revolution. T* **183** *and similar multicoloured designs each including the "Philexfrance" International Stamp Exhibition logo.* W w **14** *(sideways on 60 c., $3.50). P* 14.

1026	10 c. Type 183		25	15
1027	60 c. Hoisting Revolutionary flag, Morne Fortune, 1791 (*horiz*)		1·00	70
1028	$1 Declaration of Rights of Man and view of St. Lucia		1·40	1·10
1029	$3.50, Arrival of Capt. La Crosse, Gros Islet, 1792 (*horiz*)		4·00	4·50
1026/9		Set of 4	6·00	5·75

184 Red Cross Headquarters, St. Lucia   **185** Christmas Lantern

(Des A. Theobald. Litho Questa)

1989 (10 Oct). *125th Anniv of International Red Cross. T* **184** *and similar horiz designs. Multicoloured.* W w **16** *(sideways). P* 14×14½.

1030	50 c. Type 184		1·00	1·00
1031	80 c. Red Cross seminar, Castries, 1987		1·50	1·50
1032	$1 Red Cross ambulance		1·75	1·75
1030/2		Set of 3	3·75	3·75

(Des Jennifer Toombs. Litho Questa)

1989 (17 Nov). *Christmas. T* **185** *and similar horiz designs showing decorative "building" lanterns.* W w **16** *(sideways). P* 14×14½.

1033	10 c. multicoloured		10	10
1034	50 c. multicoloured		35	35
1035	90 c. multicoloured		60	60
1036	$1 multicoloured		70	70
1033/6		Set of 4	1·60	1·60

MINIMUM PRICE

The minimum price quote is 10p which represents a handling charge rather than a basis for valuing common stamps. For further notes about prices see introductory pages.

186 Gwi Gwi   **187** Father Tapon and Original College Building

(Des R. Gorringe. Litho B.D.T.)

1990 (21 Feb–25 June). *Endangered Trees. T* **186** *and similar vert designs. Multicoloured.* W w **16**. *P* 14.

1037	10 c. Chinna (12 Apr)		20	15
1038	15 c. Latanier (12 Apr)		20	15
1039	20 c. Type 186		10	10
1040	25 c. L'Encens		10	15
1041	50 c. Bois Lélé		30	35
1042	80 c. Bois D'Amande (12 Apr)		35	40
1043	95 c. Mahot Piman Grand Bois (25 June)		40	45
1044	$1 Balata (25 June)		45	50
1045	$1.50, Pencil Cedar (12 Apr)		70	75
1046	$2.50, Bois Cendre (25 June)		1·10	1·25
1047	$5 Lowye Cannelle (25 June)		2·25	2·40
1048	$25 Chalantier Grand Bois		10·50	11·00
1037/48		Set of 12	15·00	16·00

(Des G. Vasarhelyi. Litho Questa)

1990 (6 June). *International Literacy Year. Centenary of St. Mary's College, Castries. T* **187** *and similar horiz designs. Multicoloured.* W w **14** *(sideways). P* 14.

1049	30 c. Type 187		15	15
1050	45 c. Brother M. C. Collins and St. Mary's College		25	25
1051	75 c. Literacy class		45	45
1052	$2 Children approaching "door to knowledge"		1·50	1·50
1049/52		Set of 4	2·10	2·10

(Des D. Miller. Litho Questa)

1990 (3 Aug). *90th Birthday of Queen Elizabeth the Queen Mother. Vert designs as T* **107** *(50 c.) or* **108** *($5) of Kenya.* W w **16**. *P* 14×15 (50 c.) *or* 14½ ($5).

1053	50 c. multicoloured		35	35
1054	$5 brownish black and deep violet-blue		2·75	3·00

Designs:—50 c. Crowning of Queen Consort, 1937; $5 Queen Elizabeth arriving at New Theatre, London, 1949.

(188)   **189** "Adoration of the Magi" (Rubens)

1990 (13 Aug). *"EXPO 90" International Garden and Greenery Exhibition, Osaka. No.* 1047 *optd with T* **188**.

1055	$5 Lowye Cannelle		2·75	3·00

(Des D. Miller. Litho Questa)

1990 (3 Dec). *Christmas. Religious Paintings. T* **189** *and similar vert designs. Multicoloured.* W w **16**. *P* 14.

1056	10 c. Type 189		15	10
1057	30 c. "Adoration of the Shepherds" (Murillo)		20	15
1058	80 c. "Adoration of the Magi" (Rubens) (*different*)		50	50
1059	$5 "Adoration of the Shepherds" (Philippe de Champaigne)		2·75	3·00
1056/9		Set of 4	3·25	3·25

190 *Vistafjord* (liner)   **191** *Battus polydamas*

(Des E. Nisbet. Litho Walsall)

1991 (27 Mar). *Cruise Ships. T* **190** *and similar horiz designs. Multicoloured.* W w **14** *(sideways). P* 14½.

1060	50 c. Type 190		45	30
1061	70 c. *Windstar* (schooner)		70	60
1062	$1 *Unicorn* (brig)		90	80
1063	$2.50, Game-fishing launch		2·50	2·75
1060/3		Set of 4	4·00	4·00
MS1064	82×65 mm. $5 Ships in Castries Harbour		3·25	3·50

(Des I. Loe. Litho Walsall)

1991 (15 Aug). *Butterflies. T* **191** *and similar vert designs. Multicoloured. W w* **16.** *P* 14.

1065	60 c. Type **191**	..	70	55
1066	80 c. *Strymon simaethis*	..	95	75
1067	$1 *Mestra cana* ..	..	1·25	1·00
1068	$2.50, *Allosmaitia piplea*	..	2·50	2·75
1065/8	..	Set of 4	4·75	4·50

192 Mural, Jacmel Church   193 Yacht and Map

(Des D. Miller. Litho Questa)

1991 (20 Nov). *Christmas. Paintings by Duncan St. Omer. T* **192** *and similar multicoloured designs. W w* **16** *(sideways on* 10, 80 c.). *P* 14½.

1069	10 c. Type **192**	..	15	10
1070	15 c. "Red Madonna" (*vert*)	..	15	10
1071	80 c. Mural, Monchy Church	..	50	45
1072	$5 "Blue Madonna" (*vert*)	..	2·50	2·75
1069/72	..	Set of 4	3·00	3·00

(Des P. Devarreaux. Litho Questa)

1991 (10 Dec). *Atlantic Rally for Cruising Yachts. T* **193** *and similar horiz design. Multicoloured. W w* **16** *(sideways). P* 14.

1073	60 c. Type **193**	..	50	50
1074	80 c. Yachts off St. Lucia ..	..	75	75

(Adapted G. Vasarhelyi. Litho Cartor)

1992 (6 July). *Organization of East Caribbean States. 500th Anniv of Discovery of America by Columbus. Vert designs as T* **66** *of St. Kitts. Multicoloured. W w* **14.** *P* 13.

1075	$1 Columbus meeting Amerindians	..	75	60
1076	$2 Ships approaching island	..	1·25	1·40

194 Amerindian Village   195 "Virgin and Child" (Delaroche)

(Des D. Miller. Litho Cartor)

1992 (7 Aug). *Discovery of St. Lucia. T* **194** *and similar horiz designs. Multicoloured. W w* **14** *(sideways). P* 13½.

1077	15 c. Type **194** ..	..	20	20
1078	40 c. Ships of Juan de la Cosa and islands, 1499	..	25	20
1079	50 c. Columbus sailing between Martinique and St. Lucia, 1502	..	30	30
1080	$5 Legendary shipwreck of Gimie	..	2·75	3·00
1077/80	..	Set of 4	3·25	3·25

1992 (Aug–11 Dec). *As Nos.* 1037/8 *and* 1041, *but W w* **14.** *P* 14.

1081	10 c. Chinna (11.12.92) ..	..	10	10
1082	15 c. Latanier (11.12.92) ..	..	10	10
1085	50 c. Bois Lélé ..	..	20	25
1081/5	..	Set of 3	35	40

No. 1081 exists with different imprint dates below the design.

(Des D. Miller. Litho Walsall)

1992 (9 Nov). *Christmas. Religious Paintings. T* **195** *and similar vert designs. Multicoloured. W w* **14.** *P* 14½.

1092	10 c. Type **195** ..	..	10	10
1093	15 c. "The Holy Family" (Rubens)	..	15	10
1094	60 c. "Virgin and Child" (Luini) ..	..	45	45
1095	80 c. "Virgin and Child" (Sassoferrato)	..	55	55
1092/5	..	Set of 4	1·10	1·10

196 "Death" and Gravestone

(Adapted D. Miller. Litho Cartor)

1993 (1 Feb). *Anti-drugs Campaign. W w* **14.** *P* 13½.

1096	**196** $5 multicoloured	..	2·25	2·40

POSTAGE DUE STAMPS

No. 4545
ST. LUCIA.
1d.
POSTAGE DUE

D 1

No. No.

Normal	Wide fount

(Type-set Government Printing Office)

1930. *Each stamp individually handstamped with different number. No wmk. No gum. Rough perf 12. (a) Horizontally laid paper.*

D1	D 1	1d. black/*blue*		2·25	8·00
		a. Wide, wrong fount "No."		8·00	21·00
		b. Missing stop after "ST"		32·00	55·00
		c. Missing stop after "LUCIA"		32·00	55·00
		d. Handstamped number double		£150	

(b) Wove paper

D2	D 1	2d. black/*yellow*		6·00	26·00
		a. Wide, wrong fount "No."		17·00	55·00
		b. Imperf between (vert pair)		£3500	
		c. Missing stop after "ST"		70·00	£110
		d. Incorrect number with correction above		£250	

It is believed that there were three settings of the 1d. and two of the 2d., the same type being used for both values.

For the initial setting of the 1d. the wide "No." variety occurs on the last four stamps in the bottom row of the sheet of 60 (6 × 10). In later settings first the second and then later the first stamps in the same row were changed to show the variety. Nos. D1b and D2c occur on R.5/3 and No. D1c on R.9/2.

Some sheets from the initial printing of the 1d. show a papermaker's watermark, "KINGSCLERE" in double-lined capitals above a crown, across a number of stamps.

The sheets had all outer edges, except that at the left, imperforate. It would appear that they were bound into books from which they could be detached, using the perforations at the left-hand edge.

The handstamped numbers were applied at the Post Office, using numbering machines. Each value had its own sequence of numbers and it is possible to recognise, by minor differences in fount, the use of two such machines. This is especially noticeable on examples of Nos. D1d and D2d where the corrections are often applied using a second machine. No. D2d shows the incorrect number partly erased and a correction struck across it.

D 2	D 3	D 4 St. Lucia Coat of Arms

(Typo D.L.R.)

1933–47. *Wmk Mult Script CA. P 14.*

D3	D 2	1d. black		4·00	4·25
D4		2d. black		10·00	6·50
D5		4d. black (28.6.47)		3·75	22·00
D6		8d. black (28.6.47)		3·75	27·00
D3/6			Set of 4	19·00	55·00
D3/6 Perf "Specimen"			Set of 4	£130	

1949 (1 Oct)**–52.** *Value in cents. Wmk Mult Script CA. Typo. P 14.*

D 7	D 3	2 c. black		1·75	15·00
		a. Chalk-surfaced paper (27.11.52)		10	4·00
		ab. Error. Crown missing, W 9*a*		65·00	
		ac. Error. St. Edward's Crown, W 9*b*		25·00	
D 8		4 c. black		3·25	12·00
		a. Chalk-surfaced paper (27.11.52)		30	5·50
		ab. Error. Crown missing, W 9*a*		80·00	
		ac. Error. St. Edward's Crown, W 9*b*		32·00	

D 9	D 3	8 c. black		2·75	15·00
		a. Chalk-surfaced paper (27.11.52)		1·40	17·00
		ac. Error. St. Edward's Crown, W 9*b*		£140	
D10		16 c. black		12·00	38·00
		a. Chalk-surfaced paper (27.11.52)		2·25	23·00
		ac. Error. St. Edward's Crown, W 9*b*		£170	
D7/10			Set of 4	18·00	70·00
D7a/10a			Set of 4	3·50	45·00

1965 (9 Mar)**.** *As Nos. D7/8, but wmk w 12. Ordinary paper. P 14.*

D11	D 3	2 c. black		35	6·50
D12		4 c. black		45	6·50

Nos D9a, D10a and D11/12 exist with a similar overprint to Type 49 in red (*Price for set of 4 £150 mint*).

(Des L. Curtis. Litho Format)

1981 (4 Aug)**.** *W w 14. P 14.*

D13	D 4	5 c. brown-purple		10	15
D14		15 c. emerald		15	20
D15		25 c. red-orange		15	20
D16		$1 deep ultramarine		50	65
D13/16			Set of 4	80	1·10

(Des L. Curtis. Litho Questa)

1991 (14 Feb)**.** *W w 16. P 15×14.*

D17	D 4	5 c. deep carmine		10	10
D18		15 c. emerald		10	10
D19		25 c. red-orange		10	15
D20		$1 ultramarine		45	50
D17/20			Set of 4	70	75

OFFICIAL STAMPS

OFFICIAL OFFICIAL

(O 1)	(O 2)

1983 (13 Oct)**.** *Nos. 537/48 optd with Type O 1.*

O 1	5 c. Type **120**		15	10
O 2	10 c. McDonnell Douglas "DC-10" airliner		15	10
O 3	15 c. Local bus		20	15
O 4	20 c. Refrigerated freighter		30	20
O 5	25 c. "Islander" aeroplane		35	20
O 6	30 c. Pilot boat		40	25
O 7	50 c. Boeing "727" airliner		55	35
O 8	75 c. *Cunard Countess* (liner)		75	50
O 9	$1 Lockheed "Tristar" airliner		95	75
O10	$2 Cargo liner		1·75	1·75
O11	$5 Boeing "707" airliner		3·50	3·50
O12	$10 *Queen Elizabeth 2* (liner)		6·50	7·50
O1/12		Set of 12	14·00	14·00

1985 (7 May)**.** *Nos. 797/811 optd with Type O 2.*

O13	5 c. Type **156**		20	20
O14	10 c. Officer, Grenadier Company, 14th Regiment, 1780.		20	20
O15	20 c. Officer, Battalion Company, 46th Regiment, 1781		20	20
O16	25 c. Officer, Royal Artillery, *c* 1782		20	20
O17	30 c. Officer, Royal Engineers, 1782		30	30
O18	35 c. Officer, Battalion Company, 54th Regiment, 1782		30	30
O19	45 c. Private, Grenadier Company, 14th Regiment, 1782.		40	40
O20	50 c. Gunner, Royal Artillery, 1796		40	40
O21	65 c. Private, Battalion Company, 85th Regiment, *c* 1796		50	50
O22	75 c. Private, Battalion Company, 76th Regiment, 1796.		60	60
O23	90 c. Private, Battalion Company, 81st Regiment, *c* 1796		65	65
O24	$1 Sergeant, 74th (Highland) Regiment, 1796		70	70
O25	$2.50, Private, Light Company, 93rd Regiment, 1803		1·75	1·75
O26	$5 Private, Battalion Company, 1st West India Regiment, 1803		3·50	4·00
O27	$15 Officer, Royal Artillery, 1850		8·00	9·00
O13/27		Set of 15	16·00	17·00

POSTAL FISCAL STAMPS

Nos. F1/28 were authorised for postal use from 14 April 1885.

CANCELLATIONS. Many used examples of the Postal Fiscal stamps have had previous pen cancellations removed before being used postally.

SHILLING STAMP	One Penny Stamp	HALFPENNY Stamp
(F 1)	(F 2)	(F 3)

1881. *Wmk Crown CC. P 14. (a) Surch as Type* F 1.

F1	1	ONE PENNY STAMP, black (C.)		30·00	38·00
		a. Surch inverted		£700	£700
		b. Surch double		£650	£700
F2		FOUR PENNY STAMP, yellow		50·00	60·00
		a. Bisected (2d.) (on cover)			
F3		SIX PENCE STAMP, mauve		90·00	£100
F4		SHILLING STAMP, orange		50·00	60·00
		a. "SHILEING"		£650	
		b. "SHILDING"		£650	£600

(b) Surch as Type F 2

F 7	1	One Penny Stamp, black (R.)		30·00	38·00
		a. Surch double		£700	
F 8		Four Pence Stamp, yellow		50·00	50·00
F 9		Six Pence Stamp, mauve		50·00	50·00
F10		Shilling Stamp, orange		55·00	70·00

(c) Surch as Type F 3

F11	1	Halfpenny Stamp, green		30·00	38·00
		a. "Stamp" double		£450	£450
F12		One Shilling Stamp, orange (*wmk Crown CA*)		55·00	55·00
		a. "Stamp" double		£450	£500

FOUR PENCE REVENUE	Revenue	REVENUE
(F 4)	(F 5)	(F 6)

1882. *Wmk Crown CA. Surch as Type* F 4. (*a*) *P* 14.

F13	1	1d. black (C.)		22·00	22·00
		a. Imperf. (pair)		£1100	
F14		2d. pale blue		12·00	9·50
		a. Imperf (pair)			
F15		3d. deep blue (C.)		42·00	38·00
F16		4d. yellow		14·00	4·00
F17		6d. mauve		26·00	23·00

(*b*) *P* 12

F18	1	1d. black (C.)		22·00	22·00
F19		3d. deep blue (C.)		32·00	20·00
F20		1s. orange		32·00	13·00

1883. *Nos. 25, 26, 30 and 32 optd locally as Type* F 5.

(a) Word 11 mm long

F21	1d. black (C.)		22·00	32·00
	a. Opt inverted			
	b. Opt double		£250	£350

(b) Word 13 mm

F22	1d. black (C.)		—	50·00

(c) Word 15½ mm

F23	½d. green		—	42·00
	a. "Revenue" double		—	£225
F24	1d. black (C.)		18·00	10·00
	a. "Revenue" double		£130	
	b. "Revenue" triple		£250	
	c. "Revenue" double, one inverted		£250	£300
F25	1d. rose (No. 30)		—	45·00
F26	4d. yellow		—	55·00

1884–85. *Optd with Type* F 6. *Wmk Crown CA. P* 14.

F27	5	1d. slate (C.)		13·00	11·00
		a. Imperf (pair)			
F28		1d. dull mauve (Die I) (1885)		13·00	7·50

St. Vincent

Although postal markings for St. Vincent are recorded as early as 1793 it was not until 1852 that the British G.P.O. opened a branch office at Kingstown, the island's capital.

The stamps of Great Britain were used between May 1858 and the end of April 1860. From 1 May in that year the local authorities assumed responsibility for the postal services and fell back on the use of No. CC1 until the introduction of St. Vincent stamps in 1861.

KINGSTOWN

CROWNED-CIRCLE HANDSTAMPS

CC 1

CC1 CC 1 ST. VINCENT (R.) (30.1.1852) *Price on cover* £750

Stamps of GREAT BRITAIN *cancelled* "A 10" *as Type Z* **1** *of Jamaica.*

1858 *to* **1860.**
Z1	1d. rose-red (1857), *perf* 14	..	..		£550
Z2	2d. blue (1855)	..	..	..	
Z3	4d. rose (1857)	..	..	..	£350
Z4	6d. lilac (1856)	..	..	..	£250
Z5	1s. green (1856)	..	..	..	£950

PRICES FOR STAMPS ON COVER TO 1945
Nos. 1/2	*from* × 5
Nos. 3/7	*from* × 8
No. 8	—
No. 9	*from* × 8
No. 10	—
Nos. 11/19	*from* × 8
Nos. 20/1	*from* × 5
Nos. 22/5	*from* × 8
Nos. 26/8	—
Nos. 29/31	*from* × 9
No. 32	—
Nos. 33/4	*from* × 8
No. 35	—
Nos. 36/8	*from* × 6
Nos. 39/41	*from* × 12
Nos. 42/5	*from* × 5
No. 46	*from* × 15
Nos. 47/54	*from* × 4
Nos. 55/8	*from* × 8
No. 59	*from* × 10
No. 60	*from* × 6
Nos. 61/3	*from* × 8
Nos. 67/75	*from* × 3
Nos. 76/84	*from* × 2
Nos. 85/92	*from* × 3
No. 93	—
Nos. 94/8	*from* × 3
Nos. 99/107	*from* × 2
Nos. 108/19	*from* × 3
No. 120	—
No. 121	*from* × 3
No. 122	*from* × 5
No. 123	—
No. 124	*from* × 5
Nos. 126/9	*from* × 10
Nos. 131/45	*from* × 3
Nos. 146/8	*from* × 6
Nos. 149/59	*from* × 2

CROWN COLONY

1	(2)	3

(T **1, 3** and **7** recess P.B.)

1861 (8 May). *No wmk.* (a) *Intermediate perf* 14 *to* 16.
1	1	1d. rose-red	..	£7000	£450
		a. Imperf vert (horiz pair)	..		£450
2		6d. deep yellow-green ..	..	£5500	£200

(b) *Rough perf* 14 *to* 16.
3	1	1d. rose-red	..	35·00	14·00
		a. Imperf vert (horiz pair)	..		£350
		b. Imperf (pair)	..		£250

1862 (Sept). *No wmk. Rough perf* 14 *to* 16.
4	1	6d. deep green	..	50·00	18·00
		a. Imperf between (horiz pair)	..		£1400
		b. Imperf (pair)	..		£450

1863–68. *No wmk.* (a) *P* 11 *to* 12½.
5	1	1d. rose-red (3.63)	..	32·00	15·00
6		4d. deep blue (*shades*) (1866)	..	£275	£110
		a. Imperf between (horiz pair)			
7		6d. deep green (7.68)	..	£200	60·00
8		1s. slate-grey (8.66)	..	£1800	£900

(b) *P* 14 *to* 16
9	1	1s. slate-grey (*shades*)	..	£300	£130

(c) *P* 11 *to* 12½ × 14 *to* 16
10	1	1d. rose-red	..	£2750	£1300
11		1s. slate-grey (*shades*)	..	£225	£120

1869. *Colours changed. No wmk. P* 11 *to* 12½.
12	1	4d. yellow	..	£350	£150
13		1s. indigo	..	£325	90·00
14		1s. brown	..	£425	£160

1871 (Apr). *Wmk Small Star, Type* w **2.** *Rough perf* 14 *to* 16.
15	1	1d. black ..	..	42·00	10·00
		a. Imperf between (vert pair)	..		£4750
16		6d. deep green	..	£250	70·00

1872. *Colour changed. W* w **2.** *P* 11 *to* 12½.
17	1	1s. deep rose-red..	..	£750	£140

1872–75. *W* w **2.** (a) *Perf about* 15.
18	1	1d. black (*shades*) (1872)	..	40·00	7·50
19		6d. dull blue-green (*shades*) (1873)		£600	30·00
		a. Deep blue-green (1875)	..	£600	38·00

(b) *P* 11 *to* 12½ × 15
20	1	1s. lilac-rose (1873)	..	£5000	£400

No. 19a always has the watermark sideways and Nos. 16 and 19 normally have it upright but are known with it sideways.

1875. *Colour changed. W* w **2.** *P* 11 *to* 12½.
21	1	1s. claret..	..	£600	£250

1876–78. *W* w **2.** (a) *P* 11 *to* 12½ × 15.
22	1	1d. black (*shades*) (1876)	..	60·00	7·00
		a. Imperf between (horiz pair)	..	—	£3750
23		6d. pale green (1877)	..	£500	45·00
24		1s. vermilion (2.77)	..	£750	85·00
		a. Imperf vert (horiz pair)			

(b) *P* 11 *to* 12½
25	1	4d. deep blue (7.77)	..	£450	90·00

(c) *Perf about* 15
26	1	6d. pale green (3.77)	..	£1500	£450
		a. Light yellow-green (1878)	..	£550	25·00
27		1s. vermilion (1878?)	..	—	£6500
		a. Imperf	..	—	£3000

Nos. 23 and 26 always have the watermark sideways but No. 26a always has the watermark upright.

1880 (May). *No. 19a divided vertically by a line of perforation gauging* 12, *and surch locally as T* **2.**
28	1	1d. on half 6d. bright blue-green (R.)	£375	£250
		a. Unsevered pair	..	£1300	£950

1880 (June). *W* w **2.** *P* 11 *to* 12½.
29	1	1d. olive-green	..	85·00	3·25
30		6d. bright green ..	..	£300	60·00
31		1s. bright vermilion	..	£650	50·00
		a. Imperf between (horiz pair)	..		£4500
32	3	5s. rose-red	..	£1000	£1200
		a. Imperf	..		£3250

d 1/2	d 1/2	ONE PENNY
(4)	Straight serif to "1" (R. 6/20)	(5)

4d

(6)

1881. *Nos.* 30/31 *surch locally. No.* 33 *is divided vertically like No.* 28.
33	4	½d. on half 6d. bright green (R.) (1.9)	£160	£160
		a. Unsevered pair	..	£400	£400
		b. Fraction bar omitted (pair with and without bar)	£3500	£4000
		c. Straight serif to "1"			
34	5	1d. on 6d. bright green (30.11)	£400	£275
35	6	4d. on 1s. bright vermilion (28.11)	£1300	£700

It is believed that Type 4 was applied as a setting of 36 (6 × 6) surcharges repeated three times on each sheet across rows 1 to 9. The missing fraction bar occurs on R. 6/3 of the setting.

The tenth vertical row of stamps appears to have been surcharged from a separate setting of 12 (2 × 6) on which the "straight serif" flaw occurs on the bottom right half-stamp.

Three unused single copies of No. 33 are known with the surcharge omitted.

It is believed that Nos. 34 and 35 were surcharged in settings of 30 (10×3).

No. 34 was only on sale between the 30 November and 3 December when supplies of No. 37 became available.

7	(8)	(9)

2½ PENCE ~~2½ PENCE~~

1881 (Dec). *W* w **2.** *P* 11 *to* 12½.
36	7	½d. orange (*shades*)	..	7·00	2·50
37	1	1d. drab (*shades*)	..	£700	5·00
38		4d. bright blue	..	£1200	£100
		a. Imperf between (horiz pair)..			

(Recess D.L.R. from Perkins, Bacon plates)

1882 (Nov)**–83.** *No.* 40 *is surch with T* **8.** *Wmk Crown CA. P* 14.
39	1	1d. drab	..	35·00	1·25
40		2½d. on 1d. lake (1883)..	..	7·50	40
41		4d. ultramarine	..	£325	28·00
		a. Dull ultramarine ..	..	£950	£350

1883–84. *Wmk Crown CA. P* 12.
42	7	½d. green (1884) ..	..	60·00	25·00
43	1	4d. ultramarine-blue	..	£275	18·00
		a. Grey-blue	..	£1000	£300
44		6d. bright green	..	£400	£325
45		1s. orange-vermilion	..	80·00	48·00

The ½d. orange, 1d. rose-red, 1d. milky blue (without surcharge) and 5s. carmine-lake which were formerly listed are now considered to be colour trials. They are, however, of great interest. (*Prices un.* ½d. £900, 1d. red £900, 1d. blue £1200, 5s. £1500.)

1885 (Mar). *No.* 40 *surch locally as in T* **9.**
46	1	1d. on 2½d. on 1d. lake ..	..	12·00	12·00

Stamps with three cancelling bars instead of two are considered to be proofs.

1885–93. *No.* 49 *is surch with T* **8.** *Wmk Crown CA. P* 14.
47	7	½d. green	..	..	60	20
		a. Deep green	..	..	2·50	50
48	1	1d. rose-red	..	..	2·00	80
		a. Rose (1886)	..	..	4·25	1·50
		b. Red (1887)	..	..	1·60	50
		c. Carmine-red (1889)	..	23·00	3·00
49		2½d. on 1d. milky blue (1889)	..	23·00	4·00
50		4d. red-brown	..	..	£850	22·00
51		4d. purple-brown (1886)	..	38·00	75
		a. Chocolate (1887)	..	38·00	1·25
52		6d. violet (1888)	..	90·00	£110
53	3	5s. lake (1888)	..	27·00	50·00
		a. Printed both sides ..	..	£3500	
		b. Brown-lake (1893) ..	..	29·00	50·00
49, 51, 52 Optd "Specimen"	Set of 3	£160	

2½d. | **5 PENCE**

(10)	(11)

1890 (Aug). *No.* 51a *surch with T* **10.**
54	1	2½d. on 4d. chocolate	..	48·00	70·00
		a. No fraction bar (R. 1/7, 2/4)	£225	£250

1890–93. *No.* 55 *is surch with T* **8.** *Colours changed. Wmk Crown CA. P* 14.
55	1	2½d. on 1d. grey-blue (1890)	..	14·00	55
		a. Blue (1893)..	..	1·00	35
56		4d. yellow (1893) (Optd S. £30)	1·60	4·75
57		6d. dull purple (1891)	..	2·00	5·50
58		1s. orange (1891)	..	5·50	9·00
		a. Red-orange (1892) ..	..	9·50	9·50

1892 (Nov). *No.* 51a *surch with T* **11,** *in purple.*
59	1	5d. on 4d. chocolate (Optd S. £30)	9·00	20·00

Some letters are known double due to loose type, the best known being the first "E", but they are not constant.

FIVE PENCE

(12)	13	14

1893–94. *Surch with T* **12.** *Wmk Crown CA. P* 14.
60	1	5d. on 6d. carmine-lake (Optd S. £45) ..	13·00	25·00
		a. Deep lake (1893)	..	80	1·75
		b. Lake (1894)	..	1·75	4·25
		c. Surch double..	..	£4000	£2750

(Recess D.L.R.)

1897 (13 July). *New values. Wmk Crown CA. P* 14.
61	1	2½d. blue	..	2·50	2·25
62		5d. sepia	..	5·50	17·00
61/2 Optd "Specimen"	Set of 2	60·00	

1897 (6 Oct). *Surch as T* **12.** *Wmk Crown CA. P* 14.
63	1	3d. on 1d. mauve (Optd S. £40) ..	6·00	15·00
		a. Red-mauve	..	9·50	23·00

(Typo D.L.R.)

1899 (1 Jan). *Wmk Crown CA. P* 14.
67	13	½d. dull mauve and green	..	..	1·25	85
68		1d. dull mauve and carmine		..	3·25	45
69		2½d. dull mauve and blue		..	4·00	2·00
70		3d. dull mauve and olive		..	4·00	8·50
71		4d. dull mauve and orange		..	4·00	13·00
72		5d. dull mauve and black		..	7·00	13·00
73		6d. dull mauve and brown		..	13·00	27·00
74	14	1s. green and carmine		..	13·00	40·00
75		5s. green and blue		..	70·00	£120
67/75		..	..	*Set of 9*	£110	£200
67/75 Optd "Specimen"			..	*Set of 9*	£170	

15   16

(Typo D.L.R.)

1902. *Wmk Crown CA. P* 14.
76	15	½d. dull purple and green		..	1·00	60
77		1d. dull purple and carmine		..	1·50	20
78	16	2d. dull purple and black		..	1·75	2·25
79	15	2½d. dull purple and blue		..	2·25	3·25
80		3d. dull purple and olive		..	2·00	2·00
81		6d. dull purple and brown		..	9·00	24·00
82	16	1s. green and carmine	..	..	13·00	42·00
83	15	2s. green and violet		..	22·00	48·00
84	16	5s. green and blue		..	48·00	90·00
76/84		..	..	*Set of 9*	90·00	£180
76/84 Optd "Specimen"			..	*Set of 9*	£120	

1904–11. *Wmk Mult Crown CA. Ordinary paper* (½d., 1d., 1s.) *or chalk-surfaced paper* (*others*). *P* 14.
85	15	½d. dull purple and green (1905)			2·25	90
		a. Chalk-surfaced paper		..	1·00	80
86		1d. dull purple and carmine		..	9·00	55
		a. Chalk-surfaced paper		..	9·00	65
88		2½d. dull purple and blue (1906)			10·00	25·00
89		6d. dull purple and brown (1905)			11·00	25·00
90	16	1s. green and carmine (1906)		..	13·00	29·00
		a. Chalk-surfaced paper		..	9·00	29·00
91	15	2s. purple and bright blue/*blue* (3.09?)			22·00	42·00
92	16	5s. green and red/*yellow* (3.09?)			17·00	45·00
93		£1 purple and black/*red* (22.7.11)			£250	£300
85/93		..	..	*Set of 8*	£300	£425
91/3 Optd "Specimen"			..	*Set of 3*	£180	

17   18

(Recess D.L.R.)

1907–08. *Wmk Mult Crown CA. P* 14.
94	17	½d. green (2.7.07)		..	1·25	90
95		1d. carmine (26.4.07)		..	2·50	15
96		2d. orange (5.08)		..	1·00	5·50
97		2½d. blue (8.07)		..	12·00	8·50
98		3d. violet (1.6.07)		..	4·25	14·00
94/8		..	..	*Set of 5*	19·00	26·00
94/8 Optd "Specimen"			..	*Set of 5*	£100	

1909. *No dot below* "d". *Wmk Mult Crown CA. P* 14.
99	18	1d. carmine (3.09)		..	1·25	25
100		6d. dull purple (16.1.09)		..	5·50	24·00
101		1s. black/*green* (16.1.09)		..	3·75	7·00
99/101		..	..	*Set of 3*	9·50	28·00
99/101 Optd "Specimen"			..	*Set of 3*	60·00	

1909 (Nov)–**11.** *T* 18, *redrawn* (*dot below* "d", *as in T* 17). *Wmk Mult Crown CA. P* 14.
102		½d. green (31.10.10)	..		1·50	40
103		1d. carmine	..	..	1·50	15
104		2d. grey (3.8.11)		..	2·00	8·00
105		2½d. ultramarine (25.7.10)		..	6·00	2·00
106		3d. purple/*yellow*		..	2·25	3·25
107		6d. dull purple		..	2·25	5·00
102/7		..	..	*Set of 6*	14·00	17·00
102 and 104/6 Optd "Specimen"			*Set of 4*	80·00	

ONE

PENNY.

19   (20)

(Recess D.L.R.)

1913 (1 Jan)–**17.** *Wmk Mult Crown CA. P* 14.
108	19	½d. green		..	35	20
109		1d. red	..	..	60	25
		a. Rose-red		..	80	45
		b. Scarlet (1.17)		..	8·00	3·25
110		2d. grey		..	5·50	20·00
		a. Slate		..	2·50	20·00
111		2½d. ultramarine		..	35	40
112		3d. purple/*yellow*		..	80	5·00
		a. On lemon		..	2·50	12·00
		b. On pale yellow		..	1·90	8·50
113		4d. red/*yellow*		..	80	2·00
114		5d. olive-green (7.11.13)			2·25	12·00

115	19	6d. claret		..	2·00	4·50
116		1s. black/*green*			1·50	3·25
117		1s. bistre (1.5.14)			3·50	13·00
118	18	2s. blue and purple			4·75	17·00
119		5s. carmine and myrtle	..		13·00	40·00
120		£1 mauve and black		..	70·00	£140
108/20		..	..	*Set of 13*	90·00	£225
108/20 Optd "Specimen"		..	*Set of 13*	£250	

Nos. 118/20 are from new centre and frame dies, the motto "PAX ET JUSTITIA" being slightly over 7 mm long, as against just over 8 mm in Nos. 99 to 107. Nos. 139/41 are also from the new dies.

1915. *Surch with T* 20.
121	19	1d. on 1s. black/*green* (R.)		..	4·00	17·00
		a. "ONE" omitted		..	£850	£750
		b. "ONE" double		..	£650	
		c. "PENNY" and bar double		..	£650	

The spacing between the two words varies from 7¾ mm to 10 mm.

WAR   WAR
STAMP.   STAMP.   WAR STAMP
(21)   (22)   (24)

1916 (June). *No. 109 optd locally with T* 21. (*a*) *First and second settings; words* 2 *to* 2½ *mm apart.*
122	19	1d. red		..	1·50	2·75
		a. Opt double		..	£140	£140
		b. Comma for stop		..	7·00	11·00

In the first printing every second stamp has the comma for stop. The second printing of this setting has full stops only. These two printings can therefore only be distinguished in blocks or pairs.

(*b*) *Third setting; words only* 1½ *mm apart*
123	19	1d. red		..	60·00	
		a. Opt double		..	£1100	

Stamps of the first setting are offered as this rare one. Care must be taken to see that the distance between the lines is not over 1½ mm.

(*c*) *Fourth setting; optd with T* 22. *Words* 3½ *mm apart*
124	19	1d. carmine-red		..	1·50	5·00
		a. Opt double		..	£200	

1916 (Aug)–**18.** *T* 19, *new printing, optd with T* 24.
126		1d. carmine-red (Optd S. £60)			30	50
127		1d. pale rose-red		..	30	50
128		1d. deep rose-red		..	20	50
129		1d. pale scarlet (1918)			15	50

1921–32. *Wmk Mult Script CA. P* 14.
131	19	½d. green (3.21)		..	40	20
132		1d. carmine (6.21)		..	40	50
		a. Red		..	40	15
132b		1½d. brown (1.12.32)			60	15
133		2d. grey (3.22)		..	55	30
133a		2½d. bright blue (12.25)			60	30
134		3d. bright blue (3.22)		..	90	6·00
135		3d. purple/*yellow* (1.12.26)			45	1·50
135a		4d. red/*yellow* (9.30)			1·75	6·00
136		5d. sage-green (8.3.24)			70	5·50
137		6d. claret (1.11.27)			80	3·50
138		1s. bistre-brown (9.21)			3·00	11·00
		a. Ochre (1927)		..	1·50	10·00
139	18	2s. blue and purple (8.3.24)			4·00	13·00
140		5s. carmine and myrtle (8.3.24)			10·00	30·00
141		£1 mauve and black (9.28)			70·00	£110
131/41		..	..	*Set of 14*	80·00	£160
131/41 Optd/Perf "Specimen"		..	*Set of 14*	£250	

1935 (6 May). *Silver Jubilee. As Nos.* 114/17 *of Jamaica, but ptd by Waterlow. P* 11×12.
142		1d. deep blue and scarlet			40	55
143		1½d. ultramarine and grey			1·00	80
144		2½d. brown and deep blue			1·90	65
145		1s. slate and purple		..	2·00	3·50
		k. Kite and horizontal log			£110	
142/5		..	..	*Set of 4*	4·75	5·00
142/5 Perf "Specimen"		..	*Set of 4*	75·00	

For illustration of plate variety see Omnibus section following Zimbabwe.

1937 (12 May). *Coronation. As Nos.* 118/20 *of Jamaica, but ptd by B.W. P* 11×11½.
146		1d. violet		..	35	15
147		1½d. carmine		..	55	10
148		2½d. blue		..	65	45
146/8		..	..	*Set of 3*	1·40	60
146/8 Perf "Specimen"		..	*Set of 3*	50·00	

25   26 Young's Island and Fort Duvernette

27 Kingstown and Fort Charlotte   28 Bathing Beach at Villa

NEW CONSTITUTION 1951 (29a)

29 Victoria Park, Kingstown

(Recess B.W.)

1938 (11 Mar)–**47.** *Wmk Mult Script CA. P* 12.
149	25	½d. blue and green		..	10	10
150	26	1d. blue and lake-brown			10	10
151	27	1½d. green and scarlet			15	10
152	25	2d. green and black			40	35
153	28	2½d. blue-black and blue-green			10	40
153a	29	2½d. green and purple-brown (1947)			15	20
154	25	3d. orange and purple		..	15	10
154a	28	3½d. blue-black and blue-green (1947)			40	85
155	25	6d. black and lake			60	40
156	29	1s. purple and green		..	60	40
157	25	2s. blue and purple		..	5·00	55
157a		2s. 6d. red-brown and blue (1947)			1·00	3·50
158		5s. scarlet and deep green			8·50	2·50
158a		10s. violet and brown (1947)			3·50	7·50
159		£1 purple and black			16·00	15·00
149/59		..	..	*Set of 15*	32·00	28·00
149/59 Perf "Specimen"		..	*Set of 15*	£250	

1946 (15 Oct). *Victory. As Nos.* 141/2 *of Jamaica.*
160	1½d. carmine ..		..	10	10
161	3½d. blue		..	10	10
160/1 Perf "Specimen"		..	*Set of 2*	50·00	

1948 (30 Nov). *Royal Silver Wedding. As Nos.* 143/4 *of Jamaica.*
162	1½d. scarlet		..	10	10
163	£1 bright purple		..	15·00	13·00

No. 163 was originally printed in black, but the supply of these was stolen in transit. A few archive examples exist, some perforated "Specimen".

(New Currency. 100 cents=1 West Indian dollar)

1949 (26 Mar)–**52.** *Value in cents and dollars. Wmk Mult Script CA. P* 12.
164	25	1 c. blue and green		..	20	15
164a		1 c. green and black (10.6.52)			30	60
165	26	2 c. green and lake-brown			15	20
166	27	3 c. green and scarlet			40	15
166a	25	3 c. orange and purple (10.6.52)			30	45
167		4 c. green and black		..	35	20
167a		4 c. blue and green (10.6.52)			25	15
168	29	5 c. green and purple-brown			15	10
169	25	6 c. orange and purple		..	40	35
169a	27	6 c. green and scarlet (10.6.52)			25	30
170	28	7 c. blue-black and blue-green			2·75	30
170a		10 c. blue-black and blue-green (10.6.52)			50	20
171	25	12 c. black and lake			35	15
172	29	24 c. purple and green			35	40
173	25	48 c. blue and purple			1·50	1·50
174		60 c. red-brown and blue..			1·75	1·75
175		$1.20, scarlet and deep green			4·25	4·00
176		$2.40, violet and brown			6·50	9·00
177		$4.80, purple and black			11·00	17·00
164/77		..	..	*Set of 19*	28·00	32·00

1949 (10 Oct). *75th Anniv of U.P.U. As Nos.* 145/8 *of Jamaica.*
178		5 c. blue		..	25	15
179		6 c. purple		..	30	40
180		12 c. magenta		..	30	40
181		24 c. blue-green		..	50	25
178/81		..	..	*Set of 4*	1·25	1·10

1951 (16 Feb). *Inauguration of B.W.I. University College. As Nos.* 149/50 *of Jamaica.*
182	3 c. deep green and scarlet			30	15
183	12 c. black and purple..		..	30	15

1951 (21 Sept). *New Constitution. Optd with T* 29a *by B.W.*
184	27	3 c. green and scarlet		..	10	15
185	25	3 c. green and black		..	10	15
186	29	5 c. green and purple-brown			10	15
187	25	12 c. black and lake		..	10	15
184/7		..	..	*Set of 4*	30	55

1953 (2 June). *Coronation. As No.* 153 *of Jamaica.*
188	4 c. black and green	..	..	30	15

30   31

(Recess Waterlow (until 1961), then D.L.R.)

1955 (16 Sept)–**63.** *Wmk Mult Script CA. P* 13½×14 (*T* 30) *or* 14 (*T* 31).
189	30	1 c. orange		..	10	10
		a. Deep orange (11.12.62)			1·75	2·00
190		2 c. ultramarine		..	10	10
		a. Blue (26.9.61)		..	15	10
191		3 c. slate		..	30	10
192		4 c. brown		..	15	10
193		5 c. scarlet		..	30	10
194		10 c. reddish violet		..	20	10
		a. Deep lilac (12.2.58)			20	10
195		15 c. deep blue		..	55	30
196		20 c. green		..	60	10
197		25 c. black-brown		..	50	10

198	31	50 c. red-brown ..	..	..	3·00	90
		a. Chocolate (11.6.58)		..	3·00	75
199		$1 myrtle-green	..	..	4·75	1·00
		a. Deep myrtle-green (11.6.58)			9·00	4·00
		b. Deep yellowish green (15.1.63)			13·00	8·00
200		$2.50, deep blue	..	..	12·00	6·50
		a. Indigo-blue (30.7.62)		..	25·00	12·00
189/200				Set of 12	20·00	8·00

See also Nos. 207/20 and **MS**633.

1958 (22 Apr). *Inauguration of British Caribbean Federation. As Nos. 175/7 of Jamaica.*

201		3 c. deep green	..	..	40	20
202		6 c. blue	..	..	55	35
203		12 c. scarlet	..	..	80	35
201/3	..		..	Set of 3	1·60	80

MINISTERIAL GOVERNMENT

1963 (4 June). *Freedom from Hunger. As No. 80 of Lesotho.*

204		8 c. reddish violet	..	..	60	50

1963 (2 Sept). *Red Cross Centenary. As Nos. 203/4 of Jamaica.*

205		4 c. red and black	..	..	15	20
206		8 c. red and blue	..	..	35	50

(Recess D.L.R.)

1964–65. *As 1955 but wmk w 12.* (a) *P 12½ (14 Jan–Feb 1964).*

207	30	10 c. deep lilac	..	..	40	45
208		15 c. deep blue	..	..	70	50
209		20 c. green (24.2.64*)	..		5·50	1·50
210		25 c. black-brown	..	..	1·00	50
211	31	50 c. chocolate	..	..	4·50	8·50
207/11	..		..	Set of 5	11·00	10·00

(b) *P 13 × 14 (T 30) or 14 (T 31)*

212	30	1 c. orange (15.12.64)	..	..	15	10
213		2 c. blue (15.12.64)	..	..	15	10
214		3 c. slate (15.12.64)	..	..	50	10
215		5 c. scarlet (15.12.64)	..	..	15	10
216		10 c. deep lilac (15.12.64)	..		15	10
217		15 c. deep blue (9.11.64)	..		80	30
218		20 c. green (1964)	..	..	45	10
219		25 c. black-brown (20.10.64)	..		1·25	25
220	31	50 c. chocolate (18.1.65)	..		4·75	7·00
212/20				Set of 9	7·50	7·00

*This is the earliest known date recorded in St. Vincent although it may have been put on sale on 14.1.64.

32 Scout Badge and Proficiency Badges   33 Tropical Fruits

(Des V. Whiteley. Litho Harrison)

1964 (23 Nov). *50th Anniv of St. Vincent Boy Scouts Association. W w 12. P 14½.*

221	32	1 c. yellow-green and chocolate		..	10	10
222		4 c. blue and brown-purple		..	10	10
223		20 c. yellow and black-violet		..	30	10
224		50 c. red and bronze-green		..	45	20
221/4	..			Set of 4	80	30

(Des V. Whiteley. Photo Harrison)

1965 (23 Mar). *Botanic Gardens Bicentenary. T 33 and similar multicoloured designs. W w 12. P 14½ × 13½ (horiz) or 13½ × 14½ (vert).*

225		1 c. Type 33	..	..	10	10
226		4 c. Breadfruit and H.M.S. *Providence*, 1791			10	10
227		25 c. Doric Temple and pond (vert)			15	10
228		40 c. Talipot Palm and Doric Temple (vert)			30	40
225/8	..		..	Set of 4	50	50

1965 (17 May). *I.T.U. Centenary. As Nos. 98/9 of Lesotho.*

229		4 c. light blue and light olive-green	..		25	10
230		48 c. ochre-yellow and orange	..		1·00	45

37 Boat-building, Bequia (inscr "BEQUIA")

(Des M. Goaman. Photo Harrison)

1965 (16 Aug)–**67.** *T 37 and similar multicoloured designs. W w 12. P 14½ × 13½ (horiz designs) or 13½ × 14½ (vert).*

231		1 c. Type 37 ("BEQUIA")	..		10	60
231a		1 c. Type 37 ("BEQUIA") (27.6.67)			10	10
232		2 c. Friendship Beach, Bequia			10	10
233		3 c. Terminal Building, Arnos Vale Airport			15	10
234		4 c. Woman with bananas (vert)	..		1·00	30
235		5 c. Crater Lake	..	..	15	10
236		6 c. Carib Stone (vert)	..		15	40
237		8 c. Arrowroot (vert)	..	..	30	10
238		10 c. Owia Salt Pond	..	..	20	10
239		12 c. Deep water wharf	..	..	30	10
240		20 c. Sea Island cotton (vert)	..		10	10
241		25 c. Map of St. Vincent and islands (vert)			35	10
242		50 c. Breadfruit (vert)	..		50	25

243		$1 Baleine Falls (vert)	..		4·00	30
244		$2.50, St. Vincent Amazon (vert)	..		16·00	4·00
245		$5 Arms of St. Vincent (vert)	..		7·00	5·50
231/45				Set of 16	27·00	10·00

The 1 c. (No. 231a), 2 c., 3 c., 5 c. and 10 c. exist with PVA gum as well as gum arabic.
See also No. 261.

1966 (24 June). *Churchill Commemoration. As Nos. 102/5 of Lesotho.*

246		1 c. new blue	..		10	10
247		4 c. deep green	..		35	10
248		20 c. brown	..		75	45
249		40 c. bluish violet	..		1·50	1·25
246/9				Set of 4	2·40	1·60

1966 (4 Feb). *Royal Visit. As Nos. 183/4 of Montserrat.*

250		4 c. black and ultramarine	..		1·50	25
251		25 c. black and magenta	..		4·00	1·25

1966 (20 Sept). *Inauguration of W.H.O. Headquarters, Geneva. As Nos. 185/6 of Montserrat.*

252		4 c. black, yellow-green and light blue	..		30	10
253		25 c. black, light purple and yellow-brown			95	80

1966 (1 Dec). *20th Anniv of U.N.E.S.C.O. As Nos. 342/4 of Mauritius.*

254		4 c. slate-violet, red, yellow and orange			40	10
255		8 c. orange-yellow, violet and deep olive			75	10
256		25 c. black, bright purple and orange	..		1·50	60
254/6				Set of 3	2·40	70

38 Coastal View of Mount Coke Area

(Des and photo Harrison)

1967 (1 Dec). *Autonomous Methodist Church. T 38 and similar horiz designs. Multicoloured. W w 12. P 14 × 14½.*

257		2 c. Type 38	..		10	10
258		8 c. Kingstown Methodist Church			10	10
259		25 c. First Licence to perform marriages			20	10
260		35 c. Conference Arms	..		20	10
257/60			..	Set of 4	45	20

1968 (20 Feb). *As No. 234, but W w 12 sideways.*

261		4 c. Woman with bananas	..		30	30

The above exists with PVA gum as well as gum arabic.

39 Meteorological Institute

(Des G. Vasarhelyi. Photo Harrison)

1968 (28 May). *World Meteorological Day. W w 12. P 14 × 14½.*

262	39	4 c. multicoloured	..		10	10
263		25 c. multicoloured	..		10	10
264		35 c. multicoloured	..		15	10
262/4	..		..	Set of 3	30	20

40 Dr. Martin Luther King and Cotton Pickers

(Des V. Whiteley. Litho D.L.R.)

1968 (28 Aug). *Martin Luther King Commemoration. W w 12 (sideways). P 13.*

265	40	5 c. multicoloured	..		10	10
266		25 c. multicoloured	..		10	10
267		35 c. multicoloured	..		10	10
265/7			..	Set of 3	20	20

41 Speaker addressing Demonstrators   42 Scales of Justice and Human Rights Emblem

(Des V. Whiteley. Photo Enschedé)

1968 (1 Nov). *Human Rights Year. P 13 × 14 (3 c.) or 14 × 13 (35 c.).*

268	41	3 c. multicoloured	..		10	10
269	42	35 c. royal blue and turquoise-blue	..		20	10

43 Male Masquerader   44 Steel Bandsman

(Des V. Whiteley. Litho Format)

1969 (17 Feb). *St. Vincent Carnival. T 43/4 and similar designs. P 14.*

270		1 c. multicoloured	..	..	10	10
271		5 c. red and deep chocolate	..		10	10
272		8 c. multicoloured	..	..	10	10
273		25 c. multicoloured	..	..	15	15
270/3	..		..	Set of 4	30	30

Designs: Horiz—8 c. Carnival Revellers. Vert—25 c. Queen of Bands.

METHODIST CONFERENCE MAY 1969
(47)

1969 (14 May). *Methodist Conference. Nos. 257/8, 241 and 260 optd with T 47.*

274		2 c. multicoloured	..		10	15
275		8 c. multicoloured	..		30	40
276		25 c. multicoloured	..		35	40
277		35 c. multicoloured	..		1·50	3·00
274/7	..		..	Set of 4	2·00	3·50

48 "Strength in Unity"   49 Map of "CARIFTA" Countries

(Des J. Cooter. Litho D.L.R.)

1969 (1 July). *First Anniv of CARIFTA (Caribbean Free Trade Area). W w 12 (sideways on T 48). P 13.*

278	48	2 c. black, pale buff and red	..		10	10
279	48	5 c. multicoloured	..		10	10
280	48	8 c. black, pale buff and pale green	..		10	10
281	49	25 c. multicoloured	..		15	15
278/81			..	Set of 4	30	30

ASSOCIATED STATEHOOD

50 Flag of St. Vincent

(Des V. Whiteley, based on local designs. Photo Harrison)

1969 (27 Oct). *Statehood. T 50 and similar horiz designs. W w 12. P 14 × 14½.*

282		4 c. multicoloured	..		10	10
283		10 c. multicoloured	..		10	10
284		50 c. grey, black and orange	..		25	10
282/4			..	Set of 3	40	20

Designs:—10 c. Battle scene with insets of Petroglyph and Carib chief Chatoyer; 50 c. Carib House with maces and scales.

51 Green Heron

(Des J.W. Photo Harrison)

1970 (12 Jan)–**71.** *T* **51** *and similar multicoloured designs. Chalk-surfaced paper. W* w **12** (*sideways on* 1, 2, 3, 6, 8, 20, 25 c., $1, $2.50 *and upright on others*). *P* 14.

285	½ c. House Wren (*vert*)	..	..	10	60
286	1 c. Type **51**	..	..	35	1·00
	a. Glazed, ordinary paper (9.8.71)..		..	30	1·00
287	2 c. Lesser Antillean Bullfinches		..	15	40
288	3 c. St. Vincent Amazons		..	15	30
289	4 c. Rufous-throated Solitaire (*vert*)			20	30
290	5 c. Red-necked Pigeon (*vert*)		..	3·00	30
	a. Glazed, ordinary paper (9.8.71)..			1·25	30
291	6 c. Bananaquits	..	..	25	20
292	8 c. Purple-throated Carib		..	25	20
293	10 c. Mangrove Cuckoo (*vert*)		..	30	10
294	12 c. Common Black Hawk (*vert*)		..	40	10
295	20 c. Bare-eyed Thrush		..	60	15
296	25 c. Hooded Tanager		..	70	20
297	50 c. Blue Hooded Euphonia ..			1·75	75
298	$1 Barn Owl (*vert*)	..	..	6·50	3·50
299	$2.50, Yellow-bellied Elaenia (*vert*)			7·00	4·00
300	$5 Ruddy Quail Dove		..	11·00	5·50
285/300			*Set of* 16	27·00	15·00

See also Nos. 361/8 and 396/8.

52 "DHC-6" Twin Otter

(Des R. Granger Barrett. Litho Enschedé)

1970 (13 Mar). *20th Anniv of Regular Air Services. T* **52** *and similar horiz designs. Multicoloured. W* w **12** (*sideways*). *P* 14 × 13.

301	5 c. Type **52**	..	..	10	10
302	8 c. Grumman "Goose"		..	15	10
303	10 c. Hawker Siddeley "HS-748"		..	20	10
304	25 c. Douglas "DC-3"		..	65	30
301/4			*Set of* 4	1·00	40

53 "Children's Nursery"

54 "Angel and the Two Marys at the Tomb" (stained-glass window)

(Des R. Granger Barrett. Photo Harrison)

1970 (1 June). *Centenary of British Red Cross. T* **53** *and similar horiz designs. Multicoloured. W* w **12.** *P* 14.

305	3 c. Type **53**	..	..	10	10
306	5 c. "First Aid"		..	15	10
307	12 c. "Voluntary Aid Detachment"		..	25	15
308	25 c. "Blood Transfusion"		..	40	15
305/8			*Set of* 4	75	30

(Des L. Curtis. Litho J.W.)

1970 (7 Sept). *150th Anniv of St. George's Cathedral, Kingstown. T* **54** *and similar multicoloured designs. W* w **12** (*sideways on horiz designs*). *P* 14.

309	½ c. Type **54**	..	..	10	10
310	5 c. St. George's Cathedral (*horiz*)		..	10	10
311	25 c. Tower, St. George's Cathedral		..	10	10
312	35 c. Interior, St. George's Cathedral (*horiz*)			15	10
313	50 c. Type **54**		..	20	30
309/13			*Set of* 5	45	35

55 "The Adoration of the Shepherds" (Le Nain)

(Des J. Cooter. Litho Questa)

1970 (23 Nov). *Christmas. T* **55** *and similar vert design. Multicoloured. W* w **12** (*sideways on* 25 c., 50 c.). *P* 14.

314	8 c. "The Virgin and Child" (Bellini)	..		10	10
315	25 c. Type **55**		..	10	10
316	35 c. As 8 c.		..	10	10
317	50 c. Type **55**		..	15	20
314/17			*Set of* 4	35	30

56 New Post Office and 6d. Stamp of 1861

(Des J. Cooter. Litho Questa)

1971 (29 Mar). *110th Anniv of First St. Vincent Stamps. T* **56** *and similar horiz design. Multicoloured. W* w **12** (*sideways*). *P* 14.

318	2 c. Type **56**	..	..	10	10
319	4 c. 1d. Stamp of 1861 and New Post Office			10	10
320	25 c. Type **56**		..	10	10
321	$1 As 4 c.		..	35	45
318/21			*Set of* 4	45	50

57 Trust Seal and Wildlife   58 "Madonna appearing to St. Anthony" (Tiepolo)

(Des G. Drummond. Litho J.W.)

1971 (4 Aug). *St. Vincent's National Trust. T* **57** *and similar horiz design. Multicoloured. W* w **12** (*sideways*). *P* 13½ × 14.

322	12 c. Type **57**	..	..	25	10
323	30 c. Old Cannon, Fort Charlotte		..	40	15
324	40 c. Type **57**		..	55	25
325	45 c. As 30 c.		..	55	30
322/5			*Set of* 4	1·60	70

(Des J. Cooter. Litho Questa)

1971 (6 Oct). *Christmas. T* **58** *and similar horiz design. Multicoloured. W* w **12** (*sideways on* 10 c. *and* $1). *P* 14½ × 14 (10 c., $1) *or* 14 × 14½ (5 c., 25 c.).

326	5 c. Type **58**	..	..	10	10
327	10 c. "The Holy Family on the Flight into Egypt" (detail, Pietro da Cortona)		..	10	10
328	25 c. Type **58**		..	10	10
329	$1 As 10 c.		..	30	35
326/9			*Set of* 4	40	40

59 Careening   60 Private, Grenadier Company, 32nd Foot (1764)

(Des J. Cooter. Litho J.W.)

1971 (25 Nov). *The Grenadines of St. Vincent. T* **59** *and similar vert designs. Multicoloured. W* w **12.** *P* 13½.

330	1 c. Type **59**	..	..	10	10
331	5 c. Seine fishermen..		..	10	10
332	6 c. Map of the Grenadines ..		..	10	10
333	15 c. Type **59**		..	10	10
334	20 c. As 5 c.		..	15	10
335	50 c. As 6 c.		..	30	60
330/5			*Set of* 6	50	80
MS336	177 × 140 mm. Nos. 330/5			7·00	11·00

(Des and litho J.W.)

1972 (14 Feb). *Military Uniforms. T* **60** *and similar vert designs. Multicoloured. W* w **12.** *P* 14 × 13½.

337	12 c. Type **60**	..	..	90	15
338	30 c. Officer, Battalion Company, 31st Foot (1772)			1·75	65
339	50 c. Private, Grenadier Company, 6th Foot (1772)			2·50	1·00
337/9			*Set of* 3	4·50	1·60

61 Breadnut Fruit   62 Candlestick Cassia

(Des P. Powell. Litho Questa)

1972 (16 May). *Fruit. T* **61** *and similar vert designs. Multicoloured. W* w **12** (*sideways*). *P* 13½.

340	3 c. Type **61**	..	..	10	10
341	5 c. Pawpaw		..	10	10
342	12 c. Plumrose or Roseapple		..	30	30
343	25 c. Mango		..	70	70
340/3			*Set of* 4	1·00	1·00

(Des Sylvia Goaman. Litho B.W.)

1972 (31 July). *Flowers. T* **62** *and similar vert designs. Multicoloured. P* 13 ($1) *or* 13½ × 14 (*others*).

344	1 c. Type **62**	..	..	10	10
345	30 c. Lobster Claw		..	20	10
346	40 c. White Trumpet		..	25	15
347	$1 Souofriere tree		..	70	80
344/7			*Set of* 4	1·10	1·00

63 Sir Charles Brisbane and Coat of Arms

(Des Jennifer Toombs. Litho J.W.)

1972 (29 Sept). *Birth Bicentenary of Sir Charles Brisbane. T* **63** *and similar horiz designs. W* w **12** (*sideways*). *P* 13½.

348	20 c. yellow-ochre, gold and red-brown		..	15	10
349	30 c. light yellow, light mauve and black		..	40	10
350	$1 multicoloured		..	1·40	70
348/50			*Set of* 3	1·75	75
MS351	171 × 111 mm. Nos. 348/50 (*sold at* $2)			4·50	6·50

Designs:—30 c. H.M.S. *Arethusa*, 1807; $1 H.M.S. *Blake*, 1808.

64 Arrowroot and Breadfruit

(Des (from photograph by D. Groves) and photo Harrison)

1972 (20 Nov). *Royal Silver Wedding. Multicoloured; background colour given. W* w **12.** *P* 14 × 14½.

| 352 | **64** | 30 c. red-brown | .. | .. | 10 | 10 |
| 353 | | $1 myrtle-green | .. | .. | 40 | 20 |

65 Sighting St. Vincent   66 "The Last Supper" (French Stained-glass Window)

(Des J. Cooter. Litho Enschedé)

1973 (31 Jan). *475th Anniv of Columbus's Third Voyage to the West Indies. T* **65** *and similar triangular designs. Multicoloured. W* w **12.** *P* 13½.

354	5 c. Type **65**	..	..	25	15
355	12 c. Caribs watching Columbus's fleet		..	45	20
356	30 c. Christopher Columbus		..	1·00	70
357	50 c. *Santa Maria*		..	1·50	1·10
354/7			*Set of* 4	3·00	2·00

(Des J. Cooter. Litho Questa)

1973 (19 Apr). *Easter. T* **66** *and similar vert designs. Multicoloured. W* w **12** (*sideways*). *P* 14 × 13½.

358	**66**	15 c. multicoloured	..		10	10
		a. Horiz strip of 3. Nos. 358/60		..	45	
359	–	60 c. multicoloured	..	..	20	20
360	–	$1 multicoloured	..	..	20	20
358/60			*Set of* 3	45	45

Nos. 358, 360 and 359 were printed, in that order, horizontally *se-tenant* throughout a sheet of 45 stamps, and form a composite design of "The Last Supper".

1973 (13 June–23 Nov). *As Nos. 285 etc, but W* w **12** *upright on* 2, 3, 6, 20 c. *and sideways on others. Glazed paper.*

361	2 c. Lesser Antillean Bullfinches (23.11)	..		30	30
362	3 c. St. Vincent Amazons (23.11)		..	30	30
363	4 c. Rufous-throated Solitaire (*vert*) (23.11) ..			30	30
364	5 c. Red-necked Pigeon (*vert*)		..	50	20
365	6 c. Bananaquits (23.11)		..	40	35
366	10 c. Mangrove Cuckoo (*vert*) (23.11)		..	55	15
367	12 c. Common Black Hawk (*vert*) (23.11)		..	85	65
368	20 c. Bare-eyed Thrush (23.11)		..	1·25	40
361/8			*Set of* 8	4·00	2·40

For the 1 c. value with watermark upright see Grenadines of St. Vincent No. 3a.

67 William Wilberforce and Poster   **68** P.P.F. Symbol

(Des Jennifer Toombs. Litho D.L.R.)

1973 (11 July). *140th Death Anniv of William Wilberforce. T* **67** *and similar horiz designs. Multicoloured. W w* **12.** *P* 14 × 13½.

369	30 c. Type 67	..	..	15	10
370	40 c. Slaves cutting cane	..	..	20	15
371	50 c. Wilberforce and medallion	..	20	15
369/71			*Set of* 3	50	35

(Des PAD Studio. Litho Walsall)

1973 (3 Oct). *21st Anniv of International Planned Parenthood Federation. T* **68** *and similar vert design. Multicoloured. W w* **12** *(sideways). P* 14.

372	12 c. Type 68	..	..	10	10
373	40 c. "IPPF" and symbol	..	..	20	20

1973 (14 Nov). *Royal Wedding. As Nos.* 322/3 *of Montserrat.*

374	50 c. deep blue	..	..	15	10
375	70 c. grey-green	..	..	20	10

69 Administrative Block, Mona

(Des PAD Studio. Litho Questa)

1973 (13 Dec). *25th Anniv of West Indies University. T* **69** *and similar multicoloured designs. W w* **12** *(sideways on* $1). *P* 14.

376	5 c. Type 69	..	..	10	10
377	10 c. University Centre, Kingstown	..	10	10
378	30 c. Aerial view, Mona University	..	15	10
379	$1 University coat of arms (*vert*)	..	50	60
376/9	..	..	*Set of* 4	65	65

(70)   **71** "The Descent from the Cross" (Sansovino)

1973 (15 Dec). *Nos.* 297, 292 *and* 298 *surch in half sheets with T* **70,** *by the Govt Printer, St. Vincent.*

380	30 c. on 50 c. multicoloured	..	2·00	70
	a. Surch double	..		30·00
	b. Surch double (on front) and single inverted (on reverse)	..	75·00
	c. Surch double, one inverted	..	60·00
	d. Surch inverted		
381	40 c. on 8 c. multicoloured	..	2·00	70
	a. Surch double	..		35·00
	b. Surch inverted	..		£130
382	$10 on $1 multicoloured	..	10·00	6·50
	a. Surch double	..		95·00
	b. Surch inverted	..		£110
	c. Surch double, one inverted		£110
380/2	..	*Set of* 3	12·50	7·00

SPECIMEN STAMPS. From No. 383 onwards the stamps of St. Vincent exist overprinted "SPECIMEN", these being produced for publicity purposes.

(Des PAD Studio. Litho Enschedé)

1974 (10 Apr). *Easter. T* **71** *and similar vert designs showing sculptures. Multicoloured. W w* **12** *(sideways). P* 14 × 13½.

383	5 c. Type 71	..	..	10	10
384	30 c. "The Deposition" (English, 14th-century)	10	10
385	40 c. "Pieta" (Fernandez)	..	10	10
386	$1 "The Resurrection" (French, 16th-century)	..	20	25
383/6	..	..	*Set of* 4	30	30

72 Istra

(Des J.W. Litho Questa)

1974 (28 June). *Cruise Ships. T* **72** *and similar horiz designs. Multicoloured. W w* **12** *(sideways). P* 14.

387	15 c. Type 72	..	..	20	10
388	20 c. *Oceanic*	..	..	25	10
389	30 c. *Aleksandr Pushkin*	..	25	10
390	$1 *Europa*	..	..	50	30
387/90			*Set of* 4	1·10	40
MS391	134 × 83 mm. Nos. 387/90	..	1·00	2·50

73 U.P.U. Emblem

(Des J.W. Litho Questa)

1974 (25 July). *Centenary of Universal Postal Union. T* **73** *and similar horiz designs. Multicoloured. W w* **12.** *P* 14.

392	5 c. Type 73	..	..	10	10
393	12 c. Globe within posthorn	..	10	10
394	60 c. Map of St. Vincent and hand-cancelling	20	10
395	90 c. Map of the World	..	25	30
392/5	..	..	*Set of* 4	50	40

74 Royal Tern   **75** Scout Badge and Emblems

(Des J.W. Litho Questa)

1974 (29 Aug). *T* **74** *and similar vert designs. Multicoloured. Glazed paper. W w* **12** *(sideways on* 40 c. *and* $10). *P* 14.

396	30 c. Type 74	..	..	2·00	75
397	40 c. Brown Pelican	..	2·00	75
398	$10 Magnificent Frigate Bird	..	18·00	9·00
396/8	..	..	*Set of* 3	20·00	9·50

(Des Sylvia Goaman. Litho Enschedé)

1974 (9 Oct). *Diamond Jubilee of Scout Movement in St. Vincent. W w* **12.** *P* 13 × 13½.

399	75	10 c. multicoloured	..	10	10
400		25 c. multicoloured	..	20	10
401		45 c. multicoloured	..	35	25
402		$1 multicoloured	..	75	50
399/402			*Set of* 4	1·25	75

76 Sir Winston Churchill   **77** The Shepherds

(Des C. Abbott. Litho Questa)

1974 (28 Nov). *Birth Centenary of Sir Winston Churchill. T* **76** *and similar vert designs. Multicoloured. W w* **12.** *P* 14.

403	25 c. Type 76	..	..	15	10
404	35 c. Churchill in military uniform	..	20	10
405	45 c. Churchill in naval uniform	..	25	10
406	$1 Churchill in air-force uniform	..	45	50
403/6	..	..	*Set of* 4	95	60

(Des Jennifer Toombs. Litho Enschedé)

1974 (5 Dec). *Christmas. T* **77** *and similar vert designs. W w* **12.** *P* 12 × 12½.

407	77	3 c. violet-blue and black	..	10	10
		a. Horiz strip of 4. Nos. 407/10	20	
408	–	3 c. violet-blue and black	..	10	10
409	–	3 c. violet-blue and black	..	10	10
410	–	3 c. violet-blue and black	..	10	10
411	77	8 c. apple-green and black	..	10	10
412	–	35 c. rose and deep maroon	..	20	10
413	–	45 c. olive-bistre and brown-black	..	20	10
414	–	$1 lavender and slate-black	..	40	50
407/14			*Set of* 8	1·00	85

Designs:—Nos. 408, 412 Mary and crib; Nos. 409, 413 Joseph, ox and ass; Nos. 410, 414 The Magi.

Nos. 407/10 were issued horizontally *se-tenant* within the sheet, together forming a composite design of the Nativity.

MINIMUM PRICE

The minimum price quote is 10p which represents a handling charge rather than a basis for valuing common stamps. For further notes about prices see introductory pages.

---

78 Faces

(Des G. Drummond. Litho D.L.R.)

1975 (7–27 Feb). *Kingstown Carnival. T* **78** *and similar horiz designs. Multicoloured. W w* **12.** *P* 14 × 13½.

415	1 c. Type 78	..	..	10	10
	a. Booklet pane. No. 415 × 2 plus printed label (27.2)	35	
	b. Booklet pane. Nos. 415, 417 and 419 (27.2)	45	
416	15 c. Pineapple women	..	20	15
	a. Booklet pane. Nos. 416, 418 and 420 (27.2)	70	
417	25 c. King of the Bands	..	20	20
418	35 c. Carnival dancers	..	25	15
419	45 c. Queen of the Bands	..	25	20
420	$1.25, "African Splendour"	..	35	55
415/20			*Set of* 6	1·10	1·10
MS421	146 × 128 mm. Nos. 415/20	..	1·25	3·00

79 French Angelfish

Two types of $2.50:

Type I. Fishing-line attached to fish's mouth. Imprint "1975".
Type II. Fishing-line omitted. Imprint "1976".

(Des G. Drummond. Litho Questa)

1975 (10 Apr)–**76.** *T* **79** *and similar horiz designs. Multicoloured. W w* **14** *(sideways). P* 14½.

422	1 c. Type 79	..	..	15	50
423	2 c. Spotfin Butterfly-fish	..	15	60
424	3 c. Horse-eyed Jack	..	15	15
425	4 c. Mackerel	..	..	20	10
426	5 c. French Grunt	..	20	30
427	6 c. Spotted Goatfish	..	20	50
428	8 c. Ballyhoo	..	20	50
429	10 c. Sperm Whale	..	30	10
430	12 c. Humpback Whale	..	40	70
431	15 c. Cowfish	..	70	55
432	15 c. Skipjack (14.10.76)	..	3·00	35
433	20 c. Queen Angelfish	..	40	10
434	25 c. Princess Parrotfish	..	45	10
435	35 c. Red Hind	..	50	50
436	45 c. Atlantic Flying Fish	..	65	50
437	50 c. Porkfish	..	65	55
438	70 c. "Albacore" or Yellowfin Tuna (14.10.76)	4·25	70
439	90 c. Pompano (14.10.76)	..	4·25	70
440	$1 Queen Triggerfish	..	90	20
441	$2.50, Sailfish (I)	..	4·00	5·50
	a. Type II (12.7.76)	..	3·50	1·50
442	$5 Dolphin Fish	..	5·00	2·50
443	$10 Blue Marlin	..	5·00	8·50
422/43			*Set of* 22	27·00	18·00

With the exception of Nos. 431, 435/6, 438/9 and 442 the above exist with different dates in the imprint at the foot of each stamp.

80 Cutting Bananas

(Des G. Drummond. Litho Questa)

1975 (26 June). *Banana Industry. T* **80** *and similar horiz designs. Multicoloured. W w* **12.** *P* 13½.

447	25 c. Type 80	..	..	15	10
448	35 c. Packaging Station, La Croix	..	15	10
449	45 c. Cleaning and boxing	..	20	15
450	70 c. Shipping bananas aboard *Geest Tide*	40	50
447/50			*Set of* 4	80	50

81 Snorkel Diving

(Des G. Drummond. Litho Questa)

1975 (31 July). *Tourism. T 81 and similar horiz designs. Multi-coloured. W w 14 (sideways). P 13½.*
451	15 c. Type 81	..	15	10
452	20 c. Aquaduct Golf Course	..	20	10
453	35 c. Steel Band at Mariner's Inn		35	15
454	45 c. Sunbathing at Young Island		45	25
455	$1.25, Yachting marina	..	1·25	1·50
451/5	.. ..	*Set of 5*	2·10	1·90

82 George Washington, John Adams, Thomas Jefferson and James Madison

(Des G. Drummond. Litho Questa)

1975 (11 Sept). *Bicentenary of American Revolution. T 82 and similar horiz designs. P 14.*
456	½ c. black and lavender	..	10	10
457	1 c. black and light emerald	..	10	10
458	1½ c. black and light magenta	..	10	10
459	5 c. black and bright yellow-green	..	10	10
460	10 c. black and light violet-blue	..	10	10
461	25 c. black and dull orange-yellow	..	15	10
462	35 c. black and light greenish blue	..	25	15
463	45 c. black and bright rose	..	30	15
464	$1 black and light orange	..	45	40
465	$2 black and light yellow-olive	..	80	75
456/65	..	*Set of 10*	2·00	1·50
MS466	179 × 156 mm. Nos. 456/65		4·25	4·00

Presidents:—1 c. Monroe, Quincy Adams, Jackson, van Buren; 1½ c. W. Harrison, Tyler, Polk, Taylor; 5 c. Fillmore, Pierce, Buchanan, Lincoln; 10 c. Andrew Johnson, Grant, Hayes, Garfield, 25 c. Arthur, Cleveland, B. Harrison, McKinley; 35 c. Theodore Roosevelt, Taft, Wilson, Harding; 45 c. Coolidge, Hoover, Franklin Roosevelt, Truman; $1 Eisenhower, Kennedy, Lyndon Johnson, Nixon; $2 Pres. Ford and White House.

Nos. 456/65 were each issued in sheets of ten stamps and two *se-tenant* labels.

83/4 "Shepherds"

(Des Jennifer Toombs. Litho Harrison)

1975 (4 Dec). *Christmas. T 83/4 and similar triangular designs. P 13½ × 14. A. W w 12 (upright). B. W w 12 (sideways).*
		A		B	
467	3 c. black and magenta	10	10	10	10
	a. Block of 4. Nos. 467/70	30	30	30	30
468	3 c. black and magenta	10	10	10	10
469	3 c. black and magenta	10	10	10	10
470	3 c. black and magenta	10	10	10	10
471	8 c. black & lt greenish blue	10	10	10	10
	a. Pair. Nos. 471/2	15	15	15	15
472	8 c. black & lt greenish blue	10	10	10	10
473	35 c. black and yellow	20	20	20	20
	a. Pair. Nos. 473/4	40	40	40	40
474	35 c. black and yellow	20	20	20	20
475	45 c. black and yellow-green	30	30	30	30
	a. Pair. Nos. 475/6	60	60	60	60
476	45 c. black and yellow-green	30	30	30	30
477	$1 black and bright lilac	65	65	65	65
	a. Pair. Nos. 477/8	1·25	1·25	1·25	1·25
478	$1 black and bright lilac	65	65	65	65
467/78	.. *Set of 12*	2·40	2·40	2·40	2·40

Designs:—No. 467, "Star of Bethlehem"; 468, "Holy Trinity"; 469, As T 83; 470, "Three Kings"; 471/2, As 468; 473/4, As 468; 475/6, T 83/4; 477/8 As 470. The two designs of each denomination (Nos. 471/8) differ in that the longest side is at the foot or at the top as shown in T 83/4.

Each denomination was printed in sheets of 16, the designs being *se-tenant* and so arranged that the watermark comes upright, inverted, sideways right and sideways left.

85 Carnival Dancers

(Des G. Drummond. Litho Questa)

1976 (19 Feb). *Kingstown Carnival. T 85 and similar horiz designs. Multicoloured. W w 14 (sideways). P 13½.*
479	1 c. Type 85		10	10
	a. Booklet pane. Nos. 479 and 480 plus printed label		20	
480	2 c. Humpty-Dumpty people		10	10
	a. Booklet pane. Nos. 480/2		35	
481	5 c. Smiling faces		10	10
482	35 c. Dragon worshippers		20	10
	a. Booklet pane. Nos. 482/4		80	
483	45 c. Carnival tableaux		25	15
484	$1.25, Bumble-Bee dancers		45	45
479/84	..	*Set of 6*	90	80

(86)

87 Blue-headed Hummingbird and Yellow Hibiscus

1976 (8 Apr). *Nos. 424 and 437 surch as T 86.*
485	70 c. on 3 c. Horse-eyed Jack	..	1·25	1·25
	a. Surch inverted	..	40·00	
486	90 c. on 50 c. Porkfish	..	1·40	1·40
	a. Surch inverted	..	45·00	

(Des G. Drummond. Litho Walsall)

1976 (20 May). *Hummingbirds and Hibiscuses. T 87 and similar vert designs. Multicoloured. W w 14 (inverted). P 13½.*
487	5 c. Type 87		35	10
488	10 c. Antillean Crested Hummingbird and Pink Hibiscus		60	15
489	35 c. Purple-throated Carib and White Hibiscus	..	1·40	55
	a. No wmk	..	35·00	
490	45 c. Blue-headed Hummingbird and Red Hibiscus		1·50	65
491	$1.25, Green-throated Carib and Peach Hibiscus		9·50	5·50
487/91	.. ..	*Set of 5*	12·00	6·25

1976 (16 Sept). *West Indian Victory in World Cricket Cup. As Nos. 419/20 of Jamaica.*
492	15 c. Map of the Caribbean		75	25
493	45 c. Prudential Cup	..	1·75	1·00

88 St Mary's Church, Kingstown

(Des G. Drummond. Litho Questa)

1976 (18 Nov). *Christmas. T 88 and similar horiz designs. Multicoloured. W w 14 (sideways). P 14.*
494	35 c. Type 88		15	10
495	45 c. Anglican Church, Georgetown		15	10
496	50 c. Methodist Church, Georgetown		20	10
497	$1.25, St. George's Cathedral, Kingstown		40	60
494/7	..	*Set of 4*	80	70

89 Barrancoid Pot-stand

(Des G. Vasarhelyi. Litho J.W.)

1976 (16 Dec). *National Trust. T 89 and similar horiz designs. Multicoloured. W w 14 (sideways). P 13½.*
498	5 c. Type 89		10	10
499	45 c. National Museum		15	10
500	70 c. Carib sculpture		25	20
501	$1 Ciboney petroglyph	..	45	50
498/501	..	*Set of 4*	80	75

90 William I, William II, Henry I and Stephen

(Des G. Vasarhelyi. Litho J.W.)

1977 (7 Feb). *Silver Jubilee. T 90 and similar horiz designs. Multicoloured. P 13½. (a) W w 14 (sideways). From sheets.*
502	½ c. Type 90	..	10	10
503	1 c. Henry II, Richard I, John, Henry III		10	10
504	1½ c. Edward I, Edward II, Edward III, Richard II		10	10
505	2 c. Henry IV, Henry V, Henry VI, Edward IV		10	10
506	5 c. Edward V, Richard III, Henry VII, Henry VIII		10	10
507	10 c. Edward VI, Lady Jane Grey, Mary I, Elizabeth I		10	10
508	25 c. James I, Charles I, Charles II, James II		15	15
509	35 c. William III, Mary II, Anne, George I		20	20
510	45 c. George II, George III, George IV		20	25
511	75 c. William IV, Victoria, Edward VII		30	35
512	$1 George V, Edward VIII, George VI		40	45
513	$2 Elizabeth II leaving Westminster Abbey		65	70
502/13		*Set of 12*	2·00	2·40
MS514	170 × 146 mm. Nos. 502/13. P 14½ × 14		2·75	3·25

(b) No wmk. From booklets
515	½ c. Type 90	..	1·60	2·50
	a. Booklet pane. Nos. 515/18 se-tenant		5·75	
516	1 c. As No. 503		1·60	2·50
517	1½ c. As No. 504		1·60	2·50
518	2 c. As No. 505		1·60	2·50
519	5 c. As No. 506		1·60	2·50
	a. Booklet pane. Nos. 519/22 se-tenant		5·75	
520	10 c. As No. 507		1·60	2·50
521	25 c. As No. 508		1·60	2·50
522	35 c. As No. 509		1·60	2·50
523	45 c. As No. 510		1·60	2·50
	a. Booklet pane. Nos. 523/6 se-tenant		5·75	
524	75 c. As No. 511		1·60	2·50
525	$1 As No. 512		1·60	2·50
526	$2 As No. 513		1·60	2·50
515/26		*Set of 12*	17·00	26·00

Nos. 502/13 were each issued in sheets of ten stamps and two *se-tenant* labels.

91 Grant of Arms

(Des G. Drummond. Litho Questa)

1977 (12 May). *Centenary of Windward Is Diocese. T 91 and similar horiz designs. Multicoloured. W w 14 (sideways). P 13½.*
527	15 c. Type 91		10	10
528	35 c. Bishop Berkeley and mitres	..	10	10
529	45 c. Map and arms of diocese	..	10	10
530	$1.25, St. George's Cathedral and Bishop Woodroffe		30	45
527/30	..	*Set of 4*	45	50

CARNIVAL 1977
JUNE 25TH-JULY 5TH
(92)

1977 (2 June). *Kingstown Carnival. Nos. 426, 429, 432/3 and 440 optd with T 92.*
531	5 c. French Grunt	..	10	10
	a. Red opt	..	50·00	
	b. Hyphen omitted	..	1·40	
532	10 c. Sperm Whale (R.)	..	10	10
	a. Opt double (R. and Blk.)	..	60·00	
	b. Hyphen omitted	..	1·60	
533	15 c. Skipjack (R.)	..	10	10
	a. Black opt	..	50·00	
	b. Hyphen omitted	..	2·00	
534	20 c. Queen Angel Fish (R.)	..	10	10
	a. Opt inverted	..	22·00	
	b. Black opt	..	55·00	
	c. Hyphen omitted	..	2·25	
535	$1 Queen Triggerfish	..	40	40
	a. Red opt	..	60·00	
	b. Hyphen omitted	..	3·50	
531/5	..	*Set of 5*	70	70

The variety showing the hyphen omitted from the second line of the overprint occurred on R.4/4 of the lower pane.

93 Guide and Emblem

CARIBBEAN VISIT 1977 (94)

(Des PAD Studio. Litho J.W.)

1977 (1 Sept). *50th Anniv of St. Vincent Girl Guides. T* **93** *and similar vert designs. The $2 value is additionally optd.* "*1930–1977*". *Multicoloured. W w* **14**. *P* 13½.
536	5 c. Type **93**	..	..	10	10
537	15 c. Early uniform, ranger, guide and brownie			15	10
538	20 c. Early uniform and guide	..	..	15	10
539	$2 Lady Baden-Powell	..	..	70	60
	a. Optd dates omitted	..	..	20·00	
	b. Optd dates double	..	..	85·00	
536/9			*Set of 4*	95	65

1977 (27 Oct). *Royal Visit. No.* 513 *optd with T* **94**.
540	$2 Queen Elizabeth leaving Westminster Abbey	..	..	40	30
	a. Opt inverted	..	..	50·00	

95 Map of St. Vincent   96 Opening Verse and Scene

(Des G. Drummond. Litho Questa)

1977–78. *Provisionals. W w* **12**. *P* 14½ × 14.
541	**95**	20 c. blk, dull violet-bl & pale bl (31.1.78)		15	15
542		40 c. black, dull orange & flesh (30.11.77)		25	20
		a. Black (value) omitted	..	50·00	
543		40 c. black, magenta and salmon (31.1.78)		20	15
541/3			*Set of 3*	55	45

Nos. 541/3 were printed in 1974, without value, for provisional use; they were locally surcharged before going on sale.

(Des Jennifer Toombs. Litho Enschedé)

1977 (1 Dec). *Christmas. Scenes and Verses from the carol "While Shepherds Watched their Flocks by Night". T* **96** *and similar vert designs. Multicoloured. W w* **14**. *P* 13 × 11.
544	5 c. Type **96**	..	..	10	10
545	10 c. Angel consoling shepherds	..		10	10
546	15 c. View of Bethlehem	..	..	10	10
547	25 c. Nativity scene	..	..	10	10
548	50 c. Throng of Angels	..	..	10	10
549	$1.25, Praising God	..	..	30	45
544/9			*Set of 6*	50	65
MS550	150 × 170 mm. Nos. 544/9. P 13½			90	1·50

97 *Cynthia cardui and Bougainvillea glabra var. alba*

(Des Daphne Padden. Litho Walsall)

1978 (6 Apr). *Butterflies and Bougainvilleas. T* **97** *and similar horiz designs. Multicoloured. W w* **14** (*sideways*). *P* 14.
551	5 c. Type **97**	..	..	10	10
552	25 c. *Dione juno* and "Golden Glow"	..	15	10
553	40 c. *Anartia amathea* and "Mrs McLean"	..	25	10
554	50 c. *Hypolimnas misippus* and "Cyphen"	30	10
555	$1.25, *Pseudolycaena marsyas* and "Thomasii"			65	55
551/5			*Set of 5*	1·25	75

(Des G. Drummond. Litho J.W.)

1978 (2 June). *25th Anniv of Coronation. Horiz designs as Nos.* 422/5 *of Montserrat. Multicoloured. W w* **14** (*sideways*). *P* 13.
556	40 c. Westminster Abbey	..	..	10	10
557	50 c. Gloucester Cathedral	..	..	10	10
558	$1.25, Durham Cathedral	..	..	20	15
559	$2.50, Exeter Cathedral	..	..	30	25
556/9			*Set of 4*	55	45
MS560	130 × 102 mm. Nos. 556/9. P 13½ × 14		60	85

Nos. 556/9 were each printed in sheets of ten stamps and two *se-tenant* labels.

98 Rotary International Emblem   **99** "Co-operation in and Motto   Education Leads to Mutual Understanding and Respect"

(Des G. Hutchins. Litho Questa)

1978 (13 July). *International Service Clubs. T* **98** *and similar horiz designs showing club emblems and mottoes. Multicoloured. W w* **14** (*sideways*). *P* 14½.
561	40 c. Type **98**	..	..	25	10
562	50 c. Lions International	..	..	25	10
563	$1 Jaycees	..	..	50	35
561/3			*Set of 3*	90	40

(Des G. Hutchins. Litho Questa)

1978 (7 Sept). *10th Anniv of Project School to School (St. Vincent-Canada school twinning project). T* **99** *and similar multicoloured design showing flags and blackboard. W w* **14** (*sideways on $2*). *P* 14.
564	40 c. Type **99**	..	..	10	10
565	$2 "Co-operation in Education Leads to the Elimination of Racial Intolerance" (*horiz*)		40	50

100 Arnos Vale Airport   101 Young Child

(Des G. Drummond. Litho Questa)

1978 (19 Oct). *75th Anniv of Powered Flight. T* **100** *and similar horiz designs. Multicoloured. W w* **14** (*sideways*). *P* 14½ × 14.
566	10 c. Type **100**	..	..	10	10
567	40 c. Wilbur Wright landing *Flyer*	..	15	10
568	50 c. Orville Wright in *Flyer*	..	15	10
569	$1.25, Orville Wright and *Flyer* airborne	45	35
566/9			*Set of 4*	70	45

(Des A. Paish. Litho Questa)

1979 (14 Feb). *International Year of the Child. T* **101** *and similar vert designs showing portraits of young children. W w* **14**. *P* 14 × 13½.
570	8 c. black, gold and pale yellow-green		10	10
571	20 c. black, gold and pale rose-lilac		15	10
572	50 c. black, gold and pale violet-blue	..	25	10
573	$2 black, gold and flesh	..	..	75	50
570/3			*Set of 4*	1·10	55

10c+5c

SOUFRIERE
RELIEF
FUND 1979
(**102**)

103 Sir Rowland Hill

(Des G. Drummond. Litho Questa)

1979 (17 Apr). *Soufrière Eruption Relief Fund. Designs as T* **95** *but surchd as T* **102** *by Reliance Printery, Kingstown. W w* **12**. *P* 14½ × 14.
574	10 c. + 5 c. violet-blue and pale rose-lilac	10	15
575	50 c. + 25 c. yellow-brown and buff	20	20
576	$1 + 50 c. reddish brown and brownish grey	30	30
577	$2 + $1 deep green and apple-green	50	50
574/7			*Set of 4*	1·00	1·00

(Des J.W. Litho Harrison)

1979 (31 May). *Death Centenary of Sir Rowland Hill. T* **103** *and similar horiz designs. Multicoloured. W w* **14** (*sideways*). *P* 14.
578	40 c. Type **103**	..	..	15	10
579	50 c. Penny Black and Twopenny Blue stamps	20	15
580	$3 1861 1d. and 6d. stamps	..	1·00	1·10
578/80			*Set of 3*	1·25	1·25
MS581	170 × 123 mm. Nos. 578/80, 594/5 and 599 (see footnote after No. 601)		1·75	3·00

Nos. 578/80 were each printed in sheets including two *se-tenant* stamp-size labels.

104 First and Latest Buccament   (**105**)
Postmarks and Map of St. Vincent

ST VINCENT AND
THE GRENADINES
AIR SERVICE 1979

(Des J.W. Litho Harrison)

1979 (31 May–1 Sept). *St. Vincent Post Offices. Horiz designs as T* **104** *showing first and latest postmarks and map of St. Vincent. Multicoloured. W w* **14** (*sideways*). *P* 14.
582	1 c. Type **104**	..	..	10	10
583	2 c. Sion Hill	..	..	10	10
584	3 c. Cumberland	..	..	10	10
585	4 c. Questelles	..	..	10	10
586	5 c. Layou	..	..	10	10
587	6 c. New Ground	..	..	10	10
588	8 c. Mesopotamia	..	..	10	10
589	10 c. Troumaca	..	..	10	10
590	12 c. Arnos Vale	..	..	15	10

591	15 c. Stubbs	..	..	15	10
592	20 c. Orange Hill	..	..	15	10
593	25 c. Calliaqua	..	..	15	10
594	40 c. Edinboro	..	..	25	20
595	50 c. Colonarie	..	..	30	25
596	80 c. Biabou	..	..	40	35
597	$1 Chateaubelair	..	..	50	50
598	$2 Head P.O., Kingstown	..	60	80
599	$3 Barrouallie	..	..	75	1·25
600	$5 Georgetown	..	..	1·25	2·00
601	$10 Kingstown	..	..	2·25	4·00
582/601			*Set of 20*	6·50	9·00

Dates of issue:—40, 50 c., $3 (from No. **MS**581 and booklets only) 31.5.79; others, and 40, 50 c., $3 from sheets, 1.9.79.
The 5, 10, 25 c. and $1 values exist with different imprint dates below the design.
See also Nos. **MS**581 and **MS**637.

1979 (6 Aug). *Opening of St. Vincent and the Grenadines Air Service. No.* 566 *optd with T* **105**, *in red, by Reliance Printery, Kingstown.*
602	10 c. Type **100**	..	..	10	10

INDEPENDENT

106 National Flag and *Ixora coccinea* (flower)

(Des J.W. Litho Enschedé)

1979 (27 Oct). *Independence. T* **106** *and similar horiz designs. Multicoloured. W w* **14** (*sideways*). *P* 12½ × 12.
603	20 c. Type **106**	..	..	15	10
604	50 c. House of Assembly and *Ixora stricta* (flower)		20	10
605	80 c. Prime Minister R. Milton Cato and *Ixora williamsii* (flower)		25	20
603/5			*Set of 3*	55	30

INDEPENDENCE 1979
(**107**)

1979 (27 Oct). *Independence. Nos.* 422, 425/30, 432, 434, 437/40, 441a *and* 443 *optd with T* **107**, *by Letchworth Press, Barbados.*
606	1 c. Type **79**	..	..	10	10
607	4 c. Mackerel	..	..	10	10
608	5 c. French Grunt	..	..	10	10
609	6 c. Spotted Goatfish	..	..	10	10
610	8 c. Ballyhoo	..	..	10	10
611	10 c. Sperm Whale	..	..	15	15
612	12 c. Humpback Whale	..	..	15	15
613	15 c. Skipjack	..	..	15	15
614	25 c. Princess Parrotfish	..	20	20
615	50 c. Porkfish	..	..	35	35
616	70 c. "Albacore" or Yellowfin Tuna	..	45	45
617	90 c. Pompano	..	..	60	50
618	$1 Queen Triggerfish	..	..	60	50
619	$2.50, Sailfish (II)	..	1·75	1·00
	a. Opt inverted	..	..	£100	
	b. Optd on Type I (No. 441)	..	9·00	9·00
620	$10 Blue Marlin	..	..	4·75	4·25
606/20			*Set of 15*	8·50	7·00

108 Virgin and Child   109 *Polistes cinctus* (wasp) and Oleander

(Des Jennifer Toombs. Litho Questa)

1979 (1 Nov). *Christmas. Scenes and Verses from the carol "Silent Night". T* **108** *and similar horiz designs. Multicoloured. W w* **14** (*sideways*). *P* 13½.
621	10 c. Type **108**	..	..	10	10
622	20 c. Jesus in manger	..	..	10	10
623	25 c. Shepherds	..	..	10	10
624	40 c. Angel	..	..	10	10
625	50 c. Angels with infant Jesus	..	10	10
626	$2 Nativity scene	..	..	40	30
621/6			*Set of 6*	55	45
MS627	151 × 170 mm. Nos. 621/6	..	55	1·00

(Des J.W. Litho Walsall)

1979 (13 Dec). *Flowers and Insects. T* **109** *and similar vert designs showing insects and different varieties of Oleander flower. Multicoloured. W w* **14**. *P* 14.
628	5 c. Type **109**	..	..	10	10
629	10 c. *Pyrophorus noctiluca* (click beetle)	10	10
630	25 c. *Stagmomantis limbata* (mantid)	..	10	10
631	50 c. *Psiloptera lampetis* (beetle)	..	10	10
632	$2 *Diaprepies abbreviatus* (weevil)	..	30	30
628/32			*Set of 5*	50	40

(Des and litho D.L.R.)

1980 (28 Feb). *Centenary of St. Vincent "Arms" Stamps. Sheet 116 × 72 mm containing designs as T **31**. W w **14** (sideways). P 14 × 13½.*
MS633 116 × 72 mm. 50 c. reddish brown; $1 deep
grey-green; $2.50 deep blue 50 75

110 Queen Elizabeth II

(Des J.W. Litho Harrison)

1980 (24 Apr). *"London 1980" International Stamp Exhibition. T **110** and similar horiz designs. Multicoloured. W w **14** (sideways). P 14.*
634 80 c. Type **110** 20 20
635 $1 Great Britain 1954 3d. and St. Vincent
 1954 5 c. definitive stamps .. 30 30
636 $2 Unadopted postage stamp design of 1971 60 60
634/6 .. .. *Set of 3* 1·00 1·00
MS637 165 × 115 mm. Nos. 596/8 and 634/6 .. 1·25 1·50
 Nos. 634/6 were each printed in sheets containing 2 *se-tenant*
stamp-size labels.

111 Steel Band .. **112** Football

(Des G. Drummond. Litho Questa)

1980 (12 June). *Kingstown Carnival. T **111** and similar horiz design. Multicoloured. W w **14** (sideways). P 13½ × 14.*
638 20 c. Type **111** 15 15
 a. Pair. Nos. 638/9 .. .. 30 30
639 20 c. Steel band (different) 15 15
 Nos. 638/9 were printed together, *se-tenant*, in horizontal and
vertical pairs throughout the sheet.

(Des Polygraphic. Litho Rosenbaum Bros, Vienna)

1980 (7 Aug). *"Sport for All". T **112** and similar vert designs. Multicoloured. W w **14** (inverted). P 13½.*
640 10 c. Type **112** 10 10
641 60 c. Cycling 20 15
642 80 c. Basketball 30 20
643 $2.50, Boxing 40 70
640/3 .. .. *Set of 4* 90 1·00

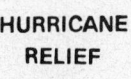
HURRICANE
RELIEF
50¢
(**113**)

114 Brazilian Agouti

1980 (7 Aug). *Hurricane Relief. Nos. 640/3 surch with T **113**. W w **14** (upright).*
644 10 c. + 50 c. Type **112** 15 15
645 60 c. + 50 c. Cycling 25 25
646 80 c. + 50 c. Basketball 35 35
647 $2.50 + 50 c. Boxing 60 60
644/7 .. .. *Set of 4* 1·25 1·25

(Des L. Curtis. Litho Questa)

1980 (2 Oct). *Wildlife. T **114** and similar horiz designs. Multicoloured. W w **14** (sideways). P 14 × 14½.*
648 25 c. Type **114** 10 10
649 50 c. Giant Toad 15 10
650 $2 Small Indian Mongoose 40 55
648/50 .. .. *Set of 3* 60 60

115 Map of World showing .. **116** Ville de Paris, 1782
St. Vincent

(Des G. Drummond. Litho Questa)

1980 (4 Dec). *St. Vincent "On the Map". T **115** and similar designs depicting maps showing St. Vincent. Multicoloured. W w **14** (sideways). P 13½ × 14.*
651 10 c. Type **115** 10 10
652 50 c. Western hemisphere 15 10
653 $1 Central America 30 15
654 $2 St. Vincent 50 30
651/4 .. .. *Set of 4* 90 50
MS655 143 × 95 mm. No. 654. P 12 .. 50 75

(Des J.W. Litho Rosenbaum Bros, Vienna)

1981 (19 Feb). *Sailing Ships. T **116** and similar vert designs. Multicoloured. W w **14**. P 13½.*
656 50 c. Type **116**. 40 20
657 60 c. H.M.S. *Ramillies*, 1782. .. 45 30
658 $1.50, H.M.S. *Providence*, 1793 .. 1·00 1·50
659 $2 *Dee* (paddle-steamer packet) .. 1·25 1·75
656/9 .. .. *Set of 4* 2·75 3·25

117 Arrowroot Cultivation

(Des G. Drummond. Litho Format)

1981 (21 May). *Agriculture. T **117** and similar horiz designs. Multicoloured. W w **14** (sideways). P 14.*
660 25 c. Type **117** 10 15
 a. Pair. Nos. 660/1 .. .. 20 30
661 25 c. Arrowroot processing 10 15
662 50 c. Banana cultivation 20 25
 a. Pair. Nos. 662/3 .. .. 40 50
663 50 c. Banana export packaging station 20 25
664 60 c. Coconut plantation 25 30
 a. Pair. Nos. 664/5 .. .. 50 60
665 60 c. Copra drying frames 25 30
666 $1 Cocoa cultivation 50 45
 a. Pair. Nos. 666/7 .. .. 1·00 90
667 $1 Cocoa beans and sun drying frames 50 45
660/7 .. .. *Set of 8* 1·90 2·00
 The two designs of each value were printed together, *se-tenant*,
in horizontal and vertical pairs throughout the sheet.

1981 (17 July–26 Nov). *Royal Wedding. Horiz designs as T **26/27** of Kiribati. Multicoloured.* (a) W w **15**. P 14.
668 60 c. *Isabella* 15 15
 a. Sheetlet. No. 668 × 6 and No. 669 1·10
669 60 c. Prince Charles and Lady Diana Spencer 30 30
670 $2.50, *Alberta* (tender) 30 30
 a. Sheetlet. No. 670 × 6 and No. 671 2·50
671 $2.50, As No. 669 .. .. 70 70
672 $4 *Britannia* 40 40
 a. Sheetlet. No. 672 × 6 and No. 673 3·25
673 $4 As No. 669 .. .. .. 1·25 1·25
668/73 .. .. *Set of 6* 2·75 2·75
MS674 120 × 109 mm. $5 As No. 669. Wmk sideways. P 12 (26 Nov) .. .. .. 1·25 1·00

 (b) *Booklet stamps. No wmk.* P 12 (26 Nov)
675 60 c. As No. 668 .. .. .. 25 25
 a. Booklet pane. No. 675 × 4 .. 1·00
676 $2.50, As No. 671 .. .. .. 1·25 1·25
 a. Booklet pane. No. 676 × 2 .. 2·50
 Nos. 668/73 were printed in sheetlets of seven stamps of the same
face value, each containing six of the "Royal Yacht" design and one
of the larger design showing Prince Charles and Lady Diana.
 Nos. 675/6 come from $9.80 stamp booklets.

118 Kingstown General Post Office **119**

(Des G. Drummond. Litho Questa)

1981 (1 Sept). *U.P.U. Membership. W w **14** (sideways). P 14.*
677 **118** $2 multicoloured 70 90
 a. Horiz pair. Nos. 677/8 .. 1·40 1·75
678 **119** $2 multicoloured 70 90
 Nos. 677/8 were printed together, *se-tenant*, in horizontal pairs
throughout the sheet, forming a composite design.

120 St. Vincent Flag with Flags of other
U.N. Member Nations

(Des L. Curtis. Litho Format)

1981 (11 Sept). *First Anniv of U.N. Membership. T **120** and similar horiz design. Multicoloured. W w **14** (sideways). P 13½ × 14.*
679 $1.50, Type **120** 55 25
680 $2.50, Prime Minister Robert Milton Cato 85 50
 Nos. 679/80 are inscribed "ST. VINCENT and the GRENA-
DINES" and were each printed in small sheets of 6 including one
se-tenant stamp-size label.

---

121 Silhouettes of Figures at Old Testament
Reading, and Bible Extract

(Des Jennifer Toombs. Litho Security Printers (M), Malaysia)

1981 (19 Nov). *Christmas. T **121** and similar horiz designs showing silhouettes of figures. Multicoloured. W w **14** (sideways). P 12.*
681 50 c. Type **121** 15 10
682 60 c. Madonna, and angel 15 10
683 $1 Madonna, and Bible extract .. 25 25
684 $2 Joseph and Mary travelling to Bethlehem 50 50
681/4 .. .. *Set of 4* 95 85
MS685 129 × 127 mm. Nos. 681/4. P 13½ 95 1·40

122 Sugar Boilers

(Des L. Curtis. Litho Format)

1982 (5 Apr). *First Anniv of Re-introduction of Sugar Industry. T **122** and similar horiz designs. Multicoloured. W w **14** (sideways). P 14.*
686 50 c. Type **122** 25 15
687 60 c. Sugar drying plant 25 20
688 $1.50, Sugar mill machinery 70 75
689 $2 Crane loading sugar cane .. 95 1·00
686/9 .. .. *Set of 4* 1·90 1·90

123 Butterfly Float .. **124** Augusta of Saxe-Gotha,
Princess of Wales, 1736

(Des G. Vasarhelyi. Photo Heraclio Fournier)

1982 (10 June). *Carnival 1982. T **123** and similar multicoloured designs. P 13½.*
690 50 c. Type **123** 20 15
691 60 c. Angel dancer (vert) 20 15
692 $1.50, Winged dancer (vert). 50 60
693 $2 Eagle float .. .. .. 70 1·25
690/3 .. .. *Set of 4* 1·50 2·10

(Des D. Shults and J. Cooter. Litho Format)

1982 (1 July). *21st Birthday of Princess of Wales. T **124** and similar vert designs. Multicoloured. W **24** of Kiribati. P 13½ × 14.*
694 50 c. Type **124** 25 20
695 60 c. Coat of arms of Augusta of Saxe-Gotha 25 25
696 $6 Diana, Princess of Wales .. 1·50 1·50
694/6 .. .. *Set of 3* 1·75 1·75

125 Scout Emblem .. **126** De Havilland "Moth", 1932

(Des L. Curtis. Litho Questa)

1982 (15 July). *75th Anniv of Boy Scout Movement. T **125** and similar vert design. Multicoloured. W w **14**. P 14.*
697 $1.50, Type **125** .. .. .. 70 1·00
698 $2.50, 75th anniv emblem .. .. 90 1·25

1982 (19 July). *Birth of Prince William of Wales. Nos. 694/6 optd with T **19** of St. Kitts.*
699 50 c. Type **124**. 20 20
700 60 c. Coat of arms of Augusta of Saxe-Gotha 25 25
 a. Opt inverted .. .. .. 50·00
701 $6 Diana, Princess of Wales .. .. 1·50 1·75
 a. Opt double .. .. .. 20·00
699/701 .. .. *Set of 3* 1·75 2·00

(Des A. Theobald. Litho Questa)

1982 (29 July). *50th Anniv of Airmail Service. T* **126** *and similar horiz designs. Multicoloured. W w* **14** *(sideways). P* 14.

702	50 c. Type **126**	..	45	30
703	60 c. Grumman "Goose", 1952	..	50	40
704	$1.50, Hawker-Siddeley "748", 1968		95	1·00
705	$2 Britten-Norman "Trislander", 1982	..	1·10	1·60
702/5	.. ..	*Set of 4*	2·75	3·00

127 *Geestport* (freighter)

(Des G. Drummond. Litho Format)

1982 (27 Dec). *Ships. T* **127** *and similar horiz designs. Multicoloured. W w* **14** *(sideways). P* 14.

706	45 c. Type **127**	..	25	25
707	60 c. *Stella Oceanic* (liner)	..	30	35
708	$1.50, *Victoria* (liner)	..	70	1·00
709	$2 *Queen Elizabeth 2* (liner)	..	95	1·50
706/9	.. .. ..	*Set of 4*	2·00	2·75

128 *Pseudocorynactis caribbeorum*

(Des McCombie-De Bay. Litho Security Printers (M), Malaysia)

1983 (10 Feb). *Marine Life. T* **128** *and similar multicoloured designs. W w* **14** *(sideways on 60 c., $1.50, $2). P* 12.

710	50 c. Type **128**	..	55	25
711	60 c. *Actinoporus elegans* (vert)	..	65	35
712	$1.50, *Arachnanthus nocturnus* (vert)	..	1·25	75
713	$2 *Hippocampus reidi* (vert). .	..	1·50	1·00
710/13		*Set of 4*	3·50	2·00

129 Satellite View of St. Vincent   **(130)**

(Des R. Vigurs. Litho Questa)

1983 (14 Mar). *Commonwealth Day. T* **129** *and similar horiz designs. Multicoloured. W w* **14** *(sideways). P* 14.

714	45 c. Type **129** ..	..	20	20
715	60 c. Flag of St. Vincent	..	25	25
716	$1.50, Prime Minister R. Milton Cato		50	65
717	$2 Harvesting bananas	..	75	90
714/17		*Set of 4*	1·50	1·75

Nos. 714/17 are inscribed "St. Vincent & The Grenadines".

1983 (26 Apr). *No. 681 surch with T* **130** *by Reliance Printery, Kingstown.*

718	45 c. on 50 c. Type 121. .	40	30

131 Symbolic Handshake   **132** Sir William Smith (founder)

(Des J.W. Litho Security Printers (M), Malaysia)

1983 (6 July). *10th Anniv of Treaty of Chaguaramas. T* **131** *and similar vert designs. Multicoloured. W w* **14** *(sideways). P* 11½ × 12.

719	45 c. Type **131**	..	25	20
720	60 c. Commerce emblem	..	30	25
721	$1.50, Caribbean map	..	60	65
722	$2 Flags of member countries and map of St. Vincent	..	85	90
719/22		*Set of 4*	1·75	1·75

(Des L. Curtis. Litho Security Printers (M), Malaysia)

1983 (6 Oct). *Centenary of Boys' Brigade. T* **132** *and similar vert designs. Multicoloured. W w* **14**. *P* 12 × 11½.

723	45 c. Type **132**	..	25	25
724	60 c. On parade	..	30	35
725	$1.50, Craftwork	..	70	1·10
726	$2 Community service	..	95	1·60
723/6		*Set of 4*	2·00	3·00

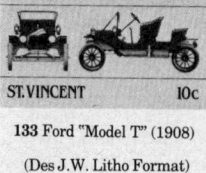

133 Ford "Model T" (1908)

(Des J.W. Litho Format)

1983 (25 Oct). *Leaders of the World. Automobiles (1st series). T* **133** *and similar horiz designs, the first in each pair showing technical drawings and the second paintings. P* 12½.

727	10 c. multicoloured	..	..	10	10
	a. Vert pair. Nos. 727/8	..	..	10	10
728	10 c. multicoloured	..	..	10	10
729	60 c. multicoloured	..	..	15	15
	a. Vert pair. Nos. 729/30	..	..	30	30
730	60 c. multicoloured	..	..	15	15
731	$1.50, multicoloured	..	..	20	20
	a. Vert pair. Nos. 731/2	..	..	40	40
732	$1.50, multicoloured	..	..	20	20
733	$1.50, multicoloured	..	..	20	20
	a. Vert pair. Nos. 733/4	..	..	40	40
734	$1.50, multicoloured	..	..	20	20
735	$2 multicoloured	..	..	30	30
	a. Vert pair. Nos. 735/6	..	..	60	60
736	$2 multicoloured	..	..	30	30
737	$2 multicoloured	..	..	30	30
	a. Vert pair. Nos. 737/8	..	..	60	60
738	$2 multicoloured	..	..	30	30
727/38			*Set of 12*	2·25	2·25

Designs:—Nos. 727/8, Ford "Model T" (1908); 729/30, Super-charged Cord "812" (1937); 731/2, Citroen "Open Tourer" (1937); 733/4, Mercedes Benz "300SL Gull-Wing" (1954); 735/6, Rolls-Royce "Phantom I" (1925); 737/8, Ferrari "Boxer 512BB" (1976).

Nos. 727/8, 729/30, 731/2, 733/4, 735/6 and 737/8 were printed together, *se-tenant*, in vertical pairs throughout the sheets.

See also Nos. 820/9, 862/7, 884/92 and 959/70.

134 Appearance of the Nativity Star

(Des Jennifer Toombs. Litho Security Printers (M), Malaysia)

1983 (15 Nov). *Christmas. T* **134** *and similar horiz designs showing the Shepherds. W w* **14**. *P* 12.

739	10 c. Type **134**	..	..	10	10
740	50 c. Message of the Angel	..	..	20	10
741	$1.50, The Heavenly Host	..	..	45	45
742	$2.40, Worshipping Jesus	..	..	65	75
739/42			*Set of 4*	1·25	1·25
MS743	130 × 130 mm. Nos. 739/42. Wmk sideways			1·25	1·75

135 *King Henry VIII*

(Des J.W. Litho Format)

1983 (8 Dec). *Leaders of the World. Railway Locomotives (1st series). T* **135** *and similar horiz designs, the first in each pair showing technical drawings and the second the locomotive at work. P* 12½.

744	10 c. multicoloured	..	..	10	10
	a. Vert pair. Nos. 744/5	..	..	10	10
745	10 c. multicoloured	..	..	10	10
746	10 c. multicoloured	..	..	10	10
	a. Vert pair. Nos. 746/7	..	..	10	10
747	10 c. multicoloured	..	..	10	10
748	25 c. multicoloured	..	..	10	10
	a. Vert pair. Nos. 748/9	..	..	20	20
749	25 c. multicoloured	..	..	10	10
750	50 c. multicoloured	..	..	20	20
	a. Vert pair. Nos. 750/1	..	..	40	40
751	50 c. multicoloured	..	..	20	20
752	60 c. multicoloured	..	..	20	20
	a. Vert pair Nos. 752/3	..	..	40	40
753	60 c. multicoloured	..	..	20	20
754	75 c. multicoloured	..	..	25	25
	a. Vert pair. Nos. 754/5	..	..	50	50
755	75 c. multicoloured	..	..	25	25
756	$2.50, multicoloured	..	..	55	55
	a. Vert pair. Nos. 756/7	..	..	1·10	1·10
757	$2.50, multicoloured	..	..	55	55
758	$3 multicoloured	..	..	70	70
	a. Vert pair. Nos. 758/9	..	..	1·40	1·40
759	$3 multicoloured	..	..	70	70
744/59			*Set of 16*	3·75	3·75

Designs:—Nos. 744/5, *King Henry VIII*, Great Britain (1927); 746/7, *Royal Scots Greys*, Great Britain (1961); 748/9, *Hagley Hall*, Great Britain (1928); 750/1, *Sir Lancelot*, Great Britain (1926); 752/3 Class "B12", Great Britain (1912); 754/5, *Deeley "Compound"* type, Great Britain (1902); 756/7, *Cheshire*, Great Britain (1927); 758/9, *Bullied "Austerity" Class Q1*, Great Britain (1942).

Nos. 744/59 were issued in a similar sheet format to Nos. 727/38. See also Nos. 792/807, 834/41, 872/83, 893/904 and 1001/8.

---

136 Fort Duvernette

(Des Walsall. Litho Questa)

1984 (13 Feb). *Fort Duvernette. T* **136** *and similar horiz designs. Multicoloured. W w* **15** *(sideways). P* 14 × 14½.

760	35 c. Type **136**	..	20	30
761	45 c. Soldiers on fortifications. .		25	30
762	$1 Cannon facing bay	..	40	60
763	$3 Map of St. Vincent and mortar	..	1·25	1·75
760/3		*Set of 4*	1·90	2·75

137 White Frangipani

(Des J. Cooter. Litho Harrison)

1984 (2 Apr). *Flowering Trees and Shrubs. T* **137** *and similar horiz designs. Multicoloured. W w* **14** *(sideways). P* 13½ × 14.

764	5 c. Type **137** ..	..	15	10
765	10 c. Genip	..	20	10
766	15 c. Immortelle	..	25	10
767	20 c. Pink Poui	..	30	10
768	25 c. Buttercup	..	40	10
769	35 c. Sandbox	..	55	20
770	45 c. Locust	..	70	25
771	60 c. Colville's Glory	..	85	40
772	75 c. Lignum Vitae	..	95	55
773	$1 Golden Shower	..	1·25	90
774	$5 Angelin	..	5·00	6·50
775	$10 Roucou	..	7·50	9·00
764/75		*Set of 12*	16·00	16·00

138 Trench Warfare, First World War   **139** Musical Fantasy Costume

(Des Court House Studio. Litho Format)

1984 (25 Apr). *Leaders of the World. British Monarchs. T* **138** *and similar vert designs. Multicoloured. P* 12½.

776	1 c. Type **138**	..	..	10	10
	a. Horiz pair. Nos. 776/7	..		10	10
777	1 c. George V and trenches	..		10	10
778	5 c. Battle of Bannockburn	..		10	10
	a. Horiz pair. Nos. 778/9	..		10	10
779	5 c. Edward II and battle	..		10	10
780	60 c. George V . .	..		20	20
	a. Horiz pair. Nos. 780/1	..		40	40
781	60 c. York Cottage, Sandringham	..		20	20
782	75 c. Edward II	..		20	20
	a. Horiz pair. Nos. 782/3	..		40	40
783	75 c. Berkeley Castle	..		20	20
784	$1 Coat of arms of Edward II	..		25	25
	a. Horiz pair. Nos. 784/5	..		50	50
785	$1 Edward II (*different*)	..		25	25
786	$4 Coat of arms of George V	..		75	75
	a. Horiz pair. Nos. 786/7	..		1·50	1·50
787	$4 George V and Battle of Jutland. .			75	75
776/87			*Set of 12*	2·75	2·75

Nos. 776/7, 778/9, 780/1, 782/3, 784/5 and 786/7 were printed together, *se-tenant*, in horizontal pairs throughout the sheets, each pair forming a composite design.

(Des G. Vasarhelyi. Litho Questa)

1984 (25 June). *Carnival 1984. T* **139** *and similar horiz designs showing Carnival costumes. Multicoloured. W w* **15** *(sideways). P* 14.

788	35 c. Type **139** ..	..	15	15
789	45 c. African princess	..	20	20
790	$1 Market woman	..	40	40
791	$3 Carib hieroglyph. .	..	1·25	1·40
788/91		*Set of 4*	1·75	2·00

IMPERFORATES AND MISSING COLOURS. Various issues between Nos. 792 and 1084 exist either imperforate or with colours omitted. Such items are not listed as there is no evidence that they fulfil the criteria outlined on page xi of this catalogue.

(Des J.W. Litho Format)

1984 (27 July). *Leaders of the World. Railway Locomotives (2nd series). Horiz designs as T* **135**, *the first in each pair showing technical drawings and the second the locomotive at work. P* 12½.

792	1 c. multicoloured	..	..	10	10
	a. Vert pair. Nos. 792/3	..		10	10
793	1 c. multicoloured			10	10

794	2 c. multicoloured		..	..	10	10
	a. Vert pair. Nos. 794/5		..	..	10	10
795	2 c. multicoloured		..	..	10	10
796	3 c. multicoloured		..	..	10	10
	a. Vert pair. Nos. 796/7		..	..	10	10
797	3 c. multicoloured		..	..	10	10
798	50 c. multicoloured		..	..	30	30
	a. Vert pair. Nos. 798/9		..	..	60	60
799	50 c. multicoloured		..	..	30	30
800	75 c. multicoloured		..	..	35	35
	a. Vert pair. Nos. 800/1		..	..	70	70
801	75 c. multicoloured		..	..	35	35
802	$1 multicoloured		..	..	40	40
	a. Vert pair. Nos. 802/3		..	..	80	80
803	$1 multicoloured		..	..	40	40
804	$2 multicoloured		..	..	55	55
	a. Vert pair. Nos. 804/5		..	..	1·10	1·10
805	$2 multicoloured		..	..	55	55
806	$3 multicoloured		..	..	65	65
	a. Vert pair. Nos. 806/7		..	..	1·25	1·25
807	$3 multicoloured		..	..	65	65
792/807				Set of 16	4·25	4·25

Designs:—Nos. 792/3, Liberation Class, France (1945); 794/5, *Dreadnought*, Great Britain (1767); 796/7, No. 242A1, France (1946); 798/9, Class "Dean Goods", Great Britain (1883); 800/1, Hetton Colliery No. 1, Great Britain (1822); 802/3, *Penydarren*, Great Britain (1804); 804/5, *Novelty*, Great Britain (1829); 806/7, Class "44", Germany (1925).

Nos. 792/807 were issued in a similar sheet format to Nos. 727/38.

140 Slaves tilling Field   141 Weightlifting

(Des G. Vasarhelyi. Litho Questa)

1984 (1 Aug). *150th Anniv of Emancipation of Slaves on St. Vincent. T* **140** *and similar horiz designs. Multicoloured.* W w **15** *(sideways). P* 14.

808	35 c. Type **140**	..	..		20	20
809	45 c. Sugar-cane harvesting		..		25	25
810	$1 Cutting sugar-cane		..		45	45
811	$3 William Wilberforce and African slave caravan		..		1·25	1·40
808/11			Set of 4		2·00	2·10

(Des Court House Studio. Litho Format)

1984 (30 Aug). *Leaders of the World. Olympic Games, Los Angeles. T* **141** *and similar vert designs. Multicoloured. P* 12½.

812	1 c. Judo	..	..		10	10
	a. Horiz pair. Nos. 812/13		..		10	10
813	1 c. Type **141**		..		10	10
814	3 c. Pursuit cycling		..		10	10
	a. Horiz pair. Nos. 814/15		..		10	10
815	3 c. Cycle road-racing		..		10	10
816	60 c. Women's backstroke swimming		..		15	15
	a. Horiz pair. Nos. 816/17		..		30	30
817	60 c. Men's butterfly swimming		..		15	15
818	$3 Sprint start		..		55	55
	a. Horiz pair. Nos. 818/19		..		1·10	1·10
819	$3 Finish of long distance race		..		55	55
812/19			Set of 8		1·40	1·40

Nos. 812/13, 814/15, 816/17 and 818/19 were printed together, *se-tenant*, in horizontal pairs throughout the sheets.

(Des J.W. Litho Format)

1984 (22 Oct). *Leaders of the World. Automobiles (2nd series). Horiz designs as T* **133**, *the first in each pair showing technical drawings and the second paintings. P* 12½.

820	5 c. black, drab and bright green		..		10	10
	a. Vert pair. Nos. 820/1		..		10	10
821	5 c. multicoloured		..		10	10
822	20 c. black, pink and pale new blue		..		15	15
	a. Vert pair. Nos. 822/3		..		30	30
823	20 c. multicoloured		..		15	15
824	55 c. black, pale green and lake-brown		..		25	25
	a. Vert pair. Nos. 824/5		..		50	50
825	55 c. multicoloured		..		25	25
826	$1.50, black, pale turq-grn & turq-grn		..		35	35
	a. Vert pair. Nos. 826/7		..		70	70
827	$1.50, multicoloured		..		35	35
828	$2.50, black, turquoise-green and lilac		..		40	40
	a. Vert pair. Nos. 828/9		..		80	80
829	$2.50, multicoloured		..		40	40
820/9			Set of 10		2·10	2·10

Designs:—Nos. 820/1, Austin-Healey "Sprite" (1958); 822/3, Maserati "Ghibli Coupe" (1971); 824/5, Pontiac "GTO" (1964); 826/7, Jaguar "D-Type" (1957); 828/9, Ferrari "365 GTB4 Daytona" (1970).

Nos. 820/9 were issued in a similar sheet format to Nos. 727/38.

142 Grenadier, 70th Regt   143 N. S. Taylor
of Foot, 1773

(Des J. Cooter. Litho Questa)

1984 (12 Nov). *Military Uniforms. T* **142** *and similar vert designs. Multicoloured.* W w **15**. *P* 14.

830	45 c. Type **142**		..		25	30
831	60 c. Grenadier, 6th Regt of Foot, 1775				30	35
832	$1.50, Grenadier, 3rd Regt of Foot, 1768				75	80
833	$2 Battalion Company officer, 14th Regt of Foot, 1780				1·00	1·10
830/3			Set of 4		2·10	2·25

(Des J.W. Litho Format)

1984 (21 Nov). *Leaders of the World. Railway Locomotives (3rd series). Horiz designs as T* **135**, *the first in each pair showing technical drawings and the second the locomotive at work. Multicoloured. P* 12½.

834	5 c. multicoloured		..		10	10
	a. Vert pair. Nos. 834/5		..		10	15
835	5 c. multicoloured		..		10	10
836	40 c. multicoloured		..		15	20
	a. Vert pair. Nos. 836/7		..		30	40
837	40 c. multicoloured		..		15	20
838	75 c. multicoloured		..		20	30
	a. Vert pair. Nos. 838/9		..		40	60
839	75 c. multicoloured		..		20	30
840	$2.50, multicoloured		..		70	1·00
	a. Vert pair. Nos. 840/1		..		1·40	2·00
841	$2.50, multicoloured		..		70	1·00
834/41			Set of 8		2·10	2·75

Designs:—Nos. 834/5 Class "20", Rhodesia (1954); 836/7, *Southern Maid*, Great Britain (1928); 838/9, *Prince of Wales*, Great Britain (1911); 840/1, Class "05", Germany (1935).

Nos. 834/41 were issued in a similar sheet format to Nos. 727/38.

(Des Court House Studio. Litho Format)

1985 (7 Jan). *Leaders of the World. Cricketers. T* **143** *and similar vert designs, the first in each pair showing a head portrait and the second the cricketer in action. P* 12½.

842	5 c. multicoloured		..		10	10
	a. Horiz pair. Nos. 842/3		..		10	10
843	5 c. multicoloured		..		10	10
844	35 c. multicoloured		..		25	20
	a. Horiz pair. Nos. 844/5		..		50	40
845	35 c. multicoloured		..		25	20
846	50 c. multicoloured		..		35	30
	a. Horiz pair. Nos. 846/7		..		70	60
847	50 c. multicoloured		..		35	30
848	$3 multicoloured		..		1·50	1·25
	a. Horiz pair. Nos. 848/9		..		3·00	2·50
849	$3 multicoloured		..		1·50	1·25
842/9			Set of 8		3·75	3·25

Designs:—Nos. 842/3, N. S. Taylor; 844/5. T. W. Graveney; 846/7, R. G. D. Willis; 848/9, S. D. Fletcher.

Nos. 842/3, 844/5, 846/7, and 848/9 were printed together, *se-tenant*, in vertical pairs throughout the sheets.

144 Eye Lash Orchid   145 Brown Pelican

(Des G. Drummond. Litho Format)

1985 (31 Jan). *Orchids. T* **144** *and similar vert designs. Multicoloured.* W w **15**. *P* 14.

850	35 c. Type **144**		..		40	30
851	45 c. *Ionopsis utricularioides*		..		50	30
852	$1 *Epidendrum secundum*		..		80	65
853	$3 *Oncidium altissimum*		..		1·75	2·00
850/3			Set of 4		3·00	3·00

(Des R. Vigurs. Litho Format)

1985 (7 Feb). *Leaders of the World. Birth Bicentenary of John J. Audubon (ornithologist). T* **145** *and similar vert designs. Multicoloured. P* 12½.

854	15 c. Type **145**		..		15	10
	a. Horiz pair. Nos. 854/5		..		30	20
855	15 c. Green Heron		..		15	10
856	40 c. Pileated Woodpecker		..		30	20
	a. Horiz pair. Nos. 856/7		..		60	40
857	40 c. Common Flicker		..		30	20
858	60 c. Painted Bunting		..		40	30
	a. Horiz pair. Nos. 858/9		..		80	60
859	60 c. White-winged Crossbill		..		40	30
860	$2.25, Red-shouldered Hawk		..		1·50	1·25
	a. Horiz pair. Nos. 860/1		..		3·00	2·50
861	$2.25, Common Caracara		..		1·50	1·25
854/61			Set of 8		4·25	3·25

Nos. 854/5, 856/7, 858/9 and 860/1 were printed together, *se-tenant*, in horizontal pairs throughout the sheets.

(Des Artists International. Litho Format)

1985 (11 Mar). *Leaders of the World. Automobiles (3rd series). Horiz designs as T* **133**, *the first in each pair showing technical drawings and the second paintings. P* 12½.

862	1 c. black, pale lemon and blue-green		..		10	10
	a. Vert pair. Nos. 862/3		..		10	10
863	1 c. multicoloured		..		10	10
864	55 c. black, pale new blue and violet-grey		..		15	15
	a. Vert pair. Nos. 864/5		..		30	30
865	55 c. multicoloured		..		15	15
866	$2 black, pale lemon & dull reddish purple		..		40	40
	a. Vert pair. Nos. 866/7		..		80	80
867	$2 multicoloured		..		40	40
862/7			Set of 6		1·00	1·00

Designs:—Nos. 862/3, Lancia "Aprilia" (1937); 864/5, Pontiac "Firebird Trans Am" (1973); 866/7, Cunningham "C-5R" (1953).

Nos. 862/7 were issued in a similar sheet format to Nos. 727/38.

146 Pepper   147 Bamboo Flute

(Des G. Drummond. Litho Format)

1985 (22 Apr). *Herbs and Spices. T* **146** *and similar vert designs. Multicoloured.* W w **15**. *P* 14.

868	25 c. Type **146**		..		20	15
869	35 c. Sweet Marjoram		..		25	25
870	$1 Nutmeg		..		55	65
871	$3 Ginger		..		1·75	2·25
868/71			Set of 4		2·50	3·00

(Des T. Hadler ($2.50), J.W. (others). Litho Format)

1985 (26 Apr). *Leaders of the World. Railway Locomotives (4th series). Horiz designs as T* **135**, *the first in each pair showing technical drawings and the second the locomotive at work. P* 12½.

872	1 c. multicoloured		..		10	10
	a. Vert pair. Nos. 872/3		..		10	10
873	1 c. multicoloured		..		10	10
874	10 c. multicoloured		..		10	10
	a. Vert pair. Nos. 874/5		..		10	15
875	10 c. multicoloured		..		10	10
876	40 c. multicoloured		..		20	30
	a. Vert pair. Nos. 876/7		..		40	60
877	40 c. multicoloured		..		20	30
878	60 c. multicoloured		..		20	30
	a. Vert pair. Nos. 878/9		..		40	60
879	60 c. multicoloured		..		20	30
880	$1 multicoloured		..		30	40
	a. Vert pair. Nos. 880/1		..		60	80
881	$1 multicoloured		..		30	40
882	$2.50, multicoloured		..		1·10	1·50
	a. Vert pair. Nos. 882/3		..		1·10	1·50
883	$2.50, multicoloured		..		60	75
872/83			Set of 12		2·40	3·25

Designs:—Nos. 872/3, *Glen Douglas*, Great Britain (1913); 874/5, *Fenchurch*, Great Britain (1872); 876/7, No. 1 "Stirling Single", Great Britain (1870); 878/9, No. 158A, Great Britain (1866); 880/1, No. 103 Class "Jones Goods", Great Britain (1893); 882/3, *The Great Bear*, Great Britain (1908).

Nos. 872/83 were issued in a similar sheet format to Nos. 727/38.

(Des J.W. (25 c.), G. Turner ($1), Artists International (others). Litho Format)

1985 (7 June). *Leaders of the World. Automobiles (4th series). Horiz designs as T* **133**, *the first in each pair showing technical drawings and the second paintings. P* 12½.

884	25 c. black, greenish grey and brown-red		..		10	10
	a. Vert pair. Nos. 884/5		..		10	15
885	25 c. multicoloured		..		10	10
886	60 c. black, pale flesh and red-orange		..		15	15
	a. Vert pair. Nos. 886/7		..		30	30
887	60 c. multicoloured		..		15	15
888	$1 black, azure and dull lavender		..		20	20
	a. Vert pair. Nos. 888/9		..		40	40
889	$1 multicoloured		..		20	20
890	$1.50, black, pale blue and scarlet		..		25	25
	a. Vert pair. Nos. 890/1		..		50	50
891	$1.50, multicoloured		..		25	25
884/91			Set of 8		1·25	1·25
MS892	180 × 121 mm. $4 × 2 As Nos. 890/1; $5 × 2 As Nos. 888/9. P 14				2·50	4·50

Designs:—Nos. 884/5, Essex "Coach" (1922); 886/7, Nash "Rambler" (1950); 888/9, Ferrari "Tipo 156" (1961); 890/1, Eagle-Weslake "Type 58" (1967).

Nos. 884/91 were issued in a similar sheet format to Nos. 727/38.

(Des J.W. (5 c., 30 c., $1), T. Hadler (others). Litho Format)

1985 (27 June). *Leaders of the World. Railway Locomotives (5th series). Horiz designs as T* **135**, *the first in each pair showing technical drawings and the second the locomotive at work. P* 12½.

893	5 c. multicoloured		..		10	10
	a. Vert pair. Nos. 893/4		..		10	10
894	5 c. multicoloured		..		10	10
895	30 c. multicoloured		..		15	20
	a. Vert pair. Nos. 895/6		..		30	40
896	30 c. multicoloured		..		15	20
897	60 c. multicoloured		..		20	30
	a. Vert pair. Nos. 897/8		..		40	60
898	60 c. multicoloured		..		20	30
899	75 c. multicoloured		..		20	30
	a. Vert pair. Nos. 899/900		..		40	60
900	75 c. multicoloured		..		20	30
901	$1 multicoloured		..		30	40
	a. Vert pair. Nos. 901/2		..		60	80
902	$1 multicoloured		..		30	40
903	$2.50, multicoloured		..		60	75
	a. Vert pair. Nos. 903/4		..		1·10	1·50
904	$2.50, multicoloured		..		60	75
893/904			Set of 12		2·50	3·50

Designs:—Nos. 893/4, Tank locomotive *Loch*, Great Britain (1874); 895/6, Class "47XX", Great Britain (1919); 897/8, Class "121", France (1876); 899/900, Class "24", Germany (1927); 901/2 Tank locomotive No. 1008, Great Britain (1889); 903/4, Class "PS-4", U.S.A. (1926).

Nos. 893/904 were issued in a similar sheet format to Nos. 727/38.

(Des Jennifer Toombs. Litho Format)

1985 (10 July). *Traditional Musical Instruments. T* **147** *and similar multicoloured designs.* W w **15** (*sideways on* $1, $2). P 15.

905	25 c. Type **147**..	..	..	15	15
906	35 c. Quatro (four-stringed guitar)	..	..	20	25
907	$1 Ba-ha (bamboo pipe) (*vert*)	..	..	50	55
908	$2 Goat-skin drum (*vert*) ..	..	..	1·00	1·10
905/8			Set of 4	1·60	1·90
MS909	141×100 mm. Nos. 905/8	..	..	3·50	4·00

148 Queen Elizabeth the Queen Mother   149 Elvis Presley

(Des Court House Studio. Litho Format)

1985 (9 Aug). *Leaders of the World. Life and Times of Queen Elizabeth the Queen Mother. Various vertical portraits as T* **148**. P 12½.

910	35 c. multicoloured..	..	..	15	20
	a. Horiz pair. Nos. 910/11..	..		30	40
911	35 c. multicoloured ..	..	..	15	20
912	85 c. multicoloured ..	..	..	20	30
	a. Horiz pair. Nos. 912/13..	..		40	60
913	85 c. multicoloured ..	..	..	20	30
914	$1.20, multicoloured ..	..	..	25	35
	a. Horiz pair. Nos. 914/15..	..		50	70
915	$1.20, multicoloured ..	..	..	25	35
916	$1.60, multicoloured ..	..	..	30	45
	a. Horiz pair. Nos. 916/17..	..		60	90
917	$1.60, multicoloured ..	..	..	30	45
910/17			Set of 8	1·60	2·40
MS918	85×114 mm. $2.10, multicoloured; $2.10, multicoloured ..	..	..	1·00	1·75

The two designs of each value were issued, *se-tenant*, in horizontal pairs within the sheets.

Each *se-tenant* pair shows a floral pattern across the bottom of the portraits which stops short of the left-hand edge on the left-hand stamp and of the right-hand edge on the right-hand stamp.

Designs as Nos. 910/11 and 912/13, but with face values of $3.50 × 2 and $6 × 2, also exist in additional miniature sheets from a restricted printing issued 19 December 1985.

(Des Court House Studio. Litho Format)

1985 (16 Aug). *Leaders of the World. Elvis Presley* (*entertainer*). *Various vertical portraits as T* **149**. *Multicoloured, background colours given.* P 12½.

919	10 c. multicoloured (T **149**)	..	..	30	10
	a. Horiz pair. Nos. 919/20..	..		60	·20
920	10 c. multicoloured (bright blue)	..	..	30	10
921	60 c. multicoloured (brown)	..	..	65	35
	a. Horiz pair. Nos. 921/2	..		1·25	70
922	60 c. multicoloured (pale grey)	..	..	65	35
923	$1 multicoloured (brown)	..	..	1·00	55
	a. Horiz pair. Nos. 923/4 ..	..		2·00	1·10
924	$1 multicoloured (bright blue)	..	..	1·00	55
925	$5 multicoloured (azure)..	..	..	3·25	2·75
	a. Horiz pair. Nos. 925/6 ..	..		6·50	5·50
926	$5 multicoloured (bright blue)	..	..	3·25	2·75
919/26			Set of 8	9·50	6·75
MS927	Four sheets each 145 × 107 mm. (a) 30 c.				

As Nos. 919/20 each × 2; (b) 50 c. As Nos. 921/2 each × 2; (c) $1.50 As Nos. 923/4 each × 2; (d) $4.50 As Nos. 925/6 each × 2   *Set of 4 sheets* 20·00 18·00

The two designs of each value were printed together, *se-tenant*, in horizontal pairs throughout the sheets.

Two similar designs, each with a face value of $4, were prepared, but not issued.

150 Silos and Conveyor Belt   151 Michael Jackson

(Des G. Vasarhelyi. Litho Format)

1985 (17 Oct). *St. Vincent Flour Milling Industry. T* **150** *and similar horiz designs. Multicoloured.* W w **15**. P 15.

928	20 c. Type **150**..	..	..	15	15
929	30 c. Roller mills	..	..	15	20
930	75 c. Administration building	..	..	40	45
931	$3 Bran finishers ..	..	..	1·60	1·75
928/31			Set of 4	2·00	2·25

1985 (27 Oct). *Royal Visit. Nos.* 672/3, 697/8, 711, 724 *and* 912/13 *optd as T* **114** *of Montserrat or surch also.*

932	– 60 c. multicoloured (No. 711)	..	..	2·50	2·00
933	– 60 c. multicoloured (No. 724)	..	..	3·00	2·50
934	– 85 c. multicoloured (No. 912)	..	..	4·00	3·50
	a. Horiz pair. Nos. 934/5 ..	..		8·00	7·00
935	– 85 c. multicoloured (No. 913)	..	..	4·00	3·50

936	125	$1.50, multicoloured ..	..	4·00	4·00
937	–	$1.60 on $4 multicoloured (No. 672) ..	2·00	2·50
		a. Sheetlet. No. 937×6 and No. 938 .	19·00	
		ab. Sheetlet. No. 937×6 and No. 938a ..	19·00	
938	–	$1.60 on $4 multicoloured (No. 673)		
		(surch $1.60 only) ..	..	9·00	9·00
		a. Additionally optd "CARIBBEAN ROYAL VISIT—1985"	..	9·00	
939	–	$2.50, multicoloured (No. 698) ..	5·50	4·50
932/9			Set of 8	30·00	29·00

No. 938 shows a new face value only. "CARIBBEAN ROYAL VISIT—1985" being omitted from the surcharge. No. 938a is the corrected version issued subsequently.

(Des Court House Studio. Litho Format)

1985 (2 Dec). *Leaders of the World. Michael Jackson* (*entertainer*). *Various vertical portraits as T* **151**. *Multicoloured.* P 12½.

940	60 c. multicoloured	..	..	25	30
	a. Horiz pair. Nos. 940/1	..		50	60
941	60 c. multicoloured	..	..	25	30
942	$1 multicoloured	..	..	40	45
	a. Horiz pair. Nos. 942/3	..		80	90
943	$1 multicoloured	..	..	40	45
944	$2 multicoloured	..	..	85	90
	a. Horiz pair. Nos. 944/5	..		1·75	1·75
945	$2 multicoloured	..	..	85	90
946	$5 multicoloured	..	..	2·10	2·25
	a. Horiz pair. Nos. 946/7	..		4·25	4·50
947	$5 multicoloured	..	..	2·10	2·25
940/7			Set of 8	6·50	7·00
MS948	Four sheets, each 144×109 mm. (a) 45 c.				

As Nos. 940/1 each × 2; (b) 90 c. As Nos. 942/3 each × 2; (c) $1.50 As Nos. 944/5 each × 2; (d) $4 As Nos. 946/7 each × 2.   *Set of 4 sheets* 7·25 7·50

The two designs for each value were printed together, *se-tenant*, in horizontal pairs throughout the sheets. The left-hand design shows the face value at top left (as on Type **151**) and the right-hand design at top right.

152 "The Serenaders" (Kim de Freitas)   153 Santa Maria

(Litho Format)

1985 (9 Dec). *Christmas. Children's Paintings. T* **152** *and similar vert designs. Multicoloured.* W w **15**. P 13½ × 14.

949	25 c. Type **152** ..	..	..	15	15
950	75 c. "Poinsettia" (Jackie Douglas) ..	..	35	40
951	$2.50, "Jesus our Master" (Bernadette Payne) ..	..	..	1·25	1·40
949/51			Set of 3	1·50	1·75

(Litho Format)

1986 (23 Jan). *500th Anniv of Discovery of America* (1992) *by Columbus* (1st issue). *T* **153** *and similar vert designs. Multicoloured.* P 12½.

952	60 c. Type **153**	..	..	30	35
	a. Horiz pair. Nos. 952/3	..		60	70
953	60 c. Christopher Columbus	..	..	30	35
954	$1.50, Columbus at Spanish Court	..	..	75	80
	a. Horiz pair. Nos. 954/5	..		1·50	1·60
955	$1.50, King Ferdinand and Queen Isabella of Spain	..	..	75	80
956	$2.75, Santa Maria and fruits	..	..	1·40	1·50
	a. Horiz pair. Nos. 956/7	..		2·75	3·00
957	$2.75, Maize and fruits ..	..	..	1·40	1·50
952/7			Set of 6	4·50	4·75
MS958	95×85 mm. $6 Christopher Columbus (*different*) ..	..	..	3·25	3·75

The two designs of each value were printed together, *se-tenant*, in horizontal pairs within the sheets.

See also Nos. 1125/31, 1305/24, 1639/57 and 1677/85.

(Des Artists International. Litho Format)

1986 (27 Jan). *Leaders of the World. Automobiles* (5th series). *Horiz designs as T* **133**, *the first in each pair showing technical drawings and the second paintings.* P 12½.

959	30 c. black, cobalt and dull orange	..	..	15	15
	a. Vert pair. Nos. 959/60 ..	..		30	30
960	30 c. multicoloured	..	..	15	15
961	45 c. black, lavender-grey and blue..	..	15	15
	a. Vert pair. Nos. 961/2 ..	..		30	30
962	45 c. multicoloured	..	..	15	15
963	60 c. black, bright blue and vermilion	..	15	15
	a. Vert pair. Nos. 963/4 ..	..		30	30
964	60 c. multicoloured	..	..	15	15
965	90 c. black, greenish yellow and bright blue	..	20	20
	a. Vert pair. Nos. 965/6 ..	..		40	40
966	90 c. multicoloured ..	..	..	20	20
967	$1.50, black, pale rose-lilac & brt magenta	25	25
	a. Vert pair. Nos. 967/8 ..	..		50	50
968	$1.50, multicoloured	..	..	25	25
969	$2.50, black, blue and bright blue	..	..	30	30
	a. Vert pair. Nos. 969/70 ..	..		60	60
970	$2.50, multicoloured	..	..	30	30
959/70			Set of 12	2·10	2·10

Designs:—Nos. 959/60, Cadillac "Type 53" (1916); 961/2, Triumph "Dolomite" (1939); 963/4, Panther "J-72" (1972); 965/6, Ferrari "275 GTB/4" (1967); 967/8, Packard "Caribbean" (1953); 969/70, Bugatti "Type 41 Royale" (1931).

Nos. 959/70 were issued in a similar sheet format to Nos. 727/38.

154 Guide Salute and Handclasp   155 Halley's Comet

(Des Court House Studio. Litho Format)

1986 (25 Feb). *75th Anniv of Girl Guide Movement and Boy Scouts of America. Two sheets, each* 85 × 113 *mm, containing vert designs as T* **154**. *Multicoloured.* P 12½.

MS971	$5 Type **154**: $5 Palette and paintbrushes	4·00	5·00
MS972	$6 Cross-tied logs: $6 Lord Baden-Powell	5·00	6·00

The two stamps in each sheet were printed together, *se-tenant*, in horizontal pairs, each forming a composite design.

Nos. MS971/2 exist with plain or decorative margins.

Overprints on these miniature sheets commemorating "Capex '87" International Stamp Exhibition, Toronto, were not authorised by the St. Vincent administration.

(Des G. Vasarhelyi. Litho Format)

1986 (14 Apr). *Appearance of Halley's Comet. T* **155** *and similar horiz designs. Multicoloured.* W w **15**. P 15.

973	45 c. Type **155**..	..	..	50	30
974	60 c. Edmond Halley ..	..	..	60	40
975	75 c. Newton's telescope and astronomers ..	75	55
976	$3 Amateur astronomer on St. Vincent	..	2·25	2·25
973/6			Set of 4	3·75	3·25
MS977	155×104 mm. Nos. 973/6	..	..	3·75	4·50

(Des Court House Studio. Litho Format)

1986 (21 Apr). *60th Birthday of Queen Elizabeth II* (1st issue). *Multicoloured designs as T* **117a** *of Montserrat.* P 12½.

978	10 c. Queen Elizabeth II	..	..	10	10
979	90 c. Princess Elizabeth	..	..	30	30
980	$2.50, Queen gathering bouquets from crowd	..	..	75	75
981	$8 In Canberra, 1982 (*vert*)	..	..	2·00	2·50
978/81			Set of 4	2·75	3·25
MS982	85×115 mm. $10 Queen Elizabeth II (*different*) ..	..	..	4·50	5·50

156 Mexican Player   157 Queen Elizabeth at Victoria Park, Kingstown

(Des Court House Studio. Litho Format)

1986 (7 May). *World Cup Football Championship, Mexico. T* **156** *and similar multicoloured designs.* P 12½ (75 c., $2, $4, $5) *or* 15 (*others*).

983	1 c. Football and world map (*horiz*)	..	10	10
984	2 c. Type **156**..	..	..	10	10
985	5 c. Mexican player (*different*)	..	..	10	10
986	5 c. Hungary v Scotland	..	..	10	10
987	10 c. Spain v Scotland	..	..	10	10
988	30 c. England v U.S.S.R. (*horiz*)	..	..	20	20
989	45 c. Spain v France ..	..	..	30	30
990	75 c. Mexican team (56×36 *mm*)	..	..	45	40
991	$1 England v Italy ..	..	..	75	55
992	$2 Scottish team (56×36 *mm*)	..	..	1·40	1·10
993	$4 Spanish team (56×36 *mm*)	..	..	2·50	2·10
994	$5 English team (56×36 *mm*)	..	..	3·00	2·10
983/94			Set of 12	8·00	7·00
MS995	Four sheets, each 84×114 mm. (a) $1.50,				

As No. 993; (b) $2.25, As No. 992; (c) $2.50, As No. 990; (d) $5.50, As No. 994. P 12½   *Set of 4 sheets* 7·00 7·00

(Des Court House Studio. Litho Questa)

1986 (14 June). *60th Birthday of Queen Elizabeth II* (2nd issue). *T* **157** *and similar vert designs showing scenes from 1985 Royal Visit. Multicoloured.* W w **15**. P 15 × 14.

996	45 c. Type **157**..	..	..	25	30
997	60 c. Queen and Prime Minister James Mitchell, Bequia	..	..	30	35
998	75 c. Queen, Prince Phillip and Mr. Mitchell, Port Elizabeth, Bequia	..	35	40
999	$2.50, Queen, Prince Phillip and Mr. Mitchell watching Independence Day parade, Victoria Park ..	..	1·25	1·40
996/9			Set of 4	1·90	2·25
MS1000	121×85 mm. $3 Queen at Victoria Park	2·00	2·40

(Des T. Hadler. Litho Format)

1986 (15 July). *Leaders of the World. Railway Locomotives (6th series). Horiz designs as T 135. Multicoloured. P 12½.*

1001	30 c. multicoloured	..	10	10
	a. Vert pair. Nos. 1001/2	..	20	20
1002	30 c. multicoloured	..	10	10
1003	50 c. multicoloured	..	15	15
	a. Vert pair. Nos. 1003/4	..	30	30
1004	50 c. multicoloured	..	15	15
1005	$1 multicoloured	..	20	20
	a. Vert pair. Nos. 1005/6	..	40	40
1006	$1 multicoloured	..	20	20
1007	$3 multicoloured	..	60	60
	a. Vert pair. Nos. 1007/8	..	1·10	1·10
1008	$3 multicoloured	..	60	60
1001/8		*Set of 8*	1·75	1·75

Designs:—Nos. 1001/2, Class "ED41 BZZB" rack and adhesion locomotive, Japan (1926); 1003/4, Locomotive *The Judge*, Chicago Railroad Exposition, U.S.A. (1883); 1005/6, Class "E60C" electric locomotive, U.S.A. (1973); 1007/8, Class "SD40-2" diesel locomotive, U.S.A. (1972).

Nos. 1001/8 were issued in a similar sheet format to Nos. 727/38.

Nos. 1007/8 exist with the green omitted from stock dispersed by the liquidator of Format International Security Printers Ltd.

(Des Court House Studio. Litho Format)

1986 (18 July–15 Oct). *Royal Wedding (1st issue). Multicoloured designs as T 118a of Montserrat. P 12½.*

1009	60 c. Profile of Prince Andrew	..	20	25
	a. Pair. Nos. 1009/10	..	40	50
1010	60 c. Miss Sarah Ferguson	..	20	25
1011	$2 Prince Andrew with Mrs. Nancy Reagan (*horiz*)..		65	85
	a. Pair. Nos. 1011/12	..	1·25	1·60
1012	$2 Prince Andrew in naval uniform (*horiz*)	..	65	85
1009/12		*Set of 4*	1·60	2·10

MS1013 115×85 mm. $10 Duke and Duchess of York in carriage after wedding (*horiz*) (15.10) .. 3·75 4·50

Nos. 1009/10 and 1011/12 were each printed together, *se-tenant*, in horizontal and vertical pairs throughout the sheets.

158 *Acrocomia aculeata*

159 Cadet Force Emblem and Cadets of 1936 and 1986

(Des J. Cooter. Litho Questa)

1986 (30 Sept). *Timber Resources of St. Vincent. T 158 and similar vert designs. Multicoloured. W w 15 (sideways). P 14.*

1014	10 c. Type 158	..	30	15
1015	60 c. *Pithecellobium saman*..		90	60
1016	75 c. White Cedar	..	1·25	75
1017	$3 *Andira inermis*	..	3·25	3·50
1014/17		*Set of 4*	5·25	4·50

(Des G. Vasarhelyi. Litho Questa)

1986 (30 Sept). *50th Anniv of St. Vincent Cadet Force (45 c., $2) and 75th Anniv of St. Vincent Girls' High School (others). T 159 and similar multicoloured designs. W w 15 (sideways on 45 c.). P 14.*

1018	45 c. Type 159	..	30	30
1019	60 c. Grimble Building, Girls' High School	..	35	35
1020	$1.50, High School pupils (*horiz*)	..	80	80
1021	$2 Cadets on parade (*horiz*)	..	1·25	1·40
1018/21		*Set of 4*	2·40	2·25

1986 (15 Oct). *Royal Wedding (2nd issue). Nos. 1009/12 optd as T 121 of Montserrat in silver.*

1022	60 c. Profile of Prince Andrew	..	30	35
	a. Pair. Nos. 1022/3	..	60	70
1023	60 c. Miss Sarah Ferguson	..	30	35
1024	$2 Prince Andrew with Mrs. Nancy Reagan (*horiz*)..		1·00	1·10
	a. Pair. Nos. 1024/5	..	2·00	2·25
1025	$2 Prince Andrew in naval uniform (*horiz*)	..	1·00	1·10
1022/5		*Set of 4*	2·40	2·50

160 King Arthur

(Des G. Vasarhelyi. Litho Format)

1986 (3 Nov). *The Legend of King Arthur. T 160 and similar horiz designs. Multicoloured. P 14×13½.*

1026	30 c. Type 160	..	40	40
1027	45 c. Merlin taking baby Arthur	..	50	50
1028	60 c. Arthur pulling sword from stone	..	60	60
1029	75 c. Camelot	..	70	70

1030	$1 Arthur receiving Excalibur from the Lady of the Lake	..	80	80
1031	$1.50, Knights at the Round Table		1·25	1·25
1032	$2 The Holy Grail	..	1·50	1·50
1033	$5 Sir Lancelot jousting	..	2·75	2·75
1026/33		*Set of 8*	7·75	7·75

Nos. 1026/9 cancelled-to-order exist imperforate from stock dispersed by the liquidator of Format International Security Printers Ltd.

161 Statue of Liberty Floodlit **162** Fishing for Tri Tri

(Des Court House Studio. Litho Format)

1986 (26 Nov). *Centenary of Statue of Liberty. T 161 and similar vert designs showing aspects of the Statue. P 14×13½.*

1034	15 c. multicoloured	..	10	10
1035	25 c. multicoloured	..	15	15
1036	40 c. multicoloured	..	20	25
1037	55 c. multicoloured	..	25	30
1038	75 c. multicoloured	..	35	40
1039	90 c. multicoloured	..	45	50
1040	$1.75, multicoloured	..	90	95
1041	$2 multicoloured	..	1·00	1·10
1042	$2.50, multicoloured	..	1·25	1·40
1043	$3 multicoloured	..	1·50	1·60
1034/43		*Set of 10*	5·50	6·00

MS1044 Three sheets, each 85×115 mm. $3.50; $4; $5 .. *Set of 3 sheets* 7·00 8·50

(Des T. Hadler. Litho Format)

1986 (10 Dec). *Freshwater Fishing. T 162 and similar horiz designs. Multicoloured. P 15.*

1045	75 c. Type 162	..	35	40
	a. Pair. Nos. 1045/6	..	70	80
1046	75 c. Tri Tri	..	35	40
1047	$1.50, Crayfishing	..	75	80
	a. Pair. Nos. 1047/8	..	1·50	1·60
1048	$1.50, Crayfish	..	75	80
1045/8		*Set of 4*	2·00	2·10

Nos. 1045/6 and 1047/8 were each printed together, *se-tenant*, in horizontal and vertical pairs throughout the sheets.

163 Baby on Scales   **(164)**

(Des C. Abbott. Litho Format)

1987 (10 June). *Child Health Campaign. T 163 and similar vert designs. Multicoloured. P 14.*

1049	10 c. Type 163	..	10	10
1050	50 c. Oral rehydration therapy	..	45	40
1051	75 c. Breast feeding	..	60	55
1052	$1 Nurse giving injection	..	85	80
1049/52		*Set of 4*	1·75	1·60

1987 (10 June). *World Population Control. Nos. 1049/52 optd with T 164.*

1053	10 c. Type 163	..	10	10
1054	50 c. Oral rehydration therapy	..	50	40
1055	75 c. Breast feeding	..	65	55
1056	$1 Nurse giving injection	..	90	70
1053/6		*Set of 4*	1·90	1·60

165 Hanna Mandlikova   **166** Miss Prima Donna, Queen of the Bands, 1986

(Litho Format)

1987 (22 June). *International Lawn Tennis Players. T 165 and similar vert designs. Multicoloured. P 12½.*

1057	40 c. Type 165	..	25	25
1058	60 c. Yannick Noah	..	35	35
1059	80 c. Ivan Lendl	..	40	40
1060	$1 Chris Evert	..	50	50
1061	$1.25, Steffi Graf	..	60	60
1062	$1.50, John McEnroe	..	75	75
1063	$1.75, Martina Navratilova with Wimbledon trophy	..	85	85
1064	$2 Boris Becker with Wimbledon trophy		95	95
1057/64		*Set of 8*	4·25	4·25

MS1065 115×85 mm. $2.25 As No. 1063; $2.25 As No. 1064 .. .. 2·75 3·25

Designs as Nos. 1063/4, but each with a face value of $10, also exist embossed on gold foil from a restricted printing.

(Des Young Phillips. Litho Format)

1987 (29 June). *10th Anniv of Carnival. T 166 and similar vert designs. Multicoloured. P 12½.*

1066	20 c. Type 166	..	10	15
1067	45 c. Donna Young, Miss Carnival, 1985		20	25
1068	55 c. Miss St. Vincent and the Grenadines, 1986		25	30
1069	$3.70, "Spirit of Hope" costume, 1986		1·60	1·75
1066/9		*Set of 4*	1·90	2·25

The 45 c. value is inscribed "Miss Carival" in error.

(167)   **168** Queen Victoria, 1841

1987 (26 Aug). *10th Death Anniv of Elvis Presley (entertainer). Nos. 919/27 optd with T 167 in silver.*

1070	10 c. multicoloured (T 149)..	..	10	10
	a. Horiz pair. Nos. 1070/1	..	10	10
1071	10 c. multicoloured (bright blue)	..	10	10
1072	60 c. multicoloured (brown)	..	25	30
	a. Horiz pair. Nos. 1072/3	..	50	60
1073	60 c. multicoloured (pale grey)	..	25	30
1074	$1 multicoloured (brown)	..	40	45
	a. Horiz pair. Nos. 1074/5	..	80	90
1075	$1 multicoloured (bright blue)	..	40	45
1076	$5 multicoloured (azure)..	..	2·10	2·25
	a. Horiz pair. Nos. 1076/7	..	4·25	4·50
1077	$5 multicoloured (bright blue)	..	2·10	2·25
1070/7		*Set of 8*	5·00	5·50

MS1078 Four sheets, each 145 × 107 mm. (a) 30 c. As Nos. 1070/1 each × 2; (b) 50 c. As Nos. 1072/3 each × 2; (c) $1.50, As Nos. 1074/5 each × 2; (d) $4.50, As Nos. 1076/7 each × 2 .. .. 7·00 7·25

(Des Young Phillips. Litho Format)

1987 (15 Oct). *Royal Ruby Wedding and 150th Anniv of Queen Victoria's Accession. T 168 and similar vert designs. Multicoloured. P 12½.*

1079	15 c. Type 168	..	15	10
1080	75 c. Queen Elizabeth and Prince Andrew, 1960	..	45	40
1081	$1 Coronation, 1953	..	60	50
1082	$2.50, Duke of Edinburgh, 1948..		1·40	1·50
1083	$5 Queen Elizabeth II, c. 1980	..	2·50	2·75
1079/83		*Set of 5*	4·50	4·75

MS1084 85×115 mm. $6 Princess Elizabeth with Prince Charles at his Christening, 1948 .. 3·75 4·00

169 Karl Benz and Benz Three-wheeler (1886)

(Litho Format)

1987 (4 Dec), *Century of Motoring. T 169 and similar horiz designs. Multicoloured. P 12½.*

1085	$1 Type 169	..	60	60
1086	$2 Enzo Ferrari and Ferrari "Dino 206SP" (1966)		1·25	1·25
1087	$4 Charles Rolls and Sir Henry Royce and Rolls-Royce "Silver Ghost" (1907) ..		2·00	2·00
1088	$5 Henry Ford and Ford "Model T" (1908)..		2·50	2·50
1085/8		*Set of 4*	5·75	5·75

MS1089 Four sheets, each 144 × 75 mm. (a) $3 As Type 169. (b) $5 As No. 1086. (c) $6 As No. 1087. (d) $8 As No. 1088 .. *Set of 4 sheets* 17·00 18·00

Nos. 1085/8 with the gold omitted and Nos. 1088 and MS1089d with Henry Ford facing right all exist from stock dispersed by the liquidator of Format International Security Printers Ltd.

170 Everton Football Team

(Litho Format)

1987 (4 Dec). *English Football Teams.* T **170** *and similar horiz designs. Multicoloured.* P 12½.

1090	$2 Type **170**	..	..	..	1·25	1·25
1091	$2 Manchester United	..	..	..	1·25	1·25
1092	$2 Tottenham Hotspur	..	..	1·25	1·25
1093	$2 Arsenal	..	..	..	1·25	1·25
1094	$2 Liverpool	..	..	..	1·25	1·25
1095	$2 Derby County	..	..	..	1·25	1·25
1096	$2 Portsmouth	..	..	..	1·25	1·25
1097	$2 Leeds United	..	..	..	1·25	1·25
1090/7		..	..	*Set of 8*	9·00	9·00

171 Five Cent Coins   172 Charles Dickens

(Des Questa ($20), Young Phillips Studio (others))

1987 (11 Dec)–**91**. *East Caribbean Currency.* T **171** *and similar multicoloured designs.* (a) *Litho Format.* P 15

1098	5 c. Type **171**	..	..	10	10
1099	6 c. Two cent coins	..	..	10	10
1100	10 c. Ten cent coins	..	..	10	10
1101	12 c. Two and ten cent coins	..	10	10
1102	15 c. Five cent coins	..	..	10	10
1103	20 c. Ten cent coins	..	..	10	10
1104	25 c. Twenty-five cent coins	..	10	15
1105	30 c. Five and twenty-five cent coins	..	10	15
1106	35 c. Twenty-five and ten cent coins	..	15	20
1107	45 c. Twenty-five and two ten cent coins	..	20	25
1108	50 c. Fifty cent coins	..	..	20	25
1109	65 c. Fifty, ten and five cent coins	..	30	35
1110	75 c. Fifty and twenty-five cent coins	..	35	40
1111	$1 One dollar note (*horiz*)	..	45	50
1112	$2 Two one dollar notes (*horiz*)	..	85	90
1113	$3 Three one dollar notes (*horiz*)	..	1·25	1·40
1114	$5 Five dollar note (*horiz*)	..	2·25	2·40
1115	$10 Ten dollar note (*horiz*)	..	4·25	4·50
1098/115			*Set of 18*	9·50	10·50

(b) *Litho Questa.* P 14 (1989–91)

1115*a*	5 c. Type **171**	..	..	10	10
1115*c*	10 c. Ten cent coins	..	..	10	10
1115*e*	15 c. Five cent coins	..	..	10	10
1115*f*	20 c. Ten cent coins	..	..	10	10
1115*g*	25 c. Twenty-five cent coins	..	10	10
1115*j*	45 c. Twenty-five and two ten cent coins	20	25
1115*k*	50 c. Fifty cent coins	..	..	20	25
1115*l*	65 c. Fifty, ten and five cent coins	..	30	35
1115*m*	75 c. Fifty and twenty-five cent coins	..	35	40
1115*n*	$1 One dollar note (*horiz*)	..	45	50
1115*o*	$2 Two one dollar notes (*horiz*)	..	85	90
1115*q*	$5 Five dollar note (*horiz*)	..	2·25	2·40
1115*s*	$20 Twenty-dollar note (*horiz*) (7.11.89)	8·75	9·00
1115*a/s*			*Set of 13*	12·50	13·00

No. 1100 overprinted "SPECIMEN" and with the blue omitted exists from stock dispersed by the liquidator of Format International Security Printers Ltd.

(Des Jennifer Toombs. Litho Format)

1987 (17 Dec). *Christmas. 175th Birth Anniv of Charles Dickens.* T **172** *and similar vert designs. Multicoloured.* P 14 × 14½.

1116	6 c. Type **172**	..	..	10	10
	a. Horiz pair. Nos. 1116/17	..	15	15
1117	6 c. "Mr. Fezziwig's Ball"	..	10	10
1118	25 c. Type **172**	..	..	15	15
	a. Horiz pair. Nos. 1118/19	..	30	30
1119	25 c. "Scrooge's Third Visitor"	..	15	15
1120	50 c. Type **172**	..	..	30	30
	a. Horiz pair. Nos. 1120/1	..	60	60
1121	50 c. "The Cratchits' Christmas"	..	30	30
1122	75 c. Type **172**	..	..	45	45
	a. Horiz pair. Nos. 1122/3	..	90	90
1123	75 c. "A Christmas Carol"	..	45	45
1116/23			*Set of 8*	1·75	1·75
MS1124	141 × 101 mm. $5 Teacher reading to class			2·75	3·25

Nos. 1116/17, 1118/19, 1120/1 and 1122/3 were printed together, *se-tenant*, in horizontal pairs throughout the sheets, each pair forming a composite design showing an open book. The first design in each pair shows Type **172** and the second a scene from *A Christmas Carol.*

---

173 Santa Maria   174 Brown Pelican

(Des M. Pollard. Litho Format)

1988 (11 Jan). *500th Anniv of Discovery of America (1992) by Columbus (2nd issue).* T **173** *and similar square designs. Multicoloured.* P 14.

1125	15 c. Type **173**	..	..	15	15
1126	75 c. *Nina* and *Pinta*	..	..	50	50
1127	$1 Compass and hourglass	..	70	70
1128	$1.50, Claiming the New World for Spain	90	90
1129	$3 Arawak village	..	..	1·50	1·50
1130	$4 Parrot, hummingbird, pineapple and maize			2·00	2·00
1125/30			*Set of 6*	5·25	5·25
MS1131	114 × 86 mm. $5 Columbus, Arms and *Santa Maria.* P 13½ × 14			4·25	4·75

Further unissued $2 and $5 miniature sheets exist from stock dispersed by the liquidator of Format International Security Printers Ltd.

(Des Maxine Marsh. Litho Format)

1988 (15 Feb). P 14.

1132	**174** 45 c. multicoloured	..	..	20	25

175 Windsurfing

(Litho Format)

1988 (26 Feb). *Tourism.* T **175** *and similar multicoloured designs.* P 15.

1133	10 c. Type **175**	..	..	10	10
1134	45 c. Scuba diving	..	..	20	25
1135	65 c. Aerial view of Young Island (*horiz*)	30	35
1136	$5 Charter yacht (*horiz*)	..	2·10	2·25
1133/6			*Set of 4*	2·40	2·50
MS1136a	115×85 mm $10 Two windsurfers off St. Vincent (60×40 mm). P 12½			4·00	4·50

176 *Nuestra Sénora del Rosario* (galleon) and Spanish Knight's Cross

(Litho Format)

1988 (29 July). *400th Anniv of Spanish Armada.* T **176** *and similar horiz designs. Multicoloured.* P 12½.

1137	15 c. Type **176**	..	..	15	10
1138	75 c. *Ark Royal* and English Armada medal	30	35
1139	$1.50, English fleet and Drake's dial	60	65
1140	$2 Dismasted Spanish ship and 16th-century shot			80	85
1141	$3.50, Attack of English fireships at Calais and 16th-century grenade		1·50	1·60
1142	$5 *Revenge* and Drake's Drum	..	2·10	2·25
1137/42			*Set of 6*	4·75	5·25
MS1143	123 × 92 mm. $8 Sighting the Armada		3·50	3·75

177 D. K. Lillee   178 Athletics

(Litho Format)

1988 (29 July). *Cricketers of 1988 International Season.* T **177** *and similar square designs. Multicoloured.* P 14.

1144	15 c. Type **177**	..	..	30	30
1145	50 c. G. A. Gooch	..	..	50	50
1146	75 c. R. N. Kapil Dev	..	70	70
1147	$1 S. M. Gavaskar	..	..	85	85
1148	$1.50, M. W. Gatting	..	1·25	1·25
1149	$2.50, Imran Khan	..	..	1·75	1·75
1150	$3 I. T. Botham	..	..	2·00	2·00
1151	$4 I. V. A. Richards	..	2·25	2·25
1144/51			*Set of 8*	8·50	8·50
MS1152	130 × 80 mm. $2 As $4; $3.50, As $3	3·50	4·00

Examples of No. **MS1152** imperforate or part perforate exist from stock dispersed by the liquidator of Format International Security Printers Ltd.

(Des S. Angela. Litho Questa)

1988 (7 Dec). *Olympic Games, Seoul.* T **178** *and similar multicoloured designs.* P 14.

1153	10 c. Type **178**	..	..	10	10
1154	50 c. Long jumping (*vert*)	..	20	25
1155	$1 Triple jumping	..	..	40	45
1156	$5 Boxing (*vert*)	..	..	2·10	2·25
1153/6			*Set of 4*	2·50	2·75
MS1157	85 × 63 mm. $10 Olympic flame		4·25	4·50

A different set of six values and a miniature sheet for this event was not issued, but exists from stock dispersed by the liquidator of Format International Security Printers Ltd.

179 Babe Ruth   180 Los Angeles Dodgers (National League Champions)

(Litho Questa)

1988 (7 Dec). *Famous Baseball Players (1st series).* P 14.

1158	**179** $2 multicoloured	..	..	1·10	1·10

No. 1158 also exists embossed on gold foil from a restricted printing.

See also Nos. 1264/75, 1407 and 1408/88.

(Des W. Storozuk. Litho Questa)

1988 (7 Dec). *1988 Baseball World Series. Sheet* 115×85 mm *containing* T **180** *and similar horiz design. Multicoloured.* P 14×13½.

MS1159	$2 Type **180**; $2 Team logos of Dodgers and Oakland Athletics			1·75	1·90

(Des Walt Disney Co. Litho Questa)

1988 (23 Dec). *Christmas. "Mickey's Christmas Train". Multicoloured designs as* T **171***a of Lesotho.* P 14×13½.

1160	1 c. Minnie Mouse in parcels van (*horiz*)	10	10
1161	2 c. Mordie and Ferdie on low-loader wagon (*horiz*)		10	10
1162	3 c. Chip n'Dale in wagon with Christmas trees (*horiz*)		10	10
1163	4 c. Donald Duck's nephews riding with reindeer (*horiz*)		10	10
1164	5 c. Donald and Daisy Duck in restaurant car (*horiz*)		10	10
1165	10 c. Grandma Duck, Uncle Scrooge McDuck, Goofy and Clarabelle carol singing in carriage (*horiz*)		10	10
1166	$5 Mickey Mouse driving locomotive (*horiz*)		2·10	2·25
1167	$6 Father Christmas in guard's van (*horiz*)		2·50	2·75
1160/7			*Set of 8*	4·50	4·75
MS1168	Two sheets, each 127 × 102 mm, (a) $5 Mickey Mouse and nephews at railway station. (b) $5 Mickey and Minnie Mouse on carousel. P 13½×14		*Set of 2 sheets*	4·25	4·50

181 Mickey Mouse as Snake Charmer

(Des Walt Disney Co. Litho Questa)

1989 (8 Feb). *"India-89" International Stamp Exhibition, New Delhi.* T **181** *and similar multicoloured designs showing Walt Disney cartoon characters in India.* P 14×13½.

1169	1 c. Type **181**	..	..	10	10
1170	2 c. Goofy with Chowsingha Antelope	10	10
1171	3 c. Mickey and Minnie Mouse with Common Peafowl		10	10
1172	5 c. Goofy with Briolette Diamond and Mickey Mouse pushing mine truck		10	10
1173	10 c. Clarabelle with Orloff Diamond	10	10
1174	25 c. Mickey Mouse as tourist and Regent Diamond, Louvre, Paris		10	15

1299	60 c. Jose Canseco	25	30
1300	60 c. Gaylord Perry	25	30
1301	60 c. Orel Hershiser	25	30
1302	60 c. Frank Viola	25	30
1294/1302	*Set of 9*	2·00	2·40

Nos. 1294/302 were printed together, *se-tenant*, in a sheetlet of 9.

193 All-Star Game Line-up
(*Illustration reduced. Actual size 115 × 80 mm*)

(Des Rosemary De Figlio. Litho Questa)

1989 (23 July). *American League v National League All-Star Game, 1989. Sheet 115×81 mm. Imperf.*
MS1303 **193** $5 multicoloured .. .. .. 2·10 2·25

194 St. Vincent Amazon **195** Queen Conch and West Indian Purpura Shells

(Des Maxine North. Litho Questa)

1989 (31 July). P 15×14.
1304 **194** 55 c. multicoloured 25 30

(Des I. MacLaury. Litho B.D.T.)

1989 (31 Aug). *500th Anniv of Discovery of America by Columbus (1992) (3rd issue). T* **195** *and similar horiz designs. P 14.*

1305	50 c. multicoloured	20	25
	a. Sheetlet. Nos. 1305/24	3·50	
1306	50 c. multicoloured	20	25
1307	50 c. dull ultramarine, black & brt new blue	20	25
1308	50 c. dull ultramarine, black & brt new blue	20	25
1309	50 c. multicoloured	20	25
1310	50 c. multicoloured	20	25
1311	50 c. multicoloured	20	25
1312	50 c. black and bright new blue	20	25
1313	50 c. multicoloured	20	25
1314	50 c. multicoloured	20	25
1315	50 c. multicoloured	20	25
1316	50 c. multicoloured	20	25
1317	50 c. multicoloured	20	25
1318	50 c. multicoloured	20	25
1319	50 c. multicoloured	20	25
1320	50 c. multicoloured	20	25
1321	50 c. multicoloured	20	25
1322	50 c. multicoloured	20	25
1323	50 c. multicoloured	20	25
1324	50 c. multicoloured	20	25
1305/24	*Set of 20*	3·50	4·50

Designs:—No. 1305, Type **195**; 1306, Caribbean reef fishes; 1307, Sperm Whale; 1308, Fleet of Columbus; 1309, Remora (fish); 1310, Columbus planting flag; 1311, Navigational instruments; 1312, Sea monster; 1313, Kemp's Ridley Turtle; 1314, Magnificent Frigate Bird; 1315, Caribbean Manatee; 1316, Caribbean Monk Seal; 1317, Mayan chief, dugout canoe and caravel; 1318, Blue-footed Boobies; 1319, Venezuelan pile village; 1320, Atlantic Wing Oyster and Lion's Paw Scallop; 1321, Great Hammerhead and Mako Sharks; 1322, Brown Pelican and Hyacinth Macaw; 1323, Venezuelan bowmen; 1324, Capuchin and Squirrel Monkeys.

Nos. 1305/24 were printed together, *se-tenant*, in a sheetlet of 20 (4×5), forming a composite design of a Caribbean map showing the voyages of Columbus.

196 Command Module *Columbia* returning to Earth

(Des W. Wright. Litho Questa)

1989 (11 Sept). *20th Anniv of First Manned Landing on Moon. T* **196** *and similar multicoloured designs. P 14.*

1325	35 c. Type **196**	15	20
1326	75 c. Lunar module *Eagle* landing	30	35
1327	$1 "Apollo 11" launch	40	45
1328	$2 Buzz Aldrin on Moon	85	90
	a. Horiz strip of 4. Nos. 1328/31	3·50	
1329	$2 Lunar module *Eagle*	85	90

1330	$2 Earthrise from the Moon	85	90
1331	$2 Neil Armstrong	85	90
1332	$3 *Eagle* and *Columbia* in Moon Orbit	1·25	1·40
1325/32	*Set of 8*	5·00	5·50

MS1333 Two sheets, each 108×79 mm. (a) $3 Command Module *Columbia*, $3 Lunar Module *Eagle*. (b) $6 Neil Armstrong stepping on to Moon (*vert*) .. .. *Set of 2 sheets* 5·00 5·25
Nos. 1328/31 were printed together, *se-tenant*, in horizontal strips of four throughout the sheet.

197 Jay Howell and Alejandro Pena

1989 (23 Sept). *Centenary of the Los Angeles Dodgers (1st issue). Baseball Players. T* **197** *and similar horiz designs. Multicoloured. Litho. P 12½.*

1334	60 c. Type **197**	25	30
	a. Sheetlet. Nos. 1334/41	2·25	
1335	60 c. Mike Davis and Kirk Gibson	25	30
1336	60 c. Fernando Valenzuela and John Shelby	25	30
1337	60 c. Jeff Hamilton and Franklin Stubbs	25	30
1338	60 c. Aerial view of Dodger stadium	25	30
1339	60 c. Ray Searage and John Tudor	25	30
1340	60 c. Mike Sharperson and Mickey Hatcher	25	30
1341	60 c. Coaching staff	25	30
1342	60 c. John Wetteland and Ramon Martinez	25	30
1343	60 c. Tim Belcher and Tim Crews	25	30
	a. Sheetlet. Nos. 1343/51	2·25	
1344	60 c. Orel Hershiser and Mike Morgan	25	30
1345	60 c. Mike Scioscia and Rick Dempsey	25	30
1346	60 c. Dave Anderson and Alfredo Griffin	25	30
1347	60 c. Dodgers emblem	25	30
1348	60 c. Kal Daniels and Mike Marshall	25	30
1349	60 c. Eddie Murray and Willie Randolph	25	30
1350	60 c. Tom Lasorda and Jose Gonzalez	25	30
1351	60 c. Lenny Harris, Chris Gwynn and Billy Bean	25	30
1334/51	*Set of 18*	4·00	4·75

Nos. 1334/42 and 1343/51 were each printed together, *se-tenant*, in sheetlets of 9.

For similar stamps, but rouletted 7, see Nos. 1541/58.

198 *Eurema venusta* **199** Young Footballers

(Des D. Bruckner. Litho Questa)

1989 (16 Oct). *Butterflies. T* **198** *and similar multicoloured designs. P 14×14½.*

1352	6 c. Type **198**	10	10
1353	10 c. *Historis odius*	10	10
1354	15 c. *Cynthia virginiensis*	10	10
1355	75 c. *Leptotes cassius*	35	40
1356	$1 *Battus polydamas*	45	50
1357	$2 *Astraptes talus*	85	90
1358	$3 *Danaus gilippus*	1·25	1·40
1359	$5 *Myscelia antholia*	2·25	2·40
1352/9	*Set of 8*	5·00	5·25

MS1360 Two sheets, each 76×103 mm. (a) $6 *Danaus plexippus* (*vert*). (b) $6 *Eurema daira* (*vert*). P 14½×14 .. .. *Set of 2 sheets* 5·25 5·50

(Des R. Vigurs. Litho B.D.T.)

1989 (16 Oct). *World Cup Football Championship, Italy (1st issue) (1990). T* **199** *and similar horiz designs. Multicoloured. P 14.*

1361	10 c. Type **199**	10	10
1362	55 c. Youth football teams	25	30
1363	$1 St. Vincent team in training	40	45
1364	$5 National team with trophies	2·10	2·25
1361/4	*Set of 4*	2·50	2·75

MS1365 Two sheets, each 103×73 mm. (a) $6 Youth team. (b) $6 National team *Set of 2 sheets* 7·00 7·50
See also Nos. 1559/63.

+10c

200 St. Vincent Amazon (**201**)

	CALIF. EARTHQUAKE RELIEF

(Des Tracy Pedersen. Litho Questa)

1989 (1 Nov). *Wildlife. T* **200** *and similar multicoloured designs. P 14.*

1366	65 c. Type **200**	35	40
1367	75 c. Whistling Warbler	45	45
1368	$5 Black Snake	2·40	2·75
1366/8	*Set of 3*	3·00	3·25

MS1369 97×70 mm. $6 Volcano Plant (*vert*) 3·00 3·50

1989 (17 Nov). *California Earthquake Relief Fund. Nos. 1276/1302 surch as T* **201**.

1370	60 c. + 10 c. Type **191**	35	35
	a. Sheetlet. Nos. 1370/8	2·75	
1371	60 c. + 10 c. Carl Yastrzemski	35	35
1372	60 c. + 10 c. Randy Johnson	35	35
1373	60 c. + 10 c. Jerome Walton	35	35
1374	60 c. + 10 c. Ramon Martinez	35	35
1375	60 c. + 10 c. Ken Hill	35	35
1376	60 c. + 10 c. Tom McCarthy	35	35
1377	60 c. + 10 c. Gaylord Perry	35	35
1378	60 c. + 10 c. John Smoltz	35	35
1379	60 c. + 10 c. Bob Milacki	35	35
	a. Sheetlet. Nos. 1379/87	2·75	
1380	60 c. + 10 c. Babe Ruth	35	35
1381	60 c. + 10 c. Jim Abbott	35	35
1382	60 c. + 10 c. Gary Sheffield	35	35
1383	60 c. + 10 c. Gregg Jeffries	35	35
1384	60 c. + 10 c. Kevin Brown	35	35
1385	60 c. + 10 c. Cris Carpenter	35	35
1386	60 c. + 10 c. Johnny Bench	35	35
1387	60 c. + 10 c. Ken Griffey Jr	35	35
1388	60 c. + 10 c. Type **192**	35	35
	a. Sheetlet. Nos. 1388/96	2·75	
1389	60 c. + 10 c. Walt Weiss	35	35
1390	60 c. + 10 c. Willie Mays	35	35
1391	60 c. + 10 c. Kirk Gibson	35	35
1392	60 c. + 10 c. Ted Williams	35	35
1393	60 c. + 10 c. Jose Canseco	35	35
1394	60 c. + 10 c. Gaylord Perry	35	35
1395	60 c. + 10 c. Orel Hershiser	35	35
1396	60 c. + 10 c. Frank Viola	35	35
1370/96	*Set of 27*	8·25	8·25

(Des Walt Disney Co. Litho Questa)

1989 (17 Nov). *"World Stamp Expo '89" International Stamp Exhibition, Washington (1st issue). Multicoloured designs as T* **234** *of Maldive Islands showing Walt Disney cartoon characters and U.S. monuments. P 13½×14.*

1397	1 c. Mickey and Minnie Mouse by Seagull Monument, Utah (*vert*)	10	10
1398	2 c. Mickey Mouse and Goofy at Lincoln Memorial (*vert*)	10	10
1399	3 c. Mickey and Minnie Mouse at Crazy Horse Memorial, South Dakota (*vert*)	10	10
1400	4 c. Mickey Mouse saluting "Uncle Sam" Wilson statue, New York (*vert*)	10	10
1401	5 c. Goofy and Mickey Mouse at Benjamin Franklin Memorial, Philadelphia (*vert*)	10	10
1402	10 c. Goofy and Mickey Mouse at George Washington statue, New York (*vert*)	10	10
1403	$3 Mickey Mouse at John F. Kennedy's birthplace, Massachusetts (*vert*)	1·25	1·40
1404	$6 Mickey and Minnie Mouse at Mount Vernon, Virginia (*vert*)	2·50	2·75
1397/1404	*Set of 8*	3·75	4·00

MS1405 Two sheets, each 127×100 mm. (a) $5 Mickey and Minnie Mouse over Mount Rushmore, South Dakota. (b) $5 Mickey Mouse and Donald Duck at Stone Mountain, Georgia. P 14×13½ .. .. *Set of 2 sheets* 4·75 5·00

(Des Design Element. Litho Questa)

1989 (17 Nov). *"World Stamp Expo '89" International Stamp Exhibition, Washington (2nd issue). Sheet 61×78 mm containing multicoloured designs as T* **193a** *of Lesotho. P 14.*
MS1406 $5 Washington Monument (*vert*) 2·10 2·25

202 Nolan Ryan

(Des W. Storozuk. Litho)

1989 (30 Nov). *Famous Baseball Players (3rd series). P 12½.*
1407 **202** $2 multicoloured 85 90
a. Sheetlet of 9 .. .. 7·75
No. 1407 was printed in sheetlets of 9, with each stamp showing a different commemorative inscription.

| 203 Early Wynn | 204 Arms and 1979 Independence 50 c. Stamp |

(Des Susan Gansbourg. Litho)

1989 (30 Nov). *Famous Baseball Players* (4th series). T **203** *and similar horiz designs.* P 12½.
1408/88 30 c. × 81 multicoloured .. Set of 81 10·00 10·50
Nos. 1408/88 were issued as nine sheetlets, each of 9 different designs. No. 1456 (Mike Greenwell) was also available in sheetlets containing nine examples of the one design.

(Des and litho Questa)

1989 (20 Dec). *10th Anniv of Independence.* P 14.
1489 **204** 65 c. multicoloured 30 35
MS1490 57×77 mm. **204** $10 multicoloured .. 4·25 4·50

(Litho Questa)

1989 (20 Dec). *Christmas. Paintings by Botticelli and Da Vinci. Vert designs as* T **193**b *of Lesotho. Multicoloured.* P 14.
1491 10 c. Holy Family (detail, "The Adoration of the Magi") (Botticelli) .. 10 10
1492 25 c. Crowd (detail, "The Adoration of the Magi") (Botticelli) .. 10 15
1493 30 c. "The Madonna of the Magnificat" (detail) (Botticelli) .. 10 15
1494 40 c. "The Virgin and Child with St. Anne and St. John the Baptist" (detail) (Da Vinci) .. 15 20
1495 55 c. Angel (detail, "The Annunciation") (Da Vinci) .. 25 30
1496 75 c. Virgin Mary (detail, "The Annunciation") (Da Vinci) .. 30 35
1497 $5 "Madonna of the Carnation" (detail) (Da Vinci) .. 2·10 2·25
1498 $6 "The Annunciation" (detail) (Botticelli) .. .. 2·50 2·75
1491/8 .. .. Set of 8 5·00 5·50
MS1499 Two sheets, each 70×94 mm. (a) $5 "The Virgin of the Rocks" (detail) (Da Vinci). (b) $5 Holy Family (detail, "The Adoration of the Magi") (Botticelli) .. Set of 2 sheets 4·25 4·50

| 205 Boy Scout, 1989 | 206 Man and Blind Girl |

(Des A. Fagbohun. Litho Questa)

1989 (20 Dec). *75th Anniv of Boy Scout and 60th Anniv of Girl Guide Movements in St. Vincent.* T **205** *and similar multicoloured designs, each showing portrait of Lord or Lady Baden-Powell.* P 14.
1500 35 c. Type **205** 25 20
1501 35 c. Guide, ranger and brownie .. 25 20
1502 55 c. Boy scout in original uniform .. 35 30
1503 55 c. Mrs. Jackson (founder of St. Vincent Girl Guides) 35 30
1504 $2 Scouts' 75th Anniv logo .. 1·10 1·25
1505 $2 Mrs. Russell (Girl Guide leader, 1989) .. .. 1·10 1·25
1500/5 .. .. Set of 6 3·00 3·25
MS1506 Two sheets, each 105×75 mm. (a) $5 Scout in canoe. (b) $5 Scout and Guide with flagpoles (horiz) .. Set of 2 sheets 5·50 6·00

(Des W. Hanson Studio. Litho Questa)

1990 (5 Mar). *25th Anniv of Lions Club of St. Vincent* (1989). T **206** *and similar multicoloured designs.* P 14.
1507 10 c. Type **206** 10 10
1508 65 c. Handing out school books (horiz) .. 30 35
1509 75 c. Teacher explaining diabetes (horiz) 35 40
1510 $2 Blood sugar testing machine (horiz) 85 90
1511 $4 Distributing book on drugs (horiz) 1·75 1·90
1507/11 .. .. Set of 5 3·00 3·25

(Des W. Wright. Litho Questa)

1990 (2 Apr). *50th Anniv of Second World War. Horiz designs as* T **242** *of Maldive Islands. Multicoloured.* P 14.
1512 5 c. Scuttling of *Admiral Graf Spee*, 1939 10 10
1513 10 c. General De Gaulle and French resistance, 1940 .. .. 10 10
1514 15 c. British tank, North Africa, 1940 .. 10 10
1515 25 c. U.S.S. *Reuben James* in periscope sight, 1941 .. .. 10 15
1516 30 c. General MacArthur and map of S.W. Pacific, 1942 .. 15 20
1517 45 c. American parachute drop on Corregidor, 1945 .. 15 20

1518 55 c. H.M.S. *King George V* engaging Bismarck, 1941 .. 20 25
1519 75 c. American battleships entering Tokyo Bay, 1945 .. .. 35 40
1520 $5 Hoisting the Soviet flag on the Reichstag, Berlin, 1945 .. 2·25 2·40
1521 $6 American carriers, Battle of Philippine Sea, 1944 .. 2·50 2·75
1512/21 .. .. Set of 10 5·25 6·00
MS1522 100×70 mm. $6 Japanese Zero fighter, Battle of Java Sea, 1942 .. .. 2·50 2·75

**Sixth No-Hitter
11 June 90
Oakland Athletics**

| 207 Two Pence Blue | (208) |

(Des M. Pollard. Litho B.D.T)

1990 (3 May). *150th Anniv of the Penny Black.* T **207** *and similar vert designs.* P 14×15.
1523 $2 black, blue-green and bright magenta 85 90
1524 $4 black and bright magenta .. 1·75 1·90
MS1525 130×99 mm. $6 black, scarlet & yellow 2·50 2·75
Designs:—$4, $6 Penny Black.

(Des Walt Disney Co. Litho Questa)

1990 (3 May). *"Stamp World London 90" International Stamp Exhibition. British Uniforms. Multicoloured designs as* T **239**a *of Maldive Islands showing Walt Disney cartoon characters.* P 13½×14.
1526 5 c. Scrooge McDuck as 18th-century admiral (vert) .. 10 10
1527 10 c. Huey as Light Infantry bugler, 1854 (vert) 10 10
1528 15 c. Minnie Mouse as Irish Guards drummer, 1900 (vert) .. 10 10
1529 25 c. Goofy as Seaforth Highlanders lance-corporal, 1944 (vert) .. 10 15
1530 $1 Mickey Mouse as 58th Regiment ensign, 1879 (vert) .. 45 50
1531 $2 Donald Duck as Royal Engineers officer, 1813 (vert) .. 85 90
1532 $4 Mickey Mouse as Duke of Edinburgh's Royal Regiment drum major (vert) .. 1·75 1·90
1533 $5 Goofy as Cameronians sergeant piper, 1918 (vert) .. .. 2·25 2·40
1526/33 .. .. Set of 8 5·00 5·50
MS1534 Two sheets, each 120x100 mm. (a) $6 Goofy as officer in King's Lifeguard of Foot, 1643. P 13½×14. (b) $6 Mickey Mouse as Grenadier Guards drummer (vert). P 14×13½
.. .. Set of 2 sheets 5·25 5·50

1990 (23 June). *Nolan Ryan–Sixth No-hitter. No.* 1407 *optd with* T **208**.
1535 **202** $2 multicoloured 85 90
a. Sheetlet of 9 .. .. 7·75

(Des Young Phillips Studio. Litho Questa)

1990 (5 July). *90th Birthday of Queen Elizabeth the Queen Mother. Vert designs as* T **198**a *of Lesotho showing portraits, 1950–59.* P 14.
1536 $2 black, bright sage-green and magenta 85 90
a. Strip of 3. Nos. 1536/8 .. 2·25
1537 $2 black, bright sage-green and magenta 85 90
1538 $2 black, bright sage-green and magenta 85 90
1536/8 .. .. Set of 3 2·25 2·40
MS1539 90×75 mm. $6 multicoloured .. 2·50 2·75
Designs:—No. 1536, Queen Elizabeth signing visitors' book; Nos. 1537, MS1539, Queen Elizabeth in evening dress; No. 1538, Queen Elizabeth the Queen Mother in Coronation robes, 1953.
Nos. 1536/8 were printed together, horizontally and vertically se-tenant, in sheetlets of 9 (3×3).

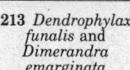

**300th Win
Milwaukee Brewers
July 31, 1990**

| (209) | 210 Maradona, Argentina |

1990 (3 Aug). *Nolan Ryan–300th Win. No.* 1407 *optd with* T **209**.
1540 **202** $2 multicoloured 85 90
a. Sheetlet of 9 .. .. 7·75

1990 (21 Sept). *Centenary of Los Angeles Dodgers (2nd issue). Baseball Players. Multicoloured designs as* T **197**. *Litho. Rouletted 7.*
1541 60 c. Mickey Hatcher and Jay Howell .. 25 30
a. Sheetlet. Nos. 1541/9 .. 2·25
1542 60 c. Juan Samuel and Mike Scioscia .. 25 30
1543 60 c. Lenny Harris and Mike Hartley .. 25 30
1544 60 c. Ramon Martinez and Mike Morgan .. 25 30

1545 60 c. Aerial view of Dodger stadium .. 25 30
1546 60 c. Stan Javier and Don Aase .. 25 30
1547 60 c. Ray Searage and Mike Sharperson .. 25 30
1548 60 c. Tim Belcher and Pat Perry .. 25 30
1549 60 c. Dave Walsh, Jose Vizcaino, Jim Neidlinger, Jose Offerman and Carlos Hernandez .. 25 30
1550 60 c. Hubie Brooks and Orel Hershiser a. Sheetlet. Nos. 1550/8 2·25 25 30
1551 60 c. Tom Lasorda and Tim Crews .. 25 30
1552 60 c. Fernando Valenzuela and Eddie Murray .. 25 30
1553 60 c. Kal Daniels and Jose Gonzalez .. 25 30
1554 60 c. Dodgers emblem .. 25 30
1555 60 c. Chris Gwynn and Jeff Hamilton .. 25 30
1556 60 c. Kirk Gibson and Rick Dempsey .. 25 30
1557 60 c. Jim Gott and Alfredo Griffin .. 25 30
1558 60 c. Ron Perranoski, Bill Russell, Joe Ferguson, Joe Amalfitano, Mark Cresse, Ben Hines and Manny Mota 25 30
1541/58 .. .. Set of 18 4·00 4·75
Nos. 1541/9 and 1550/8 were each printed together, se-tenant, in sheetlets of nine.

(Des Young Phillips Studio. Litho Questa)

1990 (24 Sept). *World Cup Football Championship, Italy (2nd issue).* T **210** *and similar vert designs. Multicoloured.* P 14.
1559 10 c. Type **210** 10 10
1560 75 c. Valderrama, Colombia .. 35 40
1561 $1 Francescoli, Uruguay .. 45 50
1562 $5 Beulemans, Belgium .. 2·25 2·40
1559/62 .. .. Set of 4 2·75 3·00
MS1563 Two sheets, each 101×85 mm. (a) $6 Klinsmann, West Germany. (b) $6 Careca, Brazil .. .. Set of 2 sheets 5·25 5·50

| | JOE DELOACH U.S.A. | STEVE LEWIS U.S.A. | PAUL ERANG KENYA |
| (211) | | (212) | |

1990 (18 Oct). *95th Anniv of Rotary International. Nos.* 1230/8 *optd with* T **211**.
1564 10 c. Type **186** 10 10
1565 40 c. *Liberté* 15 20
1566 50 c. *Mauretania* (launched 1906) .. 20 25
1567 75 c. *France* 35 40
1568 $1 *Aquitania* 45 50
1569 $2 *United States* 85 90
1570 $3 *Olympic* .. .. 1·25 1·40
1571 $4 *Queen Elizabeth* .. .. 1·75 1·90
1564/71 .. .. Set of 8 4·50 5·00
MS1572 Two sheets, each 141×108 mm. (a) $6 *Queen Mary* (85×28 mm). (b) $6 *Queen Elizabeth 2* (85×28 mm) .. Set of 2 sheets 5·25 5·50

1990 (18 Oct). *Olympic Medal Winners, Seoul. Nos.* 1153/7 *optd as* T **212**.
1573 10 c. Type **178** 10 10
1574 50 c. Long jumping (optd "CARL LEWIS U.S.A.") 20 25
1575 $1 Triple jumping (optd "HRISTO MARKOV BULGARIA") .. 45 50
1576 $5 Boxing (optd "HENRY MASKE E. GERMANY") .. 2·25 2·40
1573/6 .. .. Set of 4 2·75 3·00
MS1577 85×63 mm $10 Olympic flame* .. 4·25 4·50
*No. MS1577 is overprinted "FINAL MEDAL STANDINGS" and medal totals for either South Korea and Spain or U.S.S.R. and U.S.A. on the margin (same price for either opt)

Christmas 1990

| 213 Dendrophylax funalis and Dimerandra emarginata | 214 "Miraculous Draught of Fishes" (detail, Rubens) |

(Litho B.D.T.)

1990 (23 Nov). *"EXPO 90" International Garden and Greenery Exposition, Osaka. Orchids.* T **213** *and similar vert designs. Multicoloured.* P 14.
1578 10 c. Type **213** 10 10
1579 15 c. *Epidendrum elongatum* .. 10 10
1580 45 c. *Comparettia falcata* 20 25
1581 60 c. *Brassia maculata* 25 30
1582 $1 *Encyclia cochleata* and *Encyclia cordigera* 45 50
1583 $2 *Cyrtopodium punctatum* .. 85 90
1584 $4 *Cattleya labiata* .. .. 1·75 1·90
1585 $5 *Bletia purpurea* .. .. 2·25 2·40
1578/85 .. .. Set of 8 5·50 5·75
MS1586 Two sheets, each 108×78 mm. (a) $6 *Vanilla planifolia Jackson.* (b) $6 *Ionopsis utricularioides* .. .. Set of 2 sheets 5·25 5·40

(Litho Questa)

1990 (3 Dec). *Christmas. 350th Death Anniv of Rubens. T* **214** *and similar vert designs. Multicoloured. P* 13½×14.

1587	10 c.	Type **214**	10	10
1588	45 c.	"Crowning of Holy Katherine" (detail)	20	25
1589	50 c.	"St. Ives of Treguier" (detail)	20	25
1590	65 c.	"Allegory of Eternity" (detail)	30	35
1591	$1	"St. Bavo receives Monastic Habit of Ghent" (detail)	45	50
1592	$2	"Crowning of Holy Katherine" (different detail)	85	90
1593	$4	"St. Bavo receives Monastic Habit of Ghent" (different detail)	1·75	1·90
1594	$5	"Communion of St. Francis" (detail)	2·25	2·40
1587/94		*Set of* 8	5·50	6·00

MS1595 Four sheets. (a) 70×100 mm. $6 "Allegory of Eternity" (different detail). P 13½×14. (b) 70×100 mm. $6 As 50 c. P 13½×14. (c) 100×70 mm. $6 As Type **214** (*horiz*). P 14×13½. (d) 100×70 mm. $6 "St. Bavo receives Monastic Habit of Ghent" (different detail) (*horiz*). P 14×13½ .. *Set of 4 sheets* 10·50 11·00

215 Geoffrey Chaucer

216 American Football Game

(Des N. Waldman. Litho Cartor)

1990 (12 Dec). *International Literacy Year* (*1st issue*). *Chaucer's Canterbury Tales. T* **215** *and similar square designs. Multicoloured. P* 13½.

1596	40 c.	Type **215**	15	20
		a. Sheetlet. Nos. 1596/1619	3·25	
1597	40 c.	"When April with his showers..."	15	20
1598	40 c.	"When Zephyr also has..."	15	20
1599	40 c.	"And many little birds..."	15	20
1600	40 c.	"And palmers to go seeking out..."	15	20
1601	40 c.	Quill in ink well and open book	15	20
1602	40 c.	Green bird in tree	15	20
1603	40 c.	Brown bird in tree and franklin's head	15	20
1604	40 c.	Purple bird in tree and banner	15	20
1605	40 c.	Canterbury	15	20
1606	40 c.	Knight's head	15	20
1607	40 c.	Black bird in tree and squire's head	15	20
1608	40 c.	Friar	15	20
1609	40 c.	Franklin	15	20
1610	40 c.	Prioress and monk holding banner	15	20
1611	40 c.	Summoner, Oxford clerk and parson	15	20
1612	40 c.	Serjeant-at-Law and knight on horseback	15	20
1613	40 c.	Squire	15	20
1614	40 c.	"In fellowship..."	15	20
1615	40 c.	Cockerel and horse's legs	15	20
1616	40 c.	Hens	15	20
1617	40 c.	Hen and rabbit	15	20
1618	40 c.	Horses' legs and butterfly	15	20
1619	40 c.	"And briefly, when the sun..."	15	20
1596/1619		*Set of* 24	3·25	4·00

Nos. 1596/1619 were printed together, *se-tenant*, as a sheetlet of 24, forming a composite design.
See also Nos. 1775/87 and 1788/800.

(Litho Cartor)

1990 (17 Dec). *Death Centenary of Van Gogh* (*painter*). *Vert designs as T* **255** *of Maldive Islands. Multicoloured. P* 13.

1620	1 c.	Self-portrait, 1889	10	10
		a. Vert strip of 4. Nos. 1620/3	15	
1621	5 c.	Self-portrait, 1886	10	10
1622	10 c.	Self-portrait with hat and pipe, 1888	10	10
1623	15 c.	Self-portrait at easel, 1888	10	10
1624	20 c.	Self-portrait, 1887	10	10
		a. Vert strip of 4. Nos. 1624/7	5·00	
1625	45 c.	Self-portrait, 1889 (*different*)	20	25
1626	$5	Self-portrait with pipe, 1889	2·25	2·40
1627	$6	Self-portrait wearing straw hat, 1887	2·50	2·75
1620/7		*Set of* 8	4·75	5·25

Nos. 1620/3 and 1624/7 were each printed in sheets of 16 (4×4) with the four values vertically *se-tenant*.

(Litho Questa)

1990 (30 Dec). *Hummel Figurines. Vert designs as T* **256** *of Maldive Islands. Multicoloured. P* 14.

1628	10 c.	"The Photographer"	10	10
1629	15 c.	"Ladder and Rope"	10	10
1630	40 c.	"Druggist"	15	20
1631	60 c.	"Hello"	25	30
1632	$1	"Boots"	45	50
1633	$2	"The Artist"	85	90
1634	$4	"Waiter"	1·75	1·90
1635	$5	"The Postman"	2·25	2·40
1628/35		*Set of* 8	5·25	5·75

MS1636 Two sheets, each 94×121 mm. (a) Nos. 1628, 1631/2 and 1635. (b) Nos. 1629/30 and 1633/4 .. .. .. *Set of 2 sheets* 5·75 6·00

1991 (15 Jan). *25th Anniv of Super Bowl American Football Championship* (*1st issue*). *T* **216** *and similar vert designs. Multicoloured. Litho. P* 13½×14.

MS1637 Twenty-five sheets, each 127×101 mm, containing 50 c. × 2 as horiz pairs forming composite designs of game scenes or 50 c. × 3 (final sheet) showing Vince Lombardi Trophy and helmets of participating teams .. *Set of 25 sheets* 11·00

217 Programme Cover of XXV Super Bowl
(*Illustration reduced. Actual size* 105×95 *mm*)

1991 (15 Jan). *25th Anniv of Super Bowl American Football Championships* (*2nd issue*). *T* **217** *and similar multicoloured designs, each showing a different programme cover illustration. Litho. Imperf.*

MS1638 Twenty-five sheets, 125×99 mm or 99×125 mm, each with a face value of $2 .. *Set of 25 sheets* 22·00

218 U.S.A. 1893 1 c.
Columbus Stamp

1991 (18 Mar). *500th Anniv of Discovery of America* (1992) *by Columbus* (*4th issue*). *T* **218** *and similar horiz designs showing U.S.A 1893 Columbian Exposition, Chicago, stamps* (*Nos. 1639/54*) *or ships* (*others*). *Multicoloured. Litho. P* 13½×14.

1639	1 c.	Type **218**	10	10
		a. Sheetlet. Nos. 1639/46 and 1655	4·75	
1640	2 c.	U.S.A. Columbus 2 c.	10	10
1641	3 c.	U.S.A. Columbus 3 c.	10	10
1642	4 c.	U.S.A. Columbus 4 c.	10	10
1643	5 c.	U.S.A. Columbus 5 c.	10	10
1644	6 c.	U.S.A. Columbus 6 c.	10	10
1645	8 c.	U.S.A. Columbus 8 c.	10	10
1646	10 c.	U.S.A. Columbus 10 c.	10	10
1647	15 c.	U.S.A. Columbus 15 c.	10	10
		a. Sheetlet. Nos. 1647/54 and 1656	11·00	
1648	30 c.	U.S.A. Columbus 30 c.	15	20
1649	50 c.	U.S.A. Columbus 50 c.	20	25
1650	$1	U.S.A. Columbus $1	45	50
1651	$2	U.S.A. Columbus $2	85	90
1652	$3	U.S.A. Columbus $3	1·25	1·40
1653	$4	U.S.A. Columbus $4	1·75	1·90
1654	$5	U.S.A. Columbus $5	2·25	2·40
1655	$10	*Santa Maria*, Scarlet Macaw and tropical flower	4·25	4·50
1656	$10	Logo, *Santa Maria* and Amerindian hut	4·25	4·50
1639/56		*Set of* 18	14·50	15·00

MS1657 Two sheets, each 98×72 mm. (a) $6 Sailors on ship's fo'c'sle. (b) $6 Ship's figurehead .. .. .. *Set of 2 sheets* 5·25 5·50

Nos. 1639/46 and 1655 and Nos. 1647/54 and 1656 were each printed together, *se-tenant*, in sheetlets of 9.

219 Pebbles and Hoppy boxing

(Des Hanna-Barbera Productions. Litho Questa)

1991 (25 Mar). *Sports. T* **219** *and similar horiz designs showing characters from the Flintstones cartoons. Multicoloured. P* 14×13½.

1658	10 c.	Type **219**	10	10
1659	15 c.	Fred Flintstone and Dino playing football	10	10
1660	45 c.	Fred losing rowing race to Barney Rubble	20	25
1661	55 c.	Betty Rubble, Wilma Flintstone and Pebbles in dressage competition	25	30
1662	$1	Fred playing basketball	45	50
1663	$2	Bamm Bamm wrestling Barney with Fred as referee	85	90
1664	$4	Fred and Barney playing tennis	1·75	1·90
1665	$5	Fred, Barney and Dino cycling	2·25	2·40
1658/65		*Set of* 8	5·50	5·75

MS1666 Two sheets, each 117×95 mm. (a) $6 Fred at the plate in baseball game. (b) $6 Fred running to homeplate .. .. *Set of 2 sheets* 5·25 5·50

220 Board Meeting

(Des Hanna-Barbera Productions. Litho Questa)

1991 (25 March). *The Jetsons* (*cartoon film*). *T* **220** *and similar multicoloured designs. P* 14×13½ (60 c., $1, $2) *or* 13½×14 (*others*).

1667	5 c.	Type **220**	10	10
1668	20 c.	Jetsons with Dog	10	10
1669	45 c.	Judy and Apollo Blue	20	25
1670	50 c.	Cosmo Spacely and George Jetson	20	25
1671	60 c.	George and Elroy catching cogs (*horiz*)	25	30
1672	$1	Judy, Apollo, Elroy and Teddy in cavern (*horiz*)	45	50
1673	$2	Drill destroying the cavern (*horiz*)	85	90
1674	$4	Jetsons celebrating with the Grungees	1·75	1·90
1675	$5	The Jetsons returning home	2·25	2·40
1667/75		*Set of* 9	5·50	6·00

MS1676 Two sheets, each 114×76 mm. (a) $6 The Jetsons in spacecraft (*horiz*). (b) $6 The Jetsons in control room (*horiz*). P 14×13½ .. .. *Set of 2 sheets* 5·25 5·50

(Des T. Agans. Litho Questa)

1991 (13 May). *500th Anniv of Discovery of America by Columbus*, (1992) (*5th issue*). *History of Exploration. Multicoloured designs as T* **64** *of St. Kitts-Nevis* (*Nevis*). *P* 14.

1677	5 c.	"Sänger 2" (projected space shuttle)	10	10
1678	10 c.	"Magellan" satellite, 1990	10	10
1679	25 c.	"Buran" space shuttle	10	15
1680	75 c.	Projected "Freedom" space station	35	40
1681	$1	Projected Mars mission space craft	45	50
1682	$2	"Hubble" telescope, 1990	85	90
1683	$4	Projected Mars mission "sailship"	1·75	1·90
1684	$5	Projected "Craf" satellite	2·25	2·40
1677/84		*Set of* 8	5·50	5·75

MS1685 Two sheets, each 105×71 mm. (a) $6 Bow of caravel (*vert*). (b) $6 Caravel under full sail .. .. .. *Set of 2 sheets* 5·25 5·50

(Des D. Miller. Litho Walsall)

1991 (5 July). *65th Birthday of Queen Elizabeth II. Horiz designs as T* **210** *of Lesotho. Multicoloured. P* 14.

1686	5 c.	Queen and Prince Philip during visit to Spain, 1988	10	10
1687	60 c.	Queen and Prince Philip in landau	25	30
1688	$2	Queen at Caen Hill Waterway, 1990	85	90
1689	$4	Queen at Badminton, 1983	1·75	1·90
1686/9		*Set of* 4	2·50	2·75

MS1690 68×91 mm. $5 Queen Elizabeth II in 1988 and Prince Philip in 1989 .. .. 2·25 2·40

(Des D. Miller. Litho Walsall)

1991 (5 July). *10th Wedding Anniv of the Prince and Princess of Wales. Horiz designs as T* **210** *of Lesotho. Multicoloured. P* 14.

1691	20 c.	Prince and Princess in hard hats, 1987	10	10
1692	25 c.	Portraits of Prince and Princess and sons	10	15
1693	$1	Prince Henry and Prince William, both in 1988	45	50
1694	$5	Princess Diana in France and Prince Charles in 1987	2·25	2·40
1691/4		*Set of* 4	2·50	2·75

MS1695 68×90 mm. $5 Princes Henry and William in Majorca, and Princess Diana presenting polo trophy to Prince Charles 2·25 2·40

221 Class "D 51" Steam
Locomotive

(Des K. Gromell. Litho Cartor)

1991 (12 Aug). *"Phila Nippon '91" International Stamp Exhibition, Tokyo. Japanese Trains. T* **221** *and similar multicoloured designs. P* 13½.

1696	75 c.	Type **221**	35	40
		a. Sheetlet. Nos. 1696/1704	3·00	
1697	75 c.	Class "9600" steam locomotive	35	40
1698	75 c.	Goods wagons and chrysanthemum emblem	35	40
1699	75 c.	Passenger coach	35	40
1700	75 c.	Decorated class "C 57" steam locomotive	35	40
1701	75 c.	Oil tanker wagon	35	40
1702	75 c.	Class "C 53" steam locomotive	35	40
1703	75 c.	First Japanese steam locomotive	35	40
1704	75 c.	Class "C 11" steam locomotive	35	40
1705	$1	Class "181" electric train	45	50
		a. Sheetlet. Nos. 1705/13	4·00	

1706	$1 Class "EH-10" electric locomotive	..	45	50
1707	$1 Passenger coaches and Special Express symbol	..	45	50
1708	$1 Sendai City class "1" tram	..	45	50
1709	$1 Class "485" electric train	..	45	50
1710	$1 Sendai City street cleaning tram	..	45	50
1711	$1 Hakari "Bullet" train	..	45	50
1712	$1 Class "ED-11" electric locomotive	..	45	50
1713	$1 Class "EF-66" electric locomotive	..	45	50
1696/1713		Set of 18	6·50	7·25

MS1714 Four sheets, each 108×77 mm. (a) $6 Class "C 55" steam locomotive (vert). P 13×13½. (b) $6 Series "400" electric train. P 13½×13. (c) $6 Class "C 62" steam locomotive (vert). P 13×13½. (d) $6 Super Hitachi electric train. P 13×13½. .. .. Set of 4 sheets 10·50 11·00

Nos. 1696/1704 and 1705/13 were each printed together, se-tenant, in sheetlets of 9.

222 Marcello Mastroianni (actor)

(Des J. Iskowitz. Litho Cartor)

1991 (22 Aug). Italian Entertainers. T 222 and similar multicoloured designs. P 13.

1715	$1 Type 222	..	45	50
	a. Sheetlet. Nos. 1715/23	..	3·75	
1716	$1 Sophia Loren (actress)	..	45	50
1717	$1 Mario Lanza (singer)	..	45	50
1718	$1 Federico Fellini (director)	..	45	50
1719	$1 Arturo Toscanini (conductor)	..	45	50
1720	$1 Anna Magnani (actress)	..	45	50
1721	$1 Giancarlo Giannini (actor)	..	45	50
1722	$1 Gina Lollobrigida (actress)	..	45	50
1723	$1 Enrico Caruso (operatic tenor)	..	45	50
1715/23		Set of 9	3·75	4·00

MS1724 117×80 mm. $6 Luciano Pavarotti (operatic tenor) (horiz) .. .. .. 2·50 2·75

Nos. 1715/23 were printed together, se-tenant, in sheetlets of 9.

223 Madonna

(Des J. Iskowitz. Litho Cartor)

1991 (22 Aug). Madonna (American singer). T 223 and similar vert portraits. Multicoloured. P 13.

1725	$1 Type 223	..	45	50
	a. Sheetlet. Nos. 1725/33	..	3·75	
1726	$1 In strapless dress	..	45	50
1727	$1 Wearing necklaces, looking right	..	45	50
1728	$1 In green dress	..	45	50
1729	$1 Wearing necklaces, looking to front	..	45	50
1730	$1 With wrist bangles	..	45	50
1731	$1 With hand to face	..	45	50
1732	$1 In purple dress	..	45	50
1733	$1 With microphone	..	45	50
1725/33		Set of 9	3·75	4·00

MS1734 79×118 mm. $6 Madonna (25×40 mm). P 12×13 .. .. 2·50 2·75

Nos. 1725/33 were printed together, se-tenant, in sheetlets of 9.

224 John Lennon

(Des J. Iskowitz. Litho Cartor)

1991 (22 Aug). John Lennon (British musician). T 224 and similar vert portraits. Multicoloured. P 13.

1735	$1 + 2 c. Type 224	..	45	50
	a. Sheetlet. Nos. 1735/43	..	3·75	
1736	$1 + 2 c. With Beatle hair cut	..	45	50
1737	$1 + 2 c. In cap	..	45	50
1738	$1 + 2 c. In red polka-dot shirt	..	45	50
1739	$1 + 2 c. In green polo-neck jumper and jacket	..	45	50
1740	$1 + 2 c. In glasses and magenta jacket	..	45	50
1741	$1 + 2 c. With long hair and glasses	..	45	50
1742	$1 + 2 c. In black jumper	..	45	50
1743	$1 + 2 c. In polo-neck jumper	..	45	50
1735/43		Set of 9	3·75	4·00

Nos. 1735/43 were printed together, se-tenant, in sheetlets of 9.

(Des W. Hanson Studio. Litho Questa)

1991 (18 Nov). 50th Death Anniv of Lord Baden-Powell and World Scout Jamboree, Korea. Multicoloured designs as T 263 of Maldive Islands. P 14.

1744	65 c. Tales around the camp fire (vert)	..	30	35
1745	$1.50, British trenches and Mafeking Siege 3d. stamp	..	65	70
1746	$3.50, Queen Angelfish and scout diver	..	1·50	1·75
1744/6		Set of 3	2·25	2·50

MS1747 117×89 mm. $5 Scout badge and Jamboree emblem .. .. .. 2·25 2·40

(Litho Questa)

1991 (18 Nov). Birth Centenary of Charles de Gaulle (French statesman) (1990). Multicoloured designs as T 209 of Lesotho. P 14.

1748	10 c. Free French Resistance fighters, 1944 (horiz)	..	10	10
1749	45 c. De Gaulle with Churchill, 1944 (horiz)	..	20	25
1750	75 c. Liberation of Paris, 1944 (horiz)	..	35	40
1748/50		Set of 3	60	70

MS1751 76×116 mm. $5 President De Gaulle .. 2·25 2·40

(Des L. Fried. Litho Questa)

1991 (18 Nov). Bicentenary of Brandenburg Gate, Berlin. Horiz designs as T 264 of Maldive Islands. Multicoloured. P 14.

1752	50 c. Protester with banner	..	20	25
1753	75 c. Building Berlin Wall	..	35	40
1754	90 c. German flag and protestors' shadows	..	40	45
1755	$1 Presidents Bush and Gorbachev shaking hands	..	45	50
1752/5		Set of 4	1·25	1·40

MS1756 101×72 mm. $4 Arms of Berlin .. 1·75 2·00

(Des J. Iskowitz. Litho Questa)

1991 (18 Nov). Death Bicentenary of Mozart. Multicoloured designs as T 265 of Maldive Islands. P 14.

1757	$1 Marriage of Figaro	..	45	50
1758	$3 The Clemency of Titus	..	1·25	1·50

MS1759 77×116 mm. $4 Mozart and signature (vert) .. .. 1·75 2·00

225 Myrvyn Bennion   226 Street Fighting, Kiev

(Des D. Ben-Ami. Litho Questa)

1991 (18 Nov). 50th Anniv of Japanese Attack on Pearl Harbor. T 225 and similar horiz designs showing recipients of Congressional Medal of Honor. Multicoloured. P 14½×15.

1760	$1 Type 225	..	45	50
	a. Sheetlet. Nos. 1760/74	..	6·00	
1761	$1 George Cannon	..	45	50
1762	$1 John Finn	..	45	50
1763	$1 Francis Flaherty	..	45	50
1764	$1 Samuel Fuqua	..	45	50
1765	$1 Edwin Hill	..	45	50
1766	$1 Herbert Jones	..	45	50
1767	$1 Isaac Kidd	..	45	50
1768	$1 Jackson Pharris	..	45	50
1769	$1 Thomas Reeves	..	45	50
1770	$1 Donald Ross	..	45	50
1771	$1 Robert Scott	..	45	50
1772	$1 Franklin van Valkenburgh	..	45	50
1773	$1 James Ward	..	45	50
1774	$1 Cassin Young	..	45	50
1760/74		Set of 15	6·00	6·75

Nos. 1760/74 were printed together, se-tenant, in sheetlets of 15.

(Des Walt Disney Co. Litho Questa)

1991 (18 Nov). International Literacy Year (1990) (2nd issue). Multicoloured designs as T 246 of Maldive Islands, but horiz, showing scenes from Disney cartoon film The Prince and the Pauper. P 14×13½.

1775	5 c. Mickey Mouse, Goofy and Pluto as pauper pals	..	10	10
1776	10 c. Mickey as the bored prince	..	10	10
1777	15 c. Donald Duck as the valet	..	10	10
1778	25 c. Mickey as the prince and the pauper	..	10	10
1779	60 c. Exchanging clothes	..	25	30
1780	75 c. Prince and pauper with suit of armour	..	35	40
1781	80 c. Throwing food from the battlements	..	35	40
1782	$1 Pete as Captain of the Guard	..	45	50
1783	$2 Mickey and Donald in the dungeon	..	85	90
1784	$3 Mickey and Donald at dungeon window	..	1·25	1·40

1785	$4 Goofy rescuing Mickey and Donald	..	1·75	1·90
1786	$5 Crowning the real prince	..	2·25	2·40
1775/86		Set of 12	7·00	7·50

MS1787 Four sheets, each 127×101 mm. (a) $6 Crowning the wrong prince. (b) $6 Pete holding Mickey. (c) $6 The pauper on the throne. (d) $6 Mickey telling troops to seize the guard .. .. .. Set of 4 sheets 10·50 11·00

(Des Walt Disney Co. Litho Questa)

1991 (18 Nov). International Literacy Year (1990) (3rd issue). Multicoloured designs as T 246 of Maldive Islands showing scenes from Disney cartoon film The Rescuers Down Under. P 14×13½.

1788	5 c. Miss Bianca	..	10	10
1789	10 c. Bernard	..	10	10
1790	15 c. Matre d'Francoise	..	10	10
1791	25 c. Wilbur the Albatross	..	10	10
1792	60 c. Jake the Kangaroo mouse	..	25	30
1793	75 c. Bernard, Bianca and Jake in the outback	..	35	40
1794	80 c. Bianca and Bernard to the rescue	..	35	40
1795	$1 Marahute the Eagle	..	45	50
1796	$2 Cody and Marahute with eggs	..	85	90
1797	$3 McLeach and his pet, Joanna the Goanna	..	1·25	1·40
1798	$4 Frank the Frill-necked Lizard	..	1·75	1·90
1799	$5 Red Kangaroo, Krebbs Koala and Polly Platypus	..	2·25	2·40
1788/99		Set of 12	7·00	7·75

MS1800 Four sheets, each 127×102 mm. (a) $6 The Rescuers. (b) $6 Ethiopia and Japanese mice delegates. (c) $6 Wilbur carrying Bianca and Bernard. (d) $6 Wilbur in pain .. Set of 4 sheets 10·50 11·00

(Des W. Wright. Litho Questa)

1991 (18 Nov). Centenary of Trans-Siberian Railway. Multicoloured design as T 266 of Maldive Islands but horiz. P 14.

1801	$1.50, Modern Trans-Siberian steam locomotive	..	70	75

(Des W. Wright. Litho Questa)

1991 (18 Nov). 700th Anniv of Swiss Confederation. Horiz design as T 269 of Maldive Islands. Multicoloured. P 14.

1802	$1.50, Map of Switzerland and woman in national costume	..	70	75

(Des W. Wright. Litho Questa)

1991 (18 Nov). Centenary of Otto Lilienthal's Gliding Experiments. Horiz design as T 267 of Maldive Islands. Multicoloured. P 14.

1803	$1.65, Lilienthal's signature and Flugzeug Nr.13 Doppeldecker	..	75	80

(Des W. Wright. Litho Questa)

1991 (18 Nov). 50th Anniv of Capture of Kiev. P 14.

1804	226	$2 multicoloured	..	85	90

(Des W. Wright. Litho Questa)

1991 (18 Nov). 750th Anniv of Hanover. Horiz design as T 268 of Maldive Islands. Multicoloured. P 14.

1805	$2 Gottfried Leibniz (mathematician)	..	85	90

227 Hans-Dietrich Genscher and "Winged Victory" Statue

228 Walt Disney Characters decorating Christmas Tree, 1982

(Des J. Puvilland. Litho Questa)

1991 (25 Nov). European History. T 227 and similar vert designs. Multicoloured. P 14½×14.

1806	$1 Type 227	..	45	50
1807	$1 Destruction of Berlin Wall	..	45	50
1808	$1 Churchill, De Gaulle and Appeal to the French, 1940	..	45	50
1809	$1 Eisenhower, De Gaulle and D-Day, 1944	..	45	50
1810	$1 Brandenburg Gate, Berlin (bicentenary)	..	45	50
1811	$1 Chancellor Helmut Kohl and meeting of Berlin Mayors, 1989	..	45	50
1812	$1 De Gaulle with Chancellor Adenauer	..	45	50
1813	$1 Pres. Kennedy's visit to Europe, 1961, Washington and Lafayette	..	45	50
1806/13		Set of 8	3·25	3·50

MS1814 106×88 mm. $6 Casablanca Conference, 1942, and demolition of Berlin Wall (24½×39 mm). P 14 .. .. 2·50 2·75

(Des J. Puvilland. Litho Questa)

1991 (25 Nov). Famous Golfers. Vert designs as T 227. Multicoloured. P 14½×14.

1815	$1 Gary Player	..	45	50
1816	$1 Nick Faldo	..	45	50
1817	$1 Severiano Ballesteros	..	45	50
1818	$1 Ben Hogan	..	45	50
1819	$1 Jack Nicklaus	..	45	50
1820	$1 Greg Norman	..	45	50
1821	$1 José-Maria Olazabal	..	45	50
1822	$1 Bobby Jones	..	45	50
1815/22		Set of 8	3·25	3·50

(Des J. Puvilland. Litho Questa)

1991 (25 Nov). *Famous Entertainers. Vert designs as T 227. Multicoloured. P 14½.*

1823	$2 Michael Jackson	..	85	90
1824	$2 Madonna	..	85	90
1825	$2 Elvis Presley	..	85	90
1826	$2 David Bowie	..	85	90
1827	$2 Prince	..	85	90
1828	$2 Frank Sinatra	..	85	90
1829	$2 George Michael	..	85	90
1830	$2 Mick Jagger	..	85	90
1823/30		*Set of 8*	6·00	6·50

MS1831 Two sheets, each 110×82 mm. (a) $6 Madonna (29×43 *mm*). (b) $6 Elvis Presley (29×43 *mm*). P 14 .. *Set of 2 sheets* 5·25 5·50

(Des J. Puvilland. Litho Questa)

1991 (25 Nov). *Famous Chess Masters. Vert designs as T 227. Multicoloured. P 14½.*

1832	$1 Francoise Philidor	..	45	50
1833	$1 Karl Anderssen	..	45	50
1834	$1 Wilhelm Steinitz	..	45	50
1835	$1 Alexandrovich Alekhine	..	45	50
1836	$1 Boris Spassky	..	45	50
1837	$1 Robert Fischer	..	45	50
1838	$1 Anatoly Karpov	..	45	50
1839	$1 Garry Kasparov	..	45	50
1832/9		*Set of 8*	3·25	3·50

(Des J. Puvilland. Litho Questa)

1991 (25 Nov). *Nobel Prizewinners. Vert designs as T 227. Multicoloured. P 14½.*

1840	$1 Albert Einstein (mathematical physicist)	45	50
1841	$1 Wilhelm Rontgen (physicist) ..	..	45	50
1842	$1 William Shockley (chemist)	..	45	50
1843	$1 Charles Townes (physicist)	..	45	50
1844	$1 Lev Landau (physicist)	..	45	50
1845	$1 Guglielmo Marconi (applied physicist)	45	50
1846	$1 Willard Libby (chemist)	..	45	50
1847	$1 Ernest Lawrence (nuclear physicist) ..	45	50
1840/7		*Set of 8*	3·25	3·50

(Des Walt Disney Co. Litho Questa)

1991 (23 Dec). *Christmas. Walt Disney Christmas Cards. T 228 and similar vert designs. Multicoloured. P 13½×14.*

1848	10 c. Type **228**		10	10
1849	45 c. Mickey and Moose, 1980 ..	20	25
1850	55 c. Mickey, Pluto and Donald carrying bauble, 1970	20	25
1851	75 c. Duckling and egg shell, 1943 ..	35	40
1852	$1.50, Walt Disney characters decorating globe, 1941 ..	70	75
1853	$2 The Lady and the Tramp by Christmas tree, 1986	85	90
1854	$4 Walt Disney characters carol singing, 1977	1·75	1·90
1855	$5 Mickey in fairy-tale castle, 1965 ..	2·25	2·40
1848/55		*Set of 8*	5·75	6·25

MS1856 Two sheets. (a) 102×128 mm. $6 Characters in balloon basket, 1966. (b) 128×102 mm. $6 Characters in national costumes, 1966 *Set of 2 sheets* 5·25 5·50

229 Kings Hill

(Litho Questa)

1992 (17 Feb). *Preserving the Environment. T 229 and similar horiz designs. Multicoloured. P 14.*

1857	10 c. Type **229**	..	10	10
1858	55 c. Planting sapling	..	20	25
1859	75 c. Doric Temple, Botanic Gardens	..	35	40
1860	$2 18th-century map of Kings Hill	..	85	90
1857/60		*Set of 4*	1·40	1·50

(Des D. Miller. Litho Questa)

1992 (2 Mar). *40th Anniv of Queen Elizabeth II's Accession. Horiz designs as T 214 of Lesotho. Multicoloured. P 14.*

1861	10 c. Kingstown from the cliffs	..	10	10
1862	20 c. Deep water wharf, Kingstown	..	10	10
1863	$1 Residential suburb, Kingstown	..	45	50
1864	$5 Kingstown from the interior	..	2·25	2·40
1861/4		*Set of 4*	2·50	2·75

MS1865 Two sheets, each 75×92 mm. (a) $6 Deep water wharf (*different*). (b) $6 Beach *Set of 2 sheets* 5·25 5·50

230 Women's Luge

(Litho Questa)

1992 (21 Apr). *Winter Olympic Games, Albertville. T 230 and similar multicoloured designs. P 14.*

1866	10 c. Type **230**	..	10	10
1867	15 c. Women's figure skating (*vert*)	10	10
1868	25 c. Two-man bobsleigh ..	..	10	10

1869	30 c. Mogul skiing (*vert*) ..	..	15	20
1870	45 c. Nordic combination ..	..	20	25
1871	55 c. Ski jump	..	20	25
1872	75 c. Men's giant slalom	..	35	40
1873	$1.50, Women's slalom (*vert*)	..	70	75
1874	$5 Ice hockey	..	2·25	2·40
1875	$8 Biathlon (*vert*)	..	3·25	3·50
1866/75		*Set of 10*	6·75	7·25

MS1876 Two sheets, each 100×70 mm. (a) $6 Women's speed skating (*vert*). (b) $6 Men's downhill skiing (*vert*) .. *Set of 2 sheets* 5·25 5·50

(Des Walt Disney Co. Litho Questa)

1992 (28 Apr). *International Stamp Exhibitions. Multicoloured designs as T 215 of Lesotho showing Walt Disney cartoon characters.*

(a) *"Granada '92", Spain. The Three Pigs in Spanish Uniforms. P 13½×14*

1877	15 c. The Wolf as General of Spanish Moors	10	10
1878	40 c. Pig as Captain of Infantry ..	..	15	20
1879	$2 Pig as Halberdier	..	85	90
1880	$4 Pig as Nobleman	..	1·75	1·90
1877/80		*Set of 4*	2·50	2·75

MS1881 128×102 mm. $6 Nobleman at castle window 2·50 2·75

(b) *"World Columbian Stamp Expo '92". Chicago Landmarks. P 14×13½*

1882	10 c. Mickey Mouse and Goofy looking at Picasso sculpture (*horiz*) ..	10	10
1883	50 c. Mickey and Donald Duck admiring Robie House (*horiz*) ..	20	25
1884	$1 Calder sculpture in Sears Tower (*horiz*)	45	50
1885	$5 Goofy in Buckingham Memorial Fountain (*horiz*) ..	2·25	2·40
1882/5		*Set of 4*	2·75	3·00

MS1886 128×102 mm. $6 Mickey painting Minnie. P 13½×14 .. 2·50 2·75

OFFICIAL STAMPS

OFFICIAL

(O 1)

1982 (11 Oct). *Nos. 668/73 optd with Type O 1.*

O1	60 c. *Isabella*	..	25	25
	a. Sheetlet. No. O1 × 6 and No. O2	2·00	
	b. Opt double		
	c. Albino opt ..	..	10·00	
O2	60 c. Prince Charles and Lady Diana Spencer	50	50
	b. Opt double		
	c. Albino opt ..	..	28·00	
O3	$2.50, *Alberta* (tender)	..	50	50
	a. Sheetlet. No. O3 × 6 and No. O4	3·50	
	b. Opt inverted	..	30·00	
	c. Opt inverted (horiz pair)..	..	80·00	
	d. Albino opt	..	20·00	
O4	$2.50, Prince Charles and Lady Diana Spencer	80	80
	b. Opt inverted	..	80·00	
	c. Albino opt ..	..	55·00	
O5	$4 *Britannia* ..	..	80	80
	a. Sheetlet. No. O5 × 6 and No. O6	5·50	
	b. Opt double		
	c. Albino opt ..	..	15·00	
	d. Opt inverted		
	e. Opt inverted (horiz pair).		
O6	$4 Prince Charles and Lady Diana Spencer	1·25	1·25
	b. Opt double		
	c. Albino opt ..	..	50·00	
	d. Opt inverted		
O1/6		*Set of 6*	3·75	3·75

Nos. O3c and O5e show the long overprint, intended for Nos. O4 or O6, inverted and struck across a horizontal pair of Nos. O3 or O5. Nos. O4b and O6d show two examples of Type O 1 inverted on the same stamp.

POSTAL FISCAL STAMPS

The following were primarily intended for the payment of passport fees, but were also valid for postal purposes and are frequently found used on parcels.

$5

STAMP DUTY

(F 1)   F 2 St. Vincent Coat of Arms

1980 (Feb). *Stamps as T 95, without value, surch as Type F 1. W w 12. P 14½ × 14.*

F1	$5 deep lavender and azure	..	3·00	2·50
F2	$10 light green and apple green	..	6·50	5·50
F3	$20 reddish purple and pale rose-lilac	12·50	12·00
F1/3		*Set of 3*	20·00	18·00

(Des Harrison. Recess D.L.R.)

1980 (19 May). *W w 14. P 14 × 13.*

F4	F **2**	$5 chalky blue ..	..	2·10	2·25
F5		$10 deep green	..	4·00	4·25
F6		$20 brown-red	..	9·50	9·75
F4/6			*Set of 3*	14·00	14·50

1984 (22 May). *As No. F6, but W w 15. P 12.*

F9	F **2**	$20 brown-red ..	..	8·50	8·75

A 10 c. in a design similar to Type F **2**, but inscribed "REVENUE", was issued in April 1988. Examples can be found used on commercial mail, but such use was unauthorised.

GRENADINES OF ST. VINCENT

A group of islands south of St. Vincent which includes Bequia, Mustique, Canouan and Union.

For stamps inscribed "The Grenadines of St. VINCENT" issued by St. Vincent in 1971, see under St. Vincent Nos. 330/6.

Stamps of the Grenadines of St. Vincent exist overprinted "SPECIMEN", these being produced for publicity purposes.

1973 (14 Nov). *Royal Wedding. As Nos. 322/3 of Montserrat.*
1	25 c. light green	10	10
2	$1 ochre	25	15

GRENADINES OF

(1)

2 Map of Bequia

1974 (24 Apr). *Stamps of St. Vincent T 51 etc. optd in litho with T 1 by Harrison & Sons. Glazed paper. W w 12 (sideways on 4, 5, 10, 12, 50 c. and $5).*
3	1 c. Green Heron	10	10
	a. Opt omitted	50·00	
	b. Albino opt	45·00	
4	2 c. Lesser Antillean Bullfinches	15	15
5	3 c. St. Vincent Amazons	75	75
6	4 c. Rufous-throated Solitaire	15	10
7	5 c. Red-necked Pigeon	15	10
8	6 c. Bananaquits	15	10
9	8 c. Purple-throated Carib	15	10
10	10 c. Mangrove Cuckoo	15	10
11	12 c. Common Black Hawk	20	15
	a. Opt double	£130	
12	20 c. Bare-eyed Thrush	35	20
13	25 c. Hooded Tanager	40	20
14	50 c. Blue-hooded Euphonia	70	40
	a. Albino opt	80·00	
15	$1 Barn Owl	1·50	75
16	$2.50, Yellow-bellied Elaenia	2·00	1·25
17	$5 Ruddy Quail Dove	3·50	2·25
3/17	Set of 15	9·25	6·00

(Des G. Drummond. Litho Enschedé)

1974 (9 May). *Maps (1st series). T 2 and similar vert designs. W w 12 (sideways). P 13 × 12½.*
18	5 c. black, light dull green and deep dull green	10	10
19	15 c. multicoloured	10	10
20	20 c. multicoloured	10	10
21	30 c. black, light rose-lilac and lake	10	10
22	40 c. black, lavender and deep ultramarine	10	10
23	$1 black, cobalt and bright ultramarine	25	20
18/23	Set of 6	60	35

Maps:—15 c. The Grenadines and Prune Island (inset); 20 c. Mayreau Island and Tobago Cays; 30 c. Mustique Island; 40 c. Union Island; $1 Canouan Island.

Nos. 18/23 were each issued in sheets of ten stamps and two *se-tenant* labels.

See also Nos. 85/8.

GRENADINES OF

(3)

4 Boat-building

1974 (7 June). *Nos. 361/2 of St. Vincent optd in typo with T 3 by Govt Printer, St. Vincent. Glazed paper. W w 12.*
24	2 c. Lesser Antillean Bullfinches	40	30
25	3 c. St. Vincent Amazons	40	30
	a. Opt double	45·00	
	b. Albino opt	11·00	
	c. Chalky paper. Wmk sideways (No. 288)	23·00	25·00

1974 (25 July). *Centenary of Universal Postal Union. As Nos. 392/5 of St. Vincent but colours and face-values changed and inscr "Grenadines of St. Vincent".*
26	2 c. U.P.U. emblem	10	10
	a. Red (U.P.U. emblem) omitted	£650	
27	15 c. Globe within posthorn	10	10
28	40 c. Map of St. Vincent and hand-cancelling	10	10
29	$1 Map of the world	25	15
26/9	Set of 4	40	25

No. 26a was caused by a paper fold.

(Des G. Drummond. Litho Questa)

1974. *Bequia Island (1st series). T 4 and similar horiz designs. Multicoloured. P 14. (a) W w 12 (sideways) (26.9.74).*
30	5 c. Type 4	90	1·75
31	30 c. Careening at Port Elizabeth	10	15
32	35 c. Admiralty Bay	10	15
33	$1 Fishing boat race	20	25

(b) W w 14 (sideways) (12.74)
34	5 c. Type 4	15	15
30/4	Set of 5	1·25	2·25

No. 34 differs in shade from No. 30, notably in the shirt of the man at right, which is red on No. 34 instead of purple.

Nos. 30/4 were each issued in sheets of ten stamps and two *se-tenant* labels.

See also Nos. 185/8.

5 Music Volute (imprint at foot showing designer, date and printer)

(Des R. Granger Barrett. Litho Questa)

1974 (27 Nov)–**77.** *Shells and Molluscs. Horiz designs as T 5. Multicoloured. W w 14 (sideways). P 14.*
A. *No imprint.* B. *Imprint at foot*

		A		B	
35	1 c. Atlantic Thorny Oyster	10	10	†	
36	2 c. Zigzag Scallop	10	10	†	
37	3 c. Reticulated Helmet	10	10	†	
38	4 c. Type 5	10	10	10	10
39	5 c. Amber Pen Shell	10	10	10	10
40	6 c. Angular Triton	10	10	10	10
41	8 c. Flame Helmet	10	10	10	10
42	10 c. Caribbean Olive	10	10	10	10
	a. Corrected imprint		†		70
43	12 c. Common Sundial	10	10	†	
44	15 c. Glory of the Atlantic Cone	25	20	80	15
45	20 c. Flame Auger	30	35	30	20
	a. Corrected imprint		†	1·25	
46	25 c. King Venus	50	20	80	15
47	35 c. Long-spined Star-shell	35	30	35	25
	a. Corrected imprint		†	1·50	
48	45 c. Speckled Tellin	35	30	†	
49	50 c. Rooster Tail Conch	40	25	45	30
50	$1 Green Star Shell	1·00	75	1·00	60
51	$2.50, Incomparable Cone	2·25	1·25	7·00	1·25
52	$5 Rough File Clam	4·00	2·75	9·00	3·00
52a	$10 Measled Cowrie	10·00	4·00		
35A/52aA	Set of 19	18·00	10·00		
38B/52B	Set of 13			18·00	5·50

Dates of issue: 27.11.74, Nos. 35A/52A; 12.7.76, Nos. 52aA, 38B/42B, 45B, 47B and 49B/50B; 2.6.77, Nos. 42a, 44B, 45a, 46B, 47a, 51B, 52B.

On Nos. 42a, 44B, 45a, 46B, 47a, 51B and 52B the designer's name is correctly spelt as "R. Granger Barrett". Previously the last name had been spelt "Barratt".

1974 (28 Nov). *Birth Centenary of Sir Winston Churchill. As Nos. 403/6 of St. Vincent but colours and face-values changed and inscr "GRENADINES OF ST. VINCENT".*
53	5 c. Type 75	10	10
54	40 c. As 35 c.	10	10
55	50 c. As 45 c.	15	10
56	$1 As $1	25	20
53/6	Set of 4	50	40

6 Cotton House, Mustique

(Des G. Drummond. Litho Questa)

1975 (27 Feb). *Mustique Island. T 6 and similar horiz designs. Multicoloured. W w 14 (sideways). P 14.*
57	5 c. Type 6	10	10
58	35 c. "Blue Waters", Endeavour Bay	10	10
59	45 c. Endeavour Bay	10	10
60	$1 "Les Jolies Eaux", Gelliceaux Bay	25	20
57/60	Set of 4	40	30

Nos. 57/60 were each issued in sheets of ten stamps and two *se-tenant* labels.

7 Danaus plexippus

(Des G. Drummond. Litho Questa)

1975 (15 May). *Butterflies. T 7 and similar horiz designs. Multicoloured. W w 14 (sideways). P 14.*
61	3 c. Type 7	20	10
62	5 c. *Agraulis vanillae*	25	10
63	35 c. *Battus polydamas*	80	10
64	45 c. *Evenus dindymus* and *Junonia evarete*	1·00	10
65	$1 *Anartia jatrophae*	1·75	35
61/5	Set of 5	3·50	65

8 Resort Pavilion

(Des G. Drummond. Litho Harrison)

1975 (24 July). *Petit St. Vincent. T 8 and similar horiz designs. Multicoloured. W w 14 (sideways). P 14.*
66	5 c. Type 8	10	10
67	35 c. The Harbour	10	10
68	45 c. The Jetty	15	10
69	$1 Sailing in coral lagoon	50	30
66/9	Set of 4	70	45

Nos. 66/9 were each issued in sheets of ten stamps and two *se-tenant* labels.

9 Ecumenical Church, Mustique

(Des G. Drummond. Litho Questa)

1975 (20 Nov). *Christmas. T 9 and similar horiz designs. Multicoloured. W w 12 (sideways). P 14.*
70	5 c. Type 9	10	10
71	25 c. Catholic Church, Union Island	10	10
72	50 c. Catholic Church, Bequia	10	10
73	$1 Anglican Church, Bequia	25	15
70/3	Set of 4	40	30

10 Sunset Scene

(Des G. Drummond. Litho J.W.)

1976 (26 Feb). *Union Island (1st series). T 10 and similar horiz designs. Multicoloured. W w 14 (sideways). P 13½.*
74	5 c. Type 10	10	10
75	35 c. Customs and Post Office, Clifton	10	10
76	45 c. Anglican Church, Ashton	10	10
77	$1 Mail schooner, Clifton Harbour	25	20
74/7	Set of 4	45	30

Nos. 74/7 were each issued in sheets of ten stamps and two *se-tenant* labels.

See also Nos. 242/5.

11 Staghorn Coral

(Des G. Drummond. Litho Questa)

1976 (13 May). *Corals. T 11 and similar horiz designs. Multicoloured. W w 14 (sideways). P 14.*
78	5 c. Type 11	10	10
79	35 c. Elkhorn coral	25	10
80	45 c. Pillar coral	30	10
81	$1 Brain coral	80	20
78/81	Set of 4	1·25	30

12 25 c. Bicentennial Coin

(Des J. Cooter. Litho Questa)

1976 (15 July). *Bicentenary of American Revolution. T 12 and similar horiz designs. W w 14 (sideways). P 13½.*
82	25 c. silver, black and light violet-blue	10	10
83	50 c. silver, black and light rose-red	20	10
84	$1 silver, black and mauve	25	20
82/4	Set of 3	50	30

Designs:—50 c. Half-dollar coin; $1 One dollar coin.

Nos. 82/4 were each issued in sheets of ten stamps and two *se-tenant* labels.

(Des G. Drummond. Litho Questa)

1976 (23 Sept). *Maps (2nd series). Vert designs as T 2, showing various islands as detailed below. W w 14. P 13½.*

A. Bequia   D. Mustique   F. Prune
B. Canouan   E. Petit St. Vincent   G. Union
C. Mayreau

To indicate individual islands, use the above letters as a suffix to the following catalogue numbers.
85	5 c. black, myrtle-green and pale emerald	10	10
	a. Booklet pane. Nos. 85/6 and 88 plus printed label	45	
	b. Booklet pane. Nos. 85 × 2 and 86 plus printed label	30	

86	10 c. black, ultramarine and greenish blue	10	10
	a. Booklet pane. Nos. 86 × 2 and 87 plus printed label	40	
87	35 c. black, red-brown and bright rose	20	20
	a. Booklet pane. Nos. 87 × 2 and 88 plus printed label	65	
88	45 c. black, scarlet and yellow-orange	25	25
85/8	Set of 4 (one island)	60	60
85/8	Set of 28 (seven islands)	4·00	4·00

Nos. 85/8 were only issued in $2.50 stamp booklets.

13 Station Hill School and Post Office

(Des G. Drummond. Litho Questa)

1976 (2 Dec). *Mayreau Island. T **13** and similar horiz designs. Multicoloured. W w **14** (sideways). P 14.*

89	5 c. Type **13**	10	10
90	35 c. Church at Old Wall	10	10
91	45 c. La Sourciere Anchorage	10	10
92	$1 Saline Bay	25	15
89/92	Set of 4	40	30

Nos. 89/92 were each issued in sheets of ten stamps and two se-tenant labels.

14 Coronation Crown Coin

(Des G. Vasarhelyi. Litho Questa)

1977 (3 Mar). *Silver Jubilee. T **14** and similar horiz designs. Multicoloured. W w **14** (sideways). P 14.*

93	25 c. Type **14**	20	10
94	50 c. Silver Wedding Crown	25	10
95	$1 Silver Jubilee Crown	30	15
93/5	Set of 3	65	30

Nos. 93/5 were each issued in sheets of ten stamps and two se-tenant labels.

15 Fiddler Crab

(Des BG Studio. Litho Questa)

1977 (19 May). *Crustaceans. T **15** and similar horiz designs. Multicoloured. W w **14** (sideways). P 14.*

96	5 c. Type **15**	10	10
97	35 c. Ghost crab	20	10
98	50 c. Blue crab	25	10
99	$1.25, Spiny lobster	55	40
96/9	Set of 4	95	55

16 Snorkel Diving

(Des G. Drummond. Litho Questa)

1977 (25 Aug). *Prune Island. T **16** and similar horiz designs. Multicoloured. W w **14** (sideways). P 14½.*

100	5 c. Type **16**	10	10
101	35 c. Palm Island Resort	10	10
102	45 c. Casuarina Beach	10	15
103	$1 Palm Island Beach Club	30	40
100/3	Set of 4	50	55

Nos. 100/3 were each issued in sheets of ten stamps and two se-tenant labels.

17 Mustique Island

(Des G. Drummond. Litho Questa)

1977 (31 Oct). *Royal Visit. Previously unissued stamps without face values, locally surch with new inscription. W w **12.** P 14½ × 14.*

104	17 40 c. turquoise-green and blue-green (Blk. (value) and R.)	20	10
105	$2 yellow-ochre and yellow-brown (R. (value) and B.)	65	25

18 The Clinic, Charlestown

(Des G. Drummond. Litho Harrison)

1977 (8 Dec). *Canouan Island (1st series). T **18** and similar horiz designs. Multicoloured. W w **14.** P 14½.*

106	5 c. Type **18**	10	10
107	35 c. Town jetty, Charlestown	10	10
108	45 c. Mail schooner arriving at Charlestown	10	10
109	$1 Grand Bay	30	35
106/9	Set of 4	50	50

Nos. 106/9 were each issued in sheets of ten stamps and two se-tenant labels.
See also Nos. 307/10.

19 Tropical Mockingbird

(Des J.W. Litho Enschedé)

1978 (11 May). *Birds and their Eggs. Horiz designs as T **19.** Multicoloured. W w **14** (sideways). P 12½ × 12.*

110	1 c. Type **19**	10	15
111	2 c. Mangrove Cuckoo	15	15
112	3 c. Osprey	20	15
113	4 c. Smooth-billed Ani	20	15
114	5 c. House Wren	20	15
115	6 c. Bananaquit	20	15
116	8 c. Carib Grackle	20	15
117	10 c. Yellow-bellied Elaenia	20	15
118	12 c. Collared Plover	30	15
119	15 c. Cattle Egret	30	15
120	20 c. Red-footed Booby	30	15
121	25 c. Red-billed Tropic Bird	30	15
122	40 c. Royal Tern	45	15
123	50 c. Grenada Flycatcher	45	20
124	80 c. Purple Gallinule	70	45
125	$1 Broad-winged Hawk	75	65
126	$2 Scaly-breasted Ground Dove	90	1·00
127	$3 Laughing Gull	1·25	1·40
128	$5 Common Noddy	2·25	1·75
129	$10 Grey Kingbird	5·00	2·75
110/29	Set of 20	13·00	9·00

See also Nos. MS155 and MS170.

(Des G. Drummond. Litho J.W.)

1978 (2 June). *25th Anniv of Coronation. Horiz designs as Nos. 422/5 of Montserrat. Multicoloured. W w **14** (sideways). P 13.*

130	5 c. Worcester Cathedral	10	10
131	40 c. Coventry Cathedral	10	10
132	$1 Winchester Cathedral	15	10
133	$3 Chester Cathedral	25	35
130/3	Set of 4	45	50
MS134	130 × 102 mm. Nos. 130/3. P 13½ × 14	60	80
	a. Top horiz pair imperf three sides	£350	

Nos. 130/3 were each issued in sheets of ten stamps and two se-tenant labels.

No. **MS**134a shows the 5 c. and 40 c. stamps in the sheet perforated along the top, but imperforate on the other three sides.

20 Green Turtle
21 Three Kings following Star

(Des R. Granger Barrett. Litho Walsall)

1978 (20 July). *Turtles. T **20** and similar horiz designs. Multicoloured. W w **14** (sideways). P 14.*

135	5 c. Type **20**	10	10
136	40 c. Hawksbill turtle	15	10
137	50 c. Leatherback turtle	15	10
138	$1.25, Loggerhead turtle	40	40
135/8	Set of 4	65	60

(Des Jennifer Toombs. Litho Questa)

1978 (2 Nov). *Christmas. Scenes and Verses from the Carol "We Three Kings of Orient Are". T **21** and similar vert designs. Multicoloured. W w **14.** P 14 × 13½.*

139	5 c. Type **21**	10	10
140	10 c. King with gift of Gold	10	10
141	25 c. King with gift of Frankincense	10	10
142	50 c. King with gift of Myrrh	10	10
143	$2 Three Kings paying homage to infant Jesus	30	20
139/43	Set of 5	45	30
MS144	154 × 175 mm. Nos. 139/43	70	1·25

22 Sailing Yachts
23 False Killer Whale

(Des G. Drummond. Litho Questa)

1979 (25 Jan). *National Regatta. T **22** and similar vert designs showing sailing yachts. W w **14.** P 14.*

145	5 c. multicoloured	10	10
146	40 c. multicoloured	20	10
147	50 c. multicoloured	25	10
148	$2 multicoloured	75	60
145/8	Set of 4	1·10	75

(Des L. Curtis. Litho Questa)

1979 (8 Mar). *Wildlife. Horiz designs as T **114** of St. Vincent. Multicoloured. W w **14** (sideways). P 14 × 14½.*

149	20 c. Green Iguana	10	10
150	40 c. Common Opossum ("Manicou")	15	10
151	$2 Red-legged Tortoise	60	65
149/51	Set of 3	75	75

Nos. 149/51 were each printed in four panes of 12 throughout the sheet, each pane including two se-tenant labels.

(Des J.W. Litho. Enschedé)

1979 (21 May). *Death Centenary of Sir Rowland Hill. Horiz designs as T **103** of St. Vincent. Multicoloured. W w **14** (sideways). P 12½ × 12.*

152	80 c. Sir Rowland Hill	25	15
153	$1 Great Britain 1d. and 4d. stamps of 1858 with "A10" (Kingstown, St. Vincent) postmark	30	25
154	$2 St. Vincent ½d. and 1d. stamps of 1894 with Bequia postmark	50	40
152/4	Set of 3	95	70
MS155	165 × 115 mm. Nos. 124/6 and 152/4	2·00	2·50

Nos. 152/4 were each printed in sheets including two se-tenant stamp-size labels.

1979 (24 Oct). *International Year of the Child. As Nos. 570/3 of St. Vincent.*

156	6 c. black, silver and pale blue	10	10
157	40 c. black, silver and salmon	10	10
158	$1 black, silver and buff	20	10
159	$3 black, silver and lilac	45	30
156/9	Set of 4	65	45

(Des J.W. Litho Enschedé)

1979 (27 Oct). *Independence. Horiz designs as T **106** of St. Vincent. Multicoloured. W w **14** (sideways). P 12½ × 12.*

160	5 c. National flag and *Ixora salici-folia* (flower)	10	10
161	40 c. House of Assembly and *Ixora odorata* (flower)	10	10
162	$1 Prime Minister R. Milton Cato and *Ixora javanica* (flower)	20	20
160/2	Set of 3	30	30

(Des R. Granger Barrett. Litho Walsall)

1980 (31 Jan). *Whales and Dolphins. T **23** and similar horiz designs. Multicoloured. W w **14** (sideways). P 14.*

163	10 c. Type **23**	20	10
164	50 c. Spinner Dolphin	45	35
165	90 c. Bottle-nosed Dolphin	65	70
166	$2 Short-finned Pilot Whale ("Blackfish")	1·25	1·10
163/6	Set of 4	2·25	2·00

(Des J.W. Litho Enschedé)

1980 (24 Apr). *"London 1980" International Stamp Exhibition. Horiz designs as T **110** of St. Vincent. Multicoloured. W w **14** (sideways). P 12½ × 12.*

167	40 c. Queen Elizabeth II	20	10
168	50 c. St. Vincent 1965 2 c. definitive	20	10
169	$3 1973 25 c. and Royal Wedding commemoratives	80	1·00
167/9	Set of 3	1·10	1·10
MS170	165 × 115 mm. Nos. 122/3, 127 and 167/9	2·25	2·50

Nos. 167/9 were printed in sheets including 2 se-tenant stamp-size labels.

(Des Polygraphic. Litho Rosenbaum Bros, Vienna)

1980 (7 Aug). *"Sport for All". Vert designs as T **112** of St. Vincent. Multicoloured. W w **14.** P 13½.*

171	25 c. Running	10	10
172	50 c. Sailing	10	10
173	$1 Long jumping	20	20
174	$2 Swimming	30	30
171/4	Set of 4	60	60

1980 (7 Aug). *Hurricane Relief. Nos. 171/4 surch with T* **113** *of St. Vincent.*

175	25 c.+50 c. Running	..	10	20
176	50 c.+50 c. Sailing	..	20	30
177	$1+50 c. Long jumping	..	25	40
178	$2+50 c. Swimming	..	40	60
175/8	..	*Set of 4*	85	1·40

24 Scene and Verse from the Carol "De Borning Day" 25 Post Office, Port Elizabeth

(Des Jennifer Toombs. Litho Questa)

1980 (13 Nov). *Christmas. T* **24** *and similar vert designs showing scenes and verses from the carol "De Borning Day". W* w **14**. *P* 14 × 13½.

179	5 c. multicoloured	..	10	10
180	50 c. multicoloured	..	10	10
181	60 c. multicoloured	..	10	10
182	$1 multicoloured	..	15	15
183	$2 multicoloured	..	25	25
179/83	..	*Set of 5*	50	50
MS184	159 × 178 mm. Nos. 179/83	..	75	1·40

(Des G. Drummond. Litho Questa)

1981 (19 Feb). *Bequia Island (2nd series). T* **25** *and similar horiz designs. Multicoloured. W* w **14** *(sideways). P* 14½ × 14.

185	50 c. Type **25**	..	15	15
186	60 c. Moonhole	..	20	20
187	$1.50, Fishing boats, Admiralty Bay	..	40	40
188	$2 *Friendship Rose* (yacht) at jetty	..	55	55
185/8	..	*Set of 4*	1·10	1·10

The $2 value was originally printed with the country name in black and the face value in white. A quantity of these were stolen in transit before issue and the remainder were not placed on sale, the stamp being reprinted with the inscriptions in red.

Nos. 185/8 were each printed in sheets including two *se-tenant* stamp-size labels.

26 Ins. Cannaouan 27 Bar Jack
(map of Windward Islands
by R. Ottens, circa 1765)

(Des J. Cooter. Litho Format)

1981 (2 Apr). *Details from Early Maps. T* **26** *and similar horiz designs. Multicoloured. W* w **14** *(sideways). P* 13½.

189	50 c. Type **26**	..	40	30
	a. Pair. Nos. 189/90	..	80	60
190	50 c. Cannouan Is. (chart by J. Parsons, 1861)	40	30
191	60 c. Ins. Moustiques (map of Windward Islands by R. Ottens, circa 1765)	45	35
	a. Pair. Nos. 191/2	..	90	70
192	60 c. Mustique Is. (chart by J. Parsons, 1861)	45	35
193	$2 Ins. Bequia (map of Windward Islands by R. Ottens circa 1765)	80	75
	a. Pair. Nos. 193/4	..	1·60	1·50
194	$2 Bequia Is. (map surveyed in 1763 by T. Jefferys)	80	75
189/94	..	*Set of 6*	3·00	2·50

The two designs of each value were printed together, *se-tenant*, in horizontal and vertical pairs throughout the sheet.

(Des D. Shults. Litho Questa)

1981 (17 July–26 Nov). *Royal Wedding. Horiz designs as T* **26/27** *of Kiribati. Multicoloured. (a) W* w **15**. *P* 14.

195	50 c. *Mary*	..	15	15
	a. Sheetlet. No. 195 × 6 and No. 196	1·10	
196	50 c. Prince Charles and Lady Diana Spencer	40	40
197	$3 *Alexandra*	..	30	30
	a. Sheetlet. No. 197 × 6 and No. 198	2·50	
198	$3 As No. 196	..	90	90
199	$3.50, *Britannia*	..	35	35
	a. Sheetlet. No. 199 × 6 and No. 200	2·75	
200	$3.50, As No. 196	..	90	90
195/200		*Set of 6*	2·75	2·75
MS201	120 × 109 mm. $5 As No. 196. Wmk sideways. P 12 (26 Nov)	1·25	1·00

(b) *Booklet stamps. No wmk. P* 12 (26 Nov)

202	50 c. As No. 195	..	20	30
	a. Booklet pane. No. 202 × 4	80	
203	$3 As No. 198	..	1·50	1·60
	a. Booklet pane. No. 203 × 2	3·00	

Nos. 195/200 were printed in sheetlets of seven stamps of the same face value, each containing six of the "Royal Yacht" design and one of the larger design showing Prince Charles and Lady Diana.

Nos. 202/3 come from $10 stamp booklets.

(Des N. Weaver. Litho Questa)

1981 (9 Oct). *Game Fish. T* **27** *and similar horiz designs. Multicoloured. W* w **14** *(sideways). P* 14.

204	10 c. Type **27**	..	15	10
205	50 c. Tarpon	..	25	10
206	60 c. Cobia	..	30	10
207	$2 Blue Marlin	..	90	70
204/7	..	*Set of 4*	1·40	85

28 H.M.S. *Experiment* 29 Prickly Pear Fruit

(Des J. Cooter. Litho Security Printers (M), Malaysia)

1982 (28 Jan). *Ships. Horiz designs as T* **28**. *Multicoloured. W* w **14**. *P* 13½ × 13.

208	1 c. Type **28**	..	10	10
209	3 c. *Lady Nelson* (cargo liner)	10	10
210	5 c. *Daisy* (brig)	..	10	10
211	6 c. Carib canoe	..	10	10
212	10 c. *Hairoun Star* (freighter)	15	10
213	15 c. *Jupiter* (liner)	..	15	10
214	20 c. *Christina* (steam yacht)	15	10
215	25 c. *Orinoco* (paddle-steamer)	20	15
216	30 c. H.M.S. *Lively*	..	20	15
217	50 c. *Alabama* (Confederate warship)	30	25
218	60 c. *Denmark* (freighter)	35	30
219	75 c. *Santa Maria*	..	40	35
220	$1 *Baffin* (cable ship)	..	50	45
221	$2 *Queen Elizabeth 2* (liner)	85	90
222	$3 *R.Y. Britannia*	..	1·25	1·40
223	$5 *Geeststar* (cargo liner)	..	2·10	2·25
224	$10 *Grenadines Star* (ferry)	4·25	4·50
208/24	..	*Set of 17*	10·00	10·00

(Des G. Drummond. Litho Harrison)

1982 (5 Apr). *Prickly Pear Cactus. T* **29** *and similar vert designs. Multicoloured. W* w **14**. *P* 14.

225	10 c. Type **29**	..	15	15
226	50 c. Prickly Pear flower buds	35	35
227	$1 Flower of Prickly Pear Cactus	60	60
228	$2 Prickly Pear Cactus	..	1·25	1·25
225/8	..	*Set of 4*	2·10	2·10

30 Anne Neville, 31 Old and New Uniforms
Princess of Wales, 1470

(Des D. Shults and J. Cooter. Litho Format)

1982 (1 July). *21st Birthday of Princess of Wales. T* **30** *and similar vert designs. Multicoloured. W* w **15**. *P* 13½ × 14.

229	50 c. Type **30**	..	20	20
230	60 c. Coat of arms of Anne Neville	20	20
231	$6 Diana, Princess of Wales	1·00	1·00
229/31	..	*Set of 3*	1·25	1·25

(Des L. Curtis. Litho W.S. Cowell Ltd)

1982 (15 July). *75th Anniv of Boy Scout Movement. T* **31** *and similar vert design. Multicoloured. W* w **14** *(inverted). P* 14½.

232	$1.50, Type **31**	..	60	60
233	$2.50, Lord Baden-Powell	..	90	90

ROYAL BABY

BEQUIA

(32) 33 Silhouette Figures
of Mary and Joseph

1982 (19 July). *Birth of Prince William of Wales. Nos. 229/31 optd with various island names as T* **32**.

A. Bequia B. Canouan C. Mayreau
D. Mustique E. Union Island

To indicate individual islands, use the above letters as a suffix to the following catalogue numbers.

234	50 c. Type **30**	..	20	20
	a. Opt A (Bequia) double	35·00	
	b. Opt C (Mayreau) inverted	28·00	
	c. Opt D (Mustique) inverted	28·00	
235	60 c. Coat of arms of Anne Neville	20	20
	a. Opt D (Mustique) inverted	35·00	
	b. Opt E (Union Island) inverted	50·00	
	c. Opt E (Union Island) double	£110	
236	$6 Diana, Princess of Wales	1·00	1·00
234/6	..	*Set of 3*	1·25	1·25

(Des Jennifer Toombs. Litho Security Printers (M), Malaysia)

1982 (18 Nov). *Christmas. T* **33** *and similar horiz designs showing silhouettes of figures. Multicoloured. W* w **14**. *P* 13½.

237	10 c. Type **33**	..	10	10
238	$1.50, Animals in stable	..	45	45
239	$2.50, Mary and Joseph with baby Jesus	60	60
237/9	..	*Set of 3*	1·00	1·00
MS240	168 × 99 mm. Nos. 237/9	..	1·00	1·75

45¢

(34) 35 Power Station, Clifton

1983 (26 Apr). *No. 123 surch with T* **34** *by Reliance Printery, Kingstown.*

241	45 c. on 50 c. Grenada Flycatcher	..	20	25

(Des G. Drummond. Litho Security Printers (M), Malaysia)

1983 (12 May). *Union Island (2nd series). T* **35** *and similar horiz designs. Multicoloured. W* w **14**. *P* 13½.

242	50 c. Type **35**	..	15	15
243	60 c. Sunrise, Clifton harbour	..	15	15
244	$1.50, Junior Secondary School, Ashton	40	40
245	$2 Frigate Rock and Conch Shell Beach	55	55
242/5	..	*Set of 4*	1·10	1·10

Nos. 242/5 were each printed in sheets including two *se-tenant* stamp-size labels.

36 British Man-of-war 37 Montgolfier Balloon, 1783

(Des J.W. Litho Questa)

1983 (4 Aug). *Bicentenary of Treaty of Versailles. T* **36** *and similar vert designs. Multicoloured. W* w **14**. *P* 14½.

246	45 c. Type **36**	..	15	15
247	60 c. American man-of-war	..	15	15
248	$1.50, Soldiers carrying U.S. flags	..	45	45
249	$2 British troops in battle	..	55	55
246/9	..	*Set of 4*	1·10	1·10

(Des A. Theobald. Litho Format)

1983 (15 Sept). *Bicentenary of Manned Flight. T* **37** *and similar multicoloured designs. W* w **14** *(sideways on Nos. 251/53). P* 14.

250	45 c. Type **37**	..	15	15
251	60 c. Ayres "Turbo-thrush Commander" (*horiz*)	15	15
252	$1.50, Lebaudy "1" dirigible (*horiz*)	45	45
253	$2 Space shuttle *Columbia* (*horiz*)	55	55
250/3	..	*Set of 4*	1·10	1·10
MS254	110 × 145 mm. Nos. 250/3. Wmk sideways	1·50	2·00

38 Coat of Arms of 39 Quarter Dollar and Half
Henry VIII Dollar, 1797

(Des Court House Studio. Litho Format)

1983 (25 Oct). *Leaders of the World. British Monarchs. T* **38** *and similar vert designs. Multicoloured. P* 12½.

255	60 c. Type **38**	..	25	25
	a. Horiz pair. Nos. 255/6	50	50
256	60 c. Henry VIII	..	25	25
257	60 c. Coat of Arms of James I	25	25
	a. Horiz pair. Nos. 257/8	50	50
258	60 c. James I	..	25	25
259	75 c. Henry VIII	..	25	25
	a. Horiz pair. Nos. 259/60	50	50
260	75 c. Hampton Court	..	25	25
261	75 c. James I	..	25	25
	a. Horiz pair. Nos. 261/2	50	50
262	75 c. Edinburgh Castle	..	25	25
263	$2.50, The *Mary Rose*	..	35	35
	a. Horiz pair. Nos. 263/4	70	70
264	$2.50, Henry VIII and Portsmouth harbour	35	35
265	$2.50, Gunpowder Plot	..	35	35
	a. Horiz pair. Nos. 265/6	70	70
266	$2.50, James I and the Gunpowder Plot	35	35
255/66	..	*Set of 12*	3·00	3·00

Nos. 255/6, 257/8, 259/60, 261/2, 263/4 and 265/6 were printed together, *se-tenant*, in horizontal pairs throughout the sheets.

(Des J. Cooter. Litho Walsall)

1983 (1 Dec). *Old Coinage. T* **39** *and similar vert designs. Multicoloured. W* w **14.** *P* 14.

267	20 c. Type 39		10	10
268	45 c. Nine Bitts, 1811–14		15	15
269	75 c. Twelve Bitts and Six Bitts, 1811–14		25	25
270	$3 Sixty-six Shillings, 1798..		80	80
267/70		*Set of* 4	1·10	1·10

40 Class "D 13"

(Des J.W. Litho Format)

1984 (15 Mar). *Leaders of the World. Railway Locomotives (1st series). T* **40** *and similar horiz designs, the first in each pair showing technical drawings and the second the locomotive at work. P* 12½.

271	5 c. multicoloured		10	10
	a. Vert pair. Nos. 271/2		10	10
272	5 c. multicoloured		10	10
273	10 c. multicoloured		10	10
	a. Vert pair. Nos. 273/4		15	15
274	10 c. multicoloured		10	10
275	15 c. multicoloured		15	15
	a. Vert pair. Nos. 275/6		30	30
276	15 c. multicoloured		15	15
277	35 c. multicoloured		20	20
	a. Vert pair. Nos. 277/8		40	40
278	35 c. multicoloured		20	20
279	45 c. multicoloured		20	20
	a. Vert pair. Nos. 279/80		40	40
280	45 c. multicoloured		20	20
281	60 c. multicoloured		25	25
	a. Vert pair. Nos. 281/2		50	50
282	60 c. multicoloured		25	25
283	$1 multicoloured		35	35
	a. Vert pair. Nos. 283/4		70	70
284	$1 multicoloured		35	35
285	$2.50, multicoloured		50	50
	a. Vert pair. Nos. 285/6		1·00	1·00
286	$2.50 multicoloured		50	50
271/86		*Set of* 16	3·00	3·00

Designs:—Nos. 271/2, Class "D 13", U.S.A. (1892); 273/4, High Speed Train "125", Great Britain (1980); 275/6, Class "T 9", Great Britain (1899); 277/8, *Claud Hamilton*, Great Britain (1900); 279/80, Class "J", U.S.A. (1941); 281/2, Class "D 16", U.S.A. (1895); 283/4, *Lode Star*, Great Britain (1907); 285/6, *Blue Peter*, Great Britain (1948).

Nos. 271/2, 273/4, 275/6, 277/8, 279/80, 281/2, 283/4 and 285/6 were printed together, *se-tenant* in vertical pairs throughout the sheet.

See also Nos. 311/26, 351/9, 390/7, 412/19, 443/58, 504/19 and 520/35.

41 Spotted Eagle Ray

(Des G. Drummond. Litho Format)

1984 (26 Apr). *Reef Fishes. T* **41** *and similar horiz designs. Multicoloured. W* w **15.** *P* 14.

287	45 c. Type 41		25	30
288	60 c. Queen Trigger Fish		30	35
289	$1.50, White Spotted File Fish		75	80
290	$2 Schoolmaster		1·00	1·10
287/90		*Set of* 4	2·10	2·25

42 R. A. Woolmer

43 Junior Secondary School

(Des Court House Studio. Litho Format)

1984 (16 Aug). *Leaders of the World. Cricketers (1st series). T* **42** *and similar vert designs, the first in each pair showing a portrait and the second the cricketer in action. P* 12½.

291	1 c. multicoloured		10	10
	a. Horiz pair. Nos. 291/2		10	10
292	1 c. multicoloured		10	10
293	3 c. multicoloured		10	10
	a. Horiz pair. Nos. 293/4		10	10
294	3 c. multicoloured		10	10
295	5 c. multicoloured		10	10
	a. Horiz pair. Nos. 295/6		10	10
296	5 c. multicoloured		10	10
297	30 c. multicoloured		20	20
	a. Horiz pair. Nos. 297/8		40	40
298	30 c. multicoloured		20	20
299	60 c. multicoloured		40	40
	a. Horiz pair. Nos. 299/300 ..		80	80

300	60 c. multicoloured		40	40
301	$1 multicoloured		50	50
	a. Horiz pair. Nos. 301/2		1·00	1·00
302	$1 multicoloured		50	50
303	$2 multicoloured		80	80
	a. Horiz pair. Nos. 303/4		1·60	1·60
304	$2 multicoloured		80	80
305	$3 multicoloured		1·10	1·10
	a. Horiz pair. Nos. 305/6		2·10	2·10
306	$3 multicoloured		1·10	1·10
291/306		*Set of* 16	5·50	5·50

Designs:—Nos. 293/4, K. S. Ranjitsinhji; 295/6, W. R. Hammond; 297/8, D. L. Underwood; 299/300, W. G. Grace; 301/2, E. A. E. Baptiste; 303/4, A. P. E. Knott; 305/6, L. E. G. Ames.

See also Nos. 331/8 and 364/9.

(Des G. Drummond. Litho Questa)

1984 (3 Sept). *Canouan Island (2nd series). T* **43** *and similar horiz designs. Multicoloured. W* **15** *(sideways). P* 14.

307	35 c. Type 43		20	20
308	45 c. Police Station		25	25
309	$1 Post Office		50	50
310	$3 Anglican Church..		1·25	1·50
307/10		*Set of* 4	2·00	2·25

IMPERFORATES AND MISSING COLOURS. Various issues between Nos. 311 and 672 exist either imperforate or with colours omitted. Such items are not listed as there is no evidence that they fulfil the criteria outlined on page xi of this catalogue.

(Des J.W. Litho Format)

1984 (9 Oct). *Leaders of the World. Railway Locomotives (2nd series). Horiz designs as T* **40**, *the first in each pair showing technical drawings and the second the locomotive at work. P* 12½.

311	1 c. multicoloured		10	10
	a. Vert pair. Nos. 311/12		10	10
312	1 c. multicoloured		10	10
313	5 c. multicoloured		10	10
	a. Vert pair. Nos. 313/14		10	10
314	5 c. multicoloured		10	10
315	20 c. multicoloured		15	15
	a. Vert pair. Nos. 315/16		30	30
316	20 c. multicoloured		15	15
317	35 c. multicoloured		15	15
	a. Vert pair. Nos. 317/18		30	30
318	35 c. multicoloured		15	15
319	60 c. multicoloured		20	20
	a. Vert pair. Nos. 319/20		40	40
320	60 c. multicoloured		20	20
321	$1 multicoloured		25	25
	a. Vert pair. Nos. 321/2		50	50
322	$1 multicoloured		25	25
323	$1.50, multicoloured		30	30
	a. Vert pair. Nos. 323/4		60	60
324	$1.50, multicoloured		30	30
325	$3 multicoloured		55	55
	a. Vert pair. Nos. 325/6		1·10	1·10
326	$3 multicoloured		55	55
311/26		*Set of* 16	3·00	3·00

Designs:—Nos. 311/12, Class "C62", Japan (1948); 313/14, Class "V", Great Britain (1903); 315/16, *Catch-Me-Who-Can*, Great Britain (1808), 317/18, Class "E10", Japan (1948); 319/20, J. B. Earle, Great Britain (1904); 321/2, *Lyn*, Great Britain (1898); 323/4, *Talyllyn*, Great Britain (1865); 325/6, *Cardean*, Great Britain (1906).

Nos. 311/26 were issued in a similar sheet format to Nos. 271/86.

44 Lady of the Night

45 Facel "Vega HK500"

(Des Jennifer Toombs. Litho Questa)

1984 (15 Oct). *Night-blooming Flowers. T* **44** *and similar vert designs. Multicoloured. W* **15.** *P* 14.

327	35 c. Type 44		35	30
328	45 c. Four o'clock		45	35
329	75 c. Mother-in-Law's Tongue		60	50
330	$3 Queen of the Night		2·00	1·75
327/30		*Set of* 4	3·00	2·50

(Des Court House Studio. Litho Format)

1984 (28 Nov). *Leaders of the World. Cricketers (2nd series). Vert designs as T* **42**, *the first in each pair listed showing a head portrait and the second the cricketer in action. P* 12½.

331	5 c. multicoloured		10	10
	a. Horiz pair. Nos. 331/2		10	10
332	5 c. multicoloured		10	10
333	30 c. multicoloured		15	15
	a. Horiz pair. Nos. 333/4		30	30
334	30 c. multicoloured		15	15
335	$1 multicoloured		30	30
	a. Horiz pair. Nos. 335/6		60	60
336	$1 multicoloured		30	30
337	$2.50, multicoloured		70	70
	a. Horiz pair. Nos. 337/8		1·40	1·40
338	$2.50, multicoloured		70	70
331/8		*Set of* 8	2·25	2·25

Designs:—Nos. 331/2, S. F. Barnes; 333/4, R. Peel; 335/6, H. Larwood; 337/8, Sir John Hobbs.

Nos. 331/8 were issued in a similar sheet format to Nos. 291/306.

(Des J.W. Litho Format)

1984 (28 Nov). *Leaders of the World. Automobiles (1st series). T* **45** *and similar horiz designs, the first in each pair showing technical drawings and the second the paintings. P* 12½.

339	5 c. black, azure and dull yellow-green		10	10
	a. Vert pair. Nos. 339/40		10	10
340	5 c. multicoloured		10	10
341	25 c. black, pale lilac and pink		10	10
	a. Vert pair. Nos. 341/2		20	20
342	25 c. multicoloured		10	10
343	50 c. black, pale blue and pale orange		15	15
	a. Vert pair. Nos. 343/4		30	30
344	50 c. multicoloured		15	15
345	$3 black, stone and brown lake		45	45
	a. Vert pair. Nos. 345/6		90	90
346	$3 multicoloured		45	45
339/46		*Set of* 8	1·25	1·25

Designs:—Nos. 339/40, Facel "Vega HK500"; 341/2, B.M.W. "328"; 343/4, Frazer-Nash "TT Replica 1.5L"; 345/6, Buick "Roadmaster Riviera".

Nos. 339/40, 341/2, 343/4 and 345/6 were printed together, se-tenant, in vertical pairs throughout the sheets.

See also Nos. 378/85 and 431/42.

46 The Three Wise Men and Star

(Des Jennifer Toombs. Litho Format)

1984 (3 Dec). *Christmas. T* **46** *and similar horiz designs. Multicoloured. W* **15** *(sideways). P* 14½.

347	20 c. Type 46		10	10
348	45 c. Journeying to Bethlehem		20	25
349	$3 Presenting gifts		1·00	1·40
347/9		*Set of* 3	1·10	1·60
MS350	177 × 107 mm. Nos. 347/9. Wmk inverted		1·25	2·00

(Des J.W. Litho Format)

1985 (31 Jan). *Leaders of the World. Railway Locomotives (3rd series). Horiz designs as T* **40**, *the first in each pair showing technical drawings and the second the locomotive at work. P* 12½.

351	1 c. multicoloured		10	10
	a. Vert pair. Nos. 351/2		10	10
352	1 c. multicoloured		10	10
353	15 c. multicoloured		10	10
	a. Vert pair Nos. 353/4		15	15
354	15 c. multicoloured		10	10
355	75 c. multicoloured		25	25
	a. Vert pair. Nos. 355/6		50	50
356	75 c. multicoloured		25	25
357	$3 multicoloured		70	70
	a. Vert pair. Nos. 357/8		1·40	1·40
358	$3 multicoloured		70	70
351/8		*Set of* 8	1·90	1·90
MS359	142 × 122 mm. Nos. 355/8. W w 15.		5·50	6·00

Designs:—Nos. 351/2, P.L.M. "Grosse C", France (1898); 353/4, Class "C12", Japan (1932); 355/6, Class "D50", Japan (1923); 357/8, *Fire Fly*, Great Britain (1840).

Nos. 351/8 were issued in a similar sheet format to Nos. 271/86.

47 Caribbean King Crab

48 Cypripedium calceolus

(Des G. Drummond. Litho Format)

1985 (11 Feb). *Shell Fish. T* **47** *and similar horiz designs. Multicoloured. W* w **15** *(sideways). P* 14.

360	25 c. Type 47		40	15
361	60 c. Queen Conch		55	35
362	$1 White Sea Urchin		80	60
363	$3 West Indian Top Shell ..		1·75	1·90
360/3		*Set of* 4	3·25	2·75

(Des Court House Studio. Litho Format)

1985 (22 Feb). *Leaders of the World. Cricketers (3rd series). Vert designs as T* **42** (55 c., 60 c.), *the first in each pair showing a head portrait and the second the cricketer in action, or horiz designs showing teams ($2). P* 12½.

364	55 c. multicoloured		30	35
	a. Horiz pair. Nos. 364/5 ..		60	70
365	55 c. multicoloured		30	35
366	60 c. multicoloured		35	40
	a. Horiz pair. Nos. 366/7		70	70
367	60 c. multicoloured		35	40
368	$2 multicoloured		80	85
369	$2 multicoloured		80	85
364/9		*Set of* 6	2·50	2·75

Designs: *Vert* (as T **42**)—Nos. 364/5, M. D. Moxon; 366/7, L. Potter. *Horiz* (59 × 42 mm)—No. 368, Kent team; 369, Yorkshire team.

Nos. 364/5 and 366/7 were issued in a similar sheet format to Nos. 291/306.

(Des Jennifer Toombs. Litho Format)

1985 (13 Mar). *Leaders of the World. Flowers. T* **48** *and similar vert designs. Multicoloured. P* 12½.

370	5 c. Type **48**	..	..	10	10
	a. Horiz pair. Nos. 370/1		..	10	10
371	5 c. *Gentiana asclepiadea*		..	10	10
372	55 c. *Clianthus formosus*		..	20	20
	a. Horiz pair. Nos. 372/3		..	40	40
373	55 c. *Clemisia coriacea*		..	20	20
374	60 c. *Erythronium americanum*			20	20
	a. Horiz pair. Nos. 374/5		..	40	40
375	60 c. *Laelia anceps*		..	20	20
376	$2 *Leucadendron discolor*		..	50	50
	a. Horiz pair. Nos. 376/7		..	1·00	1·00
377	$2 *Meconopsis horridula*		..	50	50
370/7			*Set of 8*	1·60	1·60

Nos. 370/1, 372/3, 374/5 and 376/7 were printed together, *se-tenant*, in horizontal pairs throughout the sheets.

(Des J.W. (5 c.), G. Turner (others). Litho Format)

1985 (9 Apr). *Leaders of the World. Automobiles* (2nd series). *Horiz designs as T* **45**, *the first in each pair showing technical drawings and the second paintings. P* 12½.

378	5 c. black, pale lemon and turquoise-blue	..		10	10
	a. Vert pair. Nos. 378/9		..	10	10
379	5 c. multicoloured		..	10	10
380	60 c. black, pale yellow and pale orange			15	15
	a. Vert pair. Nos. 380/1		..	30	30
381	60 c. multicoloured		..	15	15
382	$1 black, pale green and azure			20	20
	a. Vert pair. Nos. 382/3		..	40	40
383	$1 multicoloured		..	20	20
384	$1.50, black, pale cobalt and light green		..	25	25
	a. Vert pair. Nos. 384/5		..	50	50
385	$1.50, multicoloured		..	25	25
378/85			*Set of 8*	1·10	1·10

Designs:—Nos. 378/9, Winton (1903); 380/1, Invicta 4½ litre (1931); 382/3, Daimler "SP250 Dart" (1959); 384/5, Brabham "Repco BT19" (1966).

Nos. 378/85 were issued in a similar sheet format to Nos. 339/46.

49 Windsurfing

(Des G. Vasarhelyi. Litho Format)

1985 (9 May). *Tourism. Watersports. T* **49** *and similar horiz designs. Multicoloured. W w* **15** (*sideways*). *P* 14.

386	35 c. Type **49**	..		20	25
387	45 c. Water-skiing		..	25	30
388	75 c. Scuba-diving		..	35	40
389	$3 Deep-sea game fishing	..		1·50	1·60
386/9	..	..	*Set of 4*	2·10	2·25

(Des J.W. (50 c.), T. Hadler (others). Litho Format)

1985 (17 May). *Leaders of the World. Railway Locomotives* (4th series). *Horiz designs as T* **40**, *the first in each pair showing technical drawings and the second the locomotive at work. P* 12½.

390	10 c. multicoloured		..	10	10
	a. Vert pair. Nos. 390/1		..	10	10
391	10 c. multicoloured		..	10	10
392	40 c. multicoloured		..	20	20
	a. Vert pair. Nos. 392/3		..	40	40
393	40 c. multicoloured		..	20	20
394	50 c. multicoloured		..	20	20
	a. Vert pair. Nos. 394/5		..	40	40
395	50 c. multicoloured		..	20	20
396	$2.50, multicoloured		..	80	80
	a. Vert pair. Nos. 396/7		..	1·60	1·60
397	$2.50, multicoloured		..	80	80
390/7			*Set of 8*	2·25	2·25

Designs:—Nos. 390/1, Class "581" 12-car train, Japan (1968); 392/3, Class "231-132BT", Algeria (1936); 394/5, *Slieve Gullion*, Great Britain (1913); 396/7, Class "Beattie" well tank, Great Britain (1974).

Nos. 390/7 were issued in a similar sheet format to Nos. 271/86.

50 Passion Fruits and
Blossom

51 Queen Elizabeth the
Queen Mother

(Des G. Drummond. Litho Format)

1985 (24 June). *Fruits and Blossoms. T* **50** *and similar horiz designs. Multicoloured. W w* **15**. *P* 15.

398	30 c. Type **50**	..	..	15	20
399	75 c. Guava	..	..	35	40
400	$1 Sapodilla	..	..	50	55
401	$2 Mango	..	..	1·00	1·10
398/401			*Set of 4*	1·75	2·00
MS402	145 × 120 mm. Nos. 398/401. Wmk sideways. P 14½ × 15.			2·00	2·25

(Des Court House Studio. Litho Format)

1985 (31 July). *Leaders of the World. Life and Times of Queen Elizabeth the Queen Mother. Various vertical portraits as T* **51**. *P* 12½.

403	40 c. multicoloured	..		15	20
	a. Horiz pair. Nos. 403/4		..	30	40
404	40 c. multicoloured		..	15	20
405	75 c. multicoloured		..	15	20
	a. Horiz pair. Nos. 405/6		..	30	40
406	75 c. multicoloured		..	15	20
407	$1.10, multicoloured		..	20	25
	a. Horiz pair. Nos. 407/8		..	40	50
408	$1.10, multicoloured		..	20	25
409	$1.75, multicoloured		..	30	40
	a. Horiz pair. Nos. 409/10		..	60	80
410	$1.75, multicoloured		..	30	40
403/10	..	..	*Set of 8*	1·40	1·90
MS411	85 × 114 mm. $2 multicoloured; $2 multicoloured			1·00	1·75

The two designs of each value were issued, *se-tenant*, in horizontal pairs within the sheets.

Each *se-tenant* pair shows a floral pattern across the bottom of the portraits which stops short of the left-hand edge on the left-hand stamp and of the right-hand edge on the right-hand stamp.

Designs as Nos. 403/4 and 407/8, but with face values of $4 × 2 and $5 × 2, also exist in additional miniature sheets from a restricted printing issued 19 December 1985.

(Des J.W. (35 c.), T. Hadler (others). Litho Format)

1985 (16 Sept). *Leaders of the World. Railway Locomotives* (5th series). *Horiz designs as T* **40**, *the first in each pair showing technical drawings and the second the locomotive at work. P* 12½.

412	35 c. multicoloured	..		15	20
	a. Vert pair. Nos. 412/13		..	30	40
413	35 c. multicoloured		..	15	20
414	70 c. multicoloured		..	20	30
	a. Vert pair. Nos. 414/15		..	40	60
415	70 c. multicoloured		..	20	30
416	$1.20, multicoloured		..	30	40
	a. Vert pair. Nos. 416/17		..	60	80
417	$1.20, multicoloured		..	30	40
418	$2 multicoloured		..	50	65
	a. Vert pair. Nos. 418/19		..	1·00	1·25
419	$2 multicoloured		..	50	65
412/19			*Set of 8*	2·10	2·75

Designs:—Nos. 412/13, *Coronation*, Great Britain (1937); 414/15, Class "E18", Germany (1935); 416/17, "Hayes" type, U.S.A. (1854), 418/19, Class "2120", Japan (1890).

Nos. 412/19 were issued in a similar sheet format to Nos. 271/86.

1985 (27 Oct). *Royal Visit. Nos. 199/200, 222, 287, 398 and 407/8 optd as T* **114** *of Montserrat or surch also.*

420	**50**	30 c. multicoloured	..	2·50	2·00
421	**41**	45 c. multicoloured	..	3·00	2·50
422	—	$1.10, multicoloured (No. 407)	..	4·50	4·00
		a. Horiz pair. Nos. 422/3	..	9·00	8·00
423	—	$1.10, multicoloured (No. 408)	..	4·50	4·00
424	—	$1.50 on $3.50, mult (No. 199)		3·00	3·00
		a. Sheetlet. No. 424 × 6 and No. 425.	25·00		
425	—	$1.50 on $3.50, mult (No. 200)		9·00	9·00
426	—	$3 multicoloured (No. 222)	..	5·50	5·00
420/6	..	..	*Set of 7*	28·00	26·00

52 Donkey Man

(Des Jennifer Toombs. Litho Format)

1985 (16 Dec). *Traditional Dances. T* **52** *and similar multicoloured designs. P* 15.

427	45 c. Type **52**	..		25	30
428	75 c. Cake Dance (*vert*)		..	35	40
429	$1 Bois-Bois Man (*vert*)		..	50	55
430	$2 Maypole Dance		..	1·00	1·10
427/30	..	..	*Set of 4*	1·90	2·10

(Des Artists International (15 c.), J.W. ($3), G. Turner (others). Litho Format)

1986 (20 Feb). *Leaders of the World. Automobiles* (3rd series). *Horiz designs as T* **45**, *the first in each pair showing technical drawings and the second paintings. P* 12½.

431	15 c. black, pale rose-lilac and dull mauve	..		10	10
	a. Vert pair. Nos. 431/2		..	15	20
432	15 c. multicoloured		..	10	10
433	45 c. black, pale yellow and light brown			15	20
	a. Vert pair. Nos. 433/4		..	30	40
434	45 c. multicoloured		..	15	20
435	60 c. black, pale green and turquoise-blue		..	20	25
	a. Vert pair. Nos. 435/6		..	40	50
436	60 c. multicoloured		..	20	25
437	$1 black, pale cinnamon and sage-green		..	25	30
	a. Vert pair. Nos. 437/8		..	50	60
438	$1 multicoloured		..	25	30
439	$1.75, black, pale yellow and pale orange		..	35	45
	a. Vert pair. Nos. 439/40		..	70	90
440	$1.75, multicoloured		..	35	45
441	$3 multicoloured		..	55	65
	a. Vert pair. Nos. 441/2		..	1·10	1·25
442	$3 multicoloured		..	55	65
431/42			*Set of 12*	2·75	3·50

Designs:—Nos. 431/2, Mercedes-Benz 4.5 litre (1914); 433/4, Rolls Royce "Silver Wraith" (1954); 435/6, Lamborghini "Countach" (1974); 437/8, Marmon "V-16" (1932); 439/40, Lotus-Ford "49 B" (1968); 441/2, Delage 1.5 litre (1927).

Nos. 431/42 were issued in a similar sheet format to Nos. 339/46.

(Des T. Hadler (15 c., $3), J.W. (others). Litho Format)

1986 (14 Mar). *Leaders of the World. Railway Locomotives* (6th series). *Horiz designs as T* **40**, *the first in each pair showing technical drawings and the second the locomotive at work. P* 12½.

443	15 c. multicoloured		..	10	10
	a. Vert pair. Nos. 443/4		..	15	20
444	15 c. multicoloured		..	10	10
445	45 c. multicoloured		..	15	20
	a. Vert pair. Nos. 445/6		..	30	40
446	45 c. multicoloured		..	15	20
447	60 c. multicoloured		..	20	30
	a. Vert pair. Nos. 447/8		..	40	60
448	60 c. multicoloured		..	20	30
449	75 c. multicoloured		..	25	35
	a. Vert pair. Nos. 449/50		..	50	70
450	75 c. multicoloured		..	25	35
451	$1 multicoloured		..	30	40
	a. Vert pair. Nos. 451/2		..	60	80
452	$1 multicoloured		..	30	40
453	$1.50, multicoloured		..	35	50
	a. Vert pair. Nos. 453/4		..	70	1·00
454	$1.50, multicoloured		..	35	50
455	$2 multicoloured		..	50	65
	a. Vert pair. Nos. 455/6		..	1·00	1·25
456	$2 multicoloured		..	50	65
457	$3 multicoloured		..	65	80
	a. Vert pair. Nos. 457/8		..	1·25	1·40
458	$3 multicoloured		..	65	80
443/58			*Set of 16*	4·50	5·50

Designs:—Nos. 443/4, Class "T15", Germany (1897); 445/6, Class "13", Great Britain (1900); 447/8, *Halesworth*, Great Britain (1879); 449/50, Class "Problem", Great Britain (1859); 451/2, Class "Western" diesel, Great Britain (1961); 453/4, Drummond's "Bug", Great Britain (1899); 455/6, Class "Clan", Great Britain (1951); 457/8, Class "1800", Japan (1884).

Nos. 443/58 were issued in a similar sheet format to Nos. 271/86.

(Des Court House Studio. Litho Format)

1986 (21 Apr). *60th Birthday of Queen Elizabeth II. Multicoloured designs as T* **117a** *of Montserrat. P* 12½.

459	5 c. Queen Elizabeth II		..	10	10
460	$1 At Princess Anne's christening, 1950	..		30	35
461	$4 Princess Elizabeth		..	90	1·10
462	$6 In Canberra, 1982 (*vert*)		..	1·40	1·90
459/62			*Set of 4*	2·40	3·00
MS463	85 × 115 mm. $8 Queen Elizabeth II (*different*)			4·00	4·25

53 Handmade Dolls

(Des G. Drummond. Litho Format)

1986 (22 Apr). *Handicrafts. T* **53** *and similar horiz designs. Multicoloured. W w* **15**. *P* 15.

464	10 c. Type **53**		..	10	10
465	60 c. Basketwork		..	35	35
466	$1 Scrimshaw work		..	55	55
467	$3 Model boat		..	1·60	1·60
464/7			*Set of 4*	2·40	2·40

54 Uruguayan Team

(Des Court House Studio. Litho Format)

1986 (7 May). *World Cup Football Championship, Mexico. T* **54** *and similar multicoloured designs. P* 12½ (1 c., 10 c., $4, $5) *or* 15 (*others*).

468	1 c. Type **54**	..		10	10
469	10 c. Polish team		..	10	10
470	45 c. Bulgarian player (28 × 42 mm)		..	25	30
471	75 c. Iraqi player (28 × 42 mm)		..	35	40
472	$1.50, South Korean player (28 × 42 mm)		..	75	80
473	$2 Northern Irish player (28 × 42 mm)		..	1·00	1·10
474	$4 Portuguese team		..	2·00	2·10
475	$5 Canadian team		..	2·50	2·75
468/75			*Set of 8*	6·25	6·75
MS476	Two sheets, 85 × 114 mm. (a) $1 As No. 474: (b) $3 Type **54**. P 12½		*Set of 2 sheets*	1·50	2·25

55 *Marasmius pallescens*

56 *Brachymesia
furcata*

(Des G. Drummond. Litho Questa)

1986 (23 May). *Fungi. T 55 and similar vert designs. Multicoloured. W w 15 (sideways). P 14.*

477	45 c. Type **55**		1·25	65
478	60 c. *Leucocoprinus fragilissimus*		1·50	80
479	75 c. *Hygrocybe occidentalis* ..		2·00	1·00
480	$3 *Xerocomus hypoxanthus*		6·00	4·00
477/80		*Set of 4*	9·75	5·75

(Des Court House Studio. Litho Format)

1986 (18 July–15 Oct). *Royal Wedding (1st issue). Multicoloured designs as T 118a of Montserrat. P 12½.*

481	60 c. Miss Sarah Ferguson and Princess Diana applauding		20	25
	a. Pair. Nos. 481/2 ..		40	50
482	60 c. Prince Andrew at shooting match		20	25
483	$2 Prince Andrew and Miss Sarah Ferguson (*horiz*)		75	80
	a. Pair. Nos. 483/4 ..		1·50	1·60
484	$2 Prince Charles, Prince Andrew, Princess Anne and Princess Margaret on balcony (*horiz*) ..		75	80
481/4		*Set of 4*	1·75	1·90
MS485	115×85 mm. $8 Duke and Duchess of York in carriage after wedding (*horiz*) (15.10.86)		3·00	3·50

Nos. 481/2 and 483/4 were each printed together, *se-tenant*, in horizontal and vertical pairs throughout the sheets.

1986 (15 Oct). *Royal Wedding (2nd issue). Nos. 481/4 optd as T 121 of Montserrat in silver.*

486	60 c. Miss Sarah Ferguson and Princess Diana applauding		30	35
	a. Pair. Nos. 486/7 ..		60	70
487	60 c. Prince Andrew at shooting match ..		30	35
488	$2 Prince Andrew and Miss Sarah Ferguson (*horiz*)		1·00	1·10
	a. Pair. Nos. 488/9 ..		2·00	2·25
489	$2 Prince Charles, Prince Andrew, Princess Anne and Princess Margaret on balcony (*horiz*) ..		1·00	1·10
486/9		*Set of 4*	2·40	2·50

(Des M. Hillier. Litho Format)

1986 (19 Nov). *Dragonflies. T 56 and similar multicoloured designs. P 15.*

490	45 c. Type **56**		30	30
491	60 c. *Lepthemis vesiculosa*		35	35
492	75 c. *Perithemis domitia*		40	40
493	$2.50, *Tramea abdominalis* (*vert*)..		1·40	1·40
490/3		*Set of 4*	2·25	2·25

(Des Court House Studio. Litho Format)

1986 (26 Nov). *Centenary of Statue of Liberty. Vert views of Statue as T 121a of Montserrat in separate miniature sheets. Multicoloured. P 14×13½.*

MS494	Nine sheets, each 85×115 mm. $1.50; $1.75; $2; $2.50; $3; $3.50; $5; $6; $8	
	Set of 9 sheets 12·00 16·00	

57 American Kestrel   **58** Santa playing Steel Band Drums

(Des Toni Lance. Litho Questa)

1986 (26 Nov). *Birds of Prey. T 57 and similar vert designs. Multicoloured. P 14.*

495	10 c. Type **57** ..		30	15
496	45 c. Common Black Hawk ..		75	45
497	60 c. Peregrine Falcon ..		1·00	55
498	$4 Osprey		3·75	4·00
495/8		*Set of 4*	5·25	4·75

(Des Court House Studio. Litho Questa)

1986 (26 Nov). *Christmas. T 58 and similar vert designs. Multicoloured. P 14.*

499	45 c. Type **58**		25	30
500	60 c. Santa windsurfing		30	35
501	$1.25, Santa skiing		60	65
502	$2 Santa limbo dancing ..		1·00	1·10
499/502		*Set of 4*	1·90	2·10
MS503	166×128 mm. Nos. 499/502 ..		6·00	6·50

(Litho Format)

1987 (5 May). *Railway Locomotives (7th series). Horiz designs as T 40, the first in each pair showing technical drawings and the second the locomotive at work. Multicoloured. P 12½.*

504	10 c. multicoloured		10	10
	a. Vert pair. Nos. 504/5 ..		10	10
505	10 c. multicoloured		10	10
506	40 c. multicoloured		20	25
	a. Vert pair. Nos. 506/7 ..		40	50
507	40 c. multicoloured		20	25
508	50 c. multicoloured		25	30
	a. Vert pair. Nos. 508/9 ..		50	60
509	50 c. multicoloured		25	30
510	60 c. multicoloured		25	30
	a. Vert pair. Nos. 510/11 ..		50	60
511	60 c. multicoloured		25	30
512	75 c. multicoloured		35	40
	a. Vert pair. Nos. 512/13 ..		70	80
513	75 c. multicoloured		35	40

514	$1 multicoloured		45	50
	a. Vert pair. Nos. 514/15 ..		90	1·00
515	$1 multicoloured		45	50
516	$1.25, multicoloured		55	60
	a. Vert pair. Nos. 516/17 ..		1·10	1·25
517	$1.25, multicoloured		55	60
518	$1.50, multicoloured		70	75
	a. Vert pair. Nos. 518/19 ..		1·40	1·50
519	$1.50, multicoloured		70	75
504/19		*Set of 16*	5·00	5·75

Designs:—Nos. 504/5, Class "1001", No. 1275, Great Britain (1874); 506/7, Class "4P Garratt", Great Britain (1927); 508/9, *Papyrus*, Great Britain (1929); 510/11, Class "V1", Great Britain (1930); 512/13, Class "40" diesel, No. D200, Great Britain (1958); 514/15, Class "42 Warship" diesel, Great Britain (1958); 516/17, Class "P-69", U.S.A. (1902); 518/19, Class "60-3 Shay", No. 15, U.S.A. (1913).
Nos. 504/19 were issued in a similar sheet format to Nos. 271/86.

(Litho Format)

1987 (26 Aug). *Railway Locomotives (8th series). Horiz designs as T 40, the first in each pair showing technical drawings and the second the locomotive at work. P 12½.*

520	10 c. multicoloured		10	10
	a. Vert pair. Nos. 520/1 ..		10	10
521	10 c. multicoloured		10	10
522	40 c. multicoloured		20	25
	a. Vert pair. Nos. 522/3 ..		40	50
523	40 c. multicoloured		20	25
524	50 c. multicoloured		25	30
	a. Vert pair. Nos. 524/5 ..		50	60
525	50 c. multicoloured		25	30
526	60 c. multicoloured		25	30
	a. Vert pair. Nos. 526/7 ..		50	60
527	60 c. multicoloured		25	30
528	75 c. multicoloured		35	40
	a. Vert pair. Nos. 528/9 ..		70	80
529	75 c. multicoloured		35	40
530	$1 multicoloured		45	50
	a. Vert pair. Nos. 530/1 ..		90	1·00
531	$1 multicoloured		45	50
532	$1.50, multicoloured		70	75
	a. Vert pair. Nos. 532/3 ..		1·40	1·50
533	$1.50, multicoloured		70	75
534	$2 multicoloured		90	95
	a. Vert pair. Nos. 534/5 ..		1·75	1·90
535	$2 multicoloured		90	95
520/35		*Set of 16*	5·75	6·25

Designs:—Nos. 520/1, Class "142", East Germany (1977); 522/3, Class "120", West Germany (1979); 524/5, Class "X", Australia (1954); 526/7, Class "59", Great Britain (1986); 528/9, New York Elevated Railroad *Spuyten Duyvel*, U.S.A. (1875); 530/1, Camden & Amboy Railroad *Stevens* (later *John Bull*), U.S.A. (1831); 532/3, "Royal Hudson" Class "H1-d", No. 2850, Canada (1938); 534/5, "Pioneer Zephyr" 3-car set, U.S.A. (1934). Nos. 520/35 were issued in a similar sheet format to Nos. 271/86.

59 Queen Elizabeth with Prince Andrew   **60** Banded Coral Shrimp

(Des Young Phillips. Litho Format)

1987 (15 Oct). *Royal Ruby Wedding and 150th Anniv of Queen Victoria's Accession. T 59 and similar vert designs. P 12½.*

536	15 c. multicoloured		15	15
537	45 c. deep chocolate, black & greenish yellow		30	30
538	$1.50, multicoloured		90	90
539	$3 multicoloured		1·75	1·75
540	$4 multicoloured		2·00	2·00
536/40		*Set of 5*	4·50	4·50
MS541	85×115 mm. $6 multicoloured ..		3·00	3·25

Designs:—45 c. Queen Victoria and Prince Albert, *c* 1855; $1.50, Queen and Prince Philip after Trooping the Colour, 1977; $3 Queen and Duke of Edinburgh, 1953; $4 Queen in her study, *c* 1980; $6 Princess Elizabeth, 1947.

(Litho Format)

1987 (17 Dec). *Marine Life. T 60 and similar horiz designs. Multicoloured. P 15.*

542	45 c. Type **60** ..		45	45
543	50 c. Arrow Crab and Flamingo Tongue ..		50	50
544	65 c. Cardinal Fish		70	70
545	$5 Moray Eel		4·00	4·00
542/5		*Set of 4*	5·00	5·00
MS546	85×115 mm. $5 Puffer Fish ..		3·50	4·00

MINIMUM PRICE

The minimum price quote is 10p which represents a handling charge rather than a basis for valuing common stamps. For further notes about prices see introductory pages.

61 *Australia IV*   **62** Seine-fishing Boats racing

(Litho Format)

1988 (31 Mar). *Ocean Racing Yachts. T 61 and similar vert designs. Multicoloured. P 12½.*

547	50 c. Type **61**		50	50
548	65 c. *Crusader II*		60	60
549	75 c. *New Zealand K27*		75	75
550	$2 *Italia*		1·50	1·50
551	$4 *White Crusader*		2·50	2·50
552	$5 *Stars and Stripes*		3·00	3·00
547/52		*Set of 6*	8·00	8·00
MS553	100×140 mm. $1 *Champosa V*		90	1·25

(Litho Format)

1988 (31 Mar). *Bequia Regatta. T 62 and similar horiz designs. Multicoloured. P 15.*

554	5 c. Type **62**		10	10
555	50 c. *Friendship Rose* (motor fishing boat) ..		20	25
556	75 c. Fishing boats racing ..		30	35
557	$3.50, Yachts racing		1·50	1·60
554/7		*Set of 4*	1·90	2·00
MS558	115×85 mm. $8 Port Elizabeth, Bequia (60×40 mm). P 12½		3·75	4·50

63 "Twin-Otter" making Night Approach

(Litho Format)

1988 (26 May). *Mustique Airways. T 63 and similar multicoloured designs. P 14×13½.*

559	15 c. Type **63**		10	10
560	65 c. Beech "Baron" aircraft in flight		30	35
561	75 c. "Twin-Otter" over forest		30	35
562	$5 Beech "Baron" on airstrip		2·10	2·25
559/62		*Set of 4*	2·50	2·75
MS563	115 × 85 mm. $10 Baleine Falls (36 × 56 mm). P 12½		4·75	5·50

64 *Sv. Petr* in Arctic (Bering)   **65** Asif Iqbal Razvi

(Litho Format)

1988 (29 July). *Explorers. T 64 and similar square designs. Multicoloured. P 14×13½.*

564	15 c. Type **64**		10	10
565	75 c. Bering's ships in pack ice		30	35
566	$1 Livingstone's steam launch *Ma-Robert* on Zambesi		45	50
567	$2 Meeting of Livingstone and H. M. Stanley at Ujiji		80	85
568	$3 Speke and Burton at Tabori		1·25	1·40
569	$3.50, Speke and Burton in canoe on Lake Victoria		1·50	1·60
570	$4 Sighting the New World, 1492		1·60	1·75
571	$4.50, Columbus trading with Indians		2·00	2·10
563/71		*Set of 8*	7·25	7·75
MS572	Two sheets, each 115 × 85 mm. (a) $5 Sextant and coastal scene. (b) $5 *Santa Maria* at anchor. P 13½ × 14 ..	*Set of 2 sheets*	4·25	4·50

An unissued $6 miniature sheet, showing the *Santa Maria*, exists from stock dispersed by the liquidator of Format International Security Printers Ltd.

(Litho Format)

1988 (29 July). *Cricketers of 1988 International Season. T 65 and similar multicoloured designs. P 15.*

573	20 c. Type **65**		30	30
574	45 c. R. J. Hadlee ..		50	50
575	75 c. M. D. Crowe		70	70
576	$1.25, C. H. Lloyd		1·00	1·00
577	$1.50, A. R. Boarder		1·25	1·25
578	$2 M. D. Marshall		1·75	1·75
579	$2.50, G. A. Hick		2·00	2·00
580	$3.50, C. G. Greenidge (*horiz*)		2·50	2·50
573/80		*Set of 8*	9·00	9·00
MS581	115 × 85 mm. $3 As $2		4·00	4·00

66 Pam Shriver

(Litho Format)

1988 (29 July). *International Tennis Players. T* **66** *and similar multicoloured designs. P* 12½.

582	15 c. Type **66**	..	10	10
583	50 c. Kevin Curran (*vert*)	..	20	25
584	75 c. Wendy Turnbull (*vert*)	..	30	35
585	$1 Evonne Cawley (*vert*) ..	..	45	50
586	$1.50, Ilie Nastase (*vert*)	..	60	65
587	$2 Billie Jean King (*vert*)	..	80	85
588	$3 Bjorn Borg (*vert*)	..	1·25	1·40
589	$3.50, Virginia Wade with Wimbledon trophy (*vert*) ..	..	1·50	1·60
582/9		*Set of 8*	4·75	5·25

MS590 115 × 85 mm. $2.25, Stefan Edberg with Wimbledon cup; $2.25, Steffi Graf with Wimbledon trophy .. .. 3·00 3·25
No. 584 is inscribed "WENDY TURNBALL" in error.

Examples of an unissued set of six values and a miniature sheet for the 1988 Olympic Games at Seoul exist from stock dispersed by the liquidator of Format International Security Printers Ltd.

67 Mickey and Minnie Mouse visiting Fatehpur Sikri

(Des Walt Disney Co. Litho Questa)

1989 (8 Feb). *"India-89" International Stamp Exhibition, New Delhi. T* **67** *and similar multicoloured designs showing Walt Disney cartoon characters in India. P* 14×13½.

591	1 c. Type **67**	..	10	10
592	2 c. Mickey and Minnie Mouse aboard "Palace on Wheels" train	..	10	10
593	3 c. Mickey and Minnie Mouse passing Old Fort, Delhi	..	10	10
594	5 c. Mickey and Minnie Mouse on camel, Pinjore Gardens, Haryana ..	..	10	10
595	10 c. Mickey and Minnie Mouse at Taj Mahal, Agra ..	..	10	10
596	25 c. Mickey and Minnie Mouse in Chandni Chowk, Old Delhi	..	10	10
597	$4 Goofy on elephant with Mickey and Minnie Mouse at Agra Fort, Jaipur ..		1·60	1·75
598	$5 Goofy, Mickey and Minnie Mouse at Gandhi Memorial, Cape Comorin	..	2·10	2·25
591/8		*Set of 8*	3·75	4·00

MS599 Two sheets, each 127 × 102 mm. (a) $6 Mickey and Minnie Mouse in vegetable cart, Jaipur. P 14 × 13½. (b) $6 Mickey and Minnie Mouse leaving carriage, Qutab Minar, New Delhi (*vert*). P 13½ × 14 .. *Set of 2 sheets* 5·50 6·00

(Litho Questa)

1989 (6 July). *Japanese Art. Horiz designs as T* **187***a of Lesotho. Multicoloured. P* 14×13½.

600	5 c. "The View at Yotsuya" (Hokusai) ..		10	10
601	30 c. "Landscape at Ochanomizu" (Hokuju)		10	15
602	45 c. "Itabashi" (Eisen)	..	20	25
603	65 c. "Early Summer Rain" (Kunisada)	..	25	30
604	75 c. "High Noon at Kasumigaseki" (Kuniyoshi) ..	..	30	35
605	$1 "The Yoshiwara Embankment by Moonlight" (Kuniyoshi) ..	..	40	45
606	$4 "The Bridge of Boats at Sano" (Hokusai) ..	..	1·75	1·90
607	$5 "Lingering Snow on Mount Hira" (Kunitora) ..	..	2·10	2·25
600/7		*Set of 8*	4·75	5·25

MS608 Two sheets, each 103×76 mm. (a) $6 "Colossus of Rhodes" (Kunitora). (b) $6 "Shinobazu Pond" (Kokan) .. *Set of 2 sheets* 5·00 5·25
Nos. 600/7 were each printed in sheetlets of 10 containing two horizontal strips of 5 stamps separated by printed labels commemorating Emperor Hirohito.

68 Player with Ball and Mt Vesuvius

69 Arawak smoking Tobacco

(Des J. Genzo. Litho B.D.T.)

1989 (10 July). *World Cup Football Championship, Italy* (1st issue). *T* **68** *and similar vert designs each showing players and Italian landmarks. Multicoloured. P* 14.

609	$1.50, Type **68**	..	80	70
	a. Sheetlet. Nos. 609/16 ..		5·75	
610	$1.50, Fallen player, opponent kicking ball and Coliseum	..	80	70
611	$1.50, Player blocking ball and Venice	..	80	70
612	$1.50, Player tackling and Forum, Rome		80	70
613	$1.50, Two players competing for ball and Leaning Tower, Pisa		80	70
614	$1.50, Goalkeeper and Florence ..	..	80	70
615	$1.50, Two players competing for ball and St. Peter's, Vatican		80	70
616	$1.50, Player kicking ball and Pantheon		80	70
609/16		*Set of 8*	5·75	5·00

Nos. 609/16 were printed together, *se-tenant*, in a sheetlet of 8.
See also Nos. 680/4.

(Des D. Miller. Litho B.D.T.)

1989 (2 Oct). *500th Anniv of Discovery of America* (1992) *by Columbus. Pre-Columbian Arawak Society. T* **69** *and similar vert designs. Multicoloured. P* 14.

617	25 c. Type **69**	..	10	15
618	75 c. Arawak rolling cigar ..	..	30	35
619	$1 Applying body paint ..	..	40	45
620	$1.50, Making fire	..	65	70
	a. Horiz strip of 4. Nos. 620/3		2·50	
621	$1.50, Cassava production	..	65	70
622	$1.50, Woman baking bread	..	65	70
623	$1.50, Using stone implement	..	65	70
624	$4 Arawak priest	..	1·75	1·90
617/24		*Set of 8*	4·75	5·00

MS625 Two sheets, each 70×84 mm. (a) $6 Arawak chief. (b) $6 Men returning from fishing expedition .. .. *Set of 2 sheets* 6·00 6·50
Nos. 620/4 were printed together, *se-tenant*, in horizontal strips of 4 throughout the sheet of 20, each strip forming a composite design.

70 Command Module Columbia

71 *Marpesia petreus*

(Des W. Wright. Litho B.D.T.)

1989 (2 Oct). *10th Anniv of First Manned Landing on Moon. T* **70** *and similar multicoloured designs. P* 14.

626	5 c. Type **70**	..	10	10
627	40 c. Astronaut Neil Armstrong saluting U.S. flag		20	20
628	55 c. *Columbia* above lunar surface	..	30	30
629	65 c. Lunar module *Eagle* leaving Moon		30	30
630	70 c. *Eagle* on Moon	..	35	35
631	$1 *Columbia* re-entering Earth's atmos-phere	..	45	45
632	$3 "Apollo 11" emblem	..	1·40	1·40
633	$5 Armstrong and Aldrin on Moon	..	2·25	2·25
626/33		*Set of 8*	4·75	4·75

MS634 Two sheets, each 110×82 mm. (a) $6 Launch of "Apollo 11" (*vert*). (b) $6 "Apollo 11" splashdown .. .. *Set of 2 sheets* 5·50 6·00

(Des D. Bruckner. Litho Questa)

1989 (16 Oct). *Butterflies. T* **71** *and similar horiz designs. Multicoloured. P* 14½.

635	5 c. Type **71**	..	15	10
636	30 c. *Papilio androgeus*	..	20	15
637	45 c. *Strymon maesites*	..	30	25
638	65 c. *Junonia coenia*	..	40	30
639	75 c. *Eurema gratiosa*	..	45	35
640	$1 *Hypolimnas misippus*	..	60	45
641	$4 *Urbanus proteus*	..	2·25	2·25
642	$5 *Junonia evarete*	..	2·40	2·50
635/42		*Set of 8*	6·00	5·75

MS643 Two sheets. (a) 76×104 mm. $6 *Phoebis agarithe*. (b) 104×76 mm. $6 *Dryas julia* .. *Set of 2 sheets* 5·50 6·00

72 *Solanum urens*

73 Goofy and Mickey Mouse in Rolls-Royce "Silver Ghost", 1907

(Des Mary Walters. Litho Questa)

1989 (1 Nov). *Flowers from St. Vincent Botanical Gardens. T* **72** *and similar vert designs. Multicoloured. P* 14.

644	80 c. Type **72**	..	50	50
645	$1.25, *Passiflora andersonii*	..	70	70
646	$1.65, *Miconia andersonii*	..	85	85
647	$1.85, *Pitcairnia sulphurea*	..	1·00	1·00
644/7		*Set of 4*	2·75	2·75

(Des Walt Disney Co. Litho Questa)

1989 (20 Dec). *Christmas. T* **73** *and similar horiz designs showing Walt Disney cartoon characters and cars. Multicoloured. P* 14×13½.

648	5 c. Type **73**	..	10	10
649	10 c. Daisy Duck driving first Stanley Steamer, 1897	..	10	10
650	15 c. Horace Horsecollar and Clarabelle Cow in Darracq "Genevieve", 1904		10	10
651	45 c. Donald Duck driving Detroit electric coupe, 1914	..	20	25
652	55 c. Mickey and Minnie Mouse in first Ford, 1896		25	30
653	$2 Mickey Mouse driving Reo "Runabout", 1904	..	85	90
654	$3 Goofy driving Winton mail truck, 1899		1·25	1·40
655	$5 Mickey and Minnie Mouse in Duryea car, 1893		2·10	2·25
648/55		*Set of 8*	4·25	4·75

MS656 Two sheets, each 127×102 mm. (a) $6 Mickey and Minnie Mouse in Pope-Hartford, 1912. (b) $6 Mickey and Minnie Mouse in Buick "Model 10", 1908. P 13½×14 .. *Set of 2 sheets* 5·50 6·00

(Des W. Wright. Litho Questa)

1990 (2 Apr). *50th Anniv of Second World War. Horiz designs as T* **242** *of Maldive Islands. Multicoloured. P* 14.

657	10 c. Destroyers in action, First Battle of Narvik, 1940 ..		10	10
658	15 c. Allied tank at Anzio, 1944	..	10	10
659	20 c. U.S. carrier under attack, Battle of Midway, 1942		10	10
660	45 c. U.S. bombers over Gustav Line, 1944		20	25
661	55 c. Map showing Allied zones of Berlin, 1945 ..		25	30
662	65 c. German U-boat pursuing convoy, Battle of the Atlantic, 1943		30	35
663	90 c. Allied tank, North Africa, 1943	..	40	45
664	$3 U.S. forces landing on Guam, 1944	..	1·25	1·40
665	$5 Crossing the Rhine, 1945	..	2·25	2·40
666	$6 Japanese battleships under attack, Leyte Gulf, 1944	..	2·50	2·75
657/66		*Set of 10*	6·75	7·25

MS667 100×70 mm. $6 Lancaster on "Dam-busters" raid, 1943 .. .. .. 2·50 2·75

(Des Walt Disney Co. Litho Questa)

1990 (3 May). *"Stamp World London 90" International Stamp Exhibition* (1st issue). *Mickey's Shakespeare Company. Multicoloured designs as T* **239***a of Maldive Islands showing Walt Disney cartoon characters. P* 14×13½.

668	20 c. Goofy as Mark Anthony (*Julius Caesar*)	..	10	10
669	30 c. Clarabelle Cow as the Nurse (*Romeo and Juliet*)	..	15	20
670	45 c. Pete as Falstaff (*Henry IV*)	..	20	25
671	50 c. Minnie Mouse as Portia (*The Merchant of Venice*)	..	20	25
672	$1 Donald Duck as Hamlet (*Hamlet*)	..	45	50
673	$2 Daisy Duck as Ophelia (*Hamlet*)	..	85	90
674	$4 Donald and Daisy Duck as Benedick and Beatrice (*Much Ado About Nothing*)	..	1·75	1·90
675	$5 Minnie Mouse and Donald Duck as Katherine and Petruchio (*The Taming of the Shrew*)	..	2·25	2·40
668/75		*Set of 8*	5·50	6·00

MS676 Two sheets, each 127×101 mm. (a) $6 Clarabelle as Titania (*A Midsummer Night's Dream*) (*vert*). (b) $6 Mickey Mouse as Romeo (*Romeo and Juliet*) (*vert*). P 13½×14 *Set of 2 sheets* 5·25 5·50

74 Exhibition Emblem

75 Scaly-breasted Ground Dove

(Des M. Pollard. Litho B.D.T.)

1990 (3 May). *"Stamp World London 90" International Stamp Exhibition* (2nd issue). *150th Anniv of Penny Black. T* **74** *and similar vert designs. P* 14×15.

677	$1 black, brown-rose and magenta	..	45	50
678	$5 black, grey-lilac and ultramarine	..	2·25	2·40

MS679 130×100 mm. $6 black and pale blue .. 2·50 2·75
Designs:—$5 Negative image of Penny Black; $6 Penny Black.

(Des Young Phillips Studio. Litho Questa)

1990 (24 Sept). *World Cup Football Championship, Italy* (2nd issue). *Multicoloured designs as T* **210** *of St. Vincent, but horiz. P* 14.

680	25 c. McCleish, Scotland	..	10	15
681	50 c. Rasul, Egypt	..	20	25
682	$2 Lindenberger, Austria	..	85	90
683	$4 Murray, U.S.A.	..	1·75	1·90
680/3		*Set of 4*	2·50	3·00

MS684 Two sheets, each 102×77 mm. (a) $6 Robson, England. (b) $6 Gullit, Netherlands *Set of 2 sheets* 5·25 5·50

(Des Dorothy Novick. Litho B.D.T.)

1990 (23 Nov). *"EXPO 90" International Garden and Greenery Exposition, Osaka. Orchids. Vert designs as T 213 of St. Vincent. Multicoloured. P 14.*

685	5 c. *Paphiopedilum*		10	10
686	25 c. *Dendrobium phalaenopsis* and *Cymbidium hybrid*		10	15
687	30 c. *Miltonia candida* hybrid		15	20
688	50 c. *Epidendrum ibaguense* and *Cymbidium* Elliot Rogers		20	25
689	$1 *Rossioglossum grande*		45	50
690	$2 *Phalaenopsis* Elisa Chamg Lou and *Masdevallia coccinea*		85	90
691	$4 *Cypripedium acaule* and *Cypripedium calceolus*		1·75	1·90
692	$5 *Orchis spectabilis*		2·25	2·40
685/92		*Set of 8*	5·25	5·75

MS693 Two sheets, each 108×78 mm. (a) $6 *Dendrobium anosmum*. (b) $6 *Epidendrium ibaguense* and *Phalaenopsis* .. *Set of 2 sheets* 5·25 5·50

(Des W. Wright. Litho B.D.T.)

1990 (26 Nov). *Birds of the Caribbean. T 75 and similar horiz designs. Multicoloured. P 14.*

694	5 c. Type 75		10	10
695	25 c. Purple Martin		10	15
696	45 c. Painted Bunting		20	25
697	55 c. Blue-hooded Euphonia		25	30
698	75 c. Blue-grey Tanager		35	40
699	$1 Red-eyed Vireo		45	50
700	$2 Palm Chat		85	90
701	$3 Northern Jacana		1·25	1·40
702	$4 Green-throated Carib		1·75	1·90
703	$5 St. Vincent Amazon		2·25	2·40
694/703		*Set of 10*	6·75	7·50

MS704 Two sheets, each 117×87 mm. (a) $3 Magnificent Frigate Bird; $3 Bananaquit. (b) $6 Red-legged Honeycreeper .. *Set of 2 sheets* 5·25 5·50

(Des Young Phillips Studio. Litho B.D.T.)

1991 (14 Feb). *90th Birthday of Queen Elizabeth the Queen Mother. Vert designs as T 198a of Lesotho. P 14.*

705	$2 multicoloured		85	90
	a. Sheetlet. Nos. 705/13		7·75	
706	$2 multicoloured		85	90
707	$2 multicoloured		85	90
708	$2 multicoloured		85	90
709	$2 multicoloured		85	90
710	$2 multicoloured		85	90
711	$2 multicoloured		85	90
712	$2 multicoloured		85	90
713	$2 multicoloured		85	90
714	$2 multicoloured		85	90
	a. Sheetlet. Nos. 714/22		7·75	
715	$2 multicoloured		85	90
716	$2 multicoloured		85	90
717	$2 black and rose-lilac		85	90
718	$2 black and rose-lilac		85	90
719	$2 black, pale yellow-olive and rose-lilac		85	90
720	$2 multicoloured		85	90
721	$2 black and rose-lilac		85	90
722	$2 multicoloured		85	90
723	$2 multicoloured		85	90
	a. Sheetlet. Nos. 723/31		7·75	
724	$2 multicoloured		85	90
725	$2 multicoloured		85	90
726	$2 multicoloured		85	90
727	$2 multicoloured		85	90
728	$2 multicoloured		85	90
729	$2 multicoloured		85	90
730	$2 multicoloured		85	90
731	$2 multicoloured		85	90
705/31		*Set of 27*	21·00	22·00

MS732 Nine sheets containing details of designs indicated. (a) 120×115 mm. $5 As No. 705. (b) 115×120 mm. $5 As No. 710. (c) 115×120 mm. $5 As No. 712. (d) 115×120 mm. $5 As No. 715. (e) 120×115 mm. $5 As No. 719. (f) 120×115 mm. $5 As No. 720. (g) 120×115 mm. $5 As No. 724. (h) 120×115 mm. $5 As No. 730. (i) 120×115 mm. $5 As No. 730. *Set of 9 sheets* 19·00 20·00

Designs:—No. 705, Lady Elizabeth Bowes-Lyon with brother; No. 706, Young Lady Elizabeth in long dress; No. 707, Young Lady Elizabeth wearing a hat; No. 708, Lady Elizabeth leaning on wall; No. 709, Lady Elizabeth in evening dress; No. 710, Studio Portrait; No. 711, Lady Elizabeth in evening dress; No. 712, Duchess of York in fur-lined cloak; No. 713, Duchess of York holding rose; No. 714, Coronation, 1937; No. 715, King and Queen with Princess Elizabeth at Royal Lodge, Windsor; No. 716, Queen Elizabeth in blue hat; No. 717, King George VI and Queen Elizabeth; No. 718, Queen Elizabeth with Princess Elizabeth; No. 719, Queen Elizabeth watching sporting fixture; No. 720, Queen Elizabeth in white evening dress; No. 721, Princess Anne's christening, 1950; No. 722, Queen Mother with yellow bouquet; No. 723, Queen Mother and policewoman; No. 724, Queen Mother at ceremonial function; No. 725, Queen Mother in pink coat; No. 726, Queen Mother in academic robes; No. 727, Queen Mother in carriage with Princess Margaret; No. 728, Queen Mother in blue coat and hat; No. 729, Queen Mother with bouquet; No. 730, Queen Mother outside Clarence House on her birthday; No. 731, Queen Mother in turquoise coat and hat.

Nos. 705/13, 714/22 and 723/31 were printed, *se-tenant*, in sheetlets of nine.

(Litho Walsall)

1991 (11 June). *Death Centenary of Vincent van Gogh (artist) (1990). Multicoloured designs as T 255 of Maldive Islands. P 13½.*

733	5 c. "View of Arles with Irises" (*horiz*)		10	10
734	10 c. "Saintes-Maries"		10	10
735	15 c. "Old Woman of Arles"		10	10
736	20 c. "Orchard in Blossom, bordered by Cypresses" (*horiz*)		10	10
737	25 c. "Three White Cottages in Saintes-Maries" (*horiz*)		10	10
738	35 c. "Boats at Saintes-Maries" (*horiz*)		15	20
739	40 c. "Interior of a Restaurant in Arles" (*horiz*)		15	20

740	45 c. "Peasant Women"		20	25
741	55 c. "Self-portrait"		20	25
742	60 c. "Pork Butcher's Shop from a Window"		25	30
743	75 c. "The Night Cafe in Arles" (*horiz*)		35	40
744	$1 "2nd Lieut. Millet of the Zouaves" (*horiz*)		45	50
745	$2 "The Café Terrace, Place du Forum, Arles at Night"		85	90
746	$3 "The Zouave"		1·25	1·50
747	$4 "The Two Lovers" (detail)		1·75	2·00
748	$5 "Still Life" (*horiz*)		2·25	2·40
733/48		*Set of 16*	7·25	8·25

MS749 Four sheets, each 112×76 mm. (a) $5 "Street in Saintes-Maries" (*horiz*). (b) $5 "Lane near Arles" (*horiz*). (c) $6 "Harvest at La Crau, with Montmajour in the Background" (*horiz*). (d) $6 "The Sower". Imperf. .. *Set of 4 sheets* 10·50 11·00

(Des D. Miller. Litho Walsall)

1991 (5 July). *65th Birthday of Queen Elizabeth II. Horiz designs as T 210 of Lesotho. Multicoloured. P 14.*

750	15 c. Inspecting the Yeomen of the Guard		10	10
751	40 c. Queen Elizabeth II with the Queen Mother at the Derby, 1988		15	20
752	$2 The Queen and Prince Philip leaving Euston, 1986		85	90
753	$4 The Queen at the Commonwealth Institute, 1987		1·75	1·90
750/3		*Set of 4*	2·50	2·75

MS754 68×90 mm. $5 Queen Elizabeth and Prince Philip with Prince Andrew in naval uniform .. .. .. 2·25 2·40

(Des D. Miller. Litho Walsall)

1991 (5 July). *10th Wedding Anniv of Prince and Princess of Wales. Horiz designs as T 210 of Lesotho. Multicoloured. P 14.*

755	10 c. Prince and Princess at polo match, 1987		10	10
756	50 c. Separate family portraits		20	25
757	$1 Prince William and Prince Henry at Kensington Palace, 1991		45	50
758	$5 Portraits of Prince Charles and Princess Diana		2·25	2·40
755/8		*Set of 4*	2·75	3·00

MS759 68×90 mm. $5 Separate portraits of Prince and Princess and sons .. .. 2·25 2·40

76 First Japanese Steam Locomotive and Map

(Des K. Gromell. Litho Cartor)

1991 (12 Aug). *"Phila Nippon '91" International Stamp Exhibition, Tokyo. Japanese Railway Locomotives. T 76 and similar designs, each in black, scarlet-vermilion and dull blue-green. P 14×13½.*

760	10 c. Type 76		10	10
761	25 c. First imported American steam locomotive		10	15
762	35 c. Class "8620" steam locomotive		15	20
763	50 c. Class "C53" steam locomotive		20	25
764	$1 Class "DD-51" diesel locomotive		45	50
765	$2 Class "KTR001 Tango Explorer" electric rail car (inscr "RF22327")		85	90
766	$4 Class "EF55" electric locomotive		1·75	1·90
767	$5 Class "EF58" electric locomotive		2·25	2·40
760/7		*Set of 8*	5·25	5·75

MS768 Four sheets, each 114×73 mm showing frontal views. (a) $6 Class "9600" steam locomotive (*vert*). (b) $6 Class "C57" steam locomotive (*vert*). (c) $6 Class "C62" steam locomotive (*vert*). (d) $6 Class "4100" steam locomotive (*vert*) .. *Set of 4 sheets* 10·50 11·00

(Des W. Hanson Studio. Litho Questa)

1991 (18 Nov). *50th Death Anniv of Lord Baden-Powell and World Scout Jamboree, Korea. Multicoloured designs as T 263 of Maldive Islands. P 14.*

769	$2 Czechoslovakia 1918 20 h. stamp and scout delivering mail		85	90
770	$4 Scouts and cog train on Snowdon (*vert*)		1·75	1·90

MS771 Two sheets, each 118×89 mm. (a) $5 Jamboree emblem (buff background). (b) $5 Jamboree emblem (bluish violet background) (*vert*) .. .. .. *Set of 2 sheets* 4·25 4·50

(Litho Questa)

1991 (18 Nov). *Birth Centenary of Charles de Gaulle (French statesman) (1990). Multicoloured designs as T 209 of Lesotho. P 14.*

772	60 c. General De Gaulle in Djibouti, 1959 (*horiz*)		25	30

MS773 Two sheets. (a) 77×112 mm. $5 De Gaulle in civilian dress (*horiz*). (b) 69×101 mm. $5 General Charles de Gaulle .. *Set of 2 sheets* 4·25 4·50

(Des L. Fried. Litho Questa)

1991 (18 Nov). *Bicentenary of Brandenburg Gate. Horiz designs as T 264 of Maldive Islands. Multicoloured. P 14.*

774	45 c. President Gorbachev and photo of Gate		20	25
775	65 c. "DIE MAUER MUSS WEG!" slogan		30	35
776	80 c. East German border guard escaping to West		35	40
774/6		*Set of 3*	75	85

MS777 Two sheets, each 100×71 mm. (a) $5 Arms of Berlin. (b) $5 Berlin police badge *Set of 2 sheets* 4·25 4·50

(Des J. Iskowitz. Litho Questa)

1991 (18 Nov). *Death Bicentenary of Mozart. Multicoloured designs as T 265 of Maldive Islands. P 14.*

778	$1 *Abduction from the Seraglio*		45	50
779	$3 Dresden, 1749		1·25	1·50

MS780 Two sheets, each 75×101 mm. (a) $5 Portrait of Mozart (*vert*). (b) $5 Bust of Mozart (*vert*) .. .. .. *Set of 2 sheets* 4·25 4·50

Grenadines of St. Vincent / $1

77 Japanese Aircraft and Submarines leaving Truk

(Des J. Batchelor. Litho Questa)

1991 (18 Nov). *50th Anniv of Japanese Attack on Pearl Harbor. T 77 and similar horiz designs. Multicoloured. P 14½×15.*

781	$1 Type 77		45	50
	a. Sheetlet. Nos. 781/90		4·00	
782	$1 *Akagi* (Japanese aircraft carrier)		45	50
783	$1 Nakajima B5 N2 "Kate" aircraft		45	50
784	$1 Torpedo bombers attacking Battleship Row		45	50
785	$1 Burning aircraft, Ford Island airfield		45	50
786	$1 Doris Miller winning Navy Cross		45	50
787	$1 U.S.S. *West Virginia* and *Tennessee* (battleships) ablaze		45	50
788	$1 U.S.S. *Arizona* (battleship) sinking		45	50
789	$1 U.S.S. *New Orleans* (cruiser)		45	50
790	$1 President Roosevelt declaring war		45	50
781/90		*Set of 10*	4·00	4·50

Nos. 781/90 were printed together, *se-tenant*, in sheetlets of 10 with the stamps arranged in two horizontal rows of 5 separated by a map of Pearl Harbor.

(Des W. Wright. Litho Questa)

1991 (18 Nov). *Centenary of Trans-Siberian Railway. Multicoloured designs as T 266 of Maldive Islands. P 14.*

791	$1.75, Trans-Siberian logo (*horiz*)		75	80
792	$1.75, Trans-Siberian steam locomotive		75	80

MS793 115×85 mm. $5 Trans-Siberian express leaving Moscow at night (43×56 *mm*) .. 2·25 2·40

(Des W. Wright. Litho Questa)

1991 (18 Nov). *700th Anniv of Swiss Confederation. Horiz designs as T 269 of Maldive Islands. Multicoloured. P 14.*

794	$2 Zurich couple maypole dancing		85	90
795	$2 Man and woman in Vaud traditional costumes		85	90

MS796 101×72 mm. $5 Arms of Appenzell and Thurgau .. .. .. 2·25 2·40

(Des W. Wright. Litho Questa)

1991 (18 Nov). *Centenary of Otto Lilienthal's Gliding Experiments. Horiz design as T 267 of Maldive Islands. Multicoloured. P 14.*

797	$1.50, Lilienthal and glider		70	75

(Des W. Wright. Litho Questa)

1991 (18 Nov). *750th Anniv of Hanover. Horiz designs as T 268 of Maldive Islands. P 14.*

798	$2 multicoloured		85	90

MS799 101×72 mm. $5 rose-lilac, yellow-green and black .. .. .. 2·25 2·40

Designs:—$2, Georg Laves (architect) and Hoftheatre; $5, Old Hanover

(Des Walt Disney Co. Litho Questa)

1991 (23 Dec). *Christmas. Walt Disney Company Christmas Cards. Multicoloured designs as T 228 of St. Vincent. P 14×13½.*

800	10 c. Pluto pulling Mickey Mouse in sledge, 1974 (*horiz*)		10	10
801	55 c. Mickey, Pluto and Donald Duck watching toy band, 1961 (*horiz*)		20	25
802	65 c. "The Same Old Wish", 1942 (*horiz*)		30	35
803	75 c. Mickey, Peter Pan, Donald and Nephews with Merlin the magician, 1963 (*horiz*)		35	40
804	$1.50, Mickey, Donald and leprechauns, 1958 (*horiz*)		65	70
805	$2 Mickey and friends with book *Old Yeller*, 1957 (*horiz*)		85	90
806	$5 Mickey controlling Pinnochio, 1953 (*horiz*)		1·75	2·00
807	$5 Cinderella and Prince dancing, 1987 (*horiz*)		2·25	2·40
800/7		*Set of 8*	5·75	6·25

MS808 Two sheets, each 128×102 mm. (a) $6 Santa Claus and American bomber, 1942. (b) $6 Snow White, 1957. P 13½×14 .. *Set of 2 sheets* 5·25 5·50

(Des D. Miller. Litho Questa)

1992 (2 Mar). *40th Anniv of Queen Elizabeth II's Accession. Horiz designs as T 214 of Lesotho. Multicoloured. P 14.*

809	15 c. View across bay		10	10
810	45 c. Schooner at anchor, Mayreau		20	25
811	$2 Hotel on hillside		85	90
812	$4 Tourist craft at anchor		1·75	1·90
809/12		*Set of 4*	2·50	2·75

MS813 Two sheets, each 74×97 mm. (a) $6 Beach and palms. (b) $6 Aerial view of hotel by beach .. .. .. *Set of 2 sheets* 5·25 5·50

(Des Walt Disney Co. Litho Questa)

1992 (28 Apr). *International Stamp Exhibitions. Multicoloured designs as T 215 of Lesotho, showing Walt Disney cartoon characters.* P 14×13½.

(*a*) "*Granada '92*", *Spain. Spanish Explorers*

814	15 c.	Big Pete as Hernando Cortes in Mexico (*horiz*)	10	10
815	40 c.	Mickey Mouse as Hernando de Soto at Mississippi River (*horiz*)	15	10
816	$2	Goofy as Vasco Nunez de Balboa sights Pacific (*horiz*)	85	90
817	$4	Donald Duck as Francisco Coronado on Rio Grande (*horiz*)	1·75	1·90
814/17		*Set of 4*	2·50	2·75
MS818		127×102 mm. $6 Mickey as Ponce de Leon. P 13½×14	2·50	2·75

(*b*) "*World Columbian Stamp Expo '92*", *Chicago. Local Personalities*

819	10 c.	Mickey Mouse and Pluto outside Walt Disney's birthplace (*horiz*)	10	10
820	50 c.	Donald Duck and nephews in George Pullman's railway sleeping car (*horiz*)	20	25
821	$1	Daisy Duck as Jane Addams (social reformer) and Hull House (*horiz*)	45	50
822	$5	Mickey as Carl Sandburg (novelist, poet and historian) (*horiz*)	2·25	2·40
819/22		*Set of 4*	2·75	2·90
MS823		127×102 mm. $6 Daisy as Mrs O'Leary with her cow (source of Chicago fire of 1871). P 13½×14	2·50	2·75

78 King Ferdinand and Queen Isabella of Spain

(Des W. Wright. Litho Questa)

1992 (22 May). *500th Anniv of Discovery of America by Columbus (2nd issue).* T **78** *and similar multicoloured designs.* P 14.

824	10 c.	Type **78**	10	10
825	45 c.	*Santa Maria* and *Nina* in Acul Bay, Haiti	20	25
826	55 c.	*Santa Maria* (*vert*)	20	25
827	$2	Ships of Columbus (*vert*)	85	90
828	$4	Wreck of *Santa Maria*	1·75	1·90
829	$5	*Pinta* and *Nina*	2·25	2·40
824/9		*Set of 6*	4·75	5·25
MS830		Two sheets, each 114×85 mm. (*a*) $6 Columbus landing on San Salvador. (*b*) $6 *Santa Maria* in storm		
		Set of 2 sheets	5·25	5·50

79 *Paulogramma* sp

(Des J. Barberis. Litho Questa)

1992 (15 June). "*Genova '92*" *International Thematic Stamp Exhibition. Butterflies.* T **79** *and similar multicoloured designs.* P 14.

831	15 c.	Type **80**	10	10
832	20 c.	*Heliconius cydno*	10	10
833	30 c.	*Eutresis hypereia*	15	20
834	45 c.	*Eurytides columbus* (*vert*)	20	25
835	55 c.	*Papilio ascolius*	20	25
836	75 c.	*Anaea pasibula*	35	40
837	80 c.	*Heliconius doris*	35	40
838	$1	*Perisama pitheas*	45	50
839	$2	*Batesia hypochlora*	85	90
840	$3	*Heliconius erato*	1·25	1·40
841	$4	*Elzunia cassandrina*	1·75	1·90
842	$5	*Sais ivcidice*	2·25	2·40
831/42		*Set of 12*	7·25	8·00
MS843		Three sheets, each 109×79 mm. (*a*) $6 *Oleria tigilla*. (*b*) $6 *Dismorphia orise*. (*c*) $6 *Podotricha telesiphe*		
		Set of 3 sheets	7·75	8·00

OFFICIAL STAMPS

1982 (11 Oct). *Nos. 195/200 optd with Type O 1 of St. Vincent.*

O1	50 c.	*Mary*	15	15
		a. Sheetlet. No. O1 × 6 and No. O2	1·10	
		b. Opt double		
		c. Albino opt	4·00	
		d. Horiz pair, one without opt		
O2	50 c.	Prince Charles and Lady Diana Spencer	35	35
		b. Opt double		
		c. Albino opt	9·50	
O3	$3	*Alexandra*	35	35
		a. Sheetlet. No. O3 × 6 and No. O4	2·75	
		b. Opt double	40·00	
		c. Albino opt	6·00	
O4	$3	Prince Charles and Lady Diana Spencer	80	80
		b. Opt double	£130	
		c. Albino opt	25·00	
O5	$3.50,	*Britannia*	50	50
		a. Sheetlet. No. O5 × 6 and No. O6	3·50	
		c. Albino opt	7·50	
O6	$3.50,	Prince Charles and Lady Diana Spencer	1·00	1·00
		c. Albino opt	20·00	
O1/6		*Set of 6*	2·75	2·75

Appendix

The following issues for individual islands in the Grenadines group fall outside the criteria for full listing as detailed on page xi of the General Catalogue Information in this edition.

BEQUIA

1984

Leaders of the World. Railway Locomotives (1st series). Two designs for each value, the first showing technical drawings and the second the locomotive at work. 1, 5, 10, 25, 35, 45 c., $1.50, $2, each × 2

Grenadines of St. Vincent 1982 Ships definitives (Nos. 208/24) optd "BEQUIA". 1, 3, 5, 6, 10, 15, 20, 25, 30, 50, 60, 75 c., $1, $2, $3, $5, $10

Leaders of the World. Automobiles (1st series). Two designs for each value, the first showing technical drawings and the second the car in action. 5, 40 c., $1, $1.50, each × 2

Leaders of the World. Olympic Games, Los Angeles. 1, 10, 60 c., $3, each × 2

Leaders of the World. Railway Locomotives (2nd series). Two designs for each value, the first showing technical drawings and the second the locomotive at work. 1, 5, 10, 35, 75 c., $1, $2.50, $3, each × 2

Leaders of the World. Automobiles (2nd series). Two designs for each value, the first showing technical drawings and the second the car in action. 5, 10, 20, 25, 75 c., $1, $2.50, $3, each × 2

1985

Leaders of the World. Railway Locomotives (3rd series). Two designs for each value, the first showing technical drawings and the second the locomotive at work. 25, 55, 60 c., $2, each × 2

Leaders of the World. Dogs. 25, 35, 55 c., $2, each × 2

Leaders of the World. Warships of the Second World War. Two designs for each value, the first showing technical drawings and the second the ship at sea. 15, 50 c., $1, $1.50, each × 2

Leaders of the World. Flowers. 10, 20, 70 c., $2.50, each × 2

Leaders of the World. Automobiles (3rd series). Two designs for each value, the first showing technical drawings and the second the car in action. 5, 25, 50 c., $1, $1.25, $2, each × 2

Leaders of the World. Railway Locomotives (4th series). Two designs for each value, the first showing technical drawings and the second the locomotive at work. 25, 55, 60, 75 c., $1, $2.50, each × 2

Leaders of the World. Life and Times of Queen Elizabeth the Queen Mother. Two designs for each value, showing different portraits. 20, 65 c., $1.35, $1.80, each × 2

Leaders of the World. Automobiles (4th series). Two designs for each value, the first showing technical drawings and the second the car in action. 20, 45 c., $1.50, $2, each × 2

1986

Leaders of the World. Automobiles (5th series). Two designs for each value, the first showing technical drawings and the second the car in action. 25, 50, 65, 75 c., $1, $3, each × 2

60th Birthday of Queen Elizabeth II. 5, 75 c., $2, $8

World Cup Football Championship, Mexico. 1, 2, 5, 10, 45, 60, 75 c., $1.50, $1.50, $2, $3.50, $6

Royal Wedding (1st issue). 60 c., $2, each × 2

Railway Engineers and Locomotives. $1, $2.50, $3, $4

Royal Wedding (2nd issue). Previous issue optd "Congratulations T.R.H. The Duke & Duchess of York". 60 c., $2, each × 2.

Automobiles (6th series). Two designs for each value, the first showing technical drawings and the second the car in action. 20, 60, 75, 90 c., $1, $3, each × 2

1987

Automobiles (7th series). Two designs for each value, the first showing technical drawings and the second the car in action. 5, 20, 35, 60, 75, 80 c., $1.25, $1.75, each × 2

Royal Ruby Wedding. 15, 75 c., $1, $2.50, $5

Railway Locomotives (5th series). Two designs for each value, the first showing technical drawings and the second the locomotive at work. 15, 25, 40, 50, 60, 75 c., $1, $2, each × 2

1988

Explorers. 15, 50 c., $1.75, $2, $2.50, $3, $3.50, $4

International Lawn Tennis Players. 15, 45, 80 c., $1.25, $1.75, $2, $2.50, $3

1989

"*Philexfrance 89*" *International Stamp Exhibition, Paris. Walt Disney Cartoon Characters.* 1, 2, 3, 4, 5, 10 c., $5, $6

1991

50th Anniv of Japanese Attack on Pearl Harbor. 50 c., $1

UNION ISLAND

1984

Leaders of the World. British Monarchs. Two designs for each value, forming a composite picture. 1, 5, 10, 20, 60 c., $3, each × 2

Leaders of the World. Railway Locomotives (1st series). Two designs for each value, the first showing technical drawings and the second the locomotive at work. 5, 60 c., $1, $2

Grenadines of St. Vincent 1982 Ships definitives (Nos. 208/24) optd "UNION ISLAND". 1, 3, 5, 6, 10, 15, 20, 25, 30, 50, 60, 75 c., $1, $2, $3, $5, $10

Leaders of the World. Cricketers. Two designs for each value, the first showing a portrait and the second the cricketer in action. 1, 10, 15, 55, 60, 75 c., $1.50, $3, each × 2

Leaders of the World. Railway Locomotives (2nd series). Two designs for each value, the first showing technical drawings and the second the locomotive at work. 5, 10, 20, 25, 75 c., $1, $2.50, $3, each × 2

1985

Leaders of the World. Automobiles (1st series). Two designs for each value, the first showing technical drawings and the second the car in action. 1, 50, 75 c., $2.50, each × 2

Leaders of the World. Birth Bicent of John J. Audubon (ornithologist). Birds. 15, 50 c., $1, $1.50, each × 2

Leaders of the World. Railway Locomotives (3rd series). Two designs for each value, the first showing technical drawings and the second the locomotive at work. 5, 50, 60 c., $2, each × 2

Leaders of the World. Butterflies. 15, 25, 75 c., $2, each × 2

Leaders of the World. Automobiles (2nd series). Two designs for each value, the first showing technical drawings and the second the car in action. 5, 60 c., $1, $1.50, each × 2

Leaders of the World. Automobiles (3rd series). Two designs for each value, the first showing technical drawings and the second the car in action. 10, 55, 60, 75, 90 c., $1, $1.50, $2, each × 2

Leaders of the World. Life and Times of Queen Elizabeth the Queen Mother. Two designs for each value, showing different portraits. 55, 70 c., $1.05, $1.70, each × 2

1986

Leaders of the World. Railway Locomotives (4th series). Two designs for each value, the first showing technical drawings and the second the locomotive at work. 15, 30, 45, 60, 75 c., $1.50, $2.50, $3, each × 2

60th Birthday of Queen Elizabeth II. 10, 60 c., $2, $8

World Cup Football Championship, Mexico. 1, 10, 30, 75 c., $1, $2.50, $3, $6

Royal Wedding (1st issue). 60 c., $2, each × 2

Automobiles (4th series). Two designs for each value, the first showing technical drawings and the second the car in action. 10, 60, 75 c., $1, $1.50, $3, each × 2

Royal Wedding (2nd issue). Previous issue optd as Bequia. 60 c., $2, each × 2

Railway Locomotives (5th series). Two designs for each value, the first showing technical drawings and the second the locomotive at work. 15, 45, 60, 75 c., $1, $1.50, $2, $3, each × 2

1987

Railway Locomotives (6th series). Two designs for each value, the first showing technical drawings and the second the locomotive at work. 15, 25, 40, 50, 60, 75 c., $1, $2, each × 2

Royal Ruby Wedding. 15, 45 c., $1.50, $3, $4

Railway Locomotives (7th series). Two designs for each value, the first showing technical drawings and the second the locomotive at work. 15, 20, 30, 45, 50, 75 c., $1, $1.50, each × 2

1989

"*Philexfrance 89*" *International Stamp Exhibition, Paris. Walt Disney Cartoon Characters.* 1, 2, 3, 4, 5, 10 c., $5, $6

Samia

Samoa

INDEPENDENT KINGDOM OF SAMOA

The first postal service in Samoa was organised by C. L. Griffiths, who had earlier run the *Fiji Times* Express post in Suva. In both instances the principal purpose of the service was the distribution of newspapers of which Griffiths was the proprietor. The first issue of the *Samoa Times* (later the *Samoa Times and South Sea Gazette*) appeared on 6 October 1877 and the newspaper continued in weekly publication until 27 August 1881.

Mail from the Samoa Express post to addresses overseas was routed via New South Wales, New Zealand or U.S.A. and received additional franking with stamps of the receiving country on landing.

Cancellations, inscribed "APIA SAMOA", did not arrive until March 1878 so that examples of Nos. 1/9 used before that date were cancelled in manuscript.

1

(Des H. H. Glover. Litho S. T. Leigh & Co, Sydney, N.S.W.)

1877 (1 Oct)–**80**.

A. *1st state: line above "X" in "EXPRESS" not broken. P 12½*
1	1	1d. ultramarine			£225	£100
2		3d. deep scarlet			£250	£110
3		6d. bright violet			£250	95.00
		a. Pale lilac			£275	95.00

B. *2nd state: line above "X" broken, and dot between top of "M" and "O" of "SAMOA". P 12½ (1878–79)*
4	1	1d. ultramarine			85.00	90.00
5		3d. bright scarlet			£250	£110
6		6d. bright violet			£150	80.00
7		1s. dull yellow			£130	80.00
		a. Line above "X" not broken			£150	£100
		b. Perf 12 (1879)			70.00	85.00
		c. Orange-yellow			85.00	90.00
8		2s. red-brown			£250	£180
		a. Chocolate			£275	£325
9		5s. green			£800	£1000

C. *3rd state: line above "X" repaired, dot merged with upper right serif of "M" (1879). (a) P 12½*
10	1	1d. ultramarine			80.00	80.00
11		3d. vermilion			£110	£110
12		6d. lilac			£110	80.00
13		2s. brown			£200	£200
		a. Chocolate			£200	£200
14		5s. green			£500	£500
		a. Line above "X" not repaired			£600	

(b) P 12
15	1	1d. blue			24.00	40.00
		a. Deep blue			32.00	70.00
		b. Ultramarine			28.00	40.00
16		3d. vermilion			45.00	65.00
		a. Carmine-vermilion			45.00	75.00
17		6d. bright violet			40.00	48.00
		a. Deep violet			40.00	80.00
18		2s. deep brown			£130	£200
19		5s. yellow-green			£400	£600
		a. Deep green			£375	£550
		b. Line above "X" not repaired			£475	

D. *4th state: spot of colour under middle stroke of "M". P 12½ (1880)*
| 20 | 1 | 9d. orange-brown | | | 60.00 | £120 |

Originals exist imperf, but are not known used in this state.

On sheets of the 1d., 1st state, at least eight stamps have a stop after "PENNY". In the 2nd state, three stamps have the stop, and in the 3rd state, only one.

In the 1st state, all the stamps, 1d., 3d. and 6d., were in sheets of 20 (5×4) and also the 1d. in the 3rd state.

All values in the 2nd state, all values except the 1d. in the 3rd state and No. 20 were in sheets of 10 (5×2).

As all sheets of all printings of the originals were imperf at the outer edges, the only stamps which can have perforations on all four sides are Nos. 1 to 3a, 10 and 15 to 15b, all other originals being imperf on one or two sides.

The perf 12 stamps, although gauge 11.8, are generally very rough but later the machine was repaired and the 1d., 3d. and 6d. are known with clean-cut perforations.

Remainders of the unissued 2d. rose, 6d. (in sheets of 21 (7×3), 3d., 9d., 1s. (in sheets of 12 (4×3) and of the 2s. and 5s. (sheet format unknown) were found in the Samoan post office

---

when the service closed down in 1881. The remainders are rare in complete sheets, but of very little value as singles, compared with the originals.

Reprints of all values, in sheets of 40 (8×5), were made after the originals had been withdrawn from sale. These are practically worthless.

The majority of both reprints and remainders are in the 4th state as the 9d. with the spot of colour under the middle stroke of the "M", but a few stamps (both remainders and reprints) do not show this, while on some it is very faint.

There are three known types of forgery, one of which is rather dangerous, the others being crude.

The last mail despatch organised by the proprietors of the Samoa Express took place on 31 August 1881, although one cover is recorded postmarked 24 September 1881.

After the withdrawal of the Samoa Express service it would appear that the Apia municipality appointed a postmaster to continue the overseas post. Covers are known franked with U.S.A. or New Zealand stamps in Samoa, or routed via Fiji. In December 1886 the municipal postmaster, John Davis, was appointed Postmaster of the Kingdom of Samoa by King Malietoa. Overseas mail sent via New Zealand was subsequently accepted without the addition of New Zealand stamps, although letters to the U.S.A. continued to require such franking until August 1891.

| 2 Palm Trees | 3 King Malietoa Laupepa | 4a 6 mm |

| 4b 7 mm | 4c 4 mm |

Description of Watermarks

(These are the same as W 12a/c of New Zealand)

W 4a. 6 mm between "N Z" and star; broad irregular star; comparatively wide "N"; "N Z" 11½ mm wide.

W 4b. 7 mm between "N Z" and star; narrower star; narrow "N"; "N Z" 10 mm wide.

W 4c. 4 mm between "N Z" and star; narrow star; wide "N"; "N Z" 11 mm wide.

(Des A. E. Cousins (T 3). Dies eng W. R. Bock and A. E. Cousins (T 2) or A. E. Cousins (T 3). Typo Govt Ptg Office, Wellington)

1886–1900. (i) *W 4a. (a) P 12½ (Oct–Nov 1886)*
21	2	½d. purple-brown			16.00	30.00
22		1d. yellow-green			5.50	12.00
23		2d. dull orange			11.00	7.50
24		4d. blue			22.00	8.50
25		1s. rose-carmine			60.00	7.50
		a. Bisected (2½d.) (on cover)*			†	£275
26		2s. 6d. reddish lilac			55.00	55.00

(b) P 12 × 11½ (July–Nov 1887)
27	2	½d. purple-brown			80.00	80.00
28		1d. yellow-green			£100	20.00
29		2d. yellow			85.00	£140
30		4d. blue			£250	£200
31		6d. brown-lake			20.00	8.00
32		1s. rose-carmine			—	£170
33		2s. 6d. reddish lilac			£300	

(ii) W 4c. P 12 × 11½ (May 1890)
34	2	½d. purple-brown			70.00	20.00
35		1d. green			50.00	27.00
36		2d. brown-orange			70.00	35.00
37		4d. blue			£130	5.00
38		6d. brown-lake			£225	11.00
39		1s. rose-carmine			£325	13.00
40		2s. 6d. reddish lilac			£375	8.50

(iii) W 4b. (a) P 12 × 11½ (1890–92)
41	2	½d. pale purple-brown			2.00	2.50
		a. Blackish purple			2.00	2.50
42		1d. myrtle-green (5.90)			13.00	1.40
		a. Green			13.00	1.40
		b. Yellow-green			13.00	1.40
43		2d. dull orange (5.90)			15.00	1.75
44	3	2½d. rose (11.92)			75.00	3.50
		a. Pale rose			75.00	3.50
45	2	4d. blue			£225	14.00
46		6d. brown-lake			£110	8.00
47		1s. rose-carmine			£225	4.00
48		2s. 6d. slate-lilac				6.00

(b) P 12½ (Mar 1891–92)
49	2	½d. purple-brown				
50		1d. green				
51		2d. orange-yellow			—	£130
52	3	2½d. rose (1.92)			20.00	4.50
53	2	4d. blue			—	£450
54		6d. brown-purple			£2000	£750
55		1s. rose-carmine			—	£425
56		2s. 6d. slate-lilac				

(c) P 11 (May 1895–1900)
57	2	½d. purple-brown			90	1.75
		a. Deep purple-brown			65	1.75
		b. Blackish purple (1900)			75	35.00

58	2	1d. green			1.50	1.75
		a. Bluish green (1897)			1.50	1.75
		b. Deep green (1900)			1.25	22.00
59		2d. pale yellow			35.00	35.00
		a. Orange (1896)			35.00	35.00
		b. Bright yellow (1.97)			6.00	4.00
		c. Pale ochre (10.97)			4.50	1.00
		d. Dull orange (1900)			5.50	
60	3	2½d. rose			70	4.50
		a. Deep rose-carmine (1900)			1.10	42.00
61	2	4d. blue			5.75	2.00
		a. Deep blue (1900)			60	50.00
62		6d. brown-lake			5.50	3.00
		a. Brown-purple (1900)			1.75	60.00
63		1s. rose			5.50	3.75
		a. Dull rose-carmine/toned (5.98)			2.00	35.00
		b. Carmine (1900)			1.25	
64		2s. 6d. purple			55.00	9.50
		a. Reddish lilac (wmk inverted) (1897)			7.50	7.50
		b. Deep purple/toned (wmk reversed) (5.98)			4.75	9.50
		ba. Imperf between (vert pair)			£350	
		c. Slate-violet			£120	

*Following a fire on 1 April 1895 which destroyed stocks of all stamps except the 1s. value perf 12½, this was bisected diagonally and used as a 2½d. stamp for overseas letters between 24 April and May 1895, and was cancelled in blue. Fresh supplies of the 2½d. did not arrive until July 1895, although other values were available from 23 May.

Examples of the 1s. rose perforated 11, No. 63, were subsequently bisected and supplied cancelled-to-order by the post office to collectors, often with backdated cancellations. Most of these examples were bisected vertically and all were cancelled in black (*Price* £7).

The dates given relate to the earliest dates of printing in the various watermarks and perforations and not to issue dates.

The perf 11 issues (including those later surcharged or over-printed), are very unevenly perforated owing to the large size of the pins. Evenly perforated copies are extremely hard to find.

For the 2½d. black, see Nos. 81/2 and for the ½d. green and 1d. red-brown, see Nos. 88/9.

| **FIVE PENCE** ▬▬ (5) | **FIVE PENCE** ▬▬▬ (6) | **5d** ▬▬ (7) |

1893 (Nov–Dec). *Handstamped singly, at Apia.*

(a) In two operations
65	5	5d. on 4d. blue (37)			48.00	42.00
		a. Bars omitted			—	£400
66		5d. on 4d. blue (45)			60.00	£100
67	6	5d. on 4d. blue (37)			85.00	£110
68		5d. on 4d. blue (45)			90.00	

(b) In three operations (Dec)
69	7	5d. on 4d. blue (37) (R.)			17.00	25.00
		a. Stop after "d"			£250	60.00
		b. Bars omitted				
70		5d. on 4d. blue (45) (R.)			18.00	50.00

In Types 5 and 6 the bars obliterating the original value vary in length from 13½ to 16½ mm and can occur with either the thick bar over the thin one or vice versa.

Double handstamps exist but we do not list them.

No. 69a came from a separate handstamp which applied the "5d." at one operation. Where the "d" was applied separately its position in relation to the "5" naturally varies.

| ★👑 **SAMOA POST** **FIVE 5 PENCE** 8 | **Surcharged 1½d.** (9) | **R 3d.** (10) |

The "R" in Type 10 indicates use for registration fee.

(Des and die eng A. E. Cousins. Typo New Zealand Govt Ptg Office)

1894–1900. *W 4b (sideways). (a) P 11½ × 12.*
| 71 | 8 | 5d. dull vermilion (3.94) | | | 18.00 | 2.75 |
| | | a. Dull red | | | 18.00 | 3.75 |

(b) P 11
| 72 | 8 | 5d. dull red (1895) | | | 10.00 | 6.50 |
| | | a. Deep red (1900) | | | 1.25 | 13.00 |

1895–1900. *W 4b.*

(i) *Handstamped with T 9 or 10. (a) P 12 × 11½ (26.1.95)*
| 73 | 2 | 1½d. on 2d. dull orange (B.) | | | 6.00 | 5.00 |
| 74 | | 3d. on 2d. dull orange | | | 23.00 | 8.00 |

(b) P 11 (6.95)
75	2	1½d. on 2d. orange (B.)			1.50	3.25
		a. Pair, one without handstamp				
76		3d. on 2d. orange			5.50	7.50
		a. On 2d. yellow			75.00	60.00

(ii) *Surch printed*. P 11*
| 77 | 2 | 1½d. on 2d. orange-yellow (B.) | | | 75.00 | 60.00 |

(iii) *Handstamped as T 9 or 10.† P 11 (1896)*
78	2	1½d. on 2d. orange-yellow (B.)			2.50	22.00
79		3d. on 2d. orange-yellow			3.00	45.00
		a. Imperf between (vert pair)			£400	
		b. Pair, one without handstamp				

(iv) *Surch typo as T 10. P 11 (Feb 1900)*
| 80 | 2 | 3d. on 2d. deep red-orange (G.) | | | 1.50 | £130 |

*It is believed that this was type-set from which clichés were made and set up in a forme and then printed on a hand press. This would account for the clear indentation on the back of the stamp and the variation in the position on the stamps which probably resulted from the clichés becoming loose in the forme.

†In No. 78 the "2" has a serif and the handstamp is in pale greenish blue instead of deep blue. In No. 79 the "R" is slightly narrower. In both instances the stamp is in a different shade.

A special printing in a distinctly different colour was made for No. 80 and the surcharge is in green.

Most of the handstamps exist double.

1896 (Aug). *Printed in the wrong colour. W 4b.* (a) *P* 10 × 11.
81	3	2½d. black	..	..	90	3·00

(b) P 11
82	3	2½d. black	..	..	60·00	65·00
		a. Mixed perfs 10 and 11	..	..	£350	

Surcharged 2½d.
(11)

PROVISIONAL GOVT.
(12)

1898–99. W 4b. P 11. (a) *Handstamped as T 11* (10.98).
83	2	2½d. on 1s. dull rose-carmine/*toned*	..	26·00	35·00

(b) Surch as T 11 (1899)
84	2	2½d. on 1s. bluish green (R.)	..	..	55	2·00
		a. Surch inverted	..	..	—	£350
85		2½d. on 1s. dull rose-carmine/*toned* (R.)		3·50	8·50
		a. Surch double	..	..	£350	
86		2½d. on 1s. dull rose-carmine/*toned* (Blk.)		3·50	8·50
		a. Surch double	..	..	£450	
87		2½d. on 2s. 6d. deep purple/*toned*	..	4·75	11·00

The typographed surcharge was applied in a setting of nine, giving seven types differing in the angle and length of the fractional line, the type of stop, etc.

1899. *Colours changed. W 4b. P* 11.
88	2	½d. dull blue-green	..	..	65	1·40
		a. Deep green	..	..	65	1·40
89		1d. deep red-brown	..	..	55	1·25

1899–1900. *Provisional Government. New printings optd with T* 12 (*longer words and shorter letters on* 5d.). *W 4b. P* 11.
90	2	½d. dull blue-green (R.)	..	..	30	1·25
		a. Yellowish green (1900)	..	30	1·75
91		1d. chestnut (B.)	..	..	1·00	2·75
92		2d. dull orange (R.)	..	..	70	3·00
		a. Orange-yellow (1900)	..	55	3·25
93		4d. deep dull blue (R.)	..	..	45	2·50
94	8	5d. dull vermilion (B.)	..	..	1·25	4·50
		a. Red (1900)	..	..	90	4·50
95	2	6d. brown-lake (R.)	..	..	1·10	3·75
96		1s. rose-carmine (B.)	..	..	1·50	10·00
97		2s. 6d. reddish purple (R.)	..	4·75	17·00

The Samoan group of islands was partitioned on 1 March 1900: Western Samoa (Upolu, Savaii, Apolima and Manono) to Germany and Eastern Samoa (Tutuila, the Manu'a Is and Rose Is) to the United States. German issues of 1900–14 will be found listed in Part 7 (*Germany*) of this catalogue, there were no U.S. issues.

The Samoan Kingdom post office run by John Davis was suspended in March 1900.

WESTERN SAMOA
NEW ZEALAND OCCUPATION

The German Islands of Samoa surrendered to the New Zealand Expeditionary Force on 30 August 1914 and were administered by New Zealand until 1962.

G.R.I. 1d.
(13)

G.R.I. 1 Shillings.
(14)

SETTINGS. Nos. 101/9 were surcharged by a vertical setting of ten, repeated ten times across the sheet. Nos. 110/14 were from a horizontal setting of four repeated five times in the sheet.

Nos. 101b, 102a and 104a occurred on position 6. The error was corrected during the printing of No. 102.

Nos. 101c, 102c, 104d and 105b are from position 10.

Nos. 101d, 102e and 104b are from position 1.

No. 108b is from position 9.

(Surch by *Samoanische Zeitung*, Apia)

1914 (3 Sept). *German Colonial issue* (*ship*) (*no wmk*) *inscr* "SAMOA" *surch as T* 13 *or* 14 (*mark values*).
101		½d. on 3 pf. brown	..	..	17·00	8·50
		a. Surch double	..	..	£650	£500
		b. No fraction bar	..	..	50·00	30·00
		c. Comma after "I"	..	..	£600	£500
		d. "1" to left of "2" in "½"	..	50·00	30·00
102		½d. on 5 pf. green	..	..	38·00	10·00
		a. No fraction bar	..	..	£110	55·00
		c. Comma after "I"	..	..	£350	£170
		d. Surch double	..	..	£650	£500
		e. "1" to left of "2" in "½"	..	95·00	40·00
103		1d. on 10 pf. carmine	..	..	95·00	40·00
		a. Surch double	..	..	£650	£500
104		2½d. on 20 pf. ultramarine	..	30·00	10·00
		a. No fraction bar	..	..	65·00	38·00
		b. "1" to left of "2" in "½"	..	65·00	40·00
		c. Surch inverted	..	..	£800	£750
		d. Comma after "I"	..	..	£450	£325
		e. Surch double	..	..	£650	£550
105		3d. on 25 pf. black and red/*yellow*	50·00	35·00
		a. Surch double	..	..	£650	£500
		b. Comma after "I"	..	..	£3500	£800
106		4d. on 30 pf. black and orange/*buff*	£110	60·00
107		5d. on 40 pf. black and carmine..	£110	70·00

108		6d. on 50 pf. black and purple/*buff*	55·00	35·00
		a. Surch double	..	..	£750	£800
		b. Inverted "9" for "6"	..	£160	£100
109		9d. on 80 pf. black and carmine/*rose*	£190	95·00
110		"1 shillings" on 1 m. carmine	..	£3000	£3250
111		"1 shilling" on 1 m. carmine	..	£9500	£7000
112		2s. on 2 m. blue	..	..	£3000	£2750
113		3s. on 3 m. violet-black..	..	£1400	£1200
		a. Surch double	..	..	£8000	£9000
114		5s. on 5 m. carmine and black	..	£1000	£950
		a. Surch double	..	..	£11000	£11000

No. 108b is distinguishable from 108, as the "d" and the "9" are not in a line, and the upper loop of the "9" turns downwards to the left.

UNAUTHORISED SURCHARGES. Examples of the 2d. on 20 pf., 3d. on 30 pf., 3d. on 40 pf., 4d. on 40 pf., 6d. on 80 pf., 2s. on 3 m. and 2s. on Marshall Islands 2 m., together with a number of errors not listed above, were produced by the printer on stamps supplied by local collectors. These were not authorised by the New Zealand Military Administration.

SAMOA.
(15)

1914 (29 Sept)–**15.** *Stamps of New Zealand. T* 50, 51, 52 *and* 27, *optd as T* 15, *but optd only* 14 *mm long on all except* 2½d. *Wmk* "N Z" *and Star, W* 43 *of New Zealand.*
115		½d. yellow-green (R.) (*p* 14×15)	..	30	30
116		1d. carmine (B.) (*p* 14×15)	..	30	10
117		2d. mauve (R.) (*p* 14×14½) (10.14)	60	95
118		2½d. deep blue (R.) (*p* 14) (10.14)	1·50	1·75
119		6d. carmine (B.) (*p* 14×14½) (10.14)	1·50	1·75
		a. Perf 14×13½	..	..	17·00	19·00
		b. Vert pair. Nos. 119/a (1915)	42·00	60·00
120		6d. pale carmine (B.) (*p* 14×14½) (10.14)	10·00	9·50
121		1s. vermilion (B.) (*p* 14×14½) (10.14)	3·50	10·00

1914–24. *Postal Fiscal stamps as Type F* 4 *of New Zealand optd with T* 15. *W* 43 *of New Zealand* (*sideways*). *Chalk-surfaced* "De La Rue" *paper.*

(a) P 14 (Nov 1914–17)
122		2s. blue (R.) (9.17) ..	..	80·00	£100
123		2s. 6d. grey-brown (B.) (9.17)	..	4·50	8·50
124		5s. yellow-green (R.)	..	..	10·00	11·00
125		10s. maroon (B.)	..	..	20·00	28·00
126		£1 rose-carmine (B.)	..	..	60·00	45·00

(b) P 14½ × 14, *comb* (1917–24)
127		2s. deep blue (R.) (3.18)	..	4·00	5·50
128		2s. 6d. grey-brown (B.) (10.24)	..	£180	£140
129		3s. purple (R.) (6.23)	..	..	12·00	28·00
130		5s. yellow-green (R.) (9.17)	..	14·00	15·00
131		10s. maroon (B.) (3.18)	..	40·00	40·00
132		£1 rose-carmine (B.) (3.18)	..	60·00	70·00

We no longer list the £2 value as it is doubtful if this was used for postal purposes.

See also Nos. 165/6e.

1916–19. *King George V stamps of New Zealand optd as T* 15, *but* 14 *mm long.* (a) *T* 61. *Typo. P* 14×15.
134		½d. yellow-green (R.)	..	..	20	40
135		1½d. slate (R.) (1917)	..	..	30	25
136		1½d. orange-brown (R.) (1919)	..	20	40
137		2d. yellow (R.) (14.2.18)	..	40	15
138		3d. chocolate (B.) (1919)	..	75	13·00

(b) T 60. *Recess. P* 14 × 14½, *etc.*
139		2½d. blue (R.)	..	..	65	60
		a. Perf 14 × 13½	..	..	35	35
		b. Vert pair. Nos. 139/9a ..	15·00	22·00
140		3d. chocolate (B.) (1917)	..	35	90
		a. Perf 14 × 13½	..	..	45	1·60
		b. Vert pair. Nos. 140/40a ..	15·00	25·00
141		6d. carmine (B.) (5.5.17)	..	1·25	90
		a. Perf 14 × 13½	..	..	1·50	3·25
		b. Vert pair. Nos. 141/1a ..	17·00	28·00
142		1s. vermilion (B.)	..	..	3·50	9·00
		a. Perf 14 × 13½	..	..	1·25	1·25
		b. Vert pair. Nos. 142/2a ..	22·00	40·00
134/42a		..	..	*Set of* 9	4·50	16·00

LEAGUE OF NATIONS MANDATE

Administered by New Zealand.

1920 (July). *Victory. Nos.* 453/8 *of New Zealand optd as T* 15, *but* 14 *mm long.*
143		½d. green (R.)	..	..	1·50	2·50
144		1d. carmine (B.)	..	..	1·25	1·25
145		1½d. brown-orange (R.)	..	1·25	4·00
146		3d. chocolate (B.)	..	..	4·00	7·00
147		6d. violet (R.)	..	..	4·00	6·50
148		1s. orange-red (B.) ..	..	13·00	11·00
143/8		..	..	*Set of* 6	23·00	29·00

SILVER JUBILEE OF KING GEORGE V 1910 - 1935.
16 Native Hut   (17)

(Eng B.W. Recess-printed at Wellington, N.Z.)

1921 (23 Dec). *W* 43 *of New Zealand.* (a) *P* 14×14½.
149	16	½d. green	..	..	50	3·50
150		1d. lake	..	..	50	20
151		1½d. chestnut	..	..	50	5·00
152		2d. yellow	..	..	70	1·90
149/52		..	..	*Set of* 4	2·00	9·50

(b) P 14 × 13½
153	16	½d. green	..	..	1·25	1·75
154		1d. lake	..	..	1·25	20
155		1½d. chestnut	..	..	6·00	7·50
156		2d. yellow	..	..	6·00	35

157	16	2½d. grey-blue	..	..	70	3·75
158		3d. sepia	..	..	75	3·00
159		4d. violet	..	..	80	3·00
160		5d. light blue	..	..	75	5·00
161		6d. bright carmine	..	80	3·50
162		8d. red-brown	..	..	1·25	9·00
163		9d. olive-green	..	..	1·25	11·00
164		1s. vermilion	..	..	1·25	12·00
153/64		..	*Set of* 12	20·00	55·00

1925–28. *Postal Fiscal stamps as Type F* 4 *of New Zealand optd with T* 15. *W* 43 *of New Zealand* (*sideways*). *P* 14½×14.

(a) Thick, opaque, white chalk-surfaced "Cowan" *paper*
165		2s. blue (R.) (12.25)	..	..	£100	£110
166		2s. 6d. deep grey-brown (B.) (10.28)	65·00	85·00
166a		3s. mauve (R.) (9.25)	..	50·00	60·00
166b		5s. yellow-green (R.) (11.26)	..	12·00	24·00
		ba. Opt at top of stamp	..	£1100	
166c		10s. brown-red (B.) (12.25)	..	75·00	65·00
166d		£1 rose-pink (B.) (11.26)	..	50·00	75·00
165/6d		..	*Set of* 6	£300	£350

(b) Thin, hard, chalk-surfaced "Wiggins Teape" *paper*
166e		£1 rose-pink (B.) (1928)	..	—	£750

1926–27. *T* 72 *of New Zealand, optd with T* 15, *in red.*

(a) "Jones" *paper*
167		2s. deep blue (11.26)	..	4·50	12·00
168		3s. mauve (10.26)	..	..	7·00	22·00

(b) "Cowan" *paper*
169		2s. light blue (10.11.27)	..	5·00	30·00
170		3s. pale mauve (10.11.27)	..	42·00	70·00

1932 (Aug). *Postal Fiscal stamps as Type F* 6 *of New Zealand optd with T* 15. *W* 43 *of New Zealand. Thick, opaque, white chalk-surfaced* "Cowan" *paper. P* 14.
171		2s. 6d. deep brown (B.)	..	15·00	27·00
172		5s. green (R.)	..	..	20·00	35·00
173		10s. carmine-lake (B.)	..	45·00	75·00
174		£1 pink (B.)	..	..	60·00	90·00
175		£2 bright purple (R.)	..	£700	
176		£5 indigo-blue (R.)	..	£1800	

The £2 and £5 values were primarily for fiscal use.

1935 (7 May). *Silver Jubilee. Optd with T* 17. *P* 14 × 13½.
177	16	1d. lake	..	..	30	30
		a. Perf 14 × 14½	..	75·00	£120
178		2½d. grey-blue	..	..	60	65
179		6d. bright carmine	..	2·50	2·50
177/9		..	*Set of* 3	3·00	3·00

18 Samoan Girl   19 Apia

21 Chief and Wife   25 Lake Lanuto'o

(Recess D.L.R.)

1935 (7 Aug). *T* 18/19, 21, 25 *and similar designs. W* 43 *of New Zealand* ("N Z" *and Star*).

(a) P 14 × 13½, (b) *P* 13½ × 14 *or* (c) *P* 14
180		½d. green (a)	..	..	10	35
181		1d. black and carmine (b)	..	10	10
182		2d. black and orange (c)	..	2·50	1·75
		a. Perf 13½ × 14	..	..	3·75	3·50
183		2½d. black and blue (a)	..	10	10
184		4d. slate and sepia (b)	..	40	15
185		6d. bright magenta (b)	..	40	10
186		1s. violet and brown (b)	..	30	10
187		2s. green and purple-brown (a)	..	50	50
188		3s. blue and brown-orange (a)	1·50	3·50
180/8		..	*Set of* 9	5·25	5·75

Designs: *Horiz*—2d. River scene; 4d. Canoe and house; 6d. R. L. Stevenson's home "Vailima"; 1s. Stevenson's Tomb. *Vert* (as *T* 25)—3s. Falefa Falls.

See also Nos. 200/3.

WESTERN SAMOA.
(27)

1935–42. *Postal Fiscal stamps as Type F* 6 *of New Zealand optd with T* 27. *W* 43 *of New Zealand. P* 14.

(a) Thick, opaque chalk-surfaced "Cowan" *paper* (7.8.35)
189		2s. 6d. deep brown (B.)	..	6·00	13·00
190		5s. green (R.)	..	..	10·00	17·00
191		10s. carmine-lake (B.)	..	45·00	60·00
192		£1 pink (B.)	..	..	60·00	90·00
193		£2 bright purple (R.)	..	£160	£300
194		£5 indigo-blue (R.)	..	£350	£650

(b) Thin, hard chalk-surfaced "Wiggins, Teape" *paper* (1941–42)
194a		5s. green (B.) (6.42)	..	65·00	75·00
194b		10s. pale carmine-lake (B.) (6.41)	£100	£120
194c		£2 bright purple (R.) (2.42)	..	£425	£550
194d		£5 indigo-blue (R.) (2.42)	..	£650	£800

The £2 and £5 values were primarily for fiscal use.

See also Nos. 207/14.

28 Coastal Scene

31 Robert Louis Stevenson

(Des J. Berry (1d. and 1½d.). L. C. Mitchell (2½d. and 7d.). Recess B.W.)

1939 (29 Aug). *25th Anniv of New Zealand Control.* T **28**, **31** *and similar horiz designs.* W **98** *of New Zealand.* P 13½ × 14 *or* 14 × 13½ (7d.).

195	1d. olive-green and scarlet	30	10
196	1½d. light blue and red-brown	45	30
197	2½d. red-brown and blue	90	65
198	7d. violet and slate-green	6·00	1·75
195/8	*Set of 4*	7·00	2·50

Designs:—1½d. Western Samoa; 2½d. Samoan dancing party.

32 Samoan Chief

33 Apia Post Office

(Recess B.W.)

1940 (2 Sept). W **98** *of New Zealand* (Mult "N Z" and Star). P 14 × 13½.

199	**32**	3d. on 1½d. brown	10	10

T **32** was not issued without surcharge.

(T **33**. Des L. C. Mitchell. Recess B.W.)

1944–49. *As Nos.* 180, 182/3 *and* T **33**. W **98** *of New Zealand* (Mult "N Z" and Star) (sideways on 2½d.). P 14 *or* 13½ × 14 (5d.).

200	½d. green	25	6·50
202	2d. black and orange	1·25	5·00
203	2½d. black and blue (1948)	3·50	16·00
205	5d. sepia and blue (8.6.49)	20	50
200/5	*Set of 4*	4·75	25·00

1945–48. *Postal Fiscal stamps as Type* F **6** *of New Zealand optd with* T **27.** W **98** *of New Zealand. Thin hard, chalk-surfaced "Wiggins Teape" paper.* P 14.

207	2s. 6d. deep brown (B.) (6.45)	2·25	5·50
208	5s. green (B.) (5.45)	5·00	7·50
209	10s. carmine-lake (B.) (4.46)	16·00	17·00
210	£1 pink (B.) (6.48)	85·00	£150
211	30s. brown (8.48)	£140	£250
212	£2 bright purple (R.) (11.47)	£140	£225
213	£3 green (8.48)	£170	£325
214	£5 indigo-blue (R.) (1946)	£250	£375
207/10	*Set of 4*	95·00	£160

The £2 to £5 values were mainly used for "fiscal purposes".
See also Nos. 232/5.

WESTERN SAMOA
(34)

1946 (4 June). *Peace Issue. Nos.* 668, 670 *and* 674/5 *of New Zealand optd with* T **34** (reading up and down at sides on 2d.).

215	1d. green	10	10
216	2d. purple (B.)	10	10
217	6d. chocolate and vermilion	10	10
218	8d. black and carmine (B.)	10	10
215/18	*Set of 4*	35	20

UNITED NATIONS TRUST TERRITORY
Administered by New Zealand.

35 Making Siapo Cloth

42 Thatching a Native Hut

43 Preparing Copra

44 Samoan Chieftainess

(Recess B.W.)

1952 (10 Mar). T **35**, **42/4** *and similar designs.* W **98** *of New Zealand* (sideways on 1s. and 3s.). P 13 (½d., 2d., 5d. and 1s.) *or* 13½ (others).

219	½d. claret and orange-brown	10	60
220	1d. olive-green and green	10	15
221	2d. carmine-red	10	10
222	3d. pale ultramarine and indigo	40	10
223	5d. brown and deep green	4·00	70
224	6d. pale ultramarine and rose-magenta	50	10
225	8d. carmine	30	30
226	1s. sepia and blue	15	10
227	2s. yellow-brown	1·40	60
228	3s. chocolate and brown-olive	3·00	2·25
219/28	*Set of 10*	9·00	4·50

Designs: *Horiz* (as T **43**)—1d. Native houses and flags; 3d. Malifa Falls (wrongly inscribed "Aleisa Falls"); 6d. Bonito fishing canoe; 8d. Cacao harvesting. *Vert* (as T **35**)—2d. Seal of Samoa; 5d. Tooth-billed Pigeon.

1953 (25 May). *Coronation. Designs as Nos.* 715 *and* 717 *of New Zealand, but inscr* "WESTERN SAMOA".

229	2d. brown	75	15
230	6d. slate-grey	1·00	35

WESTERN

SAMOA
(45)

1955 (14 Nov). *Postal Fiscal stamps as Type* F **6** *of New Zealand optd with* T **45**. W **98**. *Chalk-surfaced "Wiggins, Teape" paper.* P 14.

232	5s. green (B.)	13·00	17·00
233	10s. carmine-lake (B.)	16·00	25·00
234	£1 pink (B.)	27·00	35·00
235	£2 bright purple (R.)	75·00	£130
232/5	*Set of 4*	£120	£180

The £2 value was mainly used for fiscal purposes.

46 Native Houses and Flags

47 Seal of Samoa

(Recess B.W.)

1958 (21 Mar). *Inauguration of Samoan Parliament.* T **46/7** *and similar horiz design.* W **98** *of New Zealand* (sideways). P 13½ × 13 (6d.) *or* 13½ (others).

236	4d. cerise	15	10
237	6d. deep reddish violet	15	15
238	1s. deep ultramarine	35	15
236/8	*Set of 3*	60	30

Design:—1s. Map of Samoa, and the Mace.

INDEPENDENT

Samoa became independent on 1 January 1962.

49 Samoan Fine Mat

50 Samoa College

(Litho B.W.)

1962 (2 July). *Independence.* T **49/50** *and similar designs.* W **98** *of New Zealand* (sideways on horiz stamps). P 13½.

239	1d. brown and rose-carmine	10	10
240	2d. brown, green, yellow and red	10	10
241	3d. brown, blue-green and blue	10	10
242	4d. magenta, yellow, blue and black	15	10
243	6d. yellow and blue	20	10
244	8d. bluish green, yellow-green and blue	20	10
245	1s. brown and bluish green	20	10
246	1s. 3d. yellow-green and blue	75	35
247	2s. 6d. red and ultramarine	1·50	1·25
248	5s. ultramarine, yellow, red and drab	3·25	2·50
239/48	*Set of 10*	5·75	4·25

Designs: *Horiz*—3d. Public library; 4d. Fono House; 6d. Map of Samoa; 8d. Airport; 1s. 3d. "Vailima"; 2s. 6d. Samoan flag; 5s. Samoan seal. *Vert*—1s. Samoan orator.
See Nos. 257/62.

59 Seal and Joint Heads of State

60 Signing the Treaty

(Des L. C. Mitchell. Photo Harrison)

1963 (1 Oct). *First Anniv of Independence.* W **98** *of New Zealand.* P 14.

249	**59**	1d. deep sepia and green	10	10
250		4d. deep sepia and blue	10	10
251		8d. deep sepia and rose-pink	10	10
252		2s. deep sepia and orange	20	15
249/52		*Set of 4*	35	30

(Des L. C. Mitchell. Photo Enschedé)

1964 (1 Sept). *2nd Anniv of New Zealand–Samoa Treaty of Friendship.* P 13½.

253	**60**	1d. multicoloured	10	10
254		8d. multicoloured	10	10
255		2s. multicoloured	20	10
256		3s. multicoloured	20	20
253/6		*Set of 4*	40	35

61 Kava Bowl

1965 (4 Oct)–**66?** *As Nos.* 239, 241/5, *but* W **61** (sideways on horiz designs).

257	1d. brown and rose-carmine	20	40
258	3d. brown, blue-green and blue (1966?)	27·00	3·75
259	4d. magenta, yellow, blue and black	25	40
260	6d. yellow and blue	45	30
261	8d. bluish green, yellow-green and blue	20	10
262	1s. brown and bluish green	25	40
257/62	*Set of 6*	27·00	4·75

62 Red-tailed Tropic Bird

63 Flying Fish

(Des L. C. Mitchell. Photo Harrison)

1965 (29 Dec). *Air.* W **61** (sideways). P 14½.

263	**62**	8d. black, red-orange and blue	40	10
264	**63**	2s. black and blue	55	20

64 Aerial View of Deep Sea Wharf

(Des Tecon Co (U.S.A.). Photo Enschedé)

1966 (3 Mar). *Opening of First Deep Sea Wharf, Apia.* T **64** *and similar horiz design. Multicoloured.* W **61** (sideways). P 13½.

265	1d. Type **64**	10	10
266	8d. Aerial view of wharf and bay	15	10
267	2s. As 8d.	25	20
268	3s. Type **64**	30	20
265/8	*Set of 4*	70	45

66 W.H.O. Building

(Des M. Goaman. Photo D.L.R.)

1966 (4 July). *Inauguration of W.H.O. Headquarters, Geneva.* T **66** *and similar horiz design.* W **61** (sideways). P 14.

269	3d. yellow-ochre, blue and light slate-lilac	35	10
270	4d. blue, yellow, green & light orange-brown	40	10
271	6d. reddish lilac, emerald and yellow-olive	45	15
272	1s. blue, yellow, green and turquoise-green	80	20
269/72	*Set of 4*	1·75	50

Designs:—3d., 6d. Type **66**; 4d., 1s. W.H.O. Building on flag.

HURRICANE RELIEF
6d
(68)

1966 (1 Sept). *Hurricane Relief Fund. No.* 261 *surch with* T **68** *by Bradbury, Wilkinson.*

273	8d. + 6d. bluish green, yellow-green and blue	10	10

69 Hon. Tuatagaloa L. S. (Minister of Justice)

(Des and photo Harrison)

1967 (16 Jan). *Fifth Anniv of Independence. T* **69** *and similar horiz designs. W* **61** *(sideways).* P 14½ × 14.

274	3d.	sepia and bluish violet	..	10	10
275	8d.	sepia and light new blue..	..	10	10
276	2s.	sepia and olive	..	10	10
277	3s.	sepia and magenta	..	15	15
274/7		*Set of* 4		30	30

Designs:—8d. Hon. F. C. F. Nelson (minister of Works, Marine and Civil Aviation); 2s. Hon. To'omata T. L. (minister of Lands); Hon. Fa'alava'au G. (minister of Post Office, Radio and Broadcasting).

73 Samoan Fales (houses), 1890

(Des V. Whiteley. Photo Harrison)

1967 (16 May). *Centenary of Mulinu'u as Seat of Government. T* **73** *and similar horiz design. Multicoloured. W* **61**. P 14½ × 14.

278	8d.	Type **73**	..	15	15
279	1s.	Fono (Parliament) House, 1967 ..		15	10

(New Currency. 100 sene or cents=1 tala or dollar)

75 Carunculated Honeyeater

76 Black-breasted Honeyeater

(Des V. Whiteley. Litho Format ($2, $4). Photo Harrison (others))

1967 (10 July)–**69**. *Decimal currency. Multicoloured designs as T* **75** *(1 s. to $1) or* **76** *($2, $4). W* **61** *(sideways).* P 13½ ($2, $4) *or* 14 × 14½ *(others).*

280	1s.	Type **75**	..	10	10
281	2s.	Pacific Pigeon	..	10	10
282	3s.	Samoan Starling	..	10	10
283	5s.	White-vented Flycatcher	..	15	10
284	7s.	Red-headed Parrot Finch	..	15	10
285	10s.	Purple Swamphen	..	20	10
286	20s.	Barn Owl	..	2·25	40
287	25s.	Tooth-billed Pigeon	..	1·50	15
288	50s.	Island Thrush	..	1·50	25
289	$1	Samoan Fantail..	..	1·75	1·50
289a	$2	Type **76** (14.7.69)	..	5·50	7·00
289b	$4	Savaii White Eye (6.10.69)	..	40·00	45·00
280/9b		*Set of* 12		48·00	48·00

85 Nurse and Child

(Des G. Vasarhelyi. Photo D.L.R.)

1967 (1 Dec). *South Pacific Health Service. T* **85** *and similar horiz designs. Multicoloured.* P 14.

290	3s.	Type **85**	..	10	10
291	7s.	Leprosarium	..	15	10
292	20s.	Mobile X-ray Unit	..	25	15
293	25s.	Apia Hospital	..	30	20
290/3		*Set of* 4		70	40

89 Thomas Trood   **93** Cocoa

(Des M. Farrar-Bell. Litho B.W.)

1968 (15 Jan). *6th Anniv of Independence. T* **89** *and similar horiz designs. Multicoloured.* P 13½.

294	2s.	Type **89**	..	10	10
295	7s.	Dr. Wilhelm Solf..	..	10	10
296	20s.	J. C. Williams	..	10	10
297	25s.	Fritz Marquardt ..	..	15	10
294/7		*Set of* 4		30	30

(Des Jennifer Toombs. Photo Enschedé)

1968 (15 Feb). *Agricultural Development. T* **93** *and similar vert designs. W* **61**. P 13 × 12½.

298	3s.	deep red-brown, yellow-green and black		10	10
299	5s.	myrtle-green, greenish yellow & lt brn	..	10	10
300	10s.	scarlet, blackish brown and olive-yellow		10	10
301	20s.	yellow-bistre, yellow and blackish olive..		15	15
298/301		*Set of* 4		30	30

Designs:—5 s. Breadfruit; 10 s. Copra; 20 s. Bananas.

97 Women weaving Mats

(Des G. Vasarhelyi. Photo Harrison)

1968 (22 Apr). *21st Anniv of the South Pacific Commission. T* **97** *and similar horiz designs. Multicoloured. W* **61**. P 14½ × 14.

302	7s.	Type **97**	..	10	10
303	20s.	Palm trees and bay	..	15	10
304	25s.	Sheltered cove	..	15	15
302/4		*Set of* 3		30	30

1928-1968
KINGSFORD-SMITH
TRANSPACIFIC FLIGHT

20
SENE ≡

(100)

1968 (13 June). *40th Anniv of Kingsford Smith's Trans-Pacific Flight. No.* **285** *surch with T* **100**.

305	20s. on 10 s. Purple Swamphen	..	..	10	10

101 Bougainville's Route

(Des Jennifer Toombs. Litho B.W.)

1968 (17 June). *Bicentenary of Bougainville's Visit to Samoa. T* **101** *and similar horiz designs. W* **61** *(sideways).* P 14.

306	3s.	new blue and black	..	10	10
307	7s.	light ochre and black	..	15	10
308	20s.	multicoloured	..	45	15
309	25s.	multicoloured	..	60	25
306/9		*Set of* 4		1·10	45

Designs:—7 s. Louis de Bougainville; 20 s. Bougainvillea flower; 25 s. Ships *La Boudeuse* and *L'Etoile*.

105 Globe and Human Rights Emblem   **106** Dr. Martin Luther King

(Des G. Vasarhelyi. Photo Harrison)

1968 (26 Aug). *Human Rights Year. W* **61**. P 14.

310	**105**	7s.	greenish blue, brown and gold	10	10
311		20s.	orange, green and gold	10	10
312		25s.	violet, green and gold	10	10
310/12			*Set of* 3	30	20

(Des and litho D.L.R.)

1968 (23 Sept). *Martin Luther King Commemoration. W* **61**. P 14½ × 14.

313	**106**	7s.	black and olive-green	10	10
314		20s.	black and bright purple	10	10

107 Polynesian Version of Madonna and Child   **108** Frangipani—*Plumeria acuminata*

(Des and litho D.L.R.)

1968 (14 Oct). *Christmas. W* **61**. P 14.

315	**107**	1s.	multicoloured	10	10
316		3s.	multicoloured	10	10
317		20s.	multicoloured	10	10
318		30s.	multicoloured	15	15
315/18			*Set of* 4	30	30

(Des J.W. Litho Format)

1969 (20 Jan). *Seventh Anniv of Independence. T* **108** *and similar multicoloured designs.* P 14½.

319	2s.	Type **108**	..	10	10
320	7s.	Hibiscus (*vert*)	..	25	10
321	20s.	Red-Ginger (*vert*)	..	65	10
322	30s.	"Moso'oi" ..	..	80	45
319/22		*Set of* 4		1·60	65

109 R. L. Stevenson and *Treasure Island*   **110** Weightlifting

(Des Jennifer Toombs. Litho D.L.R.)

1969 (21 Apr). *75th Death Anniv of Robert Louis Stevenson. Horiz designs, each showing portrait as in T* **109**. *Multicoloured. W* **61** *(sideways).* P 14.

323	3s.	Type **109**	..	15	10
324	7s.	*Kidnapped*	..	20	10
325	20s.	*Dr. Jekyll and Mr. Hyde*..	..	45	10
326	22s.	*Weir of Hermiston*	..	55	15
323/6		*Set of* 4		1·25	40

(Des J. Mason. Photo Note Ptg Branch, Reserve Bank of Australia)

1969 (21 July). *Third South Pacific Games, Port Moresby. T* **110** *and similar vert designs.* P 13½.

327	3s.	black and sage-green	..	10	10
328	20s.	black and light blue	..	10	10
329	22s.	black and dull orange	..	15	15
327/9		*Set of* 3		30	30

Designs:—20 s. Yachting; 22 s. Boxing.

113 U.S. Astronaut on the Moon and the Splashdown near Samoan Islands

(Des J. Mason. Photo Note Ptg Branch, Reserve Bank of Australia)

1969 (24 July). *First Man on the Moon.* P 13½.

330	**113**	7s.	multicoloured	15	15
331		20s.	multicoloured	15	15

OMNIBUS ISSUES

Details, together with prices for complete sets, of the various Omnibus issues from the 1935 Silver Jubilee series to date are included in a special section following Zimbabwe at the end of Volume 2.

114 "Virgin with Child" (Murillo)

(Des and photo Heraclio Fournier)

1969 (13 Oct). *Christmas. T* **114** *and similar vert designs. Multicoloured. P* 14.

332	1 s.	Type **114**				10	10
333	3 s.	"The Holy Family" (El Greco)				10	10
334	20 s.	"The Nativity" (El Greco)				25	10
335	30 s.	"The Adoration of the Magi" (detail, Velazquez)				30	15
332/5					*Set of* 4	50	30
MS336	116 × 126 mm. Nos. 332/5					60	1·25

115 Seventh Day Adventists' Sanatorium, Apia

(Des V. Whiteley. Litho Format)

1970 (19 Jan). *Eighth Anniv of Independence. T* **115** *and similar designs. W* **61** *(sideways on* 2, 7 *and* 22 s.*). P* 14.

337	2 s.	yellow-brown, pale slate and black			10	10
338	7 s.	violet, buff and black			10	10
339	20 s.	rose, lilac and black			15	10
340	22 s.	olive-green, cinnamon and black			15	15
337/40				*Set of* 4	30	30

Designs: *Horiz*—7 s. Rev. Father Violette and Roman Catholic Cathedral, Apia; 22 s. John Williams, 1797–1839, and London Missionary Society Church, Sapali'i. *Vert*—20 s. Mormon Church of Latter Day Saints, Tuasivi-on-Safotulafai.

119 Wreck of S.M.S. *Adler*

(Des J.W. Litho Questa)

1970 (27 Apr). *Great Apia Hurricane of 1889. T* **119** *and similar horiz designs. Multicoloured. W* **61** *(sideways). P* 13½.

341	5 s.	Type **119**				45	10
342	7 s.	U.S.S. *Nipsic*				50	10
343	10 s.	H.M.S. *Calliope*				65	25
344	20 s.	Apia after the hurricane				2·00	1·25
341/4					*Set of* 4	3·25	1·50

120 Sir Gordon Taylor's *Frigate Bird III*

(Des R. Honisett. Photo. Note Ptg Branch, Reserve Bank of Australia)

1970 (27 July). *Air. Aircraft. T* **120** *and similar horiz designs. Multicoloured. P* 13½ × 13.

345	3 s.	Type **120**				35	10
346	7 s.	Polynesian Airlines "DC-3"				70	10
347	20 s.	Pan-American "Samoan Clipper"				1·75	60
348	30 s.	Air Samoa Britten-Norman "Islander"				2·00	1·25
	a.	Pale purple omitted				£250	
345/8					*Set of* 4	4·25	1·75

121 Kendal's Chronometer and Cook's Sextant

122 "Peace for the World" (F. B. Eccles)

(Des J. Berry, adapted J. Cooter. Litho Questa)

1970 (14 Sept). *Cook's Exploration of the Pacific. T* **121** *and similar designs. W* **61** *(sideways on* 30 s.*). P* 14.

349	1 s.	carmine, silver and black			20	15
350	2 s.	multicoloured			35	25
351	20 s.	black, bright blue and gold			1·75	1·00
352	30 s.	multicoloured			2·75	1·75
349/52				*Set of* 4	4·50	2·75

Designs: *Vert*—2 s. Cook's statue, Whitby; 20 s. Cook's head. *Horiz* (83 × 25 *mm*)—30 s. Cook, H.M.S. *Endeavour* and island.

(Des from paintings. Photo Heraclio Fournier)

1970 (26 Oct). *Christmas. T* **122** *and similar vert designs. Multicoloured. P* 13.

353	2 s.	Type **122**			10	10
354	3 s.	"The Holy Family" (W. E. Jahnke)			10	10
355	20 s.	"Mother and Child" (F. B. Eccles)			15	10
356	30 s.	"Prince of Peace" (Meleane Fe'ao)			20	15
353/6				*Set of* 4	35	30
MS357	111 × 158 mm. Nos. 353/6				60	1·25

123 Pope Paul VI

124 Native and Tree

(Des J. Cooter. Litho Format)

1970 (20 Nov). *Visit of Pope Paul to Samoa. W* **61**. *P* 14×14½.

358	123	8 s. black and grey-blue			15	15
359		20 s. black and plum			35	15

(Des G. Drummond from sketches by the American Timber Co. Litho Questa)

1971 (1 Feb). *Timber Industry. T* **124** *and similar multicoloured designs. P* 13½.

360	3 s.	Type **124**			10	10
361	8 s.	Bulldozer in clearing (*horiz*)			15	10
362	20 s.	Log in sawmill (*horiz*)			30	10
363	22 s.	Floating logs and harbour			30	15
360/3				*Set of* 4	70	30

125 Fautasi (canoe) in Apia Harbour and first stamps of Samoa and U.S.A.

(*Half-sized illustration. Actual size* 84 × 26 *mm*)

(Des E. Roberts. Photo Courvoisier)

1971 (12 Mar). *"Interpex" Stamp Exhibition, New York. Sheet* 138 × 80 *mm. P* 11½.

MS364	**125**	70 s. multicoloured			85	1·40

126 Siva Dance

127 "Queen Salamasina"

(Des and litho J.W.)

1971 (9 Aug). *Tourism. T* **126** *and similar horiz designs. Multicoloured. W* **61** *(sideways). P* 14.

365	5 s.	Type **126**			40	10
366	7 s.	Samoan cricket			1·00	60
367	8 s.	Hideaway Hotel			1·00	35
368	10 s.	Aggie Grey and her hotel			1·00	60
365/8				*Set of* 4	3·00	1·40

(Des Jennifer Toombs. Litho J.W.)

1971 (20 Sept). *Myths and Legends of Old Samoa* (1st series). *T* **127** *and similar vert designs from carvings by S. Ortquist. Multicoloured. W* **61** *(sideways). P* 14 × 13½.

369	3 s.	Type **127**			10	10
370	8 s.	"Lu and his Sacred Hens"			15	10
371	10 s.	"God Tagaloa fishes Samoa from the sea"			20	10
372	22 s.	"Mount Vaea and the Pool of Tears"			35	20
369/72				*Set of* 4	70	30

See also Nos. 426/9.

128 "The Virgin and Child" (Bellini)

129 Map and Scales of Justice

(Des J. Cooter. Litho J.W.)

1971 (4 Oct). *Christmas. T* **128** *and similar design. W* **61**. *P* 14 × 13½.

373	**128**	2 s. multicoloured			10	10
374		3 s. multicoloured			10	10
375	—	20 s. multicoloured			20	10
376	—	30 s. multicoloured			30	20
373/6				*Set of* 4	55	35

Design: *Vert*—20 s., 30 s. "The Virgin and Child with St. Anne and John the Baptist" (Leonardo da Vinci).

(Des E. Roberts. Photo Courvoisier)

1972 (10 Jan). *First South Pacific Judicial Conference. P* 11½ × 11.

377	**129**	10 s. multicoloured			15	15

Issued on matt, almost invisible gum.

130 Asau Wharf, Savaii

131 Flags of Member Countries

(Des V. Whiteley. Litho A. & M.)

1972 (10 Jan). *Tenth Anniv of Independence. T* **130** *and similar horiz designs. Multicoloured. W* **61** *(sideways). P* 13.

378	1 s.	Type **130**			10	10
379	8 s.	Parliament Building			10	10
380	10 s.	Mothers' Centre			10	10
381	22 s.	"Vailima" Residence and rulers			20	25
378/81				*Set of* 4	40	30

(Des V. Whiteley. Litho Questa)

1972 (17 Mar). *25th Anniv of South Pacific Commission. T* **131** *and similar multicoloured designs. W* **61** *(sideways on* 8 s. *and* 10 s.*). P* 14 × 13½ (3 *and* 7 s.) *or* 13½ × 14 (*others*).

382	3 s.	Type **131**			10	15
383	7 s.	Flag and Afoafouvale Misimoa (Gen Sec)			10	15
384	8 s.	H.Q. building, Nouméa (*horiz*)			15	15
385	10 s.	Flags and area map (*horiz*)			15	15
382/5				*Set of* 4	40	55

132 Expedition Ships

133 Bull Conch

(Des J. Berry; adapted J. Cooter. Litho Questa)

1972 (14 June). *250th Anniv of sighting of Western Samoa by Jacob Roggeveen. T 132 and similar horiz designs. Multi-coloured. W 61 (sideways, except 2 s.). P 14½.*

386	2 s. Type 132	..	15	10
387	8 s. Ships in storm	..	45	10
388	10 s. Ships passing island	..	50	10
389	30 s. Route of Voyage (85 × 25 mm) ..		1·75	1·50
386/9		Set of 4	2·50	1·60

(Des Format ($5) or J.W. (others). Litho Format ($5), Questa (others))

1972 (18 Oct)–76. *T 133 and similar multicoloured designs. W 61 (sideways, on 1 s. to 50 s.). White, ordinary paper. P 13½ ($1 to $5) or 14½ (others).*

390	1 s. Type 133	..	20	10
	a. Cream, chalk-surfaced paper (30.11.76)		1·50	1·50
391	2 s. *Oryctes rhinoceros* (beetle) ..		20	10
	a. Cream, chalk-surfaced paper (30.11.76)		1·50	1·50
392	3 s. Skipjack (fish)	..	30	20
393	4 s. Painted Crab	..	30	10
	a. Cream, chalk-surfaced paper (30.11.76)		1·50	1·50
394	5 s. Butterfly Fish	..	35	10
	a. Cream, chalk-surfaced paper (30.11.76)		1·50	1·50
395	7 s. *Danaus hamata* (butterfly) ..		1·25	30
396	10 s. Triton Shell	..	1·00	40
397	20 s. *Chrysochroa abdominalis* (beetle) ..		1·25	30
398	50 s. Spiny Lobster	..	2·00	1·75
399	$1 *Gnathothlibus erotus* (moth) (29×45 mm)		7·00	3·25
399a	$2 Green Turtle (29×45 mm) (18.6.73)		8·00	4·00
399b	$4 Black Marlin (29×45 mm) (27.3.74)		5·00	7·00
399c	$5 Green Tree Lizard (29×45 mm) (30.6.75)		5·50	7·50
390/9c		Set of 13	29·00	22·00

134 "The Ascension"

135 Erecting a Tent

(Des PAD Studio. Litho Harrison)

1972 (1 Nov). *Christmas. Stained-glass Windows in Apia. T 134 and similar vert designs. Multicoloured. W 61. P 14 × 14½.*

400	1 s. Type 134	..	10	10
401	4 s. "The Blessed Virgin and Infant Christ"		10	10
402	10 s. "St. Andrew blessing Samoan canoe"		10	10
403	30 s. "The Good Shepherd" ..		40	30
400/3		Set of 4	50	40
MS404	70 × 159 mm. Nos. 400/3 ..		90	1·25

(Des G. Drummond. Litho Format)

1973 (29 Jan). *Boy Scout Movement. T 135 and similar horiz designs. Multicoloured. W 61 (sideways). P 14.*

405	2 s. Saluting the flag ..		10	10
406	3 s. First-aid	..	10	10
407	8 s. Type 135 ..		25	10
408	20 s. Samoan action-song	..	90	85
405/8		Set of 4	1·10	95

136 Hawker Siddeley "748"

(Des E. Roberts. Photo Courvoisier)

1973 (9 Mar). *Air. T 136 and similar horiz designs showing aircraft at Faleolo Airport. Multicoloured. P 11½.*

409	8 s. Type 136 ..		45	15
410	10 s. H.S. "748" in flight	..	55	15
411	12 s. H.S. "748" on runway	..	65	35
412	22 s. B.A.C. 1-11	..	1·00	60
409/12		Set of 4	2·40	1·10
	Issued on matt, almost invisible gum.			

ALTERED CATALOGUE NUMBERS

Any Catalogue numbers altered from the last edition are shown as a list in the introductory pages.

---

137 Apia General Hospital

138 Mother and Child, and Map

(Des C. Abbott. Litho Questa)

1973 (20 Aug). *25th Anniv of W.H.O. T 137 and similar vert designs. Multicoloured. W 61. P 14.*

413	2 s. Type 137 ..		10	10
414	8 s. Baby clinic	..	20	10
415	20 s. Filariasis research	..	45	20
416	22 s. Family welfare ..		45	30
413/16		Set of 4	1·10	55

(Des W. E. Jahnke (3 s.), Fiasili Keil (4 s.), E. Cooter (others); adapted Jennifer Toombs. Litho J.W.)

1973 (15 Oct). *Christmas. T 138 and similar vert designs. Multicoloured. W 61. P 14.*

417	3 s. Type 138 ..		10	10
418	4 s. Mother and child, and village	..	10	10
419	10 s. Mother and child, and beach	..	10	10
420	30 s. Samoan stable ..		45	50
417/20		Set of 4	55	55
MS421	144×103 mm. Nos. 417/20 ..		60	75

139 Boxing

(Des G. Drummond. Litho Questa)

1974 (24 Jan). *Commonwealth Games, Christchurch. T 139 and similar horiz designs. Multicoloured. W 61 (sideways). P 14.*

422	8 s. Type 139 ..		10	10
423	10 s. Weightlifting	..	10	10
424	20 s. Bowls	..	20	10
425	30 s. Athletics stadium	..	35	45
422/5		Set of 4	70	60

(Des Jennifer Toombs. Litho Questa)

1974 (13 Aug). *Myths and Legends of Old Samoa (2nd series). Vert designs as T 127 from carvings by S. Ortquist. Multicoloured. W 61. P 14 × 13½.*

426	2 s. Tigilau and sacred dove	..	10	10
427	8 s. Pili, his sons and fishing net	..	10	10
428	20 s. Sina and the origin of the coconut	..	30	10
429	30 s. The warrior, Nafanua	..	45	45
426/9		Set of 4	80	55

140 Mail-van at Faleolo Airport

(Des E. Roberts. Photo Heraclio Fournier)

1974 (4 Sept). *Centenary of Universal Postal Union. T 140 and similar horiz designs. Multicoloured. P 13 × 12½ (50 s.) or 13 (others).*

430	8 s. Type 140..		15	10
431	20 s. Cargo liner at Apia Wharf	..	35	15
432	22 s. Early Post Office, Apia and letter	..	40	25
433	50 s. William Willis and *Age Unlimited* (sailing-raft) (87×29 mm) ..		80	1·00
430/3		Set of 4	1·50	1·40
MS434	140×82 mm. No. 433	..	1·25	2·25

141 "Holy Family" (Sebastiano)

(Des PAD Studio. Litho Enschedé)

1974 (25 Nov). *Christmas. T 141 and similar horiz designs. Multicoloured. W 61 (sideways). P 13×13½.*

435	3 s. Type 141 ..		10	10
436	4 s. "Virgin and Child with Saints" (Lotto) ..		10	10
437	10 s. "Madonna and Child with St. John" (Titian)	..	10	10
438	30 s. "Adoration of the Shepherds" (Rubens) ..		35	45
435/8		Set of 4	45	50
MS439	128 × 87 mm. Nos. 435/8 ..		70	1·40

---

142 Winged Passion Flower

(Des J.W. Litho Questa)

1975 (15 Jan). *Tropical Flowers. T 142 and similar multicoloured designs. W 61 (sideways on 8 and 30 s.). P 14.*

440	8 s. Type 142	..	20	10
441	20 s. Gardenia (vert)	..	50	45
442	22 s. *Barringtonia samoensis* (vert)	..	55	50
443	30 s. Malay apple	..	85	85
440/3		Set of 4	1·90	1·75

143 *Joyita* loading at Apia

144 "Pate" Drum

(Des E. Roberts. Photo Heraclio Fournier)

1975 (14 Mar). *"Interpex 1975" Stamp Exhibition, New York, and "Joyita Mystery". T 143 and similar horiz designs. Multicoloured. P 13½.*

444	1 s. Type 143	..	10	10
445	8 s. *Joyita* sails for Tokelau Islands	..	15	10
446	20 s. Taking to rafts	..	35	25
447	22 s. *Joyita* abandoned	..	40	30
448	50 s. Discovery of *Joyita* north of Fiji ..		1·00	1·25
444/8		Set of 5	1·75	1·75
MS449	150 × 100 mm. Nos. 444/8. Imperf		2·50	3·50

(Des Iosua To'afa; adapted L. Curtis. Litho Harrison)

1975 (30 Sept). *Musical Instruments. T 144 and similar vert designs. Multicoloured. W 61 (sideways). P 14.*

450	8 s. Type 144	..	10	10
451	20 s. "Lali" drum	..	20	10
452	22 s. "Logo" drum	..	20	10
453	30 s. "Pu" shell horn	..	35	30
450/3		Set of 4	75	50

145 "Mother and Child" (Meleane Fe'ao)

146 "The Boston Massacre, 1770" (Paul Revere)

(Des local artists; adapted G. Vasarhelyi. Litho Walsall)

1975 (25 Nov). *Christmas. T 145 and similar vert designs. Multicoloured. W 61 (inverted). P 14.*

454	3 s. Type 145	..	10	10
455	4 s. "The Saviour" (Polataia Tuigamala) ..		10	10
456	10 s. "A Star is Born" (Iosua To'afa) ..		10	10
457	30 s. "Madonna and Child" (Ernesto Coter) ..		30	45
454/7		Set of 4	45	50
MS458	101 × 134 mm. Nos. 454/7	..	60	1·25

(Des J. Cooter. Litho Walsall)

1976 (20 Jan). *Bicentenary of American Revolution. T 146 and similar horiz designs. Multicoloured. W 61 (sideways). P 13½.*

459	7 s. Type 146	..	20	15
460	8 s. "The Declaration of Independence" (Trumbull) ..		20	15
461	20 s. "The Ship that Sank in Victory, 1779" (Ferris) ..		60	35
462	22 s. "Pitt addressing the Commons, 1782" (R. A. Hickel) ..		60	35
463	50 s. "The Battle of Princetown" (Mercer) ..		1·50	1·75
459/63		Set of 5	2·75	2·50
MS464	160 × 125 mm. Nos. 459/63 ..		6·00	7·00

147 Mullet Fishing

(Des V. Whiteley Studio. Litho Harrison)

1976 (27 Apr). *Fishing. T 147 and similar horiz designs. Multicoloured. W 61. P 14.*

465	10 s. Type 147 ..		10	10
466	12 s. Fish traps	..	15	10
467	22 s. Samoan fishermen	..	30	10
468	50 s. Net fishing	..	85	70
465/8		Set of 4	1·25	90

148 Paul Revere's Ride

(Des J. Berry. Photo Heraclio Fournier)

1976 (29 May). *"Interphil" Stamp Exhibition. Sheet* 120 × 80 *mm.*
P 13.
MS469 148 $1 gold, black and emerald .. .. 2·75 2·50

149 Boxing   150 Mary and Joseph going
to Bethlehem

(Des C. Abbott. Litho Questa)

1976 (21 June). *Olympic Games, Montreal. T* 149 *and similar horiz designs. Multicoloured. W* 61 *(sideways). P* 14.
470 10 s. Type 149 .. .. 10 10
471 12 s. Wrestling 10 10
472 22 s. Javelin 15 10
473 50 s. Weightlifting 45 50
470/3 .. .. *Set of* 4 70 60

(Des C. Abbott. Litho Questa)

1976 (18 Oct). *Christmas. T* 150 *and similar vert designs. Multi-coloured. W* 61. *P* 13½.
474 3 s. Type 150 .. .. .. 10 10
475 5 s. The Shepherds 10 10
476 22 s. The Holy Family.. .. 15 10
477 50 s. The Magi 55 65
474/7 .. .. .. *Set of* 4 70 75
MS478 124×115 mm. Nos. 474/7 .. 80 1·75

151 Queen Elizabeth and View of Apia

(Des BG Studio. Litho Questa)

1977 (11 Feb). *Silver Jubilee and Royal Visit. T* 151 *and similar horiz designs. Multicoloured. W* 61 *(sideways). P* 13½.
479 12 s. Type 151 .. .. .. 20 10
480 26 s. Presentation of Spurs of Chivalry 35 20
481 32 s. Queen and Royal Yacht *Britannia* 50 25
482 50 s. Queen leaving Abbey .. 55 80
479/82 .. .. *Set of* 4 1·40 1·25

152 Map of Flight Route

(Des C. Abbott. Litho Walsall)

1977 (20 May). *50th Anniv of Lindbergh's Transatlantic Flight. Horiz designs showing the "Spirit of St. Louis". Multicoloured. W* 61 *(sideways). P* 14.
483 22 s. Type 152 .. .. .. 25 10
484 24 s. In flight 35 15
485 26 s. Landing 35 15
486 50 s. Col. Lindbergh 80 75
483/6 .. .. *Set of* 4 1·60 1·00
MS487 194 × 93 mm. Nos. 483/6 .. 2·40 2·75

153 3d. Express Stamp and First
Mail Notice

(Des J. Cooter. Litho Questa)

1977 (29 Aug). *Stamp Centenary. T* 153 *and similar horiz designs. W* 61 *(sideways). P* 13½.
488 12 s. lemon, red and sepia 20 10
489 13 s. multicoloured 20 15
490 26 s. multicoloured 45 30
491 50 s. multicoloured .. .. 80 1·00
488/91 .. .. .. *Set of* 4 1·50 1·40
Designs:—13 s. Early cover and 6d. Express; 26 s. Apia Post Office and 1d. Express; 50 s. Schooner *Energy*, 1877, and 6d. Express.

154 Apia Automatic   155 "Samoan
Telephone Exchange   Nativity" (P.
Feata)

(Des J.W. Litho Questa)

1977 (28 Oct*). *Telecommunications Project. T* 154 *and similar horiz designs. Multicoloured. W* 61 *(sideways). P* 14.
492 12 s. Type 154 .. .. .. 15 10
493 13 s. Mulinuu Radio Terminal .. 15 10
494 26 s. Old and new telephones .. 30 20
495 50 s. "Global communication" .. 50 70
492/5 .. .. .. *Set of* 4 1·00 1·00
*The above were originally scheduled for release on 11 July and were put on sale by the Crown Agents in England on that date.

(Designs adapted by J.W. Litho Questa)

1977 (31 Oct). *Christmas. T* 155 *and similar vert designs. Multicoloured. W* 61. *P* 14.
496 4 s. Type 155 .. .. .. 10 10
497 6 s. "The Offering" (E. Saofaiga) .. 10 10
498 26 s. "Madonna and Child" (F. Tupou) .. 20 10
499 50 s. "Emmanuel" (M. Sapa'u) .. 35 40
496/9 .. .. .. *Set of* 4 55 50
MS500 117×159 mm. Nos. 496/9 .. 55 85

156 Polynesian Airlines Boeing "737"

(Des E. Roberts. Litho Heraclio Fournier)

1978 (21 Mar). *Aviation Progress. T* 156 *and similar horiz designs. Multicoloured. P* 14.
501 12 s. Type 156 .. .. .. 20 10
502 24 s. Wright brothers' *Flyer* .. 40 20
503 26 s. Kingsford Smith's *Southern Cross* 40 20
504 50 s. "Concorde" .. .. 1·10 85
501/4 .. .. *Set of* 4 1·90 1·25
MS505 150×120 mm. Nos. 501/4 .. 2·25 2·75

157 Hatchery, Aleipata   158 Pacific Pigeon

(Des J.W. Litho Questa)

1978 (14 Apr). *Hawksbill Turtle Conservation Project. T* 157 *and similar horiz design. Multicoloured. W* 61 *(sideways). P* 14½ × 14.
506 24 s. Type 157 .. .. .. 35 30
507 $1 Turtle .. .. .. 1·60 1·60

(Des Jennifer Toombs. Litho Questa)

1978 (21 Apr). *25th Anniv of Coronation. T* 158 *and similar vert designs. P* 15.
508 26 s. black, brown and deep magenta.. 25 30
a. Sheetlet. Nos. 508/10 × 2 .. 1·50
509 26 s. multicoloured 25 30
510 26 s. black, brown and deep magenta.. 25 30
508/10 .. .. .. *Set of* 3 70 80
Designs:—No. 508, King's Lion; No. 509, Queen Elizabeth II; No. 510, Type 158.
Nos. 508/10 were printed together in small sheets of 6, containing two *se-tenant* strips of 3, with horizontal gutter margin between.

159 Flags of Western Samoa and   160 Captain Cook
Canada with Canadian National Tower

(Des BG Studio. Litho Walsall)

1978 (9 June). *"Capex '78" International Stamp Exhibition, Toronto. Sheet* 119 × 79 *mm. W* 61. *P* 14½.
MS511 159 $1 blue, red and black.. .. 1·25 1·75

(Des J. Berry. Litho Harrison)

1978 (28 Aug). *250th Birth Anniv of Captain Cook. T* 160 *and similar vert designs. Multicoloured. W* 61. *P* 14½ × 14.
512 s. Type 160 .. .. .. 30 15
513 24 s. Cook's cottage, Gt Ayton, Yorkshire 60 35
514 26 s. Old drawbridge over the river Esk, Whitby 70 35
515 50 s. H.M.S. *Resolution* .. 1·25 1·50
512/15 .. .. .. *Set of* 4 2·50 2·10

161 Thick-edged Cowry   162 "Madonna on
the Crescent"

(Photo Courvoisier)

1978 (15 Sept)–80. *Shells. Horiz designs as T* 161. *Multicoloured. P* 12½.
516 1 s. Type 161 .. .. .. 15 10
517 2 s. Isabella cowry 15 10
518 3 s. Money cowry 25 10
519 4 s. Eroded cowry 30 10
520 6 s. Honey cowry 30 10
521 7 s. Banded cowry 35 10
522 10 s. Globe cowry 40 10
523 11 s. Mole cowry 40 10
524 12 s. Children's cowry .. 40 10
525 13 s. Flag cone (20.11.78) .. 40 10
526 14 s. Soldier cone (20.11.78) .. 40 10
527 24 s. Cloth-of-gold cone (20.11.78) .. 40 10
528 26 s. Lettered cone (20.11.78).. 45 10
529 50 s. Tiled cone (20.11.78) .. 50 15
530 $1 Black Marble cone (20.11.78) .. 95 60
530a $2 Marlin-spike auger (18.7.79) .. 1·50 90
530b $3 Scorpion Spider Conch (18.7.79).. 2·25 1·50
530c $5 Common Harp (26.8.80) .. 3·75 3·00
516/30c .. .. .. *Set of* 18 12·00 6·00
Nos. 530a/c are larger, size 36 × 26 mm.
Issued on matt, almost invisible gum.

(Des C. Abbott. Litho Questa)

1978 (6 Nov). *Christmas. Woodcuts by Dürer. T* 162 *and similar vert designs. Multicoloured. W* 61. *P* 14.
531 4 s. black and yellow-brown .. 10 10
532 6 s. black and turquoise-blue .. 10 10
533 26 s. black and bright blue .. 15 10
534 50 s. black and bright violet .. 35 50
531/4 .. .. .. *Set of* 4 50 55
MS535 103 × 154 mm. Nos. 531/4 .. 70 1·00
Designs:—6 s. "Nativity"; 26 s. "Adoration of the Magi"; 50 s. "Annunciation".

163 Boy with Coconuts   164 *Charles W. Morgan*

(Des G. Drummond. Litho Questa)

1979 (10 Apr). *International Year of the Child. T* 163 *and similar horiz designs. Multicoloured. W* 61 *(sideways). P* 14.
536 12 s. Type 163 .. .. .. 15 10
537 24 s. White knitting 30 15
538 26 s. Children at pump 35 15
539 50 s. Young girl with ukulele .. 70 80
536/9 .. .. *Set of* 4 1·40 1·10

(Des J. Cooter. Litho Format)

1979 (29 May). *Sailing Ships (1st series). Whaling Ships. T* **164** *and similar horiz designs. Multicoloured. W* **61** *(sideways). P* 13½.

540	12 s. Type **164** ..	..	..	..	40	10
541	14 s. *Lagoda*	..	..	..	45	10
542	24 s. *James T. Arnold*	..	..	60	20
543	50 s. *Splendid* ..	..	..	1·10	85
540/3 ..	..	..	..	*Set of* 4	2·25	1·10

See also Nos. 561/4 and 584/7.

165 Launch of "Apollo 11" **166** Sir Rowland Hill (statue) and Penny Black

(Des J.W. Litho Questa)

1979 (20 June). *10th Anniv of Moon Landing. T* **165** *and similar designs in chocolate and dull vermilion (12 s.) or multicoloured (others). W* **61** *(sideways on 14, 26 s. and $1). P* 14½ × 14 (12, 24, 50 s.) *or* 14 × 14½ (*others*).

544	12 s. Type **165** ..	..	..	20	10
545	14 s. Lunar module and astronaut on Moon (*horiz*)	..	..	25	10
546	24 s. View of Earth from Moon	..	..	30	15
547	26 s. Astronaut on Moon (*horiz*)	..	30	15
548	50 s. Lunar and Command modules in Space	..	55	55
549	$1 Command module after splash-down (*horiz*)	..	1·25	1·50
544/9 ..	..	..	..	*Set of* 6	2·50	2·25
MS550	90 × 130 mm. No. 549	..	..	1·00	1·75

No. MS550 is inscribed "Spashdown" in error.

(Des and litho J.W.)

1979 (27 Aug). *Death Centenary of Sir Rowland Hill. T* **166** *and similar vert designs. Multicoloured. W* **61**. *P* 14.

551	12 s. Type **166** ..	..	..	15	10
552	24 s. Two-penny Blue with "Maltese Cross" postmark ..	..	..	20	15
553	26 s. Sir Rowland Hill and Penny Black	..	20	15
554	$1 Two-penny Blue and Sir Rowland Hill (statue)	..	..	60	75
551/4 ..	..	..	..	*Set of* 4	1·00	1·00
MS555	128 × 95 mm. Nos. 551/4 ..	..	1·00	1·60

167 Anglican Church, Apia

(Des A. Peake. Photo Courvoisier)

1979 (22 Oct). *Christmas. Churches. T* **167** *and similar horiz designs. P* 11½.

556	4 s. black and pale blue	..	..	10	10
557	6 s. black and bright yellow-green	..	10	10
558	26 s. black and yellow-ochre	..	15	10
559	50 s. black and reddish lilac	..	30	30
556/9 ..	..	..	*Set of* 4	45	35
MS560	150 × 124 mm. Nos. 556/9	..	50	75

Designs:—6 s. Congregational Christian, Leulumoega; 26 s. Methodist, Piula; 50 s. Protestant, Apia.

Issued on matt, almost invisible gum.

(Des J. Cooter. Litho Format)

1980 (22 Jan). *Sailing Ships (2nd series). Whaling Ships. Horiz designs as T* **164**. *Multicoloured. W* **61** *(sideways) P* 13½.

561	12 s. *William Hamilton*	..	..	40	40
562	14 s. *California*	..	..	45	15
563	24 s. *Liverpool II*	..	..	60	25
564	50 s. *Two Brothers*	..	..	1·10	70
561/4 ..	..	..	*Set of* 4	2·25	1·10

168 "Equipment for a Hospital"

(Des M. Goaman (12, 50 s.), E. Roberts (others). Photo Heraclio Fournier)

1980 (26 Mar). *Anniversaries. T* **168** *and similar horiz designs. Multicoloured. P* 13½ × 14.

565	12 s. Type **168** ..	..	..	40	10
566	13 s. John Williams, dove with olive twig and commemorative inscription	..	40	15
567	14 s. Dr. Wilhelm Solf (instigator), flag and commemorative inscription	..	45	15
568	24 s. Cairn Monument	..	..	60	25
569	26 s. Williams Memorial, Savai'i	..	65	25
570	50 s. Paul P. Harris (founder) ..	..	1·10	60
565/70	..	..	*Set of* 6	3·25	1·40

Commemorations:—12, 50 s. 75th anniversary of Rotary International; 13, 26 s. 150th anniversary of John Williams' (missionary) arrival in Samoa; 14, 24 s. 80th anniversary of raising of German flag.

169 Samoan Village Scene

(Des J.W. Litho Walsall)

1980 (6 May). *"London 1980" International Stamp Exhibition. Sheet* 140 × 81 *mm. W* **61** *(sideways). P* 14.

| MS571 | **169** $1 multicoloured | .. | .. | 80 | 1·25 |

170 Queen Elizabeth the Queen Mother in 1970

(Des Harrison. Litho Questa)

1980 (4 Aug). *80th Birthday of Queen Elizabeth the Queen Mother. P* 14.

| 572 | **170** 50 s. multicoloured | .. | .. | 50 | 35 |

171 1964 2nd Anniversary of New Zealand–Samoa Treaty of Friendship 2 s. Commemorative and "Zeapex '80" Emblem

(Des E. Roberts. Photo Heraclio Fournier)

1980 (23 Aug). *"Zeapex '80" International Stamp Exhibition, Auckland. Sheet* 130 × 80 *mm. P* 14.

| MS573 | **171** $1 multicoloured | .. | .. | 1·25 | 1·40 |

172 Afiamalu Satellite Earth Station

(Des and photo Courvoisier)

1980 (20 Sept). *Afiamalu Satellite Earth Station. T* **172** *and similar horiz designs. Multicoloured. P* 11½.

574	12 s. Type **172** ..	..	..	15	10
575	14 s. Satellite station (*different*)	..	20	10
576	24 s. Satellite station and map of Savai'i and Upolu	..	..	30	15
577	50 s. Satellite and globe	..	60	60
574/7 ..	..	..	*Set of* 4	1·10	85

173 Afiamalu Satellite Earth Station 24 s. Commemorative Stamp and "Sydpex 80" Emblem

(Des E. Roberts. Litho Sprintpak, Mayne Nickless Ltd, Australia)

1980 (29 Sept). *"Sydpex 80" International Stamp Exhibition, Sydney. Sheet* 130 × 80 *mm. Imperf.*

| MS578 | **173** $2 multicoloured | .. | .. | 2·00 | 2·00 |

174 "The Saviour" (J. Poynton) **175** President Franklin D. Roosevelt and Hyde Park (family home)

(Des G. Vasarhelyi. Litho Format)

1980 (28 Oct). *Christmas. Paintings. T* **174** *and similar vert designs. Multicoloured. W* **61**. *P* 13½.

579	8 s. Type **174** ..	..	..	10	10
580	14 s. "Madonna and Child" (Lealofi F. Siaopo)	..	10	10
581	27 s. "Nativity" (Pasila Feata)	..	15	10
582	50 s. "Yuletide" (R. P. Aiono)	..	25	40
579/82 ..	..	..	*Set of* 4	55	55
MS583	90 × 105 mm. Nos. 579/82	..	1·00	1·50

(Des J. Cooter. Litho Format)

1981 (26 Jan). *Sailing Ships (3rd series). Horiz designs as T* **164**. *Multicoloured. P* 13½.

584	12 s. *Ocean* (whaling ship)	..	..	20	10
585	18 s. *Horatio* (whaling ship)	..	30	15
586	27 s. H.M.S. *Calliope*	..	..	45	25
587	32 s. H.M.S. *Calypso*	..	..	50	50
584/7 ..	..	..	*Set of* 4	1·25	90

(Des J.W. Litho Format)

1981 (29 Apr). *International Year for Disabled Persons. President Franklin D. Roosevelt Commemoration. T* **175** *and similar horiz designs. P* 14.

588	12 s. Type **175** ..	..	..	15	10
589	18 s. Roosevelt's inauguration, 4 March 1933	..	25	15
590	27 s. Franklin and Eleanor Roosevelt	..	35	20
591	32 s. Roosevelt's Lend-lease Bill (Atlantic convoy, 1941)	..	40	30
592	38 s. Roosevelt the philatelist..	..	45	35
593	$1 Campobello House (summer home)	..	1·00	1·00
588/93	..	..	*Set of* 6	2·40	1·90

176 Hotel Tusitala **177** Wedding Bouquet from Samoa

(Des and litho Walsall)

1981 (29 June). *Tourism. T* **176** *and similar horiz designs. Multicoloured. W* **61** *(sideways). P* 14½ × 14.

594	12 s. Type **176** ..	..	..	15	10
595	18 s. Apia Harbour	..	..	25	15
596	27 s. Aggie Grey's Hotel	..	..	25	20
597	32 s. Preparation for Ceremonial Kava	..	30	30
598	54 s. Piula water pool	..	..	55	55
594/8 ..	..	..	*Set of* 5	1·40	1·10

(Des J.W. Litho Walsall)

1981 (22 July). *Royal Wedding. T* **177** *and similar vert designs. Multicoloured. W* **61**. *P* 14.

599	18 s. Type **177** ..	..	..	25	10
600	32 s. Prince Charles as Colonel-in-Chief, Gordon Highlanders	..	35	20
601	$1 Prince Charles and Lady Diana Spencer	..	70	90
599/601	..	..	*Set of* 3	1·10	1·10

178 Tattooing Instruments **179** Black Marlin

(Des E. Roberts. Litho Cambec Press, Melbourne)

1981 (29 Sept). *Tattooing. T* **178** *and similar horiz designs. Multicoloured. P* 13½.

602	12 s. Type **178** ..	..	..	20	20
	a. Horiz strip of 4. Nos. 602/5	..	1·25	
603	18 s. First stage of tattooing ..	..	25	25
604	27 s. Progressive stage	..	..	30	30
605	$1 Completed tattoo ..	..	70	70
602/5 ..	..	..	*Set of* 4	1·25	1·25

Nos. 602/5 were printed together, *se-tenant*, in horizontal strips of 4 throughout the sheet.

(Des E. Roberts. Litho Cambec Press, Melbourne)

1981 (9 Oct). *"Philatokyo '81" International Stamp Exhibition, Tokyo. Sheet* 130 × 80 *mm. P* 14 × 13½.

| MS606 | **179** $2 multicoloured | .. | .. | 1·25 | 1·50 |

180 *Thespesia populnea* **181** George Washington's Pistol

(Des and litho J.W.)

1981 (30 Nov). *Christmas. Flowers. T* **180** *and similar vert designs. Multicoloured. W* **61**. *P* 13½.

607	11 s. Type **180** ..	..	..	15	10
608	15 s. Copper Leaf	..	..	20	15
609	23 s. *Allamanda cathartica*	..	30	25
610	$1 Mango	..	..	1·00	1·00
607/10	..	..	*Set of* 4	1·50	1·40
MS611	86 × 120 mm. Nos. 607/10	..	1·60	2·25

(Des J.W. Litho Format)

1982 (26 Feb). *250th Birth Anniv of George Washington. T* **181** *and similar horiz designs, each in black, ochre and stone. P* 13½.
612	23 s.	Type **181**	..	30	30
613	25 s.	Mount Vernon (Washington's house)	..	30	30
614	34 s.	George Washington	..	40	40
612/14			*Set of 3*	90	90
MS615	104 × 103 mm. $1 Washington taking Oath of Office as President			95	1·00

182 *Forum Samoa*
(container ship)

(Des E. Roberts. Litho Cambec Press, Melbourne)

1982 (24 May). *20th Anniv of Independence. T* **182** *and similar horiz designs. Multicoloured. P* 13½ × 14.
616	18 s.	Type **182**	..	30	20
617	23 s.	"Air services"	..	40	30
618	25 s.	N.P.F. (National Provident Fund) Building, Apia		40	30
619	$1	"Telecommunications"	..	1·10	1·00
616/19			*Set of 4*	2·00	1·60

183 Scouts map-reading and "75" 184 Boxing

(Des J.W. Litho Walsall)

1982 (20 July). *75th Anniv of Boy Scout Movement. T* **183** *and similar horiz designs. Multicoloured. W* **61** *(sideways). P* 14½.
620	5 s.	Type **183**	..	10	10
621	38 s.	Scout salute and "75"	..	40	40
622	44 s.	Scout crossing river by rope, and "75"	..	50	50
623	$1	"Tower" of Scouts and "75"	..	1·00	1·00
620/23			*Set of 4*	1·75	1·75
MS624	93 × 81 mm. $1 As No. 623 but with portrait of Lord Baden-Powell replacing emblem (47 × 35 mm). P 11			1·00	1·10

(Des Garden Studio. Litho Walsall)

1982 (20 Sept). *Commonwealth Games, Brisbane. T* **184** *and similar vert designs. Multicoloured. W* w **14.** *P* 14½.
625	23 s.	Type **184**	..	25	20
626	25 s.	Hurdling	..	25	20
627	34 s.	Weightlifting	..	35	40
628	$1	Bowling	..	95	1·75
625/8			*Set of 4*	1·60	2·25

185 "Mary and Joseph"   186 Satellite View of Australasia
(Emma Dunlop)

(Des J.W. Litho Questa)

1982 (15 Nov). *Christmas. Children's Pictures. T* **185** *and similar horiz designs. Multicoloured. W* **61** *(sideways). P* 14 × 14½.
629	11 s.	Type **185**	..	15	10
630	15 s.	"Mary, Joseph and baby Jesus" (Marie Tofaeono)	..	15	15
631	38 s.	"Madonna and Child" (Ralph Laban and Fetalaiga Fareni)	..	40	30
632	$1	"Mother and Child" (Panapa Pouesi)	..	90	1·10
629/32			*Set of 4*	1·40	1·50
MS633	130 × 119 mm. Nos. 629/32			1·60	2·25

(Des Walsall. Litho Enschedé)

1983 (23 Feb). *Commonwealth Day. T* **186** *and similar horiz designs. Multicoloured. W* w **14** *(sideways). P* 13 × 13½.
634	14 s.	Type **186**	..	10	10
635	29 s.	Flag of Samoa	..	15	20
636	43 s.	Harvesting copra	..	25	25
637	$1	Head of State Malietoa Tanumafili II	..	50	80
634/7			*Set of 4*	90	1·25

187 Douglas "DC-1"

(Des J.W. Litho Questa)

1983 (7 June). *Bicentenary of Manned Flight and 50th Anniv of Douglas Commercial Aircraft. Sheet,* 215 × 113 *mm, containing horiz designs as T* **187.** *Multicoloured. W* w **14** *(sideways). P* 14.
MS638	32 s. × 10, each design showing a different Douglas aircraft from the "DC-1" to the "DC-10"			2·50	2·75

188 Pole-vaulting   189 Lime

(Des McCombie Skinner Studio. Litho Format)

1983 (31 Aug). *South Pacific Games. T* **188** *and similar vert designs. Multicoloured. W* w **14.** *P* 14 × 14½.
639	8 s.	Type **188**	..	35	10
640	15 s.	Netball	..	45	20
641	25 s.	Tennis	..	70	50
642	32 s.	Weight-lifting	..	70	70
643	35 s.	Boxing	..	75	75
644	46 s.	Football	..	90	90
645	48 s.	Golf	..	1·00	1·10
646	56 s.	Rugby	..	1·10	1·25
639/46			*Set of 8*	5·50	5·00

(Des E. Roberts. Litho Enschedé)

1983 (28 Sept)–**84.** *Fruit. T* **189** *and similar vert designs. Multicoloured. W* w **14** *(inverted on 1 s.). P* 13½ *($2 to $5) or* 14 × 13½ *(others).*
647	1 s.	Type **189**	..	10	15
648	2 s.	Star fruit	..	10	20
649	3 s.	Mangosteen	..	10	20
650	4 s.	Lychee	..	10	20
651	7 s.	Passion fruit	..	10	20
652	8 s.	Mango	..	10	20
653	11 s.	Pawpaw	..	15	25
654	13 s.	Pineapple	..	20	30
655	14 s.	Breadfruit	..	20	30
656	15 s.	Banana	..	30	30
657	21 s.	Cashew Nut (30.11.83)	..	80	30
658	25 s.	Guava (30.11.83)	..	90	20
659	32 s.	Water Melon (30.11.83)	..	85	35
660	48 s.	Sasalapa (30.11.83)	..	1·00	60
661	56 s.	Avocado (30.11.83)	..	1·25	60
662	$1	Coconut (30.11.83)	..	1·40	1·00
663	$2	Vi Apple (11.4.84)	..	1·50	2·00
664	$4	Grapefruit (11.4.84)	..	2·00	3·25
665	$5	Orange (11.4.84)	..	2·50	3·50
647/65			*Set of 19*	12·00	13·00

Nos. 663/5 are larger, size 25 × 35½ mm.

Samoa $1

190 On Parade   191 Togitogiga Falls, Upolu

(Des Brian Melton Studio. Litho Format)

1983 (10 Oct). *Centenary of Boys' Brigade. Sheet* 120 × 83 *mm. W* w **14.** *P* 14.
MS668	**190** $1 multicoloured			2·50	2·00

(Litho Format)

1984 (15 Feb). *Scenic Views. T* **191** *and similar horiz designs. Multicoloured. W* w **14** *(sideways). P* 14.
669	25 s.	Type **191**	..	30	15
670	32 s.	Lano Beach, Savai'i	..	50	60
671	48 s.	Mulinu'u Point, Upolu	..	75	95
672	56 s.	Nu'utele Island	..	80	1·25
669/72			*Set of 4*	2·10	2·75

192 Apia Harbour   (193)

(Des Jennifer Toombs. Litho Questa)

1984 (24 May). *250th Anniv of "Lloyd's List" (newspaper). T* **192** *and similar vert designs. Multicoloured. W* w **14.** *P* 14 × 14½.
673	32 s.	Type **192**	..	25	20
674	48 s.	Apia hurricane, 1889	..	40	45
675	60 s.	*Forum Samoa* (container ship)	..	45	50
676	$1	*Matua* (cargo liner)	..	75	80
673/6			*Set of 4*	1·75	1·75

(Des J.W. Litho Questa)

1984 (7 June). *Universal Postal Union Congress, Hamburg. No.* 662 *optd with T* **193.**
677	$1	Coconut	..	1·10	80

194 Olympic Stadium

(Des Garden Studio. Litho Format)

1984 (26 June). *Olympic Games, Los Angeles. T* **194** *and similar horiz designs. Multicoloured. W* w **14** *(sideways). P* 14½.
678	25 s.	Type **194**	..	20	20
679	32 s.	Weightlifting	..	25	25
680	48 s.	Boxing	..	40	45
681	$1	Running	..	75	90
678/81			*Set of 4*	1·40	1·50
MS682	170 × 120 mm. Nos. 678/81			1·40	1·60

195 Nomad "N24" Aircraft

(Des E. Roberts. Litho Walsall)

1984 (21 Sept). *"Ausipex" International Stamp Exhibition, Melbourne. Sheet* 131 × 80 *mm. W* w **14** *(sideways). P* 14.
MS683	**195** $2.50, multicoloured			3·50	3·50

196 "Faith"

(Litho Walsall)

1984 (7 Nov). *Christmas. "The Three Virtues" (Raphael). T* **196** *and similar horiz designs. Multicoloured. W* w **14** *(sideways). P* 14.
684	25 s.	Type **196**	..	20	15
685	35 s.	"Hope"	..	25	20
686	$1	"Charity"	..	75	90
684/6			*Set of 3*	1·10	1·10
MS687	63 × 76 mm. Nos. 684/6			1·25	2·00

197 *Dendrobium biflorum*   198 Ford "Model A", 1903

(Des Jennifer Toombs. Litho Format)

1985 (23 Jan). *Orchids (1st series). T* **197** *and similar vert designs. Multicoloured. P* 14.
688	48 s.	Type **197**	..	55	35
689	56 s.	*Dendrobium vaupelianum* Kraenzl	..	65	45
690	67 s.	*Glomera montana*	..	80	60
691	$1	*Spathoglottis plicata*	..	1·10	1·10
688/91			*Set of 4*	2·75	2·25

See also Nos. 818/21.

(Des A. Theobald. Litho Walsall)

1985 (26 Mar). *Veteran and Vintage Cars. T* **198** *and similar horiz designs. Multicoloured. P* 14.
692	48 s.	Type **198**	..	60	35
693	56 s.	Chevrolet "Tourer", 1912	..	70	40
694	67 s.	Morris "Oxford", 1913	..	80	45
695	$1	Austin "Seven", 1923	..	1·00	70
692/5			*Set of 4*	2·75	1·75

199 *Dictyophora*   200 The Queen Mother at
indusiata   Liverpool Street Station

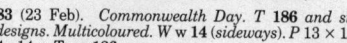

(Des Doreen McGuinness. Litho Walsall)

1985 (17 Apr). *Fungi.* T **199** *and similar vert designs. Multicoloured. P* 14½.

696	48 s. Type 199..				55	45
697	56 s. *Ganoderma tornatum*				70	55
698	67 s. *Mycena chlorophos*				90	75
699	$1 *Mycobonia flava*..				1·40	1·25
696/9	..	..	..	*Set of 4*	3·25	2·75

(Des A. Theobald ($2), C. Abbott (others). Litho Questa)

1985 (7 June). *Life and Times of Queen Elizabeth the Queen Mother.* T **200** *and similar vert designs. Multicoloured.* W w **16**. *P* 14½ × 14.

700	32 s. At Glamis Castle, aged 9			20	25
701	48 s. At Prince Henry's Christening with other members of the Royal family	..		30	35
702	56 s. Type 200..			35	40
703	$1 With Prince Henry at his christening (from photo by Lord Snowdon)..			65	70
700/3	..		*Set of 4*	1·40	1·50
MS704	91 × 73 mm. $2 Arriving at Tattenham Corner Station with the Queen. Wmk sideways..			2·00	1·50

201 Map of Pacific and Exhibition Logo   **202** I.Y.Y. Emblem and Map (Alaska—Arabian Gulf)

(Des D. Hartley. Litho Enschedé)

1985 (26 Aug). *"Expo '85" World Fair, Japan. Sheet* 70 × 45 *mm. P* 14.

MS705	201	$2 multicoloured	..	..	1·25	1·40

(Des Garden Studio. Litho B.D.T.)

1985 (18 Sept) *International Youth Year.* T **202** *and similar vert designs, showing background map and emblem* (Nos. 706 *and* 710) *or raised arms* (others). *Multicoloured P* 14.

706	60 s. Type 202..			40	45
	a. Horiz strip of 5. Nos. 706/10	..		1·75	
707	60 s. Raised arms (Pakistan–Mexico)		40	45
708	60 s. Raised arms (Central America–China)			40	45
709	60 s. Raised arms (Japan–Greenland)	..	40	45
710	60 s. As Type 202 (Iceland–Siberia)..		40	45
706/10	..	..	*Set of 5*	1·75	2·00

Nos. 706/10 were printed together, *se-tenant*, in horizontal strips of 5, throughout the sheet, the background forming a composite design of three continuous world maps.

203 "System"   **204** *Hypolimnas bolina*

(Des L. Curtis. Litho Format)

1985 (5 Nov). *Christmas.* T **203** *and similar vert designs showing illustrations by Millicent Sowerby for R. L. Stevenson's "A Child's Garden of Verses". Multicoloured. P* 14 × 14½.

711	32 s. Type 203..			20	25
712	48 s. "Time to Rise"			30	35
713	56 s. "Auntie's Skirts"			35	40
714	$1 "Good Children"			65	70
711/14	..		*Set of 4*	1·40	1·50
MS715	87 × 109 mm. Nos. 711/14	..		1·50	2·25

(Des Annette Robinson. Litho Walsall)

1986 (13 Feb). *Butterflies.* T **204** *and similar vert designs. Multicoloured.* W w **16**. *P* 14½ × 14.

716	25 s. Type 204			30	15
717	32 s. *Belenois java* ..			35	20
718	48 s. *Deudorix epijarbas*	..		55	35
719	56 s. *Badamia exclamationis*	..		60	40
720	60 s. *Danaus hamata*	..		60	40
721	$1 *Catochrysops taitensis*			90	65
716/21	..		*Set of 6*	3·00	1·90

205 Halley's Comet over Apia   **206** U.S.S. *Vincennes*

(Des N. Shewring. Litho Walsall)

1986 (24 Mar). *Appearance of Halley's Comet.* T **205** *and similar horiz designs. Multicoloured.* W w **16** (*sideways*). *P* 14 × 14½.

722	32 s. Type 205..			15	20
723	48 s. Edmond Halley..			30	35
724	60 s. Comet passing Earth	..		35	40
725	$2 Preparing *Giotto* spacecraft	..		1·10	1·25
722/5	..		*Set of 4*	1·75	2·00

(Des A. Theobald. Litho Questa)

1986 (21 Apr). *60th Birthday of Queen Elizabeth II. Vert designs as* T **230a** *of Jamaica. Multicoloured.* W w **16**. *P* 14½ × 14.

726	32 s. Engagement photograph, 1947	15	20
727	48 s. Queen with Liberty Bell, U.S.A., 1976..	30	35
728	56 s. At Apia, 1977		35	40
729	67 s. At Badminton Horse Trials, 1978	40	45
730	$2 At Crown Agents Head Office, London, 1983			
			1·10	1·25
726/30	*Set of 5*		2·10	2·40

(Des E. Nisbet. Litho Questa)

1986 (22 May). *"Ameripex '86" International Stamp Exhibition, Chicago.* T **206** *and similar horiz designs. Multicoloured. P* 14 × 14½.

731	48 s. Type 206..			30	35
732	56 s. Sikorsky "S-42" flying boat	..		35	40
733	60 s. U.S.S. *Swan*	..		35	40
734	$2 "Apollo 10" descending..	..		1·10	1·25
731/4	..		*Set of 4*	1·90	2·10

207 Vailima

(Des E. Roberts. Litho Cambec Press, Melbourne)

1986 (4 Aug). *"Stampex '86" Stamp Exhibition, Adelaide. Sheet* 158 × 97 *mm. P* 13½.

MS735	207	$3 multicoloured		..	3·00	3·00

208 Spotted Grouper

(Des P. Rymers. Litho Walsall)

1986 (13 Aug). *Fishes.* T **208** *and similar horiz designs. Multicoloured. P* 14.

736	32 s. Type 208..		..	30	20
737	48 s. Sabel Squirrelfish		..	50	35
738	60 s. Lunartail Grouper		..	55	40
739	67 s. Longtail Snapper		..	60	45
740	$1 Berndt's Soldierfish		..	85	65
736/40	..		*Set of 5*	2·50	1·90

209 Samoan Prime Ministers, American Presidents and Parliament House   **210** *Hibiscus rosa-sinensis* and Map of Samoa

(Des N. Shewring. Litho Format)

1986 (1 Dec). *Christmas. 25th Anniv of United States Peace Corps.* T **209** *and similar horiz design. Multicoloured. P* 14½.

741	45 s. Type 209..		..	25	30
742	60 s. French and American Presidents, Samoan Prime Minister and Statue of Liberty			35	40
MS743	131 × 72 mm. Nos. 741/2 ..		..	3·00	3·50

No. MS743 also commemorates the Centenary of the Statue of Liberty.

(Des local artist, adapted G. Vasarhelyi. Litho Format)

1987 (16 Feb). *25th Anniv of Independence.* T **210** *and similar multicoloured designs. P* 14½ × 14 ($2) *or* 14 × 14½ (*others*).

744	15 s. Type 210..			30	10
745	45 s. Parliament Building, Apia			50	30
746	60 s. Boat race at Independence celebration		65	40
747	70 s. Peace dove and laurel wreath ..		75	50
748	$2 Head of State Malietoa Tanumafili II and national flag (*horiz*)			
			1·60	1·75
744/8	..		*Set of 5*	3·50	2·75

NEW INFORMATION

The editor is always interested to correspond with people who have new information that will improve or correct the Catalogue.

211 Gulper (*Eurypharynx*)

(Des J. Walker. Litho Format)

1987 (31 Mar). *Deep Ocean Fishes.* T **211** *and similar horiz designs. Multicoloured. P* 14.

749	45 s. Type 211..		..	45	30
750	60 s. Hatchet Fish		..	50	35
751	70 s. Angler Fish		..	60	45
752	$2 Gulper (*Saccopharynx*)..		..	1·40	1·40
749/52			*Set of 4*	2·75	2·25

212 Workmen trimming Logs and building Fale (traditional house)

(Des Jennifer Toombs. Litho Questa)

1987 (13 June). *"Capex 87" International Stamp Exhibition, Toronto. Sheet* 122 × 66 *mm. P* 14½.

MS753	212	$3 multicoloured		..	1·60	1·75

213 Lefaga Beach, Upolu   **214** Abel Tasman

(Des D. Miller. Litho Questa)

1987 (29 July). *Coastal Scenery.* T **213** *and similar horiz designs. Multicoloured. P* 14.

754	45 s. Type 213..		..	45	30
755	60 s. Vaisala Beach, Savaii		..	55	35
756	70 s. Sololosolo Beach, Upolu ..		..	70	45
757	$2 Neiafu Beach, Savaii		..	1·60	1·25
754/7	..		*Set of 4*	3·00	2·10

(Des M. Bradbery. Litho Questa)

1987 (30 Sept). *Bicentenary of Australian Settlement* (1988) (*1st issue*). *Explorers of the Pacific.* T **214** *and similar horiz designs. Multicoloured. P* 14 × 14½.

758	40 s. Type 214..			30	25
759	45 s. Capt. James Cook	..		45	30
760	80 s. Comte Louis-Antoine de Bougainville			50	50
761	$2 Comte Jean de la Perouse			1·10	1·25
758/61	..		*Set of 4*	2·10	2·10
MS762	90 × 73 mm. No. 761	..		1·10	1·25

See also Nos. 768/72.

(**215**)   **216** Christmas Tree

1987 (16 Oct). *"Hafnia" International Stamp Exhibition, Copenhagen. No.* MS762 *optd with* T **215** *in red.*

MS763	90 × 73 mm. $2 Comte Jean de la Perouse ..		..	1·10	1·25

(Des Josephine Martin. Litho Questa)

1987 (30 Nov). *Christmas.* T **216** *and similar square designs. Multicoloured. P* 14.

764	40 s. Type 216..		..	20	25
765	45 s. Family going to church		..	25	30
766	50 s. Bamboo fire-gun		..	25	30
767	80 s. Inter-island transport ..		..	45	50
764/7	..		*Set of 4*	1·00	1·25

217 Samoa Coat of Arms and Australia Post Logo   **218** Airport Terminal and Airliner taking off

(Des A. Theobald. Litho Questa)

1988 (27 Jan). *Bicentenary of Australian Settlement (2nd issue). Postal Services. T* **217** *and similar vert designs. Multicoloured. P* 14½ × 14.

768	45 s. Type **217**..	55	40
	a. Horiz strip of 5. Nos. 768/72	2·50	
769	45 s. Samoan mail van and aircraft..	55	40
770	45 s. Loading mail plane	55	40
771	45 s. Australian mail van and aircraft	55	40
772	45 s. "Congratulations Australia" message on airmail letter	55	40
768/72	*Set of 5*	2·50	1·75

Nos. 768/72 were printed together, *se-tenant*, in horizontal strips of 5 throughout the sheet, Nos. 769/71 forming a composite design.

(Des E. Nisbet. Litho Walsall)

1988 (24 Mar). *Opening of Faleolo Airport. T* **218** *and similar horiz designs. Multicoloured. P* 13 × 13½.

773	40 s. Type **218**..	35	25
774	45 s. Boeing "727"	40	30
775	60 s. DHC "Twin Otter"	45	35
776	70 s. Boeing "737"	55	50
777	80 s. Boeing "727" and control tower	70	60
778	$1 "DC9" over "fale" (house)	80	70
773/8	*Set of 6*	3·00	2·40

219 "Expo '88" Pacific Islands Village

220 Mormon Temple, Apia

(Des C. Abbott. Litho Walsall)

1988 (30 Apr). *"Expo '88" World Fair, Brisbane. T* **219** *and similar horiz designs. Multicoloured. P* 14 × 14½.

779	45 s. Type **219**	25	30
780	70 s. Expo Complex and monorail	35	40
781	$2 Map of Australia showing Brisbane	1·00	1·10
779/81	*Set of 3*	1·40	1·60

(Des Jennifer Toombs. Litho CPE Australia Ltd, Melbourne)

1988 (9 June). *Centenary of Arrival of the Latter-Day Saints in Samoa. Sheet* 86 × 77 mm. P 13½.

MS782	**220** $3 multicoloured	1·50	1·60

221 Athletics

222 Spotted Triller

(Des D. Miller. Litho Format)

1988 (10 Aug). *Olympic Games, Seoul. T* **221** *and similar vert designs. Multicoloured. P* 14.

783	15 s. Type **221**	10	10
784	60 s. Weightlifting..	30	35
785	80 s. Boxing	40	45
786	$2 Olympic stadium	1·00	1·10
783/6	*Set of 4*	1·60	1·75
MS787	85 × 100 mm. Nos. 783/6	1·75	2·00

(Des D. Johnston. Litho CPE Australia Ltd, Melbourne (Nos. 788/97), Questa (Nos. 798/803))

1988 (17 Aug)–89. *Birds. Multicoloured.*

(a) Vert designs as T **222**. *P* 13½

788	10 s. Type **222**	10	10
789	15 s. Samoan Wood Rail	10	10
790	20 s. Flat-billed Kingfisher	10	15
791	25 s. Samoan Fantail	10	15
792	35 s. Scarlet Robin	15	20
793	40 s. Black-breasted Honeyeater ("Mao")	20	25
794	50 s. Cardinal Honeyeater ..	25	30
795	65 s. Yellow-fronted Whistler	30	35
796	75 s. Many-coloured Fruit Dove	35	40
797	85 s. White-throated Pigeon	40	45

(b) Horiz designs, each 45 × 28 mm. P 13½ × 14.

798	75 s. Silver Gull (28.2.89)	35	40
799	85 s. Great Frigate Bird (28.2.89)	40	45
800	90 s. Eastern Reef Heron (28.2.89)..	45	50
801	$3 Short-tailed Albatross (28.2.89)	1·50	1·60
802	$10 White Tern (31.7.89)	5·00	5·25
803	$20 Shy Albatross (31.7.89)	10·00	10·50
788/803	*Set of 16*	17·00	18·00

223 Forest

224 Congregational Church of Jesus, Apia

(Des G. Vasarhelyi. Litho Questa)

1988 (25 Oct). *National Conservation Campaign. T* **223** *and similar multicoloured designs. P* 14 × 13½ (15, 40, 45 s.) *or* 13½ × 14 *(others).*

807	15 s. Type **223**	15	10
808	40 s. Samoan handicrafts ..	30	25
809	45 s. Forest wildlife	35	30
810	50 s. Careful use of water *(horiz)*	40	30
811	60 s. Fishing *(horiz)*	45	35
812	$1 Coconut plantation *(horiz)*	70	60
807/12	*Set of 6*	2·10	1·75

(Des N. Shewring. Litho Format)

1988 (14 Nov). *Christmas. Samoan Churches. T* **224** *and similar vert designs. Multicoloured. P* 14.

813	15 s. Type **224**	10	10
814	40 s. Roman Catholic Church, Leauva'a	20	25
815	45 s. Congregational Christian Church, Moataa	25	30
816	$2 Baha'i Temple, Vailima	1·00	1·25
813/16	*Set of 4*	1·40	1·75
MS817	143 × 64 mm. Nos. 813/16	1·75	1·90

225 *Phaius flavus*

226 *Eber* (German warship)

(Des H. Bevan. Litho Questa)

1989 (31 Jan). *Orchids (2nd series). T* **225** *and similar vert designs. Multicoloured. P* 14 × 13½.

818	15 s. Type **225**	30	10
819	45 s. *Calanthe triplicata*	80	35
820	60 s. *Luisia teretifolia*	1·10	45
821	$3 *Dendrobium mohlianum*	2·75	2·25
818/21	*Set of 4*	4·50	2·75

(Des E. Nisbet. Litho Walsall)

1989 (16 Mar). *Centenary of Great Apia Hurricane. T* **226** *and similar horiz designs. Multicoloured. P* 14.

822	50 s. Type **226**	60	60
	a. Horiz strip of 4. Nos. 822/5	3·75	
823	65 s. *Olga* (German warship)	80	80
824	85 s. H.M.S. *Calliope* (screw corvette)	1·00	1·00
825	$2 U.S.S. *Vandalia*	1·75	1·75
822/5	*Set of 4*	3·75	3·75

Nos. 822/5 were printed together, *se-tenant*, in horizontal strips of 4 throughout the sheet.
See also No. MS839.

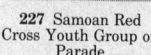
227 Samoan Red Cross Youth Group on Parade

228 Virgin Mary and Joseph

(Des L. Curtis. Litho Questa)

1989 (15 May). *125th Anniv of International Red Cross. T* **227** *and similar vert designs. Multicoloured. P* 14½ × 14.

826	50 s. Type **227**	50	40
827	65 s. Blood donors	70	55
828	75 s. Practising first aid	80	65
829	$3 Red Cross volunteers carrying patient	2·50	3·00
826/9	*Set of 4*	4·00	4·25

(Des A. Theobald ($3), D. Miller (others). Litho Questa)

1989 (20 July). *20th Anniv of First Manned Landing on Moon. Multicoloured designs as T* **126** *of Ascension. W w* **16** *(sideways on* 50, 65 c.). *P* 14×13½ (18 s., $2) *or* 14 *(others).*

830	18 s. Saturn rocket on mobile launcher	15	10
831	50 s. Crew of "Apollo 14" (30×30 mm)	30	30
832	65 s. "Apollo 14" emblem (30×30 mm)	45	55
833	$2 Tracks of lunar transporter	1·25	2·00
830/3	*Set of 4*	2·00	2·75
MS834	100×83 mm. $3 Aldrin with U.S. flag on Moon. P 14×13½	1·75	2·25

(Des T. Chance. Litho Cartor, France)

1989 (1 Nov). *Christmas. T* **228** *and similar horiz designs. Multicoloured. P* 13½.

835	18 s. Type **228**	10	10
836	50 s. Shepherds	30	30
837	55 s. Donkey and ox	35	35
838	$2 Three Wise Men	1·50	2·00
835/8	*Set of 4*	2·00	2·50

(Litho Walsall)

1989 (17 Nov). *"World Stamp Expo '89" International Stamp Exhibition, Washington. Sheet* 91×105 *mm containing designs as Nos.* 824/5. *Multicoloured. W* **61**. *Imperf.*

MS839	85 s. H.M.S. *Calliope*; $2 U.S.S. *Vandalia*	4·00	4·25

229 Pao Pao Outrigger

(Des R. Roberts. Litho Note Ptg Branch, Reserve Bank of Australia)

1990 (31 Jan). *Local Transport. T* **229** *and similar horiz designs. Multicoloured. P* 14×15.

840	18 s. Type **229**	15	15
841	55 s. Fautasi (large canoe)	35	40
842	60 s. Polynesian Airlines aircraft	40	45
843	$3 *Lady Samoa* (ferry)	1·75	2·00
840/3	*Set of 4*	2·40	2·75

230 Bismarck and Brandenburg Gate, Berlin

(Des G. Vasarhelyi. Litho Cartor, France)

1990 (19 Apr). *Treaty of Berlin, 1889, and Opening of Berlin Wall, 1989. T* **230** *and similar horiz design. Multicoloured. P* 14×13½.

844	75 s. Type **230**	1·00	1·00
	a. Horiz pair. Nos. 844/5	3·00	3·00
845	$3 *Adler* (German steam gunboat)	2·00	2·00

Nos. 844/5 were printed together, *se-tenant*, in horizontal pairs throughout the sheet, each pair forming a composite design showing Berliners on the Wall near the Brandenburg Gate.

231 Penny Black and Alexandra Palace, London

(Des G. Vasarhelyi. Litho Cartor, France)

1990 (3 May). *"Stamp World London 90" International Stamp Exhibition. P* 14×13½.

846	**231** $3 multicoloured	2·40	2·75

232 Visitors' Bureau

(Des D. Miller. Litho B.D.T.)

1990 (30 July). *Tourism. T* **232** *and similar horiz designs. Multicoloured. P* 14.

847	18 s. Type **232**	25	10
848	50 s. Village resort	45	35
849	65 s. Aggie's Hotel	60	50
850	$3 Swimming pool, Tusitala Hotel	2·25	2·50
847/50	*Set of 4*	3·25	3·00

233 1964 2nd Anniv of Treaty of Friendship 3 s. Commemorative and "NZ 1990" Logo

(Des N. Eustis. Litho Leigh-Mardon Ltd, Melbourne)

1990 (24 Aug). *"New Zealand 1990" International Stamp Exhibition, Auckland. Sheet 130×85 mm. P 13.*

MS851 **233** $3 multicoloured .. .. .. 2·10 2·25

234 "Virgin and Child" (Bellini)

235 William Draper III (administrator) and 40th Anniv Logo

(Des G. Vasarhelyi. Litho Security Printers (M), Malaysia)

1990 (31 Oct). *Christmas. Paintings. T 234 and similar vert designs. Multicoloured. P 12½.*

852	18 s. Type **234**	30	10
853	50 s. "Virgin and Child with St. Peter and St. Paul" (Bouts)	70	25
854	55 s. "School of Love" (Correggio)	75	30
855	$3 "Virgin and Child" (Cima)	3·00	3·50
852/5	*Set of 4*	4·25	3·75

The 55 s. value should have shown "The Madonna of the Basket" by the same artist and is so inscribed.

(Des D. Miller. Litho Cartor, France)

1990 (26 Nov). *40th Anniv of U.N. Development Programme. P 13½.*

856 **235** $3 multicoloured .. .. .. 2·00 2·25

236 Black-capped Lory

237 Peter Fatialofa (Samoan captain)

(Des R. Roberts. Litho B.D.T.)

1991 (8 Apr). *Parrots. T 236 and similar vert designs. Multicoloured. P 13½.*

857	18 s. Type **236**	20	10
858	50 s. Eclectus Parrot	45	35
859	65 s. Scarlet Macaw	55	40
860	$3 Palm Cockatoo	2·50	2·50
857/60	*Set of 4*	3·25	3·00

(Des D. Miller. Litho Questa)

1991 (17 June). *65th Birthday of Queen Elizabeth II and 70th Birthday of Prince Philip. Vert designs as T 58 of Kiribati. Multicoloured. W w 16 (sideways). P 14½×14.*

861	75 s. Prince Philip in the countryside	60	60
	a. Horiz pair. Nos. 861/2 separated by label	2·10	2·10
862	$2 Queen wearing yellow lei	1·50	1·50

Nos. 861/2 were printed together in a similar sheet format to Nos. 366/7 of Kiribati.

(Des G. Vasarhelyi. Litho Questa)

1991 (21 Oct). *World Cup Rugby Championships. Sheet 121×75 mm. P 14½×14.*

MS863 **237** $5 multicoloured .. .. .. 3·50 3·75

238 "O Come All Ye Faithful"

239 Herse convolvuli

(Des Jennifer Toombs. Litho Questa)

1991 (31 Oct). *Christmas. Carols (1st series). T 238 and similar horiz designs. Multicoloured. P 14×14½.*

864	20 s. Type **238**	25	15
865	60 s. "Joy to the World"	65	40
866	75 s. "Hark the Herald Angels sing"	75	50
867	$4 "We wish you a Merry Christmas"	3·00	3·50
864/7	*Set of 4*	4·25	4·00

See also Nos. 886/9.

(Des I. Loe. Litho Questa)

1991 (16 Nov). *"Phila Nippon '91" International Stamp Exhibition, Tokyo. Samoan Hawkmoths. T 239 and similar horiz designs. P 13½×14.*

868	60 s. Type **239**	70	60
869	75 s. Gnathothlibus erotus	80	70
870	85 s. Deilephila celerio	85	75
871	$3 Cephonodes armatus ..	2·50	2·75
868/71	*Set of 4*	4·25	4·25

240 Head of State inspecting Guard of Honour

241 Samoa Express 1d. Stamp, 1877

(Des G. Vasarhelyi and D. Miller. Litho Walsall)

1992 (8 Jan). *30th Anniv of Independence. T 240 and similar horiz designs. Multicoloured. P 14.*

872	50 s. Type **240**	40	30
873	65 s. Siva ceremony	50	40
874	$1 Commemorative float	80	80
875	$3 Raising Samoan flag	2·25	2·50
872/5	*Set of 4*	3·50	3·50

(Des D. Miller. Litho Questa ($3), Leigh-Mardon Ltd, Melbourne (others))

1992 (6 Feb). *40th Anniv of Queen Elizabeth II's Accession. Horiz designs as T 113 of Kenya. Multicoloured. W w 14 (sideways) ($3) or w 16 (sideways) (others). P 14.*

876	20 s. Queen and Prince Philip with umbrellas	20	10
877	60 s. Queen and Prince Philip on Royal Yacht..	45	35
878	75 s. Queen in multicoloured hat	55	40
879	85 s. Three portraits of Queen Elizabeth	65	50
880	$3 Queen Elizabeth II	2·00	2·50
876/80	*Set of 5*	3·50	3·50

(Des L. Curtis. Litho Questa)

1992 (17 Apr). *500th Anniv of Discovery of America by Columbus. Sheet 91×70 mm. P 14½×14.*

MS881 **241** $4 multicoloured .. .. 3·00 3·25

242 Weightlifting

243 Batfish

(Des D. Miller. Litho Questa)

1992 (28 July). *Olympic Games, Barcelona. T 242 and similar vert designs. Multicoloured. P 14.*

882	60 s. Type **242**	45	45
883	75 s. Boxing	50	50
884	85 s. Running	60	60
885	$3 Montjuic Olympic Stadium, Barcelona	2·00	2·25
882/5	*Set of 4*	3·25	3·50

(Des Jennifer Toombs. Litho Walsall)

1992 (28 Oct). *Christmas. Carols (2nd series). Horiz designs as T 238. Multicoloured. P 14×14½.*

886	50 s. "God rest you Merry Gentle-men"	40	40
887	60 s. "While Shepherds watched their Flocks by Night"	45	45
888	75 s. "Away in a Manger, no Crib for a Bed"	50	50
889	$4 "O little Town of Bethlehem"	2·75	3·00
886/9	*Set of 4*	3·75	4·00

(Des G. Drummond. Litho Walsall)

1993 (17 Mar). *Fishes. T 243 and similar horiz designs. Multicoloured. P 14.*

890	60 s. Type **243**	30	35
891	75 s. Lined Surgeonfish	35	40
892	$1 Red Tail Snapper	50	55
893	$3 Long Nosed Emperor	1·50	1·60
890/3	*Set of 4*	2·40	2·50

Sarawak
see Malaysia

Seychelles

Seychelles was administered as a dependency of Mauritius from 1810 until 1903, although separate stamp issues were provided from April 1890 onwards.

The first post office was opened, at Victoria on Mahé, on 11 December 1861 and the stamps of Mauritius were used there until 1890. No further post offices were opened until 1901.

Z 1

Stamps of MAURITIUS *cancelled with Type* Z 1.

1848–59
Z1   2d. blue (intermediate impression) (No. 14)   ..

1859–61.
Z2	6d. blue (No. 32)			£500
Z3	6d. dull purple-slate (No. 33)			£800
Z4	1s. vermilion (No. 34)			£600

1860–63. *(Nos. 45/53).*
Z 5	1d. purple-brown			£110
Z 6	2d. blue			£140
Z 7	4d. rose			£100
Z 8	6d. green			£375
Z 9	6d. slate			£275
Z10	9d. dull purple			70·00
Z11	1s. buff			£130
Z12	1s. green			£300

1862.
Z13	6d. slate (No. 54)			£600

1863–72. *(Nos. 56/72).*
Z14	1d. purple-brown			65·00
Z14a	1d. brown			55·00
Z15	1d. bistre			55·00
Z16	2d. pale blue			75·00
Z17	2d. bright blue			75·00
Z18	3d. deep red			85·00
Z19	3d. dull red			65·00
Z20	4d. rose			45·00
Z21	6d. dull violet			£150
Z22	6d. yellow-green			65·00
Z23	6d. blue-green			55·00
Z24	9d. yellow-green			£500
Z25	10d. maroon			£180
Z26	1s. yellow			85·00
Z27	1s. blue			£200
Z28	1s. orange			85·00
Z29	5s. rosy mauve			£425
Z30	5s. bright mauve			£425

1876. *(Nos. 76/7).*
Z31	½d. on 9d. dull purple			£160
Z32	½d. on 10d. maroon			£160

1877. *(Nos. 79/82).*
Z33	½d. on 10d. rose			
Z34	1d. on 4d. rose-carmine			
Z35	1s. on 5s. rosy mauve			
Z36	1s. on 5s. bright mauve			

1878. *(Nos. 83/91).*
Z37	2 c. dull rose (lower label blank)			50·00
Z38	4 c. on 1d. bistre			£200
Z39	8 c. on 2d. blue			35·00
Z40	13 c. on 3d. orange-red			75·00
Z41	17 c. on 4d. rose			35·00
Z42	25 c. on 6d. slate-blue			65·00
Z43	38 c. on 9d. pale violet			£150
Z44	50 c. on 1s. green			65·00
Z45	2 r. 50 on 5s. bright mauve			£190

1879–80. *(Nos. 92/100).*
Z46	2 c. Venetian red			£100
Z47	4 c. orange			£110
Z48	8 c. blue			30·00
Z49	13 c. slate			£550
Z50	17 c. rose			70·00
Z51	25 c. olive-yellow			£120
Z52	38 c. bright purple			£800
Z53	50 c. green			£425
Z54	2 r. 50, brown-purple			£550

1883–90.
Z55	2 c. Venetian red (No. 102)			65·00
Z56	2 c. green (No. 103)			£110
Z57	4 c. orange (No. 104)			55·00
Z58	4 c. carmine (No. 105)			65·00
Z59	16 c. chestnut (No. 109)			35·00
Z60	25 c. olive-yellow (No. 110)			75·00
Z61	50 c. orange (No. 111)			£375

1883.
Z62	16 c. on 17 c. rose (No. 112)			

1883.
Z63	16 c. on 17 c. rose (No. 115)			30·00

1885.
Z64	2 c. on 38 c. bright purple (No. 116)			

1887.
Z65	2 c. on 13 c. slate (No. 117)			

POSTAL FISCAL

1889.
ZR1	4 c. lilac (No. R2)			

We no longer list the G.B. 1862 6d. lilac with this obliteration as there is no evidence that the stamps of Great Britain were sold by the Victoria post office.

PRICES FOR STAMPS ON COVER TO 1945
Nos. 1/8	*from* × 10
Nos. 9/21	*from* × 20
Nos. 22/5	*from* × 6
Nos. 26/7	*from* × 8
Nos. 28/36	*from* × 5
Nos. 37/40	*from* × 30
Nos. 41/5	*from* × 6
Nos. 46/81	*from* × 5
Nos. 82/131	*from* × 3
Nos. 132/4	*from* × 10
Nos. 135/49	*from* × 3

DEPENDENCY OF MAURITIUS

PRINTERS. Nos. 1 to 123 were typographed by De La Rue & Co.

1

Die I   Die II

In Die I there are lines of shading in the middle compartment of the diadem which are absent from Die II.

1890 (5 April)**–92.** *Wmk Crown CA. P* 14. (i) *Die* I.
1	1	2 c. green and carmine			75	7·00
2		4 c. carmine and green			9·50	9·00
3		8 c. brown-purple and blue			3·50	3·50
4		10 c. ultramarine and brown			3·75	10·00
5		13 c. grey and black			4·50	9·00
6		16 c. chestnut and blue			2·00	2·75
7		48 c. ochre and green			16·00	16·00
8		96 c. mauve and carmine			38·00	45·00
1/8				*Set of* 8	70·00	90·00
1/8 Optd "Specimen"				*Set of* 8	£160	

(ii) *Die* II (1892)
9	1	2 c. green and rosine			65	90
10		4 c. carmine and green			90	85
11		8 c. brown-purple and ultramarine			2·75	1·40
12		10 c. bright ultramarine and brown			3·00	2·25
13		13 c. grey and black			85	1·50
14		16 c. chestnut and ultramarine			30·00	7·00
9/14				*Set of* 6	35·00	12·50

3 cents   **18 CENTS**   SEYCHELLES POSTAGE 1R.

(2)   (3)   4

1893 (1 Jan). *Surch locally as T* 2.
15	3 c. on 4 c. (No. 10)			85	1·25
	a. Surch inverted			£300	£375
	b. Surch double			£450	
	c. Surch omitted (in pair with normal)			£4250	
16	12 c. on 16 c. (No. 6)			1·00	3·50
	a. Surch inverted			£450	
	b. Surch double			—	£4000

17	12 c. on 16 c. (No. 14)			2·50	1·25
	a. Surch double			£3500	£3500
	b. Surch omitted (in pair with normal)				
18	15 c. on 16 c. (No. 6)			8·00	11·00
	a. Surch inverted			£300	£350
	b. Surch double			£800	£750
19	15 c. on 16 c. (No. 14)			7·00	2·00
	a. Surch inverted			£650	£650
	b. Surch double			£750	£800
	c. Surch treble			£2250	
*20	45 c. on 48 c. (No. 7)			8·50	4·00
21	90 c. on 96 c. (No. 8)			23·00	25·00
15/21			*Set of* 7	45·00	42·00

Nos. 15, 16, 18, 19 and 20 exist with "cents" omitted and with "cents" above value and are due to misplacement of the surcharge.

1893 (Nov). *New values. Die* II. *Wmk Crown CA. P* 14.
22	1	3 c. dull purple and orange		75	30
23		12 c. sepia and green		75	40
24		15 c. sage-green and lilac		3·25	2·00
25		45 c. brown and carmine		22·00	26·00
22/5			*Set of* 4	24·00	26·00
22/5 Optd "Specimen"			*Set of* 4	70·00	

1896 (1 Aug). *No. 25 surch as T* **3.**
26	1	18 c. on 45 c. brown and carmine		7·00	2·50
		a. Surch double		£1200	£1200
		b. Surch treble		£1400	
27		36 c. on 45 c. brown and carmine		10·00	35·00
		a. Surch double		£1100	
26/27 H/S "Specimen"			*Set of* 2	70·00	

Normal   Malformed "S"   Repaired "S"

The malformed "S" occurs on R. 7/3 of the left pane from Key Plate 2. It is believed that the repair to it took place in mid-1898. Both states may occur on other stamps in Types **1** and **4**. Stamps subsequently printed from Key Plate 3 showed the "S" normal.

1897–1900. *Colours changed and new values. Die* II. *Wmk Crown CA. P* 14.
28	1	2 c. orange-brown and green (1900)		40	45
		a. Repaired "S"		90·00	
29		6 c. carmine (1900)		2·25	40
		a. Repaired "S"		£130	
30		15 c. ultramarine (1900)		2·50	2·50
		a. Repaired "S"		£140	
31		18 c. ultramarine		1·60	90
32		36 c. brown and carmine		15·00	4·00
33	4	75 c. yellow and violet (1900)		35·00	60·00
		a. Repaired "S"		£225	
34		1 r. bright mauve and deep red		8·50	3·50
		a. Repaired "S"		£250	
35		1 r. 50, grey and carmine (1900)		48·00	75·00
		a. Repaired "S"		£250	
36		2 r. 25, bright mauve and green (1900)		55·00	75·00
		a. Repaired "S"		£250	
28/36			*Set of* 9	£150	£190
28/36 Optd "Specimen"			*Set of* 9	£160	

3 cents

6 cents

(5)   (5a)

1901 (21 June–Oct). *Surch locally with T* 5 *or* 5a.
37	3 c. on 10 c. bright ultramarine and brown (No. 12) (10.01)			30	60
	a. Surch double			£600	
	b. Malformed "S"			85·00	
38	3 c. on 16 c. chestnut and ultramarine (No. 14) (8.01)			30	85
	a. Surch inverted			£600	£600
	b. Surch double			£500	
	c. "3 cents" omitted			£500	£550
39	3 c. on 36 c. brown and carmine (No. 32)			30	50
	a. Surch double			£650	£800
	b. "3 cents" omitted			£550	£650
40	6 c. on 8 c. brown-purple and ultramarine (No. 11) (8.01)			30	1·50
	a. Surch inverted			£650	£750
37/40			*Set of* 4	1·00	3·00
37/40 H/S "Specimen"			*Set of* 4	£100	

1902 (June). *Surch locally as T* 5.
41	1	2 c. on 4 c. carmine and green (No. 10)		90	2·75
42	4	30 c. on 75 c. yellow and violet (No. 33)		80	4·00
		a. Narrow "0" in "30" (R. 3/6, 5/2-4)		10·00	40·00
		b. Repaired "S"		£120	
43		30 c. on 1 r. bright mauve & dp red (No. 34)		3·25	17·00
		a. Narrow "0" in "30" (R. 3/6, 5/2-4)		20·00	70·00
		b. Surch double		£850	
44		45 c. on 1 r. bright mauve & dp red (No. 34)		3·50	17·00
		a. Surch double		£650	
45		45 c. on 2 r. 25, brt mauve & grn (No. 36)		22·00	38·00
		a. Narrow "5" in "45" (R. 4/1)		£110	£180
		b. Repaired "S"		£190	
41/5			*Set of* 5	27·00	70·00
41/5 H/S "Specimen"			*Set of* 5	£110	

3 cents

6   **7**   **(8)**

Dented frame (R. 1/6 of left pane)

1903 (26 May). *Wmk Crown CA. P 14.*

46	6	2 c. chestnut and green	..	60	40
		a. Dented frame	..	30·00	
47		3 c. dull green	..	1·00	1·25
		a. Dented frame	..	35·00	
48		6 c. carmine	..	1·50	30
		a. Dented frame	..	42·00	
49		12 c. olive-sepia and dull green		1·50	1·25
		a. Dented frame	..	45·00	
50		15 c. ultramarine ..	..	3·25	1·25
		a. Dented frame	..	65·00	
51		18 c. sage-green and carmine		3·00	6·00
		a. Dented frame	..	65·00	
52		30 c. violet and dull green		5·50	8·50
		a. Dented frame	..	75·00	
53		45 c. brown and carmine	..	7·00	11·00
		a. Dented frame	..	£100	
54	7	75 c. yellow and violet	..	9·00	17·00
		a. Dented frame	..	£110	
55		1 r. 50, black and carmine		32·00	50·00
		a. Dented frame	..	£170	
56		2 r. 25, purple and green	..	24·00	60·00
		a. Dented frame	..	£160	
46/56			Set of 11	80·00	£140
46/56 Optd "Specimen" ..			Set of 11	£180	

1903. *Surch locally with T 8.*

57	6	3 c. on 15 c. ultramarine (3.7)		55	1·25
		a. Dented frame	..	50·00	
58		3 c. on 18 c. sage-green and carmine (2.9)		1·75	22·00
		a. Dented frame	..	90·00	
59		3 c. on 45 c. brown and carmine (21.7)		70	1·50
		a. Dented frame	..	55·00	
57/9			Set of 3	2·75	22·00
57/9 H/S "Specimen" ..			Set of 3	80·00	

CROWN COLONY

The Seychelles became a Separate Crown Colony by Letters Patent dated 31 August 1903.

1906. *Wmk Mult Crown CA. P 14.*

60	6	2 c. chestnut and green		50	1·75
		a. Dented frame	..	30·00	
61		3 c. dull green	..	70	30
		a. Dented frame	..	35·00	
62		6 c. carmine	..	1·00	15
		a. Dented frame	..	38·00	
63		12 c. olive-sepia and dull green		3·00	1·25
		a. Dented frame	..	65·00	
64		15 c. ultramarine ..	..	1·60	2·00
		a. Dented frame	..	50·00	
65		18 c. sage-green and carmine		3·00	5·50
		a. Dented frame	..	60·00	
66		30 c. violet and dull green		6·00	7·50
		a. Dented frame	..	£110	
67		45 c. brown and carmine	..	3·00	5·00
		a. Dented frame	..	£100	
68	7	75 c. yellow and violet	..	8·50	38·00
		a. Dented frame	..	£130	
69		1 r. 50, black and carmine		38·00	35·00
		a. Dented frame	..	£180	
70		2 r. 25, purple and green	..	30·00	35·00
		a. Dented frame	..	£170	
60/70	..	.. ..	Set of 11	85·00	£120

9   **10**

1912 (Apr)–**13.** *Wmk Mult Crown CA. P 14.*

71	9	2 c. chestnut and green ..		20	1·10
		a. Split "A"	..	22·00	
72		3 c. green	..	35	40
		a. Split "A"	..	32·00	
73		6 c. aniline carmine (6.13)		8·50	4·50
		a. Carmine-red	..	2·25	45
		b. Split "A"	..	60·00	
74		12 c. olive-sepia and dull green (1.13)		80	3·50
		a. Split "A"	..	38·00	
75		15 c. ultramarine	..	1·25	40
		a. Split "A"	..	45·00	
76		18 c. sage-green and carmine (1.13)		1·25	3·50
		a. Split "A"	..	45·00	
77		30 c. violet and green (1.13)		5·00	1·25
		a. Split "A"	..	75·00	
78		45 c. brown and carmine (1.13)		2·50	24·00
		a. Split "A"	..	55·00	
79	10	75 c. yellow and violet (1.13) ..		2·50	5·50
		a. Split "A"	..	60·00	

80	10	1 r. 50, black and carmine (1.13)		5·50	85
		a. Split "A"	..	95·00	
81		2 r. 25, rose-purple and green (1.13)		55·00	55·00
		a. Bright purple and green	..	30·00	2·50
		b. Split "A"	..	£200	
71/81a		.. .. ..	Set of 11	45·00	38·00
71/81 Optd "Specimen"			Set of 11	£180	

For illustration of "Split A" flaw see above St. Helena No. 83.

11   **12**   **13**

1917–22. *Wmk Mult Crown CA. Chalk-surfaced paper (18 c. to 5 r.). P 14.*

82	11	2 c. chestnut and green	..	15	1·00
83		3 c. green	..	65	40
84	12	5 c. deep brown (1920)	..	70	2·75
85	11	6 c. carmine	..	65	50
		a. Rose (1919)	..	3·50	80
86		12 c. grey (1919)	..	30	1·00
87		15 c. ultramarine	..	30	85
88		18 c. purple/yellow (1919)		1·75	13·00
		a. On orange-buff (1920)	..	13·00	45·00
		b. On pale yellow (Die II) (1922)		75	13·00
89	13	25 c. black and red/yellow		1·50	16·00
		a. On orange-buff (1920)	..	38·00	65·00
		b. On pale yellow (Die II) (1922)		1·00	5·50
90	11	30 c. dull purple and olive		1·50	5·50
91		45 c. dull purple and orange (1919)		3·00	19·00
92	13	50 c. dull purple and black (1920)		3·00	12·00
93		75 c. black/blue-green (olive back)		1·25	8·00
		a. On emerald back (Die II) (1922)		1·40	14·00
94		1 r. dull purple and red (1920)		7·00	24·00
95		1 r. 50, reddish purple and blue/blue		9·00	35·00
		a. Blue-pur & blue/blue (Die II) (1922)		9·00	26·00
96		2 r. 25, yellow-green and violet		29·00	90·00
97		5 r. green and blue (1920)		48·00	£150
82/97			Set of 16	95·00	£325
82/97 Optd "Specimen"			Set of 16	£250	

1921–32. *Wmk Mult Script CA. Chalk-surfaced paper (18 c. and 25 c. to 5 r.). P 14.*

98	11	2 c. chestnut and green		10	15
99		3 c. green	..	30	15
100		3 c. black (1922)	..	50	30
101		4 c. green (1922)	..	70	65
102		4 c. sage-green and carmine (1928)		3·50	10·00
103	12	5 c. deep brown	..	75	3·00
104	11	6 c. carmine	..	1·25	5·00
105		6 c. deep mauve (1922)		30	10
106	13	9 c. red (1927)	..	1·25	2·75
107	11	12 c. grey (Die II)	..	50	15
108		12 c. carmine-red (1922)		45	15
109		12 c. grey (Die I) (1932)		3·75	65
110		15 c. bright blue	..	2·00	42·00
111		15 c. yellow (1922)	..	50	2·50
112		18 c. purple/pale yellow (1925)		2·00	7·00
113	13	20 c. bright blue (1922)		1·25	35
		a. Dull blue (1926)	..	4·00	55
114		25 c. black and red/pale yellow (1925)		2·50	6·00
115	11	30 c. dull purple and olive		80	8·50
116		45 c. dull purple and orange		80	5·00
117	13	50 c. dull purple and black		90	2·25
118		75 c. black/emerald (1924)		7·50	15·00
119		1 r. dull purple and red (Die II)		7·00	17·00
120		1 r. dull purple and red (Die I) (1932)		12·00	30·00
121		1 r. 50, purple and blue/blue (1924)		8·00	15·00
122		2 r. 25, yellow-green and violet		8·00	13·00
123		5 r. yellow-green and blue		48·00	95·00
98/123			Set of 24	80·00	£225
98/123 Optd "Specimen"			Set of 24	£350	

The 3 c. green and 12 c. grey (Die II) were reissued in 1927. "Specimens" of these also exist.

1935 (6 May). *Silver Jubilee. As Nos. 114/17 of Jamaica. P 11×12.*

128		6 c. ultramarine and grey-black		70	50
		a. Extra flagstaff	..	£160	
		b. Short extra flagstaff ..	..	£110	
		c. Lightning conductor	..	£110	
		d. Flagstaff on right-hand turret	..	£110	
		e. Double flagstaff	..	£110	
129		12 c. green and indigo	..	2·00	30
		a. Extra flagstaff	..	£2500	£2500
		b. Short extra flagstaff ..	..	£150	
		c. Lightning conductor	..	£500	
		d. Flagstaff on right-hand turret	..	£150	
		e. Double flagstaff	..	£150	
130		20 c. brown and deep blue		2·00	40
		a. Extra flagstaff	..	£200	
		b. Short extra flagstaff ..	..	£130	
		c. Lightning conductor	..	£130	
		d. Flagstaff on right-hand turret	..	£130	
		e. Double flagstaff	..	£130	
131		1 r. slate and purple	..	3·00	7·75
		a. Extra flagstaff	..	£150	
		b. Short extra flagstaff ..	..	£150	
		c. Lightning conductor	..	£100	
		d. Flagstaff on right-hand turret	..	£150	
128/31			Set of 4	7·00	8·00
128/31 Perf "Specimen"			Set of 4	80·00	

For illustrations of plate varieties see Omnibus section following Zimbabwe.

1937 (12 May). *Coronation. As Nos. 118/20 of Jamaica, but ptd by B.W. P 11×11½.*

132		6 c. sage-green	..	35	15
133		12 c. orange	..	50	30
134		20 c. blue	..	70	50
132/4			Set of 3	1·40	85
132/4 Perf "Specimen"			Set of 3	55·00	

14 Coco-de-mer Palm   15 Giant Tortoise

16 Fishing Pirogue

(Photo Harrison)

1938 (1 Jan)–**49.** *Wmk Mult Script CA. Chalk-surfaced paper. P 14½×13½ (vert) or 13½×14½ (horiz).*

135	14	2 c. purple-brown (10.2.38)		45	30
		a. Ordinary paper (18.11.42)		20	40
136	15	3 c. green	..	4·50	1·25
136a		3 c. orange (8.8.41)	..	55	40
		a. Ordinary paper (18.11.42)		55	60
137	16	6 c. orange	..	4·25	2·50
137a		6 c. greyish green (8.8.41)		2·00	55
		ab. Ordinary paper. Green (18.11.42)		40	50
		ac. Green (5.4.49)	..	1·25	65
138	14	9 c. scarlet (10.2.38)	..	8·00	1·75
138a		9 c. grey-blue (8.8.41)		1·25	30
		ab. Ordinary paper (18.11.42)		60	60
		ac. Ordinary paper. Dull bl (19.11.45)		2·00	1·00
		ad. Dull blue (5.4.49) ..		2·25	1·25
139	15	12 c. reddish violet	..	28·00	85
139a		15 c. brown-carmine (8.8.41)		1·50	30
		a. Ordinary paper. Brn-red (18.11.42)		70	60
139c	14	18 c. carmine-lake (8.8.41)		2·25	40
		ca. Ordinary paper (18.11.42)		1·50	1·25
		cb. Rose-carmine (5.4.49)		2·25	1·75
140	16	20 c. blue	..	35·00	5·50
140a		20 c. brown-ochre (8.8.41)		1·75	30
		ab. Ordinary paper (18.11.42)		85	55
141	14	25 c. brown-ochre	..	50·00	11·00
142	15	30 c. carmine (10.2.38) ..		60·00	6·50
142a		30 c. blue (8.8.41)	..	1·75	40
		ab. Ordinary paper (18.11.42)		40	1·00
143	16	45 c. chocolate (10.2.38)		2·25	75
		a. Ordinary paper. Pur-brn (18.11.42)		1·00	1·00
		b. Purple-brown (5.4.49)		2·75	2·00
144	14	50 c. deep reddish violet (10.2.38)		2·25	40
		a. Ordinary paper (18.11.42)		30	1·00
144b		50 c. bright lilac (13.6.49)		40	1·25
145	15	75 c. slate-blue (10.2.38)		80·00	38·00
145a		75 c. deep slate-lilac (8.8.41)		2·00	90
		ab. Ordinary paper (18.11.42)		60	90
146	16	1 r. yellow-green (10.2.38)		95·00	48·00
146a		1 r. grey-black (8.8.41)		1·50	60
		ab. Ordinary paper (18.11.42)		1·00	1·25
147	14	1 r. 50, ultramarine (10.2.38)		4·00	1·00
		a. Ordinary paper (18.11.42)		2·00	1·25
148	15	2 r. 25, olive (10.2.38)		5·50	4·00
		a. Ordinary paper (18.11.42)		3·75	4·50
149	16	5 r. red (10.2.38)	..	4·50	3·00
		a. Ordinary paper (18.11.42)		8·50	7·00
135/49			Set of 25	£350	£120
135/49 (excl No. 144b) Perf "Specimen"			Set of 24	£350	

Lamp on mast flaw (R. 1/5)

1946 (23 Sept). *Victory. As Nos. 141/2 of Jamaica.*

150		9 c. light blue	..	10	10
151		30 c. deep blue	..	10	10
		a. Lamp on mast flaw	..	10·00	
150/1 Perf "Specimen"			Set of 2	50·00	

1948 (5 Nov). *Royal Silver Wedding. As Nos. 143/4 of Jamaica.*

152		9 c. ultramarine	..	15	25
153		5 r. carmine	..	7·00	12·00

1949 (10 Oct). *75th Anniv of U.P.U. As Nos. 145/8 of Jamaica, but inscribed "SEYCHELLES" in recess.*

154		18 c. bright reddish purple		15	15
155		50 c. purple	..	35	40
156		1 r. grey	..	30	15
157		2 r. 25, olive	..	50	40
154/7	..		Set of 4	1·10	1·00

PRICES OF SETS

Set prices are given for many issues, generally those containing three stamps or more. Definitive sets include one of each value or major colour change, but do not cover different perforations, die types or minor shades. Where a choice is possible the set prices are based on the cheapest versions of the stamps included in the listings.

SEYCHELLES — 1952

17 Sail-fish

18 Map of Indian Ocean

(Photo Harrison)

1952 (3 Mar). *Various designs as T* **14/16** *but with new portrait and crown as in T* **17/18**. *Chalk-surfaced paper. Wmk Mult Script CA. P* 14½ × 13½ (*vert*) *or* 13½ × 14½ (*horiz*).

158	**17**	2 c. lilac			50	60
		a. Error. Crown missing, W **9***a*			£250	
		b. Error. St. Edward's Crown, W **9***b*			90·00	
159	**15**	3 c. orange			50	30
		a. Error. Crown missing, W **9***a*			£225	
		b. Error. St. Edward's Crown, W **9***b*			85·00	
160	**14**	9 c. chalky blue			50	50
		a. Error. Crown missing, W **9***a*			£350	
		b. Error. St. Edward's Crown, W **9***b*			£140	
161	**16**	15 c. deep yellow-green			40	65
		a. Error. Crown missing, W **9***a*			£300	
		b. Error. St. Edward's Crown, W **9***b*			£140	
162	**18**	18 c. carmine-lake			65	20
		a. Error. Crown missing, W **9***a*			£375	
		b. Error. St. Edward's Crown, W **9***b*			£160	
163	**16**	20 c. orange-yellow			90	60
		a. Error. Crown missing, W **9***a*			£400	
		b. Error. St. Edward's Crown, W **9***b*			£200	
164	**15**	25 c. vermilion			70	70
		a. Error. Crown missing, W **9***a*			£400	
		b. Error. St. Edward's Crown, W **9***b*			£190	
165	**17**	40 c. ultramarine			60	80
		a. Error. Crown missing, W **9***a*			£425	
		b. Error. St. Edward's Crown, W **9***b*			£225	
166	**16**	45 c. purple-brown			60	30
		a. Error. Crown missing, W **9***a*			£475	
		b. Error. St. Edward's Crown, W **9***b*			£275	
167	**14**	50 c. reddish violet			1·25	60
		a. Error. Crown missing, W **9***a*			£550	
		b. Error. St. Edward's Crown, W **9***b*			£275	
168	**18**	1 r. grey-black			2·00	1·50
		b. Error. St. Edward's Crown, W **9***b*			£550	
169	**14**	1 r. 50, blue			4·00	6·50
		b. Error. St. Edward's Crown, W **9***b*			£650	
170	**15**	2 r. 25, brown-olive			4·50	8·00
		b. Error. St. Edward's Crown, W **9***b*			£600	
171	**18**	5 r. red			4·50	11·00
		b. Error. St. Edward's Crown, W **9***b*			£500	
172	**17**	10 r. green			9·00	15·00
158/72				*Set of 15*	28·00	42·00

See *Introduction* re the watermark errors.

1953 (2 June). *Coronation. As No. 153 of Jamaica.*

173		9 c. black and deep bright blue			15	20

19 Sail-fish

20 Seychelles Flying Fox

(Photo Harrison)

1954 (1 Feb)**–61**. *Designs previously used for King George VI issue, but with portrait of Queen Elizabeth II, as in T* **19** *and T* **20**. *Chalk-surfaced paper. Wmk Mult Script CA. P* 14½ × 13½ (*vert*) *or* 13½ × 14½ (*horiz*).

174	**19**	2 c. lilac			10	10
175	**–**	3 c. orange			10	10
175*a*	**20**	5 c. violet (25.10.57)			30	30
176	**–**	9 c. chalky blue			10	10
176*a*	**–**	10 c. chalky blue (15.9.56)			30	40
		ab. Blue (11.7.61)			2·50	1·25
177	**–**	15 c. deep yellow-green			15	15
178	**–**	18 c. crimson			10	10
179	**–**	20 c. orange-yellow			30	20
180	**–**	25 c. vermilion			60	70
180*a*	**–**	35 c. crimson (15.9.56)			1·75	90
181	**19**	40 c. ultramarine			30	25
182	**–**	45 c. purple-brown			20	15
183	**–**	50 c. reddish violet			30	20
183*a*	**–**	70 c. purple-brown (15.9.56)			1·75	1·25
184	**–**	1 r. grey-black			50	40
185	**–**	1 r. 50, blue			3·25	2·75
186	**–**	2 r. 25, brown-olive			3·25	6·50
187	**–**	5 r. red			13·00	7·00
188	**19**	10 r. green			24·00	17·00
174/88				*Set of 19*	45·00	35·00

Designs: *Horiz*—15 c., 20 c., 45 c., 70 c. Fishing pirogue; 18 c., 35 c., 1 r., 5 r. Map of Indian Ocean. *Vert*—3 c., 25 c., 2 r. 25, Giant Tortoise; 9 c., 50 c., 1 r. 50, Coco de Mer Palm.

21 "La Pierre de Possession"

(**22**)

(Photo Harrison)

1956 (15 Nov). *Bicentenary of "La Pierre de Possession". Wmk Mult Script CA. P* 14½ × 13½.

189	**21**	40 c. ultramarine			10	10
190		1 r. black			10	10

| 191 | 191a | 191 | 191b | 191 | 191c |

1957 (16 Sept). *No. 182 surch with T* **22**.

191		5 c. on 45 c. purple-brown			10	10
		a. Italic "e"			3·00	
		b. Italic "s"			3·00	
		c. Italic "c"			2·50	
		d. Thick bars omitted			£475	
		e. Surch double			£225	

23 Mauritius 6d. Stamp with Seychelles "B 64" Cancellation

(Recess: cancellation typo B.W.)

1961 (11 Dec). *Centenary of First Seychelles Post Office. W w* **12**. *P* 11½.

193	**23**	10 c. blue, black and purple			15	10
194		35 c. blue, black and myrtle-green			25	10
195		2 r. 25, blue, black and orange-brown			60	35
193/5				*Set of 3*	90	40

24 Black Parrot

29 Anse Royale Bay

40 Colony's Badge

(Des V. Whiteley. Photo Harrison)

1962 (21 Feb)**–68**. *T* **24**, **29**, **40** *and similar designs. W w* **12** (*upright*). *P* 13½ × 14½ (*horiz designs and* 10 *r.*) *or* 14½ × 13½ (*others*).

196		5 c. multicoloured			30	10
197		10 c. multicoloured			80	10
198		15 c. multicoloured			10	10
199		20 c. multicoloured			10	10
200		25 c. multicoloured			10	10
200*a*		30 c. multicoloured (15.7.68)			2·25	90
201		35 c. multicoloured			1·50	2·00
202		40 c. multicoloured			20	50
203		45 c. multicoloured (1.8.66)			3·50	3·25
204		50 c. multicoloured			25	25
205		70 c. ultramarine and light blue			5·50	3·00
206		75 c. multicoloured (1.8.66)			2·00	2·75
207		1 r. multicoloured			30	10
208		1 r. 50, multicoloured			4·00	5·00
209		2 r. 25, multicoloured			4·00	3·00
210		3 r. 50, multicoloured			2·25	4·50
211		5 r. multicoloured			3·50	2·50
212		10 r. multicoloured			11·00	4·50
196/212				*Set of 18*	38·00	29·00

Designs: *Vert* (*as T* **24**)—10 c. Vanilla vine; 15 c. Fisherman; 20 c. Denis Island lighthouse; 25 c. Clock Tower, Victoria; 50 c. Cascade Church; 70 c. Sail-fish; 75 c. Coco-de-Mer palm. *Horiz* (*as T* **29**)—30 c., 35 c. Anse Royale Bay; 40 c. Government House; 45 c. Fishing pirogue; 1 r. Cinnamon; 1r. 50, Copra; 2r. 25 Map; 3r. 50, Land settlement; 5 r. Regina Mundi convent.

The 1 r. exists with PVA gum as well as gum arabic, but the 30 c. exists with PVA gum only.

See also Nos. 233/7.

For stamps of the above issue overprinted "B.I.O.T" see under British Indian Ocean Territory.

1963 (4 June). *Freedom from Hunger. As No. 80 of Lesotho.*

213		70 c. reddish violet		60	25

1963 (16 Sept). *Red Cross Centenary. As Nos. 203/4 of Jamaica.*

214		10 c. red and black		25	10
215		75 c. red and blue		75	40

---

45 CENTS

(**41**)

42 Seychelles Flying Fox

1965 (15 Apr). *Nos. 201 and 205 surch as T* **41**.

216		45 c. on 35 c. multicoloured		10	15
217		75 c. on 70 c. ultramarine and light blue		20	15

1965 (1 June). *I.T.U. Centenary. As Nos. 98/9 of Lesotho.*

218		5 c. orange and ultramarine		15	10
219		1 r. 50, mauve and apple-green		65	25

1965 (25 Oct). *International Co-operation Year. As Nos. 100/1 of Lesotho.*

220		5 c. reddish purple and turquoise-green		10	10
221		40 c. deep bluish green and lavender		20	20

1966 (24 Jan). *Churchill Commemoration. As Nos. 102/5 of Lesotho.*

222		5 c. new blue		15	10
223		15 c. deep green		40	10
224		75 c. brown		80	10
225		1 r. 50, bluish violet		1·25	60
222/5			*Set of 4*	2·25	80

1966 (1 July). *World Cup Football Championships. As Nos. 57/8 of Pitcairn Islands.*

226		15 c. violet, yellow-green, lake & yellow-brn		10	10
227		1 r. chocolate, blue-green, lake & yellow-brn		20	20

1966 (20 Sept). *Inauguration of W.H.O. Headquarters, Geneva. As Nos. 185/6 of Montserrat.*

228		20 c. black, yellow-green and light blue		15	10
229		50 c. black, light purple and yellow-brown		25	20

1966 (1 Dec). *20th Anniv of U.N.E.S.C.O. As Nos. 342/4 of Mauritius.*

230		5 c. slate-violet, red, yellow and orange		25	10
231		1 r. orange-yellow, violet and deep olive		45	10
232		5 r. black, bright purple and orange		1·25	1·00
230/2			*Set of 3*	1·75	1·00

1967–69. *As Nos. 196/7, 204 and new values as T* **42** *but wmk w* **12** (*sideways*).

233		5 c. multicoloured (7.2.67)		35	60
234		10 c. multicoloured (4.6.68)		25	15
235		50 c. multicoloured (13.5.69)		1·75	2·50
236		60 c. red, blue and blackish brown (15.7.68)		1·75	45
237		85 c. ultramarine and light blue (as No. 205) (15.7.68)		90	40
233/7			*Set of 5*	4·50	3·75

The 10 c. exists with PVA gum as well as gum arabic, but the 50 c. to 85 c. exist with PVA gum only.

UNIVERSAL ADULT SUFFRAGE 1967

(**43**)

44 Cowrie Shells

1967 (18 Sept). *Universal Adult Suffrage. As Nos. 198 and 206, but W w* **12** (*sideways*), *and Nos. 203 and 210* (*wmk upright*), *optd with T* **43**.

238		15 c. multicoloured		10	10
		a. Opt double			
239		45 c. multicoloured		10	10
240		75 c. multicoloured		10	10
241		3 r. 50, multicoloured		20	15
238/41			*Set of 4*	30	30

(Des V. Whiteley. Photo Harrison)

1967 (4 Dec). *International Tourist Year. T* **44** *and similar horiz designs. Multicoloured. W w* **12**. *P* 14 × 13.

242		15 c. Type **44**		15	10
243		40 c. Cone Shells		20	10
244		1 r. Arthritic Spider Conch		25	10
245		2 r. 25, Subulate Auger and Triton Shells		55	45
242/5			*Set of 4*	1·00	45

30

(**48**)

49 Farmer with Wife and Children at Sunset

1968 (16 Apr). *Nos. 202/3 and as No. 206 surch as T* **48** (30 c.) *or with "CENTS" added, and three bars* (*others*). *W w* **12** (*sideways on No. 248*).

246		30 c. on 40 c. multicoloured		10	10
247		60 c. on 45 c. multicoloured		10	10
248		85 c. on 75 c. multicoloured		15	15
246/8			*Set of 3*	30	30

(Des Mary Hayward. Litho Harrison)

1968 (2 Sept). *Human Rights Year.* W w **12**. *P* 14½ × 13½.
249	49 20 c. multicoloured		10	10
250	50 c. multicoloured		10	10
251	85 c. multicoloured		10	10
252	2 r. 25, multicoloured		20	30
249/52		*Set of* 4	30	40

50 Expedition landing at Anse Possession | 54 Apollo Launch

(Des Mary Hayward. Litho and die-stamped Harrison)

1968 (30 Dec). *Bicentenary of First Landing on Praslin. T* **50** *and similar multicoloured designs.* W w **12** (*sideways on* 50 c., 85 c.). *P* 14.
253	20 c. Type 50		20	10
254	50 c. French warships at anchor (*vert*)		25	15
255	85 c. Coco-de-Mer and Black Parrot (*vert*)		60	20
256	2 r. 25, French warships under sail		65	50
253/6		*Set of* 4	1·50	80

(Des V. Whiteley. Litho Format)

1969 (9 Sept). *First Man on the Moon. T* **54** *and similar horiz designs. Multicoloured.* W w **12** (*sideways on horiz designs*). *P* 13½.
257	5 c. Type 54		10	10
258	20 c. Module leaving Mother-ship for Moon		15	10
259	50 c. Astronauts and Space Module on Moon		20	15
260	85 c. Tracking station		25	15
261	2 r. 25, Moon craters with Earth on the "Horizon"		45	65
257/61		*Set of* 5	1·00	95

59 Picault's Landing, 1742 | 60 Badge of Seychelles

(Des Mary Hayward. Litho Enschedé)

1969 (3 Nov)–**75**. *Horiz designs as T* **59/60**. *Multicoloured.* W w **12** (*sideways*). *Slightly toned paper. P* 13 × 12½.
262	5 c. Type 59		10	10
263	10 c. U.S. satellite-tracking station		10	10
	a. Whiter paper (8.3.73)		70	40
264	15 c. *Königsberg I* at Aldabra, 1914†		1·75	75
	a. Whiter paper (8.3.73)		4·25	1·50
265	20 c. Fleet re-fuelling off St. Anne, 1939–45		30	10
	a. Whiter paper (13.6.74)		1·25	1·50
266	25 c. Exiled Ashanti King Prempeh		20	10
	a. Whiter paper (8.3.73)		65	75
267	30 c. Laying Stone of Possession, 1756		1·00	3·00
268	40 c. As 30 c. (11.12.72)		90	1·25
	a. Whiter paper (13.6.74)		1·60	1·60
269	50 c. Pirates and treasure		30	15
	a. Whiter paper (13.6.74)		1·25	1·50
270	60 c. Corsairs attacking merchantman		1·00	1·50
271	65 c. As 60 c. (11.12.72)		2·00	3·00
	a. Whiter paper (13.8.75)		6·00	7·50
272	85 c. Impression of proposed airport		1·25	1·50
273	95 c. As 85 c. (11.12.72)		4·00	3·50
	a. Whiter paper (13.6.74)		4·00	3·25
274	1 r. French Governor capitulating to British naval officer, 1794		35	15
	a. Whiter paper (8.3.73)		1·00	70
275	1 r. 50, H.M.S. *Sybille* and *Chiffone* in battle, 1801		1·75	2·00
	a. Whiter paper (8.3.73)		3·25	5·50
276	3 r. 50, Visit of the Duke of Edinburgh, 1956		1·50	2·00
	a. Whiter paper (13.8.75)		2·50	9·00
277	5 r. Chevalier Queau de Quincy		1·50	2·00
278	10 r. Indian Ocean chart, 1574		3·25	4·00
279	15 r. Type 60		4·00	8·50
262/79		*Set of* 18	21·00	29·00
263a/76a		*Set of* 11	24·00	30·00

†The design is incorrect in that it shows *Königsberg II* and the wrong date ("1915").

The stamps on the whiter paper are highly glazed, producing shade variations and are easily distinguishable from the original printings on toned paper.

74 White Terns, French Warship and Island

(Des A. Smith; adapted V. Whiteley. Litho D.L.R.)

1970 (27 Apr). *Bicentenary of First Settlement, St. Anne Island. T* **74** *and similar horiz designs. Multicoloured.* W w **12** (*sideways*). *P* 14.
280	20 c. Type 74		20	10
281	50 c. Flying Fish, ship and island		20	10
282	85 c. Compass and chart		20	10
283	3 r. 50, Anchor on sea-bed		30	45
280/3		*Set of* 4	80	55

78 Girl and Optician's Chart | 79 Pitcher Plant

(Des A. Smith. Litho Questa)

1970 (4 Aug). *Centenary of British Red Cross. T* **78** *and similar multicoloured designs.* W w **12** (*sideways on horiz designs*). *P* 14.
284	20 c. Type 78		15	10
285	50 c. Baby, scales and milk bottles		20	10
286	85 c. Woman with child and umbrella (*vert*)		20	10
287	3 r. 50, Red Cross local H.Q. building		1·00	80
284/7		*Set of* 4	1·40	85

(Des G. Drummond. Litho J.W.)

1970 (29 Dec). *Flowers. T* **79** *and similar vert designs. Multicoloured.* W w **12**. *P* 14.
288	20 c. Type 79		45	15
289	50 c. Wild Vanilla		55	15
290	85 c. Tropic-Bird Orchid		1·40	30
291	3 r. 50, Vare Hibiscus		2·50	1·50
288/91		*Set of* 4	4·50	1·90
MS292	81 × 133 mm. Nos. 288/91. Wmk inverted		8·00	13·00

80 Seychelles "On the Map" | 81 Piper "Navajo"

(Des and litho J.W.)

1971 (18 May). *"Putting Seychelles on the Map". Sheet* 152 × 101 mm. W w **12** (*sideways*). *P* 13½.
MS293	80 5 r. multicoloured		2·25	8·50

(Des and litho J.W.)

1971 (28 June). *Airport Completion. T* **81** *and similar multicoloured designs showing aircraft.* W w **12** (*sideways on horiz designs*). *P* 14 × 14½ (5, 20 and 60 c.) or 14½ (others).
294	5 c. Type 81		10	10
295	20 c. Westland "Wessex"		20	10
296	50 c. "Catalina" flying-boat (*horiz*)		40	10
297	60 c. Grumman "Albatross"		45	10
298	85 c. Short "G" Class flying-boat (*horiz*)		65	10
299	3 r. 50, Vickers Supermarine "Walrus" (*horiz*)		3·50	3·00
294/9		*Set of* 6	4·75	3·25

82 Santa Claus delivering Gifts (Jean-Claude Waye Hive) | (83)

(Des Jennifer Toombs. Litho A. & M.)

1971 (12 Oct). *Christmas. Drawings by local children. T* **82** *and similar horiz designs. Multicoloured.* W w **12** (*sideways*). *P* 13½.
300	10 c. Type 82		10	10
301	15 c. Santa Claus seated on turtle (Edison Thérésine)		10	10
302	3 r. 50, Santa Claus landing on island (Isabelle Tirant)		40	70
300/2		*Set of* 3	50	70

1971 (21 Dec). *Nos. 267, 270 and 272 surch in grey as T* **83**.
303	40 c. on 30 c. Laying Stone of Possession, 1756		30	55
304	65 c. on 60 c. Corsairs attacking merchantman		40	75
305	95 c. on 85 c. Impression of proposed airport		45	1·00
303/5		*Set of* 3	1·00	2·10

85 Seychelles Brush Warbler

ROYAL VISIT 1972 (84)

1972 (20 Mar). *Royal Visit. Nos.* 265 *and* 277 *optd with T* **84**.
306	20 c. Fleet re-fuelling off St. Anne, 1939–45		15	20
307	5 r. Chevalier Queau de Quincy (Gold)		1·50	2·50

(Des R. Gillmor. Litho Questa)

1972 (24 July). *Rare Seychelles Birds. T* **85** *and similar vert designs. Multicoloured.* W w **12** (*sideways*). *P* 13½.
308	5 c. Type 85		30	10
309	20 c. Bare-legged Scops Owl		1·00	20
310	50 c. Seychelles Blue Pigeon		1·25	65
311	65 c. Seychelles Magpie Robin		1·50	75
312	95 c. Seychelles Paradise Flycatcher		2·25	2·00
313	3 r. 50, Seychelles Kestrel		6·50	8·00
308/13		*Set of* 6	11·50	10·50
MS314	144 × 162 mm. Nos. 308/13		17·00	24·00

86 Fireworks Display | 87 Giant Tortoise and Sailfish

(Des V. Whiteley. Litho Questa)

1972 (18 Sept). *"Festival '72". T* **86** *and similar multicoloured designs.* W w **12** (*sideways on* 10 *and* 25 c.). *P* 14.
315	10 c. Type 86		10	10
316	15 c. Pirogue race (*horiz*)		10	10
317	25 c. Floats and costumes		10	10
318	5 r. Water skiing (*horiz*)		60	80
315/18		*Set of* 4	65	80

(Des (from photograph by D. Groves) and photo Harrison)

1972 (20 Nov). *Royal Silver Wedding. Multicoloured; background colour given.* W w **12**. *P* 14 × 14½.
319	87 95 c. turquoise-blue		15	10
320	1 r. 50, red-brown		15	10

1973 (14 Nov). *Royal Wedding. As Nos.* 322/3 *of Montserrat.*
321	95 c. ochre		10	10
322	1 r. 50, dull deep blue		10	10

88 Soldier Fish

(Des G. Drummond. Litho Questa)

1974 (5 Mar). *Fishes. T* **88** *and similar horiz designs. Multicoloured.* W w **12**. *P* 14½ × 14.
323	20 c. Type 88		15	10
324	50 c. File Fish		25	10
325	95 c. Butterfly Fish		30	20
326	1 r. 50, Gaterin		75	1·00
323/6		*Set of* 4	1·25	1·25

89 Globe and Letter

(Des Sylvia Goaman. Litho Enschedé)

1974 (9 Oct). *Centenary of Universal Postal Union. T* **89** *and similar horiz designs. Multicoloured.* W w **12** (*sideways*). *P* 12½ × 12.
327	20 c. Type 89		10	10
328	50 c. Globe and radio beacon		20	10
329	95 c. Globe and postmark		35	40
330	1 r. 50, Emblems within "UPU"		50	70
327/30		*Set of* 4	1·00	1·10

90 Sir Winston Churchill   (91)

VISIT OF Q.E. II

(Des G. Vasarhelyi. Litho Questa)

1974 (30 Nov). *Birth Centenary of Sir Winston Churchill. T* **90** *and similar horiz design. Multicoloured.* W w **12.** P 14.

331	95 c. Type 90	20	15
332	1 r. 50, Profile portrait	35	40
MS333	81 × 109 mm. Nos. 331/2 ..	60	1·75

1975 (8 Feb). *Visit of R.M.S. "Queen Elizabeth II". Nos.* 265a, 269a, 273a *and* 275a *optd with T* **91**.

334	20 c. Fleet re-fuelling off St. Anne, 1939–45 ..	15	15
335	50 c. Pirates and treasure	20	20
336	95 c. Impression of proposed airport (Sil.)	25	35
337	1 r. 50, H.M.S. *Sybille* and *Chiffone* in battle, 1801 ..	35	60
334/7	*Set of 4*	85	1·10

INTERNAL SELF-GOVERNMENT OCTOBER 1975

(92)   93 Queen Elizabeth I

1975 (1 Oct). *Internal Self-Government. Nos.* 265a, 271a, 274a *and* 276a *optd with T* **92** *in gold, by Enschedé.*

338	20 c. Fleet re-fuelling off St. Anne, 1939–45 ..	15	15
339	65 c. Corsairs attacking merchantman	25	30
340	1 r. French Governor capitulating to British naval officer, 1794	30	35
341	3 r. 50, Visit of Duke of Edinburgh, 1956 ..	1·00	1·50
338/41	*Set of 4*	1·50	2·00

(Des C. Abbott. Litho Walsall)

1975 (15 Dec). *International Women's Year. T* **93** *and similar vert designs. Multicoloured.* W w **14** (*inverted*). P 13½.

342	10 c. Type 93	10	10
343	15 c. Gladys Aylward ..	10	10
344	20 c. Elizabeth Fry	10	10
345	25 c. Emmeline Pankhurst ..	10	10
346	65 c. Florence Nightingale	25	20
347	1 r. Amy Johnson	40	35
348	1 r. 50, Joan of Arc	50	60
349	3 r. 50, Eleanor Roosevelt	1·50	2·25
342/9	*Set of 8*	2·50	3·25

94 Map of Praslin and   95 First Landing, 1609
Postmark   (inset portrait of
                             Premier James Mancham)

(Des J.W. Litho Questa)

1976 (30 Mar). *Rural Posts. T* **94** *and similar vert designs showing maps and postmarks. Multicoloured.* W w **14.** P 14.

350	20 c. Type 94	15	10
351	65 c. La Digue	25	20
352	1 r. Mahé with Victoria postmark	30	25
353	1 r. 50, Mahé with Anse Royale postmark ..	45	70
350/3	*Set of 4*	1·00	1·10
MS354	166 × 127 mm. Nos. 350/3 ..	2·00	3·00

INDEPENDENT

(Des G. Drummond. Litho J.W.)

1976 (29 June). *Independence. T* **95** *and similar vert designs. Multicoloured.* W w **12** (*sideways*). P 13½.

355	20 c. Type 95	10	10
356	25 c. The Possession Stone	10	10
357	40 c. First settlers, 1770	15	15
358	75 c. Chevalier Queau de Quincy	20	20
359	1 r. Sir Bickham Sweet-Escott	25	20
360	1 r. 25, Legislative Building ..	40	50
361	1 r. 50, Seychelles badge ..	45	60
362	3 r. 50, Seychelles flag	90	1·40
355/62	*Set of 8*	2·25	2·75

---

96 Flags of Seychelles and U.S.A.

(Des and litho J.W.)

1976 (12 July). *Seychelles Independence and American Independence Bicentenary. T* **96** *and similar horiz design. Multicoloured.* W w **12** (*sideways*). P 13½.

363	1 r. Type 96	25	15
364	10 r. Statehouses of Seychelles and Philadelphia ..	1·25	1·50

97 Swimming   98 Seychelles Paradise
                             Flycatcher

(Des J.W. Litho Questa)

1976 (26 July). *Olympic Games, Montreal. T* **97** *and similar horiz designs.* W w **14** (*sideways*). P 14.

365	20 c. ultramarine, cobalt and sepia	10	10
366	65 c. bottle-green, apple-green and grey-black	20	10
367	1 r. chestnut, blue-green and grey-black	25	10
368	3 r. 50, crimson, rose and grey-black	50	1·00
365/8 ..	*Set of 4*	90	1·10

Designs:—65 c. Hockey; 1 r. Basketball; 3 r. 50, Football.

(Des Mrs. R. Fennessy. Litho Questa)

1976–77. *Fourth Pan-African Ornithological Congress, Seychelles. T* **98** *and similar multicoloured designs.* W w **14** (*sideways on Nos.* 370/1). P 14. A. *Ordinary paper* (8.11.76). B. *Chalky paper* (7.3.77).

		A		B	
369	20 c. Type 98	20	10	15	10
370	1 r. 25, Seychelles Sunbird (*horiz*)	75	65	65	65
371	1 r. 50, Seychelles Brown White Eye (*horiz*)	95	80	80	80
372	5 r. Black Parrot ..	2·00	2·00	2·00	2·00
369/72 ..	*Set of 4*	3·50	3·25	3·25	3·25
MS373	161 × 109 mm. Nos. 369/72 ..	4·50	5·50		†
	a. 5 r. value in miniature sheet imperf		£850		

Independence 1976

(99)   100 Inauguration of George Washington

1976 (22 Nov). *Independence. Nos.* 265a, 269, 271a, 273a, 274a, 276a *and* 277/9 *optd with T* **99** (*No.* 271 *additionally surch.*). W w **12** (*sideways*).

374	20 c. Fleet re-fuelling off St. Anne, 1939–45 ..	25	55
375	50 c. Pirates and treasure ..	40	75
376	95 c. Impression of proposed airport ..	55	1·00
	a. Opt inverted ..	85·00	
377	1 r. French Governor capitulating to British naval officer, 1794	55	1·00
378	3 r. 50, Visit of Duke of Edinburgh, 1956 ..	2·75	3·50
	a. Opt inverted ..	75·00	
	b. On No. 276	3·25	3·50
	ba. Opt inverted ..	£100	
379	5 r. Chevalier Queau de Quincy	3·00	3·50
380	10 r. Indian Ocean chart, 1574	5·50	9·00
381	15 c. Type 60	7·50	9·00
382	25 r. on 65 c. Corsairs attacking merchantman	11·00	16·00
374/82	*Set of 9*	28·00	40·00

(Des Jennifer Toombs. Litho Questa)

1976 (21 Dec). *Bicentenary of American Revolution. T* **100** *and similar horiz designs.* P 14 × 13½.

383	1 c. crimson and light rose	10	10
384	2 c. violet and light lilac	10	10
385	3 c. bright blue and azure	10	10
386	4 c. chestnut and light yellow	10	10
387	5 c. emerald and light yellow-green..	10	10
388	1 r. 50, sepia and cinnamon ..	60	35
389	3 r. 50, dp turquoise-blue & pale blue-green..	80	80
390	5 r. chestnut and light yellow	1·00	1·00
391	10 r. chalky blue and azure	1·75	1·75
383/91	*Set of 9*	4·00	3·75
MS392	141 × 141 mm. 25 r. plum and magenta	4·00	5·50

Designs:—2 c. Jefferson and Louisiana Purchase; 3 c. William Seward and Alaska Purchase; 4 c. Pony Express, 1860; 5 c. Lincoln's Emancipation Proclamation; 1 r. 50 Transcontinental Railroad, 1869; 3 r. 50 Wright Brothers flight, 1903; 5 r. Henry Ford's assembly-line, 1913; 10 r. J. F. Kennedy and 1969 Moonlanding; 25 r. Signing Independence Declaration, 1776.

---

101 Silhouette of the Islands   102 Cruiser *Aurora* and Flag

(Des G. Hutchins (Nos. 395/8), J.W. (others). Litho Questa)

1977 (5 Sept). *Silver Jubilee. T* **101** *and similar multicoloured designs.* W w **14** (*sideways on* 20 *and* 40 c., 5 *and* 10 r.). P 14.

393	20 c. Type 101	10	10
394	40 c. Silhouette (*different*)	10	10
395	50 c. The Orb (*vert*)	10	10
396	1 r. St. Edward's Crown (*vert*)	15	10
397	1 r. 25, Ampulla and Spoon (*vert*)	20	15
398	1 r. 50, Sceptre with Cross (*vert*)	20	20
399	5 r. Silhouette (*different*)	50	50
400	10 r. Silhouette (*different*)	90	90
393/400	*Set of 8*	1·75	1·75
MS401	133 × 135 mm. 20 c., 50 c., 1 r., 10 r. all wmk sideways	75	1·40

(Litho State Printing Works, Moscow)

1977 (7 Nov). *60th Anniv of Russian October Revolution.* P 12 × 12½.

402	**102** 1 r. 50, multicoloured ..	35	30
MS403	101 × 129 mm. No. 402 ..	80	80

103 Coral Scene

(Des G. Drummond. Litho Walsall (40 c., 1 r., 1 r. 25, 1 r. 50), J.W. or Questa (25 c. (No. 408B)), J.W. (others))

1977–84. *Multicoloured designs as T* **103.** *Rupee values show "Re" or "Rs".* W w **14** (*sideways on* 10, 20, 50 *and* 75 c.). P 14½ × 14 (40 c., 1 r., 1 r. 25, 1 r. 50), 13 (5, 10, 15, 20 r.) *or* 14 (*others*).

A. *No imprint.* B. *Imprint date at foot*

		A		B	
404	5 c. Reef Fish	10	10		†
405	10 c. Hawksbill Turtle	30	10	10	10
406	15 c. Coco-de-Mer	10	10	10	10
407	20 c. Wild Vanilla Orchid	90	10	10	10
408	25 c. *Hypolimnas misippus* (butterfly)	1·00	35	10	10
409	40 c. Type 103	30	10	10	10
410	50 c. Giant Tortoise	20	10	30	10
411	75 c. Crayfish	20	10	20	25
412	1 r. Madagascar Red Fody	1·25	10	5·00	10
413	1 r. 25, White Tern ..	1·25	15		†
414	1 r. 50, Seychelles Flying Fox	1·50	15	2·00	50
415	3 r. 50, Green Gecko	75	1·00		†
416	5 r. Octopus	2·00	40		†
417	10 r. Giant Tiger Cowrie	2·25	2·25		†
418	15 r. Pitcher Plant	2·25	2·50		†
419	20 r. Coat of arms	2·50	2·50		†
404A/19A	*Set of 16*	15·00	9·00		
405B/14B	*Set of 9*			7·00	1·25

Dates of issue: Without imprint 10.11.77, 40 c., 1 r. to 1 r. 50; 6.2.78, 10, 20, 50, 75 c., 5 r., 20 r.; 10.4.78, others. With imprint 14.3.80, 10, 15, 25, 40, 50, 75, 1 r., 1 r. 50; 5.84, 20 c.

The 40 c., 1 r., 1 r. 25 and 1 r. 50 values are horizontal designs, 31 × 27 mm; the 5, 10, 15 and 20 r. are vertical, 28 × 36 mm; the others are horizontal, 29 × 25 mm.

The 10 c. and 25 c. (Nos. 405B and 408B) exist with different imprint dates.

For rupee values showing face value as "R" see Nos. 487/94.

For 10 c. and 50 c. with watermark w **14** (upright) and printed by Questa see Nos. 718 and 722. A printing of the 25 c. by Questa on the same date has the same perforation and watermark as J.W. printings of No. 408B.

For 50 c. and 3 r. (inscr "Rs") with watermark w **16** and printed by Questa see Nos. 732/8.

104 St. Roch Roman Catholic Church, Bel Ombre

(Des G. Drummond. Litho Walsall)

1977 (5 Dec). *Christmas. T* **104** *and similar horiz designs. Multicoloured.* W w **14** (*sideways*). P 13½ × 14.

420	20 c. Type 104	10	10
421	1 r. Anglican cathedral, Victoria	10	10
422	1 r. 50, Roman Catholic cathedral, Victoria	15	10
423	5 r. St. Mark's Anglican church, Praslin ..	30	45
420/3	*Set of 4*	50	55

105 Liberation Day ringed on Calendar

106 Stamp Portraits of Edward VII, George V and George VI

(Des local artists; adapted L. Curtis. Litho Questa)

1978 (5 June). *Liberation Day. T **105** and similar vert designs. Multicoloured. W w* 14. *P* 14 × 13½.

424	40 c. Type **105**		10	10
425	1 r. 25, Hands holding bayonet, torch and flag		15	10
426	1 r. 50, Fisherman and farmer		15	15
427	5 r. Soldiers and rejoicing people		35	40
424/7		*Set of* 4	60	60

(Des G. Drummond. Litho Questa)

1978 (21 Aug). *25th Anniv of Coronation. T **106** and similar vert designs. Multicoloured. W w* 14. *P* 14.

428	40 c. Type **106**		10	10
429	1 r. 50, Victoria and Elizabeth II		10	10
430	3 r. Queen Victoria Monument		20	20
431	5 r. Queen's Building, Victoria		30	35
428/31		*Set of* 4	60	65
MS432	87 × 129 mm. Nos. 428/31		60	85

107 Gardenia

(Des G. Hutchins. Litho Questa)

1978 (16 Oct). *Wildlife. T **107** and similar horiz designs. Multi-coloured. W w* 14 *(sideways). P* 13½ × 14.

433	40 c. Type **107**		10	10
434	1 r. 25, Seychelles Magpie Robin		40	25
435	1 r. 50, Seychelles Paradise Flycatcher		45	35
436	5 r. Green Turtle		70	85
433/6		*Set of* 4	1·50	1·40

108 Possession Stone

109 Seychelles Fody

(Des G. Hutchins. Litho Questa)

1978 (15 Dec). *Bicentenary of Victoria. T **108** and similar horiz designs. Multicoloured. W w* 14 *(sideways). P* 13½ × 14.

437	20 c. Type **108**		10	10
438	1 r. 25, Plan of 1782 "L'Etablissement"		15	15
439	1 r. 50, Clock Tower		15	15
440	5 r. Bust of Pierre Poivre		40	50
437/40		*Set of* 4	65	75

(Des G. Drummond. Litho Questa)

1979 (27 Feb). *Birds (1st series). T **109** and similar vert designs. Multicoloured. W w* 14. *P* 14.

441	2 r. Type **109**		50	50
	a. Horiz strip of 5. Nos. 441/5		2·25	
442	2 r. Green Heron		50	50
443	2 r. Thick-billed Bulbul		50	50
444	2 r. Seychelles Cave Swiftlet		50	50
445	2 r. Grey-headed Lovebird		50	50
441/5		*Set of* 5	2·25	2·25

Nos. 441/5 were printed together, *se-tenant*, in horizontal strips of 5 throughout the sheet.
See also Nos. 463/7, 500/4 and 523/7.

---

110 Patrice Lumumba

111 1978 5 r. Liberation Day Commemorative and Sir Rowland Hill

(Des G. Vasarhelyi. Litho Questa)

1979 (5 June). *African Liberation Heroes. T **110** and similar vert designs. W w* 14. *P* 14 × 14½.

446	40 c. black, deep violet and lilac		10	10
447	2 r. black, blue and pale blue		25	25
448	2 r. 25, black, reddish brown & orange-brn		30	30
449	5 r. black, bronze-green and dull green		65	80
446/9		*Set of* 4	1·10	1·25

Designs:—2 r. Kwame Nkrumah; 2 r. 25, Dr. Eduardo Mondlane; 5 r. Hamilcar Cabral.

(Des J.W. Litho Questa)

1979 (27 Aug). *Death Centenary of Sir Rowland Hill. T **111** and similar vert designs showing stamps and Sir Rowland Hill. Multicoloured. W w* 14. *P* 14.

450	40 c. Type **111**		10	10
451	2 r. 25, 1972 50 c. Rare Birds commemorative		45	40
452	3 r. 1962 50 c. definitive		50	55
450/2		*Set of* 3	95	95
MS453	112 × 88 mm. 5 r. 1892 4 c. definitive. Wmk inverted		40	55

112 Child with Book

113 The Herald Angel

(Des BG Studio. Litho Questa)

1979 (26 Oct). *International Year of the Child. T **112** and similar multicoloured designs. W w* 14 *(sideways on 40 c. and 2 r. 25). P* 14½.

454	40 c. Type **112**		10	10
455	2 r. 25, Children of different races		20	30
456	3 r. Young child with ball *(vert)*		30	45
457	5 r. Girl with glove-puppet *(vert)*		40	65
454/7		*Set of* 4	85	1·25

Nos. 454/7 were each printed in sheets including two *se-tenant* stamp-size labels.

(Des J. Cooter. Litho Walsall)

1979 (3 Dec). *Christmas. T **113** and similar multicoloured designs. W w* 14 *(sideways on 3 r.). P* 14½ × 14 *(3 r.) or* 14 × 14½ *(others).*

458	20 c. Type **113**		10	10
459	2 r. 25, The Virgin and Child		30	30
460	3 r. The Three Kings *(horiz)*		40	45
458/60		*Set of* 3	65	70
MS461	87 × 75 mm. 5 r. The Flight into Egypt *(horiz) (wmk sideways). P* 14½ × 14		50	70

(114)

115 Seychelles Kestrel

1979 (7 Dec). *As No. 415 but with imprint, surch with T **114**.*

462	1 r. 10 on 3 r. 50, Green Gecko		30	30

(Des G. Drummond. Litho Questa)

1980 (29 Feb). *Birds (2nd series). Seychelles Kestrel. T **115** and similar vert designs. Multicoloured. W w* 14 *(inverted). P* 14.

463	2 r. Type **115**		60	50
	a. Horiz strip of 5. Nos. 463/7		2·75	
464	2 r. Pair of Seychelles Kestrels		60	50
465	2 r. Seychelles Kestrel with eggs		60	50
466	2 r. Seychelles Kestrel on nest with chick		60	50
467	2 r. Seychelles Kestrel chicks in nest		60	50
463/7		*Set of* 5	2·75	2·25

Nos. 463/7 were printed together, *se-tenant*, in horizontal strips of 5 throughout the sheet.

---

116 10 Rupees Banknote

117 Sprinting

(Des B. Grout. Litho Questa)

1980 (18 Apr). *"London 1980" International Stamp Exhibition. New Currency. T **116** and similar multicoloured designs showing banknotes. W w* 14 *(sideways on 40 c. and 1 r. 50). P* 14.

468	40 c. Type **116**		10	10
469	1 r. 50, 25 rupees		25	15
470	2 r. 25, 50 rupees *(vert)*		35	25
471	5 r. 100 rupees *(vert)*		65	55
468/71		*Set of* 4	1·25	90
MS472	119 × 102 mm. Nos. 468/71 (wmk sideways)		1·25	1·40

(Des J.W. Litho Questa)

1980 (13 June). *Olympic Games, Moscow. T **117** and similar vert designs. Multicoloured. W w* 14. *P* 14 × 14½.

473	40 c. Type **117**		10	10
474	2 r. 25, Weightlifting		20	20
475	3 r. Boxing		30	30
476	5 r. Yachting		60	40
473/6		*Set of* 4	1·10	80
MS477	90 × 121 mm. Nos. 473/6		1·10	1·90

118 "Jumbo Jet" Airliner

119 Female Palm

(Des A. Theobald. Litho Questa)

1980 (22 Aug). *International Tourism Conference, Manila. T **118** and similar horiz designs. Multicoloured. W w* 14 *(sideways). P* 14.

478	40 c. Type **118**		10	10
479	2 r. 25, Bus		35	35
480	3 r. Cruise liner		50	50
481	5 r. *La Belle Coralline* (tourist launch)		70	75
478/81		*Set of* 4	1·50	1·50

(Des L. Curtis. Litho Harrison)

1980 (14 Nov). *Coco-de-Mer (palms). T **119** and similar vert designs. Multicoloured. W w* 14. *P* 14.

482	40 c. Type **119**		10	10
483	2 r. 25, Male Palm		25	20
484	3 r. Artefacts		40	35
485	5 r. Fisherman's gourd		55	55
482/5		*Set of* 4	1·10	1·00
MS486	82 × 140 mm. Nos. 482/5		2·00	2·00

1981 (9 Jan)–**91**. *As Nos. 412/14, 415 (but new value), and 416/19 all with face values redrawn to show "R" instead of "Re" or "Rs" and imprint date at foot. Chalk-surfaced paper.*

487	1 r. Madagascar Red Fody		1·00	40
	a. Ordinary paper (11.86)		25	30
488	1 r. 10, Green Gecko		25	30
489	1 r. 50, White Tern		2·25	75
490	1 r. 50, Seychelles Flying Fox		45	55
	a. Ordinary paper (11.91)		35	40
491	5 r. Octopus		1·25	1·40
492	10 r. Giant Tiger Cowrie		2·40	2·50
493	15 r. Pitcher Plant		3·75	4·00
494	20 r. Coat of arms		5·00	5·50
487/94		*Set of* 8	14·00	14·00

The 1 r., 1 r. 50 and 5 r. values exist with different imprint dates below the design.
For 1 r. 25, 3 r. and 5 r. watermarked w **16** see Nos. 735/8.

120 Vasco da Gama's *Sao Gabriel*, 1497

121 Male White Tern

(Des J.W. Litho Format)

1981 (27 Feb). *Ships.* T **120** *and similar horiz designs. Multicoloured.* W w 14 (*sideways*). *P* 14½ × 14.

495	40 c. Type **120**	15	10
496	2 r. 25, Mascarenhas' caravel, 1505	60	55
497	3 r. 50, Darwin's H.M.S. *Beagle*, 1831	90	1·00
498	5 r. *Queen Elizabeth 2* (liner), 1968	1·10	1·40
495/8	*Set of 4*	2·50	2·75
MS499	141 × 91 mm. Nos. 495/98	2·50	3·25

(Des G. Drummond. Litho Questa)

1981 (10 Apr). *Birds* (3rd series). *White Tern.* T **121** *and similar vert designs. Multicoloured.* W w 14. *P* 14.

500	2 r. Type **121**	85	65
	a. Horiz strip of 5. Nos. 500/4	3·75	
501	2 r. Pair of White Terns	85	65
502	2 r. Female White Tern	85	65
503	2 r. Female White Tern on nest, and egg	85	65
504	2 r. White Tern and chick	85	65
500/4	*Set of 5*	3·75	3·00

Nos. 500/4 were printed together, *se-tenant*, in horizontal strips of 5 throughout the sheet.

(Des D. Shults. Litho Questa)

1981 (23 June–16 Nov). *Royal Wedding. Horiz designs as T* **26/27** *of Kiribati. Multicoloured.* (a) W w 15. *P* 14.

505	1 r. 50, *Victoria and Albert I*	20	25
	a. Sheetlet. No. 505 × 6 and No. 506	1·60	
506	1 r. 50, Prince Charles and Lady Diana Spencer	50	50
507	5 r. *Cleveland*	60	60
	a. Sheetlet. No. 507 × 6 and No. 508	4·50	
508	5 r. As No. 506	1·50	2·00
509	10 r. *Britannia*	1·00	1·50
	a. Sheetlet. No. 509 × 6 and No. 510	7·50	
510	10 r. As No. 506	2·25	2·25
505/10	*Set of 6*	5·50	6·50
MS511	120 × 109 mm. 7 r. 50, As No. 506. Wmk sideways. *P* 12 (16 Nov)	1·50	1·50

(b) *Booklet stamps. No wmk. P* 12 (16 Nov)

512	1 r. 50, As No. 505	25	40
	a. Booklet pane. No. 512 × 4	1·00	
513	5 r. As No. 508	1·00	1·60
	a. Booklet pane. No. 513 × 2	2·00	

Nos. 505/10 were printed in sheetlets of seven stamps of the same face value, each containing six of the "Royal Yacht" design and one of the larger design showing Prince Charles and Lady Diana. Nos. 512/13 come from 22 r. stamp booklets.

122 Britten-Norman "Islander"   123 Seychelles Flying Foxes in Flight

(Litho Harrison)

1981 (27 July). *10th Anniv of Opening of Seychelles International Airport. Aircraft.* T **122** *and similar horiz designs. Multicoloured.* W w 14 (*sideways*). *P* 14½.

514	40 c. Type **122**	15	10
515	2 r. 25, Britten-Norman "Trislander"	55	45
516	3 r. 50, BAC (Vickers) "VC10" airliner	80	70
517	5 r. Boeing "747" airliner	1·00	1·00
514/17	*Set of 4*	2·25	2·00

(Litho Format)

1981 (9 Oct). *Seychelles Flying Fox* (*Roussette*). T **123** *and similar vert designs. Multicoloured.* W w 14. *P* 14.

518	40 c. Type **123**	10	10
519	2 r. 25, Flying Fox eating	45	45
520	3 r. Flying Fox climbing across tree branch	70	70
521	5 r. Flying Fox hanging from tree branch	1·00	1·00
518/21	*Set of 4*	2·00	2·00
MS522	95 × 130 mm. Nos. 518/21	3·00	3·50

124 Chinese Little Bittern (male)   125 Silhouette Island and La Digue

(Des G. Drummond. Litho Questa)

1982 (4 Feb). *Birds* (4th series). *Chinese Little Bittern.* T **124** *and similar vert designs. Multicoloured.* W w 14. *P* 14.

523	3 r. Type **124**	1·75	80
	a. Horiz strip of 5. Nos. 523/7	8·00	
524	3 r. Chinese Little Bittern (female)	1·75	80
525	3 r. Hen on nest	1·75	80
526	3 r. Nest and eggs	1·75	80
527	3 r. Hen with chicks	1·75	80
523/7	*Set of 5*	8·00	3·50

Nos. 523/7 were printed together, *se-tenant*, in horizontal strips of 5 throughout the sheet.

(Des J. Cooter. Litho Format)

1982 (22 Apr). *Modern Maps.* T **125** *and similar vert designs. Multicoloured.* W w 14. *P* 14½.

528	40 c. Type **125**	15	10
529	1 r. 50, Denis and Bird Islands	40	25
530	2 r. 75, Praslin	65	65
531	7 r. Mahé	1·60	2·00
528/31	*Set of 4*	2·50	2·75
MS532	92 × 128 mm. Nos. 528/31	3·25	4·00

126 "Education"

(Des PAD Studio. Litho Harrison)

1982 (5 June). *5th Anniv of Liberation.* T **126** *and similar horiz designs. Multicoloured.* W w 14 (*sideways*). *P* 14.

533	40 c. Type **126**	10	10
534	1 r. 75, "Health"	25	25
535	2 r. 75, "Agriculture"	45	45
536	7 r. "Construction"	1·40	1·40
533/6	*Set of 4*	2·00	2·00
MS537	128 × 120 mm. Nos. 533/6. *P* 14½	4·50	5·50

127 Tourist Board Emblem   128 Tata Bus

(Des and litho Harrison)

1982 (1 Sept). *Tourism.* T **127** *and similar horiz designs. Multicoloured.* W w 14 (*sideways*). *P* 14.

538	1 r. 75, Type **127**	40	35
539	1 r. 75, Northolme Hotel	40	35
540	1 r. 75, Reef Hotel	40	35
541	1 r. 75, Barbarous Beach Hotel	40	35
542	1 r. 75, Coral Strand Hotel	40	35
543	1 r. 75, Beau Vallon Bay Hotel	40	35
544	1 r. 75, Fisherman's Cove Hotel	40	35
545	1 r. 75, Mahé Beach Hotel	40	35
538/45	*Set of 8*	2·75	2·50

(Des C. Abbott. Litho Harrison)

1982 (18 Nov). *Land Transport.* T **128** *and similar horiz designs. Multicoloured.* W w 14 (*sideways*). *P* 14.

546	20 c. Type **128**	10	10
547	1 r. 75, Mini-moke	30	25
548	2 r. 75, Ox-cart	50	50
549	7 r. Truck	1·40	1·75
546/9	*Set of 4*	2·10	2·40

129 Radio Seychelles Control Room

(Des A. Theobald. Litho Questa)

1983 (25 Feb). *World Communications Year.* T **129** *and similar horiz designs. Multicoloured.* W w 14 (*sideways*). *P* 14.

550	40 c. Type **129**	10	10
551	2 r. 75, Satellite Earth Station	45	50
552	3 r. 50, Radio Seychelles Television control room	70	75
553	5 r. Postal services sorting office	1·00	1·25
550/3	*Set of 4*	2·00	2·25

130 Agricultural Experimental Station

(Des L. Curtis. Litho Questa)

1983 (14 Mar). *Commonwealth Day.* T **130** *and similar horiz designs. Multicoloured.* W w 14 (*sideways*). *P* 14.

554	40 c. Type **130**	10	10
555	2 r. 75, Food processing plant	45	50
556	3 r. 50, Unloading fish catch	70	75
557	7 r. Seychelles flag	1·40	1·50
554/7	*Set of 4*	2·40	2·50

131 Denis Island Lighthouse

(Des Harrison. Litho Format)

1983 (14 July). *Famous Landmarks.* T **131** *and similar horiz designs. Multicoloured.* W w 14 (*sideways*). *P* 14 × 13½.

558	40 c. Type **131**	10	10
559	2 r. 75, Victoria Hospital	40	45
560	3 r. 50, Supreme Court	60	65
561	7 r. State House	1·25	1·40
558/61	*Set of 4*	2·10	2·25
MS562	110 × 98 mm. Nos. 558/61	4·50	5·50

132 *Royal Vauxhall Balloon, 1836*

(Des A. Theobald. Litho Harrison)

1983 (15 Sept). *Bicentenary of Manned Flight.* T **132** *and similar horiz designs. Multicoloured.* W w 14 (*sideways*). *P* 14.

563	40 c. Type **132**	15	10
564	1 r. 75, De Havilland "D.H.50J"	50	30
565	2 r. 75, Grumman "Albatross" flying boat	75	55
566	7 r. Swearingen "Merlin"	1·60	1·75
563/6	*Set of 4*	2·75	2·25

133 "DC 10" Aircraft   134 Swamp Plant and Moorhen

(Des Park Advertising. Litho Walsall)

1983 (26 Oct). *1st International Flight of Air Seychelles.* W w 14 (*sideways*). *P* 14.

567	**133** 2 r. multicoloured	1·00	1·00

(Des L. Curtis. Litho Questa)

1983 (17 Nov). *Centenary of Visit to Seychelles by Marianne North* (*botanic artist*). T **134** *and similar vert designs. Multicoloured.* W w 14. *P* 14.

568	40 c. Type **134**	15	10
569	1 r. 75, *Wormia flagellaria*	50	30
570	2 r. 75, Asiatic Pancratium	65	60
571	7 r. Pitcher Plant	1·50	1·60
568/71	*Set of 4*	2·50	2·25
MS572	90 × 121 mm. Nos. 568/71	3·75	4·50

50c   ▬▬▬

(135)

1983 (28 Dec). *Nos.* 505/10 *surch as T* **135**.

573	50 c. on 1 r. 50, *Victoria and Albert I*	15	15
	a. Sheetlet. No. 573 × 6 and No. 574	1·10	
	b. Albino surch	32·00	
	c. Surch double, one albino	35·00	
	d. Surch double, one inverted	55·00	
	e. Surch double, one in 2 r. 25 value	45·00	
574	50 c. on 1 r. 50, Prince Charles and Lady Diana Spencer	40	45
	b. Albino surch	75·00	
	c. Surch double, one albino	85·00	
	d. Surch double, one inverted	£130	
	e. Surch double, one in 2 r. 25 value	£110	
575	2 r. 25 on 5 r. *Cleveland*	45	50
	a. Sheetlet. No. 575 × 6 and No. 576	3·25	
576	2 r. 25 on 5 r. As No. 574	1·00	1·25
577	3 r. 75 on 10 r. *Britannia*	75	80
	a. Sheetlet. No. 577 × 6 and No. 578	5·50	
	b. Albino surch	30·00	
	c. Surch double	75·00	
578	3 r. 75 on 10 r. As No. 574	1·40	1·75
	b. Albino surch	65·00	
	c. Surch double	£225	
573/8	*Set of 6*	3·75	4·50

MINIMUM PRICE

The minimum price quote is 10p which represents a handling charge rather than a basis for valuing common stamps. For further notes about prices see introductory pages.

136 Coconut Vessel   **137** Victoria Port

(Des Jennifer Toombs. Litho Format)

1984 (29 Feb). *Traditional Handicrafts. T* **136** *and similar horiz designs. Multicoloured.* W w 14 (*sideways*). *P* 14.

579	50 c. Type **136**		15	10
580	2 r. Scarf and doll		50	60
581	3 r. Coconut-fibre roses		70	80
582	10 r. Carved fishing boat and doll		2·00	3·00
579/82		*Set of 4*	3·00	4·00

(Des C. Collins. Litho Questa)

1984 (21 May). *25th Anniv of "Lloyd's List" (newspaper). T* **137** *and similar vert designs. Multicoloured.* W w 14. *P* 14½ × 14.

583	50 c. Type **137**		20	10
584	2 r. Cargo liner		55	55
585	3 r. *Sun Viking* (liner)		80	80
586	10 r. Loss of R.F.A. *Ennerdale II*		2·25	2·75
583/6		*Set of 4*	3·50	3·75

138 Old S.P.U.P. Office

(Des D. Miller. Litho B.D.T.)

1984 (2 June). *20th Anniv of Seychelles People's United Party. T* **138** *and similar multicoloured designs.* W w 14 (*sideways on 50 c., 3 r.*). *P* 14.

587	50 c. Type **138**		15	10
588	2 r. Liberation statue (*vert*)		40	50
589	3 r. New S.P.U.P. office		60	80
590	10 r. President René (*vert*)		2·00	3·00
587/90		*Set of 4*	2·75	4·00

139 1949 U.P.U. 2 r. 25 Stamp

(Des M. Joyce. Litho Harrison)

1984 (18 June). *Universal Postal Union Congress, Hamburg. Sheet* 70 × 85 *mm.* W w 14 (*sideways*). *P* 14½.

MS591	**139** 5 r. yellow-olive, flesh and black	1·40	2·25

140 Long Jumping

(Des L. Curtis. Litho Questa)

1984 (28 July). *Olympic Games, Los Angeles. T* **140** *and similar horiz designs. Multicoloured.* W w 14 (*sideways*). *P* 14.

592	50 c. Type **140**		10	10
593	2 r. Boxing		40	45
594	3 r. Swimming		60	75
595	10 r. Weightlifting		1·75	2·50
592/5		*Set of 4*	2·50	3·50
MS596	100 × 100 mm. Nos. 592/5		2·50	4·00

141 Sub-aqua Diving

(Des A. Theobald. Litho Questa)

1984 (24 Sept). *Water Sports. T* **141** *and similar horiz designs. Multicoloured.* W w 14 (*sideways*). *P* 14.

597	50 c. Type **141**		20	10
598	2 r. Paragliding		60	45
599	3 r. Sailing		80	75
600	10 r. Water-skiing		2·25	2·50
597/600		*Set of 4*	3·50	3·50

142 Humpback Whale   **143** Two Bare-legged Scops Owls in Tree

(Des A. Jardine. Litho Questa)

1984 (19 Nov). *Whale Conservation. T* **142** *and similar horiz designs. Multicoloured.* W w 14 (*sideways*). *P* 14.

601	50 c. Type **142**		85	15
602	2 r. Sperm Whale		2·00	1·10
603	3 r. Black Right Whale		2·25	1·50
604	10 r. Blue Whale		4·50	5·00
601/4		*Set of 4*	8·75	7·00

(Des I. Lewington. Litho Walsall)

1985 (11 Mar). *Birth Bicentenary of John J. Audubon (ornithologist). Bare-legged Scops Owl. T* **143** *and similar vert designs. Multicoloured.* W w 14. *P* 14.

605	50 c. Type **143**		85	15
606	2 r. Owl on branch		1·75	1·10
607	3 r. Owl in flight		2·00	1·50
608	10 r. Owl on ground		3·75	5·00
605/8		*Set of 4*	7·50	7·00

144 Giant Tortoises   **145** The Queen Mother with Princess Anne and Prince Andrew, 1970

(Des D. Miller. Litho Format)

1985 (15 Mar). *"Expo '85" World Fair, Japan. T* **144** *and similar vert designs. Multicoloured.* W w 14. *P* 14.

609	50 c. Type **144**		40	10
610	2 r. White Terns		1·50	75
611	3 r. Windsurfing		1·50	95
612	5 r. Coco-de-Mer		1·60	1·75
609/12		*Set of 4*	4·50	3·25
MS613	130 × 80 mm. Nos. 609/12		4·50	5·00

For these designs without "Expo '85" inscription see No. MS650.

(Des A. Theobald (10 r.), C. Abbott (others). Litho Questa)

1985 (7 June). *Life and Times of Queen Elizabeth the Queen Mother. T* **145** *and similar vert designs. Multicoloured.* W w 16. *P* 14½ × 14.

614	50 c. The Queen Mother in 1930		10	10
615	2 r. Type **145**		45	50
616	3 r. On her 75th Birthday		65	70
617	5 r. With Prince Henry at his christening (from photo by Lord Snowdon)		1·10	1·25
614/17		*Set of 4*	2·10	2·40
MS618	91 × 73 mm. 10 r. Arriving at Blenheim Palace by helicopter. Wmk sideways		2·50	2·50

146 Boxing   **147** Agriculture Students

(Des O. Bell. Litho Questa)

1985 (24 Aug). *2nd Indian Ocean Islands Games. T* **146** *and similar horiz designs. Multicoloured.* W w 14 (*sideways*). *P* 14.

619	50 c. Type **146**		15	10
620	2 r. Football		55	50
621	3 r. Swimming		75	70
622	10 r. Windsurfing		2·40	2·40
619/22		*Set of 4*	3·50	3·25

1985 (1 Nov). *Acquisition of 1st Air Seychelles "Airbus" As No.* 735, *but additionally inscribed* "AIR SEYCHELLES FIRST AIRBUS".

623	1 r. 25, White Tern	1·00	1·00

(Des Joan Thompson. Litho Questa)

1985 (28 Nov). *International Youth Year. T* **147** *and similar vert designs. Multicoloured.* W w 16. *P* 14.

624	50 c. Type **147**		10	10
625	2 r. Construction students building wall		45	50
626	3 r. Carpentry students		65	70
627	10 r. Science students		2·25	2·40
624/7		*Set of 4*	3·00	3·25

148 Ford "Model T" (1919)   **149** Five Foot Transit Instrument

(Des J.W. Litho Questa)

1985 (18 Dec). *Vintage Cars. T* **148** *and similar horiz designs. Multicoloured.* W w 16 (*sideways*). *P* 14.

628	50 c. Type **148**		30	10
629	2 r. Austin "Seven" (1922)		1·00	50
630	3 r. Morris "Oxford" (1924)		1·25	70
631	10 r. Humber "Coupé" (1929)		2·75	2·40
628/31		*Set of 4*	4·75	3·25

(Des Harrison. Litho Format)

1986 (28 Feb). *Appearance of Halley's Comet. T* **149** *and similar vert designs. Multicoloured.* W w 16. *P* 14.

632	50 c. Type **149**		30	10
633	2 r. Eight foot quadrant		1·00	50
634	3 r. Comet's orbit		1·25	70
635	10 r. Edmond Halley		2·75	2·40
632/5		*Set of 4*	4·75	3·50

150 Ballerina   **151** Ferry to La Digue

(Des C. Abbott. Litho Format)

1986 (4 Apr). *Visit of Ballet du Louvre Company. "Giselle". T* **150** *and similar vert designs. Multicoloured.* W w 16. *P* 13½.

636	2 r. Type **150**		75	60
637	3 r. Male dancer		1·00	90
MS638	80 × 90 mm. 10 r. Pas de deux		2·25	2·40

(Des A. Theobald. Litho Questa)

1986 (21 Apr). *60th Birthday of Queen Elizabeth II. Vert designs as T* **230a** *of Jamaica. Multicoloured.* W w 16. *P* 14½ × 14.

639	50 c. Wedding photograph, 1947		10	10
640	1 r. 25, At State Opening of Parliament, 1982		30	35
641	2 r. Queen accepting bouquet, Seychelles, 1972		45	50
642	3 r. On board Royal Yacht *Britannia*, Qatar, 1979		70	75
643	5 r. At Crown Agents Head Office, London, 1983		1·10	1·25
639/43		*Set of 5*	2·40	2·75

(Des G. Drummond. Litho Questa)

1986 (22 May). *"Ameripex '86" International Stamp Exhibition, Chicago. Inter-island Communications. T* **151** *and similar multicoloured designs.* W w 16 (*sideways on 50 c., 1r.*). *P* 14.

644	50 c. Type **151**		50	10
645	2 r. Telephone kiosk (*vert*)		1·10	60
646	3 r. Post Office counter, Victoria (*vert*)		1·40	85
647	7 r. Air Seychelles Britten-Norman "Trislander" aircraft		3·00	2·00
644/7		*Set of 4*	5·50	3·25

152 Crests of Seychelles and Knights of Malta   (**153**)

(Des Jennifer Toombs. Litho Format)

1986 (7 June). *Seychelles Knights of Malta Day.* W w 16 (*sideways*). *P* 14.

648	**152** 5 r. multicoloured	1·10	1·25
MS649	101 × 81 mm. No. 648	2·25	2·75

1986 (12 July). *Seychelles Philatelic Exhibition, Tokyo. Miniature sheet, 130×80 mm, containing stamps as Nos. 609/12, but without "Expo '85" inscription and emblem.* W w **16**. P 14.
MS650 As Nos. 609/12 .. .. 3·00 3·00

(Des D. Miller. Litho Questa)

1986 (23 July). *Royal Wedding. Vert designs as T 231a of Jamaica. Multicoloured.* W w **16**. P 14.
651 2 r. Prince Andrew and Miss Sarah Ferguson 45 50
652 10 r. Prince Andrew boarding Wessex helicopter, 1983 .. .. .. 2·25 2·40

1986 (28 Oct). *International Creole Day. No. 487a optd with T 153.*
653 1 r. Madagascar Red Fody .. .. 1·50 70

154 Pope John Paul at Seychelles Airport
155 *Melanitis leda*

(Des L. Curtis. Litho Questa)

1986 (1 Dec). *Visit of Pope John Paul II. T 154 and similar vert designs, each showing Pope and Seychelles scene. Multicoloured.* W w **16**. P 14½×14.
654 50 c. Type **154**.. .. .. 60 10
655 2 r. Catholic Cathedral, Victoria .. 1·75 60
656 3 r. Baie Lazare Parish Church .. 2·25 90
657 10 r. Aerial view of People's Stadium .. 3·75 2·75
654/7 .. .. .. Set of 4 7·50 4·00
MS658 95×106 mm. Nos. 654/7. Wmk inverted.. 9·00 9·50

(Des R. Lewington. Litho Questa)

1987 (18 Feb). *Butterflies. T 155 and similar horiz designs. Multicoloured.* W w **16** (sideways). P 14½.
659 1 r. Type **155**.. .. .. 80 25
660 2 r. *Phalanta philiberti* .. .. 1·40 75
661 3 r. *Danaus chrysippus* .. .. 1·60 1·25
662 10 r. *Euploea mitra* .. .. 4·50 4·50
659/62 .. .. .. Set of 4 7·50 6·00

156 *Gloripallium pallium*
157 Statue of Liberation

(Des Josephine Martin. Litho Walsall)

1987 (7 May). *Seashells. T 156 and similar vert designs. Multicoloured.* W w **14**. P 14½×14.
663 1 r. Type **156**.. .. .. 80 25
664 2 r. *Spondylus aurantius* .. .. 1·40 75
665 3 r. *Harpa ventricosa* and *Lioconcha ornata* .. .. .. 1·60 1·25
666 10 r. *Strombus lentiginosus* .. .. 4·50 4·50
663/6 .. .. .. Set of 4 7·50 6·00

(Des Harrison. Litho Format)

1987 (5 June). *10th Anniv of Liberation. T 157 and similar multicoloured designs.* W w **16** (sideways on 2 r., 3 r.). P 14.
667 1 r. Type **157**.. .. .. 20 50
668 2 r. Seychelles Hospital (*horiz*) .. 45 50
669 3 r. Orphanage Village (*horiz*) .. 70 75
670 10 r. Proposed Sail-fish Monument .. 2·25 2·50
667/70 .. .. .. Set of 4 3·25 3·50

158 Seychelles Savings Bank, Praslin

(Des A. Theobald. Litho Format)

1987 (25 June). *Centenary of Banking in Seychelles. T 158 and similar horiz designs.* W w **16** (sideways). P 14.
671 1 r. bronze-green and sage-green .. 20 25
672 2 r. bistre-brown and salmon .. 45 50
673 10 r. royal blue and cobalt .. .. 2·50
671/3 .. .. .. Set of 3 2·50 3·00
Designs:—2 r. Development Bank; 10 r. Central Bank.

1987 (9 Dec). *Royal Ruby Wedding. Nos. 639/43 optd with T 45a of Kiribati in silver.*
674 50 c. Wedding photograph, 1947 .. 15 15
  a: Opt inverted .. .. 75·00
675 1 r. 25, At State Opening of Parliament, 1982 .. .. .. 30 35
676 2 r. Queen accepting bouquet, Seychelles, 1972 .. .. .. 45 50
677 3 r. On board Royal Yacht *Britannia*, Qatar, 1979 .. .. 70 75
678 5 r. At Crown Agents Head Office, London, 1983 .. .. .. 1·10 1·25
674/8 .. .. .. Set of 5 2·40 2·75

159 Tuna-canning Factory

(Des O. Bell. Litho B.D.T.)

1987 (11 Dec). *Seychelles Fishing Industry. T 159 and similar diamond-shaped designs. Multicoloured.* W w **16**. P 14.
679 50 c. Type **159**.. .. .. 15 15
680 2 r. Trawler 45 50
681 3 r. Weighing catch 70 75
682 10 r. Unloading net .. .. 2·25 2·40
679/82 .. .. .. Set of 4 3·25 3·50

160 Water Sports
161 Young Turtles making for Sea

(Des Jennifer Toombs. Litho Questa)

1988 (9 Feb). *Tourism. T 160 and similar horiz designs, each showing beach hotel. Multicoloured.* W w **16** (sideways). P 14½.
683 1 r. Type **160**.. .. .. 20 25
684 2 r. Speedboat and yachts 45 50
685 3 r. Yacht at anchor.. .. .. 70 75
686 10 r. Hotel at night .. .. 2·25 2·40
683/6 .. .. .. Set of 4 3·25 3·50

(Des Doreen McGuinness. Litho Questa)

1988 (22 Apr). *The Green Turtle. T 161 and similar vert designs. Multicoloured.* W w **14**. P 14½ × 14.
687 2 r. Type **161** .. .. 1·50 1·50
  a. Vert pair. Nos. 687/8 .. .. 3·00 3·00
688 2 r. Young turtles hatching .. 1·50 1·50
689 3 r. Female turtle leaving sea .. 1·75 1·75
  a. Vert pair. Nos. 689/90 .. 3·50 3·50
690 3 r. Female laying eggs .. .. 1·75 1·75
687/90 .. .. .. Set of 4 6·00 6·00
Nos. 687/8 and 689/90 were each printed together, *se-tenant*, in vertical pairs throughout the sheets, each pair forming a composite design.

162 Shot Put
163 Police Motorcyclists

(Des O. Bell. Litho Walsall)

1988 (29 July). *Olympic Games, Seoul. T 162 and similar vert designs. Multicoloured.* W w **16**. P 14½.
691 1 r. Type **162** 30 25
692 2 r. Type **162** 55 45
  a. Horiz strip of 5. Nos. 692/6 .. 2·50
693 2 r. High jump 55 45
694 2 r. Gold medal winner on podium .. 55 45
695 2 r. Athletics 55 45
696 2 r. Javelin 55 45
697 3 r. As No. 694 .. .. .. 60 65
698 4 r. As No. 695 .. .. .. 80 85
699 5 r. As No. 696 .. .. .. 1·00 1·10
691/9 .. .. .. Set of 9 4·75 4·50
MS700 121 × 52 mm. 10 r. Tennis. W w **14** (sideways) .. .. .. 3·25 2·75
Nos. 691, 693 and 697/9 were each printed in sheets of 50 of one design. No. 693 also exists from sheets containing Nos. 692/6 printed together, *se-tenant*, in horizontal strips of five.

(Des D. Miller (1 r.), L. Curtis and D. Miller (2 r.), E. Nisbet and D. Miller (3 r.), S. Noon and D. Miller (10 r.). Litho Questa)

1988 (30 Sept). *300th Anniv of Lloyd's of London. Multicoloured designs as T 167a of Malawi.* W w **16** (sideways on 2, 3 r.). P 14.
701 1 r. Leadenhall Street, London, 1928 .. 60 25
702 2 r. *Cinq Juin* (travelling post office) (*horiz*) .. 1·25 55
703 3 r. *Queen Elizabeth 2* (liner) (*horiz*) .. 1·75 80
704 10 r. Loss of *Hindenburg* (airship), 1937 .. 4·50 3·25
701/4 .. .. .. Set of 4 7·25 4·25

(Des A. Theobald. Litho Questa)

1988 (25 Nov). *1st Anniv of Defence Forces Day. T 163 and similar horiz designs. Multicoloured.* W w **14** (sideways). P 14.
705 1 r. Type **163** 80 25
706 2 r. Air Wing helicopter .. .. 1·40 1·25
707 3 r. Patrol boat .. .. .. 1·75 1·60
708 10 r. BRDM armoured car .. .. 5·00 5·50
705/8 .. .. .. Set of 4 8·00 7·75

164 Father Christmas with Basket of Presents
165 *Dendrobium sp.*

(Des S. Hoareau (50 c.), R. Leste (2 r.), F. Anacoura (3 r.), A. McGaw (10 r.), adapted N. Harvey. Litho B.D.T.)

1988 (1 Dec). *Christmas. T 164 and similar vert designs. Multicoloured.* W w **14**. P 13½.
709 50 c. Type **164** 10 10
710 2 r. Bird and gourd filled with presents .. 50 45
711 3 r. Father Christmas basket weaving .. 70 65
712 10 r. Christmas bauble and palm tree .. 2·00 2·10
709/12 .. .. .. Set of 4 3·00 3·00

(Des Annette Robinson. Litho Questa)

1988 (21 Dec). *Orchids (1st series). T 165 and similar multicoloured designs.* W w **16** (sideways on 2, 10 r.). P 14.
713 1 r. Type **165** 45 25
714 2 r. *Arachnis hybrid* (*horiz*) .. 75 55
715 3 r. *Vanda caerulea* 95 75
716 10 r. *Dendrobium phalaenopsis* (*horiz*) .. 2·75 3·00
713/16 .. .. .. Set of 4 4·50 4·00
See also Nos. 767/70 and 795/8.

(Litho Questa)

1988 (30 Dec). *As Nos. 405B and 410B, but W w 14 (upright). P 14.*
718 10 c. Hawksbill Turtle 10 10
722 50 c. Giant Tortoise 30 30
A Questa new printing of the 25 c. was issued on the same date. It has the same watermark and perforation as No. 408B.

166 India 1976 25 p. Nehru Stamp
167 Pres. Rene addressing Rally at Old Party Office

(Des O. Bell. Litho B.D.T.)

1989 (30 Mar). *Birth Centenary of Jawaharlal Nehru (Indian statesman). T 166 and similar horiz design, each showing flags of Seychelles and India. Multicoloured.* W w **16** (sideways). P 13½.
724 2 r. Type **166** 60 50
725 10 r. Jawaharlal Nehru .. .. 2·50 3·00

(Litho Walsall (1 r. 25), Questa (others))

1989 (May)–**91**. *As Nos. 410, 415 (but new value), 489 and 491, but W w 16. Chalk-surfaced paper (1 r. 25). Imprint date at foot. P 14½×14 (1 r. 25), 14×14½ (5 r.) or 14 (others).*
732 50 c. Giant Tortoise (11.91) 10 10
735 1 r. 25, White Tern 30 35
736 3 r. Green Gecko (as No. 415) (11.91) .. 70 75
738 5 r. Octopus (1.91) .. .. 1·25 1·40
732/8 .. .. .. Set of 4 2·10 2·40

(Des D. Miller. Litho Walsall)

1989 (5 June). *25th Anniv of Seychelles People's United Party. T 167 and similar vert designs. Multicoloured.* W w **16**. P 14.
742 1 r. Type **167** 20 25
743 2 r. Women with Party flags and Maison du Peuple 40 45
744 3 r. President Rene making speech and Torch of Freedom 60 65
745 10 r. President Rene, Party flag and Torch of Freedom .. .. 2·00 2·25
742/5 .. .. .. Set of 4 2·75 3·25

(Des A. Theobald (10 r.), D. Miller (others). Litho Questa)

1989 (20 July). *20th Anniv of First Manned Landing on Moon. Multicoloured designs as T 51a of Kiribati. W w 16 (sideways on 2, 3 r.). P 14×13¹⁄₂ (1, 5 r.) or 14 (others).*
746	1 r. Lift off of "Saturn 5" rocket		20	25
747	2 r. Crew of "Apollo 15" (30×30 mm)		40	45
748	3 r. "Apollo 15" emblem (30×30 mm)		60	65
749	5 r. James Irwin saluting U.S. flag on Moon	1·00	1·10
746/9		Set of 4	2·00	2·25
MS750	100×83 mm. 10 r. Aldrin alighting from "Apollo 11" on Moon. P 14×13¹⁄₂		4·50	5·00

168 British Red Cross Ambulance, Franco-Prussian War, 1870

169 Black Parrot and Map of Praslin

(Des A. Theobald. Litho Questa)

1989 (12 Sept). *125th Anniv of International Red Cross. T 168 and similar horiz designs. W w 16 (sideways). P 14¹⁄₂.*
751	1 r. black and orange-vermilion		55	25
752	2 r. black, light green and orange-vermilion	95	85
753	3 r. black and orange-vermilion		1·40	1·25
754	10 r. black and orange-vermilion		4·25	5·00
751/4		Set of 4	6·50	6·50

Designs:—2 r. H.M. Hospital Ship *Liberty*, 1914-18; 3 r. Sunbeam "Standard" army ambulance, 1914-18; 10 r. "White Train", South Africa, 1899-1902.

(Des I. Loe. Litho Questa)

1989 (16 Oct). *Island Birds. T 169 and similar vert designs. Multicoloured. W w 16. P 14¹⁄₂×14.*
755	50 c. Type 169		75	15
756	2 r. Sooty Tern and Ile aux Vaches		1·60	1·00
757	3 r. Seychelles Magpie Robin and Frégate	1·90	1·40
758	5 r. Roseate Tern and Aride		2·50	2·75
755/8		Set of 4	6·00	4·75
MS759	83×109 mm. Nos. 755/8		6·50	6·50

170 Flags of Seychelles and France

(Adapted D. Miller from local artwork. Litho B.D.T.)

1989 (17 Nov). *Bicentenary of French Revolution and "World Stamp Expo '89", International Stamp Exhibition, Washington. T 170 and similar horiz designs. W w 16 (sideways). P 14.*
760	2 r. multicoloured		1·25	1·25
761	5 r. black, new blue and scarlet		2·50	2·75
MS762	78×100 mm. 10 r. multicoloured		4·50	5·00

Designs:—5 r. Storming the Bastille, Paris, 1789; 10 r. Reading Revolutionary proclamation, Seychelles, 1791.

171 Beau Vallon School

172 *Disperis tripetaloides*

(Des L. Curtis. Litho B.D.T.)

1989 (29 Dec). *25th Anniv of African Development Bank. T 171 and similar multicoloured designs. W w 16 (sideways on 1, 2 r.). P 14.*
763	1 r. Type 171		45	25
764	2 r. Seychelles Fishing Authority Headquarters	80	65
765	3 r. *Variola* (fishing boat) (*vert*)	1·40	1·00
766	10 r. *Deneb* (fishing boat) (*vert*)	4·00	4·50
763/6		Set of 4	6·00	5·75

(Des N. Shewring. Litho Questa)

1990 (26 Jan). *Orchids (2nd series). T 172 and similar vert designs. Multicoloured. W w 16. P 14.*
767	1 r. Type 172		65	25
768	2 r. *Vanilla phalaenopsis*		1·10	75
769	3 r. *Angraecum eburneum* subsp *superbum*	1·40	95
770	10 r. *Polystachya concreta*		4·00	4·50
767/70		Set of 4	6·50	5·75

See also Nos. 795/8.

173 Seychelles 1903 2 c. and Great Britain 1880 1¹⁄₂d. Stamps

174 Fumiyo Sako

(Des D. Miller. Litho Security Printers (M), Malaysia)

1990 (3 May). *"Stamp World London 90" International Stamp Exhibition. T 173 and similar horiz designs, each showing stamps. Multicoloured. W w 14 (sideways). P 12¹⁄₂.*
771	1 r. Type 173		55	25
772	2 r. Seychelles 1917 25 c. and G.B. 1873 1s.	95	75
773	3 r. Seychelles 1917 2 c. and G.B. 1874 6d.	1·40	1·25
774	5 r. Seychelles 1890 2 c. and G.B. 1841 1d. red-brown	2·00	2·25
771/4		Set of 4	4·50	4·00
MS775	88×60 mm. 10 r. Seychelles 1961 Post Office Centenary 2 r. 25 and G.B. 1840 Penny Black. Wmk upright		4·50	5·00

(Des D. Miller. Litho B.D.T.)

1990 (8 June). *"EXPO 90" International Garden and Greenery Exhibition, Osaka. T 174 and similar vert designs. Multicoloured. W w 14. P 14.*
776	2 r. Type 174		75	75
777	3 r. Male and female Coco-de-Mer palms	1·00	1·00
778	5 r. Pitcher Plant and Aldabra Lily	1·60	1·60
779	7 r. Arms of Seychelles and Gardenia	2·25	2·25
776/9		Set of 4	5·00	5·00
MS780	130×85 mm. Nos. 776/9. Wmk inverted	5·50	6·00

175 Air Seychelles Boeing "767-200ER" over Island

176 Adult Class

(Des D. Miller. Litho Questa)

1990 (27 July). *Air Seychelles "Boeing 767-200ER" World Record-breaking Flight (1989). W w 16. P 14×14¹⁄₂.*
781	175 3 r. multicoloured		1·60	1·60

No. 781 was printed in sheetlets of 10, containing two horizontal strips of 5, separated by a central gutter showing a map of the flight route from Grand Rapids, U.S.A. to the Seychelles.

(Des D. Miller. Litho Questa)

1990 (4 Aug). *90th Birthday of Queen Elizabeth the Queen Mother. Vert designs as T 107 (2 r.) or 108 of Kenya. W w 16. P 14×15 (2 r.) or 14¹⁄₂ (10 r.).*
782	2 r. multicoloured		75	60
783	10 r. brownish black and violet		2·75	3·00

Designs:—2 r. Queen Elizabeth in Coronation robes, 1937; 10 r. Queen Elizabeth visiting Lord Roberts Workshops, 1947.

(Des G. Vasarhelyi. Litho Questa)

1990 (8 Sept). *International Literacy Year. T 176 and similar vert designs. Multicoloured. W w 14. P 14.*
784	1 r. Type 176		40	25
785	2 r. Reading a letter		75	65
786	3 r. Following written instructions		1·00	85
787	10 r. Typewriter, calculator and crossword	3·25	3·50
784/7		Set of 4	4·75	4·75

177 Sega Dancers

178 Beach

(Des Jennifer Toombs. Litho Cartor, France)

1990 (27 Oct). *Kreol Festival. Sega Dancing. T 177 and similar vert designs. Multicoloured. W w 14. P 13¹⁄₂×14.*
788	2 r. Type 177		85	90
	a. Horiz strip of 5. Nos. 788/92		3·75	
789	2 r. Dancing couple (girl in yellow dress)	85	90
790	2 r. Female Sega dancer		85	90
791	2 r. Dancing couple (girl in floral pattern skirt)		85	90
792	2 r. Dancing couple (girl in red patterned skirt)		85	90
788/92		Set of 5	3·75	4·00

Nos. 788/92 were printed together, *se-tenant*, in horizontal strips of 5 throughout the sheet.

(Des D. Miller. Litho Questa)

1990 (10 Dec). *First Indian Ocean Regional Seminar on Petroleum Exploration. T 178 and similar horiz design. Multicoloured. W w 16 (sideways). P 14¹⁄₂.*
793	3 r. Type 178		1·00	1·00
794	10 r. Geological map		3·00	3·00

(Des N. Shewring. Litho Questa)

1991 (1 Feb). *Orchids (3rd series). Vert designs as T 172. Multicoloured. W w 16. P 14.*
795	1 r. *Bulbophyllum intertextum*		40	25
796	2 r. *Agrostophyllum occidentale*		75	60
797	3 r. *Vanilla planifolia*		1·10	85
798	10 r. *Malaxis seychellarum*		3·25	3·50
795/8		Set of 4	5·00	4·75

(Des D. Miller. Litho Questa)

1991 (17 June). *65th Birthday of Queen Elizabeth II and 70th Birthday of Prince Philip. Vert designs as T 58 of Kiribati. Multicoloured. W w 16 (sideways). P 14¹⁄₂×14.*
799	4 r. Queen in evening dress		1·40	1·50
	a. Horiz pair. Nos. 799/800 separated by label		2·75	3·00
800	4 r. Prince Philip in academic robes	1·40	1·50

Nos. 799/800 were printed in a similar sheet format to Nos. 366/7 of Kiribati.

179 *Precis rhadama*

180 "The Holy Virgin, Joseph, The Holy Child and St. John" (S. Vouillemont after Raphael)

(Des I. Loe. Litho Walsall)

1991 (15 Nov). *"Phila Nippon '91" International Stamp Exhibition, Tokyo. Butterflies. T 179 and similar horiz designs. W w 14 (sideways). P 14×14¹⁄₂.*
801	1 r. 50, Type 179		70	40
802	3 r. *Lampides boeticus*		1·25	1·00
803	3 r. 50, *Zizeeria knysna*		1·40	1·25
804	10 r. *Phalanta phalantha*		4·00	4·50
801/4		Set of 4	6·50	6·50
MS805	78×81 mm. 10 r. *Eagris sabadius*		3·75	4·25

(Des D. Miller. Litho B.D.T.)

1991 (2 Dec). *Christmas. Woodcuts. T 180 and similar vert designs. W w 16. P 13¹⁄₂×14.*
806	50 c. black, brown-ochre and bright crimson	20	15
807	1 r. black, brown-ochre and myrtle-green	35	25
808	2 r. black, brown-ochre and blue		60	60
809	7 r. black, brown-ochre & deep violet-blue	2·00	2·25
806/9		Set of 4	2·75	3·00

Designs:—1 r. "The Holy Virgin, the Child and Angel" (A. Blooting after Van Dyck); 2 r. "The Holy Family, St. John and St. Anna" (L. Vorsterman after Rubens); 7 r. "The Holy Family, Angel and St. Cathrin" (C. Bloemaert).

(Des D. Miller. Litho Questa (5 r.), Walsall (others))

1992 (6 Feb). *40th Anniv of Queen Elizabeth II's Accession. Horiz designs as T 113 of Kenya. Multicoloured. W w 14 (sideways). P 14.*
810	1 r. Seychelles coastline		45	25
811	1 r. 50, Clock Tower, Victoria		60	40
812	3 r. Victoria harbour		1·10	1·10
813	3 r. 50, Three portraits of Queen Elizabeth	1·25	1·25
814	5 r. Queen Elizabeth II		1·50	1·75
810/14		Set of 5	4·50	4·25

181 Brush Warbler

(Des I. Loe. Litho B.D.T.)

1993 (1 Mar). *Flora and Fauna.* T **181** *and similar multicoloured designs.* W w **14** (*sideways on horiz designs*). P 13½.

815	10 c.	Type **181**	..	..	10	10
816	25 c.	Bronze Gecko (*vert*)	..	..	10	10
817	50 c.	Seychelles Tree Frog	..	..	10	10
818	1 r.	Seychelles Splendid Palm (*vert*)	..	25	30
819	1 r. 50,	Seychelles Skink (*vert*)	..	35	40
820	2 r.	Giant Tenebrionid Beetle	..	50	55
821	3 r.	Seychelles Sunbird	..	..	70	75
822	3 r. 50,	Seychelles Killifish	..	85	90
823	4 r.	Magpie Robin	..	..	1·00	1·10
824	5 r.	Seychelles Vanilla (plant) (*vert*)	..	1·25	1·40
825	10 r.	Tiger Chameleon	..	..	2·40	2·50
826	15 r.	Coco-de-mer (*vert*)	..	..	3·75	4·00
827	25 r.	Paradise Flycatcher (*vert*)	..	6·25	6·50
828	50 r.	Giant Tortoise	..	..	12·50	13·00
815/28	..	..	..	*Set of* 14	27·00	29·00

POSTAGE DUE STAMPS

D 1

(Frame recess, value typo B.W.)

1951 (1 Mar). *Wmk Mult Script CA. P* 11½.

D1	D **1**	2 c. scarlet and carmine	..	..	80	1·50
D2		3 c. scarlet and green	..	..	1·25	1·50
D3		6 c. scarlet and bistre	..	..	1·25	1·25
D4		9 c. scarlet and orange	..	..	1·50	1·25
D5		15 c. scarlet and violet	..	..	1·75	7·50
D6		18 c. scarlet and blue	..	..	1·75	7·50
D7		20 c. scarlet and brown	..	..	1·75	7·50
D8		30 c. scarlet and claret	..	..	1·75	7·50
D1/8	..	..	..	*Set of* 8	10·50	32·00

1964 (7 July)–**65.** *As* 1951 *but W w* **12.**

D 9	D **1**	2 c. scarlet and carmine	..	..	1·50	7·50
D10		3 c. scarlet and green (14.9.65)	..	1·00	8·50

(Litho Walsall)

1980 (29 Feb). *Design as Type* D **1** *but redrawn, size* 18 × 22 *mm.* W w **14** (*sideways*). P 14.

D11	5 c.	rosine and magenta	..	..	15	30
D12	10 c.	rosine and deep blue-green	..	15	30
D13	15 c.	rosine and bistre	..	..	20	30
D14	20 c.	rosine and orange-brown	..	..	20	40
D15	25 c.	rosine and bright violet	..	..	20	40
D16	75 c.	rosine and maroon	..	..	30	50
D17	80 c.	rosine and deep grey-blue	..	30	50
D18	1 r.	rosine and deep reddish purple	..	30	55
D11/18	..	..	..	*Set of* 8	1·60	3·00

ZIL ELWANNYEN SESEL

(SEYCHELLES OUTER ISLANDS)

For use from Aldabra, Coetivy, Farquhar and the Amirante Islands, served by the M.V. *Cinq-Juin* travelling post office.

I Inscr "ZIL ELOIGNE SESEL"

1 Reef Fish   2 *Cinq Juin*

1980 (20 June)–**81.** *Designs as Nos. 404/11 (with imprint) and 487/94 of Seychelles but inscr. "ZIL ELOIGNE SESEL" as in T* 1. W w **14** (*sideways on* 10, 20, 50, 75 *c.*). P 14½ × 14 (40 *c.*, 1 *r.*, 1 *r.* 25, 1*r.* 50), 13½ (5, 10, 15, 20 *r.*) *or* 14 (*others*).

1	5 c. Type 1		15	20
2	10 c. Hawksbill Turtle		15	20
3	15 c. Coco-de-Mer		15	20
4	20 c. Wild Vanilla		20	20
5	25 c. *Hypolimnas misippus* (butterfly)		60	30
6	40 c. Coral scene		30	30
7	50 c. Giant Tortoise		30	30
8	75 c. Crayfish		35	30
9	1 r. Madagascar Red Fody		75	40
10	1 r. 10, Green Gecko		40	40
11	1 r. 25, White Tern		90	45
12	1 r. 50, Seychelles Flying Fox		45	35
13	5 r. Octopus		70	1·00
	a. Perf 13 (1981)		65	90
14	10 r. Giant Tiger Cowrie		1·50	1·50
	a. Perf 13 (1981)		1·00	2·00
15	15 r. Pitcher Plant		2·00	2·50
	a. Perf 13 (1981)		1·75	2·50
16	20 r. Seychelles coat of arms		2·00	3·25
	a. Perf 13 (1981)		2·00	3·75
1/16		*Set of 16*	9·00	10·50

Nos. 1/12 exist with imprint dates of either "1980" or "1981", Nos. 13/16 with "1980" only and Nos. 13a/16a "1981" only.

(Des L. Curtis. Litho Walsall)

1980 (24 Oct). *Establishment of Travelling Post Office. T* 2 *and similar horiz designs. Multicoloured.* W w **14** (*sideways*). P 14.

17	1 r. 50, Type 2		30	15
18	2 r. 10, Hand-stamping covers		40	20
19	5 r. Map of Zil Eloigne Sesel		70	40
17/19		*Set of 3*	1·25	65

Nos. 17/19 were printed in sheets including two *se-tenant* stamp-size labels.

The original version of No. 19 incorrectly showed the Agalega Islands as Seychelles territory. A corrected version was prepared prior to issue and stamps in the first type were intended for destruction. Mint examples and some used on first day covers are known, originating from supplies sent to some philatelic bureau standing order customers in error. Such stamps are not listed as they were not available from Seychelles post offices or valid for postage.

3 Yellowfin Tuna

(Des G. Drummond. Litho Rosenbaum Bros, Vienna)

1980 (28 Nov). *Marine Life. T* 3 *and similar horiz designs. Multicoloured.* W w **14**. P 14.

20	1 r. 50, Type 3		20	15
21	2 r. 10, Blue Marlin (fish)		35	20
22	5 r. Sperm Whale		70	50
20/2		*Set of 3*	1·10	75

Nos. 20/2 were printed in sheets including two *se-tenant* stamp-size labels.

(Des D. Shults. Litho Questa)

1981 (23 June–16 Nov). *Royal Wedding. Horiz designs as T* 26/27 *of Kiribati. Multicoloured.* (*a*) W w **15**. P 14.

23	40 c. Royal Escape		10	10
	a. Sheetlet. No. 23 × 6 and No. 24		90	
24	40 c. Prince Charles and Lady Diana Spencer		40	40
25	5 r. *Victoria and Albert II*		40	40
	a. Sheetlet. No. 25 × 6 and No. 26		3·50	
26	5 r. As No. 24		1·40	1·40
27	10 r. *Britannia*		85	85
	a. Sheetlet. No. 27 × 6 and No. 28		6·25	
28	10 r. As No. 24		2·00	2·50
23/8		*Set of 6*	4·50	5·00
MS29	120 × 109 mm. 7 r. 50, As No. 24. Wmk sideways. P 12 (16 Nov)		2·00	2·00

(*b*) *Booklet stamps. No wmk.* P 12 (16 Nov)

30	40 c. As No. 23		35	55
	a. Booklet pane. No. 30 × 4		1·25	
31	5 r. As No. 26		1·00	1·50
	a. Booklet pane. No. 31 × 2		2·00	

Nos. 23/8 were printed in sheetlets of seven stamps of the same face value, each containing six of the "Royal Yacht" design and one of the larger design showing Prince Charles and Lady Diana.

Nos. 30/1 come from 13 r. 20 stamp booklets.

---

4 Wright's Skink

(Des and litho Walsall)

1981 (11 Dec). *Wildlife* (1st series). *T* 4 *and similar horiz designs. Multicoloured.* W w **14** (*sideways*). P 14.

32	1 r. 40, Type 4		15	15
33	2 r. 25, Tree Frog		20	20
34	5 r. Robber Crab		40	40
32/4		*Set of 3*	65	65

See also Nos. 45/7.

5 *Cinq Juin* ("Communications")

(Des L. Curtis. Litho Harrison)

1982 (11 Mar). *Island Development. Ships. T* 5 *and similar horiz designs.* W w **14**. P 14 × 14½.

35	1 r. 75, black and orange		50	20
36	2 r. 10, black and turquoise-blue		60	30
37	5 r. black and bright scarlet		70	50
35/7		*Set of 3*	1·60	90

Designs:—2 r. 10, *Junon* ("fisheries protection"); 5 r. *Diamond M. Dragon* (drilling ship).

II Inscr "ZIL ELWAGNE SESEL"

6 *Paulette*

(Des L. Curtis. Litho Harrison)

1982 (22 July). *Local Mail Vessels. T* 6 *and similar horiz designs. Multicoloured.* W w **14** (*sideways*). P 14.

38	40 c. Type 6		20	10
39	1 r. 75, *Janette*		40	30
40	2 r. 75, *Lady Esme*		50	40
41	3 r. 50, *Cinq Juin*		60	50
38/41		*Set of 4*	1·50	1·10

7 Birds flying over Island   8 Red Land Crab

(Des Harrison. Litho Format)

1982 (19 Nov). *Aldabra, World Heritage Site. T* 7 *and similar horiz designs. Multicoloured.* W w **14** (*sideways*). P 14.

42	40 c. Type 7		30	15
43	2 r. 75, Map of the atoll		70	35
44	7 r. Giant Tortoises		1·25	75
42/4		*Set of 3*	2·00	1·10

(Des G. Drummond. Litho Questa)

1983 (25 Feb). *Wildlife* (2nd series). *T* 8 *and similar horiz designs. Multicoloured.* W w **14** (*sideways*). P 14 × 14½.

45	1 r. 75, Type 8		25	25
46	2 r. 75, Black Terrapin		35	35
47	7 r. Madagascar Green Gecko		80	80
45/7		*Set of 3*	1·25	1·25

9 Map of Poivre Island   10 Aldabra Warbler
and Île du Sud

(Des J. Cooter. Litho Format)

1983 (27 Apr). *Island Maps. T* 9 *and similar vert designs. Multicoloured.* W w **14**. P 14.

48	40 c. Type 9		10	10
49	1 r. 50, Île des Roches		25	25
50	2 r. 75, Astove Island		40	40
51	7 r. Coëtivy Island		1·10	1·10
48/51		*Set of 4*	1·75	1·75
MS52	93 × 129 mm. Nos. 48/51		2·75	3·25

(Des G. Drummond. Litho Harrison)

1983 (13 July). *Birds. T* 10 *and similar multicoloured designs.* W w **14** (*sideways on* 5 c. to 2 r. 75). P 14.

53	5 c. Type 10		40	40
54	10 c. Zebra Dove ("Barred Ground Dove")		60	30
55	15 c. Madagascar Nightjar		10	10
56	20 c. Madagascar Cisticola ("Malagasy Grass Warbler")		10	10
57	25 c. Madagascar White Eye		75	30
58	40 c. Mascarene Fody		10	10
59	50 c. White-throated Rail		90	30
60	75 c. Black Bulbul		20	25
61	2 r. Western Reef Heron ("Dimorphic Little Egret")		1·50	85
62	2 r. 10, Souimanga Sunbird		50	55
63	2 r. 50, Madagascar Turtle Dove		60	65
64	2 r. 75, Sacred Ibis		65	70
65	3 r. 50, Black Coucal (*vert*)		85	90
66	7 r. Seychelles Kestrel (*vert*)		1·75	1·90
67	15 r. Comoro Blue Pigeon (*vert*)		3·75	4·00
68	20 r. Greater Flamingo (*vert*)		5·00	5·25
53/68		*Set of 16*	16·00	15·00

For 5 c., 10 c., 25 c., 50 c. and 2 r. values in these designs, but inscribed "Zil Elwannyen Sesel", see Nos. 100/7, 165/73 and 226.

11 Windsurfing

(Des G. Wilby. Litho Questa)

1983 (27 Sept). *Tourism. T* 11 *and similar horiz designs. Multicoloured.* W w **14** (*sideways*). P 14.

69	50 c. Type 11		10	10
70	2 r. Hotel		25	25
71	3 r. View of beach		35	35
72	10 r. Islands at sunset		1·40	1·75
69/72		*Set of 4*	1·75	2·10

1983 (16–28 Dec). *Nos. 23/8 surch as T* 135 *of Seychelles.*

73	30 c. on 40 c. Royal Escape		25	25
	a. Sheetlet. No. 73 × 6 and No. 74		1·50	
	b. Surch double		50·00	
	c. Error. Surch 50 c. (as Seychelles No. 573)		60·00	
74	30 c. on 40 c. Prince Charles and Lady Diana Spencer		40	50
	b. Surch double		£130	
	c. Error. Surch 50 c. (as Seychelles No. 574)		£140	
75	2 r. on 5 r. *Victoria and Albert II* (28.12.83)		70	70
	a. Sheetlet. No. 75 × 6 and No. 76		4·75	
	b. Albino surch		40·00	
	c. Surch double		75·00	
76	2 r. on 5 r. As No. 74 (28.12.83)		1·00	1·40
	b. Albino surch		65·00	
	c. Surch double		£200	
77	3 r. on 10 r. *Britannia* (28.12.83)		85	85
	a. Sheetlet. No. 77 × 6 and No. 78		6·00	
78	3 r. on 10 r. As No. 74 (28.12.83)		1·40	1·75
73/8		*Set of 6*	4·25	5·00

12 Map of Aldabra and
Commemorative Postmark

(Des L. Curtis. Litho Questa)

1984 (30 Mar). *Re-opening of Aldabra Post Office. T* 12 *and similar horiz designs. Multicoloured.* W w **14** (*sideways*). P 14.

79	50 c. Type 12		15	25
80	2 r. 75, White-throated Rail		60	95
81	3 r. Giant Tortoise		60	1·10
82	10 r. Red-footed Booby		2·25	2·75
79/82		*Set of 4*	3·25	4·50

13 Fishing from Launch

(Des L. Curtis. Litho Walsall)

1984 (31 May). *Game Fishing. T* 13 *and similar multicoloured designs.* W w **14** (*sideways on* 50 c., 10 r.). P 14.

83	1 r. 75, Type 13		15	15
84	2 r. Hooked fish (*vert*)		45	55
85	3 r. Weighing catch (*vert*)		60	75
86	10 r. Fishing from boat (*different*)		2·00	2·50
83/6		*Set of 4*	2·75	3·50

14 Giant Hermit Crab   15 Constellation of "Orion"

(Des G. Drummond. Litho Format)

1984 (24 Aug). *Crabs. T **14** and similar horiz designs. Multi-coloured. W w 14 (sideways). P 14½.*

87	50 c. Type **14**	..	..	..	25	30
88	2 r. Fiddler Crabs	..	..	..	65	85
89	3 r. Sand Crab	..	..	..	80	1·25
90	10 r. Spotted Pebble Crab	..	..	2·50	3·25
87/90	..	..	..	*Set of 4*	3·75	5·00

(Des A. Theobald. Litho Format)

1984 (16 Oct). *The Night Sky. T **15** and similar vert designs. Multicoloured. W w 14. P 14.*

91	50 c. Type **15**	..	..	..	15	15
92	2 r. "Cygnus"	..	..	..	50	55
93	3 r. "Virgo"	..	..	..	75	80
94	10 r. "Scorpio"	..	..	..	2·00	2·25
91/4	..	..	..	*Set of 4*	3·00	3·25

III Inscr "ZIL ELWANNYEN SESEL"

16 *Lenzites elegans*   17 The Queen Mother attending Royal Opera House, Covent Garden

(Des G. Drummond. Litho Walsall)

1985 (31 Jan). *Fungi. T **16** and similar vert designs. Multicoloured. W w 14. P 14.*

95	50 c. Type **16**	..	..	..	30	20
96	2 r. *Xylaria telfairei*	..	..	80	65
97	3 r. *Lentinus sajor-caju*	..	..	1·10	90
98	10 r. *Hexagonia tenuis*..	..	..	3·00	3·00
95/8	..	..	..	*Set of 4*	4·75	4·25

(Litho Harrison)

1985 (May)–**87**. *As Nos. 54, 57, 59 and 61 but inscr "Zil Elwannyen Sesel". W w 14 (sideways). P 14.*

100	10 c. Zebra Dove ("Barred Ground Dove")	60	60
103	25 c. Madagascar White Eye	..	10	10
105	50 c. White-throated Rail (1.7.87)	..	70	70
107	2 r. Western Reef Heron ("Dimorphic Little Egret")		2·75	2·75
100/7	..	..	*Set of 4*	3·75	3·75

The 10 c. exists with different imprint dates below the design.
For 10 c., 50 c., and 2 r. values watermarked w **16** (sideways) see Nos. 165/73 and 226.

(Des A. Theobald (10 r.), C. Abbott (others). Litho Questa)

1985 (7 June). *Life and Times of Queen Elizabeth the Queen Mother. T **17** and similar vert designs. Multicoloured. W w 16. P 14½×14.*

115	1 r. The Queen Mother, 1936 (from photo by Dorothy Wilding)	..	20	25
116	2 r. With Princess Anne at Ascot, 1974	..	45	50
117	3 r. Type **17**	..	..	65	70
118	5 r. With Prince Henry at his christening (from photo by Lord Snowdon)		1·10	1·25
115/18	..	..	*Set of 4*	2·25	2·40
MS119	91×73 mm. 10 r. In a launch, Venice, 1985. Wmk sideways	..	2·25	2·75

18 Giant Tortoise

(Des. G. Vasarhelyi. Litho J.W.)

1985 (27 Sept). *Giant Tortoises of Aldabra (1st series). T **18** and similar horiz designs. Multicoloured. W w 16 (sideways). P 14.*

120	50 c. Type **18**	..	..	..	45	25
121	75 c. Giant Tortoises at stream	..	50	40
122	1 r. Giant Tortoises on grassland	..	65	45
123	2 r. Giant Tortoise (side view)	..	1·00	80
120/3	..	..	*Set of 4*	2·40	1·75
MS124	70×60 mm. 10 r. Two Giant Tortoises. P 13×13½	..	2·25	2·75

For stamps as Nos. 120/3, but without circular inscription around W.W.F. emblem, see Nos. 153/6.

19 Phoenician Trading Ship (600 B.C.)   20 *Acropora palifera* and *Tubastraea coccinea*

(Des N. Shewring. Litho Format)

1985 (25 Oct). *Famous Visitors. T **19** and similar horiz designs. Multicoloured. W w 14 (sideways). P 14.*

125	50 c. Type **19**	..	..	..	40	30
126	2 r. Sir Hugh Scott and H.M.S. *Sealark*, 1908		1·25	80
127	10 r. Vasco da Gama and *Sao Gabriel*, 1502	3·50	2·75
125/7	..	..	*Set of 3*	4·75	3·50

(Des A. Theobald. Litho Questa)

1986 (21 Apr). *60th Birthday of Queen Elizabeth II. Vert designs as T **230**a of Jamaica. Multicoloured. W w 16. P 14½×14.*

128	75 c. Princess Elizabeth at Chester, 1951	..	20	25
129	1 r. Queen and Duke of Edinburgh at Falklands Service, St. Paul's Cathedral, 1985		20	25
130	1 r. 50, At Order of St. Michael and St. George service, St. Paul's Cathedral, 1968		35	40
131	3 r. 75, In Mexico, 1975	..	..	85	90
132	5 r. At Crown Agents Head Office, London, 1983		1·10	1·25
128/32	..	..	*Set of 5*	2·40	2·75

(Des D. Miller. Litho Questa)

1986 (23 July). *Royal Wedding. Square designs as T **231**a of Jamaica. Multicoloured. W w 16. P 14.*

133	3 r. Prince Andrew and Miss Sarah Ferguson on Buckingham Palace balcony..	..	70	75
134	7 r. Prince Andrew in naval uniform	..	1·60	1·75

(Des I. Loe. Litho Harrison)

1986 (17 Sept). *Coral Formations. T **20** and similar vert designs. Multicoloured. W w 16. P 14.*

135	2 r. Type **20**	..	..	..	60	60
	a. Horiz strip of 5. Nos. 135/9	..	2·75	
136	2 r. *Echinopora lamellosa* and *Favia pallida*	60	60
137	2 r. *Sarcophyton sp.* and *Porites lutea*	..	60	60
138	2 r. *Goniopora sp.* and *Goniastrea retiformis*	60	60
139	2 r. *Tubipora musica* and *Fungia fungites*	..	60	60
135/9	..	..	*Set of 5*	2·75	2·75

Nos. 135/9 were printed together, *se-tenant*, in horizontal strips of 5 throughout the sheet, forming a composite design.

21 *Hibiscus tiliaceus*   22 *Chaetodon unimaculatus*

(Des Annette Robinson. Litho Walsall)

1986 (12 Nov). *Flora. T **21** and similar vert designs. Multicoloured. W w 16. P 14.*

140	50 c. Type **21**	..	..	..	35	20
141	2 r. *Crinum angustum*	..	..	1·60	1·10
142	3 r. *Phaius tetragonus*	..	..	2·25	1·40
143	10 r. *Rothmannia annae*	..	..	3·75	3·50
140/3	..	..	*Set of 4*	7·00	5·50

(Des G. Drummond. Litho Questa)

1987 (26 Mar). *Coral Reef Fishes. T **22** and similar vert designs. Multicoloured. W w 16. P 14.*

144	2 r. Type **22**	..	..	..	60	60
	a. Horiz strip of 5. Nos. 144/8	..	2·75	
145	2 r. *Ostorhincus fleurieu*	..	..	60	60
146	2 r. *Platax orbicularis*	..	..	60	60
147	2 r. *Abudefduf annulatus*	..	..	60	60
148	2 r. *Chaetodon lineolatus*	..	..	60	60
144/8	..	..	*Set of 5*	2·75	2·75

Nos. 144/8 were printed together, *se-tenant*, in horizontal strips of 5 throughout the sheet, forming a composite design.

23 Coconut   24 "Vallee de Mai" (Christine Harter)

(Des R. Gorringe. Litho Walsall)

1987 (26 Aug). *Trees. T **23** and similar vert designs. Multicoloured. W w 16. P 14½.*

149	1 r. Type **23**	..	..	..	55	45
150	2 r. Mangrove..	..	..	..	95	1·00
151	3 r. Pandanus Palm	..	..	1·40	1·50
152	5 r. Indian Almond	..	..	2·25	2·50
149/52	..	..	*Set of 4*	4·75	5·00

(Des G. Vasarhelyi. Litho Questa)

1987 (9 Sept). *Giant Tortoises of Aldabra (2nd series). Designs as Nos. 120/3, but without circular inscr around W.W.F. emblem. Multicoloured. W w 16 (sideways). P 14.*

153	50 c. As Type **18**	..	..	75	65
154	75 c. Giant Tortoises at stream	..	1·10	1·00
155	1 r. Giant Tortoises on grassland	..	1·40	1·25
156	2 r. Giant Tortoise (side view)	..	2·40	2·75
153/6	..	..	*Set of 4*	5·25	5·00

1987 (9 Dec). *Royal Ruby Wedding. Nos. 128/32 optd with T **45**a of Kiribati in silver.*

157	75 c. Princess Elizabeth at Chester, 1951	..	20	20
158	1 r. Queen and Duke of Edinburgh at Falklands Service, St. Paul's Cathedral, 1985		25	25
159	1 r. 50, At Order of St. Michael and St. George service, St. Paul's Cathedral, 1968		40	40
160	3 r. 75, In Mexico, 1975	..	..	90	90
161	5 r. At Crown Agents Head Office, London, 1983		1·25	1·25
157/61	..	..	*Set of 5*	2·75	2·75

(Des D. Miller. Litho Questa)

1987 (16 Dec). *Tourism. T **24** and similar vert designs. Multicoloured. W w 16. P 14.*

162	3 r. Type **24**	..	..	..	1·50	1·25
	a. Horiz strip of 3. Nos. 162/4	..	4·00	
163	3 r. Ferns	..	..	..	1·50	1·25
164	3 r. Bamboo	..	..	..	1·50	1·25
162/4	..	..	*Set of 3*	4·00	3·25

Nos. 162/4 were printed together, *se-tenant*, in horizontal strips of 3 throughout the sheet, forming the complete picture.

(Litho Harrison)

1988 (July–24 Nov). *As No. 53, but inscr "Zil Elwannyen Sesel", and Nos. 100, 105 and 107, all W w 16 (sideways). P 14.*

165	5 c. Type **10** (24.11)	..	..	10	10
166	10 c. Zebra Dove ("Barred Ground Dove") (24.11)	..	10	10
171	50 c. White-throated Rail (24.11)	..	10	15
173	2 r. Western Reef Heron ("Dimorphic Little Egret")		1·25	1·25
165/73	..	..	*Set of 4*	1·40	1·40

For 2 r. printed by Walsall and perforated 14×14½ see No. 226.

25 *Yanga seychellensis* (beetle)

(Des I. Loe. Litho Walsall)

1988 (28 July). *Insects. T **25** and similar horiz designs. Multicoloured. W w 14 (sideways). P 14.*

180	1 r. Type **25**	..	..	..	50	30
181	2 r. *Belenois aldabrensis* (butterfly)	..	75	55
182	3 r. *Polyspilota seychelliana* (mantid)	..	85	75
183	5 r. *Polposipus herculeanus* (beetle)	..	1·40	1·25
180/3	..	..	*Set of 4*	3·25	2·50

26 Olympic Rings

(Des Joan Thompson. Litho Format)

1988 (31 Aug). *Olympic Games, Seoul. Sheet 99 × 73 mm. W w 16 (sideways). P 14.*

MS184	**26** 10 r. multicoloured	..	..	2·00	2·10

(Des D. Miller (1 r.), E. Nisbet and D. Miller (2 r.), O. Bell and D. Miller (3 r.), A. Theobald and D. Miller (5 r.). Litho Walsall)

1988 (28 Oct). *300th Anniv of Lloyd's of London. Multicoloured designs as T **167**a of Malawi. W w 14 (sideways on 2, 3 r.). P 14.*

185	1 r. Modern Lloyd's Building, London	..	60	40
186	2 r. *Retriever* (cable ship) (horiz)	..	90	70
187	3 r. *Chantel* (fishing boat) (horiz) ..	..	1·50	1·25
188	5 r. Wreck of *Torrey Canyon* (tanker), Cornwall, 1967		2·00	1·60
185/8	..	..	*Set of 4*	4·50	3·50

NEW INFORMATION

The editor is always interested to correspond with people who have new information that will improve or correct the Catalogue.

27 "Father Christmas landing with
Presents" (Jean-Claude
Boniface)

(Adapted G. Vasarhelyi. Litho Questa)

1988 (18 Nov). *Christmas. Children's Paintings.* T **27** and
similar multicoloured designs. W w **16** (*sideways on* 1, 5 *r.*).
P 13½ × 14 (*horiz*) *or* 14 × 13½ (*vert*).
189	1 r. Type **27**			..	25	25
190	2 r. "Church" (Francois Barra) (*vert*)				45	45
191	3 r. "Father Christmas flying on Bird" (Wizy Ernesta) (*vert*)				65	65
192	5 r. "Father Christmas in Sleigh over Island" (Federic Lang)				1·10	1·10
189/92	..	..	..	*Set of* 4	2·25	2·25

(Des A. Theobald (10 r.), D. Miller (others). Litho Questa)

1989 (20 July). *20th Anniv of First Manned Landing on Moon.*
Multicoloured designs as T **51a** *of Kiribati.* W w **16** (*sideways*
on 2, 3 *r.*). *P* 14×13½ (1, 5 *r.*) *or* 14 (*others*).
193	1 r. Firing Room, Launch Control Centre	..		35	35
194	2 r. Crews of "Apollo-Soyuz" mission (30×30 mm)			60	60
195	3 r. "Apollo-Soyuz" emblem (30×30 mm)	..		80	80
196	5 r. "Apollo" and "Soyuz" docking in space			1·40	1·40
193/6			*Set of* 4		2·75	2·75
MS197	82×100 mm. 10 r. Recovery of "Apollo 11". P 14×13½ ..	..		4·00	4·50

28 Dumb Cane   **29** Tec-Tec Broth

(Des Lynn Chadwick. Litho Questa)

1989 (9 Oct). *Poisonous Plants (1st series).* T **28** and similar
horiz designs. Multicoloured. W w **16** (*sideways*). *P* 14.
198	1 r. Type **28**	..		50	50
199	2 r. Star of Bethlehem	..		80	80
200	3 r. Indian Liquorice	..		1·10	1·10
201	5 r. Black Nightshade	..		1·60	1·60
198/201			*Set of* 4	3·50	3·50

See also Nos. 214/17.

(Des O. Bell. Litho B.D.T.)

1989 (18 Dec). *Creole Cooking.* T **29** and similar vert designs.
Multicoloured. W w **16**. *P* 14.
202	1 r. Type **29**	..		50	50
203	2 r. Pilaff á la Seychelloise	..		80	80
204	3 r. Mullet grilled in banana leaves	..	1·10	1·10
205	5 r. Daube	..		1·60	1·60
202/5			*Set of* 4	3·50	3·50
MS206	125×80 mm. Nos. 202/5	..		5·00	5·50

Stamps from No. **MS206** have the white margin omitted on
one or both vertical sides.

30 1980 Marine Life 5 r.
Stamp

(Des D. Miller. Litho Security Printers (M), Malaysia)

1990 (3 May). *"Stamp World London 90" International Stamp
Exhibition.* T **30** and similar horiz designs showing stamps.
Multicoloured. W w **14** (*sideways*). *P* 12½.
207	1 r. Type **30**	..		50	50
208	2 r. 1980 5 r. definitive	..		80	80
209	3 r. 1983 2 r. 75 definitive	..		1·10	1·10
210	5 r. 1981 Wildlife 5 r.	..		1·60	1·60
207/10			*Set of* 4	3·50	3·50
MS211	124×84 mm. Nos. 207/10. Wmk upright	4·50	5·00

(Des D. Miller. Litho Questa)

1990 (4 Aug). *90th Birthday of Queen Elizabeth the Queen
Mother.* Vert designs as T **107** (2 r.) or **108** (10 r.) of Kenya.
W w **16**. *P* 14×15 (2 r.) or 14½ (10 r.).
212	2 r. multicoloured	..		60	60
213	10 r. black and orange-brown	..		2·40	2·40

Designs:—2 r. Duchess of York with baby Princess Elizabeth,
1926; 10 r. King George VI and Queen Elizabeth visiting
bombed district, London, 1940.

(Des Lynn Chadwick. Litho Security Printers (M), Malaysia)

1990 (5 Nov). *Poisonous Plants (2nd series). Horiz designs as*
T **28**. *Multicoloured.* W w **14** (*sideways*). *P* 12½.
214	1 r. Ordeal Plant	..	..	40	40
215	2 r. Thorn Apple	..	..	70	70
216	3 r. Strychnine Tree	..	..	90	90
217	5 r. Bwa Zasmen	..		1·40	1·40
214/17	..	..	*Set of* 4	3·00	3·00

(Litho Walsall)

1991 (Jan). *As No.* 173, *but different printer.* W w **16**
(*sideways*). *P* 14×14½.
226	2 r. Western Reef Heron ("Dimorphic Little Egret")	50	55

(Des D. Miller. Litho Questa)

1991 (17 June). *65th Birthday of Queen Elizabeth II and 70th
Birthday of Prince Philip.* Vert designs as T **58** of Kiribati.
Multicoloured. W w **16** (*sideways*). *P* 14½×14.
234	4 r. Queen Elizabeth II	..	1·40	1·50
	a. Horiz pair. Nos. 234/5 separated by label	..	2·75	3·00
235	4 r. Prince Philip	..	1·40	1·50

Nos. 234/5 were printed in a similar sheet format to Nos.
366/7 of Kiribati.

31 *St. Abbs* (full-rigged ship),
1860   **32** *Lomatopyllum
aldabrense* (plant)

(Des J. Batchelor. Litho Walsall)

1991 (28 Oct). *Shipwrecks.* T **31** and similar horiz designs.
Multicoloured. W w **14** (*sideways*). *P* 14.
236	1 r. 50, Type **31**	..	..	50	50
237	3 r. *Norden* (barque), 1862	..		95	95
238	3 r. 50, *Clan Mackay* (freighter), 1894	..	1·10	1·10
239	10 r. *Glenlyon* (freighter), 1905	..	2·75	2·75
236/9			*Set of* 4	4·75	4·75

(Des D. Miller. Litho Questa (5 r.), Walsall (others))

1992 (6 Feb). *40th Anniv of Queen Elizabeth II's Accession.
Horiz designs as* T **113** *of Kenya. Multicoloured.* W w **14**
(*sideways*). *P* 14.
240	1 r. Beach	..	..	35	35
241	1 r. 50, Aerial view of Desroches	..	50	50
242	3 r. Tree-covered coastline	..	95	95
243	3 r. 50, Three portraits of Queen Elizabeth II	1·10	1·10
244	5 r. Queen Elizabeth II	..	1·50	1·50
240/4	..	..	*Set of* 5	4·00	4·00

(Des D. Miller. Litho Questa)

1992 (19 Nov). *10th Anniv of Aldabra as a World Heritage
Site.* T **32** and similar vert designs. Multicoloured. W w **14**.
P 14½×14.
245	1 r. 50, Type **32**	..	..	50	50
246	3 r. White-throated Rail	..	..	95	95
247	3 r. 50, Robber Crab	..	..	1·10	1·10
248	10 r. Aldabra Drongo	..	..	3·00	3·00
245/8			*Set of* 4	5·00	5·00

Sierra Leone

PRICES FOR STAMPS ON COVER TO 1945

Nos. 1/3	from × 10
Nos. 4/15	from × 6
Nos. 16/26	from × 10
Nos. 27/34	from × 12
Nos. 35/7	from × 6
No. 38	—
No. 39	from × 10
Nos. 41/52	from × 4
No. 53	—
No. 54	from × 25
Nos. 55/63	from × 3
Nos. 64/71	—
Nos. 73/84	from × 3
No. 85	—
Nos. 86/97	from × 3
No. 98	—
Nos. 99/110	from × 3
No. 111	—
Nos. 112/26	from × 2
Nos. 127/30	—
Nos. 131/45	from × 2
Nos. 146/8	—
Nos. 155/66	from × 2
No. 167	—
Nos. 168/78	from × 2
Nos. 179/80	—
Nos. 181/4	from × 6
Nos. 185/7	from × 5
Nos. 188/200	from × 2

CROWN COLONY AND PROTECTORATE

The first settlement in Sierra Leone intended as a home for repatriated Africans, and subsequently those released by the Royal Navy from slave ships, was established in 1787. The Sierra Leone Company was created by Act of Parliment in 1791, but its charter was surrendered in 1808 and the coastal settlements then became a Crown Colony. The inland region was proclaimed a British protectorate on 21 August 1896.

A post office was established in 1843 but, until the inclusion of Freetown in the British Post Office packet system in 1852, overseas mail was carried at irregular intervals by passing merchant or naval vessels.

The stamps of GREAT BRITAIN were not sold at Sierra Leone post offices, although examples from ships of the West African Squadron do exist with local cancellations.

PRINTERS. All issues of Sierra Leone until 1932 were typographed by De La Rue & Co. Ltd, London.

HALF
PENNY

| 1 | 2 | (3) |

1859 (21 Sept)–**74.** *No wmk. P* 14.
1	1	6d. dull purple	£200	45·00
2		6d. grey-lilac (1865)	£225	40·00
3		6d. reddish violet (p 12½) (1872)	£300	55·00
4		6d. reddish lilac (1874)	35·00	26·00

Imperforate proofs exist.
The paper used for the 6d. value often shows varying degrees of blueing, caused by a chemical reaction.

1872–73. *Wmk Crown CC. P* 12½. (a) *Wmk sideways* (April 1872).
7	2	1d. rose-red	65·00	27·00
8		3d. buff	£110	35·00
9		4d. blue	£150	38·00
10		1s. green	£250	50·00

(b) *Wmk upright* (Sept 1873)
11	2	1d. rose-red	55·00	30·00
12		2d. magenta	£100	48·00
13		3d. saffron-yellow	£475	85·00
14		4d. blue	£200	50·00
15		1s. green	£375	90·00

1876–77. *Wmk Crown CC. P* 14.
16	2	½d. brown	2·00	4·75
17		1d. rose-red	40·00	16·00
18		1½d. lilac (1877)	40·00	5·00
19		2d. magenta	45·00	3·75
20		3d. buff	42·00	4·00
21		4d. blue	95·00	6·50
22		1s. green	50·00	6·00
16/22			Set of 7 £250	35·00

1883 (June–26 Sept). *Wmk Crown CA. P* 14.
23	2	½d. brown	17·00	38·00
24		1d. rose-red (26.9.83)	£200	35·00
25		2d. magenta	38·00	6·50
26		4d. blue	£850	28·00

1884 SIERRA 5s. LEONE SURCHARGE. From 2 June 1884 the administration decided that, as a temporary measure, revenue and fiscal duties were to be paid with ordinary postage stamps. At that time there was no postage value higher than 1s., so a local surcharge, reading "SIERRA 5s. LEONE" was applied to No. 22. Until its withdrawal on 1 March 1885 this surcharge was valid for both fiscal and postal purposes, although no genuine postal cover or piece has yet been found. One mint example is known with overprint inverted.
Remainders of the surcharge were cancelled by a horizontal red brush stroke (*Price* £30).

1884 (July)–**91.** *Wmk Crown CA. P* 14.
27	2	½d. dull green	30	40
28		1d. carmine	1·75	45
		a. Rose-carmine (1885?)	28·00	8·50
29		1½d. pale violet (1889)	2·00	5·00
30		2d. grey	18·00	12·00
31		2½d. ultramarine (1891)	7·00	65
32		3d. yellow (1889)	1·75	4·00
33		4d. brown	1·50	1·00
34		1s. red-brown (1888)	12·00	9·50
27/34			Set of 8 40·00	21·00
27/8, 30/1, 33/4 (*perf* 14) Optd "Specimen"			Set of 6	£400
27/8, 30, 33 (*perf* 12) Optd "Specimen"			Set of 4	£450

1885–96. *Wmk Crown CC. P* 14.
35	1	6d. dull violet (1885)	55·00	22·00
		a. Bisected (3d.) (on cover)		† £2500
36		6d. brown-purple (1890)	13·00	14·00
37		6d. purple-lake (1896)	2·00	6·50
36 Optd "Specimen"			60·00	

1893 (18 Jan). *Surch with T* 3. (a) *On No.* 18. *Wmk Crown CC.*
38	2	½d. on 1½d. lilac	£400	£450
		a. "PFNNY" (R. 3/1)	£1800	£2250

(b) *On No.* 29. *Wmk Crown CA*
39	2	½d. on 1½d. pale violet	2·75	3·00
		a. Surch inverted	£100	£100
		b. "PFNNY" (R. 3/1)	70·00	70·00
		ba. Ditto. Surch inverted	£1400	

The 6d. fiscal, inscribed "STAMP DUTY" as Type 6, surcharged "ONE-PENNY" is known used for postage between June and August 1894, but no official sanction for such usage has been found.

| 4 | 5 |

1896–97. *Wmk Crown CA. P* 14.
41	4	½d. dull mauve and green (1897)	75	1·10
42		1d. dull mauve and carmine	75	55
43		1½d. dull mauve and black (1897)	2·50	7·00
44		2d. dull mauve and orange	2·25	5·00
45		2½d. dull mauve and ultramarine	1·40	80
46	5	3d. dull mauve and slate	7·00	7·00
47		4d. dull mauve and carmine (1897)	7·00	13·00
48		5d. dull mauve and black (1897)	7·50	11·00
49		6d. dull mauve (1897)	7·00	13·00
50		1s. green and black	6·00	15·00
51		2s. green and ultramarine	20·00	27·00
52		5s. green and carmine	38·00	80·00
53		£1 purple/red	£140	£275
41/53			Set of 13 £200	£400
41/53 Optd "Specimen"			Set of 13	£225

POSTAGE
AND
REVENUE

| 6 | (7) |

$2\frac{1}{2}$d. $2\frac{1}{2}$d. $2\frac{1}{2}$d.

(8)   (9)   (10)

$2\frac{1}{2}$d. $2\frac{1}{2}$d. $2\frac{1}{2}$d.

(11)   (12)   (13)

POSTAGE AND
REVENUE

(14)

1897 (1 Mar). *Fiscal stamps as T* 6. *Wmk CA over Crown, w* 7. *P* 14. (a) *Optd with T* 7.
54		1d. dull purple and green	1·60	2·00
		a. Opt double	£1100	£1100

(b) *Optd with T* 7 *and surch T* 8, 10, 11 (*with square stop*) *or* 12 *with six thin bars across the original face value.*
55	8	2½d. on 3d. dull purple and green	11·00	12·00
		a. Surch double		£9500
		b. Surch double (Types 8 + 10)		£7500
		c. Surch double (Types 8 + 11)		£13000
56	10	2½d. on 3d. dull purple and green	50·00	65·00
57	11	2½d. on 3d. dull purple and green	£140	£160
58	12	2½d. on 3d. dull purple and green	£300	£350
59	8	2½d. on 6d. dull purple and green	8·50	12·00
60	10	2½d. on 6d. dull purple and green	40·00	50·00
61	11	2½d. on 6d. dull purple and green	£100	£110
62	12	2½d. on 6d. dull purple and green	£225	£250

Nos. 55/8 and 59/62 were surcharged from a setting of 30 (10×3) which contained twenty-two examples of Type 8 (including three with square stops), five of Type 10, two of Type 11 and one of Type 12.

Two examples are known of No. 55a, five of No. 55b (of which two are in the Royal Collection) and two of No. 55c (one in the Royal Collection). A unique example of a double surcharge on No. 55 showing Types 8 + 12 is also in the Royal Collection.

(c) *Optd with T* 14 *and surch T* 8, 9, 10, 11 (*with round stop*) *or* 13 *with five thin bars across the original face value.*
63	8	2½d. on 1s. dull lilac	80·00	60·00
64	9	2½d. on 1s. dull lilac	£1200	£1200
65	10	2½d. on 1s. dull lilac	£700	£700
66	11	2½d. on 1s. dull lilac	£400	£400
66a	13	2½d. on 1s. dull lilac	£1200	£1200
67	8	2½d. on 2s. dull lilac	£1300	£1600
68	9	2½d. on 2s. dull lilac	£27000	
69	10	2½d. on 2s. dull lilac	£11000	
70	11	2½d. on 2s. dull lilac	£6500	
71	13	2½d. on 2s. dull lilac	£27000	

The setting of 30 (10×3) used for both Nos. 63/6a and 67/71 contained twenty-two examples of Type 8 (including one with square stop), one of Type 9, two of Type 10, four of Type 11 and one of Type 13.

Most examples of Nos. 63/6a are water-stained. Stamps in this condition are worth about 30% of the price quoted.

| 15 | 16 |

1903. *Wmk Crown CA. P* 14.
73	15	½d. dull purple and green	3·00	2·50
74		1d. dull purple and rosine	1·25	30
75		1½d. dull purple and black	1·25	4·00
76		2d. dull purple and brown-orange	3·75	9·50
77		2½d. dull purple and ultramarine	4·50	4·75
78	16	3d. dull purple and grey	6·00	8·00
79		4d. dull purple and rosine	6·50	8·50
80		5d. dull purple and black	6·50	15·00
81		6d. dull purple	11·00	9·50
82		1s. green and black	12·00	26·00
83		2s. green and ultramarine	32·00	42·00
84		5s. green and carmine	48·00	70·00
85		£1 purple/red	£200	£225
73/85			Set of 13 £275	£325
73/85 Optd "Specimen"			Set of 13	£225

1904–5. *Wmk Mult Crown CA. Ordinary paper* (1d.) *or chalk-surfaced paper* (*others*). *P* 14.
86	15	½d. dull purple and green (1905)	5·00	2·25
87		1d. dull purple and rosine	65	35
		a. Chalk-surfaced paper (1905)	1·00	85
88		1½d. dull purple and black (1905)	2·75	8·00
89		2d. dull purple and brown-orange (1905)	4·25	3·50
90		2½d. dull purple and ultramarine (1905)	4·50	2·00
91	16	3d. dull purple and grey (1905)	16·00	3·00
92		4d. dull purple and rosine (1905)	4·50	4·75
93		5d. dull purple and black (1905)	8·50	16·00
94		6d. dull purple (1905)	3·50	9·50
95		1s. green and black (1905)	7·50	8·50
96		2s. green and ultramarine (1905)	14·00	19·00
97		5s. green and carmine (1905)	28·00	48·00
98		£1 purple/red (1905)	£200	£225
86/98			Set of 13 £250	£300

1907–12. *Wmk Mult Crown CA. Ordinary paper* (½d. *to* 2½d.) *or chalk-surfaced paper* (*others*). *P* 14.
99	15	½d. green	35	25
100		1d. carmine	6·00	20
		a. Red	2·25	15
101		1½d. orange (1910)	30	2·00
102		2d. greyish slate (1909)	80	1·50
103		2½d. blue	1·75	1·00
104	16	3d. purple/yellow (1909)	5·00	2·75
		a. Ordinary paper (1912)	5·00	5·50
105		4d. black and red/yellow (1908)	2·25	1·10
106		5d. purple and olive-green (1908)	5·50	4·25
107		6d. dull and bright purple (1908)	3·50	4·75
108		1s. black/green (1908)	5·50	4·50
109		2s. purple and bright blue/blue (1908)	15·00	12·00
110		5s. green and red/yellow (1908)	27·00	38·00
111		£1 purple and black/red (1911)	£170	£170
99/111			Set of 13 £200	£200
99/111 Optd "Specimen"			Set of 13	£300

USED HIGH VALUES. The £2 and £5 values of the King George V series were intended for fiscal use only. Before the introduction of the airmail service at the end of 1926 there was no postal rate for which they could be used. Under the airmail rates used between 1926 and 1932 it is just possible that a very heavy letter may have required a £2 value. Postmarks on the £5 and on the £2 before December 1926 can only have been applied "by favour" or, in the case of the cds type, are on stamps removed from telegraph forms. Used prices quoted for Nos. 129/30 and 147/8 are for "by favour" cancellations.

| 17 | 18 |

| 19 | 20 |

1912–21. *Wmk Mult Crown CA. Chalk-surfaced paper (3d. and 6d. to £5). P 14.*

112	17	½d. blue-green	..	..	1·00	75
		a. *Yellow-green*	..	..	1·10	75
		b. *Deep green*	..	..	3·00	1·40
113		1d. carmine-red	..	..	1·25	10
		a. *Scarlet* (1916)	..	..	1·25	50
		b. *Rose-red*	..	..	2·50	30
114		1½d. orange (1913)	..	..	1·00	95
		a. *Orange-yellow*	..	..	2·75	95
115		2d. greyish slate (1913)	..	1·00	10	
116		2½d. deep blue (1913)	..	7·50	2·25	
		a. *Ultramarine*	..	..	1·00	65
116b	20	3d. purple/*yellow*	..	..	3·00	2·50
		ba. *On pale yellow*	..	..	3·00	3·25
117	18	4d. black and red/*yellow* (Die I) (1913)	1·50	5·00	
		a. *On lemon*	..	..	3·75	5·50
		b. *On pale yellow* (Die II) (5.21)	2·75	2·75	
118		5d. purple and olive-green (1913)	85	3·00	
119		6d. dull and bright purple (1913)	3·25	3·75	
120	19	7d. purple and orange (1913)	..	2·00	4·25
121		9d. purple and black (1913)	..	5·00	6·00
122	18	10d. purple and red (1913)	..	3·00	13·00
124	20	1s. black/*green*	..	..	4·25	3·50
		a. *On blue-green, green back*	..	4·00	2·50	
125		2s. blue and purple/*blue*	..	8·00	3·50	
126		5s. red and green/*yellow*	..	11·00	18·00	
127		10s. red and green/*yellow*	..	45·00	75·00	
		a. *Carmine and blue-green/green*	60·00	90·00	
		b. *Carmine and yellow-green/green*	60·00	90·00	
128		£1 black and purple/*red*	..	£110	£140	
129		£2 blue and dull purple (S. £100)	£475	£600	
130		£5 orange and green (S. £225)	£1200	£1400	
112/28			Set of 17	£180	£250	
112/28 Optd "Specimen"			Set of 17	£300		

1921–28. *Wmk Mult Script CA. Chalk-surfaced paper (6d. to £5). P 14.*

131	17	½d. dull green ..		..	70	15
		a. *Bright green*	..	..	2·00	75
132		1d. bright violet (Die I) (1924)	1·25	60	
		a. *Die II* (1926)	..	..	1·75	10
133		1½d. scarlet (1925)	..	..	50	30
134		2d. grey (1922)	..	..	40	10
135		2½d. ultramarine	..	..	45	2·00
136	18	3d. bright blue (1922)	..	40	30	
137		4d. black and red/*pale yellow* (1925)	1·75	1·50	
138		5d. purple and olive-green	..	50	55	
139		6d. grey-purple and bright purple	1·25	2·00	
140	19	7d. purple and orange (1928)	..	2·00	11·00
141		9d. purple and black (1922)	..	2·50	8·00
142	18	10d. purple and red (1926)	..	2·00	14·00
143	20	1s. black/*emerald* (1925)	..	3·75	4·00
144		2s. blue and dull purple/*blue* (1925)	8·00	7·00	
145		5s. red and green/*yellow* (1927)	8·50	32·00	
146		10s. red and green/*green* (1927)	55·00	£100	
147		£2 bl & dull pur (1923) (Optd S. £100)	£425	£600	
148		£5 orange & grn (1923) (Optd S. £225)	£1100	£1400	
131/46			Set of 16	80·00	£160	
131/46 Optd "Specimen" ..			Set of 16	£250		

21 Rice Field   **22** Palms and Cola Tree

(Eng J.A.C. Harrison (T **21**))

1932 (1 Mar). *Wmk Mult Script CA.* (a) *Recess Waterlow. P 12½.*

155	21	½d. green	..	..	15	20
156		1d. violet	..	..	15	10
157		1½d. carmine	..	..	20	1·25
		a. Imperf between (horiz pair)			
158		2d. brown	..	..	20	10
159		3d. blue	..	..	50	85
160		4d. orange	..	..	50	2·25
161		5d. bronze-green	..	..	65	1·60
162		6d. light blue	..	..	50	1·50
163		1s. lake	..	..	90	2·50

(b) *Recess B.W. P 12.*

164	22	2s. chocolate	..	..	2·75	3·50
165		5s. deep blue	..	..	8·00	15·00
166		10s. green	..	..	48·00	85·00
167		£1 purple	..	..	75·00	£140
155/67			Set of 13	£120	£225	
155/67 Perf "Specimen" ..			Set of 13	£180		

23 Arms of Sierra Leone   **24** Old Slave Market, Freetown

27 African Elephant   **28** King George V

(Des Father F. Welsh. Recess B.W.)

1933 (2 Oct). *Centenary of Abolition of Slavery and of Death of William Wilberforce. T 23/4, 27/8 and similar designs. Wmk Mult Script CA (sideways on horiz designs). P 12.*

168		½d. green	..	..	35	70
169		1d. black and brown	..	30	10	
170		1½d. chestnut	..	..	3·50	4·00
171		2d. purple	..	..	2·50	20
172		3d. blue	..	..	2·00	1·50
173		4d. brown	..	..	6·00	10·00
174		5d. green and chestnut	..	6·50	16·00	
175		6d. black and brown-orange	..	6·50	8·00	
176		1s. violet	..	..	4·50	14·00
177		2s. brown and light blue	..	19·00	27·00	
178		5s. black and purple	..	£120	£150	
179		10s. black and sage-green	..	£130	£180	
180		£1 violet and orange	..	£325	£375	
168/180			Set of 13	£550	£700	
168/80 Perf "Specimen"			Set of 13	£550		

Designs: *Vert*—1d. "Freedom"; 1½d. Map of Sierra Leone; 4d. Government sanatorium. *Horiz*—3d. Native fruit seller; 5d. Bullom canoe; 6d. Punting near Banana; 1s. Government buildings; 2s. Bunce Island; £1 Freetown harbour.

1935 (6 May). *Silver Jubilee. As Nos. 114/17 of Jamaica. P 11×12.*

181		1d. ultramarine and grey-black	..	70	55	
		a. Extra flagstaff	..	..	40·00	
		b. Short extra flagstaff	..	48·00		
		c. Lightning conductor	..	27·00		
182		3d. brown and deep blue	..	1·00	3·25	
		a. Extra flagstaff	..	..	60·00	
		b. Short extra flagstaff	..	75·00		
		c. Lightning conductor	..	45·00		
183		5d. green and indigo	..	1·40	5·50	
		a. Extra flagstaff	..	..	90·00	
		b. Short extra flagstaff	..	£110		
		c. Lightning conductor	..	70·00		
184		1s. slate and purple	..	4·75	2·75	
		a. Extra flagstaff	..	..	£180	
		b. Short extra flagstaff	..	£150		
		c. Lightning conductor	..	£120		
181/4			Set of 4	7·00	11·00	
181/4 Perf "Specimen"			Set of 4	80·00		

For illustrations of plate varieties see Omnibus section following Zimbabwe.

1937 (12 May). *Coronation. As Nos. 118/20 of Jamaica, but ptd by B.W.*

185		1d. orange	..	..	70	25
186		2d. purple	..	..	90	30
187		3d. blue	..	..	1·75	1·75
185/7			Set of 3	3·00	2·10	
185/7 Perf "Specimen"			Set of 3	55·00		

30 Freetown from the Harbour

31 Rice Harvesting

(Recess Waterlow)

1938 (1 May)–**44.** *Wmk Mult Script CA (sideways). P 12½.*

188	30	½d. black and blue-green	..	10	20	
189		1d. black and lake	..	..	30	10
		a. Imperf between (vert pair)	..	†	
190	31	1½d. scarlet	..	..	18·00	30
190a		1½d. mauve (1.2.41)	..	..	15	10
191		2d. mauve	..	..	40·00	1·25
191a		2d. scarlet (1.2.41)	..	..	15	40
192	30	3d. black and ultramarine	..	30	30	
193		4d. black and red-brown (20.6.38)	70	75	
194	31	5d. olive-green (20.6.38)	..	4·75	2·75
195		6d. grey (20.6.38)	..	..	50	50
196	30	1s. black and olive-green (20.6.38)	50	30	
196a	31	1s. 3d. yellow-orange (1.7.44)	30	30	
197	30	2s. black and sepia (20.6.38)	2·00	90	
198	31	5s. red-brown (20.6.38)	..	5·50	3·25
199		10s. emerald-green (20.6.38)	..	10·00	7·00
200	30	£1 deep blue (20.6.38)	..	16·00	9·00
188/200			Set of 16	90·00	24·00	
188/200 Perf "Specimen" ..			Set of 16	£250		

1946 (1 Oct). *Victory. As Nos. 141/2 of Jamaica.*

201		1½d. lilac	..	..	10	10
202		3d. ultramarine	..	..	15	10
201/2 Perf "Specimen"			Set of 2	55·00		

1948 (1 Dec). *Royal Silver Wedding. As Nos. 143/4 of Jamaica.*

203		1½d. bright purple	..	..	15	15
204		£1 indigo	..	..	15·00	15·00

1949 (10 Oct). *75th Anniv of U.P.U. As Nos. 145/8 of Jamaica.*

205		1½d. purple	..	..	15	20
206		3d. deep blue	..	..	35	90
207		6d. grey	..	..	35	90
208		1s. olive	..	..	35	95
205/8	..		Set of 4	1·10	2·75	

1953 (2 June). *Coronation. As No. 153 of Jamaica, but ptd by B.W.*

209		1½d. black and purple	..	20	20	

---

32 Cape Lighthouse   **33** Cotton Tree, Freetown

(Recess Waterlow)

1956 (2 Jan)–**61.** *Designs as T 32/3. Wmk Mult Script CA. P 13½ × 13 (horiz) or 14 (vert).*

210		½d. black and deep lilac	..	55	80	
211		1d. black and olive ..		..	55	30
212		1½d. black and ultramarine ..		90	2·25	
213		2d. black and brown	..	40	10	
214		3d. black and bright blue	..	75	10	
		a. Perf 13 × 13½	..	1·25	6·00	
215		4d. black and slate-blue	..	2·25	85	
216		6d. black and violet	..	80	20	
217		1s. black and scarlet	..	80	10	
218		1s. 3d. black and sepia	..	6·50	10	
219		2s. 6d. black and chestnut ..		7·50	2·75	
220		5s. black and deep green	..	1·00	1·00	
221		10s. black and bright reddish purple	3·00	2·50	
		a. *Black and purple* (19.4.61)	9·00	24·00	
222		£1 black and orange	..	9·00	16·00	
210/22			Set of 13	30·00	24·00	

Designs: *Horiz*—1d. Queen Elizabeth II Quay; 1½d. Piassava workers; 4d. Iron ore production, Marampa; 6d. Whale Bay, York Village; 1s. 3d. Aeroplane and map; 10s. Law Courts, Freetown; £1, Government House. *Vert*—3d. Rice harvesting; 1s. Bullom canoe; 2s.6d. Orugu Railway Bridge; 5s. Kuranko Chief. Nos. 210/11 and 214 exist in coils, constructed from normal sheets.

INDEPENDENT

45 Palm Fruit Gathering   **46** Licensed Diamond Miner

52

(Des K. Penny (½d., 1s.), Messrs Thoma, Turrell and Larkins (1d., 3d., 6d., 2s. 6d.), W. G. Rumley (1½d., 5s.), J. H. Vandi (2d., 10s.), R. A. Sweet (4d., 1s 3d.), J. White (£1). Recess B.W.)

1961 (27 Apr). *Independence. T 45/6 and similar designs. W 52. P 13½.*

223		½d. chocolate and deep bluish green	10	10	
224		1d. orange-brown and myrtle-green	..	75	10
225		1½d. black and emerald	..	10	10	
226		2d. black and ultramarine ..		10	10	
227		3d. orange-brown and blue	..	10	10	
228		4d. turquoise-blue and scarlet	..	10	10	
229		6d. black and purple	..	10	10	
230		1s. chocolate and yellow-orange	..	10	10	
231		1s. 3d. turquoise-blue and violet	..	15	10	
232		2s. 6d. deep green and black	..	2·25	10	
233		5s. black and red	..	90	90	
234		10s. black and green	..	1·00	1·25	
235		£1 carmine-red and yellow	..	6·50	4·00	
223/235			Set of 13	11·00	6·50	

Designs: *Vert*—1½d., 5s. Bundu mask; 2d., 10s. Bishop Crowther and Old Fourah Bay College; 1s. Palm fruit gathering; £1, Forces Bugler. *Horiz*—3d., 6d. Sir Milton Margai; 4d., 1s. 3d. Lumley Beach, Freetown; 2s. 6d. Licensed diamond miner.

53 Royal Charter, 1799   **55** Old House of Representatives, Freetown, 1924

(Des C. P. Rang (3d., 4d.), F. H. Burgess (1s. 3d.). Recess B.W.)

1961 (25 Nov). *Royal Visit. T* **53, 55** *and similar designs. W* **52.** *P* 13½.

236	3d. black and rose-red	.. ..	10	10
237	4d. black and violet	..	10	30
238	6d. black and yellow-orange	.. ..	10	10
239	1s. 3d. black and blue	.. ..	1·75	30
236/9		Set of 4	1·90	65

Designs: *Vert—*4d. King's Yard Gate, Freetown, 1817. *Horiz—*1s. 3d. Royal Yacht *Britannia* at Freetown.

57 Campaign Emblem

(Recess B.W.)

1962 (7 Apr). *Malaria Eradication. W* **52.** *P* 11 × 11½.

240	**57**	3d. carmine-red	..	10	10
241		1s. 3d. deep green	.. ..	10	10

58 Fireball Lily   **59** Jina-gbo

(Des M. Goaman. Photo Harrison)

1963 (1 Jan). *Flowers. Vert designs as T* **58** (½d., 1½d., 3d., 4d., 1s., 2s. 6d., 5s., 10s.) *or horiz as T* **59** (*others*). *Multicoloured. W* **52** (*sideways on vert designs*). *P* 14.

242	½d. Type **58** ..	.. ..	10	10
243	1d. Type **59** ..	.. ..	10	10
244	1½d. Stereospermum	.. ..	10	10
245	2d. Black-eyed Susan	..	10	10
246	3d. Beniseed	.. ..	10	10
247	4d. Blushing Hibiscus	.. ..	15	10
248	6d. Climbing Lily	.. ..	30	10
249	1s. Beautiful Crinum	.. ..	40	10
250	1s. 3d. Blue Bells	.. ..	1·00	20
251	2s. 6d. Broken Hearts	..	1·00	30
252	5s. Ra-ponthi ..	.. ..	1·25	80
253	10s. Blue Plumbago ..	..	2·00	1·50
254	£1 African Tulip Tree	.. ..	7·50	7·00
242/254		Set of 13	12·50	9·00

71 Threshing Machine and Corn Bins

(Des V. Whiteley. Recess B.W.)

1963 (21 Mar). *Freedom from Hunger. T* **71** *and similar horiz design. W* **52.** *P* 11½ × 11.

255	3d. black and yellow-ochre..	..	15	10
256	1s. 3d. sepia and emerald-green	..	35	10

Design:—1s. 3d. Girl with onion crop.

2ND YEAR OF INDEPENDENCE **19** PROGRESS 63 DEVELOPMENT **3**d.	2nd Year Independence Progress Development 1963 **10**d.
(**73**)	(**74**)

(Optd by Govt Printer, Freetown)

1963 (27 Apr). *Second Anniv of Independence. Surch or optd as T* **73/4.** (*a*) *Postage.*

257	3d. on ½d. black & deep lilac (No. 210) (R.)	20	10
	a. Small "c" in "INDEPENDENCE"	3·00	4·50
258	4d. on 1½d. black & ultram (No. 212) (Br.) ..	10	10
259	6d. on ½d. black & deep lilac (No. 210) (O.)	20	10
	a. Small "c" in "INDEPENDENCE"	3·50	4·75
260	10d. on 3d. black & bright blue (No. 214) (R.)	40	10
261	1s. 6d. on 3d. black & brt bl (No. 214) (V.)	20	10
262	3s. 6d. on 3d. black & brt bl (No. 214) (Ult.)	30	15

(*b*) *Air. Additionally optd* "AIR MAIL"

263	7d. on 1½d. black & ultram (No. 212) (C.)	10	10
264	1s. on 1½d. blk & ultram (No. 212) (R.)	10	10
265	2s. 6d. black and chestnut (No. 219) (V.)	40	15
266	3s. on 3d. black & bright blue (No. 214) (B.)	30	15
267	6s. on 3d. black & bright blue (No. 214) (Br.)	80	20
268	11s. on 10s. black and bright reddish purple (No. 221) (V.)	1·25	75
269	11s. on £1 black and orange (No. 222) (C.)	£500	£180
257/268		Set of 12	3·50	1·60

75 Centenary Emblem

(Des M. Goaman. Recess B.W.)

1963 (1 Nov). *Centenary of Red Cross. T* **75** *and similar vert designs. W* **52.** *P* 11 × 11½.

270	3d. red and violet	.. ..	30	10
271	6d. red and black	.. ..	45	15
272	1s. 3d. red and deep bluish green	65	20
270/2		Set of 3	1·25	40

Designs:—6d. Red Cross emblem; 1s. 3d. Centenary emblem.

1853–1859–1963 Oldest Postal Service Newest G.P.O. in West Africa **1s.**	1853–1859–1963 Oldest Postage Stamp Newest G.P.O. in West Africa AIRMAIL
(**78**)	(**79**)

1963 (4 Nov). *Postal Commemorations. Optd or surch by Govt Printer, Freetown.* (*a*) *Postage. As T* **78.**

273	3d. black and bright blue (No. 214) ..	10	10
	a. "1895" for "1859" (R. 3/3)		2·50
274	4d. on 1½d. black & ultram (No. 212) (C.)	10	10
	a. "1895" for "1859" (R. 1/2)		3·50
275	9d. on 1½d. black & ultram (No. 212) (V.)	10	10
276	1s. on 1s. 3d. turq-blue & vio (No. 231) (C.)	10	10
277	1s. 6d. on ½d. black & deep lilac (No. 210) (Mag.)	15	10
278	2s. on 3d. black & brt blue (No. 214) (Br.)	15	10
	a. "1895" for "1859" (R. 4/10)		8·00

(*b*) *Air. As T* **79**

279	7d. on 3d. black & rose-red (No. 236) (Br.)	15	30
	a. "1895" for "1859" (R. 3/6, 4/4)		3·00
280	1s. 3d. black and blue (No. 239) (C.)	1·00	55
	a. "1895" for "1859" (R. 7/3)		12·00
281	2s. 6d. on 4d. turquoise-bl & scar (No. 228)	55	20
	a. "1895" for "1859" (R. 7/3)		35·00
282	3s. on 3d. black and rose-red (No. 236) (V.)	1·00	1·25
	a. "1895" for "1859" (R. 3/3)		£180
283	6s. on 6d. black & yell-orge (No. 238) (Ult.)	70	60
	a. "1895" for "1859" (R. 1/1)		40·00
284	£1 black and orange (No. 222) (R.)	13·00	13·00
	a. "1895" for "1859" (R. 11/4)		£160
273/84		Set of 12	15·00	14·50

The events commemorated are: 1853, "First Post Office"; 1859, "First Postage Stamps"; and 1963, "Newest G.P.O." in West Africa. Nos. 273, 278 have the opt. in five lines; Nos. 279, 282 in six lines (incl "AIRMAIL").

80 Lion Emblem and Map   **81** Globe and Map

(Recess and litho Walsall Lithographic Co, Ltd)

1964 (10 Feb). *World's Fair, New York. Imperf. Self-Adhesive.*

(*a*) *Postage. T* **80**

285	1d. multicoloured	.. ..	10	10
286	3d. multicoloured	.. ..	10	10
	a. Lion omitted	.. ..		
287	4d. multicoloured	.. ..	10	10
288	6d. multicoloured	.. ..	10	10
289	1s. multicoloured	.. ..	10	10
	a. "POSTAGE 1/-" omitted ..	35·00	
290	2s. multicoloured	.. ..	15	10
291	5s. multicoloured	.. ..	25	20
	a. "POSTAGE 5/-" omitted ..	35·00	

(*b*) *Air. T* **81**

292	7d. multicoloured	.. ..	10	10
293	9d. multicoloured	.. ..	10	10
	a. "AIR MAIL 9d." omitted..		
294	1s. 3d. multicoloured	..	10	10
	a. "AIR MAIL 1/3" omitted..	35·00	
295	2s. 6d. multicoloured	..	15	10
296	3s. 6d. multicoloured	..	15	10
	a. "AIR MAIL 3/6" omitted..		
297	6s. multicoloured	.. ..	25	25
	a. "AIR MAIL 6/–" omitted..	40·00	
298	11s. multicoloured	..	35	50
	a. "AIR MAIL 11/-" omitted	42·00	
285/298		Set of 14	1·40	1·40

Nos. 285/98 were issued in sheets of 30 (6 × 5) on green (postage) or yellow (airmail) backing paper with the emblems of Samuel Jones & Co. Ltd, self-adhesive paper-makers, on the back.

WARNING. These and later self-adhesive stamps should be kept on their backing paper except commercially used, which should be retained on cover or piece.

82 Inscription and Map   **83** Pres. Kennedy and Map

(Recess and litho Walsall)

1964 (11 May). *President Kennedy Memorial Issue. Imperf. Self-adhesive.* (*a*) *Postage. Green backing paper.*

299	**82**	1d. multicoloured	.. ..	10	10
300		3d. multicoloured	.. ..	10	10
301		4d. multicoloured	.. ..	10	10
302		6d. multicoloured	.. ..	10	10
303		1s. multicoloured	.. ..	10	10
304		2s. multicoloured	.. ..	10	10
305		5s. multicoloured	.. ..	25	20

(*b*) *Air. Yellow backing paper*

306	**83**	7d. multicoloured	.. ..	10	10
307		9d. multicoloured	.. ..	10	10
308		1s. 3d. multicoloured	..	10	10
309		2s. 6d. multicoloured	..	15	20
310		3s. 6d. multicoloured	..	15	20
311		6s. multicoloured	..	30	40
312		11s. multicoloured	..	45	60
299/312			Set of 14	1·50	1·75

(**New Currency. 100 cents = 1 leone**)

3c AIRMAIL **7c**	LE **1·00**
(**84**) (**85**)	(**86**)

1964–66. *Decimal currency. Various stamps surch locally.*

(i) *First issue* (4.8.64). (*a*) *Postage. Surch as T* **84**

313	1 c. on 6d. multicoloured (No. 248) (R.) ..	10	10
314	2 c. on 3d. black and rose-red (No. 236)	10	10
315	3 c. on 3d. multicoloured (No. 246) ..	10	10
	a. Surch inverted		£140
316	5 c. on ½d. chocolate and deep bluish green (No. 223) (B.)	10	10
317	8 c. on 3d. black & yell-ochre (No. 255) (R.) ..	10	10
318	10 c. on 1s. 3d. multicoloured (No. 250) (R.)	10	10
319	15 c. on 1s. multicoloured (No. 249)	15	10
320	25 c. on 6d. black & yell-orge (No. 238) (V.)	25	25
321	50 c. on 2s. 6d. dp green & blk (No. 232) (O.)	50	50

(*b*) *Air. As T* **85** *or* **86** (*Nos.* **326/7**)

322	7 c. on 1s. 3d. sepia and emerald-green (No. 256) (B.)	10	10
	a. Surch omitted (in horiz pair with normal)		
323	20 c. on 4d. turquoise-blue & scar (No. 228)	20	15
324	30 c. on 10s. black and green (No. 234) (R.)	30	30
325	40 c. on 5s. black and red (No. 233) (R.)	40	40
326	1 l. on 1s. 3d. multicoloured (No. 308) (R.)	60	80
327	2 l. on 11s. multicoloured (No. 312)	1·10	1·40
313/27		Set of 15	3·50	3·75

TWO LEONES

1c	Le **2·00**
(**87**)	(**88**)

(ii) *Second issue* (20.1.65). *Surch as T* **87** *or* **88** (*Nos.* **332/3**)

(*a*) *Postage*

328	1 c. on 3d. orange-brown and blue (No. 227)..	10	10
329	2 c. on 1d. multicoloured (No. 299) ..	10	10
330	4 c. on 3d. multicoloured (No. 300) ..	10	10
	a. Error. 4 c. on 1d. (No. 299)		
	b. Stamp omitted (in pair with normal)		
331	5 c. on 3d. multicoloured (No. 245) ..	10	10
332	1 l. on 5s. multicoloured (No. 252) (Gold)	1·25	1·25
333	2 l. on £1 carmine-red & yellow (No. 235) (B.)	2·25	2·25
	a. Surch double (B. + Blk.) ..	—	65·00

(*b*) *Air*

334	7 c. on 7d. multicoloured (No. 306) (R.) ..	10	10
335	60 c. on 9d. multicoloured (No. 307) ..	50	45
328/35		Set of 8	3·75	4·25

On No. 330b the stamp became detached before the surcharge was applied so that "4c" appears on the backing paper.

1c	**1c**
Normal	Small "c" (R. 3/3)

(iii) Third issue (4.65). Surch in figures (various sizes).
(a) Postage

336		1 c. on 1½d. black & emerald (No. 225) (R.)		10	10
	a.	Small "c"		4·00	
337		2 c. on 3d. multicoloured (No. 300)	..	10	10
338		2 c. on 4d. multicoloured (No. 287)	..	10	10
339		3 c. on 1d. multicoloured (No. 243)	..	10	10
340		3 c. on 2d. black and ultram (No. 226) (R.)		10	10
341		5 c. on 1s. 3d. turq-bl & violet (No. 231) (R.)		10	10
	a.	Surch inverted			
342		15 c. on 6d. multicoloured (No. 302)		80	50
343		15 c. on 1s. multicoloured (No. 303) (R.)	..	1·25	90
344		20 c. on 6d. black and purple (No. 229) (R.)		30	10
345		25 c. on 6d. multicoloured (No. 248) (R.)	..	35	20
346		50 c. on 3d. orange-brn & blue (No. 227) (R.)		80	55
347		60 c. on 5s. multicoloured (No. 291) (V.)	..	3·25	1·75
348		1 l. on 4d. multicoloured (No. 301) (R.)	..	3·75	2·75
349		2 l. on £1 carmine-red & yell (No. 235) (B.)		6·00	3·75

(b) Air

350	7 c. on 9d. multicoloured (No. 293)	..		15	10
336/350	.. .. ..		Set of 15	15·00	9·75

TWO 2c Leones

(89) (90)

(iv) Fourth issue (9.11.65). Surch as T 89. (a) Postage

351	80	1 c. on 6d. multicoloured (V.)	..	2·75	7·00
352		1 c. on 2s. multicoloured (V.)	..	2·75	7·00
353	82	1 c. on 3s. multicoloured (V.)	..	2·75	7·00
354		1 c. on 5s. multicoloured (V.)	..	2·75	7·00

(b) Air

355	81	2 c. on 1s. 3d. multicoloured	..	2·75	7·00
356	83	2 c. on 1s. 3d. multicoloured	..	2·75	7·00
357		2 c. on 3s. 6d. multicoloured	..	2·75	7·00
358	81	3 c. on 7d. multicoloured	..	2·75	7·00
359	83	3 c. on 9d. multicoloured	..	2·75	7·00
360	81	5 c. on 2s. 6d. multicoloured	..	2·75	7·00
361	83	5 c. on 2s. 6d. multicoloured	..	2·75	7·00
362	81	5 c. on 3s. 6d. multicoloured	..	2·75	7·00
363		5 c. on 6s. multicoloured	..	2·75	7·00
364	83	5 c. on 6s. multicoloured	..	2·75	7·00
351/364		.. .. ..	Set of 14	35·00	90·00

(v) Fifth issue (28.1.66). Air. No. 374 further surch with T 90

365	2 l. on 30 c. on 6d. multicoloured	..	2·50	2·00

IN MEMORIAM 2c
TWO GREAT LEADERS

SIR MILTON MARGAI 1895-1964 SIR WINSTON CHURCHILL 1874-1965

(91 Margai and Churchill)

1965 (19 May). *Sir Milton Margai and Sir Winston Churchill Commemoration. Nos. 242/3, 245/50 and 252/4 surch as T 91 on horiz designs or with individual portraits on vert designs as indicated.*
(a) Postage

366	2 c. on 1d. Type 59	..	10	10
367	3 c. on 3d. Beniseed (Margai)	..	10	10
368	10 c. on 1s. Beautiful Crinum (Churchill)	..	20	10
369	20 c. on 1s. 3d. Blue Bells	..	40	10
370	50 c. on 4d. Blushing Hibiscus (Margai)		90	35
371	75 c. on 5s. Ra-ponthi (Churchill)	..	2·25	1·25

(b) Air. Additionally optd "AIR MAIL"

372	7 c. on 2d. Black-eyed Susan.	..	20	10
373	15 c. on ½d. Type 58 (Margai)	..	35	10
374	30 c. on 6d. Climbing Lily (O. and W.)	..	1·25	25
375	1 l. on £1 African Tulip Tree	..	4·00	1·50
376	2 l. on 10s. Blue Plumbago (Churchill)	..	11·00	5·00
	a. Surch value omitted	..	£250	
366/376	.. ..	Set of 11	18·00	8·00

92 Cola Plant and Nut

93 Arms of Sierra Leone

94 Inscription and Necklace

(Des M. Meers. Manufactured by Walsall Lithographic Co, Ltd)

1965 (Nov). *Imperf. Self-adhesive.*

A. *Embossed on silver foil, backed with paper bearing advertisements. Emerald, olive-yellow and carmine; denominations in colours given. Postage.*

377	92	1 c. emerald	.. .. ..	25	10
378		2 c. carmine	..	25	10
379		3 c. olive-yellow..		25	10
380		4 c. silver/emerald		30	10
381		5 c. silver/carmine		30	10

B. *Typo and embossed on cream paper backed with advertisements*
(a) Postage

382	93	20 c. multicoloured	..	1·00	35
383		50 c. multicoloured	..	2·50	1·60

(b) Air

384	93	40 c. multicoloured	..	2·25	1·60

C. *Foil-backed and litho, with advertisements on white paper backing (see footnote). Air*

385	94	7 c. multicoloured	..	55	15
386		15 c. multicoloured	..	85	50
377/386		.. ..	Set of 10	7·50	4·25

The above stamps were issued in single form with attached tabs to remove the backing paper, with the exception of No. 385 which was in sheets of 25 bearing a single large advertisement on the back.

For other stamps in Type 92 see Nos. 421/31 and 435/42a. For 10 c. stamps in Type 93 see Nos. 433/b.

2c 15c
AIRMAIL

FIVE YEARS	FIVE YEARS
INDEPENDENCE	INDEPENDENCE
1961-1966	1961-1966
(95)	(96)

1966 (27 Apr). *Fifth Anniv of Independence. Various stamps surch.*
(a) Postage. As T 95

387	1 c. on 6d. multicoloured (No. 248)	..		10	10
388	2 c. on 4d. multicoloured (No. 247)	..		10	10
389	3 c. on 1½d. black & ultram (No. 212) (B.)		10	10
390	8 c. on 1s. multicoloured (No. 249) (B.)		15	10
391	10 c. on 2s. 6d. multicoloured (No. 251) (B.)		15	10
392	20 c. on 2d. black and brown (No. 213) (B.)		20	10

(b) Air. As T 96

393	7 c. on 3d. red and violet (No. 270)	..		10	10
394	15 c. on 1s. multicoloured (No. 249)	..		20	10
395	25 c. on 2s. 6d. multicoloured (No. 251)		40	60
396	50 c. on 1½d. multicoloured (No. 244)		60	80
397	1 l. on 4d. multicoloured (No. 247)		1·00	1·60
387/397	.. .. ..	Set of 11	2·50	3·00

The inscription on No. 387 is in larger type.

97 Lion's Head

98 Map of Sierra Leone

(Des and embossed Walsall)

1966 (12 Nov). *First Sierra Leone Gold Coinage Commemoration. Circular designs, embossed on gold foil, backed with paper bearing advertisements. Imperf. (a) Postage.*

(i) ¼ golde coin. Diameter 1½ in.

398	97	2 c. magenta and yellow-orange	..	10	10
399	98	3 c. emerald and bright purple..	..	10	10

(ii) ½ golde coin. Diameter 2⅛ in.

400	97	5 c. vermilion and ultramarine	..	10	10
401	98	8 c. turquoise-blue and black	..	15	15

(iii) 1 golde coin. Diameter 3¼ in.

402	97	25 c. violet and emerald ..		35	35
403	98	1 l. orange and cerise	..	2·25	2·25

(b) Air. (i) ¼ golde coin. Diameter 1½ in.

404	98	7 c. red-orange and cerise	..	10	10
405	97	10 c. cerise and greenish blue	..	15	15

(ii) ½ golde coin. Diameter 2⅛ in.

406	98	15 c. orange and cerise	..	25	25
407	97	30 c. bright purple and black	..	40	45

(iii) 1 golde coin. Diameter 3¼ in.

408	98	50 c. bright green and purple	..	75	75
409	97	2 l. black and emerald ..		3·50	3·50
398/409		.. ..	Set of 12	7·25	7·25

12½ 17½ =17½

(99) (100) (101)

1967 (2 Dec). *Decimal Currency Provisionals. Surch as T 99 (Nos. 410/13), T 100 (Nos. 415/17) or T 101 (others). (a) Postage.*

410	6½ c. on 75 c. on 5s. mult (No. 371) (R.)	..	15	15
411	7½ c. on 75 c. on 5s. mult (No. 371) (S.)	..	15	15
412	9½ c. on 50 c. on 4d. mult (No. 370) (G.)	..	20	20
413	12½ c. on 20 c. on 1s. 3d. multicoloured (No. 369) (V.)	..	25	25
414	17½ c. on 50 c. multicoloured (No. 383)	..	1·40	1·40
415	17½ c. on 1 l. on 4d. mult (No. 348) (B.)	..	1·40	1·40
416	18½ c. on 1 l. on 4d. multicoloured (No. 348)	..	1·40	1·40
417	18½ c. on 60 c. on 5s. multicoloured (No. 347)	..	4·00	4·00
418	25 c. on 50 c. multicoloured (No. 383)	..	60	60

(b) Air

419	11½ c. on 40 c. multicoloured (No. 384)	..	20	20
420	25 c. on 40 c. multicoloured (No. 384)	..	60	60
410/20	.. ..	Set of 11	9·25	9·25

102 Eagle

(Manufactured by Walsall)

1967 (2 Dec)–**69**. *Decimal Currency. Imperf. Self-adhesive.*

(a) *Postage. As T 92, but embossed on white paper, backed with paper bearing advertisements. Background colours given first, and value tablet colours in brackets*

421	92	½ c. carmine-red (carmine/white)	..	10	10
422		1 c. carmine (carmine/white)	..	15	10
423		1½ c. orange-yellow (green/white)	..	20	15
424		2 c. carmine-red (green/white)..		35	10
425		2½ c. apple-green (yellow/white)	..	50	40
426		3 c. carmine-red (white/carmine)		30	10
427		3½ c. reddish purple (white/green)		50	40
428		4 c. carmine-red (white/green)..		50	15
429		4½ c. dull green (green/white)	..	50	40
430		5 c. carmine (yellow/white)	..	50	15
431		5½ c. brown-red (green/white)	..	50	50

(b) *Air. T 102 embossed on black paper, backed with paper bearing advertisements; or, (No. 433), as T 93, typo and embossed on cream paper, also with advertisements*

432	102	9½ c. red and gold/black	..	60	60
432a		9½ c. blue and gold/black (10.9.69)		4·00	4·00
433	93	10 c. multicoloured (red frame)	..	65	65
	a.	Face value omitted			
433b		10 c. mult (black frame) (10.9.69)		4·50	4·00
434	102	15 c. green and gold/black	..	85	85
434a		15 c. red and gold/black (10.9.69)		5·00	5·00
421/34a		.. ..	Set of 17	18·00	16·00

The ½, 1½, 2, 2½, 3, 3½ and 5 c. also exist without advertisements.

The footnote below Nos. 377/86 also applies here.

Although only released for collectors on 2 December, the 5 c. was known to be in use locally in February and the 3 c. in March. The 1 c. and 2 c. were also released locally some months earlier.

See also Nos. 538/44.

1968. *No advertisements on back, and colours in value tablet reversed. Background colours given first, and value tablet colours in brackets.*

435	92	½ c. carmine-red (white/*green*)..	..	10	10
436		1 c. carmine (white/*carmine*)	..	15	10
437		2 c. carmine (white/*green*)	..	4·25	4·25
438		2½ c. apple-green (white/*yellow*)	..	4·75	4·75
439		3 c. carmine-red (carmine/*white*)	..	1·75	65

On Nos. 435 and 438, the figure "½" is larger than in Nos. 421 and 425.

It is believed that the ½ c. was released in February, the 2½ c. in April and the others in March.

The 1 c. also exists with advertisements on the backing paper.
The footnote below Nos. 377/86 also applies here.

1968-69. *No advertisements on back, colours changed and new value (7 c.). Background colours given first, and value tablet colours in brackets.* (a) *Postage.*

440	92	2 c. pink (white/*brown-lake*)	..	1·75	1·25
441		2½ c. deep bluish green (white/*orange*)	..	1·75	1·25
442		3½ c. olive-yellow (blue/*white*)	..	2·25	1·40

(b) Air

442a	92	7 c. yellow (carmine/*white*) (10.9.69)	..	6·50	3·25
435/42a			Set of 9	21·00	15·00

On Nos. 441/2 the fraction "½" is larger than in Nos. 425 and 427.

It is believed that the 3½ c. was released in March 1968 and the 2 and 2½ c. in May 1968.

The 2 c. also exists with advertisements on the backing paper.
The footnote below Nos. 377/86 also applies here.

103 Outline Map of Africa

(Litho Walsall)

1968 (25 Sept). *Human Rights Year. Each value comes in six types, showing different territories in yellow, as below. Imperf. Self-adhesive.*

A. Portuguese Guinea.   D. Rhodesia.
B. South Africa.   E. South West Africa.
C. Mozambique.   F. Angola.

To indicate yellow territory use above letters as suffix to the following catalogue numbers.

(a) Postage

					Each	Territory
443	103	½ c. multicoloured	..	..	10	10
444		2 c. multicoloured	..	..	10	10
445		2½ c. multicoloured	..	..	10	10
446		3½ c. multicoloured	..	..	10	10
447		10 c. multicoloured	..	..	15	15
448		11½ c. multicoloured	..	..	20	20
449		15 c. multicoloured	..	..	25	25

(b) Air

450	103	7½ c. multicoloured	..	..	15	15
451		9½ c. multicoloured	..	..	20	20
452		14½ c. multicoloured	..	..	25	25
453		18½ c. multicoloured	..	..	30	30
454		25 c. multicoloured	..	..	40	40
455		1 l. multicoloured	..	..	6·50	5·50
456		2 l. multicoloured	..	..	14·00	12·00
443/56	Each territory	..	..	Set of 14	20·00	18·00
443/56	Six territories	..	..	Set of 84	£120	£100

Nos. 443/56 were issued in sheets of 30 (6 × 5) on backing paper depicting diamonds or the coat of arms on the reverse. The six types occur once in each horizontal row.

OLYMPIC
PARTICIPATION

MEXICO   1968

POSTAGE

✱ 6½

(104)

1968 (30 Nov). *Mexico Olympics Participation.*

(a) Postage. No. 383 surch or optd (No. 461) as T 104

457	93	6½ c. on 50 c. multicoloured	..	20	15
458		17½ c. on 50 c. multicoloured	..	25	20
459		22½ c. on 50 c. multicoloured	..	40	30
	a. Surch double	..	..	£170	
460		28½ c. on 50 c. multicoloured	..	50	40
461		50 c. multicoloured	..	80	60

(b) Air. No. 384 surch or optd (No. 466) as T 104 in red

462	93	6½ c. on 40 c. multicoloured	..	20	15
	a. Surch double	..	..	£190	
463		17½ c. on 40 c. multicoloured	..	25	20
464		22½ c. on 40 c. multicoloured	..	40	30
465		28½ c. on 40 c. multicoloured	..	50	40
466		40 c. multicoloured	..	80	60
457/66	..	..	Set of 10	3·75	3·00

105 1859 6d.

111 1965 15 c. Self-adhesive

(Litho Walsall)

1969 (1 Mar). *Fifth Anniv of World's First Self-adhesive Postage Stamps. Reproductions of earlier issues. Multicoloured. Imperf. Self-adhesive.* (a) *Postage. Vert designs.*

467		1 c. Type 105	..	10	10
468		2 c. 1965 2 c. self-adhesive	..	10	10
469		3½ c. 1961 Independence 2 c. commemorative	..	10	10
470		5 c. 1965 20 c. self-adhesive	..	10	10
471		12½ c. 1948 Royal Silver Wedding £1 commemorative	..	30	15
472		1 l. 1923 £2	..	4·25	2·75

(b) Air. Horiz designs

473		7½ c. Type 111	..	20	10
474		9½ c. 1967 9½ c. self-adhesive	..	20	10
475		20 c. 1964 1s. 3d. self-adhesive	..	40	25
476		30 c. 1964 President Kennedy Memorial 6s. commemorative self-adhesive	55	35
477		50 c. 1933 Centenary of Abolition of Slavery £1 commemorative	..	2·00	1·00
478		2 l. 1963 2nd Anniversary of Independence 11s. commemorative	..	16·00	13·00
467/478			Set of 12	22·00	16·00

Nos. 467 and 473 were issued with tabs as note under Nos. 377/86 and No. 474 exists with tabs and also in the normal version on backing paper.

All values are on white backing paper with advertisements printed on the reverse.

117 Ore Carrier, Globe and Flags of Sierra Leone and Japan

118 Ore Carrier, Map of Europe and Africa and Flags of Sierra Leone and Netherlands

The 3½ c., 9½ c., 2 l. and 10 c., 50 c., 1 l. are as T 118 but show respectively the flags of Great Britain and West Germany instead of the Netherlands.

(Litho Walsall)

1969 (10 July). *Pepel Port Improvements. Imperf. Self-adhesive, backed with paper bearing advertisements.* (a) *Postage.*

479	117	1 c. multicoloured	..	10	10
480	118	2 c. multicoloured	..	10	10
481	–	3½ c. multicoloured	..	10	10
482	–	10 c. multicoloured	..	10	10
483	118	18½ c. multicoloured	..	20	25
484	–	50 c. multicoloured	..	70	85

(b) Air

485	117	7½ c. multicoloured	..	10	10
486	–	9½ c. multicoloured	..	15	10
487	117	15 c. multicoloured	..	20	25
488	118	25 c. multicoloured	..	30	35
489	–	1 l. multicoloured	..	1·25	1·75
490	–	2 l. multicoloured	..	2·50	4·00
479/90			Set of 12	5·00	7·00

119 African Development Bank Emblem   120 Boy Scouts Emblem in "Diamond"

(Litho and embossed Walsall)

1969 (10 Sept). *Fifth Anniv of African Development Bank. Self-adhesive, backed with paper bearing advertisements. Imperf.*

(a) Postage

491	119	3½ c. deep green, gold and blue	..	25	20

(b) Air

492	119	9½ c. bluish violet, gold and apple-green	..	35	45

(Litho Walsall)

1969 (6 Dec). *Boy Scouts Diamond Jubilee. T 120 and similar design. Imperf. Self-adhesive, backed with paper bearing advertisements.*

(a) Postage

493	120	1 c. multicoloured	..	10	10
494		2 c. multicoloured	..	10	10
495		3½ c. multicoloured	..	15	10
496		4½ c. multicoloured	..	15	15
497		5 c. multicoloured	..	15	15
498		75 c. multicoloured	..	9·00	5·00

(b) Air

499	–	7½ c. multicoloured	..	35	30
500	–	9½ c. multicoloured	..	45	35
501	–	15 c. multicoloured	..	70	50
502	–	22 c. multicoloured	..	1·25	70
503	–	55 c. multicoloured	..	7·50	4·00
504	–	3 l. multicoloured	..	85·00	60·00
493/504			Set of 12	95·00	65·00

Design: *Octagonal Shape* (65 × 51 *mm*)—Nos. 499/504 Scout saluting, Baden-Powell and badge.

(121)

1970 (28 Mar). *Air. No. 443 surch as T 121.*

				Each	Territory
505	103	7½ c. on ½ c. multicoloured (G.)	..	20	10
506		9½ c. on ½ c. multicoloured (P.)	..	20	10
507		15 c. on ½ c. multicoloured (B.)	..	40	25
508		28 c. on ½ c. multicoloured (G.)	..	70	55
509		40 c. on ½ c. multicoloured (B.)	..	1·25	1·40
510		2 l. on ½ c. multicoloured (Sil.)	..	6·00	9·00
505/10	Each Territory	..	Set of 6	8·00	10·00
505/10	Six Territories	..	Set of 36	45·00	55·00

122 Expo Symbol and Maps of Sierra Leone and Japan

(Litho Walsall)

1970 (22 June). *World Fair, Osaka. T 122 and similar design. Imperf. Self-adhesive, backed with paper bearing advertisements.*

(a) Postage

511	122	2 c. multicoloured	..	10	10
512		3½ c. multicoloured	..	10	10
513		10 c. multicoloured	..	15	10
514		12½ c. multicoloured	..	15	10
515		20 c. multicoloured	..	20	10
516		45 c. multicoloured	..	45	45

(b) Air

517	–	7½ c. multicoloured	..	10	10
518	–	9½ c. multicoloured	..	15	10
519	–	15 c. multicoloured	..	20	10
520	–	25 c. multicoloured	..	40	20
521	–	50 c. multicoloured	..	55	50
522	–	3 l. multicoloured	..	3·00	4·00
511/22			Set of 12	4·50	5·00

Design: *Chrysanthemum shape* (43 × 42 *mm*)—Nos. 517/22 Maps of Sierra Leone and Japan.

123 Diamond

124 Palm Nut

(Litho and embossed Walsall)

1970 (3 Oct). *Imperf. Self-adhesive, backed with paper bearing advertisements.*

523	123	1 c. multicoloured				10	10
524		1½ c. multicoloured				10	10
525		2 c. multicoloured				10	10
526		2½ c. multicoloured				10	10
527		3 c. multicoloured				15	10
528		3½ c. multicoloured				15	10
529		4 c. multicoloured				15	10
530		5 c. multicoloured				20	10
531	124	6 c. multicoloured				25	10
532		7 c. multicoloured				30	10
533		8½ c. multicoloured				40	15
534		9 c. multicoloured				40	15
535		10 c. multicoloured				45	15
536		11½ c. multicoloured				55	20
537		18½ c. multicoloured				75	45

1970 (3 Oct). *Air. As T 102, but embossed on white paper. Backed with paper bearing advertisements.*

538	102	7½ c. gold and red				35	10
539		9½ c. rose and bright green			40	10
540		15 c. pink and greenish blue			55	20
541		25 c. gold and purple				90	50
542		50 c. bright green and orange			2·00	1·50
543		1 l. royal blue and silver			5·00	7·00
544		2 l. ultramarine and gold			10·00	16·00
523/44					*Set of 22*	21·00	24·00

126 "Jewellery Box" and Sewa Diadem

(Litho and embossed Walsall)

1970 (30 Dec). *Diamond Industry. T 126 and similar design. Imperf (backing paper roul 20). Self-adhesive, backed with paper bearing advertisements. (a) Postage.*

545	126	2 c. multicoloured				30	10
546		3½ c. multicoloured				30	10
547		10 c. multicoloured				55	15
548		12½ c. multicoloured				75	25
549		40 c. multicoloured				1·75	1·00
550		1 l. multicoloured				10·00	8·50

(b) Air

551	—	7½ c. multicoloured				50	10
552	—	9½ c. multicoloured				60	10
553	—	15 c. multicoloured				95	30
554	—	25 c. multicoloured				1·40	60
555	—	75 c. multicoloured				5·50	4·50
556	—	2 l. multicoloured				24·00	20·00
545/556					*Set of 12*	42·00	32·00

Design: *Horiz (63 × 61 mm)*—Nos. 551/6, Diamond and curtain.

ALTERED CATALOGUE NUMBERS

Any Catalogue numbers altered from the last edition are shown as a list in the introductory pages.

10c AIRMAIL

127 "Traffic Changeover" **(128)**

1971 (1 Mar). *Changeover to Driving on the Right of the Road. Imperf (backing paper roul 20). Self-adhesive, backed with paper bearing advertisements. (a) Postage.*

557	127	3½ c. yellow-orange, ultram & blk	1·50	50

(b) Air

558	127	9½ c. ultramarine, yell-orge & blk	2·00	1·75

1971 (1 Mar). *Air. Surch as T 128, in red (No. 559), blue (Nos. 560 and 562) or black (others).*

559		10 c. on 2d. black and ultramarine (No. 226) ..	40	20
560		20 c. on 1s. chocolate & yell-orge (No. 230) ..	70	45
561		50 c. on 1d. multicoloured (No. 243) ..	1·25	1·10
562		70 c. on 30 c. multicoloured (No. 476)..	2·00	2·75
563		1 l. on 30 c. multicoloured (No. 476)..	3·00	3·75
559/63		.. .. .. *Set of 5*	6·50	7·50

REPUBLIC

129 Flag and Lion's Head

130 Pres. Siaka Stevens

(Manufactured by Walsall)

1971 (27 Apr). *Tenth Anniv of Independence. T 129 and similar design. Imperf. Self-adhesive, backed with paper bearing advertisements. (a) Postage.*

564	129	2 c. multicoloured				10	10
565		3½ c. multicoloured				10	10
566		10 c. multicoloured				15	10
567		12½ c. multicoloured				20	10
568		40 c. multicoloured				70	40
569		1 l. multicoloured				1·50	2·50

(b) Air

570	—	7½ c. multicoloured				15	10
571	—	9½ c. multicoloured				15	10
572	—	15 c. multicoloured				25	10
573	—	25 c. multicoloured				35	35
574	—	75 c. multicoloured				1·25	1·50
575	—	2 l. multicoloured				4·00	6·50
564/75		.. .. *Set of 12*	8·00	10·50

Design: *"Map" shaped as T 129*—Nos. 570/5, Bugles and lion's head.

(Litho D.L.R.)

1972 (5 Dec)–*78. Multicoloured; colour of background given. P 13.*
A. *Glazed ordinary paper.*
B. *Chalk-surfaced paper (1975–78).*

			A		B	
576	130	1 c. light rose-lilac	10	10	40	40
577		2 c. lavender (*shades*)	10	10	30	30
578		4 c. cobalt ..	10	10	65	40
579		5 c. light cinnamon	10	10	65	30
580		7 c. light rose ..	15	10	90	30
581		10 c. olive-bistre ..	15	10	90	30
582		15 c. pale yellow-green	25	15	1·50	60
583		18 c. yellow-ochre ..	25	15	1·50	85
584		20 c. pale greenish blue	30	15	1·50	1·00
585		25 c. orange-ochre ..	35	15	1·50	1·00
586		50 c. light turquoise-green	1·00	55	4·00	2·50
587		1 l. bright reddish mauve (*shades*)	1·50	1·00	4·50	3·50
588		2 l. orange-salmon ..	3·50	3·50	11·00	15·00
589		5 l. light stone ..	8·00	8·50	18·00	32·00
576/89 ..		*Set of 14*	14·00	13·00	42·00	55·00

131 Guma Valley Dam and Bank Emblem

(Litho D.L.R.)

1975 (14 Jan). *Tenth Anniv of African Development Bank (1974). P 13½ × 13. (a) Postage.*

590	131	4 c. multicoloured	45·00	28·00

(b) Air

591	131	15 c. multicoloured	..	1·00	80

---

132 Opening Ceremony

(Litho D.L.R.)

1975 (25 Aug). *Opening of New Congo Bridge and President Stevens' 70th Birthday. P 12½ × 13. (a) Postage.*

592	132	5 c. multicoloured		5·00	1·75

(b) Air

593	132	20 c. multicoloured		70	25

133 Presidents Tolbert and Stevens, and Handclasp

(Litho D.L.R.)

1975 (3 Oct). *1st Anniv of Mano River Union. P 12½ × 13. (a) Postage.*

594	133	4 c. multicoloured	..	75	50

(b) Air

595	133	15 c. multicoloured	..	35	25

134 "Quaid-i-Azam" (Mohammed Ali Jinnah)

135 Queen Elizabeth II

(Litho Pakistan Security Printing Corporation)

1977 (28 Jan). *Birth Centenary of Mohammed Ali Jinnah (Quaid-i-Azam). P 13.*

596	134	30 c. multicoloured	..	75	30

(Des A. Larkins. Litho De La Rue, Colombia)

1977 (28 Nov). *Silver Jubilee. P 12½ × 12.*

597	135	5 c. multicoloured	..	10	10
598		1 l. multicoloured	..	90	80

136 College Buildings

137 St. Edward's Crown and Sceptres

(Des A. Larkins. Litho De La Rue, Colombia)

1977 (19 Dec). *150th Anniv of Fourah Bay College. T 136 and similar vert design. Multicoloured. P 12 × 12½ (5 c.) or 12½ × 12 (20 c.).*

599		5 c. Type 136		10	10
600		20 c. The old college	..	35	30

(Des L. Curtis. Litho Harrison)

1978 (14 Sept). *25th Anniv of Coronation. T 137 and similar vert designs. Multicoloured. P 14½ × 14.*

601		5 c. Type 137		10	10
602		50 c. Queen Elizabeth II in Coronation Coach	30	40
603		1 l. Queen Elizabeth II and Prince Philip	40	60
601/3 ..		*Set of 3*	65	1·00

138 *Myrina silenus*

139 Young Child's Face

(Des J. Cooter. Litho Questa)

1979 (9 Apr). *Butterflies* (1st series). *T* **138** *and similar horiz designs. Multicoloured.* P 14½ × 14.
604	5 c. Type **138**	10	10
605	15 c. *Papilio nireus*	25	15
606	25 c. *Catacroptera cloanthe*	40	15
607	1 l. *Druryia antimachus*	2·00	1·50
604/7	*Set of* 4	2·50	1·60

See also Nos. 646/9.

(Des BG Studio. Litho Walsall)

1979 (13 Aug). *International Year of the Child and 30th Anniv of S.O.S. International (child distress organisation). T* **139** *and similar vert designs. Multicoloured.* W w 14. P 14 × 13½.
608	5 c. Type **139**	10	10
609	27 c. Young child with baby	20	25
610	1 l. Mother with young child	50	1·10
608/10	*Set of* 3	65	1·25
MS611	114 × 84 mm. No. 610. Wmk sideways	1·00	1·75

140 Presidents Stevens (Sierra Leone) and Tolbert (Liberia), Dove with Letter and Bridge

(Des L. Curtis. Litho Questa)

1979 (3 Oct). *5th Anniv of Mano River Union and 1st Anniv of Postal Union.* W w 14 *(sideways).* P 13½ × 14.
612	**140** 5 c. sepia, orange and greenish yellow	10	10
613	22 c. sepia, orge-yell & brt reddish violet	10	15
614	27 c. sepia, light blue and orange	10	15
615	35 c. sepia, blue-green and orange-red	15	20
616	1 l. sepia, brt reddish violet & lt blue	50	1·00
612/16	*Set of* 5	75	1·40
MS617	144 × 73 mm. No. 616	55	1·00

141 Great Britain 1848 10d. Stamp   142 Knysna Touraco

(Des J.W. Litho Walsall)

1979 (19 Dec). *Death Centenary of Sir Rowland Hill. T* **141** *and similar vert designs showing stamps.* W w 14. P 14 × 14½.
618	10 c. black, orange-brown and new blue	15	10
619	15 c. black, brown-ochre and greenish blue	25	15
620	50 c. black, carmine and greenish yellow	60	70
618/20	*Set of* 3	90	85
MS621	90 × 99 mm. 1 l. black, carm-red & flesh	60	80

Designs:—15 c. 1872 4d.; 50 c. 1961 £1 Independence commemorative; 1 l. 1912 £1.

(Des J.W. Litho Format)

1980 (29 Jan)–**82**. *Birds. Multicoloured designs as T* **142**. W w 14 *(sideways on* 1, 2, 3, 5, 7 c., 1, 2 *and* 5 l.). P 14.

A. *No imprint.* B. *Imprint date at foot*
		A		B	
622	1 c. Type **142**	20	50	30	70
623	2 c. Olive-bellied Sunbird	20	50	40	70
624	3 c. Western Black-headed Oriole	50	50	30	70
625	5 c. Spur-winged Goose	50	30	30	40
626	7 c. Didric Cuckoo	40	30	7·00	3·00
627	10 c. Grey Parrot (*vert*)	50	40	30	45
628	15 c. Blue Quail (*vert*)	75	80	40	1·00
629	20 c. African Wood Owl (*vert*)	1·00	1·25	40	1·00
630	30 c. Great Blue Turaco (*vert*)	1·00	1·25	50	1·25
631	40 c. Blue-breasted Kingfisher (*vert*)	1·25	1·40	60	1·50
632	50 c. Black Crake (*vert*)	1·25	1·40	60	1·75
633	1 l. Hartlaub's Duck	1·40	2·00	60	2·25
634	2 l. Black Bee Eater	2·50	3·50	1·75	5·00
635	5 l. Barrow's Bustard	3·50	4·50	4·25	9·00
622/35	*Set of* 14	15·00	20·00	16·00	25·00

Dates of issue: No Imprint—29.1.80. With Imprint—21.12.81 5, 10, 15, 30, 40, 50 c., 1 l., 2 l., 5 l.; 15.3.82 1, 2, 3, 20 c.; 11.10.82 7 c.

Nos. 622A/35A exist imperforate from stock dispersed by the liquidator of Format International Security Printers Ltd.

For similar stamps, but without watermark, see Nos. 760/73.

143 Paul P. Harris (founder), President Stevens of Sierra Leone and Rotary Emblem

(Des BG Studio. Litho Walsall)

1980 (23 Feb). *75th Anniv of Rotary International.* W w 14 (*sideways*). P 13½.
636	**143** 5 c. multicoloured	10	10
637	27 c. multicoloured	10	10
638	50 c. multicoloured	20	25
639	1 l. multicoloured	40	55
636/9	*Set of* 4	65	85

144 *Maria*, 1884   145 Organisation for African Unity Emblem

(Des L. Dunn. Litho Walsall)

1980 (6 May). *"London 1980" International Stamp Exhibition. Mail Ships. T* **144** *and similar horiz designs. Multicoloured.* W w 14 (*sideways*). P 14.
640	6 c. Type **144**	10	10
641	31 c. *Tarquah*, 1902	25	30
642	50 c. *Aureol*, 1951	40	60
643	1 l. *Africa Palm*, 1974	55	95
640/3	*Set of* 4	1·10	1·75

(Des L. Curtis. Litho Questa)

1980 (1 July). *African Summit Conference, Freetown.* W w 14. P 14 × 14½.
644	**145** 20 c. black, light blue and bright purple	10	10
645	1 l. black, bright purple and light blue	45	45

146 *Graphium policenes*   147 Arrival at Freetown Airport

(Des I. Loe. Litho Questa)

1980 (6 Oct). *Butterflies* (2nd series). *T* **146** *and similar vert designs. Multicoloured.* W w 14. P 13½.
646	5 c. Type **146**	10	10
647	27 c. *Charaxes varanes*	30	15
648	35 c. *Charaxes brutus*	35	25
649	1 l. *Euphaedra zaddachi*	1·10	1·40
646/9	*Set of* 4	1·75	1·75

(Des L. Curtis. Litho Format)

1980 (5 Dec). *Tourism. T* **147** *and similar vert designs. Multicoloured.* W w 14. P 13½.
650	6 c. Type **147**	10	10
651	26 c. Welcome to tourists	20	20
652	31 c. Freetown cotton tree	25	25
653	40 c. Beinkongo Falls	30	30
654	50 c. Sports facilities	40	40
655	1 l. African Elephant	95	95
650/5		2·00	2·00

148 Servals   149 Soldiers (Defence)

(Des P. Oxenham. Litho Questa)

1981 (28 Feb). *Wild Cats. T* **148** *and similar horiz designs. Multicoloured.* W w 14 (*sideways*). P 13½ × 14.
656	6 c. Type **148**	10	10
	a. Horiz pair. Nos. 656/7	10	10
657	6 c. Serval cubs	10	10
658	31 c. African Golden Cats	30	30
	a. Horiz pair. Nos. 658/9	60	60
659	31 c. African Golden Cat cubs	30	30
660	50 c. Leopards	45	45
	a. Horiz pair. Nos. 660/1	90	90
661	50 c. Leopard cubs	45	45
662	1 l. Lions	80	80
	a. Horiz pair. Nos. 662/3	1·60	1·60
663	1 l. Lion cubs	80	80
656/63	*Set of* 8	2·75	2·75

The two designs of each value were printed together, *se-tenant*, in horizontal pairs throughout the sheet, forming composite designs.

(Des G. Hutchins. Litho Walsall)

1981 (18 Apr). *20th Anniv of Independence and 10th Anniv of Republic. National Services. T* **149** *and similar multicoloured designs.* W w 14 (*sideways on* 31 c. *and* 1 l.). P 14½.
664	6 c. Type **149**	40	10
665	31 c. Nurses administering first aid, and ambulance (Health) (*horiz*)	1·00	20
666	40 c. Controlling traffic (Police Force)	1·75	30
667	1 l. Patrol boat (Coastguard) (*horiz*)	2·50	1·25
664/7	*Set of* 4	5·00	1·60

150 Wedding Bouquet from Sierra Leone   151 Sandringham

(Des J.W. Litho Harrison)

1981 (22 July). *Royal Wedding* (1st issue). *T* **150** *and similar vert designs. Multicoloured.* W w 14. P 14.
668	31 c. Type **150**	20	20
669	45 c. Prince Charles as helicopter pilot	25	30
670	1 l. Prince Charles and Lady Diana Spencer	45	1·10
668/70	*Set of* 3	80	1·40

(Des J.W. Litho Format)

1981 (9 Sept–30 Nov). *Royal Wedding* (2nd issue). *T* **151** *and similar vert designs. Multicoloured.* (a) *Sheet stamps.* P 12.
671	35 c. Type **151**	30	35
672	60 c. Prince Charles in outdoor clothes	50	40
673	1 l. 50. Prince Charles and Lady Diana Spencer	1·00	1·40
671/3	*Set of* 3	1·60	1·90
MS674	96 × 83 mm. 3 l. Royal Landau. P 14	1·50	1·50

(b) *Booklet stamps.* P 14 (30 Nov)
675	70 c. Type **151**	75	90
	a. Booklet pane. Nos. 675/6 × 2 plus two printed labels	3·00	
676	1 l. 30, As 60 c.	1·00	1·25
677	2 l. As 1 l. 50	3·25	3·50
	a. Booklet pane of 1	3·25	
675/7	*Set of* 3	4·50	5·00

Nos. 671/3 were each printed in small sheets of 6 including one *se-tenant* stamp-size label.

152 "Physical Recreation"   153 Pineapples

(Des BG Studio. Litho Questa)

1981 (30 Sept). *25th Anniv of Duke of Edinburgh Award Scheme and President's Award Scheme Publicity. T* **152** *and similar vert designs. Multicoloured.* W w 14. P 14.
678	6 c. Type **152**	10	10
679	31 c. "Community service"	15	10
680	1 l. Duke of Edinburgh	40	40
681	1 l. President Siaka Stevens	40	40
678/81	*Set of* 4	90	85

(Des BG Studio. Litho Questa)

1981 (16 Oct). *World Food Day* (1st issue). *T* **153** *and similar vert designs. Multicoloured.* W w 14. P 14.
682	6 c. Type **153**	10	10
683	31 c. Groundnuts	15	10
684	50 c. Cassava fruits	20	15
685	1 l. Rice plants	50	50
682/5	*Set of* 4	75	70

154 Groundnuts

(Litho Format)

1981 (2 Nov). *World Food Day* (2nd issue). *Agricultural Industry. T* **154** *and similar horiz designs. Multicoloured.* P 14½.
686	6 c. Type **154**	10	10
687	31 c. Cassava	25	10
688	50 c. Rice	45	25
689	1 l. Pineapples	45	70
686/9	*Set of* 4	1·50	1·00

Examples of Nos. 686/9 *se-tenant* come from unissued sheetlets dispersed by the liquidator of Format International Security Printers Ltd.

155 Scouts with Cattle   (156)

(Des M. Diamond. Litho Questa)

1982 (23 Aug). *75th Anniv of Boy Scout Movement. T* **155** *and similar horiz designs. Multicoloured. P* 14.

690	20 c. Type **155**		25	10
691	50 c. Scouts picking flowers		50	40
692	1 l. Lord Baden-Powell		90	1·00
693	2 l. Scouts fishing		1·90	2·00
690/3		*Set of* 4	3·25	3·00
MS694	101 × 70 mm. 3 l. Scouts raising flag		2·75	3·25

1982 (30 Aug)–85. *Nos.* 668/74 *surch as T* **156.**

695	50 c. on 31 c. Type **150**		40	40
696	50 c. on 35 c. Type **151**		40	40
697	50 c. on 45 c. Prince Charles as helicopter pilot		40	40
698	50 c. on 60 c. Prince Charles in outdoor clothes		40	40
699	90 c. on 1 l. Prince Charles and Lady Diana Spencer		75	75
699a	1 l. 30 on 60 c. Prince Charles in outdoor clothes (1985)		1·75	1·75
699b	2 l. on 35 c. Type **151** (1985)		2·75	2·75
	ba. Surch double		20·00	
700	2 l. on 1 l.50 Prince Charles and Lady Diana Spencer		1·50	1·50
700a	8 l. on 1 l.50 Prince Charles and Lady Diana Spencer (1985)		8·75	8·75
695/700a		*Set of* 9	15·00	15·00
MS701	95 × 83 mm. 3 l. 50 on 3 l. Royal Landau		1·50	1·50

Nos. 699a/b and 700a also exist surcharged in blue from a limited printing (*Price for set of 3* £50 *mint*).

157 Heading   158 Prince and Princess of Wales

(Des PAD Studio. Litho Questa)

1982 (7 Sept). *World Cup Football Championship, Spain. T* **157** *and similar vert designs. Multicoloured. P* 14.

702	20 c. Type **157**		45	15
703	30 c. Dribbling		70	20
704	1 l. Tackling		2·25	2·00
705	2 l. Goalkeeping		3·50	3·25
702/5		*Set of* 4	6·25	5·00
MS706	92 × 75 mm. 3 l. Shooting		4·50	3·00

Nos. 702/5 were each printed in small sheets of 6 including one, *se-tenant*, stamp-sized label.

(Des PAD Studio. Litho Questa)

1982 (15 Sept). *21st Birthday of Princess of Wales. T* **158** *and similar vert designs. Multicoloured. P* 14½ × 14.

707	31 c. Caernarvon Castle		35	15
708	50 c. Type **158**		40	25
709	2 l. Princess of Wales		1·10	1·50
707/9		*Set of* 3	1·75	1·75
MS710	103 × 75 mm. 3 l. Princess of Wales (*different*)		1·50	1·50

Nos. 707/9 also exist in sheetlets of 5 stamps and 1 label.

1982 (15 Oct). *Birth of Prince William of Wales. Nos.* 707/10 *optd with T* **212a** *of Jamaica.*

711	31 c. Caernarvon Castle		35	15
712	50 c. Type **158**		40	25
713	2 l. Princess of Wales		1·10	1·50
711/13		*Set of* 3	1·75	1·75
MS714	103 × 75 mm. 3 l. Princess of Wales (*different*)		1·50	1·50

Nos. 711/13 also exist in sheetlets of 5 stamps and 1 label.

159 Washington with Troops   160 Temptation of Christ

(Des C. Mill. Litho Questa)

1982 (30 Oct). *250th Birth Anniv of George Washington. T* **159** *and similar multicoloured designs. P* 14.

715	6 c. Type **159**		10	10
716	31 c. Portrait of Washington (*vert*)		20	20
717	50 c. Washington with horse		35	35
718	1 l. Washington standing on battlefield (*vert*)		65	80
715/18		*Set of* 4	1·10	1·25
MS719	103 × 71 mm. 2 l. Washington at home		1·00	1·50

(Des N. Waldman Studio. Litho Questa)

1982 (18 Nov). *Christmas. Stained-glass Windows. T* **160** *and similar vert designs. Multicoloured. P* 13½ × 14.

720	6 c. Type **160**		10	10
721	31 c. Baptism of Christ		15	20
722	50 c. Annunciation		20	40
723	1 l. Nativity		55	90
720/3		*Set of* 4	85	1·40
MS724	74 × 104 mm. 2 l. Mary and Joseph		70	1·10

WORLD CUP
WINNERS
ITALY (3)
vs.
W. GERMANY (1)

(161)   162 Long Snouted Crocodile

1982 (2 Dec). *World Cup Football Championship Winners. Nos.* 702/6 *optd with T* **161.**

725	20 c. Type **157**		15	20
726	30 c. Dribbling		20	30
727	1 l. Tackling		55	55
728	2 l. Goalkeeping		1·00	1·75
725/8		*Set of* 4	1·75	2·75
MS729	91 × 75 mm. 3 l. Shooting		1·00	2·00

(Des G. Drummond. Litho Questa)

1982 (10 Dec). *Death Centenary of Charles Darwin. T* **162** *and similar horiz designs. Multicoloured. P* 14.

730	6 c. Type **162**		40	15
731	31 c. Rainbow Lizard		1·10	75
732	50 c. River Turtle		1·60	1·40
733	1 l. Chameleon		2·75	3·00
730/3		*Set of* 4	5·25	4·75
MS734	90 × 70 mm. 2 l. Royal Python (*vert*)		2·25	2·75

163 Diogenes

(Des Design Images. Litho Questa)

1983 (28 Jan). *500th Birth Anniv of Raphael. Details from painting "The School of Athens". T* **163** *and similar multicoloured designs. P* 13½.

735	6 c. Type **163**		10	10
736	31 c. Euclid, Ptolemy, Zoroaster, Raphael and Sodoma		20	30
737	50 c. Euclid and his pupils		35	45
738	2 l. Pythagoras, Francesco della Rovere and Heraclitus		1·25	1·40
735/8		*Set of* 4	1·60	2·00
MS739	101 × 126 mm. 3 l. Plato and Aristotle (*vert*)		1·25	2·00

164 Agricultural Training   165 Map of Africa and Flag of Sierra Leone

(Litho Questa)

1983 (14 Mar). *Commonwealth Day. T* **164** *and similar horiz designs. Multicoloured. P* 14.

740	6 c. Type **164**		10	10
741	10 c. Tourism development		10	10
742	50 c. Broadcasting training		45	45
743	1 l. Airport services		90	90
740/3		*Set of* 4	1·40	1·40

(Des M. Diamond. Litho J.W.)

1983 (29 Apr). *25th Anniv of Economic Commission for Africa. P* 13.

744	165	1 l. multicoloured	80	1·10

166 Chimpanzees in Tree

(Des J. Iskowitz. Litho Questa)

1983 (19 May). *Endangered Species. T* **166** *and similar multi-coloured designs. P* 14.

745	6 c. Type **166**		65	20
746	10 c. Three Chimpanzees (*vert*)		80	20
747	31 c. Chimpanzees swinging in tree (*vert*)		1·90	80
748	60 c. Group of Chimpanzees		3·50	4·00
745/8		*Set of* 4	6·25	4·75
MS749	115 × 80 mm. 3 l. African Elephant		1·50	2·25

167 Traditional Communications   168 Montgolfier Balloon, Paris, 1783

(Des R. Sauber. Litho Questa)

1983 (14 July). *World Communications Year. T* **167** *and similar horiz designs. Multicoloured. P* 14.

750	6 c. Type **167**		10	10
751	10 c. Mail via Mano River		10	10
752	20 c. Satellite ground station		10	10
753	1 l. British packet, *circa* 1805		55	65
750/3		*Set of* 4	70	80
MS754	115 × 85 mm. 2 l. Telecommunications		80	1·25

(Des Artists International. Litho Questa)

1983 (31 Aug). *Bicentenary of Manned Flight. T* **168** *and similar multicoloured designs. P* 14.

755	6 c. Type **168**		25	10
756	20 c. *Deutschland* airship, Berlin, 1879 (*horiz*)		45	20
757	50 c. *Norge I*, North Pole, 1926 (*horiz*)		90	90
758	1 l. *Cape Sierra* sport balloon, Freetown, 1983		1·25	1·60
755/8		*Set of* 4	2·50	2·50
MS759	115 × 85 mm. 2 l. Airship of 21st century		1·00	1·75

1983 (Oct). *Birds. As Nos.* 622B/35B *but without wmk.*

760	1 c. Type **142**		70	1·00
761	2 c. Olive-bellied Sunbird		70	1·00
763	5 c. Spur-winged Goose		90	50
765	10 c. Grey Parrot (*vert*)		90	50
766	15 c. Blue Quail (*vert*)		1·25	60
767	20 c. African Wood Owl (*vert*)		2·25	1·00
768	30 c. Great Blue Turaco (*vert*)		1·50	1·25
769	40 c. Blue-breasted Kingfisher (*vert*)		2·50	2·00
770	50 c. Black Crake (*vert*)		2·50	2·00
772	2 l. Black Bee Eater		5·00	7·50
773	1 l. Barrow's Bustard		10·00	15·00
760/73		*Set of* 11	25·00	29·00

Nos. 760/73 exist imperforate from stock dispersed by the liquidator of Format International Security Printers Ltd.

The imprint date on Nos. 760/73 is 1983. Examples of the 1, 2, 3 c. and 2 l. with 1981 date come from the liquidator's stock.

169 Mickey Mouse

(Litho Format)

1983 (18 Nov). *Space Ark Fantasy. T* **169** *and similar horiz designs featuring Disney cartoon characters. Multicoloured. P* 13½.

774	1 c. Type **169**		10	10
775	1 c. Huey, Dewey and Louie		10	10
776	3 c. Goofy in spaceship		10	10
777	3 c. Donald Duck		10	10
778	10 c. Ludwig von Drake		10	10
779	10 c. Goofy		10	10
780	2 l. Mickey Mouse and Giraffe in spaceship		1·10	1·25
781	3 l. Donald Duck floating in space		1·60	1·75
774/81		*Set of* 8	2·75	3·00
MS782	140 × 116 mm. 5 l. Mickey Mouse leaving spaceship		2·75	3·00

170 Graduates from Union Training Programme

(Des G. Vasarhelyi. Litho Format)

1984 (8 Feb). *10th Anniv of the Mano River Union. T* **170** *and similar horiz designs. Multicoloured. P* 15.

783	6 c. Type **170**		10	10
784	25 c. Intra-Union trade		10	10
785	31 c. Member Presidents on map		15	15
786	41 c. Signing ceremony marking Guinea's accession		20	20
783/6		*Set of* 4	45	45
MS787	75 × 113 mm. No. 786		50	70

171 Gymnastics   172 "Apollo 11" Lift-off

(Des J. Iskowitz. Litho Questa)

1984 (27 Mar). *Olympic Games, Los Angeles. T* **171** *and similar horiz designs. Multicoloured.* P 14.

788	90 c. Type **171**	30	40
789	1 l. Hurdling	30	40
790	3 l. Javelin-throwing	75	1·25
788/90	*Set of 3*	1·25	1·90
MS791	104 × 71 mm. 7 l. Boxing	1·40	2·00

(Des J. Iskowitz. Litho Questa)

1984 (14 May). *15th Anniv of First Moonwalk. T* **172** *and similar multicoloured designs.* P 14.

792	50 c. Type **172**	20	20
793	75 c. Lunar module	30	30
794	1 l. 25, First Moonwalk	45	45
795	2 l. 50, Lunar exploration	85	85
792/5	*Set of 4*	1·60	1·60
MS796	99 × 69 mm. 5 l. Family watching Moonwalk on television (*horiz*)	1·60	2·25

173 "Concorde"

(Des Susan David. Litho Walsall)

1984 (19 June). *Universal Postal Union Congress, Hamburg. T* **173** *and similar horiz design. Multicoloured.* P 14.

797	4 l. Type **173**	2·75	1·75
MS798	100 × 70 mm. 4 l. Heinrich von Stephan (founder of U.P.U.)	2·00	2·75

174 Citroen "Traction Avante"   (175)

(Des Susan David. Litho Format)

1984 (16 July). *United Nations Decade for African Transport. T* **174** *and similar horiz designs. Multicoloured.* P 14½ × 15.

799	12 c. Type **174**	20	10
800	60 c. Locomobile	40	25
801	90 c. A.C. "Ace"	55	35
802	1 l. Vauxhall "Prince Henry"	55	35
803	1 l. 50, Delahaye "135"	70	50
804	2 l. Mazda "1105"	90	65
799/804	*Set of 6*	3·00	1·90
MS805	107 × 75 mm. 6 l. Volkswagen "Beetle". P 15	3·25	3·50

1984 (3 Aug). *Surch as T* **175**. (*a*) *On Nos. 625, 627 and 634. A. No imprint. B. Imprint date at foot.*

		A		B	
806	25 c. on 10 c. Grey Parrot (*vert*)	3·50	3·50	3·50	3·50
807	40 c. on 10 c. Grey Parrot (*vert*)	3·50	3·50	3·50	3·50
808	50 c. on 2 l. Black Bee Eater	3·50	3·50	3·50	3·50
809	70 c. on 5 c. Spur-winged Goose	3·50	3·50	3·50	3·50
810	10 l. on 5 c. Spur-winged Goose	7·00	7·00	7·00	7·00
806/10	*Set of 5*	19·00	19·00	19·00	19·00

(*b*) *On Nos. 763, 765 and 772*

811	25 c. on 10 c. Grey Parrot (*vert*)	75	85
812	40 c. on 10 c. Grey Parrot (*vert*)	50	70
813	50 c. on 2 l. Black Bee Eater	50	70
814	70 c. on 5 c. Spur-winged Goose	50	70
815	10 l. on 5 c. Spur-winged Goose	3·00	3·50
811/15	*Set of 5*	4·75	5·75

Nos. 806B/10B exist with either "1981" or "1982" imprint dates.

AUSIPEX 84   177 Portuguese Caravel
(176)

1984 (22 Aug). *"Ausipex" International Stamp Exhibition, Melbourne, Optd with T* **176**. (*a*) *On Nos. 632 and 635. A. No imprint. B. Imprint date at foot.*

		A		B	
816	50 c. Black Crake	5·00	5·00	5·00	5·00
817	5 l. Barrow's Bustard	15·00	15·00	15·00	15·00

(*b*) *On Nos. 770 and 773*

818	50 c. Black Crake	1·00	75
819	5 l. Barrow's Bustard	2·25	2·00

Nos. 816B/17B exist with either "1981" or "1982" imprint dates.

(Des G. Drummond. Litho Questa)

1984 (5 Sept)–85. *History of Shipping. T* **177** *and similar horiz designs. Multicoloured.* A. *Without imprint date below design.* P 14. B. *With imprint date below design.* P 12.

		A		B	
820	2 c. Type **177**	35	60	20	40
821	5 c. Merlin of Bristol	50	50	25	30
822	10 c. Golden Hind	65	50	35	30
823	15 c. Mordaunt	75	50		†
824	20 c. Atlantic (transport)	80	50	50	30
825	25 c. H.M.S. Lapwing	80	50	50	30
826	30 c. Traveller (brig)	90	50	50	35
827	40 c. Amistad (schooner)	1·00	55	60	35
828	50 c. H.M.S. Teazer	1·00	55	70	35
829	70 c. Scotia (cable ship)	1·25	90	85	50
830	1 l. H.M.S. Alecto	1·40	90	90	50
831	2 l. H.M.S. Blonde	6·00	2·50	1·25	75
832	5 l. H.M.S. Fox	10·00	4·75	1·75	1·50
833	10 l. Accra (liner)	13·00	11·00	2·25	2·00
833c	15 l. H.M.S. Favourite	2·00	2·25		†
833d	25 l. H.M.S. Euryalus	2·75	3·00		†
820A/33dA	*Set of 16*	38·00	27·00		
820B/33B	*Set of 13*			9·50	7·00

Dates of issue:—Without imprint 5.9.84, 2 c., to 1 l.; 9.10.84, 2 l., 5 l.; 7.11.84, 10 l.; 15.11.85, 15 l., 25 l. With imprint 7.85, 2 c. to 10 l.

178 Mail Runner approaching   179 "Madonna and Child"
Mano River Depot, *c* 1843   (Pisanello)

(Des Susan David. Litho Walsall)

1984 (9 Oct). *125th Anniv of First Postage Stamps. T* **178** *and similar horiz designs. Multicoloured.* P 14.

834	50 c. Type **178**	35	15
835	2 l. Isaac Fitzjohn, First Postmaster, receiving letters, 1855	1·25	65
836	3 l. 1859 packet franked with four 6d. stamps	1·75	1·00
834/6	*Set of 3*	3·00	1·75
MS837	100 × 70 mm. 5 l. Sierra Leone 1859 6d. purple and Great Britain 1840 Penny Black stamps	1·50	1·60

(Litho Walsall)

1984 (15 Nov). *Christmas. Madonna and Child paintings by artists named. T* **179** *and similar vert designs. Multicoloured.* P 14.

838	20 c. Type **179**	10	10
839	1 l. Memling	40	30
840	2 l. Raphael	75	55
841	3 l. Van der Werff	1·10	80
838/41	*Set of 4*	2·00	1·60
MS842	100 × 69 mm. 6 l. Picasso	2·50	1·90

180 Donald Duck in the "The Wise Little Hen"

(Litho Questa)

1984 (26 Nov). *50th Birthday of Donald Duck. Walt Disney Cartoon Characters. T* **180** *and similar horiz designs. Multicoloured.* P 12 (2 *l.*) or 14 × 13½ (*others*).

843	1 c. Type **180**	10	10
844	2 c. Mickey Mouse and Donald Duck in "Boat Builders"	10	10
845	3 c. Panchito, Donald Duck and Jose Carioca in "The Three Caballeros"	10	10
846	4 c. Donald Duck meeting Pythagoras in "Mathmagic Land"	10	10
847	5 c. Donald Duck and nephew in "The Mickey Mouse Club"	10	10
848	10 c. Mickey Mouse, Goofy and Donald Duck in "Donald on Parade"	10	10
849	1 l. Donald Duck riding donkey in "Don Donald"	75	75
850	2 l. Donald Duck in "Donald Gets Drafted"	1·75	1·50
851	4 l. Donald Duck meeting children in Tokyo Disneyland	2·75	2·50
843/51	*Set of 9*	5·00	4·50
MS852	126 × 102 mm. 5 l. Style sheet for Donald Duck	2·50	1·75

No. 850 was printed in sheetlets of 8.

181 Fischer's Whydah

(Des Susan David. Litho Walsall)

1985 (31 Jan). *Birth Bicentenary of John J. Audubon (ornithologist). Songbirds of Sierra Leone. T* **181** *and similar horiz designs. Multicoloured.* P 14.

853	40 c. Type **181**	1·25	55
854	90 c. Spotted Flycatcher	2·25	1·40
855	1 l. 30, Garden Warbler	2·50	2·50
856	3 l. Speke's Weaver	4·00	5·00
853/6	*Set of 4*	9·00	8·50
MS857	100 × 70 mm. 5 l. Great Grey Shrike	2·25	3·00

182 Fishing

(Des M. Zacharow. Litho Walsall)

1985 (14 Feb). *International Youth Year. T* **182** *and similar horiz designs. Multicoloured.* P 14.

858	1 l. Type **182**	30	35
859	1 l. 50, Sawing timber	40	45
860	2 l. 15, Rice farming	55	60
858/60	*Set of 3*	1·10	1·25
MS861	100 × 70 mm. 5 l. Polishing diamonds	1·25	1·50

183 Eddie Rickenbacker and Spad "XIII", 1918

(Des K. Gromol. Litho Walsall)

1985 (28 Feb). *40th Anniv of International Civil Aviation Organization. T* **183** *and similar horiz designs. Multicoloured.* P 14.

862	70 c. Type **183**	1·25	75
863	1 l. 25, Samuel P. Langley and *Aerodrome No. 5*, 1903	1·75	1·50
864	1 l. 30, Orville and Wilbur Wright with *Flyer No. 1*, 1903	1·75	1·50
865	2 l. Charles Lindbergh and *Spirit of St. Louis*, 1927	2·00	2·50
862/5	*Set of 4*	6·00	5·75
MS866	100 × 69 mm. 5 l. Sierra Leone Airlines Boeing "707-384C"	1·50	1·75

184 "Temptation of Christ"   185 The Queen
(Botticelli)   Mother at St. Paul's
                 Cathedral

(Des C. Walters. Litho Questa)

1985 (29 Apr). *Easter. Religious Paintings. T* **184** *and similar multicoloured designs.* P 14.

867	45 c. Type **184**	30	15
868	70 c. "Christ at the Column" (Velasquez)	55	25
869	1 l. 55, "Pietà" (Botticelli) (*vert*)	90	45
870	10 l. "Christ on the Cross" (Velasquez) (*vert*)	4·75	3·25
867/70	*Set of 4*	6·00	3·75
MS871	106 × 76 mm. 12 l. "Man of Sorrows" (Botticelli)	3·50	3·75

(Des J.W. Litho Questa)

1985 (8 July). *Life and Times of Queen Elizabeth the Queen Mother. T* **185** *and similar multicoloured designs.* P 14.

872	1 l. Type **185**	20	25
873	1 l. 70, With her racehorse, "Double Star", at Sandown (*horiz*)	30	40
874	10 l. At Covent Garden, 1971	2·00	2·50
872/4	*Set of 3*	2·25	2·75
MS875	56 × 85 mm. 12 l. With Princess Anne at Ascot	2·00	2·75

75th ANNIVERSARY OF GIRL GUIDES

(186)

1985 (25 July). *75th Anniv of Girl Guide Movement. Nos. 690/4 surch as T* **186**.

876	70 c. on 20 c. Type **155**	..	25	25
877	1 l. 30 on 50 c. Scouts picking flowers	..	45	40
878	5 l. on 1 l. Lord Baden-Powell	..	1·40	1·40
879	7 l. on 2 l. Scouts fishing	..	1·90	1·90
876/9		*Set of 4*	3·50	3·50
MS880	101×70 mm. 15 l. on 3 l. Scouts raising flag..		3·75	4·00

MA YANHONJG
CHINA
GOLD MEDAL

Le2

(187)

1985 (25 July). *Olympic Gold Medal Winners, Los Angeles. Nos.* 788/91 *surch as T* **187**.

881	2 l. on 90 c. Type **171** (surch T **187**)..		50	55
882	4 l. on 1 l. Hurdling (surch "E. MOSES U.S.A. GOLD MEDAL")..		1·00	1·25
883	8 l. on 3 l. Javelin-throwing (surch "A. HAERKOENEN FINLAND GOLD MEDAL")..		2·00	2·10
881/3		*Set of 3*	3·25	3·50
MS884	104×71 mm. 15 l. on 7 l. Boxing (surch "M. TAYLOR U.S.A. GOLD MEDAL")..		3·25	3·75

188 Chater-Lea (1905) at Hill Station House (189)

(Des A. DiLorenzo. Litho Questa)

1985 (15 Aug). *Centenary of the Motor Cycle and Decade for African Transport. T* **188** *and similar horiz designs. Multicoloured. P* 14.

885	1 l. 40, Type **188**		1·00	1·00
886	2 l. Honda "XR 350 R" at Queen Elizabeth II Quay, Freetown		1·40	1·40
887	4 l. Kawasaki "Vulcan" at Bo Clock Tower ..		2·50	2·50
888	5 l. Harley-Davidson "Electra-Glide" in Makeni village		2·75	2·75
885/8		*Set of 4*	7·00	7·00
MS889	104×71 mm. 12 l. Millet (1893)..		3·00	3·50

(Des Susan David. Litho Questa)

1985 (3 Sept). *300th Birth Anniv of Johann Sebastian Bach (composer). Vert designs as T* **204***a of Maldive Islands. P* 14.

890	70 c. multicoloured		40	25
891	3 l. multicoloured		1·10	80
892	4 l. multicoloured		1·40	1·10
893	5 l. multicoloured		1·60	1·40
890/3		*Set of 4*	4·00	3·25
MS894	103×77 mm. 12 l. black		3·50	3·50

Designs:—70 c. Viola pomposa; 3 l. Spinet; 4 l. Lute; 5 l. Oboe; 12 l. "Johann Sebastian Bach" (Toby E. Rosenthal).

1985 (30 Sept). *Surch as T* **189**. *(a) On Nos.* 707/10

895	70 c. on 31 c. Caernarvon Castle		30	30
896	4 l. on 50 c. Type **158**		2·50	2·50
897	7 l. on 2 l. Princess of Wales		3·00	3·00
MS898	103×75 mm. 15 l. on 3 l. Princess of Wales (*different*) ..		6·00	6·00

(b) On Nos. 711/14

899	1 l. 30 on 31 c. Caernarvon Castle		80	80
900	5 l. on 50 c. Type **158**		3·00	3·00
901	7 l. on 2 l. Princess of Wales ..		3·00	3·00
895/901		*Set of 6*	12·00	12·00
MS902	103×75 mm. 15 l. on 3 l. Princess of Wales (*different*) ..		6·00	6·00

190 "Madonna and Child" (Crivelli) 191 Player kicking Ball

(Litho Questa)

1985 (18 Oct). *Christmas. "Madonna and Child" Paintings by artists named. T* **190** *and similar vert designs. Multicoloured. P* 14.

903	70 c. Type **190**..		25	10
904	3 l. Bouts		80	40
905	4 l. Da Messina		95	55
906	5 l. Lochner		1·10	65
903/6		*Set of 4*	2·75	1·50
MS907	113×85 mm. 12 l. Miniature from Book of Kells		1·50	1·60

1985 (30 Oct). *150th Birth Anniv of Mark Twain (author). Vert designs as T* **160***a of Lesotho showing Walt Disney cartoon characters illustrating Mark Twain quotations. Multicoloured. P* 13½×14.

908	1 l. 50, Snow White and Bashful	..	30	25
909	3 l. Three Little Pigs	..	50	40
910	4 l. Donald Duck and nephew	..	60	55
911	5 l. Pinocchio and Figaro the cat	..	75	65
908/11		*Set of 4*	1·90	1·60
MS912	126×101 mm. 15 l. Winnie the Pooh ..		2·50	2·00

(Des Walt Disney Productions. Litho Questa)

1985 (3 Oct). *Birth Bicentenaries of Grimm Brothers (folklorists). Designs as T* **160***b of Lesotho, but horiz, showing Walt Disney cartoon characters from "Rumpelstiltskin". Multicoloured. P* 14×13½.

913	70 c. The Miller (Donald Duck) and his daughter (Daisy Duck) meet the King (Uncle Scrooge) ..		20	25
914	1 l. 30, The King puts the Miller's daughter to work ..		35	40
915	2 l. Rumpelstiltskin demands payment ..		50	55
916	10 l. The King with gold spun from straw ..		2·75	3·25
913/16		*Set of 4*	3·50	4·00
MS917	126×100 mm. 15 l. The King and Queen with baby ..		4·00	4·25

(Litho Format)

1985 (28 Nov). *40th Anniv of United Nations Organization. Multicoloured designs as T* **159** *of Lesotho showing United Nations (New York) stamps. P* 14½.

918	2 l. John Kennedy and 1954 Human Rights 8 c..		70	70
919	4 l. Albert Einstein (scientist) and 1958 Atomic Energy 3 c.		1·40	1·40
920	7 l. Maimonides (physician) and 1956 W.H.O. 8 c.		3·75	3·75
918/20		*Set of 3*	5·25	5·25
MS921	110×85 mm. 12 l. Martin Luther King (civil rights leader) (*vert*)..		1·50	1·75

(Des M. Lemel. Litho Questa)

1986 (3 Mar). *World Cup Football Championship, Mexico. T* **191** *and similar vert designs. Multicoloured. P* 14.

922	70 c. Type **191**		25	10
923	3 l. Player controlling ball ..		70	50
924	4 l. Player chasing ball		85	70
925	5 l. Player kicking ball (*different*) ..		1·25	80
922/5		*Set of 4*	2·75	1·90
MS926	105×74 mm. 12 l. Player kicking ball (*different*) ..		1·50	1·75

191*a* Times Square, 1905 192 Chicago-Milwaukee "Hiawatha Express'

(Des J. Iskowitz. Litho Questa)

1986 (11 Mar). *Centenary of Statue of Liberty (1st issue). T* **191***a and similar multicoloured designs. P* 14.

927	40 c. Type **191***a*		10	10
928	70 c. Times Square, 1986 ..		15	10
929	1 l. "Tally Ho" coach, *c* 1880 (*horiz*)		25	15
930	10 l. Express bus, 1986 (*horiz*)		1·75	1·90
927/30		*Set of 4*	2·00	2·00
MS931	105×75 mm. 12 l. Statue of Liberty		2·00	2·00

See also Nos. 1001/9.

(Des W. Hanson. Litho Questa)

1986 (1 Apr). *Appearance of Halley's Comet (1st issue). Horiz designs as T* **162***a of Lesotho. Multicoloured. P* 14.

932	15 c. Johannes Kepler (astronomer) and Paris Observatory		10	10
933	50 c. N.A.S.A. Space Shuttle landing, 1985..		10	10
934	70 c. Halley's Comet (from Bayeux Tapestry)		10	10
935	10 l. Comet of 530 A.D. and Merlin predicting coming of King Arthur		1·25	1·40
932/5		*Set of 4*	1·40	1·50
MS936	101×70 mm. 12 l. Halley's Comet ..		1·50	1·60

See also Nos. 988/92.

(Des and litho Questa)

1986 (23 Apr). *60th Birthday of Queen Elizabeth II. Vert designs as T* **163***a of Lesotho. P* 14.

937	10 c. black and yellow		10	10
938	1 l. 70, multicoloured		25	30
939	10 l. multicoloured		1·25	1·40
937/9		*Set of 3*	1·40	1·60
MS940	120×85 mm. 12 l. black and grey-brown		1·50	1·60

Designs:—10 c. Princess Elizabeth inspecting guard of honour, Cranwell, 1951; 1 l. 70, In Garter robes; 10 l. At Braemar Games, 1970; 12 l. Princess Elizabeth, Windsor Castle, 1943.

(Des P. Rhymer. Litho Questa)

1986 (22 May). *"Ameripex" International Stamp Exhibition, Chicago. American Trains. T* **192** *and similar horiz designs. Multicoloured. P* 14.

941	50 c. Type **192**..		60	25
942	2 l. Rock Island Line "The Rocket" ..		1·25	80
943	4 l. Rio Grande "Prospector"		2·00	1·60
944	7 l. Southern Pacific "Daylight Express"..		2·50	2·50
941/4		*Set of 4*	5·75	4·75
MS945	105×85 mm. 12 l. Pennsylvania "Broadway" ..		2·25	2·00

(Litho Questa)

1986 (1 July). *Royal Wedding. Vert designs as T* **170***a of Lesotho. Multicoloured. P* 14.

946	10 c. Prince Andrew and Miss Sarah Ferguson		10	10
947	1 l. 70, Prince Andrew at clay pigeon shoot		30	35
948	10 l. Prince Andrew in naval uniform ..		1·40	1·75
946/8		*Set of 3*	1·60	2·00
MS949	88×88 mm. 12 l. Prince Andrew and Miss Sarah Ferguson (*different*) ..		2·00	1·60

193 *Monodora myristica* 194 Handshake and Flags of Sierra Leone and U.S.A.

(Des G. Drummond. Litho Format)

1986 (25 Aug). *Flowers of Sierra Leone. T* **193** *and similar vert designs. Multicoloured. P* 15.

950	70 c. Type **193**..		15	10
951	1 l. 50, *Gloriosa simplex*		20	15
952	4 l. *Mussaenda erythrophylla*		35	25
953	6 l. *Crinum ornatum*		50	40
954	8 l. *Bauhinia purpurea*		60	60
955	10 l. *Bombax costatum*		70	70
956	20 l. *Hibiscus rosasinensis* ..		1·25	1·50
957	30 l. *Cassia fistula*		1·75	2·00
950/7		*Set of 8*	5·00	5·00
MS958	Two sheets, each 101×92 mm. (a) 40 l. *Clitoria ternatea*. (b) 40 l. *Plumbago auriculata*			
		Set of 2 sheets	4·00	4·00

(Litho Questa)

1986 (26 Aug). *25th Anniv of United States Peace Corps. P* 14.

959	**194** 10 l. multicoloured		70	70

195 Transporting Goods by Canoe (196) (197)

(Des T. O'Toole. Litho Questa)

1986 (1 Sept). *International Peace Year. T* **195** *and similar horiz designs. Multicoloured. P* 14.

960	1 l. Type **195**..		10	10
961	2 l. Teacher and class		15	15
962	5 l. Rural post office..		30	30
963	10 l. Fishermen in longboat ..		55	55
960/3 ..		*Set of 4*	1·00	1·00

1986 (15 Sept). *Various stamps surch.*

(a) As T **196** *on Nos.* 820A, 826/7A *and* 829A

964	30 l. on 2 c. Type **177**..		1·50	1·60
965	40 l. on 30 c. *Traveller* (brig)..		2·10	2·25
966	45 l. on 40 c. *Amistad* (schooner)		2·40	2·50
967	50 l. on 70 c. *Scotia* (cable ship) ..		2·75	2·75

(b) As T **197** *on Nos.* 937 *and* 939/40 (*in silver on Nos.* 968/9)

968	70 c. on 10 c. black and yellow		10	10
969	45 l. on 10 l. multicoloured		2·40	2·50
MS970	120×85 mm. 50 l. on 12 l. black and grey-brown		3·00	3·00

(c) As T **197** *on Nos.* 946 *and* 948/9, *in silver*

971	70 c. on 10 c. Prince Andrew and Miss Sarah Ferguson..		10	10
972	45 l. on 10 l. Prince Andrew in naval uniform		2·40	2·50
964/72		*Set of 8*	12·00	12·50
MS973	88×88 mm. 50 l. on 12 l. Prince Andrew and Miss Sarah Ferguson (*different*) ..		3·50	3·00

1986 (15 Sept). *World Cup Football Championship Winners, Mexico. Nos.* 922/6 *optd with T* **213***a of Maldive Islands or surch also, all in gold.*

974	70 c. Type **191** ..		20	10
975	3 l. Player controlling ball ..		40	30
976	4 l. Player chasing ball		50	40
977	40 l. on 5 l. Player kicking ball (*different*) ..		3·50	4·00
974/7		*Set of 4*	4·25	4·25
MS978	105×74 mm. 40 l. on 12 l. Player kicking ball (*different*) ..		2·50	2·50

198 Mickey and Minnie Mouse as Jack and Jill

(Des Walt Disney Co. Litho Format)

1986 (22 Sept). *"Stockholmia '86" International Stamp Exhibition, Sweden. T* **198** *and similar horiz designs showing Walt Disney cartoon characters in scenes from nursery rhymes. Multicoloured. P* 11.

979	70 c. Type **198**	..	..	10	10
980	1 l. Donald Duck as Wee Willie Winkie	..	15	15
981	2 l. Minnie Mouse as Little Miss Muffet	..	20	20
982	4 l. Goofy as Old King Cole	..	..	40	40
983	5 l. Clarabelle as Mary Quite Contrary	..	50	50
984	10 l. Daisy Duck as Little Bo Peep	..	90	90
985	25 l. Daisy Duck and Minnie Mouse in "Polly put the Kettle on"		..	2·00	2·00
986	35 l. Goofy, Mickey Mouse and Donald Duck as the Three Men in a Tub			2·50	2·50
979/86			*Set of* 8	6·00	6·00

MS987 Two sheets, each 127×102 mm. P 14×13½. (a) 40 l. Aunt Matilda as the Old Woman in the Shoe. (b) 40 l. Goofy as Simple Simon .. .. .. *Set of 2 sheets* 5·00 5·50

1986 (15 Oct). *Appearance of Halley's Comet (2nd issue). Nos. 932/6 optd as T* **213***b of Maldive Islands (in silver on 50 l.) or such also.*

988	50 c. N.A.S.A. Space Shuttle landing, 1985 ..		10	10
989	70 c. Halley's Comet (from Bayeux Tapestry)		..	10	10
990	1 l. 50 on 15 c. Johannes Kepler (astronomer) and Paris Observatory ..		10	10
991	45 l. on 10 l. Comet of 530 A.D. and Merlin predicting coming of King Arthur		3·00	3·50
988/91		*Set of* 4	3·00	3·50

MS992 101×70 mm. 50 l. on 12 l. Halley's Comet 3·25 3·50

199 "Virgin and Child with St. Dorothy"

200 Nomoli (soapstone figure)

(Litho Questa)

1986 (17 Nov). *Christmas. Paintings by Titian. T* **199** *and similar multicoloured designs. P* 14.

993	70 c. Type **199**	..	..	10	10
994	1 l. 50, "The Gypsy Madonna" (*vert*)	..	15	10
995	20 l. "The Holy Family"	..	..	2·25	2·25
996	30 l. "Virgin and Child in an Evening Landscape" (*vert*)		..	2·75	2·75
993/6			*Set of* 4	4·75	4·75

MS997 76×102 mm. 40 l. "Madonna with the Pesaro Family" (*vert*) .. .. .. 5·00 6·00

(Des A. DiLorenzo. Litho Format)

1987 (2 Jan). *Bicentenary of Sierra Leone. T* **200** *and similar vert designs. Multicoloured. P* 15.

998	2 l. Type **200**	..	..	10	15
999	5 l. King's Yard Gate, Royal Hospital, 1817..		20	30

MS1000 100×70 mm. 60 l. Early 19th-century British warship at Freetown .. .. 2·50 2·75

201 Removing Top of Statue's Torch

202 Emblem, Mother with Child and Syringe

(Litho Questa)

1987 (2 Jan). *Centenary of Statue of Liberty (1986) (2nd issue). T* **201** *and similar multicoloured designs. P* 14.

1001	70 c. Type **201**	..	..	10	10
1002	1 l. 50, View of Statue's torch and New York Harbour (*horiz*)		..	10	10
1003	2 l. Crane lifting torch	..	..	10	10
1004	3 l. Workman steadying torch	..	10	15
1005	4 l. Statue's crown (*horiz*)	..	..	15	20
1006	5 l. Statue of Liberty (side view) and fireworks		..	20	25
1007	10 l. Statue of Liberty and fireworks	..	40	45
1008	25 l. Bedloe Island, Statue and fireworks (*horiz*)		..	1·00	1·25
1009	30 l. Statue's face	..	..	1·25	1·60
1001/9			*Set of* 9	3·00	3·75

(Litho Questa)

1987 (18 Mar). *40th Anniv of U.N.I.C.E.F. P* 14.
1010 **202** 10 l. multicoloured 40 55

ALTERED CATALOGUE NUMBERS

Any Catalogue numbers altered from the last edition are shown as a list in the introductory pages.

---

203 *U.S.A.*, 1987

204 Mickey Mouse as Mountie and Parliament Building, Ottawa

(Des S. Heinmann. Litho Questa)

1987 (15 June). *America's Cup Yachting Championship. T* **203** *and similar multicoloured designs. P* 14.

1011	,1 l. Type **203**	..	..	10	10
1012	1 l. 50, New Zealand, 1987 (*horiz*)	..	10	10
1013	2 l. 50, French Kiss, 1987 ..	..	10	10
1014	10 l. Stars and Stripes, 1987 (*horiz*)	..	40	45
1015	15 l. Australia II, 1983	..	..	60	65
1016	25 l. Freedom, 1980 ..	..	1·00	1·10
1017	30 l. Kookaburra III, 1987 (*horiz*)	..	1·25	1·40
1011/17			*Set of* 7	3·00	3·50

MS1018 100×70 mm. 50 l. Constellation, 1964 .. 2·00 2·50

(Des Walt Disney Co. Litho Format)

1987 (15 June). *"Capex '87" International Stamp Exhibition, Toronto. T* **204** *and similar horiz designs showing Walt Disney cartoon characters in Canada. Multicoloured. P* 11.

1019	2 l. Type **204**	..	..	10	10
1020	5 l. Goofy dressed as Mountie and totem poles		..	20	25
1021	10 l. Goofy windsurfing and Donald Duck fishing off Perce Rock ..		40	45
1022	20 l. Goofy with mountain goat in Rocky Mountains		..	80	85
1023	25 l. Donald Duck and Mickey Mouse in Old Quebec..		..	1·00	1·10
1024	45 l. Goofy emerging from igloo and *Aurora Borealis*..		..	1·75	1·90
1025	50 l. Goofy as gold prospector and post office, Yukon		..	2·00	2·10
1026	75 l. Dumbo flying over Niagara Falls ..		3·25	3·25
1019/26			*Set of* 8	8·25	9·00

MS1027 Two sheets, each 127×101 mm. (a) 100 l. Mickey Mouse driving chuckwagon in Calgary Stampede. (b) 100 l. Mickey Mouse and Goofy as Vikings in Newfoundland. P 14×13½
Set of 2 sheets 8·00 8·50

205 *Salamis temora*

206 Cycling

(Des S. Heinmann. Litho Questa)

1987 (4 Aug)–**91**. *Butterflies. T* **205** *and similar vert designs. Multicoloured. A. Without imprint date. P* 14. B. *Without imprint date. P* 12.

			A		B	
1028	10 c. Type **205**	..	50	20	30	20
1029	20 c. Stugeta marmorea	60	20	30	20
1030	40 c. Graphium ridleyanus	60	20	30	20
1031	1 l. Papilio bromius	60	20	40	20
1032	2 l. Iterus zalmoxis	70	40	50	30
1033	3 l. Cymothoe sangaris	70	40	50	30
1034	5 l. Graphium tynderaeus	85	40	10	10
1035	10 l. Graphium policenes	1·60	70	10	10
1036	20 l. Tanuetheira timon	2·50	2·00	10	10
1037	25 l. Danaus limniace	3·25	2·50	10	10
1038	30 l. Papilio hesperus	4·00	3·00	10	10
1039	45 l. Charaxes smaragdalis	5·50	4·00	10	15
1040	60 l. Charaxes lucretius	2·00	3·00	20	25
1041	75 l. Antanartia delius	2·50	3·25	20	25
1042	100 l. Abisara talantus	3·25	4·00	30	35
1028/42		*Set of* 15	26·00	22·00	2·75	2·40

C. *With imprint date. P* 12½×11½ (50 c., 50 l., 80 l., 300 l.) *or* 14 (*others*)

1028C	10 c. Type **205**	..	10	10
1029C	20 c. Stugeta marmorea	..	10	10
1030C	40 c. Graphium ridleyanus	..	10	10
1030aC	50 c. As 40 c.	..	10	10
1031C	1 l. Papilio bromius	..	10	10
1032C	2 l. Iterus zalmoxis	..	10	10
1033C	3 l. Cymothoe sangaris	..	10	10
1039aC	50 l. Type **205**	..	15	20
1041aC	80 l. As 20 c. ..	..	25	30
1042aC	300 l. As 30 c.	..	90	95
1028C/42C		*Set of* 10	1·50	1·75

Nos. 1030aC, 1039aC, 1041aC and 1042aC show a larger perforation hole on every sixth perforation, both vertically and horizontally.
Dates of issue:—4.8.87, Nos. 1028A/42A; 6.88, Nos. 1028B/37B; 8.88, Nos. 1038B/9B; 10.88, Nos. 1040B/1B; 3.89, No. 1042B; 1989, Nos. 1028C/30C and 1031C/3C; 8.91, Nos. 1030aC, 1039aC, 1041aC and 1042aC.

(Des BG Studio. Litho Questa)

1987 (10 Aug). *Olympic Games, Seoul (1988) (1st issue). T* **206** *and similar vert designs. Multicoloured. P* 14.

1043	5 l. Type **206**	..	..	20	25
1044	10 l. Three Day Eventing	..	40	45
1045	45 l. Athletics	..	..	1·75	1·90
1046	50 l. Tennis	..	..	2·00	2·10
1043/6			*Set of* 4	4·25	

MS1047 73×84 mm. 100 l. Olympic gold medal.. 4·00 4·50
See also Nos. 1137/41.

206a "The Quarrel" (Chagall)

206b "Apollo 8" Spacecraft (first manned Moon orbit), 1968

(Litho Questa)

1987 (17 Aug). *Birth Centenary of Marc Chagall (artist). T* **206***a and similar multicoloured designs. P* 13½×14.

1048	3 l. Type **206***a*	..	..	15	15
1049	5 l. "Rebecca giving Abraham's Servant a Drink"		..	20	25
1050	10 l. "The Village"	..	..	40	45
1051	20 l. "Ida at the Window"	..	40	45
1052	25 l. "Promenade"	..	..	1·00	1·10
1053	45 l. "Peasants"	..	..	1·75	1·90
1054	50 l. "Turquoise Plate" (ceramic)	..	2·00	2·10
1055	75 l. "Cemetery Gate"	..	..	3·00	3·25
1048/55			*Set of* 8	8·25	9·00

MS1056 Two sheets, each 110 × 95 mm. (a) 100 l. "Wedding Feast" (stage design) (104 × 78 mm). (b) 100 l. "The Falling Angel" (104 × 78 mm). Imperf .. .. .. *Set of 2 sheets* 8·00 8·50

(Des W. Wright. Litho Format)

1987 (28 Aug). *Milestones of Transportation. T* **206***b and similar multicoloured designs. P* 15.

1057	3 l. Type **206***b*	..	..	15	15
1058	5 l. Blanchard's balloon (first U.S. balloon flight), 1793 (*horiz*)			20	20
1059	10 l. Amelia Earhart's Lockheed "Vega" (first solo transatlantic flight by woman), 1932 (*horiz*)			40	40
1060	15 l. Vicker's "Vimy" (first non-stop transatlantic flight), 1919 (*horiz*)			60	60
1061	20 l. British "Mk 1" tank (first combat tank), 1916 (*horiz*)			80	80
1062	25 l. Sikorsky "VS-300" (first U.S. helicopter flight), 1939 (*horiz*)			90	90
1063	30 l. Wright brother's *Flyer 1* (first powered flight), 1903 (*horiz*)			1·10	1·10
1064	35 l. Bleriot "XI" (first cross Channel flight), 1909 (*horiz*)			1·25	1·25
1065	40 l. Paraplane (first flexible-wing ultralight), 1983		..	1·50	1·50
1066	50 l. Daimler's first motorcycle, 1885	..	1·75	1·75
1057/66			*Set of* 10	7·75	7·75

MS1067 114×83 mm. 100 l. "Rhinegold Express" (first electric railway) (*horiz*) .. .. 3·75 4·00

207 Evonne Goolagong

(Des W. Storozuk. Litho Questa)

1987 (4 Sept). *Wimbledon Tennis Champions. T* **207** *and similar horiz designs. Multicoloured. P* 14.

1068	2 l. Type **207**	..	..	20	20
1069	5 l. Martina Navratilova	..	35	35
1070	10 l. Jimmy Connors	..	..	60	60
1071	15 l. Bjorn Borg	..	..	90	90
1072	30 l. Boris Becker	..	..	1·75	1·75
1073	40 l. John McEnroe	..	..	2·00	2·00
1074	50 l. Chris Evert Lloyd	..	2·25	2·25
1075	75 l. Virginia Wade	..	..	3·00	3·00
1068/75			*Set of* 8	10·00	10·00

MS1076 Two sheets, each 105 × 75 mm. (a) 100 l. Boris Becker (*different*). (b) 100 l. Steffi Graf
Set of 2 sheets 10·00 10·00

208 Ducats, *Santa Maria* and Issac Abravanel (financier)

209 Cotton Tree

(Litho Questa)

1987 (11 Sept). *500th Anniv of Discovery of America by Columbus (1992). T 208 and similar horiz designs. Multicoloured. P 14.*

1077	5 l. Type 208	25	20
1078	10 l. Astrolabe, *Pinta* and Abraham Zacuto (astronomer)	40	35
1079	45 l. Maravedis (coins), *Nina* and Luis de Santangel (financier)	1·50	1·60
1080	50 l. Carib and Spaniard with tobacco plant and Luis de Torres (translator)	1·75	2·00
1077/80	*Set of 4*	3·50	3·75
MS1081	101 × 70 mm. 100 l. Christopher Columbus and map	3·00	3·50

(Des Mary Walters. Litho Questa)

1987 (15 Sept). *Flora and Fauna. T 209 and similar horiz designs. Multicoloured. P 14.*

1082	3 l. Type 209	10	10
1083	5 l. Dwarf Crocodile	15	20
1084	10 l. Kudu	30	35
1085	20 l. Yellowbells	60	65
1086	25 l. Hippopotamus and calf	75	80
1087	45 l. Comet Orchid	1·25	1·40
1088	50 l. Baobab Tree	1·50	1·60
1089	75 l. Elephant and calf	2·25	2·40
1082/9	*Set of 8*	6·25	6·75
MS1090	Two sheets, each 100 × 70 mm. (a) 100 l. Bananas, Coconut Palm, Papayas and Pineapple. (b) 100 l. Leopard *Set of 2 sheets*	5·75	6·50

210 Scouts at Ayers Rock	**210a** White House

(Des R. Vigurs. Litho Format)

1987 (5 Oct). *World Scout Jamboree, Australia. T 210 and similar horiz designs. Multicoloured. P 15.*

1091	5 l. Type 210	20	20
1092	15 l. Scouts sailing yacht	55	60
1093	40 l. Scouts and Sydney skyline	1·50	1·60
1094	50 l. Scout, Sydney Harbour Bridge and Opera House	1·75	1·90
1091/4	*Set of 4*	3·50	3·75
MS1095	114 × 78 mm. 100 l. Flags of Sierra Leone, Australia and Boy Scouts	3·00	3·50

Stamps in the design of the 50 l., but with a face value of 1 l. 50, exist from stock dispersed by the liquidator of Format International Security Printers Ltd.

(Des and litho Questa)

1987 (9 Nov). *Bicentenary of U.S. Constitution. T 210a and similar multicoloured designs. P 14.*

1096	5 l. Type 210a	15	20
1097	10 l. George Washington (Virginia delegate) (*vert*)	30	35
1098	30 l. Patrick Henry (statesman) (*vert*)	90	95
1099	65 l. State Seal, New Hampshire	1·90	2·00
1096/9	*Set of 4*	3·00	3·25
MS1100	105 × 75 mm. 100 l. John Jay (jurist) (*vert*)	3·00	3·50

210b Mickey and Minnie Mouse on Space Mountain

(Des Walt Disney Company. Litho Questa)

1987 (9 Dec). *60th Anniv of Mickey Mouse (Walt Disney cartoon character). T 210b and similar horiz designs showing cartoon characters at Tokyo Disneyland. Multicoloured. P 14×13½.*

1101	20 c. Type 210b	10	10
1102	40 c. Mickey Mouse at Country Bear Jamboree	10	10
1103	80 c. Mickey Mouse as bandleader and Minnie Mouse, Goofy and Pluto as musicians	10	10
1104	1 l. Goofy, Mickey Mouse and children in canoe and Mark Twain's river boat	10	10
1105	2 l. Mickey Mouse, Goofy and Chip n'Dale on Western River Railroad	10	10
1106	3 l. Goofy and Mickey Mouse as Pirates of the Caribbean	10	10
1107	10 l. Mickey Mouse, Goofy and children aboard Big Thunder Mountain train	40	40
1108	20 l. Mickey Mouse, Morty and Ferdie in boat and Goofy on flying carpet	75	75
1109	30 l. Mickey and Minnie Mouse in kimonos at Disneyland entrance	1·25	1·25
1101/9	*Set of 9*	2·50	2·50
MS1110	127 × 102 mm. 65 l. Mickey and Minnie Mouse in kimonos at Cinderella's Castle	2·40	2·75

211 "The Annunciation" (detail) (Titian)	**211a** Wedding of Princess Elizabeth and Duke of Edinburgh, 1947

(Litho Questa)

1987 (21 Dec). *Christmas. Religious Paintings by Titian. T 211 and similar multicoloured designs. P 14.*

1111	2 l. Type 211	15	10
1112	10 l. "Madonna and Child with Saints"	50	35
1113	20 l. "Madonna and Child with Saints Ulfus and Brigid"	90	90
1114	35 l. "The Madonna of the Cherries"	1·60	1·75
1111/14	*Set of 4*	2·75	2·75
MS1115	70 × 100 mm. 65 l. "The Pesaro Altarpiece" (*vert*)	3·25	3·75

(Des and litho Questa)

1988 (15 Feb). *Royal Ruby Wedding. T 211a and similar vert designs. P 14.*

1116	2 l. deep brown, black and grey	10	10
1117	3 l. multicoloured	10	10
1118	10 l. deep brown, black and orange	30	35
1119	50 l. multicoloured	1·75	2·00
1116/19	*Set of 4*	1·90	2·00
MS1120	76 × 100 mm. 65 l. multicoloured	1·90	2·00

Designs:—3 l. Prince Charles' christening photograph, 1949; 10 l. Queen Elizabeth II with Prince Charles and Princess Anne, c. 1951; 50 l. Queen Elizabeth, c. 1960; 65 l. Wedding photograph, 1947.

212 *Russula cyanoxantha*	**213** Golden Pheasant Fish

(Des L. Nelson. Litho Questa)

1988 (29 Feb). *Fungi. T 212 and similar vert designs. Multicoloured. P 14.*

1121	3 l. Type 212	35	30
1122	10 l. *Lycoperdon perlatum*	90	60
1123	20 l. *Lactarius deliciosus*	1·50	1·50
1124	30 l. *Boletus edulis*	2·00	2·25
1121/4	*Set of 4*	4·25	4·25
MS1125	100 × 70 mm. 65 l. *Amanita muscaria*	2·75	3·25

(Des Mary Walters. Litho Format)

1988 (13 Apr). *Fishes of Sierra Leone. T 213 and similar horiz designs. Multicoloured. P 15.*

1126	3 l. Type 213	10	10
1127	10 l. Banded Toothcarp	30	35
1128	20 l. Jewel Fish	60	65
1129	35 l. Butterfly Fish	1·00	1·10
1126/9	*Set of 4*	1·75	1·90
MS1130	99 × 69 mm. 65 l. African Longfin	1·90	2·25

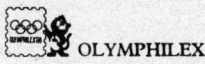 OLYMPHILEX '88

(213a)

1988 (19 Apr). *Stamp Exhibitions. Nos. 1016, 1072 and 1079 optd as T 213a with various emblems.*

1131	25 l. *Freedom*, 1980 (optd "INDEPEND-ENCE 40, Israel")	75	80
1132	30 l. Boris Becker (optd Type 213a)	90	95
1133	45 l. Maravedis (coins), *Nina* and Luis de Santangel (financier) (optd "PRAGA 88", Prague)	1·25	1·40
1131/3	*Set of 3*	2·50	2·75

214 Hands holding Coffee Beans and Woman with Cocoa	**215** Basketball

(Des L. Lamm. Litho Questa)

1988 (3 May). *International Fund for Agricultural Development. T 214 and similar horiz designs. Multicoloured. P 14.*

1134	3 l. Type 214	15	15
1135	15 l. Tropical fruits and man climbing palm tree	55	60
1136	25 l. Sheaf of rice and harvesters	90	1·00
1134/6	*Set of 3*	1·40	1·60

(Des L. Fried. Litho Questa)

1988 (15 June). *Olympic Games, Seoul (2nd issue). T 215 and similar vert designs. Multicoloured. P 14.*

1137	3 l. Type 215	10	10
1138	10 l. Judo	30	35
1139	15 l. Gymnastics	45	50
1140	40 l. Synchronized swimming	1·25	1·40
1137/40	*Set of 4*	2·00	2·10
MS1141	73 × 101 mm. 65 l. Sierra Leone athlete	1·90	2·50

216 Swallow-tailed Bee Eater	**217** *Aureol* (cargo liner)

(Des L. Nelson. Litho Questa)

1988 (25 June). *Birds. T 216 and similar vert designs. Multicoloured. P 14.*

1142	3 l. Type 216	20	20
1143	5 l. Double-toothed Barbet	30	30
1144	8 l. African Golden Oriole	45	45
1145	10 l. Red Bishop	50	50
1146	12 l. Red-billed Shrike	55	55
1147	20 l. European Bee Eater	95	95
1148	35 l. Common Gonolek ("Barbary Shrike")	1·60	1·60
1149	40 l. Western Black-headed Oriole	1·75	1·75
1142/9	*Set of 8*	5·75	5·75
MS1150	Two sheets, each 111 × 82 mm. (a) 65 l. Purple Heron. (b) 65 l. Saddle-bill Stork *Set of 2 sheets*	3·75	4·50

(Des D. Miller. Litho Questa)

1988 (1 July). *Ships. T 217 and similar horiz designs. Multicoloured. P 14.*

1151	3 l. Type 217	30	30
1152	10 l. *Dunkwa* (freighter)	80	80
1153	15 l. *Melampus* (container ship)	1·10	1·10
1154	30 l. *Dumbaia* (freighter)	1·90	1·90
1151/4	*Set of 4*	3·75	3·75
MS1155	95 × 95 mm. 65 l. Loading container ship, Freetown	1·90	2·25

(Litho Questa)

1988 (22 Aug). *500th Birth Anniv of Titian (artist). Vert designs as T 186a of Lesotho showing paintings. Multicoloured. P 13½×14.*

1156	1 l. "The Concert" (detail)	10	10
1157	2 l. "Philip II of Spain"	10	10
1158	3 l. "Saint Sebastian" (detail)	10	10
1159	5 l. "Martyrdom of St. Peter Martyr"	15	20
1160	15 l. "St. Jerome"	45	50
1161	20 l. "St. Mark enthroned with Saints"	60	65
1162	25 l. "Portrait of a Young Man"	75	80
1163	30 l. "St. Jerome in Penitence"	90	95
1156/63	*Set of 8*	2·75	3·00
MS1164	Two sheets, each 110 × 95 mm. (a) 50 l. "Self Portrait". (b) 50 l. "Orpheus and Eurydice" *Set of 2 sheets*	3·00	3·50

218 Helicopter lowering "Mercury" Capsule to Flight Deck	**219** Famine Relief Convoy crossing Desert

(Des W. Hanson. Litho B.D.T.)

1988 (26 Sept). *25th Death Anniv of John F. Kennedy (American statesman). U.S. Space Achievements. T 218 and similar horiz designs. Multicoloured. P 14.*

1165	3 l. Type 218	10	10
1166	5 l. Liberty Bell 7 capsule descending (*vert*)	15	20
1167	15 l. Launch of first manned American capsule (*vert*)	45	50
1168	40 l. *Freedom 7* orbiting Earth	1·25	1·40
1165/8	*Set of 4*	1·75	2·00
MS1169	98 × 69 mm. 65 l. President Kennedy and quotation	1·90	2·25

(Des J. Genzo. Litho B.D.T.)

1988 (1 Nov). *125th Anniv of International Red Cross. T 219 and similar multicoloured designs. P 14.*
1170	3 l.	Type **219**	30	30
1171	10 l.	Rifle and map of Battle of Solferino, 1859	75	75
1172	20 l.	World War II hospital ship in Pacific	1·25	1·25
1173	40 l.	Red Cross tent and World War I German biplanes	2·25	2·25
1170/3		*Set of 4*	4·00	4·00

MS1174 100 × 70 mm. 65 l. Henri Dunant (founder), Alfred Nobel and Peace Prize scroll (*horiz*) .. .. 2·40 2·75

(Des Walt Disney Company. Litho Questa)

1988 (1 Dec). *Christmas. "Mickey's Christmas Dance". Vert designs as T 171a of Lesotho showing Walt Disney cartoon characters. Multicoloured. P 13½×14.*
1175	10 l.	Donald Duck's nephews playing as band	45	45
		a. Sheetlet. Nos. 1175/82	3·25	
1176	10 l.	Clarabelle	45	45
1177	10 l.	Goofy	45	45
1178	10 l.	Scrooge McDuck and Grandma Duck	45	45
1179	10 l.	Donald Duck	45	45
1180	10 l.	Daisy Duck	45	45
1181	10 l.	Minnie Mouse	45	45
1182	10 l.	Mickey Mouse	45	45
1175/82		*Set of 8*	3·25	3·25

MS1183 Two sheets, each 127 × 102 mm. (a) 70 l. Mickey Mouse dancing the Charleston. (b) 70 l. Mickey Mouse jiving .. .. *Set of 2 sheets* 4·50 5·00

Nos. 1175/82 were printed together, *se-tenant* as a composite design, in sheetlets of eight.

Sierra Leone Le3
CHRISTMAS 1988
Adoration of the Magi (Detail) RUBENS 1577–1640

220 "Adoration of the Magi" (detail)	GRAND SLAM WINNER (221)

(Litho Questa)

1988 (15 Dec). *Christmas. Religious Paintings by Rubens. T 220 and similar vert designs. Multicoloured. P 13½ × 14.*
1184	3 l.	Type **220**	10	10
1185	3 l. 60,	"Adoration of the Shepherds" (detail)	10	10
1186	5 l.	"Adoration of the Magi" (detail)	20	20
1187	10 l.	"Adoration of the Shepherds" (different detail)	35	35
1188	20 l.	"Virgin and Child surrounded by Flowers"	65	65
1189	40 l.	"St. Gregory the Great and Other Saints" (detail)	1·40	1·40
1190	60 l.	"Adoration of the Magi" (detail)	1·90	1·90
1191	80 l.	"Madonna and Child with Saints" (detail)	2·40	2·40
1184/91		*Set of 8*	6·50	6·50

MS1192 Two sheets, each 76 × 113 mm. (a) 100 l. "Virgin and Child enthroned with Saints". (b) 100 l. "St. Gregory the Great and Other Saints" .. .. .. *Set of 2 sheets* 5·75 6·50

1989 (16 Jan). *Steffi Graf's "Grand Slam" Tennis Victories. No. MS1076b optd "GOLD MEDALIST" (No. MS1193e) or with T 221 (others), each with different inscription on sheet margin, all in gold.*
MS1193 105×75 mm. 100 l. Steffi Graf. (a) Optd "AUSTRALIAN OPEN JANUARY 11–24, 1988 GRAF v EVERET". (b) Optd "FRENCH OPEN MAY 23–JUNE 5, 1988 GRAF v ZVEREVA". (c) Optd "WIMBLEDON JUNE 20–JULY 4, 1988 GRAF v NAVRATILOVA". (d) Optd "U.S. OPEN AUGUST 29–SEPTEMBER 11, 1988 GRAF v SABATINI". (e) Optd "SEOUL OLYMPICS 1988 GRAF v SABATINI"
.. .. .. *Set of 5 sheets* 4·00 4·00
Each marginal overprint includes score of match involved.

222 Brazil v. Sweden, 1958	223 Decathlon (Gold, C. Schenk, East Germany)

(Des J. McDaniel. Litho B.D.T.)

1989 (28 Apr). *World Cup Football Championship, Italy. T 222 and similar vert designs, each showing action from previous World Cup finals. Multicoloured. P 14.*
1194	3 l.	Type **222**	10	10
1195	6 l.	West Germany v. Hungary, 1954	15	15
1196	8 l.	England v. West Germany, 1966	15	15
1197	10 l.	Argentina v. Netherlands, 1978	20	20
1198	12 l.	Brazil v. Czechoslovakia, 1962	20	20
1199	20 l.	West Germany v. Netherlands, 1974	25	25
1200	30 l.	Italy v. West Germany, 1982	30	30
1201	40 l.	Brazil v. Italy, 1970	35	35
1194/201		*Set of 8*	1·50	1·50

MS1202 Two sheets, each 73×104 mm. (a) 100 l. Argentina v. West Germany, 1986. (b) 100 l. Uruguay v. Brazil, 1950 .. *Set of 2 sheets* 1·60 1·75

(Des L. Fried. Litho B.D.T.)

1989 (28 Apr). *Olympic Medal Winners, Seoul (1988). T 223 and similar horiz designs. Multicoloured. P 14.*
1203	3 l.	Type **223**	10	10
1204	6 l.	Men's heavyweight judo (Gold, H. Saito, Japan)	15	15
1205	10 l.	Women's cycle road race (Silver, J. Niehaus, West Germany)	15	15
1206	15 l.	Men's single sculls (Gold, T. Lange, East Germany)	15	15
1207	20 l.	Men's 50 metres freestyle swimming (Gold, M. Biondi, U.S.A.)	20	20
1208	30 l.	Men's 100 metres (Gold, C. Lewis, U.S.A.)	25	25
1209	40 l.	Dressage (Gold, West Germany)	35	35
1210	50 l.	Greco-Roman wrestling (57 kg) (Gold, A. Sike, Hungary)	40	40
1203/10		*Set of 8*	1·60	1·60

MS1211 Two sheets, each 70×100 mm. (a) 100 l. Olympic gold medal. (b) 100 l. Olympic torch and rings .. .. .. *Set of 2 sheets* 1·60 1·75

224 Map of Union States, Mail Lorry and Post Office

(Des J. Genzo. Litho B.D.T.)

1989 (19 May). *15th Anniv of Mano River Union. T 224 and similar horiz designs. Multicoloured. P 14.*
1212	1 l.	Type **224**	10	10
1213	3 l.	Map of West Africa and Presidents Momoh, Conte and Doe	10	10
1214	10 l.	Construction of Freetown–Monrovia Highway	20	20
1212/14		*Set of 3*	30	30

MS1215 96×68 mm. 15 l. Presidents signing anniversary meeting communique 30 30

225 Richard III	226 Centenary Logo

(Des G. Vasarhelyi. Litho B.D.T.)

1989 (30 May). *425th Birth Anniv of Shakespeare. T 225 and similar horiz designs. Multicoloured. P 13.*
1216	15 l.	Type **225**	25	25
		a. Sheetlet. Nos. 1216/23	1·75	
1217	15 l.	Othello (Iago)	25	25
1218	15 l.	Two Gentlemen of Verona	25	25
1219	15 l.	Macbeth (Lady Macbeth)	25	25
1220	15 l.	Hamlet	25	25
1221	15 l.	The Taming of the Shrew	25	25
1222	15 l.	The Merry Wives of Windsor	25	25
1223	15 l.	Henry IV (Sir John Falstaff)	25	25
1224	15 l.	Macbeth (The Witches)	25	25
		a. Sheetlet. Nos. 1224/31	1·75	
1225	15 l.	Romeo and Juliet	25	25
1226	15 l.	Merchant of Venice	25	25
1227	15 l.	As You Like It	25	25
1228	15 l.	The Taming of the Shrew (banquet scene)	25	25
1229	15 l.	King Lear	25	25
1230	15 l.	Othello (Othello and Desdemona)	25	25
1231	15 l.	Henry IV (Justice Shallow)	25	25
1216/31		*Set of 16*	3·50	3·50

MS1232 Two sheets, each 117×82 mm. (a) 100 l. Shakespeare and arms (49×36 mm). (b) 100 l. Shakespeare (49×36 mm) .. *Set of 2 sheets* 2·75 3·00

Nos. 1216/23 and 1224/31 were each printed together, *se-tenant*, in sheetlets of eight stamps and one central stamp-size label.

(Litho Questa)

1989 (8 June). *Centenary of Ahmadiyya Muslim Society. P 14.*
1233 **226**	3 l.	brownish black and new blue	10	10

(Litho Questa)

1989 (3 July). *Japanese Art (1st series). Paintings by Seiho. Multicoloured designs as T 187a of Lesotho. P 14×13½ (3, 10, 12, 40 l.) or 13½×14 (others).*
1234	3 l.	"Lapping Waves"	10	10
1235	6 l.	"Hazy Moon" (*vert*)	15	15
1236	8 l.	"Passing Spring" (*vert*)	15	15
1237	10 l.	"Mackerels"	15	15
1238	12 l.	"Calico Cat"	15	15
1239	30 l.	"The First Time to be a Model" (*vert*)	25	25
1240	40 l.	"Kingly Lion"	35	35
1241	75 l.	"After a Shower" (*vert*)	60	60
1234/41		*Set of 8*	1·60	1·60

MS1242 Two sheets, each 102×77 mm. (a) 150 l. "Dozing in the midst of all the Chirping" (detail) (*vert*). P 13½×14. (b) 150 l. "Domesticated Monkeys and Rabbits" (detail). P 14×13½ .. .. .. *Set of 2 sheets* 2·25 2·50

Nos. 1234/41 were each printed in sheetlets of 10 containing two horizontal or vertical strips of 5 stamps separated by printed labels commemorating Emperor Hirohito.
See also Nos. 1321/51.

227 Robespierre and Bastille

(Des Design Element. Litho B.D.T.)

1989 (13 July). *"Philexfrance '89" International Stamp Exhibition, Paris, and Bicentenary of French Revolution. T 227 and similar multicoloured designs. P 14.*
1243	6 l.	Type **227**	15	15
1244	20 l.	Danton and Louvre	20	20
1245	45 l.	Queen Marie Antoinette and Notre Dame	35	35
1246	80 l.	Louis XVI and Palace of Versailles	60	60
1243/6		*Set of 4*	1·10	1·10

MS1247 77×107 mm. 150 l. Celebrating crowd, Paris (*vert*) .. .. .. 1·25 1·50

228 "Sputnik" Satellite in Orbit, 1957	229 Bulbophyllum barbigerum

(Des G. Vasarhelyi. Litho B.D.T.)

1989 (20 July). *History of Space Exploration. T 228 and similar horiz designs. P 14.*
1248/301 10 l.×27, 15 l.×27 multicoloured
.. .. .. *Set of 54* 4·00 4·50
MS1302 Three sheets, each 112×90 mm. 100 l. ×3 multicoloured .. .. *Set of 3 sheets* 2·25 2·50
Nos. 1248/301 were issued as six sheetlets, each of nine different designs.

(Des W. Hanson Studio. Litho B.D.T.)

1989 (8 Sept). *Orchids of Sierra Leone. T 229 and similar vert designs. Multicoloured. P 14.*
1303	3 l.	Type **229**	15	15
1304	6 l.	Bulbophyllum falcatum	15	15
1305	12 l.	Habenaria macrara	15	15
1306	20 l.	Eurychone rothchildiana	20	20
1307	50 l.	Calyptrochilum christyanum	45	45
1308	60 l.	Bulbophyllum distans	55	55
1309	70 l.	Eulophia guineensis	60	60
1310	80 l.	Diaphananthe pellucida	70	70
1303/10		*Set of 8*	2·75	2·75

MS1311 Two sheets, each 112×80 mm. (a) 100 l. Cyrtorchis arcuata and Pagoda, Kew Gardens. (b) 100 l. Eulophia cucullata .. *Set of 2 sheets* 1·75 2·00

230 Salamis temora

(Des Mary Walters. Litho B.D.T.)

1989 (11 Sept). *Butterflies. T 230 and similar multicoloured designs. P 14.*
1312	6 l.	Type **230**	15	15
1313	12 l.	Pseudacraea lucretia	15	15
1314	18 l.	Charaxes boueti (*vert*)	20	20
1315	30 l.	Graphium antheus (*vert*)	30	30
1316	40 l.	Colotis protomedia	35	35
1317	60 l.	Asterope pechueli (*vert*)	50	50
1318	72 l.	Coenyra aurantiaca	60	60
1319	80 l.	Precis octavia (*vert*)	70	70
1312/19		*Set of 8*	2·75	2·75

MS1320 Two sheets, each 100×70 mm. (a) 100 l. Charaxes cithaeron (*vert*). (b) 100 l. Euphaedra themis .. .. .. *Set of 2 sheets* 1·75 2·00

(Litho Questa)

1989 (13 Nov). *Japanese Art (2nd series). Paintings by Hiroshige of "The Fifty-three Stations on the Tokaido Road". Horiz designs as T 187a of Lesotho. Multicoloured.* P 14×13½.

1321	25 l.	"Ferry-boat to Kawasaki"	20	20
1322	25 l.	"The Hilly Town of Hodogaya"	20	20
1323	25 l.	"Lute Players at Fujisawa"	20	20
1324	25 l.	"Mild Rainstorm at Oiso"	20	20
1325	25 l.	"Lake Ashi and Mountains of Hakone"	20	20
1326	25 l.	"Twilight at Numazu"	20	20
1327	25 l.	"Mount Fuji from Hara"	20	20
1328	25 l.	"Samurai Children riding through Yoshiwara"	20	20
1329	25 l.	"Mountain Pass at Yui"	20	20
1330	25 l.	"Harbour at Ejiri"	20	20
1331	25 l.	"Halt at Fujieda"	20	20
1332	25 l.	"Misty Kanaya on the Oi River"	20	20
1333	25 l.	"The Bridge to Kakegawa"	20	20
1334	25 l.	"Teahouse at Fukuroi"	20	20
1335	25 l.	"The Ford at Mistuke"	20	20
1336	25 l.	"Coolies warming themselves at Hamamatsu"	20	20
1337	25 l.	"Imakiri Ford at Maisaka"	20	20
1338	25 l.	"Pacific Ocean from Shirasuka"	20	20
1339	25 l.	"Futakawa Street-singers"	20	20
1340	25 l.	"Repairing Yoshida Castle"	20	20
1341	25 l.	"The Inn at Akasaka"	20	20
1342	25 l.	"The Bridge to Okazaki"	20	20
1343	25 l.	"Samurai's Wife entering Narumi"	20	20
1344	25 l.	"Harbour at Kuwana"	20	20
1345	25 l.	"Autumn in Ishiyakushi"	20	20
1346	25 l.	"Snowfall at Kameyama"	20	20
1347	25 l.	"The Frontier-station of Seki"	20	20
1348	25 l.	"Teahouse at Sakanoshita"	20	20
1349	25 l.	"Kansai Houses at Minakushi"	20	20
1350	25 l.	"Kusatsu Station"	20	20
1321/50		*Set of 30*	5·50	5·50

MS1351 Two sheets, each 102×75 mm. (a) 120 l. "Nihom Bridge, Edo". (b) 120 l. "Sanjo Bridge, Kyoto" .. .. .. *Set of 2 sheets* 1·60 1·75
The English captions of the two miniature sheets of No. MS1351 are transposed. The sheet showing the Nihom Bridge, Edo, has a group of fishmongers in the left foreground.

(Des Design Element. Litho Questa)

1989 (17 Nov). *"World Stamp Expo '89" International Stamp Exhibition, Washington (1st issue). Landmarks of Washington. Sheet 78×61 mm containing horiz design as T 193a of Lesotho. Multicoloured.* P 14.

MS1352 100 l. Jefferson Memorial 60 75

231 Formosan Sika Deer

(Des J. Genzo. Litho B.D.T.)

1989 (29 Nov). *"World Stamp Expo '89" International Stamp Exhibition, Washington (2nd issue). Endangered Fauna. T 231 and similar multicoloured designs.* P 14.

1353	6 l.	Humpback Whale	15	15
1354	9 l.	Type 231	15	15
1355	16 l.	Spanish Lynx	20	20
1356	20 l.	Goitred Gazelle	20	20
1357	30 l.	Japanese Sea Lion	30	30
1358	50 l.	Long-eared Owl	50	50
1359	70 l.	Lady Amherst's ("Chinese Copper") Pheasant	65	65
1360	100 l.	Siberian Tiger	90	90
1353/60		*Set of 8*	2·75	2·75

MS1361 Two sheets, each 103×75 mm. (a) 150 l. Mauritius Kestrel (*vert*). (b) 150 l. Japanese Crested Ibis (*vert*) .. .. *Set of 2 sheets* 2·00 2·25

(Des Walt Disney Co. Litho Questa)

1989 (18 Dec). *Christmas. Horiz designs as T 73 of St. Vincent Grenadines showing Walt Disney cartoon characters with cars. Multicoloured.* P 14×13½.

1362	3 l.	Mickey Mouse and Goofy in Rolls-Royce "Phantom II Roadstar", 1934	10	10
1363	6 l.	Mickey and Minnie Mouse in Mercedes-Benz "500K", 1935	15	15
1364	10 l.	Mickey and Minnie Mouse with Jaguar "SS-100", 1938	15	15
1365	12 l.	Mickey Mouse and Goofy with U.S. army jeep, 1941	15	15
1366	20 l.	Mickey and Minnie Mouse with Buick Roadmaster Sedan "Model 91", 1937	20	20
1367	30 l.	Mickey Mouse driving 1948 Tucker	30	30
1368	40 l.	Mickey and Minnie Mouse in Alfa Romeo, 1933	40	40
1369	50 l.	Mickey and Minnie Mouse with 1937 Cord	45	45
1362/9		*Set of 8*	1·60	1·60

MS1370 Two sheets, each 127×101 mm. (a) 100 l. Mickey in Fiat Topolino, 1938. (b) 100 l. Mickey Mouse with gifts and Pontiac "Model 401", 1931 .. .. *Set of 2 sheets* 1·75 2·00

(Litho Questa)

1989 (22 Dec). *Christmas. Paintings by Rembrandt. Vert designs as T 193b of Lesotho. Multicoloured.* P 14.

1371	3 l.	"The Adoration of the Magi"	10	10
1372	6 l.	"The Holy Family with a Cat"	15	15
1373	10 l.	"The Holy Family with Angels"	15	15
1374	15 l.	"Simeon in the Temple"	15	15
1375	30 l.	"The Circumcision"	25	25
1376	90 l.	"The Holy Family"	70	70

1377	100 l.	"The Visitation"	85	85
1378	120 l.	"The Flight into Egypt"	1·00	1·00
1371/8		*Set of 8*	3·00	3·00

MS1379 Two sheets, each 70×95 mm. (a) 150 l. "The Adoration of the Shepherds" (detail). (b) 150 l. "The Presentation of Jesus in the Temple" (detail) .. .. *Set of 2 sheets* 1·60 1·75

232 Johann Kepler
(astronomer)

(Des G. Vasarhelyi. Litho Questa)

1990 (15 Jan). *Exploration of Mars. T 232 and similar horiz designs showing astronomers, spacecraft and Martian landscapes.* P 14.

1380/1415 175 l. × 36 multicoloured .. *Set of 36* 22·00 23·00
MS1416 Two sheets, each 105×85 mm. (a) 150 l. The "Face" on Mars. (b) 150 l. Section of space station .. .. .. *Set of 2 sheets* 1·60 1·75
Nos. 1380/1415 were issued as four sheetlets each of nine different designs.

232a Dolittle's B-25
Ruptured Duck, 1942

(Des J. Batchelor. Litho Questa)

1990 (5 Feb). *50th Anniv of Second World War. American Aircraft. T 232a and similar horiz designs. Multicoloured.* P 14.

1417	1 l.	Type 232a	10	10
1418	2 l.	B-24 Liberator	10	10
1419	3 l.	A-20 Boston attacking Japanese convoy, Bismark Sea, 1943	10	10
1420	9 l.	P-38 Lightning	10	10
1421	12 l.	B-26 bomber	10	10
1422	16 l.	Two B-17 F bombers	10	10
1423	50 l.	B-25 D bomber	15	20
1424	80 l.	B-29 Superfortress	25	30
1425	90 l.	B-17 G bomber	25	30
1426	100 l.	B-29 Superfortress *Enola Gay*	30	35
1417/26		*Set of 10*	1·10	1·25

MS1427 Two sheets, each 106×77 mm. (a) 150 l. Dolittle B-25 taking off from the U.S.S. *Hornet*, 1942. (b) 150 l. B-17 G of 447th Bomber Group .. .. *Set of 2 sheets* 90 95

233 Mickey Mouse at Bauxite Mine

234 Olivier as Antony in *Antony and Cleopatra*, 1951

(Des Walt Disney Co. Litho Questa)

1990 (23 Apr). *Sierra Leone Sites and Scenes. T 233 and similar multicoloured designs, each showing Walt Disney cartoon characters.* P 14×13½.

1428	3 l.	Type 233	10	10
1429	6 l.	Scrooge McDuck panning for gold	10	10
1430	10 l.	Minnie Mouse at Lungi Airport	10	10
1431	12 l.	Mickey Mouse at Old Fourah Bay College	10	10
1432	16 l.	Mickey Mouse mining bauxite	10	10
1433	20 l.	Huey, Dewey and Louie harvesting rice	10	10
1434	30 l.	Mickey and Minnie Mouse admire the Freetown Cotton Tree	10	15
1435	100 l.	Mickey Mouse flying over Rutile Mine	30	35
1436	200 l.	Mickey Mouse fishing at Goderich	60	65
1437	225 l.	Mickey and Minnie Mouse at Bintumani Hotel	65	70
1428/37		*Set of 10*	2·00	2·00

MS1438 Two sheets, each 130×100 mm. (a) 250 l. Dwarfs with diamonds. P 14×13½. (b) 250 l. Mickey and Minnie Mouse at King Jimmy Market (*vert*). P 13½×14 .. *Set of 2 sheets* 1·50 1·60

(Des J. Iskowitz. Litho Questa)

1990 (27 Apr). *Sir Laurence Olivier (actor) Commemoration. T 234 and similar vert designs. Multicoloured.* P 14.

1439	3 l.	Type 234	10	10
1440	9 l.	As King Henry V in *Henry V*, 1943	10	10
1441	16 l.	As Oedipus in *Oedipus*, 1945	10	10
1442	20 l.	As Heathcliff in *Wuthering Heights*, 1939	10	10
1443	30 l.	As Szell in *Marathon Man*, 1976	10	15
1444	70 l.	As Othello in *Othello*, 1964	20	25
1445	175 l.	As Michael in *Beau Geste*, 1929	50	55
1446	200 l.	As King Richard III in *Richard III*, 1956	60	65
1439/46		*Set of 8*	1·40	1·60

MS1447 Two sheets, each 98×68 mm. (a) 250 l. As Hamlet in *Hamlet*, 1947. (b) 250 l. As Sir Hugh Dowding in *The Battle of Britain*, 1969 .. .. *Set of 2 sheets* 1·50 1·60

235 Penny Black   **236** Cameroons World Cup Team

(Des M. Pollard. Litho Questa)

1990 (3 May). *150th Anniv of the Penny Black.* P 14×13½.

1448	235	50 l. deep ultramarine	15	20
1449		100 l. purple-brown	30	35
MS1450		145×106 mm. 235 250 l. black	75	80

(Des Young Phillips Studio. Litho Questa)

1990 (11 May). *World Cup Football Championship, Italy. Finalists. T 236 and similar horiz designs. Multicoloured.* P 14×13½.

1451/74 15 l. × 8 (Type 236, Colombia, Costa Rica, Egypt, Rumania, South Korea, U.A.E., Yugoslavia), 30 l. × 8 (Austria, Belgium, Czechoslovakia, Netherlands, Scotland, Sweden, Uruguay, U.S.S.R.), 45 l. × 8 (Argentina, Brazil, England, Ireland, Italy, Spain, U.S.A., West Germany) .. .. .. *Set of 24* 2·10 2·25
Each design of Nos. 1451/74 was issued in separate sheetlets of 8 stamps with a central label showing the World Cup and Championship logo.

237 Great Crested Grebe

(Des Mary Walters. Litho Questa)

1990 (4 June). *Birds. T 237 and similar horiz designs. Multicoloured.* P 14.

1475	3 l.	Type 237	10	10
1476	6 l.	Green Wood Hoopoe	10	10
1477	10 l.	African Jacana	10	10
1478	12 l.	Avocet	10	10
1479	20 l.	Peters's Finfoot	10	15
1480	80 l.	Glossy Ibis	25	30
1481	150 l.	Hammerkop	45	50
1482	200 l.	Black-throated Honeyguide	60	65
1475/82		*Set of 8*	1·40	1·50

MS1483 Two sheets, each 100×70 mm. (a) 250 l. African Palm Swift. (b) 250 l. Painted Snipe .. .. *Set of 2 sheets* 1·50 1·60

(Des Walt Disney Co. Litho Questa)

1990 (6 June). *"Stamp World London 90" International Stamp Exhibition. British Costumes. Multicoloured designs as T 239a of Maldive Islands showing Walt Disney cartoon characters.* P 13½×14.

1484	3 l.	Mickey Mouse as a Yeoman Warder (*vert*)	10	10
1485	6 l.	Scrooge McDuck as a lamplighter (*vert*)	10	10
1486	12 l.	Goofy as a medieval knight (*vert*)	10	10
1487	15 l.	Clarabelle as Anne Boleyn (*vert*)	10	10
1488	75 l.	Minnie Mouse as Queen Elizabeth I (*vert*)	20	25
1489	100 l.	Donald Duck as a chimney sweep (*vert*)	30	35
1490	125 l.	Pete as King Henry VIII (*vert*)	35	40
1491	150 l.	Clarabelle, Minnie Mouse and Daisy Duck as May dancers (*vert*)	45	50
1484/91		*Set of 8*	1·40	1·50

MS1492 Two sheets, each 127×102 mm. (a) 250 l. Donald Duck as a lawyer (*vert*). P 13½×14. (b) 250 l. Minnie Mouse as Queen Boadicea. P 14×13½ .. *Set of 2 sheets* 1·50 1·60

(Des Young Phillips Studio. Litho Questa)

1990 (5 July). *90th Birthday of Queen Elizabeth the Queen Mother. Vert designs as* T **198***a of Lesotho showing portraits, 1980–89. Multicoloured.* P 14.

1493	75 l.	Queen Mother on Remembrance Sunday	20	25
		a. Strip of 3. Nos. 1493/5	55	
1494	75 l.	Queen Mother in yellow hat	20	25
1495	75 l.	Waving to crowds on 85th birthday	20	25
1493/5		*Set of 3*	55	70
MS1496		90×75 mm. 250 l. As No. 1495	75	80

Nos. 1493/5 were printed together, horizontally and vertically *se-tenant*, in sheetlets of 9 (3×3).

238 Golden Cat

239 Rabbit

(Des S. Barlowe. Litho Questa)

1990 (24 Sept). *Wildlife.* T **238** *and similar multicoloured designs.* P 14.

1497	25 l.	Type **238**	10	10
		a. Sheetlet. Nos. 1497/1514	80	
1498	25 l.	White-backed Night Heron	10	10
1499	25 l.	Bateleur	10	10
1500	25 l.	Marabou Stork	10	10
1501	25 l.	White-faced Whistling Duck	10	10
1502	25 l.	Aardvark	10	10
1503	25 l.	Royal Antelope	10	10
1504	25 l.	Pygmy Hippopotamus	10	10
1505	25 l.	Leopard	10	10
1506	25 l.	Sacred Ibis	10	10
1507	25 l.	Mona Monkey	10	10
1508	25 l.	African Darter	10	10
1509	25 l.	Chimpanzee	10	10
1510	25 l.	African Elephant	10	10
1511	25 l.	Potto	10	10
1512	25 l.	African Manatee	10	10
1513	25 l.	African Fish Eagle	10	10
1514	25 l.	African Spoonbill	10	10
1497/1514		*Set of 18*	80	80
MS1515		106×76 mm. 150 l. Crowned Eagle (*vert*)	45	50

Nos. 1497/1514 were printed together, *se-tenant*, in sheetlets of 18 with the background forming a map of Sierra Leone.

(Litho Questa)

1990 (22 Oct). *Fairground Carousel Animals.* T **239** *and similar vert designs. Multicoloured.* P 14.

1516	5 l.	Type **239**	10	10
1517	10 l.	Horse with panther saddle	10	10
1518	20 l.	Ostrich	10	10
1519	30 l.	Zebra	10	15
1520	50 l.	Horse	15	20
1521	80 l.	Sea monster	25	30
1522	100 l.	Giraffe	30	35
1523	150 l.	Armoured horse	45	50
1524	200 l.	Camel	60	65
1516/24		*Set of 9*	1·75	2·10
MS1525		Two sheets (a) 98×68 mm. 300 l. Masked horse. (b) 68×98 mm. 300 l. Baden-Powell as Centaur		
		Set of 2 sheets	1·75	1·90

(Des B. Grout. Litho B.D.T.)

1990 (12 Nov). *Olympic Games, Barcelona* (1992). *Multicoloured designs as* T **202** *of Lesotho.* P 14.

1526	5 l.	Start of Men's 100 metres	10	10
1527	10 l.	Men's 4×400 metres relay	10	10
1528	20 l.	Men's 100 metres in progress	10	10
1529	30 l.	Weightlifting	10	15
1530	40 l.	Freestyle wrestling	10	15
1531	80 l.	Water polo	25	30
1532	150 l.	Women's gymnastics	45	50
1533	200 l.	Cycling	60	65
1526/33		*Set of 8*	1·50	1·75
MS1534		Two sheets, each 103×75 mm. (a) 400 l. Boxing (*horiz*). (b) 400 l. Olympic flag (*horiz*)		
		Set of 2 sheets	2·40	2·50

240 Morty assembling Bicycle by Christmas Tree

241 "Holy Family with St. Elizabeth" (Mantegna)

(Des Walt Disney Co. Litho B.D.T.)

1990 (17 Dec). *Christmas. "The Night before Christmas".* T **240** *and similar designs showing Walt Disney cartoon characters in scenes from Clement Moore's poem.* P 13.

1535/58	50 l. × 8, 75 l. × 8, 100 l. × 8	*Set of 24*	5·50	5·75
MS1559	Six sheets, each 129×107 mm. 400 l. × 6 multicoloured	*Set of 6 sheets*	7·25	7·50

Nos. 1535/58 were issued as three sheetlets of eight, each containing stamps of the same face value *se-tenant*. Of the stamps in No. **MS**1559 four horizontal and two vertical.

(Litho Cartor, France)

1990 (17 Dec). *Christmas Paintings.* T **241** *and similar vert designs. Multicoloured.* P 13.

1560	10 l.	"Holy Family resting" (Rembrandt)	10	10
1561	20 l.	Type **241**	10	10
1562	30 l.	"Virgin and Child with an Angel" (Correggio)	10	15
1563	50 l.	"Annunciation" (Bernardo Strozzi)	15	20
1564	100 l.	"Madonna and Child appearing to St. Anthony" (Lippi)	30	35
1565	175 l.	"Virgin and Child" (Giovanni Boltraffio)	50	55
1566	200 l.	"Esterhazy Madonna" (Raphael)	60	65
1567	300 l.	"Coronation of Mary" (Andrea Orcagna)	90	95
1560/7		*Set of 8*	2·40	2·75
MS1568		Two sheets, each 75×114 mm. (a) 400 l. "Adoration of the Shepherds" (Bronzino). (b) 400 l. "Adoration of the Shepherds" (Gerard David)		
		Set of 2 sheets	2·40	2·50

(Litho Questa)

1990 (24 Dec). *350th Death Anniv of Rubens* (1st issue). *Multicoloured designs as* T **250** *of Maldive Islands, but vert.* P 13½×14.

1569	5 l.	"Helena Fourment as Hagar in the Wilderness" (detail)	10	10
1570	10 l.	"Isabella Brant"	10	10
1571	20 l.	"Countess of Arundel and her Party" (detail)	10	10
1572	60 l.	"Countess of Arundel and her Party" (different detail)	20	25
1573	80 l.	"Nicolaas Rockox"	25	30
1574	100 l.	"Adriana Perez"	30	35
1575	150 l.	"George Villiers, Duke of Buckingham" (detail)	45	50
1576	300 l.	"Countess of Buckingham"	90	95
1569/76		*Set of 8*	2·00	2·25
MS1577		Two sheets, each 71×100 mm. (a) 350 l. "Giovanni Carlo Dorio" (detail). (b) 350 l. "Veronica Spinola Dorio" (detail) *Set of 2 sheets*	2·10	2·25

See also Nos. 1595/603.

242 *Chlorophyllum molybdites*

243 "The Flight of St. Barbara" (detail) (Rubens)

(Des Mary Walters. Litho Questa)

1990 (31 Dec). *Fungi.* T **242** *and similar vert designs. Multicoloured.* P 14.

1578	3 l.	Type **242**	10	10
1579	5 l.	*Lepista nuda*	10	10
1580	10 l.	*Clitocybe nebularis*	10	10
1581	15 l.	*Cyathus striatus*	10	10
1582	20 l.	*Bolbitius vitellinus*	10	10
1583	25 l.	*Leucoagaricus naucinus*	10	10
1584	30 l.	*Suillus luteus*	10	10
1585	40 l.	*Podaxis pistillaris*	10	10
1586	50 l.	*Oudemansiella radicata*	15	20
1587	60 l.	*Phallus indusiatus*	20	25
1588	80 l.	*Macrolepiota rhacodes*	25	30
1589	100 l.	*Mycena pura*	30	35
1590	150 l.	*Volvariella volvacea*	45	50
1591	175 l.	*Omphalotus olearius*	50	55
1592	200 l.	*Sphaerobolus stellatus*	60	65
1593	250 l.	*Schizophyllum commune*	75	80
1578/93		*Set of 16*	3·25	3·50
MS1594		Four sheets, each 101×70 mm. (a) 350 l. *Hypholoma fasciculare.* (b) 350 l. *Psilocybe coprophila.* (c) 350 l. *Agaricus campestris.* (d) 350 l. *Suillus granulatus*		
		Set of 4 sheets	4·25	4·50

(Litho Questa)

1991 (8 Apr). *Easter. 350th Death Anniv of Rubens* (1990) (2nd issue). T **243** *and similar vert designs. Multicoloured.* P 13½×14.

1595	10 l.	Type **243**	10	10
1596	20 l.	"The Last Judgement" (detail)	10	10
1597	30 l.	"St. Gregory of Nazianzus"	10	10
1598	50 l.	"Doubting Thomas"	15	20
1599	80 l.	"The Way to Calvary" (detail)	25	30
1600	100 l.	"St. Gregory with Sts. Domitilla, Maurus and Papianus"	30	35
1601	175 l.	"Sts. Gregory, Maurus and Papianus"	50	55
1602	300 l.	"Christ and the Penitent Sinners"	90	95
1595/602		*Set of 8*	2·10	2·40
MS1603		Two sheets, each 70×101 mm. (a) 400 l. "The Last Judgement" (different detail). (b) 400 l. "The Way to Calvary" (different detail)		
		Set of 2 sheets	2·50	2·75

244 Class "1400" Steam Locomotive

(Des K. Gromell. Litho Questa)

1991 (13 May). *"Phila Nippon '91" International Stamp Exhibition, Tokyo. Japanese Trains.* T **244** *and similar horiz designs. Each multicoloured* (Nos. 1604/11) *or black and rosine* (No. **MS**1612). P 14.

1604	10 l.	Type **244**	10	10
1605	20 l.	Class "C 55" streamline steam locomotive	10	10
1606	30 l.	Class "ED 17" electric locomotive	10	10
1607	60 l.	Class "EF 13" double-ended electric locomotive	20	25
1608	100 l.	Baldwin Class "Mikado" steam locomotive	30	35
1609	150 l.	Class "C 62" steam locomotive	45	50
1610	200 l.	Class "KiHa 81" diesel train	60	65
1611	300 l.	Class "8550" steam locomotive	90	95
1604/11		*Set of 8*	2·50	2·75
MS1612		Four sheets, each 106×76 mm. (a) 400 l. Class "9600" steam locomotive. (b) 400 l. Class "D 51" steam locomotive. (c) 400 l. Class "7000" electric train. (d) 400 l. Hikari "Bullet" train		
		Set of 4 sheets	5·00	5·25

245 *Aphyosemion spurrelli*

(Des W. Hanson Studio. Litho Questa)

1991 (3 June). *Fishes.* T **245** *and similar horiz designs. Multicoloured.* P 14.

1613	10 l.	Type **245**	10	10
1614	20 l.	*Epiplatys dageti*	10	10
1615	30 l.	*Aphyosemion petersi*	10	10
1616	60 l.	*Fundulosoma thierryi*	20	25
1617	100 l.	*Pantodon bulcholzi peters*	30	35
1618	150 l.	*Epiplatys spilargyreius*	45	50
1619	200 l.	*Epiplatys sexfasciatus*	60	65
1620	300 l.	*Tetraodon lineatus*	90	95
1613/20		*Set of 8*	2·50	2·75
MS1621		Two sheets, each 96×70 mm. (a) 400 l. *Synodontis robbianus.* (b) 400 l. *Epiplatys bifasciatus*		
		Set of 2 sheets	2·50	2·75

(Litho Walsall)

1991 (28 June). *Death Centenary of Vincent van Gogh* (artist). *Multicoloured designs as* T **255** *of Maldive Islands.* P 13½.

1622	10 c.	"The Langlois Bridge at Arles" (*horiz*)	10	10
1623	50 c.	"Tree in Garden at Saint-Paul Hospital"	10	10
1624	1 l.	"Wild Flowers and Thistles in a Vase"	10	10
1625	2 l.	"Still Life: Vase with Oleanders and Books" (*horiz*)	10	10
1626	5 l.	"Farmhouses in a Wheatfield near Arles" (*horiz*)	10	10
1627	10 l.	"Self-portrait, September 1889"	10	10
1628	20 l.	"Patience Escalier"	10	10
1629	30 l.	"Doctor Félix Rey"	10	10
1630	50 l.	"The Iris"	15	20
1631	60 l.	"The Shepherdess"	20	25
1632	80 l.	"Vincent's House in Arles" (*horiz*)	25	30
1633	100 l.	"The Road Menders" (*horiz*)	30	35
1634	150 l.	"The Garden of Saint-Paul Hospital"	45	50
1635	200 l.	"View of the Church, Saint-Paul-de-Mausole" (*horiz*)	60	65
1636	250 l.	"Seascape at Saintes-Maries" (*horiz*)	75	80
1637	300 l.	"Pietà"	90	95
1622/37		*Set of 16*	3·50	4·00
MS1638		Six sheets. (a) 102×76 mm. 400 l. "Haystacks in Provence" (96×70 *mm*). (b) 102×76 mm. 400 l. "The Trinquetaille Bridge" (96×70 *mm*). (c) 102×76 mm. 400 l. "Vineyards with a View of Auvers" (96×70 *mm*). (d) 102×76 mm. 400 l. "The Garden of Saint-Paul Hospital" (96×107 *mm*). (e) 76×102 mm. 400 l. "Church at Auvers-sur-Dise" (70×96 *mm*). (f) 76×102 mm. 400 l. "Two Poplars on a Road through the Hills" (70×96 *mm*). Imperf		
		Set of 6 sheets	7·50	7·75

(Des D. Miller. Litho Walsall)

1991 (5 July). *65th Birthday of Queen Elizabeth II. Horiz designs as* T **210** *of Lesotho. Multicoloured.* P 14.

1639	10 l.	The Queen and Prince Charles at polo match	10	10
1640	20 l.	The Queen at Windsor, 1989	10	10
1641	200 l.	The Queen and Princess Diana in Nigeria, 1989	60	65
1642	250 l.	The Queen and Prince Philip	75	80
1639/42		*Set of 4*	1·40	1·50
MS1643		68×90 mm. 400 l. Separate photographs of the Queen and Prince Philip in 1987 and 1988	1·25	1·40

(Des D. Miller. Litho Walsall)

1991 (5 July). *10th Wedding Anniv of Prince and Princess of Wales. Horiz designs as T 210 of Lesotho. Multicoloured. P 14.*
1644	20 l.	Prince and Princess of Wales in August 1987	10	10
1645	80 l.	Separate photographs of Prince, Princess and sons	25	30
1646	100 l.	Prince Henry in Majorca and Prince William on his first day at school ..	30	35
1647	300 l.	Prince Charles at Caister, April 1988, and Princess Diana in Hyde Park, May 1989 ...	90	95
1644/7		*Set of 4*	1·40	1·50
MS1648		68×90 mm. 400 l. Prince, Princess and Prince Henry in Majorca and Prince William going to school ..	1·25	1·40

246 *Graphium latreillianus* and *Ancistrochilus rothschildianus*

(Des I. Maclaury. Litho Cartor)

1991 (5 Aug). *Butterflies and Flowers. T 246 and similar horiz designs. Multicoloured. P 14×13½.*
1649	10 l.	Type 246	10	10
1650	30 l.	*Euphraedra eleus* and *Clitoria ternatea*	10	10
1651	50 l.	*Graphium antheus* and *Gloriosa simplex*	15	20
1652	60 l.	*Salamis cacta* and *Stenandriopsis guineensis*	20	25
1653	80 l.	*Kallima rumia* and *Cassia fistula* ..	25	30
1654	100 l.	*Hypolimnas salmacis* and *Amorphophallus abyssinicus*	30	35
1655	200 l.	*Danaus formosa* and *Nephthytis afzelii*	60	65
1656	300 l.	*Graphium leonidas* and *Clappertonia ficifolia*	90	95
1649/56		*Set of 8*	2·40	2·75

MS1657 Four sheets, each 102×74 mm. (a) 400 l. *Charaxes cynthia* and *Plumbago auriculata.* (b) 400 l. *Colias electo* and *Combretum grandiflorum.* (c) 400 l. *Cynandra opis* and *Bombax costatum.* (d) 400 l. *Eurema brigitta* and *Monodora myristica.* P 13×12 .. *Set of 4 sheets* 5·00 5·25

247 Audie Murphy in *To Hell and Back*

248 Meissen China Parrot Ornament, Munich Botanic Garden

(Des R. Jung. Litho Questa)

1991 (14 Oct). *Films of Second World War. T 247 and similar horiz designs. Multicoloured. P 14.*
1658	2 l.	Type 247	10	10
1659	5 l.	Jack Palance in *Attack*	10	10
1660	10 l.	Greer Garson and Walter Pidgeon in *Mrs. Miniver*	10	10
1661	20 l.	Heavy artillery from *The Guns of Navarone*	10	10
1662	30 l.	Charlie Chaplin and Paulette Goddard in *The Great Dictator*	10	10
1663	50 l.	Steam locomotive from *The Train*	15	20
1664	60 l.	Diary and fountain pen from *The Diary of Anne Frank*	20	25
1665	80 l.	William Holden in *The Bridge on the River Kwai*	25	30
1666	100 l.	Tallulah Bankhead and Alfred Hitchcock (director) of *Lifeboat* ..	30	35
1667	200 l.	John Wayne in *Sands of Iwo Jima*	60	65
1668	300 l.	Van Johnson and Spencer Tracy in *Thirty Seconds over Tokyo*	90	95
1669	350 l.	Humphrey Bogart and Ingrid Bergman in *Casablanca* ..	1·00	1·10
1658/69		*Set of 12*	3·25	3·75

MS1670 Three sheets, each 116×76 mm. (a) 450 l. George C. Scott in *Patton.* (b) 450 l. Gregory Peck in *Twelve O'Clock High.* (c) 450 l. Burning cruiser from *Tora! Tora! Tora!*
Set of 3 sheets 3·75 4·00

(Des Dot Barlowe. Litho Questa)

1991 (28 Oct). *Botanical Gardens of the World. T 248 and similar multicoloured designs. P 14.*
1671/718 60 l. × 48 *Set of 48* 8·75 11·00
MS1719 Three sheets, each 97×69 mm. (a) 600 l. Munich Botanic Garden. (b) 600 l. Kyoto Botanic Garden. (c) 600 l. Brooklyn Botanic Garden
Set of 3 sheets 4·25 4·50
Nos. 1671/718 were issued as *se-tenant* sheetlets, each of 16 (4×4), depicting features and plants from Munich (Nos. 1671/86), Kyoto (Nos. 1687/701) and Brooklyn (Nos. 1702/18). The single designs in the three miniature sheets of No. **MS**1719 are horizontal.

(Litho Walsall)

1991 (9 Dec). *Christmas. Drawings and Paintings by Albrecht Dürer. Vert designs as T 211 of Lesotho. P 12.*
1720	6 l.	black and bright magenta ..	10	10
1721	60 l.	black and new blue	20	25
1722	80 l.	multicoloured	25	30
1723	100 l.	multicoloured	30	35
1724	200 l.	multicoloured	60	65
1725	300 l.	multicoloured	90	95
1726	700 l.	multicoloured	2·10	2·25
1720/6		*Set of 6*	4·00	4·50

MS1727 Two sheets, each 102×127 mm. (a) 600 l. multicoloured. (b) 600 l. multicoloured. P 14 *Set of 2 sheets* 2·75 3·00
Designs:—6 l. "Mary being Crowned by Two Angels"; 60 l. "St. Christopher"; 80 l. "Virgin and Child with St. Anne" (detail); 100 l. "Virgin with the Pear" (detail); 200 l. "Madonna and Child" (detail); 300 l. "The Virgin in Half-Length" (detail); 700 l. "The Madonna with the Siskin" (detail); 600 l. (No. **MS**1727a) "Virgin and Child with St. Anne"; 600 l. (No. **MS**1727b) "The Feast of the Rose Garlands" (detail).

(Des W. Hanson Studio. Litho Questa)

1991 (20 Dec). *50th Death Anniv of Lord Baden-Powell and World Scout Jamboree, Korea. Multicoloured designs as T 263 of Maldive Islands. P 14.*
1728	250 l.	Sea Scouts learning sailing	75	80
1729	300 l.	Sierra Leone scouts emblem and Lord Baden-Powell	90	95
1730	400 l.	Scouts playing baseball at Mt. Sorak Jamboree	1·25	1·40
1728/30		*Set of 3*	2·50	2·75

MS1731 89×117 mm. 750 l. 17th World Scout Jamboree emblem (*vert*) 2·25 2·40

(Des J. Iskowitz. Litho Questa)

1991 (20 Dec). *Death Bicentenary of Mozart. Multicoloured designs as T 265 of Maldive Islands. P 14.*
1732	50 l.	National Theatre, Prague ..	15	20
1733	100 l.	St. Peter's Abbey, Salzburg	30	35
1734	500 l.	Scene from *Idomeneo*	1·50	1·60
1732/4		*Set of 3*	1·75	1·90

MS1735 75×105 mm. 600 l. Bust of Mozart (*vert*) 1·75 1·90

249 Aichi D3A1 "Val" Dive Bomber

(Des. J. Batchelor. Litho Questa)

1991 (20 Dec). *50th Anniv of Japanese Attack on Pearl Harbor. T 249 and similar horiz designs. Multicoloured. P 14½×15.*
1736	75 l.	Type 249 ..	20	25
		a. Sheetlet. Nos. 1736/50		2·75
1737	75 l.	Japanese bomber and smoke ..	20	25
1738	75 l.	Battleship Row burning	20	25
1739	75 l.	Planes and burning dockyard ..	20	25
1740	75 l.	Burning installations ..	20	25
1741	75 l.	Two Japanese dive bombers	20	25
1742	75 l.	Burning ships and hangars	20	25
1743	75 l.	Airfield under attack	20	25
1744	75 l.	American fighter	20	25
1745	75 l.	Japanese torpedo bombers ..	20	25
1746	75 l.	Japanese bombers over suburb	20	25
1747	75 l.	Japanese bombers attacking ships	20	25
1748	75 l.	Japanese aircraft on fire	20	25
1749	75 l.	Japanese torpedo bombers over jungle	20	25
1750	75 l.	Nakasima B5N2 "Kate" torpedo bomber	20	25
1736/50		*Set of 15*	2·75	3·50

Nos. 1736/50 were printed together, *se-tenant*, in sheetlets of 15 forming a composite design showing an aerial view.

(Des Walt Disney Co. Litho Questa)

1991 (24 Dec). *Christmas. Walt Disney Christmas Cards. Multicoloured designs as T 228 of St. Vincent. P 14×13½.*
1751	12 l.	Mickey Mouse, Donald Duck and characters from *Peter Pan,* 1952 (*horiz*)	10	10
1752	30 l.	Disney characters reading *Alice in Wonderland,* 1950 (*horiz*) ..	10	10
1753	60 l.	Sleepy and animals, 1938 (*horiz*) ..	20	25
1754	75 l.	Mickey, Minnie, Donald and Pluto posting card, 1936 (*horiz*)	20	25
1755	100 l.	Disney cartoon characters, 1984 (*horiz*)	30	35
1756	125 l.	Mickey and Donald singing carols with Donald's nephews and Pluto reading, 1954 (*horiz*)	35	40
1757	150 l.	*101 Dalmatians,* 1960 (*horiz*)	45	50
1758	200 l.	Mickey and Donald opening presents, 1956 (*horiz*)	60	65
1759	300 l.	Mickey, Minnie, Morte and Ferde decorating tree, 1983 (*horiz*)	90	95
1760	400 l.	Donald decorating tree and nephews watching television, 1956 (*horiz*)	1·25	1·40
1761	500 l.	Characters from Disney films, 1972 (*horiz*)	1·50	1·60
1762	600 l.	Mickey, Donald, Pluto and friends singing, 1964 (*horiz*)	1·75	1·90
1751/62		*Set of 12*	7·00	7·50

MS1763 Three sheets, each 128×102 mm. (a) 900 l. Mad Hatter's tea party, 1951. (b) 900 l. Disneyland, 1955. (c) 900 l. Seven Dwarfs in toboggan, 1959. P 13½×14 .. *Set of 3 sheets* 8·00 8·25

(Des Walt Disney Co. Litho B.D.T.)

1992 (9 Mar). *Mickey's World Tour. Multicoloured designs as T 270 of Maldive Islands showing Walt Disney cartoon characters in different countries. P 13.*
1764	6 l.	Minnie Mouse as Chiquita with Pluto, Cuba	10	10
1765	10 l.	Goofy as Olympic discus champion, Greece	10	10
1766	20 l.	Donald and Daisy Duck as flamenco dancers, Spain	10	10
1767	30 l.	Goofy and Donald as guardsman, England	10	10
1768	50 l.	Mickey and Minnie at Paris fashion show, France	15	20
1769	100 l.	Goofy in the Alps, Switzerland	30	35
1770	200 l.	Daisy and Minnie in grass skirts, Hawaii	60	65
1771	350 l.	Mickey, Donald and Goofy as ancient Egyptians (*horiz*)	1·00	1·10
1772	500 l.	Daisy and Minnie as cancan dancers, France (*horiz*)	1·50	1·60
1764/72		*Set of 9*	3·50	3·75

MS1773 Three sheets, each 83×105 mm. (a) 700 l. Mickey playing bagpipes, Scotland. (b) 700 l. Donald the gondolier, Italy. (c) 700 l. Mickey and Goofy smashing plates, Greece
Set of 3 sheets 6·25 6·50

(Des D. Miller. Litho Questa)

1992 (9 Mar). *40th Anniv of Queen Elizabeth II's Accession. Horiz designs as T 214 of Lesotho. Multicoloured. P 14.*
1774	60 l.	State House	20	25
1775	100 l.	Beach	30	35
1776	300 l.	Parliament Building	90	95
1777	400 l.	Canoe on beach	1·25	1·40
1774/7		*Set of 4*	2·40	2·75

MS1778 Two sheets, each 75×97 mm. (a) 700 l. Jungle hillside. (b) 700 l. Freetown
Set of 2 sheets 4·25 4·50

250 "Visit of St. Thomas Aquinas to St. Bonaventure" (Zurbarán)

251 Rhamphorhynchus

(Litho B.D.T.)

1992 (25 May). *"Granada '92" International Stamp Exhibition, Spain. Paintings by Francisco Zurbarán. T 250 and similar vert designs. Multicoloured. P 13.*
1779	1 l.	Type 250	10	10
1780	10 l.	"St. Gregory"	10	10
1781	30 l.	"St. Andrew"	10	10
1782	50 l.	"St. Gabriel the Archangel"	15	20
1783	60 l.	"The Blessed Henry Suso"	20	25
1784	100 l.	"St. Lucy"	30	35
1785	300 l.	"St. Casilda"	90	95
1786	400 l.	"St. Margaret of Antioch"	1·25	1·40
1787	500 l.	"St. Apollonia"	1·50	1·60
1788	600 l.	"St. Bonaventure at Council of Lyons"	1·75	1·90
1789	700 l.	"St. Bonaventure on his Bier"	2·10	2·25
1790	800 l.	"The Martyrdom of St. James" (detail)	2·40	2·50
1779/90		*Set of 12*	9·75	10·50

MS1791 Three sheets. (a) 95×112 mm. 900 l. "The Martyrdom of St. James". (b) 95×112 mm. 900 l. "The Young Virgin". (c) 112×95 mm. 900 l. "St. Hugh in the Refectory". Imperf
Set of 3 sheets 8·25 8·50

(Des D. Burkhart. Litho B.D.T.)

1992 (8 June). *Prehistoric Animals. T 251 and similar vert designs. Multicoloured. P 14.*
1792	50 l.	Type 251	15	20
		a. Sheetlet. Nos. 1792/811		2·75
1793	50 l.	Pteranodon	15	20
1794	50 l.	Dimorphodon	15	20
1795	50 l.	Pteradactyl	15	20
1796	50 l.	Archaeopteryx	15	20
1797	50 l.	Iguanodon	15	20
1798	50 l.	Hypsilophodon	15	20
1799	50 l.	Nothosaurus	15	20
1800	50 l.	Brachiosaurus	15	20
1801	50 l.	Kentrosaurus	15	20
1802	50 l.	Plesiosaurus	15	20
1803	50 l.	Trachodon	15	20
1804	50 l.	Hesperornis	15	20
1805	50 l.	Henodus	15	20
1806	50 l.	Stenosaurus	15	20
1807	50 l.	Stenopterygius	15	20
1808	50 l.	Eurhinosaurus	15	20
1809	50 l.	Placodus	15	20
1810	50 l.	Mosasaurs	15	20
1811	50 l.	Mixosaurus	15	20
1792/1811		*Set of 20*	2·75	3·50

MS1812 106×76 mm. No. 1804 3·00 3·25
Nos. 1792/811 were printed together, *se-tenant*, in sheetlets of 20 forming a composite design.

252 Greater Flamingo

253 Minnie Mouse and Chip decorating Christmas Tree

(Des P. Chinelli. Litho B.D.T.)

1992 (20 July). *Birds.* T **252** *and similar vert designs. Multicoloured.* P 14.

1813	30 l.	Type **252**	10	10
1814	50 l.	White-crested Hornbill	15	20
1815	100 l.	Verreaux's Touraco	30	35
1816	170 l.	Yellow-spotted Barbet	50	55
1817	200 l.	African Spoonbill	60	65
1818	250 l.	Saddle-bill Stork	75	80
1819	300 l.	Red-faced Lovebird ("Red Headed Lovebird")	90	95
1820	600 l.	Yellow-billed Barbet	1·75	2·00
1813/20		*Set of 8*	4·50	5·00

MS1821 Two sheets, each 72×101 mm. (a) 1000 l. Fire-bellied Woodpecker. (b) 1000 l. Swallow-tailed Bee Eater .. *Set of 2 sheets* 6·00 6·25

(Litho Questa)

1992 (8 Sept). *Olympic Games, Albertville and Barcelona. Multicoloured designs as* T **216** *of Lesotho.* P 14.

1822	10 l.	Marathon	10	10
1823	20 l.	Men's parallel bars	10	10
1824	30 l.	Men's discus	10	10
1825	50 l.	Men's 110 metres hurdles (*horiz*)	15	20
1826	60 l.	Women's longjump	20	25
1827	100 l.	Men's floor exercise (*horiz*)	30	35
1828	200 l.	Windsurfing	60	65
1829	250 l.	Women's biathlon	75	80
1830	300 l.	Cycle road race	90	95
1831	400 l.	Weightlifting	1·25	1·40
1832	500 l.	Men's speed skating	1·50	1·60
1833	600 l.	Men's downhill skiing (*horiz*)	1·75	1·90
1822/33		*Set of 12*	7·00	7·50

MS1834 Three sheets, each 102×71 mm. (a) 900 l. Football (*horiz*). (b) 900 l. Men's single luge (*horiz*). (c) 900 l. Pairs ice dancing *Set of 3 sheets* 8·25 8·50

(Des Walt Disney Co. Litho Questa)

1992 (16 Nov). *Christmas.* T **253** *and similar multicoloured designs, each showing Walt Disney cartoon characters.* P 13½×14.

1835	10 l.	Type **253**	10	10
1836	20 l.	Goofy as Father Christmas	10	10
1837	30 l.	Daisy Duck and Minnie decorating Christmas tree	10	10
1838	50 l.	Mickey Mouse, and Goofy lighting candle	15	20
1839	80 l.	Big Pete as Father Christmas	25	30
1840	100 l.	Donald Duck as Father Christmas	30	35
1841	150 l.	Morty and Ferdie decorating cake	45	50
1842	200 l.	Mickey and bauble	60	65
1843	300 l.	Goofy and toy Father Christmas	90	95
1844	500 l.	Chip and Dale with sledge	1·50	1·60
1845	600 l.	Donald and Dale with musical instruments	1·75	1·90
1846		Huie, Dewey and Louie making patterns in snow	2·50	2·75
1835/46		*Set of 12*	7·75	8·50

MS1847 Three sheets, each 128×102 mm. (a) 900 l. Mickey as Father Christmas. P 13½×14. (b) 900 l. Chip and Christmas tree fairy (*horiz*). P 14×13½. (c) 900 l. Mickey and Minnie (*horiz*). P 14×13½ .. *Set of 3 sheets* 7·75 8·50

254 Toy Pennsylvannia Railroad GG-1 Electric Locomotive No. 6-18306, 1992

255 African Pygmy Goose

(Des W. Hanson. Litho B.D.T.)

1992 (23 Nov). *"Genova '92" International Thematic Stamp Exhibition. Toy Trains.* T **254** *and similar horiz designs showing electric locomotives and rolling stock manufactured by Lionel. Multicoloured.* P 14.

1848	150 l.	Type **254**	45	50
		a. Sheetlet. Nos. 1848/56	3·50	
1849	150 l.	Wabash Railroad Hudson locomotive No. 8610, 1985	45	50
1850	150 l.	Locomotive No. 1911, 1911	45	50
1851	150 l.	Chesapeake & Ohio locomotive No. 6-18627, 1992	45	50
1852	150 l.	Gang car No. 50, 1954	45	50
1853	150 l.	Rock Island & Peoria locomotive No. 8004, 1980	45	50
1854	150 l.	Western Maryland Railroad Shay locomotive No. 6-18023, 1992	45	50

1855	150 l.	Boston & Albany Railroad Hudson locomotive No. 784, 1986	45	50
1856	150 l.	Locomotive No. 6, 1906	45	50
1857	170 l.	Special F-3 diesel locomotive, 1947	50	55
		a. Sheetlet. Nos. 1857/65	4·00	
1858	170 l.	Pennsylvannia Railroad switcher locomotive No. 6-18905, 1992	50	55
1859	170 l.	No. 1 Trolley, 1913	50	55
1860	170 l.	Seaboard Railroad freight diesel locomotive, 1958	50	55
1861	170 l.	Pennsylvannia S-2 turbine locomotive, 1991	50	55
1862	170 l.	Western Pacific diesel locomotive No. 6-18302, 1992	50	55
1863	170 l.	Locomotive No. 10, 1929	50	55
1864	170 l.	Locomotive No. 400E, 1931	50	55
1865	170 l.	Locomotive No. 384E, 1928	50	55
1866	170 l.	Pennsylvannia Railroad Torpedo locomotive No. 238EW, 1936	50	55
		a. Sheetlet. Nos. 1866/74	4·00	
1867	170 l.	Denver & Rio Grande Western Alco locomotive No. 6-18107, 1992	50	55
1868	170 l.	Locomotive No. 408E, 1930	50	55
1869	170 l.	Mickey Mouse 60th Birthday boxcar No. 19241, 1991	50	55
1870	170 l.	Polished brass locomotive No. 54, 1913	50	55
1871	170 l.	Broadway Limited locomotive No. 392E, 1936	50	55
1872	170 l.	Great Northern EP-5 locomotive No. 18302, 1988	50	55
1873	170 l.	Locomotive No. 6, 1918	50	55
1874	170 l.	Locomotive No. 400E, 1933	50	55
1848/74		*Set of 27*	12·00	13·00

MS1875 Three sheets, each 119×90 mm. (a) 1000 l. Joshua Lionel Cowen commemorative locomotive (50×37 mm). (b) 1000 l. Trolley No. 300 (50×37 mm). (c) 1000 l. Locomotive No. 381E, 1928 (50×37 mm). P 13 .. *Set of 3 sheets* 9·00 13·00
Nos. 1848/56, 1857/65 and 1866/74 were each printed together, *se-tenant*, in sheetlets of 9.

(Litho Questa)

1992 (1 Dec). *Birds.* T **255** *and similar horiz designs. Multicoloured.* P 14×15.

1876	50 c.	Type **255**	10	10
1877	1 l.	Spotted Eagle Owl	10	10
1878	2 l.	Verreaux's Touraco	10	10
1879	5 l.	Saddle-bill Stork	10	10
1880	10 l.	African Golden Oriole	10	10
1881	20 l.	Malachite Kingfisher	10	10
1882	30 l.	Red-crowned Bishop ("Fire-crowned Bishop")	10	10
1883	40 l.	Fire-bellied Woodpecker	10	10
1884	50 l.	Red-billed Fire Finch	15	20
1885	80 l.	Blue Fairy Flycatcher	25	30
1886	100 l.	Crested Malimbe	30	35
1887	150 l.	Vitelline Masked Weaver	45	50
1888	170 l.	Great Blue Turaco ("Blue Plantain-eater")	50	55
1889	200 l.	Superb Sunbird	60	65
1890	250 l.	Swallow-tailed Bee Eater	75	80
1891	300 l.	Cabani's Yellow Bunting	90	95
1892	500 l.	Egyptian Plover ("Crocodile Bird")	1·50	1·60
1893	750 l.	White-faced Scops Owl	2·25	2·50
1894	1000 l.	African Blue Cuckoo Shrike	3·00	3·25
1876/94		*Set of 19*	10·00	11·00

(Litho Questa)

1992 (7 Dec). *Christmas. Religious Paintings. Vert designs as* T **218** *of Lesotho. Multicoloured.* P 13½×14.

1896	1 l.	"Virgin and Child" (Fiorenzo di Lorenzo)	10	10
1897	10 l.	"Madonna and Child on a Wall" (School of Bouts)	10	10
1898	20 l.	"Virgin and Child with the Flight into Egypt" (Master of Hoogstraeten)	10	10
1899	30 l.	"Madonna and Child before Firescreen" (Robert Campin)	10	10
1900	50 l.	"Mary in a Rosegarden" (detail) (Hans Memling)	15	20
1901	100 l.	"Virgin Mary and Child" (Lucas Cranach the Elder)	30	35
1902	170 l.	"Virgin and Child" (Rogier van der Weyden)	50	55
1903	200 l.	"Madonna and Saints" (detail) (Perugino)	60	65
1904	250 l.	"Madonna Enthroned with Sts Catherine and Barbara" (Master of Hoogstraeten)	75	80
1905	300 l.	"The Virgin in a Rose Arbour" (Stefan Lochner)	90	95
1906	500 l.	"Madonna with Child and Angels" (Botticelli)	1·50	1·60
1907	1000 l.	"Madonna and Child with young St. John the Baptist" (Fra Bartolemmeo)	3·00	3·25
1896/907		*Set of 12*	7·25	7·75

MS1908 Three sheets, each 76×102 mm. (a) 900 l. "Virgin and Child" (detail) (Jan Gossaert). (b) 900 l. "Virgin and Child" (detail) (Lucas Cranach the Younger). (c) 900 l. "The Virgin with the Green Cushion" (detail) (Andrea Solario) .. *Set of 3 sheets* 8·25 8·50

The new-issue supplement to this Catalogue appears each month in

GIBBONS STAMP MONTHLY

—from your newsagent or by postal subscription— sample copy and details on request.

256 Mickey Mouse and Sousaphone (magazine cover, 1936)

257 Emblems

(Des Walt Disney Co. Litho Questa)

1992 (17 Dec). *Mickey Mouse in Literature.* T **256** *and similar multicoloured designs each showing Walt Disney cartoon characters on magazine or book covers.* P 13½×14.

1909	10 l.	Type **256**	10	10
1910	20 l.	Mickey and Minnie Mouse, 1936	10	10
1911	30 l.	Mickey and Donald Duck, 1936	10	10
1912	40 l.	Mickey, Minnie and Goofy in car, 1937	10	10
1913	50 l.	Mickey as Ringmaster, 1937	15	20
1914	60 l.	Mickey as Father Christmas, 1937	20	25
1915	70 l.	Donald and Goofy representing 1937 and 1938	20	25
1916	150 l.	Mickey and Minnie steering ship, 1935	45	50
1917	170 l.	Mickey and Tanglefoot the horse, 1936	50	55
1918	200 l.	Mickey tied up	60	65
1919	300 l.	Mickey and Goofy in jungle	90	95
1920	400 l.	Mickey and Goofy on submarine	1·25	1·40
1921	500 l.	Mickey and Minnie singing and dancing, 1931	1·50	1·60
1909/21		*Set of 13*	5·50	6·00

MS1922 Three sheets. (a) 127×102 mm. 900 l. Mickey reading to Morty and Ferdie, 1933 (*horiz*). P 14×13½. (b) 102×127 mm. 900 l. Mickey with book, 1935 (*horiz*). P 14×13½. (c) 102×127 mm. 900 l. Mickey the hunter, 1948. P 13½×14 .. *Set of 3 sheets* 8·25 8·50

(Litho B.D.T.)

1993 (14 Jan). *International Conference on Nutrition, Rome.* T **257** *and similar horiz design. Multicoloured.* P 14.

1923	150 l.	Type **257**	45	50
1924	170 l.	Cow and cereal with emblems	50	55

258 The *Graf Zeppelin*

(Litho B.D.T.)

1993 (14 Jan). *75th Death Anniv of Count Ferdinand von Zeppelin (airship pioneer).* T **258** *and similar multicoloured designs.* P 14.

1925	170 l.	Type **258**	50	55
1926	700 l.	Construction drawings of *Graf Zeppelin*	2·10	2·25

MS1927 100×70 mm. 900 l. Count Von Zeppelin (*vert*) .. 2·75 3·00

259 Starving Child and W.H.O. Emblem

(Litho B.D.T.)

1993 (14 Jan). *United Nations World Health Organization Projects.* P 14.

1928	**259**	200 l. multicoloured	60	65

260 Summit Emblem and Cottonwood Tree

(Litho B.D.T.)

1993 (14 Jan). *United Nations Earth Summit '92, Rio de Janeiro.* T **260** *and similar horiz design. Multicoloured.* P 14.

1929	250 l.	Type **260**	75	80
1930	300 l.	Emblem and African Elephant	90	95

261 Lions Club Emblem on
Map of World

(Litho B.D.T.)

1993 (14 Jan). *75th Anniv of International Association of Lions Clubs. P* 14.
1931 **261** 250 l. multicoloured 75 80

262 Columbus, King
Ferdinand and Queen Isabella

(Litho B.D.T.)

1993 (14 Jan). *500th Anniv of Discovery of America by Columbus. T* **262** *and similar multicoloured designs. P* 14.
1932 300 l. Type **262** 90 95
1933 500 l. Landing in the New World .. 1·50 1·60
MS1934 97×67 mm. 900 l. Christopher Columbus (*vert*) .. .. 2·75 3·00

263 American Space Shuttle

(Des W. Wright and L. Fried. Litho B.D.T.)

1993 (14 Jan). *International Space Year. T* **263** *and similar horiz design. Multicoloured. P* 14.
1935 600 l. Type **263** .. .. .. 1·75 1·90
MS1936 101×70 mm. 900 l. American astronaut on space walk .. .. 2·75 3·00

Singapore

A Crown Colony until the end of 1957. From 1 August 1958, an internally self-governing territory designated the State of Singapore. From 16 September 1963, part of the Malaysian Federation until 9 August 1965, when it became an independent republic within the Commonwealth.

CROWN COLONY
(Typo D.L.R.)

1948 (1 Sept)–**52.** As T **58** of Malaysia (Straits Settlements), but inscribed "SINGAPORE" at foot. Wmk Mult Script CA. Chalk-surfaced paper. (a) P 14.

1	1 c. black	..	..	15	10
2	2 c. orange	..	..	15	10
3	3 c. green	..	..	30	10
4	4 c. brown	..	..	20	50
5	6 c. grey	..	..	25	15
6	8 c. scarlet (1.10.48)	..	..	25	15
7	10 c. purple	..	..	20	10
8	15 c. ultramarine (1.10.48)	..	3·25	10
9	20 c. black and green (1.10.48)	..	2·75	20
10	25 c. purple and orange (1.10.48)	..	2·00	15
11	40 c. red and purple (1.10.48) ..	..	4·75	5·00
12	50 c. black and blue (1.10.48) ..	..	3·25	10
13	$1 blue and purple (1.10.48)	..	10·00	75
14	$2 green and scarlet (25.10.48)	..	48·00	2·50
15	$5 green and brown (1.10.48)	..	£100	2·50
1/15		..	Set of 15	£150	11·00

(b) P 17½×18

16	1 c. black (21.5.52)	..	..	50	1·75
17	2 c. orange (31.10.49)	..	..	70	80
19	4 c. brown (1.7.49)	..	..	70	10
19a	5 c. bright purple (1.9.52)	..	2·50	55
20	6 c. grey (10.12.52)	..	..	70	30
21a	8 c. scarlet (1.9.52) ..	..	4·00	2·50
22	10 c. purple (9.2.50)	..	..	50	10
22a	12 c. scarlet (1.9.52)	..	..	4·00	4·00
23	15 c. ultramarine (9.2.50)	..	6·00	10
24	20 c. black and green (31.10.49)	..	2·75	1·40
24a	20 c. bright blue (1.9.52)	..	4·00	10
25	25 c. purple and orange (9.2.50)	..	80	10
25a	35 c. scarlet and purple (1.9.52)	..	4·00	90
26	40 c. red and purple (4.5.51*)	..	16·00	8·50
27	50 c. black and blue (9.2.50)	..	6·50	10
28	$1 blue and purple (31.10.49)	..	11·00	20
	a. Error. St. Edward's Crown, W **9**b	£3500	
29	$2 green and scarlet (24.5.51)	..	£110	1·75
	a. Error. St. Edward's Crown, W **9**b	£3500	
30	$5 green and brown (19.12.51)	..	£160	1·75
16/30		..	Set of 18	£300	22·00

* Earliest known postmark date.
Nos. 28a and 29a occur on rows in the watermark in which the crowns and letters "CA" alternate.
Postal forgeries of the 50 c., $1 and $2 exist on unwatermarked paper and perforated 14×14½.

1948 (25 Oct). Royal Silver Wedding. As Nos. 143/4 of Jamaica.

31	10 c. violet	..	..	75	30
32	$5 brown	..	..	95·00	27·00

1949 (10 Oct). 75th Anniv of U.P.U. As Nos. 145/8 of Jamaica.

33	10 c. purple	..	..	75	30
34	15 c. deep blue ..	..	..	3·25	1·40
35	25 c. orange	..	..	3·75	1·50
36	50 c. blue-black	..	..	5·50	2·50
33/6	..	..	Set of 4	12·00	5·25

1953 (2 June). Coronation. As No. 153 of Jamaica.

37	10 c. black and reddish purple	..	1·25	10

1 Chinese Sampan

2 Raffles Statue

3 Singapore River   4 Arms of Singapore

(Des Dr. C. A. Gibson-Hill, except 25 c., 30 c., 50 c. and $5 (from photographs, etc.). Photo Harrison (1 c. to 50 c.). Recess (centre typo on $5) B.W. (others))

1955 (4 Sept)–**59.** Designs as T **1**/**4**. Wmk Mult Script CA. P 13½×14½ (1 c. to 50 c.) or 14 (others).

38	1 c. black	..	..	10	40
39	2 c. yellow-orange	..	..	60	1·00
40	4 c. brown	..	..	45	15

41	5 c. bright purple	..	..	35	15
42	6 c. deep grey-blue	..	..	35	30
43	8 c. turquoise-blue	..	..	55	70
44	10 c. deep lilac	..	..	2·25	10
45	12 c. rose-carmine	..	..	2·25	2·50
46	20 c. ultramarine	..	..	1·10	10
	a. Blue (13.3.58)	..	..	1·40	10
47	25 c. orange-red and bluish violet	..	75	10
	a. Orange-red and purple (21.1.59)	..	4·00	55
48	30 c. violet and brown-purple	..	2·00	10
49	50 c. blue and black	..	..	1·25	10
50	$1 blue and deep purple	..	22·00	10
	a. Deep purple (Queen's head) omitted	£3500	
51	$2 blue-green and scarlet	..	28·00	65
52	$5 yellow, red, brown and slate-black ..	35·00	3·00
38/52	..	..	Set of 15	85·00	8·00

Designs: Horiz as T **1**—2 c. Malay kolek; 4 c. Twa-kow lighter; 5 c. Lombok sloop; 6 c. Trengganu pinas; 8 c. Palari schooner; 10 c. Timber tongkong; 12 c. Hainan junk; 20 c. Cocos-Keeling schooner; 25 c. "Argonaut" aircraft; 30 c. Oil tanker; 50 c. Chusan III (liner).
Plate 2A and 2B of the 10 c. (12 April 1960) and the blue "3A" and "3B" plates of the 50 c. "3A–2A", "3B–2B" (part of the 24 January 1961 issue and later printings) were printed with a finer screen (250 dots per inch, instead of the normal 200) (Price 10 c., £2·75 un, 20p us. 50 c. £2 un, 10p us).
No. 50a was caused by a paper fold.

INTERNAL SELF-GOVERNMENT

16 The Singapore Lion

17 State Flag

(Photo Harrison)

1959 (1 June). New Constitution. W w **12**. P 11½×12.

53	16	4 c. yellow, sepia and rose-red	..	30	30
54		10 c. yellow, sepia and reddish purple	..	40	20
55		20 c. yellow, sepia and bright blue	..	1·10	2·00
56		25 c. yellow, sepia and green	..	1·10	1·25
57		30 c. yellow, sepia and violet	..	1·25	2·00
58		50 c. yellow, sepia and deep slate ..	1·50	2·00
53/8		..	Set of 6	5·00	7·00

(Litho Enschedé)

1960 (3 June). National Day. W w **12** (sideways). P 13½.

59	17	4 c. red, yellow and blue ..	..	30	40
60		10 c. red, yellow and grey ..	..	60	10

18 Clasped Hands

(Photo Enschedé)

1961 (3 June). National Day. W w **12**. P 13½.

61	18	4 c. black, brown and pale yellow	..	20	40
62		10 c. black, deep green and pale yellow	..	35	10

19 Arachnis "Maggie Oei" (orchid)   20 Sea-Horse

21 Six-banded Barb

24 Vanda "Tan Chay Yan" (orchid)

26a Black-naped Tern   30 White-rumped Shama

(Photo Harrison (orchids, fish and 15 c. bird) D.L.R. (birds, except 15 c.))

1962 (31 Mar)–**66.** T **19**/**21**, **24**, **26**a, **30** and similar designs. W w **12**. P 12½ (i), 14½×13½ (ii), 13½×14½ (iii), 13½×13 (iv) or 13×13½ (v).

63	1 c. multicoloured (i) (10.3.63)	..	10	75
64	2 c. brown and green (ii)	..	10	1·00
65	4 c. black and orange-red (iii)	..	10	30
	a. Black omitted	..	£140	
66	5 c. red and black (iii)	..	10	10
	a. Red omitted	..	£140	
67	6 c. black and greenish yellow (ii)	..	45	60
68	8 c. multicoloured (i) (10.3.63)	..	55	2·75
69	10 c. red-orange and black (iii)	..	15	10
	a. Red-orange omitted	..	95·00	
70	12 c. multicoloured (i) (10.3.63)	..	55	2·50
70a	15 c. multicoloured (i) (9.11.66)	..	80	10
	ab. Orange (eye) omitted	..	13·00	
71	20 c. orange and blue (ii)	..	30	10
	a. Orange omitted	..	£170	
72	25 c. black and orange (iii)	..	55	10
73	30 c. multicoloured (i) (10.3.63)	..	1·00	10
	a. Yellow (flowers) omitted	..	35·00	
74	50 c. multicoloured (iv) (10.3.63)	..	95	10
75	$1 multicoloured (iv) (10.3.63)	..	10·00	35
76	$2 multicoloured (iv) (10.3.63)	..	13·00	75
77	$5 multicoloured (v) (10.3.63)	..	27·00	3·00
63/77		Set of 16	48·00	11·50

Designs: Horiz (as T **21**)—5 c. Clown fish; 10 c. Harlequin; 25 c. Two-spot Gourami. (As T **30**)—$1 White-breasted Kingfisher. Vert (as T **20**)—6 c. Archer fish; 20 c. Butterfly fish. (As T **24**)—12 c. Grammaphotyllum speciosum (orchid); 30 c. Vanda "Miss Joaquim" (orchid). (As T **26**a)—$2 Yellow-bellied Sunbird; $5 White-bellied Sea Eagle.
The 15 c., 30 c., $2 and $5 exist with PVA gum as well as gum arabic.
See also Nos. 83/88.

34 "The Role of Labour in Nation-Building"

35 Blocks of Flats, Singapore

(Photo Courvoisier)

1962 (3 June). National Day. P 11½×12.

78	34	4 c. yellow, rose-carmine and black	..	15	40
79		10 c. yellow, blue and black	..	35	10

(Photo Harrison)

1963 (3 June). National Day. W w **12**. P 12½.

80	35	4 c. orange-red, black, blue & turq-blue	..	15	40
81		10 c. orange-red, blk, yell-olive & turq-bl	..	35	10

36 Dancers in National Costume

37 Workers

1st ANNIVERSARY

(Photo Harrison)

1963 (8 Aug). South East Asia Cultural Festival. W w **12**. P 14×14½.

82	36	5 c. multicoloured	..	..	15	30

INDEPENDENT REPUBLIC

1966 (1 Mar)–**67.** As Nos. 63, 66, 69, 72, 74/5, but W w **12** (sideways).

83	1 c. multicoloured (22.2.67)	..	10	1·75
84	5 c. red and black (30.5.67)	..	1·75	65
85	10 c. red-orange and black (30.5.67)	..	65	40
86	25 c. black and orange (9.66*)	..	70	65
87	50 c. multicoloured (29.1.66*) ..	..	4·00	1·75
	a. Imperf (pair)	..	£350	
88	$1 multicoloured (18.5.67)	..	7·50	5·50
83/8		Set of 6	13·00	9·50

*The 25 and 50 c. values were not released in London until 30.5.67 and 9.6.66. The 25 c. value, however, is known used in September 1966 and the 50 c. on 29.1.66.
The 1 c. and 25 c. exist with PVA gum as well as gum arabic.

(Photo D.L.R.)

1966 (9 Aug). First Anniv of Republic. W w **12** (30 c.) or no wmk (others). P 12½×13.

89	37	15 c. multicoloured	..	..	40	30
90		20 c. multicoloured	..	..	60	80
91		30 c. multicoloured	..	..	80	1·10
89/91	..		Set of 3	1·60	2·00

38 Flag Procession

(Photo D.L.R.)

1967 (9 Aug). *National Day*. P 14 × 14½.

92	38	6 c. rosine, brown and slate			20	50
93		15 c. reddish purple, brown and slate			40	10
94		50 c. bright blue, brown and slate..			75	1·25
92/4				*Set of 3*	1·25	1·60

Nos. 92/4 are respectively inscribed "Build a Vigorous Singapore" in Chinese, Malay and Tamil in addition to the English inscription.

39 Skyscrapers and Afro-Asian Map

40 Symbolical Figure wielding Hammer, and Industrial Outline of Singapore

(Photo D.L.R.)

1967 (7 Oct). *2nd Afro-Asian Housing Congress*. P 14 × 13.

95	39	10 c. multicoloured			25	10
		a. Opt omitted			£200	£200
96		25 c. multicoloured			45	80
97		50 c. multicoloured			70	1·40
95/7				*Set of 3*	1·25	2·10

The above were originally scheduled for release in 1966, and when finally issued were overprinted with the new date and a black oblong obliterating the old date.

(Photo Harrison)

1968 (9 Aug). *National Day*. Inscription at top in Chinese (6 c.), Malay (15 c.) or Tamil (50 c.). P 13½ × 14.

98	40	6 c. orange-red, black and gold..			20	30
99		15 c. apple-green, black and gold			25	15
100		50 c. greenish blue, black and gold			65	70
98/100				*Set of 3*	1·00	1·00

41 Half check Pattern

42 Scrolled "S" multiple

43 Mirudhangam

44 Pi Pa

45 Sword Dance

51 Dragon Dance

(Photo D.L.R. (5 c. to $1), Japanese Govt Printing Bureau, Tokyo (others))

1968–73. *T 43/5, 51 and similar designs.* 5 c. to $1: Chalk-surfaced paper; W 41; P 14. Others: Ordinary paper; W 42 upright (1 c., $5) or sideways (4 c., $2, $10); P 13½.

101		1 c. multicoloured (10.11.69)			15	1·75
102		4 c. multicoloured (10.11.69)			30	2·00

103		5 c. multicoloured (29.12.68)			50	60
		a. Glazed unsurfaced paper (16.12.70)			3·75	4·25
		b. Chalky paper. Perf 13 (27.6.73)..			3·25	4·25
104		6 c. black, lemon and orange (1.12.68)			30	85
105		10 c. multicoloured (29.12.68)			20	10
		a. Glazed unsurfaced paper (16.12.70)			4·00	4·25
		b. Chalky paper. Perf 13 (14.7.73*)			3·50	4·25
106		15 c. multicoloured (29.12.68)			30	10
107		20 c. multicoloured (1.12.68) ..			20	30
		a. Perf 13 (12.9.73)..			4·25	6·00
108		25 c. multicoloured (29.12.68)			50	50
		a. Perf 13 (27.6.73)..			4·25	6·50
109		30 c. multicoloured (1.12.68) ..			30	50
		a. Perf 13 (12.9.73)..			5·00	6·50
110		50 c. blk, orge-red & lt yell-brown (1.12.68)			50	40
		a. Perf 13 (12.9.73)..			6·50	12·00
111		75 c. multicoloured (1.12.68) ..			1·25	80
112		$1 multicoloured (29.12.68)			2·50	80
		a. Perf 13 (12.9.73)..			8·00	12·00
113		$2 multicoloured (10.11.69)			3·50	1·00
114		$5 multicoloured (10.11.69)			9·00	2·00
115		$10 multicoloured (6.12.69)			30·00	13·00
101/15				*Set of 15*	45·00	22·00
103b/12a				*Set of 7*	32·00	45·00

Designs: *Vert (as T 45)*—6 c. Lion dance; 10 c. Bharatha Natyam; 15 c. Tari Payong; 20 c. Kathak Kali; 25 c. Lu Chih Shen and Lin Chung; 50 c. Tari Lilin; 75 c. Tarian Kuda Kepang; $1 Yao Chi. (*As T 44*)—$2, Rebab; $10 Ta Ku. *Horiz* (as T 43)—$5 Vina.

*Earliest known date of use.

58 E.C.A.F.E. Emblem

59 "100000" and Slogan as Block of Flats

(Des Eng Siak Loy. Photo Japanese Govt Ptg Bureau, Tokyo)

1969 (15 Apr). *25th Plenary Session of the U.N. Economic Commission for Asia and the Far East.* P 13.

116	58	5 c. black, silver and pale blue ..			35	15
117		30 c. black, silver and red			70	90
118		75 c. black, silver and violet-blue			1·25	1·75
116/18				*Set of 3*	2·00	2·50

(Des Tay Siew Chiah. Litho B.W.)

1969 (20 July). *Completion of "100,000 Homes for the People" Project.* P 13½.

119	59	25 c. black and emerald ..			70	50
120		50 c. black and deep blue			90	1·00

60 Aircraft over Silhouette of Singapore Docks

61 Sea Shells

(Des Eng Siak Loy and Han Kuan Cheng. Litho B.W.)

1969 (9 Aug). *150th Anniv of Founding of Singapore. T 60 and similar vert designs.* P 14 × 14½.

121		15 c. black, vermilion and yellow			1·25	30
122		30 c. black, blue and new blue			1·75	75
123		75 c. multicoloured			3·00	2·00
124		$1 black and vermilion			3·50	3·25
125		$5 vermilion and black			35·00	45·00
126		$10 black and bright green ..			48·00	48·00
121/6				*Set of 6*	80·00	90·00
MS127		120 × 120 mm. Nos. 121/6. P 13½			£350	£375

Designs:—30 c. U.N. emblem and outline of Singapore; 75 c. Flags and outline of Malaysian Federation; $1 Uplifted hands holding crescent and stars; $5 Tail of Japanese aircraft and searchlight beams; $10 Bust from statue of Sir Stamford Raffles.

(Des Tay Siew Chiah (15 c.), Eng Siak Loy (others). Litho Rosenbaum Bros, Vienna)

1970 (15 Mar). *World Fair, Osaka. T 61 and similar vert designs. Multicoloured.* P 13½.

128		15 c. Type 61			90	15
129		30 c. Tropical fish			1·75	90
130		75 c. Greater Flamingo and Helmeted Hornbill			4·75	3·75
131		$1 Orchid			4·75	6·00
128/31				*Set of 4*	11·00	9·75
MS132		94 × 154 mm. Nos. 128/31			20·00	21·00

OMNIBUS ISSUES

Details, together with prices for complete sets, of the various Omnibus issues from the 1935 Silver Jubilee series to date are included in a special section following Zimbabwe at the end of Volume 2.

62 "Kindergarten"

63 Soldier charging

(Des Choy Weng Yang. Litho B.W.)

1970 (1 July). *Tenth Anniv of People's Association. T 62 and similar square designs.* P 13½.

133		15 c. agate and bright orange..			50	15
134		50 c. ultramarine and yellow-orange ..			1·40	1·40
135		75 c. bright purple and black ..			2·25	2·75
133/5				*Set of 3*	3·75	3·75

Designs:—50 c. "Sport"; 75 c. "Culture".

(Des Choy Weng Yang. Litho Rosenbaum Bros, Vienna)

1970 (9 Aug). *National Day. T 63 and similar vert designs. Multicoloured.* P 13½.

136		15 c. Type 63 ..			70	15
137		50 c. Soldier on assault course			2·75	2·75
138		$1 Soldier jumping ..			3·75	6·00
136/8				*Set of 3*	6·50	8·00

64 Sprinters

(Des Choy Weng Yang. Photo Japanese Govt Ptg Bureau, Tokyo)

1970 (23 Aug). *Festival of Sports. T 64 and similar horiz designs.* P 13 × 13½.

139		10 c. magenta, black and ultramarine			90	1·50
		a. Horiz strip of 4. Nos. 139/42			4·50	
140		15 c. black, ultramarine and red-orange			1·25	1·90
141		25 c. black, red-orange and bright green			1·40	2·00
142		50 c. black, bright green and magenta			1·50	2·25
139/42				*Set of 4*	4·50	7·00

Designs:—15 c. Swimmers; 25 c. Tennis-players; 50 c. Racing-cars.

Nos. 139/42 were issued together *se-tenant* in horizontal strips of four within the sheet.

65 *Neptune Aquamarine* (freighter)

(Des W. Lee. Litho Rosenbaum Bros, Vienna)

1970 (1 Nov). *Singapore Shipping. T 65 and similar horiz designs.* P 12.

143		15 c. multicoloured			1·10	55
144		30 c. yellow-ochre and ultramarine			3·25	3·75
145		75 c. yellow-ochre and vermilion			5·00	6·00
143/5				*Set of 3*	8·50	8·50

Designs:—30 c. Container berth; 75 c. Ship-building.

66 Country Names forming Circle

(Des W. Lee. Litho D.L.R.)

1971 (1 Jan). *Commonwealth Heads of Government Meeting, Singapore. T 66 and similar horiz designs. Multicoloured.* P 14 ($1) or 15 × 14½ (others).

146		15 c. Type 66 ..			60	15
147		30 c. Flags in circle			1·10	65
148		75 c. Commonwealth flags			2·50	2·75
149		$1 Commonwealth flags linked to Singapore (63 × 61 mm)			3·00	3·75
146/9				*Set of 4*	6·50	6·50

Imperforate examples of Nos. 146/7 overprinted "Specimen" are from printer's sample sheets.

67 Bicycle Rickshaws   68 Chinese New Year

(Des Eng Siak Loy (15, 20 and 30 c.), W. Lee (others). Litho B.W.)

1971 (4 Apr). *Visit A.S.E.A.N. Year (A.S.E.A.N. = Association of South East Asian Nations). T 67 and similar designs. P 13 × 13½ (50, 75 c.) or 11½ (others).*

150	15 c. black, deep bluish violet and orange		40	25
151	20 c. indigo, orange and turquoise-blue		55	40
152	30 c. vermilion and deep maroon		80	1·00
153	50 c. multicoloured		2·75	4·50
154	75 c. multicoloured		3·50	6·00
150/4		*Set of 5*	7·00	11·00

Designs: As *T* 67—20 c. Houseboat "village" and sampans; 30 c. Bazaar. *Horiz* (68 × 18 *mm*)—50 c. Modern harbour skyline; 75 c. Religious buildings.

(Des W. Lee. Litho Rosenbaum Bros, Vienna)

1971 (9 Aug). *Singapore Festivals. T* **68** *and similar vert designs. Multicoloured. P* 14.

155	15 c. Type **68**		70	15
156	30 c. Hari Raya		2·00	2·00
157	50 c. Deepavali		2·75	4·50
158	75 c. Christmas		3·25	5·50
155/8		*Set of 4*	8·00	11·00
MS159	150 × 125 mm. Nos. 155/8		45·00	38·00

69 "Dish" Aerial

(Des W. Lee. Litho B.W.)

1971 (23 Oct). *Opening of Satellite Earth Station. P* 13½.

160	**69**	15 c. multicoloured	2·75	75
161	–	30 c. multicoloured	8·00	8·00
		a. Block of 4. Nos. 161/4	32·00	
162	–	30 c. multicoloured	8·00	8·00
163	–	30 c. multicoloured	8·00	8·00
164	–	30 c. multicoloured	8·00	8·00
160/4		*Set of 5*	32·00	30·00

Designs:—Nos. 161/4 were printed in *se-tenant* blocks of four throughout the sheet, the four stamps forming a composite design similar to T **69**. They can be identified by the colour of the face value which is: yellow (No. 161), green (No. 162), magenta (No. 163) or orange (No. 164).

70 "Singapore River and Fort Canning, 1843–7" (Lieut. E. A. Porcher)

(Des W. Lee. Litho B.W.)

1971 (5 Dec). *Art. T* **70** *and similar horiz designs. Multicoloured. P* 12½ × 13 (50 c. and $1) or 13 (others).

165	10 c. Type **70**		1·75	1·25
166	15 c. "The Padang, 1851" (J. T. Thomson)		2·50	2·00
167	20 c. "Singapore Waterfront, 1848–9"		3·25	3·00
168	35 c. "View from Fort Canning, 1846" (J. T. Thomson)		6·50	5·50
169	50 c. "View from Mt Wallich, 1857" (P. Carpenter) (69 × 47 *mm*)		9·00	9·50
170	$1 "Singapore Waterfront, 1861" (W. Gray) (69 × 47 *mm*)		12·00	15·00
165/70		*Set of 6*	32·00	32·00

ALTERED CATALOGUE NUMBERS

Any Catalogue numbers altered from the last edition are shown as a list in the introductory pages.

---

71 One Dollar of 1969

(Des W. Lee. Litho B.W.)

1972 (4 June). *Coins. T* **71** *and similar horiz designs. P* 13½.

171	15 c. orange, black and deep green		45	15
172	35 c. black and vermilion		1·00	1·25
173	$1 yellow, black and bright blue		3·25	4·75
171/3		*Set of 3*	4·25	5·50

Designs:—15 c. One-cent coin of George V; $1 One hundred and fifty dollar gold coin of 1969.

72 "Moon Festival" (Seah Kim Joo)   73 Lanterns and Fish

(Des W. Lee. Litho State Bank Note Printing Works, Helsinki)

1972 (9 July). *Contemporary Art. T* **72** *and similar multicoloured designs. P* 12½.

174	15 c. Type **72**		40	20
175	35 c. "Complimentary Forces" (Thomas Yeo) (36 × 54 *mm*)		1·25	1·50
176	50 c. "Rhythm in Blue" (Yusman Aman) (36 × 54 *mm*)		2·00	2·25
177	$1 "Gibbons" (Chen Wen Hsi)		3·75	4·75
174/7		*Set of 4*	6·75	8·00

(Des Eng Siak Loy. Litho State Bank Note Printing Works, Helsinki)

1972 (9 Aug). *National Day. T* **73** *and similar vert designs symbolising Festivals. Multicoloured. P* 12½.

178	15 c. Type **73**		45	15
179	35 c. Altar and candles		1·00	1·25
180	50 c. Jug, bowl and gifts		1·40	2·75
181	75 c. Candle		2·25	4·25
178/81		*Set of 4*	4·75	7·50

74 Student Welding   75 *Maria Rickmers*

(Des Eng Siak Loy. Photo Kultura, Budapest)

1972 (1 Oct). *Youth. T* **74** *and similar horiz designs. P* 12.

182	15 c. multicoloured		50	10
183	35 c. multicoloured		1·00	1·50
184	$1 red-orange, blue-violet & yellowish grn		3·00	6·00
182/4		*Set of 3*	4·00	7·00

Designs:—35 c. Sport; $1 Dancing.

(Des Choy Weng Yang (Nos. 185/7), Eng Siak Loy (MS188). Litho Harrison)

1972 (17 Dec). *Shipping. T* **75** *and similar multicoloured designs. P* 14 × 14½.

185	15 c. *Neptune Ruby* (container ship) (42 × 29 *mm*)		70	50
186	75 c. *Cutty Sark*		3·75	5·00
187	$1 Chinese junk		5·00	6·50
185/7		*Set of 3*	8·50	11·00
MS188	152 × 84 mm. Nos. 185/7		20·00	26·00

76 P.Q.R. Slogan   77 Jurong Bird Park

(Des W. Lee. Litho B.W.)

1973 (25 Feb). *"Prosperity through Quality and Reliability" Campaign. T* **76** *and similar vert designs. P* 14.

189	**76**	15 c. multicoloured	40	15
190	–	35 c. multicoloured	85	75
191	–	75 c. multicoloured	1·40	2·75
192	–	$1 multicoloured	1·75	3·50
189/92		*Set of 4*	4·00	6·50

Nos. 190/2 show various P.Q.R. emblems.

(Des Han Kuan Cheng. Litho Harrison)

1973 (29 Apr). *Singapore Landmarks. T* **77** *and similar vert designs. P* 12½.

193	15 c. black and red-orange		55	15
194	35 c. black and myrtle-green		1·00	1·00
195	50 c. black and red-brown		2·00	2·75
196	$1 black and purple		3·25	7·50
193/6		*Set of 4*	6·25	7·50

Designs:—35 c. National Theatre; 50 c. City Hall; $1 Fullerton Building and Singapore River.

78 Aircraft Tail-fins   79 "Culture"

(Des W. Lee. Litho B.W.)

1973 (24 June). *Aviation. T* **78** *and similar horiz designs. Multicoloured. P* 13½ × 13.

197	10 c. Type **78**		25	10
198	35 c. Emblem of Singapore Airlines and destinations		75	75
199	75 c. Emblem on tail-fin		1·40	1·60
200	$1 Emblems encircling the globe		2·00	2·50
197/200		*Set of 4*	4·00	4·50

(Des Eng Siak Loy. Litho Harrison)

1973 (9 Aug). *National Day. T* **79** *and similar vert designs. P* 13½.

201	**79**	10 c. orange and black	1·25	55
		a. Block of 4. Nos. 201/4	6·00	
202	–	35 c. orange and black	1·50	1·25
203	–	50 c. orange and black	1·75	1·50
204	–	75 c. orange and black	2·00	1·75
201/4		*Set of 4*	6·00	4·50

Nos. 201/4 were printed in *se-tenant* blocks of four within the sheet, and form a composite design representing Singapore's culture.

80 Athletics, Judo and Boxing   81 Agave   82 Mangosteen

(Des C. Lim. Photo Heraclio Fournier)

1973 (1 Sept). *Seventh S.E.A.P.* Games. T* **80** *and similar designs. P* 14 (10 to 35 c.) or 13 × 14 (others).

205	10 c. gold, silver and indigo		25	20
206	15 c. gold and grey-black		50	30
207	25 c. gold, silver and black		65	65
208	35 c. gold, silver and deep blue		1·10	90
209	50 c. multicoloured		1·75	2·50
210	$1 silver, royal blue and yellow-green		3·25	5·00
205/10		*Set of 6*	7·00	9·00
MS211	130 × 111 mm. No. 205/10. P 13 × 14		14·00	17·00

Designs: As *T* **80**—15 c. Cycling, weight-lifting, pistol-shooting and sailing; 25 c. Footballs; 35 c. Table-tennis bat, shuttlecock, tennis ball and hockey stick. *Horiz* (41 × 25 *mm*):—50 c. Swimmers; $1 Stadium.

*S.E.A.P. = South East Asian Peninsula.

(Des W. Lee (1 c. to 75 c.), Eng Siak Loy (others). Photo Heraclio Fournier)

1973. *Various multicoloured designs as T* **81/2**. *With fluorescent security markings.*

(a) *Stylized flowers and plants, size as T* **81**. *P* 13 (30.9.73)

212	1 c. Type **81**		30	55
213	5 c. *Coleus blumei*		10	35
	a. Booklet pane. Nos. 213×4, 214×4, 216×2		2·50	
214	10 c. *Vinca rosea*		15	10
215	15 c. *Helianthus angustifolius*		35	10
	a. Green printed double		†	
216	20 c. *Licuala grandis*		35	50
217	25 c. *Wedelia trilobata*		60	45
218	35 c. *Chrysanthemum frutescens*		60	70
219	50 c. *Costus malortieanus*		1·00	40
220	75 c. *Gerbera jamesonii*		1·75	90

(b) *Fruits, size as T* **82**. *P* 12½ × 13 (1.11.73)

221	$1 Type **82**		1·50	30
222	$2 Jackfruit		3·25	1·25
223	$5 Coconut		6·00	6·00
224	$10 Pineapple		12·00	16·00
212/24		*Set of 13*	25·00	25·00

83 Tiger and Orang-Utans   84 Multicolour Guppy

(Des Eng Siak Loy. Litho B.W.)

1973 (16 Dec). *Singapore Zoo. T* 83 *and similar vert designs. Multicoloured.* P 13.
225	5 c. Type 83	..	..	25	20
226	10 c. Leopard and Waterbuck	..	..	45	20
227	35 c. Leopard and Thamin	..	..	1·75	1·75
228	75 c. Horse and Lion	..	..	2·75	5·00
225/8	..	..	*Set of 4*	4·50	6·50

(Des Eng Siak Loy. Photo Heraclio Fournier)

1974 (21 Apr). *Tropical Fish. T* 84 *and similar vert designs. Multicoloured.* P 14.
229	5 c. Type 84	..	..	20	10
230	10 c. Half Black Guppy	..	..	40	15
231	35 c. Multicolour Guppy (*different*)	..	..	1·10	1·40
232	$1 Black Guppy	..	..	2·75	4·00
229/32	..	..	*Set of 4*	4·00	5·00

85 Scout Badge within "9"   86 U.P.U. Emblem and Multiple "Centenary"

(Des W. Lee. Litho Harrison)

1974 (9 June). *Ninth Asia-Pacific Scout Conference.* P 13½ × 14½.
233	85	10 c. multicoloured	..	40	10
234		75 c. multicoloured	..	1·60	1·40

(Des W. Lee. Litho Harrison)

1974 (7 July). *Centenary of Universal Postal Union. T* 86 *and similar vert designs.* P 14 × 13½.
235	10 c. orange-brown, purple-brown and gold	..	20	10
	a. Gold (U.P.U. symbol) omitted	..		£170	
236	35 c. new blue, deep blue and gold	..	55	75
237	75 c. multicoloured	..	..	1·25	2·75
235/7	..	..	*Set of 3*	1·75	3·25

Designs:—35 c. U.P.U. emblem and multiple U.N. symbols; 75 c. U.P.U. emblem and multiple peace doves.

87 Family Emblem   88 "Tree and Sun" (Chia Keng San)

(Des Eng Siak Loy. Litho B.W.)

1974 (9 Aug). *World Population Year. T* 87 *and similar horiz designs. Multicoloured.* P 12½ × 13½.
238	10 c. Type 87	..	..	20	10
239	35 c. Male and female symbols	..	80	1·00
	a. Emerald (male symbol) omitted	..		£250	
240	75 c. World population map	..	1·75	3·25
238/40	..	..	*Set of 3*	2·50	4·00

(Des Eng Siak Loy. Photo Heraclio Fournier)

1974 (1 Oct). *Universal Children's Day. T* 88 *and similar vert designs showing children's paintings. Multicoloured.* P 13½.
241	5 c. Type 88	..	..	20	20
242	10 c. "My Daddy and Mummy" (Angeline Ang)	35	20
243	35 c. "A Dump Truck" (Si-Hoe Yeen Joong)	1·75	2·50
244	50 c. "My Aunt" (Raymond Teo)	..	2·25	3·75
241/4	..	..	*Set of 4*	4·00	6·00
MS245	138 × 100 mm. Nos. 241/4. P 13	..	9·00	11·00

89 Street Scene

(Des Loy Chin. Litho Secura, Singapore)

1975 (26 Jan). *Singapore Views. T* 89 *and similar horiz designs. Multicoloured.* P 14.
246	15 c. Type 89	..	..	45	10
247	20 c. Singapore River	..	..	60	70
248	$1 "Kelong" (fish-trap)	..	..	2·75	6·00
246/8	..	..	*Set of 3*	3·50	6·00

90 Emblem and Lighters' Prows   91 Satellite Earth Station, Sentosa

(Des Choy Weng Yang. Litho Secura, Singapore)

1975 (10 Mar). *Ninth Biennial Conference of International Association of Ports and Harbours, Singapore. T* 90 *and similar horiz designs. Multicoloured.* P 14.
249	5 c. Type 90	..	..	15	10
250	25 c. Freighter and ship's wheel	..	70	90
251	50 c. Oil-tanker and flags	..	1·40	2·25
252	$1 Container-ship and propellers	..	2·25	4·50
249/52	..	..	*Set of 4*	4·00	7·00

(Des Sim Tong Khern. Photo Heraclio Fournier)

1975 (29 June). *"Science and Industry". T* 91 *and similar multicoloured designs.* P 13½.
253	10 c. Type 91	..	..	25	10
254	35 c. Oil refineries (*vert*)	..	75	1·00
255	75 c. "Medical Sciences"	..	1·50	3·00
253/5	..	..	*Set of 3*	2·25	3·75

92 "Homes and Gardens"   93 South African Crowned Cranes

(Des Tay Siew Chiah. Litho Secura, Singapore)

1975 (9 Aug). *Tenth National Day. T* 92 *and similar square designs. Multicoloured.* P 13½.
256	10 c. Type 92	..	..	20	10
257	35 c. "Shipping and Ship-building"	..	75	75
258	75 c. "Communications and Technology"	1·90	3·25
259	$1 "Trade, Commerce and Industry"	2·10	3·75
256/9	..	..	*Set of 4*	4·50	7·00

(Des Eng Siak Loy. Litho Harrison)

1975 (5 Oct). *Birds. T* 93 *and similar vert designs. Multicoloured.* P 14½ × 13½.
260	5 c. Type 93	..	..	1·00	30
261	10 c. Great Indian Hornbill	..	1·50	20
262	35 c. White-breasted Kingfisher and White-collared Kingfisher	..	4·00	3·00
263	$1 Sulphur-crested Cockatoo and Blue and Yellow Macaw	..	10·00	13·00
260/3	..	..	*Set of 4*	15·00	15·00

94 "Equality"   95 Yellow Flame

(Des Tay Siew Chiah. Litho Secura, Singapore)

1975 (7 Dec). *International Women's Year. T* 94 *and similar square designs. Multicoloured.* P 13½.
264	10 c. Type 94	..	..	25	10
265	35 c. "Development"	..	..	1·50	1·50
266	75 c. "Peace"	..	..	2·75	5·00
264/6	..	..	*Set of 3*	4·00	6·00
MS267	128 × 100 mm. Nos. 264/6	..	7·00	8·00

(Des Tay Siew Chiah. Litho Secura, Singapore)

1976 (18 Apr). *Wayside Trees. T* 95 *and similar vert designs. Multicoloured.* P 14.
268	10 c. Type 95	..	..	50	10
269	35 c. Cabbage Tree	..	..	1·25	1·00
270	50 c. Rose of India	..	..	2·00	2·75
271	75 c. Variegated Coral Tree	..	2·25	4·50
268/71	..	..	*Set of 4*	5·50	7·50

96 *Arachnis hookeriana* × *Vanda* Hilo Blue   97 Festival Symbol and Band

(Des Eng Siak Loy. Litho Secura, Singapore)

1976 (20 June). *Singapore Orchids. T* 96 *and similar vert designs. Multicoloured.* P 14.
272	10 c. Type 96	..	..	70	10
273	35 c. *Arachnis Maggie Oei* × *Vanda insignis*	2·00	1·10
274	50 c. *Arachnis Maggie Oei* × *Vandu Rodman*	3·50	3·50
275	75 c. *Arachnis hookeriana* × *Vanda* Dawn Nishimura	..	3·75	6·00
272/5	..	..	*Set of 4*	9·00	9·50

(Des Han Kuan Cheng. Litho Harrison)

1976 (9 Aug). *Tenth Anniv of Singapore Youth Festival. Horiz designs showing festival symbol as T* 97. *Multicoloured.* P 12½.
276	10 c. Type 97	..	..	20	10
277	35 c. Athletes	..	..	60	75
278	75 c. Dancers	..	..	1·40	1·60
276/8	..	..	*Set of 3*	2·00	2·25

98 "Queen Elizabeth Walk"

(Des H. Weepaul. Litho Secura, Singapore)

1976 (14 Nov). *Paintings of Old Singapore, circa 1905–10, by A. L. Watson. T* 98 *and similar horiz designs. Multicoloured. With fluorescent security markings.* P 14.
279	10 c. Type 98	..	..	30	10
280	50 c. "The Padang"	..	..	1·75	1·75
281	$1 "Raffles Place"	..	..	3·25	3·50
279/81	..	..	*Set of 3*	4·75	4·75
MS282	164 × 91 mm. Nos. 279/81. P 13½	..	8·00	12·00

99 Chinese Costume   100 Radar, Missile and Soldiers

(Des Margaret Heng. Litho Harrison)

1976 (19 Dec). *Bridal Costumes. T* 99 *and similar vert designs. Multicoloured.* P 14½.
283	10 c. Type 99	..	..	25	10
284	35 c. Indian costume	..	..	1·00	1·00
285	75 c. Malay costume	..	..	1·75	2·25
283/5	..	..	*Set of 3*	2·75	3·00

(Des Eng Siak Loy. Litho Harrison)

1977 (12 Mar). *Tenth Anniv of National Service. T* 100 *and similar vert designs. Multicoloured.* P 14½.
286	10 c. Type 100	..	..	30	10
287	50 c. Tank and soldiers	..	..	1·25	90
288	75 c. Soldiers, wireless operators, pilot and aircraft	..	2·00	2·00
286/9	..	..	*Set of 3*	3·25	2·75

101 Lyrate Cockle   102 Spotted Hermit Crab

(Des Tay Siew Chiah. Litho Secura, Singapore)

1977. *Multicoloured designs as T* 101/2. *With fluorescent security markings.* P 13×13½. (*a*) Shells as T 101 (9.4.77).
289	1 c. Type 101	..	..	30	85
290	5 c. Folded Scallop	..	..	20	10
	a. Booklet pane. Nos. 290 × 4 and 291 × 8 se-tenant	..		1·75	

291	10 c. Marble Cone	.. ..	20	10
	a. Imperf (pair)	.. ..	£300	
292	15 c. Scorpion Conch	.. ..	45	10
293	20 c. Amplustre Bubble	.. ..	70	10
294	25 c. Spiral Babylon	.. ..	80	60
295	35 c. Regal Thorny Oyster	.. ..	1·00	1·00
296	50 c. Winged Frog Shell	.. ..	1·25	10
297	75 c. Troschel's Murex..	.. ..	2·00	20

(b) Fish and Crustaceans as T 102 (4.6.77)

298	$1 Type 102	.. ..	1·75	15
299	$2 Stingray ..	.. ..	1·75	50
300	$5 Cuttlefish	.. ..	4·00	2·25
301	$10 Lionfish ..	.. ..	7·50	5·50
289/301	..	Set of 13	20·00	10·50

103 Shipbuilding   104 Keyhole and Banknotes

(Des W. Lee. Litho Secura, Singapore)

1977 (1 May). *Labour Day. T 103 and similar horiz designs. Multicoloured. P 13 × 12½.*

302	10 c. Type 103	.. ..	15	10
303	50 c. Building construction	.. ..	75	60
304	75 c. Road construction	.. ..	1·00	1·00
302/4	..	Set of 3	1·75	1·75

(Des Tay Siew Chiah. Litho Secura, Singapore)

1977 (16 July). *Centenary of Post Office Savings Bank. T 104 and similar vert designs. Multicoloured. P 13.*

305	10 c. Type 104	.. ..	15	10
	a. Perf 14			
306	35 c. On-line banking service	.. ..	75	50
	a. Perf 14			
307	75 c. GIRO service ..	.. ..	1·50	1·25
	a. Perf 14			
305/7	..	Set of 3	2·25	1·60

105 Flags of Member Nations   106 "Chingay Procession" (Liang Yik Yin)

(Des Eng Siak Loy. Litho Secura, Singapore)

1977 (8 Aug). *Tenth Anniv of A.S.E.A.N. (Association of South-East Asian Nations). T 105 and similar vert designs. Multi-coloured. P 14.*

308	10 c. Type 105	.. ..	15	10
309	35 c. "Agriculture"	.. ..	60	50
310	75 c. "Industry"	.. ..	1·25	1·10
308/10	..	Set of 3	1·75	1·50

(Des H. Weepaul. Litho Secura, Singapore)

1977 (1 Oct). *Children's Art. T 106 and similar horiz designs. Multicoloured. P 14½.*

311	10 c. Type 106	.. ..	20	10
312	35 c. "At the Bus Stop" (Chong Khing Ann)	75	50
313	75 c. "Playground" (Yap Li Hwa)	1·60	1·40
311/13	..	Set of 3	2·25	1·75
MS314	160 × 97 mm. Nos. 311/13	5·50	6·00

107 "Life Sciences"   108 Botanical Gardens and Esplanade, Jurong Bird Park

(Des Tay Siew Chiah. Litho Format)

1977 (10 Dec). *Singapore Science Centre. T 107 and similar vert designs. Multicoloured. P 14½×14.*

315	10 c. Type 107..	.. ..	10	10
316	35 c. "Physical sciences"	.. ..	45	30
	a. Deep green and brown omitted	£160	
317	75 c. "Science and technology"	..	1·00	1·00
318	$1 Singapore Science Centre	..	1·25	1·25
315/18	..	Set of 4	2·50	2·40

(Des C. Kiat. Litho Harrison)

1978 (22 Apr). *Parks and Gardens. T 108 and similar multi-coloured designs. P 14½.*

319	10 c. Type 108	.. ..	15	10
320	45 c. Lagoon, East Coast Park (vert)	45	45
321	75 c. Botanical Gardens (vert)	75	1·00
319/21	..	Set of 3	1·25	1·40

109 Red-whiskered Bulbul   111 Map of South East Asia showing Cable Network

110 Thian Hock Keng Temple

(Des Eng Siak Loy. Litho Secura, Singapore)

1978 (1 July). *Singing Birds. T 109 and similar vert designs. Multicoloured. P 13½×14.*

322	10 c. Type 109	.. ..	35	10
323	35 c. Oriental White Eye	.. ..	85	55
324	50 c. White-rumped Shama	..	1·10	1·10
325	75 c. White-crested Laughing Thrush and Huamei ..	.. ..	1·50	2·00
322/5	..	Set of 4	3·50	3·25

(Des Eng Siak Loy. Litho Secura, Singapore)

1978 (9 Aug). *National Monuments. T 110 and similar horiz designs. Multicoloured. P 13½.*

326	10 c. Type 110	.. ..	20	25
327	10 c. Hajjah Fatimah Mosque..	..	20	25
328	10 c. Armenian Church	.. ..	20	25
329	10 c. Sri Mariamman Temple..	..	20	25
326/9	..	Set of 4	70	90
MS330	173 × 86 mm. 35 c. × 4, as Nos. 326/9	3·00	3·25

Stamps from No. MS330 are similar in design to Nos. 326/9 but have no borders and the inscriptions are slightly larger.

(Des J. Heng. Litho Secura, Singapore)

1978 (3 Oct). *A.S.E.A.N. (Association of South East Asian Nations) Submarine Cable Network (1st issue). Completion of Philippines–Singapore section. P 14 (around design as well as stamp).*

331	111	10 c. multicoloured	10	10
332		35 c. multicoloured	40	40
333		50 c. multicoloured	50	50
334		75 c. multicoloured	80	1·00
331/4	..	Set of 4	1·60	1·75

See also Nos. 385/8 and 458/62.

112 Neptune Spinel (bulk carrier)

(Des Paul Wee Hui Hong. Litho Secura, Singapore)

1978 (18 Nov). *10th Anniv of Neptune Orient Shipping Lines. T 112 and similar horiz designs. Multicoloured. P 13½×14.*

335	10 c. Type 112..	.. ..	15	10
336	35 c. Neptune Aries (tanker)..	40	50
337	50 c. Anro Temasek (container ship)	45	85
338	75 c. Neptune Pearl (container ship)	80	1·60
335/8	..	Set of 4	1·60	2·75

113 "Concorde"   114 10 Kilometre Marker

(Des Paul Wee Hui Hong. Litho Secura, Singapore)

1978 (16 Dec). *Aviation. T 113 and similar horiz designs. Multicoloured. P 13½.*

339	10 c. Type 113	.. ..	35	15
340	35 c. Boeing "747B"	.. ..	50	30
341	50 c. Vickers "Vimy"	.. ..	70	1·00
342	75 c. Wright Brothers' Flyer 1..	80	2·00
339/42	..	Set of 4	2·10	3·00

(Des W. Lee. Litho Secura, Singapore)

1979 (24 Feb). *Metrication. T 114 and similar vert designs. Multicoloured. P 13½.*

343	10 c. Type 114	.. ..	10	10
344	35 c. Tape measure	.. ..	20	20
345	75 c. Weighing scales	.. ..	45	60
343/5	..	Set of 3	65	80

115 Vanda Hybrid   116 Envelope with new Singapore Postcode

(Des Paul Wee Hui Hong. Litho Harrison)

1979 (14 Apr). *Orchids. T 115 and similar designs showing different varieties of Vanda Hybrid. P 15×14 (10, 35 c.) or 14×15 (others).*

346	10 c. multicoloured	.. ..	15	10
347	35 c. multicoloured	.. ..	35	20
348	50 c. multicoloured (vert)	.. ..	50	35
349	75 c. multicoloured (vert)	.. ..	70	60
346/9	..	Set of 4	1·50	1·10

(Des Paul Wee Hui Hong. Litho Secura, Singapore)

1979 (1 July). *Postal Code Publicity. P 13.*

350	116	10 c. multicoloured	10	10
351	–	50 c. multicoloured	30	35

The 50 c. design is as Type 116, but the envelope is addressed to the Philatelic Bureau, General Post Office and has the postcode "Singapore 0104".

117 Early Telephone and Overhead Cables   118 "Lantern Festival" (Eng Chun-Ngan)

(Des Eng Siak Loy. Litho J.W.)

1979 (5 Oct). *Centenary of Telephone Service. T 117 and similar horiz designs. P 13½×13.*

352	10 c. yellow-brown and new blue	..	10	10
353	35 c. bright orange, blue and reddish violet	20	25
354	50 c. blue, dp turquoise-grn & yellowish grn	35	50
355	75 c. yellowish green and bright orange	60	90
352/5	..	Set of 4	1·00	1·60

Designs:—35 c. Telephone dial and world map; 50 c. Modern telephone and city scene; 75 c. Latest computerised telephone and circuit diagram.

(Des Han Kuan Cheng. Litho Secura, Singapore)

1979 (10 Nov). *International Year of the Child. Children's Drawings. T 118 and similar horiz designs. Multicoloured. P 13.*

356	10 c. Type 118 ..	.. ..	10	10
357	35 c. "Singapore Harbour" (Wong Chien Chien)	.. ..	30	35
358	50 c. "Use Your Hands" (Leong Choy Yeen)	40	55
359	75 c. "Soccer" (Tan Cheong Hin)	60	90
356/9	..	Set of 4	1·25	1·75
MS360	154 × 98 mm. Nos. 356/9 ..	3·00	3·00

119 View of Gardens   120 Hainan Junk

(Des Eng Siak Loy. Litho Secura, Singapore)

1979 (15 Dec). *120th Anniv of Botanic Gardens. T 119 and similar horiz designs showing different views of the gardens. P 13½.*

361	10 c. multicoloured	.. ..	15	10
	a. Imperf (pair)	.. ..	£400	
362	50 c. multicoloured	.. ..	60	85
363	$1 multicoloured	.. ..	1·10	2·25
361/3	..	Set of 3	1·75	2·75

(Des Eng Siak Loy. Litho J.W.)

1980 (5 Apr)–84. *Ships. Multicoloured designs as T 120. Ordinary paper (1 c., 10 c.), phosphorised paper ($1 to $10) and ordinary or phosphorised paper (others). P 14 (1 to 75 c.) or 13½ ($1 to $10).*

364	1 c. Type 120 (26.4.80)	..	30	70
365	5 c. Clipper (26.4.80)	..	10	45
366	10 c. Fujian junk (26.4.80)	..	10	10
	p. One narrow (4 mm) phosphor band (12.81)	45	30
	pa. One wide (10 mm) phosphor band (2.84)	90	90
367	15 c. Golekkan (26.4.80)	..	15	15
368	20 c. Palari schooner (26.4.80)	..	20	30
369	25 c. East Indiaman (26.4.80)	..	25	40
370	35 c. Galleon (26.4.80)	..	35	40
371	50 c. Caravel (26.4.80)	..	50	40
372	75 c. Jiangsu trading junk (26.4.80)	65	75
373	$1 Kedah (coaster) (42 × 25 mm)	70	45
	a. Imperf (pair)	£250	
374	$2 Murex (oil tanker) (42 × 25 mm)	1·25	90
375	$5 Chusan (screw steamer) (42 × 25 mm)	3·00	3·00
376	$10 Braganza (paddle-steamer) (42×25 mm)	6·00	6·00
364/76	..	Set of 13	12·00	12·50

121 Straits Settlements 1867 1½ c. Stamp and Map of Singapore, 1843

122 C.P.F. Emblem and "Keys to Retirement Benefits"

(Des Paul Wee Hui Hong. Litho Secura, Singapore)

1980 (6 May). *"London 1980" International Stamp Exhibition. T* **121** *and similar vert designs. Multicoloured. P* 13.

377	10 c. Type **121**		20	10
378	35 c. Straits Settlements 1906 $500 stamp and treaty between Johore and British Colony of Singapore		35	25
379	$1 1948 $2 stamp and map of Malaysia		70	1·10
380	$2 1969 150th Anniversary of Singapore $10 commemorative and letter to Col. Addenbrooke from Sir Stamford Raffles		1·25	2·25
377/80		*Set of 4*	2·25	3·25
MS381	148 × 104 mm. Nos. 377/80		3·50	4·25

(Des Paul Wee Hui Hong. Litho Secura, Singapore)

1980 (1 July). *25th Anniv of Central Provident Fund Board. T* **122** *and similar vert designs showing C.P.F. emblem. Multicoloured. P* 13.

382	10 c. Type **122**		10	10
383	50 c. "C.P.F. savings for home ownership"		40	40
384	$1 "C.P.F. savings for old-age"		75	1·00
382/4		*Set of 3*	1·10	1·40

123 Map of South East Asia showing Cable Network

124 A.S.E.A.N. Trade Fair Emblem

(Des J. Heng. Litho Secura, Singapore)

1980 (8 Aug). *A.S.E.A.N.* (*Association of South East Asian Nations*) *Submarine Cable Network* (2nd issue). *Completion of Indonesia–Singapore Section. P* 14 (*around design as well as stamp*).

385	**123**	10 c. multicoloured		10	10
386		35 c. multicoloured		40	30
387		50 c. multicoloured		50	55
388		75 c. multicoloured		65	1·25
385/8			*Set of 4*	1·50	2·00

(Des Paul Wee Hui Hong. Litho Secura, Singapore)

1980 (3 Oct). *A.S.E.A.N.* (*Association of South East Asian Nations*) *Trade Fair. P* 13.

389	**124**	10 c. multicoloured		10	10
		a. Perf 13½×14			
390		35 c. multicoloured		30	20
		a. Perf 13½×14			
391		75 c. multicoloured		60	80
		a. Perf 13½×14			
389/91			*Set of 3*	85	1·00

125 Ixora

126 International Currency Symbols

(Des S. Tan and Chua Ban Har. Litho J.W.)

1980 (8 Nov). *National Tree Planting Day. Flowers. T* **125** *and similar horiz designs. Multicoloured. P* 13½ × 13.

392	10 c. Type **125**		10	10
393	35 c. Allamanda		40	25
394	50 c. Sky Vine		50	40
395	75 c. Bougainvillea		60	75
392/5		*Set of 4*	1·40	1·40

(Des Paul Wee Hui Hong. Litho Secura, Singapore)

1981 (24 Jan). *10th Anniv of Monetary Authority of Singapore. P* 14.

396	**126**	10 c. black, vermilion & greenish yellow	10	10
397		35 c. multicoloured		30	20
398		75 c. multicoloured		55	60
396/8			*Set of 3*	80	75

(127)

128 Woodwork

1981 (4 Mar). *No.* 65 *surch with T* **127**.

399	**21**	10 c. on 4 c. black and orange-red	20	40

(Des Sng Tong Beng. Litho J.W.)

1981 (11 Apr). *Technical Training. T* **128** *and similar vert designs. Multicoloured. P* 13 × 13½.

400	10 c. Type **128**		10	10
401	35 c. Building construction		25	20
402	50 c. Electronics		40	45
403	75 c. Precision machining		50	75
400/3		*Set of 4*	1·10	1·40

129 Figures representing various Sports

130 "The Rights to Environmental Aids"

(Des Lim Ching San. Litho J.W.)

1981 (25 Aug). *"Sports for All". T* **129** *and similar vert designs showing figures representing various sports. P* 14.

404	10 c. multicoloured		15	10
405	75 c. multicoloured		1·50	1·75
406	$1 multicoloured		1·75	2·50
404/6		*Set of 3*	3·00	3·75

(Des Chua Ban Har. Litho Harrison)

1981 (24 Nov). *International Year for Disabled Persons. T* **130** *and similar vert designs. Multicoloured. One centre phosphor band* (10 *c.*) *or phosphorised paper* (*others*). *P* 14½.

407	10 c. Type **130**		10	10
408	35 c. "The right to social integration"		40	25
409	50 c. "The right to education"		60	50
410	75 c. "The right to work"		80	90
407/10		*Set of 4*	1·75	1·60

Nos. 407/10 were printed with phosphor bands or on phosphorised paper similar to that used on contemporary Great Britain issues.

131 Control Tower and Passenger Terminal Building, Changi Airport

132 *Parthenos sylvia*

(Des J. Heng. Litho Secura, Singapore Ltd)

1981 (29 Dec). *Opening of Changi Airport. P* 14 × 13½.

411	**131**	10 c. multicoloured		10	10
412		35 c. multicoloured		35	20
413		50 c. multicoloured		45	40
414		75 c. multicoloured		70	80
415		$1 multicoloured		80	1·25
411/15			*Set of 5*	2·25	2·50
MS416	154 × 105 mm. Nos. 411/15			2·25	3·75

The five values show different background emblems representing the Parks and Recreation Dept, Public Works Dept, Telecommunications Authority, Port of Singapore and Dept of Civil Aviation.

(Des Eng Siak Loy. Litho J.W.)

1982 (3 Mar). *Butterflies. T* **132** *and similar horiz designs. Multicoloured. One centre phosphor band* (10 *c.*) *or phosphorised paper* (*others*). *P* 14.

417	10 c. Type **132**		20	10
418	50 c. *Danaus vulgaris*		70	50
419	$1 *Trogonoptera brookiana*		1·10	1·40
417/19		*Set of 3*	1·75	1·75

133 A.S.E.A.N. Emblem

134 Football and Stylised Player

(Des Paul Wee Hui Hong. Litho Secura, Singapore)

1982 (14 June). *15th Anniv of A.S.E.A.N.* (*Association of South East Asian Nations*). *One centre phosphor band* (10 *c.*) *or phosphorised paper* (*others*). *P* 14½ × 14.

420	**133**	10 c. multicoloured		10	10
421		35 c. multicoloured		25	30
422	–	50 c. multicoloured		35	50
423	–	75 c. multicoloured		50	85
420/3			*Set of 4*	1·00	1·60

The 50 and 75 c. values are as Type **133**, but are inscribed "15th ASEAN Ministerial Meeting".

(Des Paul Wee Hui Hong. Litho Secura, Singapore)

1982 (9 July). *World Cup Football Championship, Spain. T* **134** *and similar vert designs. One centre phosphor band* (10 *c.*) *or phosphorised paper* (*others*). *P* 12.

424	10 c. black, bright blue and greenish blue	20	10
425	75 c. multicoloured		75	1·25
426	$1 multicoloured		95	1·50
424/6		*Set of 3*	1·75	2·50

Designs:—75 c. Football and World Cup, Asian Zone Four emblem; $1 Football and globe.

135 Sultan Shoal Lighthouse, 1896

136 Yard Gantry Cranes

(Des Eng Siak Loy. Litho Secura, Singapore)

1982 (7 Aug). *Lighthouses of Singapore. T* **135** *and similar horiz designs. Multicoloured. One centre phosphor band* (10 *c.*) *or phosphorised paper* (*others*). *P* 12.

427	10 c. Type **135**		10	10
428	75 c. Horsburgh Lighthouse, 1855		55	1·00
429	$1 Raffles Lighthouse, 1855		75	1·40
427/9		*Set of 3*	1·25	2·25
MS430	148 × 104 mm. Nos. 427/9		3·00	3·75

No. **MS**430 was printed on plain paper without phosphor.

(Des Goh Seng Lim. Litho Secura, Singapore)

1982 (15 Sept). *10th Anniv of Container Terminal. T* **136** *and similar horiz designs. Multicoloured. One centre phosphor band* (10 *c.*) *or phosphorised paper* (*others*). *P* 13½.

431	**136**	10 c. Type **136**		10	10
432		35 c. Computer		20	25
433		50 c. Freightlifter		30	30
434		75 c. Straddle carrier		45	50
431/4			*Set of 4*	90	1·00

137 Scouts on Parade

138 Productivity Movement Slogans

(Des Poh Siew Wah. Litho Secura, Singapore)

1982 (15 Oct). *75th Anniv of Boy Scout Movement. T* **137** *and similar vert designs. Multicoloured. One centre phosphor band* (10 *c.*) *or phosphorised paper* (*others*). *P* 14×13½.

435	10 c. Type **137**		15	10
436	35 c. Scouts hiking		45	25
437	50 c. Scouts building tower		65	35
438	75 c. Scouts canoeing		95	80
435/8		*Set of 4*	2·00	1·25

(Des M. Gan. Litho Secura, Singapore)

1982 (17 Nov). *Productivity Movement. T* **138** *and similar diamond-shaped designs. One centre phosphor band* (10 *c.*) *or phosphorised paper* (*others*). *P* 13½.

439	10 c. orange and emerald		10	10
440	35 c. yellow-ochre and deep dull blue		35	35
441	50 c. maroon, bistre-yellow and brownish grey	55	70
442	75 c. maroon and lemon		75	1·00
439/42		*Set of 4*	1·60	1·90

Designs:—35 c. Family and housing ("Benefits of Productivity"); 50 c. Works meeting ("Quality Control Circles"); 75 c. Aspects of Singapore business ("Everybody's Business").

139 Commonwealth Logo and Country Names

140 Soccer

(Des Eng Siak Loy. Litho Secura, Singapore)

1983 (14 Mar). *Commonwealth Day. One centre phosphor band (10 c.) or phosphorised paper (others). P 13 × 13½.*

443	139	10 c. multicoloured	..	..	10	10
444		35 c. multicoloured	..	..	20	25
445		75 c. multicoloured	..	..	45	70
446		$1 multicoloured	..	..	65	90
443/6	..			*Set of 4*	1·25	1·75

(Des Lim Ching San. Litho Secura, Singapore)

1983 (28 May). *12th South-East Asia Games. T 140 and similar vert designs. Multicoloured. One centre phosphor band (10 c.) or phosphorised paper (others). P 13½ × 13.*

447	10 c. Type 140	..	..	10	10
448	35 c. Racket games	..	..	20	25
449	75 c. Athletics	..	..	45	50
450	$1 Swimming	..	..	65	70
447/50	..	..	*Set of 4*	1·25	1·40

141 Policeman and Family

142 1977 ASEAN Stamps and Statue of King Chulalongkorn

(Des Lim Ching San. Litho J.W.)

1983 (24 June). *Neighbourhood Watch Scheme. T 141 and similar horiz designs. Multicoloured. One wide centre phosphor band (10 c.) or phosphorised paper (others). P 14.*

451	10 c. Type 141	..	..	15	10
452	35 c. Policeman and children	..	..	45	30
453	75 c. Policeman and inhabitants with linked arms	..	..	80	70
451/3	..	..	*Set of 3*	1·25	95

(Des Sylvia Tan and Ko Hui-Huy. Litho J.W.)

1983 (4 Aug). *Bangkok International Stamp Exhibition. T 142 and similar vert designs. Multicoloured. One wide centre phosphor band (10 c.), phosphorised paper (35 c., $1) or ordinary paper (miniature sheet). P 14.*

454	10 c. Type 142	..	..	10	10
455	35 c. 1980 ASEAN stamps and map of South-East Asia	..	..	25	35
456	$1 1982 ASEAN stamps and signatures of Heads of State	..	..	65	1·10
454/6	..	..	*Set of 3*	85	1·40
MS457	147 × 104 mm. Nos. 454/6			1·75	3·00

143 Map of South-East Asia showing Cable Network

(Des J. Heng. Litho Secura, Singapore)

1983 (27 Sept). *A.S.E.A.N. (Association of South-East Asian Nations) Submarine Cable Network (3rd issue). Completion of Malaysia-Singapore-Thailand section. One centre phosphor band (10 c.), phosphorised paper (35 c. to 75 c.) or ordinary paper (miniature sheet). P 13½ (around design as well as stamp).*

458	143	10 c. multicoloured	..	..	10	10
459		35 c. multicoloured	..	..	20	25
460		50 c. multicoloured	..	..	35	45
461		75 c. multicoloured	..	..	45	70
458/61	..	..		*Set of 4*	90	1·40
MS462	146 × 100 mm. Nos. 331, 388, 458/61		..	1·60	2·75

144 Teletex Service

(Des Sylvia Tan and Ko Hui-Huy. Litho Enschedé)

1983 (10 Nov). *World Communications Year. T 144 and similar horiz designs. Phosphorised paper. P 12½ × 13.*

463	10 c. greenish yellow, light emerald and black			10	10
464	35 c. greenish yellow, brt rose-red & chocolate			20	35
465	75 c. bright yellow-green, greenish blue and deep violet-blue			55	80
466	$1 greenish yell, olive-brn & brownish blk			65	95
463/6	..			*Set of 4*	1·40	2·00

Designs:—35 c. World telephone numbering plan; 75 c. Satellite transmission; $1 Sea communications.

145 Blue-breasted Banded Rail

146 House of Tan Yeok Nee

(Des Poh Siew Wah. Litho Harrison)

1984 (15 Mar). *Coastal Birds. T 145 and similar horiz designs. Multicoloured. One wide centre phosphor band (10 c.) or phosphorised paper (others). P 14½ × 13½.*

467	10 c. Type 145	..	..	30	10
468	35 c. Black Bittern	..	..	70	45
469	50 c. Brahminy Kite	..	..	85	85
470	75 c. Moorhen	..	..	1·10	1·75
467/70	..	..	*Set of 4*	2·75	2·75

(Des Poh Siew Wah. Litho Secura, Singapore)

1984 (7 June). *National Monuments. T 146 and similar vert designs. Multicoloured. One centre phosphor band (10 c.) or phosphorised paper (others). P 12.*

471	10 c. Type 146	..	..	10	10
472	35 c. Thong Chai building	..	..	30	35
473	50 c. Telok Ayer market	..	..	40	60
474	$1 Nagore Durgha shrine	..	..	80	1·40
471/4	..	..	*Set of 4*	1·40	2·25

147 1970 $1 National Day Stamp   148 Schoolchildren

(Des P. Hong. Litho Secura, Singapore)

1984 (9 Aug–23 Nov). *"25 Years of Nation Building." T 147 and similar vert designs showing various Singapore stamps. Multicoloured. One centre phosphor band (10 c.) or phosphorised paper (others). P 14 × 14½.*

475	10 c. Type 147	..	..	10	10
476	35 c. 1981 $1 "Sports for All" stamp	..	..	30	35
477	50 c. 1969 25 c. "100,000 Homes for the People" stamp			40	55
478	75 c. 1976 10 c. Wayside Trees stamp	..	..	60	80
479	$1 1981 $1 Opening of Changi Airport stamp			80	1·25
480	$2 1981 10 c. Monetary Authority stamp			1·75	3·00
475/80	..	..	*Set of 6*	3·50	5·50
MS481	132 × 106 mm. Nos. 475/80. P 12½ (23 Nov)		4·50	6·50

No. MS481 is on ordinary paper without a phosphor band on the 10 c. stamp.

(Des Lim Ching San. Litho Secura, Singapore)

1984 (26 Oct). *"Total Defence". T 148 and similar vert designs. One centre phosphor band. P 12.*

482	10 c. brown and orange-vermilion	..		15	20
	a. Horiz strip of 5. Nos. 482/6			65	
483	10 c. brown, yellow-olive and new blue	..		15	20
484	10 c. brown, bright violet and pale salmon	..		15	20
485	10 c. brown, orange-brown and mauve	..		15	20
486	10 c. brown, yellow and yellow-olive	..		15	20
482/6	..	..	*Set of 5*	65	90

Designs:—No. 482, Type 148; 483, People of Singapore; 484, Industrial workers; 485, Civil Defence first aid worker; 486, Anti-aircraft gun crew.

Nos. 482/6 were printed together, *se-tenant*, in horizontal strips of five throughout the sheet.

STANLEY GIBBONS STAMP COLLECTING SERIES

Introductory booklets on *How to Start, How to Identify Stamps* and *Collecting by Theme.* A series of well illustrated guides at a low price.
Write for details.

149 Coleman Bridge

150 *Ceriagrion cerinorubellum* (damselfly)

(Des Eng Siak Loy. Recess Harrison)

1985 (15 Mar). *Bridges of Singapore. T 149 and similar horiz designs. One phosphor band (10 c.) or phosphorised paper (others). P 14½ × 14.*

487	10 c. black (Type 149)	..	..	15	10
488	35 c. black (Cavenagh Bridge)	..	..	30	30
489	75 c. black (Elgin Bridge)	..	..	55	55
490	$1 black (Benjamin Sheares Bridge)			70	70
487/90	..	..	*Set of 4*	1·50	1·50

(Des Eng Siak Loy. Litho Japanese Govt Ptg Bureau, Tokyo, to 1987, thereafter Leigh-Mardon Ltd, Melbourne (5 c. to 75 c.). Recess and photo Japanese Govt Ptg Bureau, Tokyo ($1 to $10))

1985 (24 Apr)–**89**. *Insects. T 150 and similar horiz designs. Multicoloured. One narrow (5 mm) phosphor band (10 c.) or phosphorised paper (others). P 13×13½.*

491	5 c. Type 150	..	35	10
	a. Leigh-Mardon ptg (13.5.88)	..	1·00	40
492	10 c. *Apis javana* (bee)	..	40	10
	a. Leigh-Mardon ptg (on phosphorised paper) (15.10.88)	..	1·00	30
493	15 c. *Delta arcuata* (wasp)	..	45	20
	a. Leigh-Mardon ptg (2.88)	..	3·75	70
494	20 c. *Xylocopa caerulea* (bee)	..	60	10
	a. Leigh-Mardon ptg (8.6.88)	..	5·00	45
495	25 c. *Donacia javana* (water beetle)		60	30
	a. Leigh-Mardon ptg (8.88)	..	5·00	90
496	35 c. *Heteroneda reticulata* (ladybird)		70	30
	a. Leigh-Mardon ptg (25.5.88)	..	6·00	90
497	50 c. *Catacanthus nigripes* (bug)	..	90	45
	a. Leigh-Mardon ptg (21.1.89)	..	11·00	1·25
498	75 c. *Chremistica pontianaka* (cicada)	..	1·00	60
	a. Leigh-Mardon ptg (3.7.89)	..	15·00	1·75
499	$1 *Homoexipha lycoides* (cricket) (5.6.85)		1·25	60
500	$2 *Traulia azureipennis* (grasshopper) (5.6.85)		1·50	1·25
501	$5 *Trithemis aurora* (dragonfly) (5.6.85)		2·75	3·25
502	$10 *Scambophyllum sanguinolentum* (grasshopper) (5.6.85)		5·75	6·00
491/502		*Set of 12*	14·50	12·00

Nos. 499/502 are larger, 35×30 mm.

Although the work of the two printers is very similar as far as shade, paper and perforation are concerned Leigh-Mardon used new printing plates taken from the original colour separations and, in consequence, each value does differ from its predecessor printed by the Japanese Government Printing Bureau:

J.G.P.B.   L.-M.

5 c. On the J.G.P.B. printing the tail of the insect is ½ mm from the bottom edge of the vignette. On the L.-M. printing the distance is 1 mm.

J.G.P.B.   L.-M.

10 c. The J.G.P.B. printing shows the petals at bottom right cut by the edge of the design. On the L.-M. printing all three petals are complete.

J.G.P.B.   L.-M.

15 c. The J.G.P.B. printing shows the rock at bottom right 1½ mm from the right-hand edge. On the L.-M. stamp this distance is 2 mm.

SINGAPORE — 1985

J.G.P.B.   L.-M.

20 c. On the J.G.P.B. stamp the pink flowers above
"SINGAPORE" touch the edge of the vignette. For the L.-M.
printing the right-hand petal is clear of the edge.

J.G.P.B.   L.-M.

25 c. The J.G.P.B. printing shows the uppermost feeler of the
water beetle touching the top of the design. On the L.-M. stamp
the feeler does not reach the edge of the design.

J.G.P.B.   L.-M.

35 c. On the J.G.P.B. printing the vein on the leaf at bottom
left stops just short of the corner of the design. The L.-M. stamp
shows this vein reaching the left-hand edge of the design above
the corner.

J.G.P.B.   L.-M.

50 c. The J.G.P.B. stamp has the uppermost leaf cut by the top
edge of the design. On the L.-M. printing the leaf is complete.

J.G.P.B.   L.-M.

75 c. On the J.G.P.B. printing the shadow of the wings is
1½mm above the bottom edge of the vignette. For the L.-M.
stamp the shadow touches the bottom edge.

151 Tennis, Canoeing, Judo and Children Playing

(Des M. Chiew. Litho Secura, Singapore)

1985 (1 July). *25th Anniv of the People's Association. T 151 and
similar horiz designs. Multicoloured. One phosphor band
(10 c.) or phosphorised paper (others). P 13½×14.*
503	10 c. Type 151.			15	10
504	35 c. Lion dance, martial arts and athletes with flags			30	30
505	50 c. Tae-kwon-do, Indian dance and Dragon dance			40	40
506	75 c. Boxing, table tennis, basketball and dancing			55	55
503/6	..		Set of 4	1·25	1·25

152 Modern Housing Estate and Squatter Settlement

(Des Eng Siak Loy. Litho Secura, Singapore)

1985 (9 Aug). *25th Anniv of Housing and Development Board.
Horiz designs as T 152 with different aspects of housing shown
at left. Multicoloured. One phosphor band (10 c.) or phosphorised paper (others). P 13½×14.*
507	10 c. Type 152.		15	10
508	35 c. Singapore family (Home-ownership)	..	30	30
509	50 c. Group of residents (Community development)		40	40
510	75 c. Construction workers (Building technology)		55	55
507/10		Set of 4	1·25	1·25
MS511	126×105 mm. Nos. 507/10	..	2·25	2·75

153 Brownies   154 Badges and Emblems of Singapore Youth Organizations

(Des Foo Lye Lin. Litho J.W.)

1985 (6 Nov). *75th Anniv of Girl Guide Movement. T 153 and
similar vert designs. One phosphor band (10 c.) or phosphorised paper (others). Multicoloured. P 14.*
512	10 c. Type 153.		10	10
513	35 c. Guides practising first aid	..	30	30
514	50 c. Senior Branch	..	40	40
515	75 c. Adult leaders and guides	..	55	55
512/15		Set of 4	1·25	1·25

(Des Eng Siak Loy. Litho Secura, Singapore)

1985 (18 Dec). *International Youth Year. T 154 and similar
horiz designs. Multicoloured. One phosphor band (10 c.) or
phosphorised paper (others). P 12.*
516	10 c. Type 154.		10	10
517	75 c. Hand protecting sapling	..	50	55
518	$1 Stylised figures and dove		65	70
516/18		Set of 3	1·10	1·25

155 Guava   156 Laboratory Technician and Salesmen with Bar Graph

(Des Poh Siew Wah. Litho J.W.)

1986 (26 Feb). *Singapore Fruits. T 155 and similar vert
designs. Multicoloured. One centre phosphor band (10 c.) or
phosphorised paper (others). P 14.*
519	10 c. Type 155.	..		10	10
520	35 c. Jambu Air	..		25	30
521	50 c. Rambutan	..		30	35
522	75 c. Ciku	..		50	55
519/22			Set of 4	1·00	1·10

(Des W. Lee. Litho Secura, Singapore)

1986 (1 May). *25th Anniv of National Trades Union Congress.
T 156 and similar vert designs. Multicoloured. One phosphor
band. P 13½.*
523	10 c. Type 156.	..		20	20
	a. Horiz strip of 4. Nos. 523/6		70		
524	10 c. Computer operator and welder		20	20
525	10 c. Draughtsmen and surveyors	..		20	20
526	10 c. Group of workers		20	20
523/6			Set of 4	70	70
MS527	148×100 mm. As Nos. 523/6, but each stamp with a face value of 35 c. Phosphorised paper			1·50	1·75

Nos. 523/6 were printed together, *se-tenant*, in horizontal
strips of 4 throughout the sheet, forming a composite design.

157 Calligraphy   158 Industrial Automation

(Des Chua Ban Har. Litho (50 c. also die-stamped) Leigh-
Mardon Ltd, Melbourne)

1986 (2 May). *"Expo '86" World Fair, Vancouver. T 157 and
similar horiz designs. Multicoloured. "All-over" phosphor.
P 14×14½.*
528	50 c. Type 157.			45	65
	a. Horiz strip of 3. Nos. 528/30	..	1·60		
529	75 c. Garland maker	..		60	85
530	$1 Batik printer	..		75	1·10
528/30			Set of 3	1·60	2·40

Nos. 528/30 were printed together, *se-tenant*, in horizontal
strips of 3 throughout the sheet.

(Des Eng Siak Loy. Litho J.W.)

1986 (1 Aug). *25th Anniv of Economic Development Board.
T 158 and similar vert designs. Multicoloured. Phosphorised
paper. P 15×14½.*
531	10 c. Type 158.		10	10
532	35 c. Manufacture of aircraft components	..	25	30
533	50 c. Electronics industry	..	30	40
534	75 c. Biotechnology industry	..	50	70
531/4	..		Set of 4	1·00	1·40

159 Map showing Route of Cable and Vercors (cable ship)

(Des J. Heng. Litho Secura, Singapore)

1986 (8 Sept). *SEA–ME–WE Submarine Cable Project. Phosphorised paper. P 13½.*
535	159 10 c. multicoloured	..	..	15	10
536	35 c. multicoloured	..	..	40	35
537	50 c. multicoloured	..	..	55	60
538	75 c. multicoloured	..	..	75	90
535/8	..		Set of 4	1·75	1·75

160 Stylized Citizens   161 Peace Doves and People of Different Races

(Des W. Lee. Litho Secura, Singapore)

1986 (15 Oct). *21st Anniv of Citizens' Consultative Committees.
T 160 and similar vert designs showing citizens. Phosphorised
paper. P 12.*
539	10 c. multicoloured	..	..	20	20
	a. Block of 4. Nos. 539/42..		1·40		
540	35 c. multicoloured	..	..	35	35
541	50 c. multicoloured	..	..	40	40
542	75 c. multicoloured	..	..	60	60
539/42	..		Set of 4	1·40	1·40

Nos. 539/42 were printed together, *se-tenant*, in blocks of 4
throughout the sheet, each block forming a composite design.

(Des Eng Siak Loy. Litho Secura, Singapore)

1986 (17 Dec). *International Peace Year. T 161 and similar
horiz designs. Multicoloured. Phosphorised paper. P 14×13½.*
543	10 c. Type 161.		10	10
544	35 c. Doves and map of ASEAN countries	..	30	30
545	$1 Doves and globe	..	70	1·10
543/5	..		Set of 3	1·00	1·40

162 Orchard Road   163 Flags of Member Nations and Logo

(Des Chua Ban Har. Litho Secura, Singapore)

1987 (25 Feb). *Singapore Skyline. T 162 and similar horiz
designs. Multicoloured. Phosphorised paper. P 12.*
546	10 c. Type 162.		15	10
547	50 c. Central Business District	..	40	50
548	75 c. Marina Centre and Raffles City	..	60	90
546/8		Set of 3	1·00	1·40

(Des Chua Ban Har. Litho Secura, Singapore)

1987 (15 June). *20th Anniv of Association of South-east Asian
Nations. Phosphorised paper. P 12.*
549	163 10 c. multicoloured	..	10	10
550	35 c. multicoloured	..	25	25
551	50 c. multicoloured	..	30	30
552	75 c. multicoloured	..	45	45
549/52		Set of 4	1·00	95

429

164 Soldier with Rocket Launcher and Tank   165 Singapore River and Dragon Boats

(Des M. Ng Puay Chiew. Litho Questa)

1987 (1 July). *20th Anniv of National Service. T **164** and similar vert designs. Multicoloured. Phosphorised paper.* P 15 × 14.

553	10 c. Type **164**..	20	30
	a. Horiz strip of 4. Nos. 553/6	70	
554	10 c. Radar operator and patrol boat	20	30
555	10 c. Fighter pilot and aircraft	20	30
556	10 c. Servicemen pledging allegiance	20	30
553/6	*Set of 4*	70	1·10
MS557	148 × 100 mm. 35 c. × 5. As Nos. 553/6 and Singapore lion symbol (scarlet and black)	1·75	1·50

Nos. 553/6 were printed together, *se-tenant*, in horizontal strips of 4 throughout the sheet.

(Des Ng Keng Seng. Litho Secura, Singapore)

1987 (2 Sept). *River Conservation. T **165** and similar square designs. Multicoloured. Phosphorised paper.* P 13½.

558	10 c. Type **165**.	10	10
559	50 c. Kallang Basin, canoe and fishing punt	45	40
560	$1 Kranji Reservoir, athletes and cyclist ..	85	80
558/60	*Set of 3*	1·25	1·10

166 Majapahit Gold Bracelet and Museum

(Des M. Ng. Litho Secura, Singapore)

1987 (12 Oct). *Centenary of National Museum. T **166** and similar horiz designs, each showing different drawings of Museum. Multicoloured. Phosphorised paper.* P 13½ × 14.

561	10 c. Type **166**..	10	10
562	75 c. Ming fluted kendi (water vessel)	50	60
563	$1 Patani hulu pekakak keris (sword) ..	65	75
561/3 ..	*Set of 3*	1·10	1·25

167 Omni-theatre

(Des Eng Siak Loy. Litho Leigh-Mardon Ltd, Melbourne)

1987 (10 Dec). *10th Anniv of Singapore Science Centre. T **167** and similar horiz designs. Multicoloured. Phosphorised paper.* P 14½.

564	10 c. Type **167**..	10	10
565	35 c. Omni-planetarium	40	30
566	75 c. Model of body cell	60	70
567	$1 Physical sciences exhibits	85	90
564/7	*Set of 4*	1·75	1·75

168 Modern Anti-aircraft Gun   169 Route Map

(Litho Secura, Singapore)

1988 (22 Feb). *Centenary of Singapore Artillery. T **168** and similar horiz designs. Multicoloured. Phosphorised paper.* P 13½ × 14.

568	10 c. Type **168**	30	10
569	35 c. 25-pounder field gun firing salute	75	35
570	50 c. Gunner and 12-pounder gun, c. 1920	1·00	60
571	$1 Gunner and Maxim gun, 1889	1·75	1·10
568/71	*Set of 4*	3·50	1·90

(Des Ng Keng Seng. Litho Secura, Singapore)

1988 (12 Mar). *Singapore Mass Rapid Transit System. T **169** and similar horiz designs. Multicoloured. Phosphorised paper.* P 13½ × 14.

572	10 c. Type **169**	20	10
573	50 c. Train on elevated section	65	45
574	$1 Train in tunnel	1·10	90
572/4	*Set of 3*	1·75	1·25

170 Camera, Film and Outside Broadcast Van

(Des E. Soriano. Litho CPE Australia Ltd, Melbourne)

1988 (4 Apr). *25th Anniv of Television in Singapore. T **170** and similar horiz designs. Multicoloured. Phosphorised paper.* P 13½ × 14.

575	10 c. Type **170**	10	10
576	35 c. Camera, studio lights and microphone	20	25
577	75 c. Television set and transmitter	40	45
578	$1 Globe on TV screen and dish aerial	55	60
575/8	*Set of 4*	1·10	1·25

MACHINE LABELS. From 19 April 1988 self-adhesive labels in the above design, with the background printed in orange and grey, were available from machines situated outside a number of Singapore post offices. Face values between 5 c. and $2 could be selected and the location of individual machines is indicated by the code number, from 0001 to 0050, at bottom left.

The design was changed to three lions' heads in red on 5 June 1989, to the Fullerton Building G.P.O. in brown on 8 September 1990, to Haw Par Villa on 2 October 1991 and to trishaws on 1 December 1992.

Vertical labels inscribed "SINGAPORE POSTAGE" with face values and, in some instances a weight, also exist. These were introduced in January 1983 and come from machines used by P.O. counter clerks to process parcels and registered mail. For a time, during 1986–87, these labels were on self-adhesive paper.

171 Water Droplet and Blocks of Flats   172 Greeting Neighbours

(Des Ng Keng Seng. Litho CPE Australia Ltd, Melbourne)

1988 (4 May). *25th Anniv of Public Utilities Board. T **171** and similar vert designs, each showing a different skyline. Multicoloured. Phosphorised paper.* P 13½.

579	10 c. Type **171**	10	10
580	50 c. Electric light bulb and city centre	45	45
581	$1 Gas flame and factories	85	85
579/81	*Set of 3*	1·25	1·25
MS582	116 × 75 mm. Nos. 579/81	1·50	1·75

(Des M. Ng Puay Chiew. Litho Leigh-Mardon Ltd, Melbourne)

1988 (6 July). *10th Anniv of National Courtesy Campaign. T **172** and similar horiz designs, each showing campaign mascot "Singa". Multicoloured. Phosphorised paper.* P 14½.

583	10 c. Type **172**	10	10
584	30 c. Queueing at checkout	20	20
585	$1 Helping the elderly	70	70
583/5	*Set of 3*	90	90

173 Modern 30 Metre Turntable Fire Appliance   174 Container Ships and Warehouses

(Des Eng Siak Loy. Litho Secura, Singapore)

1988 (1 Nov). *Centenary of Fire Service. T **173** and similar horiz designs. Multicoloured. Phosphorised paper.* P 13½.

586	10 c. Type **173**	30	15
587	$1 Steam fire engine, c. 1890	1·75	1·25

(Des Ng Keng Seng. Litho Secura, Singapore)

1989 (3 Apr). *25th Anniv of Singapore Port Authority. T **174** and similar vert designs. Multicoloured. Phosphorised paper.* P 14 × 13½.

588	10 c. Type **174**	15	10
589	30 c. Shipping and oil storage depot	35	30
590	75 c. Container ships and Singapore skyline	80	75
591	$1 Container port at night	90	90
588/91	*Set of 4*	2·00	1·75

175 "Sago Street"   176 North-west Singapore City, 1920

(Litho Questa)

1989 (17 May). *Paintings of Chinatown by Choo Keng Kwang. T **175** and similar square designs. Multicoloured. Phosphorised paper.* P 14½.

592	10 c. Type **175**	20	10
593	35 c. "Pagoda Street"	55	40
594	75 c. "Trengganu Street"	1·10	90
595	$1 "Temple Street"	1·25	1·00
592/5	*Set of 4*	2·75	2·25

(Des Leo Teck Chong. Litho Harrison)

1989 (26 July). *Maps of Singapore. T **176** and similar multicoloured designs. Phosphorised paper.* P 14 × 14½ (15 c.) or 12½ × 13 (others).

596	15 c. Type **176** (top left)	30	30
	a. Block of 4. Nos. 596/9 ..	1·10	
597	15 c. North-east Singapore (top right)	30	30
598	15 c. South-west Singapore (bottom left) ..	30	30
599	15 c. South-east Singapore (bottom right)	30	30
600	50 c. Singapore Island and Dependencies, 1860s	85	85
601	$1 British Settlement of Singapore, 1820s	1·40	1·40
596/601	*Set of 6*	3·00	3·00

Nos. 596/9 were printed together, *se-tenant*, in blocks of 4 throughout the sheet, each block forming a composite design. Individual stamps can be identified by the position of the lion emblem which is quoted in brackets.

177 Clown Triggerfish   178 "Hari Raya Puasa" (Loke Yoke Yun)

(Des Eng Siak Loy. Litho Harrison)

1989 (6 Sept). *Fishes. T **177** and similar horiz designs. Multicoloured. Phosphorised paper.* P 13½.

602	15 c. Type **177**	40	10
603	30 c. Majestic Angelfish	75	40
604	75 c. Emperor Angelfish	1·60	1·10
605	$1 Royal Empress Angelfish	1·75	1·25
602/5	*Set of 4*	4·00	2·50

(Adapted S. Ang Woon Beng. Litho Harrison)

1989 (25 Oct). *Festivals of Singapore. Children's Drawings. T **178** and similar vert designs. Multicoloured. Phosphorised paper.* P 14½.

606	15 c. Type **178**	20	10
607	35 c. "Chinese New Year" (Simon Koh)	40	30
608	75 c. "Thaipusam" (Henry Setiono)	85	70
609	$1 "Christmas" (Wendy Ang Lin Min)	1·10	1·00
606/9	*Set of 4*	2·25	1·90
MS610	126 × 75 mm. Nos. 606/9. P 14	2·25	2·50

179 North Entrance of Stadium   180 "Singapore River, 1839" (Louis le Breton)

(Des Lim Ching San. Litho Harrison)

1989 (27 Dec). *Opening of Singapore Indoor Stadium. T **179** and similar horiz designs. Multicoloured. Phosphorised paper.* P 14.

611	30 c. Type **179**	50	30
612	75 c. Arena	1·10	80
613	$1 East entrance	1·25	1·10
611/13	*Set of 3*	2·50	2·00
MS614	104 × 104 mm. Nos. 611/13	2·50	2·25

(Des Choy Weng Yang. Litho Leigh-Mardon Ltd, Melbourne)

1990 (21 Mar). *Lithographs of 19th-century Singapore. T* **180** *and similar horiz designs. Multicoloured. Phosphorised paper.* P 13.

615	15 c. Type **180**	..	20	10
616	a. Booklet pane. No. 615×10	..	1·90	
616	30 c. "Chinatown, 1837" (Barthelemy Lauvergne)		40	30
617	75 c. "Singapore Harbour, 1837" (Barthelemy Lauvergne)		85	70
618	$1 "View from the French Resident's House, 1824" (Deroy)..		1·00	90
615/18		*Set of* 4	2·25	1·75

The upper and lower edges of booklet pane No. 615a are imperforate.

181 1969 150th Anniv of Singapore Stamp Issue

(Des Sylvia Tan. Litho Leigh-Mardon Pty Ltd, Melbourne)

1990 (3 May). *150th Anniv of the Penny Black. T* **181** *and similar horiz designs, each showing a different map in the background. Multicoloured. Phosphorised paper.* P 13½.

619	50 c. Type **181**	..	65	40
620	75 c. Indian stamps, including bisect, used from Singapore in 1859		90	80
621	$1 Indian stamps used from Singapore in 1854		1·40	1·10
622	$2 Penny Black and Two Pence Blue		2·25	2·25
619/22		*Set of* 4	4·75	4·00
MS623	134×90 mm. Nos. 619/22		4·75	4·00

No. **MS623** also commemorates the "Stamp World London 90" international stamp exhibition.

182 Zoological Gardens   **183** Chinese Opera Singer and Siong Lim Temple

(Des Ng Keng Seng (5 to 75 c.), Lim Ching San ($1 to $10). Photo (5 to 75 c.) or recess and photo ($1 to $10) Harrison)

1990 (4 July)–**91**. *Tourism. Multicoloured. Phosphorised paper.* (*a*) *T* **182** *and similar square designs.* P 14½.

624	5 c. Type **182**	..	10	10
625	15 c. Sentosa Island	..	10	10
	a. Booklet pane. No. 625×10	..	2·00	
626	20 c. Singapore River	..	15	20
	a. Booklet pane. No. 626×10 (6.3.91)	1·40	
627	25 c. Dragon Boat Festival	..	20	25
628	30 c. Raffles Hotel	..	20	25
629	35 c. Coffee shop bird singing contest	25	30
630	40 c. Jurong Bird Park	..	30	35
631	50 c. Chinese New Year boat float	40	45
632	75 c. Peranakan Place	..	60	65

(*b*) *T* **183** *and similar horiz designs.* P 15×14 (9.10.90)

633	$1 Type **183**	..	80	85
634	$2 Malay dancer and Sultan Mosque	1·60	1·75
635	$5 Indian dancer and Sri Mariamman Temple		4·00	4·25
636	$10 Ballet dancer and Victoria Memorial Hall		7·75	8·00
624/36		*Set of* 13	15·00	16·00

The upper and lower edges of booklet panes Nos. 625a and 626a are imperforate.

184 Armed Forces Personnel   **185** Stag's Horn Fern

(Des Chua Ban Har. Litho Harrison)

1990 (16 Aug). *25th Anniv of Independence. T* **184** *and similar horiz designs. Multicoloured. Phosphorised paper.* P 14×15.

637	15 c. Type **184**	..	30	15
	a. Perf 14	..	30	40
	ab. Booklet pane. No. 637a×10	2·75	
638	35 c. Inhabitants of Singapore	60	45
639	75 c. Workers and technological achievements		1·10	90
640	$1 Cultural activities	..	1·25	1·10
637/40		*Set of* 4	3·00	2·40

Booklet pane No. 637a has margins at the vertical edges of the pane.

(Des Poh Siew Wah. Litho Questa)

1990 (14 Nov). *Ferns. T* **185** *and similar horiz designs. Multicoloured. Phosphorised paper.* P 14.

641	15 c. Type **185**	..	15	10
642	35 c. Maiden Hair Fern	..	35	35
643	75 c. Bird's Nest Fern	..	70	70
644	$1 Rabbit's Foot Fern	..	90	90
641/4		*Set of* 4	1·90	1·90

186 Carved Dragon Pillar, Hong San See Temple   **187** *Vanda* "Miss Joaquim"

(Des Leo Teck Chong. Litho Leigh-Mardon Ltd, Melbourne)

1991 (23 Jan). *National Monuments. T* **186** *and similar multicoloured designs. Phosphorised paper.* P 14½.

645	20 c. Type **186**	..	30	30
	a. Vert pair. Nos. 645/6	60	60
646	20 c. Hong San See Temple (40×25 *mm*)	30	30
647	50 c. Interior of dome, Abdul Gaffoor Mosque		55	55
	a. Vert pair. Nos. 647/8	1·10	1·10
648	50 c. Abdul Gaffoor Mosque (40×25 *mm*)	55	55
649	75 c. Statue of Vishnu, Sri Perumal Hindu Temple		80	80
	a. Vert pair. Nos. 649/50	1·60	1·60
650	75 c. Sri Perumal Temple (40×25 *mm*)	80	80
651	$1 Stained glass window, St Andrew's Cathedral		90	90
	a. Vert pair. Nos. 651/2	1·75	1·75
652	$1 St Andrew's Cathedral (40×25 *mm*)	90	90
645/52		*Set of* 8	4·50	4·50

The two designs for each value were printed together, *se-tenant*, in vertical pairs throughout the sheets.

(Des Chua Ban Har. Litho Leigh-Mardon Ltd, Melbourne)

1991 (24 Apr). *"Singapore '95" International Stamp Exhibition. Orchids (1st issue). T* **187** *and similar horiz design. Multicoloured. Phosphorised paper.* P 14.

653	$2 Type **187**	..	1·90	1·90
	a. Horiz pair. Nos. 653/4	3·75	3·75
654	$2 Dendrobium "Anocha"	1·90	1·90
MS655	123×80 mm. Nos. 653/4	3·75	4·50

Nos. 653/4 were issued together, *se-tenant*, in sheets of 30 (6×5), showing No. 653 in vertical rows 1 and 4, No. 654 in vertical rows 3 and 5, and stamp-size labels with exhibition emblem in vertical rows 2 and 4.

See also Nos. 674/6.

188 Changi Airport Terminal II, 1991, and B747-400   **189** *Arachnopsis* "Eric Holttum"

(Des Leo Teck Chong. Recess and litho Harrison)

1991 (1 June). *Singapore Civil Aviation. T* **188** *and similar horiz designs. Multicoloured. Phosphorised paper.* P 13½×14½.

656	20 c. Type **188**	..	35	20
657	75 c. Changi Airport Terminal I, 1981, and B747-200		90	75
658	$1 Paya Lebar Airport, 1955–1981, and Concorde		1·10	95
659	$2 Kallang Airport, 1937–1955, and DC-2	2·00	1·90
656/9		*Set of* 4	4·00	3·50

(Des Chua Ban Har. Litho Questa)

1991 (7 Aug). *Orchid Dress Motifs. T* **189** *and similar horiz designs. Multicoloured. Phosphorised paper.* P 14½×14.

660	20 c. Type **189**	..	35	25
661	30 c. *Cattleya meadii*	..	45	35
662	$1 *Calanthe vestita*	..	1·50	1·50
660/2		*Set of* 3	2·10	1·90

190 Long-tailed Tailor Bird   **191** Productivity Discussion

(Des M. Ng Puay Chiew. Litho Leigh-Mardon Ltd, Melbourne)

1991 (19 Sept). *Garden Birds. T* **190** *and similar horiz designs. Multicoloured. Phosphorised paper.* P 14.

663	20 c. Type **190**	..	30	20
	a. Booklet pane. No. 663×10	2·75	
664	35 c. Scarlet-backed Flowerpecker	50	40
665	75 c. Black-naped Oriole	..	90	90
666	$1 Common Iora	..	1·10	1·10
663/6		*Set of* 4	2·50	2·40

Booklet pane No. 663a has the upper and lower edges imperforate and there are margins at left and right.

(Des Foo Lye Lin. Litho Questa)

1991 (1 Nov). *10th Anniv of Productivity Movement. T* **191** *and similar vert design. Multicoloured. Phosphorised paper.* P 14×14½.

667	20 c. Type **191**	..	30	20
668	$1 Construction workers	95	1·25

192 Railway Creeper   **193** "Singapore Waterfront" (Georgette Chen Liying)

(Des Eng Siak Loy. Litho Leigh-Mardon Ltd, Melbourne)

1991 (16 Nov). *"Phila Nippon '91" International Stamp Exhibition, Tokyo. Wild Flowers. T* **192** *and similar vert designs. Multicoloured. Phosphorised paper.* P 14½×14.

669	30 c. Type **192**	..	30	25
670	75 c. Asystasia	..	60	60
671	$1 Singapore Rhododendron	80	90
672	$2 Coat Buttons ..	..	1·60	1·75
669/72		*Set of* 4	3·00	3·25
MS673	132×90 mm. Nos. 669/72	3·50	4·00

(Des Chua Ban Har. Litho Leigh-Mardon Ltd, Melbourne)

1992 (22 Jan). *"Singapore '95" International Stamp Exhibition. Orchids (2nd issue). Horiz designs as T* **187**. *Multicoloured. Phosphorised paper.* P 14.

674	$2 Dendrobium "Sharifah Fatimah"	1·75	1·75
	a. Horiz pair. Nos. 674/5	3·50	3·50
675	$2 Phalaenopsis "Shim Beauty" ..	1·75	1·75
MS676	123×80 mm. Nos. 674/5	3·50	3·50

Nos. 674/5 were printed in the same sheet format as Nos. 653/4.

(Des Lim Ching San. Litho Secura, Singapore)

1992 (11 Mar). *Local Artists. T* **193** *and similar square designs. Multicoloured. Phosphorised paper.* P 14.

677	20 c. Type **193**	..	30	20
678	75 c. "Kampung Hut" (Lim Cheng Hoe)	75	80
679	$1 "The Bridge" (Poh Siew Wah)	95	1·10
680	$2 "Singapore River" (Lee Boon Wang)	1·90	2·25
677/80		*Set of* 4	3·50	3·75

194 Football   **195** Chinese Family and Samfu Pattern

(Des Leo Teck Chong. Litho Leigh-Mardon Ltd, Melbourne)

1992 (24 Apr). *Olympic Games, Barcelona. T* **194** *and similar horiz designs. Multicoloured. Phosphorised paper.* P 14.

681	20 c. Type **194**	..	25	20
682	35 c. Athletics	..	35	30
683	50 c. Swimming	..	55	55
684	75 c. Basketball	..	75	75
685	$1 Tennis	..	95	95
686	$2 Yachting	..	1·90	2·00
681/6		*Set of* 6	4·25	4·25
MS687	132×90 mm. Nos. 681/6	4·25	4·50

(Des Chua Ban Har. Litho Leigh-Mardon Ltd, Melbourne)

1992 (22 May). *Singapore Costumes of 1910. T* **195** *and similar vert designs. Multicoloured. Phosphorised paper.* P 14½.

688	20 c. Type **195**	..	25	20
689	35 c. Malay family and sarong pattern	35	35
690	75 c. Indian family and sari pattern	80	80
691	$2 Straits Chinese family and belt pattern	1·90	1·90
688/91		*Set of* 4	3·00	

NEW INFORMATION

The editor is always interested to correspond with people who have new information that will improve or correct the Catalogue.

196 Infantryman, Air Force Pilot and Navy Gunner

197 Crafts from A.S.E.A.N. Countries

(Des T. Koh. Litho Leigh-Mardon Ltd, Melbourne)

1992 (1 July). *25th Anniv of National Service. T 196 and similar horiz designs. Multicoloured. Phosphorised paper. P 14½.*

692	20 c. Type 196	..	25	20
693	35 c. Navy diver, F-16 Fighting Falcon and FH-88 155 mm howitzer		35	35
694	$1 F-16 in flight, corvette and AMX-13SM1 tank	..	1·25	1·40
692/4		*Set of 3*	1·75	1·75

(Des Chua Ban Har. Litho Questa)

1992 (8 Aug). *25th Anniv of A.S.E.A.N (Association of South East Asian Nations). T 197 and similar horiz designs. Multicoloured. Phosphorised paper. P 14×14½.*

695	20 c. Type 197	..	20	20
696	35 c. National dances	..	30	30
697	$1 National landmarks	..	1·10	1·10
695/7		*Set of 3*	1·40	1·40

198 Mosaic Crab

199 Coins

(Des Chua Ban Har. Litho Leigh-Mardon Ltd, Melbourne)

1992 (21 Aug). *Crabs. T 198 and similar horiz designs. Multicoloured. Phosphorised paper. P 14½.*

698	20 c. Type 198	..	20	20
	a. Booklet pane. No. 698×10	..	1·90	
699	50 c. Johnson's Freshwater Crab	..	50	50
700	75 c. Singapore Freshwater Crab	..	80	80
701	$1 Swamp Forest Crab	..	1·10	1·10
698/701		*Set of 4*	2·40	2·40

The upper and lower edges of booklet pane No. 698a are imperforate.

(Des L. Ching San. Litho Leigh-Mardon Ltd, Melbourne)

1992 (2 Oct). *25th Anniv of Singapore Currency. T 199 and similar square designs. Multicoloured. Phosphorised paper. P 14½.*

702	20 c. Type 199	..	25	25
	a. Block of 4. Nos. 702/5	..	3·25	
703	75 c. Currency note from "orchid" series	..	80	80
704	$1 Currency note from "ship" series	..	95	95
705	$2 Currency note from "bird" series	..	1·75	1·75
702/5		*Set of 4*	3·25	3·25

Nos. 702/5 were printed together, *se-tenant*, as blocks of four throughout the sheet of 20, each block forming a composite design.

200 Sun Bear

201 "Thank You"

(Des Eng Siak Loy. Litho Leigh-Mardon Ltd, Melbourne)

1993 (13 Jan). *South-East Asian Mammals. T 200 and similar horiz designs. Multicoloured. Phosphorised paper. P 14½.*

706	20 c. Type 200	..	15	20
707	30 c. Orang-utan	..	20	25
708	75 c. Slow Loris	..	60	65
709	$2 Greater Malay Chevrotain ("Large Mouse Deer")	..	1·60	1·75
706/9		*Set of 4*	2·25	2·50

1993 (10 Feb). *Greetings Stamps. T 201 and similar square designs. Multicoloured. Litho. Phosphorised paper. P 14½×14.*

710	20 c. Type 201	..	15	20
	a. Booklet pane. Nos. 710/14 × 2	..	70	
711	20 c. "Congratulations"	..	15	20
712	20 c. "Best Wishes"	..	15	20
713	20 c. "Happy Birthday"	..	15	20
714	20 c. "Get Well Soon"	..	15	20
710/14		*Set of 5*	70	90

Nos. 710/14 were only available from $2 booklets. The upper and lower edges of booklet pane No. 710a are imperforate and there are margins at both left and right.

202 Shophouses

(Des Ng Keng Seng ($2), W. Kee (others). Litho Leigh-Mardon Ltd, Melbourne)

1993 (10 Mar). *Conservation of Tanjong Pagar District. T 202 and similar horiz designs. Multicoloured. Phosphorised paper. P 14.*

715	20 c. Type 202	..	15	20
716	30 c. Jinrikisha Station	..	20	25
717	$2 View of Tanjong Pagar	..	1·60	1·75
715/17		*Set of 3*	1·75	2·00

POSTAGE DUE STAMPS

The postage due stamps of Malayan Postal Union were in use in Singapore until replaced by the following issues.

D 1   D 2   D 3

(Litho B.W.)

1968 (1 Feb)–**69.** *Toned paper. W w 12. P 9.*

D1	D 1	1 c. green	..	40	1·50
D2		2 c. red	..	40	2·00
D3		4 c. yellow-orange	..	55	2·50
D4		8 c. chocolate	..	50	90
D5		10 c. magenta	..	50	90
		a. White paper (16.12.69)	..	80	2·00
D6		12 c. slate-violet	..	1·00	1·50
		a. White paper (16.12.69)	..	2·75	4·25
D7		20 c. new blue	..	2·00	3·25
		a. White paper (16.12.69)	..	5·50	8·00
D8		50 c. drab	..	6·00	5·00
D1/8			*Set of 8*	10·00	16·00

1973. *White paper. W w 12. P 13 × 13½.*

D 9	D 1	10 c. bright magenta (27.4)		75	4·50
D10		50 c. sage-green (24.8)	..	5·00	12·00

1977–78. *White paper. No wmk. P 13 × 13½.*

D11	D 1	1 c. green	..	28·00	32·00
D12		4 c. yellow-orange	..	28·00	32·00
D13		10 c. bright magenta	..	28·00	32·00
D14		20 c. new blue	..	38·00	42·00
D15		50 c. sage-green	..	45·00	48·00
D11/15			*Set of 5*	£150	£170

(Litho Secura, Singapore)

1978 (25 Sept)–**81.** *No wmk. P 13 × 13½.*

D16	D 2	1 c. blue-green	..	55	1·75
		a. Perf 12 × 11½ (1981)	..	15	55
D17		4 c. pale orange	..	65	1·75
		a. Perf 12 × 11½ (1981)	..	20	75
D18		10 c. cerise	..	75	1·75
		a. Perf 12 × 11½ (1981)	..	50	80
D19		20 c. light blue	..	85	1·90
		a. Perf 12 × 11½ (1981)	..	65	1·25
D20		50 c. yellow-green	..	1·40	2·25
		a. Perf 12 × 11½ (1981)	..	90	1·75
D16/20			*Set of 5*	3·75	8·50
D16a/20a			*Set of 5*	2·25	4·75

(Litho Secura, Singapore)

1989 (12 July). *P 13×13½.*

D21	D 3	5 c. bright mauve	..	10	10
D22		10 c. carmine	..	10	10
D23		20 c. bright greenish blue	..	15	20
D24		50 c. yellow-green	..	40	45
D21/4			*Set of 4*	70	80

Solomon Islands
(*formerly* British Solomon Islands)

BRITISH PROTECTORATE

1   2

(Des C. M. Woodford. Litho W. E. Smith & Co, Sydney)

1907 (14 Feb). *No wmk. P* 11.

1	1	½d. ultramarine		6·50	12·00
2		1d. rose-carmine		20·00	30·00
3		2d. indigo		25·00	30·00
		a. Imperf between (horiz pair)		£10000	
4		2½d. orange-yellow		30·00	35·00
		a. Imperf between (vert pair)		£4000	
		b. Imperf between (horiz pair)		£4750	£4000
5		5d. emerald-green		50·00	65·00
6		6d. chocolate		55·00	60·00
		a. Imperf between (vert pair)		£3500	
7		1s. bright purple		75·00	75·00
1/7			*Set of* 7	£225	£275

Three types exist of the ½d. and 2½d., and six each of the other values, differing in minor details.

Forgeries of Nos. 1/7 show different perforations and have the boat paddle touching the shore. Genuine stamps show a gap between the paddle and the shore.

(Recess D.L.R.)

1908 (1 Nov)**–11.** *Wmk Mult Crown CA* (*sideways*). *P* 14.

8	2	½d. green		50	80
9		1d. red		1·00	50
10		2d. greyish slate		1·25	1·00
11		2½d. ultramarine		2·00	2·50
11a		4d. red/*yellow* (6.3.11)		3·00	11·00
12		5d. olive		8·50	9·00
13		6d. claret		7·50	7·50
14		1s. black/*green*		9·50	12·00
15		2s. purple/*blue* (7.3.10)		28·00	50·00
16		2s. 6d. red/*blue* (7.3.10)		42·00	70·00
17		5s. green/*yellow* (7.3.10)		70·00	£100
8/17			*Set of* 11	£150	£225
8/17 Optd "Specimen"			*Set of* 11	£250	

The ½d. and 1d. were issued in 1913 on rather thinner paper and with brownish gum.

3   4

(T 3 and 4. Typo D.L.R.)

1913. *Inscribed* "POSTAGE POSTAGE". *Wmk Mult Crown CA. P* 14.

18	3	½d. green (1.4)		80	3·50
19		1d. red (1.4)		80	10·00
20		3d. purple/*yellow* (27.2)		80	4·00
		a. On orange-buff		3·25	22·00
21		11d. dull purple and scarlet (27.2)		3·00	14·00
18/21			*Set of* 4	4·75	28·00
18/21 Optd "Specimen"			*Set of* 4	70·00	

1914 (Mar)**–23.** *Inscribed* "POSTAGE REVENUE". *Wmk Mult Crown CA. Chalk-surfaced paper* (3d. to £1). *P* 14.

22	4	½d. green		70	7·00
23		½d. yellow-green (1917)		2·50	12·00
24		1d. carmine-red		1·00	90
25		1d. scarlet (1917)		3·75	6·50
26		2d. grey (7.14)		1·50	9·00
27		2½d. ultramarine (7.14)		2·00	5·00
28		3d. purple/*pale yellow* (3.23)		18·00	65·00
29		4d. black and red/*yellow* (7.14)		2·00	2·50
30		5d. dull purple and olive-green (7.14)		15·00	27·00
31		5d. brown-purple and olive-green (7.14)		15·00	29·00
32		6d. dull and bright purple (7.14)		6·00	14·00
33		1s. black/*green* (7.14)		3·00	7·00
		a. On blue-green, olive back (1923)		6·50	18·00
34		2s. purple and blue/*blue* (7.14)		6·50	10·00
35		2s. 6d. black and red/*blue* (7.14)		7·50	20·00
36		5s. green and red/*yellow* (7.14)		25·00	40·00
		a. On orange-buff (1920)		42·00	65·00

37	4	10s. green and red/*green* (7.14)		75·00	80·00
38		£1 purple and black/*red* (7.14)		£200	£130
22/38			*Set of* 14	£325	£375
22/38 Optd "Specimen"			*Set of* 14	£400	

Variations in the coloured papers are mostly due to climate and do not indicate separate printings.

1922–31. *Wmk Mult Script CA. Chalk-surfaced paper* (4d. and 5d. to 10s.). *P* 14.

39	4	½d. green (10.22)		30	2·00
40		1d. scarlet (4.23)		10·00	8·50
41		1d. dull violet (2.27)		1·00	5·50
42	3	1½d. bright scarlet (7.24)		1·75	30
43	4	2d. slate-grey (4.23)		2·50	9·00
44		3d. pale ultramarine (11.23)		60	2·50
45		4d. black and red/*yellow* (7.27)		3·50	15·00
45a		4½d. red-brown (1931)		3·00	15·00
46		5d. dull purple and olive-green (12.27)		2·75	20·00
47		6d. dull and bright purple (12.27)		3·75	16·00
48		1s. black/*emerald* (12.27)		2·75	12·00
49		2s. purple and blue/*blue* (2.27)		7·50	30·00
50		2s. 6d. black and red/*blue* (12.27)		7·50	32·00
51		5s. green and red/*pale yellow* (12.27)		24·00	48·00
52		10s. green and red/*emerald* (1.25)		80·00	90·00
39/52			*Set of* 15	£130	£250
39/52 Optd/Perf "Specimen"			*Set of* 15	£300	

1935 (6 May). *Silver Jubilee. As Nos.* 114/17 *of Jamaica, but ptd by D.L.R. P* 13½×14.

53		1½d. deep blue and carmine		1·00	50
		f. Diagonal line by turret		45·00	
		h. Dot by flagstaff		60·00	
54		3d. brown and deep blue		2·75	4·00
		f. Diagonal line by turret		80·00	
		h. Dot by flagstaff		£100	
55		6d. light blue and olive-green		6·50	8·50
		a. Frame printed double, one albino		£1000	
		b. Frame printed triple, two albino		£1200	
		h. Dot by flagstaff		£140	
56		1s. slate and purple		6·50	7·00
		f. Diagonal line by turret		£130	
53/6			*Set of* 4	15·00	18·00
53/6 Perf "Specimen"			*Set of* 4	90·00	

For illustrations of plate varieties see Omnibus section following Zimbabwe.

1937 (13 May). *Coronation. As Nos.* 118/20 *of Jamaica, but ptd by B.W. P* 11×11½.

57		1d. violet		30	40
58		1½d. carmine		30	50
59		3d. blue		40	40
57/9			*Set of* 3	90	1·10
57/9 Perf "Specimen"			*Set of* 3	60·00	

5 Spears and Shield   6 Native Constable and Chief

7 Canoe House   8 Roviana Canoe

(Recess D.L.R. (2d., 3d., 2s. and 2s. 6d.), Waterlow (others))

1939 (1 Feb)**–1951.** *T* 5/8 *and similar designs. Wmk Mult Script CA. P* 13½ (2d., 3d., 2s. and 2s. 6d.) *or* 12½ (others).

60		½d. blue and blue-green		15	60
61		1d. brown and deep violet		15	40
62		1½d. blue-green and carmine		35	90
63		2d. orange-brown and black		30	1·00
		a. Perf 12 (7.11.51)		30	2·00
64		2½d. magenta and sage-green		70	65
		a. Imperf horiz (vert pair)		£7500	
65		3d. black and ultramarine		30	70
		a. Perf 12 (7.11.51)		30	2·00
66		4½d. green and chocolate		8·00	13·00
67		6d. deep violet and reddish purple		35	70
68		1s. green and black		70	40
69		2s. black and orange		6·00	3·00
70		2s. black and violet		25·00	4·50
71		5s. emerald-green and scarlet		25·00	8·00
72		10s. sage-green and magenta (27.4.42)		7·00	8·50
60/72			*Set of* 13	65·00	38·00
60/72 Perf "Specimen"			*Set of* 13	£275	

Designs: *Horiz* (as T 8)—1½d. Artificial Island, Malaita; 1s. Breadfruit; 5s. Malaita canoe. (As T 7)—3d. Roviana canoes; 2s. Tinakula volcano; 2s. 6d. Common Scrub Hen. *Vert* (as T 6)—4½d., 10s. Native house, Reef Islands; 6d. Coconut plantation.

1946 (15 Oct). *Victory. As Nos.* 141/2 *of Jamaica.*

73		1½d. carmine		15	40
74		3d. blue		15	10
73/4 Perf "Specimen"			*Set of* 2	55·00	

COVER PRICES

Cover factors are quoted at the beginning of each country for most issues to 1945. An explanation of the system can be found on page x. The factors quoted do not, however, apply to philatelic covers.

Pocket handkerchief flaw (R. 1/6)

1949 (14 Mar). *Royal Silver Wedding. As Nos.* 143/4 *of Jamaica.*

75		2d. black		50	30
		a. Pocket handkerchief flaw		12·00	
76		10s. magenta		12·00	8·50

1949 (10 Oct). *75th Anniv of U.P.U. As Nos.* 145/8 *of Jamaica.*

77		2d. red-brown		1·00	60
78		3d. deep blue		1·25	70
79		5d. deep blue-green		1·25	85
80		1s. blue-black		1·75	60
77/80			*Set of* 4	4·75	2·50

1953 (2 June). *Coronation. As No.* 153 *of Jamaica.*

81		2d. black and grey-black		30	55

17 Ysabel Canoe   18 Roviana Canoe

24 Native Constable and Chief   25 Arms of the Protectorate

(Des Miss I. R. Stinson (½d.), R. Bailey (2½d.), R. A. Sweet (5d., 1s., 1s. 3d.), Capt. J. Brett Hilder (6d., 8d., 9d., 5s.). Recess B.W. (½d., 2½d., 5d., 6d., 8d., 9d., 1s., 1s. 3d., 5s.), D.L.R. (1d., 2d., 2s.), Waterlow (1½d., 3d., 2s. 6d., 10s., £1), until 1962, then D.L.R.)

1956 (1 Mar)**–63.** *T* 17/18, 24/5 *and similar horiz designs. Wmk Mult Script CA. P* 12 (1d., 2d., 2s.), 13 (1½d., 3d., 2s 6d., 10s., £1) *or* 11½ (others).

82		½d. orange and purple		15	50
83		1d. yellow-green and red-brown		15	15
84		1½d. slate-green and carmine-red		15	40
		a. Slate-green and brown-red (31.7.63)		60	30
85		2d. deep brown and dull green		20	30
86		2½d. black and blue		30	45
87		3d. blue-green and red		25	15
88		5d. black and blue		30	55
89		6d. black and turquoise-green		50	25
90		8d. bright blue and black		25	15
90a		9d. emerald and black (28.1.60)		3·25	80
91		1s. slate and yellow-brown		50	50
		a. Slate and orange-brown (13.6.61)		3·00	2·50
91b		1s. 3d. black and blue (28.1.60)		6·00	1·75
		ba. Black and pale ultramarine (11.12.62)		10·00	3·25
92		2s. black and carmine		12·00	90
93		2s. 6d. emerald and bright purple		7·50	45
		a. Emerald and reddish purple (19.2.63)		11·00	1·75
94		5s. red-brown		12·00	2·00
95		10s. sepia		17·00	3·00
96		£1 black and blue (5.11.58)		42·00	35·00
82/96			*Set of* 17	90·00	40·00

Designs: (As T 17)—5d., 1s. 3d. Map; 6d. Miena (schooner); 1s. Voyage of H.M.S. Swallow, 1767; 2s. 6d. Native house, Reef Islands; 5s. Mendaña and Todos los Santos. (As T 25)—1d. Roviana canoe; 1½d. Artificial Island, Malaita; 2d. Canoe house; 3d. Malaita Canoe; 8d., 9d. Henderson airfield, Guadalcanal; 2s. Tinakula volcano.

LEGISLATIVE COUNCIL

32 Great Frigate Bird

(Litho Enschedé)

1961 (19 Jan). *New Constitution, 1960.* W w **12** (*sideways*). P 13 × 12½.

97	**32**	2d. black and turquoise-green	10	15
98		3d. black and rose-carmine	10	10
99		9d. black and reddish purple	15	15
97/9		*Set of* 3	30	30

1963 (4 June). *Freedom from Hunger.* As No. 80 of *Lesotho.*

100	1s. 3d. ultramarine		2·50	35

1963 (2 Sept). *Red Cross Centenary.* As Nos. 203/4 of *Lesotho.*

101	2d. red and black		60	20
102	9d. red and blue		1·40	70

1963–64. *As Nos. 83/5, 87, 89, 90a and 91a/3, but wmk* w **12**.

103	1d. yellow-green and red-brown (9.7.64)		25	30
104	1½d. slate-green and red (9.7.64)		25	50
105	2d. deep brown and dull green (9.7.64)		20	20
106	3d. light blue-green and scarlet (16.11.63)		40	15
	a. *Yellowish green and red* (9.7.64)		1·25	1·75
107	6d. black and turquoise (7.7.64)		60	40
108	9d. emerald and black (7.7.64)		20	35
109	1s. 3d. black and blue (7.7.64)		60	70
110	2s. black and carmine (9.7.64)		1·00	5·50
111	2s. 6d. emerald & reddish purple (9.7.64)		10·00	10·00
103/11	*Set of* 9		12·00	16·00

33 Makira Food Bowl (48)

(Des M. Farrar-Bell. Litho D.L.R.)

1965 (24 May). *Horiz designs as T* **33**. W w **12**. P 13 × 12½.

112	½d. black, deep slate-blue and light blue		10	30
113	1d. black, orange and yellow		50	20
114	1½d. black, blue and yellow-green		35	35
115	2d. black, ultramarine and light blue		50	30
116	2½d. black, light brown & pale yellow-brown		10	35
117	3d. black, green and light green		10	10
118	6d. black, magenta and yellow-orange		35	20
119	9d. brownish blk, dp bluish grn & pale yell		40	15
120	1s. black, chocolate and magenta		80	15
121	1s. 3d. black and rose-red		3·50	2·25
122	2s. black, bright purple and lilac		5·50	2·75
123	2s. 6d. black, olive-brown and light brown		1·00	70
124	5s. black, ultramarine and violet		10·00	4·50
125	10s. black, olive-green and yellow		12·00	4·00
126	£1 black, deep reddish violet and pink		11·00	5·00
112/126	*Set of* 15		42·00	18·00

Designs:—1d. *Dendrobium veratrifolium* (orchid); 1½d. Scorpion Shell; 2d. Blyth's Hornbill; 2½d. Ysabel shield; 3d. Rennellese club; 6d. Moorish Idol; 9d. Lesser Frigate Bird; 1s. *Dendrobium macrophyllum* (orchid); 1s. 3d. *Dendrobium spectabilis* (orchid); 2s. Sanford's Sea Eagle; 2s. 6d. Malaita belt; 5s. *Ornithoptera victoreae* (butterfly); 10s. Ducorp's Cockatoo; £1, Western canoe figurehead.

1965 (28 June). *I.T.U. Centenary.* As Nos. 98/9 of *Lesotho.*

127	2d. orange-red and turquoise-blue		20	10
128	3d. turquoise-blue and olive-brown		20	10

1965 (25 Oct). *International Co-operation Year.* As Nos. 100/1 of *Lesotho.*

129	1d. reddish purple and turquoise-green		15	10
130	2s. 6d. deep bluish green and lavender		60	15

1966 (24 Jan). *Churchill Commemoration.* As Nos. 102/5 of *Lesotho.*

131	2d. new blue		15	10
132	9d. deep green		25	10
133	1s. 3d. brown		35	10
134	2s. 6d. bluish violet		40	15
131/4	*Set of* 4		1·00	30

(New Currency. 100 cents = 1 Australian dollar)

8 c.   8 c.

Normal "8"   Inverted "8"
(No. 142a)
(R. 9/2. Later corrected)

1966–67. *Decimal Currency. Nos. 112/26 variously surch as T* **48** *by De La Rue.* A. *Wmk upright.* B. *Wmk sideways.*

				A		B	
135	1 c. on ½d.			10	10	10	10
136	2 c. on 1d.			10	10	10	10
137	3 c. on 1½d.			10	10	15	10
138	4 c. on 2d.			15	10	15	10
139	5 c. on 6d.			15	10	15	10
140	6 c. on 2½d.			15	10	15	10
141	7 c. on 3d.			10	10	10	10
142	8 c. on 9d.			25	10	15	10
	a. Inverted "8"			20·00	16·00	†	
	b. Surch omitted (vert pair)			—	—	†	
143	10 c. on 1s.			30	10	40	10
144	12 c. on 1s. 3d.			†		40	10
145	13 c. on 1s. 3d.			1·50	15	4·50	1·75
146	14 c. on 3d.			†		40	10
147	20 c. on 2s.			75	25	3·25	30
148	25 c. on 2s. 6d.			60	40	2·50	35
149	35 c. on 2d.			†		1·75	25
	a. Surch omitted (horiz pair with normal)			†	£2000	—	
	b. Surch value only omitted			†	—	—	
150	50 c. on 5s. (R.)			6·50	2·75	10·00	5·50
151	$1 on 10s.			4·00	3·00	4·25	1·25
152	$2 on £1			3·25	6·50	5·00	3·00
135A/152A	*Set of* 15			16·00	12·00		
135B/152A	*Set of* 18					29·00	11·50

Dates of issue: 1967—1 March, 12 c., 14 c., 35 c. 1966—14 February. All watermark upright. 1966—All other watermark sideways.

The positions of the bars in the surcharge vary considerably from stamp to stamp within the sheets.

The stamps with sideways watermark are all from new printings and in some instances there are marked shade variations from Nos. 112/26 which were used for making Nos. 135A/152A.

No. 142b comes from the bottom left-hand corner of the sheet and was covered by a paper fold. The bottom stamp in the pair is completely without surcharge and the upper has the surcharge value and one bar missing.

1966 (1 July). *World Cup Football Championships.* As Nos. 57/8 of *Pitcairn Islands.*

153	8 c. violet, yellow-green, lake & yellow-brn		15	10
154	35 c. chocolate, blue-green, lake & yellow-brn·		30	10

1966 (20 Sept). *Inauguration of W.H.O. Headquarters, Geneva.* As Nos. 185/6 of *Montserrat.*

155	3 c. black, yellow-green and light blue		25	10
156	50 c. black, light purple and yellow-brown		1·00	20

1966 (1 Dec). *20th Anniv of U.N.E.S.C.O.* As Nos. 342/4 of *Mauritius.*

157	3 c. slate-violet, red, yellow and orange		20	10
158	25 c. orange-yellow, violet and deep olive		55	15
159	$1 black, bright purple and orange		1·50	70
157/9	*Set of* 3		2·00	85

49 Henderson Field

(Des V. Whiteley. Photo Harrison)

1967 (28 Aug). *25th Anniv of Guadalcanal Campaign (Pacific War). T* **49** *and similar horiz design. Multicoloured.* W w **12**. P 14 × 14½.

160	8 c. Type **49**		10	10
161	35 c. Red Beach landings		10	10

51 Mendaña's *Todos los Santos* off Point Cruz

(Des V. Whiteley. Photo Harrison)

1968 (7 Feb). *Quatercentenary of the Discovery of Solomon Is. T* **51** *and similar horiz designs. Multicoloured.* W w **12**. P 14.

162	3 c. Type **51**		15	10
163	8 c. Arrival of missionaries		15	10
164	35 c. Pacific Campaign, World War II		30	10
165	$1 Proclamation of the Protectorate		50	1·10
162/5	*Set of* 4		1·00	1·25

55 Vine Fishing

(Des R. Granger Barrett. Photo Harrison)

1968 (20 May)–**71**. *Horiz designs as T* **55**. *Chalk-surfaced paper.* W w **12** (*inverted on No. 167a*). P 14½.

166	1 c. turquoise-blue, black and brown		10	10
	a. Glazed, ordinary paper (9.8.71).		90	90
167	2 c. apple-green, black and brown		10	10
	a. Glazed, ordinary paper (9.8.71).		90	90
168	3 c. green, myrtle-green and black		10	10
	a. Glazed, ordinary paper (9.8.71).		90	90
169	4 c. bright purple, black and brown		15	10
	a. Glazed, ordinary paper (9.8.71).		90	90
170	6 c. multicoloured		30	10
171	8 c. multicoloured		25	10
	a. Glazed, ordinary paper (9.8.71).		1·50	1·60
172	12 c. yellow-ochre, brown-red and black		65	40
	a. Glazed, ordinary paper (9.8.71).		2·25	2·50
173	14 c. orange-red, chocolate and black		1·50	90
174	15 c. multicoloured		80	50
	a. Glazed, ordinary paper (9.8.71).		2·50	3·25
175	20 c. bright blue, red and black		2·25	1·00
	a. Glazed, ordinary paper (9.8.71).		4·25	5·50
176	24 c. rose-red, black and yellow		2·00	1·25
177	35 c. multicoloured		1·75	70
178	45 c. multicoloured		1·50	75
179	$1 violet-blue, light green and black		2·50	2·00
180	$2 multicoloured		4·00	5·00
166/80	*Set of* 15		15·00	11·50
166a/75a	*Set of* 8		13·00	15·00

Designs:—2 c. Kite fishing; 3 c. Platform fishing; 4 c. Net fishing; 6 c. Gold Lip shell diving; 8 c. Night fishing; 12 c. Boat building; 14 c. Cocoa; 15 c. Road building; 20 c. Geological survey; 24 c. Hauling timber; 35 c. Copra; 45 c. Harvesting rice; $1, Honiara Port; $2, Internal air service.

The stamps on glazed, ordinary paper exist with PVA gum only. The 1 c. to 12 c. and 20 c. on chalk-surfaced paper exist with PVA gum as well as gum arabic, but the others exist with gum arabic only.

70 Map of Australasia and Diagram   71 Basketball Player

(Des R. Gates. Litho Enschedé)

1969 (10 Feb). *Inaugural Year of the South Pacific University.* P 12½ × 12.

181	**70**	3 c. multicoloured	10	10
182		12 c. multicoloured	10	10
183		35 c. multicoloured	15	10
181/3		*Set of* 3	30	15

(Des J. Cooter. Photo Harrison)

1969 (13 Aug). *Third South Pacific Games, Port Moresby. T* **71** *and similar vert designs. Multicoloured.* W w **12** (*sideways*). P 14½ × 14.

184	3 c. Type **71**		10	10
185	8 c. Footballer		10	10
186	14 c. Sprinter		10	10
187	45 c. Rugby player		20	15
184/7	*Set of* 4		40	30
MS188	126 × 120 mm. Nos. 184/7		3·50	8·00

Stamps from the miniature sheets differ slightly from those in the ordinary sheets, particularly the 14 c. value, which has a shadow below the feet on the runner. The footballer and rugby player on the 8 c. and 45 c. values also have shadows below their feet, but these are more pronounced than on the stamps from the ordinary sheets.

75 South Sea Island with Star of Bethlehem   76 Southern Cross, "PAX" and Frigatebird (stained glass window)

(Des L. Curtis. Photo Harrison)

1969 (21 Nov). *Christmas.* W w **12** (*sideways*). P 14½ × 14.

189	**75**	8 c. black, violet and turquoise-green	10	10
190	**76**	35 c. multicoloured	20	10

77 "Paid" Stamp, New South Wales 1896–1906 2d. Stamp and 1906–07 Tulagi Postmark

(Des G. Drummond. Litho B.W.)

1970 (15 Apr). *Inauguration of New G.P.O. Honiara. T* **77** *and similar horiz designs.* W w **12** (*sideways*). P 13.

191	7 c. light magenta, deep blue and black		20	15
192	14 c. sage-green, deep blue and black		25	15
193	18 c. multicoloured		25	15
194	23 c. multicoloured		30	20
191/4	*Set of* 4		90	60

Designs:—14 c. 1906–07 2d. stamp. C. M. Woodford; 18 c. 1910–14 5s. stamp and Tulagi postmark, 1913; 23 c. New G.P.O., Honiara.

81 Coat of Arms   83 British Red Cross H.Q., Honiara

(Des V. Whiteley. Photo Harrison)

1970 (15 June). *New Constitution. T* **81** *and similar design.* W w **12** (*sideways on 18 c.*). P 14½ × 14 (18 c.) or 14 × 14½ (35 c.).

195	18 c. multicoloured		15	10
196	35 c. pale apple-green, deep blue and ochre		30	20

Design: *Horiz*—35 c. Map.

(Des L. Curtis. Litho Questa)

1970 (17 Aug). *Centenary of British Red Cross. T* **83** *and similar horiz design.* W w **12** (*sideways*). *P* 14 × 14½.
197	3 c. multicoloured		10	10
198	35 c. blue, vermilion and black		25	20

Design:—35 c. Wheelchair and map.

86 Reredos (Altar Screen)

(Des L. Curtis. Litho J.W.)

1970 (19 Oct). *Christmas. T* **86** *and similar design.* W w **12** (*sideways on* 45 c.). *P* 14 × 13½ (8 c.) *or* 13½ × 14 (45 c.).
199	8 c. ochre and bluish violet		10	10
200	45 c. chestnut, yellow-orange & blackish brn		25	20

Design: *Vert*—8 c. Carved angel.

87 La Perouse and *La Boussole*

(Des J.W. Litho Questa)

1971 (28 Jan). *Ships and Navigators (1st series). T* **87** *and similar horiz designs. Multicoloured.* W w **12** (*sideways*). *P* 14.
201	3 c. Type **87**		55	20
202	4 c. Astrolabe and Polynesian Reed Map		65	20
203	12 c. Abel Tasman and *Heemskerk*		1·50	45
204	35 c. Te Puki canoe, Santa Cruz		3·00	75
201/4		*Set of* 4	5·00	1·40

See also Nos. 215/18, 236/9, 254/7 and 272/5.

88 J. Atkin, Bishop Patteson and S. Taroaniara

(Des J.W. Litho Questa)

1971 (5 April). *Death Centenary of Bishop Patteson. T* **88** *and similar multicoloured designs.* W w **12** (*sideways on* 2 c., 4 c.). *P* 14½ × 14 (2 c., 4 c.) *or* 14 × 14½ (*others*).
205	2 c. Type **88**		10	10
206	4 c. Last Landing at Nukapu		10	10
207	14 c. Memorial Cross and Nukapu (*vert*)		10	10
208	45 c. Knotted Leaf and canoe (*vert*)		20	10
205/8		*Set of* 4	30	30

89 Torch Emblem and Boxers   **90** Melanesian Lectern

(Des C. Debenham. Litho Questa)

1971 (9 Aug). *Fourth South Pacific Games, Tahiti. T* **89** *and similar horiz designs. Multicoloured.* W w **12** (*sideways*). *P* 14.
209	3 c. Type **89**		10	10
210	8 c. Emblem and footballers		10	10
211	12 c. Emblem and runner		10	10
212	35 c. Emblem and skin-diver		15	15
209/12		*Set of* 4	30	30

(Des C. Abbott. Litho A. & M.)

1971 (15 Nov). *Christmas. T* **90** *and similar vert design. Multicoloured.* W w **12**. *P* 13½.
213	9 c. Type **90**		10	10
214	45 c. "United we Stand" (Margarita Bara)		20	20

(Des J.W. Litho Questa)

1972 (1 Feb). *Ships and Navigators (2nd series). Horiz designs as T* **87**. *Multicoloured.* W w **12** (*sideways*). *P* 14.
215	4 c. Bougainville and *La Boudeuse*		30	10
216	9 c. Horizontal planisphere and ivory backstaff		60	10
217	15 c. Philip Carteret and H.M.S. *Swallow*		85	15
218	45 c. Malaita canoe		3·75	1·25
215/18		*Set of* 4	5·00	1·40

91 *Cupha woodfordi*

(Des R. Granger Barrett. Litho Questa)

1972 (3 July)–73. *T* **91** *and similar horiz designs. Multicoloured. Cream paper.* W w **12** (*upright on* $5, *sideways on others*). *P* 14.
219	1 c. Type **91**		15	30
220	2 c. *Ornithoptera priamus*		25	40
221	3 c. *Vindula sapor*		25	40
222	4 c. *Papilio ulysses*		25	40
223	5 c. Great Trevally		25	30
224	8 c. Little Bonito		40	50
225	9 c. Sapphire Demoiselle		50	55
226	12 c. *Costus speciosus*		1·25	80
227	15 c. Orange Anenome Fish		1·25	1·00
228	20 c. *Spathoglottis plicata*		3·25	1·75
229	25 c. *Ephemerantha comata*		3·25	1·50
230	35 c. *Dendrobium cuthbertsonii*		3·50	2·25
231	45 c. *Heliconia salomonica*		3·50	3·00
232	$1 Blue Finned Triggerfish		6·00	4·50
233	$2 *Ornithoptera alottei*		13·00	12·00
233*a*	$5 Great Frigate Bird (2.7.73)		10·00	10·00
219/33*a*		*Set of* 16	42·00	35·00

The 1 to 4 c. and $2 are butterflies; the 5 to 9 c., 15 c. and $1 are fishes; the 12 c. and 20 to 45 c. are flowers and the $5 a bird.

92 Greetings and Message Drum

(Des (from photograph by D. Groves) and photo Harrison)

1972 (20 Nov). *Royal Silver Wedding. Multicoloured; background colour given.* W w **12**. *P* 14 × 14½.
234	**92** 8 c. rose-carmine		10	10
235	45 c. deep yellow-olive		20	20

(Des J.W. Litho Questa)

1973 (9 Mar). *Ships and Navigators (3rd series). Horiz designs as T* **87**. *Multicoloured.* W w **12**. *P* 14.
236	4 c. D'Entrecasteaux and *Recherche*		30	15
237	9 c. Ship's hour-glass and chronometer		60	15
238	15 c. Lt. Shortland and H.M.S. *Alexander*		75	20
239	35 c. Tomoko (war canoe)		3·25	1·75
236/9		*Set of* 4	4·50	2·00

93 Pan Pipes

(Des and litho J.W.)

1973 (1 Oct). *Musical Instruments. T* **93** *and similar horiz designs. Multicoloured.* W w **12**. *P* 13½.
240	4 c. Type **93**		10	10
241	9 c. Castanets		10	10
242	15 c. Bamboo flute		15	10
243	35 c. Bauro gongs		35	25
244	45 c. Bamboo band		35	30
240/4		*Set of* 5	90	65

(Des PAD Studio. Litho Questa)

1973 (14 Nov). *Royal Wedding. As Nos.* 322/3 *of Montserrat.*
245	4 c. deep grey-blue		10	10
246	35 c. bright blue		15	10

94 "Adoration of the Kings" (Jan Brueghel)

(Des PAD Studio. Litho Questa)

1973 (26 Nov). *Christmas. T* **94** *and similar designs showing "Adoration of the Kings" by the artists listed. Multicoloured.* W w **12** (*sideways on* 22 c.). *P* 13½ (45 c.) *or* 14 (*others*).
247	8 c. Type **94**		10	10
248	22 c. Pieter Brueghel (*vert*)		25	25
249	45 c. Botticelli (48 × 35 *mm*)		50	50
247/9		*Set of* 3	70	70

95 Queen Elizabeth II and Map   **96** "Postman"

(Des G. Drummond. Litho Questa)

1974 (18 Feb). *Royal Visit.* W w **12**. *P* 13½.
250	**95** 4 c. multicoloured		25	10
251	9 c. multicoloured		50	10
252	15 c. multicoloured		60	20
253	35 c. multicoloured		1·10	1·25
250/3		*Set of* 4	2·25	1·40

(Des and litho J.W.)

1974 (15 May). *Ships and Navigators (4th series). Horiz designs as T* **87**. *Multicoloured.* W w **12** (*sideways*). *P* 14.
254	4 c. Commissioner landing from S.S. *Titus*		20	10
255	9 c. Radar scanner		25	10
256	15 c. Natives being transported to a "Blackbirder" brig		40	15
257	45 c. Lieut. John F. Kennedy's *P.T.* 109		2·00	1·25
254/7		*Set of* 4	2·50	1·40

(Des Jennifer Toombs. Litho Questa)

1974 (29 Aug). *Centenary of Universal Postal Union. T* **96** *and similar designs showing Origami figures.* W w **12** (*sideways on* 9 *and* 45 c.). *P* 14.
258	4 c. light yellow-green, deep green and black		10	10
259	9 c. light olive-bistre, lake-brown and black		10	10
260	15 c. mauve, purple and black		15	10
261	45 c. cobalt, dull ultramarine and black		35	70
258/61		*Set of* 4	65	80

Designs: *Horiz*—9 c. Carrier-pigeon; 45 c. Pegasus. *Vert*—15 c. St. Gabriel.

97 "New Constitution" Stamp of 1970

(Des R. Granger Barrett. Litho Questa)

1974 (16 Dec). *New Constitution. T* **97** *and similar horiz design.* W w **14** (*sideways*). *P* 14.
262	**97** 4 c. multicoloured		10	10
263	— 9 c. dull rose-red, black & lt yell-ochre		10	10
264	— 15 c. dull rose-red, blk & lt greenish yell		15	10
265	**97** 35 c. multicoloured		45	50
262/5		*Set of* 4	70	60
MS266	134 × 84 mm. Nos. 262/5		2·75	3·50

Design:—9 c., 15 c. "New Constitution" stamp of 1961 (inscr "1960").

98 Golden Whistler

(Des G. Drummond. Litho Questa)

1975 (7 Apr). *Birds. T* **98** *and similar horiz designs. Multicoloured.* W w **12**. *P* 14.
267	1 c. Type **98**		45	55
268	2 c. Common Kingfisher		50	70
269	3 c. Red-bibbed Fruit Dove		55	75
270	4 c. Little Button Quail		55	75
271	$2 Duchess Lorikeet		11·00	9·50
267/71		*Set of* 5	12·00	11·00

See also Nos. 305/20.

(Des and litho J.W.)

1975 (29 May). *Ships and Navigators (5th series). Horiz designs as T* **87**. *Multicoloured.* W w **12**. *P* 13½.
272	4 c. *Walande* (coaster)		25	10
273	9 c. *Melanesian* (coaster)		30	10
274	15 c. *Marsina* (container ship)		35	15
275	45 c. *Himalaya* (liner)		1·00	1·50
272/5		*Set of* 4	1·75	1·60

99 800-Metres Race

(Des PAD Studio. Litho Walsall)

1975 (4 Aug). *Fifth South Pacific Games, Guam.* T 99 *and similar horiz designs. Multicoloured.* W w 14 (*sideways*). P 13½.

276	4 c. Type 99	10	10
277	9 c. Long-jump	10	10
278	15 c. Javelin-throwing	15	10
279	45 c. Football	45	45
276/9	*Set of 4*	70	55
MS280	130 × 95 mm. Nos. 276/9	4·00	4·00

100 Christmas Scene and Candles   (101)

(Des G. Vasarhelyi. Litho Questa)

1975 (13 Oct). *Christmas.* T 100 *and similar horiz designs. Multicoloured.* W w 12 (*sideways*). P 14.

281	15 c. Type 100	20	10
282	35 c. Shepherds, angels and candles	40	15
283	45 c. The Magi and candles	50	40
281/3	*Set of 3*	1·00	60
MS284	140 × 130 mm. Nos. 281/3	4·00	4·00

1975 (12 Nov). *Nos. 267/70, 223/32, 271 and 233a with obliterating bar as* T 101 *over* "BRITISH".

285	1 c. Type 98	25	45
286	2 c. Common Kingfisher	30	45
287	3 c. Red-bibbed Fruit Dove	30	45
288	4 c. Little Button Quail	35	45
289	5 c. Great Trevally	35	45
290	8 c. Little Bonito	50	60
291	9 c. Sapphire Demoiselle	50	60
292	12 c. *Costus speciosus*	1·50	1·00
293	15 c. Orange Anemone Fish	1·50	1·25
294	20 c. *Spathoglottis plicata*	2·75	1·50
295	25 c. *Ephemerantha comata*	2·75	1·75
296	35 c. *Dendrobium cuthbertsonii*	3·50	1·75
297	45 c. *Heliconia salomonica*	3·50	3·00
298	$1 Blue Finned Triggerfish (*cream paper*)	3·00	2·50
	a. White paper	4·75	4·00
299	$2 Duchess Lorikeet	8·00	10·00
300	$5 Great Frigate Bird (*white paper*)	15·00	18·00
	a. Cream paper	23·00	23·00
285/300	*Set of 16*	38·00	40·00

SELF-GOVERNMENT

102 Ceremonial Food-bowl

(Des J. Cooter. Litho Questa)

1976 (12 Jan). *Artefacts (1st series).* T 102 *and similar multicoloured designs.* W w 12 (*upright on 35 c.; sideways on others*). P 14.

301	4 c. Type 102	10	10
302	15 c. Chieftains' money	10	10
303	35 c. Nguzu-nguzu (canoe protector spirit) (*vert*)	25	20
304	45 c. Nguzu-nguzu canoe prow	30	25
301/4	*Set of 4*	65	55

See also Nos. 337/40, 353/6 and 376/9.

103 Golden Whistler

(Des G. Drummond. Litho Questa)

1976 (8 Mar–6 Dec). *Nos. 267/71 with new country inscr (omitting* "BRITISH") *as* T 103, *and new values. Multicoloured.* W w 14 (*sideways*). P 14.

305	1 c. Type 103	30	50
306	2 c. Common Kingfisher	30	60
307	3 c. Red-bibbed Fruit Dove	30	50
308	4 c. Little Button Quail	30	50
309	5 c. Willie Wagtail	30	60
310	6 c. Golden Cowrie	60	50
311	10 c. Glory of the Sea Cone	60	60
312	12 c. Rainbow Lory	60	80
313	15 c. Pearly Nautilus	65	40
314	20 c. Venus Comb Murex	1·00	45
315	25 c. Commercial Trochus	85	50
316	35 c. Melon or Baler Shell	1·00	70
317	45 c. Orange Spider Conch	1·50	1·25
318	$1 Pacific Triton	3·25	3·00
319	$2 Duchess Lorikeet	6·50	4·75
320	$5 Great Frigate Bird (6.12)	6·50	6·00
305/20	*Set of 16*	22·00	19·00

104 Coastwatchers, 1942   105 Alexander Graham Bell

(Des J. Cooter. Litho Walsall)

1976 (24 May). *Bicentenary of American Revolution.* T 104 *and similar horiz designs. Multicoloured.* W w 14 (*sideways*). P 14.

321	6 c. Type 104	20	10
322	20 c. *Amagiri* ramming *PT109* and Lt. J. F. Kennedy	60	30
323	35 c. Henderson Airfield	1·00	40
324	45 c. Map of Guadalcanal	1·10	70
321/4	*Set of 4*	2·75	1·40
MS325	95 × 115 mm. Nos. 321/4	5·50	7·50

(Des P. Powell. Litho Harrison)

1976 (26 July). *Telephone Centenary.* T 105 *and similar vert designs.* W w 14 (*sideways*). P 14½ × 14.

326	6 c. multicoloured	10	10
327	20 c. multicoloured	15	10
328	35 c. brown-orange, lt orange & lt vermilion	30	15
329	45 c. multicoloured	40	35
326/9	*Set of 4*	85	55

Designs:—20 c. Radio telephone via satellite; 35 c. Ericson's magneto telephone; 45 c. Stick telephone and first telephone.

106 B.A.C. "1–11"   107 The Communion Plate

(Des and litho Walsall)

1976 (13 Sept). *50th Anniv of First Flight to Solomon Islands.* T 106 *and similar horiz designs. Multicoloured.* W w 14 (*sideways*). P 14.

330	6 c. Type 106	20	10
331	20 c. Britten-Norman "Islander"	35	10
332	35 c. "Dakota DC3"	65	15
333	45 c. De Havilland "DH50A"	75	45
330/3	*Set of 4*	1·75	65

(Des Jennifer Toombs. Litho Questa)

1977 (7 Feb). *Silver Jubilee.* T 107 *and similar vert designs. Multicoloured.* W w 14. P 13½.

334	6 c. Queen's visit, 1974	10	10
335	35 c. Type 107	15	20
336	45 c. The Communion	25	45
334/6	*Set of 3*	45	65

108 Carving from New Georgia   109 Spraying Roof and Mosquito

(Des J. Cooter. Litho Questa)

1977 (9 May). *Artefacts (2nd series).* T 108 *and similar vert designs showing carvings.* W w 14. P 14.

337	6 c. multicoloured	10	10
338	20 c. multicoloured	10	10
339	35 c. slate-black, grey and rose-red	20	15
340	45 c. multicoloured	25	30
337/40	*Set of 4*	55	50

Designs:—20 c. Sea adaro (spirit); 35 c. Shark-headed man; 45 c. Man from Ulawa or Malaita.

(Des G. Vasarhelyi. Litho Questa)

1977 (27 July). *Malaria Eradication.* T 109 *and similar horiz designs. Multicoloured.* W w 14 (*sideways*). P 14.

341	6 c. Type 109	10	10
342	20 c. Taking blood samples	20	10
343	35 c. Microscope and map	30	15
344	45 c. Delivering drugs	40	40
341/4	*Set of 4*	90	60

110 The Shepherds   111 Feather Money

(Des M. and G. Shamir. Litho Questa)

1977 (12 Sept). *Christmas.* T 110 *and similar vert designs. Multicoloured.* W w 14. P 14.

345	6 c. Type 110	10	10
346	20 c. Mary and Jesus in stable	10	10
347	35 c. The Three Kings	20	15
348	45 c. "The Flight into Egypt"	25	25
345/8	*Set of 4*	50	45

(Des D.L.R. Litho Harrison)

1977 (24 Oct). *Introduction of Solomon Islands Coins and Banknotes.* T 111 *and similar horiz designs. Multicoloured.* W w 14. P 14 × 14½.

349	6 c. Type 111	10	10
	a. Horiz pair. Nos. 349/50	20	20
350	6 c. New currency coins	10	10
351	45 c. New currency notes	35	25
	a. Horiz pair. Nos. 351/2	70	50
352	45 c. Shell money	35	25
349/52	*Set of 4*	80	60

The two designs of each value were printed in horizontal se-tenant pairs throughout their sheets.

112 Figure from Shortland Island   113 Sandford's Sea Eagle

(Des J. Cooter. Litho Questa)

1978 (11 Jan). *Artefacts (3rd series).* T 112 *and similar vert designs.* W w 14. P 14.

353	6 c. multicoloured	10	10
354	20 c. multicoloured	10	10
355	35 c. deep brown, black and orange	20	15
356	45 c. multicoloured	25	30
353/6	*Set of 4*	55	50

Designs:—20 c. Ceremonial shield; 35 c. Santa Cruz ritual figure; 45 c. Decorative combs.

(Des Jennifer Toombs. Litho Questa)

1978 (21 Apr). *25th Anniv of Coronation.* T 113 *and similar vert designs. Multicoloured.* P 15.

357	45 c. black, vermilion and silver	25	30
	a. Sheetlet. Nos. 357/9 × 2	1·25	
358	45 c. multicoloured	25	30
359	45 c. black, vermilion and silver	25	30
357/9	*Set of 3*	65	80

Designs:—No. 357, King's Dragon; No. 358, Queen Elizabeth II; No. 359, Type 113.

Nos. 357/9 were printed together in small sheets of 6, containing two se-tenant strips of 3, with horizontal gutter margin between.

INDEPENDENT

114 National Flag   115 John

(Des L. Curtis. Litho Questa)

1978 (7 July). *Independence.* T 114 *and similar vert designs. Multicoloured.* W w 14. P 14.

360	6 c. Type 114	10	10
361	15 c. Governor-General's flag	20	10
362	35 c. The Cenotaph, Honiara	35	30
363	45 c. National coat of arms	40	50
360/3	*Set of 4*	95	85

(Des J.W. Litho Questa)

1978 (4 Oct). *450th Death Anniv of Dürer. Details from his Painting "Four Apostles". T 115 and similar vert designs. Multicoloured. W w 14. P 14.*

364	6 c. Type 115			10	10
365	20 c. Peter			10	10
366	35 c. Paul			15	15
367	45 c. Mark			20	30
364/7			Set of 4	45	50

116 Firelighting **117** H.M.S. *Discovery*

(Des K. G. Watkinson; adapted J.W. Litho Questa)

1978 (15 Nov). *50th Anniv of Scouting in Solomon Islands. T 116 and similar horiz designs. Multicoloured. W w 14 (sideways). P 14.*

368	6 c. Type 116			15	10
369	20 c. Camping			20	20
370	35 c. Solomon Islands Scouts			40	40
371	45 c. Canoeing			50	70
368/71			Set of 4	1·10	1·25

(Des and litho (45 c. also embossed) Walsall)

1979 (16 Jan). *Bicentenary of Captain Cook's Voyages, 1768–79. T 117 and similar vert designs. P 11.*

372	8 c. multicoloured			30	10
373	18 c. multicoloured			40	15
374	35 c. black, yellowish green and silver			55	25
375	45 c. multicoloured			60	40
372/5			Set of 4	1·75	80

Designs:—18 c. "Captain Cook" (Nathaniel Dance); 35 c. Sextant; 45 c. Flaxman/Wedgwood medallion of Captain Cook.

118 Fish Net Float **119** Running

(Des J. Cooter. Litho Questa)

1979 (21 Mar). *Artefacts (4th series). T 118 and similar designs. W w 14 (sideways on 8 and 35 c.). P 14.*

376	8 c. multicoloured			10	10
377	20 c. multicoloured			10	10
378	35 c. black, grey and rose			15	15
379	45 c. black, chestnut and apple-green			20	30
376/9			Set of 4	45	50

Designs: *Vert*—20 c. Armband of shell money; 45 c. Forehead ornament. *Horiz*—35 c. Ceremonial food bowl.

(Des L. Curtis. Litho Format)

1979 (4 June). *South Pacific Games, Fiji. T 109 and similar horiz designs. Multicoloured. W w 14 (sideways). P 13½.*

380	8 c. Type 119			10	10
381	10 c. Hurdling			10	10
382	35 c. Football			15	15
383	45 c. Swimming			25	35
380/3			Set of 4	55	50

120 1908 6d. Stamp **121** Sea Snake

(Des J.W. Litho Format)

1979 (16 Aug). *Death Centenary of Sir Rowland Hill. T 120 and similar vert designs showing stamps. W w 14. P 14.*

384	8 c. carmine and pale rose			10	10
385	20 c. deep mauve and pale mauve			20	30
386	35 c. multicoloured			35	45
384/6			Set of 3	60	75
MS387	121 × 121 mm. 45 c. rosine, deep dull green and pink			45	65

Designs:—20 c. Great Britain 1856 6d.; 35 c. 1978 45 c. Independence commemorative; 45 c. 1922 10s.

(Des L. Curtis. Litho Enschedé)

1979 (18 Sept)–83. *Reptiles. Vert designs as T 121. Multicoloured. W w 14 (inverted on Nos. 394B and 397B). P 13½ × 13.*
A. *No imprint.* B. *Imprint date at foot.*

				A		B	
388	1 c. Type 121			10	20	†	
389	3 c. Red-banded Tree Snake			10	20	†	
390	4 c. Whip Snake			10	20	†	
391	6 c. Pacific Boa			10	20	†	
392	8 c. Skink			10	10	†	
393	10 c. Gecko (*Lepidodactylus lugubris*)			10	20	†	
394	12 c. Monitor			50	40	20	50
395	15 c. Anglehead			30	25	†	
396	20 c. Giant Toad			30	30	†	
397	25 c. Marsh Frog			60	50	30	60
398	30 c. Horned Frog			1·50	60	1·00	1·25
399	35 c. Tree Frog			30	40	†	
399a	40 c. Burrowing Snake			†		45	1·25
400	45 c. Guppy's Snake			30	70	†	
400a	50 c. Tree Gecko			†		50	40
401	$1 Large Skink			1·25	1·75	1·50	70
402	$2 Guppy's Frog			1·25	2·00	†	
403	$5 Estuarine Crocodile			3·00	6·00	4·00	4·00
403a	$10 Hawksbill Turtle			†		6·50	6·75
388/403		Set of 16		8·50	12·50		
394/403a		Set of 8				13·00	14·00

Dates of issue:—18.9.79, Nos. 388A/403A; 25.1.82, Nos. 401B, 403B; 27.8.82, Nos. 394B, 397B; 20.9.82, No. 403a; 24.1.83, Nos. 399aB, 400aB; 31.8.83, No. 398B.

122 "Madonna and Child" (Morando) **123** H.M.S. *Curacao*, 1839

(Des BG Studio. Litho Questa)

1979 (15 Nov). *Christmas. International Year of the Child. T 122 and similar vert designs showing "Madonna and Child" paintings by various artists. Multicoloured. W w 14. P 14 × 14½.*

404	4 c. Type 122			10	10
405	20 c. Luini			20	15
406	35 c. Bellini			30	15
407	50 c. Raphael			35	50
404/7			Set of 4	85	80
MS408	92 × 133 mm. Nos. 404/7			1·00	1·50

(Des L. Curtis. Litho Questa)

1980 (23 Jan). *Ships and Crests (1st series). T 123 and similar horiz designs. Multicoloured. W w 14 (sideways). P 14.*

409	8 c. Type 123			20	10
410	20 c. H.M.S. *Herald*, 1854			35	15
411	35 c. H.M.S. *Royalist*, 1889			55	55
412	45 c. H.M.S. *Beagle*, 1878			70	55
409/12			Set of 4	1·60	1·00

See also Nos. 430/3.

124 Steel Fishery Training Vessel

(Des G. Hutchins. Litho Secura, Singapore)

1980 (27 Mar). *Fishing. Ancillary Craft. T 124 and similar horiz designs. Multicoloured. W w 14 (sideways). P 13½.*

413	8 c. Type 124			15	10
414	20 c. *Solomon Hunter* (fishery training vessel)			20	15
415	45 c. *Ufi Na Tasi* (refrigerated fish transport)			35	40
416	80 c. Research Vessel			60	1·00
413/16			Set of 4	1·10	1·50

125 *Comliebank* (cargo-liner) and 1935 Tulagi Registered Letter Postmark

(Des A. Theobald. Litho Questa)

1980 (6 May). *"London 1980" International Stamp Exhibition. Mail-carrying Transport. T 125 and similar horiz designs. Multicoloured. W w 14 (sideways). P 14½ × 14.*

417	45 c. Type 125			25	40
	a. Sheetlet. Nos. 417/20			90	
418	45 c. Douglas "C-47" aeroplane (U.S. Army Postal Service, 1943)			25	40
419	45 c. B.A.C. "1-11" airliner and 1979 Honiara postmark			25	40
420	45 c. *Corabank* (container ship) and 1979 Auki postmark			25	40
417/20			Set of 4	90	1·40

Nos. 417/20 were printed together as a sheetlet containing a *se-tenant* block of 4.

126 Queen Elizabeth the Queen Mother **127** Angel with Trumpet

(Des Harrison. Litho Questa)

1980 (4 Aug). *80th Birthday of Queen Elizabeth the Queen Mother. W w 14 (sideways). P 14.*

421	**126** 45 c. multicoloured			40	35

(Des C. Abbott. Litho Walsall)

1980 (2 Sept). *Christmas. T 127 and similar vert designs. Multicoloured. W w 14. P 14½ × 14.*

422	8 c. Type 127			10	10
423	20 c. Angel with fiddle			10	10
424	45 c. Angel with trumpet (*different*)			25	25
425	80 c. Angel with lute			40	45
422/5			Set of 4	70	75

128 *Parthenos sylvia* **129** Francisco Antonio Maurelle

(Des J. Cooter. Litho Secura, Singapore)

1980 (12 Nov). *Butterflies (1st series). T 128 and similar horiz designs. Multicoloured. W w 14 (sideways. P 13½.*

426	8 c. Type 128			10	10
427	20 c. *Delias schoenbergi*			25	20
428	45 c. *Jamides cephion*			40	40
429	80 c. *Ornithoptera victoriae*			1·00	1·00
426/9			Set of 4	1·60	1·50

See also Nos. 456/9 and 610/13.

(Des L. Curtis. Litho Questa)

1981 (14 Jan). *Ships and Crests (2nd series). Horiz designs as T 123. Multicoloured. W w 14 (sideways). P 14.*

430	8 c. H.M.S. *Mounts Bay*			15	10
431	20 c. H.M.S. *Charybdis*			25	15
432	45 c. H.M.S. *Hydra*			50	35
433	$1 Royal Yacht *Britannia*			1·25	1·00
430/3			Set of 4	1·90	1·40

(Des J. Cooter. Litho Questa)

1981 (23 Mar). *Bicentenary of Maurelle's Visit and Production of Bauche's Chart, 1791 (No. MS438). T 129 and similar designs. Wmk CA Diagonal (sideways on 8 c. and $1). P 13½ × 14 (8 c., $1) or 14 × 13½ (others).*

434	8 c. black, deep brown and greenish yellow			15	10
435	10 c. black, vermilion and stone			20	10
436	45 c. multicoloured			60	65
437	$1 multicoloured			1·00	1·10
434/7			Set of 4	1·75	1·75
MS438	126 × 91 mm. 25 c. × 4, each black, vermilion and stone (wmk sideways). P 14½			1·25	1·40

Designs: *Horiz*—10 c. Bellin's map of 1742 showing route of *La Princesa*; 45 c. *La Princesa*. *Vert*—$1 Spanish compass cards, 1745 and 1757. No. MS438, "Chart of a part of the South Sea" (each stamp 44 × 28 mm).
Stamps in No. MS438 were printed to form a composite design.

130 Netball **131** Prince Charles as Colonel-in-Chief, Royal Regiment of Wales

(Des R. Granger Barrett. Litho Security Printers (M), Malaysia)

1981 (7 July). *Mini South Pacific Games. T 130 and similar vert designs. Multicoloured. W w 14. P 12.*

439	8 c. Type 130			10	10
440	10 c. Tennis			15	15
441	25 c. Running			25	25
442	30 c. Football			25	25
443	45 c. Boxing			40	40
439/43			Set of 5	1·00	1·00
MS444	102 × 67 mm $1 Stylised athletes (wmk sideways)			1·00	1·10

(Des and litho J.W.)

1981 (22 July). *Royal Wedding. T* **131** *and similar vert designs. Multicoloured.* W w **14**. P 13½ × 13.

445	8 c. Wedding bouquet from Solomon Islands		10	10
446	45 c. Type **131**		30	40
447	$1 Prince Charles and Lady Diana Spencer		60	1·00
445/7		*Set of 3*	90	1·25

132 "Music"　　　**133** Primitive Church

(Des BG Studio. Litho Questa)

1981 (28 Sept). *25th Anniv of Duke of Edinburgh Award Scheme. T* **132** *and similar vert designs. Multicoloured.* W w **14**. P **14**.

448	8 c. Type **132**		10	10
449	25 c. "Handicrafts"		10	10
450	45 c. "Canoeing"		20	20
451	$1 Duke of Edinburgh		50	70
448/51		*Set of 4*	75	95

(Des BG Studio. Litho Format)

1981 (12 Oct). *Christmas. Churches. T* **133** *and similar horiz designs.* W w **14** (*sideways*). P 14.

452	8 c. black, buff and cobalt		10	10
453	10 c. multicoloured		10	10
454	25 c. black, buff and dull green		15	10
455	$2 multicoloured		1·00	1·25
452/5		*Set of 4*	1·25	1·25

Designs:—10 c. St. Barnabas Anglican Cathedral, Honiara; 25 c. Early church; $2 Holy Cross Cathedral, Honiara.

(Des J. Cooter. Litho Secura, Singapore)

1982 (5 Jan). *Butterflies* (2nd series). *Horiz designs as T* **128**. *Multicoloured.* W w **14** (*sideways*). P 13½ × 13.

456	10 c. *Doleschallia bisaltide*		15	10
457	25 c. *Papilio bridgei*		35	25
458	35 c. *Taenaris phorcas*		40	30
	a. Wmk inverted		50·00	
459	$1 *Graphium sarpedon*		1·50	1·50
456/9		*Set of 4*	2·25	1·90

No. 458a shows a change of watermark position from sideways to inverted.

(134)	**135** Pair of Sanford's Sea Eagles constructing Nest

5 CENTS SURCHARGE
CYCLONE RELIEF FUND
1982

"0" of "50" omitted from surcharge (R. 4/5)

1982 (3 May). *Cyclone Relief Fund. No.* 447 *surch with T* **134** *in red.*

460	$1 + 50 c. Prince Charles and Lady Diana Spencer		2·50	2·75
	a. "0" omitted		10·00	

(Des N. Arlott. Litho Walsall)

1982 (15 May). *Sanford's Sea Eagle. T* **135** *and similar vert designs. Multicoloured.* W w **14**. P **14**.

461	12 c. Type **135**		35	40
	a. Horiz strip of 5. Nos. 461/5		1·75	
462	12 c. Egg and chick		35	40
463	12 c. Hen feeding chicks		35	40
464	12 c. Fledgelings		35	40
465	12 c. Young bird in flight		35	40
466	12 c. Pair of birds and village dwellings		35	40
461/6		*Set of 6*	1·90	2·25

Nos. 461/6 were printed together, *se-tenant*, in various combinations throughout sheets also including one stamp-size label.

136 Wedding Portrait	**137** Flags of Solomon Islands and United Kingdom

(Des Jennifer Toombs. Litho Walsall)

1982 (1 July). *21st Birthday of Princess of Wales. T* **136** *and similar vert designs. Multicoloured.* W w **14**. P 14½ × 14.

467	12 c. Solomon Islands coat of arms		15	10
468	40 c. Lady Diana Spencer at Broadlands, May 1981		30	30
469	50 c. Type **136**		35	35
470	$1 Formal portrait		65	65
467/70		*Set of 4*	1·25	1·25

(Des Studio 53. Litho Questa)

1982 (11 Oct). *Royal Visit (Nos.* 471/2, **MS**475) *and Commonwealth Games, Brisbane (Nos.* 473/4, **MS**476). *T* **137** *and similar square designs. Multicoloured.* W w **14** (*sideways*). P 14.

471	12 c. Type **137**		15	20
	a. Pair. Nos. 471/2		30	40
472	12 c. Queen and Prince Philip		15	20
473	25 c. Running		30	45
	a. Pair. Nos. 473/4		60	90
474	25 c. Boxing		30	45
471/4		*Set of 4*	80	1·25
MS475	123 × 123 mm. Nos. 471/2 and $1 Royal Yacht *Britannia*		1·60	2·50
MS476	123 × 123 mm. Nos. 473/4 and $1 Royal Yacht *Britannia*		1·60	2·50

Nos. 471/2 and 473/4 were each printed in small sheets of 10, including 2 *se-tenant*, stamp-size, labels, the two stamp designs appearing *se-tenant*, both horizontally and vertically.

138 Boy Scouts

(Des McCombie Skinner. Litho Format)

1982 (4 Nov). *75th Anniv of Boy Scout Movement (Nos.* 477, 479, 481, 483) *and Centenary of Boys' Brigade (others). T* **138** *and similar horiz designs. Multicoloured.* W w **14** (*sideways*). P 14.

477	12 c. Type **138**		20	15
478	12 c. Boys' Brigade cadets		20	15
479	25 c. Lord Baden-Powell		35	40
480	25 c. Sir William Smith		35	40
481	35 c. Type **138**		40	50
482	35 c. As No. 478		40	50
483	50 c. As No. 479		60	1·10
484	50 c. As No. 480		60	1·10
477/84		*Set of 8*	2·75	3·75

139 Leatherback Turtle

(Des L. Curtis. Litho Format)

1983 (5 Jan). *Turtles. T* **139** *and similar horiz designs. Multicoloured.* W w **14** (*sideways*). P 14½.

485	18 c. Type **139**		25	25
486	35 c. Loggerhead turtle		45	45
487	45 c. Pacific Ridley turtle		60	60
488	50 c. Green turtle		65	65
485/8		*Set of 4*	1·75	1·75

140 *Oliva vidum, Conus generalis* and *Murex tribulus*

(Des W. Fenton. Litho Questa)

1983 (14 Mar). *Commonwealth Day. Shells. T* **140** *and similar horiz designs. Multicoloured.* W w **14** (*sideways*). P 14.

489	12 c. Type **140**		15	15
490	35 c. Romu, Kurila, Kakadu and money belt		35	40
491	45 c. Shells from "Bride-price" necklaces		50	60
492	50 c. *Trochus niloticus* polished and in its natural state		55	65
489/92		*Set of 4*	1·40	1·60

141 Montgolfier Balloon

(Des A. Theobald. Litho Format)

1983 (30 June). *Bicentenary of Manned Flight. T* **141** *and similar horiz designs. Multicoloured.* W w **14** (*sideways*). P 14.

493	30 c. Type **141**		55	40
494	35 c. R.A.A.F. Lockheed "Hercules"		60	45
495	40 c. Wright brothers' *Flyer III*		70	55
496	45 c. Space shuttle *Columbia*		75	60
497	50 c. Beechcraft "Baron-Solair"		80	65
493/7		*Set of 5*	3·00	2·40

142 Weto Dancers

(Des J.W. Litho Format)

1983 (25 Aug). *Christmas. T* **142** *and similar horiz designs. Multicoloured.* W w **14** (*sideways*). P 14.

498	12 c. Type **142**		15	10
499	15 c. Custom wrestling		20	20
500	18 c. Girl dancers		20	20
501	20 c. Devil dancers		20	20
502	25 c. Bamboo band		30	35
503	35 c. Gilbertese dancers		40	45
504	40 c. Pan pipers		45	55
505	45 c. Girl dancers		50	65
506	50 c. Cross surrounded by flowers		55	70
498/506		*Set of 9*	2·50	3·00
MS507	153 × 112 mm. Nos. 498/506		2·50	3·00

Stamps from No. **MS**507 are without the inscription, "Christmas 1983", shown on Nos. 498/506.

143 Earth Satellite Station	**144** *Calvatia gardneri*

(Des Jennifer Toombs. Litho Format)

1983 (19 Dec). *World Communications Year. T* **143** *and similar horiz designs. Multicoloured.* W w **14** (*sideways*). P 14.

508	12 c. Type **143**		20	15
509	18 c. Ham radio operator		25	20
510	25 c. 1908 2½d. Canoe stamp		35	30
511	$1 1908 6d. Canoe stamp		1·25	1·40
508/11		*Set of 4*	1·90	1·90
MS512	131 × 103 mm. No. 511		1·40	2·25

(Des Gillian Tomblin. Litho Enschedé)

1984 (30 Jan). *Fungi. T* **144** *and similar vert designs. Multicoloured.* W w **14**. P 13½.

513	6 c. Type **144**		10	10
514	18 c. *Marasmiellus inoderma*		20	25
	a. Booklet pane of 6		1·25	
515	35 c. *Pycnoporus sanguineus*		35	45
	a. Booklet pane of 6		2·10	
516	$2 *Filoboletus manipularis*		2·25	2·50
513/16		*Set of 4*	2·50	3·00

Booklet panes Nos. 514a and 515a were from special sheets providing blocks of 6 (3 × 2) with vertical margins at both the left and right of each pane.

145 Cross surrounded by Flowers	**146** *Olivebank*, 1892

(Des J.W. Litho Format)

1984 (16 Apr). *Visit of Pope John Paul II.* W w **14** (*sideways*). P 14.

517	**145** 12 c. multicoloured		20	10
518	50 c. multicoloured		65	80

(Des Studio 53. Litho Questa)

1984 (21 Apr). *250th Anniv of "Lloyd's List" (newspaper). T* **146** *and similar vert designs. Multicoloured.* W w **14**. P 14.

519	12 c. Type **146**		45	10
520	15 c. S.S. *Tinhow*, 1906		50	40
521	18 c. *Oriana* at Point Cruz, Honiara		60	50
522	$1 Point Cruz, Honiara		1·75	2·50
519/22		*Set of 4*	3·00	3·25

(Des Jennifer Toombs. Litho Format)

1984 (18 June). *Universal Postal Union Congress, Hamburg. As No.* **MS**512 *but with changed sheet inscriptions and U.P.U. logo in margin. Multicoloured.* W w **14** (*sideways*). P 14.

MS523	$1 1908 6d. Canoe stamp		1·25	1·40

147 Village Drums   148 Solomon Islands Flag and Torch-bearer

(Des McCombie Skinner Studio. Litho Questa)

1984 (2 July). *20th Anniv of Asia-Pacific Broadcasting Union. T 147 and similar horiz designs. Multicoloured. W w 14 (sideways). P 13½ × 14.*

524	12 c. Type 147	..	15	15
525	45 c. Radio City, Guadalcanal	..	60	60
526	60 c. S.I.B.C. studios, Honiara	..	75	80
527	$1 S.I.B.C. Broadcasting House	..	1·25	1·40
524/7		Set of 4	2·50	2·75

(Des McCombie Skinner Studio. Litho Format)

1984 (4 Aug–22 Sept). *Olympic Games, Los Angeles. T 148 and similar multicoloured designs. W w 14 (sideways on 25 c. to $1). P 14 × 13½ (12 c.) or 13½ × 14 (others).*

528	12 c. Type 148	..	15	20
529	25 c. Lawson Tama Stadium, Honiara (horiz)		30	35
	a. Booklet pane Nos. 529/30, each × 2 (22.9.84)		1·90	
530	50 c. Honiara Community Centre (horiz)		65	70
531	95 c. Alick Wickham inventing crawl stroke, Bronte Baths, New South Wales, 1898 (horiz) (22.9.84)		2·25	3·00
	a. Booklet pane of 1		2·25	
532	$1 Olympic Stadium, Los Angeles (horiz)		1·25	1·40
528/32		Set of 5	4·25	5·00

No. 531 only exists from $3·95 stamp booklets.

149 Little Pied Cormorant   150 The Queen Mother with Princess Margaret at Badminton Horse Trials

(Des I. Loe. Litho Questa)

1984 (21 Sept). *"Ausipex" International Stamp Exhibition, Melbourne. Birds. T 149 and similar vert designs. Multicoloured. W w 14. P 14½.*

533	12 c. Type 149	..	20	15
534	18 c. Spotbill Duck	..	30	30
535	35 c. Rufous Night Heron	..	50	50
536	$1 Eastern Broad-billed Roller ("Dollarbird")		1·25	2·00
533/6		Set of 4	2·00	2·75
MS537	130 × 96 mm. Nos. 533/6	..	2·00	2·75

(Des A. Theobald ($1.50), C. Abbott (others). Litho Questa)

1985 (7 June). *Life and Times of Queen Elizabeth the Queen Mother. T 150 and similar vert designs. Multicoloured. W w 16. P 14½×14.*

538	12 c. With Winston Churchill at Buckingham Palace, VE Day, 1945		10	10
539	25 c. Type 150	..	25	30
540	35 c. At a St. Patrick's Day parade	..	30	35
541	$1 With Prince Henry at his christening (from photo by Lord Snowdon)		90	95
538/41		Set of 4	1·40	1·50
MS542	91 × 73 mm. $1.50, In a gondola, Venice, 1985. Wmk sideways		1·40	1·50

151 Japanese Memorial Shrine, Mount Austen, Guadalcanal

(Des D. Slater. Litho Questa)

1985 (28 June). *"Expo '85" World Fair, Japan. T 151 and similar horiz designs. Multicoloured. W w 14 (sideways). P 14.*

543	12 c. Type 151	..	10	10
544	25 c. Digital telephone exchange equipment		25	30
545	45 c. Fishing vessel *Soltai No. 7*	..	40	45
546	85 c. Coastal village scene	..	75	80
543/6		Set of 4	1·40	1·50

152 Titiana Village   153 Girl Guide Activities

(Des O. Bell. Litho Walsall)

1985 (30 Aug). *Christmas. "Going Home for the Holiday". T 152 and similar horiz designs. Multicoloured. W w 14 (sideways). P 14½.*

547	12 c. Type 152	..	10	10
548	25 c. Sigana, Santa Isabel	..	25	30
549	35 c. Artificial Island and Langa Lagoon		30	35
547/9		Set of 3	60	70

(Des D. Slater. Litho Walsall)

1985 (30 Sept). *75th Anniv of Girl Guide Movement (12, 45 c.) and International Youth Year (others). T 153 and similar vert designs. Multicoloured. W w 16. P 14.*

550	12 c. Type 153	..	40	10
551	15 c. Boys playing and child in wheelchair (Stop Polio)		45	30
552	25 c. Runners and Solomon Island scenes		70	40
553	35 c. Runners and Australian scenes ("Run Round Australia")		85	45
554	45 c. Guide colour party and badges		95	60
550/4		Set of 5	3·00	1·60
MS555	100 × 75 mm. Nos. 552/3	..	55	60

154 Osprey   155 Water-powered Generator. Iriri

(Des Annette Robinson and C. Abbott. Litho Format)

1985 (25 Nov). *Birth Bicentenary of John J. Audubon (ornithologist). Sheet 121 × 107 mm containing T 154 and similar vert design. W w 16. P 14.*

MS556	45 c. black, gold and deep blue; 50 c. (×2) multicoloured		2·50	2·50

Design:—45 c. John J. Audubon.

(Des B. Drake. Litho Walsall)

1986 (24 Jan). *Village Hydro-electric Schemes. Sheet 109 × 135 mm. containing T 155 and similar vert design. Multicoloured. W w 16. P 14.*

MS557	30 c. Type 155; 60 c. Domestic lighting	..	75	80

156 Building Red Cross Centre, Gizo   157 U.S. Memorial Obelisks, Henderson Airfield, Guadalcanal

(Des N. Shewring. Litho Walsall)

1986 (27 Mar). *Operation Raleigh (volunteer project). T 156 and similar diamond-shaped designs. Multicoloured. W w 14. P 14½×14.*

558	18 c. Type 156	..	60	20
559	30 c. Exploring rainforest	..	90	45
560	60 c. Observing Halley's Comet	..	1·50	1·10
561	$1 Sir Walter Raleigh and Zebu	..	2·00	1·60
558/61		Set of 4	4·50	3·00

Details of watermark and perforation for the stamps are given with the designs orientated so that the royal cypher appears in the top left corner.

(Des A. Theobald. Litho Questa)

1986 (21 Apr). *60th Birthday of Queen Elizabeth II. Vert designs as T 230a of Jamaica. Multicoloured. W w 16. P 14½×14.*

562	5 c. Princess Elizabeth and Duke of Edinburgh at Clydebank Town Hall, 1947		10	10
563	18 c. At St. Paul's Cathedral for Queen Mother's 80th birthday service, 1980		15	20
564	22 c. With children, Solomon Islands, 1982		20	25
565	55 c. At Windsor Castle on her 50th birthday, 1976		40	45
566	$2 At Crown Agents Head Office, London, 1983		1·40	1·50
562/6		Set of 5	2·00	2·25

(Des D. Miller. Litho Cambec Press, Melbourne)

1986 (22 May). *"Ameripex '86" International Stamp Exhibition, Chicago. International Peace Year. Sheet 100 × 75 mm containing T 157 and similar horiz design. Multicoloured. P 13½.*

MS567	55 c. Type 157; $1.65 Peace Corps emblem, President Kennedy and Statue of Liberty (25th anniv of Peace Corps)		1·50	1·60

(Des D. Miller. Litho Questa)

1986 (23 July). *Royal Wedding. Square designs as T 231a of Jamaica. Multicoloured. W w 16. P 14.*

568	55 c. Prince Andrew and Miss Sarah Ferguson		40	45
569	60 c. Prince Andrew at helm of Yacht *Bluenose II* off Nova Scotia, 1985	..	45	50

158 *Freedom* (winner 1980)   + 50c Cyclone Relief Fund 1986 (159)

(Des J. Dixon. Litho Leigh-Mardon Ltd, Melbourne)

1986 (22 Aug). *America's Cup Yachting Championship (1987) (1st issue). T 158 and similar vert designs. P 14½.*

570	18 c. multicoloured	..	15	20
	a. Sheet of 50	..	25·00	
571	30 c. multicoloured	..	50	70
572	$1 multicoloured	..	75	80
570/2		Set of 3	1·25	1·50

Nos. 570/2 were issued as a sheet of 50, each horizontal strip of 5 being separated by gutter margins. The sheet contains 20 different designs at 18 c., 10 at 30 c. and 20 at $1. Individual stamps depict yachts, charts, the America's Cup or the emblem of the Royal Perth Yacht Club.
See also No. MS575.

1986 (23 Sept). *Cyclone Relief Fund. Nos. 541 and MS567 surch as T 159 in red.*

573	$1 + 50 c. Queen Mother with Prince Henry at his christening (from photo by Lord Snowdon)		1·10	1·25
MS574	100 × 75 mm. 55 c. + 25 c. Type 157; $1.65 + 75 c. Peace Corps emblem, President Kennedy and Statue of Liberty (25th anniv of Peace Corps)		3·00	3·00

The surcharges on No. MS574 are vertical, in smaller type (length 16½ mm) and do not include "1986".

(Des J. Dixon. Litho Leigh-Mardon Ltd, Melbourne)

1987 (4 Feb). *America's Cup Yachting Championship (2nd issue). Sheet 111 × 75 mm, containing vert design as T 158. Multicoloured. P 14½.*

MS575	$5 Stars and Stripes (1987 winner)	..	3·25	3·50

No. MS575 was also issued printed on gold foil and sold at a premium of $20 over the face value of the stamp.

160 *Dendrophyllia gracilis*   161 *Cassia fistula*

(Des D. Miller. Litho Format)

1987 (11 Feb). *Corals. T 160 and similar horiz designs. Multicoloured. W w 16 (sideways). P 14.*

576	18 c. Type 160	..	20	15
577	45 c. *Dendronephthya sp*	..	60	50
578	60 c. *Clavularia sp*	..	80	80
579	$1.50, *Melithaea squamata*	..	1·60	1·75
576/9		Set of 4	3·00	3·00

(Des Gill Tomblin. Litho Walsall)

1987 (12 May)–88. *Flowers. T 161 and similar vert designs. Multicoloured. W w 16. P 14½×14.*

580	1 c. Type 161	..	10	10
581	5 c. *Allamanda cathartica*	..	15	10
582	10 c. *Catharanthus roseus*	..	15	10
583	18 c. *Mimosa pudica*	..	20	10
584	20 c. *Hibiscus rosa-sinensis*	..	20	15
585	22 c. *Clerodendrum thomsonae*	..	20	15
586	25 c. *Bauhinia variegata*	..	20	20
587	28 c. *Gloriosa rothschildiana*	..	20	20
588	30 c. *Heliconia solomonensis*	..	25	20
589	40 c. *Episcia hybrid*	..	25	20
590	45 c. *Bougainvillea hybrid*	..	30	25
591	50 c. *Alpinia purpurata*	..	30	25
592	55 c. *Plumeria rubra*	..	35	35
593	60 c. *Acacia farnesiana*	..	40	40
594	$1 *Ipomea purpurea*	..	65	50
595	$2 *Dianella ensifolia*	..	1·25	1·40
596	$5 *Passiflora foetida*	..	3·00	3·50
597	$10 *Hemigraphis sp* (1.3.88)	..	6·00	7·00
580/97		Set of 18	13·00	13·50

162 Mangrove Kingfisher on Branch   163 *Dendrobium conanthum*

(Des Josephine Martin. Litho Format)

1987 (15 July). *Mangrove Kingfisher. T 162 and similar vert designs. Multicoloured. W w 14. P 14.*

598	60 c. Type 162.	1·40	1·50
	a. Horiz strip of 4. Nos. 598/601	5·00	
599	60 c. Kingfisher diving	1·40	1·50
600	60 c. Entering water	1·40	1·50
601	60 c. Kingfisher with prey	1·40	1·50
598/601	*Set of 4*	5·00	5·50

Nos. 598/601 were printed together, *se-tenant*, in horizontal strips of 4 throughout the sheet, forming a composite design.

(Des Sue Wickison. Litho Walsall)

1987 (23 Sept). *Christmas. Orchids (1st series). T 163 and similar vert designs. Multicoloured. W w 16. P 13½×13.*

602	18 c. Type 163.	55	10
603	30 c. *Spathoglottis plicata*	85	20
604	55 c. *Dendrobium gouldii*	1·10	50
605	$1.50, *Dendrobium goldfinchii*	2·40	1·75
602/5	*Set of 4*	4·50	2·25

See also Nos. 640/3 and 748/51.

164 Telecommunications Control Room and Satellite   165 Pupa of *Ornithoptera victoriae*

(Des D. Hartley. Litho CPE Australia Ltd, Melbourne)

1987 (16 Nov). *Asia-Pacific Transport and Communications Decade. T 164 and similar horiz designs. Multicoloured. P 13½.*

606	18 c. Type 164.	15	15
607	30 c. De Havilland "Twin Otter" mail plane	20	20
608	60 c. Guadalcanal road improvement project	45	50
609	$2 Beechcraft "Queen Air" and Henderson Control Tower	1·25	1·50
606/9	*Set of 4*	1·90	2·10

(Des R. Lewington. Litho Questa)

1987 (25 Nov). *Butterflies (3rd series). Ornithoptera victoriae (Queen Victoria's Birdwing). T 165 and similar vert designs. Multicoloured. W w 16 (sideways). P 14½×14.*

610	45 c. Type 165.	1·50	1·00
	a. Strip of 4. Nos. 610/13	5·50	
611	45 c. Larva	1·50	1·00
612	45 c. Female butterfly	1·50	1·00
613	45 c. Male butterfly	1·50	1·00
610/13	*Set of 4*	5·50	3·50

Nos. 610/13 were printed together, *se-tenant*, in horizontal and vertical strips of 4 throughout the sheet of 16.

166 Student and National Agriculture Training Institute   167 Building a Fishing Boat

(Des D. Miller. Litho Format)

1988 (12 Feb). *10th Anniv of International Fund for Agricultural Development. T 166 and similar square designs. Multicoloured. W w 16. P 14½.*

614	50 c. Type 166.	30	35
	a. Horiz pair. Nos. 614/15.	60	70
615	50 c. Students working in fields	30	35
616	$1 Transport by lorry	55	60
	a. Horiz pair. Nos. 616/17.	1·10	1·25
617	$1 Canoe transport.	55	60
614/17	*Set of 4*	1·50	1·75

Nos. 614/15 and 616/17 were printed together, *se-tenant*, in horizontal pairs throughout the sheets, each pair forming a composite design.

(Des N. Shewring. Litho CPE Australia Ltd, Melbourne)

1988 (28 Apr). *"Expo '88" World Fair, Brisbane. T 167 and similar horiz designs. Multicoloured. P 13½×14.*

618	22 c. Type 167	15	15
619	80 c. War canoe	40	45
620	$1.50, Traditional village	80	85
618/20	*Set of 3*	1·25	1·25
MS621	130 × 53 mm. Nos. 618/20	1·25	1·40

No. MS621 also exists, as a restricted issue, surcharged $3.50 for "New Zealand 1990" International Stamp Exhibition, Auckland.

168 *Todos los Santos* in Estrella Bay, 1568   169 *Papuan Chief* (container ship)

(Des M. Bradbury and J. Sayer. Litho Walsall)

1988 (6 July). *10th Anniv of Independence. T 168 and similar horiz designs. Multicoloured. W w 14 (sideways). P 13×13½.*

622	22 c. Type 168	35	15
623	55 c. Raising the Union Jack, 1893	65	40
624	80 c. High Court Building	85	60
625	$1 Dancers at traditional celebration	1·00	90
622/5	*Set of 4*	2·50	1·90

(Des E. Nisbet. Litho Walsall)

1988 (30 July). *Bicentenary of Australian Settlement and "Sydpex '88" National Stamp Exhibition, Sydney. T 169 and similar horiz designs. Multicoloured. W w 16 (sideways). P 14.*

626	35 c. Type 169	30	25
627	60 c. *Nimos* (container ship)	45	35
628	70 c. *Malaita* (liner)	55	45
629	$1.30, *Makambo* (freighter)	90	75
626/9	*Set of 4*	2·00	1·60
MS630	140 × 76 mm. Nos. 626/9. W w 14 (sideways)	2·00	1·75

170 Archery   171 *Bulbophyllum dennisii*

(Des Joan Thompson. Litho Walsall)

1988 (5 Aug). *Olympic Games, Seoul. T 170 and similar multicoloured designs. W w 16. P 14½.*

631	22 c. Type 170	30	15
632	55 c. Weightlifting	50	40
633	70 c. Athletics	60	55
634	80 c. Boxing	70	60
631/4	*Set of 4*	1·90	1·50
MS635	100 × 80 mm. $2 Olympic Stadium (horiz). W w 14 (sideways)	1·25	1·25

(Des D. Miller (22, 65 c.), O. Bell and D. Miller (50 c.), E. Nisbet and D. Miller ($2). Litho Questa)

1988 (31 Oct). *300th Anniv of Lloyd's of London. Designs as T 167a of Malawi. W w 16 (sideways on 50, 65 c.). P 14.*

636	22 c. brownish black and brown	30	15
637	50 c. multicoloured	50	30
638	65 c. multicoloured	60	55
639	$2 multicoloured	1·75	1·75
636/9	*Set of 4*	2·75	2·50

Designs: *Vert*—22 c. King George V and Queen Mary laying foundation stone of Leadenhall Street Building, 1925; $2 *Empress of China*, 1911. *Horiz*—50 c. *Forthbank* (container ship); 65 c. Soltel satellite communications station.

(Des Sue Wickison. Litho Walsall)

1989 (20 Jan). *Orchids (2nd series). T 171 and similar vert designs. Multicoloured. W w 14. P 13½ × 13.*

640	22 c. Type 171	35	15
641	35 c. *Calanthe langei*	45	30
642	55 c. *Bulbophyllum blumei*	65	45
643	$2 *Grammatophyllum speciosum*	1·60	1·75
640/3	*Set of 4*	2·75	2·40

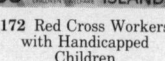

172 Red Cross Workers with Handicapped Children   173 *Phyllidia varicosa*

(Des A. Theobald. Litho Questa)

1989 (16 May). *125th Anniv of International Red Cross. T 172 and similar horiz designs. Multicoloured. W w 16 (sideways). P 14½.*

644	35 c. Type 172	30	35
	a. Horiz pair. Nos. 644/5	60	70
645	35 c. Handicapped Children Centre minibus	30	35
646	$1.50, Blood donor	1·10	1·25
	a. Horiz pair. Nos. 646/7	2·10	2·50
647	$1.50, Balance test	1·10	1·25
644/7	*Set of 4*	2·50	3·00

Nos. 644/5 and 646/7 were each printed together, *se-tenant*, in horizontal pairs throughout the sheets, each pair forming a composite design.

(Des Sue Wickison. Litho Questa)

1989 (30 June). *Nudibranchs (Sea Slugs). T 173 and similar horiz designs. Multicoloured. W w 14 (sideways). P 14×14½.*

648	22 c. Type 173	25	10
649	70 c. *Chromodoris bullocki*	70	60
650	80 c. *Chromodoris leopardus*	75	70
651	$1.50, *Phidiana indica*	1·50	1·60
648/51	*Set of 4*	3·00	2·75

(Des A. Theobald ($4), D. Miller (others). Litho Questa)

1989 (20 July). *20th Anniv of First Manned Landing on Moon. Multicoloured designs as T 51a of Kiribati. W w 16 (sideways on 35, 70 c.). P 14×13½ (22, 80 c.) or 14 (others).*

652	22 c. "Apollo 16" descending by parachute	20	10
653	35 c. Launch of "Apollo 16" (30×30 mm)	35	30
654	70 c. "Apollo 16" emblem (30×30 mm)	70	60
655	80 c. Ultra-violet colour photograph of Earth	75	90
652/5	*Set of 4*	1·75	1·50
MS656	100×83 mm. $4 Moon's surface seen from Space. Wmk inverted. P 14×13½	2·50	2·75

174 Five Stones Catch   175 Fishermen and Butterfly

(Des D. Miller ($3), R. Stewart (others). Litho B.D.T. ($3) or Walsall (others))

1989 (19 Nov). *"World Stamp Expo '89", International Stamp Exhibition, Washington. Children's Games. T 174 and similar multicoloured designs. W w 16 (sideways on 67, 73 c.). P 14.*

657	5 c. Type 174	10	10
658	67 c. Blowing soap bubbles (horiz)	60	50
659	73 c. Coconut shell game (horiz)	60	50
660	$1 Seed wind sound	95	90
657/60	*Set of 4*	2·00	1·75
MS661	72×72 mm. $3 Softball. W w 14	2·40	2·75

(Des N. Kohia and C. Vendi, adapted G. Vasarhelyi. Litho Questa)

1989 (30 Nov). *Christmas. T 175 and similar horiz designs. Multicoloured. W w 16 (sideways). P 14.*

662	18 c. Type 175	20	10
663	25 c. The Nativity	25	20
664	45 c. Hospital ward at Christmas	45	30
665	$1.50, Village tug-of-war	1·40	1·40
662/5	*Set of 4*	2·10	1·75

176 Man wearing Headband, Necklace and Sash   177 Spindle Cowrie

(Des Sue Wickison. Litho Questa)

1990 (14 Mar). *Personal Ornaments. T 176 and similar vert designs. Multicoloured. W w 14. P 14.*

666	5 c. Type 176	10	15
667	12 c. Pendant	15	15
668	18 c. Man wearing medallion, nose ring and earrings	15	15
669	$2 Forehead ornament	1·60	2·00
666/9	*Set of 4*	1·75	2·25

First day covers of Nos. 666/9 were postmarked 26 February 1990, which was the originally intended date of issue, but the stamps were not placed on sale until 14 March.

(Des Lynn Chadwick. Litho Questa)

1990 (23 July). *Cowrie Shells. T 177 and similar horiz designs. Multicoloured. W w 14 (sideways). P 14.*

670	4 c. Type 177	15	10
671	20 c. Map Cowrie	20	20
672	35 c. Sieve Cowrie	35	25
673	50 c. Egg Cowrie	50	50
674	$1 Prince Cowrie	90	1·10
670/4	*Set of 5*	1·90	1·90

(Des D. Miller. Litho Questa)

1990 (4 Aug). *90th Birthday of Queen Elizabeth the Queen Mother. Vert designs as T 107 (25 c.) or 108 ($5) of Kenya. P 14×15 (25 c.) or 14½ ($5).*

675	25 c. multicoloured	25	25
676	$5 black and deep claret	3·00	3·00

Designs:—25 c. Queen Mother, 1987; $5 King George VI and Queen Elizabeth inspecting bomb damage to Buckingham Palace, 1940.

178 Postman with Mail Van

(Des N. Shewring. Litho Questa)

1990 (15 Oct). *150th Anniv of the Penny Black. T* **178** *and similar horiz designs. Multicoloured. W* w **14** *(sideways). P* 14.
677	35 c. Type **178**	..	..	..	30	20
678	45 c. General Post Office	..	..		40	35
679	50 c. 1907 ¹/₂d. stamp	..	..		40	40
680	55 c. Child collecting stamps		..		45	50
681	60 c. Penny Black and Solomon Islands 1913					
	1d. stamp	..	..		45	55
677/81		..	..	*Set of 5*	1·75	1·75

179 Purple Swamphen   **180** *Cylas formicarius*
   (weevil)

(Des N. Arlott. Litho Questa)

1990 (5 Dec). *"Birdpex '90" Stamp Exhibition, Christchurch, New Zealand. T* **179** *and similar horiz designs showing birds. Multicoloured. W* w **14** *(sideways). P* 14.
682	10 c. Type **179**	..	..		15	10
683	25 c. Mackinlay's Cuckoo Dove ("Rufous					
	Brown Pheasant Dove")		..		20	15
684	30 c. Superb Fruit Dove		..		25	20
685	45 c. Cardinal Honeyeater		..		35	30
686	$2 Finsch's Pygmy Parrot		..		1·25	1·50
682/6			..	*Set of 5*	2·00	2·00

(Des Josephine Martin. Litho B.D.T.)

1991 (16 Jan). *Crop Pests. T* **180** *and similar vert designs. Multicoloured. W* w **14**. *P* 14.
687	7 c. Type **180**		..		15	10
688	25 c. *Dacus cucurbitae* (fruit-fly)		..		25	15
689	40 c. *Papuana uninodis* (beetle)		..		35	25
690	90 c. *Pantorhytes biplagiastus* (weevil)				70	70
691	$1.50, *Scapanes australis* (beetle)				1·10	1·25
687/91		..	..	*Set of 5*	2·25	2·25

(Des D. Miller. Litho Questa)

1991 (17 June). *65th Birthday of Queen Elizabeth II and 70th Birthday of Prince Philip. Vert designs as T* **58** *of Kiribati. Multicoloured. W* w **16** *(sideways). P* 14¹/₂×14.
692	90 c. Prince Philip in evening dress		..		70	80
	a. Horiz pair. Nos. 692/3 separated by					
	label	..	..		2·10	2·40
693	$2 Queen Elizabeth II		..		1·40	1·60

Nos. 692/3 were printed in a similar sheet format to Nos. 366/7 of Kiribati.

181 Child drinking from   **182** Volley Ball
   Coconut

(Des G. Vasarhelyi. Litho Walsall)

1991 (24 June). *Health Campaign. T* **181** *and similar horiz designs. Multicoloured. W* w **14** *(sideways). P* 14.
694	5 c. Type **181**	..	..		10	10
695	75 c. Mother feeding child	..			45	55
696	80 c. Breast feeding		..		50	60
697	90 c. Local produce		..		60	70
694/7	..	..	..	*Set of 4*	1·50	1·75

(Des N. Shewring. Litho Questa)

1991 (8 Aug). *9th South Pacific Games. T* **182** *and similar vert designs. Multicoloured. W* w **16**. *P* 14.
698	25 c. Type **182**	..	..		25	10
699	40 c. Judo	..	..		35	30
700	65 c. Squash	..	..		60	65
701	90 c. Bowling	..	..		75	90
698/701		..	..	*Set of 4*	1·75	1·75
MS702	92×112 mm. $2 Games emblem. Wmk					
	sideways	..	..		1·60	1·75

183 Preparing Food for   **184** Yellowfin Tuna
   Christmas

(Des G. Vasarhelyi. Litho B.D.T.)

1991 (28 Oct). *Christmas. T* **183** *and similar horiz designs. Multicoloured. W* w **14** *(sideways). P* 14.
703	10 c. Type **183**	..	..		15	10
704	25 c. Christmas Day church service		..		20	15
705	65 c. Christmas Day feast		..		50	40
706	$2 Cricket match	..	..		1·25	1·50
703/6		..	..	*Set of 4*	1·90	1·90
MS707	138×110 mm. Nos. 703/6		..		2·00	2·25

(Des O. Bell. Litho Leigh-Mardon Ltd, Melbourne)

1991 (16 Nov). *"Phila Nippon '91" International Stamp Exhibition, Tokyo. Tuna Fishing. T* **184** *and similar multicoloured designs. W* w **16** *(sideways). P* 14.
708	5 c. Type **184**	..	..		10	10
709	30 c. Pole and line tuna fishing boat		..		20	20
710	80 c. Pole and line fishing		..		60	70
711	$2 Processing "arabushi" (smoked tuna)				1·10	1·25
708/11		..	..	*Set of 4*	1·75	2·00
MS712	101×80 mm. 80 c. Plate of "tori nanban"					
	(25×42 *mm*); 80 c. Bowl of "aka miso"					
	(25×42 *mm*). *P* 14¹/₂	..	..		95	1·10

(Des D. Miller. Litho Questa ($5), Leigh-Mardon Ltd, Melbourne (others))

1992 (6 Feb). *40th Anniv of Queen Elizabeth II's Accession. Horiz designs as T* **113** *of Kenya. Multicoloured. W* w **14** *(sideways)* (20 c., 40 c., $5) *or* w **16** (5 c., 60 c.). *P* 14.
713	5 c. Aerial view of Honiara		..		10	10
714	20 c. Sunset across lagoon		..		15	15
715	40 c. Honiara harbour		..		30	30
716	60 c. Three portraits of Queen Elizabeth		..		50	50
717	$5 Queen Elizabeth II	..	..		3·00	3·25
713/17		..	..	*Set of 5*	3·50	3·75

185 Mendana's Fleet in   **186** Sgt-major
   Thousand Ships Bay   Jacob Vouza

(Des J. Batchelor. Litho Leigh-Mardon Ltd, Melbourne)

1992 (24 Apr). *"Granada '92" International Stamp Exhibition, Spain. Mendana's Discovery of Solomon Islands. T* **185** *and similar horiz designs. W* w **14** *(sideways). P* 15×14¹/₂.
718	10 c. Type **185**	..	..		15	10
719	65 c. Map of voyage		..		45	45
720	80 c. Alvaro Mendana de Niera		..		70	70
721	$1 Settlement at Graciosa Bay		..		90	90
722	$5 Mendana's fleet at sea		..		3·00	3·25
718/22		..	..	*Set of 5*	4·75	4·75

(Des T. Rider, adapted G. Vasarhelyi. Litho Enschedé)

1992 (3 May). *Birth Centenary of Sgt-major Jacob Vouza (war hero). T* **186** *and similar vert designs. Multicoloured. W* w **14**. *P* 14×13¹/₂.
723	25 c. Type **186**	..	..		15	10
	a. Booklet pane. Nos. 723 and 725, each					
	× 2, with margins all round	..			1·25	
724	70 c. Vouza in U.S. Marine corps battle dress				50	50
	a. Booklet pane. Nos. 724 and 726, each					
	× 2, with margins all round	..			3·25	
725	90 c. Vouza in U.S. Marine corps uniform				60	60
726	$2 Statue of Vouza	..	..		1·25	1·40
723/6		..	..	*Set of 4*	2·25	2·40
MS727	113×76 mm. $4 Sgt-major Vouza in					
	ceremonial uniform	..	..		2·50	2·75

187 Solomon Airlines   **188** Japanese Troops
   Domestic Routes   landing at Esperance

(Des D. Miller. Litho Enschedé)

1992 (22 May). *500th Anniv of Discovery of America by Columbus and "World Columbian Stamp Expo '92" Exhibition, Chicago. T* **187** *and similar vert designs. Multicoloured. W* w **14**. *P* 14×13¹/₂.
728	25 c. Type **187**	..	..		15	10
729	80 c. Solomon Airlines Boeing 737-400					
	Guadalcanal		..		55	55
730	$1.50, Solomon Airlines international					
	routes	..	..		95	95
731	$5 Columbus and *Santa Maria*		..		3·00	3·25
728/31		..	..	*Set of 4*	4·25	4·50
MS732	120×94 mm. Nos. 728/31		..		4·50	4·75

(Des J. Batchelor. Litho Questa)

1992 (7 Aug). *50th Anniv of Battle of Guadalcanal. T* **188** *and similar horiz designs. Multicoloured. P* 14.
733	30 c. Type **188**	..	..		20	20
	a. Sheetlet. Nos. 733/7		..		90	
734	30 c. American troops in landing-craft				20	20
735	30 c. Australian cruiser		..		20	20
736	30 c. U.S. Navy post office		..		20	20
737	30 c. R.N.Z.A.F Catalina flying boat		..		20	20
738	80 c. U.S. Marine Corps Wildcat fighters		..		55	55
	a. Sheetlet. Nos. 738/47		..		5·00	
739	80 c. Henderson Field		..		55	55
740	80 c. U.S.S. *Quincy* (heavy cruiser)		..		55	55
741	80 c. H.M.A.S. *Canberra* (heavy cruiser)		..		55	55
742	80 c. U.S. Marine Corps landing craft				55	55
743	80 c. *Ryujo* (Japanese aircraft carrier)		..		55	55
744	80 c. Japanese Zeke fighters		..		55	55
745	80 c. Japanese bombers		..		55	55
746	80 c. Japanese destroyer		..		55	55
747	80 c. *Chockai* (Japanese heavy cruiser)		..		55	55
733/47		..	..	*Set of 15*	5·50	5·50

Nos. 733/7 and 738/47 were each printed together, *se-tenant*, in sheetlets with the 30 c. designs as a horizontal strip of 5 below a label showing Henderson Field and the 80 c. designs in two horizontal strips of 5 separated by a gutter showing night naval action off Savo Island.

It was originally intended that the 30 c. sheetlet should also contain ten stamps, but the top row of five was removed before the sheetlets were issued.

189 *Dendrobium* hybrid   **190** Stalk-eyed Ghost Crab

(Des Annette Robinson. Litho Leigh-Mardon Ltd, Melbourne)

1992 (14 Dec). *Orchids (3rd series). T* **189** *and similar horiz designs. Multicoloured. W* w **14** *(sideways). P* 14¹/₂.
748	15 c. Type **189**	..	..		15	10
749	70 c. *Vanda* "Amy Laycock"		..		55	55
750	95 c. *Dendrobium mirbelianum*		..		65	65
751	$2.50, *Dendrobium macrophyllum*		..		1·75	1·90
748/51		..	..	*Set of 4*	2·75	2·75

(Des G. Drummond. Litho Cartor)

1993 (15 Jan). *Crabs. T* **190** *and similar horiz designs. Multicoloured. W* w **14** *(sideways). P* 13.
752	5 c. Type **190**	..	..		10	10
753	10 c. Red-spotted Crab		..		10	10
754	25 c. Flat Crab		..		10	10
755	30 c. Land Hermit Crab		..		10	10
756	40 c. Grapsid Crab		..		15	20
757	45 c. Red and White Painted Crab		..		20	25
758	55 c. Swift-footed Crab		..		25	30
759	60 c. Spanner Crab		..		25	30
760	70 c. Red Hermit Crab		..		30	35
761	80 c. Red-eyed Crab		..		35	40
762	90 c. Rathbun Red Crab		..		35	40
763	$1 Coconut Crab		..		40	45
764	$1.10, Red-spotted White Crab		..		50	55
765	$4 Ghost Crab	..	..		1·75	1·90
766	$10 Mangrove Fiddler Crab		..		4·25	4·50
752/66		..	..	*Set of 15*	8·25	9·00

POSTAGE DUE STAMPS

D **1**

(Typo B.W.)

1940 (1 Sept). *Wmk Mult Script CA. P* 12.
D1	D **1**	1d. emerald-green		..	3·75	6·50
D2		2d. scarlet	..	..	4·25	6·50
D3		3d. brown	..	..	4·50	10·00
D4		4d. blue	..	..	7·00	11·00
D5		5d. grey-green	..	..	8·00	14·00
D6		6d. purple	..	..	8·50	15·00
D7		1s. violet	..	..	12·00	26·00
D8		1s. 6d. turquoise-green	..		22·00	45·00
D1/8			..	*Set of 8*	65·00	£120
D1/8 Perf "Specimen"			..	*Set of 8*	£150	

Somaliland Protectorate

Egyptian post offices were opened in Somaliland during 1876 and the stamps of Egypt were used there until the garrisons were withdrawn in 1884.

Cancellations for these offices have been identified as follows (for illustrations of postmark types see after EGYPT):

BARBARA (Berbera). Open 1876? to 1884. Circular datestamp

ZEILA Open 1876 to 1884. Circular datestamps, sometimes inscr ZEJLA. One example with seal type cancellation is also known.

Stamps of India were used at the two post offices from 1 January 1887 until 1903 usually cancelled with circular datestamps or the "B" obliterator used by all offices controlled from Bombay.

The Protectorate Post Office was established on 1 June 1903, when control of British Somaliland was transferred from the Indian Government to the British Foreign Office.

PRICES FOR STAMPS ON COVER TO 1945

Nos. 1/11	from × 25
Nos. 12/13	
Nos. 18/22	from × 12
Nos. 23/4	—
Nos. 25/30	from × 30
Nos. 32/59	from × 12
Nos. 60/92	from × 6
Nos. 93/104	from × 3
Nos. 105/16	from × 4
Nos. O1/13	from × 6
Nos. O14/15	—

BRITISH SOMALILAND

(1) 2 3

SETTINGS OF TYPE 1

In all printings the ½, 1, 2, 2½, 3, 4, 8, 12 a. and 1 r. values were overprinted from a setting of 240 (2 panes 12 × 10, one above the other), covering the entire sheet at one operation.

The 6 a., which was in sheets of 320 (4 panes, each 8 × 10), had a modified setting of 160, applied twice to each sheet.

The high values were overprinted in sheets of 96 (8 panes, each 4 × 3).

The settings for the low value stamps contained two slightly different styles of overprint, identified by the position of "B" of "BRITISH". Type A shows this letter over the "M" of "SOMALI-LAND" and Type B over the "OM".

For the first printing with the overprint at the top of the design the 240 position setting showed all the stamps in the upper pane and 63 in the lower as Type A, with the remaining 57 as Type B. When the setting was used for the printing with overprint at foot it was amended slightly so that one of the Type A examples in the upper pane became a Type B.

The 6 a. value with overprint at top shows 250 examples of Type A and 70 as Type B in each sheet. This proportion altered in the printing with overprint at foot to 256 as Type A and 64 as Type B.

OVERPRINT VARIETIES

Missing second "I" in "BRITISH"—Occurs on the stamps with overprint at top from R.2/6 of the upper pane and R.5/1 of the lower, although it is believed that the example on the 2½ a. (No. 4a) only occurs from the second position. On the later printing with overprint at foot a similar error can be found on R.7/12 of the upper pane. Some examples of both these errors show traces of the letter remaining, but the prices quoted are for stamps with it completely omitted.

Figure "1" for first "I" in "BRITISH"—Occurs on R.6/4 of the upper pane for all printings of the 240 impression setting. In addition it has been reported from R.7/12 of the Queen Victoria 2½ a., 12 a. and 1 r. with overprint at foot. Both versions of the 6 a. show the variety on R.6/4 of the upper left and upper right panes.

Curved overprint—Occurs on R.3/4 of the top right-hand pane of the high values.

"SUMALILAND"—Occurs on R.2/9 of the upper pane for all low values with the overprint at foot, except the 6 a. A similar variety occurs on the high values from the same series on R.1/3 of the top left pane.

"SOMAL.LAND"—Occurs on R.7/5 of the lower pane from the 240 impression setting with the overprint at foot. In addition the Edwardian values of this series also have an example on R.6/7. The 6 a. has examples of the flaw on R.6/9 and R.7/5 of both lower right and left panes. A similar variety occurs on the high values from the same series at R.3/4 of the third pane in the left-hand column.

1903 (1 June). Nos. 80, 94, 96, 98, 100, 106/9, 114/16 and 118 of India (Queen Victoria) optd with T 1, at top of stamp, in Calcutta. Wmk Elephant Head (6 a.) or Star (others).

1	½ a. yellow-green	..	..	1·50	2·00
	a. "BRIT SH"	..	..	£130	
2	1 a. carmine	..	..	1·50	1·75
	a. "BRIT SH"	..	..	£150	£225
	b. "BR1TISH"	..	..	£110	
3	2 a. pale violet	..	..	1·00	50
	a. "BRIT SH"	..	..	£250	
	b. "BR1TISH"	..	..	£200	
	c. Opt double	..	..	£600	

4	2½ a. ultramarine	..	..	2·00	1·75
	a. "BR1TISH"	..	..	£325	
	b. "BR1TISH"	..	..	£225	
5	3 a. brown-orange	..	..	1·50	1·75
	a. "BRIT SH"	..	..	£350	
	b. "BR1TISH"	..	..	£250	
6	4 a. slate-green	..	..	1·75	2·75
	a. "BR1TISH"	..	..	£250	
7	6 a. olive-bistre	..	..	3·75	4·50
	a. "BR1TISH"	..	..	£180	
8	8 a. dull mauve	..	..	1·50	5·00
	a. "BR1TISH"	..	..	£250	
9	12 a. purple/red	..	..	1·75	7·00
	a. "BR1TISH"	..	..	£250	
10	1 r. green and aniline carmine	..	..	3·25	10·00
	a. "BR1TISH"	..	..	£275	
11	2 r. carmine and yellow-brown	..	..	23·00	35·00
	a. Curved opt	..	..	£140	
12	3 r. brown and green	..	..	17·00	38·00
	a. Curved opt	..	..	£150	
13	5 r. ultramarine and violet	..	..	20·00	48·00
	a. Curved opt	..	..	£160	
1/13			Set of 13	70·00	£140

1903 (1 Sept–2 Nov). Stamps of India optd with T 1, at bottom of stamp, in Calcutta. (a) On Nos. 80, 100, 106/9 and 118 (Queen Victoria).

18	2½ a. ultramarine (2.11)	..	..	1·25	4·25
	a. "BR1TISH"	..	..	£140	
	b. "SUMALILAND"	..	..	£180	
	c. "SOMAL.LAND"	..	..	£180	
19	6 a. olive-bistre (2.11)	..	..	2·25	4·25
	a. "BR1TISH"	..	..	£160	
	b. "SOMAL.LAND"	..	..	£100	
20	12 a. purple/red (2.11)	..	..	3·50	12·00
	a. "BR1TISH"	..	..	£160	
	b. "SUMALILAND"	..	..	£250	
	c. "SOMAL.LAND"	..	..	£250	
21	1 r. green and aniline carmine (2.11)	..	..	2·00	10·00
	a. "BR1TISH"	..	..	£180	
	b. "SUMALILAND"	..	..	£300	
	c. "SOMAL.LAND"	..	..	£300	
22	2 r. carmine and yellow-brown (2.11)	..	..	50·00	70·00
	a. Curved opt	..	..	£275	
	b. "SUMALILAND"	..	..	£275	
	c. "SOMAL.LAND"	..	..	£275	
23	3 r. brown and green (2.11)	..	..	50·00	75·00
	a. Opt double, both inverted with one albino	..	..	£475	
	b. Curved opt	..	..	£275	
	c. "SUMALILAND"	..	..	£275	
	d. "SOMAL.LAND"	..	..	£275	
24	5 r. ultramarine and violet (2.11)	..	..	40·00	60·00
	a. Curved opt	..	..	£225	
	b. "SUMALILAND"	..	..	£225	
	c. "SOMAL.LAND"	..	..	£225	

(b) On Nos. 122/4, 127/8 and 133 (King Edward VII)

25	½ a. green	..	..	85	55
	a. "BRIT SH"	..	..	£275	
	b. "BR1TISH"	..	..	60·00	
	c. "SUMALILAND"	..	..	60·00	
	d. "SOMAL.LAND"	..	..	20·00	
26	1 a. carmine (8.10)	..	..	60	30
	a. "BRIT SH"	..	..	£180	
	b. "BR1TISH"	..	..	65·00	65·00
	c. "SUMALILAND"	..	..	65·00	
	d. "SOMAL.LAND"	..	..	22·00	22·00
27	2 a. violet (2.11)	..	..	1·00	2·50
	a. "BRIT SH"	..	..	£750	
	b. "BR1TISH"	..	..	£140	
	c. "SUMALILAND"	..	..	£140	
	d. "SOMAL.LAND"	..	..	38·00	
28	3 a. orange-brown (2.11)	..	..	1·00	2·50
	a. "BRITISH"	..	..	£140	
	b. "SUMALILAND"	..	..	£140	
	c. "SOMAL.LAND"	..	..	38·00	
29	4 a. olive (2.11)	..	..	1·00	4·00
	a. "BR1TISH"	..	..	£150	
	b. "SUMALILAND"	..	..	£150	
	c. "SOMAL.LAND"	..	..	45·00	
30	8 a. purple (2.11)	..	..	1·25	2·25
	a. "BR1TISH"	..	..	£170	
	b. "SUMALILAND"	..	..	£170	
	c. "SOMAL.LAND"	..	..	55·00	
18/30	..	..	Set of 13	£140	£225

(Typo D.L.R.)

1904 (15 Feb–3 Sept). (a) Wmk Crown CA. P 14.

32	2	½ a. dull green and green	..	30	2·50
33		1 a. grey-black and red (3.9)	..	2·00	1·75
34		2 a. dull and bright purple (3.9)	..	1·50	1·00
35		2½ a. bright blue (3.9)	..	1·75	3·00
36		3 a. chocolate and grey-green (3.9)	..	1·00	2·25
37		4 a. green and black (3.9)	..	1·50	2·75
38		6 a. green and violet (3.9)	..	3·00	8·50
39		8 a. grey-black and pale blue (3.9)	..	2·75	5·50
40		12 a. grey-black and orange-buff (3.9)	..	5·50	11·00

(b) Wmk Crown CC. P 14

41	3	1 r. green (3.9)	..	12·00	29·00
42		2 r. dull and bright purple (3.9)	..	28·00	55·00
43		3 r. green and black (3.9)	..	28·00	60·00
44		5 r. grey-black and red (3.9)	..	30·00	60·00
32/44			Set of 13	£100	£200
32/44	Optd "Specimen"		Set of 13	£180	

1905 (July)–11. Wmk Mult Crown CA. Ordinary paper. P 14.

45	2	½ a. dull green and green	..	60	3·75
46		1 a. grey-black and red (10.7.05)	..	3·50	1·60
		a. Chalk-surfaced paper (1906)	..	4·50	1·40
47		2 a. dull and bright purple	..	5·00	7·50
		a. Chalk-surfaced paper (1909)	..	4·00	8·00
48		2½ a. bright blue	..	3·00	10·00
49		3 a. chocolate and grey-green	..	1·50	7·50
		a. Chalk-surfaced paper (1911)	..	4·50	8·50
50		4 a. green and black	..	2·75	10·00
		a. Chalk-surfaced paper (1911)	..	5·50	12·00
51		6 a. green and violet	..	2·25	14·00
		a. Chalk-surfaced paper (1911)	..	6·50	15·00
52		8 a. grey-black and pale blue	..	2·75	6·50
		a. Chalk-surfaced paper. Black and blue (27.1.11)	..	40·00	70·00

| 53 | 2 | 12 a. grey-black and orange-buff | .. | 2·75 | 10·00 |
| | | a. Chalk-surfaced paper. Black and orange-brown (9.11.11) | .. | 16·00 | 50·00 |

1909 (30 Apr–May). Wmk Mult Crown CA. P 14.
58	2	½ a. bluish green (May)	..	9·00	13·00
59		1 a. red (Optd S. £25)	..	2·50	75
45/59			Set of 11	30·00	75·00

4 5

(Typo D.L.R.)

1912 (Nov)–19. Wmk Mult Crown CA. Chalk-surfaced paper (2 a. and 3 a. to 5 r.). P 14.

60	4	½ a. green (11.13)	..	30	4·00
61		1 a. red	..	90	50
		a. Scarlet (1917)	..	3·00	1·25
62		2 a. dull and bright purple (12.13)	..	3·50	8·00
		a. Dull purple and violet-purple (4.19)	..	11·00	18·00
63		2½ a. bright blue (10.13)	..	80	5·00
64		3 a. chocolate and grey-green (10.13)	..	80	3·75
65		4 a. green and black (12.12)	..	80	5·50
66		6 a. green and violet (4.13)	..	1·00	3·25
67		8 a. grey-black and pale blue (10.13)	..	1·00	3·25
68		12 a. grey-black and orange-buff (10.13)	..	1·50	14·00
69	5	1 r. green	..	5·50	8·50
70		2 r. dull purple and purple (4.19)	..	18·00	48·00
71		3 r. green and black (4.19)	..	48·00	85·00
72		5 r. black and scarlet (4.19)	..	48·00	£110
60/72			Set of 13	£110	£275
60/72	Optd "Specimen"		Set of 13	£150	

1921. Wmk Mult Script CA. Chalk-surfaced paper (2 a. and 3 a. to 5 r.). P 14.

73	4	½ a. blue-green	..	1·00	4·00
74		1 a. carmine-red	..	1·25	30
75		2 a. dull and bright purple	..	1·50	1·00
76		2½ a. bright blue	..	75	3·50
77		3 a. chocolate and green	..	2·50	7·00
78		4 a. green and black	..	2·50	4·00
79		6 a. green and violet	..	1·50	11·00
80		8 a. grey-black and pale blue	..	1·75	5·00
81		12 a. grey-black and orange-buff	..	6·50	15·00
82	5	1 r. dull green	..	6·00	30·00
83		2 r. dull purple and purple	..	15·00	32·00
84		3 r. dull green and black	..	26·00	85·00
85		5 r. black and scarlet	..	48·00	£120
73/85			Set of 13	£100	£275
73/85	Optd "Specimen"		Set of 13	£150	

1935 (6 May). Silver Jubilee. As Nos. 114/17 of Jamaica, but ptd by Waterlow. P 11×12.

86		1 a. deep blue and scarlet	..	1·50	1·50
87		2 a. ultramarine and grey	..	1·50	1·50
		j. Kite and vertical log	..	42·00	
88		3 a. brown and deep blue	..	2·00	4·00
		j. Kite and vertical log	..	70·00	
		k. Kite and horizontal log	..	60·00	
89		1 r. slate and purple	..	5·00	7·50
		j. Kite and vertical log	..	95·00	
		k. Kite and horizontal log	..	85·00	
86/9			Set of 4	9·00	13·00
86/9	Perf "Specimen"		Set of 4	75·00	

For illustrations of plate varieties see Omnibus section following Zimbabwe.

1937 (13 May). Coronation. As Nos. 118/20 of Jamaica.

90		1 a. scarlet	..	15	10
91		2 a. grey-black	..	45	55
92		3 a. bright blue	..	60	55
90/2			Set of 3	1·10	1·10
90/2	Perf "Specimen"		Set of 3	55·00	

6 Berbera Blackhead Sheep   7 Lesser Kudu

8 Somaliland Protectorate

(Des H. W. Claxton. Recess Waterlow)

1938 (10 May). Portrait to left. Wmk Mult Script CA. P 12½.

93	6	½ a. green	..	15	1·60
94		1 a. scarlet	..	15	10
95		2 a. maroon	..	15	15
96		3 a. bright blue	..	4·00	4·00
97	7	4 a. sepia	..	1·50	2·25
98		6 a. violet	..	2·75	6·50
99		8 a. grey	..	75	5·50
100		12 a. red-orange	..	75	7·00

101	**8**	1 r. green	..	..	..	7·50	22·00
102		2 r. purple	..		..	8·50	22·00
103		3 r. bright blue	..			11·00	17·00
104		5 r. black	..		..	13·00	17·00
		a. Imperf between (horiz pair)				£7500	
93/104			..	Set of 12		45·00	95·00
93/104	Perf "Specimen"		..	Set of 12		£130	

Following the Italian Occupation during 1940–41 the stamps of ADEN were used at Berbera from 1 July 1941 until 26 April 1942.

5 Cents (10)   **1 Shilling** (11)

9 Berbera Blackhead Sheep

(Recess Waterlow)

1942 (27 Apr). *As T 6/8 but with full-face portrait of King George VI, as in T 9. Wmk Mult Script CA. P 12½.*

105	**9**	½ a. green				10	10
106		1 a. scarlet	..	..		10	10
107		2 a. maroon		..		40	10
108		3 a. bright blue	..			60	10
109	**7**	4 a. sepia		..		60	10
110		6 a. violet			..	90	10
111		8 a. grey	..			55	10
112		12 a. red-orange	..			1·50	10
113	**8**	1 r. green				45	30
114		2 r. purple			..	1·00	2·00
115		3 r. bright blue	..			1·10	6·50
116		5 r. black	..			3·25	4·00
105/16				Set of 12		9·50	12·00
105/16	Perf "Specimen"			Set of 12		£140	

1946 (15 Oct). *Victory. As Nos. 141/2 of Jamaica. P 13½×14.*

117		1 a. carmine	..			10	10
		a. Perf 13½	..			4·75	30·00
118		3 a. blue		..		10	10
117/18	Perf "Specimen"			Set of 2		45·00	

1949 (28 Jan). *Royal Silver Wedding. As Nos. 143/4 of Jamaica.*

119		1 a. scarlet	..			10	10
120		5 r. black	..	..		3·25	3·25

1949 (10 Oct). *75th Anniv of U.P.U. As Nos. 145/8 of Jamaica. Surch with face values in annas.*

121		1 a. on 10 c. carmine	..			15	10
122		3 a. on 30 c. deep blue (R.)				30	30
123		6 a. on 50 c. purple	..			30	30
124		12 a. on 1s. red-orange	..			45	30
121/4				Set of 4		1·10	90

1951 (2 Apr). *1942 issue surch as T 10/11.*

125		5 c. on ½ a. green				10	10
126		10 c. on 2 a. maroon				10	10
127		15 c. on 3 a. bright blue				30	10
128		20 c. on 4 a. sepia				40	10
129		30 c. on 6 a. violet				60	10
130		50 c. on 8 a. grey				55	10
131		70 c. on 12 a. red-orange				90	1·50
132		1 s. on 1 r. green				50	10
133		2 s. on 2 r. purple				1·00	3·50
134		2 s. on 3 r. bright blue				1·25	2·50
135		5 s. on 5 r. black (R.)	..			2·25	4·00
125/35				Set of 11		7·00	11·00

At least one cover is known postmarked 1 April, in error, at Burao.

1953 (2 June). *Coronation. As No. 153 of Jamaica.*

136		15 c. black and green	..			15	15

12 Camel and Gurgi   13 Askari

(Recess B.W.)

1953 (15 Sept)–58. *T 12/13 and similar horiz designs. Wmk Mult Script CA. P 12½.*

137	**12**	5 c. slate-black				10	30
138	**13**	10 c. red-orange				1·40	30
		a. Salmon (20.3.58)				3·50	90
139	**12**	15 c. blue-green	..			50	30
140		20 c. scarlet	..			50	30
141	**13**	30 c. reddish brown	..			1·75	90
142	—	35 c. blue	..			1·25	80
143	—	50 c. brown and rose-carmine	..			1·50	35
144	—	1 s. light blue	..			50	20
145	—	1 s. 30, ultramarine and black (1.9.58)				5·50	3·00
146	—	2 s. brown and bluish violet				11·00	2·00
147	—	5 s. red-brown and emerald				11·00	5·50
148	—	10 s. brown and reddish violet				6·00	11·00
137/48				Set of 12		35·00	22·00

Designs:—35 c., 2 s. Somali Stock Dove; 50 c., 5 s. Martial Eagle; 1 s. Berbera Blackhead Sheep; 1 s. 30, Sheikh Isaaq's Tomb; 10 s. Taleh Fort.

OPENING OF THE LEGISLATIVE COUNCIL 1957 (19)	LEGISLATIVE COUNCIL UNOFFICIAL MAJORITY, 1960 (20)

1957 (21 May). *Opening of Legislative Council. Nos. 140 and 144 optd with T 19.*

149		20 c. scarlet	..			10	10
150		1 s. light blue	..			20	10

1960 (5 Apr). *Legislative Council's Unofficial Majority. Nos. 140 and 145 optd as T 20.*

151		20 c. scarlet	..			10	10
152		1 s. 30, ultramarine and black	..			20	10

OFFICIAL STAMPS

SERVICE

BRITISH SOMALILAND (O 1)

BRITISH SOMALILAND (O 2)

O.H.M.S. (O 3)

SETTING OF TYPE O 1

The 240 impression setting used for the Official stamps differs considerably from that on the contemporary postage issue with overprint at foot, although the "BR1TISH" error can still be found on R.6/4 of the upper pane. The Official setting is recorded as consisting of 217 overprints as Type A and 23 as Type B.

OVERPRINT VARIETIES

Figure "1" for first "I" in "BRITISH". Occurs on R.6/4 of the upper pane as for the postage issue.
"BRITIS H"—Occurs on R.8, stamps 4 and 10 of the lower pane.

1903 (1 June). *Nos. O45, O48, O49a and O50/1 of India (Queen Victoria optd "O.H.M.S.") additionally optd with Type O 1 in Calcutta.*

O1	½ a.	yellow-green	..		..	3·50	48·00
		a. "BR1TISH"	..			£250	
		b. "BRITIS H"				£130	
O2	1 a.	carmine	..		..	10·00	7·50
		a. "BR1TISH"				£275	£225
		b. "BRITIS H"	..			£140	
O3	2 a.	pale violet	..		..	8·00	48·00
		a. "BR1TISH"				£300	
		b. "BRITIS H"				£180	
O4	8 a.	dull mauve	..		..	10·00	£350
		a. "BR1TISH"				£600	
		b. "BRITIS H"				£300	
		c. Stop omitted after "M" of "O.H.M.S." (lower pane R. 12/10)				£600	
O5	1 r.	green and carmine	..		..	10·00	£475
		a. "BR1TISH"				£600	
		b. "BRITIS H"	..			£300	
O1/5				Set of 5		38·00	£800

No. O4c was caused by an attempt to correct a minor spacing error of the "O.H.M.S." overprint which is known on the equivalent India Official stamp.

SETTING OF TYPE O 2

This 240 impression setting of "BRITISH SOMALILAND" also differs from that used to prepare the postage issue with overprint at foot, although many of the errors from the latter still occur in the same positions for the Official stamps. The setting used for Nos. O6/9f contained 180 overprints as Type A and 60 as Type B.

OVERPRINT VARIETIES

Missing second "I" in "BRITISH"—Occurs R.7/12 of upper pane as for the postage issue.
Figure "1" for first "I" in "BRITISH"—Occurs R.6/4 of upper pane as for the postage issue.
"SUMALILAND"—Occurs R.2/9 of the upper pane as for the postage issue.
"SOMAL.LAND"—Occurs R.6/7 of the lower pane as for the postage issue.

SERVICE (O 2a)

"SERVICE" in wrong fount (Type O 2a)—Occurs R.1/7 of lower pane.

1903. *Prepared for use but not issued. Nos. 106, 122/4 and 133 of India (1 r. Queen Victoria, rest King Edward VII), optd with Type O 2 in Calcutta.*

O6	½ a.	green	..		..	40
		a. "BRIT SH"	..			70·00
		b. "BR1TISH"	..			50·00
		c. "SUMALILAND"				50·00
		d. "SOMAL.LAND"				35·00
		e. "SERVICE" as Type O 2a				45·00
O7	1 a.	carmine	..		..	40
		a. "BRIT SH"				70·00
		b. "BR1TISH"	..			50·00
		c. "SUMALILAND"				50·00
		d. "SOMAL.LAND"				35·00
		e. "SERVICE" as Type O 2a				45·00
O8	2 a.	violet	..		..	70
		a. "BRIT SH"				£100
		b. "BR1TISH"	..			70·00
		c. "SUMALILAND"				70·00
		d. "SERVICE" as Type O 2a				50·00
O9	8 a.	purple			..	5·00
		a. "BRIT SH"	..			£1400
		b. "BR1TISH"	..			£400
		c. "SUMALILAND"				£400
		d. "SERVICE" as Type O 2a				£400

O9f		1 r. green and aniline carmine	..	..		20·00
		fa. "BRIT SH"	..			£1400
		fb. "BR1TISH"	..			£400
		fc. "SUMALILAND"				£400
		fd. "SOMAL.LAND"				£400
		fe. "SERVICE" as Type O 2a				£400
O6/9f				Set of 5		24·00

Used examples of Nos. O6/9f are known, but there is no evidence that such stamps did postal duty.

SETTING OF TYPE O 3

The anna values were overprinted in sheets of 120 (2 panes 6 × 10) from a setting matching the pane size. The full stop after the "M" on the fifth vertical column was either very faint or completely omitted. The prices quoted are for stamps with the stop missing; examples with a partial stop are worth much less.

The 1 r. value was overprinted from a separate setting of 60 which did not show the "missing stop" varieties.

1904 (1 Sept)–05. *Stamps of Somaliland Protectorate optd with Type O 3. P 14. (a) Wmk Crown CA.*

O10	**2**	½ a. dull green and green	..			3·25	48·00
		a. No stop after "M"				£400	
O11		1 a. grey-black and carmine	..			3·25	7·00
		a. No stop after "M"				£300	£375
O12		2 a. dull and bright purple	..			£120	48·00
		a. No stop after "M"				£1400	£650
O13		8 a. grey-black and pale blue	..			60·00	£130
		a. No stop after "M"				£550	

(b) Wmk Mult Crown CA

O14	**2**	2 a. dull and bright purple, O (7.05?)				75·00	£550
		a. No stop after "M"				£1200	

(c) Wmk Crown CC

O15	**3**	1 r. green	..			£150	£450
O10/13, O15				Set of 5		£250	£600
O10/13, O15	Optd "Specimen"			Set of 5		£120	

All Somaliland Protectorate stamps were withdrawn from sale on 25 June 1960 and until the unification on 1 July, issues of Italian Somalia together with Nos. 353/5 of Somalia Republic were used. Later issues will be found listed in Part 14 (*Africa since Independence N–Z*) of this catalogue.

South Africa

The South African provinces of Cape of Good Hope (including Griqualand West), Natal (including New Republic and Zululand), Orange Free State and Transvaal produced their own issues before federation on 31 May 1910.

CAPE OF GOOD HOPE

PRICES FOR STAMPS ON COVER	
Nos. 1/4	*from* × 4
Nos. 5/14	*from* × 3
Nos. 18/21	*from* × 5
No. 22	—
Nos. 23/6	*from* × 5
Nos. 27/31	*from* × 8
Nos. 32/3	*from* × 10
No. 34	*from* × 25
No. 35	*from* × 20
No. 36	*from* × 10
Nos. 37/8	*from* × 25
Nos. 39/40	*from* × 10
Nos. 41/2	*from* × 12
Nos. 43/54	*from* × 10
Nos. 55/6	*from* × 25
No. 57	*from* × 50
Nos. 58/69	*from* × 10
Nos. 70/8	*from* × 6

PRICES. Our prices for early Cape of Good Hope are for stamps in very fine condition. Exceptional copies are worth more, poorer copies considerably less.

1 Hope

2

(Des Charles Bell, Surveyor-General. Eng W. Humphrys. Recess P.B.)

1853 (1 Sept). *W* **2**. *Imperf.* (*a*) *Paper deeply blued.*
1	1	1d. pale brick-red		£3500	£275
		a. Deep brick-red		£5000	£300
2		4d. deep blue		£2000	£160

Plate proofs of the 4d. in a shade similar to the issued stamp exist on ungummed watermarked paper. The blueing on the reverse of these proofs is uneven giving a blotchy appearance.

(*b*) *Paper slightly blued (blueing not so pronounced at back)*
3	1	1d. brick-red		£3000	£200
		a. Brown-red		£3250	£225
4		4d. deep blue		£1300	£110
		a. Blue		£1400	£150

Both values are known with wmk sideways.

1855–8. *W* **2**. (*a*) *Imperf.*
5	1	1d. brick-red/*cream toned paper* (1857)		£5000	£900
		a. Rose (1858)		£450	£200
		b. Deep rose-red		£600	£225
6		4d. deep blue/*white paper* (1855)		£475	45·00
		a. Blue		£275	45·00
7		6d. slate-lilac/*blued paper* (18.2.58)		£4250	£450
		b. Pale rose-lilac/white paper		£700	£200
		c. Deep rose-lilac/white paper		£1700	£300
		d. Slate-purple/blued paper		£3500	£1000
8		1s. bright yellow-green/*white paper* (18.2.58)		£2500	£180
		a. Deep dark green		£225	£500

The method adopted for producing the plate of the 4d., 6d., and 1s. stamps involved the use of two dies, so that there are two types of each of these values, differing slightly in detail, but produced in equal numbers.

All values of this issue are known with watermark sideways. The 1d. value in dull rose on ungummed watermarked paper with watermark sideways is a plate proof. The 6d. is known bisected and used with 1d. for 4d. rate.

The paper of No. 5 is similar to that of Nos. 1/4, but is without the blueing. It is much thicker than the white paper used for later printings of the 1d. The evolution of the paper on these Cape of Good Hope stamps is similar to that on the line-engraved issues of Great Britain. Examples of the 6d. slate-lilac apparently on white paper have had the blueing washed out.

The 4d. value is known printed in black on white watermarked paper. Eleven authenticated copies have been recorded, the majority of which show cancellations or, at least, some indication that they have been used.

It was, at one time, believed that these stamps came from a small supply printed in black to mark the death of the Prince Consort, but references to examples can be found in the philatelic press before news of this event reached Cape Town.

It is now thought that these stamps represent proof sheets, possibly pressed into service during a shortage of stamps in 1861. There is, however, no official confirmation of this theory. (*Price £30000 un, £25000 with obliteration*).

(*b*) *Unofficially rouletted*
9	1	1d. brick-red		—	£2750
10		4d. blue		—	£2250
11		6d. rose-lilac		—	£1500
12		1s. bright yellow-green		—	£2750
		a. Deep dark green		—	£3000

These rouletted stamps are best collected on cover.

3 Hope

(Local provisional (so-called "wood-block") issue. Engraved on steel by C. J. Roberts. Printed from stereotyped plates by Saul Solomon & Co, Cape Town)

1861 (Feb–April). *Laid paper. Imperf.*
13	3	1d. vermilion (27 February)		£13000	£2000
		a. Carmine (7 March)		£22000	£3000
		b. Brick-red (10 April)		£30000	£4250
		c. Error. Pale milky blue		—	£28000
		ca. Pale bright blue		—	£30000
14		4d. pale milky blue (23 February)		£9000	£1500
		aa. Retouch or repair to rt-hand corner		—	£5500
		a. Pale grey-blue (March?)		£10000	£1500
		b. Pale bright blue (March?)		£10000	£1900
		ba. Retouch or repair to rt-hand corner		—	£5500
		c. Deep bright blue (12 April)		£75000	£4500
		d. Blue		£12000	£3000
		e. Error. Vermilion		£85000	£40000
		ea. Carmine		—	£80000
		f. Sideways tête-bêche (pair)		†	£60000

Nos. 13/14 were each issued in *tête-bêche* pairs normally joined at edges bearing the same inscription ("POSTAGE" against "POSTAGE", etc). No. 14f, of which only one used example is known, comes from the first printing and shows the right-hand stamp misplaced so that "FOUR PENCE" adjoins "POSTAGE".

Both values were officially reprinted in March, 1883, on wove paper. The 1d. is in deep red, and the 4d. in a deeper blue than that of the deepest shade of the issued stamp.

Specimens of the reprints have done postal duty, but their use thus was not intended. There are no reprints of the errors or of the retouched 4d.

Further reprints were made privately but with official permission, in 1940/41, in colours much deeper than those of any of the original printings, and on thick carton paper.

Examples of the 4d. are known unofficially rouletted.

Early in 1863, Perkins Bacon Ltd handed over the four plates used for printing the triangular Cape of Good Hope stamps to De La Rue & Co, Ltd, who made all the subsequent printings.

(Printed from the P.B. plates by D.L.R.)

1863–4. *Imperf.* (*a*) *W* **2**.
18	1	1d. deep carmine-red		£100	£225
		a. Deep brown-red		£350	£225
		b. Brownish red		£350	£225
19		4d. deep blue		£100	42·00
		a. Blue		£120	60·00
		b. Slate-blue		£2000	£500
		c. Steel-blue		£2000	£300

20	1	6d. bright mauve		£150	£450
21		1s. bright emerald-green		£350	£450
		a. Pale emerald-green		£1000	

(*b*) *Wmk Crown CC* (*sideways*)
22	1	1d. deep carmine-red		£15000	

No. 22 was a trial printing, and is only known unused.

Our prices for the 4d. blue are for stamps which are blue by comparison with the other listed shades. An exceptionally pale shade is recognised by specialists and is rare.

All values of this issue are known with watermark lying sideways.

With the exception of the 4d., these stamps may be easily distinguished from those printed by Perkins Bacon by their colours, which are quite distinct.

The De La Rue stamps of all values are less clearly printed, the figure of Hope and the lettering of the inscriptions standing out less boldly, while the fine lines of the background appear blurred and broken when examined under a glass. The background as a whole often shows irregularity in the apparent depth of colour, due to wear of the plates.

For note regarding the two dies of the 4d., 6d., and 1s. values, see after No. 8.

All the triangular stamps were demonetised as from 1 October 1900.

Four Pence.

4 "Hope" seated, with vine and ram. (With outer frame-line)

(5)

(Des Charles Bell; die engraved on steel and stamps typo by D.L.R.)

1864–77. *With outer frame-line surrounding the design. Wmk Crown CC. P* 14.
23	4	1d. carmine-red (5.65)		75·00	10·00
		a. Rose-red		75·00	10·00
24		4d. pale blue (8.65)		90·00	2·00
		a. Blue		£100	2·00
		b. Ultramarine		£250	50·00
		c. Deep blue (1872)		£130	2·00
25		6d. pale lilac (before 21.3.64)		£100	15·00
		a. Deep lilac		£200	6·50
		b. Violet (to bright) (1877)		£110	1·50
26		1s. deep green (1.64)		£475	14·00
		a. Green		90·00	2·00
		b. Blue-green		95·00	3·00

The 1d. rose-red, 6d. lilac, and 1s. blue-green are known imperf, probably from proof sheets.

The 1d. and 4d. stamps of this issue may be found with side and/or top outer frame-lines missing, due to wear of the plates.

(Surch by Saul Solomon & Co, Cape Town)

1868 (17 Nov). *No. 25a surch with T* **5**.
27	4	4d. on 6d. deep lilac (R.)		£130	11·00
		a. "Peuce" for "Pence"		£1800	£700
		b. "Fonr" for "Four"		—	£700

Specimens may also be found with bars omitted or at the top of the stamp, due to misplacement of the sheet.

The space between the words and bars varies from 12½ to 16 mm, stamps with spacing 15½ and 16 mm being rare. There were two printings, one of 120,000 in November 1868 and another of 1,000,000 in December. Stamps showing widest spacings are probably from the earlier printing.

6 (No outer frame-line)

(Die re-engraved. Typo D.L.R.)

1871–6. *Outer frame-line removed. Wmk Crown CC. P* 14.
28	6	½d. grey-black (*shades*) (12.75)		4·00	2·75
29		1d. carmine-red (*shades*) (2.72)		20·00	35
30		4d. deep blue (*shades*) (12.76)		85·00	50
		b. Ultramarine		£190	28·00
31		5s. yellow-orange (25.8.71)		£170	9·00

The ½d., 1d. and 5s. are known imperf, probably from proof sheets.

For the 3d. of this issue see Nos. 36 and 39.

ONE PENNY | **THREE PENCE**

(7) | (8)

(Surch by Saul Solomon & Co, Cape Town)

1874–6. *Nos. 25a and 26a surch with T* **7**.
32	4	1d. on 6d. deep lilac (R.) (1.9.74)		£275	48·00
		a. "E" of "PENNY" omitted		—	£650
33		1d. on 1s. green (11.76)		35·00	22·00

These provisionals are found with the bar only, either across the centre of the stamp or at top, with value only; or with value and bar close together, either at top or foot. Such varieties are due to misplacement of sheets during surcharging.

1879 (1 Nov). *No. 30 surch with T* **8**.
34	6	3d. on 4d. blue (R.)		70·00	90
		a. "PENCB" for "PENCE"		£1300	£275
		b. "THE.EE" for "THREE"		£1600	£350
		c. Surch double		£6500	£2750
		d. Variety b. double			

The double surcharge must also have existed showing variety a. but only variety b. is known.

There are numerous minor varieties, including letters broken or out of alignment, due to defective printing and use of poor type.

The spacing between the bar and the words varies from 16½ to 18 mm.

THREEPENCE **3** **3**

(9) (10) (11)

(Surch by D.L.R.)

1880 (Feb). *Special printing of the 4d. in new colour, surch, with T* **9**. *Wmk Crown CC.*
35	9	3d. on 4d. pale dull rose		40·00	1·50

A minor constant variety exists with foot of "P" in "PENCE" broken off, making the letter appear shorter.

1880 (1 July). *Wmk Crown CC. P* 14.
36	6	3d. pale dull rose		£140	12·00

(Surch by Saul Solomon & Co, Cape Town)

1880 (Aug). *No. 36 surch.*
37	10	"3" on 3d. pale dull rose		35·00	75
		a. Surch inverted		£650	40·00
		b. Vert pair. Nos. 37/8		£475	£250
38	11	"3" on 3d. pale dull rose		95·00	3·25
		a. Surch inverted		£6500	£900

The "3" (T **10**) is sometimes found broken. Vertical pairs are known showing the two types of surcharge *se-tenant*, and vertical strips of three exist, the top stamp having surcharge T **10**, the middle stamp being without surcharge, and the lower stamp having surcharge T **11** (*price for strip of 3 un. £3000*).

1881 (Jan). *Wmk Crown CC. P* 14.
39	6	3d. pale claret		70·00	1·75
		a. Deep claret		75·00	1·50

This was a definite colour change made at the request of the Postmaster-General owing to the similarity between the colours of the 1d. stamp and the 3d. in pale dull rose. Imperf copies are probably from proof sheets.

Proofs of this value were printed in brown, on unwatermarked wove paper and imperf, but the colour was rejected as unsuitable.

1882 (July). *Wmk Crown CA. P* 14.
40	6	3d. pale claret		5·50	90
		a. Deep claret		6·50	75

One Half-penny.

(12) 13 "Cabled Anchor"

(Surch by Saul Solomon & Co, Cape Town)

1882 (July). *Nos. 39a and 40a surch with T* **12**.
41	6	½d. on 3d. deep claret (Wmk CC)		£1700	£120
		a. Hyphen omitted		—	£3250
42		½d. on 3d. deep claret (Wmk CA)		3·75	2·00
		a. "p" in "penny" omitted		£2000	£700
		b. "y" in "penny" omitted		£1000	
		c. Hyphen omitted		£450	£350

Varieties also exist with broken and defective letters, and with the obliterating bar omitted or at the top of the stamp.

1882–83. *Wmk Crown CA. P* 14.
43	6	½d. black (1.9.82)		7·50	40
		a. Grey-black		3·50	15
44		1d. rose-red (7.82)		23·00	15
		a. Deep rose-red		22·00	15
45		2d. pale bistre (1.9.82)		60·00	15
		a. Deep bistre		65·00	10
46	4	6d. mauve (to bright) (8.82)		48·00	70
47	6	5s. orange (8.83)		£700	£200

Imperf pairs of the ½d., 1d., and 2d. are known, probably from proof sheets.

For the 3d. stamp with this watermark see No. 40.

1884–90. *W* **13**. *P* 14.
48	6	½d. black (1.86)		1·00	10
		a. Grey-black		1·00	10
49		1d. rose-red (12.85)		1·00	10
		a. Carmine-red		1·00	10
50		2d. pale bistre (12.84)		8·50	20
		a. Deep bistre		2·25	10
51		4d. blue (6.90)		3·25	15
		a. Deep blue		3·00	15
52	4	6d. reddish purple (12.84)		55·00	1·60
		a. Purple (shades)		2·75	15
		b. Bright mauve		9·00	40
53		1s. yellow-green (12.85)		75·00	3·50
		a. Blue-green (1889)		22·00	90
54	6	5s. orange (7.87)		45·00	3·00
48/54			Set of 7	70·00	3·50

All the above stamps are known in imperf pairs, probably from proof sheets.

For later shade and colour changes, etc., see Nos. 59, etc.

ONE PENNY.

2½d

(14) 15 (16)

(Surch by D.L.R.)

1891 (Mar). *Special printing of the 3d. in new colour, surch with T 14.*

55	6	2½d. on 3d. pale magenta	..	..	2·75	70
		a. *Deep magenta*	..	..	90	20
		b. "1" with horiz serif ..	..	..	42·00	32·00

No. 55b occurs on two stamps (Nos. 8 and 49) of the pane of 60.
Two types of "d" are found in the surcharge, one with square end to serif at top, and the other with pointed serif.

1892 (June). *W 13. P 14.*

56	15	2½d. sage-green	..	..	2·00	10
		a. *Olive-green* ..	..	..	4·50	55

(Surch by W. A. Richards & Sons, Cape Town)

1893 (Mar). *Nos. 50/a surch with T 16.*

57	6	1d. on 2d. pale bistre	..	..	1·75	10
		a. *Deep bistre*	..	..	70	10
		b. No stop after "PENNY"	..	35·00	11·00
		c. Surch double	..	..	—	£400

No. 57b occurs on stamp No. 42 of the upper left-hand pane, and on No. 6 of the lower right-hand pane.
Minor varieties exist showing broken letters and letters out of alignment or widely spaced. Also with obliterating bar omitted, due to misplacement of the sheet during surcharging.

17 "Hope" standing. Table Bay in background

18 Table Mountain and Bay with Arms of the Colony

(Des Mr. Mountford. Typo D.L.R.)

1893 (Oct). *W 13. P 14.*

58	17	1d. rose-red	..	..	60	10
		a. *Carmine*	..	..	30	10

The above stamp is known in imperf pairs, probably from proof sheets.

1893–98. *New colours, etc. W 13. P 14.*

59	6	½d. pale yellow-green (12.96)	..	1·25	10
		a. *Green*	..	..	2·75	20
60		2d. chocolate-brown (3.97)	..	1·25	10
61	15	2½d. pale ultramarine (3.96)	..	2·00	15
		a. *Ultramarine* ..	..	..	1·75	10
62	6	3d. bright magenta (9.98)	..	2·00	40
63		4d. sage-green (3.97)	..	..	3·25	60
64		1s. blue-green (12.93)	..	..	23·00	70
		a. *Deep blue-green* ..	..	42·00	5·50
65		1s. yellow-ochre (5.96) ..	..	6·00	50
66		5s. brown-orange (6.96) ..	..	30·00	3·50
59/66			*Set of 8*	75·00	5·50

1898–1902. *W 13. P 14.*

67	17	½d. green (9.98) ..	..	..	30	10
68		3d. magenta (3.02)	..	..	3·50	50

(Des E. Sturman. Typo D.L.R.)

1900 (Jan). *W 13. P 14.*

69	18	1d. carmine	..	..	45	10

19   20   21

22   23   24

25   26   27

(Typo D.L.R.)

1902 (Dec)–04. *W 13. P 14.*

70	19	½d. green	..	..	40	10
71	20	1d. carmine	..	..	40	10
72	21	2d. brown (10.04)	..	..	2·75	55
73	22	2½d. ultramarine (3.04) ..	..	2·50	5·00
74	23	3d. magenta (4.03)	..	..	2·75	30
75	24	4d. olive-green (2.03)	..	..	3·25	55
76	25	6d. bright mauve (3.03)	..	..	3·25	30
77	26	1s. yellow-ochre	..	..	6·00	40
78	27	5s. brown-orange (2.03)	..	40·00	6·50
70/8			*Set of 9*	55·00	12·50

All values exist in imperf pairs, from proof sheets.

Cape of Good Hope became a province of the Union of South Africa on 31 May 1910.

BRITISH KAFFRARIA

The history of the Cape eastern frontier was punctuated by a series of armed conflicts with the native population, known as the Kaffir Wars. After a particularly violent outbreak in 1846 the Governor, Sir Harry Smith, advanced the line of the Cape frontier to the Keikama and Tyumie Rivers. In the area between the new frontier and the Kei River a buffer state, British Kaffraria, was established on 17 December 1847. This area was not annexed to the Cape, but was administered as a separate Crown dependency by the Governor of Cape Colony in his capacity as High Commissioner for South Africa.

The territory, with its administration based on King William's Town, used the stamps of the Cape of Good Hope from 1853 onwards, the mail being sent via Port Elizabeth or overland from the Cape. Covers from British Kaffraria franked with the triangular issues are rare.

The first postal marking known from British Kaffraria is the 1849 type octagonal numeral No. 47 from Port Beaufort. Oval post-marks of the 1853 type were used at Alice, Aliwal North, Bedford, Fort Beaufort, King William's Town and Queenstown. In 1864 numeral cancellations were issued to all post offices within the Cape system and it is known that the following numbers were initially assigned to post towns in Kaffraria: 4 (King William's Town), 7 (Bedford), 11 (Queenstown), 29 (East London), 32 (Fort Beaufort), 38 (Aliwal North) and 104 (Cathcart).

It is believed that post offices may have also existed at Adelaide, Barkly East, Sterkstroom and Stutterheim, but, to date, no examples of handstamps or cancellations are known from them during the British Kaffraria period.

Following the decimation by famine of the Xhosa tribes in 1857 British Kaffraria was annexed to Cape Colony in 1865. The area eventually formed the basis of the Ciskei independent "homeland".

MAFEKING SIEGE STAMPS

PRICES FOR STAMPS ON COVER	
Nos. 1/16	*from* × 8
Nos. 17/22	*from* × 10

23 MARCH to 17 MAY 1900

There are numerous forgeries of the Mafeking overprints, many of which were brought home by soldiers returning from the Boer War.

MAFEKING,   MAFEKING

3d.   **3d.**

BESIEGED.   BESIEGED.

(1)   (2)

(Surcharged by Townsend & Co, Mafeking)

1900 (23 Mar–25 Apr). *Various stamps surch as T 1 and 2.*

(a) Cape of Good Hope stamps surch as T 1 (23 Mar)

1	6	1d. on ½d. green	..	£150	48·00
2	17	1d. on ½d. green (24.3)	..	£180	55·00
3		3d. on 1d. carmine	..	£150	48·00
4	6	6d. on 3d. magenta (24.3)	..	£7000	£250
5		1s. on 4d. sage-green (24.3)	..	£3500	£325

A variety in the setting of each value exists without comma after "MAFEKING".

(b) Nos. 59 and 61/3 of Bechuanaland Protectorate (optd on Great Britain) surch as T 1

6		1d. on ½d. vermilion (28.3)	..	£150	48·00
		a. Surch inverted	..	†	£4000
		b. Vert pair, surch tête-bêche	..	†	£8000
7		3d. on 1d. lilac (4.4)	..	£850	65·00
		a. Surch double	..	†	£6500
8		6d. on 2d. green and carmine (6.4)	£1000	65·00
9		6d. on 6d. purple/*yellow* (30.3)	..	£3250	£250
		a. Surch inverted	..	†	£13000
		b. Surch double			

(c) Nos. 12 and 35 of British Bechuanaland (optd on Great Britain) surch as T 1

10		6d. on 3d. lilac and black (27.3)	..	£350	60·00
11		1s. on 4d. green and purple-brown (29.3)	£1200	65·00
		a. Surch double	..	†	£11000
		b. Surch treble	..	†	£12000
		c. Surch double, one inverted	..	†	£12000

(d) Nos. 61/2 and 65 of Bechuanaland Protectorate (optd on Great Britain) surch as T 2 (25 Apr)

12		3d. on 1d. lilac	..	£900	55·00
		a. Surch double	..	†	£6000
13		6d. on 2d. green and carmine	..	£1100	60·00
14		1s. on 6d. purple/*rose-red*	..	£800	80·00

(e) Nos. 36/7 of British Bechuanaland (optd on Great Britain) surch as T 2

15		1s. on 6d. purple/*rose-red* (3.5)	..	£6500	£600
16		2s. on 1s. green (25.4)	..	£6000	£300

No. 11a has both surcharges T 1. Copies exist with normal surcharge T 1 and the second surcharge T 2 but are believed to be trials (*Price £3750, unused or used*).

On the stamps overprinted "BECHUANALAND PROTECT-ORATE" and "BRITISH BECHUANALAND" the local surcharge is so adjusted as not to overlap the original overprint.

3 Cadet Sergt.-major   4 General Baden-Powell
Goodyear

(Des Dr. W. A. Hayes (T 3), Capt. H. Greener (T 4))

1900 (7–11 Apr). *Produced photographically by Dr. D. Taylor. Horiz laid paper with sheet wmk "OCEANA FINE". P 12.*

(a) 18½ mm wide. (b) 21 mm wide

17	3	1d. pale blue/*blue*	..	£800	£275
18		1d. deep blue/*blue*	..	£800	£275
19	4	3d. pale blue/*blue* (a)	..	£1100	£400
		a. Reversed design	..	£35000	£25000
20		3d. deep blue/*blue* (a)..	..	£1200	£350
		a. Imperf between (horiz pair)	..	†	£40000
		b. Double print	..	†	£14000
21		3d. deep blue/*blue* (b) (11.4)	..	£6000	£750
22		3d. deep blue/*blue* (b) (11.4)	..	£6500	£950

These stamps vary a great deal in colour from deep blue to pale grey.
No. 18 imperforate and without gum is believed to be a proof (*Price for unused pair £10000*).
No. 19a comes from a sheet of 12 printed in reverse.

VRYBURG

PRICES FOR STAMPS ON COVER	
Nos. 1/4	*from* × 5
Nos. 11/12	*from* × 2

BOER OCCUPATION

Vryburg was occupied by Boer forces on 15 October 1899. Unoverprinted stamps of Transvaal were used initially. Nos. 1/4 were only available from 24 to 29 November. The Boers evacuated the town on 7 May 1900.

½ PENCE

Z.A.R.

(1)

1899 (24 Nov). *Cape stamps surch as T 1. With 12 mm between the lines on No. 3 and 10 mm on all other values.*

1	6	½ PENCE, green	..	£200	80·00
		a. Italic "Z"	..	£1600	£700
		b. 12 mm between lines of surch	..	£1600	£700
2	17	1 PENCE, rose	..	£225	£100
		a. Italic "Z"	..	£1800	£800
		b. 12 mm between lines of surch	..	£1800	£800
3	4	2 PENCE on 6d. mauve	..	£2250	£500
		a. Italic "Z"	..	£10000	£4250
4	15	2½ PENCE on 2½d. blue	..	£2000	£425
		a. Italic "Z"	..	£10000	£4250
		b. 12 mm between lines of surch	..	£10000	£4250

The "2 PENCE" on 6d. has a gap of 12 mm between the two lines of type. It is possible that this was the first value surcharged as the remaining three show this gap reduced to 10 mm with the exception of one position in the second vertical row of the setting. The italic "Z" occurs on one position in the sixth vertical row. It is believed that the setting was of 60 (6×10).

BRITISH REOCCUPATION

V. R. SPECIAL POST

(2)

1900 (May). *Provisionals issued by the Military Authorities. Stamps of Transvaal handstamped with T 2.*

11	30	½d. green	..		—	£1600
12		1d. carmine and green	..	£7000	£2750
13		2d. deep brown and green			
14		2½d. blue and green	..	..	

GRIQUALAND WEST

Griqualand West was situated to the North of Cape Colony, bounded on the north by what became British Bechuanaland and on the east by the Orange Free State.

The area was settled in the early nineteenth century by the Griqua tribal group, although many members of the tribe, including the paramount chief, migrated to Griqualand East (between Basutoland and the east coast of South Africa) in 1861–63. There was little European involvement in Griqualand West before 1866, but in that year the diamond fields along the Vaal River were discovered. Sovereignty was subsequently claimed by the Griqua Chief, the Orange Free State and the South African Republic (Transvaal). In 1871 the British authorities arbitrated in favour of the Griqua Chief who promptly ceded his territory to Great Britain. Griqualand West became a separate Crown Colony in January 1873.

During the initial stages of the prospecting boom mail was passed via the Orange Free State, but a post office connected to the Cape Colony postal system was opened at Klip Drift (subsequently Barkly) in late 1870. Further offices at De Beer's New Rush (subsequently Kimberley), Douglas and Du Toit's Pan (subsequently Beaconsfield) were open by September 1873.

Cape of Good Hope stamps to the 5s. value were in use from October 1871, but those originating in Griqualand West can only be identified after the introduction of Barred Oval Diamond Numeral cancellations in 1873. Numbers known to have been issued in the territory are:

1 De Beers N.R. (New Rush) (subsequently Kimberley)
3 Junction R. & M. (Riet and Modder Rivers)
4 Barkly
6 or 9 Du Toit's Pan (subsequently Beaconsfield)
8 Langford (transferred to Douglas)
10 Thornhill

FORGED OVERPRINTS. Many stamps show forged overprints. Great care should be taken when purchasing the scarcer items.

Stamps of the Cape of Good Hope, Crown CC, perf 14, overprinted.

1874 (Sept). *No. 24a of Cape of Good Hope surch* "1d." *in red manuscript by the Kimberley postmaster.*

1	1d. on 4d. blue	.. .. ..	£600	£1100

G. W.
(1)

1877 (Mar). *Nos. 29/30 of Cape of Good Hope optd with T 1.*

2	1d. carmine-red	.. ..	£400	70·00
	a. Opt double	.. ..	† £1100	
3	4d. deep blue (R.)	.. ..	£300	60·00

G G G G G G
(1a) (2) (3) (4) (5) (6)

G G G G G
(7) (8) (9) (10) (11)

G *G* *G*
(12) (13) (14)

1877 (Apr)–78. *Nos. 24a, 25b, 26a and 28/31 of Cape of Good Hope optd with capital* "G".

(a) First printing. Optd with T 1a/6 and 8 in black (1d.) or red (others)

4	½d. grey-black			
	a. Opt Type 1a	.. .. ..	11·00	12·00
	b. Opt Type 2	.. ..	24·00	26·00
	c. Opt Type 3	.. ..	15·00	16·00
	d. Opt Type 4	.. ..	24·00	26·00
	e. Opt Type 5	.. ..	28·00	30·00
	f. Opt Type 6	.. ..	14·00	15·00
	g. Opt Type 8	.. ..		
5	1d. carmine-red			
	a. Opt Type 1a	.. .. ..	11·00	7·00
	b. Opt Type 2	.. ..	26·00	19·00
	c. Opt Type 3	.. ..	16·00	10·50
	d. Opt Type 4	.. ..	26·00	19·00
	e. Opt Type 5	.. ..	35·00	24·00
	f. Opt Type 6	.. ..	14·00	9·00
	g. Opt Type 8	.. ..	*	
6	4d. blue (with frame-line) (No. 24a)			
	a. Opt Type 1a	.. ..	£100	17·00
	b. Opt Type 2	.. ..	£250	60·00
	c. Opt Type 3	.. ..	£170	28·00
	d. Opt Type 4	.. ..	£250	60·00
	e. Opt Type 5	.. ..	£300	75·00
	f. Opt Type 6	.. ..	£150	26·00
	g. Opt Type 8	.. ..		
7	4d. deep blue (without frame-line) (No. 30)			
	a. Opt Type 1a	.. ..	80·00	12·00
	b. Opt Type 2	.. ..	£180	40·00
	c. Opt Type 3	.. ..	£130	18·00
	d. Opt Type 4	.. ..	£180	40·00
	e. Opt Type 5	.. ..	£225	55·00
	f. Opt Type 6	.. ..	£120	17·00
	g. Opt Type 8	.. ..	£1000	
8	6d. violet			
	a. Opt Type 1a	.. ..	55·00	16·00
	b. Opt Type 2	.. ..	£120	45·00
	c. Opt Type 3	.. ..	80·00	21·00
	d. Opt Type 4	.. ..	£120	45·00
	e. Opt Type 5	.. ..	£160	60·00
	f. Opt Type 6	.. ..	75·00	20·00
	g. Opt Type 8	.. ..		
9	1s. green			
	a. Opt Type 1a	.. ..	70·00	12·00
	ab. Opt inverted	.. ..	—	£275
	b. Opt Type 2	.. ..	£160	26·00
	ba. Opt inverted	.. ..		
	c. Opt Type 3	.. ..	£110	16·00
	d. Opt Type 4	.. ..	£160	26·00
	da. Opt inverted	.. ..		
	e. Opt Type 5	.. ..	£200	32·00
	f. Opt Type 6	.. ..	£100	15·00
	fa. Opt inverted	.. ..		
	g. Opt Type 8	.. ..	—	£350
10	5s. yellow-orange			
	a. Opt Type 1a	.. ..	£275	11·00
	b. Opt Type 2	.. ..	—	25·00
	c. Opt Type 3	.. ..	£375	15·00
	d. Opt Type 4	.. ..	—	25·00
	e. Opt Type 5	.. ..	£650	35·00
	f. Opt Type 6	.. ..	£350	14·00
	g. Opt Type 8	.. ..	£1500	

*The 1d. with overprint Type 8 from this setting can only be distinguished from that of the second printing when *se-tenant* with overprint Type 3.

Nos. 4/10 were overprinted by a setting of 120 covering two panes of 60 (6×10). This setting contained 41 examples of Type 1a, 10 of Type 2, 23 of Type 3, 10 of Type 4, 8 of Type 5, 27 of Type 6 and 1 of Type 8. Sub-types of Types 1a and 2 exist. The single example of Type 8 occurs on R. 7/4 of the right-hand pane.

It is believed that there may have been an additional setting used for the 5s. which was in considerable demand to cover the postage and registration on diamond consignments. It is also possible that single panes of this value and of the 1s. were overprinted using the right-hand half of the normal 120 setting.

(b) Second printing. Optd with T 6/14 in black (1878)

11	1d. carmine-red			
	a. Opt Type 6	.. ..	*	
	b. Opt Type 7	.. ..	16·00	11·00
	c. Opt Type 8	.. ..	28·00	20·00
	d. Opt Type 9	.. ..	17·00	13·00
	e. Opt Type 10	.. ..	55·00	50·00
	f. Opt Type 11	.. ..	35·00	27·00
	g. Opt Type 12	.. ..	50·00	45·00
	h. Opt Type 13	.. ..	85·00	75·00
	i. Opt Type 14	.. ..	£350	£300
12	4d. deep blue (without frame-line) (No. 30)			
	a. Opt Type 6	.. ..	£170	38·00
	b. Opt Type 7	.. ..	65·00	14·00
	c. Opt Type 8	.. ..	£160	35·00
	d. Opt Type 9	.. ..	75·00	15·00
	e. Opt Type 10	.. ..	£250	60·00
	f. Opt Type 11	.. ..	£180	42·00
	g. Opt Type 12	.. ..	£225	55·00
	h. Opt Type 13	.. ..	£400	£120
	i. Opt Type 14	.. ..	—	£375
13	6d. violet			
	a. Opt Type 6	.. ..	£275	95·00
	b. Opt Type 7	.. ..	£140	50·00
	ba. Opt double	.. ..		
	c. Opt Type 8	.. ..	£250	90·00
	d. Opt Type 9	.. ..	£160	60·00
	da. Opt double	.. ..	—	£450
	e. Opt Type 10	.. ..	£350	£130
	ea. Opt double	.. ..	†	£550
	f. Opt Type 11	.. ..	£300	£100
	g. Opt Type 12	.. ..	£325	£120
	h. Opt Type 13	.. ..	£475	£200
	i. Opt Type 14	.. ..	£1200	£475

*The 1d. with overprint Type 6 from this setting can only be distinguished from that of the first printing when *se-tenant* with Types 11, 12 or 13.

Nos. 11/13 were overprinted by another double-pane setting of 120 in which only Types 6 and 8 were repeated from that used for the first printing. The second printing setting contained 12 examples of Type 6, 30 of Type 7, 13 of Type 8, 27 of Type 9, 9 of Type 10, 11 of Type 11, 11 of Type 12, 6 of Type 13 and 1 of Type 14. Sub-types of Types 7 and 12 exist.

G *G* G
(15) (16) (17)

1878 (July). *Nos. 24a, 25b and 28/30 of Cape of Good Hope optd with small capital* "G", *T 15/16.*

14	15	½d. grey-black (R.)	.. ..	4·50	6·00
		a. Opt inverted	.. ..	6·00	6·00
		b. Opt double	.. ..	32·00	
		c. Opt double, both inverted	..	55·00	
		d. Black opt	.. ..	£140	75·00
		da. Opt inverted	.. ..	£140	
		db. Opt double, one inverted in red		£275	
		dc. Opt double, one inverted (Type 16) in red	.. ..	75·00	
15	16	½d. grey-black (R.)	.. ..	6·00	6·00
		a. Opt inverted	.. ..	6·00	7·50
		b. Opt double	.. ..	55·00	55·00
		c. Opt double, both inverted	..		
		d. Black opt	.. ..	25·00	25·00
		da. Opt inverted	.. ..	25·00	25·00
		db. Opt double, one inverted (Type 15) in red	.. ..	95·00	
16	15	1d. carmine-red	..	6·00	4·25
		a. Opt inverted	.. ..	6·00	6·00
		b. Opt double	.. ..	£130	32·00
		c. Opt double, both inverted	..	£130	48·00
		d. Opt double, both inverted with one in red	.. ..	21·00	23·00
		e. Opt double, both inverted with one (Type 16) in red	.. ..		
17	16	1d. carmine-red	..	6·00	6·00
		a. Opt inverted	.. ..	50·00	20·00
		b. Opt double	.. ..	—	60·00
		c. Opt double, both inverted	..	—	75·00
		d. Opt double, both inverted with one in red	.. ..	50·00	50·00
18	15	4d. blue (with frame-line) (No. 24a)		—	90·00
19	16	4d. blue (with frame-line) (No. 24a)		—	95·00
20	15	4d. deep blue (without frame-line) (No.30)	60·00	14·00
		a. Opt inverted	..	£140	60·00
		b. Opt double	.. ..	—	£140
		c. Opt double, both inverted	..	—	£190
		d. Red opt	.. ..	£200	75·00
		da. Opt inverted	.. ..	£650	55·00
21	16	4d. deep blue (without frame-line) (No.30)	£100	7·50
		a. Opt inverted	..	£150	20·00
		b. Opt double	.. ..	—	£150
		c. Opt double, both inverted	..	—	£190
		d. Red opt	.. ..	—	60·00
		da. Opt inverted	.. ..	£200	60·00
22	15	6d. violet	.. ..	65·00	16·00
23	16	6d. violet	.. ..	—	16·00

Nos. 14/23 were also overprinted using a double-pane setting of 120. Based on evidence from surviving ½d. and 1d. sheets all overprints in the left-hand pane were roman, Type 15, and all those in the right-hand pane italic, Type 16, except for R. 1/6, 4/5, 6/6, 7/6, 8/6, 9/6 and 10/6 which were Type 15. There is considerable evidence to suggest that after the ½d. value had been overprinted the setting was amended to show a Type 15, instead of a Type 16, on R. 10/5 of the right-hand pane. Two strikes of the setting were required to overprint the sheets of 240 and it would appear that on many sheets the bottom two panes had the overprints inverted.

1879. *Nos. 25b, 26b and 28/31 of Cape of Good Hope optd with small capital* "G", *T 17.*

24	½d. grey-black	.. ..	7·00	4·75
	a. Opt double	.. ..	£225	£225
25	1d. carmine-red	.. ..	7·00	3·50
	a. Opt inverted	.. ..	—	75·00
	b. Opt double	.. ..	—	£120
	c. Opt treble	.. ..	—	£160
26	4d. deep blue	.. ..	12·00	3·50
	a. Opt double	.. ..	—	95·00
27	6d. violet	.. ..	70·00	6·00
	a. Opt inverted	.. ..	—	23·00
	b. Opt double	.. ..	£400	£140

28	1s. green	.. ..	50·00	3·50
	a. Opt double	.. ..	£190	80·00
29	5s. yellow-orange	.. ..	£225	6·00
	a. Opt double	.. ..	£300	60·00
	b. Opt treble	.. ..	—	£250

Nos. 24/9 were also overprinted using a setting of 120 which contained a number of minor type varieties.

Griqualand West was merged with Cape Colony in October 1880. The remaining stock of the overprinted stamps was returned from Kimberley to Cape Town and redistributed among various post offices in Cape Colony where they were used as ordinary Cape stamps.

NATAL

1   2

3   4

5

(Embossed in plain relief on coloured wove paper)

1857 (26 May, *the 1d. in 1858*). *Imperf.*

1	1	1d. rose	.. .. ..	—	£1700
2		1d. buff	.. .. ..	—	£950
3		1d. blue	.. .. ..	—	£1100
4	2	3d. rose	.. ..	—	£400
		a. Tête-bêche (pair)	.. ..	—	£10000
5	3	6d. green	.. ..	—	£1100
6	4	9d. blue	.. ..	—	£7000
7	5	1s. buff	.. ..	—	£5500

All the above have been reprinted more than once, and the early reprints of some values cannot always be distinguished with certainty from originals.

Stamps on surface-coloured paper, perforated 12½, are fiscals.

NOTE. The value of the above stamps depends on their dimensions, and the clearness of the embossing, but our prices are for fine used.

6   7

(Eng C. H. Jeens. Recess P.B.)

1859–60. *No wmk. P 14.*

9	6	1d. rose-red	.. ..	£120	70·00
10		3d. blue	.. ..	£110	42·00
		a. Imperf between (vert pair)	..	† £3750	

No. 10a is only known from a cover of 1867 franked with two such pairs.

1861. *No wmk. Intermediate perf 14 to 16.*
11 6 3d. blue .. .. .. £180 65·00

1862. *No wmk. Rough perf 14 to 16.*
12 6 3d. blue .. .. 85·00 32·00
　a. Imperf between (pair).. .. £1600
　b. Imperf (pair) .. — £1100
13 6d. grey .. .. £130 45·00

1862. *Wmk Small Star. Rough perf 14 to 16.*
15 6 1d. rose-red.. .. £100 55·00
The 1d. and 3d. wmk. Star, imperf, are proofs, and are therefore not included. The 3d. wmk Star, perforated, is believed to exist only with forged watermark.

(Recess D.L.R.)
1863. *Thick paper. No wmk. P 13.*
18 6 1d. lake .. .. 75·00 27·00
19 1d. carmine-red .. .. 75·00 20·00

1864. *Wmk Crown CC. P 12½.*
20 6 1d. brown-red .. .. £110 35·00
21 1d. rose .. .. 80·00 28·00
22 1d. bright-red .. .. 80·00 28·00
23 6d. lilac .. .. 55·00 15·00
24 6d. violet .. .. .. 38·00 25·00

(Typo D.L.R.)
1867 (April). *Wmk Crown CC. P 14.*
25 7 1s. green .. .. .. £120 26·00

1869 (23 Aug). *Optd horiz in Natal. No wmk (3d.), wmk Crown CC (others). P 14 or 14–16 (3d.), 12½ (1d., 6d) or 14 (1s.).*

POSTAGE
Tall capitals
26 6 1d. rose .. .. £250 55·00
27 1d. bright red .. .. £250 55·00
28 3d. blue (No. 10) .. £375 £190
28a 3d. blue (No. 11) .. — 55·00
28b 3d. blue (No. 12) .. £350 75·00
29 6d. lilac .. .. — 55·00
30 6d. violet .. .. £300 55·00
31 7 1s. green .. .. — £950

Postage.
12¾ mm long
32 6 1d. rose .. .. £225 50·00
33 1d. bright red .. .. £225 50·00
　a. Opt double .. .. — £550
34 3d. blue (No. 10) .. — £200
34a 3d. blue (No. 11) .. £350 £160
34b 3d. blue (No. 12) .. £325 65·00
35 6d. lilac .. .. £325 50·00
36 6d. violet .. .. £250 50·00
37 7 1s. green .. .. — £450

Postage.
13¾ mm long
38 6 1d. rose £450 £120
39 1d. bright red .. .. — £120
40 3d. blue (No. 10) ..
40a 3d. blue (No. 11) ..
40b 3d. blue (No. 12) .. £900 £250
41 6d. lilac .. .. — £120
42 6d. violet £850 £120
43 7 1s. green .. .. — £1400

Postage.
14½ to 15½ mm long
44 6 1d. rose £400 £190
45 1d. bright red £400 £170
46 3d. blue (No. 10) ..
46a 3d. blue (No. 11) .. — £250
46b 3d. blue (No. 12) .. — £190
47 6d. lilac .. .. — 75·00
48 6d. violet .. .. £800 75·00
49 7 1s. green .. .. — £1400

POSTAGE.
With a stop
50 6 1d. rose .. .. 65·00 25·00
51 1d. bright red .. .. £120 25·00
52 3d. blue (No. 10) .. £190 55·00
53 3d. blue (No. 11) .. £110 38·00
54 3d. blue (No. 12) .. £140 35·00
　a. Opt double .. .. — £600
54b 6d. lilac .. .. £120 55·00
55 6d. violet .. .. £100 45·00
56 7 1s. green .. .. £110 48·00
All values exist with this overprint at top or bottom of stamp.

(8)

1870. *No. 25 optd with T 8.*
57 7 1s. green (C.) £3000
58 1s. green (Blk.) .. £1500 £950
　a. Opt double £2750 £1000
59 1s. green (G.) .. 48·00 10·00
For 1s. orange, see No. 108.

(9) (10) (11)

1870–73. *Optd with T 9. Wmk Crown CC. P 12½.*
60 6 1d. bright red .. .. 55·00 13·00
61 3d. bright blue (R.).. .. 55·00 13·00
62 6d. mauve .. .. £110 25·00

1873 (July). *Optd up centre of stamp with T 10. Wmk Crown CC. P 14.*
63 7 1s. purple-brown .. .. 90·00 16·00

1874 (July). *No. 21 optd with T 11.*
65 7 1d. rose .. .. £120 50·00
　a. Opt double ..

12 13 14

15 16

(Typo D.L.R.)
1874–78. *Wmk Crown CC. P 14.*
66 12 1d. dull rose .. .. 21·00 1·75
67 1d. bright rose .. .. 21·00 1·75
68 13 3d. blue .. .. 75·00 14·00
　a. Perf 14 × 12½ .. £1400 £850
69 14 4d. brown (1878) .. .. 85·00 11·00
　a. Perf 12½ .. .. £325 65·00
70 15 6d. lilac .. .. 30·00 6·00
71 16 5s. maroon .. .. £100 32·00
　a. Perf 15½ × 15 .. £110 70·00
72 5s. rose .. .. 65·00 28·00
73 5s. carmine (H/S S. £160).. .. 60·00 26·00
The 5s. stamps normally have wmk sideways.

POSTAGE POSTAGE ½HALF
(17) (18) (19)

1875. *Wmk Crown CC. P 14 (1s.) or 12½ (others). (a) Optd with T 17.*
76 6 1d. rose .. .. 85·00 38·00
　a. Opt double £475 £425
77 1d. bright red .. .. 80·00 48·00

(b) Optd with T 18 (14½ mm long, without stop)
81 6 1d. rose .. .. 70·00 45·00
　a. Opt inverted £700 £400
82 1d. yellow .. .. 70·00 65·00
83 6d. violet .. .. 50·00 5·50
　a. Opt double .. .. — £550
　b. Opt inverted £650 £150
84 7 1s. green .. .. 75·00 4·50
　a. Opt double .. .. — £325

TYPE 19. There are several varieties of this surcharge, of which T 19 is an example. They may be divided as follows:
(a) "½" 4½ mm high, "2" has straight foot.
(b) As last but "½" is 4 mm high.
(c) As last but "2" has curled foot.
(d) "½" 3½ mm. high, "2" has straight foot.
(e) As last but "2" has curled foot.
(f) As last but "2" smaller.

As the "½" and "HALF" were overprinted separately, they vary in relative position, and are frequently overlapping.

1877 (13 Feb). *No. 66 surch as T 19.*
85 12 ½d. on 1d. rose (a).. .. .. 20·00 65·00
　a. "½" double .. ..
86 ½d. on 1d. rose (b).. .. 95·00
87 ½d. on 1d. rose (c).. .. 85·00
88 ½d. on 1d. rose (d).. .. 45·00
89 ½d. on 1d. rose (e).. .. 48·00
90 ½d. on 1d. rose (f).. .. 48·00

NEW INFORMATION
The editor is always interested to correspond with people who have new information that will improve or correct the Catalogue.

POSTAGE Half-penny ONE HALF-PENNY.
(21) 23 (24)

1877–79. *T 6 (wmk Crown CC, P 12½) surch as T 21.*
91 ½d. on 1d. yellow .. .. 8·00 11·00
　a. Surch inverted £225 £180
　b. Surch double £225 £180
　c. Surch omitted (lower stamp, vertical pair) £950 £850
　d. "POSTAGE" omitted (in pair with normal) £1000
　e. "S" of "POSTAGE" omitted .. £180 £170
　f. "T" of "POSTAGE" omitted .. £180
92 1d. on 6d. violet .. .. 45·00 8·50
　a. "S" of "POSTAGE" omitted .. £275 £150
93 1d. on 6d. rose .. .. 85·00 28·00
　a. Surch inverted .. .. — £160
　b. Surch double .. .. — £190
　c. Surch double, one inverted .. £250 £250
　d. Surch four times £325 £160
　e. "S" of "POSTAGE" omitted .. £275
No. 93c. is known with one surcharge showing variety "S" of "POSTAGE" omitted.
Other minor varieties exist in these surcharges.

(Typo D.L.R.)
1880 (13 Oct). *Wmk Crown CC. P 14.*
96 23 ½d. blue-green .. .. 9·00 11·00
　a. Imperf between (vert pair) ..

1882–89. *Wmk Crown CA. P 14.*
97 23 ½d. blue-green .. .. 85·00 15·00
　a. Dull green 65 30
99 12 1d. rose (shades).. .. 85 10
　a. Carmine .. .. 1·90 15
100 13 3d. blue .. .. 90·00 17·00
101 3d. grey (11.89) .. .. 1·75 95
102 14 4d. brown .. .. 2·75 65
103 15 6d. mauve .. .. 3·25 70
97a/103 Set of 6 90·00 17·00
97a, 99a, 101/3 H/S "Specimen" Set of 5 £250

1885 (26 Jan). *No. 99 surch with T 24.*
104 12 ½d. on 1d. rose .. .. 16·00 11·00

TWO PENCE TWO PENCE TWOPENCE HALFPENNY
(25) 26 (27)

1886. *No. 101 surch with T 25 by D.L.R.*
105 13 2d. on 3d. grey .. .. 18·00 5·50

(Typo D.L.R.)
1887–89. *Wmk Crown CA. P 14.*
106 26 2d. olive-green Die I* (Optd S. £60) .. 24·00 85
107 2d. olive-green, Die II (H/S S. £60) .. 1·75 85
*The differences between Dies I and II are shown in the Introduction.

1888 (16 Mar). *As No. 84, but colour changed and wmk Crown CA, optd with T 8 by D.L.R.*
108 7 1s. orange (C.) (H/S S. £90) .. 3·50 85
　a. Opt double .. .. — £1500

1890. *Surch locally with T 27.*
109 14 2½d. on 4d. brown (H/S S. £50).. .. 11·00 8·50
　a. "TWOPENGE" .. .. 60·00 60·00
　b. "HALFPENN" £225 £180
　c. Surch double £250 £180
　d. Surch inverted £325 £250

POSTAGE.
Half-Penny POSTAGE.
2½ Varieties of long-tailed letters
28 (29)

(Typo D.L.R.)
1891 (June). *Wmk Crown CA. P 14.*
113 28 2½d. bright blue (H/S S. £60) .. .. 3·25 50

1895 (12 Mar). *No. 24 surch with T* **29** *in carmine.*

114	½d. on 6d. violet (H/S S. £50)	..	..	1·00	2·75
	a. "Ealf-Penny"	..	..	18·00	20·00
	b. "Half-Pennv" and long "P"	..	15·00	
	ba. "Half Pennv" and long "T" and "A"	15·00	
	c. No stop after "POSTAGE" and long "P", "T" and "A"	..	15·00	
	d. Long "P"	..	..	2·00	3·50
	e. Long "T"	..	..	2·00	3·50
	f. Long "A"	..	..	3·00	4·25
	g. Long "P" and "T"	..	2·00	3·50
	h. Long "P" and "A"	..	2·00	3·50
	i. Long "T" and "A"	..	2·75	4·00
	k. Long "P", "T" and "A"	..	2·75	4·00
	ka. Long "P", "T" and "A" with comma after "POSTAGE"	..	6·00	8·50
	l. Surcharge double, one vertical ..	£250	

No. 114 is known with surcharge double and widely spaced, but the second surcharge is extremely faint.

The surcharge was applied as a setting of 60 (12×5) which contained seventeen normals, one each of Nos. 114a, 114b, 114ba, 114c, six of No. 114d, six of 114e, three of 114f, six of 114g, seven of 114h, five of No. 114i, four of No. 114k and two of No. 114ka.

HALF

(30)   31   32

1895 (18 Mar). *No. 99 surch with T* **30**.

125	HALF on 1d. rose (*shades*) (H/S S. £50)			70	75
	a. Surch double	..	..	£325	£325
	b. "H" with longer left limb	..	20·00	
	c. Pair, one without surcharge		

No. 125b occurs on the second, fourth, sixth etc., stamps of the first vertical row of the righthand pane. It was very soon corrected.
In some printings what appears to be a broken "E" (with the top limb removed) was used instead of "L" in "HALF" on the last stamp in the sheet (*Price* £30)

(Typo D.L.R.)

1902–3. *Inscr* "POSTAGE REVENUE". *Wmk Crown CA. P* 14.

127	**31**	½d. blue-green	..	..	65	15
128		1d. carmine	..	..	1·00	15
129		1½d. green and black	..	1·25	90
130		2d. red and olive-green..	..	80	25
131		2½d. bright blue ..	..	90	3·00
132		3d. purple and grey	..	80	30
133		4d. carmine and cinnamon	..	2·75	7·50
134		5d. black and orange	..	1·25	2·50
135		6d. green and brown-purple	..	1·25	1·10
136		1s. carmine and pale blue	..	3·50	1·10
137		2s. green and bright violet	..	45·00	9·00
138		2s. 6d. purple	..	..	35·00	12·00
139		4s. deep rose and maize	..	50·00	45·00
		a. Imperf between (horiz pair)		
127/139				*Set of* 13	£130	75·00
127/39 Optd "Specimen"			*Set of* 13	£150	

No. 139a is also imperforate between stamp and left-hand margin.

(Typo D.L.R.)

1902–3. *Wmk Crown CC. P* 14.

140	**32**	5s. dull blue and rose	..	..	16·00	7·50
141		10s. deep rose and chocolate	..	48·00	24·00
142		£1 black and bright blue	..	£110	42·00
143		£1 10s. green and violet (Optd S. £65)	£225	65·00
144		£5 mauve and black (Optd S. £100)	..	£1300	£275
145		£10 green and orange (Optd S. £200)	..	£6000	£2250
145a		£20 red and green (Optd S. £325)	..£12000	
140/2 Optd "Specimen"		..	*Set of* 3	£100	

USED HIGH VALUES. Collectors are warned against fiscally used high value Natal stamps with penmarks cleaned off and forged postmarks added.

1904–8. *Wmk Mult Crown CA. Chalk-surfaced paper* (£1 10s.). *P* 14.

146	**31**	½d. blue-green ..	..	2·00	15
147		1d. rose-carmine	..	..	2·00	15
148		1d. deep carmine	..	..	3·00	20
149		2d. red and olive-green	..	2·25	3·25
152		4d. carmine and cinnamon	..	2·00	1·00
153		5d. black and orange (1908)	..	2·50	2·75
155		1s. carmine and pale blue	..	48·00	6·00
156		2s. dull green and bright violet	..	40·00	23·00
157		2s. 6d. purple	..	..	38·00	25·00
162	**32**	£1 10s. brown-orange and deep purple (1908) (Optd S. £170)	..	£1000	
146/157				*Set of* 9	£120	55·00

1908–9. *Inscr* "POSTAGE POSTAGE". *Wmk Mult Crown CA. P* 14.

165	**31**	6d. dull and bright purple	..	4·50	2·00
166		1s. black/*green*	..	..	6·00	2·00
167		2s. purple and bright blue/*blue*..	15·00	3·00
168		2s. 6d. black and red/*blue*	..	25·00	3·00
169	**32**	5s. green and red/*yellow*	..	18·00	18·00
170		10s. green and red/*green*..	..	48·00	50·00
171		£1 purple and black/*red*	..	£225	£160
165/71				*Set of* 7	£300	£200
165/71 Optd "Specimen"			*Set of* 7	£170	

FISCALS USED FOR POSTAGE

1869. *Embossed on coloured wove, surfaced paper. P* 12½.

F1	**1**	1d. yellow ..	..	..	50·00	80·00

Examples of 1d. yellow and 6d. rose values as Type **6**, 1s. purple-brown as Type **7** and various values between 5s. and £10 in the design illustrated above are believed to exist postally used, but, as such use was not authorised, they are not now listed.

OFFICIAL STAMPS

OFFICIAL

(O 1)

1904. *T* **31**, *wmk Mult Crown CA, optd with Type* O 1. *P* 14.

O1	½d. blue-green	..	..	3·00	35
O2	1d. carmine	..	..	1·50	60
O3	2d. red and olive-green	..	12·00	7·50
O4	3d. purple and grey	..	7·50	4·00
O5	6d. green and brown-purple ..	..	25·00	27·00
O6	1s. carmine and pale blue	..	65·00	£110
O1/6			*Set of* 6	£100	£130

The use of stamps overprinted as above was discontinued after 30 May 1907. Stamps perforated with the letters "N.G.R." were for use on Government Railways.

Natal became a province of the Union of South Africa on 31 May 1910.

NEW REPUBLIC

During the unrest following the death of Cetshwayo, the Zulu king, in 1884, a group of Boers from the Transvaal offered their support to his son, Dinizulu. The price for this support was the cession of a sizeable portion of Zulu territory to an independent Boer republic. The New Republic, centred on Vryheid, was proclaimed on 16 August 1884 with the remaining Zulu territory becoming a protectorate of the new administration.
Alarmed by these developments the British authorities annexed the southernmost part of the land grant, around St. Lucia Bay, to prevent direct access to the Indian Ocean. The remainder of the New Republic was, however, recognised as independent on 22 October 1886. Zululand was annexed by the British on 22 May 1887.
Difficulties beset the New Republic, however, and its Volksraad voted for union with the South African Republic (Transvaal). The two republics united on 21 July 1888. In 1903 the territory of the former New Republic was transferred to Natal.
Mail from Vryheid in 1884–85 was franked with issues of Transvaal (for dispatches made via Utrecht) or Natal (for those sent via Dundee). Issues of the New Republic were never accepted as internationally valid by these administrations so that all external mail continued to show Transvaal or Natal stamps used in combination with those of the republic.

> **PRICES FOR STAMPS ON COVER**
> Nos. 1/95 *from* × 10

1

Printed with a rubber handstamp on paper bought in Europe and sent out ready gummed and perforated.

1886 (7 Jan)–**87.** *Various dates indicating date of printing.*
P 11½.

A. *Without Arms.* (i) *Yellow paper*

1	**1**	1d. black (9.1.86)	..	..	—	£2500
2		1d. violet (9.1.86)	..	10·00	12·00
		a. "1d." omitted (in pair with normal) (24.4.86)	..	£1500	
3		2d. violet (9.1.86)	..	10·00	15·00
		a. "d" omitted (13.10.86)	..		
4		3d. violet (13.1.86)	..	23·00	
		a. "d" omitted (13.10.86)		
5		4d. violet (30.8.86)	..	35·00	
6		6d. violet (20.2.86)	..	30·00	
		a. "6d." omitted (in pair with normal) (2.7.86)	..		
7		9d. violet (13.1.86)	..	30·00	
8		1s. violet (30.8.86)	..	65·00	
		a. "1s." omitted (in pair with normal) (6.9.86)		
9		1/s. violet (13.10.86)	..	£500	
10		1/6 violet (30.8.86)	..	65·00	
11		1s. 6d. violet (13.1.86)	..	£400	
		a. "d" omitted (13.10.86)	..	85·00	
12		2s. violet (30.8.86)	..	38·00	
		a. Tête-bêche (pair) (6.9.86)	..	£475	
13		2/6 violet (13.1.86)	..	£150	
14		2s. 6d. violet (1.86)	..	95·00	
15		4/s. violet (17.1.87)	..	£400	
16		5s. violet (1.86)	..	28·00	30·00
		a. "s" omitted (in pair with normal) (7.3.86)	..	£2000	
17		5/6 violet (20.2.86)	..	35·00	
18		5s. 6d. violet (13.1.86)	..	£160	
19		7/6 violet (13.1.86)	..	£170	
20		7s. 6d. violet (24.5.86)	..	95·00	
21		10s. violet (13.1.86)	..	95·00	
22		10s. 6d. violet (1.86)	..	£170	
		a. "d" omitted (1.86)	..	48·00	

23	**1**	13s. violet (24.11.86)	..	..	£400
24		£1 violet (13.1.86)	..	..	£120
25		30s. violet (13.1.86)	..	95·00	
		a. Tête-bêche (pair) (24.11.86)	£500	

(ii) *Blue granite paper*

26	**1**	1d. violet (20.1.86)	..	13·00	14·00
		a. "d" omitted (24.11.86)	£375	
		b. "1" omitted (in pair with normal) (24.11.86)		
27		2d. violet (13.1.86)	..	13·00	14·00
		a. "d" omitted (24.4.86)	£750	
		b. "2d." omitted (in pair with normal) (24.4.86)		
28		3d. violet (13.10.86)	..	16·00	18·00
		a. Tête-bêche (pair) (13.10.86)	£275	
29		4d. violet (24.5.86)	..	13·00	16·00
30		6d. violet (24.5.86)	..	25·00	21·00
		a. "6" omitted (in pair with normal) (24.5.86)	..£1500	
31		9d. violet (6.9.86)	..	24·00	
32		1s. violet (1.86)	..	28·00	30·00
		a. Tête-bêche (pair) (21.5.86)	£300	
		b. "1s." omitted (in pair with normal) (29.4.86)	..£1500	
33		1s. 6d. violet (2.7.86)	..	35·00	
		a. Tête-bêche (pair) (6.9.86)	£475	
34		1/6 violet (6.9.86)	..	£150	
35		2s. violet (21.5.86)	..	£120	
		a. "2s" omitted (in pair with normal) (24.5.86)	..£1500	
36		2s. 6d. violet (19.8.86)	..	£140	
37		2/6 violet (19.8.86)	..	£180	
38		4/s. violet (17.1.87)	..	£200	
39		5s. 6d. violet (13.1.86)	..	£170	
40		5/6 violet (13.1.86)	..	£200	
		a. "/" omitted (13.1.87)	£200	
41		7/6 violet (13.1.86)	..	£200	
41a		7s. 6d. violet (13.1.86)		
42		10s. violet (1.86)	..	£200	£200
		a. Tête-bêche (pair) (2.7.86)	£400	
		b. "s" omitted (13.1.86)		
43		10s. 6d. violet (1.86)	..	£200	
		a. Tête-bêche (pair) (13.1.86)		
		b. "d" omitted (1.86)	£450	
44		12s. violet (13.1.86)	..	£300	
45		13s. violet (17.1.87)	..	£400	
46		£1 violet (13.1.86)	..	£250	
47		30s. violet (13.1.86)	..	£250	

B. *With embossed Arms of New Republic.* (i) *Yellow paper*

48	**1**	1d. violet (20.1.86)	..	13·00	15·00
		a. Arms inverted (20.1.86)	..	25·00	25·00
		b. Arms tête-bêche (pair) (14.4.86)	£100	£120
49		2d. violet (2.12.86)	..	13·00	15·00
		a. Arms inverted (24.11.86)	..	23·00	28·00
50		4d. violet (2.12.86)	..	18·00	22·00
		a. Arms inverted (12.86)	..	95·00	60·00
		b. Arms tête-bêche (pair) (12.86)	..	£250	
51		6d. violet (2.12.86)	..	45·00	

(ii) *Blue granite paper*

52	**1**	1d. violet (20.1.86)	..	14·00	16·00
		a. Arms inverted (10.2.86)	..	35·00	40·00
		b. Arms tête-bêche (pair) (3.11.86)		
53		2d. violet (30.8.86)	..	14·00	16·00
		a. Arms inverted (30.8.86)	..	48·00	
		b. Arms tête-bêche (pair) (2.12.86)	£500	£500

Stamps as Type **1** were produced as and when stocks were required, each printing including in its design the date on which it was prepared. The dates quoted above for Nos. 1/53 are those on which the various stamps first appeared. Details of the various printing dates are given below. From these dates it can be seen that some values share common printing dates, and, it is believed, that the different values were produced *se-tenant* within the same sheet, at least in some instances. A reported proof sheet in the Pretoria Postal Museum, on yellow paper and embossed, contains 4 examples of the 6d. value and 3 each of the 3d., 4d., 9d., 1s., 1/6, 2/-, 2/6, 3s., 4s., 5s., 5/6, 7/6, 10/-, 10/6, £1 and 30/-.
The significance, if any, of the two coloured papers and the use of the embossing machine have never been satisfactorily explained. Both the different papers and the embossing machine were introduced in January 1886, and occur throughout the period that the stamps with dates were used.

PRINTINGS

Date	Paper	Face value	Cat. No.	Un.	Us.
Jan 86	Yellow	5s.	16	28·00	30·00
		10s. 6d.	22	£170	
	Blue	10s. 6d.	22a	80·00	
		1s.	32		
		10s.	42	£200	£200
		10s. 6d.	43	£200	
		10s. 6d.	43b	£450	
7 Jan 86	Yellow	10s. 6d.	22	£160	
	Blue	10s.	42		
		10s. 6d.	43	£450	
9 Jan 86	Yellow	1d.	1	—	£2500
		1d.	2	10·00	12·00
		2d.	3	10·00	15·00
13 Jan 86	Yellow	1d.	2	35·00	
		2d.	3	14·00	15·00
		3d.	4	40·00	
		9d.	7	£200	
		1s. 6d.	11	£400	
		2/6	13	£160	
		2s. 6d.	14	95·00	
		5s. 6d.	18		
		7/6	19	£170	
		10s.	21		
		£1	24	£130	
		30s.	25	95·00	
	Blue	2d.	27		
		5s. 6d.	39	£170	
		5/6	40	£200	
		7/6	41	£200	
		7s. 6d.	41a		
		10s.	42	£400	
		10s.	42b		
		10s. 6d.	43	£200	
		10s. 6d.	43a		
		12s.	44	£300	
		£1	46	£250	
		30s.	47	£250	

Date	Paper	Face value	Cat. No.	Un.	Us.
20 Jan 86	Yellow	1d.	2		
		2s. 6d.	14		
	Blue	1d.	26	£250	
	Yellow, embossed	1d.	48	32·00	
		1d.	48a	48·00	
	Blue, embossed	1d.	52	95·00	
Jan 20 86	Blue	1d.	26	23·00	
	Yellow, embossed	1d.	48a		
	Blue, embossed	1d.	52	£100	
24 Jan 86	Blue	1d.	26	18·00	
		2d.	27	30·00	
10 Feb 86	Yellow	1d.	2		
	Yellow, embossed	1d.	48		
		1d.	48a	48·00	
	Blue, embossed	1d.	52	£130	
		1d.	52a	35·00	
20 Feb 86	Yellow	6d.	6		
		2s. 6d.	14	£130	
		5/6	17	£120	
		5s. 6d.	18		
7 Mar 86	Yellow	1d.	2	£110	
		2/6	13		
		2s. 6d.	14	95·00	
		5s.	16	£200	85·00
		5s.	16a		
		5/6	17	35·00	
		5s. 6d.	18	£160	
	Blue	2d.	27	95·00	
		1s.	32		
17 Mar 86	Yellow	1d.	2	95·00	
	Yellow, embossed	1d.	48	48·00	
	Blue, embossed	1d.	52	95·00	
		1d.	52a	80·00	
26 Mar 86	Blue, embossed	1d.	52a	£130	
14 Apr 86	Yellow	1d.	2		
	Yellow, embossed	1d.	48	23·00	
		1d.	48a	£120	
		1d.	48b	£100	£120
	Blue, embossed	1d.	52	45·00	
		1d.	52a		
24 Apr 86	Yellow	1d.	2	£100	
		1d.	2a	£1500	
		5s.	16		
	Blue	2d.	27	28·00	
		2d.	27a	£750	
		2d.	27b		
		1s.	32		
29 Apr 86	Blue	1s.	32	£110	
		1s.	32b		
21 May 86	Yellow	6d.	6	£130	
	Blue	1d.	26	85·00	
		1s.	32	28·00	30·00
		1s.	32a	£300	
		1s.	32b	£1500	
		2s.	35	£275	
23 May 86	Yellow, embossed	1d.	48		
	Blue, embossed	1d.	52a	95·00	
24 May 86	Yellow	1d.	2	95·00	
		2d.	3	£120	
		5s.	16	70·00	
		7/6	19	£170	
		7s. 6d.	20	95·00	
	Blue	1d.	26	13·00	14·00
		2d.	27		
		4d.	29	85·00	
		6d.	30	£120	
		6d.	30a		
		1s.	32	£200	
		1s.	32b		
		2s.	35	£120	
		2s.	35a	£1500	
26 May 86	Yellow	1d.	2		
	Blue	1d.	26	£110	
	Yellow, embossed	1d.	48	£250	
		1d.	48a	95·00	
	Blue, embossed	1d.	52	£130	
		1d.	52a	48·00	50·00
28 May 86	Yellow, embossed	1d.	48	32·00	
30 Jun 86	Yellow	1d.	2		
	Blue	1d.	26		
Jun 30 86	Blue	1d.	26	15·00	16·00
	Yellow, embossed	1d.	48	14·00	16·00
		1d.	48a	25·00	28·00
		1d.	48b	£200	£225
	Blue, embossed	1d.	52	45·00	40·00
2 Jul 86	Yellow	6d.	6		
		6d.	6a		
		9d.	7	95·00	95·00

Date	Paper	Face value	Cat. No.	Un.	Us.
	Blue	1s.	32		
		1s. 6d.	33	35·00	
		10s.	42	£200	
		10s.	42a	£400	
		10s. 6d.	43		
		10s. 6d.	43b		
Jul 7 86	Yellow	1d.	2		
	Blue	1d.	26		
		10s. 6d.	43		
	Yellow, embossed	1d.	48	25·00	
		1d.	48a	95·00	95·00
	Blue, embossed	1d.	52	14·00	16·00
		1d.	52a	55·00	40·00
4 Aug 86	Yellow	1d.	2		
	Yellow, embossed	1d.	48	55·00	
	Blue, embossed	1d.	52	35·00	
		1d.	52a		
19 Aug 86	Yellow	2/6	13		
		2s. 6d.	14	£140	
		2s. 6d.	36	£140	
	Blue	2/6	37	£180	
30 Aug 86	Yellow	1d.	2	10·00	12·00
		2d.	3	11·00	
		3d.	4	23·00	
		4d.	5	48·00	
		6d.	6	32·00	
		9d.	7	48·00	
		1s.	8	65·00	
		1/6	10	65·00	
		2s.	12	95·00	
		2/6	13	£150	
	Blue	1d.	26		
		2d.	27	13·00	14·00
	Yellow, embossed	1d.	48		
	Blue, embossed	2d.	53	42·00	
		2d.	53a	£110	
6 Sep 86	Yellow	1d.	2	12·00	
		2d.	3	8·50	9·00
		3d.	4	38·00	
		4d.	5	40·00	
		6d.	6	30·00	
		9d.	7	30·00	
		1s.	8	95·00	
		1s.	8a		
		1/6	10	70·00	
		1s. 6d.	11	£400	
		2s.	12	£100	
		2s.	12a	£475	
		2/6	13	£150	
		2s. 6d.	14		
		5s.	16	£140	
		7s. 6d.	20	£200	
		10s.	21	95·00	
		£1	24	£120	
	Blue	6d.	30	20·00	21·00
		9d.	31	£110	
		1s.	32	65·00	
		1s.	32b	£1300	
		1s. 6d.	33	£140	
		1s. 6d.	33a	£475	
		1/6	34		
		2/6	37	£400	
		10s. 6d.	43		
13 Sep 86	Yellow	1d.	2		
	Yellow, embossed	1d.	48	48·00	
		1d.	48a	48·00	
	Blue, embossed	1d.	52	85·00	
6 Oct 86	Yellow	1d.	2		
	Blue	1d.	26	85·00	
	Yellow, embossed	1d.	48	23·00	18·00
		1d.	48a		
	Blue, embossed	1d.	52	45·00	18·00
		1d.	52a	85·00	
13 Oct 86	Yellow	1d.	2	12·00	12·00
		2d.	3	10·00	11·00
		2d.	3a		
		3d.	4	23·00	25·00
		3d.	4a		
		4d.	5	35·00	
		6d.	6	30·00	32·00
		9d.	7	35·00	
		1s.	8	70·00	
		1/s.	9	£500	
		1/6	10	£150	
		1s. 6d.	11a	85·00	
		2s.	12	38·00	
		2/6	13	£160	
		5s.	16	42·00	
		10s.	21	95·00	£100

Date	Paper	Face value	Cat. No.	Un.	Us.
		10s. 6d.	22a	48·00	
		£1	24	£120	
	Blue	2d.	27	13·00	14·00
		3d.	28	16·00	18·00
		3d.	28a	£275	
		4d.	29	28·00	28·00
		1s.	32	28·00	
		1/6	34	£150	
		2s.	35	£120	
3 Nov 86	Yellow	1d.	2	28·00	
		9d.	7		
	Blue	1d.	26		
	Yellow, embossed	1d.	48	13·00	15·00
		1d.	48a	25·00	28·00
		1d.	48b	£100	£120
	Blue, embossed	1d.	52	14·00	
		1d.	52a	35·00	40·00
		1d.	52b		
13 Nov 86	Yellow	1d.	2	35·00	
24 Nov 86	Yellow	1d.	2	14·00	
		2d.	3	10·00	11·00
		3d.	4	30·00	32·00
		1/6	10		
		10s.	21	£200	
		13s.	23	£400	
		30s.	25	95·00	
		30s.	25a	£500	
	Blue	1d.	26	38·00	17·00
		1d.	26a	£375	
		1d.	26b		
		2d.	27	18·00	
		2d.	27a		
		4d.	29	13·00	16·00
		6d.	30	20·00	21·00
		9d.	31	24·00	
		1s.	32	45·00	48·00
		1/6	34	£160	
		2s.	35	£140	
	Yellow, embossed	2d.	49	£160	
		2d.	49a		
26 Nov 86	Yellow	1/6	10	£140	
2 Dec 86	Yellow	1d.	2		
		2d.	3		
	Yellow, embossed	1d.	48	13·00	15·00
		1d.	48a	£160	
		2d.	49	13·00	15·00
		2d.	49a	23·00	28·00
		4d.	50	80·00	
		6d.	51	45·00	
	Blue, embossed	1d.	52	28·00	
		1d.	52a	£160	
		2d.	53	14·00	16·00
		2d.	53a	48·00	
		2d.	53b	£500	£500
Dec 86	Yellow	6d.	6		
	Blue	4d.	29		
		6d.	30		
	Yellow, embossed	4d.	50	18·00	22·00
		4d.	50a	95·00	60·00
		4d.	50b	£250	
		6d.	51	42·00	
4 Jan 87	Yellow	1d.	2	35·00	
		2d.	3	32·00	
		13s.	23	£400	
	Blue	1d.	26	13·00	14·00
		2d.	27	16·00	14·00
	Blue, embossed	2d.	53	42·00	
13 Jan 87	Blue	5/6	40	£400	
		5/6	40a		
		7/6	41	£400	
17 Jan 87	Yellow	1d.	2	38·00	
		2d.	3	30·00	
		3d.	4	45·00	
		4/s.	15	£200	
	Blue	1d.	26	75·00	
		4/s.	38	£200	
		13s.	45	£400	
		30s.	47	£250	
20 Jan 87	Blue	2d.	27	32·00	
	Yellow, embossed	2d.	49	50·00	
		2d.	49a	£140	
	Blue, embossed	2d.	53	42·00	
		2d.	53a	95·00	
Jan 20 87	Yellow, embossed	1d.	48a	£400	

1887 (Feb–Mar). *As T* **1**, *but without date. With embossed Arms.*

(a) Blue granite paper

72	1d. violet	..	..	14·00 14·00
	a. Imperf between (pair)	..	..	
	b. Stamps *tête-bêche* (pair)	..	£325	
	c. Arms *tête-bêche* (pair)	..		
	d. Arms inverted	..	..	23·00 23·00
	e. Arms omitted	..	..	£110 £110
	f. Arms sideways	..	..	
73	2d. violet	..	..	8·50 8·50
	a. Stamps *tête-bêche* (pair)	..	£275	
	b. Arms inverted	..	..	23·00 23·00
	c. Arms omitted	..	..	£110 95·00
	d. Arms *tête-bêche* (pair)	..		
74	3d. violet	..	..	13·00 13·00
	a. Stamps *tête-bêche* (pair)	..	£375	
	b. Arms *tête-bêche* (pair)	..		
	c. Arms inverted	..	..	48·00 48·00
75	4d. violet	..	..	13·00 13·00
	a. Stamps *tête-bêche* (pair)	..	£325	
	b. Arms *tête-bêche* (pair)	..	£275	
	c. Arms inverted	..	..	85·00
76	6d. violet	..	..	13·00 13·00
	a. Arms inverted	..	..	85·00
77	1/6 violet	..	..	14·00 14·00
	a. Arms inverted	..	..	80·00
77*b*	2/6d. violet	..	..	— £750

(b) Yellow paper (March 1887)

78	2d. violet (*arms omitted*)	..	..	13·00
79	3d. violet	..	..	13·00 13·00
	a. Imperf between (pair)	..	..	
	b. Stamps *tête-bêche* (pair)	..	£325 £350	
	c. Arms *tête-bêche* (pair)	..	£200	
	d. Arms inverted	..	..	23·00 23·00
	da. Double impression	..		
80	4d. violet	..	..	13·00 13·00
	a. Arms inverted	..	..	14·00 14·00
81	6d. violet	..	..	8·00 8·00
	a. Arms *tête-bêche* (pair)	..	£350	
	b. Arms inverted	..	..	42·00 42·00
	c. Arms omitted	..	..	80·00
	ca. Double impression	..		
82	9d. violet	..	..	8·50 8·50
	a. Arms inverted	..	..	£200
	b. Arms *tête-bêche* (pair)	..	£350	
83	1s. violet	..	..	8·50 8·50
	a. Arms inverted	..	..	70·00
84	1/6 violet	..	..	17·00 14·0
85	2s. violet	..	..	18·00 16·00
	a. Arms inverted	..	..	55·00 50·00
	b. Arms omitted	..	..	70·00
86	2/6 violet	..	..	23·00 23·00
	a. Arms inverted	..	..	28·00 28·00
87	3s. violet	..	..	42·00 42·00
	a. Arms inverted	..	..	45·00 45·00
	b. Stamps *tête-bêche* (pair)..	£450		
88	4s. violet	..	..	11·00 11·00
	a. Arms omitted (4s.)	..	£180	
	b. Arms omitted (4/-)	..	£130	
89	5s. violet	..	..	13·00 13·00
	a. Imperf between (pair)	..	..	— 80·00
	b. Arms inverted	..	..	
90	5/6 violet	..	..	12·00 12·00
91	7/6 violet	..	..	14·00 17·00
	a. Arms *tête-bêche* (pair)	..		
	b. Arms inverted	..	..	45·00
92	10s. violet	..	..	12·00 12·00
	a. Imperf between (pair)	..	..	
	b. Arms *tête-bêche* (pair)	..	£120	
	c. Arms inverted	..	..	23·00
	d. Arms omitted	..	..	£110 45·00
93	10/6 violet	..	..	16·00 16·00
	a. Imperf between (pair)	..	..	
	b. Arms inverted	..	..	
94	£1 violet	..	..	45·00 45·00
	a. Stamps *tête-bêche* (pair)	..	£300 £350	
	b. Arms inverted	..	..	55·00
95	30s. violet	..	..	£110

New Republic united with the South African Republic (Transvaal) on 21 July 1888. In 1903 the territory of the former New Republic was transferred to Natal.

ORANGE FREE STATE

PRICES FOR STAMPS ON COVER

Nos. 1/9	*from* × 12
Nos. 10/13	*from* × 10
Nos. 18/19	*from* × 12
No. 20	
Nos. 21/42	*from* × 10
Nos. 48/51	*from* × 20
Nos. 52/138	*from* × 10
Nos. 139/51	*from* × 7
Nos. F1/17	—
Nos. PF1/3	—
No. M1	—

1

(Typo D.L.R.)

1868 (1 Jan)–**94**. *P* 14.

1	1	1d. pale brown	..	2·25	65
2		1d. red-brown	..	2·25	35
3		1d. deep brown	..	3·75	40
4		6d. pale rose (1868)	..	10·00	4·00
5		6d. rose (1871)	..	3·50	3·25
6		6d. rose-carmine (1891)	..	11·00	12·00
7		6d. bright carmine (1894)	..	3·25	2·00
8		1s. orange-buff	..	50·00	5·00
9		1s. orange-yellow	..	12·00	1·50
		a. Double print		—£2500	

4 **4** **4** **4**

(2) (a) — (b) — (c) — (d)

1877. *No. 6 surcharged T* **2** (*a*) *to* (*d*).

10	1	4d. on 6d. rose (*a*)	..	£180	45·00
		a. Surch inverted		—	£550
		b. Surch double (*a + c*)	..		
		c. Surch double. one inverted (*a + c* inverted)		—£1100	
		d. Surch double, one inverted (*a* inverted + *c*)			
11		4d. on 6d. rose (*b*)	..	£1100	£160
		a. Surch inverted		—	£900
		b. Surch double (*b + d*)	..		
12		4d. on 6d. rose (*c*) ..		85·00	25·00
		a. Surch inverted		—	£325
		b. Surch double			
13		4d. on 6d. rose (*d*)	..	£120	35·00
		a. Surch inverted		£1000	£375

1878 (July). *P* 14.

18	1	4d. pale blue	..	9·50	2·50
19		4d. ultramarine	..	4·00	2·50
20		5s. green	..	8·50	9·50

1d. **1d.** **1d.** **1d.** **1d.** **1d.**

(3) (*a*) — (*b*) — (*c*) — (*d*) — (*e*) — (*f*)

Type 3: (*a*) Small "1" and "d." (*b*) Sloping serif. (*c*) Same size as (*b*), but "1" with straighter horizontal serif. (*d*) Taller "1" with horizontal serif and antique "d". (*e*) Same size as (*d*) but with sloping serif and thin line at foot. (*f*) as (*d*) but with Roman "d".

1881 (19 May). *No. 20 surch T* **3** (*a*) *to* (*f*) *with heavy black bar cancelling the old value.*

21	1	1d. on 5s. green (*a*)	..	45·00	10·00
22		1d. on 5s. green (*b*)	..	28·00	10·00
		a. Surch inverted		—	£500
		b. Surch double		—	£500
23		1d. on 5s. green (*c*)	..	90·00	42·00
		a. Surch inverted		—	£600
		b. Surch double		—	£700
24		1d. on 5s. green (*d*)	..	40·00	10·00
		a. Surch inverted		£600	£500
		b. Surch double		—	£550
25		1d. on 5s. green (*e*)	..	£250	£200
		a. Surch inverted		—	£1300
		b. Surch double		—	£1100
26		1d. on 5s. green (*f*)	..	40·00	10·00
		a. Surch inverted		—	£450
		b. Surch double		—	£500

No. 21 was the first printing in one type only. Nos. 22 to 25 constitute the second printing about a year later, and are all found on the same sheet; and No. 26 the third printing of which about half have the stop raised.

Owing to defective printing examples of Nos. 22 and 24/5 may be found with the obliterating bar at the top of the stamps or, from the top row, without the bar.

½d

(4)

1882 (Aug). *No. 20 surch with T* **4** *and with a thin black line cancelling old value.*

36	1	½d. on 5s. green	..	2·75	3·25
		a. Surch double..		£350	£300
		b. Surch inverted	..		

3d **3*d*** **3*d*** **3d** **3*d***

(5) (*a*) — (*b*) — (*c*) — (*d*) — (*e*)

1882. *No. 19 surch with T* **5** (*a*) *to* (*e*) *with thin black line cancelling value.*

38	1	3d. on 4d. ultramarine (*a*)	..	50·00	23·00
		a. Surch double		—	£650
39		3d. on 4d. ultramarine (*b*)	..	42·00	17·00
		a. Surch double		—	£650
40		3d. on 4d. ultramarine (*c*)	..	25·00	16·00
		a. Surch double		—	£650
41		3d. on 4d. ultramarine (*d*)	..	48·00	17·00
		a. Surch double		—	£650
42		3d. on 4d. ultramarine (*e*)	..	£110	60·00
		a. Surch double		—	£750

Examples of Nos. 39 and 41/2 exist without the cancelling bar due to the misplacement of the surcharge.

1883–84. *P* 14.

48	1	½d. chestnut	..	60	50
49		2d. pale mauve	..	3·00	40
50		2d. bright mauve	..	3·00	30
51		3d. ultramarine	..	1·75	2·00

For 1d. purple, see No. 68.

2d **2d** **2d**

(6) (*a*) — (*b*) — (*c*)

1888 (Sept–Oct). *No. 51 surch with T* **6** (*a*), (*b*) *or* (*c*).

(a) Wide "2". (b) Narrow "2"

52	1	2d. on 3d. ultramarine (*a*) (Sept)		26·00	9·00
		a. Surch inverted		—	£700
53		2d. on 3d. ultramarine (*b*)		11·00	2·00
		a. Surch inverted		—	£300
		b. "2" with curved foot (*c*)	..		

1d **1d** **1d**

(7) (*a*) — (*b*) — (*c*)

1890 (Dec)–**91**. *Nos. 51 and 19 surch with T* **7** (*a*) *to* (*c*).

54	1	1d. on 3d. ultramarine (*a*)		1·10	60
		a. Surch double		75·00	
		c. "1" and "d" wide apart	..	£140	£110
55		1d. on 3d. ultramarine (*b*)		6·00	2·50
		a. Surch double..		£140	£160
57		1d. on 4d. ultramarine (*a*)		13·00	3·25
		a. Surch double..		£120	£110
		b. Surch double (*a + b*)..		£180	
		c. Surch triple			
58		1d. on 4d. ultramarine (*b*)		70·00	48·00
		a. Surch double..		£250	£250
59		1d. on 4d. ultramarine (*c*)		£1000	£450
		a. Surch double..			

The settings of the 1d. on 3d. and on 4d. are not identical. The variety (*c*) does not exist on the 3d.

2½d.

(8)

1892 (Oct). *No 51 surch with T* **8**.

67	1	2½d. on 3d. ultramarine	..	3·00	70
		a. No stop after "d"	..	40·00	

1894 (Sept). *Colour changed. P* 14.

68	1	1d. purple	..	85	30

½d **½d** **½d**

(9) (*a*) — (*b*) — (*c*)

½d **½d** **½d** **½d**

(*d*) — (*e*) — (*f*) — (*g*)

Types (*a*) and (*e*) differ from types (*b*) and (*f*) respectively, in the serifs of the "1", but owing to faulty overprinting this distinction is not always clearly to be seen.

1896 (Sept). *No. 51 surch with T* **9** (*a*) *to* (*g*).

69	1	½d. on 3d. ultramarine (*a*)	..	2·25	4·00
70		½d. on 3d. ultramarine (*b*)	..	5·00	4·00
71		½d. on 3d. ultramarine (*c*)	..	5·00	2·50
72		½d. on 3d. ultramarine (*d*)	..	5·00	2·25
73		½d. on 3d. ultramarine (*e*)	..	4·25	2·25
74		½d. on 3d. ultramarine (*f*)	..	4·25	4·50
75		½d. on 3d. ultramarine (*g*)	..	2·00	2·25
		a. Surch double	..	12·00	10·00
		b. Surch triple	..	60·00	

The double and triple surcharges are often different types, but are always type (*g*), or in combination with type (*g*).

Double surcharges in the same type, but without the "d" and bar, also exist, probably from a trial sheet prepared by the printer. Both mint and used examples are known.

Halve Penny.

——— **2½**

(10) — (11)

1896. *No. 51 surch with T* **10**.

77	1	½d. on 3d. ultramarine	..	35	50

(i) Errors in setting

78	1	½d. on 3d. (no stop)	..	8·00	13·00
79		½d. on 3d. ("Peuny")	..	8·50	13·00

(ii) Surch inverted

81	1	½d. on 3d.	..	50·00	
81*a*		½d. on 3d. (no stop)	..		
81*b*		½d. on 3d. ("Peuny")	..		

(iii) Surch double, one inverted

81*c*	1	½d. on 3d. (Nos. 77 and 81)	..	£180	£200
81*d*		½d. on 3d. (Nos. 77 and 81*a*)	..	£450	
81*e*		½d. on 3d. (Nos. 77 and 81*b*)	..	£500	
81*f*		½d. on 3d. (Nos. 81 and 78)	..		
82		½d. on 3d. (Nos. 81 and 79)	..	—	£425

Examples from the top horizontal row can be found without the bar due to the surcharge being misplaced.

Nos. 69 to 75 also exist surcharged as last but they are considered not to have been issued with authority.

1897 (1 Jan). *No. 51 surch with T* **11**. (*a*) *As in illustration.* (*b*) *With Roman "1" and antique "2" in fraction.*

83	1	2½d. on 3d. ultramarine (*a*)	..	1·25	80
83*a*		2½d. on 3d. ultramarine (*b*)	..	£130	90·00

1897. *P 14.*

84	1	½d. yellow (March)	.. ..	80	35
85		½d. orange	.. ..	80	35
87		1s. brown (Aug)	.. ..	7·50	1·50

The 6d. blue was prepared for use in the Orange Free State, but had not been brought into use when the stamps were seized in Bloemfontein. A few have been seen without the "V.R.I." overprint, but they were not authorized or available for postage. (*Price* £45.)

BRITISH OCCUPATION

V. R. I.	V. R. I.	V. R. I.
4d	**½d**	**½d**
31 (Level stops)	(32) (Raised stops) Thin "V"	(33) Thick "V"

V. R I.

Inserted "R"

(Surch by Curling & Co, Bloemfontein)

1900. *T 1 surch as T 31/33 (2½d. on 3d. optd "V.R.I." only).*

(a) First printings surch as T 31 with stops level (March)

101	½d. on ½d. orange	.. ..	1·25	1·25
	a. No stop after "V" ..		15·00	15·00
	b. No stop after "I" ..		£160	£160
	c. "½" omitted		£160	£160
	d. "I" omitted			
	e. "V.R.I." omitted ..		£160	
	f. Value omitted		£100	
	g. Small "½"		45·00	45·00
	h. Surch double		£140	
102	1d. on 1d. purple		1·00	60
	a. Error. Brown		£600	£400
	b. No stop after "V" ..		10·00	10·00
	c. No stop after "R" ..		£150	£160
	d. No stop after "I" ..			
	e. "1" omitted		£170	
	f. "I" omitted		65·00	65·00
	g. "I" and stop after "R" omitted ..		75·00	75·00
	h. "V.R.I." omitted ..		£140	
	i. "d" omitted		£300	
	j. Value omitted		80·00	
	k. Inverted stop after "R"		£160	
	l. Wider space between "1" and "d"		£100	£100
	m. "V" and "R" close..		£150	
	n. Pair, one without surch ..		£400	
	o. "V" omitted		£650	
103	2d. on 2d. bright mauve		45	70
	a. No stop after "V"..		9·00	11·00
	b. No stop after "R" ..		£250	
	c. No stop after "I" ..		£250	
	d. "V.R.I." omitted ..		£300	
	e. Value omitted			
104	2½d. on 3d. ultramarine (a) ..		4·75	3·50
	a. No stop after "V"..		65·00	60·00
105	2½d. on 3d. ultramarine (b) ..		£170	£170
106	3d. on 3d. ultramarine		1·25	85
	a. No stop after "V"..		12·00	12·00
	b. Pair, one without surch ..		£325	
	c. "V.R.I." omitted ..			
	d. Value omitted			
107	4d. on 4d. ultramarine		4·25	5·50
	a. No stop after "V"..		48·00	50·00
108	6d. on 6d. bright carmine		35·00	35·00
	a. No stop after "V"..		£250	£275
	b. "6" omitted		£300	£300
109	6d. on 6d. blue		2·75	3·25
	a. No stop after "V"..		28·00	30·00
	b. "6" omitted		55·00	55·00
	c. "V.R.I." omitted ..			
110	1s. on 1s. brown		3·50	3·25
	a. Error. Orange-yellow		£2750	£2250
	b. No stop after "V"..		28·00	28·00
	c. "1" omitted		£100	£100
	d. "1" omitted and spaced stop after "s"		£120	
	e. "V.R.I." omitted ..		£150	£150
	f. Value omitted		£150	£150
	g. Raised stop after "s"		9·00	9·50
	h. Wider space between "1" and "s"		£150	£150
111	5s. on 5s. green		17·00	28·00
	a. No stop after "V"..		£180	£180
	b. "5" omitted		£750	£750
	c. Inverted stop after "R"		£600	£600
	d. Wider space between "5" and "s"		£120	£120
	e. Value omitted			

All values are found with a rectangular, instead of an oval, stop after "R". Misplaced surcharges (upwards or sideways) occur.

(b) Subsequent printings. (i) *Surch as T 32*

112	½d. on ½d. orange		20	20
	a. Raised and level stops mixed		1·40	1·60
	b. Pair, one with level stops		8·00	12·00
	c. No stop after "V"..		2·00	2·00
	d. No stop after "I" ..		24·00	24·00
	e. "V" omitted		£550	
	f. Small "½"		11·00	12·00
	g. As a, and small "½"		11·00	12·00
	i. Space between "V" and "R"			
	j. Value omitted			
113	1d. on 1d. purple		20	20
	a. Raised and level stops mixed		1·25	1·40
	b. Pair, one with level stops		16·00	16·00
	c. No stop after "V"..		3·25	4·75
	d. No stop after "R"..		13·00	13·00
	e. No stop after "I" ..		13·00	13·00
	f. No stops after "V" and "I"		£275	
	g. Surch inverted		£300	
	h. Surch double		95·00	85·00
	i. Pair, one without surch ..		£200	

---

	j. Short figure "1"		£100	£100
	k. Space between "V" and "R"		70·00	75·00
	l. Space between "R" and "I"		£100	
	m. Space between "1" and "d"		£180	
	n. Inserted "R"		£300	
114	2d. on 2d. bright mauve		35	30
	a. Raised and level stops mixed		4·00	4·00
	b. Pair, one with level stops		6·50	6·50
	c. Surch inverted		£300	£300
	d. "I" raised			
	e. Pair, one without surch ..			
	f. No stop after "V"		£1000	
115	2½d. on 3d. ultramarine (a) ..		£180	£160
	a. Raised and level stops mixed			
116	2½d. on 3d. ultramarine (b) ..		£1200	
117	3d. on 3d. ultramarine		30	30
	a. Raised and level stops mixed		6·00	6·00
	b. Pair, one with level stops		14·00	14·00
	c. No stop after "V"..		£140	£140
	d. No stop after "R"..		—	£500
	e. "I" omitted		£400	
	f. Surch double		£400	
	g. Surch double, one diagonal		£350	
	h. Ditto, diagonal surch, with mixed stops		£6500	
	n. Inserted "R"			
	o. Space between "3" and "d"			
118	4d. on 4d. ultramarine		1·10	1·75
	a. Raised and level stops mixed		6·00	
	b. Pair, one with level stops		14·00	14·00
119	6d. on 6d. bright carmine		35·00	48·00
	a. Raised and level stops mixed		£140	£140
	b. Pair, one with level stops		£200	
120	6d. on 6d. blue		70	40
	a. Raised and level stops mixed		6·00	6·00
	b. Pair, one with level stops		14·00	14·00
	c. No stop after "V"..		£500	
	d. No stop after "R"..			
	e. Value omitted			
121	1s. on 1s. brown		70	45
	a. Error. Orange-yellow		£1300	£1300
	b. Raised and level stops mixed		9·00	
	c. Pair, one with level stops		20·00	22·00
	f. "s" omitted			
	g. "V.R.I." omitted ..			
122	5s. on 5s. green (H/S £50)		4·25	6·50
	a. Raised and level stops mixed		£300	£300
	b. Pair, one with level stops		£900	
	c. Short top to "5"		55·00	55·00

(ii) *Surch as T 33*

123	½d. on ½d. orange		1·25	60
124	1d. on 1d. purple		1·00	35
	a. Inverted "1" for "I"		14·00	14·00
	b. No stops after "R" and "I"		85·00	65·00
	c. No stop after "R"..		35·00	30·00
	d. Surch double		£300	£300
	n. Inserted "R"			
125	2d. on 2d. bright mauve		2·00	2·50
	a. Inverted "1" for "I"		16·00	16·00
126	2½d. on 3d. ultramarine (a)		£550	£650
127	2½d. on 3d. ultramarine (b)			
128	3d. on 3d. ultramarine		3·00	3·75
	a. Inverted "1" for "I"		75·00	60·00
	b. Surch double			
	ba. Surch double, one diagonal		£400	
129	6d. on 6d. bright carmine		£425	
130	6d. on 6d. blue		4·75	8·50
131	1s. on 1s. brown		7·50	7·00
132	5s. on 5s. green (H/S £150)		25·00	35·00

Stamps with thick "V" occur in certain positions in *later* settings of the type with stops above the line (T 32). *Earlier* settings with stops above the line have all stamps with thin "V".

Some confusion has previously been caused by the listing of certain varieties as though they occurred on stamps with thick "V", in fact they occur on stamps showing the normal thin "V", included in the settings which also contained the thick "V".

As small blocks of unsurcharged Free State stamps could be handed in for surcharging, varieties thus occur which are not found in the complete settings.

The inserted "R" variety occurs on positions 6 (T 32) and 12 (T 33) of the forme. The "R." of the original surcharge failed to print and the "R", but not the full stop, was added by the use of a handstamp. Traces of the original letter are often visible. The broken "V" flaw, also shown in the illustration, does not appear on No. 124n.

ORANGE RIVER COLONY

CROWN COLONY

ORANGE		**E. R. I.**
RIVER	**4d**	
COLONY.	**—**	**6d**
(34)	(35)	(36)

1900 (10 Aug)–02. *Nos. 58a, 61a and 67 of Cape of Good Hope (wmk Cabled Anchor. P 14) optd with T 34 by W. A. Richards and Sons, Cape Town.*

133	½d. green (13.10.00)		20	10
	a. No stop		7·00	10·00
	b. Opt double		£550	£600
134	1d. carmine (May 1902)		25	10
	a. No stop		9·00	13·00
135	2½d. ultramarine		30	35
	a. No stop		40·00	50·00
133/5		*Set of 3*	65	45

In the ½d. and 2½d., the "no stop" after "COLONY" variety was the first stamp in the left lower pane. In the 1d. it is the twelfth stamp in the right lower pane on which the stop was present at the beginning of the printing but became damaged and soon failed to print.

1902 (14 Feb). *Surch with T 35 by "Bloemfontein Express".*

136	4d. on 6d. blue (No. 120) (R.) ..		50	70
	a. No stop after "R"		30·00	30·00
	b. No stop after "I"			
	c. Surch on No. 130 (Thick "V").		1·75	3·75
	ca. Inverted "1" for "I"		4·75	8·00

1902 (Aug). *Surch with T 36.*

137	1	6d. on 6d. blue		1·75	4·50
	a. Surch double, one inverted			
	b. Wide space between "6" and "d" (R.4/2) ..		60·00	75·00

One Shilling	
❋	
(37)	**38** King Edward VII, Springbok and Gnu

1902 (Sept). *Surch with T 37.*

138	1	1s. on 5s. green (O.)		4·00	5·50
	a. Thick "V"		10·00	16·00
	b. Short top to "5"		65·00	65·00
	c. Surch double			

(Typo D.L.R.)

1903 (3 Feb)–04. *Wmk Crown CA. P 14.*

139	38	½d. yellow-green (6.7.03) ..		4·25	90
140		1d. scarlet		90	10
141		2d. brown (6.7.03)		2·75	70
142		2½d. bright blue (6.7.03)..		90	50
143		3d. mauve (6.7.03)		3·50	90
144		4d. scarlet and sage-green (6.7.03) ..		15·00	2·00
		a. "IOSTAGE" for "POSTAGE"		£800	£450
145		6d. scarlet and mauve (6.7.03)		5·00	70
146		1s. scarlet and bistre (6.7.03)		16·00	1·75
147		5s. blue and brown (31.10.04)		65·00	20·00
139/47			*Set of 9*	£100	24·00
139/47 Optd "Specimen"			*Set of 9*	£150	

No. 144a occurs on R.10/2 of the upper left pane.

Several of the above values are found with the overprint "C.S.A.R.", in black, for use by the Central South African Railways.

1905 (Nov)–09. *Wmk Mult Crown CA. P 14.*

148	38	½d. yellow-green (28.7.07)		3·75	30
149		1d. scarlet		2·50	20
150		4d. scarlet and sage-green (8.11.07)		4·25	1·75
		a. "IOSTAGE" for "POSTAGE"		£180	£150
151		1s. scarlet and bistre (2.09)		27·00	8·50
148/51			*Set of 4*	35·00	9·50

POSTCARD STAMPS

From 1889 onwards the Orange Free State Post Office sold postcards franked with adhesives as Type 1, some subsequently surcharged, over which the State Arms had been overprinted.

There are five known dies of the Arms overprint which can be identified as follows:
(a) Shield without flags. Three cows (two lying down, one standing) at left. Point of shield complete.
(b) Shield with flags. Four cows (two lying down, two standing) at left (*illustrated*).
(c) Shield with flags. Three cows (one lying down, two standing) at left.
(d) Shield without flags. Three cows (one lying down, two standing) at left.
(e) Shield without flags. Three cows (two lying down, one standing) at left. Point of shield broken.
There are also other differences between the dies.

PRICES. Those in the left-hand column are for unused examples on complete postcard; those on the right for used examples off card. Examples used on postcard are worth more.

1889 (Feb). *No. 2 (placed sideways on card) optd Shield Type (a).*

P1	1	1d. red-brown..		60·00	30·00
		a. Optd Shield Type (b)		20·00	5·00

1891 (Aug). *No. 48 optd Shield Type (b).*

P2	1	½d. chestnut		2·00	1·00
		a. Optd Shield Type (c)		6·00	3·00
		b. Optd Shield Type (d)		3·00	1·50
		c. Optd Shield Type (e)		7·00	3·50

1892 (June). *No. 54 optd Shield Type (b).*

P3	1	1d. on 3d. ultramarine		60·00	35·00
		a. Optd Shield Type (c)		7·00	2·00

1½d.	**1½d.**	**1½d.**
(P 1)	(P 2)	(P 3)

1892 (Sept)–95. *Nos. 50/1 optd Shield Type (b) or (d) (No. P6) and surch with Types P 1/3.*

P4	1	1½d. on 2d. bright mauve (Type P 1) (11.92)	5·00	2·50
P5		1½d. on 2d. bright mauve (Type P 2) (9.93)	2·00	1·00
		a. Surch inverted			
P6		1½d. on 2d. brt mauve (Type P 3) (R.) (6.95)	7·00	3·00
P7		1½d. on 3d. ultramarine (8.94)		5·00	1·50

No. P5a shows the stamp affixed to the card upside down with the surcharge correctly positioned in relation to the card.

½d.
(P 4)

1895 (Aug). *No. 48 optd Shield Type* (e) *and surch with Type P 4.*
P8 1 ½d. on ½d. chestnut .. .. .. 6·00 2·00

1½d. 1½d.
(P 5) (P 6)

1895 (Dec)–**97.** *No. 50 optd Shield Type* (e) *and surch with Types P 5/6.*
P 9 1 1½d. on 2d. bright mauve (Type P 5) 3·00 2·00
P10   1½d. on 2d. brt mauve (Type P 6) (12.97) 3·50 2·50
P11   1½d. on 2d. bright mauve (as Type P 6, but without stop) (12.97) .. 3·50 2·50

1897 (Mar). *No. 85 optd Shield Type* (d).
P12 1 ½d. orange .. .. .. 6·00 1·00
          a. Optd Shield Type (e) .. .. 7·00 2·00

V.R.I.
(P 7)

1900. *Nos. P11/12 optd as T 31/2 or with Type P 7.*
P13 1 1½d. on 2d. bright mauve (No. P11) (T 31) .. 15·00 4·00
P14   1½d. on 2d. bright mauve (No. P12) (T 31) .. 15·00 4·00
P15   1½d. on 2d. bright mauve (No. P11) (T 32) .. 15·00 4·00
P16   1½d. on 2d. bright mauve (No. P12) (T 32) .. 15·00 4·00
P17   1½d. on 2d. brt mve (No. P11) (Type P 7) 25·00 7·50
P18   1½d. on 2d. brt mve (No. P12) (Type P 7) 25·00 7·50

POLICE FRANK STAMPS

The following frank stamps were issued to members of the Orange Free State Mounted Police ("Rijdende Dienst Macht") for use on official correspondence.

PF 1 (eight ornaments at left and right) PF 2

1896. *P 12.*
PF1 PF 1 (–) Black .. ..
No. PF1 was printed in horizontal strips of 5 surrounded by wide margins.

1898. *As Type PF 1, but with nine ornaments at left and right. P 12.*
PF2 (–) Black £120
No. PF2 was printed in blocks of 4 (2×2) surrounded by wide margins.

1899. *P 12.*
PF3 PF 2 (–) Black/yellow .. £100 80·00
No. PF3 was printed in sheets of 24 (6×4) with the edges of the sheet imperforate. It is believed that they were produced from a setting of 8 (2×4) repeated three times.

Examples of No. PF3 are known postmarked as late as 28 April 1900. The O.F.S. Mounted Police were disbanded by the British authorities at the end of the following month.

MILITARY FRANK STAMP

M 1

(Typeset Curling & Co, Bloemfontein)
1899 (15 Oct). *P 12.*
M1 M 1 (–) Black/*bistre-yellow* .. 10·00 40·00
Supplies of No. M1 were issued to members of the Orange Free State army on active service during the Second Boer War. To pass free through the O.F.S. fieldpost system letters had to be franked with No. M1 or initialled by the appropriate unit commander. The franks were in use between October 1899 and February 1900.
No. M1 was printed in sheets of 20 (5×4) using a setting of five different types in a horizontal row. The colour in the paper runs in water.
Typeset forgeries can be identified by the appearance of 17 pearls, instead of the 16 of the originals, in the top and bottom frames. Forgeries produced by lithography omit the stops after "BRIEF" and "FRANKO".

FISCAL STAMPS USED FOR POSTAGE

The following were issued in 1878 (Nos. F1 and F3 in 1882) and were authorised for postal use between 1882 and 1886.

F 1 F 2

(Typo D.L.R.)

1882–86. *P 14.*
F 1 F 1 6d. pearl-grey .. .. 2·75 7·00
F 2   6d. purple-brown .. .. — 10·00
F 3 F 2 1s. purple-brown .. .. 4·00 10·00
F 4   1s. pearl-grey .. .. 20·00 27·00
F 5   1s. 6d. blue .. .. 7·00 5·50
F 6   2s. magenta .. .. 7·00 5·00
F 7   3s. chestnut .. .. 10·00 27·00
F 8   4s. grey .. ..
F 9   5s. rose .. .. 11·00
F10   6s. green .. .. — 27·00
F11   7s. violet .. ..
F12   10s. orange .. .. 22·00 16·00
F13   £1 purple .. .. 30·00 20·00
F14   £2 red-brown .. .. 32·00
F14a   £4 carmine .. ..
F15   £5 green .. .. 50·00 24·00
A fiscally used example of No. F2 exists showing "ZES PENCE" double, one inverted.
The 8s. yellow was prepared but we have no evidence of its use postally without surcharge Type F 3.

ZES PENCE.
(F 3)

1886. *Surch with Type F 3.*
F16 F 2 6d. on 4s. grey .. ..
F17   6d. on 8s. yellow £110
Postage stamps overprinted for use as Telegraph stamps and used postally are omitted as it is impossible to say with certainty which stamps were genuinely used for postal purposes.

Orange Free State became a province of the Union of South Africa on 31 May 1910.

TRANSVAAL
(formerly South African Republic)

PRICES FOR STAMPS ON COVER

Nos. 1/6 are rare used on cover.

Nos. 7/80   from × 20
Nos. 86/155   from × 3
Nos. 156/62   from × 6
Nos. 163/9   from × 5
Nos. 170/225   from × 10
Nos. 226/34   from × 20
Nos. 235/7
Nos. 238/43   from × 12
Nos. 244/55   from × 4
Nos. 256/7   from × 6
Nos. 258/9   —
Nos. 260/76   from × 20
Nos. D1/7   from × 20

The issues for Pietersburg, Lydenburg, Rustenburg, Schweizer Renecke, Volksrust and Wolmaransstad are very rare when on cover.

1 (Eagle with spread wings) 2 3

(Typo Adolph Otto, Gustrow, Mecklenburg-Schwerin)
1869. *Thin paper, clear and distinct impressions.* (a) *Imperf.*
1 1 1d. brown-lake £350
       a. Orange-red £350 £350
2   6d. bright ultramarine .. £130 £130
       a. Pale ultramarine .. £150 £160
3   1s. deep green £550 £550
       a. Tête-bêche (pair)

(b) *Fine roulette,* 15½ *to* 16
4 1 1d. brown-lake .. .. 85·00
       a. Brick-red .. .. 65·00
       b. Orange-red .. .. 65·00
       c. Vermilion .. .. 65·00
5   6d. bright ultramarine .. 60·00 60·00
       a. Pale ultramarine .. 70·00
6   1s. deep green £130 £130
       a. Yellow-green .. .. 90·00 90·00
       b. Emerald-green .. .. 75·00 75·00
A tête-bêche pair of the 6d. imperforate is also said to exist.

PLATES. The German printings of the 1d., 6d. and 1s. in Type 1 were from two pairs of plates, each pair printing sheets of 80 in two panes of five horizontal rows of eight.
One pair of plates, used for Nos. 4a, 4c, 5a and 6/a, produced stamps spaced 1¼ to 1½ mm apart with the rouletting close to the design on all four sides. The 1d. from these "narrow" plates shows a gap in the outer frame line at the bottom right-hand corner. The second pair, used for Nos. 1/3, 4, 4b, 5/a and 6b, had 2½ to 3½ mm between the stamps. These "wide" plates were sent to the Transvaal in 1869 and were used there to produce either single or double pane printings until 1883.
The 6d. and 1s. "wide" plates each had an inverted *cliché*. When printed these occurred on right-hand pane R. 4/1 of the 6d. and right-hand pane R.1/1 of the 1s. These were never corrected and resulted in *tête-bêche* pairs of these values as late as 1883.

REPRINTS AND IMITATIONS. A number of unauthorised printings were made of these stamps by the German printer. Many of these can be identified by differences in the central arms, unusual colours or, in the case of the 1d., by an extra frame around the numeral tablets at top.
Genuine stamps always show the "D" of "EENDRAGT" higher than the remainder of the word, have no break in the border above "DR" and depict the flagstaff at bottom right, behind "MAGT", stopping short of the central shield. They also show the eagle's eye as a clear white circle. On the forgeries the eye is often blurred.
The most difficult of the reprints to detect is the 1s. yellow-green which was once regarded as genuine, but was subsequently identified, by J. N. Luff in *The Philatelic Record* 1911–12, as coming from an unauthorised plate of four. Stamps from this plate show either a white dot between "EEN" and "SHILLING" or a white flaw below the wagon pole.

(Typo M. J. Viljoen, Pretoria)
1870 (4 Apr–4 July).
I. *Thin gummed paper from Germany. Impressions coarse and defective.* (a) *Imperf*
8 1 1d. dull rose-red .. .. 70·00
       a. Reddish pink .. .. 60·00
       b. Carmine-red .. .. 55·00 65·00
9   6d. dull ultramarine .. £250 60·00
       a. Tête-bêche (pair)

(b) *Fine roulette,* 15½ *to* 16
10 1 1d. carmine-red £700 £200
11   6d. dull ultramarine .. £180 90·00
       a. Imperf between (vert pair) .. £550

(c) *Wide roulette,* 6½
12 1 1d. carmine-red .. .. — £850

II. *Thick, hard paper with thin yellow smooth gum (No. 15) or yellow streaky gum (others).* (a) *Imperf* (26 Apr)
13 1 1d. pale rose-red .. .. 60·00
       a. Carmine-red .. .. 60·00 70·00
14   1s. yellow-green .. .. 70·00 70·00
       a. Tête-bêche (pair) .. £8000
       b. Bisected (6d.) (on cover) .. †£1100

(b) *Fine roulette,* 15½ *to* 16
15 1 1d. carmine-red (24 May) .. 80·00
16   6d. ultramarine (10 May) .. 80·00 80·00
       a. Tête-bêche (pair) .. £14000 £13000
17   1s. yellow-green (26 Apr) .. £550 £550

III. *Medium paper, blotchy heavy printing and whitish gum. Fine roulette* 15½ *to* 16 (4 July)
18 1 1d. rose-red .. .. 60·00 60·00
       a. Carmine-red .. .. 38·00 45·00
       b. Crimson. From over-inked plate .. £130
19   6d. ultramarine .. .. 65·00 65·00
       a. Tête-bêche (pair)
       b. Deep ultram. From over-inked plate £400 £150
20   1s. deep green .. .. 75·00 65·00
       a. From over-inked plate .. £400 £150
The rouletting machine producing the wide 6½ gauge was not introduced until 1875.
Nos. 18b, 19b and 20a were printed from badly over-inked plates giving heavy blobby impressions.

(Typo J. P. Borrius, Potchefstroom)
1870 (Sept)–**71.** *Stout paper, but with colour often showing through, whitish gum.* (a) *Imperf*
21 1 1d. black £120 £120

(b) *Fine roulette,* 15½ *to* 16
22 1 1d. black .. .. .. 15·00 20·00
       a. Grey-black .. .. 15·00 20·00
23   6d. blackish blue (7.71) .. £120 50·00
       a. Dull blue .. .. 90·00 48·00

(Typo Adolph Otto, Gustrow, Mecklenburg-Schwerin)
1871 (July). *Thin paper, clear and distinct impressions. Fine roulette,* 15½ *to.* 16.
24 2 3d. pale reddish lilac .. 80·00 75·00
       a. Deep lilac .. .. 85·00 75·00
No. 24 and later printings in the Transvaal were produced from a pair of plates in the same format as the 1869 issue. All genuine stamps have a small dot on the left leg of the eagle.
Imperforate examples in the issued shade, without the dot on eagle's leg, had been previously supplied by the printer, probably as essays, but were not issued for postal purposes. They exist tête-bêche (price for un pair £3250).
Imperforate and rouletted stamps in other colours are reprints.

(Typo J. P. Borrius, Potchefstroom)
1872–74. *Fine roulette,* 15½ *to.* 16. (a) *Thin transparent paper*
25 1 1d. black £170 £550
26   1d. bright carmine .. £140 50·00
27   6d. ultramarine .. .. £100 40·00
28   1s. green .. .. .. £100 40·00

(b) *Thinnish opaque paper, clear printing* (Dec 1872)
29 1 1d. reddish pink .. .. 55·00 38·00
       a. Carmine-red .. .. 55·00 38·00
30 2 3½d. grey-lilac .. .. 75·00 38·00

31	1	6d. ultramarine		55·00	27·00
		a. Pale ultramarine		60·00	27·00
32		1s. yellow-green		60·00	27·00
		a. Green		60·00	29·00
		aa. Bisected (6d.) (on cover)			

(c) Thickish wove paper (1873–74)

33	1	1d. dull rose		400·00	70·00
		a. Brownish rose		£475	£110
		b. Printed on both sides			
34		6d. milky blue		£140	40·00
		a. Deep dull blue		80·00	35·00
		aa. Imperf (pair)		£600	
		ab. Imperf between (horiz pair)		£650	
		ac. Wide roulette 6½			

(d) Very thick dense paper (1873–74)

35	1	1d. dull rose		£475	£110
		a. Brownish rose		£350	85·00
36		6d. dull ultramarine		£170	60·00
		a. Bright ultramarine		£180	60·00
37		1s. yellow-green		£750	£550

(Typo P. Davis & Son, Pietermaritzburg)
1874 (Sept). *P 12½.* (a) *Thin transparent paper.*

38	1	1d. pale brick-red		80·00	35·00
		a. Brownish red		75·00	35·00
39		6d. deep blue		£100	35·00

(b) Thicker opaque paper

40	1	1d. pale red		£130	65·00
41		6d. blue		95·00	40·00
		a. Imperf between (pair)			
		b. Deep blue		90·00	40·00

(Typo Adolph Otto, Gustrow, Mecklenburg-Schwerin)
1874 (Oct). *Thin smooth paper, clearly printed. Fine roulette 15½ to 16.*

42	3	6d. bright ultramarine		60·00	20·00
		a. Bisected (3d.) (on cover)			

Stamps in other shades of blue, brown or red, often on other types of paper, are reprints.

(Typo J. F. Celliers on behalf of Stamp Commission, Pretoria)
1875 (29 Apr)–77.
I. *Very thin, soft opaque (semi-pelure) paper.* (a) *Imperf*

43	1	1d. orange-red		£120	40·00
		a. Pin-perf			
44	2	3d. lilac		80·00	40·00
45	1	6d. blue		75·00	38·00
		a. Milky blue		£120	38·00
		aa. Tête-bêche (pair)		£6000	
		ab. Pin-perf		—	£250

(b) Fine roulette, 15½ to 16

46	1	1d. orange-red		£400	£130
47	2	3d. lilac		£425	£140
48	1	6d. blue		£400	£130

(c) Wide roulette, 6½

49	1	1d. orange-red		—	£150
50	2	3d. lilac		£550	£200
51	1	6d. blue		—	£120
		a. Bright blue		—	£120
		b. Milky blue		—	£120

II. *Very thin, hard transparent (pelure) paper (1875–76)*
(a) *Imperf*

52	1	1d. brownish red		48·00	24·00
		a. Orange-red		38·00	22·00
		b. Dull red		42·00	42·00
		ba. Pin-perf		£425	£250
53	2	3d. lilac		42·00	38·00
		a. Pin-perf		—	£225
		b. Deep lilac		55·00	38·00
54	1	6d. pale blue		38·00	38·00
		a. Blue		38·00	20·00
		ab. Tête-bêche (pair)		†£10000	
		ac. Pin-perf		—	£200
		b. Deep blue		38·00	20·00

(b) Fine roulette 15½ to 16

55	1	1d. orange-red		£250	£120
		a. Brown-red		£250	£120
56	2	3d. lilac		£325	£110
57	1	6d. blue		£150	95·00
		a. Deep blue		£150	£110

(c) Wide roulette, 6½

58	1	1d. orange-red		£700	£150
		a. Bright red		—	£130
59	2	3d. lilac		—	£180
60	1	6d. deep blue		£700	85·00

III. *Stout hard-surfaced paper with smooth, nearly white, gum* (1876). (a) *Imperf*

61	1	1d. bright red		20·00	14·00
62	2	3d. lilac			
63	1	6d. bright blue		85·00	20·00
		a. Tête-bêche (pair)			
		b. Pale blue		85·00	20·00
		c. Deep blue (deep brown gum)		50·00	16·00
		ca. Tête-bêche (pair)		—£10000	

(b) Fine roulette, 15½ to 16

64	1	1d. bright red		£400	£150
65	2	3d. lilac		£275	
66	1	6d. bright blue		—	£100
		a. Deep blue (deep brown gum)		—	£250

(c) Wide roulette, 6½

67	1	1d. bright red		£450	£140
68		6d. pale blue		—	£200
		a. Deep blue (deep brown gum)		£500	£225

IV. *Coarse, soft white paper* (1876–77). (a) *Imperf*

69	1	1d. brick-red		85·00	45·00
70		6d. deep blue		£150	45·00
		a. Milky blue		£275	85·00
71		1s. yellow-green		£250	85·00
		a. Bisected (6d.) (on cover)			

(b) Fine roulette, 15½ to 16

72	1	1d. brick-red		—	£250
73		6d. deep blue		—	£130
74		1s. yellow-green		£550	£250

(c) Wide roulette, 6½

75	1	1d. brick-red		—	£300
76		6d. deep blue			
77		1s. yellow-green		—	£800

(d) Fine × wide roulette

78	1	1d. brick-red		£550	£250

V. *Hard, thick, coarse yellowish paper* (1876–77)

79	1	1d. brick-red (imperf)		—	£200
80		1d. brick-red (wide roulette)		—	£300

The pin-perforated stamps have various gauges and were probably produced privately or by one or more post offices other than Pretoria.

On Nos. 63c/ca, 66a and 68a the brown gum used was so intense that it caused staining of the paper which is still visible on used examples.

See also Nos. 171/4.

FIRST BRITISH OCCUPATION

By 1876 conditions in the Transvaal had deteriorated and the country was faced by economic collapse, native wars and internal dissension. In early 1877 Sir Theophilus Shepstone, appointed Special Commissioner to the South African Republic by the British Government, arrived in Pretoria and on 12 April annexed the Transvaal with the acquiesence of at least part of the European population.

V. R.   **V. R.**

TRANSVAAL.   **TRANSVAAL.**
(4)   **(5)**

T 4 is the normal overprint, but in some printings No. 11 (R.2/3) on the pane has a wider-spaced overprint, as T 5.

1877 (Apr). *Optd with T 4 in red.* (a) *Imperf*

86	2	3d. lilac (semi-pelure) (No. 44)		£1100	£225
		a. Opt Type 5			
87		3d. lilac (pelure) (No. 53)		£1100	£160
		a. Opt Type 5		£4750	
		b. Opt on back		£3000	
		c. Opt double, in red and in black		£4750	
88	1	6d. milky blue (No. 70)		£1300	£160
		a. Opt inverted		—	£4250
		b. Opt double		£3500	£750
		c. Opt Type 5		£4250	
		d. Deep blue		—	£225
89		1s. yellow-green (No. 71)		£475	£160
		a. Bisected (6d.) (on cover)		†£1200	
		b. Opt inverted		—	£3250
		c. Opt Type 5		£3000	£750

(b) Fine roulette, 15½ to 16

90	2	3d. lilac (pelure) (No. 56)		—	£1100
91	1	6d. deep blue (No. 73)		—	£1100
92		1s. yellow-green (No. 74)		£1000	£450
		a. Opt Type 5			

(c) Wide roulette, 6½

93	2	3d. lilac (pelure) (No. 59)		—	£1100
		a. Opt Type 5			
94	1	6d. deep blue (No. 76)		—	£1100
		a. Opt Type 5			
95		1s. yellow-green (No. 77)		£2750	£1000
		a. Opt inverted		—	£3500

Nos. 88a, 89b and 95a occurred on the inverted *cliché* of the basic stamps.

1877 (June). *Optd with T 4 in black.*
I. *Very thin, hard transparent (pelure) paper*

96	1	1d. orange-red (imperf) (No. 52)		£170	95·00
97		1d. orange-red (fine roulette) (No. 55)		—	£1000

II. *Stout hard-surfaced paper with smooth, nearly white, gum*

98	1	1d. bright red (imperf) (No. 61)		20·00	20·00
		a. Opt inverted		£475	£400
		b. Opt Type 5		£550	£600
99		1d. bright red (fine roulette) (No. 64)		£140	45·00
		a. Opt inverted			
		b. Opt double		—	£750
		c. Imperf between (horiz pair)		£650	
100		1d. bright red (wide roulette) (No. 67)		£475	£140

III. *New ptgs on coarse, soft white paper.* (a) *Imperf*

101	1	1d. brick-red (5.77)		20·00	20·00
		a. Opt double		—	£900
		b. Opt Type 5			
102	2	3d. lilac		70·00	32·00
		a. Opt inverted			
		b. Deep lilac		£140	80·00
103	1	6d. dull blue		85·00	30·00
		a. Opt double		£2750	
		b. Opt inverted		£1200	£150
		c. Tête-bêche (pair)			
		d. Opt Type 5		—	£750
		da. Opt Type 5 inverted			
		e. Blue (bright to deep)		£150	22·00
		ea. Bright blue, opt inverted		£475	
		f. Pin-perf		—	£450
104		1s. yellow-green		80·00	40·00
		a. Opt inverted		£900	£180
		b. Tête-bêche (pair)		£10000	£10000
		c. Opt Type 5		£2750	£900
		d. Bisected (6d.) (on cover)		†	£900

(b) Fine roulette, 15½ to 16

105	1	1d. brick-red		65·00	65·00
		a. Imperf horiz (vert strip of 3)			
		b. Imperf between (horiz pair)		†	£600
106	2	3d. lilac		£140	55·00

107	1	6d. dull blue		£160	42·00
		a. Opt inverted		—	£550
		b. Opt Type 5		£3500	
108		1s. yellow-green		£150	80·00
		a. Opt inverted		£800	£375
		b. Opt Type 5		—	£2500

(c) Wide roulette, 6½

109	1	1d. brick-red		£550	£140
		a. Opt Type 5		—	£650
110	2	3d. lilac		—	£475
111	1	6d. dull blue		—	£1100
		a. Opt inverted			
112		1s. yellow-green		£350	£120
		a. Opt inverted		£1100	£475

1877 (31 Aug). *Optd with T 4 in black.*

113	1	6d. blue/rose (imperf)		65·00	42·00
		a. Bisected (3d.) (on cover)			
		b. Opt inverted		85·00	42·00
		c. Tête-bêche (pair)			
		d. Opt omitted		£2750	
114		6d. blue/rose (fine roulette)		£150	60·00
		a. Opt inverted		£425	60·00
		b. Tête-bêche (pair)			
		c. Opt omitted			
115		6d. blue/rose (wide roulette)			
		a. Opt inverted			
		b. Opt omitted			

Nos. 113/15 were overprinted from a setting of 40 which was applied upright to one pane in each sheet and inverted on the other.

V. R.   **V. R.**

Transvaal   **Transvaal**
(6)   **(7)**

1877 (28 Sept)–79. *Optd with T 6 in black.* (a) *Imperf*

116	1	1d. red/blue		42·00	22·00
		a. "Transvral" (Right pane R. 2/3)		£4000	£2000
		b. Opt double		£3000	
		c. Opt inverted		£600	£300
		d. Opt omitted			
117		1d. red/orange (6.12.77)		14·00	15·00
		a. Pin-perf			
		b. Printed both sides			
		c. Opt double		£2500	
		d. Optd with Type 7 (15.4.78)		42·00	35·00
118	2	3d. mauve/buff (24.10.77)		32·00	22·00
		a. Opt inverted		—	£550
		b. Pin-perf			
		c. Optd with Type 7 (15.4.78)		48·00	30·00
		ca. Opt inverted		£550	£550
119		3d. mauve/green (18.4.79)		£140	40·00
		a. Pin-perf			
		b. Opt inverted		—	£1500
		c. Opt double			
		d. Optd with Type 7		90·00	30·00
		da. Opt inverted		—	£1500
		db. Opt omitted		—	£2750
		dc. Printed both sides			
120	1	6d. blue/green (27.11.77)		75·00	32·00
		a. Deep blue/green		90·00	35·00
		b. Broken "Y" for "V" in "V. R." (Left pane R. 3/7)			
		c. Small "v" in "Transvaal" (Left pane R. 5/2)			
		d. "V..R" (Right pane R. 3/4)		—	£550
		e. Tête-bêche (pair)		—	£10000
		f. Opt inverted		—	£700
		g. Pin-perf			
121		6d. blue/blue (20.3.78)		48·00	22·00
		a. Tête-bêche (pair)			
		b. Opt inverted		—	£700
		c. Opt omitted		—	£1600
		d. Opt double		—	£2500
		e. Pin-perf			
		f. Bisected (3d.) (on cover)		†	£550
		g. Optd with Type 7		90·00	22·00
		ga. Tête-bêche (pair)		£7500	
		gb. Opt inverted		—	£400

(b) Fine roulette, 15½ to 16

122	1	1d. red/blue		70·00	32·00
		a. "Transvral" (Right pane R. 2/3)		—	£2250
123		1d. red/orange (6.12.77)		28·00	22·00
		a. Imperf between (pair)		£500	
		b. Optd with Type 7 (15.4.78)		£130	£110
124	2	3d. mauve/buff (24.10.77)		85·00	22·00
		a. Imperf horiz (vert pair)		£600	
		b. Opt inverted		—	£2500
		c. Optd with Type 7 (15.4.78)		£130	95·00
		ca. Imperf between (pair)			
125		3d. mauve/green (18.4.79)		£550	£150
		a. Optd with Type 7		£500	£150
126		6d. blue/green (27.11.77)		70·00	22·00
		a. "V..R" (Right pane R. 3/4)		—	£1000
		b. Tête-bêche (pair)			
		c. Opt omitted		—	£500
		d. Opt double		—	£3000
		e. Bisected (3d.) (on cover)		†	£550
127		6d. blue/blue (20.3.78)		£180	45·00
		a. Opt inverted		—	£900
		b. Opt omitted		—	£2500
		c. Imperf between (pair)			
		d. Bisected (3d.) (on cover)		†	£475
		e. Optd with Type 7		£300	95·00
		ea. Opt inverted		—	£800

(c) Wide roulette, 6¼

128	1	1d. red/orange (15.4.78)		£225	95·00
		a. Optd with Type 7		—	£225
129	2	3d. mauve/buff (24.10.77)		—	95·00
		a. Optd with Type 7 (15.4.78)		—	£275
130		3d. mauve/green (18.4.79)		£350	£250
		a. Optd with Type 7		—	£275

131	1	6d. blue/*green* (27.11.77)	..	—	£850
132		6d. blue/*blue* (20.3.78)	..	—	£225
		a. Opt inverted			
		b. Optd with Type **7**	..	—	£275
		ba. Opt inverted			

Nos. 116/32 were overprinted from various settings covering sheets of 80 or panes of 40 (8 ×5). Initially these settings contained Type **6** only, but the type was reset in March 1878 to contain examples of Type **7** also.

V.R.	V.R.
Transvaal	Transvaal
(8)	(8a)

9

1879 (Aug–Sept). *Optd with T* **8** *in black.* (a) *Imperf.*

145	1	1d. red/*yellow*	..	38·00	32·00
		a. Small "T", Type 8a	..	£225	£150
		b. Red/*orange*	..	32·00	25·00
		ba. Small "T", Type 8a	..	£160	£150
146	2	3d. mauve/*green*	..	35·00	20·00
		a. Small "T", Type 8a	..	£160	85·00
147		3d. mauve/*blue*	..	40·00	25·00
		a. Small "T", Type 8a	..	£170	85·00

(b) *Fine roulette,* 15½ *to* 16

148	1	1d. red/*yellow*	..	£350	£200
		a. Small "T", Type 8a	..	£800	£550
		b. Red/*orange*	..	£750	£375
		ba. Small "T", Type 8a			
149	2	3d. mauve/*green*	..	£700	£225
		a. Small "T", Type 8a			
150		3d. mauve/*blue*	..	—	£160
		a. Small "T", Type 8a	..	—	£600

(c) *Wide roulette,* 6½

151	1	1d. red/*yellow*	..	£600	£600
		a. Small "T", Type 8a			
		b. Red/*orange*			
152	2	3d. mauve/*green*			
		a. Small "T", Type 8a			
153		3d. mauve/*blue*			

(d) *Pin-perf, about* 17

154	1	1d. red/*yellow*	..		£450
		a. Small "T", Type 8a			
155	2	3d. mauve/*blue*	..		£600

The small "T" variety occurs on right pane R. 2/8, 3/8, 4/8 and 5/8 of the 1d. and on the same positions, but from the left pane, for the 3d.

(Recess B.W.)

1878 (26 Aug)–80. *P* 14, 14½.

156	9	½d. vermilion (1880)	..	16·00	40·00
157		1d. pale red-brown	..	5·50	3·00
		a. Brown-red	..	5·00	2·25
158		3d. dull rose	..	7·50	5·00
		a. Claret	..	10·00	4·50
159		4d. sage-green	..	9·00	4·25
160		6d. olive-black	..	4·50	3·25
		a. Black-brown	..	6·50	2·75
161		1s. green	..	90·00	30·00
162		2s. blue	..	£110	65·00

The above prices are for specimens perforated on all four sides. Stamps from margins of sheets, with perforations absent on one or two sides, can be supplied for about 30% less.

1 Penny	1 Penny	1 Penny
(10)	(11)	(12)

1 Penny	1 Penny
(13)	(14)

1 PENNY	1 Penny
(15)	(16)

1879 (22 April). *No.* 160a *surch with T* **10** *to* **16**.

A. *In black.* B. *In red.*

				A	B
				A		B	
163	10	1d. on 6d.	..	65·00	40·00	£180	£120
164	11	1d. on 6d.	..	£160	75·00	£450	£250
165	12	1d. on 6d.	..	£160	75·00	£450	£250
166	13	1d. on 6d.	..	70·00	45·00	£200	£140
167	14	1d. on 6d.	..	£425	£130	—	£1500
168	15	1d. on 6d.	..	35·00	22·00	£110	60·00
169	16	1d. on 6d.	..	£150	70·00	£400	£225

Nos. 163/9 were surcharged from a setting of 60 containing eleven examples of Type **10**, four of Type **11**, four of Type **12**, nine of Type **13**, two of Type **14**, twenty-five of Type **15** and five of Type **16**.

The red surcharges may have been produced first.

SECOND REPUBLIC

Following the first Boer War the independence of the South African Republic was recognised by the Convention of Pretoria from 8 August 1881.

Nos. 156/62 remained valid and some values were available for postage until 1885.

EEN PENNY

(17)

1882 (11 Aug). *No.* 159 *surch with T* **17**.

170	9	1d. on 4d. sage-green	..	4·75	3·50
		a. Surch inverted	..	£300	£200

Used examples of a similar, but larger, surcharge (width 20 mm) are known. These were previously considered to be forgeries, but it is now believed that some, at least, may represent a trial printing of the "EEN PENNY" surcharge.

(Typo J. F. Celliers)

1883 (20 Feb). *Re-issue of T* **1** *and* **2**. *P* 12.

171	1	1d. grey (*to* black) (Apr)	..	2·00	75
		a. Imperf vert (horiz pair)	..	£250	
172	2	3d. grey-black (*to* black)/*rose*	..	11·00	2·25
		a. Bisected (1d.) (on cover)	..	†	£475
173		3d. pale red (Mar)	..	5·50	1·00
		a. Bisected (1d.) (on cover)			
		b. Chestnut	..	20·00	2·25
		c. Vermilion	..	18·00	2·50
174	1	1s. green (*to* deep) (July)	..	13·00	1·50
		a. Bisected (6d.) (on cover)	..	†	£350
		b. Tête-bêche (pair)	..	£600	£100

Reprints are known of Nos. 172, 173, 173b and 173c. The paper of the first is *bright rose* in place of *dull rose*, and the impression is brownish black in place of grey-black to deep black. The reprints on white paper have the paper thinner than the originals, and the gum yellowish instead of white. The colour is a dull deep orange-red.

18

PERFORATIONS. Stamps perforated 11½×12 come from the first vertical row of sheets of the initial printing otherwise perforated 12½×12 .

REPRINTS. Reprints of the general issues 1885–93, 1894–95, 1895–96 and 1896–97 exist in large quantities. They cannot readily be distinguished from genuine originals except by comparison with used stamps, but the following general characteristics may be noted. The reprints are all perf 12½, large holes; the paper is whiter and thinner than that usually employed for the originals and their colours lack the lustre of those of the genuine stamps.

Forged surcharges have been made on these reprints.

(Des J. Vurtheim. Typo Enschedé)

1885 (13 Mar)–1893. *P* 12½.

175	18	½d. grey (30.3.85)	..	30	10
		a. Perf 13½	..	3·75	80
		b. Perf 12½×12	..	1·75	10
		ba. Perf 11½×12			
176		1d. carmine	..	30	10
		a. Perf 12½×12	..	30	10
		aa. Perf 11½×12	..	70	10
		b. Rose	..	6·50	2·25
		ba. Perf 12½×12	..	30	10
177		2d. brown-purple (p 12½×12) (9.85)	..	30	10
178		2d. olive-bistre (14.4.87)	..	40	10
		a. Perf 12½×12	..	3·50	10
179		2½d. mauve (*to* bright) (8.93)*	..	1·25	20
180		3d. mauve (*to* bright)	..	1·50	60
		a. Perf 12½×12	..	5·50	75
		aa. Perf 11½×12	..	22·00	13·00
181		4d. bronze-green	..	2·25	30
		a. Perf 13½	..	4·75	65
		b. Perf 12½×12	..	12·00	65
		ba. Perf 11½×12	..	£140	55·00
182		6d. pale dull blue	..	1·50	15
		a. Perf 13½	..	4·50	70
		b. Perf 12½×12	..	5·50	15
		ba. Perf 11½×12			
183	18	1s. yellow-green	..	2·50	35
		a. Perf 13½	..	12·00	4·50
		b. Perf 12½×12	..	6·50	20
184		2s. 6d. orange-buff (*to* buff) (2.12.85)	..	3·50	1·40
		a. Perf 12½×12	..	6·50	3·00
185		5s. slate (2.12.85)	..	4·50	1·75
		a. Perf 12½×12	..	5·50	1·50
186		10s. fawn (2.12.85)	..	23·00	2·50
187		£5 dp grn (3.92)* (Optd "Monster" £150)	£3000	£170

Singles of the 6d. pale dull blue imperforate have been reported used in 1893.

*Most examples of No. 187 on the market are either forgeries or reprints.

HALVE PENNY

(19)

1885 (22 May–Aug). *Surch with T* **19**. A. *Reading down.* B. *Reading up.*

				A		B	
188	2	½d. on 3d. (No. 173)	..	1·25	2·50	1·25	2·50
189	1	½d. on 1s. (No. 174) (Aug)	..	4·00	6·50	4·00	6·50
		a. Tête-bêche (pair)	..	†		£550	£250

Nos. 188/9 were surcharged by a setting of 40. After the left pane had been surcharged reading down the sheets were turned so that the right pane had the surcharges reading up.

HALVE PENNY	TWEE PENCE	HALVE
Z.A.R	Z.A.R.	PENNY
(20)	(21)	(22)

1885 (1 Sept). *No.* 160a *surch with T* **20/1** *in red.*

190	9	½d. on 6d. black-brown	..	8·00	14·00
191		2d. on 6d. black-brown	..	1·75	1·75

1885 (28 Sept). *No.* 180a *surch with T* **21**.

192	18	½d. on 3d. mauve	..	1·25	1·25
		a. "PRNNY" (R. 6/6)	..	22·00	
		b. 2nd "N" inverted (R. 3/8)	..	50·00	
		c. Perf 11½×12	..	3·25	

2d	2d
(23)	(24)

1887 (15 Jan). *No.* 180a *surch with T* **23/4**.

193	18	2d. on 3d. mauve (Type 23)	..	3·25	3·25
		a. Surch double	..		£200
		b. Perf 11½×12	..	5·50	5·50
194		2d. on 3d. mauve (Type 24)	..	55	85
		a. Surch double	..		£160
		b. Perf 11½×12	..	3·25	3·25

Nos. 193/4 were surcharged from the same setting of 60 (10 × 6) which showed Type **24** on the top five horizontal rows and Type **23** on the sixth horizontal row.

Halve Penny	1 Penny
(25)	(26)

2½ Pence	2½ Pence
(27)	(28)

Two types of surcharge:

A. Vertical distance between bars 12½ mm.
B. Distance 13½ mm.

1893. *T* **18** *surch. P* 12½. (a) *In red.*

195	25	½d. on 2d. olive-bistre (A) (27 May)	..	60	65
		a. Surch Type B	..	1·25	1·25
		b. Surch Type B	..	1·10	1·10
		ba. Surch inverted	..	4·00	

(b) *In black*

196	25	½d. on 2d. olive-bistre (A) (2 July)	..	50	50
		a. Surch inverted	..	3·00	3·00
		b. Extra surch on back inverted	..	£120	
		c. Surch Type B	..	70	70
		ca. Surch inverted	..	—	8·00
		cb. Extra surch on back inverted	..	£180	
197	26	1d. on 6d. blue (A) (26 Jan)	..	30	20
		a. Surch double	..	38·00	32·00
		b. Surch inverted	..	90	1·00
		c. Surch Type B	..	55	55
		ca. Surch inverted	..	2·75	2·75
		cb. Surch double	..	—	50·00
		d. Pair with and without surch	..	£120	
198	27	2½d. on 1s. green (A) (2 Jan)	..	60	60
		a. "2½" for "2½"(R. 1/10)	..	15·00	15·00
		b. Surch inverted	..	1·00	1·10
		ba. Surch inverted and "2½" for "2½"	..	£200	£150
		c. Extra surch on back inverted	..	£225	
		d. Surch Type B	..	1·00	1·10
		da. Surch inverted	..	4·50	5·25
199	28	2½d. on 1s. green (A) (24 June)	..	1·75	1·75
		a. Surch double	..	23·00	23·00
		b. Surch inverted	..	4·50	4·50
		c. Surch Type B	..	4·00	4·00
		ca. Surch double	..	50·00	50·00
		cb. Surch inverted	..	9·00	9·00

Surcharge Types **25/8** all show a similar setting of the horizontal bars at top and bottom. On horizontal rows 1 to 4 and 6 the bars are 12½ mm apart and on row 5 the distance is 13½ mm.

29 (Wagon with shafts)	30 (Wagon with pole)

1894 (July). *P* 12½.

200	29	½d. grey	..	20	10
201		1d. carmine	..	20	10
202		2d. olive-bistre	..	20	10
203		6d. pale dull blue	..	90	40
204		1s. yellow-green	..	4·00	4·50

For note *re* reprints, see below T **18**.

1895 (16 Mar)–96. *P* 12½.
205	30	½d. pearl-grey (1895)			20	10
		a. Lilac-grey			20	10
206		1d. rose-red			20	10
207		2d. olive-bistre (1895)			20	10
208		3d. mauve (1895)			30	10
209		4d. olive-black (1895)			1·10	55
210		6d. pale dull blue (1895)			1·00	40
211		1s. yellow-green (18.3.95)			1·10	75
212		5s. slate (1896)			3·50	4·50
212a		10s. pale chestnut (1896)			4·25	1·50
		205/8, 211 Optd "Monster"		*Set of* 5	£150	

For note *re* reprints, see below T **18**.

Halve Penny

(31)

(32—Round dot)   (32a—Square dot)

1895 (July–August). *Nos.* 211 *and* 179 *surch with* T **31/2**.
213	30	½d. on 1s. green (R.)			30	10
		a. Surch spaced			85	65
		b. "Pennij" for "Penny" (R. 6/6)		35·00		
		c. Surch inverted			3·00	2·75
		d. Surch double			48·00	
214	18	1d. on 2½d. bright mauve (G.)			30	10
		a. Surch inverted			16·00	12·00
		b. Surch double				
		c. Surch on back only				
		d. Surch Type 32a			1·10	1·10
		da. Surch inverted			42·00	

The normal space between "Penny" and the bars is 3 mm. On No. 213a, which comes from the fifth horizontal row of the setting, this is increased to 4 mm. Copies may be found in which one or both of the bars have failed to print.

Type **32a** with square stop occurred on R. 3/3-4, 3/6-8, 4/4-5, 4/7-8, 4/10, 6/3, 6/7-8 and 6/10 of the setting of 60.

33

34

1895 (July). *Fiscal stamp optd* "POSTZEGEL". *P* 11½.
215	33	6d. bright rose (G.)			50	65
		a. Imperf between (pair)				

(Litho The Press Printing and Publishing Works, Pretoria)

1895 (6 Sept). *Introduction of Penny Postage. P* 11.
215b	34	1d. red (pale *to* deep)			75	50
		ba. Imperf between (pair)		55·00	55·00	

1896–97. *P* 12½.
216	30	½d. green (1896)			20	10
217		1d. rose-red and green (1896)			20	10
218		2d. brown and green (2.97)			20	10
219		2½d. dull blue and green (6.96)			30	10
220		3d. purple and green (3.97)			30	45
221		4d. sage-green and green (3.97)			30	45
222		6d. lilac and green (11.96)			30	45
223		1s. ochre and green (3.96)			45	15
224		2s. 6d. dull violet and green (6.96)		1·00	1·00	

For note *re* reprints, see below T **18**.

SECOND BRITISH OCCUPATION

The Second Boer War began on 11 October 1899 and was concluded by the Peace of Vereeniging on 31 May 1902. Pretoria was occupied by the British on 5 June 1900 and a civilian postal service began operating thirteen days later.

FORGERIES. The forgeries of the "V.R.I." and "E.R.I." overprints most often met with can be recognised by the fact that the type used is perfect and the three stops are always in alignment with the bottom of the letters. In the genuine overprints, which were made from old type, it is impossible to find all three letters perfect and all three stops perfect and in exact alignment with the bottom of the letters.

E. R. I.

V. R. I.   E. R. I.

(35)   (36)

Half Penny

(37)

1900 (18 June). *Optd with* T **35**.
226	30	½d. green			15	15
		a. No stop after "V"			10·00	
		b. No stop after "R"			8·00	
		c. No stop after "I"			6·00	
		d. Opt inverted			7·00	
		e. Opt double				
		f. "V.I.R." (R.4/4)			£500	

227	30	1d. rose-red and green			15	15
		a. No stop after "V"			10·00	
		b. No stop after "R"			8·00	
		c. No stop after "I"			4·00	
		d. Opt inverted			7·00	
		e. Opt double			42·00	
		f. No stops after "R" and "T"		48·00	48·00	
		g. Opt omitted (in pair with normal)	£250		
228		2d. brown and green			1·25	50
		a. No stop after "V"			18·00	
		c. No stop after "T"			24·00	
		d. Opt inverted			10·00	
		e. Opt double				
		f. "V.I.R." (R.4/4)			£500	
229		2½d. dull blue and green			50	55
		a. No stop after "V"			15·00	
		b. No stop after "R"			38·00	
		c. No stop after "T"			11·00	
		d. Opt inverted			7·00	
230		3d. purple and green			50	55
		a. No stop after "V"			20·00	
		b. No stop after "R"			30·00	
		c. No stop after "T"			22·00	
		d. Opt inverted			42·00	
231		4d. sage-green and green			85	20
		a. No stop after "V"			26·00	
		b. No stop after "R"			35·00	
		c. No stop after "T"			22·00	
		d. Opt inverted			16·00	
		f. "V.I.R." (R.4/4)			£500	
232		6d. lilac and green			85	50
		a. No stop after "V"			12·00	
		b. No stop after "R"			18·00	
		c. No stop after "T"			16·00	
		d. Opt inverted			16·00	
233		1s. ochre and green			85	80
		a. No stop after "V"			13·00	
		b. No stop after "R"				
		c. No stop after "T"			25·00	
		d. Opt inverted			20·00	
		e. Opt double			45·00	
234		2s. 6d. dull violet and green			1·75	2·50
		a. No stop after "V"			20·00	
		b. No stop after "R"			45·00	
235		5s. slate			2·75	4·25
		a. No stop after "V"			60·00	
236		10s. pale chestnut			4·25	5·50
		a. No stop after "V"			60·00	
		c. No stop after "T"			60·00	
237	18	£5 deep green*			£1800	£750
		a. No stop after "V"				
		234/7 Optd "Specimen"		*Set of* 4	£200	

*Many examples of No. 237 on the market are forgeries and the stamps should only be purchased if accompanied by a recent expert committee certificate.

The error "V.I.R." occurred on R.4/4 in the first batch of stamps to be overprinted—a few sheets of the ½d., 2d. and 4d. The error was then corrected and stamps showing it are very rare.

A number of different settings were used to apply the overprint to Nos. 226/37. The missing stop varieties listed above developed during overprinting and occur on different positions in the various settings.

1901 (Jan)–02. *Optd with* T **36**.
238	30	½d. green			20	15
239		1d. rose-red and green (20.3.01)			20	10
		a. "E" of opt omitted			50·00	
240		3d. purple and green (6.02)			1·25	1·25
241		4d. sage-green and green (6.02)			1·25	1·50
242		2s. 6d. dull violet and green (10.02)		4·25	4·75	

1901 (July). *Surch with* T **37**.
243	30	½d. on 2d. brown and green			20	20
		a. No stop after "E" (R.4/6)			38·00	

 ...

38 (POSTAGE REVENUE)   39 (POSTAGE POSTAGE)

(Typo D.L.R.)

1902 (1 April)–1903. *Wmk Crown CA. P* 14.
244	38	½d. black and bluish green			80	20
245		1d. black and carmine			75	15
246		2d. black and purple			1·25	20
247		2½d. black and blue			2·00	75
248		3d. black and sage-green (1903)			3·25	30
249		4d. black and brown (1903)			3·00	50
250		6d. black and orange-brown			1·50	50
251		1s. black and sage-green			7·00	3·25
252		2s. black and brown			13·00	14·00
253	39	2s. 6d. magenta and black			8·50	6·50
254		5s. black and purple/*yellow*			11·00	11·00
255		10s. black and purple/*red*			28·00	17·00
		244/55		*Set of* 12	70·00	48·00
		244/55 Optd "Specimen"		*Set of* 12	£130	

The colour of the "black" centres varies from brownish grey or grey to black.

1903. *Wmk Crown CA. P* 14.
256	39	1s. grey-black and red-brown			3·50	1·10
257		2s. grey-black and yellow			7·00	6·00
258		£1 green and violet			90·00	60·00
259		£5 orange-brown and violet			£1200	£400
		256/9 Optd "Specimen"		*Set of* 4	£180	

1904–9. *Wmk Mult Crown CA. Ordinary paper. P* 14.
260	38	½d. black and bluish green			1·75	40
261		1d. black and carmine			2·00	15
262		2d. black and purple (*chalk-surfaced paper*) (1906)		2·50	30	

263	38	2½d. black and blue (1905)			3·50	2·00
		a. Chalk-surfaced paper			2·00	80
264		3d. black & sage-green (*chalk-surfaced paper*) (1906)		2·25	15	
265		4d. black and brown (*chalk-surfaced paper*) (1906)		2·25	30	
266		6d. black and orange (1905)			2·50	30
		a. Chalk-surfaced paper. *Black and brown-orange*		1·50	30	
267	39	1s. black and red-brown (1905)			2·25	30
268		2s. black and yellow (1906)			10·00	2·75
269		2s. 6d. magenta and black (1909)			19·00	2·00
270		5s. black and purple/*yellow*			8·50	1·50
271		10s. black and purple/*red* (1907)		20·00	2·25	
272		£1 green and violet (1908)			90·00	14·00
		a. Chalk-surfaced paper			90·00	10·00
		260/72		*Set of* 13	£150	19·00

There is considerable variation in the "black" centres as in the previous issue.

1905–9. *Wmk Mult Crown CA. P* 14.
273	38	½d. yellow-green			1·00	10
		a. Deep green (1908)			1·25	20
274		1d. scarlet			85	10
		a. Wmk Cabled Anchor, T **13** of Cape of Good Hope		†	£325	
275		2d. purple (1909)			2·75	20
276		2½d. bright blue (1909)			7·50	2·25
		273/6		*Set of* 4	11·00	2·25
		273/6 Optd "Specimen"		*Set of* 4	50·00	

A 2d. grey, T **38**, was prepared for use but not issued. It exists overprinted "Specimen", price £120.

The monocoloured ½d. and 1d. are printed from new combined plates. These show a slight alteration in that the frame does not touch the crown.

Many of the King's Head stamps are found overprinted or perforated "C.S.A.R.", for use by the Central South African Railways.

FISCALS WITH POSTAL CANCELLATIONS

Various fiscal stamps are found apparently postally used, but these were used on telegrams not on postal matter.

POSTAGE DUE STAMPS

D 1

(Typo D.L.R.)

1907. *Wmk Mult Crown CA. P* 14.
D1	D 1	½d. black and blue-green			1·75	1·25
D2		1d. black and scarlet			2·50	70
D3		2d. brown-orange			2·50	1·25
D4		3d. black and blue			3·25	2·00
D5		5d. black and violet			1·75	8·00
D6		6d. black and red-brown			3·75	8·50
D7		1s. scarlet and black			6·50	5·00
		D1/7		*Set of* 7	20·00	24·00

Transvaal became a province of the Union of South Africa on 31 May 1910.

PIETERSBURG

After the fall of Pretoria to the British in June 1900 the Transvaal government withdrew to the north of the country. Those post offices in areas not occupied by the British continued to function, but by early the following year supplies of stamps were exhausted. The following stamps were then authorised by the State Secretary and remained in use in some towns to early May 1901. Pietersburg itself was taken by British forces on 9 April.

PRICES. Genuinely used examples are very rare. Stamps cancelled by favour exist and are worth the same as the unused prices quoted.

The issued stamps are initialled by the Controller J. T. de V. Smit. All values exist without his signature and these are believed to come from remainders abandoned when the Boers evacuated Pietersburg.

P 1

P 2

P 3

TYPES P 1/3. Each value was printed in sheets of 24 (6×4) of which the first two horizontal rows were as Type P 1, the third row as Type P 2 and the fourth as Type P 3. The stamps were issued to post offices in blocks of 12.

(Type-set *De Zoutpansberg Wachter* Press, Pietersburg)

1901 (20 Mar (1*d.*)–3 Apr (*others*)). A. *Imperf.*

(a) Controller's initials in black

1	P 1	½d. black/*green*	..	15·00
		e. Controller's initials omitted	..	95·00
2	P 2	½d. black/*green*..	..	45·00
		d. Controller's initials omitted	..	95·00
3	P 3	½d. black/*green*..	..	45·00
		d. Controller's initials omitted	..	95·00
4	P 1	1d. black/*red*	..	3·50
5	P 2	1d. black/*red* ..	..	5·50
6	P 3	1d. black/*red* ..	..	7·00
7	P 1	2d. black/*orange*	..	6·00
8	P 2	2d. black/*orange*..	..	14·00
9	P 3	2d. black/*orange*..	..	22·00
10	P 1	4d. black/*blue*	..	5·50
11	P 2	4d. black/*blue* ..	..	9·50
12	P 3	4d. black/*blue* ..	..	32·00
13	P 1	6d. black/*green*	..	9·50
14	P 2	6d. black/*green*..	..	15·00
15	P 3	6d. black/*green*..	..	40·00
16	P 1	1s. black/*yellow*	..	8·00
17	P 2	1s. black/*yellow*..	..	14·00
18	P 3	1s. black/*yellow*..	..	25·00

(b) Controller's initials in red

19	P 1	½d. black/*green*..	..	15·00
20	P 2	½d. black/*green*..	..	35·00
21	P 3	½d. black/*green*..	..	40·00

B. P 11½. (a) Controller's initials in red

22	P 1	½d. black/*green*..	..	5·50
		c. Imperf vert (horiz pair)	..	95·00
23	P 2	½d. black/*green*..	..	17·00
		c. Imperf vert (horiz pair)	..	£120
24	P 3	½d. black/*green*..	..	12·00
		b. Imperf vert (horiz pair)	..	£120

(b) Controller's initials in black

25	P 1	1d. black/*red*	..	2·00
		m. Imperf vert (horiz pair)	..	55·00
		n. Imperf between (vert pair: No. 25 + No. 26)		
		o. Imperf horiz (vert pair)		
26	P 2	1d. black/*red*	..	2·75
		f. Imperf vert (horiz pair)	..	80·00
		g. Imperf horiz (vert pair: No. 26 + No. 27)		
27	P 3	1d. black/*red*	..	4·00
		f. Imperf vert (horiz pair)	..	80·00
28	P 1	2d. black/*orange*	..	5·50
29	P 2	2d. black/*orange*	..	8·00
30	P 3	2d. black/*orange*	..	14·00

CONSTANT VARIETIES

Rows 1 and 2 are as Type P **1**, *Row 3 as Type* P **2** *and Row 4 as Type* P **3**.

½d. value

First printing—Imperf

R.1/2	No stop after left "AFR"	(No. 1a)	60·00
R.1/3	"⅓" at top left, no bar over lower right "½"	(No. 1b)	60·00
R.1/6	No stop after date	(No. 1c)	60·00
R.2/5	"BEP" at left, no stop after date	(No. 1d)	60·00
R.3/3	"AFB" at left	(No. 2a)	60·00
R.3/4	"POSTZEGEI" ..	(No. 2b)	60·00
R.3/6	No bar over lower right "½"	(No. 2c)	60·00
R.4/1	No stop after right "AFR"	(No. 3a)	60·00
R.4/4	No stop after left "Z", no bar under top right "½"	(No. 3b)	60·00
R.4/5	"POSTZECEL AER" at left	(No. 3c)	60·00

Second printing

R.1/4	No stop after right "AFR"	.. *Imperf*	(No. 19a)	70·00
		Perf	(No. 22a)	40·00
R.2/1	Left side of inner frame too high	*Imperf*	(No. 19b)	70·00
		Perf	(No. 22b)	40·00
R.3/5	Centre figures "½" level	.. *Imperf*	(No. 20a)	70·00
		Perf	(No. 23a)	40·00
R.3/6	No stop after right "AFR"	.. *Imperf*	(No. 20b)	70·00
		Perf	(No. 23b)	40·00
R.4/6	Hyphen between right "AFR" and "REP"	.. *Imperf*	(No. 21a)	70·00
		Perf	(No. 24a)	40·00

Third printing—Imperf

R.1/1	& 4 Top left "½" inverted, no stop after right "AFR"	(No. 19c)	70·00
R.1/2	Top right "½" inverted	(No. 19d)	90·00
R.1/3	"⅓" at lower right	(No. 19e)	90·00
R.1/5	"POSTZFGEL"	(No. 19f)	90·00
R.1/6	Left spray inverted, "AFB" at right	(No. 19g)	90·00
R.2/1	"REB" at left, left side of inner frame too high	(No. 19h)	90·00
R.2/2	"BEP" at left	(No. 19i)	90·00
R.2/3	"POSTZEOEL"	(No. 19j)	90·00
R.2/4	"AER" at right	(No. 19k)	90·00
R.2/5	No stop after date	(No. 19l)	90·00
R.3/1	"⅓" at top left, "PE" of "PENNY" spaced	(No. 20c)	90·00
R.3/2	Right spray inverted	(No. 20d)	90·00
R.3/3	Top left "½" inverted	(No. 20e)	90·00
R.4/3	"⅓" at top right	(No. 21b)	90·00
R.4/4	Lower left "½" inverted	(No. 21c)	90·00
R.4/5	"¼" at top left ..	(No. 21d)	90·00

1d. value

First printing

R.1/2	Inverted "1" at lower left, first "1" of date dropped	.. *Imperf*	(No. 4a)	35·00
		Perf	(No. 25a)	22·00
R.1/3	No bar under top left "1"	.. *Imperf*	(No. 4b)	35·00
		Perf	(No. 25b)	22·00
R.1/4	No bar over lower right "1"	.. *Imperf*	(No. 4c)	35·00
		Perf	(No. 25c)	22·00
R.1/5	"POSTZFGEL"	.. *Imperf*	(No. 4d)	35·00
		Perf	(No. 25d)	22·00
R.1/6	"AFB" at right..	.. *Imperf*	(No. 4e)	35·00
		Perf	(No. 25e)	22·00
R.2/1	"REB" at left	.. *Imperf*	(No. 4f)	35·00
		Perf	(No. 25f)	22·00
R.2/2	"BEP" at left	.. *Imperf*	(No. 4g)	35·00
		Perf	(No. 25g)	22·00
R.2/3	"POSTZEOEL"	.. *Imperf*	(No. 4h)	35·00
		Perf	(No. 25h)	22·00

R.2/4	"AER" at right..	.. *Imperf*	(No. 4i)	35·00
		Perf	(No. 25i)	22·00
R.2/5	No stop after date	.. *Imperf*	(No. 4j)	35·00
		Perf	(No. 25j)	22·00
R.2/6	No stop after "PENNY"	.. *Imperf*	(No. 4k)	35·00
		Perf	(No. 25k)	22·00
R.3/2	Right spray inverted ..	.. *Imperf*	(No. 5a)	35·00
		Perf	(No. 26a)	22·00
R.3/3	No bar over lower left "1"	.. *Imperf*	(No. 5b)	35·00
		Perf	(No. 26b)	22·00
R.3/4	No stop after left "Z"	.. *Imperf*	(No. 5c)	35·00
		Perf	(No. 26c)	22·00
R.3/6	"POSTZEGFL", no stop after right "AFR"	.. *Imperf*	(No. 5d)	35·00
		Perf	(No. 26d)	22·00
R.4/1	No stop after right "AFR"	.. *Imperf*	(No. 6a)	35·00
		Perf	(No. 27a)	22·00
R.4/2 & 6	Left spray inverted..	.. *Imperf*	(No. 6b)	35·00
		Perf	(No. 27b)	13·00
R.4/3	"POSTZEGEI"	.. *Imperf*	(No. 6c)	35·00
		Perf	(No. 27c)	22·00
R.4/4	No bar under top right "1"	.. *Imperf*	(No. 6d)	35·00
		Perf	(No. 27d)	22·00

Second printing

R.1/2	First "1" in date dropped	.. *Imperf*	(No. 4l)	35·00
		Perf	(No. 25l)	22·00
R.3/6	No stop after right "AFR"	.. *Imperf*	(No. 5e)	35·00
		Perf	(No. 26e)	22·00
R.4/5	Dropped "P" in "PENNY"	.. *Imperf*	(No. 6e)	35·00
		Perf	(No. 27e)	22·00

It has been suggested that there may have been a third printing.

2d. value

First printing—Imperf

R.1/1	"1" at lower right	(No. 7a)	45·00
R.1/2	No stop after left "AFR" (*on small part of printing*)	(No. 7b)	90·00
R.1/3	No bar over lower right "2" (*on small part of printing*)	(No. 7c)	90·00
R.1/3	"PENNY" for "PENCE"	(No. 7d)	90·00
R.1/5	"POSTZFGEL"	(No. 7e)	45·00
R.1/6	"AFB" at right ..	(No. 7f)	45·00
R.2/1	"REB" at left ..	(No. 7g)	45·00
R.2/2	"AFB" at left	(No. 7h)	45·00
R.2/3	"POSTZEOEL"	(No. 7i)	45·00
R.2/4	"AER" at right ..	(No. 7j)	45·00
R.2/5	No stop after date	(No. 7k)	45·00
R.2/6	No stop after date, vertical line after "POSTZEGEL"	(No. 7l)	45·00
R.3/2	Right spray inverted	(No. 8a)	45·00
R.3/3	No bar over lower left "2"	(No. 8b)	45·00
R.3/4	Centre "2" inverted, no stop after left "Z"	(No. 8c)	45·00
R.3/6	"POSTZEGFL", no stop after right "AFR"	(No. 8d)	45·00
R.4/1	Centre "2" inverted, no stop after right "AFR" (*occurs on second printing also*)	(No. 9a)	38·00
R.4/2	Centre "2" wider, left spray inverted ..	(No. 9b)	45·00
R.4/3	"POSTZEGEI"	(No. 9c)	45·00
R.4/4	No bar under top right "2"	(No. 9d)	45·00
R.4/5	"1" at lower left, "P" in "PENCE" dropped	(No. 9e)	45·00
R.4/6	Left spray inverted	(No. 9f)	45·00

Second printing

R.1/2	First "1" in date dropped	.. *Imperf*	(No. 7m)	45·00
		Perf	(No. 28a)	30·00
R.2/1	No stop after left "REP"	.. *Imperf*	(No. 7n)	45·00
		Perf	(No. 28b)	30·00
R.3/4	No stop after left "Z"	.. *Imperf*	(No. 8e)	45·00
R.3/6	No stop after right "AFR"	.. *Imperf*	(No. 8f)	45·00
		Perf	(No. 29a)	30·00
R.4/1	Centre 2 wider, no stop after right "AFR" (*occurs on first printing also*)	.. *Imperf*	(No. 9a)	38·00
		Perf	(No. 30a)	30·00
R.4/2	Centre "2" wider	.. *Imperf*	(No. 9g)	45·00
		Perf	(No. 30b)	30·00
R.4/5	"P" in "PENCE" dropped	.. *Imperf*	(No. 9h)	45·00
		Perf	(No. 30c)	30·00

It has been suggested that there was a third printing of this value.

4d. value

First printing

R.1/2	No stop after left "AFR"	(No. 10a)	45·00
R.1/3	No bar over lower right "4" ..	(No. 10b)	45·00
R.1/3	"PENNY" for "PENCE" (*on small part of printing*)	(No. 10c)	90·00
R.1/5	"POSTZFGEL"	(No. 10d)	45·00
R.1/6	"AFB" at right ..	(No. 10e)	45·00
R.2/1	"REB" at left..	(No. 10f)	45·00
R.2/2	"AFB" at left	(No. 10g)	45·00
R.2/3	"POSTZEOEL"	(No. 10h)	45·00
R.2/4	"AER" at right ..	(No. 10i)	45·00
R.2/5	No stop after date	(No. 10j)	45·00
R.3/2	Right spray inverted	(No. 11a)	45·00
R.3/3	No bar over lower left "4" (*on small part of printing*)	(No. 11b)	45·00
R.3/4	No stop after left "Z"	(No. 11c)	90·00
R.3/6	"POSTZEGFL"	(No. 11d)	45·00
R.4/1	Centre "4" wider, no stop after right "AFR"	(No. 12a)	45·00
R.4/2	Centre "4" wider, left spray inverted ..	(No. 12b)	45·00
R.4/3	"POSTZEGEI" ..	(No. 12c)	45·00
R.4/4	No bar under top right "4"	(No. 12d)	45·00
R.4/5	"AER" at left, "P" in "PENCE" dropped	(No. 12e)	45·00
R.4/6	Left spray inverted	(No. 12f)	45·00

Second printing

R.2/1	Left inner frame too high	(No. 10k)	45·00
R.4/1–2	Centre "4" wider	(No. 12g)	35·00
R.4/5	"P" in "PENCE" dropped	(No. 12h)	45·00

6d. value

First printing

R.1/2	No stop after left "AFR"	(No. 13a)	55·00
R.1/3	No bar over lower right "6" ..	(No. 13b)	55·00
R.1/3	"PENNY" for "PENCE" (*on small part of printing*)	(No. 13c)	£100
R.1/5	"POSTZFGEL"	(No. 13d)	55·00
R.1/6	"AFB" at right ..	(No. 13e)	55·00
R.2/1	"REB" at left ..	(No. 13f)	55·00
R.2/2	"AFB" at left	(No. 13g)	55·00
R.2/3	"POSTZEOEL"	(No. 13h)	55·00

R.2/4	"AER" at right..	(No. 13i)	55·00
R.2/5	No stop after date	(No. 13j)	55·00
R.3/2	Right spray inverted	(No. 14a)	55·00
R.3/4	Centre "6" inverted, no stop after left "Z" (*on small part of printing*)	(No. 14b)	£100
R.3/4	No stop after left "Z"	(No. 14c)	55·00
R.3/6	"POSTZEGFL"	(No. 14d)	55·00
R.4/1	Centre "6" wider, no stop after right "AFR"	(No. 15a)	55·00
R.4/2	Centre "6" wider, left spray inverted ..	(No. 15b)	55·00
R.4/3	"POSTZEGEI" ..	(No. 15c)	55·00
R.4/4	No bar under top right "6"	(No. 15d)	55·00
R.4/5	"AER" at left, "P" in "PENCE" dropped	(No. 15e)	55·00
R.4/6	Left spray inverted	(No. 15f)	55·00

Second printing

R.2/1	Left inner frame too high, no stop after left "REP"	(No. 13k)	55·00
R.4/1–2	Centre "6" wider	(No. 15g)	40·00
R.4/5	"P" in "PENCE" dropped	(No. 15h)	55·00

1s. value

R.1/2	No stop after left "AFR"	(No. 16a)	40·00
R.1/3	No bar over lower right "1"	(No. 16b)	40·00
R.2/5	No stop after date	(No. 16c)	40·00
R.3/4	"POSTZEGEI", no stop after left "Z"	(No. 17a)	40·00
R.4/1	No stop after right "AFR"	(No. 18a)	40·00
R.4/4	No bar under top right "1"	(No. 18b)	40·00
R.4/5	"AER" at left	(No. 18c)	40·00

LOCAL BRITISH OCCUPATION ISSUES DURING THE SOUTH AFRICAN WAR 1900–2

Stamps of the Transvaal Republic, unless otherwise stated, variously overprinted or surcharged.

LYDENBURG

Lydenburg fell to the British on 6 September 1900.

V.R.I.
3d.
(L 1)

1900 (Sept). *No. 217 surch with Type* L **1**, *others optd* "V.R.I" *only.*

1	**30**	½d. green	..	90·00	70·00
2		1d. rose-red and green	..	75·00	70·00
3		2d. brown and green	..	£700	£550
4		2½d. blue and green	..	£1800	£950
5		3d. on 1d. rose-red and green	..	75·00	60·00
6		3d. purple and green			
7		4d. sage-green and green	..	£1800	£600
8		6d. lilac and green	..	£1800	£500
9		1s. ochre and green	..	£3000	£2000

Only one genuine copy of No. 6 (unused) is known.

Type 34 surcharged "V.R.I. 1d." is now considered by experts to be bogus.

The above were cancelled by British Army postal service postmarks. These overprints with Transvaal cancellations are believed to be forgeries.

RUSTENBURG

The British forces in Rustenburg, west of Pretoria, were besieged by the Boers during June 1900. When relieved on the 22 June 1900 no "V.R.I" stamps were available so a local handstamp was applied.

V.R.
(R 1)

1900 (23 June). *Handstamped with Type* R **1** *in violet.*

1	**30**	½d. green	..	£110	75·00
2		1d. rose-red and green	..	85·00	60·00
3		2d. brown and green	..	£190	75·00
4		2½d. blue and green	..	£110	65·00
5		3d. purple and green	..	£170	75·00
6		6d. lilac and green	..	£600	£300
7		1s. ochre and green	..	£1400	£970
8		2s. 6d. dull violet and green	..	£5000	£3750

SCHWEIZER RENECKE

BESIEGED
(SR 1)

1900 (Aug). *Handstamped with Type* SR **1** *in black, reading vert up or down.* (a) *On stamps of Transvaal.*

1	**30**	½d. green		†	£225
2		1d. rose-red and green	..	†	£225
3		2d. brown and green		†	£300
4		6d. lilac and green	..	†	£750

(b) *On stamps of Cape of Good Hope*

5	**17**	½d. green		†	£400
6		1d. carmine	..	†	£400

Schweizer Renecke, near the Bechuanaland border, was under siege from 1 August 1900 to 9 January 1901. The British commander authorised the above stamps shortly after 19 August. All stamps were cancelled with the dated circular town postmark ("Schweizer Renecke, Z.A.R."), usually after having been stuck on paper before use. Unused, without the postmark, do not exist.

VOLKSRUST

1902 (Mar). *Optd with* T **35**. *P* 12.

1	**33**	1d. pale blue	—	45·00
2		6d. dull carmine	—	55·00
3		1s. olive-bistre	—	70·00
4		1s. 6d. brown	—	80·00
5		2s. 6d. dull purple	—	80·00

These are the normal Transvaal Revenue stamps of the period, authorised for postal use in Volksrust.

WOLMARANSSTAD

Cancelled   *Cancelled*

V-R-I.   V-R-I.

(L 3)   (L 4)

1900 (June). *Optd with Type* L **3**.
1	30	½d. green (B.)	..	..	£200	£300
		a. Opt inverted			£600	
2		1d. rose-red and green (B.)			£140	£200
3		2d. brown and green (B.)			£1300	£1300
4		2½d. blue and green (R.)	..		£1200	
		a. Opt in blue	..		£2750	£2750
5		3d. purple and green (B.)			£2500	£2750
6		4d. sage-green and green (B.)	..		£3000	£3500
7		6d. lilac and green (B.)	..		£3000	£3500
8		1s. ochre and green (B.)			—	£6000

1900 (July). *Optd with Type* L **4**.
9	34	1d. red (B.)	..	..	£150	£225

ZULULAND

PRICES FOR STAMPS ON COVER
Nos. 1/10	*from* × 20	
No. 11	—	
Nos. 12/16	*from* × 12	
Nos. 20/6	*from* × 20	
Nos. 27/9	—	
No. F1	*from* ×100	

ZULULAND   ZULULAND,
(1)   (2)

1888 (1 May)–**93.** (a) *Nos. 173, 180, 197, 200/2, 205a, 207a/8, 209 and 211 of Great Britain (Queen Victoria) optd with* T **1.**
1	½d. vermilion (11.88)	..	2·00	2·50
2	1d. deep purple	..	23·00	4·75
3	2d. grey-green and carmine		11·00	17·00
4	2½d. purple/*blue* (9.91)	..	14·00	18·00
5	3d. purple/*yellow*	..	23·00	20·00
6	4d. green and deep brown..		28·00	35·00
7	5d. dull purple and blue (3.93)		80·00	95·00
8	6d. purple/*rose-red*	..	11·00	16·00
9	9d. dull purple and blue (4.92)	..	70·00	70·00
10	1s. dull green (4.92)	..	95·00	£100
11	5s. rose (4.92)	..	£475	£500
1/11		Set of 11	£750	£800
1 and 3/11 H/S "Specimen"		Set of 10	£600	

(b) *No. 97a of Natal optd with* T **2.**
12	½d. green (with stop) (7.88)	..	50·00	60·00
	a. Opt double	..	£1000	£1100
	b. Opt inverted	..	£1100	
	d. Opt omitted (vert pair with normal)	£4750	£4750	
13	½d. green (without stop)	..	19·00	28·00
	a. Opt double	..	£1000	£1200

1894 (Jan). *No. 103 of Natal optd with* T **1.**
16	15	6d. mauve	..	48·00	48·00

    3   4

(Typo D.L.R.)

1894 (18 Apr)–**96.** *Wmk Crown CA. P* 14.
20	3	½d. dull mauve and green	..	1·75	3·75
21		1d. dull mauve and carmine	..	5·00	80
22		2½d. dull mauve and ultramarine	..	12·00	7·00
23		3d. dull mauve and olive-brown	..	8·00	2·75
24	4	6d. dull mauve and black	..	18·00	16·00
25		1s. green	..	30·00	35·00
26		2s. 6d. green and black (2.96)..		70·00	70·00
27		4s. green and carmine	..	95·00	£120
28		£1 purple/*red*	..	£450	£475
29		£5 purple and black/*red* (Optd S. £375)	£3500	£1200	
20/8			Set of 9	£600	£650
20/8 Optd "Specimen"			Set of 9	£350	

Dangerous forgeries exist of the £1 and £5.

FISCAL STAMP USED FOR POSTAGE

1891 (27 June). *Fiscal stamp of Natal (Wmk Crown, CA, P 14) optd with* T **1.**
F1	1d. dull mauve (Optd S. £60)	..	3·00	3·00

Other values, 1s. to £20 as No. F1 exist apparently with postmarks, but, as these were never authorised for postal use, they are no longer listed.

Zululand was annexed to Natal on 31 December 1897 and its stamps were withdrawn from sale on 30 June 1898.

UNION OF SOUTH AFRICA

Although South Africa is now a republic, outside the British Commonwealth, all its stamp issues are listed together here purely as a matter of convenience to collectors.

The province continued to use their existing issues until the introduction of Nos. 3/17. From 19 August 1910 the issues of any province were valid for use throughout the Union until they were demonetised on 31 December 1937.

PRICES FOR STAMPS ON COVER TO 1945
Nos. 1/15	*from* × 4
Nos. 16/17	*from* × 4
Nos. 18/21	*from* × 6
Nos. 26/32	*from* × 2
No. 33	*from* × 4
Nos. 34/110	*from* × 1
Nos. D1/7	*from* × 4
Nos. D8/33	*from* × 6
Nos. O1/33	*from* × 4

1

(Des H. S. Wilkinson. Recess D.L.R.)

1910 (4 Nov). *Opening of Union Parliament. Inscribed bilingually. Wmk Multiple Rosettes. P* 14.
1	1	2½d. deep blue (H/S S. £325)	..	3·50	3·00
2		2½d. blue	..	2·00	1·25

The deep blue shade is generally accompanied by a blueing of the paper.

The price quoted for the "Specimen" handstamp is for the small italic type with capital and lower case letters.

   2   3   4 Springbok's Head

(Typo D.L.R.)

1913 (1 Sept)–**24.** *Inscribed bilingually. W* 4. (*a*) *P* 14.
3	2	½d. green	..	1·00	20
		a. Stamp doubly printed	..	£10000	
		b. Blue-green	..	1·75	20
		c. Yellow-green	..	2·25	30
		d. Booklet pane of 6	..	35·00	
4		1d. rose-red (*shades*)..	..	70	10
		a. Carmine-red	..	1·50	10
		b. Scarlet (*shades*)	..	1·25	15
		c. Booklet pane of 6	..	38·00	
5		1½d. chestnut (*shades*) (23.8.20)	30	10
		a. Tête-bêche (*pair*)	..	1·75	16·00
		b. Booklet pane of 6 (1921)	38·00	
6	3	2d. dull purple	..	1·25	10
		a. Deep purple	..	2·50	10
		b. Booklet pane of 6 (1922)	60·00	
7		2½d. bright blue	..	2·50	1·00
		a. Deep blue..	..	5·00	3·00
8		3d. black and orange-red	..	6·50	30
		a. Black and dull orange-red	7·50	70
9		3d. ultramarine (*shades*) (4.10.22)	4·50	1·75
10		4d. orange-yellow and olive-green ..	9·00	45
		a. Orange-yellow and sage-green	7·50	45
11		6d. black and violet ..	..	5·50	30
		a. Black and bright violet ..	7·50	50
12		1s. orange	..	15·00	70
		a. Orange-yellow	..	25·00	90
13		1s. 3d. violet (*shades*) (1.9.20)	12·00	7·00
14		2s. 6d. purple and green	..	55·00	1·00
15		5s. purple and blue	..	£130	5·00
		a. Reddish purple and light blue	£130	8·00
16		10s. deep blue and olive-green	..	£225	5·50
17		£1 green and red (7.16)	..	£700	£350
		a. Pale olive-green and red (1924)	£900	£1200
3/17			Set of 15	£1000	£350
3/8, 10/17 Optd or H/S "Specimen"		Set of 14	£1300	

(*b*) *Coil stamps. P* 14 × *imperf*
18	2	½d. green	..	4·75	1·00
19		1d. rose-red (13.2.14)	..	6·50	3·75
		a. Scarlet	..	7·50	4·50
20		1½d. chestnut (15.11.20)..	..	7·50	8·00
21	3	2d. dull purple (7.10.21)	..	8·00	4·25
18/21			Set of 4	24·00	15·00

The 6d. exists with "Z" of "ZUID" wholly or partly missing due to wear of plate (*Price wholly missing*, £75 *un*, £38 *us*).

MINIMUM PRICE

The minimum price quote is 10p which represents a handling charge rather than a basis for valuing common stamps. For further notes about prices see introductory pages.

5

(Eng A. J. Cooper. Litho *Cape Times* Ltd)

1925 (26 Feb). *Air. Inscr bilingually. P* 12.
26	5	1d. carmine	..	4·00	7·00
27		3d. ultramarine..	..	7·00	8·50
28		6d. magenta	..	10·00	14·00
29		9d. green	..	18·00	48·00
26/9		..	Set of 4	35·00	70·00

Beware of forgeries of all values perforated 11, 11½ or 13.

INSCRIPTIONS. From 1926 until 1951 (also Nos. 167 and 262/5), most issues were inscribed in English and Afrikaans alternately throughout the sheets.

PRICES for Nos. 30/135 are for unused horizontal pairs, used horizontal pairs and used singles (either inscription), *unless otherwise indicated.* Vertical pairs are worth 50% of those prices quoted for horizontal pairs.

6 Springbok   7 *Dromedaris*
            (Van Riebeeck's ship)

8 Orange Tree   9

(Typo Waterlow until 1927, thereafter Govt Printer, Pretoria)

1926 (2 Jan)–**27.** *W* 9. *P* 14½×14.

					Un pair	Used pair	Used single
30	6	½d. black and green	..		2·50	2·00	10
		a. Missing "1" in "½"	..		£1700		
		b. Booklet pane of 6	..		70·00		
		c. Perf 13½ × 14 (1927)	..		35·00	35·00	2·25
		ca. Tête-bêche (*pair*)	..		£850		
		cb. Booklet pane of 6	..		£350		
31	7	1d. black and carmine	..		2·00	45	10
		a. Booklet pane of 6	..		60·00		
		b. Perf 13½ × 14 (1927)	..		30·00	30·00	2·00
		ba. Tête-bêche (*pair*)	..		£950		
		bb. Booklet pane of 6	..		£300		
32	8	6d. green and orange (1.5.26)		30·00	20·00	1·50
30/2			Set of 3	30·00	20·00	1·50

No. 30a exists in Afrikaans only. Nos. 30c and 31b were only issued in booklets.

Nos. 30/1 exist in coils, constructed from normal sheets.

For ½d. with pale grey centre, see No. 126.

For rotogravure printing see Nos. 42, etc.

10 "Hope"

(Recess B.W.)

1926 (2 Jan). T **10.** *Inscribed in English* (E) *or Afrikaans* (A). *W* 9. *Imperf.*

			Single stamps			
			E		A	
33		4d. grey-blue (*shades*)..	1·00	60	1·00	60

In this value the English and Afrikaans inscriptions are on separate sheets.

This stamp is known with private perforations or roulettes.

11 Union Buildings, Pretoria   12 Groot Schuur

12a A Native Kraal

13 Black and Blue Wildebeest

14 Ox-wagon inspanned   15 Ox-wagon outspanned

16 Cape Town and Table Bay

(Recess B.W.)

1927 (1 Mar)–30. *W* 9. *P* 14.

			Un pair	Used pair	Used single
34	11	2d. grey and maroon ..	11·00	17·00	60
		a. Perf 14×13½ (2.30) ..	11·00	18·00	70
35	12	3d. black and red ..	20·00	26·00	60
		a. Perf 14×13½ (1930) ..	30·00	32·00	80
35b	12a	4d. brown (23.3.28) ..	26·00	45·00	1·00
		ba. Perf 14×13½ (1930) ..	38·00	55·00	1·25
36	13	1s. brown and deep blue ..	35·00	45·00	1·00
		a. Perf 14×13½ (1930) ..	45·00	48·00	1·25
37	14	2s. 6d. green and brown ..	£110	£250	14·00
		a. Perf 14×13½ (1930) ..	£180	£300	20·00
38	15	5s. black and green ..	£225	£450	30·00
		a. Perf 14×13½ (1930) ..	£300	£500	40·00
39	16	10s. bright blue and brown ..	£150	£130	9·00
		a. Centre inverted (single stamp) ..	£9000		
		b. Perf 14×13½ (1930) ..	£160	£140	11·00
34/9		Set of 7	£500	£850	48·00
34/9 H/S "Specimen" ..		Set of 7	£850		

17 D.H. "Moth"

(Typo Govt Ptg Wks, Pretoria)

1929 (16 Aug). *Air. Inscribed bilingually. No wmk. P* 14 × 13½.

			Un single	Us single
40	17	4d. green ..	5·00	2·50
41		1s. orange ..	11·00	11·00

PRINTER. All the following issues, except *where stated otherwise*, are printed by rotogravure (the design having either plain lines or a dotted screen) by the Government Printer, Pretoria.

I   II

The two types of the 1d. differ in the spacing of the horizontal lines in the side panels:—Type I close; Type II wide. The Afrikaans had the spacing of the words POSSEEL-INKOMSTE close in Type I and more widely spaced in Type II.

Window flaw (R. 20/4 on all ptgs before 1937)

1930–45. *T* 6 to 8 *and* 11 to 14 *redrawn,* "SUIDAFRIKA" (*in one word*) *on Afrikaans stamps. W* 9. *P* 15 × 14 (½d., 1d., and 6d.) or 14.

			Un pair	Used pair	Used single
42		½d. black and green (5.30) ..	1·75	1·50	10
		a. Two English or two Afrikaans stamps se-tenant (vert strip of 4)	40·00		
		b. Tête-bêche ..	£850		
		c. Booklet pane of 6 ..	18·00		
43		1d. black and carmine (I) (4.30) ..	2·75	1·00	10
		a. Tête-bêche ..	£850		
		b. Frame omitted (single stamp) ..	£450		
		c. Booklet pane of 6 ..	20·00		
43d		1d. black and carmine (II) (8.32) ..	28·00	2·25	10
44		2d. slate-grey and lilac (4.31) ..	15·00	4·50	20
		a. Tête-bêche ..	£2250		
		b. Frame omitted (single stamp) ..	£1000		
		c. Booklet pane of 6 ..	£130		
44d		2d. blue and violet (3.38) ..	£170	50·00	2·50
45		3d. black and red (11.31) ..	48·00	55·00	2·50
		a. Window flaw ..	£110		
45b		3d. blue (10.33) ..	7·00	3·00	20
		ba. Window flaw ..	30·00		
46		4d. brown (19.11.32) ..	£140	90·00	8·00
46a		4d. brown (shades) (again redrawn) (1936) ..	3·00	2·25	10
47		6d. green and orange (5.31) ..	17·00	2·00	10
48		1s. brown and deep blue (14.9.32) ..	48·00	18·00	35
49		2s. 6d. grn & brn (shades) (24.12.32)	90·00	75·00	3·00
49a		2s. 6d. blue and brown (1945) ..	16·00	8·00	20
42/9a		Set of 13	£500	£275	15·00

For similar designs with "SUID-AFRIKA" hyphenated, see Nos. 54 etc. and Nos. 114 etc.

Nos. 42/3, 43d/4 exist in coils.

No. 42a comes from the coil printing on the cylinder for which two horizontal rows were incorrectly etched so that two Afrikaans-inscribed stamps were followed by two English. This variety is normally without a coil join, although some examples do occur showing a repair join.

The 1d. (Type I) exists without watermark from a trial printing (*Price* £80 *un*).

The Rotogravure printings may be distinguished from the preceding Typographed and Recess printed issues by the following tests:—

	TYPO	ROTO
	R	R
	RECESS	ROTO
2d.		
3d.		
4d.	No. 35a	No. 46 · No. 46a
1s.		
2s. 6d.		
5s.	R	R

ROTOGRAVURE:

½d., 1d. and 6d. Leg of "R" in "AFR" ends squarely on the bottom line.

2d. The newly built War Memorial appears to the left of the value.

3d. Two fine lines have been removed from the top part of the frame.

4d. No. 46. The scroll is in solid colour.
No. 46a. The scroll is white with a crooked line running through it. (No. 35a. The scroll is shaded by the diagonal lines.)

1s. The shading of the last "A" partly covers the flower beneath.

2s. 6d. The top line of the centre frame is thick and leaves only one white line between it and the name.

5s. (Nos. 64/a). The leg of the "R" is straight.

Rotogravure impressions are generally coarser.

18 Church of the Vow   19 "The Great Trek" (C. Michell)

20 A Voortrekker   21 Voortrekker Woman

(Des J. Prentice (½d., 2d., 3d.)

1933 (3 May)–36. *Voortrekker Memorial Fund. W* 9 (*sideways*). *P* 14.

50	18	½d. + ½d. black and green (16.1.36)	3·75	3·50	50
51	19	1d. + ½d. grey-black and pink ..	3·25	1·50	25
52	20	2d. + 1d. grey-green and purple ..	4·00	4·00	55
53	21	3d. + 1½d. grey-green and blue ..	6·50	5·00	70
50/3		Set of 4	16·00	12·50	1·75

22 Gold Mine   22a Groot Schuur

I   II   III
Dies of 6d.

23 Groot Constantia

1933–48. "SUID-AFRIKA" (*hyphenated*) *on Afrikaans stamps. W* 9. *P* 15×14 (½d., 1d. and 6d.) or 14 (*others*).

			Un	Used	single
54	6	½d. grey and green (9.35) ..	3·00	1·00	10
		a. Coil stamp. Perf 13½×14 (1935) ..	28·00	40·00	1·00
		b. Booklet pane of 6 (with adverts on margins) ..	18·00		
56	7	1d. grey and carmine (shades) (19.4.34) ..	40	55	10
		a. Imperf (pair) ..	£130		
		b. Frame omitted (single stamp) ..	£250		
		c. Coil stamp. Perf 13½×14 (1935) ..	32·00	40·00	1·00
		d. Booklet pane of 6 (with adverts on margins) (1935)	8·50		
		e. Booklet pane of 6 (with blank margins) (1937) ..	9·00		
		f. Booklet pane of 2 (1937) ..	2·00		
		g. Booklet pane of 6 (without margins) (1938) ..	12·00		
		h. Booklet pane of 6 (with postal slogans on margins) (1948) ..	4·00		
		i. Grey and brt rose-carmine (7.48) ..	55	50	10
57	22	1½d. green & brt gold (12.11.36)	1·50	1·00	10
		a. Shading omitted from mine dump (in pair with normal)	95·00		
		b. Blue-grn & dull gold (8.40) ..	6·00	2·00	10
		c. Booklet pane of 4 (1941) ..	19·00		
58	11	2d. blue and violet (11.38) ..	60·00	28·00	1·00
58a		2d. grey and dull purple (5.41) ..	32·00	45·00	1·25
59	22a	3d. ultramarine (2.40) ..	5·50	1·00	10
61	8	6d. green & verm (I) (10.37) ..	75·00	20·00	70
61a		6d. green & vermilion (II) (6.38) ..	25·00	1·00	10
61b		6d. grn & red-orge (III) (11.46)	13·00	75	10
62	13	1s. brown & chalky blue (2.39) ..	35·00	5·50	10
		a. Frame omitted (single stamp) ..	£1000		
64	15	5s. black and green (10.33) ..	50·00	40·00	1·50
		a. Black and blue-green (9.44) ..	35·00	14·00	50
64b	23	10s. blue and sepia (8.39) ..	60·00	14·00	70
		ba. Blue & blackish brn (8.39) ..	40·00	3·75	30
54/64ba (only one 6d.) ..		Set of 10	£200	90·00	3·00

The ½d. and 1d. coil stamps may be found in blocks emanating from the residue of the large rolls which were cut into sheets and distributed to Post Offices.

Nos. 54 and 56 also exist in coils.

1d. Is printed from Type II. Frames of different sizes exist due to reductions made from time to time for the purpose of providing more space for the perforations.

3d. In No. 59 the frame is unscreened and composed of solid lines. Centre is diagonally screened. Scrolls above "3d." are clear lined, light in the middle and dark at sides.

6d. Die I. Green background lines faint. "SUID-AFRIKA" 16¼ mm long.
Die II. Green background lines heavy. "SUID-AFRIKA" 17 mm long. "S" near end of tablet. Scroll open.
Die III. Scroll closed up and design smaller (18 × 22 mm).

Single specimens of the 1933–48 issue inscribed in English may be distinguished from those of 1930–45 as follows:—
½d. and 1d. Centres in grey instead of varying intensities of black.
2d. The letters of "SOUTH AFRICA" are narrower and thinner.
3d. The trees are taller and the sky is without lines.
6d. The frame is vermilion.
1s. The frame is chalky blue.
For similar designs, but printed in screened rotogravure, see Nos. 114 to 122a.

BOOKLET PANES. Booklets issued in 1935 contained ½d. and 1d. stamps in panes with advertisements in the top and bottom margins and no margin at right (Nos. 54b and 56d). These were replaced in 1937 by editions showing blank margins on all four sides (Nos. 56e and 64ca). Following a period when the booklet panes were without margins, a further 3s. booklet was issued in 1948 which had four margins on the panes and postal slogans at top and bottom (Nos. 56h, 87b and 114a).

JIPEX

1936

24   (24a)

"Cleft skull" flaw (R. 14/2)

(Des J. Booysen)

1935 (1 May). *Silver Jubilee. Inscr bilingually. W* 9. *P* 15 × 14.

				Un	Us	
65	24	½d. black and blue-green		2·50	12·00	10
		a. "Cleft skull" flaw	..	6·00		
66		1d. black and carmine		2·75	4·00	10
		a. "Cleft skull" flaw	..	6·00		
67		3d. blue ..	..	23·00	48·00	2·25
		a. "Cleft skull" flaw	..	40·00		
68		6d. green and orange	..	42·00	60·00	3·25
		a. "Cleft skull" flaw	..	75·00		
65/8			*Set of* 4	65·00	£110	5·00

In stamps with English at top the ½d., 3d. and 6d. have "SILVER JUBILEUM" to left of portrait, and "POSTAGE REVENUE" or "POSTAGE" (3d. and 6d.) in left value tablet. In the 1d., "SILVER JUBILEE" is to the left of portrait. In alternate stamps the positions of English and Afrikaans inscriptions are reversed.

1936 (2 Nov). *Johannesburg International Philatelic Exhibition. Optd with T* 24a.

				Un	Us
				sheet	sheet
MS69	6	½d. grey and green (No. 54)		4·25	10·00
MS70	7	1d. grey and carmine (No. 56)..		3·25	7·00

Issued each in miniature sheet of six stamps with marginal advertisements.

25   25a

"Mouse" flaw (R. 4/1)

(Des J. Prentice)

1937 (12 May). *Coronation. W* 9 (*sideways*). *P* 14.

71	25	½d. grey-black and blue-green	..	25	50	10
72		1d. grey-black and carmine		35	40	10
73		1½d. orange and greenish blue	..	50	50	10
		a. "Mouse" flaw	..	3·75		
74		3d. ultramarine ..	..	3·75	1·75	10
75		1s. red-brown and turquoise-blue		6·00	3·75	15
		a. Hyphen on Afrikaans stamp omitted (R. 2/13)	..	42·00		
71/5			*Set of* 5	9·75	6·25	40

No. 75a shows the hyphen completely omitted and the top of the "K" damaged. A less distinct flaw, on which part of the hyphen is still visible and with no damage to the "K", occurs on R. 4/17.

1937–40. *W* 9. *P* 15×14.

75b	25a	½d. grey and green	..	7·00	90	10
		ba. Booklet pane of 6 (with blank margins) (1937)	..	42·00		
		bb. Booklet pane of 2 (1937)	..	15·00		
		bc. Booklet pane of 6 (without margins) (1938)	..	40·00		
		bd. Grey and blue-green (1940)		4·50	75	10

The lines of shading in T 25a are all horizontal and thicker than in T 6. In Nos. 75b and 75bd the design is composed of solid lines. For stamps with designs composed of dotted lines, see No. 114. Later printings of No. 75bd have a smaller design.

---

26 Voortrekker Ploughing   27 Wagon crossing Drakensberg

28 Signing of Dingaan–Retief Treaty

29 Voortrekker Monument

(Des W. Coetzer and J. Prentice)

1938 (14 Dec). *Voortrekker Centenary Memorial Fund. W* 9. *P* 14 (*Nos.* 76/7) *or* 15 × 14 (*others*).

76	26	½d. + ½d. blue and green	..	10·00	4·00	30
77	27	1d. + 1d. blue and carmine	..	11·00	5·00	40
78	28	1½d. + 1½d. chocolate & blue-grn		15·00	9·50	80
79	29	3d. + 3d. bright blue	..	17·00	11·00	1·00
76/9			*Set of* 4	48·00	27·00	2·25

30 Wagon Wheel

31 Voortrekker Family

(Des W. Coetzer and J. Prentice)

1938 (14 Dec). *Voortrekker Commemoration. W* 9. *P* 15 × 14.

80	30	1d. blue and carmine	..	4·00	1·50	25
81	31	1½d. greenish blue and brown	..	6·00	1·50	25

32 Old Vicarage, Paarl,   33 Symbol of the Reformation
now a museum

34 Huguenot Dwelling, Drakenstein Mountain Valley

(Des J. Prentice)

1939 (17 July). *250th Anniv of Huguenot Landing in South Africa and Huguenot Commemoration Fund. W* 9. *P* 14 (*Nos.* 82/3) *or* 15 × 14 (*No.* 84).

82	32	½d. + ½d. brown and green		4·75	4·25	30
83	33	1d. + 1d. green and carmine	..	10·00	4·50	30
84	34	1½d. + 1½d. blue-green and purple	20·00	10·00	90	
82/4		..	..	*Set of* 3	32·00	17·00	1·40

34a Gold Mine

1941 (Aug)–**48.** *W* 9 (*sideways*). *P* 14 × 15.

87	34a	1½d. blue-grn and yellow-buff (shades)	..	30	30	10
		a. Yellow-buff (centre) omitted £1000				
		b. Booklet pane of 6 (with postal slogans on margins) (1948)	..	3·50		

---

35 Infantry   36 Nurse and Ambulance   37 Airman

38 Sailor, Destroyer and Lifebelts   39 Women's Auxiliary Services

40 Artillery   41 Electric Welding

42 Tank Corps   42a Signaller

"Stain" on uniform (R. 14/11)

1941–46. *War Effort. W* 9 (*sideways on* 2d., 4d., 6d.). *P* 14 (2d., 4d., 6d.) *or* 15 × 14 (*others*). (*a*) *Inscr alternately.*

88	35	½d. green (19.11.41)	..	75	75	10
		a. Blue-green (7.42)	..	2·75	1·60	10
89	36	1d. carmine (3.10.41)	..	1·50	70	10
		a. "Stain" on uniform flaw		5·00		
90	37	1½d. myrtle-green (12.1.42)		1·00	75	10
91	39	3d. blue (1.8.41)	..	15·00	14·00	50
92	40	4d. orange-brown (20.8.41)		12·00	9·00	15
		a. Red-brown (6.42)	..	28·00	23·00	1·25
93	41	6d. red-orange (3.9.41)	..	8·50	7·00	15
94	42a	1s. 3d. olive-brown (2.1.43)	..	8·50	6·00	20
		a. Blackish brown (5.46)	..	5·50	6·00	20

(*b*) *Inscr bilingually*

					Un	Us
					single	single
95	38	2d. violet (15.9.41) ..	..	..	55	20
96	42	1s. brown (27.10.41) ..	..		2·50	50
88/96 ..		..	*Set of* 7 *pairs and* 2 *singles*	42·00	35·00	

43 Infantry   44 Nurse   45 Airman   46 Sailor

47 Women's Auxiliary Services   48 Electric Welding   49 Heavy Gun in Concrete Turret

50 Tank Corps

Unit (pair)

Unit (triplet)

1942–44. War Effort. Reduced sizes. In pairs perf 14 (P) or strips of three, perf 15 × 14 (T), subdivided by roulette 6½. W **9** (sideways on 3d., 4d. and 1s.). (a) Inscr alternately.

			Un unit	Us unit	Us single
97	43	½d. blue-green (T) (10.42) ..	70	80	10
		a. Green (3.43) ..	2·50	1·10	10
		b. Greenish blue (7.44)..	2·00	80	10
		c. Roulette omitted	£400		
98	44	1d. carmine-red (T) (5.1.43)	1·00	60	10
		a. Bright carmine (3.44)	1·00	40	10
		b. Roulette omitted	£375		
99	45	1½d. red-brown (P) (9.42)	65	55	10
		a. Roulette 13 (8.42) ..	1·50	3·00	15
		b. Roulette omitted	£225	£250	
100	46	2d. violet (P) (2.43)	90	85	10
		a. Reddish violet (6.43)	1·50	50	10
		b. Roulette omitted	£300		
101	47	3d. blue (T) (10.42)	7·00	10·00	10
102	48	6d. red-orange (P) (10.42)	2·00	1·40	10

(b) Inscr bilingually

103	49	4d. slate-green (T) (10.42)	13·00	4·00	10
104	50	1s. brown (P) (11.42) ..	10·00	1·50	10
97/104		Set of 8	32·00	17·00	65

52

53

1943. Coil stamps. Redrawn. In single colours with plain background. W **9**. P 15 × 14.

			Un pair	Used pair	Used single
105	52	½d. blue-green (18.2.43) ..	75	2·75	20
106	53	1d. carmine (9.43) ..	1·25	2·50	15

Quoted prices are for vertical pairs.

54 Union Buildings, Pretoria

1945–46. Redrawn. W **9**. P 14.

107	54	2d. slate and violet (3.45)	9·00	2·50	10
		a. Slate & brt vio (shades) (10.46)	2·25	5·50	15

In Nos. 107 and 107a the Union Buildings are shown at a different angle from Nos. 58 and 58a. Only the centre is screened i.e., composed of very small square dots of colour arranged in straight diagonal lines. For whole design screened and colours changed, see No. 116. No. 107a also shows "2" of "2d." clear of white circle at top.

55 "Victory"

56 "Peace"

57 "Hope"

1945 (3 Dec). Victory. W **9**. P 14.

108	55	1d. brown and carmine..	20	80	10
109	56	2d. slate-blue and violet	20	85	10
110	57	3d. deep blue and blue ..	20	1·25	10
108/10		Set of 3	55	2·75	25

58 King George VI

59 King George VI and Queen Elizabeth

60 Queen Elizabeth II as Princess, and Princess Margaret

"Bird" on "2" (Cyl 6912 R. 10/6)

(Des J. Prentice)

1947 (17 Feb). Royal Visit. W **9**. P 15 × 14.

111	58	1d. black and carmine ..	10	10	10
112	59	2d. violet ..	15	20	10
		a. "Bird" on "2" flaw ..	2·00		
113	60	3d. blue ..	15	20	10
111/13		Set of 3	35	45	20

"Flying saucer" flaw (Cyl 17 R. 17/2)

5s.

1947–54. "SUID-AFRIKA" hyphenated on Afrikaans stamps. Printed from new cylinders with design in screened rotogravure. W **9**. P 15 × 14 (½d., 1d. and 6d.) or 14 (others).

114	25a	½d. grey and green (frame only screened) (1947) ..	40	1·00	10
		a. Booklet pane of 6 (with postal slogans on margins) (1948) ..	3·00		
		b. Entire design screened (2.49) ..	50	1·00	10
		ba. Booklet pane of 6 (with margin at right) (1951) ..	3·50		
115	7	1d. grey and carmine (1.9.50)	35	40	10
		a. Booklet pane of 6 (with margin at right) (1951) ..	5·00		
116	54	2d. slate-blue and purple (3.50)	40	3·25	10
117	22a	3d. dull blue (4.49) ..	2·00	3·25	10
117a		3d. blue (3.51) ..	2·00	2·50	10
		ab. "Flying saucer" flaw ..	10·00		
		b. Deep blue (1954) ..	60·00	50·00	2·00
118	12a	4d. brown (22.8.52) ..	1·00	4·00	10
119	8	6d. green & red-orge (III) (1.50)	1·50	40	10
		a. Grn & brn-orge (III) (1951)	1·50	40	10
120	13	1s. brown & chalky blue (1.50)	10·00	3·25	10
		a. Blackish brown & ultram (4.52) ..	18·00	6·50	15
121	14	2s. 6d. green and brown (8.49)	10·00	17·00	30
122	15	5s. black and pale blue-grn (I) (9.49) ..	45·00	22·00	50
122a		5s. black & deep yellow-green (II) (1.54) ..	70·00	55·00	1·25
114/22		Set of 9	65·00	48·00	1·25

In screened rotogravure the design is composed of very small squares of colour arranged in straight diagonal lines.

½d. Size 17¾ × 21¾ mm. Early printings have only the frame screened.

1d. Size 18 × 22 mm. For smaller, redrawn design, see No. 135.

2d. For earlier issue with centre only screened, and in different colours, see Nos. 107/a.

3d. No. 117. Whole stamp screened with irregular grain. Scrolls above "3d." solid and toneless. Printed from two cylinders.

No. 117a/b. Whole stamp diagonally screened. Printed from one cylinder. Clouds more pronounced.

4d. Two groups of white leaves below name tablet and a clear white line down left and right sides of stamp.

61 Gold Mine

62 King George VI and Queen Elizabeth

1948 (1 Apr). W **9**. In pair, perf 14, sub-divided by roulette 6½.

			Un unit of 4	Us unit single	Used
124	61	1½d. blue-green and yellow-buff	90	2·00	10

(Des J. Booysen and J. Prentice)

1948 (26 Apr). Silver Wedding. W **9**. P 14.

			Un pair	Used pair	Used single
125	62	3d. blue and silver ..	50	50	10

(Typo Government Printer, Pretoria)

1948 (July). W **9**. P 14½ × 14.

126	6	½d. pale grey and blue-green ..	60	4·50	25

This was an economy printing made from the old plates of the 1926 issue for the purpose of using up a stock of cut paper. For the original printing in black and green, see No. 30.

63 Wanderer entering Durban

(Des J. Prentice)

1949 (2 May). Centenary of Arrival of British Settlers in Natal. W **9**. P 15 × 14.

127	63	1½d. claret ..	30	30	10

"Lake" in East Africa (R. 2/19)

64 Hermes

65 Wagons approaching Bingham's Berg

(Des J. Booysen and J. Prentice)

1949 (1 Oct). 75th Anniv of Universal Postal Union. As T **64** inscr "UNIVERSAL POSTAL UNION" and "WERELDPOSUNIE" alternately. W **9** (sideways). P 14 × 15.

128	64	½d. blue-green ..	60	70	10
129		1½d. brown-red ..	75	85	10
130		3d. bright blue ..	1·40	1·40	10
		a. "Lake" in East Africa	16·00		
128/30		Set of 3	2·50	2·75	25

(Des W. Coetzer and J. Prentice)

1949 (1 Dec). Inauguration of Voortrekker Monument, Pretoria. T **65** and similar horiz designs. W **9**. P 15 × 14.

			Un single	Us single
131		1d. magenta ..	10	10
132		1½d. blue-green ..	10	10
133		3d. blue ..	10	10
131/3		Set of 3	20	20

Designs:—1½d. Voortrekker Monument, Pretoria; 3d. Bible, candle and Voortrekkers.

68 Union Buildings, Pretoria

1950 (Apr)–51. W **9** (sideways). P 14 × 15.

			Un pair	Used pair	Used single
134	68	2d. blue and violet ..	30	40	10
		a. Booklet panes of 6 (with margin at right) (1951) ..	8·00		

1951 (22 Feb). *As No. 115, but redrawn with the horizon clearly defined. Size reduced to 17¼ × 21¼ mm.*
135   7   1d. grey and carmine   ..   60   50   10

> **PRICES.** All later issues except Nos. 167 and 262/5 are inscribed bilingually and prices are for single copies, unused and used.

69 Seal and Monogram   70 "Maria de la Quellerie" (D. Craey)

(Des Miss R. Reeves and J. Prentice (1d., 4½d.), Mrs T. Campbell and J. Prentice (others))

1952 (14 Mar). *Tercentenary of Landing of Van Riebeeck. T 69/70 and similar designs. W 9 (sideways on 1d. and 4½d.). P 14 × 15 (1d. and 4½d.) or 14 × 15 (others).*
136   ½d. brown-purple and olive-grey   10   10
137   1d. deep blue-green ..   10   10
138   2d. deep violet   20   10
139   4½d. blue   10   10
140   1s. brown   15   10
136/40   *Set of 5*   40   30
Designs: *Horiz*—2d. Arrival of Van Riebeeck's ships; 1s. "Landing at the Cape" (C. Davidson Bell). *Vert*—4½d. "Jan van Riebeeck" (D. Craey).

SATISE   SADIPU
(74)   (75)   76 Queen Elizabeth II

1952 (26 Mar). *South African Tercentenary International Stamp Exhibition, Cape Town. No. 137 optd with T 74 and No. 138 with T 75.*
141   1d. deep blue-green   15   1·00
142   2d. deep violet   20   50

(Des H. Kumst)

1953 (3 June). *Coronation. W 9 (sideways). P 14 × 15.*
143   76   2d. deep violet-blue   ..   30   10
     a. Ultramarine   30   10

77 1d. "Cape Triangular" Stamp

(Des H. Kumst)

1953 (1 Sept). *Centenary of First Cape of Good Hope Stamp. T 77 and similar horiz design. W 9. P 15 × 14.*
144   1d. sepia and vermilion   ..   10   10
145   4d. deep blue and light blue ..   20   15
Design:—4d. Four pence "Cape Triangular" stamp.

79 Merino Ram   80 Springbok

81 Aloes

(Des A. Hendriksz and J. Prentice (4½d.))

1953 (1 Oct). *W 9. P 14.*
146   79   4½d. slate-purple and yellow ..   20   10
147   80   1s. 3d. chocolate   ..   1·00   10
148   81   1s. 6d. vermilion and deep blue-green   80   30
146/8   ..   ..   *Set of 3*   1·75   40

---

82 Arms of Orange Free State and Scroll

(Des H. Kumst)

1954 (23 Feb). *Centenary of Orange Free State. W 9. P 15 × 14.*
149   82   2d. sepia and pale vermilion ..   10   10
150   4½d. purple and slate   ..   20   40

83 Warthog   92 Springbok   93 Gemsbok

(Des H. Kumst)

1954 (14 Oct). *T 83, 92/3 and similar designs. W 9 (sideways on large vert designs). P 15 × 14 (½d. to 2d.), 14 (others).*
151   ½d. deep blue-green   10   10
152   1d. brown-lake   10   10
153   1½d. sepia   10   10
154   2d. plum   10   10
155   3d. chocolate and turquoise-blue   15   10
156   4d. indigo and emerald   ..   40   10
157   4½d. blue-black and grey-blue   60   1·50
158   6d. sepia and orange   ..   50   10
159   1s. deep brown and pale chocolate ..   60   10
160   1s. 3d. brown and bluish green   1·00   10
161   1s. 6d. brown and rose   ..   1·75   60
162   2s. 6d. brown-black and apple-green   3·50   20
163   5s. black-brown and yellow-orange ..   10·00   1·25
164   10s. black and cobalt..   ..   17·00   4·50
151/64   ..   *Set of 14*   32·00   7·50
Designs: *Vert* (as T 83)—1d. Black Wildebeest; 1½d. Leopard; 2d. Mountain Zebra. (As T 93)—3d. White Rhinoceros; 4d. African Elephant; 4½d. Hippopotamus; 1s. Greater Kudu; 2s. 6d. Nyala; 5s. Giraffe; 10s. Sable Antelope. *Horiz* (as T 92)—6d. Lion.
No. 152 exists in coils.
See also Nos. 170/7 and 185/97.

97 President Kruger   98 President M. Pretorius

(Des H. Kumst)

1955 (21 Oct). *Centenary of Pretoria. W 9 (sideways). P 14 × 15.*
165   97   3d. slate-green   10   10
166   98   6d. maroon   10   20

99 A. Pretorius, Church of the Vow and Flag   100 Settlers' Block-wagon and House

(Des H. Kumst)

1955 (1 Dec). *Voortrekker Covenant Celebrations, Pietermaritzburg. W 9. P 14.*

			Un pair	Us pair	Us single
167	99	2d. blue and magenta ..	45	3·00	10

(Des H. Kumst)

1958 (1 July). *Centenary of Arrival of German Settlers in South Africa. W 9. P 14.*
168   100   2d. chocolate and pale purple ..   10   10

101 Arms of the Academy

(Des H. Kumst)

1959 (1 May). *50th Anniv of the South African Academy of Science and Art, Pretoria. W 9. P 15 × 14.*
169   101   3d. deep blue and turquoise-blue   10   10
     a. Deep blue printing omitted   .. £1200

---

    1 1 / S S / I II

102 Union Coat of Arms   I   II

1959–60. *As Nos. 151/2, 155/6, 158/9 and 162/3, but W 102 (sideways on Nos. 172/3 and 175/7).*
170   ½d. deep greenish blue (12.60)   ..   15   4·50
171   1d. brown-lake (I) (11.59)   ..   10   10
     a. Redrawn. Type II (10.60)   ..   20   10
172   3d. chocolate and turquoise-blue (9.59) ..   15   10
173   4d. indigo and emerald (1.60)   ..   50   20
174   6d. sepia and orange (2.60)   ..   70   70
175   1s. deep brown and pale chocolate (11.59)   6·00   30
176   2s. 6d. brown-black & apple-green (12.59) ..   2·75   40
177   5s. black-brown & yellow-orange (10.60) ..   6·00   27·00
170/7   ..   *Set of 8*   14·50   32·00
Nos. 171/a. In Type II "1d. Posgeld Postage" is more to the left in relation to "South Africa", with "1" almost central over "S" instead of to right as in Type I.
No. 171 exists in coils.

103 Globe and Antarctic Scene

(Des H. Kumst)

1959 (16 Nov). *South African National Antarctic Expedition. W 102. P 14 × 15.*
178   103   3d. blue-green and orange   ..   20   10

104 Union Flag   106 "Wheel of Progress"

(Des V. Ivanoff and H. Kumst (1s.), H. Kumst (others))

1960 (2 May). *50th Anniv of Union of South Africa. T 104, 106 and similar designs. W 102 (sideways on 4d. and 6d.). P 14 × 15 (4d., 6d.) or 15 × 14 (others).*
179   4d. orange-red and blue   ..   30   10
180   6d. red, brown and light green   ..   30   10
181   1s. deep blue and light yellow   ..   30   10
182   1s. 6d. black and light blue ..   ..   1·10   2·00
179/82   *Set of 4*   1·75   2·00
Designs: *Vert*—6d. Union Arms. *Horiz*—1s. 6d. Union Festival emblem.
See also No. 190, 192/3.

108 Locomotives of 1860 and 1960

(Des V. Ivanoff)

1960 (2 May). *Centenary of South African Railways. W 102. P 15 × 14.*
183   108   1s. 3d. deep blue   ..   ..   2·00   30

109 Prime Ministers Botha, Smuts, Hertzog, Malan, Strijdom and Verwoerd

1960 (31 May). *Union Day. W 102. P 15 × 14.*
184   109   3d. brown and pale brown   ..   10   10
     a. Pale brown omitted*   ..   £1800
*This is due to a rectangular piece of paper adhering to the background cylinder, resulting in R.2/1 missing the colour completely and six adjoining stamps having it partially omitted. The item in block of eight is probably unique.

(New Currency. 100 cents=1 rand)

1961 (14 Feb). *As previous issues but with values in cents and rand.* W 102 (*sideways on* 3½ c., 7½ c., 20 c., 50 c., 1 r.). P 15 × 14 (½ c., to 2½ c., 10 c.), 14 × 15 (3½ c., 7½ c.) *or* 14 (*others*).

185	½ c. deep bluish green (as 151)	10	10
186	1 c. brown-lake (as 152)	10	10
187	1½ c. sepia (as 153)	10	10
188	2 c. plum (as 154)	10	10
189	2½ c. brown (as 184)..	10	10
190	3½ c. orange-red and blue (as 179) ..	15	90
191	5 c. sepia and orange (as 158) ..	20	10
192	7½ c. red, brown and light green (as 180) ..	20	1·25
193	10 c. deep blue and light yellow (as 181) ..	30	20
194	12½ c. brown and bluish green (as 160) ..	1·00	1·75
195	20 c. brown and rose (as 161) ..	2·25	3·00
196	50 c. black-brown & orange-yellow (as 163)	6·00	10·00
197	1 r. black and cobalt (as 164) ..	18·00	25·00
185/97	.. .. .. *Set of* 13	25·00	38·00

REPUBLIC OF SOUTH AFRICA

110 African Pygmy Kingfisher

111 Kafferboom Flower

112 Afrikander Bull

113 Pouring Gold

114 Groot Constantia

115 Burchell's Gonolek

116 Baobab Tree

117 Maize

118 Cape Town Castle Entrance

119 Protea

120 Secretary Bird

121 Cape Town Harbour

122 Strelitzia

Two types of ½ c.:

I   II

Type I from sheets. Spurs of branch indistinct.
Type II from coils. Spurs strengthened.

Three types of 1 c.:

I   II

III

Type I. Lowest point of flower between "OS" of "POSTAGE". Right-hand petal over "E".
Type II. Flower has moved fractionally to the right so that lowest point is over "S" of "POSTAGE". Right-hand petal over "E".
Type III. Lowest point directly over "O". Right-hand petal over "G".

Two types of 2½ c.

In Type I the lines of the building are quite faint. In Type II all lines of the building have been strengthened by re-engraving.

(Des Mrs. T. Campbell (½ c., 3 c., 1 r.); Miss N. Desmond (1 c.); De La Rue (2½ c., 5 c., 12½ c.); H. L. Prager (50 c.); Govt. Ptg Dept artist (others))

1961 (31 May)–**63**. *Unsurfaced paper.* W 102 (*sideways on* ½ c., 1½ c., 2½ c., 5 c. *to* 20 c.). P 14 × 15 (½ c., 1½ c.), 15 × 14 (1 c.), *or* 14 (*others*).

198	110	½ c. bright blue, carmine & brown (I)	10	10
		a. Perf 14 (3.63)	10	15
		b. Type II (coils) (18.5.63) ..	60	60
199	111	1 c. red and olive-grey (I) ..	10	10
		a. Type II (1.62)	10	10
		b. Type III (coils) (5.63) ..	1·00	1·00
200	112	1½ c. brown-lake and light purple	10	10
201	113	2 c. ultramarine and yellow	45	10
202	114	2½ c. violet and green (I)	15	10
		a. Type II. Dp violet & green (9.61)	20	10
203	115	3 c. red and deep blue	80	10
204	116	5 c. yellow and greenish blue	30	10
205	117	7½ c. yellow-brown and light green	60	10
206	118	10 c. sepia and green ..	75	10
207	119	12½ c. red, yellow and black-green ..	20	30
		a. Yellow omitted ..	£180	
		b. Red omitted		
208	120	20 c. turquoise-blue, carm & brn-orge	3·50	30
209	121	50 c. black and bright blue	35·00	2·00
210	122	1 r. orange, olive-green & light blue	20·00	2·00
198/210		.. .. *Set of* 13	55·00	4·00

1961–74 Definitives
Key to designs, perfs, watermarks, papers and phosphors

Value	Type	Perf	W 102. Ordinary	No wmk. Ordinary	W 127. Chalky
½ c.	110 (I)	14×15	198	—	—
	(I)	14	198a	—	—
	(II)	14×15	198b	—	—
1 c.	111 (I)	15×14	199	211	—
	(II)		199a	211a	227
	(III)		199b	—	—
1½ c.	112 (I)	14×15	200	—	228
2 c.	113	14	201	212	229
2½ c.	114 (I)	14	202	—	—
	(II)		202a	213/a	230/a
3 c.	115	14	203	214	—
5 c.	116	14	204	215	231
7½ c.	117	14	205	216	232
10 c.	118	14	206	217/b	233/a
12½ c.	119	14	207	—	—
20 c.	120	14	208	218	234/a
50 c.	121	14	209	219	235
1 r.	122	14	210	—	236

Redrawn Designs

			W 127. Upright or Tête-bêche. Plain or phosphorised	W 127 Tête-bêche. Phos frame	No wmk. Phosphorised Glossy	Chalky
½ c.	130a	14	238	—	—	—
		14×15	238b	—	—	—
		14	238c/d	—	—	—
1 c.	131	15×14	239	—	—	—
		13½×14	239a	—	—	—
1½ c.	132	14×15	240/b	284	—	—
		14×13½	240c	—	—	—
2 c.	133	14	241/a	285/a	315a	—
		12½	—	315	315b	
2½ c.	134	14	242/a	286/a	—	—
3 c.	135	14	243/a	287	—	—
		12½	—	—	316	316a
4 c.	134	14	243b	288	—	—

---

5 c.	136	14	244/a	289	318a
		12½	—	—	318	318b
6 c.	137	14	—	290	
		12½	—	—	—	319
7½ c.	137	14	245	291	
9 c.	139	14	245a	292	
		12½	—	—	320/a	
10 c.	138	14	246/a	293	321a
		12½	—	—	321	321b
12½ c.	139	14	247/a	294	
15 c.	140	14	248	295	
20 c.	141	14	249/a	296/a	
		12½	—	—	323	323a
50 c.	142	14	250		
		12½	—	—	324	324a
1 r.	143	14	251		
		12½	—	—	325	

New Designs

			W 127 Tête-bêche. Plain or phosphorised	W 127 Tête-bêche. Phos frame	No wmk. Phosphorised Glossy	Chalky
½ c.	168	14 × 13½	276	282	—	—
		14 × 14½	276a	—	313	—
		14 × 15	—	282a	—	—
1 c.	169	13½ × 14	277	283	—	—
		14	—	—	314	—
4 c.	182	14	310/a	—	—	—
		12½	—	—	317/b	317c
15 c.	182a	14	311	—	—	—
		12½	—	—	—	322

1961 (Aug)–**63**. *As Nos.* 199, 201/6 *and* 208/9 *but without wmk.*

211	111	1 c. red and olive-grey (I) ..	20	30
		a. Type II (9.62)	45	40
212	113	2 c. ultramarine and yellow (8.63)	4·00	30
213	114	2½ c. deep violet and green (II)	30	10
		a. Violet and green (12.61)	30	10
214	115	3 c. red and deep blue (10.61)	45	10
215	116	5 c. yellow & greenish blue (12.61)	50	10
216	117	7½ c. yellow-brown & lt green (3.62)	80	10
217	118	10 c. sepia and green (11.61)	1·00	30
		a. Sepia and emerald ..	40·00	10·00
		b. Sepia-brown & lt green (7.63)	2·00	35
218	120	20 c. turq-bl, carm & brn-orge (4.63)	13·00	2·25
219	121	50 c. black and bright blue (8.62)	13·50	3·50
211/19		.. .. .. *Set of* 9	30·00	6·00

123 Blériot Monoplane and Boeing 707 Airliner over Table Mountain

124 Folk-dancers

1961 (1 Dec). *50th Anniv of First South African Aerial Post.* W 102 (*sideways*). P 14 × 15.

220	123	3 c. blue and red	20	10

(Des K. Esterhuysen)

1962 (1 Mar). *50th Anniv of Volkspele (folk-dancing) in South Africa.* W 102 (*sideways*). P 14 × 15.

221	124	2½ c. orange-red and brown	15	10

125 The *Chapman*

1962 (20 Aug). *Unveiling of Precinct Stone, British Settlers Monument, Grahamstown.* W 102. P 15 × 14.

222	125	2½ c. turquoise-green and purple ..	40	10
223		12½ c. blue and deep chocolate ..	2·50	1·75

126 Red Disa (orchid), Castle Rock and Gardens

(Des M. F. Stern)

1963 (14 Mar). *50th Anniv of Kirstenbosch Botanic Gardens, Cape Town.* P 13½ × 14.

224	126	2½ c. multicoloured	20	10
		a. Red (orchid, etc) omitted ..	£950	

127 (normal version)

128 Centenary Emblem and Nurse

129 Centenary Emblem and Globe

1963 (30 Aug). *Centenary of Red Cross. Chalk-surfaced paper. Wmk* **127** (*sideways on* 2½ c.). P 14 × 13½ (2½ c.) *or* 15 × 14 (12½ c.).

225	128	2½ c. red, black and reddish purple	20	10
226	129	12½ c. red and indigo	4·00	1·00
		a. Red cross omitted	£1200	

1963–67. *As 1961–3 but chalk-surfaced paper and W* **127** (*sideways on* 1½ c., 2½ c., 5 c., 7½ c., 10 c., 20 c.). P 15 × 14 (1 c.), 14 × 15 (1½ c.), *or* 14 (*others*).

227	111	1 c. red and olive-grey (II) (9.63)	10	10
228	112	1½ c. brown-lake & lt purple (1.67)	1·75	1·25
229	113	2 c. ultramarine and yellow (11.64)	15	15
230	114	2½ c. violet and green (II) (10.63)	10	10
		a. Bright reddish violet and emerald (II) (3.66)	35	20
231	116	5 c. yellow and greenish blue (9.66)	1·25	30
232	117	7½ c. yellow-brn & brt grn (23.2.66)	7·00	2·50
233	118	10 c. sepia-brown & lt emerald (9.64)	40	10
		a. Sepia-brown and green (1.67)	45	10
234	120	20 c. turq-bl, carm & brn-orge (7.64)	1·50	60
		a. Deep turquoise-blue, carmine and flesh (20.7.65)	1·75	60
235	121	50 c. black and ultramarine (4.66)	30·00	8·00
236	122	1 r. orange, lt green & pale bl (7.64)	55·00	29·00
227/36		*Set of 10*	90·00	38·00

In the 2½ c. (No. 230a), 5 c., 7½ c., 10 c. (Jan 1967 printing only) and 50 c. the watermark is indistinct but they can easily be distinguished from the stamps without watermark by their shades and the chalk-surfaced paper which is appreciably thicker and whiter.

130 Assembly Building, Umtata

1963 (11 Dec). *First Meeting of Transkei Legislative Assembly. Chalk-surfaced paper. W* **127.** P 14 × 14.

237	130	2½ c. sepia and light green	10	10
		a. Light green omitted	£1200	

130a African Pygmy Kingfisher

131 Kafferboom Flower

132 Afrikander Bull

133 Pouring Gold

134 Groot Constantia

135 Burchell's Gonolek

136 Baobab Tree

137 Maize

138 Cape Town Castle Entrance

139 Protea

140 Industry

141 Secretary Bird

142 Cape Town Harbour

143 Strelitzia

(15 c. des C. E. F. Skotnes)

Redrawn types.

½ c. "½C" larger and "REPUBLIEK VAN REPUBLIC OF" smaller.

3 c. and 12½ c. Inscriptions and figures of value larger.

Others. "SOUTH AFRICA" and "SUID-AFRIKA" larger and bolder. The differences vary in each design but are easy to see by comparing the position of the letters of the country name with "REPUBLIC OF" and "REPUBLIEK VAN".

1964–72. *As 1961–63 but designs redrawn and new values* (4 c., 9 c. *and* 15 c.). *Chalk-surfaced paper. W* **127** (*sideways on* ½, 1½, 2½, 4, 5, 7½, 9, 10, 15 *and* 20 c.). P 14 × 15 (1½ c.), 15 × 14 (1 c.) *or* 14 (*others*).

238	130a	½ c. brt blue, carm & brn (21.5.64)	10	10
		a. Imperf (pair)	£250	
		b. Perf 14×15. Brt blue, carmine and yellow-brown (6.7.67)	20	20
		c. Perf 14. Bright blue, lake and yellow-brown (3.68)	20	20
		d. Perf 14. Bright blue, carmine-lake and yellow-brown (9.68)	30	10
239	131	1 c. red and olive-grey (9.3.67)	10	10
		a. Perf 13½×14 (7.68)	30	10
240	132	1½ c. dull red-brn & lt pur (21.9.67)	15	10
		a. Purple-brown & lt pur (1968)	15	10
		b. Brt red-brown & lt pur (5.68)	15	10
		c. Perf 14×13½. Red-brown and light purple (14.8.69)	45	45
241	133	2 c. ultramarine and yellow (8.1.68)	20	10
		a. Blue and yellow (10.71)	30	10
242	134	2½ c. violet and green (19.4.67)	20	10
		a. Reddish violet and green (8.67)	20	10
243	135	3 c. red and deep blue (11.64)	30	10
		a. Brown-red & deep blue (3.72)	35	10
243b	134	4 c. violet and green (10.71)	75	30
244	136	5 c. yellow & greenish bl (14.2.68)	40	10
		a. Lemon & dp greenish bl (10.71)	7·50	70
245	137	7½ c. yellow-brn & brt grn (26.7.67)	60	10
245a	139	9 c. red, yellow & slate-grn (2.72)	9·00	2·50
246	138	10 c. sepia and green (10.6.68)	1·50	10
		a. Brown and pale green (7.68)	4·25	3·25
247	139	12½ c. red, yellow & black-grn (3.64)	1·75	40
		a. Red, pale yell & bl-grn (2.2.66)	2·50	40
248	140	15 c. black, light olive-yellow and red-orange (1.3.67)	1·75	25
249	141	20 c. turquoise-blue, carmine and brown-orange (2.68)	4·50	15
		a. Turquoise-blue, carmine and orange-buff (12.71)	5·00	65
250	142	50 c. black and bright blue (17.6.68)	4·00	40
251	143	1 r. orange, lt green & lt bl (6.65)	4·00	1·00
238/51		*Set of 16*	25·00	4·75

WATERMARK. Two forms of the watermark Type **127** exist in the above issue: the normal Type **127** (sometimes indistinct), and a very faint *tête-bêche* watermark, i.e. alternately facing up and down, which was introduced in mid-1967. As it is extremely difficult to distinguish these on single stamps we do not list it.

The ½ (both perfs), 1, 2, 2½, 3, 15 c. and 1 r. are known in both forms, the 1½, 4, 5, 7½, 9, 10, 20 and 50 c. only in the *tête-bêche* form, and the 12½ c. Type **127** only.

GUM. The 2, 3, 5, 20, 50 c. and 1 r. exist with PVA gum as well as gum arabic.

PHOSPHORISED PAPER. From October 1971 onwards phosphor bands (see Nos. 282/96) gave way to phosphorised paper which cannot be distinguished from non-phosphor stamps without the aid of a lamp. For this reason we do not distinguish these printings in the above issue, but some are slightly different shades which are listed in the *Elizabethan Catalogue* and all have PVA gum.

The 4 c. and 9 c. are on phosphorised paper only and differ from Nos. 288 and 292 by the lack of phosphor bands.

COVER PRICES

Cover factors are quoted at the beginning of each country for most issues to 1945. An explanation of the system can be found on page x. The factors quoted do not, however, apply to philatelic covers.

145 "Springbok" Badge of Rugby Board

147 Calvin

1964 (8 May). *75th Anniv of South African Rugby Board. Chalk-surfaced paper. T* **145** *and similar horiz design. W* **127** (*sideways on* 2½ c.). P 14 × 15 (2½ c.) *or* 15 × 14 (12½ c.).

252		2½ c. yellow-brown and deep green	15	10
253		12½ c. black and light yellow-green	5·50	4·25

Design:—12½ c. Rugby footballer.

1964 (10 July). *400th Death Anniv of Calvin (Protestant reformer). Chalk-surfaced paper. W* **127** (*sideways*). P 14 × 13½.

254	147	2½ c. cerise, violet and brown	10	10

148 Nurse's Lamp

149 Nurse holding Lamp

I. Screened base to lamp II. Clear base to lamp

1964 (12 Oct). *50th Anniv of South African Nursing Association. Chalk-surfaced paper. W* **127** (*sideways on* 2½ c.). P 14 × 15 (2½ c.) *or* 15 × 14 (12½ c.).

255	148	2½ c. ultramarine and dull gold (Type I)	10	10
256		2½ c. brt blue & yellow-gold (Type II)	30	10
		a. Ultramarine and dull gold	15	10
257	149	12½ c. bright blue and gold	3·25	2·00
		a. Gold omitted	£900	
255/7		*Set of 3*	3·25	2·00

150 I.T.U. Emblem and Satellites

1965 (17 May). *I.T.U. Centenary. T* **150** *and similar horiz design. Chalk-surfaced paper. W* **127.** P 15 × 14.

258		2½ c. orange and blue	25	10
259		12½ c. brown-purple and green	3·00	1·75

Design:—12½ c. I.T.U. emblem and symbols.

152 Pulpit in Groote Kerk, Cape Town

153 Church Emblem

1965 (21 Oct). *Tercentenary of Nederduites Gereformeerde Kerk (Dutch Reformed Church) in South Africa. Chalk-surfaced paper. W* **127** (*sideways on* 2½ c., *inverted on* 12½ c.). P 14 × 15 (2½ c.) *or* 15 × 14 (12½ c.).

260	152	2½ c. brown and light yellow	15	10
261	153	12½ c. black, light orange and blue	1·75	1·25

154 Diamond

155 Bird in flight

(Des C. E. F. Skotnes)

1966 (31 May). *Fifth Anniv of Republic. T* **154/5** *and similar designs. Chalk-surfaced paper. W* **127** *(sideways on* 1 c., 3 c.*). P* 14 × 13½ (1 c.), 13½ × 14 (2½ c.), 14 × 15 (3 c.) *or* 15 × 14 (7½ c.).

			Un pair	Us pair	Us single
262		1 c. black, bluish green & olive-yell	45	45	10
263		2½ c. blue, deep blue & yellow-green	1·25	1·25	10
264		3 c. red, greenish yellow & red-brn	4·75	4·75	10
265		7½ c. blue, ultramarine and yellow	5·50	6·00	20
262/5		Set of 4	11·00	11·00	40

Designs: *Vert*—3 c. Maize plants. *Horiz*—7½ c. Mountain landscape.

Nos. 262/5 exist on Swiss-made paper with *tête-bêche* watermark from a special printing made for use in presentation albums for delegates to the U.P.U. Congress in Tokyo in 1969, as supplies of the original Harrison paper were by then exhausted (*Set of 4 pairs price* £140 *mint*).

158 Verwoerd and Union Buildings, Pretoria

(Des from portrait by Dr. Henkel)

1966 (6 Dec). *Verwoerd Commemoration. T* **158** *and similar designs. · Chalk-surfaced paper. W* **127** *(sideways on* 3 c.*). P* 14 × 15 (3 c.) *or* 15 × 14 (*others*).

266		2½ c. blackish brown and turquoise	..	10	10
267		3 c. blackish brown and yellow-green	..	10	10
268		12½ c. blackish brown and greenish blue	..	70	60
266/8		Set of 3		80	60

Designs: *Vert*—3 c. "Dr. H. F. Verwoerd" (I. Henkel). *Horiz*—12½ c. Verwoerd and map of South Africa.

161 "Martin Luther" (Cranach the Elder)
162 Wittenberg Church Door

1967 (31 Oct). *450th Anniv of Reformation. W* **127** *((sideways), normal on* 2½ c., *tête-bêche on* 12½ c.*). P* 14 × 15.

269	161	2½ c. black and rose-red	..	10	10
270	162	12½ c. black and yellow-orange	.. ..	1·75	2·00

163 "Profile of Pres. Fouché" (I. Henkel)
164 Portrait of Pres. Fouché

1968 (10 Apr). *Inauguration of President Fouché. W* **127** *(sideways). P* 14 × 15.

271	163	2½ c. chocolate and pale chocolate	..	10	10
272	164	12½ c. deep blue and light blue	..	80	1·25

No. 272 also exists with the watermark *tête-bêche* (*Price un* £1; *used* £1.50).

165 Hertzog in 1902

1968 (21 Sept). *Inauguration of General Hertzog Monument, Bloemfontein. T* **165** *and similar designs. W* **127** *(tête-bêche on* 2½ c., *inverted on* 3 c., *sideways on* 12½ c.*). P* 14 × 13½ (12½ c.) *or* 13½ × 14 (*others*).

273		2½ c. black, brown and olive-yellow	..	10	10
274		3 c. black, red-brown, red-orange and yellow	..	15	10
275		12½ c. black, red and yellow-orange	..	2·00	1·25
273/5		Set of 3		2·00	1·25

Designs: *Horiz*—3 c. Hertzog in 1924. *Vert*—12½ c. Hertzog Monument.

NEW INFORMATION

The editor is always interested to correspond with people who have new information that will improve or correct the Catalogue.

168 Natal Kingfisher
169 Kafferboom Flower

1969. *W* **127** *(tête-bêche, sideways on* ½ c.*). P* 14 × 13½ (½ c.) *or* 13½ × 14 (1 c.).

276	168	½ c. new bl, carm-red & yell-ochre (1.69)	10	30
		a. Coil. Perf 14 × 14½ (5.69)..	2·00	1·75
277	169	1 c. rose-red and olive-brown (1.69)	10	10

See also Nos. 282/3 and 313/14.

170 Springbok and Olympic Torch
171 Professor Barnard and Groote Schuur Hospital

1969 (15 Mar). *South African Games, Bloemfontein. W* **127** *(tête-bêche, sideways). P* 14 × 13½.

278	170	2½ c. black, blue-black, red & sage-grn	15	10
279		12½ c. black, blue-blk, red & cinnamon ..	1·00	1·25

1969 (7 July). *World's First Heart Transplant and 47th South African Medical Association Congress. T* **171** *and similar horiz design. W* **127** *(tête-bêche). P* 13½ × 14 (2½ c.) *or* 15 × 14 (12½ c.).

280		2½ c. plum and rose-red	..	15	10
281		12½ c. carmine-red and royal blue	.. ..	1·75	2·25

Design:—12½ c. Hands holding heart.

1969–72. *As 1964–72 issue, Nos.* 276/7, *and new value* (6 c.), *but with phosphor bands printed horizontally and vertically between the stamp designs, over the perforations, producing a frame effect. W* **127** *arranged tête-bêche (upright on* 1, 2 *and* 3 c., *sideways on others). P* 14×13½ (½, 1½ c.), 13½×14 (1 c.), *or* 14 (*others*).

282	168	½ c. new blue, carmine-red and yellow-ochre (1.70)	..	15	60
		a. Coil. Perf 14×15 (2.71)		3·25	3·25
283	169	1 c. rose-red & olive-brown (12.69)		15	10
284	132	1½ c. red-brown & lt purple (12.69)		20	10
285	133	2 c. ultramarine and yellow (11.69)		30	10
		a. Deep ultramarine & yell (8.70)		90	40
286	134	2½ c. violet and green (1.70)		25	10
		a. Purple and green (24.7.70)..		75	10
287	135	3 c. red and deep blue (30.9.69)		70	10
288	134	4 c. violet and green (1.3.71)		40	40
289	136	5 c. yellow & greenish bl (17.11.69)		85	10
290	137	6 c. yellow-brn & brt grn (3.5.71)		1·00	30
291		6 c. yell-brn & brt grn (17.11.69)		4·00	30
292	139	9 c. red, yell & black-grn (17.5.71)		1·50	30
293	138	10 c. brown and pale green (1.70) ..		2·00	10
294	139	12½ c. red, yell & black-grn (2.5.70)		5·50	1·75
295	140	15 c. blk, lt ol-yell & red-orge (1.70)		2·75	1·40
296	141	20 c. turquoise-blue, carmine and brown-orange (18.2.70) ..		11·00	60
		a. Turquoise-blue, carmine and orange-buff (9.72)		11·00	60
282/96		Set of 15		27·00	5·50

No. 286 exists on normal RSA wmk as well as RSA *tête-bêche* wmk.

The 1, 2, 2½, 3, 10, 15 and 20 c. exist with PVA gum as well as gum arabic, but the 4, 6 and 9 c. exist with PVA gum only.

For stamps without wmk, see Nos. 313, etc.

173 Mail Coach
174 Transvaal Stamp of 1869

1969 (6 Oct). *Centenary of First Stamps of South African Republic (Transvaal). Phosphor bands on all four sides* (2½ c.). *W* **127** *(tête-bêche, sideways on* 12½ c.*). P* 13½ × 14 (2½ c.) *or* 14 × 13½ (12½ c.).

297	173	2½ c. yellow, indigo and yellow-brown	15	10
298	174	12½ c. emerald, gold and yellow-brown	3·25	3·00

PHOSPHOR FRAME. Nos. 299/306 have phosphor applied on all four sides as a frame.

175 "Water 70" Emblem
177 "The Sower"

1970 (14 Feb). *Water 70 Campaign. T* **175** *and similar design. W* **127** *(tête-bêche, sideways on* 2½ c.*)). P* 14 × 13½ (2½ c.) *or* 13½ × 14 (3 c.).

299		2½ c. green, bright blue and chocolate	..	30	10
300		3 c. Prussian blue, royal blue and buff	..	30	20

Design: *Horiz*—3 c. Symbolic waves.

1970 (24 Aug). *150th Anniv of Bible Society of South Africa. T* **177** *and similar horiz design (gold die-stamped on* 12½ c.*). W* **127** *(tête-bêche, sideways on* 2½ c.*). P* 14 × 13½ (2½ c.) *or* 13½ × 14 (12½ c.).

301		2½ c. multicoloured ..		15	10
302		12½ c. gold, black and blue ..	..	2·50	2·50

Design:—12½ c. "Biblia" and open book.

178 J. G. Strijdom and Strijdom Tower
179 Map and Antarctic Landscape

1971 (22 May). *"Interstex" Stamp Exhibition, Cape Town. P* 14 × 13½. A. *W* **127** *(sideways tête-bêche). B. W* **102** *(sideways).*

			A		B
303	178	5 c. light greenish blue, black and pale yellow	20	10	1·75 4·50

1971 (22 May). *Tenth Anniv of Antarctic Treaty. W* **127** *(tête-bêche). P* 13½ × 14.

304	179	12½ c. blue-black, greenish bl & orge-red	6·00	5·50

180 "Landing of British Settlers, 1820" (T. Baines)

1971 (31 May). *Tenth Anniv of the Republic of South Africa. T* **180** *and similar design. W* **127** *(tête-bêche sideways on* 4 c.*). P* 13½ × 14 (2 c.) *or* 14 × 13½ (4 c.).

305		2 c. pale flesh and brown-red..	.. ..	15	10
306		4 c. green and black	..	15	10

Design: *Vert*—4 c. Presidents Steyn and Kruger and Treaty of Vereeniging Monument.
No. 306 exists with PVA gum as well as gum arabic.

PHOSPHORISED PAPER. All issues from here are on phosphorised paper *unless otherwise stated*.

181 View of Dam

(Des C. Bridgeford (4 c.), C. Lindsay (others))

1972 (4 Mar). *Opening of Hendrik Verwoerd Dam. T* **181** *and similar horiz designs. Multicoloured. W* **127** *(tête-bêche). P* 13½ × 14.

307		4 c. Type 181 ..		20	10
308		5 c. Aerial view of Dam	.. ..	25	10
309		10 c. Dam and surrounding country (58 × 21 mm)	..	1·50	2·25
307/9		.. ..	Set of 3	1·75	2·25

182 Sheep
182a Lamb

(Des K. Esterhuysen (4 c.), H. Botha (15 c.))

1972 (15 May–Oct). W **127** (*tête-bêche*). P 14.
310	182	4 c. olive-brn, yell, pale bl & slate-bl	..		30	10
		a. *Grey-olive, yellow, bright blue and slate-blue* (10.72)			30	10
311	182a	15 c. pale stone, deep blue and dull blue		3·00	20

Other shades exist of the 4 c.
See also Nos. 317 and 322.

183 Black and Siamese Cats   **184** Transport and Industry

1972 (19 Sept). *Centenary of Societies for the Prevention of Cruelty to Animals.* W **127** (*sideways tête-bêche*). P 14 × 13½.
312	183	5 c. multicoloured	..	..	1·75	10

1972–74. As Nos. 310/11 and 282 etc. but no wmk. P 14 × 14½ (½ c.), 14 (1 c.) or 12½ (others). *Phosphorised, glossy paper.*
313	168	½ c. bright blue, scarlet and yellow-ochre (coil) (6.73)		15·00	15·00
314	169	1 c. rose-red and olive-brown (1.74)		40	10
315	133	2 c. blue and orange-yellow (11.72)		15	10
		a. Perf 14. *Deep ultramarine and orange-yellow* (coil) (7.73)		11·00	11·00
		b. Chalky paper (17.7.74)		40	60
316	135	3 c. scarlet and deep blue (8.5.73)		50	15
		a. Chalky paper (18.2.74)		1·25	1·25
317	182	4 c. grey-blue, yellow, blue and bluish slate* (1.10.73)		30	30
		a. *Olive-sepia, yellow, azure and slate-blue* (18.2.74)		50	30
		b. *Lavender-brown, pale yellow, blue and bluish slate** (26.7.74)		30	20
		c. Chalky paper* (22.8.74)		60	45
318	136	5 c. orge-yell & greenish bl (4.10.73)		2·00	80
		a. Perf 14. *Yellow and light greenish blue* (coil) (7.73)		12·00	12·00
		b. Chalky paper (5.74)		2·25	1·10
319	137	6 c. yellow-brown and bright green (*chalky paper*) (22.7.74)		2·25	2·25
320	139	9 c. red, yellow-green & grn-blk (6.73)		1·75	2·00
		a. *Red, deep yellowish green and green-black* (4.74)		2·75	1·50
321	138	10 c. reddish brown & brt grn (8.5.73)		85	30
		a. Perf 14 (coil) (6.73)		14·00	14·00
		b. Chalky paper (17.7.74)		1·50	70
322	182a	15 c. pale stone, deep blue and dull blue (*chalky paper*) (4.9.74)		3·25	4·00
323	141	20 c. turquoise-blue, rose-carmine and orange-buff (8.5.73)		3·25	45
		a. Chalky paper (5.74)		5·00	70
324	142	50 c. black and bright blue (6.73)		4·50	1·25
		a. Chalky paper (22.7.74)		9·50	6·50
325	143	1 r. orange, lt green & lt blue (8.10.73)		14·00	2·00
		a. Orange omitted		£1000	
313/25			Set of 13	42·00	25·00

*On these stamps the colours are known to vary within the sheet.
No. 314 also differs in that the central design has been moved down about 1 mm.
Nos. 317/c also differ from No. 310 by measuring 26¼ × 21 mm instead of 27¼ × 21¾ mm.
No. 325a exists on the bottom row of one sheet.

(Des J. Hoekstra (4 c.), M. Barnett (others))

1973 (1 Feb). *50th Anniv of ESCOM (Electricity Supply Commission).* T **184** *and similar vert designs. Multicoloured.* P 12 × 12½ (4 c.) or 12½ (others).
326		4 c. Type **184**	..	20	10
327		5 c. Pylon (21 × 28 mm)	..	30	10
328		15 c. Cooling Towers (21 × 28 mm)		3·00	3·50
326/8			Set of 3	3·25	3·50

185 University Coat of arms   **187** C. J. Langenhoven

186 Rescuing Sailors

(Des P. de Wet (15 c.), H. Meiring (others))

1973 (2 Apr). *Centenary of University of South Africa.* T **185** *and similar designs.* W **127** (*tête-bêche*) (5 c.) or no wmk (others). P 12 × 12½ (5 c.) or 12½ (others).
329		4 c. multicoloured	..	20	10
330		5 c. multicoloured	..	30	15
331		15 c. black and gold	..	3·00	3·25
329/31			Set of 3	3·25	3·25

Designs: *Horiz* (37 × 21 mm)—5 c. University Complex, Pretoria. *Vert* (*As* T **185**)—15 c. Old University Building, Cape Town.

WATERMARK. All issues from this date are on unwatermarked paper, *unless otherwise stated.*

(Des M. Barnett)

1973 (2 June). *Bicentenary of Rescue by Wolraad Woltemade.* T **186** *and similar horiz designs.* P 11½ × 12½.
332		4 c. lt red-brown, lt yellow-green and black	..	25	10
333		5 c. yellow-olive, light yellow-green & black		40	10
334		15 c. red-brown, light yellow-green and black		5·50	6·00
332/4			Set of 3	5·50	6·00

Designs:—5 c. *De Jong Thomas* foundering; 15 c. *De Jong Thomas* breaking up and sailors drowning.

(Des J. Mostert)

1973 (1 Aug). *Birth Centenary of C. J. Langenhoven (politician and composer of national anthem).* T **187** *and similar designs.* P 12½ (4 and 5 c.) or 11½ × 12½ (15 c.).
335	187	4 c. multicoloured	..	25	10
336	–	5 c. multicoloured	..	35	10
337	–	15 c. multicoloured	..	5·00	5·50
335/7			Set of 3	5·00	5·50

Nos. 336/7 are as T **187** but with motifs rearranged. The 5 c. is vert, 21 × 38 mm, and the 15 c. is horiz, 38 × 21 mm.

188 Communications Map

(Des C. Webb)

1973 (1 Oct). *World Communications Day.* P 12½.

(a) No wmk. Glossy paper
338	188	15 c. multicoloured	..	80	1·40

*(b) W **127** (tête-bêche). Chalky paper*
339	188	15 c. multicoloured	..	1·50	4·50

189 Restored Buildings   **190** Burgerspond (obverse and reverse)

(Des W. Jordaan)

1974 (14 Mar). *Restoration of Tulbagh.* T **189** *and similar multicoloured design.* P 12½.
340		4 c. Type **189**	..	15	10
341		5 c. Restored Church Street (58 × 21 mm)	..	40	60

(Des P. de Wet. Litho)

1974 (6 Apr). *Centenary of the Burgerspond (coin).* P 12½ × 12.
342	190	9 c. brown, orange-red & pale yell-olive	60	95

191 Dr. Malan   **192** Congress Emblem

(Des I. Henkel)

1974 (22 May). *Birth Centenary of Dr. D. F. Malan (Prime Minister).* P 12½ × 12.
343	191	4 c. blue and light blue	..	..	15	10

(Des Ingrid Paul)

1974 (13 June). *15th World Sugar Congress, Durban.* P 12 × 12½.
344	192	15 c. deep ultramarine and silver	..	1·00	1·50

193 "50" and Radio Waves

(Des Ingrid Paul)

1974 (13 July). *50th Anniv of Broadcasting in South Africa.* P 12 × 12½.
345	193	4 c. red and black	..	..	10	10

---

194 Monument Building

(Des G. Cunningham)

1974 (13 July). *Inauguration of British Settlers' Monument, Grahamstown.* P 12 × 12½.
346	194	5 c. red and black	..	10	10

195 Stamps of the South African Provinces

(Des K. Esterhuysen)

1974 (9 Oct). *Centenary of Universal Postal Union.* P 12½.
347	195	15 c. multicoloured	..	..	80	80

196 Iris   **197** Bokmakierie Shrikes

(Des E. de Jong. Recess and photo)

1974 (20 Nov)–**76.** *Multicoloured. Glossy paper* (2, 3, 4, 6, 7, 30 c. *and* 1 r.) *or chalk-surfaced paper* (others). P 12½ (1 to 25 c.) or 12×12½ (others).

*(a) Vert designs as T **196** showing flowers, or horiz designs showing birds or fish.*
348		1 c. Type **196**	..	10	10
349		2 c. Wild Heath	..	15	10
		a. Chalk-surfaced paper (2.75)		10	10
350		3 c. Geranium	..	30	10
		a. Chalk-surfaced paper (*deep claret background*) (6.75)		10	10
		ab. Imperf (pair)		£200	
		ac. *Brown-purple background* (6.76)		10	10
351		4 c. Arum Lily	..	30	10
		a. Chalk-surfaced paper (2.75)		10	10
		ab. Imperf (pair)		£160	
352		5 c. Cape Gannet	..	20	10
353		6 c. Galjoen (fish)	..	25	10
354		7 c. Zebra Fish	..	25	10
355		9 c. Angel Fish	..	30	10
356		10 c. Moorish Idol	..	30	10
357		14 c. Roman (fish)	..	30	10
358		15 c. Greater Double-collared Sunbird		30	10
359		20 c. Yellow-billed Hornbill	..	45	10
360		25 c. Barberton Daisy	..	45	10

*(b) Horiz designs as T **197***
361		30 c. Type **197**	..	8·00	50
362		50 c. Stanley Cranes	..	2·50	35
363		1 r. Bateleurs	..	8·50	2·75
348/63			Set of 16	20·00	3·75

A used block of 4 and a single on cover of No. 351 have been seen with the yellow omitted.

1974 (20 Nov)–**76.** *Coil stamps. As Nos. 348/9, 352 and 356 but photo, colours changed. Glossy paper.* P 12½.
370		1 c. reddish violet and pink	..	75	50
		a. Perf 14. Chalk-surfaced paper (12.75)		55	50
371		2 c. bronze-green and yellow-ochre	..	80	50
		a. Chalk-surfaced paper (7.75)		1·10	50
		b. Perf 14. Chalk-surfaced paper (11.76?)		1·40	40
372		5 c. black and light slate-blue	..	1·75	80
373		10 c. deep violet-blue and light blue	..	4·25	4·75
		a. Perf 14. Chalk-surfaced paper (4.76)		4·00	4·00
370/3			Set of 4	6·50	5·25

198 Voortrekker Monument and Encampment

(Des J. Hoekstra)

1974 (6 Dec). *25th Anniv of Voortrekker Monument, Pretoria.* P 12½.
374	198	4 c. multicoloured	..	..	20	30

---

199 SASOL Complex

200 President Diederichs

(Des C. Webb)

1975 (26 Feb). *25th Anniv of SASOL (South African Coal, Oil and Gas Corporation Ltd). P 11½ × 12½.*
375 **199** 15 c. multicoloured .. .. .. 1·25 1·75

(Des J. L. Booysen. Recess (4 c.) or photo (15 c.))

1975 (19 Apr). *Inauguration of the State President. P 12½ × 11½.*
376 **200** 4 c. agate and gold 10 10
377   15 c. royal blue and gold .. .. 70 1·25

201 Jan Smuts

202 "Dutch East Indiaman, Table Bay"

(Des J. Hoekstra. Recess and photo)

1975 (24 May). *Jan Smuts Commemoration. P 12½ × 11½.*
378 **201** 4 c. black and olive-black 10 10

(Des J. Hoekstra. Photo (Nos. 379/82) or litho (**MS**383))

1975 (18 June). *Death Centenary of Thomas Baines (painter). T **202** and similar horiz designs. Multicoloured. P 11½ × 12½.*
379   5 c. Type **202** 20 10
380   9 c. "Cradock, 1848" 30 20
381 15 c. "Thirsty Flat, 1848" .. 50 50
382 30 c. "Pretoria, 1874" .. .. 1·00 1·75
379/82 .. .. .. *Set of 4* 1·75 2·25
MS383 120 × 95 mm. Nos. 379/82 .. .. 1·90 4·25

203 Gideon Malherbe's House, Paarl

(Des P. de Wet. Recess and photo)

1975 (14 Aug). *Centenary of Genootskap van Regte Afrikaners (Afrikaner Language Movement). P 12½.*
384 **203** 4 c. multicoloured 10 10

204 "Automatic Sorting"

205 Title Page of *Die Afrikaanse Patriot*

(Des J. Sampson)

1975 (11 Sept). *Postal Mechanisation. P 12½ × 11½.*
385 **204** 4 c. multicoloured 10 10

(Des K. Esterhuysen. Recess and photo (4 c.). Des P. de Wet. Litho (5 c.))

1975 (10 Oct). *Inauguration of the Language Monument, Paarl. T **205** and similar vert design. P 12½ × 11½.*
386   4 c. pale stone and bright orange .. 10 10
387   5 c. multicoloured 10 10
Design:—5 c. "Afrikaanse Taalmonument".

206 Table Mountain

(Des P. Bosman and J. Hoekstra. Litho)

1975 (13 Nov). *Tourism. T **206** and similar horiz designs. Multicoloured. P 12½.*
388 15 c. Type **206** .. .. .. 4·50 5·00
 a. Block of 4. Nos. 388/91 .. 16·00
 ab. Yellow-orange and pale lemon ("RSA 15 c") omitted .. .. .. † —
389 15 c. Johannesburg .. .. 4·50 5·00
390 15 c. Cape Vineyards .. .. 4·50 5·00
391 15 c. Lions in Kruger National Park .. 4·50 5·00
388/91 .. .. .. *Set of 4* 16·00 18·00
Nos. 388/91 were printed together, *se-tenant*, in blocks of 4 throughout the sheet.
Nos. 388/91 were printed in six colours. At least one sheet, subsequently used to prepare official first day covers at Pretoria, had the final two colours, yellow-orange and pale lemon, omitted.

207 Globe and Satellites

(Des J. Hoekstra. Litho)

1975 (3 Dec). *Satellite Communication. P 12½.*
392 **207** 15 c. multicoloured 40 40

208 Bowls

(209)

(Des J. Maskew. Litho)

1976. *Sporting Commemorations. T **208** and similar vert designs. P 12½ × 11½.*
393 15 c. black and light sage-green (18.2) .. 30 70
394 15 c. black and bright yellow-green (15.3) 75 1·40
395 15 c. black and pale yellow-olive (16.8) 40 60
396 15 c. black and apple-green (2.12) .. 30 55
393/6 .. .. .. *Set of 4* 1·60 3·00
MS397 161 × 109 mm. Nos. 393/6 (2.12) .. 2·75 4·50
Designs:—No. 393, Type **208** (World Bowls Championships, Johannesburg); No. 394, Batsman (Centenary of Organised Cricket in South Africa); No. 395, Polo player; No. 396, Gary Player (golfer).

1976 (6 Apr). *South Africa's Victory in World Bowls Championships. No. 393 optd with T **209** in gold.*
398 **208** 15 c. black and light sage-green .. 30 70

210 "Picnic under a Baobab Tree"

(Des J. Hoekstra. Photo (4 c.) or litho (others and **MS**403))

1976 (20 Apr). *Birth Centenary of Erich Mayer (painter). T **210** and similar horiz designs. Multicoloured. P 11½ × 12½.*
399   4 c. Type **210** 15 10
 a. Imperf (pair) £400
400 10 c. "Foot of the Blaawberg" .. 35 25
401 15 c. "Harbeespoort Dam" .. 60 1·00
402 20 c. "Street scene, Doornfontein" .. 80 1·50
399/402 .. .. *Set of 4* 1·75 2·50
MS403 121 × 95 mm. Nos. 399/402 .. 2·00 4·00

211 Cheetah

212 "Emily Hobhouse" (H. Naude)

(Des P. Bosman. Photo (3 c.) or litho (others))

1976 (5 June). *World Environmental Day. T **211** and similar horiz designs. Multicoloured. P 11½ × 12½.*
404   3 c. Type **211** 15 10
405 10 c. Black Rhinoceros 70 35
406 15 c. Blesbok .. .. 85 1·10
407 20 c. Mountain Zebra .. .. 1·25 1·75
404/7 .. .. .. *Set of 4* 2·75 3·00

(Des J. Hoekstra)

1976 (8 June). *50th Death Anniv of Emily Hobhouse (welfare worker). P 12½ × 11½.*
408 **212** 4 c. multicoloured 10 10

213 Steam Packet, 1876

214 Family with Globe

(Des K. Esterhuysen. Litho)

1976 (5 Oct). *Ocean Mail Service Centenary. P 11½ × 12½.*
409 **213** 10 c. multicoloured 60 85
 a. Imperf (horiz pair) £375

(Des I. Ross)

1976 (6 Nov). *Family Planning and Child Welfare. P 12½ × 11½.*
410 **214** 4 c. chestnut and light salmon .. 10 10

215 Glasses of Wine

216 Dr. Jacob du Toit

First "die" of Afrikaans inscription at left omitted (R. 1/3 on every third sheet)

(Des H. Botha. Litho)

1977 (14 Feb). *International Wine Symposium, Cape Town. P 12½ × 11½.*
411 **215** 15 c. multicoloured 40 85
 a. "die" omitted .. .. 15·00

(Des J. Hoekstra)

1977 (21 Feb). *Birth Centenary of J. D. du Toit (theologian and poet). P 12½ × 11½.*
412 **216** 4 c. multicoloured 10 10

217 Palace of Justice

218 Protea repens

(Des H. Meiring)

1977 (18 May). *Centenary of Transvaal Supreme Court. P 11½ × 12½.*
413 **217** 4 c. red-brown 10 10

(Des D. Findlay. Photo (1, 2, 3 c. (No. 416), 4, 5, 8, 10 to 20 c. (Nos. 425/a) and coil stamps) or litho (others))

1977 (27 May)–**82**. *Vert designs as T **218** showing Proteas or other Succulents. Multicoloured. (a) Sheet stamps. P 12½.*
414   1 c. Type **218** 10 10
415   2 c. P punctata 15 30
416   3 c. P neriifolia (photo) (p 12½) .. 10 10
416a   3 c. P neriifolia (litho) (p 14 × 13½) (1.10.79) 10 20
417   4 c. P longifolia 10 10
 a. Imperf (pair) £100
418   5 c. P cynaroides 10 10
 a. Perf 14 × 13½ (4.3.81) .. 10 10
 b. Imperf (pair) £130
419   6 c. P canaliculata 35 40
 a. Black (face value and inscr at foot) omitted £120
 b. Perf 14 × 13½ (25.10.79*) .. 30 40
420   7 c. P lorea 25 40
 a. Emerald ("RSA") omitted .. £150
 b. Perf 14 × 13½ (19.9.80) .. 20 40

421	8 c.	*P mundii* ..	..	20	30
	a. Perf 14 × 13½ (10.7.81) ..		..	15	10
422	9 c.	*P roupelliae*	..	20	40
	a. Perf 14 × 13½ (22.12.78)		..	3·75	2·00
423	10 c.	*P arista* ..	..	30	10
	a. Perf 14 × 13½ (12.1.82) ..		..	20	30
424	15 c.	*P eximia* ..	..	25	10
425	20 c.	*P magnifica* (photo) ..	..	30	10
	a. Perf 14 × 13½ (16.2.78) ..		..	60	90
425b	20 c.	*P magnifica* (litho) (p 14 × 13½) (24.5.82)		85	60
426	25 c.	*P grandiceps*	..	60	40
	a. Emerald ("RSA" and leaves) omitted			£160	
	b. Black (face value and inscr) omitted				
	c. Perf 14×13½ (3.6.80)		..	40	40
427	30 c.	*P amplexicaulis*	..	45	10
	a. Perf 14×13½ (19.10.80)		..	40	40
428	50 c.	*Leucospermum cordifolium*		65	15
	a. Perf 14×13½ (9.10.80)		..	45	15
429	1 r.	*Paranomus reflexus*	..	1·00	95
	a. Perf 14×13½ (30.7.80)		..	80	75
430	2 r.	*Orothamnus zeyheri*	..	3·00	2·50
	a. Perf 14×13½ (22.5.81)		..	1·50	1·00

(b) *Coil stamps. Imperf × perf 14*

431	1 c.	*Leucadendron argenteum*		35	60
432	2 c.	*Mimetes cucullatus*		35	60
433	5 c.	*Serruria florida*	..	35	60
434	10 c.	*Leucadendron sessile*	..	35	70
414/34		.. .. *Set of 21*		6·25	6·25

*Sheets dated 15 August 1979.

There were two emerald plates used for the 7 c.; one for the design and background and a second, common with other values in the issue, used to apply "RSA". No. 420a shows this second emerald plate omitted.

Later printings of the coil stamps come with every fifth stamp numbered on the back.

219 Gymnast

220 Metrication Symbol on Globe

(Des D. Cowie. Litho)

1977 (15 Aug). *Eighth Congress of International Association of Physical Education and Sports for Girls and Women.* P 12½ × 11½.
435 **219** 15 c. black, salmon-red and yellow .. 30 30

(Des L. Wilsenach. Litho)

1977 (15 Sept). *Metrication.* P 12 × 12½.
436 **220** 15 c. multicoloured 30 30

221 Atomic Diagram

(Des R. Sargent. Litho)

1977 (8 Oct). *Uranium Development.* P 12 × 12½.
437 **221** 15 c. multicoloured 30 30

222 National Flag

(Des J. Hoekstra)

1977 (11 Nov). *50th Anniv of National Flag.* P 12 × 12½.
438 **222** 5 c. multicoloured 10 10

223 Walvis Bay, 1878

(Des A. H. Barrett. Litho)

1978 (10 Mar). *Centenary of Annexation of Walvis Bay.* P 12½.
439 **223** 15 c. multicoloured .. 60 40

COVER PRICES

Cover factors are quoted at the beginning of each country for most issues to 1945. An explanation of the system can be found on page x. The factors quoted do not, however, apply to philatelic covers.

---

224 Dr. Andrew Murray

225 Steel Rail

(Des J. Hoekstra. Litho)

1978 (9 May). *150th Birth Anniv of Dr. Andrew Murray (church statesman).* P 12½ × 12.
440 **224** 4 c. multicoloured 10 10

(Des H. Botha. Litho)

1978 (5 June). *50th Anniv of I.S.C.O.R. (South African Iron and Steel Industrial Corporation).* P 12½.
441 **225** 15 c. multicoloured .. 40 30

226 Richards Bay

(Des A. H. Barrett. Litho)

1978 (31 July). *Harbours.* T **226** and similar horiz design. Multicoloured. P 12½.
442 15 c. Type **226** .. .. .. 80 1·25
  a. Pair. Nos. 442/3 .. .. 1·60 2·50
443 15 c. Saldanhabaai .. .. 80 1·25

Nos. 442/3 were printed together, *se-tenant*, in horizontal and vertical pairs throughout the sheet.

227 "Shepherd's Lonely Dwelling, Riversdale"

228 Pres. B. J. Vorster

(Des G. Mynhardt. Litho)

1978 (21 Aug). *125th Birth Anniv of J. E. A. Volschenk (painter).* T **227** and similar horiz designs. Multicoloured. P 12½.
444 10 c. Type **227** 20 20
445 15 c. "Clouds and Sunshine, Laneberg Range, Riversdale" 50 35
446 20 c. "At the Foot of the Mountain" .. 70 1·00
447 25 c. "Evening on the Veldt" .. .. 80 1·75
444/7 .. .. *Set of 4* 2·00 3·00
MS448 124 × 90 mm. Nos. 444/7 .. 3·00 4·50

(Des A. H. Barrett. Litho)

1978 (10 Oct). *Inauguration of President Vorster.* P 14 × 13½.
449 **228** 4 c. brown-purple and gold .. 60 20
  a. Perf 12½ × 12 .. .. 10 10
450 15 c. dull violet and gold 25 60

229 Golden Gate

(Des A. H. Barrett. Litho)

1978 (13 Nov). *Tourism.* T **229** and similar horiz designs. Multicoloured. P 12½.
451 10 c. Type **229** 25 15
452 15 c. Blyde River Canyon 55 50
453 20 c. Amphitheatre, Drakensberg .. 75 1·25
454 25 c. Cango Caves .. .. .. 90 1·75
451/4 .. .. *Set of 4* 2·25 3·25

230 Dr. Wadley (inventor) and Tellurometer

(Des A. H. Barrett. Litho)

1979 (12 Feb). *25th Anniv of Tellurometer (radio distance measurer).* P 12½.
455 **230** 15 c. multicoloured 20 20

231 1929 4d. Airmail Stamp

(Des G. Mynhardt. Litho)

1979 (30 Mar). *50th Anniv of Stamp Production in South Africa.* P 14.
456 **231** 15 c. green, cream and slate .. 20 20

232 "Save Fuel"

(Des A. H. Barrett)

1979 (2 Apr). *Fuel Conservation.* P 12 × 12½.
457 **232** 4 c. black and vermilion .. 25 50
  a. Pair. Nos. 457/8 .. .. 50 1·00
458 — 4 c. black and vermilion .. 25 50

No. 458 is as T **232** but has face value and country initials in bottom left-hand corner, and Afrikaans inscription above English. Nos. 457/8 were printed together, *se-tenant*, in horizontal and vertical pairs throughout the sheet.

233 Isandlwana

234 "Health Care"

(Des A. H. Barrett. Litho)

1979 (25 May). *Centenary of Zulu War.* T **233** and similar horiz designs in black and rose-red, showing drawings. P 14.
459 4 c. Type **233** 15 10
460 15 c. Ulundi 45 45
461 20 c. Rorke's Drift 60 75
459/61 .. .. *Set of 3* 1·10 1·10
MS462 125 × 90 mm. Nos. 459/61. P 12½ 2·75 3·50

(Des J. Hoekstra. Litho)

1979 (19 June). *Health Year.* P 12½ × 12.
463 **234** 4 c. multicoloured 10 10
  a. Perf 14 × 13½ 30 30

235 Children looking at Candle

(Des G. Mynhardt. Litho)

1979 (13 Sept). *50th Anniv of Christmas Stamp Fund.* P 14.
464 **235** 4 c. multicoloured 10 10

236 University of Cape Town

237 "Gary Player"

(Des G. Mynhardt. Litho)

1979 (1 Oct). *50th Anniv of University of Cape Town.* P 13½ × 14.
465 **236** 4 c. multicoloured 20 30
  a. Perf 12 × 12½ 15 15

(Des H. de Klerk. Litho)

1979 (4 Oct). *"Rosafari 1979" World Rose Convention, Pretoria.* T **237** and similar vert designs. Multicoloured. P 14 × 13½.
466 4 c. Type **237** 15 10
467 15 c. "Prof. Chris Barnard" 40 40
468 20 c. "Southern Sun" 50 50
469 25 c. "Soaring Wings" 65 65
466/9 .. .. *Set of 4* 1·50 1·40
MS470 100 × 125 mm. Nos. 466/9 .. 1·75 2·50

238 University of Stellenbosch   **239** F.A.K. Emblem

(Des A. H. Barrett. Litho)

1979 (8 Nov). *300th Anniv of Stellenbosch (oldest town in South Africa). T 238 and similar horiz design. Multicoloured. P 14.*
471	4 c. Type 238		10	10
472	15 c. Rhenish Church on the Braak	..	20	40

(Des J. Hoekstra)

1979 (18 Dec). *50th Anniv of F.A.K. (Federation of Afrikaans Cultural Societies). P 12½ × 12.*
473	**239**	4 c. multicoloured	10	15

240 "Still-life with Sweet Peas"   **241** "Cullinan II"

(Des G. Mynhardt. Litho)

1980 (6 May). *Paintings by Pieter Wenning. T 240 and similar multicoloured design. P 14 × 13½.*
474	5 c. Type 240		10	10
475	25 c. "House in the Suburbs, Cape Town" (44½ × 37 mm)		30	60
MS476	94 × 121 mm. Nos. 474/5		1·25	1·60

(Des A. H. Barrett. Litho)

1980 (12 May). *World Diamond Congresses, Johannesburg. T 241 and similar vert design. Multicoloured. P 14.*
477	15 c. Type 241		60	60
478	20 c. "Cullinan I (Great Star of Africa)"	..	65	65

242 C. L. Leipoldt   **243** University of Pretoria

(Des J. Hoekstra. Litho)

1980 (3 Sept). *Birth Centenary of C. L. Leipoldt (poet). P 14 × 13½.*
479	**242**	5 c. multicoloured	10	10

(Des P. de Wet. Litho)

1980 (9 Oct). *50th Anniv of University of Pretoria. P 14 × 13½.*
480	**243**	5 c. multicoloured	10	10

244 "Marine with Shipping" (Willem van de Velde)

(Des G. Mynhardt. Litho)

1980 (3 Nov). *Paintings from South African National Gallery, Cape Town. T 244 and similar multicoloured designs. P 14.*
481	5 c. Type 244		10	10
482	10 c. "Firetail and his Trainer" (George Stubbs)	15	20
483	15 c. "Lavinia" (Thomas Gainsborough) (vert)	20	45
484	20 c. "Classical Landscape" (Pieter Post)	25	65
481/4		Set of 4	65	1·25
MS485	126 × 90 mm. Nos. 481/4		1·00	1·75

245 Joubert, Kruger and M. Pretorius (Triumvirate Government)   **246** Boers advancing up Amajuba Mountain

(Des A. H. Barrett. Litho)

1980 (15 Dec). *Centenary of Paardekraal Monument (cairn commemorating formation of Boer Triumvirate Government). T 245 and similar multicoloured design. P 14 × 13½ (5 c.) or 13½ × 14 (10 c.).*
486	5 c. Type 245		10	10
487	10 c. Paardekraal Monument (vert)	..	20	40

(Des Diana Arbuthnot. Litho)

1981 (27 Feb). *Centenary of Battle of Amajuba. T 246 and similar multicoloured design. P 13½ × 14 (5 c.) or 14 × 13½ (15 c.).*
488	5 c. Type 246		20	10
489	15 c. British troops defending hill (horiz)	..	45	50

247 Ballet *Raka*

(Des H. Botha. Litho)

1981 (23 May). *Opening of State Theatre, Pretoria. T 247 and similar horiz design. Multicoloured. P 14.*
490	20 c. Type 247	..	25	30
491	25 c. Opera *Aida*	..	30	35
MS492	110 × 90 mm. Nos. 490/1	..	60	70

248 Former Presidents C. R. Swart, J. J. Fouché, N. Diederichs and B. J. Vorster

(Des A. H. Barrett. Litho)

1981 (30 May). *20th Anniv of Republic. T 248 and similar design. P 14.*
493	5 c. black, grey-olive and bistre	15	10
494	15 c. multicoloured	..	30	30

Design: (28 × 22 mm)—15 c. President Marais Viljoen.

249 Girl with Hearing Aid   **250** Microscope   **251** *Calanthe natalensis*

(Des Mare Mouton. Litho)

1981 (12 June). *Centenary of Institutes for Deaf and Blind, Worcester. T 249 and similar vert design. Multicoloured. P 13½ × 14.*
495	5 c. Type 249		10	10
496	15 c. Boy reading braille	..	20	25

(Des N. Hanna. Litho)

1981 (10 July). *50th Anniv of National Cancer Association. P 13½ × 14.*
497	**250**	5 c. multicoloured	10	10

(Des Jeanette Stead. Litho)

1981 (11 Sept). *Tenth World Orchid Conference, Durban. T 251 and similar vert designs. Multicoloured. P 14.*
498	5 c. Type 251		15	10
499	15 c. *Eulophia speciosa*	..	30	35
500	20 c. *Disperis fanniniae*	..	40	55
501	25 c. *Disa uniflora*	..	50	65
498/501		Set of 4	1·25	1·50
MS502	120 × 91 mm. Nos. 498/501		2·25	1·75

252 Voortrekkers in Uniform   **253** Lord Baden-Powell   **254** Dr. Robert Koch

(Des J. Hoekstra. Litho)

1981 (30 Sept). *50th Anniv of Voortrekker Movement (Afrikaans cultural youth organization). P 14.*
503	**252**	5 c. multicoloured	10	10

(Des J. Meyer. Litho)

1982 (22 Feb). *75th Anniv of Boy Scout Movement. P 13½ × 14.*
504	**253**	15 c. multicoloured	15	15

(Des J. Meyer. Litho)

1982 (24 Mar). *Centenary of Discovery of Tubercle Bacillus by Dr. Robert Koch. P 13½ × 14.*
505	**254**	20 c. multicoloured	15	30

255 *Maria van Riejbeck* (submarine)   **256** Old Provost, Grahamstown

(Des A. H. Barrett. Litho)

1982 (2 Apr). *25th Anniv of Simonstown as South African Navy Base. T 255 and similar horiz designs. Multicoloured. P 14.*
506	8 c. Type 255		10	10
507	15 c. Missile patrol vessel	..	15	30
508	20 c. Minesweeper	..	25	50
509	25 c. Harbour patrol boats	..	30	70
506/9		Set of 4	70	1·40
MS510	125 × 90 mm. Nos. 506/9	..	2·00	2·00

(Des A. H. Barrett. Recess (Nos. 511, 512b, 513, 514, 515a, 516a, 521, 522a, 524, 525, 526 and 527), photo (Nos. 528/31) or litho (others))

1982 (15 July)–**87**. *South African Architecture. Designs as T 256. (a) Sheet stamps. P 14.*
511	1 c. reddish brown (recess)		15	20
511a	1 c. reddish brown (litho) (2.4.84)	..	30	30
	ab. Imperf (horiz pair)			
512	2 c. yellow-olive (litho)	..	20	30
512a	2 c. deep green (litho) (9.5.83)		75	30
512b	2 c. bottle green (recess) (28.11.83)		10	20
512c	2 c. bottle green (litho) (21.11.85)		40	30
513	3 c. violet (recess)		30	30
513a	3 c. violet (litho) (28.11.85)	..	80	40
514	4 c. brown-olive (recess)	..	20	15
514a	4 c. brown-olive (litho) (25.3.85)	..	40	15
515	5 c. carmine (litho)		30	30
515a	5 c. brown-purple (recess) (11.11.83)		10	10
	ab. Imperf (pair)			
516	6 c. deep blue-green (litho)		45	30
516a	6 c. blackish green (recess) (9.8.84)		45	20
517	7 c. dull yellowish green (litho)	..	20	20
518	8 c. greenish blue (litho)	..	30	30
518a	8 c. indigo (litho) (3.1.83)	..	20	10
519	9 c. deep mauve (litho)	..	30	20
520	10 c. Venetian red (litho)	..	40	30
520a	10 c. purple-brown (litho) (26.1.83)		35	10
520b	11 c. cerise (litho) (2.4.84)		40	15
520c	12 c. deep violet-blue (litho) (1.4.85)		60	10
520d	14 c. lake-brown (litho) (1.4.86)		75	10
521	15 c. deep violet-blue (recess)		30	15
521a	16 c. rosine (litho) (1.4.87)		80	40
522	20 c. vermilion (litho)		65	30
522a	20 c. brownish black (recess) (15.6.83)		80	10
522b	20 c. brownish black (litho) (14.11.85)		1·00	15
523	25 c. bistre (litho)	..	40	30
523a	25 c. ochre (litho) (3.6.87)		1·50	45
524	30 c. agate (recess)		65	30
524a	30 c. reddish brown (litho) (12.3.86)		75	30
525	50 c. deep turquoise-blue (recess)		80	30
	a. Deep slate-blue (18.3.83)		1·50	65
525b	50 c. turquoise-blue (litho) (13.10.86)		1·50	20
526	1 r. deep violet (recess)	..	1·00	15
526a	1 r. deep violet (litho) (17.12.86)		1·00	40

527	2 r. deep carmine (recess)		2·00	30
527a	2 r. deep carmine (litho) (5.12.85)		2·00	50
511/27		Set of 21 (one of each value)	9·50	3·50

Designs: (28 × 20 mm)—2 c. Tuynhuys, Cape Town; 3 c. Appelhof, Bloemfontein; 4 c. Raadsaal, Pretoria; 5 c. Cape Town Castle; 6 c. Goewermentsgebou, Bloemfontein; 7 c. Drostdy, Graaff-Reinet; 8 c. Leeuwenhof, Cape Town; 9 c. Libertas, Pretoria; 10 c. City Hall, Pietermaritzburg; 11 c. City Hall, Kimberley; 12 c. City Hall, Port Elizabeth; 14 c. City Hall, Johannesburg; 15 c. Matjesfontein; 16 c. City Hall, Durban; 20 c. Post Office, Durban; 25 c. Melrose House, Pretoria. (45 × 28 mm)—30 c. Old Legislative Assembly Building, Pietermaritzburg; 50 c. Raadsaal, Bloemfontein; 1 r. Houses of Parliament, Cape Town; 2 r. Uniegebou, Pretoria.

For certain printings of Nos. 511/27a the design width of each stamp was reduced by a millimetre. Of the original set of 17 all showed "wide" designs with the exception of the 1 r. Changes in design size occurred in subsequent printings so that Nos. 512c, 513, 521 and 524 can be found in both wide and narrow versions. Of the remainder Nos. 511a, 512b, 513a, 514a, 515a, 516a, 520b/d, 521a, 522a/b, 524a, 525a/b, 526 and 527a exist as "narrow" designs only.

(b) Coil stamps. P 14 × imperf

528	1 c. brown		30	50
529	2 c. yellow-green		30	55
530	5 c. lake-brown		30	55
531	10 c. light brown		30	60
528/31		Set of 4	1·10	2·00

Designs: (28 × 20 mm)—1 c. Drostdy, Swellendam; 2 c. City Hall, East London; 5 c. Head Post Office, Johannesburg; 10 c. Morgenster, Somerset West.

257 Bradysaurus **258** Gough Island Base

(Des Sheila Nowers. Litho)

1982 (1 Dec). *Karoo Fossils.* T **257** and similar horiz designs. Multicoloured. P 14.

532	8 c. Type **257**		40	10
533	15 c. Lystrosaurus		55	60
534	20 c. Euparkeria		70	75
535	25 c. Thrinaxodon		80	85
532/5		Set of 4	2·25	2·00
MS536	107 × 95 mm. Nos. 532/5		2·75	2·75

(Des D. Thorpe. Litho)

1983 (19 Jan). *Weather Stations.* T **258** and similar horiz designs. Multicoloured. P 13½ × 14.

537	8 c. Type **258**		20	10
538	20 c. Marion Island base		45	45
539	25 c. Taking meteorological readings		45	50
540	40 c. Launching weather balloon, Sanae		70	90
537/40		Set of 4	1·60	1·75

259 Class "S2" Light Shunting **260** Rugby
Locomotive

(Des H. Botha. Litho)

1983 (27 Apr). *Steam Railway Locomotives.* T **259** and similar horiz designs. Multicoloured. P 14.

541	10 c. Type **259**		35	10
542	20 c. Class "16E" express locomotive		60	65
543	25 c. Class "6H" locomotive		70	90
544	40 c. Class "15F" main-line locomotive		1·00	1·40
541/4		Set of 4	2·40	2·75

(Des Sheila Nowers. Litho)

1983 (20 July). *Sport in South Africa.* T **260** and similar multicoloured designs. P 14.

545	10 c. Type **260**		10	10
546	20 c. Soccer (horiz)		30	35
547	25 c. Yachting		40	45
548	40 c. Horse-racing (horiz)		60	75
545/8		Set of 4	1·25	1·50

261 Plettenberg Bay **262** Thomas Pringle

(Des A. H. Barrett. Litho)

1983 (12 Oct). *Tourism. Beaches.* T **261** and similar horiz designs. Multicoloured. P 14.

549	10 c. Type **261**		10	10
550	20 c. Durban		25	30
551	25 c. West coast		30	35
552	40 c. Clifton		50	65
549/52		Set of 4	1·10	1·25
MS553	128 × 90 mm. Nos. 549/52		2·25	2·75

(Des J. van Ellinckhuijzen. Litho)

1984 (24 Feb). *South African English Authors.* T **262** and similar vert designs. P 14.

554	10 c. olive-brown, yellow-brown and grey		10	10
555	20 c. olive-brown, deep bluish green and grey		25	40
556	25 c. olive-brown, deep brown-rose and grey		30	50
557	40 c. olive-brown, olive-ochre and grey		50	85
554/7		Set of 4	1·10	1·75

Designs:—20 c. Pauline Smith; 25 c. Olive Schreiner; 40 c. Sir Percy Fitzpatrick.

263 Manganese

(Des H. Botha. Litho)

1984 (8 June). *Strategic Minerals.* T **263** and similar horiz designs. Multicoloured. P 14.

558	11 c. Type **263**		40	10
559	20 c. Chromium		75	65
560	25 c. Vanadium		90	90
561	30 c. Titanium		1·00	1·25
558/61		Set of 4	2·75	2·50

 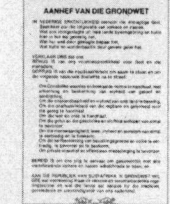

264 Bloukrans River Bridge **265** Preamble to the Constitution
in Afrikaans

(Des D. Bagnall. Litho)

1984 (24 Aug). *South African Bridges.* T **264** and similar horiz designs. Multicoloured. P 14.

562	11 c. Type **264**		40	10
563	25 c. Durban four level interchange		80	70
564	30 c. Mfolozi rail bridge		85	75
565	45 c. Gouritz River bridge		1·10	1·50
562/5		Set of 4	2·75	2·75

(Des G. Mynhardt. Litho)

1984 (3 Sept). *New Constitution.* T **265** and similar vert designs. P 14.

566	11 c. stone, black and bistre		75	90
	a. Horiz pair. Nos. 566/7		1·50	1·75
567	11 c. stone, black and bistre		75	90
568	25 c. stone, deep claret and bistre		50	55
569	30 c. multicoloured		55	60
566/9		Set of 4	2·25	2·75

Designs:—No. 566, Preamble to the Constitution in English; 568, Last two lines of National Anthem; 569, South African coat of arms.

Nos. 566/7 were printed together, *se-tenant*, in horizontal pairs.

266 Pres. P. W. Botha **267** Pro Patria Medal

1984 (2 Nov). *Inauguration of President Botha. Litho.* P 14.

570	**266**	11 c. multicoloured	30	10
571		25 c. multicoloured	55	40

(Des B. Jackson. Litho)

1984 (9 Nov). *Military Decorations.* T **267** and similar vert designs. Multicoloured. P 14.

572	11 c. Type **267**		25	10
573	25 c. De Wet Decoration		55	45
574	30 c. John Chard Decoration		60	65
575	45 c. Honoris Crux (Diamond) Decoration		85	1·10
572/5		Set of 4	2·00	2·10
MS576	71 × 116 mm. Nos. 572/5		2·50	2·75

268 "Reflections" (Frans Oerder) **269** Cape Parliament
Building

(Des J. van Ellinckhuijzen. Litho)

1985 (22 Feb). *Paintings by Frans Oerder.* T **268** and similar horiz designs. Multicoloured. Litho. P 14.

577	11 c. Type **268**		30	15
578	25 c. "Ladies in a Garden"		45	35
579	30 c. "Still-life with Lobster"		50	45
580	50 c. "Still-life with Marigolds"		80	70
577/80		Set of 4	1·90	1·50
MS581	129 × 74 mm. Nos. 577/80		2·50	2·75

(Des A. H. Barrett. Litho)

1985 (15 May). *Centenary of Cape Parliament Building.* T **269** and similar horiz designs. Multicoloured. P 14.

582	12 c. Type **269**		30	10
583	25 c. Speaker's Chair		45	35
584	30 c. "National Convention 1908–9" (Edward Roworth)		60	60
585	50 c. Republic Parliamentary emblem		95	1·00
	a. Black (inscr and outline) omitted		£160	
582/5		Set of 4	2·10	1·90

270 Freesia **271** Sugar Bowl

(Des Sheila Nowers. Litho)

1985 (23 Aug). *Floral Emigrants.* T **270** and similar vert designs. Multicoloured. P 14.

586	12 c. Type **270**		30	10
587	25 c. Nerine		55	55
588	30 c. Ixia		65	70
589	50 c. Gladiolus		90	1·10
586/9		Set of 4	2·25	2·25

(Des H. Botha. Litho)

1985 (5 Nov). *Cape Silverware.* T **271** and similar multicoloured designs. P 14.

590	12 c. Type **271**		30	10
591	25 c. Teapot		60	50
592	30 c. Loving cup (vert)		65	65
593	50 c. Coffee pot (vert)		95	1·25
590/3		Set of 4	2·25	2·25

272 Blood Donor Session **273** National Flag

(Des Sheila Nowers. Litho)

1986 (20 Feb). *Blood Donor Campaign.* T **272** and similar horiz designs. Multicoloured. P 14.

594	12 c. Type **272**		45	10
595	20 c. Baby receiving blood transfusion		75	60
596	25 c. Operation in progress		80	75
597	30 c. Ambulanceman and accident victim		95	1·10
594/7		Set of 4	2·75	2·25

(Des J. Hoekstra. Litho)

1986 (30 May). *25th Anniv of Republic of South Africa.* T **273** and similar horiz design. Multicoloured. P 14.

598	14 c. Type **273**		75	1·00
	a. Horiz pair. Nos. 598/9		1·50	2·00
599	14 c. As Type **273**, but inscr "UNITY IS STRENGTH"		75	1·00

Nos. 598/9 were printed together, *se-tenant*, in horizontal pairs throughout the sheet.

274 Drostdyhof, Graaff-Reinet

(Des A. H. Barrett. Litho)

1986 (14 Aug). *Restoration of Historic Buildings.* T **274** and similar horiz designs. Multicoloured. P 14.

600	14 c. Type **274**		40	10
601	20 c. Pilgrim's Rest mining village		70	50
602	25 c. Strapp's Store, Bethlehem		75	70
603	30 c. Palmdene, Pietermaritzburg		90	1·00
600/3		Set of 4	2·50	2·10

NEW INFORMATION

The editor is always interested to correspond with people who have new information that will improve or correct the Catalogue.

MACHINE LABELS. From 14 August 1986 gummed labels in the above design, ranging in value from 1 c. to 99 r. 99, were available from an experimental machine at Sunnyside Post Office in Pretoria. The machine was moved to the "Johannesburg 100" exhibition from 6 to 11 October 1986 and was then reinstalled at Sunnyside on 17 October 1986. Further machines were introduced subsequently and each can be identified by a code number, between P.001 and P.034, at right.

275 Von Brandis Square, Johannesburg, c 1900

(Des J. van Niekerk. Litho)

1986 (25 Sept). *Centenary of Johannesburg. T 275 and similar horiz designs. Multicoloured. P 14.*

604	14 c. Type 275. .	..	..	35	15
605	20 c. Gold mine (26 × 20 mm)	..	..	90	65
606	25 c. Johannesburg skyline, 1986	..	95	80
607	30 c. Gold bars (26 × 20 mm)..	..	..	1·25	1·25
604/7	..	..	..	..	Set of 4	3·00	2·50

276 Gordon's Rock, Paarlberg   **277** *Cicindela regalis*

(Des A. H. Barrett. Litho)

1986 (20 Nov). *Rock Formations. T 276 and similar vert designs. Multicoloured. P 14.*

608	14 c. Type 276. .	..	..	..	50	10
609	20 c. The Column, Drakensberg	..	75	70
610	25 c. Maltese Cross, Sederberge	..	85	90
611	30 c. Bourke's Luck Potholes, Blyde River Gorge	..	..	1·10	1·25
608/11	..	..	..	Set of 4	3·00	2·75

(Des E. Holm. Litho)

1987 (6 Mar). *South African Beetles. T 277 and similar vert designs. Multicoloured. P 14.*

612	14 c. Type 277. .	..	..	..	50	10
613	20 c. Trichostetha fasciculatus	..	70	70
614	25 c. Julodis viridipes	..	..	85	90
615	30 c. Ceroplesis militaris	..	..	1·10	1·25
612/15	..	..	..	Set of 4	2·75	2·75

278 Eland, Sebaaieni Cave

(Des H. Botha. Litho)

1987 (4 June). *Rock Paintings. T 278 and similar horiz designs. Multicoloured. P 14.*

616	16 c. Type 278. .	..	..	..	50	10
617	20 c. Leaping lion, Clocolan	..	75	65
618	25 c. Black Wildebeest, uMhlwazini Valley	90	90
619	30 c. Bushman dance, Floukraal	..	1·10	1·25
616/19	..	..	..	Set of 4	3·00	2·50

279 Oude Pastorie, Paarl

(Des A. H. Barrett. Litho)

1987 (3 Sept). *300th Anniv of Paarl. T 279 and similar horiz designs. Multicoloured. P 14.*

620	16 c. Type 279. .	..	..	..	40	10
621	20 c. Grapevines	..	..	..	65	60
622	25 c. Wagon-building..	..	..	70	75
623	30 c. KWV Cathedral Wine Cellar	..	95	1·10
620/3	..	..	..	Set of 4	2·50	2·25

VLOEDRAMP NATAL

(280)   **281** "Belshazzar's Feast" (Rembrandt)

1987 (16 Nov). *Natal Flood Relief Fund (1st issue). No. 521a surch as T 280 in Afrikaans or English.*

624	16 c. + 10 c. rosine (surch T 280)	..	45	65
	a. Pair. Nos. 624/5. .	..	..	90	1·25
625	16 c. + 10 c. rosine (surch "NATAL FLOOD DISASTER")	..	..	45	65

Nos. 624/5 were surcharged together, *se-tenant*, in horizontal and vertical pairs throughout the sheet.
See also Nos. 629/30 and 635/6.

(Des Sheila Nowers. Litho)

1987 (19 Nov). *The Bible Society of South Africa. T 281 and similar multicoloured designs. P 14.*

626	16 c. "The Bible" in 75 languages (54 × 34 mm)	40	10
627	30 c. Type 281..	..	..	..	70	45
628	50 c. "St. Matthew and the Angel" (Rembrandt) (vert)	..	..	90	70
626/8	..	..	..	Set of 3	1·75	1·10

A 40 c. value, showing the inscription "The Word of God" in various languages, was prepared, but due to religious objections was recalled before issue. Isolated examples are known to have been sold to the public and some used have also been reported.

1987 (1 Dec). *Natal Flood Relief Fund (2nd issue). No. 626 surch as T 280, but larger (Afrikaans version 32 mm wide).*

629	16 c. + 10 c. multicoloured (surch "NATAL FLOOD DISASTER")	..	45	65
	a. Pair. Nos. 629/30	..	90	1·25
630	16 c. + 10 c. multicoloured (surch as T 280)	..	45	65

Nos. 629/30 were surcharged together, *se-tenant*, in horizontal and vertical pairs throughout the sheet.
These stamps are known postmarked at Mooirivier on 25 November 1987.

282 Bartolomeu Dias and Cape of Good Hope   **283** Huguenot Monument, Franschhoek

(Des Sheila Nowers. Litho)

1988 (3 Feb). *500th Anniv of Discovery of Cape of Good Hope by Bartolomeu Dias. T 282 and similar horiz designs. Multicoloured. P 14.*

631	16 c. Type 282..	..	..	55	10
632	30 c. Kwaaihoek Monument..	..	80	65
633	40 c. Caravels..	..	..	90	90
634	50 c. Martellus map, c. 1489..	..	1·25	1·40
631/4	..	..	..	Set of 4	3·25	2·75

1988 (1 Mar). *Natal Flood Relief Fund (3rd issue). No. 631 surch as T 280, but larger (Afrikaans version 19 mm wide).*

635	16 c. + 10 c. multicoloured (surch as T 280)	45	65
	a. Pair. Nos. 635/6..	..	90	1·25
636	16 c. + 10 c. multicoloured (surch "NATAL FLOOD DISASTER")	..	45	65

Nos. 635/6 were surcharged together, *se-tenant*, in horizontal and vertical pairs throughout the sheet.

(Des H. Botha. Litho)

1988 (13 Apr). *300th Anniv of Arrival of First French Huguenots at the Cape. T 283 and similar vert designs. Multicoloured. P 14.*

637	16 c. Type 283	..	..	30	10
638	30 c. Map of France showing Huguenot areas..	..	..	60	60
639	40 c. Title page of French/Dutch New Testament of 1672	..	..	70	70
640	50 c. St. Bartholomew's Day Massacre, Paris, 1572	..	..	85	1·00
637/40	..	..	..	Set of 4	2·25	2·25

National Flood Disaster   **+10c**

(284)   **285** Pelican Point Lighthouse, Walvis Bay

1988 (13 Apr). *National Flood Relief Fund. Nos. 637/40 surch as T 284 in English (E) or in Afrikaans ("Nasionale Vloedramp") (A).*

641	16 c. + 10 c. multicoloured (E)	..	..	40	40
	a. Pair. Nos. 641/2	..	..	80	80
642	16 c. + 10 c. multicoloured (A)	..	..	40	40
643	30 c. + 10 c. multicoloured (A)	..	..	55	55
	a. Pair. Nos. 643/4	..	..	1·10	1·10
644	30 c. + 10 c. multicoloured (E)	..	..	55	55
645	40 c. + 10 c. multicoloured (E)	..	..	70	70
	a. Pair. Nos. 645/6	..	..	1·40	1·40
646	40 c. + 10 c. multicoloured (E)	..	..	70	70
647	50 c. + 10 c. multicoloured (E)	..	..	90	90
	a. Pair. Nos. 647/8	..	..	1·75	1·75
648	50 c. + 10 c. multicoloured (A)	..	..	90	90
641/8	..	..	Set of 8	4·50	4·50

The two versions of each surcharge were printed together, *se-tenant*, both horizontally and vertically, throughout the sheets.

(Des Sheila Nowers. Litho)

1988 (9 June). *Lighthouses. T 285 and similar horiz designs. Multicoloured. P 14.*

649	16 c. Type 285	..	..	50	10
650	30 c. Green Point, Cape Town	..	70	55
651	40 c. Cape Agulhas	..	..	90	75
652	50 c. Umhlanga Rocks, Durban	..	1·25	95
649/52	..	..	Set of 4	3·00	2·00
MS653	132 × 112 mm. Nos. 649/52	3·00	2·50

286 *Huernia zebrina*   **287** Map of Great Trek Routes

(Des H. Botha)

1988 (1 Sept)–**90**. *Succulents. T 286 and similar horiz designs. Multicoloured.*

(a) Sheet stamps. Litho. P 14.

654	1 c. Type 286	..	..	10	10
655	2 c. Euphorbia symmetrica	..	10	10
656	5 c. Lithops dorotheae	..	10	10
657	7 c. Gibbaeum nebrownii	..	10	10
658	10 c. Didymaotus lapidiformis	..	10	10
659	16 c. Vanheerdea divergens	..	10	10
659a	18 c. Faucaria tigrina (1.4.89)	..	10	10
660	20 c. Conophytum mundum	..	10	10
660a	21 c. Gasteria armstrongii (2.4.90)	..	10	10
661	25 c. Cheiridopsis peculiaris	..	10	15
662	30 c. Tavaresia barklyi	..	15	20
663	35 c. Dinteranthus wilmotianus	..	15	20
664	40 c. Frithia pulchra	..	20	25
665	50 c. Lapidaria margaretae	..	20	25
666	90 c. Dioscorea elephantipes	..	40	45
667	1 r. Trichocaulon cactiforme	..	45	50
668	2 r. Crassula columnaris	..	85	90
668a	5 r. Anacampseros albissima (1.3.90)	2·25	2·40
654/68a	..	..	Set of 18	4·75	5·25

(b) Coil stamps. Photo. P 14 × imperf.

669	1 c. Adromischus marianiae	..	10	10
670	2 c. Titanopsis calcarea	..	10	10
671	5 c. Dactylopsis digitata	..	10	10
672	16 c. Pleiospilos bolusii	..	10	10
669/72	..	..	Set of 4	20	20

(Des J. van Niekerk (16 c.). Litho)

1988 (21 Nov). *150th Anniv of Great Trek. T 287 and similar multicoloured designs. P 14.*

673	16 c. Type 287	..	..	50	10
674	30 c. "Exodus" (tapestry by W. Coetzer) (56 × 20 mm)	..	..	70	70
675	40 c. "Crossing the Drakensberg" (tapestry by W. Coetzer) (77 × 20 mm)	..	85	95
676	50 c. "After the Service, Church of the Vow" (J. H. Pierneef) (horiz)	..	1·00	1·40
673/6	..	..	Set of 4	2·75	2·75

288 Coelacanth   **289** Man-made Desert

(Des A. McBride. Litho)

1989 (9 Feb). *50th Anniv of Discovery of Coelacanth. T 288 and similar horiz designs. Multicoloured. P 14.*

677	16 c. Type 288	..	..	45	15
678	30 c. Prof. J. L. B. Smith and Dr. M. Courtenay-Latimer examining Coelacanth	..	75	55
679	40 c. J. L. B. Smith Institute of Ichthyology, Grahamstown	..	85	90
680	50 c. Coelacanth and GEO midget submarine	..	..	1·00	1·25
677/80	..	..	Set of 4	2·75	2·50

(Des D. Murphy. Litho)

1989 (3 May). *National Grazing Strategy. T* **289** *and similar horiz designs. Multicoloured. P* 14.

681	18 c.	Type 289	40	15
682	30 c.	Formation of erosion gully	75	70
683	40 c.	Concrete barrage in gully	80	85
684	50 c.	Reclaimed veldt	90	1·10
681/4		*Set of 4*	2·50	2·50

290 South Africa v France Match, 1980   291 "Composition in Blue"

(Des B. Jackson. Litho)

1989 (22 June). *Centenary of South African Rugby Board. T* **290** *and similar horiz designs. Multicoloured. P* 14.

685	18 c.	Type 290	30	15
686	30 c.	South Africa v Australia, 1963	50	50
687	40 c.	South Africa v New Zealand, 1937	65	65
688	50 c.	South Africa v British Isles, 1896	75	80
685/8		*Set of 4*	2·00	1·90

1989 (3 Aug). *Paintings by Jacob Hendrik Pierneef. T* **291** *and similar horiz designs. Multicoloured. Litho. P* 14.

689	18 c.	Type 291	30	15
690	30 c.	"Zanzibar"	50	40
691	40 c.	"The Bushveld"	65	55
692	50 c.	"Cape Homestead"	75	65
689/92		*Set of 4*	2·00	1·60
MS693	114×86 mm. Nos. 689/92		2·00	2·00

292 Pres. F. W. de Klerk   293 Gas-drilling Rig, Mossel Bay

1989 (20 Sept). *Inauguration of President F. W. de Klerk. T* **292** *and similar vert design. Multicoloured. Litho. P* 14.

694	18 c.	Type 292	30	10
695	45 c.	F. W. de Klerk (*different*)	60	75

(Des H. Botha. Litho)

1989 (19 Oct). *Energy Sources. T* **293** *and similar horiz designs. Multicoloured. P* 14×14½.

696	18 c.	Type 293	30	10
697	30 c.	Coal to oil conversion plant	50	40
698	40 c.	Nuclear power station	55	50
699	50 c.	Thermal electric power station	65	65
696/9		*Set of 4*	1·75	1·50

294 Electric Goods Train and Map of Railway Routes   295 Great Britain 1840 Penny Black

(Des A. H. Barrett. Litho)

1990 (15 Feb). *Co-operation in Southern Africa. T* **294** *and similar horiz designs. Multicoloured. P* 14½×14.

700	18 c.	Cahora Bassa Hydro-electric Scheme, Mozambique, and map of transmission lines (68×26 *mm*)	40	15
701	30 c.	Type 294	55	40
702	40 c.	Projected dam on upper Orange River, Lesotho and map of Highlands Water Project (68×26 *mm*)	70	55
703	50 c.	Cow, syringe, and outline map of Africa	80	60
700/3		*Set of 4*	2·25	1·50
MS704	136×78 mm. Nos. 700/3		2·25	2·00

1990 (12 May). *National Stamp Day. T* **295** *and similar vert designs showing stamps. Multicoloured. Litho. P* 14.

705	21 c.	Type 295	40	40
		a. Horiz strip of 5. Nos. 705/9	1·75	
706	21 c.	Cape of Good Hope 1853 4d. triangular pair	40	40
707	21 c.	Natal 1857 1s.	40	40
708	21 c.	Orange Free State 1868 1s.	40	40
709	21 c.	Transvaal 1869 1s.	40	40
705/9		*Set of 5*	1·75	1·75

Nos. 705/9 were printed together, *se-tenant*, in horizontal strips of 5 throughout the sheet.

296 Knysna Turaco   297 Karoo Landscape near Britstown

(Des C. Finch-Davies. Litho)

1990 (2 Aug). *Birds. T* **296** *and similar vert designs. Multicoloured. P* 14.

710	21 c.	Type 296	30	10
711	35 c.	Red-capped Robin Chat	40	40
712	40 c.	Rufous-naped Bush Lark	40	40
713	50 c.	Bokmakierie Shrike	55	65
710/13		*Set of 4*	1·50	1·40

1990 (1 Nov). *Tourism. T* **297** *and similar horiz designs. Multicoloured. Litho. P* 14.

714	50 c.	Type 297	65	65
		a. Block of 4. Nos. 714/17	2·40	
715	50 c.	Camps Bay, Cape of Good Hope	65	65
716	50 c.	Giraffes in Kruger National Park	65	65
717	50 c.	Boschendal Vineyard, Drakenstein Mts	65	65
714/17		*Set of 4*	2·40	2·40

Nos. 714/17 were printed together, *se-tenant*, in blocks of 4 throughout the sheet.

298 Woltemade Cross for Bravery   299 Boer Horses

(Des J. Hoekstra. Litho)

1990 (6 Dec). *National Orders. T* **298** *and similar vert designs. Multicoloured. P* 14.

718	21 c.	Type 298	25	25
		a. Horiz strip of 5. Nos. 718/22	1·10	
719	21 c.	Order of the Southern Cross	25	25
720	21 c.	Order of the Star of South Africa	25	25
721	21 c.	Order for Meritorious Service	25	25
722	21 c.	Order of Good Hope	25	25
718/22		*Set of 5*	1·10	1·10
MS723	143×70 mm. Nos. 718/22		1·10	1·10

Nos. 718/22 were printed together, *se-tenant*, in horizontal strips of 5 throughout the sheet.

(Des A. Ainslie. Litho)

1991 (12 Feb). *Animal Breeding in South Africa. T* **299** *and similar horiz designs. Multicoloured. P* 14.

724	21 c.	Type 299	30	30
		a. Horiz strip of 5. Nos. 724/8	1·40	
725	21 c.	Bonsmara bull	30	30
726	21 c.	Dorper sheep	30	30
727	21 c.	Ridgeback dogs	30	30
728	21 c.	Putterie racing pigeons	30	30
724/8		*Set of 5*	1·40	1·40

Nos. 724/8 were printed together, *se-tenant*, in horizontal strips of five throughout the sheet.

300 Diagram of Human Heart and Transplant Operation   301 State Registration of Nurses Act, 1891

(Des A. H. Barrett. Litho)

1991 (30 May). *30th Anniv of Republic. Scientific and Technological Achievements. T* **300** *and similar multicoloured designs. P* 14.

729	25 c.	Type 300	20	10
730	40 c.	Matimba Power Station (*horiz*)	35	35
731	50 c.	Dolos design breakwater (*horiz*)	45	45
732	60 c.	Western Deep Levels gold mine	60	60
729/32		*Set of 4*	1·40	1·40

(Des T. Marais. Litho)

1991 (15 Aug). *Centenary of State Registration for Nurses and Midwives. P* 14.

733	301	60 c. multicoloured	60	60

302 South Africa Post Office Ltd Emblem   303 Sir Arnold Theiler (veterinarian)

(Des Liza van der Wal. Litho)

1991 (1 Oct). *Establishment of Post Office Ltd and Telekom Ltd. T* **302** *and similar horiz design. Multicoloured. P* 14×14½.

734	27 c.	Type 302	25	25
		a. Vert pair. Nos. 734/5	50	50
735	27 c.	Telekom SA Ltd emblem	25	25

Nos. 734/5 were printed together, *se-tenant*, in vertical pairs throughout the sheet.

(Des A. H. Barrett. Litho)

1991 (9 Oct). *South African Scientists. T* **303** *and similar horiz designs. Multicoloured. P* 14.

736	27 c.	Type 303	20	15
737	45 c.	Sir Basil Schonland (physicist)	40	40
738	65 c.	Dr. Robert Broom (palaeontologist)	50	50
739	85 c.	Dr. Alex du Toit (geologist)	65	65
736/9		*Set of 4*	1·60	1·50

304 Agulhas (research ship)   305 Soil Conservation

(Des Liza van der Wal (27 c.), T. Marais (65 c.). Litho)

1991 (5 Dec). *30th Anniv of Antarctic Treaty. T* **304** *and similar horiz design. Multicoloured. P* 14.

740	27 c.	Type 304	30	10
741	65 c.	Chart showing South African National Antarctic Expedition base	80	70

(Des J. van Niekerk. Litho)

1992 (6 Feb). *Environmental Conservation. T* **305** *and similar horiz designs. Multicoloured. P* 14×14½.

742	27 c.	Type 305	20	10
743	65 c.	Water pollution	55	55
744	85 c.	Air pollution	75	75
742/4		*Set of 3*	1·40	1·25

306 Dutch Fleet approaching Table Bay   307 Queen Anne Settee, c 1750

(Des J. van Niekerk. Litho)

1992 (9 May). *National Stamp Day. Cape of Good Hope Postal Stones. T* **306** *and similar horiz designs. Multicoloured. P* 14.

745	35 c.	Type 306	25	25
		a. Horiz strip of 5. Nos. 745/9	1·10	
746	35 c.	Landing for water and provisions	25	25
747	35 c.	Discovering a postal stone	25	25
748	35 c.	Leaving letters under a stone	25	25
749	35 c.	Reading letters	25	25
745/9		*Set of 5*	1·10	1·10

Nos. 745/9 were printed together, *se-tenant*, in horizontal strips of 5 throughout the sheet

1992 (9 July). *Antique Cape Furniture. T* **307** *and similar multicoloured designs. Litho. P* 14.

750	35 c.	Type 307	25	25
		a. Sheetlet. Nos. 750/9	2·25	
751	35 c.	Stinkwood settee, c 1800	25	25
752	35 c.	Canopy bed, c 1800 (*vert*)	25	25
753	35 c.	19th-century rocking cradle	25	25
754	35 c.	Waterbutt, c 1800 (*vert*)	25	25
755	35 c.	Flemish style cabinet, c 1700 (*vert*)	25	25
756	35 c.	Armoire, c 1780 (*vert*)	25	25
757	35 c.	Late 17th-century church chair (*vert*)	25	25
758	35 c.	Tub chair, c 1770 (*vert*)	25	25
759	35 c.	Bible desk, c 1750 (*vert*)	25	25
750/9		*Set of 10*	2·25	2·25

Nos. 750/9 were printed together, *se-tenant*, as a sheetlet of 10.

MINIMUM PRICE

The minimum price quote is 10p which represents a handling charge rather than a basis for valuing common stamps. For further notes about prices see introductory pages.

308 Grand Prix Motor
Racing

309 "Women's
Monument" (Van
Wouw)

(Des Liza van der Wal (35 c. (No. 761)), C. Prinsloo (55 c.),
B. Jackson (70, 90 c., 1 r. 05). Litho)
1992 (24 July). *Sports. T* **308** *and similar horiz designs.*
Multicoloured. P 14×14½.
760	35 c. Type **308**			25	25
761	35 c. Football			25	25
762	55 c. Total Paris–Cape Motor Rally		35	35
763	70 c. Athletics			50	50
764	90 c. Rugby			65	65
765	1 r. 05, Cricket			75	75
760/5		Set of 6	2·50	2·50
MS766	167×69 mm. Nos. 760/5		2·75	2·75

1992 (8 Oct). *130th Birth Anniv of Anton van Wouw (sculptor).*
T **309** *and similar vert designs. Multicoloured. Litho. P* 14.
767	35 c. Type **309**			25	20
768	70 c. "Sekupu Player"			50	50
769	90 c. "The Hunter"			70	70
770	1 r. 05, "Postman Lehman"		80	85
767/70		Set of 4	2·00	2·00
MS771	96×149 mm. Nos. 767/70		2·25	2·40

310 Walvis Bay Harbour

1993 (28 Jan). *South African Harbours. T* **310** *and similar*
horiz designs. Multicoloured. Litho. P 14.
772	35 c. Type **310**			25	20
773	55 c. East London			35	35
774	70 c. Port Elizabeth			50	50
775	90 c. Cape Town			70	70
776	1 r. 05, Durban			80	85
772/6		Set of 5	2·40	2·40
MS777	147×112 mm. Nos. 772/6		2·40	2·50

POSTAGE DUE STAMPS

D 1

(A)   (B)

(Typo D.L.R.)

1914–22. *Inscribed bilingually. Lettering as A. W 4. P 14.*

				Un Used single single
D1	D 1	½d. black and green (19.3.15) ..	..	1·25 3·75
D2		1d. black and scarlet (19.3.15) ..	..	1·50 10
		a. Black ptd double ..		£1400
D3		2d. black and reddish violet (12.12.14)		4·00 15
		a. Black and bright violet (1922)		5·00 30
D4		3d. black and bright blue (2.2.15)		2·25 35
D5		5d. black and sepia (19.3.15) ..		3·50 14·00
D6		6d. black and slate (19.3.15) ..		7·00 17·00
D7		1s. red and black (19.3.15) ..		60·00 £120
D1/7		..	*Set of 7*	70·00 £140

There are interesting minor varieties in some of the above values, e.g. ½d. to 3d., thick downstroke to "d"; 1d., short serif to "1"; raised "d"; 2d., forward point of "2" blunted; 3d., raised "d"; very thick "d".

(Litho Govt Printer, Pretoria)

1922. *Lettering as A. No wmk. Rouletted.*

D 8	D 1	½d. black and bright green (6.6.22) ..	85	6·50
D 9		1d. black and rose-red (3.10.22) ..	55	75
D10		1½d. black and yellow-brown (3.6.22) ..	1·00	1·75
D8/10 ..		.. .. ..	*Set of 3* 2·25	8·00

(Litho Govt Printer, Pretoria)

1922–26. *Type D 1 redrawn. Lettering as B. P 14.*

D11		½d. black and green (1.8.22)	30	1·75
D12		1d. black and rose (16.5.23)..	35	15
D13		1½d. black and yellow-brown (12.1.24)	50	1·25
D14		2d. black and pale violet (16.5.23) ..	55	70
		a. Imperf (pair)	£190	£225
		b. Black and deep violet	5·00	3·00
D15		3d. black and blue (3.7.26) ..	6·50	11·00
D16		6d. black and slate (9.23) ..	9·00	6·00
D11/16		.. ..	*Set of 6* 15·00	18·00

The locally printed stamps, perf 14, differ both in border design and in figures of value from the rouletted stamps. All values except the 3d. and 6d. are known with closed "G" in "POSTAGE" usually referred to as the "POSTADE" variety. This was corrected in later printings.

D 2   D 3   D 4

(Typo Pretoria)

1927–28. *Inscribed bilingually. No wmk. P 13½ × 14.*

D17	D 2	½d. black and green ..	35	2·00
D18		1d. black and carmine ..	35	30
D19		2d. black and mauve ..	1·25	30
		a. Black and purple ..	6·50	80
D20		3d. black and blue ..	5·50	14·00
D21		6d. black and slate ..	9·50	6·00
D17/21		.. .. ..	*Set of 5* 15·00	20·00

Blunt "2" (R. 3/6, 8/6)

1932–42. *Type D 2 redrawn. W 9. P 15 × 14.*

(a) Frame roto, value typo

D22		½d. black and blue-green (1934)	1·00	1·60
		a. Blunt "2"	6·00	
D23		2d. black and deep purple (10.4.33)	3·75	1·10

(b) Whole stamp roto

D25		1d. black and carmine (3.34)	1·10	10
D26		2d. black and deep purple (1940)	8·50	10
		a. Thick (double) "2D." (R. 5/6, R. 18/2)	£140	16·00
D27		3d. black and Prussian blue (3.8.32)	12·00	11·00
D28		3d. deep blue and blue (1935)	4·50	15
		a. Indigo and milky blue (1942)	22·00	2·00
D29		6d. green and brown-ochre (7.6.33)	17·00	4·50
		a. Green and bright orange (1938)	7·50	2·50
D22/9a		..	*Set of 7* 35·00	15·00

In No. D26 the value, when magnified, has the meshed appearance of a photogravure screen, whereas in No. D23 the black of the value is solid.

1943–44. *Inscr bilingually. Roto. W 9. In units of three, perf 15 × 14 subdivided by roulette 6½.*

			Un unit	Us unit	Us single
D30	D 3	½d. blue-green (1944) ..	7·00	27·00	30
D31		1d. carmine ..	6·50	4·00	10
D32		2d. dull violet ..	6·50	8·00	15
		a. Bright violet ..	16·00	35·00	65
D33		3d. indigo (1943) ..	40·00	65·00	1·25
D30/3 ..		..	*Set of 4* 55·00	95·00	1·90

Split "D" (R. 7/5 on every fourth sheet)

1948–49. *New figure of value and capital "D". Whole stamp roto. W 9. P 15 × 14.*

D34	D 4	½d. black and blue-green ..	5·00	6·50
D35		1d. black and carmine ..	5·00	3·00
D36		2d. black and violet (1949) ..	7·00	3·00
		a. Thick (double) "2D." (R. 15/5–6, R. 16/5–6)	48·00	22·00
D37		3d. deep blue and blue ..	15·00	10·00
		a. Split "D"	95·00	
D38		6d. green and bright orange (1949)	25·00	8·00
D34/8		..	*Set of 5* 50·00	27·00

1950–58. *As Type D 4, but "SUID-AFRIKA" hyphenated. Whole stamp roto. W 9. P 15 × 14.*

D39		1d. black and carmine (5.50) ..	70	30
D40		2d. black and violet (4.51) ..	50	20
		a. Thick (double) "2D." (R. 15/5–6, R. 16/5–6) ..	8·00	6·00
		b. Black and reddish violet (12.52)	50	20
		ba. Thick (double) "2D." ..	8·00	6·00
D41		3d. deep blue and blue (5.50) ..	4·00	1·75
		a. Split "D" ..	48·00	
D42		4d. deep myrtle-green and emerald (2.58)	6·00	7·50
D43		6d. green and bright orange (3.50)	7·00	7·00
D44		1s. black-brown and purple-brown (2.58)	8·00	9·00
D39/44		..	*Set of 6* 24·00	23·00

D 5   D 6 Afrikaans at top   D 7 English at top

1961 (14 Feb). *Values in cents as Type D 5. Whole stamp roto. W 102. P 15 × 14.*

D45		1 c. black and carmine ..	20	2·75
D46		2 c. black and violet ..	35	2·75
D47		4 c. deep myrtle-green and emerald ..	80	5·50
D48		5 c. deep blue and blue ..	1·75	6·00
D49		6 c. green and orange-red ..	6·00	5·00
D50		10 c. sepia and brown-lake ..	7·50	9·00
D45/50		..	*Set of 6* 15·00	28·00

1961 (31 May)**–69.** *Roto. W 102. P 15 × 14.*

D51	D 6	1 c. black and carmine..	40	60
D52	D 7	1 c. black and carmine (6.62) ..	40	3·25
D53		2 c. black and deep reddish violet ..	40	55
D54	D 6	4 c. dp myrtle-green & light emerald ..	2·00	2·00
D54a	D 7	4 c. dp myrtle-grn & lt emerald (6.69) ..	7·00	10·00
D55		5 c. deep blue and grey-blue ..	2·00	3·00
D56		5 c. black and grey-blue (6.62)..	1·75	7·00
D57	D 6	6 c. deep green and red-orange ..	5·50	4·50
D58	D 7	10 c. sepia and purple-brown ..	3·50	2·25
D51/8 ..		..	*Set of 9* 21·00	30·00

1967 (Dec)**–71.** *Roto. W 127 (tête-bêche). P 15 × 14.*

D59	D 6	1 c. black and carmine..	20	55
D60	D 7	1 c. black and carmine..	20	30
D61	D 6	2 c. black and deep reddish violet	30	85
D62	D 7	2 c. black and deep reddish violet	30	85
D62b		4 c. dp myrtle-green & emerald (6.69)*	15·00	20·00
D62c	D 6	4 c. dp myrtle-green & emerald (6.69)*	£120	95·00
D63		4 c. black and pale green (4.71)	17·00	20·00
D64	D 7	4 c. black and pale green (4.71)	17·00	20·00
D65	D 6	5 c. black and deep blue ..	50	50
D66	D 7	5 c. black and deep blue ..	50	50
D67	D 6	6 c. green and orange-red (1968)	3·50	7·00
D68	D 7	6 c. green and orange-red (1968)	3·50	7·00
D69	D 6	10 c. black and purple-brown ..	1·00	2·75
		a. Black and brown-lake (12.69)	1·00	2·75
D70	D 7	10 c. black and purple-brown ..	1·00	2·75
		a. Black and brown-lake (12.69)	1·00	2·75
D59/70a except D62b/c		..	*Set of 12* 40·00	55·00

Nos. D59/70 were printed in two panes, one with inscriptions as Type D 6 and the other as Type D 7.

*Nos. D54a, D62b/c and further supplies of D54 were part of a printing released in June 1969. Most sheets were printed on paper with the Arms watermark, but some were printed on RSA paper with the watermark upright and faint. Of these many were spoilt, but a few sheets were issued in Types D 7 and D 6, the latter being very scarce.

1971 *Roto. W 127 (tête-bêche). P 14.*

D71	D 6	2 c. black and deep reddish violet ..	19·00	7·00
D72	D 7	2 c. black and deep reddish violet ..	19·00	7·00
D74		4 c. deep myrtle-green & light emerald	45·00	38·00
D71/4		..	*Set of 3* 75·00	48·00

Nos. D71/4 were also printed in double panes as Nos. D59/70. Although the 4 c. as Type D 6 must have been printed it has not been possible to confirm that any were actually issued.

D 8

1972 (22 Mar). *English at right (1, 4 and 8 c.) or at left (others). W 127 (sideways tête-bêche). Chalk-surfaced paper (4 c. to 10 c.). P 14×13½.*

D75	D 8	1 c. deep yellowish green ..	50	1·75
D76		2 c. bright orange ..	70	2·00
D77		4 c. plum ..	1·50	2·50
D78		6 c. chrome-yellow ..	1·75	3·50
D79		8 c. ultramarine ..	2·00	4·50
D80		10 c. bright scarlet ..	4·00	6·00
D75/80		..	*Set of 6* 9·50	18·00

The 6 c. also exists on phosphorised paper.

The use of Postage Due stamps ceased in 1975.

OFFICIAL STAMPS

OFFICIAL.   **OFFISIEEL.**   **OFFISIEEL**   **OFFICIAL**

(O 1)   (O 2)

(Approximate measurements between lines of opt are shown in mm in brackets)

1926 (1 Dec). *Optd vertically upwards, with stops, as Type O 1.*

(a) On 1913 issue

O1	3	2d. Nos. 6/6a (12½) ..	.. 17·00	1·75

(b) On 1926 issue

				Un pair	Us pair	Us single
O2	6	½d. No. 30 (12½)	..	4·25	11·00	75
O3	7	1d. No. 31 (12½)	..	2·00	4·00	50
O4	8	6d. No. 32 (12½)	..	£550	75·00	10·00

This overprint is found on the ½d., 1d. and 6d. values of both the London and Pretoria printings. The London printings of the ½d. and 1d. stamps are considerably scarcer than the Pretoria, but the 6d. Pretoria printing is scarcer still.

1928–29. *Optd vertically upwards, as Type O 1, but without stops.*

O5	11	2d. No. 34 (17½)	..	4·75	17·00	2·00
O6		2d. No. 34 (19) (1929)	..	3·50	10·00	1·50
O7	8	6d. No. 32 (11½)	..	17·00	24·00	2·75

1929. *Typographed stamps optd with Type O 2.*

O 8	6	½d. No. 30 (13½)		2·00	2·25	35
		a. Stop after "OFFISIEEL" on English stamp		28·00	28·00	3·25
		b. Ditto. On Afrikaans stamp		28·00	28·00	3·25
O 9	7	1d. No. 31 (13½)		3·00	3·75	45
O10	8	6d. No. 32 (13½)		9·00	32·00	3·25
		a. Stop after "OFFISIEEL" on English stamp		55·00	90·00	10·00
		b. Ditto. On Afrikaans stamp		55·00	90·00	10·00
O8/10		..	*Set of 3* 12·50	35·00	3·50

1930–47. *Rotogravure stamps ("SUIDAFRIKA" in one word) optd with Type O 2.*

O11	6	½d. No. 42 (9½–12) (1931)		2·25	3·50	40
		a. Stop after "OFFISIEEL" on English stamp		27·00	32·00	3·50
		b. Ditto. On Afrikaans stamp		27·00	32·00	3·50
O12		½d. No. 42 (12½) (1932)		3·50	4·00	50
O13	7	1d. No. 43 (12½ and 13½)		4·25	4·50	55
		a. Stop after "OFFISIEEL" on English stamp		27·00	28·00	3·25
		b. Ditto. On Afrikaans stamp		27·00	28·00	3·25
O14		1d. No. 43d (12½) (1932)		10·00	9·00	90
		a. Opt double ..		£250	£275	
O15	11	2d. No. 44 (21) (1931)		6·00	11·00	1·50
O15a		2d. No. 44d (20½) (1938)		85·00	90·00	9·00
O16	8	6d. No. 47 (12½) (1931)		7·00	8·50	85
		a. Stop after "OFFISIEEL" on English stamp		45·00	48·00	5·00
		b. Ditto. On Afrikaans stamp		45·00	48·00	5·00
O17	13	1s. No. 48 (19) (1933)		42·00	65·00	7·50
O18		1s. No. 48 (1933)		42·00	65·00	7·50
O19	14	2s. 6d. No. 49 (18) (1933)		65·00	£110	13·00
O20		2s. 6d. No. 49 (21) (1934)		45·00	70·00	8·00
O20a		2s. 6d. No. 49a (19½–20) (1947)		60·00	60·00	6·50
		ab. Diaeresis on second "E"		£550	£700	

Nos. O8a/b, O10a/b, O11a/b, O13a/b and O16a/b. The pairs include one stamp with variety and the other normal. Pairs of No. O20ab exist with the variety on either stamp (English or Afrikaans). Pairs with both stamps showing the variety are worth much more.

1931. *Recess-printed stamps opt with Type O 2.*

O21	13	1s. No. 36 (17½, 18 and 20½)	.. 30·00	75·00	8·50
		a. Stop after "OFFICIAL" on Afrikaans stamp		£100	£190	
O22	14	2s. 6d. No. 37 (17½ and 18)		55·00	£130	17·00
		a. Stop after "OFFICIAL" on Afrikaans stamp		£275	£425	

Nos. O21a and O22a. The pairs include one stamp with variety and the other normal.

OFFICIAL   **OFFISIEEL**   **OFFICIAL**   **OFFISIEEL**

(O 3)   (O 4)

1935–50. *Rotogravure stamps ("SUID-AFRIKA" hyphenated).*

  (a) *Optd with Type O 2 ("OFFICIAL" at right)*

O23	6	½d. No. 54 (12½) (1936)		3·00	12·00 1·40
O24	25a	½d. No. 75b (11 and 12½)			
		(1938)		6·00	7·50 75
O24a		½d. No. 75bd (12) (1947)		90	4·75 50
O24b		½d. No. 114 (11) (1949)		1·00	5·50 60
O25	7	1d. No. 56 (11½–13) ..		65	1·25 15
O26	22	1½d. No. 57 (20) (1937)		12·00	14·00 1·50
O26a		1½d. No. 57b (20) (1939)		25·00	8·50 85
O26b	34a	1½d. No. 87 (14½) (1944)		2·50	6·50 70
		ba. Diaeresis on second "E"			
		(1946?)		£110	£110
O26c		1½d. No. 87 (16) (1948)		2·25	3·75 45
O27	11	2d. No. 58 (20) (1939)		50·00	18·00 2·25
O27a	54	2d. No. 107 (20) (1947)		2·25	15·00 1·75
		ab. Diaeresis on second "E"			
		(1947)		£225	£350
O27b		2d. No. 107a (20) (1949)		5·50	14·00 1·60
O28	8	6d. No. 61 (12 and 13) (1937)		60·00	35·00 3·50
O28a		6d. No. 61a (11½–13) (1939)		9·00	10·00 1·25
O28b		6d. No. 61b (12) (1947)		4·00	80 85
O29	13	1s. No. 62 (20) (1939)		35·00	18·00 2·00
		aa. Diaeresis on second "E"			
		(1944?)		£850	£700
O29a		1s. No. 120 (17½–18½) (1950)		9·00	22·00 2·50
O29b	15	5s. No. 64a (20) (1948)		35·00	85·00 11·00
O29c	23	10s. No. 64b (19½) (1948)		65·00	£140 19·00

  (b) *Optd with Type O 3 ("OFFICIAL" at left)*

O30	15	5s. No. 64a (18) (1940)		45·00	85·00 11·00
O31	23	10s. No. 64b (19) (1940)		£180	£225 30·00

Prices for Nos. O26ba and O27ab are for horizontal pairs with the variety on both stamps. No. O29aa shows the variety on one stamp only, but pairs also exist with it on both.

1944. *Optd with Type O 4 reading up and down and with diaeresis over the second "E" of "OFFISIEEL".*

O32	25a	½d. No. 75bd (10)		9·50	16·00 1·75

(O 5)   (O 6)

1944. *Optd with Type O 5 reading upwards ("OFFICIAL" at right).*

O33	11	2d. No. 58a (18½)		3·00	15·00 1·75

1949–50. *Optd with Type O 6 reading upwards ("OFFICIAL" at left).*

O34	34a	1½d. No. 87 (16) ..		12·00	25·00 2·75
O35	68	2d. No. 134 (16) (1950)		£1000	£1300 £150

(O 7)

1950–54. *Optd as Type O 7.*

O35a	25a	½d. No. 75bd (10) (1951)		1·00	6·50 65
O35b		½d. No. 114 (10) (1953)		70	1·50 15
O36	7	1d. No. 56i (10)		1·00	4·50 45
O36a		1d. No. 115 (10) (1951)		1·00	1·50 15
O36b		1d. No. 135 (10) (1952)		90	1·75 20
O37	34a	1½d. No. 87 (14½) (1951)		1·40	2·50 25
O38	68	2d. No. 134 (14½)		1·00	2·00 20
		a. Opt inverted		£1000	
O39	8	6d. No. 119 (10)		1·00	3·50 35
O39a		6d. No. 119a (10) (1951)		1·50	3·50 35
O40	13	1s. No. 120 (10)		5·50	17·00 1·75
O40a		1s. No. 120a (19) (1953)		£100	£140 17·00
O41	14	2s. 6d. No. 121 (19)		8·50	30·00 3·50
O41a	15	5s. No. 64a (19) (1951)		£110	75·00 9·00
O41b		5s. No. 122 (19) (1953)		23·00	50·00 6·00
O41c		5s. No. 122 (19) (1954)		48·00	75·00 9·00
O42	23	10s. No. 64ba (19)		55·00	£130 18·00

On No. O36a the overprint is thicker.

The use of official stamps ceased in January 1955.

South Arabian Federation

ADEN

The first post office in Aden opened during January 1839, situated in what became known as the Crater district. No stamps were initially available, but, after the office was placed under the Bombay Postal Circle, stocks of the 1854 ½ a. and 1 a. stamps were placed on sale in Aden from 10 October 1854. Supplies of the 2 a. and 4 a. values did not arrive until December. Most Indian issues from the 1854 lithographs up to 1935 Silver Jubilee set can be found with Aden postmarks.

During January 1858 a further office, Aden Steamer Point, was opened in the harbour area and much of the business was transferred to it by 1869. The original Aden post office, in Crater, was renamed Aden Cantonment, later to be changed again to Aden Camp.

The first cancellation used with the Indian stamps was a plain diamond of dots. This type was also used elsewhere so that attri-

bution to Aden is only possible when on cover. Aden was assigned "124" in the Indian postal number system and this formed the main feature of marks from 1858, either on its own or as part of a duplex.

1858 "124" Cancellation

1870 Aden Duplex

1872 Aden Steamer Point Duplex

Both post offices used this number until 1871 when Aden Cantonment was assigned "125", only to have this swiftly amended to "124A" in the same year.

1871 Aden Cantonment "125"   1871 Aden Cantonment "124A"
Cancellation   Cancellation

Cancellations inscribed "Aden Steamer Point" disappear after 1874 and this office was then known simply as Aden. Following this change the office was given number "B-22" under the revised Indian P.O. scheme and this number appears as a major part of the cancellations from 1875 to 1886, either on its own or as part of a duplex, Aden Camp, the alternative name for the Cantonment office, became "B-22/1".

1875 Aden Duplex

Squared-circle types for Aden and Aden Cantonment were introduced in 1884 and 1888 to be in turn replaced by standard Indian double and single circle from 1895 onwards.

A number of other post offices were opened between 1891 and 1937:

Dthali (*opened* 1903, *initially using* "EXPERIMENTAL P.O. B-84" *postmark; closed* 1907)
Kamaran (*opened c* 1915, *but no civilian postmarks known before* 1925)
Khormaksar (*opened* 1892; *closed* 1915; *reopened* 1925)
Maalla (*opened* 1923; *closed* 1931)
Nobat-Dakim (*opened* 1904, *initially using* "EXPERIMENTAL P.O. B-84" *postmark; closed* 1905)
Perim (*opened* 1915; *closed* 1936)
Sheikh Othman (*opened* 1891; *closed* 1915; *reopened* 1922; *closed* 1937)

PRICES FOR STAMPS ON COVER TO 1945

Nos. 1/15   *from* × 5
Nos. 16/27 *from* × 3

---

1 Dhow   3 Aidrus Mosque, Crater

(Recess D.L.R.)

1937 (1 Apr). *Wmk Mult Script CA sideways. P 13 × 12.*

1	1	½ a. yellow-green		2·75	1·25
2		9 p. deep green		2·75	1·40
3		1 a. sepia		2·75	60
4		2 a. scarlet		2·75	2·00
5		2½ a. bright blue		2·75	80
6		3 a. carmine		9·00	6·50
7		3½ a. grey-blue		3·75	2·00
8		8 a. pale purple		19·00	5·50
9		1 r. brown		23·00	7·00
10		2 r. yellow		48·00	16·00
11		5 r. deep purple		85·00	60·00
12		10 r. olive-green		£160	£150
1/12			*Set of 12*	£325	£225
1/12 Perf "Specimen"			*Set of 12*	£250	

1937 (12 May). *Coronation. As Nos. 118/20 of Jamaica. P 14.*

13		1 a. sepia		75	70
14		2½ a. light blue		1·25	1·25
15		3½ a. grey-blue		1·50	2·50
13/15			*Set of 3*	3·25	4·00

(Recess Waterlow)

1939 (19 Jan)–48. *Horiz designs as T 3. Wmk Mult Script CA. P 12½.*

16		½ a. yellowish green		50	60
		a. Bluish green (9.48)		1·25	2·50
17		¾ a. red-brown		1·00	1·25
18		1 a. pale blue		20	25
19		1½ a. scarlet		45	60
20		2 a. sepia		20	25
21		2½ a. deep ultramarine		30	30
22		3 a. sepia and carmine		50	25
23		8 a. red-orange		35	40
23a		14 a. sepia and light blue (15.1.45)		2·25	1·00
24		1 r. emerald-green		1·50	1·50
25		2 r. deep blue and magenta		4·50	1·75
26		5 r. red-brown and olive-green		11·00	6·00
27		10 r. sepia and violet		24·00	11·00
16/27			*Set of 13*	42·00	22·00
16/27 Perf "Specimen"			*Set of 13*	£160	

Designs:—½ a., 2 a., Type 3; ¾ a., 5 r. Adenese Camel Corps; 1 a., 2 r. The Harbour; 1½ a., 1 r. Adenese Dhow; 2½ a., 8 a. Mukalla; 3 a., 14 a., 10 r. "Capture of Aden, 1839" (Capt. Rundle).

1946 (15 Oct). *Victory. As Nos. 141/2 of Jamaica.*

28		1½ a. carmine		15	50
29		2½ a. blue		15	30
28/9 Perf "Specimen"			*Set of 2*	50·00	

1949 (7 Jan). *Royal Silver Wedding. As Nos. 143/4 of Jamaica.*

30		1½ a. scarlet (p 14×15)		40	60
31		10 r. mauve (p 11½×11)		23·00	26·00

1949 (10 Oct). *75th Anniv of U.P.U. As Nos. 145/8 of Jamaica, surch with new values by Waterlow.*

32		2½ a. on 20 c. ultramarine		60	1·00
33		3 a. on 30 c. carmine-red		1·50	1·00
34		8 a. on 50 c. orange		1·60	1·00
35		1 r. on 1 s. blue		2·10	2·50
32/5			*Set of 4*	5·25	5·00

5 CENTS

(12)

1951 (1 Oct). *Currency changed. Nos. 18 and 20/7 surch with new values, in cents or shillings, as T 12, or in one line between bars (30 c.) by Waterlow.*

36		5 c. on 1 a. pale blue		15	40
37		10 c. on 2 a. sepia		15	45
38		15 c. on 2½ a. deep ultramarine		20	1·00
		a. Surch double		£550	
39		20 c. on 3 a. sepia and carmine		25	40
40		30 c. on 8 a. red-orange (R.)		25	55
41		50 c. on 8 a. red-orange		25	35
42		70 c. on 14 a. sepia and light blue		75	1·00
43		1 s. on 1 r. emerald-green		35	30
44		2 s. on 2 r. deep blue and magenta		4·00	2·50
		a. Surch albino		£225	
45		5 s. on 5 r. red-brown and olive-green		16·00	4·50
46		10 s. on 10 r. sepia and violet		22·00	9·00
36/46			*Set of 11*	40·00	18·00

1953 (2 June). *Coronation. As No. 153 of Jamaica.*

47		15 c. black and green		40	1·00

14 Minaret   25 "Aden in 1572" (F. Hogenberg)

(Recess Waterlow, until 1961, then D.L.R.)

1953 (15 June)–63. *T 14 and similar designs, and T 25. Wmk Mult Script CA. P 13½×13 (No. 72), 12×13½ (Nos. 57, 64, 66, 68) or 12 (others).*

48		5 c. yellowish green		15	10
49		5 c. bluish green (1.6.55)		30	70
		a. Perf 12 × 13½ (12.4.56)		10	30
50		10 c. orange		30	10
51		10 c. vermilion (1.2.55)		10	30
52		15 c. blue-green		85	45
53		15 c. greenish grey (26.4.59)		1·00	2·00
		a. Deep greenish grey (16.1.62)		2·75	4·00
		b. Greenish slate (13.11.62)		3·75	5·50
54		25 c. carmine-red		45	30
55		25 c. deep rose-red (15.3.56)		75	40
		a. Rose-red (13.3.62)		2·50	90

56	35 c. deep ultramarine	2·25	1·75
57	35 c. deep blue (15.10.58)	1·50	1·50
	a. *Violet-blue* (17.2.59)	2·00	1·50
58	50 c. dull blue	15	10
59	50 c. deep blue (1.7.55)	60	85
	a. Perf 12 × 13½ (12.4.56)	60	10
60	70 c. brown-grey	15	10
61	70 c. black (20.9.54)	60	35
	a. Perf 12 × 13½ (12.4.56)	60	10
62	1 s. sepia and reddish violet	30	10
63	1 s. black and violet (1.7.55)	55	10
64	1 s. 25, blue and black (16.7.56)	2·25	50
	a. *Dull blue and black* (16.1.63)	5·00	50
65	2 s. sepia and rose-carmine	1·25	40
66	2 s. black and carmine-red (1.3.56)	3·25	50
	a. *Black and carmine-rose* (22.1.63)	8·50	3·75
67	5 s. sepia and dull blue	1·25	40
68	5 s. black and deep dull blue (11.4.56)	2·00	40
	a. *Black and blue* (11.12.62)	15·00	5·00
69	10 s. sepia and olive	1·75	8·00
70	10 s. black and bronze-green (20.9.54)	5·50	1·25
71	20 s. chocolate and reddish lilac	6·50	10·00
72	20 s. black and deep lilac (7.1.57)	32·00	13·00
	a. *Deep black and deep lilac* (14.5.58)	35·00	14·00
48/72	*Set of 25*	55·00	38·00

Designs: (as Type 14). Horiz—10 c. Camel transport; 15 c. Crater; 25 c. Mosque; 1 s. Dhow building. *Vert*—35 c. Dhow; 50 c. Map; 70 c. Salt works; 1 s. 25 Colony's badge; 2 s. Aden Protectorate levy; 5 s. Crater Pass; 10 s. Tribesman.
On No. 70 the tribesman's skirt is shaded with cross-hatching instead of with mainly diagonal lines as in No. 69.

1954 (27 Apr). *Royal Visit. As No. 62 but inscr "ROYAL VISIT 1954" at top.*

73	1 s. sepia and reddish violet	30	30

تعديل
الدستور
١٩٥٩
(**26**)

REVISED
CONSTITUTION
1959
(**27**)

1959 (26 Jan). *Revised Constitution. No. 53 optd with T 26, and No. 64 optd with T 27, in red, by Waterlow.*

74	15 c. slate-green	15	90
75	1 s. 25, blue and black	45	90

1963 (4 June). *Freedom from Hunger. As No. 80 of Lesotho.*

76	1 s. 25, bluish green	1·50	1·40

1964 (5 Feb)–**65.** *As Nos. 48, etc. but wmk w 12. P 12 (10 c., 15 c., 25 c., 1 s.) or 12 × 13½ (others).*

77	5 c. green (16.2.65)	30	75
78	10 c. bright orange	20	40
79	15 c. greenish grey	30	2·00
80	25 c. carmine-red	30	30
81	35 c. indigo-violet	1·00	1·50
82	50 c. indigo-blue	20	15
	a. *Pale indigo-blue* (16.2.65)	30	30
83	70 c. black	30	55
	a. *Brownish grey* (16.2.65)	30	40
84	1 s. black and violet (10.3.64)	6·00	1·25
85	1 s. 25, ultramarine and black (10.3.64)	8·00	2·00
86	2 s. black and carmine-rose (16.2.65)	2·75	22·00
77/86	*Set of 10*	17·00	27·00

The stamps of Aden were withdrawn on 31 March 1965 and superseded by those of the South Arabian Federation.

ADEN PROTECTORATE STATES

KATHIRI STATE OF SEIYUN

The stamps of ADEN were used in Kathiri State of Seiyun from 22 May 1937 until 1942. A further office was opened at Tarim on 11 December 1940.

PRICES FOR STAMPS ON COVER TO 1945
Nos. 1/11 *from* × 10

1 Sultan of Seiyun   2 Seiyun

(Recess D.L.R.)

1942 (July–Oct). *Designs as T 1/2. Wmk Mult Script CA. T 1, perf 14; others, perf 12 × 13 (vert) or 13 × 12 (horiz).*

1	½ a. blue-green	15	35
2	¾ a. brown	15	15
3	1 a. blue	15	35
4	1½ a. carmine	15	40
5	2 a. sepia	15	50
6	2½ a. blue	20	85
7	3 a. sepia and carmine	45	50
8	8 a. red	30	50
9	1 r. green	60	50
10	2 r. blue and purple	6·00	8·50
11	5 r. brown and green	14·00	12·00
1/11	*Set of 11*	20·00	22·00
1/11 Perf "Specimen"	*Set of 11*	£110	

Designs:—½ to 1 a. Type **1**. *Vert as T* **2**—2 a. Tarim; 2½ a. Mosque, Seiyun; 1 r. South Gate, Tarim; 5 r. Mosque entrance, Tarim. *Horiz as T* **2**—3 a. Fortress, Tarim; 8 a. Mosque, Seiyun; 2 r. A Kathiri house.

VICTORY
ISSUE
8TH JUNE 1946
(10)

1946 (15 Oct). *Victory. No. 4 optd with T 10, and No. 6 optd similarly but in four lines, by De La Rue.*

12	1½ a. carmine	10	20
13	2½ a. blue (R.)	10	10
	a. Opt inverted	£375	
12/13 Perf "Specimen"	*Set of 2*	50·00	

No. 13 is known with surcharge double but the second impression is almost coincident with the first.

1949 (17 Jan). *Royal Silver Wedding. As Nos. 143/4 of Jamaica.*

14	1½ a. scarlet	30	1·00
15	5 r. green	11·00	9·00

1949 (10 Oct). *75th Anniv of U.P.U. As Nos. 145/8 of Jamaica, surch with new values by Waterlow.*

16	2½ a. on 20 c. ultramarine	25	50
17	3 a. on 30 c. carmine-red	40	65
18	8 a. on 50 c. orange	40	75
19	1 r. on 1 s. blue	60	90
16/19	*Set of 4*	1·50	2·50

5 CTS
(11)

50 CENTS
(12)

5/-
(13)

1951 (1 Oct). *Currency changed. Nos. 3 and 5/11 surch as T 11 (5 c.), 12 (10 c. ("CTS"), 15 c. ("CTS"), 20 c. and 50 c.) or 13 (1s. to 5s.), by Waterlow.*

20	5 c. on 1 a. blue (R.)	15	20
21	10 c. on 2 a. sepia	30	20
22	15 c. on 2½ a. blue	15	20
23	20 c. on 3 a. sepia and carmine	15	20
24	50 c. on 8 a. red	15	20
25	1 s. on 1 r. green	20	25
26	2 s. on 2 r. blue and purple	2·00	8·50
27	5 s. on 5 r. brown and green	9·00	23·00
20/27	*Set of 8*	11·00	29·00

1953 (2 June). *Coronation. As No. 153 of Jamaica.*

28	15 c. black and deep green	30	1·25

14 Sultan Hussein   15 Tarim

(Des Freya Stark and H. Ingram. Recess D.L.R.)

1954 (15 Jan). *As Nos. 1/11 (but with portrait of Sultan Hussein as in T 14/15). Wmk Mult Script CA. T 14, perf 12½; others, perf 12 × 13 (vert) or 13 × 12 (horiz).*

29	5 c. sepia	10	10
30	10 c. deep blue	15	10
31	15 c. deep bluish green	15	10
32	25 c. carmine-red	15	10
33	35 c. deep blue	15	10
34	50 c. deep brown and carmine-red	15	10
35	1 s. brown-orange	15	10
36	2 s. deep yellow-green	3·75	1·50
37	5 s. deep blue and violet	4·00	3·00
38	10 s. yellow-brown and violet	5·00	6·50
29/38	*Set of 10*	12·50	10·00

16 Qarn Adh Dhabi   17 Seiyun

(Recess D.L.R.)

1964 (1 July). *Designs as T 16/17. W w 12. P 12 × 13 (70 c.) or 13 × 12 (others).*

39	70 c. black	85	65
40	1 s. 25 c. blue-green	85	4·00
41	1 s. 50 c. deep reddish violet	85	4·00
39/41	*Set of 3*	2·25	7·75

Design: *Horiz as T* 17—1 s. 50 c. Gheil Omer.

STANLEY GIBBONS
STAMP COLLECTING SERIES

Introductory booklets on *How to Start, How to Identify Stamps* and *Collecting by Theme.* A series of well illustrated guides at a low price.
Write for details.

(New Currency. 1000 fils = 1 dinar)

SOUTH ARABIA
الجنوب العربي
5 FILS ٥ فلوس
19

SOUTH ARABIA
الجنوب العربي
500 ٥٠٠
FILS فلس
(20)

SOUTH ARABIA
الجنوب العربي
50 ٥٠
FILS فلس
(21)

1966 (1 Apr). *New Currency. Nos. 29/41 surch as T 19/21.*

42	5 f. on 5 c. (19)	15	10
	a. Surch quadruple, one inverted	45·00	
43	5 f. on 10 c. (19) (R.)	15	10
44	10 f. on 15 c. (21) (R.)	15	20
	a. Surch inverted	75·00	
45	15 f. on 25 c. (20)	20	20
46	20 f. on 35 c. (20) (R.)	15	20
47	25 f. on 50 c. (21) (R.)	15	30
48	35 f. on 70 c. (20) (R.)	20	90
49	50 f. on 1 s. (21)	20	15
50	65 f. on 1 s. 25 (21)	20	15
51	75 f. on 1 s. 50 (21)	20	30
52	100 f. on 2 s. (20) (R.)	22·00	27·00
53	250 f. on 5 s. (21) (R.)	1·40	3·50
54	500 f. on 10 s. (20)	1·75	3·75
42/54	*Set of 13*	24·00	32·00

SOUTH ARABIA

SOUTH ARABIA
الجنوب العربي
(22)

SOUTH ARABIA
الجنوب العربي
(23)

الجنوب العربي
5 FILS ٥ فلوس
(22)

50 FILS ٥٠ فلس
(23)

15 ١٥
FILS فلس
(24)

1966. *Nos. 29/41 surch with T 22/4.*

55	5 f. on 5 c. (22) (B.)	30	10
	a. Surch inverted	50·00	
56	5 f. on 10 c. (22) (R.)	45	10
57	10 f. on 15 c. (23) (Y.)	45	10
	a. Surch inverted	50·00	
58	15 f. on 25 c. (24) (B.)	45	10
	a. Surch inverted	50·00	
59	20 f. on 35 c. (24) (Y.)	50	10
60	25 f. on 50 c. (23) (B.)	50	10
61	35 f. on 70 c. (24) (Br.)	50	20
62	50 f. on 1 s. (23) (G.)	50	20
	a. Stop after "FILS"	12·00	
63	65 f. on 1 s. 25 (23) (Y.)	40	45
64	75 f. on 1 s. 50 (23) (G.)	40	50
	a. Surch inverted	50·00	
65	100 f. on 2 s. (24) (Y.)	2·50	85
	a. Surch inverted	35·00	
66	250 f. on 5 s. (23) (Y.)	2·50	2·75
	a. Surch inverted	60·00	
67	500 f. on 10 s. (24) (G.)	2·75	5·00
55/67	*Set of 13*	11·00	9·00

HELSINKI 1952
⬡
(25)

INTERNATIONAL COOPERATION
THROUGH OLYMPICS
(26)

1966. *History of Olympic Games. Nos. 57, 59, 61/7 Optd as T 25/6 in red.*

68	10 f. on 15 c. deep bluish green (25 ("LOS ANGELES 1932"))	15	10
69	20 f. on 35 c. deep blue (25 ("BERLIN 1936"))	20	15
70	35 f. on 70 c. black (26)	20	15
	a. Opt T 26 inverted	7·00	
71	50 f. on 1 s. brown-orange (25 ("LONDON 1948"))	25	20
	a. Stop after "FILS"	9·00	
72	65 f. on 1 s. 25, blue-green (25)	35	50
73	75 f. on 1 s. 50, deep reddish violet (25 ("MELBOURNE 1956"))	40	55
74	100 f. on 2 s. deep yellow-green (25 ("ROME 1960"))	50	65
75	250 f. on 5 s. deep blue and violet (25 ("TOKYO 1964"))	1·00	1·50
	a. Surch inverted	50·00	
76	500 f. on 10 s. yellow-brown and violet (25 ("MEXICO CITY 1968"))	1·40	2·75
68/76	*Set of 9*	4·00	6·00

CHAMPION:
ENGLAND ⚽
(27)

FOOTBALL
1966 ⚽
(28)

1966 (19 Sept). *World Cup Football Championships. Nos. 57, 59, 61/2, 65/7 optd with T 27/8.*

77	10 f. on 15 c. deep bluish green (27)	50	30
78	20 f. on 35 c. deep blue (28)	70	40
79	35 f. on 70 c. black (28)	80	40
80	50 f. on 1 s. brown-orange (27)	90	40
	a. Stop after "FILS"	15·00	
81	100 f. on 2 s. deep yellow-green (28)	3·25	1·75
82	250 f. on 5 s. deep blue and violet (27)	7·00	4·50
83	500 f. on 10 s. yellow-brown and violet (28)	9·00	7·00
77/83	*Set of 7*	20·00	13·50

29 "Telstar"

(Photo State Ptg Wks, Vienna)

1966 (25 Oct). *I.T.U. Centenary (1965). T **29** and similar vert designs. P 13½.*
84	5 f. blackish green, black and reddish violet		85	25
85	10 f. maroon, black and bright green..		1·00	30
86	15 f. Prussian blue, black and orange		1·40	40
87	25 f. blackish green, black and orange-red ..		2·00	50
88	35 f. maroon, black and deep olive-yellow		2·50	70
89	50 f. Prussian blue, black and orange-brown		3·00	1·10
90	65 f. blackish green, black and orange-yellow		3·75	1·25
84/90			*Set of 7* 13·00	4·00

Designs:—10, 35 f. "Relay"; 15, 50 f. "Ranger"; others, Type **29**.

32 Churchill at Easel

(Photo State Ptg Wks, Vienna)

1966 (Dec). *Sir Winston Churchill's Paintings. T **32** and similar designs in black and gold (5 f.) or multicoloured (others). P 13½.*
91	5 f. Type **32**	..	1·00	15
92	10 f. "Antibes"..	..	1·25	15
93	15 f. "Flowers" (*vert*)	..	1·25	20
94	20 f. "Tapestries"	..	1·40	35
95	25 f. "Village, Lake Lugano" ..		1·60	35
96	35 f. "Church, Lake Como" (*vert*) ..		1·75	40
97	50 f. "Flowers at Chartwell" (*vert*) ..		2·25	65
98	65 f. Type **32**	..	2·75	90
91/8			*Set of 8* 12·00	2·75

WORLD PEACE PANDIT NEHRU

(39)

40 "Master Crewe as Henry VIII" (Sir Joshua Reynolds)

1967. *"World Peace". Nos. 57, 59, 61/7 optd as T **39** in various sizes of type.*
99	10 f. on 15 c. deep bluish green (Type **39**) (R.)		35	35
100	20 f. on 35 c. deep blue ("WINSTON CHURCHILL") (R.)		4·00	1·50
101	35 f. on 70 c. black ("DAG HAMMARSKJOLD") (B.)..		50	50
102	50 f. on 1 s. brown-orange ("JOHN F. KENNEDY") (R.)		60	60
	a. Stop after "FILS"	..	14·00	
103	65 f. on 1 s. 25, blue-green ("LUDWIG ERHARD") (Pk.)		70	70
104	75 f. on 1 s. 50 dp reddish violet ("LYNDON JOHNSON") (B.)		80	80
105	100 f. on 2 s. deep yellow-green ("ELEANOR ROOSEVELT") (B.) ..		1·00	1·00
106	250 f. on 5 s. dp blue and violet ("WINSTON CHURCHILL") (R.)		11·00	7·50
107	500 f. on 10 s. yellow-brown & violet ("JOHN F. KENNEDY") (R.) ..		5·00	7·50
99/107	.. .. ..	..	*Set of 9* 22·00	18·00

(Photo State Ptg Wks, Vienna)

1967. *Paintings. T **40** and similar multicoloured designs. P 13½.*
108	5 f. Type **40**	..	30	25
109	10 f. "The Dancer" (Degas) ..		35	30
110	15 f. "The Fifer" (Manet) ..		40	35
111	20 f. "Stag at Sharkey's" (boxing match, G. Burrows)..		45	40
112	25 f. "Don Manuel Osorio" (Goya) ..		50	45
113	35 f. "St. Martin distributing his Cloak" (A. van Dyck)..		70	65
114	50 f. "The Blue Boy" (Gainsborough)..		85	75
115	65 f. "The White Horse" (Gauguin) ..		1·10	1·00
116	75 f. "Mona Lisa" (Da Vinci) (45 × 62 *mm*).		1·40	1·25
108/16			*Set of 9* 5·50	4·75

---

(49)

50 Churchill Crown

1967. *American Astronauts. Nos. 57, 59, 61/2 and 65/6 optd as T **49** in various sizes of type, in red.*
117	10 f. on 15 c. deep bluish green ("ALAN SHEPARD, JR.")		55	70
118	20 f. on 35 c. dp blue ("VIRGIL GRISSOM")		70	85
119	35 f. on 70 c. black ("JOHN GLENN, JR.") ..		95	1·25
120	50 f. on 1 s. brown-orange (Type **49**)		95	1·25
	a. Stop after "FILS"	..	15·00	
121	100 f. on 2 s. deep yellow-green ("WALTER SCHIRRA, JR.")		2·25	3·00
122	250 f. on 5 s. deep blue & violet ("GORDON COOPER, JR.")		3·50	4·50
	a. Opt (as T **49**) double ..		90·00	
117/122	.. ..		*Set of 6* 8·00	10·50

1967 (Mar). *Churchill Commemoration. Photo. P 13½.*
123	**50** 75 f. multicoloured	.. ..	8·50	6·50

Appendix

The following stamps have either been issued in excess of postal needs, or have not been made available to the public in reasonable quantities at face value. Miniature sheets, imperforate stamps etc., are excluded from this section.

1967

Hunting. 20 f.
Olympic Games, Grenoble. Postage 10, 25, 35, 50, 75 f. *Air* 100, 200 f.
Scout Jamboree, Idaho. Air 150 f.
Paintings by Renoir. Postage 10, 35, 50, 65, 75 f. *Air* 100, 200, 250 f.
Paintings by Toulouse-Lautrec. Postage 10, 35, 50, 65, 75 f. *Air* 100, 200, 250 f.

The National Liberation Front is said to have taken control of Kathiri State of Seiyun on 1 October 1967.

QU'AITI STATE IN HADHRAMAUT

The stamps of ADEN were used in Qu'aiti State in Hadhramaut from 22 April 1937 until 1942. The main post office was at Mukalla. Other offices existed at Du'an (*opened* 1940), Gheil Ba Wazir (*opened* 1942), Haura (*opened* 1940), Shibam (*opened* 1940) and Shihr (*opened* 1939).

> **PRICES FOR STAMPS ON COVER TO 1945**
> Nos. 1/11 *from* × 6

I. ISSUES INSCR "SHIHR AND MUKALLA"

1 Sultan of Shihr and Mukalla	**2** Mukalla Harbour

VICTORY
ISSUE
8TH JUNE
1946
(10)

(Recess D.L.R.)

1942 (July)–**46**. *Wmk Mult Script CA. Designs as T **1** (½ to 1 a.) or T **2** (others). P 14 (½ to 1 a.), 12 × 13 (1½, 2, 3 a. and 1 r.) or 13 × 12 (others).*
1	½ a. blue-green		15	25
	a. Olive-green (12.46)	..	20·00	26·00
2	¾ a. brown ..		20	25
3	1 a. blue		40	25
4	1½ a. carmine ..		45	20
5	2 a. sepia		40	30
6	2½ a. blue		30	20
7	3 a. sepia and carmine		45	25
8	8 a. red		30	40
9	1 r. green		40	50
10	2 r. blue and purple..		8·00	7·50
11	5 r. brown and green		10·00	8·00
1/11	..		*Set of 11* 19·00	15·00
1/11 Perf "Specimen"			*Set of 11* £110	

Designs: *Vert*—2 a. Gateway of Shihr; 3 a. Outpost of Mukalla; 1 r. Du'an. *Horiz*—2½ a. Shibam; 8 a. 'Einat; 2 r. Mosque in Hureidha; 5 r. Meshhed.

1946 (15 Oct). *Victory. No. 4 optd with T **10** and No. 6 optd similarly, but in three lines, by De La Rue.*
12	1½ a. carmine	.. ..	10	20
13	2½ a. blue (R.) ..	..	10	10
12/13 Perf "Specimen"			*Set of 2* 55·00	

1949 (17 Jan). *Royal Silver Wedding. As Nos. 143/4 of Jamaica.*
14	1½ a. scarlet	.. ..	40	1·00
15	5 r. green	.. ..	11·00	9·00

1949 (10 Oct). *75th Anniv of U.P.U. As Nos. 145/8 of Jamaica, surch with new values by Waterlow.*
16	2½ a. on 20 c. ultramarine	..	20	20
17	3 a. on 30 c. carmine-red	..	55	50
18	8 a. on 50 c. orange	..	55	60
19	1 r. on 1s. blue	..	55	60
	a. Surch omitted	..	£800	
16/19	.. .. ..		*Set of 4* 1·75	1·60

1951 (1 Oct). *Currency changed. Surch with new values in cents or shillings as T **11** (5 c.), **12** (10 c. ("CTS"), 15 c., 20 c. and 50 c.) or **13** (1 s. to 5 s.) of Seiyun, by Waterlow.*
20	5 c. on 1 a. blue (R.)	..	15	15
21	10 c. on 2 a. sepia	..	15	15
22	15 c. on 2½ a. blue	..	15	15
23	20 c. on 3 a. sepia and carmine	..	15	20
	a. Surch double, one albino..		£110	
24	50 c. on 8 a. red	..	15	40
25	1 s. on 1 r. green	..	30	25
26	2 s. on 2 r. blue and purple	..	4·00	5·00
27	5 s. on 5 r. brown and green ..		6·50	8·00
20/27	..		*Set of 8* 10·50	13·00

1953 (2 June). *Coronation. As No. 153 of Jamaica.*
28	15 c. black and deep blue	.. ..	40	55

II. ISSUES INSCR "HADHRAMAUT"

11 Metal Work	**22** Metal Work

(Des Mme M. de Sturler Raemaekers. Recess D.L.R.)

1955 (1 Sept)–**63**. *T **11** and similar designs. Wmk Mult Script CA. P 11½ × 13–13½ (vert) or 14 (horiz).*
29	5 c. greenish blue ..		10	10
30	10 c. grey-black ..		15	10
31	15 c. deep green ..		15	10
	a. Bronze-green (9.3.63)	..	15	20
32	25 c. carmine-red ..		15	10
33	35 c. blue ..		15	10
34	50 c. orange-red ..		15	10
	a. Red-orange (9.3.63)	..	30	30
35	90 c. sepia ..		15	15
36	1 s. black and deep lilac ..		20	10
37	1 s. 25, black and red-orange	..	30	45
38	2 s. black and indigo ..		2·50	60
39	5 s. black and bluish green ..		3·75	1·25
40	10 s. black and lake ..		4·00	2·50
29/40			*Set of 12* 10·50	5·00

Designs: *Vert*—10 c. Mat-making; 15 c. Weaving; 25 c. Pottery; 35 c. Building; 50 c. Date cultivation; 90 c. Agriculture. *Horiz*—1 s. Fisheries; 1 s. 25, 10 s. Lime-burning; 2 s. Dhow building; 5 s. Agriculture.

1963 (20 Oct). *As Nos. 29/40 but with inset portrait of Sultan Awadh bin Saleh el-Qu'aiti as in T **22** and wmk w **12**.*
41	5 c. greenish blue ..		10	10
42	10 c. grey-black ..		10	10
43	15 c. bronze-green ..		10	10
44	25 c. carmine-red ..		10	10
45	35 c. blue ..		10	10
46	50 c. red-orange ..		10	10
47	70 c. deep brown (as 90 c.) ..		15	20
48	1 s. black and deep lilac ..		20	10
49	1 s. 25, black and red-orange	..	45	75
50	2 s. black and indigo-blue ..		2·25	1·00
51	5 s. black and bluish green ..		8·50	9·00
52	10 s. black and lake ..		8·50	11·00
41/52			*Set of 12* 18·00	20·00

(New Currency. 1000 fils = 1 dinar)

1966 (1 Apr). *New currency. Nos. 41/52 surch as T **20/21** of Kathiri State of Seiyun.*
53	5 f. on 5 c. greenish blue (**20**) (R.) ..		10	30
54	5 f. on 10 c. grey-black (**20**) (R.)	..	10	30
55	10 f. on 15 c. bronze-green (**20**) (R.) ..		10	20
56	15 f. on 25 c. carmine-red (**20**)		10	30
57	20 f. on 35 c. blue (**20**) (R.) ..		10	50
58	25 f. on 50 c. red-orange (**20**)..		10	30
59	35 f. on 70 c. deep brown (**20**) (R.) ..		10	30
60	50 f. on 1 s. black and deep lilac (**21**) (R.)		10	15
61	65 f. on 1 s. 25, black and red-orange (**21**) (R.)		30	30
62	100 f. on 2 s. black and indigo-blue (**21**) (R.) ..		55	75
63	250 f. on 5 s. black and bluish green (**21**) (R.)..		1·00	1·50
64	500 f. on 10 s. black and lake (**21**) (R.) ..		14·00	3·00
53/64	..		*Set of 12* 15·00	7·00

1874-1965 **WINSTON CHURCHILL** (23)	1917-1963 **JOHN F. KENNEDY** (24)

1966. *Churchill Commemoration. Nos. 54/6 optd with T* **23.**
65	5 f. on 10 c. grey-black (R.)	..	..	..	4·50	6·00
66	10 f. on 15 c. bronze-green (R.)		..	..	5·50	7·00
	a. Opt T **23** inverted		..	..	75·00	
67	15 f. on 25 c. carmine-red (B.)..		..	..	7·50	9·00
65/7			..	*Set of* 3	16·00	20·00

1966. *President Kennedy Commemoration. Nos. 57/9 optd with* **T 24.**
68	20 f. on 35 c. blue (R.) ..		..	..	1·50	4·00
69	25 f. on 50 c. red-orange (B.) ..		..	..	1·75	4·75
70	35 f. on 70 c. deep brown (B.) ..		..	..	2·75	5·50
68/70			..	*Set of* 3	5·50	13·00

25 World Cup Emblem

(Photo State Ptg Wks. Vienna)

1966. *World Cup Football Championship, England. T* **25** *and similar diamond-shaped designs. P* 13½.
71	5 f. maroon and yellow-orange		..	..	1·75	25
72	10 f. slate-violet and light green		..	..	2·00	25
73	15 f. maroon and yellow-orange		..	..	2·25	30
74	20 f. slate-violet and light green		..	..	2·50	40
75	25 f. blackish green and orange-red		..	..	2·75	55
76	35 f. blue and yellow		..	..	3·25	80
77	50 f. blackish green and orange-red		..	..	3·75	1·10
78	65 f. blue and yellow		..	..	4·50	1·40
71/78			..	*Set of* 8	20·00	4·50

Designs:—10, 35 f. Wembley Stadium; 15, 50 f. Footballers; 20 f. Jules Rimet Cup and football; 25, 65 f. Type **25.**

29 Mexican Hat and Blanket

(Photo State Ptg Wks, Vienna)

1966 (25 Oct). *Pre-Olympic Games, Mexico* (1968). *P* 13½.
79	**29**	75 f. sepia and light yellow-green		..	1·25	1·25

30 Telecommunications Satellite

(Photo State Ptg Wks, Vienna)

1966 (Dec). *International Co-operation Year* (1965). *T* **30** *and similar horiz designs. P* 13½.
80	5 f. maroon, bright purple and emerald		..	2·00	35
81	10 f. violet, orange, blue-green and new blue			2·25	35
82	15 f. maroon, new blue and red		...	..	2·50	40
83	20 f. Prussian blue, purple and red		..	2·75	45
84	25 f. violet, olive-yellow, red and emerald		..	3·00	50
85	35 f. maroon, rose-red and new blue		..	4·00	80
	a. New blue (face values) omitted		..	£150	
86	50 f. maroon, green and red		..	5·50	1·25
87	65 f. chocolate, bluish violet and red		..	6·00	1·75
80/87			..	*Set of* 8	25·00	5·25

Designs:—10 f. Olympic runner (inscribed "ROME 1960"); 15 f. Fishes; 25 f. Olympic runner (inscribed "TOKIO 1964"); 50 f. Tobacco plant; others, Type **30.**

NEW INFORMATION

The editor is always interested to correspond with people who have new information that will improve or correct the Catalogue.

Appendix

The following stamps have either been issued in excess of postal needs, or have not been made available to the public in reasonable quantities at face value. Miniature sheets, imperforate stamps etc. are excluded from this section.

1967

Stampex Stamp Exhibition, London. Postage 5, 10, 15, 20, 25 f. *Air* 50, 65 f.
Amphilex International Stamp Exhibition, Amsterdam. Air 75 f.
Olympic Games, Mexico (1968), 75 f.
Paintings. Postage 5, 10, 15, 20, 25 f. *Air* 50, 65 f.
Scout Jamboree, Idaho. Air 35 f.
Space Research. Postage 10, 25, 35, 50, 75 f. *Air* 100, 250 f.

The National Liberation Front is said to have taken control of Qu'aiti State in Hadhramaut on 17 September 1967.

MAHRA SULTANATE OF QISHN AND SOCOTRA

(Currency. 1000 fils = 1 dinar)

1 Mahra Flag

(Des and litho Harrison)

1967 (12 Mar). *Flag in green, black and vermilion; inscriptions in black; background colours given. P* 14 × 14½.
1	1	5 f. mauve		..	1·10	10
2		10 f. buff		..	1·10	15
3		15 f. sage-green ..		..	1·10	15
4		20 f. red-orange		..	1·10	20
5		25 f. yellow-brown		..	1·10	25
6		35 f. turquoise-green		..	1·10	25
7		50 f. new blue		..	1·10	25
8		65 f. blackish brown		..	1·10	25
9		100 f. violet		..	1·10	25
10		250 f. rose-red		..	1·25	35
11		500 f. grey-green		..	1·50	50
1/11				*Set of* 11	11·50	2·40

Appendix

The following stamps have either been issued in excess of postal needs, or have not been made available to the public in reasonable quantities at face value. Miniature sheets, imperforate stamps etc., are excluded from this section.

1967

Scout Jamboree, Idaho. 15, 75, 100, 150 f.
President Kennedy Commemoration. Postage 10, 15, 25, 50, 75, 100, 150 f. *Air* 250, 500 f.
Olympic Games, Mexico (1968). *Postage* 10, 25, 50 f. *Air* 250, 500 f.

The National Liberation Front is said to have taken control of Mahra Sultanate of Qishn and Socotra on 1 October 1967.

SOUTH ARABIAN FEDERATION

Comprising Aden and most of the territories of the former Western Aden Protectorate plus one from the Eastern Aden Protectorate.

(Currency. 100 cents=1 shilling)

1 Red Cross Emblem

1963 (25 Nov). *Red Cross Centenary. W w* 12. *P* 13½.
1	1	15 c. red and black ..		..	30	15
2		1 s. 25, red and blue		..	60	35

(New Currency. 1000 fils=1 dinar)

2 Federal Crest   3 Federal Flag

(Des V. Whiteley. Photo Harrison)

1965 (1 Apr). *P* 14½ × 14 (*T* 2) *or* 14½ (*T* 3).
3	2	5 f. blue		..	10	10
4		10 f. violet-blue	..	..	10	10
5		15 f. turquoise-green	..	..	10	10
6		20 f. green	..	..	10	10
7		25 f. yellow-brown	..	..	10	10
8		30 f. yellow-bistre	..	..	10	10
9		35 f. chestnut	..	..	10	10
10		50 f. red	..	..	10	10
11		65 f. yellow-green	..	..	30	30
12		75 f. crimson	..	..	30	10

13	3	100 f. multicoloured		..	30	10
14		250 f. multicoloured		..	1·25	25
15		500 f. multicoloured		..	3·00	65
16		1 d. multicoloured		..	5·00	3·00
3/16				*Set of* 14	9·50	4·25

4 I.C.Y. Emblem

(Des V. Whiteley. Litho Harrison)

1965 (24 Oct). *International Co-operation Year. W w* **12.** *P* 14½.
17	4	5 f. reddish purple and turquoise-green	20	10
18		65 f. deep bluish green and lavender	..	50	20

5 Sir Winston Churchill and St. Paul's Cathedral in Wartime

(Des Jennifer Toombs. Photo Harrison)

1966 (24 Jan). *Churchill Commemoration. No wmk. P* 14.
19	5	5 f. black, cerise, gold and new blue ..	10	10
20		10 f. black, cerise, gold and deep green	25	10
21		65 f. black, cerise, gold and brown	65	10
22		125 f. black, cerise, gold and bluish violet	90	90
19/22			*Set of* 4	1·75	1·00

6 Footballer's Legs, Ball and Jules Rimet Cup

(Des V. Whiteley. Litho Harrison)

1966 (1 July). *World Cup Football Championship, England. No wmk. P* 14.
23	6	10 f. violet, yellow-green, lake & yell-brn	30	10
24		50 f. chocolate, blue-grn, lake & yell-brn	95	20

7 W.H.O. Building

(Des M. Goaman. Litho Harrison)

1966 (20 Sept). *Inauguration of W.H.O. Headquarters, Geneva. No wmk. P* 14.
25	7	10 f. black, yellow-green and light blue	30	10
26		75 f. black, light purple and yellow-brown	55	45

8 "Education"

9 "Science"

10 "Culture"

(Des Jennifer Toombs. Litho Harrison)

1966 (15 Dec). 20th Anniv of U.N.E.S.C.O. No wmk. P 14.
27	8	10 f. slate-violet, red, yellow and orange		20	15
28	9	65 f. orange-yellow, vio & dp olive		70	70
29	10	125 f. black, bright purple and orange		2·25	2·25
27/9			Set of 3	2·75	2·75

The South Arabian Federation became fully independent on 30 November 1967. Later issues for this area will be found listed in Part 19 (*Middle East*) of this catalogue under Yemen People's Democratic Republic.

South Australia
see Australia

Southern Cameroons

The following issue, although ordered by the Southern Cameroons authorities, was also on sale in Northern Cameroons, until the latter joined Nigeria. The stamps therefore can be found with Nigerian postmarks.

CAMEROONS U.K.T.T.
(1)

1960 (1 Oct)–61. Nos. 69/71, 72 ca/cc and 73/80 of Nigeria optd with T 1, in red.
1	18	½d. black and orange		10	20
2	—	1d. black and bronze-green		10	10
		a. Grey-blk & dull bronze-grn (19.9.61)		60	70
3	—	1½d. blue-green		10	15
4	21	2d. grey (Type B)		10	15
		a. Slate-blue (Type A)		†	—
		b. Bluish grey (Type B)		30·00	10·00
		c. Pale grey (Type B) (19.9.61)		10	20
5	—	3d. black and deep lilac		15	10
6	—	4d. black and blue		10	40
7	24	6d. orange-brown and black (p 14)		20	10
		a. Perf 13×13½ (19.9.61)		20	60
8	—	1s. black and maroon		15	10
9	26	2s. 6d. black and green		80	80
10	—	5s. black and red-orange		90	2·75
11	—	10s. black and red-brown		2·25	3·00
12	29	£1 black and violet		6·50	11·00
1/12			Set of 12	10·00	17·00

Nos. 2 and 4/b were overprinted on stamps printed by Waterlows' subsidiary, Imprimerie Belge de Securité.
Nos. 2a, 4c and 7a were from new printings produced by De La Rue instead of Waterlow.

The above stamps were withdrawn on 30 September 1961, when Southern Cameroons became part of the independent republic of Cameroun.

Southern Nigeria
see Nigeria

Southern Rhodesia
see Zimbabwe

South Georgia and the South Sandwich Islands

As South Georgia was a dependency of the Falkland Islands between 1963 and 1980 stamps so inscribed are listed under FALKLAND ISLANDS DEPENDENCIES.
Under the new constitution, effective 3 October 1985, South Georgia and South Sandwich Islands ceased to be dependencies of the Falkland Islands.

(Des A. Theobald. Litho Questa)

1986 (21 Apr). 60th Birthday of Queen Elizabeth II. Vert designs as T 230a of Jamaica. Multicoloured. W w 16. P 14½×14.
153	10p. Four generations of Royal Family at Prince Charles' christening, 1948			25	25
154	24p. With Prince Charles and Lady Diana Spencer, Buckingham Palace, 1981			55	55
155	29p. In robes of Order of the British Empire, St. Paul's Cathedral, London			60	60
156	45p. At banquet, Canada, 1976			95	95
157	58p. At Crown Agents Head Office, London, 1983			1·25	1·25
153/7			Set of 5	3·25	3·25

25a Prince Andrew and Miss Sarah Ferguson at Ascot

26 Southern Black-backed Gull

(Des D. Miller. Litho Questa)

1986 (10 Nov). Royal Wedding. T 25a and similar vert designs. Multicoloured. W w 16. P 14½×14.
158	17p. Type 25a			75	85
159	22p. Wedding photograph			85	1·00
160	29p. Prince Andrew with Lynx helicopter on board H.M.S. Brazen			1·00	1·25
158/60			Set of 3	2·40	2·75

(Des T. Chater. Litho Walsall)

1987 (24 Apr). Birds. T 26 and similar multicoloured designs. W w 16 (sideways on horiz designs). P 14½.
161	1p. Type 26			10	10
162	2p. Blue-eyed Cormorant			10	10
163	3p. Snowy Sheathbill (vert)			10	10
164	4p. Great Skua (vert)			10	10
165	5p. Pintado Petrel ("Cape Pigeon")			10	15
166	6p. Georgian Diving Petrel			10	15
167	7p. South Georgia Pipit (vert)			15	20
168	8p. Georgian Teal ("South Georgian Pintail") (vert)			15	20
169	9p. Fairy Prion			20	25
170	10p. Chinstrap Penguin			20	25
171	20p. Macaroni Penguin (vert)			40	45
172	25p. Light-mantled Sooty Albatross (vert)		50	55
173	50p. Giant Petrel (vert)			1·00	1·10
174	£1 Wandering Albatross			2·00	2·10
175	£3 King Penguin (vert)			6·00	6·25
161/75			Set of 15	10·00	10·50

26a I.G.Y. Logo

27 Gaimardia trapesina

(Des L. Curtis. Litho Questa)

1987 (5 Dec). 30th Anniv of International Geophysical Year. T 26a and similar vert designs. W w 16. P 14½×14.
176	24p. black and pale turquoise-blue			50	55
177	29p. multicoloured			55	60
178	58p. multicoloured			1·10	1·25
176/8			Set of 3	1·90	2·10

Designs:—29p. Grytviken; 58p. Glaciologist using hand-drill to take core sample.

(Des I. Strange. Litho Questa)

1988 (26 Feb). Sea Shells. T 27 and similar horiz designs. Multicoloured. W w 16 (sideways). P 14×14½.
179	10p. Type 27			30	30
180	24p. Margarella tropidophoroides			50	60
181	29p. Trophon scotianus			55	65
182	58p. Chlanidota densesculpta			1·10	1·25
179/82			Set of 4	2·25	2·50

(Des E. Nisbet and D. Miller (24p.), D. Miller (others). Litho Questa)

1988 (17 Sept). 300th Anniv of Lloyd's of London. Designs as T 167a of Malawi. W w 16 (sideways on 24, 29p.). P 14.
183	10p. brownish black and brown			30	30
184	24p. multicoloured			50	55
185	29p. brownish black and emerald			60	65
186	58p. brownish black and carmine-red		1·10	1·25
183/6			Set of 4	2·25	2·50

Designs: Vert—10p. Queen Mother at opening of new Lloyd's building, 1957; 58p. Horatio (tanker) on fire, 1916. Horiz—24p. Lindblad Explorer (cruise liner); 29p. Whaling station, Leith Harbour.

28 Glacier Headwall

29 Retracing Shackleton's Trek

(Des I. Loe. Litho Questa)

1989 (31 July). Glacier Formations. T 28 and similar horiz designs. Multicoloured. W w 16 (sideways). P 14.
187	10p. Type 28			35	35
188	24p. Accumulation area			70	70
189	29p. Ablation area			80	80
190	58p. Calving front			1·40	1·40
187/90			Set of 4	3·00	3·00

(Des O. Bell. Litho Questa)

1989 (28 Nov). 25th Anniv of Combined Services Expedition to South Georgia. T 29 and similar horiz designs. Multicoloured. W w 16 (sideways). P 14×14½.
191	10p. Type 29			35	35
192	24p. Surveying at Royal Bay			70	70
193	29p. H.M.S. Protector (ice patrol ship)		80	80
194	58p. Raising Union Jack on Mount Paget		1·40	1·40
191/4			Set of 4	3·00	3·00

(Des D. Miller. Litho Questa)

1990 (15 Sept). 90th Birthday of Queen Elizabeth the Queen Mother. Vert designs as T 107 (26p.) or 108 (£1) of Kenya. W w 16. P 14×15 (26p.) or 14½ (£1).
195	26p. multicoloured			75	75
196	£1 black and dull ultramarine		2·75	2·75

Designs:—26p. Queen Mother; £1 King George VI and Queen Elizabeth with A.R.P. wardens, 1940.

30 Brutus, Prince Olav Harbour

31 Contest between two Bull Elephant Seals

(Des D. Miller. Litho Questa)

1990 (22 Dec). Wrecks and Hulks. T 30 and similar vert designs. Multicoloured. W w 16. P 14×14½.
197	12p. Type 30			40	40
198	26p. Bayard, Ocean Harbour			80	80
199	31p. Karrakatta, Husvik			95	95
200	62p. Louise, Grytviken			1·75	1·75
197/200			Set of 4	3·50	3·50

(Des D. Miller. Litho Questa)

1991 (2 July). 65th Birthday of Queen Elizabeth II and 70th Birthday of Prince Philip. Vert designs as T 58 of Kiribati. Multicoloured. W w 16 (sideways). P 14½×14.
201	31p. Queen Elizabeth II			1·00	1·00
	a. Horiz pair. Nos. 201/2 separated by label		2·00	2·00
202	31p. Prince Philip in Grenadier Guards uniform			1·00	1·00

Nos. 201/2 were printed in a similar sheet format to Nos. 366/7 of Kiribati.

(Des D. Miller. Litho Questa)

1991 (2 Nov). Elephant Seals. T 31 and similar horiz designs. W w 14 (sideways). P 14.
203	12p. Type 31			40	40
204	26p. Adult Elephant Seal			85	85
205	29p. Seal throwing sand			95	95
206	31p. Head of Elephant Seal			1·00	1·00
207	34p. Seals on beach			1·10	1·25
208	62p. Cow seal with pup			1·75	1·90
203/8			Set of 6	5·50	5·75

(Des D. Miller. Litho Questa (68p.), Walsall (others))

1992 (6 Feb). 40th Anniv of Queen Elizabeth II's Accession. Horiz designs as T 113 of Kenya. Multicoloured. W w 14 (sideways). P 14.
209	7p. Ice-covered mountains			30	30
210	14p. Zavodovski Island			55	55
211	29p. Gulbrandsen Lake			95	95
212	34p. Three portraits of Queen Elizabeth		1·10	1·10
213	68p. Queen Elizabeth II			1·75	1·75
209/13			Set of 5	4·25	4·25

MINIMUM PRICE

The minimum price quote is 10p which represents a handling charge rather than a basis for valuing common stamps. For further notes about prices see introductory pages.

32 Adult Teal and Young
Bird

(Des G. Drummond. Litho Questa)

1992 (12 Mar). *Endangered Species. Georgian Teal ("South Georgia Teal"). T* **32** *and similar horiz designs. Multicoloured.* W w **16** (*sideways*). P 14.

214	2p. Type **32**	..	..	..	15	15
215	6p. Adult with eggs	..	..	..	20	20
216	12p. Teals swimming	..	..	..	40	40
217	20p. Adult and two chicks	..		..	80	80
214/17	..	..	..	Set of 4	1·40	1·40

(Des N. Shewring. Litho Questa)

1992 (20 June). *10th Anniv of Liberation. Square designs as T* **169** *of St. Helena. Multicoloured.* W w **16** (*sideways*). P 14.

218	14p. + 6p. King Edward Point	..	60	70
219	29p. + 11p. *Queen Elizabeth 2* in Cumberland Bay	..	1·10	1·25
220	34p. + 16p. Royal Marines hoisting Union Jack on South Sandwich Islands		1·40	1·60
221	68p. + 32p. H.M.S. *Endurance* and Wasp helicopter	..	2·75	3·00
218/21	..	Set of 4	5·25	6·00
MS222	116×116 mm. Nos. 218/21	..	5·50	6·00

The premiums on Nos. 218/22 were for the S.S.A.F.A.

South West Africa
see Namibia

Sri Lanka
(*formerly* Ceylon)

CEYLON

PRICES FOR STAMPS ON COVER TO 1945

Nos. 1/4	*from* × 5
Nos. 5/19	*from* × 4
Nos. 23/117	*from* × 8
Nos. 118/20	*from* × 15
Nos. 121/38	*from* × 6
Nos. 139/41	†
Nos. 142/3	*from* × 10
Nos. 146/51	*from* × 6
Nos. 151*a*/2	†
Nos. 153/93	*from* × 8
Nos. 194/201	*from* × 12
Nos. 202/43	*from* × 6
Nos. 245/9	*from* × 4
Nos. 250/5	*from* × 5
Nos. 256/64	*from* × 4
Nos. 265/76	*from* × 3
Nos. 277/88	*from* × 4
Nos. 289/300	*from* × 8
Nos. 301/25	*from* × 2
Nos. 326/9*a*	—
Nos. 330/7*a*	*from* × 4
Nos. 338/52	*from* × 2
Nos. 353/4	—
Nos. 355/9	*from* × 2
No. 360	—
Nos. 360*a*/*g*	*from* × 2
Nos. 361/2	*from* × 5
Nos. 363/71	*from* × 3
Nos. 372/82	*from* × 2
Nos. 383/5	*from* × 3
Nos. 386/97	*from* × 2
Nos. 398/9	*from* × 8
Nos. O1/17	*from* × 30

CROWN COLONY

PRICES. The prices of the imperf stamps of Ceylon vary greatly according to condition. The following prices are for fine copies with four margins.

Poor to medium specimens can be supplied at much lower prices.

1

2

(Recess P.B.)

1857 (1 April). *Blued paper. Wmk Star* W w **1**. *Imperf.*

1	1	6d. purple-brown	£7500	£450

Collectors should beware of proofs with faked watermark, often offered as originals.

(Typo D.L.R.)

1857 (Oct)–**58**. *No wmk. Imperf.* (*a*) *Blue glazed paper.*

3	2	½d. lilac	£3250	£450

(*b*) *White glazed paper*

4	2	½d. lilac (1858)	£160	£150

3

4

NOTE. Beware of stamps of Type **3** which are often offered with corners added.

(Recess P.B.)

1857–9. *White paper. Wmk Star,* W w **1**. (*a*) *Imperf.*

5	1	1d. blue (24.8.57)	£600	19·00
		a. Blued paper	—	£150
6		1d. deep blue	£700	29·00
7		2d. deep green (24.8.57)	£150	50·00
8		2d. yellow-green	£500	90·00

9	3	4d. dull rose (23.4.59)		£50000	£4500
10	1	5d. chestnut (2.7.57)		£1500	£150
11		6d. purple-brown		£1800	£130
12		6d. brown		£6000	£400
12*a*		6d. deep brown		£7000	£1000
13	3	8d. brown (23.4.59)		£20000	£1500
14		9d. purple-brown (23.4.59)		£30000	£900
15	4	10d. orange-vermilion (2.7.57)		£800	£250
16		1s. dull violet (2.7.57)		£4500	£200
17	3	1s. 9d. green (23.4.59)		£700	£800
18		1s. 9d. pale yellow-green		£3000	£2000
19		2s. blue (23.4.59)		£5000	£1100

(*b*) "*Unofficial*" P 7½ (*No. 22a*) *or rouletted* (*Nos. 20/2*)

20	2	½d. lilac (*No wmk*)		£5000
21	1	1d. blue (*Wmk Star*)		£5000
22		2d. deep green (*Wmk Star*)	£1800	£1000
22*a*		1s. 9d. green (*Wmk Star*)		£4000

These stamps are believed to have been made by a Ceylon firm, or firms, for their own convenience.

(Recess P.B.)

1861. *Wmk Star,* W w **1**. (*a*) *Clean-cut perf* 14 *to* 15½.

23	1	1d. deep blue		95·00	14·00
24		1d. pale blue		£325	50·00
25		2d. green		£200	35·00
27		5d. chestnut		75·00	8·00
29	4	1s. dull violet		80·00	26·00
30	3	2s. blue		£1900	£400

(*b*) *Intermediate perf* 14 *to* 15½

31	1	1d. deep blue		75·00	12·00
32		1d. blue		75·00	15·00
33		2d. green		75·00	24·00
		a. Imperf between (vert pair)		†	—
34	3	4d. dull rose		£1800	£250
34*a*	1	5d. chestnut		£350	£130
35		6d. brown		£1300	75·00
36		6d. yellowish brown		—	£120
36*a*		6d. olive-brown		—	85·00
37	3	8d. brown		£1300	£250
38		9d. dull purple-brown		£4250	£225
40	4	1s. bright violet		£120	26·00
41		1s. dull violet		65·00	13·00

(*c*) *Rough perf* 14 *to* 15½

42	1	1d. blue		60·00	6·00
43		1d. blue (*bleuté paper*)		£325	42·00
44	3	4d. rose-red		£170	42·00
45		4d. deep rose-red		£180	48·00
47	1	6d. yellowish brown		£1200	£100
48		6d. blackish brown		£475	65·00
48*a*		6d. olive-brown		£500	55·00
49	3	8d. brown		£1200	£300
50		8d. yellow-brown		£1000	£250
51		9d. olive-brown		£375	28·00
52		9d. yellowish brown		£500	55·00
53		9d. deep brown		55·00	28·00
53*a*	4	10d. orange-vermilion		£180	20·00
		b. Imperf vert (horiz pair)		†	—
54		1s. dull violet		£225	15·00
55	3	2s. blue		£500	90·00
56		2s. deep blue		£650	£110

(*d*) *Rough perf* 14 *to* 15½. *Prepared for use, but not issued*

57	3	1s. 9d. green		£475

No. 34 is distinguished from Nos. 44/5 with fraudulently altered perfs by its colour.

5

6

T **5**. 23 mm high. "CC" oval.
T **6**. 21½ mm high. "CC" round and smaller.

(Recess or typo (T **2**). D.L.R.)

1862–64. *No wmk.* (*a*) *Smooth paper. P* 13.

58	1	1d. blue		65·00	6·00
59		5d. deep red-brown		£850	£150
60		6d. reddish brown		75·00	22·00
61		6d. deep brown		85·00	22·00
62	3	9d. brown		£900	65·00
63	4	1s. cold violet		£1500	80·00

(*b*) *Smooth paper. P* 11½, 12

64	1	1d. blue		£650	95·00
		a. Imperf between (horiz pair)		†	£4750

(*c*) *Glazed paper. P* 12½ (1864)

65	2	½d. pale lilac		£190	£120

The 1s. is known imperf, but not used. The "no wmk" stamps were printed on paper having the papermaker's name and date, "T H SAUNDERS 1862" across the sheets, and one or more of these letters or figures are often found on the stamps.

(Recess P.B., perforated by D.L.R.)

1864 (Sept). *Wmk Star,* W w **1**. *P* 12½.

66	4	10d. vermilion (*shades*)		£225	15·00

(Recess or typo (T **2**) D.L.R.)

1863–6. *Paper medium thin and slightly soft.* W **5**. *Wmks arranged in four panes, each of* 60, *with the words* "CROWN COLONIES" *between the panes. Portions of these letters often appear on the stamps.*

(*a*) *P* 11½, 12

68	1	1d. blue		£1700	£190

(*b*) *P* 13

69	1	6d. brown		£1200	85·00
70	3	9d. brown		£2500	£400

(*c*) *P* 12½

71	2	½d. mauve		19·00	18·00
72		½d. lilac		24·00	15·00
73		½d. deep lilac		38·00	26·00
74	1	1d. dark blue		55·00	3·00
75		1d. blue		55·00	3·00
76		2d. yellow-green		£6000	£350
77		2d. deep bottle-green		—	£3250
78		2d. grey-green		32·00	6·00
79		2d. emerald-green		90·00	65·00
80		2d. maize		£225	£225
81	3	4d. lake-rose		£375	75·00
82		4d. rose		£180	38·00
83	1	5d. reddish brown		90·00	32·00
84		5d. deep sage-green		£1200	£250
84*a*		5d. pale sage-green		£700	£160
85		6d. brown		60·00	8·00
86		6d. reddish brown		80·00	9·00
87		6d. deep brown		65·00	4·00
88	3	8d. light carmine-brown		70·00	38·00
89		8d. dark carmine-brown		42·00	22·00
90		9d. brown		£200	21·00
91	4	10d. vermilion		£900	35·00
91*a*		10d. orange		£1500	£160
92	3	2s. dark blue		£160	26·00

The ½d. lilac; 1d. blue; 2d. grey-green; 2d. maize; and 5d. deep sage-green and pale sage-green, are known imperf.

1867. *Paper hand-made. Prepared and used only for these Ceylon stamps.* W **6**. *Wmks arranged in one pane of* 240 *in* 20 *rows of* 12, *with the words* "CROWN COLONIES" *twice in each side margin. P* 12½.

93	1	1d. pale blue		55·00	5·00
94		1d. Prussian blue		50·00	4·00
95		2d. maize		50·00	5·00
96		2d. olive-yellow		28·00	6·00
97		2d. greenish yellow		£130	42·00
98		2d. orange-yellow		27·00	5·00
99	3	4d. pale rose		£110	38·00
100		4d. rose		27·00	9·00
101	1	5d. pale sage-green		35·00	6·00
102		5d. deep olive-green		60·00	7·00
103		5d. deep myrtle-green		16·00	26·00
104		6d. deep brown		38·00	8·00
105		6d. blackish brown		50·00	9·50
106		6d. red-brown		18·00	26·00
107	3	8d. pale carmine-brown		70·00	50·00
108		8d. deep carmine-brown		28·00	40·00
109		9d. bistre-brown		£225	25·00
110		9d. deep brown		22·00	6·00
111	4	10d. vermilion		£1000	£140
111*a*		10d. red-orange		25·00	5·00
112		10d. orange		42·00	7·50
113		1s. lilac		£325	32·00
114		1s. violet		60·00	5·50
115	3	2s. pale blue		£200	45·00
116		2s. blue		85·00	14·00
117		2s. Prussian blue		60·00	11·00

The 1d. pale blue, 1d. Prussian blue, 6d. deep brown, 9d. deep brown and 10d. orange are known imperf but only unused.

PRINTERS. All stamps from No. 118 to 367 were typographed by De La Rue & Co, Ltd, London.

7

8

1866. *Wmk Crown CC. P* 12½.

118	7	3d. rose		£160	55·00

1867–8. *Wmk Crown CC. P* 14.

119	8	1d. blue		10·00	4·50
120	7	3d. pale rose (1867)		42·00	20·00
		a. Deep rose		45·00	25·00

(**New Currency.** 100 cents = 1 rupee)

9

10

11

12

13

14

15   16   17

18   19

1872–80. *Wmk Crown CC. (a) P* 14.

121	9	2 c. pale brown (*shades*)	..	5·50	1·40
122	10	4 c. grey	..	26·00	1·00
123		4 c. rosy-mauve (1880)	..	45·00	1·50
124	11	8 c. orange-yellow	..	38·00	4·00
		a. Yellow	..	23·00	4·25
126	12	16 c. pale violet	..	50·00	2·75
127	13	24 c. green	..	28·00	2·00
128	14	32 c. slate (1877)	..	90·00	13·00
129	15	36 c. blue	..	75·00	14·00
130	16	48 c. rose	..	60·00	15·00
131	17	64 c. red-brown (1877)	..	£170	55·00
132	18	96 c. drab	..	£150	26·00
121/132		.. .. ..	*Set of* 11	£650	£110

(b) P 14 × 12½

133	9	2 c. brown	£350	48·00
134	10	4 c. grey	£425	23·00
135	11	8 c. orange-yellow	£300	35·00

(c) P 12½

136	9	2 c. brown	£1600	90·00
137	10	4 c. grey	£800	£150

(d) P 12½ × 14

138	19	2 r. 50 c. dull-rose (1879)	£425	£275

(e) Prepared for use and sent out to Ceylon, but not issued unsurcharged

139	14	32 c. slate (*p* 14 × 12½)	..	£700
140	17	64 c. red-brown (*p* 14 × 12½)	..	£900
141	19	2 r. 50, dull rose (*p* 12½)	..	£950

FORGERIES.—Beware of forged overprint and surcharge varieties on Victorian issues.

SIXTEEN

16

CENTS
(20)

1882 (Oct). *Nos. 127 and 131 surch as T 20 by Govt Printer.*

142	13	16 c. on 24 c. green	..	17·00	6·50
		a. Surch inverted	..		
143	17	20 c. on 64 c. red-brown	..	9·00	3·50
		a. Surch double	..		† £1100

1883–98. *Wmk Crown CA. (a) P* 14.

146	9	2 c. pale brown	..	38·00	1·50
147		2 c. dull green (1884) (Optd S. £150)	..	1·25	15
148	10	4 c. rosy mauve	..	1·40	30
149		4 c. rose (1884) (Optd S. £150)	..	3·00	10·00
150	11	8 c. orange	..	2·75	6·00
		a. Yellow (1898)	..	2·75	6·00
151	12	16 c. pale violet	..	£950	£140

(b) Trial perforation. P 12

151a	9	2 c. dull green	..	£1600
151b	10	4 c. rose	..	£1600
151c	13	24 c. brown-purple	..	£1700

(c) Prepared for use and sent out to Ceylon, but not issued unsurcharged. P 14

152	13	24 c. brown-purple (Optd S. £300)	..	£750

Although delivered in 1884 it is believed that the 4 c. rose, No. 149, was not used until the early 1890s.

Postage &

FIVE CENTS

Revenue
(21)

TEN CENTS
(22)

Twenty Cents
(23)

One Rupee Twelve Cents
(24)

1885. *T* 10/19 *surch locally as T* 21/24.

I. Wmk Crown CC. (a) P 14

153	21	5 c. on 16 c. pale violet	..	..	† £1500
154		5 c. on 24 c. green	..	£1100	90·00
155		5 c. on 32 c. slate	..	50·00	15·00
		a. Surch inverted	..	†	£750
		b. Dark grey	..	60·00	19·00
156		5 c. on 36 c. blue	..	95·00	8·00
		a. Surch inverted	..	†	£900
157		5 c. on 48 c. rose	..	£425	29·00
158		5 c. on 64 c. red-brown	..	50·00	4·50
		a. Surch double	..	†	£650
159		5 c. on 96 c. drab	..	£250	48·00
161	22	10 c. on 16 c. pale violet	..		
162		10 c. on 24 c. green	..	£275	70·00
163		10 c. on 36 c. blue	..	£300	£150
164		10 c. on 64 c. red-brown	..	£225	60·00
165		20 c. on 24 c. green	..	32·00	13·00
166	23	20 c. on 32 c. slate	..	25·00	21·00
		a. Dark grey	..	32·00	22·00
167		25 c. on 32 c. slate	..	9·50	4·25
		a. Dark grey	..	14·00	7·00
168		28 c. on 48 c. rose	..	27·00	5·00
		a. Surch double	..	†	£800
169	22	30 c. on 36 c. blue	..	8·50	7·50
		a. Surch inverted	..	£170	90·00
170		56 c. on 96 c. drab	..	13·00	9·50

(b) P 14 × 12½

172	21	5 c. on 32 c. slate	..	£170	32·00
173		5 c. on 64 c. red-brown	..	£180	26·00
174	22	10 c. on 64 c. red-brown	..	38·00	60·00
		a. Imperf between (vert pair)	..		£1700
175	24	1 r. 12 c. on 2 r. 50 c. dull rose (*p* 12½)	£250	65·00
176		1 r. 12 c. on 2 r. 50 c. dull rose (*p* 12½ × 14)	..	55·00	32·00

II. Wmk Crown CA. P 14

178	21	5 c. on 4 c. rose	..	11·00	3·25
		a. Surch inverted	..	†	£275
179		5 c. on 8 c. orange-yellow	..	32·00	6·00
		a. Surch double	..	†	£650
		b. Surch inverted	..	†	£750
180		5 c. on 16 c. pale violet	..	45·00	8·50
		a. Surch inverted	..	†	£150
182		5 c. on 24 c. brown-purple	..	—	£500
184	22	10 c. on 16 c. pale violet	..	£2500	£550
185		10 c. on 24 c. brown-purple	..	9·00	5·50
186		15 c. on 16 c. pale violet	..	7·50	5·50

Only seven examples, all used, are recorded of No. 153.

The 5 c. on 4 c. rosy mauve and 5 c. on 24 c. green, both watermarked Crown CA, previously catalogued are now considered to be forgeries.

REVENUE AND POSTAGE

5 CENTS	10 CENTS	1 R. 12 C.
(25)	(26)	(27)

1885. *T* 11/15, 18 *and* 19 *surch with T* 25/7 *by D.L.R. P* 14.

(a) Wmk Crown CA

187	25	5 c. on 8 c. lilac	..	6·50	80
188	26	10 c. on 24 c. brown-purple	..	8·50	4·50
189		15 c. on 16 c. orange-yellow	..	35·00	5·00
190		28 c. on 32 c. slate	..	12·00	2·50
191		30 c. on 36 c. olive-green	..	27·00	12·00
192		56 c. on 96 c. drab	..	32·00	7·00

(b) Wmk Crown CC (sideways)

193	27	1 r. 12 c. on 2 r. 50, dull rose	..	27·00	65·00
187/93			*Set of* 7	£130	85·00
187/93 Optd "Specimen"		..	*Set of* 7	£600	

28   29

1886. *Wmk Crown CA. P* 14.

195	28	5 c. dull purple	..	1·25	10
196	29	15 c. sage-green	..	2·50	75
197		15 c. olive-green	..	2·75	65
198		25 c. yellow-brown	..	1·50	1·00
		a. Value in yellow	..	85·00	65·00
199		28 c. slate	..	9·50	1·40
195, 197/9 Optd "Specimen"			*Set of* 4	£130	

Six plates were used for the 5 c., No. 195, between 1885 and 1901, each being replaced by its successor as it became worn. Examples from the worn plates show thicker lines in the background and masses of solid colour under the chin, in front of the throat, at the back of the neck and at the base.

30

1887. *Wmk Crown CC (sideways). White or blued paper. P* 14.

201	30	1 r. 12, dull rose (Optd S. £80)	..	17·00	15·00
		a. Wmk upright	..	27·00	38·00

TWO CENTS	Two	2 Cents
(31)	(32)	(33)

Two Cents	
	2 Cents
(34)	(35)

1888–90. *Nos.* 148/9 *surch with T* 31/5.

202	31	2 c. on 4 c. rosy mauve	..	90	40
		a. Surch inverted	..	11·00	12·00
		b. Surch double, one inverted	..	—	75·00
203		2 c. on 4 c. rose	..	60	30
		a. Surch inverted	..	11·00	12·00
		b. Surch double	..	—	85·00
204	32	2 (c.) on 4 c. rosy mauve	..	60	20
		a. Surch inverted	..	24·00	26·00
		b. Surch double	..	32·00	32·00
		c. Surch double, one inverted	..	28·00	26·00
205		2 (c.) on 4 c. rose	..	1·90	20
		a. Surch inverted	..	80·00	
		b. Surch double	..	32·00	35·00
		c. Surch double, one inverted	..	35·00	42·00
206	33	2 c. on 4 c. rosy mauve	..	32·00	25·00
		a. Surch inverted	..	—	30·00
		b. Surch double, one inverted	..	42·00	
207		2 c. on 4 c. rose	..	1·75	75
		a. Surch inverted	..	8·50	8·00
		b. Surch double	..	75·00	75·00
		c. Surch double, one inverted	..	8·00	8·00
208	34	2 c. on 4 c. rosy mauve	..	38·00	16·00
		a. Surch inverted	..	60·00	29·00
209		2 c. on 4 c. rose	..	1·75	80
		a. Surch inverted	..	11·00	5·50
		b. Surch double	..	30·00	35·00
		c. Surch double, one inverted	..	11·00	5·50
210	35	2 c. on 4 c. rosy mauve	..	32·00	21·00
		a. Surch inverted	..	48·00	38·00
		b. Surch double, one inverted	..	48·00	50·00
		c. Surch double	..	—	85·00
		d. "s" of "Cents" inverted	..	—	£180
		e. As d. Whole surch inverted	..		
211		2 c. on 4 c. rose	..	4·00	60
		a. Surch inverted	..	12·00	5·50
		b. Surch double	..	45·00	38·00
		c. Surch double, one inverted	..	13·00	8·00
		d. "s" of "Cents" inverted	..	—	80·00
209, 211 Optd "Specimen"			*Set of* 2	60·00	

The 4 c. rose and the 4 c. rosy mauve are found surcharged "Postal Commission 3 (or 'Three') Cents". They denote the extra commission charged by the Post Office on postal orders which had not been cashed within three months of the date of issue. For a short time the Post Office did not object to the use of these stamps on letters.

POSTAGE

Five Cents

REVENUE
(36)

FIFTEEN CENTS
(37)

1890. *No.* 197 *surch with T* 36.

233		5 c. on 15 c. olive-green (Optd S. £30)	1·25	1·25
		a. Surch inverted	22·00	24·00
		b. Surch double	85·00	80·00
		c. "Flve" for "Five"	85·00	75·00
		d. Variety as c, inverted	—	£700
		e. "REVENUE" omitted	85·00	75·00
		f. Inverted "s" in "Cents"	22·00	27·00
		g. Variety as f, and whole surch inverted	£700	
		h. "REVENUE" omitted and inverted "s" in "Cents"	£325	
		i. "POSTAGE" spaced between "T" and "A"	38·00	45·00

1891. *Nos.* 198/9 *surch with T* 37.

239	29	15 c. on 25 c. yellow-brown	6·00	9·00
240		15 c. on 28 c. slate	5·50	8·50

3 Cents
(38)

39

1892. *Nos.* 148/9 *and* 199 *surch with T* 38.

241	10	3 c. on 4 c. rosy mauve	50	1·75
242		3 c. on 4 c. rose (Optd S. £30)	1·10	5·50
243	29	3 c. on 28 c. slate	1·25	1·75
		a. Surch double	60·00	
241/3			*Set of* 3	2·50	8·00

1893–99. *Wmk Crown CA. P* 14.

245	39	3 c. terracotta and blue-green	1·40	45
246	10	4 c. carmine-rose (1898)	6·50	6·50
247	29	30 c. bright mauve and chestnut	3·75	1·60
		a. Bright violet and chestnut	3·75	1·60
249	19	2 r. 50, purple/red (1899)	21·00	42·00
245/9			*Set of* 4	29·00	45·00
245, 247/9 Optd "Specimen"			*Set of* 3	60·00	

Six Cents	2 R. 25 C.
(40)	(41)

1899. (*a*) No. 196 *surch with T* **40**.
250   29   6 c. on 15 c. sage-green   45   45

(*b*) *As No.* 138 *but colour changed and perf* 14, *surch as T* **41**.
254   19   1 r. 50 c. on 2 r. 50, slate   . .   20·00 38·00
255   2 r. 25 c. on 2 r. 50, yellow   . .   27·00 65·00
250/5 Optd "Specimen"   . .   . .   *Set of* 3 70·00

43

1899–1900. *Wmk Crown CA* (1 r. 50, 2 r. 25 *wmk Crown CC*). *P* 14.
256   9   2 c. pale orange-brown . .   . .   . .   1·00   30
257   39   3 c. deep green   . .   . .   . .   1·25   55
258   10   4 c. yellow   . .   . .   . .   1·25   2·25
259   46   6 c. rose and black   75   45
260   39   12 c. sage-green and rose   . .   2·75   5·50
261   29   15 c. blue   . .   . .   . .   4·50   1·25
262   39   75 c. black and red-brown   . .   4·25   4·25
263   43   1 r. 50, rose   . .   . .   . .   15·00 32·00
264   2 r. 25, dull blue   . .   . .   28·00 32·00
256/64   . .   . .   . .   *Set of* 9 50·00 70·00
256/64 Optd "Specimen"   . .   *Set of* 9 £130

44   45   46

47   48

1903 (29 May)–05.   *Wmk Crown CA. P* 14.
265   44   2 c. red-brown (21.7.03). .   . .   70   20
266   45   3 c. green (11.6.03)   80   70
267   4 c. orange-yellow and blue   . .   1·25   2·50
268   46   5 c. dull purple (2.7.03)   . .   1·50   30
269   47   6 c. carmine (5.11.03)   . .   4·00   1·25
270   45   12 c. sage-green and rosine (13.8.03)   . .   3·75   6·00
271   48   15 c. blue (2.7.03). .   . .   6·50   1·75
272   25 c. bistre (11.8.03)   . .   . .   4·00   7·00
273   30 c. dull violet and green   . .   3·25   4·00
274   45   75 c. dull blue and orange (31.3.05)   . .   2·75 16·00
275   48   1 r. 50, greyish slate (7.4.04)   . .   50·00 45·00
276   2 r. 25, brown and green (12.4.04)   . .   45·00 38·00
265/76   . .   . .   . .   *Set of* 12 £110 £110
265/76 Optd "Specimen"   . .   *Set of* 12 £140

1904 (13 Sept)–05.   *Wmk Mult Crown CA. Ordinary paper. P* 14.
277   44   2 c. red-brown (17.11.04)   . .   55   10
278   45   3 c. green (17.11.04)   75   15
279   4 c. orange and ultramarine   . .   50   50
280   46   5 c. dull purple (29.11.04)   . .   1·75   1·00
   a. Chalk-surfaced paper (5.10.05)   . .   2·00   80
281   47   6 c. carmine (11.10.04)   . .   1·10   15
282   45   12 c. sage-green and rosine (29.9.04)   . .   1·50   1·75
283   48   15 c. blue (1.12.04)   90   50
284   25 c. bistre (5.1.05)   . .   . .   6·00   3·75
285   30 c. violet and green (7.9.05)   . .   2·50   1·50
286   45   75 c. dull blue and orange (25.5.05)   . .   5·25   8·00
287   48   1 r. 50, purple (5.1.05)   . .   15·00 10·00
288   2 r. 25, brown and green (22.12.04)   . .   18·00 27·00
277/88   . .   . .   . .   *Set of* 12 48·00 48·00

50   51

1908. *Wmk Mult Crown CA. P* 14.
289   50   5 c. deep purple (26 May)   . .   . .   1·60   10
290   5 c. dull purple   . .   . .   2·25   30
291   51   6 c. carmine (6 June)   70   10
289, 291 Optd "Specimen"   . .   *Set of* 2 48·00

1910 (1 Aug)–11.   *Wmk Mult Crown CA. P* 14.
292   44   2 c. brown-orange (20.5.11)   . .   1·50   1·00
293   48   3 c. green (5.7.11)   . .   . .   1·00   75
294   10 c. sage-green and maroon   . .   1·50   90
295   25 c. grey   . .   . .   . .   2·50   70
296   50 c. chocolate   . .   . .   4·00   7·00
297   1 r. purple/*yellow*   . .   . .   7·50 10·00
298   2 r. red/*yellow*   . .   . .   15·00 27·00
299   5 r. black/*green*   . .   . .   35·00 65·00
300   10 r. black/*red*   . .   . .   65·00 £150
292/300   . .   . .   . .   *Set of* 9 £120 £225
292/300 Optd "Specimen"   . .   *Set of* 9 £180

52   53

(A)   (B)

Most values in Type **52** were produced by two printing operations, using "Key" and "Duty" plates. Differences in the two Dies of the Key plate are described in the introduction to this catalogue.
In the Ceylon series, however, the 1 c. and 5 c. values, together with later printings of the 3 c. and 6 c., were printed from special plates at one operation. These plates can be identified by the large "C" in the value tablet (see illustration A). Examples of these values from Key and Duty plates printing have value tablet as illustration B. The 3 c. and 5 c. stamps from the single plates *resemble* Die I, and the 1 c. and 6 c. Die II, although in the latter case the inner top corners of the side panels are square and not curved.

1912–25.   *Wmk Mult Crown CA. Chalk-surfaced paper* (30 c. to 1000 r.). *P* 14.

(*a*) *Printed from single plates. Value tablet as A*
301   52   1 c. brown   50   10
302   3 c. blue-green . .   . .   . .   2·25   45
303   5 c. purple   . .   . .   . .   4·50   2·25
304   5 c. bright magenta   70   50
   a. Wmk sideways   . .   . .   65·00
305   6 c. pale scarlet   . .   . .   8·50   85
306   6 c. carmine   . .   . .   9·00   1·25
   a. Wmk sideways   . .   . .   17·00 27·00

(*b*) *Printed from Key and Duty plates at two operations. Die I. 3 c. and 6 c. have value tablet as B*
307   52   2 c. brown-orange   40   30
308   2 c. deep orange-brown   . .   30   20
309   3 c. yellow-green . .   . .   5·50   2·10
310   3 c. deep green   . .   . .   3·25   90
311   6 c. scarlet   . .   . .   1·10   50
312   6 c. bright scarlet . .   . .   2·00   90
313   10 c. sage-green   . .   . .   2·75   1·75
314   10 c. deep sage-green   . .   4·25   2·25
315   15 c. ultramarine   . .   . .   1·50   1·25
316   15 c. deep bright blue   . .   2·75   1·75
317   25 c. yellow and blue   . .   1·75   1·75
318   25 c. orange and blue   . .   5·50   4·25
319   30 c. blue-green and violet   . .   4·00   2·25
320   30 c. yellow-green and violet   . .   6·00   3·00
   a. Wmk sideways   . .   . .   7·50
321   50 c. black and scarlet   . .   1·25   1·75
322   1 r. purple/*yellow*   . .   1·90   3·00
   a. White back (1914) (Optd S. £32)   1·40   3·00
   b. On lemon (1916) (Optd S. £32)   4·00   7·00
   c. On orange-buff   . .   22·00 30·00
   d. On pale yellow (Optd S. £32)   4·25   9·00
323   2 r. black and red/*yellow*   . .   3·25   8·00
   a. White back (1914)   . .   2·25   8·50
   b. On lemon (1915) (Optd S. £32)   18·00 27·00
   c. On orange-buff   . .   32·00 35·00
   d. On pale yellow   . .   32·00 35·00
324   5 r. black/*green*   . .   11·00 20·00
   a. White back (1914) (Optd S. £35)   11·00 25·00
   b. On blue-green, olive back (1921) (Optd S. £40)   14·00 23·00
   c. On emerald back (Die II) (1923) (Optd S. £50)   45·00 80·00
325   10 r. purple and black/*red*   . .   45·00 55·00
   a. Die II (1923)   . .   . .   55·00 85·00
326   20 r. black and red/*blue*   . .   70·00 65·00
327   53   50 r. dull purple (Optd S. £100)   . .   £300
   a. Break in scroll   . .   £500
   b. Broken crown and scroll   . .   £500
328   100 r. grey-black (Optd S. £250)   . .   £1300
   a. Break in scroll   . .   £1900
   b. Broken crown and scroll   . .   £1900
329   500 r. dull green (Optd S. £350)   . .   £3750
   a. Break in scroll   . .   £5500
   b. Broken crown and scroll   . .   £5500
329c   1000 r. purple/*red* (1925) (Optd S. £650) £14000
   cb. Broken crown and scroll   . .   £18000
301/25   . .   . .   . .   *Set of* 14 65·00 85·00
301/26 Optd "Specimen" . .   *Set of* 15 £190
For illustrations of the varieties on Nos. 327/9c see above No. 58 of Leeward Islands.

WAR STAMP   **WAR STAMP ONE CENT**

(54)   (55)

1918 (18 Nov).   (*a*) *Optd with T* **54**.
330   52   2 c. brown-orange   . .   20   40
   a. Opt inverted   . .   24·00 27·00
   b. Opt double   . .   24·00 27·00
   c. Opt omitted in pair with opt inverted   £300
331   3 c. blue-green (No. 302)   . .   15   20
332   3 c. yellow-green (No. 309)   . .   85   2·50
   a. Opt double   . .   42·00 45·00
333   5 c. purple   30   30
   a. Opt double   . .   24·00 27·00
334   5 c. bright magenta   . .   60   1·10
   a. Opt inverted   . .   24·00 27·00
   b. Opt double . .   . .   24·00 29·00

(*b*) *Surch with T* **55**
335   52   1 c. on 5 c. purple   . .   40   30
336   1 c. on 5 c. bright magenta   . .   50   20
330/1, 333, 335 Optd "Specimen"   *Set of* 4 85·00
Collectors are warned against forgeries of the errors in the "WAR STAMP" overprints.

1918. *Surch as T* **55**, *but without* "WAR STAMP".
337   52   1 c. on 5 c. purple (Optd S. £30) .   . .   15   25
337a   1 c. on 5 c. bright magenta   . .   65   1·40
   ab. Opt double   . .   . .   90·00

1921–33. *Wmk Mult Script CA. Chalk-surfaced paper* (30 c. to 100 r.). *P* 14.

A. **1921–27.**   *The original issue.*

(*a*) *Printed from single plates. Value tablet as A*
338   52   1 c. brown (1927)   35   35
339   3 c. green (5.5.22)   45   75
340   5 c. bright magenta (1927)   . .   20   15
341   6 c. carmine-red (3.8.21)   . .   45   75

(*b*) *Printed from Key and Duty plates at two operations. Die I* (10 c. to 30 c. *and* 1 r.) *or Die II* (2 c., 50 c., 2 r. *to* 20 r.)
342   52   2 c. brown-orange (1927)   . .   30   25
343   10 c. sage-green (16.9.21)   . .   60   40
344   15 c. ultramarine (30.5.22)   . .   2·50   5·00
345   20 c. bright blue (1922)   . .   2·50   3·75
346   25 c. yellow and blue (17.10.21)   . .   80   1·25
347   30 c. yellow-green and violet (15.3.22)   1·40   2·50
348   50 c. black and scarlet (1922)   . .   1·00   80
349   1 r. purple/*pale yellow* (1923)   . .   12·00 18·00
350   2 r. black and red/*pale yellow* (1923)   3·50   6·50
351   5 r. black/*emerald* (1925)   . .   16·00 32·00
352   20 r. black and red/*blue* (1924)   . .   70·00 70·00
353   53   50 r. dull purple (1924) (Optd S. £100)   £325
   a. Break in scroll £550
   b. Broken crown and scroll   . .   £550
354   100 r. grey-black (1924) (Optd S. £250)   £1400
   a. Break in scroll £1900
   b. Broken crown and scroll   . .   £1900
338/51   . .   . .   . .   *Set of* 14 35·00 65·00
338/52 Optd "Specimen" . .   *Set of* 15 £190

B. **1922–27.**   *New values and colour changed.*

(*a*) *Printed from single plates. Value tablet as A*
355   52   3 c. slate-grey (1923)   20   20
   a. Wmk sideways £375
356   6 c. bright violet   20   15

(*b*) *Printed from Key and Duty plates at two operations. Die I* (12 c., 15 c.) *or Die II* (9 c.)
357   52   9 c. red/*yellow* (1926)   40   35
358   12 c. rose-scarlet (1924)   . .   2·75   4·25
359   15 c. green/*pale yellow* (1923)   . .   1·25   1·25
360   53   100 r. dull purple and blue (24.10.27) (Optd S. £250)   . .   £1300
   a. Break in scroll £1800
   b. Broken scroll and crown   . .   £1800
355/9 Optd "Specimen" . .   *Set of* 5 £120

C. **1924–25.**   *Key and Duty plates. Change to Die II.*
360c   52   10 c. sage-green   55   60
360d   12 c. rose-scarlet   80   1·50
360e   15 c. green/*pale yellow* . .   . .   1·25   1·25
360f   20 c. bright blue   70   45
360g   25 c. yellow and blue   . .   2·00   1·50
360h   30 c. yellow-green and violet   . .   1·60   1·25
360i   1 r. purple/*pale yellow*   . .   6·50 15·00
360c/i   . .   . .   . .   *Set of* 7 12·00 19·00

D. **1933** (Dec).   *Key and Duty plates. Reappearance of Die I* (Key Plate 23).
360j   52   50 c. black and scarlet   . .   . .   42·00 70·00
For illustrations of the varieties on Nos. 353/4 and 360 see above No. 58 of Leeward Islands.

2 Cents.

(56)   57

(Surch at Ceylon Govt Printing Works)

1926 (27 Nov).   *Surch as T* **56**.
361   52   2 c. on 3 c. slate-grey   70   1·00
   a. Surch double   . .   . .   65·00
   b. Bar omitted . .   . .   55·00 65·00
362   5 c. on 6 c. bright violet. .   . .   50   40
361/2 Optd "Specimen"   . .   *Set of* 2 50·00
No. 361b comes from the bottom horizontal row of the sheet which was often partially obscured by the selvedge during surcharging.

1927 (27 Nov)–29.   *Wmk Mult Script CA. Chalk-surfaced paper. P* 14.
363   57   1 r. dull and bright purple (1928)   . .   1·75   1·25
364   2 r. green and carmine (1929) . .   3·75   2·75
365   5 r. green and dull purple (1928)   . .   12·00 17·00
366   10 r. green and brown-orange   . .   28·00 70·00
367   20 r. dull purple and blue   . .   65·00 £150
363/7   . .   . .   . .   *Set of* 5 £100 £200
363/7 Optd "Specimen"   . .   *Set of* 5 £130
No. 364. Collectors are warned against faked 2 r. stamps, showing what purports to be a double centre.

NEW INFORMATION

The editor is always interested to correspond with people who have new information that will improve or correct the Catalogue.

58 Tapping Rubber   **60** Adam's Peak

(Recess D.L.R. (2, 3, 20, 50 c.), B.W. (others))

1935 (1 May)–36. *T* **58**, **60** *and similar designs. Wmk Mult Script CA (sideways on 10, 15, 25, 30 c. and 1 r.). Various perfs.*

368	2 c. black and carmine (*p* 12 × 13)	..	30	40
	a. Perf 14	..	8·00	40
369	3 c. blk & ol-green (*p* 13 × 12) (1.10.35)		35	40
	a. Perf 14	..	21·00	35
370	6 c. black & blue (*p* 11 × 11½) (1.1.36)		30	30
371	9 c. green & orange (*p* 11 × 11½) (1.1.36)		80	50
372	10 c. black & purple (*p* 11½ × 11) (1.6.35)		1·25	1·10
373	15 c. red-brown and green (*p* 11½ × 11)		1·00	50
374	20 c. black & grey-blue (*p* 12 × 13) (1.1.36)		1·75	1·75
375	25 c. deep blue & chocolate (*p* 11½ × 11)		1·40	1·00
376	30 c. carm & green (*p* 11½ × 11) (1.8.35)		3·00	1·25
377	50 c. black and mauve (*p* 14) (1.1.36)		5·50	60
378	1 r. vio-bl & chocolate (*p* 11½ × 11) (1.7.35)		8·50	7·50
368/78		*Set of* 11	22·00	14·00
368/78 Perf "Specimen"		*Set of* 11	£130	

Designs: *Vert*—6 c. Colombo Harbour; 9 c. Plucking tea; 20 c. Coconut Palms. *Horiz*—10 c. Hill paddy (rice); 15 c. River scene; 25 c. Temple of the Tooth, Kandy; 30 c. Ancient irrigation tank; 50 c. Wild elephants; 1 r. Trincomalee.

1935 (6 May). *Silver Jubilee. As Nos.* 114/17 *of Jamaica, but ptd by D.L.R. P* 13½ × 14.

379	6 c. ultramarine and grey	..	45	30
	g. Dot to left of chapel	..	27·00	
	h. Dot by flagstaff	..	27·00	
	i. Dash by turret	..	32·00	
380	9 c. green and indigo	..	70	50
	g. Dot to left of chapel	..	45·00	
	h. Dot by flagstaff	..	45·00	
381	20 c. brown and deep blue	..	4·25	1·75
	f. Horiz line from turret	..	90·00	
	g. Dot to left of chapel	..	90·00	
382	50 c. slate and purple	..	5·25	4·00
	h. Dot by flagstaff	..	£120	
379/82		*Set of* 4	9·50	6·00
379/82 Perf "Specimen"		*Set of* 4	80·00	

For illustrations of plate varieties, see Omnibus section following Zimbabwe.

1937 (12 May). *Coronation. As Nos.* 118/20 *of Jamaica, but ptd by B.W. & Co. P* 11 × 11½.

383	6 c. carmine	..	65	15
384	9 c. green	..	2·25	1·75
385	20 c. blue	..	3·25	3·25
383/5		*Set of* 3	5·50	4·75
383/5 Perf "Specimen"		*Set of* 3	55·00	

69 Tapping Rubber   **70** Sigiriya (Lion Rock)

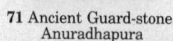

71 Ancient Guard-stone,   **72** King George VI
Anuradhapura

COCONUT PALMS

Apostrophe flaw (Frame P1 1 R. 6/6) (ptg of 1 Jan 1943 only)

(Recess B.W. (stamps perf 11 × 11½ or 11½ × 11), D.L.R. (all others) T **72** typo D.L.R.)

1938–49. *T* **69/72** *and designs as* 1935–36, *but with portrait of King George VI instead of King George V,* "POSTAGE & REVENUE" *omitted and some redrawn. Wmk Mult Script CA (sideways on 10, 15, 25, 30 c. and 1 r.). Chalk-surfaced paper (5 r.). Various perfs.*

386	69	2 c. blk & carm (*p* 11½×13) (25.4.38)		7·00	90
		a. Perf 13½×13 (1938)	..	75·00	1·75
		b. Perf 13½ (25.4.38)	..	30	10
		c. Perf 11×11½ (17.2.44)	..	40	50
		d. Perf 12 (22.4.49)	..	55	1·75
387	60	3 c. black & dp blue-green (*p* 13×11½) (21.3.38)	..	8·00	30
		a. Perf 13×13½ (1938)	..	£200	5·50
		b. Perf 13½ (21.3.38)	..	1·50	10
		c. Perf 14 (7.41)	..	80·00	95
		d. Perf 11½×11 (14.5.42)	..	50	10
		e. Perf 12 (14.1.46)	..	20	15
387*f*		5 c. sage-grn & orge (*p* 13½) (1.1.43)		20	10
		fa. Apostrophe flaw	..	28·00	
		g. Perf 12 (1947)	..	60	30
388		6 c. black and blue (*p* 11×11½) (1.1.38)		30	10
389	70	10 c. blk & light bl (*p* 11½×11) (1.2.38)		80	10
		a. Wmk upright (1.6.44)	..	1·50	30
390		15 c. grn & red-brn (*p* 11½×11) (1.1.38)		80	10
		a. Wmk upright (23.7.45)	..	1·25	40
391		20 c. blk & grey-bl (*p* 11½×11) (15.1.38)		2·25	10
392		25 c. dp bl & choc (*p* 11½×11) (15.1.38)		2·25	30
		a. Wmk upright (1944)	..	1·50	10
393		30 c. carm & grn (*p* 11½×11) (1.2.38)		8·50	75
		a. Wmk upright (16.4.45)	..	8·00	2·00
394		50 c. blk & mve (*p* 13×11½) (25.4.38)		£150	42·00
		a. Perf 13×13½ (1938)	..	£300	2·50
		b. Perf 13½ (25.4.38)	..	10·00	20
		c. Perf 14 (4.42)	..	85·00	25·00
		d. Perf 11½×11 (14.5.42)	..	2·50	1·75
		e. Perf 12 (14.1.46)	..	2·25	20
395		1 r. blue-violet & chocolate (*p* 11½×11) (1.2.38)	..	9·50	35
		a. Wmk upright (1944)	..	9·50	80
396	71	2 r. blk and carm (*p* 11×11½) (1.2.38)		5·00	1·25
396*a*		2 r. blk & vio (*p* 11×11½) (15.3.47)		1·25	85
397	72	5 r. green and purple (*p* 14) (10.10.38)		28·00	3·50
		a. Ordinary paper. *Green and pale purple* (19.2.43)	..	11·00	2·00
386/97*a* (*cheapest*)			*Set of* 14	38·00	5·25
386/97 Perf "Specimen"			*Set of* 14	£275	

Designs: *Vert*—5 c. Coconut Palms; 6 c. Colombo Harbour; 20 c. Plucking tea. *Horiz*—15 c. River scene; 25 c. Temple of the Tooth, Kandy; 30 c. Ancient irrigation tank; 50 c. Wild elephants; 1 r. Trincomalee.

3 CENTS

=   ☰

(73)   (74)

1940–41. *Nos.* **388** *and* **391** *surch.*

398	73	3 c. on 6 c. (10.5.41)	10	10
399	74	3 c. on 20 c. (5.11.40)	1·00	70

1946 (10 Dec). *Victory. As Nos.* 141/2 *of Jamaica.*

400	6 c. blue	..	10	10
401	15 c. brown	..	10	30
400/1 Perf "Specimen"		*Set of* 2	48·00	

75 Parliament Building   **76** Adam's Peak

(Des R. Tenison and M. S. V. Rodrigo. Recess B.W.)

1947 (25 Nov). *Inauguration of New Constitution. T* **75/6** *and similar designs. Wmk Mult Script CA. P* 11 × 12 (*horiz*) *or* 12 × 11 (*vert*).

402	6 c. black and blue	..	10	15
403	10 c. black, orange and carmine	..	10	20
404	15 c. green and purple	..	10	30
405	25 c. ochre and emerald-green	..	10	15
402/5		*Set of* 4	35	70
402/5 Perf "Specimen"		*Set of* 4	80·00	

Designs: *Horiz*—15 c. Temple of the Tooth. *Vert*—25 c. Anuradhapura.

DOMINION

79 Lion Flag of   **80** D. S. Senanayake
Dominion

---

81 Lotus Flowers and Sinhalese Letters "Sri"

(Recess (flag typo) B.W.)

1949 (4 Feb–5 Apr). *First Anniv of Independence. (a) Wmk Mult Script CA (sideways on* 4 *c.). P* 12½×12 (4 *c.*) *or* 12×12½ (5 *c.*).

406	79	4 c. yellow, carmine and brown	..	10	20
407	80	5 c. brown and green	..	10	10

(*b*) *W* **81** (*sideways on* 15 *c.*). *P* 13 × 12½ (15 *c.*) *or* 12 × 12½ (25 *c.*) (5 April).

408	79	15 c. yellow, carmine and vermilion	..	25	15
409	80	25 c. brown and blue	..	15	10
406/9			*Set of* 4	40	55

The 15 c. is larger, measuring 28 × 12 mm.

82 Globe and Forms of Transport

83   **84**

(Recess D.L.R.)

1949 (10 Oct). *75th Anniv of Universal Postal Union. W* **81**. *P* 13 (25 *c.*) *or* 12 (*others*).

410	82	5 c. brown and bluish green	..	75	10
411	83	15 c. black and carmine	..	1·40	75
412	84	25 c. black and ultramarine	..	1·40	65
410/12			*Set of* 3	3·25	1·40

85 Kandyan   **88** Sigiriya
Dancer   (Lion Rock)

89 Octagon Library, Temple   **90** Ruins at Madirigiriya
of the Tooth

(Recess B.W.)

1950 (4 Feb). *T* **85**, **88/90** *and similar designs. W* **81**. *P* 11 × 11½ (75 *c.*), 11½ × 11 (1 *r.*), 12 × 12½ (*others*).

413	4 c. purple and scarlet	..	10	10
414	5 c. green	..	10	10
415	15 c. blue-green and violet	..	1·50	30
416	30 c. carmine and yellow	..	30	30
417	75 c. ultramarine and orange	..	75	10
418	1 r. deep blue and brown	..	1·50	10
413/18		*Set of* 6	3·75	75

Designs: *Vert* (as *T* **88**)—5 c. Kiri Vehera, Polonnaruwa; 15 c. Vesak Orchid.

For these values with redrawn inscriptions see Nos. 450/1, 454, 456, 460 and 462.

NEW INFORMATION

The editor is always interested to correspond with people who have new information that will improve or correct the Catalogue.

91 Sambars, Ruhuna National Park **92** Ancient Guard-stone, Anuradhapura **96** Star Orchid

97 Rubber Plantation **99** Tea Plantation

I. No. 424   II. No. 424a (Dot added)

(Photo Courvoisier)

1951 (1 Aug)–54. *T* **91/2, 96/7, 99** *and similar designs. No wmk.*
P 11½.

419	2 c. brown and blue-green (15.5.54) ..		10	30
420	3 c. black and slate-violet (15.5.54) ..		10	40
421	6 c. brown-black & yellow-green (15.5.54) ..		10	15
422	10 c. green and blue-grey ..		75	30
423	25 c. orange-brown & bright blue (15.3.54) ..		10	10
424	35 c. red and deep green (I) (1.2.52) ..		1·50	85
	a. Type II (1954) ..		3·75	50
425	40 c. deep brown (15.5.54) ..		2·00	50
426	50 c. indigo and slate-grey (15.3.54) ..		30	10
427	85 c. black and deep blue-green (15.5.54) ..		50	10
428	2 r. blue and deep brown (15.5.54) ..		4·50	50
429	5 r. brown and orange (15.3.54) ..		4·75	70
430	10 r. red-brown and buff (15.3.54) ..		15·00	4·50
419/30		*Set of 12*	26·00	7·50

Designs: *Vert* (*as T* **91**)—6 c. Harvesting rice; 10 c. Coconut trees;
25 c. Sigiriya fresco. (*As T* **99**)—5 r. Bas-relief, Anuradhapura;
10 r. Harvesting rice. *Horiz* (*as T* **97**)—50 c. Outrigger canoe;
(*as T* **99**)—2 r. River Gal Dam.
For these values with redrawn inscriptions see Nos. 448, etc.

103 Ceylon Mace and Symbols of Progress

(Photo Harrison)

1952 (23 Feb). *Colombo Plan Exhibition. Chalk-surfaced paper.*
W **81** (*sideways*). *P* 14½ × 14.

431	**103** 5 c. green		10	10
432	15 c. ultramarine		20	15

104 Queen Elizabeth II **105** Ceremonial Procession

(Recess B.W.)

1953 (2 June). *Coronation. W* **81**. *P* 12 × 13.

433	**104** 5 c. green		60	10

(Recess D.L.R.)

1954 (10 Apr). *Royal Visit. W* **81** (*sideways*). *P* 13 × 12½.

434	**105** 10 c. deep blue		15	10

106 King Coconuts **107** Farm Produce

(Photo Courvoisier)

1954 (1 Dec). *No wmk. P* 11½.

435	**106** 10 c. orange, bistre-brown and buff ..		10	10

For this design with redrawn inscription see No. 453.

(Photo Harrison)

1955 (10 Dec). *Royal Agricultural and Food Exhibition. W* **81**
(*sideways*). *P* 14 × 14½.

436	**107** 10 c. brown and orange		10	10

108 Sir John Kotelawala and House of Representatives

(Photo Courvoisier)

1956 (26 Mar). *Prime Minister's 25 Years of Public Service.*
P 11½.

437	**108** 10 c. deep bluish green		10	10

109 Arrival of Vijaya in Ceylon **110** Lampstand and Dharmachakra

111 Hand of Peace and Dharmachakra **112** Dharmachakra encircling the Globe

(Photo Courvoisier)

1956. *Buddha Jayanti. P* 11½.

438	**109** 3 c. blue and brownish grey (23 May) ..	20	15
439	**110** 4 c. + 2 c. grnish yell & dp bl (10 May)	20	45
440	**111** 10 c. + 5 c. carm, yellow & grey (10 May)	20	40
441	**112** 15 c. bright blue (23 May)	20	10
438/41		*Set of 4*	70	1·00

113 Mail Transport **114** Stamp of 1857

(Photo Enschedé (4 c., 10 c.), Courvoisier (others))

1957 (1 Apr). *Centenary of First Ceylon Postage Stamp.*
P 12½ × 13 (4 c., 10 c.) *or* 11½ (*others*).

442	**113** 4 c. orange-red and deep bluish green	40	30
443	10 c. vermilion and blue ..	40	10
444	**114** 35 c. brown, yellow and blue ..	30	20
445	85 c. brown, yellow and grey-green ..	70	95
442/5	..	*Set of 4*	1·60	1·40

(115)   (116)   **117** Kandyan Dancer

1958 (15 Jan). *Nos. 439/40 with premium obliterated as T* **115**
(4 c.) *or T* **116** (10 c.).

446	**110** 4 c. greenish yellow and deep blue ..		10	10
	a. Opt inverted		8·00	
	b. Opt double		10·00	
447	**111** 10 c. carmine, yellow and grey ..		10	10
	a. Opt inverted		13·00	15·00

The 4 c. exists with opt misplaced to right so that some stamps
show the vertical bar on the left (*Price* £18 *un.*).

(Recess B.W. (4 c., 5 c., 15 c., 30 c., 75 c., 1 r.). Photo Courvoisier
(others))

1958 (14 May)–62. *As earlier types, but inscriptions redrawn*
as in T **117**. *W* **81** (4, 5, 15, 30, 75 c., 1 r.) *or no wmk* (*others*).
P 11×11½ (75 c.), 11½×11 (1 r.), 12×12½ (4, 5, 15 , 30 c.), *or*
11½ (*others*).

448	**91** 2 c. brown and blue-green ..		10	30
449	**92** 3 c. black and slate-violet ..		10	45
450	**117** 4 c. purple and scarlet ..		10	10
451	– 5 c. green (1.10.58) ..		10	10
	a. *Yellow-green* (13.6.61) ..		40	10
	b. *Deep green* (19.6.62) ..		40	10
452	– 6 c. brown-black and yellow-green ..		10	45

453	**106** 10 c. orge, bistre-brown & buff (1.10.58)	10	10
454	– 15 c. blue-green and violet (1.10.58) ..	2·75	60
455	– 25 c. orange-brown and bright blue	10	10
456	**88** 30 c. carmine and yellow (1.5.59)	15	60
457	**96** 35 c. red and deep green (II) (15.7.58)	4·00	15
459	– 50 c. indigo and slate-grey (15.7.58) ..	30	10
460	**89** 75 c. ultramarine and orange (1.5.59)	1·00	60
	a. *Ultramarine & brown-orge* (3.4.62)	1·00	50
461	**99** 85 c. black and deep blue-green (1.5.59)	3·75	2·50
462	**90** 1 r. deep blue and brown (1.10.58) ..	40	10
463	– 2 r. blue and deep brown ..	75	10
464	– 5 r. brown and orange	1·25	10
465	– 10 r. red-brown and buff	4·00	70
448/65		*Set of 17*	17·00	6·00

Designs: *Vert* (as *T* **117**)—5 c. Kiri Vehera Polonnaruwa; 6 c.
Harvesting rice; 15 c. Vesak Orchid; 25 c. Sigiriya fresco. (as
T **99**)—5 r. Bas-relief, Anuradhapura; 10 r. Harvesting rice. *Horiz*
(as *T* **97**)—50 c. Outrigger canoe. (as *T* **99**)—2 r. River Gal Dam.

118 "Human Rights" **119** Portraits of Founders and University Buildings

(Photo Enschedé)

1958 (10 Dec). *Tenth Anniv of Declaration of Human Rights.*
P 13 × 12½.

466	**118** 10 c. vermilion and dull purple ..		10	10
467	85 c. vermilion and deep blue-green ..		30	45

(Photo Enschedé)

1959 (31 Dec). *Institution of Pirivena Universities. P* 13 × 12½.

468	**119** 10 c. red-orange and ultramarine ..		10	10

120 Uprooted Tree **121** S.W.R.D. Bandaranaike

(Des W. A. Ariyasena. Photo Courvoisier)

1960 (7 Apr). *World Refugee Year. P* 11½.

469	**120** 4 c. red-brown and gold.. ..		10	40
470	25 c. blackish violet and gold		10	15

(Photo Courvoisier)

1961 (8 Jan–15 June). *Prime Minister Bandaranaike Com-*
memoration. P 11½.

471	**121** 10 c. deep blue and greenish blue ..		10	10
	a. Portrait redrawn (15.6.61)* ..		10	10

*Earliest known postmark date.
No. 471a can be identified by Mr. Bandaranaike's dark hair at
temples.

122 Ceylon Scout Badge **123** Campaign Emblem

(Des W. A. Ariyasena. Photo Courvoisier)

1962 (26 Feb). *Golden Jubilee of Ceylon Boy Scouts Association.*
P 11½.

472	**122** 35 c. buff and blue		15	10

(Photo Harrison)

1962 (7 Apr). *Malaria Eradication. W* **81**. *P* 14½ × 14.

473	**123** 25 c. red-orange and sepia		10	10

124 "DH85 Leopard-Moth" and "Comet" Airliner **125** "Produce" and Campaign Emblem

(Photo Courvoisier)

1963 (28 Feb). *25th Anniv of Airmail. P* 11½.

474	**124** 50 c. black and light blue		20	40

(Photo Courvoisier)

1963 (21 Mar). *Freedom from Hunger. P* 11½.

475	**125** 5 c. vermilion and blue		30	75
476	25 c. brown and yellow-olive		1·25	30

(126) 127 "Rural Life"

1963 (1 June). *No.* 450 *surch with T* 126.
477 117 2 c. on 4 c. purple and scarlet .. 10 10
a. Surch inverted .. .. 16·00
b. Surch double .. .. 15·00

(Photo Harrison)

1963 (5 July). *Golden Jubilee of Ceylon Co-operative Movement* (1962). *W* 81. *P* 14 × 14½.
478 127 60 c. rose-red and black .. 15 30

128 S. W. R. D. Bandaranaike 129 Terrain, Elephant and Tree

(Recess Courvoisier)

1963 (26 Sept). *P* 11½.
479 128 10 c. light blue 10 10

(Photo Harrison)

1963 (9 Dec). *National Conservation Week. W* 81 (*sideways*). *P* 14 × 14½.
480 129 5 c. sepia and blue 30 30

130 S. W. R. D. Bandaranaike 131 Anagarika Dharmapala (Buddhist missionary)

(T 130/1. Photo Courvoisier)

1964 (1 July). *P* 11½.
481 130 10 c. deep violet-blue and greenish grey 10 10

1964 (16 Sept). *Birth Centenary of Anagarika Dharmapala* (*founder of Maha Bodhi Society*). *P* 11½.
482 131 25 c. sepia and olive-yellow 10 10

134 Southern Grackle 138 Ruins at Madirigiriya

135 D. S. Senanayake 136

146 Tea Plantation 149 Map of Ceylon

(Des A. Dharmasiri (5 r.); P. A. Miththapala (10 r.). Photo Courvoisier (10 c. (486), 20 c.), Harrison (10 c. (487), 60 c., 1 r., 5 r., 10 r.), D.L.R. (others incl sheet))

1964 (1 Oct)–**72.** T 134/6, 138, 146, 149 *and similar designs. No wmk* (*Nos.* 486, 489), *W* 81 (*others; sideways on Nos.* 487, 494, 499). *P* 11½ (*Nos.* 486, 489), 14½ × 14 (*No.* 494) *or* 14 (*others*).
485 134 5 c. multicoloured 60 80
486 135 10 c. myrtle-green (22.3.66) .. 10 10
487 136 10 c. myrtle-green (23.9.68) .. 10 10
a. Imperf (pair) .. 40·00
488 — 15 c. multicoloured (5.2.66) .. 90 30
489 138 20 c. brown-purple and buff .. 10 15
494 — 60 c. multicoloured (5.2.66) .. 1·25 70
a. Red omitted. . .. 30·00
b. Blue and green omitted* .. 30·00
495 — 75 c. multicoloured (5.2.66) .. 1·25 50
a. No wmk (8.6.72) .. .. 5·50 5·50
497 146 1 r. brown and bluish green .. 1·00 20
a. Brown omitted .. £110
b. Bluish green omitted .. £160
499 — 5 r. multicoloured (15.8.69) .. 2·00 2·00
500 149 10 r. multicoloured (1.10.69) .. 9·50 2·00
485/500 *Set of* 10 15·00 6·00
MS500a 148 × 174 mm. As Nos. 485, 488, 494 and 495. Imperf. .. .. 7·00 6·00
Designs: *Horiz* (as T 134)—15 c. Common Peafowl; 60 c. Ceylon Junglefowl; 75 c. Asian Black-headed Oriole. (*as T* 138)—5 r. Girls transplanting rice.
The 5 c., 75 c. and 1 r. exist with PVA gum as well as gum arabic.
In the miniature sheet the inscriptions on the 60 c. have been rearranged to conform with the style of the other values.
*Actually only the blue printing is omitted on this sheet, but where this was printed over the yellow to form the leaves it appeared as green.

150 Exhibition Buildings and Cogwheels 151 Trains of 1864 and 1964

(Photo State Printing Works, Budapest)

1964 (1 Dec). *Industrial Exhibition. T* 150 *and similar horiz design. No wmk. P* 11.
501 — 5 c. multicoloured 10 40
a. Pair. Nos. 501/2 .. 20 1·50
502 150 5 c. multicoloured 10 40
No. 501 is inscribed "INDUSTRIAL EXHIBITION" in Sinhala and Tamil, No. 502 in Sinhala and English. The stamps were issued together *se-tenant* in alternate vertical rows, producing horizontal pairs.

(Photo Harrison)

1964 (21 Dec). *Centenary of Ceylon Railways. T* 151 *and similar horiz design. W* 81 (*sideways*). *P* 14 × 14½.
503 — 60 c. blue, reddish purple & yellow-grn 1·50 30
a. Pair. Nos. 503/4 .. 3·00 3·50
504 151 60 c. blue, reddish purple & yellow-grn 1·50 30
No. 503 is inscribed "RAILWAY CENTENARY" in Sinhala and Tamil, No. 504 in Sinhala and English. The stamps were issued together *se-tenant* in alternate horizontal rows, producing vertical pairs.

152 I.T.U. Emblem and Symbols 153 I.C.Y. Emblem

(Photo Harrison)

1965 (17 May). *I.T.U. Centenary. W* 81 (*sideways*). *P* 14½.
505 152 2 c. bright blue and red 20 80
506 30 c. brown and red .. .. 1·90 45
a. Value omitted £100
No. 506a was caused by the misplacement of the red.

(Photo Courvoisier)

1965 (26 June). *International Co-operation Year. T* 153 *and similar horiz design. P* 11½.
507 3 c. deep blue and rose-carmine .. 30 75
508 50 c. black, rose-carmine and gold .. 2·00 50
No. 508 is similar to T 153 but has the multilingual inscription "CEYLON" rearranged.

154 Town Hall, Colombo (155)

(Photo Courvoisier)

1965 (29 Oct). *Centenary of Colombo Municipal Council. P* 11 × 11½.
509 154 25 c. myrtle-green and sepia .. 10 10

1965 (18 Dec). *No.* 481 *surch with T* 155.
510 130 5 c. on 10 c. dp vio-bl & greenish grey 10 20

---

157 Kandy and Council Crest 158 W.H.O. Building

(Photo Harrison)

1966 (15 June). *Kandy Municipal Council Centenary. W* 81. *P* 14 × 13½.
512 157 25 c. multicoloured 10 10

(Litho D.L.R.)

1966 (8 Oct). *Inauguration of W.H.O. Headquarters. Geneva. P* 14.
513 158 4 c. multicoloured .. .. 1·00 1·75
514 1 r. multicoloured .. .. 4·50 1·50

159 Rice Paddy and Map of Ceylon 160 Rice Paddy and Globe

(Photo Courvoisier)

1966 (25 Oct). *International Rice Year. P* 11½.
515 159 6 c. multicoloured 20 60
516 160 30 c. multicoloured 30 15

161 U.N.E.S.C.O. Emblem 162 Water-resources Map

(Litho State Ptg Wks, Vienna)

1966 (3 Nov). *20th Anniv of U.N.E.S.C.O. P* 12.
517 161 3 c. multicoloured 50 50
518 50 c. multicoloured .. .. 2·50 30

(Litho D.L.R.)

1966 (1 Dec). *International Hydrological Decade. P* 14.
519 162 2 c. orange-brown, greenish yellow & bl 15 85
520 2 r. orge-brn, grnish yell, bl & yell-grn 60 1·40

163 Devotees at Buddhist Temple 167 Galle Fort and Clock Tower

(Photo State Ptg Wks, Vienna)

1967 (2 Jan). *Poya Holiday System. T* 163 *and similar horiz designs. Multicoloured. P* 12.
521 5 c. Type 163 .. .. .. 10 30
522 20 c. Mihintale 10 10
523 35 c. Sacred Bo-tree, Anuradhapura .. 10 15
524 60 c. Adam's Peak 10 10
521/4 .. .. .. *Set of* 4 30 45

(Litho Rosenbaum Brothers, Vienna)

1967 (5 Jan). *Centenary of Galle Municipal Council. P* 13½.
525 167 25 c. multicoloured 30 20

168 Field Research

(Litho Rosenbaum Bros, Vienna)

1967 (1 Aug). *Centenary of Ceylon Tea Industry. T* 168 *and similar horiz designs. Multicoloured. P* 13½.
526 4 c. Type 168 .. .. 20 60
527 40 c. Tea-tasting equipment 65 60
528 50 c. Leaves and bud 65 30
529 1 r. Shipping tea .. .. 1·00 10
526/9 .. .. .. *Set of* 4 2·25 1·40

172 Elephant Ride

173 Ranger, Jubilee Emblem
and Flag

(Litho Rosenbaum Bros, Vienna)

1967 (15 Aug). *International Tourist Year. P* 13½.
530 **172** 45 c. multicoloured 90 40

1967 (16 Sept). *1st National Stamp Exhibition. No.* **MS500a**
optd "FIRST NATIONAL STAMP EXHIBITION 1967".
MS531 148 × 174 mm. Nos. 485, 488, 494/5. Imperf 4·00 4·75

(Litho D.L.R.)

1967 (19 Sept). *Golden Jubilee of Ceylon Girl Guides Association.*
P 12½ × 13.
532 **173** 3 c. multicoloured 10 10
533 25 c. multicoloured 25 10

174 Col. Olcott and Buddhist Flag

(Litho Rosenbaum Bros, Vienna)

1967 (8 Dec). *60th Death Anniv of Colonel H. S. Olcott (theoso-*
phist). P 13½.
534 **174** 15 c. multicoloured 20 20

175 Independence Hall

176 Lion Flag and Sceptre

(Photo Harrison)

1968 (2 Feb). *20th Anniv of Independence. W* 81 (*sideways*). *P* 14.
535 **175** 5 c. multicoloured 10 45
536 **176** 1 r. multicoloured 20 10

177 Sir D. B. Jayatilleke

178 Institute of Hygiene

(Litho D.L.R.)

1968 (14 Feb). *Birth Centenary of Sir Baron Jayatilleke (scholar*
and statesman). P 14.
537 **177** 25 c. yellow-brown and sepia .. 10 10

(Litho B.W.)

1968 (7 Apr). *20th Anniv of World Health Organization. W* 81.
P 12.
538 **178** 50 c. multicoloured 10 10

179 Aircraft over Terminal
Building

181 Open Koran and "1400"

(Des and litho B.W.)

1968 (5 Aug). *Opening of Colombo Airport. W* 81. *P* 13½.
539 **179** 60 c. grey-blue, chestnut, red and yellow 10 10

(Des M. I. M. Mohideen. Photo Harrison)

1968 (14 Oct). *1400th Anniv of the Holy Koran. W* 81. *P* 14.
541 **181** 25 c. multicoloured 10 10

COVER PRICES

Cover factors are quoted at the beginning of each
country for most issues to 1945. An explanation of
the system can be found on page x. The factors
quoted do not, however, apply to philatelic covers.

182 Human Rights Emblem

183 All Ceylon Buddhist Congress
Headquarters

(Photo Pakistan Security Printing Corp)

1968 (10 Dec). *Human Rights Year. P* 12½ × 13½.
542 **182** 2 c. multicoloured 10 15
543 20 c. multicoloured 10 10
544 40 c. multicoloured 10 10
545 2 r. multicoloured .. .. 45 2·50
542/5 .. .. *Set of 4* 55 2·50

(Des A. Dharmasiri. Litho Rosenbaum Bros, Vienna)

1968 (19 Dec). *Golden Jubilee of All Ceylon Buddhist Congress.*
P 13½.
546 **183** 5 c. multicoloured 10 40
A 50 c. value showing a footprint was prepared but its release
was stopped the day before it was due for issue. However, some are
known to have been released in error at rural offices (*Price* £15
mint).

184 E. W. Perera
(patriot)

185 Symbols of
Strength in Savings

(Photo Harrison)

1969 (17 Feb). *E. W. Perera Commemoration. W* 81. *P* 14 × 13½.
547 **184** 60 c. brown 10 10

(Des A. Dharmasiri. Photo Harrison)

1969 (20 Mar). *Silver Jubilee of National Savings Movement.*
W 81. *P* 14.
548 **185** 3 c. multicoloured .. 10 30

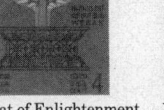

186 Seat of Enlightenment
under Sacred Bodhi Tree

187 Buduresmala (Six
fold Buddha-Rays)

(Des L. T. P. Manjusree. Litho D.L.R.)

1969 (10 Apr). *Vesak Day (inscr "Wesak"). W* 81 (*sideways*). *P* 15.
549 **186** 4 c. multicoloured 10 30
550 **187** 6 c. multicoloured 10 30
551 **186** 35 c. multicoloured 10 10
549/51 .. .. .. *Set of 3* 15 60
No. 549 exists with the gold apparently omitted. Normally the
gold appears (without a separate plate number) over an underlay
of olive-green on carmine. In one sheet we have seen, the gold only
shows as tiny specks under a strong magnifying glass and as there
may be intermediate stages of faint printing we do not list this.

188 A. E. Goonesinghe

189 I.L.O. Emblem

(Des and photo Harrison)

1969 (29 Apr). *Commemoration of Goonesinghe (founder of*
Labour Movement in Ceylon). W 81. *P* 14.
552 **188** 15 c. multicoloured 10 10

(Photo Harrison)

1969 (4 May). *50th Anniv of International Labour Organisation.*
W 81 (*sideways*). *P* 14.
553 **189** 5 c. black and turquoise-blue .. 10 10
554 25 c. black and carmine-red .. 10 10

190 Convocation Hall,
University of Ceylon

192 Uranium Atom

(Des Ahangama Edward (35 c.); L. D. P. Jayawardena (50 c.); A.
Dharmasiri (60 c.); 4 c. from photograph. Litho Rosenbaum Bros,
Vienna)

1969 (1 Aug). *Educational Centenary. T* 190, 192 *and similar*
multicoloured designs. P 13½.
555 4 c. Type **190** 10 60
556 35 c. Lamp of Learning, Globe and flags (*horiz*) 10 10
557 50 c. Type **192** 15 10
558 60 c. Symbols of Scientific education .. 15 10
555/8 .. .. .. *Set of 4* 40 80

194 Ath Pana
(Elephant Lamp)

195 Rock Fortress
of Sigiriya

(Des from photographs. Litho Rosenbaum Bros, Vienna)

1969 (1 Aug). *Archaeological Centenary. P* 13½.
559 **194** 6 c. multicoloured 15 60
560 **195** 1 r. multicoloured 25 10

196 Leopard

197 Emblem and Symbols

(Litho Rosenbaum Bros, Vienna)

1970 (11 May). *Wildlife Conservation. T* 196 *and similar horiz*
designs. Multicoloured. P 13½.
561 5 c. Water Buffalo 15 85
562 15 c. Slender Loris 50 30
a. Brown-black and orange-brown colours
omitted .. .. .. 50·00
563 50 c. Spotted Deer .. .. 70 1·25
a. Imperf (in vert pair with stamp perf 3
sides) £160
564 1 r. Type **196** .. .. 90 1·75
561/4 .. .. .. *Set of 4* 2·00 3·75
In No. 562a the sky is blue instead of violet and the animal is in
green and yellow only.

(Des A. Dharmasiri. Litho Rosenbaum Bros, Vienna)

1970 (17 June). *Asian Productivity Year. P* 13½.
565 **197** 60 c. multicoloured 10 10

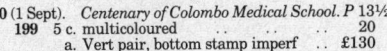

198 New U.P.U. H.Q.
Building

199 Oil Lamp and Caduceus

(Litho Rosenbaum Bros, Vienna)

1970 (14 Aug). *New U.P.U. Headquarters Building. P* 13½.
566 **198** 50 c. yellow-orange, black and new blue 20 10
a. New blue (Building) omitted .. 60·00
567 1 r. 10, vermilion, black and new blue 80 30

(Des A. Dharmasiri. Litho Rosenbaum Bros, Vienna)

1970 (1 Sept). *Centenary of Colombo Medical School. P* 13½.
568 **199** 5 c. multicoloured 20 50
a. Vert pair, bottom stamp imperf .. £130
569 45 c. multicoloured 30 50

200 Victory March and
S. W. R. D. Bandaranaike

201 U.N. Emblem and Dove
of Peace

(Des A. Dharmasiri. Litho D.L.R.)

1970 (25 Sept). *Definitive issue marking establishment of United Front Government.* P 13½.
570 **200** 10 c. multicoloured 10 10

(Des A. Dharmasiri. Photo Pakistan Security Printing Corp)

1970 (24 Oct). *25th Anniv of United Nations.* P 12½ × 13½.
571 **201** 2 r. multicoloured .. .. 1·25 2·00

202 Keppetipola Dissawa   **203** Ola Leaf Manuscript

(Des A. Dharmasiri. Litho Harrison)

1970 (26 Nov). *152nd Death Anniv of Keppetipola Dissawa (Kandyan patriot).* P 14 × 14½.
572 **202** 25 c. multicoloured 10 10

(Des A. Dharmasiri. Photo Pakistan Security Printing Corp)

1970 (21 Dec). *International Education Year.* P 13.
573 **203** 15 c. multicoloured 50 75

204 C. H. de Soysa   **205** D. E. H. Pedris (patriot)   **206** Lenin

(Des L. D. P. Jayawardena. Litho Pakistan Security Printing Corp)

1971 (3 Mar). *135th Birth Anniv of C. H. de Soysa (philanthropist).* P 13½.
574 **204** 20 c. multicoloured 15 40

(Des L. D. P. Jayawardena. Litho Harrison)

1971 (8 July). *D. E. H. Pedris Commemoration.* P 14 × 14½.
575 **205** 25 c. multicoloured 15 50

(Des L. D. P. Jayawardena. Litho Harrison)

1971 (31 Aug). *Lenin Commemoration.* P 14½.
576 **206** 40 c. multicoloured 15 40

207 Ananda Rajakaruna   **(208)**

(Des A. Dharmasiri (Nos. 577 and 579), P. A. Miththapala (Nos. 578 and 580), L. D. P. Jayawardena (No. 581). Litho Harrison)

1971 (29 Oct). *Poets and Philosophers.* T **207** *and similar vert designs.* P 14 × 13½.
577   5 c. royal blue 10 15
578   5 c. lake-brown 10 15
579   5 c. red-orange 10 15
580   5 c. deep slate-blue 10 15
581   5 c. brown 10 15
577/81 .. .. *Set of 5* 30 70
Portraits: No. 577, Type **207**; No. 578, Arumuga Navalar; No. 579, Rev. S. Mahinda; No. 580, Ananda Coomaraswamy; No. 581, Cumaratunga Munidasa.

1971 (26 Nov–2 Dec). *Nos. 549/50, 555, 559 and 570 surch as* T **208** *(obliterating shape differs).*
582 **186**   5 c. on 4 c. multicoloured .. .. 1·75 1·75
   a. Surch inverted .. .. 5·50
   b. Pair, one with "X" omitted .. 50·00
   c. Surch double, one inverted .. 8·50
   d. Ditto. Pair, one with "X" omitted 32·00
583 **190**   5 c. on 4 c. multicoloured 10 80
   a. Surch inverted .. .. 4·25
   b. Surch double, one inverted .. 8·00
584 **200** 15 c. on 10 c. multicoloured (2 Dec) .. 10 15
   a. Surch inverted .. .. 4·00
   b. Surch double .. .. 8·00
   c. Surch and dot transposed ..
   d. Surch at right, dot omitted ..
585 **187** 25 c. on 6 c. multicoloured 30 60
   a. Surch double, one inverted .. 16·00
   b. Surch inverted .. .. 13·00
586 **194** 25 c. on 6 c. multicoloured 30 60
   a. Surch inverted .. .. 4·00
582/6 .. .. *Set of 5* 2·25 3·50
Nos. 584c/d were caused by a misplacement of the surcharge on one sheet.

209 Colombo Plan Emblem and Ceylon   **210** Globe and CARE Package

(Des P. A. Miththapala. Litho Harrison)

1971 (28 Dec). *20th Anniv of Colombo Plan.* P 14 × 14½.
587 **209** 20 c. multicoloured 15 30

(Des A. Dharmasiri. Litho Harrison)

1971 (28 Dec). *20th Anniv of CARE (Co-operative for American Relief Everywhere).* P 14 × 13½.
588 **210** 50 c. new blue, lilac and violet 35 30

211 W.H.O. Emblem and Heart   **212** Map of Asia and U.N. Emblem

(Des A. Miththapala. Litho D.L.R.)

1972 (2 May). *World Health Day.* P 13 × 13½.
589 **211** 25 c. multicoloured 60 45

(Des L. D. P. Jayawardena. Litho B.W.)

1972 (2 May). *25th Anniv of ECAFE (Economic Commission for Asia and the Far East).* P 13.
590 **212** 85 c. multicoloured .. .. 2·25 2·25

SRI LANKA

REPUBLIC

Ceylon became the Republic of Sri Lanka on 22 May 1972.

208 National Flower and Mountain of the Illustrious Foot   **209** Map of World with Buddhist Flag

(Des L. D. P. Jayawardena. Litho D.L.R.)

1972 (22 May). *Inauguration of the Republic of Sri Lanka.* P 13.
591 **208** 15 c. multicoloured 30 30

(Des L. D. P. Jayawardena. Litho Harrison)

1972 (26 May). *Tenth Conference of the World Fellowship of Buddhists.* P 14 × 13.
592 **209** 5 c. multicoloured 10 40
   a. "1972" ptd double .. ..
   b. "1972" ptd double, one inverted .. 20·00
This stamp was scheduled for release in May 1971, and when finally released had the year "1972" additionally overprinted in red. Sheets are known without this overprint but their status has not been established.

210 Book Year Emblem   **211** Imperial Angelfish

(Des L. D. P. Jayawardena. Photo Pakistan Security Printing Corp)

1972 (8 Sept). *International Book Year.* P 13.
593 **210** 20 c. light yellow-orange and lake-brown 20 30

(Des G. D. Kariyawasam. Litho Rosenbaum Bros, Vienna)

1972 (12 Oct). T **211** *and similar horiz designs showing fish. Multicoloured.* P 13 × 13½.
594   2 c. Type **211** 10 60
   a. Plum colour omitted .. 3·00
595   3 c. Green Chromide 10 60
596 30 c. Skipjack .. .. 1·00 30
597   2 r. Black Ruby Barb .. .. 3·00 3·50
594/7 .. .. *Set of 4* 3·75 4·50
On No. 594a the stripes of the fish are in green instead of plum.

NEW INFORMATION

The editor is always interested to correspond with people who have new information that will improve or correct the Catalogue.

212 Memorial Hall

(Des R. B. Mawilmada. Litho D.L.R.)

1973 (17 May). *Opening of Bandaranaike Memorial Hall.* P 14.
598 **212** 15 c. light cobalt and deep grey-blue .. 30 30

213 King Vessantara giving away his Children   **214** Bandaranaike Memorial Conference Hall

(Des P. Wanigatunga. Litho D.L.R.)

1973 (3 Sept). *Rock and Temple Paintings.* T **213** *and similar vert designs. Multicoloured.* P 13½ × 14.
599 35 c. Type **213** 30 10
600 50 c. The Prince and the Grave-digger .. 35 10
601 90 c. Bearded old man 50 65
602   1 r. 55, Two female figures .. 65 1·25
599/602 .. .. *Set of 4* 1·60 1·90
MS603   115 × 141 mm. Nos. 599/602 .. 1·60 2·00

(Des and litho Harrison)

1974 (6 Sept). *20th Commonwealth Parliamentary Conference, Colombo.* P 14½.
604 **214** 85 c. multicoloured 30 30

215 Prime Minister Bandaranaike   **216** "UPU" and "100"

(Des and photo Harrison)

1974 (25 Sept). P 14½.
605 **215** 15 c. multicoloured 15 10
   a. Red (face value) omitted .. .. 3·00
   b. Pale blue (background) omitted .. 4·00
   c. Ultramarine (country inscr) omitted .. ..
   d. Imperf (pair) .. ..

(Des P. Jayatillake. Litho German Bank Note Ptg Co, Leipzig)

1974 (9 Oct). *Centenary of Universal Postal Union.* P 13½ × 13.
606 **216** 50 c. multicoloured 65 65

217 Sri Lanka Parliament Building   **218** Sir Ponnambalam Ramanathan (politician)

(Litho Toppan Printing Co, Japan)

1975 (1 Apr). *Inter-Parliamentary Meeting.* P 13.
607 **217** 1 r. multicoloured 30 50

(Des A. Rasiah. Litho Toppan Ptg Co, Japan)

1975 (4 Sep). *Ramanathan Commemoration.* P 13.
608 **218** 75 c. multicoloured 30 50

219 D. J. Wimalasurendra (engineer)   **220** Mrs. Bandaranaike, Map and Dove

(Des A. Dharmasiri. Litho Toppan Ptg Co, Japan)

1975 (17 Sept). *Wimalasurendra Commemoration.* P 13.
609 219 75 c. blue-black and new blue 30 50

(Des B. U. Ananda Somatilaka. Litho Toppan Ptg Co, Japan)

1975 (22 Dec). *International Women's Year.* P 13.
610 220 1 r. 15, multicoloured .. .. 1·25 1·25

221 Ma-ratmal

222 Mahaweli Dam

(Des and litho Toppan Ptg Co, Japan)

1976 (1 Jan). *Indigenous Flora.* T **221** *and similar vert designs. Multicoloured.* P 13.
611 25 c. Type **221** 10 10
    a. Imperf (pair) .. .. .. 55·00
612 50 c. Binara 10 10
613 75 c. Daffodil orchid 15 15
614 10 r. Diyapara .. .. .. 3·00 4·00
611/14 .. .. .. *Set of 4* 3·00 4·00
MS615 153 × 153 mm. Nos. 611/14 .. 6·00 7·50
    A used example of No. 613 has been seen with the yellow printing apparently omitted. This results in the leaves appearing blue instead of green.

(Des R. B. Mawilmada. Litho German Bank Note Ptg Co, Leipzig)

1976 (8 Jan). *Diversion of the Mahaweli River.* P 13 × 12½.
616 222 85 c. turquoise, violet-blue and azure .. 30 50

223 Dish Aerial

224 Conception of the Buddha

(Des P. A. Miththapala. Litho German Bank Note Ptg Co, Leipzig)

1976 (6 May). *Opening of Satellite Earth Station, Padukka.* P 14 × 13½.
617 223 1 r. multicoloured 65 75

(Des P. Wanigatunga. Litho Toppan Ptg Co, Japan)

1976 (7 May). *Vesak.* T **224** *and similar horiz designs showing paintings from the Dambava Temple. Multicoloured.* P 13.
618 5 c. Type **224** 10 10
619 10 c. King Suddhodana and the astrologers .. 10 10
620 1 r. 50, The astrologers being entertained .. 20 30
621 2 r. The Queen in a palanquin 25 35
622 2 r. 25, Royal procession 30 70
623 5 r. Birth of the Buddha .. .. 70 1·40
618/23 .. .. .. *Set of 6* 1·40 2·50
MS624 161 × 95 mm. Nos. 618/23 .. .. 6·50 8·50

225 Blue Sapphire

226 Prime Minister Mrs. S. Bandaranaike

(Des State Gem Corporation. Litho Toppan Ptg Co, Japan)

1976 (16 June). *Gems of Sri Lanka.* T **225** *and similar horiz designs. Multicoloured.* P 12 × 12½.
625 60 c. Type **225** .. .. .. 2·25 30
626 1 r. 15, Cat's Eye .. .. .. 3·25 1·25
627 2 r. Star sapphire .. .. .. 3·75 3·25
628 5 r. Ruby .. .. .. 5·50 6·00
625/8 .. .. .. *Set of 4* 13·50 9·75
MS629 152 × 152 mm. Nos. 625/8 .. .. 17·00 17·00

(Photo Harrison)

1976 (3 Aug). *Non-aligned Summit Conference, Colombo.* P 14 × 14½.
630 226 1 r. 15, multicoloured 25 20
631 2 r. multicoloured 40 35

227 Statue of Liberty

228 Bell, Early Telephone and Telephone Lines

(Des A. Harischandra. Litho German Bank Note Ptg Co, Leipzig)

1976 (29 Nov). *Bicentenary of American Revolution.* P 13½.
632 227 2 r. 25, cobalt and indigo 65 75

(Des A. Harischandra. Litho German Bank Note Ptg Co, Leipzig)

1976 (21 Dec). *Telephone Centenary.* P 13.
633 228 1 r. multicoloured 30 20

229 Maitreya (pre-carnate Buddha)

230 Kandyan Crown

(Des P. Wanigatunga. Litho German Bank Note Ptg Co, Leipzig)

1977 (1 Jan). *Centenary of Colombo Museum.* T **229** *and similar vert designs showing statues. Multicoloured.* P 12½.
634 50 c. Type **229** 15 15
635 1 r. Sundara Murti Swami (Tamil psalmist) 30 30
636 5 r. Tara (goddess) .. .. 1·10 2·00
634/6 .. .. .. *Set of 3* 1·40 2·25

(Des R. B. Mawilmada. Litho Toppan Ptg Co, Japan)

1977 (18 Jan). *Regalia of the Kings of Kandy.* T **230** *and similar vert design. Multicoloured.* P 13.
637 1 r. Type **230** 35 40
638 2 r. Throne and footstool .. .. 75 2·00

231 Sri Rahula Thero (poet)

232 Sir Ponnambalam Arunachalam (social reformer)

(Des S. Dissanayaka. Litho Toppan Ptg Co, Japan)

1977 (23 Feb). *Sri Rahula Commemoration.* P 13.
639 231 1 r. multicoloured 40 55

(Litho Toppan Ptg Co, Japan)

1977 (10 Mar). *Ponnambalam Arunachalam Commemoration.* P 13.
640 232 1 r. multicoloured 30 55

233 Brass Lamps

234 Siddi Lebbe (author and educationalist)

(Des A. Harischandra. Litho Toppan Ptg Co, Japan)

1977 (7 Apr). *Handicrafts.* T **233** *and similar vert designs. Multicoloured.* P 13.
641 20 c. Type **233** 15 15
642 25 c. Jewellery box 15 15
643 50 c. Caparisoned elephant 30 20
644 5 r. Mask .. .. .. 1·60 3·00
641/4 .. .. .. *Set of 4* 2·00 3·25
MS645 205 × 89 mm. Nos. 641/4 .. .. 3·25 3·75

(Des Sarasvati Rockwood. Litho Toppan Ptg Co, Japan)

1977 (11 June). *Siddi Lebbe Commemoration.* P 13½.
646 234 1 r. multicoloured 30 60

235 Girl Guide

236 Parliament Building and "Wheel of Life"

(Des and litho Asher & Co, Melbourne)

1977 (13 Dec). *60th Anniv of Sri Lanka Girl Guides Association.* P 14½ × 15.
647 235 75 c. multicoloured 85 30

(Des R. B. Mawilmada. Photo Enschedé)

1978 (4 Feb). *Election of New President.* P 12 × 12½.
648 236 15 c. gold, brt yellow-green & emerald 20 10
    No. 648 was re-issued on 7 September 1978, additionally dated "1978.09.07" to mark the Promulgation of the Constitution for the Democratic Socialist Republic of Sri Lanka. This re-issue was only available on First Day Covers (*Price on F.D.C.* £2).
    See also Nos. 680/c.

237 Youths Running

238 Prince Siddhartha's Renunciation

(Des M. Dissanayake. Litho Asher & Co, Melbourne)

1978 (27 Apr). *National Youth Service Council.* P 15 × 14½.
649 237 15 c. multicoloured 20 30

(Des P. Wanigatunga. Litho Metal Box Singapore Ltd)

1978 (16 May). *Vesak. Rock Carvings from Borobudur Temple.* T **238** *and similar horiz design in buff, brown and ultramarine.* P 13.
650 15 c. Type **238** 25 10
651 50 c. Prince Siddhartha shaving his hair .. 45 40

•05
(239)

240 Veera Puran Appu

1978 (18 May–20 Nov). *Nos. 559, 601/2, 605 and 648/9 surch as* T **239**.
652 5 c. on 90 c. Bearded old man (26.6) .. 20 50
    a. Surch inverted .. .. .. 12·00
    b. Surch double .. .. ..
653 10 c. on 35 c. Type **213** 20 50
    a. Surch inverted .. .. .. 12·00
654 25 c. on 15 c. Type **215** (20.11) .. 2·25 1·75
    a. Dot after "25" (R.3/4) .. 11·00
655 25 c. on 15 c. Type **236** (20.11) .. 2·25 1·75
    a. Surch inverted .. .. .. 10·00
    b. Surch quadruple .. .. ..
656 25 c. on 15 c. Type **237** (Blk & Pink) (20.11) 2·25 1·75
    a. Surch and obliterating square inverted 9·00
    ab. Surch only inverted .. .. 8·50
657 1 r. on 1 r. 55, Two female figures (17.11) 60 45
    a. Surch inverted .. .. ..
652/7 .. .. .. *Set of 6* 7·00 6·00
    No. 656 has the surcharge applied in black on a pink square, previously printed over the original face value.

(Des A. Dharmasiri. Litho Metal Box Singapore Ltd)

1978 (8 Aug). *130th Death Anniv of Veera Puran Appu (revolutionary).* P 13.
658 240 15 c. multicoloured 15 20

241 *Troides helena*

(242)

(Des G. Ratnavira. Litho J.W. or Questa (ptgs of 25 c. from 5 Jan 1990))

1978 (28 Nov). *Butterflies. T 241 and similar vert designs. Multicoloured. P 14.*

659	25 c. Type 241			15	10
660	50 c. *Cethosia nietneri*			40	10
661	5 r. *Kallima horsfieldi* (s sp *philarchus*)		1·00	1·00
662	10 r. *Papilio polymnestor*			1·25	1·50
659/62			Set of 4	2·50	2·40
MS663	203×147 mm. Nos. 659/62			6·50	7·00

1979 (22 Mar). *No. 486 surch with T 242 in black and turquoise-blue.*

664	15 c. on 10 c. myrtle-green			80	65
	a. Surch double			12·00	
	b. Turq-blue surch omitted.			20·00	

Type **242** shows only part of the turquoise-blue section of the overprint ("SRI LANKA"), which also includes a rectangle obliterating the original face value. The new value is printed on this rectangle in black.

243 Prince Danta and Princess Hema Mala bringing the Sacred Tooth Relic from Kalinga

244 Piyadasa Sirisena

(Des A. Dharmasiri. Litho J.W.)

1979 (3 May). *Vesak. Kelaniya Temple Paintings. T 243 and similar vert designs. Multicoloured. P 13 × 13½.*

665	25 c. Type 243			10	10
666	1 r. Theri Sanghamitta bringing the Bodhi Tree branch to Sri Lanka		15	15
667	10 r. King Kirti Sri Rajasinghe offering fan of authority to the Sangha Raja		95	1·10
665/7			Set of 3	1·00	1·10
MS668	120 × 80 mm. Nos. 665/7			1·40	2·00

(Des P. Jayatillake. Litho Toppan Ptg Co, Japan)

1979 (22 May). *Piyadasa Sirisena (writer) Commemoration. P 13.*

669	**244**	1 r. 25, multicoloured		20	20

245 Wrestlers

246 Dudley Senanayake

(Des R. B. Mawilmada. Litho Metal Box Singapore Ltd)

1979 (28 May). *Wood Carvings from Embekke Temple. T 245 and similar vert design. P 14.*

670	20 c. chocolate, ochre and deep green		95	1·50
671	50 c. agate, bistre-yellow and deep green		2·25	3·00

Design:—50 r. Dancer.

(Photo Heraclio Fournier)

1979 (19 June). *Dudley Senanayake (former Prime Minister) Commemoration. P 14.*

672	**246**	1 r. 25, bottle green		15	20

247 Mother with Child

248 Ceylon 1857 6d. Stamp and Sir Rowland Hill

(Des A. Dharmasiri and R. Mawilmada. Litho Metal Box Singapore Ltd)

1979 (31 July). *International Year of the Child. T 247 and similar horiz designs. Multicoloured. P 12½.*

673	5 c. Type 247			10	10
674	3 r. Superimposed heads of children of different races		30	70
675	5 r. Children playing.			40	80
673/5			Set of 3	65	1·40

(Des A. Dharmasiri. Litho Toppan Ptg Co, Japan)

1979 (27 Aug). *Death Centenary of Sir Rowland Hill. P 13.*

676	**248**	3 r. multicoloured		25	45

249 Conference Emblem and Parliament Building

250 Airline Emblem on Aircraft Tail-fin

(Des A. Harischandra. Litho Toppan Ptg Co, Japan)

1979 (28 Aug). *International Conference of Parliamentarians on Population and Development, Colombo. P 13.*

677	**249**	2 r. multicoloured		30	60

(Des S. Saparamadu. Litho Metal Box Singapore Ltd)

1979 (1 Sept). *Inauguration of "Airlanka" Airline. P 12½.*

678	**250**	3 r. black, deep blue-green & vermilion	30	65

251 Coconut Tree

252 Swami Vipulananda

(Des G. Wathuwalagedara. Litho Metal Box Singapore Ltd)

1979 (10 Sept). *10th Anniv of Asian and Pacific Coconut Community. P 14.*

679	**251**	2 r. multicoloured		40	60

1979 (10 Oct)—87. *Design as No. 648 but smaller, 20 × 24 mm. P 12½ × 13.*

680	**236**	25 c. gold, brt yellow-green & emerald	15	20
680a		50 c. gold, brt yell-grn & emer (6.6.81)	1·50	10
680b		60 c. gold, bright yellow-green and emerald (30.12.83)	3·00	1·25
680c		75 c. gold, bright yellow-green and emerald (1.7.87)	10	10
680/c			Set of 4	4·25	1·50

(Des R. B. Mawilmada. Litho Metal Box Singapore Ltd)

1979 (18 Nov). *Swami Vipulananda (philosopher) Commemoration. P 12½.*

681	**252**	1 r. 25, multicoloured		20	30

253 Inscription and Crescent

254 "The Great Teacher" (Institute emblem)

(Des Q. V. Saldin. Litho Metal Box Singapore Ltd)

1979 (22 Nov). *1500th Anniv of the Hegira (Mohammedan religion). P 12½.*

682	**253**	3 r. 75, black, deep green and blue-green	35	1·00

(Des H. P. Rupasinghe. Litho Metal Box Singapore Ltd)

1979 (29 Nov). *50th Anniv of Institute of Ayurveda (school of medicine). P 13 × 12½.*

683	**254**	15 c. multicoloured		30	40

255 Ceylon Blue Magpie

256 Rotary International Emblem and Map of Sri Lanka

(Des G. Ratnavira. Litho German Bank Note Ptg Co, Leipzig)

1979 (13 Dec). *Birds (1st series). T 255 and similar vert designs. Multicoloured. P 13½×14.*

684	10 c. Type 255			10	10
685	15 c. Ceylon Hanging Parrot ("Ceylon Lorikeet")		10	10
686	75 c. Ceylon Whistling Thrush ("Ceylon Arrenga")		15	15
687	1 r. Ceylon Spurfowl			15	15
688	5 r. Yellow-fronted Barbet		60	1·00
689	10 r. Yellow-tufted Bulbul		75	1·75
684/9			Set of 6	1·75	2·75
MS690	151×151 mm. Nos. 684/9			3·50	4·00

See also Nos. 827/31 and 985/9.

(Des A. Harischandra. Litho Metal Box Singapore Ltd)

1979 (27 Dec). *50th Anniv of Sri Lanka Rotary Movement and 75th Anniv of Rotary International. P 14.*

691	**256**	1 r. 50, multicoloured		30	55

257 A. Ratnayake

(258)

259 Tank and Stupa (symbols of Buddhist culture)

(Photo Govt Ptg Works, Rome)

1980 (7 Jan). *80th Birth Anniv of A. Ratnayake (politician). P 13½.*

692	**257**	1 r. 25, deep grey-green		20	30

1980 (17 Mar). *No. 680 surch with T 258.*

693	**236**	35 c. on 25 c. gold, brt yell-grn & emer	15	15
	a. Surch ".33" (R. 6/1)			15·00	
	b. Dot omitted (R. 7/6)			3·00	

(Des R. B. Mawilmada. Photo Govt Ptg Works, Rome)

1980 (25 Mar). *60th Anniv of All Ceylon Buddhist Congress. T 259 and similar horiz design showing symbols of Buddhist culture. Multicoloured. P 13½.*

694	10 c. Type 259			10	30
695	35 c. Bo-leaf wheel and fan		10	20

260 Colonel Olcott

261 Patachara's Journey through Forest

(Des S. Senevirante. Litho J.W.)

1980 (17 May). *Centenary of Arrival of Colonel Olcott (campaigner for Buddhism). P 14.*

696	**260**	2 r. multicoloured		50	60

(Des A. Dharmasiri. Litho Metal Box Singapore Ltd)

1980 (23 May). *Vesak. Details from Temple Paintings, Purvaramaya, Kataluwa. T 261 and similar horiz design. Multicoloured. P 13½.*

697	35 c. Type 261			15	15
698	1 r. 60, Patachara crossing river		40	80

262 George E. de Silva

263 Dalada Maligawa

(Des A. Rasiah. Litho German Bank Note Ptg Co, Leipzig)

1980 (8 June). *George E. de Silva (politician) Commemoration. P 13.*

699	**262**	1 r. 60, multicoloured		15	30

(Des A. Dharmasiri and R. B. Mawilmada. Litho Metal Box Singapore Ltd)

1980 (25 Aug). *U.N.E.S.C.O.—Sri Lanka Cultural Triangle Project. T 263 and similar horiz designs. P 13.*

700	35 c. claret			10	15
701	35 c. grey			10	15
702	35 c. rose-carmine			10	15
703	1 r. 60, olive-green			20	40
704	1 r. 60, slate-green			20	40
705	1 r. 60, sepia			20	40
700/5			Set of 6	70	1·50
MS706	215 × 115 mm. Nos. 700/5			70	1·50

Designs:—No. 701, Dambulla; No. 702, Alahana Pirivena; No. 703, Jetavanarama; No. 704, Abhayagiri; No. 705, Sigiri.

264 Co-operation Symbols

265 Lanka Mahila Samiti Emblem

(Des R. B. Mawilmada. Litho Metal Box Singapore Ltd)

1980 (1 Oct). *50th Anniv of Co-operative Department.* P 13.
707 **264** 20 c. multicoloured 10 20

(Des R. B. Mawilmada. Photo Govt Ptg Works, Rome)

1980 (7 Nov). *50th Anniv of Lanka Mahila Samiti (Rural Women's Movement).* P 14 × 13.
708 **265** 35 c. violet, rosine and yellow 10 20

266 The Holy Family   **267** Colombo Public Library

(Des L. Priyantha Silva. Litho Metal Box Singapore Ltd)

1980 (20 Nov). *Christmas. T 266 and similar vert design. Multi-coloured.* P 12 × 11½.
709 35 c. Type **266** 10 10
710 3 r. 75, The Three Wise Men 35 60
MS711 125 × 75 mm. Nos. 709/10. P 13½ .. 40 70

(Des P. Jayatillake. Litho Toppan Ptg Co, Japan)

1980 (17 Dec). *Opening of Colombo Public Library.* P 12 × 12½.
712 **267** 35 c. multicoloured 10 10

268 Flag of Walapane   **269** Fishing Cat
Disawa

(Des Mrs. J. L. M. Fernando. Litho Toppan Ptg Co, Japan)

1980 (18 Dec). *Ancient Flags. T 268 and similar horiz designs.* P 13.
713 10 c. black, green and brown-purple .. 10 10
714 25 c. black, greenish yellow and brown-purple 10 10
715 1 r. 60, black, greenish yellow & brn-purple 15 20
716 20 r. black, greenish yellow and brown-purple 1·25 2·50
713/16 *Set of 4* 1·40 2·50
MS717 215 × 140 mm. Nos. 713/16 .. .. 1·60 2·50
Designs:—25 c. Flag of the Gajanayaka, Huduhumpola, Kandy; 1 r. 60, Sinhala royal flag; 20 r. Sinhala royal flag, Ratnapura.

(Des L. Ranasinghe. Litho J.W.)

1981 (10 Feb). *Animals. T 269 and similar horiz designs. Multi-coloured.* P 13½ × 14.
718 2 r. 50 on 1 r. 60, Type **269** 15 15
719 3 r. on 1 r. 50, Golden Palm Civet .. 15 20
720 4 r. on 2 r. Indian Spotted Chevrotain .. 25 30
721 5 r. on 3 r. 75, Rusty-spotted Cat .. 35 45
718/21 *Set of 4* 80 1·00
MS722 165 × 89 mm. Nos. 718/21 .. .. 1·00 2·00
Nos. 718/21 are previously unissued stamps surcharged as in T 269.
For redrawn designs with revised face values see Nos. 780/3 and No. 1081.

270 Heads and Houses on   **271** Sri Lanka Light Infantry
Map of Sri Lanka   Regimental Badge

(Des D. Hemaratna. Litho Toppan Ptg Co, Japan)

1981 (2 Mar). *Population and Housing Census.* P 12½ × 12.
723 **270** 50 c. multicoloured 20 40

(Des D. Karunaratne. Litho Metal Box Singapore Ltd)

1981 (1 Apr). *Centenary of Sri Lanka Light Infantry.* P 12 × 11½.
724 **271** 2 r. multicoloured 65 40

ALTERED CATALOGUE NUMBERS

Any Catalogue numbers altered from the last edition are shown as a list in the introductory pages.

---

272 Panel from "The Great Stupa" in Honour of the Buddha, Sanci, India, 1st-century A.D.

273 St. John Baptist de la Salle

(Des P. Jayatillake. Litho German Bank Note Ptg Co, Leipzig)

1981 (5 May). *Vesak. T 272 and similar vert designs.* P 13 × 13½.
725 35 c. black, blackish green and sage-green .. 10 10
726 50 c. multicoloured 10 10
727 7 r. black and flesh .. .. .. 40 1·40
725/7 .. .. .. *Set of 3* 45 1·40
MS728 147 × 108 mm. Nos. 725/7. P 13 × 14. 2·50 2·00
Designs:—50 c. Silk banner representing a Bodhisattva from "Thousand Buddhas", Tun-Huang, Central Asia; 7 r. Bodhisattva from Fondukistan, Afghanistan.

(Des Grant Kenyon and Eckhardt Ltd. Litho State Printing Works, Moscow)

1981 (15 May). *300th Anniv of De La Salle Brothers (Religious Order of the Brothers of the Christian Schools).* P 12½ × 12.
729 **273** 2 r. brt rose, deep violet-blue & new blue 70 70

274 Rev. Polwatte   **275** Dr. Al-Haj T. B. Jayah
Sri Buddadatta

(Des G. Fernando. Litho Metal Box Singapore Ltd)

1981 (22 May). *National Heroes. T 274 and similar vert designs, each showing scholar, writer and Buddhist campaigner.* P 12.
730 50 c. bistre 30 55
731 50 c. brown-rose 30 55
732 50 c. deep mauve 30 55
730/2 .. .. .. *Set of 3* 80 1·50
Designs:—No. 731, Rev. Mohottiwatte Gunananda; No. 732, Dr. Gnanaprakasar.

(Des P. Jayatillake. Litho Metal Box Singapore Ltd)

1981 (31 May). *Dr. Al-Haj T. B. Jayah (statesman) Commemoration.* P 12.
733 **275** 50 c. grey-green 30 50

276 Dr. N. M. Perera   **277** Stylised Disabled Person and Globe

(Des P. Jayatillake. Litho Metal Box Singapore Ltd)

1981 (6 June). *Dr. N. M. Perera (campaigner for social reform) Commemoration.* P 12.
734 **276** 50 c. rose-red 30 50

(Des A. Adhikari. Litho State Printing Works, Moscow)

1981 (19 June). *International Year for Disabled Persons.* P 12 × 12½.
735 **277** 2 r. vermilion, black and grey .. 50 60

278 Hand placing Vote into Ballot Box

(Des J. Vincent (50 c.), R. Mawilmada (7 r.). Litho State Printing Works, Moscow)

1981 (7 July). *50th Anniv of Universal Franchise. T 278 and similar multicoloured design.* P 12½ × 12 (50 c.) or 12 × 12½ (7 r.)
736 50 c. Type **278** 15 10
737 7 r. Ballot box, and people forming map of Sri Lanka (vert) .. .. .. 1·00 90

---

279 T. W. Rhys Davids   **280** Federation Emblem
(founder)   and "25"

(Des P. Jayatillake. Litho State Printing Works, Moscow)

1981 (14 July). *Centenary of Pali Text Society.* P 12½ × 12.
738 **279** 35 c. stone, dp brown & orange-brown .. 50 20

(Des R. Mawilmada. Litho Secura, Singapore)

1981 (21 July). *25th Anniv of All Ceylon Buddhist Students' Federation.* P 13½.
739 **280** 2 r. black, greenish yellow & dull verm 60 30

281 "Plan for Happiness"   **282** Dove Symbol with Acupuncture Needle and "Yin-Yang" (Chinese universe duality emblem)

(Des D. Wijesinghe. Litho Secura, Singapore)

1981 (25 Sept). *Population and Family Planning.* P 13½ × 13.
740 **281** 50 c. multicoloured 50 30

(Des F. Perera. Litho State Printing Works, Moscow)

1981 (20 Oct). *World Acupuncture Congress.* P 12 × 12½.
741 **282** 2 r. black, yellow and red-orange .. 1·75 2·25

283 Union and Sri Lanka Flags   **284** "Conserve our Forests"

(Des and litho J.W.)

1981 (21 Oct). *Royal Visit.* P 14.
742 **283** 50 c. multicoloured 30 25
743 5 r. multicoloured .. .. .. 1·25 1·75
MS744 165 × 90 mm. Nos. 742/3 .. .. 2·00 2·50

(Des Ravi Advertising. Litho German Bank Note Co, Leipzig)

1981 (27 Nov). *Forest Conservation. T 284 and similar horiz designs.* P 13.
745 35 c. multicoloured 10 10
746 50 c. olive-brown and stone 10 15
747 5 r. multicoloured .. .. .. 1·25 2·00
745/7 .. .. .. *Set of 3* 1·25 2·00
MS748 180 × 90 mm. Nos. 745/7. P 14 × 13 1·75 2·50
Designs:—50 c. "Plant a tree"; 5 r. Jak (tree).

285 Sir James Peiris   **286** F. R. Senanayaka

(Des P. Jayatillake. Litho Metal Box Singapore Ltd)

1981 (20 Dec). *Birth Centenary of Sir James Peiris (politician).* P 12.
749 **285** 50 c. light brown 45 50

(Des M. Katugampola. Litho J.W.)

1982 (1 Jan). *Birth Centenary of F. R. Senanayaka (national hero).* P 14.
750 **286** 50 c. olive-brown 45 55

287 Philip Gunawardhane **288** Department of Inland Revenue Building, Colombo

(Des P. Jayatillake. Litho J.W.)

1982 (11 Jan). *10th Death Anniv of Philip Gunawardhane (politician). P* 14.
751 **287** 50 c. cerise 45 55

(Des S. Mallikerachchi. Litho J.W.)

1982 (9 Feb). *50th Anniv of Department of Inland Revenue. P* 14.
752 **288** 50 c. black, blue-black & reddish orange 45 55

289 Rupavahini Emblem **290** Cricketer and Ball

(Des G. Arthasad. Litho J.W.)

1982 (15 Feb). *Inauguration of Rupavahini (national television service). P* 14.
753 **289** 2 r. 50, lemon, purple-brown and grey 1·50 2·00

(Des R. Mawilmada. Litho J.W.)

1982 (17 Feb). *First Sri Lanka–England Cricket Test Match, Colombo. P* 14.
754 **290** 50 c. multicoloured .. .. 3·25 3·25

291 *Obsbeckia wightiana* **292** Mother breast-feeding Child

(Des P. Jayatillake. Litho Security Printers (M), Malaysia)

1982 (1 Apr). *Flowers. T* **291** *and similar horiz designs. Multicoloured. P* 12.
755 35 c. Type **291** 10 10
756 2 r. *Mesua nagassarium* 20 20
757 7 r. *Rhodomyrtus tomentosa* 50 90
758 20 r. *Phaius tancarvilleae* .. .. 1·40 2·50
755/8 .. .. *Set of* 4 2·00 3·25
MS759 180 × 110 mm. Nos. 755/8 .. .. 5·00 6·00

(Des A. Ratnapala. Litho Pakistan Security Printing Corp)

1982 (6 Apr). *Food and Nutrition Policy Planning. P* 13.
760 **292** 50 c. multicoloured 75 75

293 Conference Emblem **294** King Vessantara giving away magical, rain-making White Elephant

(Des M. Hussain. Litho J.W.)

1982 (21 Apr). *World Hindu Conference. P* 14.
761 **293** 50 c. multicoloured 75 75

(Des A. Dharmasiri. Litho J.W.)

1982 (23 Apr). *Vesak. Legend of Vessantara Jataka. Details of Cloth Painting from Arattana Rajamaha Vihara (temple), Hanguranketa, District of Nuwara Eliya. T* **294** *and similar horiz designs. Multicoloured. P* 14.
762 35 c. Type **294** 35 10
763 50 c. King Vessantara with family in Vanka-giri Forest 45 15
764 2 r. 50, Vessantara giving away his children as slaves .. .. .. 1·50 1·75

765 5 r. Vessantara and family returning to Jetut-tara in royal chariot .. .. 2·25 3·00
762/5 .. .. *Set of* 4 4·00 4·50
MS766 160 × 115 mm. Nos. 762/5 .. 5·00 5·00

295 Parliament Buildings, Sri Jayawardanapura **296** Dr. C. W. W. Kannangara

(Des M. Katugampola. Litho J.W.)

1982 (29 Apr). *Opening of Parliament Building Complex, Sri Jayawardanapura, Kotte. P* 14.
767 **295** 50 c. multicoloured 75 75

(Des M. Katugampola. Litho State Printing Works, Moscow)

1982 (22 May). *Dr. C. W. W. Kannangara ("Father of Free Education") Commemoration. P* 12 × 12½.
768 **296** 50 c. yellow-olive 75 75

297 Lord Baden-Powell **298** Dr. G. P. Malalasekara

(Des W. Rohana. Litho State Printing Works, Moscow)

1982 (24 May). *125th Birth Anniv of Lord Baden-Powell. P* 12½ × 12.
769 **297** 50 c. multicoloured .. .. 1·25 75

(Des A. Rasiah. Litho State Printing Works, Moscow)

1982 (26 May). *Dr. G. P. Malalasekara (founder of World Fellowship of Buddhists) Commemoration. P* 12 × 12½.
770 **298** 50 c. deep bluish green 75 75

299 Wheel encircling Globe **300** Wildlife

(Des A. Ratnapala. Litho State Printing Works, Moscow)

1982 (1 June). *World Buddhist Leaders Conference. P* 12½ × 12.
771 **299** 50 c. multicoloured 75 75

(Des U. Karunaratna. Litho State Printing Works, Moscow)

1982 (5 June). *World Environment Day. P* 12½ × 12.
772 **300** 50 c. multicoloured .. .. 1·25 75

301 Sir Waitialingam Duraiswamy

(Des A. Rasiah. Litho State Printing Works, Moscow)

1982 (14 June). *Sir Waitialingam Duraiswamy (statesman and educationalist) Commemoration. P* 12 × 12½.
773 **301** 50 c. blackish brown and brown 75 75

302 Y.M.C.A. Emblem

(Des R. Mawilmada. Litho State Printing Works, Moscow)

1982 (24 June). *Centenary of Colombo Y.M.C.A. P* 11½ × 11.
774 **302** 2 r. 50, multicoloured .. .. 2·25 2·50

303 Rev. Weliwita Sri Saranankara Sangharaja **304** Maharagama Sasana Sevaka Samithiya Emblem

(Des M. Katugampola. Litho State Printing Works, Moscow)

1982 (5 July). *Rev. Weliwita Sri Saranankara Sangharaja (Buddhist leader) Commemoration. P* 12 × 12½.
775 **303** 50 c. brown and yellow-orange .. 75 75

(Des A. Ratnapala. Litho Toppan Ptg Co, Japan)

1982 (4 Aug). *Silver Jubilee of Maharagama Sasana Sevaka Samithiya (Buddhist Social Reform Movement). P* 12 × 12½.
776 **304** 50 c. multicoloured 75 75

305 Dr. Robert Koch **306** Sir John Kotelawala

(Des W. Rohana. Litho Toppan Ptg Co, Japan)

1982 (21 Sept). *Centenary of Robert Koch's Discovery of Tubercle Bacillus. P* 12 × 12½.
777 **305** 50 c. multicoloured .. .. 1·75 85

(Des A. Rasiah. Litho State Printing Works, Moscow)

1982 (2 Oct). *2nd Death Anniv of Sir John Kotelawala. P* 12 × 12½.
778 **306** 50 c. deep olive 75 75

307 Eye Donation Society and Lions Club Emblems **308** 1859 4d. Dull Rose and 1948 15 c. Independence Commemorative

(Des Grant Kenyon and Eckhardt Ltd. Litho State Printing Works, Moscow)

1982 (16 Nov). *World-Wide Sight Conservation Project. P* 12 × 12½.
779 **307** 2 r. 50, multicoloured .. .. 1·75 2·00

(Des L. Ranasinghe. Litho Questa (5 r.) or J.W. (others))

1982 (16 Nov)–89. *As Nos. 718/21, but without surcharges and showing revised face values. P* 14.
780 2 r. 50, Type **269** (1.6.83) 10 10
781 3 r. Golden Palm Civet (21.6.83) .. 70 70
782 4 r. Indian Spotted Chevrotain .. 10 15
783 5 r. Rusty-spotted Cat (1.12.89) .. 15 20
780/3 .. .. *Set of* 4 95 1·00
For the 3 r. in similar design, but printed by Questa with imprint date see No. 1081.

(Des D. Karunaratne. Litho Security Printers (M), Malaysia)

1982 (2 Dec). *125th Anniv of First Postage Stamps. T* **308** *and similar horiz design. Multicoloured. P* 13 × 13½.
784 50 c. Type **308**.. .. .. 20 25
785 2 r. 50, 1859 1s. 9d. green and 1981 50 c. "Just Society" stamp .. .. 75 1·25
MS786 59 × 84 mm. Nos. 784/5 (*sold at* 5 r.) 95 1·50

309 Sir Oliver Goonetilleke   **310** Sarvodaya Emblem

(Des A. Ratnapala. Litho State Printing Works, Moscow)

1982 (17 Dec). *4th Death Anniv of Sir Oliver Goonetilleke (statesman). P 12 × 12½.*
787 **309** 50 c. olive-grey, bistre-brown and black 40 60

(Des P. Gunasinghe. Litho Secura, Singapore)

1983 (1 Jan). *25th Anniv of Sarvodaya Movement. P 13 × 13½.*
788 **310** 50 c. multicoloured 70 70

311 Morse Key, Radio Aerial and Radio Amateur Society Emblem   **312** Customs Co-operation Council Emblem and Sri Lanka Flag

(Des W. Rohana. Litho Secura, Singapore)

1983 (17 Jan). *Amateur Radio Society. P 13 × 13½.*
789 **311** 2 r. 50, multicoloured .. .. 2·25 2·75

(Des W. Rohana. Litho Secura, Singapore)

1983 (26 Jan). *30th Anniv of International Customs Day. P 12 × 11½.*
790 **312** 50 c. multicoloured 30 30
791   5 r. multicoloured .. .. 2·50 2·75

313 Bottle-nosed Dolphin   **314** *Lanka Athula* (container ship)

(Des G. Ratnavira. Litho Harrison)

1983 (22 Feb). *Marine Mammals. T 313 and similar horiz designs. P 14½ × 14.*
792 50 c. black, new blue and grey-green 30 15
793 2 r. multicoloured 55 60
794 2 r. 50, black, dp grey-blue & dp bluish grey 80 80
795 10 r. multicoloured .. .. 2·25 2·50
792/5 ..   *Set of 4* 3·50 3·50
Designs:—2 r. Dugongs; 2 r. 50, Humpback Whale; 10 r. Sperm Whale.

(Des Vision Ltd. Litho Security Printers (M), Malaysia)

1983 (1 Mar). *Ships of the Ceylon Shipping Corporation. T 314 and similar horiz designs. Multicoloured. P 11½ × 12.*
796 50 c. Type **314** 10 10
797 2 r. 50, Map of routes .. 15 30
798 5 r. *Lanka Kalyani* (freighter) .. 25 65
799 20 r. *Tammanna* (tanker) .. 1·10 2·50
796/9 .. .. *Set of 4* 1·40 3·25

315 Woman with I.W.D. Emblem and Sri Lanka Flag   **316** Waterfall

(Des R. Mawilmada. Litho Secura, Singapore)

1983 (8 Mar). *International Women's Day. T 315 and similar vert design. Multicoloured. P 13.*
800 50 c. Type **315** 10 20
801 5 r. Woman, emblem, map and symbols of progress .. 40 80

(Des S. Lankatilake. Litho Secura, Singapore)

1983 (14 Mar). *Commonwealth Day. T 316 and similar horiz designs. Multicoloured. P 13.*
802 50 c. Type **316** 10 10
803 2 r. 50, Tea plucking .. 15 25
804 5 r. Harvesting rice .. 25 40
805 20 r. Decorated elephants .. 80 2·00
802/5 .. .. *Set of 4* 1·10 2·50

317 Lions Club International Badge   **318** "The Dream of Queen Mahamaya"

(Des U. Karunaratna. Litho J.W.)

1983 (7 May). *25th Anniv of Lions Club International in Sri Lanka. P 14.*
806 **317** 2 r. 50, multicoloured .. .. 1·75 1·75

(Des G. Keyt and A. Dharmasiri. Litho Toppan Ptg Co, Japan)

1983 (13 May). *Vesak. Life of Prince Siddhartha from temple murals at Gotami Vihara. T 318 and similar vert designs. Multicoloured. P 12½ × 12.*
807 35 c. Type **318**.. .. 10 10
808 50 c. "Prince Siddhartha given to Maha Brahma".. .. 10 10
809 5 r. "Prince Siddhartha and the Sleeping Dancers".. .. 25 60
810 10 r. "The Meeting with Mara" .. 55 1·50
807/10 .. *Set of 4* 80 2·10
MS811 150 × 90 mm. Nos. 807/10 .. 90 2·10

319 First Telegraph Transmission Colombo to Galle, 1858   **320** Henry Woodward Amarasuriya (philanthropist)

(Des W. Rohana. Litho Toppan Ptg Co, Japan)

1983 (17 May). *125th Anniv of Telecommunications in Sri Lanka (2 r.) and World Communications Year (10 r.). T 319 and similar horiz design. Multicoloured. P 12 × 12½.*
812 2 r. Type **319**.. .. .. 10 35
813 10 r. World Communications Year emblem.. 55 1·40

(Litho Security Printers (M), Malaysia (No. 810), Pakistan Security Printing Corp (others))

1983 (22 May). *National Heroes. T 320 and similar vert designs. P 12 × 11½ (No. 814) or 13 (others).*
814 50 c. bright emerald 20 35
815 50 c. new blue.. .. 20 35
816 50 c. magenta.. .. 20 35
817 50 c. turquoise-green.. .. 20 35
814/17 .. .. *Set of 4* 70 1·25
Designs:—No. 815, Father Simon Perera (historian); No. 816, Charles Lorenz (lawyer and newspaper editor); No. 817, Noordeen Abdul Cader (first President of All-Ceylon Muslim League).
  A fifth design to commemorate C. W. Thamotheram Pillai was prepared for this set, but was withdrawn at the last moment when it was realised that the wrong portrait had been used. It is understood, however, that supplies were sold at some rural post offices where the instruction was not received in time. A corrected version was later issued, see No. 825.

321 Family and Village   **322** Caravan of Bulls

(Des K. Gunasiri and U. Karunaratna. Litho Toppan Ptg Co, Japan)

1983 (23 June). *Gam Udawa (Village Re-awakening Movement). T 321 and similar horiz design. Multicoloured. P 12 × 12½.*
818 50 c. Type **321**.. .. 10 15
819 5 r. Village view 40 85

(Des A. Rasiah (35 c., 2 r.), D. Hemaratna (2 r. 50), U. Karunaratna (5 r.). Litho State Printing Office, Budapest)

1983 (22 Aug). *Transport. T 322 and similar horiz designs. Multicoloured. P 12*
820 35 c. Type **322**.. .. 10 10
821 2 r. Steam train 65 75
822 2 r. 50, Ox and cart 65 65
823 5 r. Ford motor car .. .. 1·10 1·90
820/3 .. .. *Set of 4* 2·25 3·25

---

323 Sir Tikiri Banda Panabokke   **324** C. W. Thamotheram Pillai

(Des and litho Harrison)

1983 (2 Sept). *20th Death Anniv of Adigar Sir Tikiri Banda Panabokke. P 14 × 14½.*
824 **323** 50 c. Indian red 75 75

(Des and litho Pakistan Security Printing Corp)

1983 (1 Oct). *C. W. Thamotheram Pillai (Tamil scholar) Commemoration. P 13.*
825 **324** 50 c. orange-brown 75 75
See note below No. 817.

325 Arabi Pasha   **326** Sri Lanka Wood Pigeon

(Des and litho Pakistan Security Printing Corp)

1983 (13 Nov). *Centenary of the Exile to Ceylon of Arabi Pasha (Egyptian nationalist). P 13 × 13½.*
826 **325** 50 c. green 75 75

(Des G. Ratnavira. Litho Format)

1983 (22 Nov)–**88**. *Birds (2nd series). T 326 and similar horiz designs. Multicoloured. P 14½.*
827 25 c. Type **326** 10 10
828 35 c. Large Sri Lanka White Eye .. 10 10
829 2 r. Sri Lanka Dusky Blue Flycatcher .. 10 10
829a 7 r. As 35 c. (28.9.88) .. 20 25
830 20 r. Ceylon Coucal 60 65
827/30 .. *Set of 5* 80 90
MS831 183 × 93 mm. Nos. 827/9 and 830 .. 4·00 4·50

327 Pelene Siri Vajiragnana   **328** Mary praying over Jesus and St. Joseph welcoming Shepherds

(Des and litho Harrison)

1983 (25 Nov). *Pelene Siri Vajiragnana (scholar) Commemoration. P 14 × 14½.*
832 **327** 50 c. red-brown.. .. 80 80

(Des P. de Silva. Litho German Bank Note Co, Leipzig)

1983 (30 Nov). *Christmas. P 12½ × 13.*
833 **328** 50 c. multicoloured .. 10 15
834   5 r. multicoloured .. 25 60
MS835 85 × 141 mm. Nos. 833/4 .. .. 50 1·25

.60   .60

(329)   (330)

1983 (1 Dec). *No. 680a surch with T 329/30 by Aitken Spence Ptg (Pte) Ltd, Sri Lanka.*
836 **236** 60 c. on 50 c. gold, bright yellow-green and emerald (surch T **329**) .. 50 50
        a. Surch inverted
837   60 c. on 50 c. gold, bright yellow-green and emerald (surch T **330**) .. 2·00 2·00

331 Paddy Field, Globe and
F.A.O. Emblem

(Des R. Mawilmada. Litho State Ptg Works, Moscow)

1984 (2 Jan). *World Food Day.* P 12½ × 12.
838 331 3 r. multicoloured 30 70

332 Modern Tea Factory 333 Students and University

(Des M. Ratnapala. Litho State Ptg Works, Moscow)

1984 (31 Jan). *Centenary of the Colombo Tea Auctions.* T 332
and similar horiz designs. Multicoloured. P 12½ × 12.
839 1 r. Type 332 .. .. .. 10 15
840 2 r. Logo 15 35
841 5 r. Girl picking tea.. .. .. 30 80
842 10 r. Auction in progress .. .. 65 1·60
839/42 .. .. *Set of 4* 1·00 2·75

(Des R. Mawilmada. Litho Security Printers (M), Malaysia)

1984 (10 Feb). *4th Anniv of Mahapola Scheme for Development
and Education.* T 333 *and similar vert designs. Multicoloured.*
P 12.
843 60 c. Type 333 .. .. 10 15
844 1 r. Teacher with Gnana Darsana class .. 10 15
845 5 r. 50, Student with books and microscope 35 1·00
846 6 r. Mahapola lamp symbol .. .. 40 1·25
843/6 .. .. *Set of 4* 75 2·25

334 King Daham Sonda 335 Development
instructing Angels Programme Logo

(Des A. Dharmasiri. Litho D.L.R)

1984 (27 Apr). *Vesak. The Story of King Daham Sonda from
ancient casket paintings.* T 334 *and similar horiz designs.
Multicoloured.* A. P 14. B. P 13 × 13½.

			A		B	
847	35 c. Type 334	..	10	10	25	20
848	60 c. Elephant paraded with gift of gold		10	25	20	30
849	5 r. King Daham Sonda leaps into mouth of God Sakra		30	85	45	1·25
850	10 r. God Sakra carrying King Daham Sonda		65	1·50	65	2·00
847/50		*Set of 4*	95	2·40	1·40	3·25
MS851	154 × 109 mm. Nos. 847/50. P 13				1·00	2·00

(Des R. Mawilmada. Litho Harrison)

1984 (5 May). *Sri Lanka Lions Clubs' Development Programme.*
P 14 × 14½.
852 335 60 c. multicoloured 80 80

336 Dodanduwe Siri 337 Association Emblem
Piyaratana Tissa
Mahanayake Thero
(Buddhist scholar)

(Litho State Ptg Works, Moscow)

1984 (22 May). *National Heroes.* T 336 *and similar vert designs.*
P 12 × 12½.
853 60 c. yellow-bistre 10 20
854 60 c. yellow-green 10 20

855 60 c. emerald-green 10 20
856 60 c. red 10 20
857 60 c. deep yellow-brown 10 20
853/7 .. .. *Set of 5* 30 90
Designs:—No. 853, Type 336; 854, G. P. Wickremarachchi
(physician); 855, Sir Mohamed Macan Markar (politician); 856,
Dr. W. Arthur de Silva (philanthropist), 857, K. Balasingham
(lawyer).

(Des A. Harischandra. Litho Govt Printing Bureau, Tokyo)

1984 (16 June). *Centenary of Public Service Mutual Provident
Association.* P 13 × 13½.
858 337 4 r. 60, multicoloured 30 90

338 Sri Lanka Village 339 World Map showing
A.P.B.U. Countries

(Des S. Herath. Litho State Ptg Wks, Moscow)

1984 (23 June). *6th Anniv of "Gam Udawa" (Village
Reawakening Movement).* P 12 × 12½.
859 338 60 c. multicoloured 20 40

(Des G. Arthasad. Litho State Ptg Wks, Moscow)

1984 (30 June). *20th Anniv of Asia-Pacific Broadcasting Union.*
P 12½ × 12.
860 339 7 r. multicoloured .. .. 1·10 1·50

340 Drummers and Elephant 341 *Vanda memoria*
carrying Royal Instructions Ernest Soysa
(orchid)

(Des R. Mawilmada. Litho State Ptg Wks, Moscow)

1984 (11 Aug). *Esala Perahera (Procession of the Tooth), Kandy.*
T 340 *and similar horiz designs. Multicoloured.* P 12½ × 12.
861 4 r. 60, Type 340 .. .. 70 90
    a. Horiz strip of 4. Nos. 861/4 .. 2·50
862 4 r. 60, Dancers and elephants .. 70 90
863 4 r. 60, Elephant carrying Tooth Relic .. 70 90
864 4 r. 60, Custodian of the Sacred Tooth and
    attendants 70 90
861/4 .. .. *Set of 4* 2·50 3·25
MS865 223 × 108 mm. Nos. 861/4 .. 2·50 3·50
Nos. 861/4 were printed together, *se-tenant,* in horizontal
strips of 4 throughout the sheet, forming a composite design.

(Des G. Ratnavira. Litho D.L.R.)

1984 (22 Aug). *50th Anniv of Ceylon Orchid Circle.* T 341 *and
similar vert designs, showing orchids. Multicoloured.* A. P 14.
B. P 13½ × 13.

		A		B	
866	60 c. Type 341	60	30	25	60
867	4 r. 60, *Acanthephippium bi-color*	1·50	2·00	65	2·00
868	5 r. *Vanda tessellata var. rufescens*	2·00	2·25	45	2·00
869	10 r. *Anoectochilus setaceus*	2·00	3·00	†	
866A/9A	*Set of 4*	5·50	6·75	†	
866B/8B	*Set of 3*	†		1·25	4·00
MS870	115 × 110 mm. Nos. 866/9. P 13			5·00	6·00

342 Symbolic Athletes 343 D. S. Senanayake,
and Stadium Temple and Fields

(Des M. Heenkenda. Litho Govt Printing Bureau, Tokyo)

1984 (5 Oct). *1st National School Games.* P 13½ × 13.
871 342 60 c. black, grey and bright new blue .. 75 75

(Des L. Jayawardena (35 c.), G. Fernando (60 c.), N. Lasantha
(4 r. 60), R. Mawilmada (6 r.). Litho J.W.)

1984 (20 Oct). *Birth Centenary of D. S. Senanayake (former Prime
Minister).* T 343 *and similar horiz designs. Multicoloured.* P 14.
872 35 c. Type 343 .. .. 10 10
873 60 c. Senanayake and statue .. 10 10
874 4 r. 60, Senanayake and irrigation project.. 25 50
875 6 r. Senanayake and House of Representa-
    tives 30 60
872/5 .. .. *Set of 4* 55 1·10

344 Lake House 345 Agricultural Workers
and Globe

(Des Grant Kenyon and Eckhardt Ltd. Litho State Printing
Office, Budapest)

1984 (19 Nov). *150th Anniv of the "Observer" Newspaper.*
P 13 × 13½.
876 344 4 r. 60, multicoloured .. .. .. 65 1·40

(Des M. Ratnapala. Litho German Bank Note Ptg Co, Leipzig)

1984 (10 Dec). *20th Anniv of World Food Programme.*
P 13 × 13½.
877 345 7 r. multicoloured 90 90

346 College Emblem 347 Dove and Stylized
Figures

(Des S. Herath. Litho J.W.)

1984 (24 Dec). *Centenary of Baari Arabic College, Weligama.*
P 13 × 12½.
878 346 4 r. 60, blackish olive, turquoise-green
    and turquoise-blue .. .. 90 1·25

(Des S. Chandrajeewa (4 r. 60), O. Weerakkody (20 r.). Litho
J.W.)

1985 (1 Jan). *International Youth Year.* T 347 *and similar
horiz design. Multicoloured.* P 12½ × 13.
879 4 r. 60, Type 347 .. .. .. 30 50
880 20 r. Dove, stylized figures and flower .. 1·25 2·00

348 Religious Symbols 349 College Crest

(Des R. Mawilmada. Litho Security Printers (M), Malaysia)

1985 (20 Jan). *World Religion Day.* P 12.
881 348 4 r. 60, multicoloured 50 70

(Des G. Arthasad. Litho J.W.)

1985 (29 Jan). *150th Anniv of Royal College, Colombo.* T 349
and similar vert design. P 13 × 12½.
882 60 c. bright yellow and deep ultramarine .. 10 25
883 7 r. multicoloured .. .. 70 1·75
Design:—7 r. Royal College.

350 Banknotes, Buildings, 351 Wariyapola Sri
Ship and "Wheel of Life" Sumangala Thero

(Des R. Mawilmada. Litho J.W.)

1985 (7 Feb). *5th Anniv of Mahapola Scheme.* P 14.
884 350 60 c. multicoloured 60 75

(Des G. Fernando. Litho State Printing Office, Budapest)

1985 (2 Mar). *Wariyapola Sri Sumangala Thero (Buddhist
priest and patriot) Commemoration.* P 13 × 13½.
885 351 60 c. blk, reddish brn & greenish yell 50 70

352 Victoria Dam 353 Cover of 50th Edition of
International Buddhist
Annual, *Vesak Sirisara*

(Des G. Arthasad. Litho State Ptg Wks, Moscow)

1985 (12 Apr). *Inauguration of Victoria Hydro-electric Project. T 352 and similar multicoloured design.* P 12½×12 (60 c.) or 12×12½ (7 r.).
886   60 c. Type 352. 60   40
887   7 r. Map of Sri Lanka enclosing dam and power station (vert) .. .. 2·25   2·75

(Des B. Harischandra (35 c.), R. Mawilmada (others). Litho J.W.)

1985 (26 Apr). *Centenary of Vesak Poya Holiday. T 353 and similar vert designs.* Multicoloured. P 13×12½.
888   35 c. Type 353. 10   10
889   60 c. Buddhists worshipping at temple .. 10   10
890   6 r. Buddhist Theosophical Society Headquarters, Colombo 30   35
891   9 r. Buddhist flag 50   55
888/91 .. .. Set of 4   80   90
MS892   180×110 mm. Nos. 888/91 .. .. 3·75   4·50

354 Ven. Waskaduwe Sri   **355** Stylised Village and
Subhuthi (priest and scholar)   People

(Des S. Silva. Litho J.W.)

1985 (22 May). *Personalities. T 354 and similar vert designs.* P 13×12½.
893   60 c. black, yellow-orange and lake-brown ..   15   20
894   60 c. black, yellow-orange and deep mauve ..   15   20
895   60 c. black, yellow-orange and light brown ..   15   20
896   60 c. black, yellow-orange and emerald ..   15   20
893/6 .. .. Set of 4   55   70
Designs:— No. 893, Type 354; 894, Revd. Fr. Peter A. Pillai (educationist and social reformer); 895, Dr. Senarath Paranavitane (scholar); 896, A. M. Wapche Marikar (architect and educationist).

(Des S. Herath. Litho German Bank Note Co, Leipzig)

1985 (23 June). *Gam Udawa '85 (Village Re-awakening Movement).* P 13½×13.
897   355   60 c. multicoloured 75   85

356 Emblem   **357** Kothmale Dam and
Reservoir

(Des B. Harischandra. Litho German Bank Note Co, Leipzig)

1985 (25 June). *50th Anniv of Colombo Young Poets' Association.* P 14.
898   356   60 c. multicoloured 30   45

(Des R. Mawilmada. Litho J.W.)

1985 (24 Aug). *Inauguration of Kothmale Hydro-electric Project. T 357 and similar horiz design.* Multicoloured. P 14.
899   60 c. Type 357. 20   15
900   6 r. Kothmale Power Station 70   85

358 Federation Logo   **359** Breast Feeding

(Des R. Mawilmada. Litho J.W.)

1985 (2 Sept). *10th Asian and Oceanic Congress of Obstetrics and Gynaecology.* P 14.
901   358   7 r. multicoloured .. .. 2·25   2·25

(Des B. Harischandra. Litho Cartor, France)

1985 (5 Sept). *U.N.I.C.E.F. Child Survival and Development Programme. T 359 and similar vert designs.* Multicoloured. W w 17. P 13½.
902   35 c. Type 359. 10   10
903   60 c. Child and oral rehydration salts .. 20   20
904   6 r. Weighing child (growth monitoring) .. 1·25   1·50
905   9 r. Immunization .. .. .. 1·75   2·00
902/5 .. .. Set of 4   3·00   3·50
MS906   99×180 mm. Nos. 902/5. P 12½   3·00   3·75

ALTERED CATALOGUE NUMBERS

Any Catalogue numbers altered from the last edition are shown as a list in the introductory pages.

---

360 Blowing Conch Shell   **361** Casket containing Land
Grant Deed

(Des G. Malaviachi. Litho Heraclio Fournier, Spain)

1985 (27 Sept). *10th Anniv of World Tourism Organization. T 360 and similar horiz designs.* Multicoloured. P 14.
907   1 r. Type 360. 10   10
908   6 r. Parliamentary Complex, Jayawardhanapura, Kotte 40   60
909   7 r. Tea plantation 50   75
910   10 r. Ruwanveliseya (Buddhist shrine), Anuradhapura 70   1·00
907/10 .. .. Set of 4   1·50   2·25
MS911   179×89 mm. Nos. 907/10. P 13½   1·50   2·25

(Des B. Harischandra. Litho Harrison)

1985 (15 Oct). *50th Anniv of Land Development Ordinance.* P 14×15.
912   361   4 r. 60, multicoloured 80   1·40

362 Koran and Map of Sri   **363** "Our Lady of Matara"
Lanka   Statue

(Des R. Mawilmada. Litho Cartor, France)

1985 (17 Oct). *Translation of The Koran into Sinhala.* W w 17. P 13½.
913   362   60 c. gold and bright violet .. 40   60

(Des S. Silva. Litho Security Printers (M), Malaysia)

1985 (5 Nov). *Christmas. T 363 and similar vert design.* Multicoloured. P 12.
914   60 c. Type 363. 15   10
915   9 r. "Our Lady of Madhu" statue 70   80
MS916   180×100 mm. Nos. 914/15 .. 3·25   4·00

.75

(364)   **365** Linked Arms and Map
of S.A.A.R.C. Countries

1985 (1 Dec)—86. *Nos. 680b, 780, 823, 860 and 879 surch as T 364 by Aitken Spence Ptg (Pte) Ltd, Sri Lanka.*
917   236   75 c. on 60 c. gold, bright yellow-green and emerald (G.) 10   10
             a. Surch double .. .. † —
918   347   1 r. on 4 r. 60, mult (29.4.86) .. 80   70
919   339   1 r. on 7 r. multicoloured (20.1.86) .. 1·25   70
920   269   5 r. 75 on 2 r. 50, multicoloured (Br) .. 1·50   45
             a. Surch double ..
921   —   7 r. on 35 c. mult (No. 828) (10.3.86) 1·60   65
             a. Surch inverted ..
             b. Surch double ..
             c. Surch triple .. .. ..
917/21 .. .. Set of 5   4·75   2·25

(Des B. Harischandra. Litho J.W.)

1985 (8 Dec). *1st Summit Meeting of South Asian Association for Regional Co-operation, Dhaka, Bangladesh. T 365 and similar horiz design.* Multicoloured. P 14.
922   60 c. Type 365. 90   2·50
923   5 r. 50, Logo and flags of member countries 90   1·25
No 922 was, reportedly, withdrawn on 11 December after Pakistan objected to the boundaries shown on the map.

366 "Viceroy Special" Train

(Des G. Malaviachi. Litho Format)

1986 (2 Feb). *Inaugural Run of "Viceroy Special" Train from Colombo to Kandy.* P 12½.
924   366   1 r. multicoloured .. .. 2·50   1·25

367 Girl and Boy Students   **368** D. R. Wijewardena

(Des S. Silva. Litho Heraclio Fournier, Spain)

1986 (14 Feb). *6th Anniv of Mahapola Scheme.* P 14.
925   367   75 c. multicoloured 40   60

(Des S. Silva. Litho J.W.)

1986 (23 Feb). *Birth Centenary of D. R. Wijewardena (newspaper publisher).* P 14×14½.
926   368   75 c. orange-brown and deep olive .. 30   60

369 Ven Welitara   **370** Red Cross Flag and Personnel
Gnanatillake Maha
Nayake Thero

(Des S. Silva. Litho Cartor, France)

1986 (26 Feb). *Ven. Welitara Gnanatillake Maha Nayake Thero (scholar) Commemoration.* W w 17. P 13½.
927   369   75 c. multicoloured 70   70

(Des W. Rohana. Litho Format)

1986 (31 Mar). *50th Anniv of Sri Lanka Red Cross Society.* P 12½.
928   370   75 c. multicoloured .. .. 1·50   85

371 Comet depicted as   **372** Woman lighting
Goddess visiting Sun-god   Lamp

(Des W. Rohana. Litho Format)

1986 (5 Apr). *Appearance of Halley's Comet. T 371 and similar horiz designs.* Multicoloured. P 12½.
929   50 c. Type 371. 10   10
930   75 c. Comet and constellations of Scorpius and Sagittarius 10   20
931   6 r. 50, Comet's orbit 55   90
932   8 r. 50, Edmond Halley 80   1·40
929/32 .. .. Set of 4   1·40   2·40
MS933   180×115 mm. Nos. 929/32 .. 5·50   6·00

(Des B. Harischandra. Litho Format)

1986 (10 Apr). *Sinhalese and Tamil New Year. T 372 and similar vert designs.* Multicoloured. P 12½.
934   50 c. Type 372. 10   10
935   75 c. Woman and festive foods .. 15   15
936   6 r. 50, Women playing drum .. 65   1·25
937   8 r. 50, Anointing and making offerings at temple 85   1·60
934/7 .. .. Set of 4   1·60   2·75
MS938   178×108 mm. Nos. 934/7 .. 3·00   3·75

373 The King donating   **374** Ven. Kalukondayave
Elephant to the Brahmin   Sri Prajnasekhara Maha
Nayake Thero (Buddhist
leader and social reformer)

(Des N. Bulathsinhala. Litho Format)

1986 (16 May). *Vesak. Wall paintings from Samudragiri Temple, Mirissa.* T **373** *and similar horiz designs. Multi-coloured.* P 12½.

939	50 c. Type **373**..	10	10
940	75 c. The Bodhisattva in the Vasavarthi heaven	10	20
941	5 r. The offering of milk rice by Sujatha ..	45	1·00
942	10 r. The offering of parched corn and honey by Thapassu and Bhalluka	75	1·50
939/42	Set of 4	1·25	2·50

(Des S. Silva. Litho Format)

1986 (22 May). *National Heroes.* T **374** *and similar vert designs. Multicoloured.* P 12½.

943	75 c. Type **374**..	20	35
944	75 c. Brahmachari Walisinghe Harischandra (social reformer) (birth centenary)	20	35
945	75 c. Martin Wickramasinghe (author and scholar)	20	35
946	75 c. G. G. Ponnambalam (politician)	20	35
947	75 c. A. M. A. Azeez (Islamic scholar) (75th birth anniv)	20	35
943/7 ..	Set of 5	90	1·60

375 Stylised Village and People   376 Co-op Flag and Emblem

(Des S. Herath. Litho German Bank Note Co, Leipzig)

1986 (23 June). *Gam Udawa '86 (Village Re-awakening Movement).* P 13½×13.

948	**375** 75 c. multicoloured	70	50

(Des A. Harischandra. Litho Format)

1986 (5 July). *75th Anniv of Sri Lanka Co-operative Movement.* P 12½.

949	**376** 1 r. multicoloured	1·25	1·25

377 Arthur V. Dias   378 Bull Elephant

(Des S. Silva. Litho Harrison)

1986 (31 July). *Birth Centenary of Arthur V. Dias (philanthropist).* P 14×15.

950	**377** 1 r. chestnut and dull violet-blue ..	75	75

(Des G. Ratnavira. Litho Harrison)

1986 (5 Aug). *Sri Lanka Wild Elephants.* T **378** *and similar horiz designs. Multicoloured.* P 15×14.

951	5 r. Type **378** ..	1·75	1·90
	a. Horiz strip of 4. Nos. 951/4 ..	6·25	
952	5 r. Cow elephant and calf ..	1·75	1·90
953	5 r. Cow elephant ..	1·75	1·90
954	5 r. Elephants bathing ..	1·75	1·90
951/4 ..	Set of 4	6·25	7·00

Nos. 951/4 were printed, together, *se-tenant*, in horizontal strips of four throughout the sheet.

379 Congress Logo   380 Map showing Route of Cable and Telephone Receiver

(Des S. Silva. Litho Govt Printing Bureau, Tokyo)

1986 (14 Aug). *2nd Indo-Pacific Congress on Legal Medicine and Forensic Sciences.* P 13½×13.

955	**379** 8 r. 50, multicoloured ..	1·00	1·25

(Des R. Mawilmada. Litho Security Printers (M), Malaysia)

1986 (8 Sept). *SEA-ME-WE Submarine Cable Project.* P 13½×14.

956	**380** 5 r. 75, multicoloured ..	90	1·25

381 Anniversary Logo   382 Logo on Flag

(Des R. Mawilmada. Litho Format)

1986 (20 Sept). *25th Anniv of Dag Hammarskjöld Award.* P 12½.

957	**381** 2 r. multicoloured ..	1·25	65

(Des A. Harischandra. Litho Security Printers (M), Malaysia)

1986 (22 Sept). *2nd National School Games.* P 12.

958	**382** 1 r. multicoloured ..	1·25	75

383 Logo   384 College Building and Crest

(Des W. Rohana. Litho Govt Printing Bureau, Tokyo)

1986 (27 Sept). *60th Anniv of Surveyors' Institute of Sri Lanka.* P 13½×13.

959	**383** 75 c. red-brown and cinnamon	40	55

(Des W. Rohana. Litho Security Printers (M), Malaysia)

1986 (1 Nov). *Centenary of Ananda College, Colombo.* T **384** *and similar horiz designs.* P 12.

960	75 c. multicoloured ..	10	10
961	5 r. multicoloured ..	30	40
962	5 r. 75, multicoloured ..	30	40
963	6 r. carmine-red, gold and rose-lilac ..	35	45
960/3 ..	Set of 4	90	1·25

Designs:—5 r. Sports field and college crest; 5 r. 75, Col. H. S. Olcott (founder), Ven. Migettuwatte Gunananda, Ven. Hikkaduwe Sri Sumangala (Buddhist leaders) and Buddhist flag; 6 r. College flag.

385 Mangrove Swamp   386 Family and Housing Estate

(Des G. Ratnavira. Litho Security Printers (M), Malaysia)

1986 (11 Nov). *Mangrove Conservation.* T **385** *and similar horiz designs. Multicoloured.* P 12.

964	35 c. Type **385**. ..	15	10
965	50 c. Mangrove tree ..	20	10
966	75 c. Germinating mangrove flower ..	25	15
967	6 r. Fiddler Crab ..	1·40	1·75
964/7 ..	Set of 4	1·75	1·90

(Des R. Mawilmada. Litho Govt Printing Bureau, Tokyo)

1987 (1 Jan). *International Year of Shelter for the Homeless.* P 13×13½.

968	**386** 75 c. multicoloured ..	80	30

387 Ven. Ambagahawatte Indasabhawaragnanasamy Thero   388 Proctor John de Silva

(Des S. Silva. Litho Security Printers (M), Malaysia)

1987 (29 Jan). *Ven. Ambagahawatte Indasabhawaragnanasamy Thero (Buddhist monk) Commemoration.* P 12.

969	**387** 5 r. 75, multicoloured ..	75	50

(Des S. Silva. Litho Security Printers (M), Malaysia)

1987 (31 Jan). *Proctor John de Silva (playwright) Commemoration.* P 12.

970	**388** 5 r. 75, multicoloured ..	60	50

389 Mahapola Logo and Aspects of Communication   390 Dr. R. L. Brohier

(Des R. Mawilmada. Litho Security Printers (M), Malaysia)

1987 (6 Feb). *7th Anniv of Mahapola Scheme.* P 12.

971	**389** 75 c. multicoloured ..	40	40

(Des S. Silva. Litho Security Printers (M), Malaysia)

1987 (10 Feb). *Dr. Richard L. Brohier (historian and surveyor) Commemoration.* P 12.

972	**390** 5 r. 75, multicoloured ..	60	45

391 Tyre Corporation Building, Kelaniya, and Logo

(Des A. Harischandra. Litho Questa)

1987 (23 Mar). *25th Anniv of Sri Lanka Tyre Corporation.* P 14.

973	**391** 5 r. 75, black, lake and bright orange ..	45	45

392 Logo   393 Clasped Hands, Farmer and Paddy Field

(Des A. Harischandra. Litho Govt Printing Bureau, Tokyo)

1987 (24 Mar). *Centenary of Sri Lanka Medical Association.* P 13×13½.

974	**392** 5 r. 75, lake-brown, greenish yellow & blk	45	45

(Des B. Harischandra. Litho Questa)

1987 (29 Mar). *Inauguration of Farmers' Pension and Social Security Benefit Scheme.* P 14.

975	**393** 75 c. multicoloured ..	20	20

394 Exhibition Logo   395 Young Children with W.H.O. and Immunization Logos

(Des W. Rohana. Litho Security Printers (M), Malaysia)

1987 (2 Apr). *Mahaweli Maha Goviya Contest and Agro Mahaweli Exhibition.* P 12.

976	**394** 75 c. multicoloured ..	20	20

(Des B. Harischandra. Litho Questa)

1987 (7 Apr). *World Health Day.* P 14.

977	**395** 1 r. multicoloured ..	1·25	40

396 Girls playing on Swing   397 Lotus Lanterns

(Des G. Fernando. Litho Security Printers (M), Malaysia)

1987 (9 Apr). *Sinhalese and Tamil New Year.* T **396** *and similar vert design. Multicoloured.* P 12.

978	75 c. Type **396**. ..	10	10
979	5 r. Girls with oil lamp and sun symbol ..	50	50

(Des W. Rohana. Litho Security Printers (M), Malaysia)

1987 (4 May). *Vesak. T* **397** *and similar horiz designs. Multi-coloured. P* 12.

980	50 c. Type 397			10	10
981	75 c. Octagonal lanterns			10	10
982	5 r. Star lanterns			30	30
983	10 r. Gok lanterns			45	55
980/3			*Set of 4*	80	90
MS984	150×90 mm. Nos. 980/3			80	1·00

398 Emerald-collared Parakeet   **399** Ven. Heenatiyana Sri Dhammaloka Maha Nayake Thero (Buddhist monk)

(Des G. Ratnavira. Litho Questa)

1987 (18 May)–**91**. *Birds* (3rd series). *T* **398** *and similar horiz designs. Multicoloured. P* 14. A. *With imprint date at bottom right.* B. *Without imprint date.*

		A		B	
985	50 c. Type 398	10	10	†	
986	1 r. Legge's Flowerpecker	10	10	†	
987	5 r. Ceylon White-headed Starling	15	20	15	20
988	10 r. Ceylon Jungle Babbler	30	35	30	35
985/8	*Set of 4*	50	60	†	
MS989	140×80 mm. Nos. 985/8	2·50	2·00	†	

Dates of issue:—9.10.90, No. 988B; 27.2.91, No. 987B.
Nos. 986A/8A exist with different imprint dates beneath the designs.

(Des S. Silva. Litho Security Printers (M), Malaysia)

1987 (22 May). *National Heroes. T* **399** *and similar vert designs. Multicoloured. P* 12.

990	75 c. Type 399			25	25
991	75 c. P. de S. Kularatne (educationist)		25	25
992	75 c. M. C. Abdul Rahuman (legislator)		25	25
990/2			*Set of 3*	65	65

400 Peasant Family and Village   **401** *Mesua nagassarium*

(Des J. Semage. Litho Security Printers (M), Malaysia)

1987 (23 June). *Gam Udawa '87* (*Village Re-awakening Movement*). *P* 12.

993	400	75 c. multicoloured		20	20

(Des P. Hewabettage (75 c.), B. Harischandra (5 r.). Litho Security Printers (M), Malaysia)

1987 (25 June). *Forest Conservation. T* **401** *and similar horiz design. Multicoloured. P* 12.

994	75 c. Type 401			10	10
995	5 r. Elephants in forest			80	50

402 Dharmaraja College, Crest and Col. H. Olcott (founder)   **403** Youth Services Logo

(Des C. Kandewela. Litho Security Printers (M), Malaysia)

1987 (30 June). *Centenary of Dharmaraja College, Kandy. P* 12.

996	402	75 c. multicoloured		85	30

(Des H. Dayaratne. Litho Security Printers (M), Malaysia)

1987 (15 July). *20th Anniv of National Youth Services. P* 12.

997	403	75 c. multicoloured		20	20

404 Arm holding Torch and Mahaweli Logo   **405** Open Bible and Logo

(Des W. Rohana. Litho Security Printers (M), Malaysia)

1987 (5 Sept). *Mahaweli Games. P* 12.

998	404	75 c. multicoloured		75	75

(Des C. Beling. Litho Security Printers (M), Malaysia)

1987 (2 Oct). *175th Anniv of Ceylon Bible Society. P* 12.

999	405	5 r. 75, multicoloured		30	30

406 Hurdler and Committee Symbol   **407** Madonna and Child, Flowers and Oil Lamp

(Des R. Mawilmada. Litho Heraclio Fournier, Spain)

1987 (8 Oct). *50th Anniv of National Olympic Committee. P* 13.

1000	406	10 r. multicoloured		85	60

(Des B. Mendis. Litho Security Printers (M), Malaysia)

1987 (17 Nov). *Christmas. T* **407** *and similar vert design. Multicoloured. P* 12 (75 c.) *or* 12½×13 (10 r.).

1001	75 c. Type 407			10	10
1002	10 r. Christ Child in manger, star and dove		35	40
MS1003	145×82 mm. Nos. 1001/2. P 12		60	70

408 Sir Ernest de Silva   **409** Society Logo

(Des P. Gunasinghe. Litho German Bank Note Co, Leipzig)

1987 (25 Nov). *Birth Centenary of Sir Ernest de Silva* (*philanthropist and philatelist*). *P* 13×13½.

1004	408	75 c. multicoloured		20	20

(Des W. Rohana. Litho German Bank Note Co, Leipzig)

1987 (28 Nov). *150th Anniv of Kandy Friend-in-Need Society. P* 13½×13.

1005	409	75 c. multicoloured		20	20

410 University Flag and Graduates   **411** Father Joseph Vaz

(Des R. Samarasinghe. Litho Security Printers (M), Malaysia)

1987 (14 Dec). *First Convocation of Buddhist and Pali University. P* 12.

1006	410	75 c. multicoloured		20	20

(Des S. Silva. Litho Security Printers (M), Malaysia)

1987 (15 Dec). *300th Anniv of Arrival of Father Joseph Vaz in Kandy. P* 12.

1007	411	75 c. multicoloured		20	20

412 Wheel of Dhamma, Dagaba and Bo Leaf   **413** Dharmayatra Lorry

(Des W. Rohana. Litho Security Printers (M), Malaysia)

1988 (1 Jan). *30th Anniv of Buddhist Publication Society, Kandy. P* 12.

1008	412	75 c. multicoloured		20	20

(Des B. Harischandra. Litho German Bank Note Co, Leipzig)

1988 (4 Jan). *5th Anniv of Mahapola Dharmayatra Service. P* 13½×13.

1009	413	75 c. multicoloured		20	20

414 Society Logo   **415** National Youth Centre, Maharagama

(Des R. Samarasinghe. Litho Security Printers (M), Malaysia)

1988 (8 Jan). *Centenary of Ceylon Society of Arts. P* 12.

1010	414	75 c. multicoloured		20	20

(Des R. Chandrajeewa. Litho Security Printers (M), Malaysia)

1988 (31 Jan). *Opening of National Youth Centre, Maharagama. P* 13½×13.

1011	415	1 r. multicoloured		90	30

416 Citizens with National Flag and Map of Sri Lanka   **417** Graduates, Clay Lamp and Open Book

(Des R. Samarasinghe. Litho Security Printers (M), Malaysia)

1988 (4 Feb). *40th Anniv of Independence. T* **416** *and similar vert design. Multicoloured. P* 12.

1012	75 c. Type 416			10	10
1013	8 r. 50, "40" in figures and lion emblem		50	50

(Des R. Samarasinghe. Litho Security Printers (M), Malaysia)

1988 (11 Feb). *8th Anniv of Mahapola Scheme. P* 12.

1014	417	75 c. multicoloured		20	20

418 Bus and Logo   **419** Ven. Weligama Sri Sumangala Maha Nayake Thero

(Des W. Rohana. Litho Security Printers (M), Malaysia)

1988 (19 Feb). *30th Anniv of Sri Lanka Transport Board. P* 12.

1015	418	5 r. 75, multicoloured		30	30

(Des S. Silva. Litho Security Printers (M), Malaysia)

1988 (13 Mar). *Ven. Weligama Sri Sumangala Maha Nayake Thero* (*Buddhist monk*) *Commemoration. P* 12.

1016	419	75 c. multicoloured		20	20

420 Regimental Colour   **421** Chevalier I. X. Pereira

(Des W. Rohana. Litho Security Printers (M), Malaysia)

1988 (20 Apr). *Centenary of Regiment of Artillery. P* 12.

1017	420	5 r. 75, multicoloured		75	40

(Des S. Silva. Litho Security Printers (M), Malaysia)

1988 (26 Apr). *Birth Centenary of Chevalier I. X. Pereira* (*politician*). *P* 12.

1018	421	5 r. 75, multicoloured		30	30

422 Invitation to the Deities and Brahmas

423 Father Ferdinand Bonnel (educationist)

(Des N. Bulathsinhala. Litho State Ptg Wks, Moscow)

1988 (13 May). *Vesak. Paintings from Narendrarama Rajamaha Temple, Suriyagoda.* T **422** *and similar horiz design. Multicoloured.* P 12¹/₂ × 12.

1019	50 c. Type **422**			15	15
1020	75 c. Bodhisathva at the Seventh Step			15	15
MS1021	150 × 92 mm. Nos. 1019/20			50	50

(Des S. Silva. Litho State Ptg Wks, Moscow)

1988 (22 May). *National Heroes.* T **423** *and similar vert designs. Multicoloured.* P 12 × 12¹/₂.

1022	75 c. Type **423**			15	15
1023	75 c. Sir Razik Fareed (politician)			15	15
1024	75 c. W. F. Gunawardhana (scholar)			15	15
1025	75 c. Edward Nugawela (politician)			15	15
1026	75 c. Chief Justice Sir Arthur Wijeyeward-ene			15	15
1022/6			Set of 5	60	60

424 Stylized Figures and Reawakened Village   **425** Maliyadeva College, Kurunegala, and Crest

(Des P. Gunasinghe. Litho Security Printers (M), Malaysia)

1988 (23 June). *10th Anniv of Gam Udawa (Village Re-awakening Movement).* P 12.

1027	**424** 75 c. multicoloured			20	20

(Des W. Rohana. Litho German Bank Note Co, Leipzig)

1988 (30 June). *Centenary of Maliyadeva College, Kurunegala.* P 13¹/₂ × 13.

1028	**425** 75 c. multicoloured			20	20

426 M.J.M. Lafir, Billiard Game and Trophy   **427** Flags of Australia and Sri Lanka, Handclasp and Map of Australia

(Des S. Silva. Litho State Ptg Wks, Moscow)

1988 (5 July). *Mohamed Junaid Mohamed Lafir (World Amateur Billiards Champion, 1973) Commemoration.* P 12¹/₂ × 12.

1029	**426** 5 r. 75, multicoloured			30	30

(Des R. Samarasinghe. Litho Security Printers (M), Malaysia)

1988 (19 July). *Bicentenary of Australian Settlement.* P 12.

1030	**427** 8 r. 50, multicoloured			30	35

428 Ven. Kataluwe Sri Gunaratana Maha Nayake Thero   **429** Athlete, Rice and Hydro-electric Dam

(Des S. Silva. Litho State Ptg Wks, Moscow)

1988 (11 Aug). *Ven. Kataluwe Sri Gunaratana Maha Nayake Thero (Buddhist monk) Commemoration.* P 12 × 12¹/₂.

1031	**428** 75 c. multicoloured			20	20

(Des P. Gunasinghe. Litho Security Printers (M), Malaysia)

1988 (3 Sept). *Mahaweli Games.* P 12.

1032	**429** 75 c. multicoloured			20	20

430 Athletics   **431** Outline Map of Sri Lanka and Anniversary Logo

(Des P. Gunasinghe. Litho State Ptg Wks, Moscow)

1988 (6 Sept). *Olympic Games, Seoul.* T **430** *and similar vert designs. Multicoloured.* P 12 × 12¹/₂.

1033	75 c. Type **430**			10	10
1034	1 r. Swimming			10	10
1035	5 r. 75, Boxing			20	25
1036	8 r. 50, Map of Sri Lanka and logos of Olympic Committee and Seoul Games			30	35
1033/6			Set of 4	55	65
MS1037	181 × 101 mm. Nos. 1033/6			75	85

(Des S. Silva. Litho Security Printers (M), Malaysia)

1988 (12 Sept). *40th Anniv of World Health Organization.* P 12.

1038	**431** 75 c. multicoloured			20	20

432 Games Logo   **433** Mahatma Gandhi

(Des A. Harischandra. Litho Security Printers (M), Malaysia)

1988 (20 Sept). *3rd National School Games.* P 12.

1039	**432** 1 r. black, gold and mauve			75	15

(Des S. Silva. Litho Security Printers (M), Malaysia)

1988 (2 Oct). *40th Death Anniv of Mahatma Gandhi.* P 12.

1040	**433** 75 c. multicoloured			30	15

434 Globe with Forms of Transport and Communications   **435** Woman with Rice Sheaf and Hydro-electric Project

(Des R. Samarasinghe. Litho State Ptg Wks, Moscow)

1988 (28 Oct). *Asia–Pacific Transport and Communications Decade.* T **434** *and similar horiz design.* P 12¹/₂ × 12.

1041	75 c. multicoloured			10	10
1042	5 r. 75, magenta, royal blue and black			40	30

Design:—5 r. 75, Antenna tower with dish aerials and forms of transport.

(Des B. Harischandra. Litho Security Printers (M), Malaysia)

1988 (31 Oct). *Commissioning of Randenigala Project.* T **435** *and similar horiz design. Multicoloured.* P 12.

1043	75 c. Type **435**			10	10
1044	5 r. 75, Randenigala Dam and reservoir			20	25

436 Handicrafts and Centre Logo in Cupped Hands   **437** Angel, Dove, Olive Branch and Globe

(Des R. Samarasinghe. Litho Secura, Singapore)

1988 (17 Nov). *Opening of Gramodaya Folk Art Centre, Colombo.* P 13¹/₂.

1045	**436** 75 c. multicoloured			20	20

(Des B. Mendis. Litho State Ptg Wks, Moscow)

1988 (21 Nov). *Christmas.* T **437** *and similar vert design. Multicoloured.* P 12×12¹/₂.

1046	75 c. Type **437**			10	10
1047	8 r. 50, Shepherds and Star of Bethlehem			30	35
MS1048	175×100 mm. Nos. 1046/7			60	60

438 Dr. E. W. Adikaram   **439** Open Book in Tree and Children reading

(Des S. Silva. Litho Security Printers (M), Malaysia)

1988 (28 Dec). *Dr. E. W. Adikaram (educationist) Commemoration.* P 12.

1049	**438** 75 c. multicoloured			20	20

(Des Lakmini Amararatne. Litho German Bank Note Co, Leipzig)

1989 (23 Jan). *10th Anniv of Free Distribution of School Text Books.* P 13¹/₂×13.

1050	**439** 75 c. multicoloured			20	20

440 Wimalaratne Kumaragama   **441** Logo and New Chamber of Commerce Building

(Des S. Silva. Litho German Bank Note Co, Leipzig)

1989 (27 Jan). *Poets of Sri Lanka.* T **440** *and similar vert designs. Multicoloured.* P 13×13¹/₂.

1051	75 c. Type **440**			10	10
1052	75 c. G. H. Perera			10	10
1053	75 c. Sagara Palansuriya			10	10
1054	75 c. P. B. Alwis Perera			10	10
1051/4			Set of 4	30	30

(Des Mel Ads Ltd. Litho Security Printers (M), Malaysia)

1989 (25 Mar). *150th Anniv of Ceylon Chamber of Commerce.* P 12.

1055	**441** 75 c. multicoloured			20	20

442 Bodhisatva at Lunch and Funeral Pyre   **443** Parawahera Vajiragnana Thero (Buddhist monk)

(Des N. Bulathsinhala. Litho State Ptg Wks, Moscow)

1989 (15 May). *Vesak. Wall Paintings from Medawala Monastery, Harispattuwa.* T **442** *and similar horiz designs. Multicoloured.* P 12¹/₂×12.

1056	50 c. Type **442**			10	10
1057	75 c. Rescue of King Vessantara's children by god Sakra			10	10
1058	5 r. Bodhisatva ploughing and his son attacked by snake			20	25
1059	5 r. 75, King Vessantara giving away his children			20	25
1056/9			Set of 4	55	65
MS1060	150×90 mm. Nos. 1056/9			75	75

(Des S. Silva. Litho Security Printers (M), Malaysia)

1989 (22 May). *National Heroes.* T **443** *and similar multicoloured designs.* P 12.

1061	75 c. Type **443**			15	15
1062	75 c. Father Maurice Jacques Le Goc (educationist)			15	15
1063	75 c. Hemapala Munidasa (author)			15	15
1064	75 c. Ananda Samarakoon (composer)			15	15
1065	75 c. Simon Casie Chitty (scholar) (*horiz*)			15	15
1061/5			Set of 5	65	65

444 College Crest   245 Dramachakra, Lamp, Buddhist Flag and Map

(Des K. Wickramanayake. Litho Security Printers (M), Malaysia)

1989 (5 June). *150th Anniv of Hartley College, Point-Pedro* (1988). *P* 12.
1066 444 75 c. multicoloured 20 20

(Des P. Gunasinghe. Litho State Ptg Wks, Moscow)

1989 (18 June). *Establishment of Ministry of Buddha Sasana. P* 12½×12.
1067 445 75 c. multicoloured 20 20

446 Hands holding Brick and Trowel, House and Family   447 Two Families and Hand turning Cogwheel

(Des P. Gunasinghe. Litho State Ptg Wks, Moscow)

1989 (23 June). *Gam Udawa '89 (Village Re-awakening Movement). P* 12½×12.
1068 446 75 c. multicoloured 20 20

(Des P. Gunasinghe. Photo State Ptg Works, Moscow)

1989 (23 June)*–90. Janasaviya Development Programme. P* 12×11½.
1069 447 75 c. multicoloured 20 20
1070   1 r. multicoloured (31.1.90) .. 20 20

448 Dunhinda Falls   449 Rev. James Chater (missionary) and Baptist Church

(Des S. Silva. Litho State Ptg Works, Moscow)

1989 (11 Aug). *Waterfalls. T* 448 *and similar vert designs. Multicoloured. P* 12.
1071   75 c. Type 448 .. .. .. 10 10
1072   1 r. Rawana Falls 10 10
1073   5 r. 75, Laxapana Falls .. 15 20
1074   8 r. 50, Diyaluma Falls .. 20 25
1071/4 .. .. .. *Set of* 4 50 60

(Des S. Silva. Litho State Ptg Works, Moscow)

1989 (19 Aug). *177th Anniv of Baptist Church in Sri Lanka. P* 12½×12.
1075 449 5 r. 75, multicoloured 20 20

450 Bicentenary Logo   451 Old and New Bank Buildings and Logo

(Des R. Samarasinghe. Litho German Bank Note Co, Leipzig)

1989 (26 Aug). *Bicentenary of French Revolution. P* 13½×13.
1076 450 8 r. 50, black, deep blue & brt carmine 20 30

(Des W. Rohana. Litho German Bank Note Co, Leipzig)

1989 (31 Aug). *50th Anniv of Bank of Ceylon. T* 451 *and similar horiz design. Multicoloured. P* 13½×13.
1077 75 c. Type 451 .. .. 10 10
1078   5 r. "Bank of Ceylon" orchid and logo .. 20 20

452 Water Lily, Dharma Chakra and Books   453 Wilhelm Geiger

(Des P. Gunasinghe. Litho Security Printers (M), Malaysia)

1989 (22 Sept). *State Literary Festival. P* 12.
1079 452 75 c. multicoloured 20 20

(Des S. Silva. Litho German Bank Note Co, Leipzig)

1989 (30 Sept). *Wilhelm Geiger (linguistic scholar) Commemoration. P* 13×13½.
1080 453 75 c. multicoloured 20 20

(Litho Questa)

1989 (11 Oct). *As No. 781, but different printer. Face value and inscriptions in black. With imprint date. P* 14.
1081 3 r. Golden Palm Civet 10 10
No. 781 has face value and inscriptions in red-brown and is without imprint date.

454 H. V. Perera, Q.C.   455 Sir Cyril de Zoysa

(Des S. Silva. Litho Security Printers (M), Malaysia)

1989 (16 Oct). *Constitutional Pioneers. T* 454 *and similar vert design. Multicoloured. P* 12.
1082   75 c. Type 454 .. .. .. 20 20
1083   75 c. Prof. Ivor Jennings 20 20

(Des S. Silva. Litho German Bank Note Co, Leipzig)

1989 (26 Oct). *Sir Cyril de Zoysa (Buddhist philanthropist) Commemoration. P* 13×13½.
1084 455 75 c. multicoloured 20 20

456 Map of South-east Asia and Telecommunications Equipment   457 Members with Offerings and Water Lily on Map of Sri Lanka

(Des W. Rohana. Litho State Ptg Works, Moscow)

1989 (1 Nov). *10th Anniv of Asia-Pacific Telecommunity. P* 12×12½.
1085 456 5 r. 75, multicoloured 20 20

(Des P. Gunasinghe. Litho Security Printers (M), Malaysia)

1989 (9 Nov). *50th Anniv of Sri Sucharitha Welfare Movement. P* 13.
1086 457 75 c. multicoloured 20 20

458 "Apollo 11" Blast-off and Astronauts   459 Shepherds

(Des W. Rohana. Litho State Ptg Works, Moscow)

1989 (10 Nov). *20th Anniv of First Manned Landing on Moon. T* 458 *and similar vert designs. Multicoloured. P* 12×12½.
1087   75 c. Type 458 .. .. .. 10 10
1088   1 r. Armstrong leaving lunar module Eagle 10 10
1089   2 r. Astronaut on Moon 10 10
1090   5 r. 75, Lunar surface and Earth from Moon 15 20
1087/90 .. .. .. *Set of* 4 30 30
MS1091 100×160 mm. Nos. 1087/90 .. .. 70 70

(Des Father P. Silva. Litho Secura, Singapore)

1989 (21 Nov). *Christmas. T* 459 *and similar vert design. Multicoloured. P* 13½.
1092   75 c. Type 459 .. .. .. 10 10
1093   8 r. 50, Magi with gifts 20 55
MS1094 160×100 mm. Nos. 1092/3 .. .. 50 80

460 Ven. Sri Devananda Nayake Thero   461 College Building, Crest and Revd. William Ault (founder)

(Des S. Silva. Litho Security Printers (M), Malaysia)

1989 (25 Nov). *Ven. Sri Devananda Nayake Thero (Buddhist monk) Commemoration. P* 12.
1095 460 75 c. multicoloured 20 20

(Des W. Rohana. Litho Security Printers (M), Malaysia)

1989 (29 Nov). *175th Anniv of Methodist Central College, Batticaloa. P* 12.
1096 461 75 c. multicoloured 20 20

462 Golf Ball, Clubs and Logo   463 "Raja"

(Des G. Bozell. Litho Pakistan Security Ptg Corp, Karachi)

1989 (8 Dec). *Centenary of Nuwara Eliya Golf Club. T* 462 *and similar horiz design. Multicoloured. P* 13½.
1097   75 c. Type 462 .. .. .. 15 10
1098   8 r. 50, Course and club house .. 40 40

(Litho German Bank Note Co, Leipzig)

1989 (12 Dec). *"Raja" Royal Ceremonial Elephant, Kandy, Commemoration. P* 13×13½.
1099 463 75 c. multicoloured 20 20

464 College Building and G. Wickremarachchi (founder)   465 Ven. Udunuwara Sri Sarananda Thero

(Des S. Silva. Litho German Bank Note Co, Leipzig)

1989 (14 Dec). *60th Anniv of Gampaha Wickremarachchi Institute of Ayurveda Medicine. P* 13½×13.
1100 464 75 c. multicoloured 20 20

(Des S. Silva. Litho State Ptg Wks, Moscow)

1989 (20 Dec). *Ven. Udunuwara Sri Sarananda Thero (Buddhist monk) Commemoration. P* 12×12½.
1101 465 75 c. multicoloured 20 20

NEW INFORMATION

The editor is always interested to correspond with people who have new information that will improve or correct the Catalogue.

466 Diesel Train on Viaduct, Ella-Demodara

467 Cardinal Thomas Cooray

(Des R. Mawilmada. Litho Security Printers (M), Malaysia)

1989 (27 Dec). *125 Years of Sri Lanka Railways. T 466 and similar horiz designs. Multicoloured. P 12.*

1102	75 c. Type 466	..	..	10	10
1103	2 r. Diesel train at Maradana Station	..		15	15
	a. Perf 13	..	..	15	15
1104	3 r. Steam train	..		20	20
	a. Perf 13	..	..	20	20
1105	7 r. Steam train, 1864	..	..	40	40
1102/5		..	Set of 4	75	75

(Des S. Silva. Litho German Bank Note Co, Leipzig)

1989 (28 Dec). *Cardinal Thomas Cooray Commemoration. P 13×13½.*

1106	467 75 c. multicoloured	..	45	15

468 Farmer and Wife with Dagaba and Dam

469 Justin Wijayawardena

(Des P. Gunasinghe. Litho Security Printers (M), Malaysia)

1989 (29 Dec). *Agro Mahaweli Development Programme. P 12.*

1107	468 75 c. multicoloured	..	..	20	20

(Des S. Silva. Litho State Ptg Wks, Moscow)

1990 (14 Jan). *Justin Wijayawardena (scholar) Commemoration. P 12×12½.*

1108	469 1 r. multicoloured	..	..	60	20

.25

(469a)

1990 (16 Feb). *No. 1059 surch with T 469a.*

1108a	25 c. on 5 r. 75, King Vessantara giving away his children	..	..	10	10

470 Ven. Induruwe Uttarananda Mahanayake Thero

471 Two Graduates, Lamp and Open Book

(Des S. Silva. Litho Security Printers (M), Malaysia)

1990 (15 Mar). *4th Death Anniv of Ven. Induruwe Uttarananda Mahanayake Thero (Buddhist theologian). P 12.*

1109	470 1 r. multicoloured	..	..	20	30

(Des P. Gunasinghe. Litho Secura, Singapore)

1990 (25 Mar). *9th Anniv of Mahapola Scheme. P 13½.*

1110	471 75 c. multicoloured	..	..	20	20

472 Traditional Drums

(Des R. Samarasinha. Litho Security Printers (M), Malaysia)

1990 (2 Apr). *25th Anniv of Laksala Traditional Handicrafts Organization. T 472 and similar horiz designs. Multicoloured. P 12.*

1111	1 r. Type 472	..	..	10	10
1112	2 r. Silverware	..	..	15	15
1113	3 r. Lacquerware	..	..	15	20
1114	8 r. Dumbara mats	..	..	35	40
1111/14	..		Set of 4	65	75

473 King Maha Prathapa visiting Queen Chandra

474 Father T. Long (educationist)

(Des N. Bulathsinhala. Litho State Ptg Wks, Moscow)

1990 (2 May). *Vesak. Wall Paintings from Buduraja Maha Viharaya, Wewurukannala. T 473 and similar horiz designs. Multicoloured. P 12½×12.*

1115	75 c. Type 473		..	10	10
1116	1 r. Execution of Prince Dharmapala	..		10	10
1117	2 r. Prince Mahinsasaka with the Water Demon			15	15
1118	8 r. King Dahamsonda with the God Sakra disguised as a demon			35	35
1115/18			Set of 4	55	55
MS1119	160×99 mm. Nos. 1115/18	..	..	80	80

(Des S. Silva. Litho Security Printers (M), Malaysia (No. 1120), State Ptg Wks, Moscow (others))

1990 (22 May). *National Heroes. T 474 and similar vert designs. Multicoloured. P 12 (No. 1120) or 12×12½ (others).*

1120	1 r. Type 474		..	10	10
1121	1 r. Prof. M. Ratnasuriya (37×25 mm)			10	10
1122	1 r. D. Wijewardene (patriot) (37×25 mm)			10	10
1123	1 r. L. Manjusri (artist) (37×25 mm)			10	10
1120/3			Set of 4	30	30

475 Janasaviya Workers

476 Gold Reliquary

(Des P. Dissanayake. Litho State Ptg Wks, Moscow)

1990 (23 June). *12th Anniv of Gam Udawa and Opening of Janasaviya Centre, Pallekele. P 12½×12.*

1124	475 1 r. multicoloured	..	..	30	15

(Des N. Bulathsinhala. Litho Security Printers (M), Malaysia)

1990 (7 July). *Centenary of Department of Archaeology. T 476 and similar vert designs. P 13 (8 r.) or 12 (others).*

1125	1 r. black and orange-yellow		..	10	10
1126	2 r. black and greenish grey	..		15	15
1127	3 r. black, apple-green and ochre	..		15	20
	a. Perf 13	..		15	20
1128	8 r. black and ochre	..		30	35
1125/8			Set of 4	60	65

Designs:—2 r. Statuette of Ganesh; 3 r. Terrace of the Bodhi-tree, Isurumuniya Vihara; 8 r. Inscription of King Nissankamalla.

477 Male Tennis Player at Left

478 Spotted Loach

(Des S. Rohana. Litho Pakistan Security Ptg Corp, Karachi)

1990 (14 Aug). *75th Anniv of Sri Lanka Tennis Association. T 477 and similar horiz designs. Multicoloured. P 13½.*

1129	1 r. Type 477		..	15	15
	a. Horiz pair. Nos. 1129/30			30	30
1130	1 r. Male tennis player at right	..		15	15
1131	8 r. Male tennis players	..		40	40
	a. Horiz pair. Nos. 1131/2			80	80
1132	8 r. Female tennis players	..		40	40
1129/32			Set of 4	1·00	1·00

Nos. 1129/30 and 1131/2 were each printed together, *se-tenant*, in horizontal pairs throughout the sheets, each pair forming a composite design of a singles (1 r.) or doubles (8 r.) match.

(Des R. Samarasinghe. Litho State Ptg Wks, Moscow)

1990 (14 Sept). *Endemic Fishes. T 478 and similar horiz designs. Multicoloured. P 11½.*

1133	25 c. Type 478		..	10	10
1134	2 r. Ornate Paradise Fish	..		10	10
1135	8 r. Mountain Labeo	..		20	25
1136	20 r. Cherry Barb	..		60	65
1133/6			Set of 4	75	85
MS1137	150×90 mm. Nos. 1133/6	..		80	90

479 Rukmani Devi

480 Innkeeper turning away Mary and Joseph

(Litho Security Printers (M), Malaysia)

1990 (28 Oct). *12th Death Anniv of Rukmani Devi (actress and singer). P 12.*

1138	479 1 r. multicoloured	..	..	50	30

(Des P. Silva. Litho Security Printers (M), Malaysia)

1990 (28 Nov). *Christmas. T 480 and similar vert design. Multicoloured. P 13.*

1139	1 r. Type 480	..	..	10	10
1140	10 r. Adoration of the Magi	..		35	40
MS1141	190×114 mm. Nos. 1139/40. P 12	..		50	75

481 Health Worker talking to Villagers

482 Main College Building and Flag

(Des S. Rohana. Litho Security Printers (M), Malaysia)

1990 (30 Nov). *World Aids Day. T 481 and similar horiz design. Multicoloured. P 12.*

1142	1 r. Type 481	..	..	10	10
1143	8 r. Emblem and Aids virus	..		35	45

(Des P. Gunasinghe. Litho Security Printers (M), Malaysia)

1990 (8 Dec). *50th Anniv of Dharmapala College, Pannipitiya. P 12.*

1144	482 1 r. multicoloured	..	..	20	20

483 Peri Sundaram

484 Letter Box, Galle, 1904

(Litho S. Rohana. Litho Security Printers (M), Malaysia)

1990 (14 Dec). *Birth Centenary of Peri Sundaram (lawyer and politician). P 12.*

1145	483 1 r. red-brown and yellow-green	..	30	30

(Des S. Rohana. Litho Security Printers (M), Malaysia)

1990 (26 Dec). *175th Anniv of Sri Lanka Postal Service. T 484 and similar vert designs. Multicoloured. P 12.*

1146	1 r. Type 484	..	..	10	10
1147	2 r. Mail runner, 1815	..		15	15
1148	5 r. Mail coach, 1832	..		35	35
1149	10 r. Nuwara-Eliya Post Office, 1894	..		65	75
1146/9			Set of 4	1·10	1·25

485 Chemical Structure Diagram, Graduating Students and Emblem   486 Kastavahana on Royal Elephant

(Des S. Rohana. Litho Security Printers (M), Malaysia)

1991 (25 Jan). *50th Anniv of Institute of Chemistry. P 12.*
1150 **485** 1 r. multicoloured 40 30

(Des U. Karunaratne. Litho Security Printers (M), Malaysia)

1991 (17 May). *Vesak. Temple Paintings from Karagampitiya Subodarama. T **486** and similar horiz designs. Multicoloured. P 12*
1151	75 c. Type **486**		10	10
1152	1 r. Polo Janaka in prison		10	10
1153	2 r. Two merchants offering food to Buddha		15	15
1154	11 r. Escape of Queen		50	50
1151/4		*Set of 4*	75	75
MS1155	150×90 mm. Nos. 1151/4		80	1·25

487 Narada Thero (Buddhist missionary)   488 Society Building

(Des S. Silva. Litho State Ptg Works, Moscow)

1991 (22 May). *National Heroes. T **487** and similar vert designs. Multicoloured. P 12×12½.*
1156	1 r. Type **487**		15	15
1157	1 r. Wallewatta Silva (novelist)		15	15
1158	1 r. Sir Muttu Coomaraswamy (lawyer and politician)		15	15
1159	1 r. Dr. Andreas Nell (opthalmic surgeon)		15	15
1156/9		*Set of 4*	55	55

(Des R. de Silva. Litho Security Printers (M), Malaysia)

1991 (31 May). *Centenary of Maha Bodhi Society. P 12.*
1160 **488** 1 r. multicoloured 20 20

489 Women working at Home   490 Globe and Plan Symbol

(Des T. Kariyawasam. Litho Security Printers (M), Malaysia)

1991 (23 June). *13th Anniv of Gam Udawa Movement. P 12½.*
1161 **489** 1 r. multicoloured 20 20

(Des R. Mawilmada. Litho Security Printers (M), Malaysia)

1991 (1 July). *40th Anniv of Colombo Plan. P 12.*
1162 **490** 1 r. bright violet and new blue 20 20

491 17th-century Map and Modern Satellite Photo of Sri Lanka   492 Ven. Henpitagedera Gnanaseeha Nayake Thero

(Des P. Mittapala. Litho Security Printers (M), Malaysia)

1991 (1 Aug). *190th Anniv of Sri Lanka Survey Department. P 12½.*
1163 **491** 1 r. multicoloured 20 20

(Des S. Silva. Litho Security Printers (M), Malaysia)

1991 (1 Aug). *10th Death Anniv of Ven. Nayak Henpitagedera Gnanaseeha Nayake Thero (Buddhist theologian). P 12½.*
1164 **492** 1 r. multicoloured 20 20

493 Police Officers of 1866 and 1991 with Badge   494 Kingswood College

(Des S. Silva. Litho Security Printers (M), Malaysia)

1991 (3 Sept). *125th Anniv of Sri Lankan Police Force. P 12½.*
1165 **493** 1 r. multicoloured 20 20

(Des S. Rohana. Litho State Ptg Wks, Moscow)

1991 (26 Oct). *Centenary of Kingswood College, Kandy. P 12½×12.*
1166 **494** 1 r. multicoloured 20 20

495 The Annunciation   496 Early Magneto Telephone

(Des P. Silva. Litho Security Printers (M), Malaysia)

1991 (19 Nov). *Christmas. T **495** and similar vert design. Multicoloured. P 12½.*
1167	1 r. Type **495**		20	20
1168	10 r. The Presentation of Jesus in the Temple		60	60
MS1169	90×150 mm. Nos. 1167/8		80	80

(Des S. Rohana. Litho Security Printers (M), Malaysia)

1991 (23 Nov). *Inauguration of Sri Lankan Telecom Corporation. T **496** and similar vert designs. Multicoloured. P 12½.*
1170	1 r. Type **496**		15	10
1171	2 r. Manual switchboard and telephonist		20	15
1172	8 r. Satellite communications system		40	45
1173	10 r. Fibre optics cable and mobile phone		50	60
1170/3		*Set of 4*	1·10	1·10

497 S.A.A.R.C. Logo and Bandaranaike Memorial Hall   498 "Pancha" (Games mascot)

(Des S. Rohana (1 r.), S. Silva (8 r.). Litho Security Printers (M), Malaysia)

1991 (21 Dec). *Sixth South Asian Association for Regional Cooperation Summit, Colombo. T **497** and similar horiz design. P 12½.*
1174	1 r. Type **497**		15	10
1175	8 r. Logo and Hall surrounded by national flags		45	50

(Des Sri Lanka National Design Centre. Litho Secura, Singapore)

1991 (22 Dec). *5th South Asian Federation Games. T **498** and similar horiz designs. P 13½×14.*
1176	1 r. Type **498**		15	10
1177	2 r. Games logo		20	15
1178	4 r. Sugathadasa Stadium		35	35
1179	11 r. Asia map on globe and national flags		75	75
1176/9		*Set of 4*	1·25	1·25

COVER PRICES

Cover factors are quoted at the beginning of each country for most issues to 1945. An explanation of the system can be found on page x. The factors quoted do not, however, apply to philatelic covers.

499 Crate, Airliner and Container Ship   500 Plucking Tea

(Des W. Rohana. Litho Security Printers (M), Malaysia)

1992 (13 Jan). *Exports Year. P 12.*
1180 **499** 1 r. multicoloured 20 20

(Des R. Mawilmada. Litho Secura, Singapore)

1992 (12 Feb). *125th Anniv of Tea Industry. T **500** and similar horiz designs. Multicoloured. P 14.*
1181	1 r. Type **500**		15	10
1182	2 r. Healthy family, tea and tea estate		20	15
1183	5 r. Ceylon tea symbol		45	45
1184	10 r. James Taylor (founder)		70	80
1181/4		*Set of 4*	1·40	1·40

501 General Ranjan Wijeratne   502 Olcott Hall, Mahinda College

(Des S. Rohana. Litho State Ptg Wks, Moscow)

1992 (2 Mar). *1st Death Anniv of General Ranjan Wijeratne. P 12×12½.*
1185 **501** 1 r. multicoloured 20 20

(Des S. Rohana. Litho Security Printers (M), Malaysia)

1992 (2 Mar). *Centenary of Mahinda College, Galle. P 12.*
1186 **502** 1 r. multicoloured 20 20

503 Newstead College and Logo   504 Student and Oil Lamp

(Des S. Silva. Litho Security Printers (M), Malaysia)

1992 (13 Mar). *175th Anniv of Newstead Girls' College, Negombo (1991). P 12.*
1187 **503** 1 r. multicoloured 20 20

(Des S. Perera. Litho Security Printers (M), Malaysia)

1992 (30 Mar). *11th Anniv of Mahapola Scholarship Fund. P 12.*
1188 **504** 1 r. multicoloured 20 20

505 Sama's Parents leaving for Forest   506 Ven. Devamottawe Amarawansa (Buddhist missionary)

(Des N. Bulathsinhala. Litho Security Printers (M), Malaysia)

1992 (5 May). *Vesak Festival. Sama Jataka Paintings from Kottimbulwala Cave Temple. T **505** and similar horiz designs. Multicoloured. P 12.*
1189	75 c. Type **505**		10	10
1190	1 r. Sama and parents in forest		10	10
1191	8 r. Sama leading blind parents		35	40
1192	11 r. Sama's parents grieving for wounded son		55	60
1189/92		*Set of 4*	1·00	1·10
MS1193	151×91 mm. Nos. 1189/92		1·10	1·25

(Des S. Silva. Litho Leigh-Mardon Ltd, Melbourne)

1992 (22 May). *National Heroes. T* **506** *and similar vert designs. Multicoloured. P* 14.

1194	1 r.	Type **506**		10	10
1195	1 r.	Richard Mirando (Buddhist philan-thropist)		10	10
1196	1 r.	Gate Mudaliyar N. Canaganayagam (Buddhist social reformer)		10	10
1197	1 r.	Abdul Azeez (Moorish social reformer)		10	10
1194/7		.. .. ..	Set of 4	30	30

507 Map of Sri Lanka, Flag and Symbol

508 Family in House

(Des S. Silva. Litho State Ptg Wks, Moscow)

1992 (14 June). *2300th Anniv of Arrival of Buddhism in Sri Lanka. P* 12×12½.

1198	**507**	1 r. multicoloured	15	15

(Des P. Miranda. Litho Security Printers (M), Malaysia)

1992 (23 June). *14th Anniv of Gam Udawa Movement. P* 12.

1199	**508**	1 r. multicoloured	15	15

509 Postal Activities and Award

510 Narilata Mask

(Des S. Rohana. Litho Leigh-Mardon Ltd, Melbourne)

1992 (11 July). *Postal Service Awards. T* **509** *and similar horiz design. Multicoloured. P* 14.

1200	1 r.	Type **509**	15	10
1201	10 r.	Medals and commemorative cachet	50	55

(Des A. Dharmasiri. Litho Secura, Singapore)

1992 (19 Aug). *Kolam Dance Masks. T* **510** *and similar vert designs. Multicoloured. P* 12½.

1202	1 r.	Type **510**	.. ..	10	10
1203	2 r.	Mudali mask	..	10	10
1204	5 r.	Queen mask	..	15	20
1205	10 r.	King mask	..	30	35
1202/5			Set of 4	60	70
MS1206	150×90 mm. Nos. 1202/5	.. ..	65	70

511 19th and 20th-century Players and Match of 1838

512 Running

(Des S. Rohana. Litho Secura, Singapore)

1992 (8 Sept). *160th Anniv of Cricket in Sri Lanka. P* 13.

1207	**511**	5 r. multicoloured	15	20

(Litho Questa)

1992 (15 Sept). *Olympic Games, Barcelona. T* **512** *and similar vert designs. Multicoloured. P* 14.

1208	1 r.	Type **512**	..	10	10
1209	11 r.	Shooting	..	40	45
1210	13 r.	Swimming	..	45	50
1211	15 r.	Weight-lifting	..	50	55
1208/11			Set of 4	1·25	1·40
MS1212	91×151 mm. Nos. 1208/11	..	1·40	1·50

NEW INFORMATION

The editor is always interested to correspond with people who have new information that will improve or correct the Catalogue.

---

513 Vijaya Kumaratunga

514 College Building and Crest

(Litho Secura, Singapore)

1992 (9 Oct). *Vijaya Kumaratunga (actor) Commemoration. P* 13.

1213	**513**	1 r. multicoloured	..	10	10

(Des S. Rohana. Litho Security Printers (M), Malaysia)

1992 (24 Oct). *Centenary of Al-Bahjathhul Ibraheemiyyah Arabic College. P* 12.

1214	**514**	1 r. multicoloured	10	10

515 Official Church Seal

516 Nativity

(Des S. Rohana. Litho Security Printers (M), Malaysia)

1992 (25 Oct). *350th Anniv of Dutch Reformed Church in Sri Lanka. P* 12.

1215	**515**	1 r. black, yellowish grn & greenish yell	10	10

(Des S. Purnajith. Litho Security Printers (M), Malaysia)

1992 (17 Nov). *Christmas. T* **516** *and similar vert design. Multicoloured. P* 12.

1216	1 r.	Type **516**	..	10	10
1217	9 r.	Family going to church	..	25	30
MS1218	150×90 mm. Nos. 1216/17	..	35	40

517 Fleet of Columbus

518 Ven. Sumedhankara Thero and Dagoba

(Des and litho Questa)

1992 (1 Dec). *500th Anniv of Discovery of America by Columbus. T* **517** *and similar horiz designs. Multicoloured. P* 14.

1219	1 r.	Type **517**		10	10
1220	11 r.	Columbus landing in New World	..	35	40
1221	13 r.	Wreck of *Santa Maria*		40	45
1222	15 r.	Columbus reporting to Queen Isabella and King Ferdinand	..	45	50
1219/22			Set of 4	1·10	1·25
MS1223	155×95 mm. Nos. 1219/22	..	1·25	1·40

(Des S. Silva. Litho Security Printers (M), Malaysia)

1992 (10 Dec). *Birth Centenary of Ven. Dambagasare Sumedhankara Nayake Thero. P* 12.

1224	**518**	1 r. multicoloured	10	10

519 University Logo, Students and Building

(Des S. Rohana. Litho Security Printers (M), Malaysia)

1992 (22 Dec). *50th Anniv of University Education in Sri Lanka. P* 12.

1225	**519**	1 r. multicoloured	10	10

OFFICIAL STAMPS

1869. *Issues of 1867–68 overprinted "SERVICE" in block letters. Although these stamps were prepared for use and sent out to the colony, they were never issued.*

Prices:

Narrow "SERVICE"		Wide "SERVICE"	
No. 98. 2d.	.. 50·00	No. 119. 1d. ..	48·00
104. 6d.	.. 60·00	120. 3d. ..	75·00
108. 8d.	.. 70·00		
113. 1s.	.. 90·00		
116. 2s.	.. 95·00		
116. 2s. imp.	.. £650		

Until 1 October 1895 all Official mail was carried free. After that date postage was paid on Official letters to the general public, on certain interdepartmental mail and on all packets over 1lb in weight. Nos. O1/17 were provided for ths purpose.

On Service

(O 3)

1895. *Optd with Type O 3 by the Govt Printer, Colombo.*

O1	9	2 c. green (No. 147)		..	5·50	25
O2	39	3 c. terracotta and blue-green (No. 245)			8·00	40
O3	28	5 c. dull purple (No. 195)		..	1·25	20
O4	29	15 c. sage-green (No. 196)		..	9·00	30
O5		25 c. yellow-brown (No. 198)		..	10·00	80
O6		30 c. bright mauve and chestnut (No. 247)			12·00	30
O7	30	1 r. 12, dull rose (wmk sideways) (No. 201)		..	50·00	45·00
		a. Opt double, one albino		..	£150	
		b. Wmk upright		..	65·00	55·00
O1/7				Set of 7	85·00	45·00

1899 (June)–**1900.** *Nos. 256/7 and 261/2 optd with Type O 3.*

O 8	9	2 c. pale orange-brown (3.00)	..	3·00	60
O 9	39	3 c. deep green (9.00)	..	7·50	60
O10	29	15 c. blue (9.00)	..	13·00	60
O11	39	75 c. black and red-brown (R.)	..	5·50	4·00
O8/11			Set of 4	26·00	5·25

1903 (26 Nov)–**04.** *Nos. 265/6, 268 and 271/3 optd with Type O 3.*

O12	44	2 c. red-brown (4.1.04)	..	6·00	70
O13	45	3 c. green	..	3·50	2·00
O14	46	5 c. dull purple	..	8·50	1·00
O15	48	15 c. blue	..	20·00	2·50
O16		25 c. bistre (15.7.04)	..	19·00	15·00
O17		30 c. dull violet and green (14.3.04)	..	6·50	1·50
O12/17			Set of 6	55·00	20·00

Stamps overprinted "On Service" were withdrawn on 1 October 1904.

POSTAL FISCALS

1952 (1 Dec). *As T* **72** *but inscr "REVENUE" at sides. Chalk-surfaced paper.*

F1	10 r. dull green and yellow-orange ..	..	50·00	28·00

This revenue stamp was on sale for postal use from 1 December 1952, until 14 March 1954.

F 1 Republic Crest

(Recess Harrison)

1979 (28 May)–**83.** *As Type F* **1,** *but with additional Sinhala and Tamil inscrs on either side of crest. W* **4** *of Maldive Islands. P* 13×12.

F2	20 r. blackish green	.. ..	4·00	2·50
F3	50 r. deep slate-violet	..	8·50	5·50
F4	100 r. deep carmine-red (14.10.83)	..	17·00	16·00

The above, together with 500 and 1000 r. values, were originally released for fiscal purposes on 24 June 1974. The dates quoted are those on which they were validated for postal use. All three were withdrawn on 6 August 1984.

(Litho Harrison)

1984 (15 Aug). *W* **77** *of Brunei. P* 14½×14.

F5	F 1	50 r. orange	..	15·00	10·00
F6		100 r. dull chocolate	..	30·00	30·00

A 500 r. value also exists, but was not valid for postal purposes.

(Recess Harrison)

1984 (21 Sept). *W* **77** *of Brunei. P* 14½×14.

F7	F 1	50 r. orange-vermilion	..	1·40	1·50
F8		100 r. deep reddish purple		2·75	3·00

Stamps in this series with face values of 500 or 1000 r. were not valid for postal purposes.

Sudan

ANGLO-EGYPTIAN CONDOMINIUM

An Egyptian post office was opened at Suakin in 1867 and the stamps of Egypt, including postage dues and the official (No. O64), were used in the Sudan until replaced by the overprinted "SOUDAN" issue of 1897.

Cancellations have been identified from eleven post offices, using the following postmark types:

A

B

C

D

E

F

G

H

I

J

K

L

BERBER (spelt BARBAR). Open 1873 to 1884. Postmark type G.
DABROUSSA. Open 1889? onwards. Postmark as type J but with 11 bars in arcs.
DONGOLA. Open 1873 to 1885 and 1896 onwards. Postmark types F, G, K, L.
GEDAREF. Open ? Postmark type H.
KASSALA. Open 1875 to 1885. Postmark type G.
KHARTOUM. Open 1873 to 1884. Postmark types E (spelt KARTUM), G (spelt HARTUM), I (with or without line of Arabic above date).
KORTI. Open 1884/5 and 1897. Postmark type K.
SUAKIN. Open 1867 onwards. Postmark types A, B, C (spelt SUAKIM), D (spelt SUAKIM and also with year replaced by concentric arcs), I (spelt SOUAKIN), J (spelt SAWAKIN, number of bars differs).
TANI. Open 1885. Postmark type K.
TOKAR. Open 1891 onwards. Postmark type J (7 bars in arcs).
WADI HALFA. Open 1873 onwards. Postmark types F (spelt WADI HALFE), G (spelt WADI HALFE), I, J (number of bars differs).
WADI HALFA CAMP. Open 1896 onwards. Postmark type I.

Official records also list post offices at the following locations, but no genuine postal markings from them have yet been reported: Chaka, Dara, Debeira, El Abiad, El Fasher, El Kalabat, Faras, Fashoda, Fazogl, Ishkeit, Kalkal, Karkok, Mesellemia, Sara, Sennar and Taoufikia (not to be confused with the town of the same name in Egypt.

M

The post office at Kassala was operated by Italy from 1894 until 1896, using stamps of Eritrea cancelled with postmark type M.

From the last years of the nineteenth century that part of Sudan lying south of the 5 degree North latitude line was administered by Uganda (the area to the east of the Nile) (until 1912) or by Belgium (the area to the west of the Nile, known as the Lado Enclave) (until 1910).

Stamps of Uganda or East Africa and Uganda were used at Gondokoro and Nimuli between 1901 and 1911, usually cancelled with circular date stamps or, probably in transit at Khartoum, by a lozenge-shaped grid of 18 × 17 dots.

Stamps of Belgian Congo were used from the Lado Enclave between 1897 and 1910, as were those of Uganda (1901–10) and Sudan (1902–10), although no local postmarks were supplied, examples being initially cancelled in manuscript.

Stamps of Sudan were used at Gambeila (Ethiopia) between 1910 and 10 June 1940 and from 22 March 1941 until 15 October 1956. Sudan stamps were also used at Sabderat (Eritrea) between March 1910 and 1940.

PRICES FOR STAMPS ON COVER TO 1945

Nos. 1/9	from × 20
Nos. 10/17	from × 6
Nos. 18/29	from × 5
Nos. 30/95	from × 2
Nos. D1/11	from × 30
Nos. O1/3	—
Nos. O4/22	from × 15
Nos. A1/16	from × 6

السودان

SOUDAN

(1)

1897 (1 Mar). *Nos. 54b, 55a, 57/a, 58a, 59, 60, 62a and 63 of Egypt optd as T 1 by Govt Ptg Wks, Bûlâq, Cairo.*

1	1 m. pale brown	..	1·50	2·00
	a. Opt inverted	..	£250	
	b. Opt omitted (in vert pair with normal)	£900	
	c. Deep brown	..	1·50	2·25
3	2 m. green	..	1·25	1·75
	a. Opt omitted (in vert pair with normal)	£3000	
4	3 m. orange-yellow	..	1·40	1·50
	a. Opt omitted (in vert pair with normal)	£3000	
5	5 m. rose-carmine	..	2·00	70
	a. Opt inverted	..	£300	
	b. Opt omitted (in vert pair with normal)	£900	
6	1 p. ultramarine	..	7·00	2·00
7	2 p. orange-brown	..	40·00	12·00

8	5 p. slate	..	40·00	12·00
	a. Opt double	..	£2000	
	b. Opt omitted (in vert pair with normal)	£2750	
9	10 p. mauve	..	30·00	40·00
1/9	.. Set of 8	£110	65·00

Numerous forgeries exist including some which show the characteristics of the varieties mentioned below.

There are six varieties of the overprint on each value most of which can be supplied in vertical strips at double the catalogue price.

In some printings the large dot is omitted from the left-hand Arabic character on one stamp in the pane of 60.

Only two examples, one unused and the other used (in the Royal Collection), are known of No. 8a. In both instances one impression is partially albino.

PRINTERS. All stamps of Sudan were printed by De La Rue & Co, Ltd, London, *except where otherwise stated.*

2 Arab Postman

3

(Des E. A. Stanton. Typo)

1898 (1 Mar). *W 3. P 14.*

10	2	1 m. brown and pink		30	50
11		2 m. green and brown		1·00	1·25
12		3 m. mauve and green		1·50	2·25
13		5 m. carmine and black		75	40
14		1 p. blue and brown		4·00	3·25
15		2 p. black and blue		14·00	6·50
16		5 p. brown and green		22·00	7·50
17		10 p. black and mauve		22·00	2·25
10/17			Set of 8	60·00	22·00

4   (5)

5 Milliemes

1902–21. *W 4. Ordinary paper. P 14.*

18	2	1 m. brown and carmine (5.05)	..	30	10
19		2 m. green and brown (11.02)	..	1·00	10
20		3 m. mauve and green (7.03)	..	1·25	25
21		4 m. blue and bistre (20.1.07)	..	1·50	2·50
22		4 m. vermilion and brown (10.07)	..	1·50	75
23		5 m. scarlet and black (12.03)	..	2·00	10
24		1 p. blue and brown (12.03)	..	1·60	15
25		2 p. black and blue (2.08)	..	22·00	1·75
26		2 p. purple & orge-yellow (*chalk-surfaced paper*) (22.12.21)	..	3·25	6·50
27		5 p. brown and green (2.08)	..	22·00	30
		a. Chalk-surfaced paper		24·00	1·25
28		10 p. black and mauve (2.11)	..	22·00	2·00
		a. Chalk-surfaced paper		22·00	4·25
18/28			Set of 11	70·00	13·00

1903 (Sept). *No. 16 surch at Khartoum with T 5, in blocks of 30.*

29	5 m. on 5 pi. brown and green	..	6·50	9·00
	a. Surch inverted	..	£300	£275

6   7

1921–23. *Chalk-surfaced paper. Typo. W 4. P 14.*

30	6	1 m. black and orange (4.2.22)	..	80	2·00
31		2 m. yellow-orange and chocolate (1922)		6·00	6·50
		a. Yellow and chocolate (1923).		7·00	7·00
32		3 m. mauve and green (25.1.22)	..	2·50	4·50
33		4 m. green and chocolate (21.3.22)	..	3·75	1·50
34		5 m. olive-brown and black (4.2.22)		1·75	10
35		10 m. carmine and black (1922)	..	1·50	10
36		15 m. bright blue and chestnut (14.12.21)		2·75	1·00
30/36			Set of 7	17·00	14·00

1927–41. *W 7. Chalk-surfaced paper. P 14.*

37	6	1 m. black and orange	..	20	10
		a. Ordinary paper (1941)		20	10
38		2 m. orange and chocolate	..	20	10
		a. Ordinary paper (1941)		50	10
39		3 m. mauve and green	..	20	10
		a. Ordinary paper (1941)		80	10

40	6	4 m. green and chocolate	.. ..	30	10
		a. Ordinary paper (1941)	..	1·00	10
41		5 m. olive-brown and black	..	30	10
		a. Ordinary paper (1941)	..	1·00	10
42		10 m. carmine and black	..	40	10
		a. Ordinary paper (1941)	..	1·25	10
43		15 m. bright blue and chestnut	..	30	10
		a. Ordinary paper (1941)	..	70	10
44	2	2 p. purple and orange-yellow	..	30	10
		a. Ordinary paper (1941)	..	70	10
44b		3 p. red-brown and blue (1.1.40)	..	2·75	10
		ba. Ordinary paper (1941)	..	4·50	10
44c		4 p. ultramarine and black (2.11.36)		2·25	10
45		5 p. chestnut and green	..	80	10
		a. Ordinary paper (1941)	..	1·25	10
45b		6 p. greenish blue and black (2.11.36)		2·25	20
		ba. Ordinary paper (1941)	..	5·00	70
45c		8 p. emerald and black (2.11.36)		3·00	1·00
		ca. Ordinary paper (1941)	..	6·00	1·50
46		10 p. black and reddish purple	..	1·00	10
		a. Ordinary paper. *Black and bright mauve* (1941)	..	8·00	70
46b		20 p. pale blue and blue (17.10.35)		2·00	10
		ba. Ordinary paper (1941)	..	2·25	10
37/46b			Set of 15	15·00	1·60

The ordinary paper of this issue is thick, smooth and opaque and was a wartime substitute for chalk-surfaced paper.

For similar stamps, but with different Arabic inscriptions, see Nos. 96/111.

AIR MAIL (8)   **AIR MAIL** (9)   **AIR** Extended foot to "R" (R.5/12)

1931 (15 Feb-Mar). *Air. Stamps of 1927 optd with T 8 or 9 (2 p.).*

47		5 m. olive-brown and black (Mar)	..	35	70
48		10 m. carmine and black	..	85	3·50
49		2 p. purple and orange-yellow		85	3·50
		a. Extended foot to "R"	..	18·00	
47/9			Set of 3	1·90	7·00

2½   2⅜

10 Statue of Gen. Gordon   (11)   **AIR MAIL**

1931 (1 Sept)-37. *Air. Recess. W 7 (sideways). P 14.*

49b	10	3 m. green and sepia (1.1.33)	..	2·50	5·50
50		5 m. black and green	..	1·00	20
51		10 m. black and carmine	..	1·00	35
52		15 m. red-brown and sepia	..	40	10
		a. Perf 11½ × 12½ (1937)	..	3·25	10
53		2 p. black and orange	..	30	10
		a. Perf 11½ × 12½ (1937)	..	4·50	13·00
53b		2½ p. magenta and blue (1.1.33)	..	3·50	10
		c. Perf 11½ × 12½ (1936)	..	1·75	15
		ca. *Aniline magenta and blue*	..	4·75	3·25
54		3 p. black and grey	..	60	15
		a. Perf 11½ × 12½ (1937)	..	85	55
55		3½ p. black and violet	..	1·50	80
		a. Perf 11½ × 12½ (1937)	..	2·50	10·00
56		4½ p. red-brown and grey	..	10·00	15·00
57		5 p. black and ultramarine	..	1·00	40
		a. Perf 11½ × 12½ (1937)	..	2·25	35
57b		7½ p. green and emerald (17.10.35)		5·50	3·75
		c. Perf 11½ × 12½ (1937)	..	3·00	6·00
57d		10 p. brown and greenish blue (17.10.35)		8·00	40
		e. Perf 11½ × 12½ (1937)	..	2·25	10·00
49b/57d			Set of 12 (p 14)	32·00	24·00
52a/7e			Set of 8 (p 11½×12½)	18·00	35·00

1932 (18 July). *Air. No. 44 surch with T 11.*

58		2½ p. on 2 p. purple and orange-yellow		2·00	3·50

12 Gen. Gordon (after C. Ouless)   13 Gordon Memorial College, Khartoum

14 Gordon Memorial Service, Khartoum (after R. C. Woodville)

1935 (1 Jan). *50th Death Anniv of General Gordon, Recess. W 7. P 14.*

59	12	5 m. green	..	35	10
60		10 m. yellow-brown	..	65	25
61		13 m. ultramarine	..	85	5·50
62		15 m. scarlet	..	1·50	25
63	13	2 p. blue	..	1·25	20
64		5 p. orange-vermilion	..	1·25	40
65		10 p. purple	..	6·50	6·50
66	14	20 p. black	..	22·00	45·00
67		50 p. red-brown	..	65·00	80·00
59/67			Set of 9	90·00	£120

7½ PIASTRES (15)   **5 MILLIEMES** (16)

٧ ١/٢ قروش   ٥ مليمًا

1935. *Air. Surch as T 15.*

68	10	15 m. on 10 m. black and carmine (Apr)		40	10
		a. Surch double	..	£600	£700
69		2½ p. on 3 m. green and sepia (Apr)		85	5·00
		a. Second arabic letter from left missing		65·00	£100
		b. Small "½"	..	2·75	16·00
70		2½ p. on 5 m. black and green (Apr)		40	2·00
		a. Second Arabic letter from left missing		35·00	55·00
		b. Small "½"	..	1·75	9·00
		c. Surch inverted	..	£600	£700
		d. Ditto with variety a.	..	£2750	
		e. Ditto with variety b.	..	£1100	
71		3 p. on 4½ p. red-brown and grey (Apr)		1·75	10·00
72		7½ p. on 4½ p. red-brown and grey (Mar)		6·00	35·00
73		10 p. on 4½ p. red-brown and grey (Mar)		6·00	35·00
68/73			Set of 6	13·00	80·00

Nos. 69a and 70a occur in position 49 of the sheet of 50; the small "½" variety occurs in positions 17, 27, 32, 36, 41, 42 and 46.

The 15 m. on 10 m. and the 7½ p. on 4½ p. surcharged in red and the 2½ p. on 3 m. and 2½ p. on 5 m in green are from proof sheets; the latter two items being known cancelled. A 7¼ p. on 4½ p. also exists from a proof sheet (*Prices from £200 each, unused*).

1938 (1 July). *Air. Surch as T 16.*

74	10	5 m. on 2½ p. (p 11½ × 12½)	..	2·25	10
75		3 p. on 3½ p. (p 14)	..	24·00	30·00
		a. Perf 11½ × 12½	..	£350	£475
76		3 p. on 7½ p. (p 14)	..	5·50	6·00
		a. Perf 11½ × 12½	..	£350	£475
77		5 p. on 10 p. (p 14)	..	1·50	4·25
		a. Perf 11½ × 12½	..	£350	£475
74/7			Set of 4	30·00	35·00

A 5 p. on 2½ p., perf 11½×12½, exists either mint or cancelled from a trial printing (*Price £350 unused*).

5 Mills. (17)   ٥ مليم   Normal ("Malime")

"Malmime" (Left-hand pane R. 5/1)   Short "mim" (Right-hand pane R. 3/1)   Broken "lam" (Right-hand pane R. 6/2)

5 M

Inserted "5" (Bottom right-hand pane R. 4/5)

1940 (25 Feb). *Surch with T 17 by McCorquodale (Sudan) Ltd, Khartoum.*

78	6	5 m. on 10 m. carmine and black	..	50	30
		a. "Malmime"	..	32·00	35·00
		b. Two dots omitted (Right-hand pane R. 8/6)	..	32·00	35·00
		c. Short "mim"	..	32·00	35·00
		d. Broken "lam"	..	32·00	35·00
		e. Inserted "5"	..	£100	

4½ Piastres (19)   ٤ ١/٢ قرش

4½ PIASTRES (18)

1940-1. *Surch as T 18 or 19 at Khartoum.*

79	6	4½ p. on 5 m. olive-brown & blk (9.2.41)	..	38·00	2·25
80	2	4½ p. on 8 p. emerald and black (12.12.40)		25·00	5·00

20 Tuti Island, R. Nile, near Khartoum   21 Tuti Island, R. Nile near Khartoum

(Des Miss H. M. Hebbert. Litho Security Printing Press, Nasik, India)

1941 (25 Mar-10 Aug). *P 14 × 13½ (T 20) or P 13½ × 14 (T 21).*

81	20	1 m. slate and orange (10.8)		10	1·25
82		2 m. orange and chocolate (10.8)	..	30	1·10
83		3 m. mauve and green (10.8)		30	10
84		4 m. green and chocolate (10.8)		15	20
85		5 m. olive-brown and black (10.8)		15	10
86		10 m. carmine and black (10.8)		6·00	1·75
87		15 m. bright blue and chestnut		20	10
88	21	2 p. purple and orange-yellow (10.8)		3·25	60
89		3 p. red-brown and blue		70	10
90		4 p. ultramarine and black		60	10
91		5 p. chestnut and green (10.8)		4·50	6·00
92		6 p. greenish blue and black (10.8)		15·00	40
93		8 p. emerald and black (10.8)		12·00	45
94		10 p. slate and purple (10.8)		45·00	75
95		20 p. pale blue and blue (10.8)		45·00	23·00
81/95			Set of 15	£120	32·00

22   23

1948 (1 Jan-June). *Arabic inscriptions below camel altered. Typo. W 7. Ordinary paper (8, 10, 20 p.) or chalk-surfaced paper (others). P 14.*

96	22	1 m. black and orange	..	35	85
97		2 m. orange and chocolate	..	80	1·25
98		3 m. mauve and green	..	30	60
99		4 m. deep green and chocolate	..	30	10
100		5 m. olive-brown and black	..	1·25	50
101		10 m. rose-red and black	..	2·00	10
		a. Centre inverted	..	†	—
102		15 m. ultramarine and chestnut	..	1·25	10
103	23	2 p. purple and orange-yellow	..	3·25	30
104		3 p. red-brown and deep blue	..	2·25	10
105		4 p. ultramarine and black	..	2·25	75
106		5 p. brown-orange and deep green	..	2·25	40
107		6 p. greenish blue and black	..	2·25	1·50
108		8 p. bluish green and black	..	2·25	1·50
109		10 p. black and mauve	..	5·00	1·25
		a. Chalk-surfaced paper (June)	..	8·00	2·00
110		20 p. pale blue and deep blue	..	2·25	10
		a. Perf 13. Chalk-surfaced paper (June)	..	42·00	80·00
111		50 p. carmine and ultramarine	..	5·00	40
96/111			Set of 16	30·00	8·50

A single used example is known of No. 101a.

For similar stamps, but with different Arabic inscriptions, see Nos. 37/46b.

24   25

1948 (1 Oct). *Golden Jubilee of "Camel Postman" design. Chalk-surfaced paper. Typo. W 7. P 13.*

112	24	2 p. black and light blue	..	10	10

1948 (23 Dec). *Opening of Legislative Assembly, Chalk-surfaced paper. Typo. W 7. P 13.*

113	25	10 m. rose-red and black	..	10	10
114		5 p. brown-orange and deep green	..	10	30

26 Blue Nile Bridge, Khartoum

(Des Col. W. L. Atkinson (2½ p., 6 p.), G. R. Wilson (3 p.), others from photographs. Recess)

1950 (1 July). *Air. T 26 and similar horiz designs. W 7. P 12.*

115		2 p. black and blue-green	..	3·50	30
116		2½ p. light blue and red-orange	..	50	55
117		3 p. reddish purple and blue	..	2·50	10
118		3½ p. purple-brown and yellow-brown	..	75	2·25
119		4 p. brown and light blue	..	70	90
120		4½ p. black and ultramarine	..	2·25	3·00
		a. *Black and steel-blue*	..	2·50	3·50
121		6 p. black and carmine	..	60	70
122		20 p. black and kassala	..	1·75	2·50
115/122			Set of 8	11·00	9·00

Designs:—2½ p. Kassala Jebel; 3 p. Sagia (water wheel); 3½ p. Port Sudan; 4 p. Gordon Memorial College; 4½ p. Gordon Pasha (Nile mail boat); 6 p. Suakin; 20 p. G.P.O., Khartoum.

34 Ibex   35 Cotton Picking

(Des Col. W. L. Atkinson (1 m., 2 m., 4 m., 5 m., 10 m., 3 p., 3½ p., 20 p.), Col. E. A. Stanton (50 p.) others from photographs. Typo)

1951 (1 Sept)–62? *Designs as T 34/5. Chalk-surfaced paper. W 7. P 14 (millieme values) or 13 (piastre values).*

123	1 m. black and orange	..	..	10	90
124	2 m. black and bright blue	..	..	55	20
125	3 m. black and green	..	..	2·25	1·75
126	4 m. black and yellow-green	..	..	40	1·25
127	5 m. black and purple	..	..	40	10
	a. *Black and reddish purple* (1962?)			1·00	10
128	10 m. black and pale blue	..	..	15	10
129	15 m. black and chestnut	..	..	60	10
	a. *Black and brown-orange* (1962?)			60	10
130	2 p. deep blue and pale blue	..	..	15	10
	a. *Deep blue and very pale blue* (1962?)			90	10
131	3 p. brown and deep ultramarine	..		1·50	10
	a. *Brown and deep blue* (1962?)			2·50	40
132	3½ p. bright green and red-brown	..		30	10
133	4 p. ultramarine and black	..		30	10
	a. *Deep blue and black* (1962?)			1·75	10
134	5 p. orange-brown and yellow-green	..		30	10
135	6 p. blue and black	..	..	2·75	85
	a. *Deep blue and black* (1962?)			4·50	2·25
136	8 p. blue and brown	..	..	3·75	70
	a. *Deep blue and brown* (1962?)			4·50	50
137	10 p. black and green	..	..	1·00	10
138	20 p. blue-green and black	..	..	3·00	55
139	50 p. carmine and black	..	..	8·00	55
123/139			*Set of 17*	23·00	6·25

Designs: *Vert as T 34*—2 m. Whale-headed Stork; 3 m. Giraffe; 4 m. Baggara girl; 5 m. Shilluk warrior; 10 m. Hadendowa; 15 m. Policeman. *Horiz as T 35*—3 p. Ambatch reed canoe; 3½ p. Nuba wrestlers; 4 p. Weaving; 5 p. Saluka farming; 6 p. Gum tapping; 8 p. Darfur chief; 10 p. Stack Laboratory; 20 p. Nile Lechwe. *Vert as T 35*—50 p. Camel postman.

SELF-GOVERNMENT

51 Camel Postman

1954 (9 Jan). *Self-Government. Chalk-surfaced paper. Typo. W 7. P 13.*

140	**51**	15 m. orange-brown and bright green	..	40	50
141		3 p. blue and indigo	..	40	75
142		5 p. black and reddish purple	..	40	40
140/2 ..			*Set of 3*	1·10	1·50

Stamps as Type **51**, but dated "1953" were released in error at the Sudan Agency in London. They had no postal validity (*Price per set £14 un*).

Later issues of Sudan as an independent republic will be found in Part 14 (*Africa since Independence N–Z*) of this catalogue.

POSTAGE DUE STAMPS

1897 (1 Mar). *Type D 3 of Egypt, optd with T 1 at Bûlâq.*

D1	2 m. green	..	..	1·75	8·00
	a. Opt omitted (in horiz pair with normal)			£2250	
D2	4 m. maroon	..	..	1·75	8·00
	a. Bisected (2 m.) (on cover)	..	†		
D3	1 p. ultramarine	..	..	8·00	5·00
D4	2 p. orange	..	..	8·50	11·00
	a. Bisected (1 p.) (on cover)	..	† £1200		
D1/4			*Set of 4*	18·00	29·00

In some printings the large dot is omitted from the left-hand Arabic character on one stamp in the pane.

No. D1 has been recorded used as a bisect.

D 1   Gunboat *Zafir*   D 2

1901 (1 Jan)–12. *Typo. W 4 (sideways). Ordinary paper. P 14.*

D5	D 1	2 m. black and brown	..	55	60
		a. Wmk upright	..		
		b. Chalk-surfaced paper (1912)	55	1·50
D6		4 m. brown and green	..	2·00	90
		a. Chalk-surfaced paper (1912)	2·50	1·40
D7		10 m. green and mauve	..	3·75	3·75
		a. Wmk upright	..		
		b. Chalk-surfaced paper (1912)	6·50	4·50
D8		20 m. ultramarine and carmine	3·25	3·25
		a. Chalk-surfaced paper (1912)	7·50	7·50
D5/8			*Set of 4*	8·00	7·50

Nos. D6 and D8 exist used as bisects.

1927–30. *W 7. Chalk-surfaced paper. P 14.*

D 9	D 1	2 m. black and brown (1930)	..	2·00	2·00
D10		4 m. brown and green	..	90	80
D11		10 m. green and mauve	..	1·25	1·60
		a. Ordinary paper ..			
D9/11			*Set of 3*	3·75	4·00

1948 (1 Jan). *Arabic inscriptions at foot altered. Chalk-surfaced paper. Typo. W 7. P 14.*

D12	D 2	2 m. black and brown-orange	..	80	14·00
D13		4 m. brown and green	..	2·00	18·00
D14		10 m. green and mauve	..	9·50	13·00
D15		20 m. ultramarine and carmine	..	12·00	18·00
D12/15			*Set of 4*	22·00	55·00

The 10 and 20 m. were reissued in 1980 on Sudan arms watermarked paper.

OFFICIAL STAMPS

1900 (8 Feb). *5 mils of 1897 punctured "S G" by hand. The "S" has 14 and the "G" 12 holes.*

O1	5 m. rose-carmine	..	..	45·00	20·00

1901 (Jan). *1 m. wmk Quatrefoil, punctured as No. O1.*

O2	1 m. brown and pink	..	..	42·00	30·00

Nos. O1/2 are found with the punctured "SG" inverted, reversed or inverted and reversed.

O.S.G.S.   O.S.G.S.

(O 1)   ("On Sudan Government (O 2) Service")

1902. *No. 10 optd at Khartoum as Type O 1 in groups of 30 stamps.*

O3	2	1 m. brown and pink	..	2·00	8·00
		a. Oval "O" (No. 19)	..	65·00	£110
		b. Round stops. (Nos. 25 to 30)	7·50	32·00
		c. Opt inverted	..	£275	£350
		d. Ditto and oval "O"	..	£2000	
		e. Ditto and round stops	..	£600	£750
		f. Opt double	..	£350	
		g. Ditto and round stops	..	£800	
		h. Ditto and oval "O"	..		

1903–12. *T 2 optd as Type O 2, by D.L.R. in sheets of 120 stamps.*

(i) *Wmk Quatrefoil* (3.06)

O 4	10 p. black and mauve	..	..	13·00	17·00
	a. Malformed "O"	..	..	£120	

(ii) *Wmk Mult Star and Crescent*

O 5	1 m. brown and carmine (9.04)	..	40	10
	a. Opt double	..	..		
	b. Malformed "O"	..	..	19·00	
O 6	3 m. mauve and green (2.04)	..	1·75	15
	a. Opt double	..	£850	£850
	b. Malformed "O"	..	40·00	
O 7	5 m. scarlet and black (1.1.03)	..	1·75	10
	a. Malformed "O"	..	40·00	
O 8	1 p. blue and brown (1.1.03)	..	1·75	10
	a. Malformed "O"	..	40·00	
O 9	2 p. black and blue (1.1.03)	..	14·00	20
	a. Malformed "O"	..	£120	
O10	5 p. brown and green (1.1.03)	..	2·00	30
	a. Malformed "O"	..	45·00	
O11	10 p. black and mauve (9.12)	..	4·00	38·00
	a. Malformed "O"	..	65·00	
O4/11			*Set of 8*	35·00	50·00

The malformed "O" is slightly flattened on the left-hand side and occurs on position 7 of the lower pane.

1913 (Jan)–22. *Nos. 18/20 and 23/8 punctured "SG" by machine. The "S" has 12 holes and the "G" 13.*

O12	2	1 m. brown and carmine	..	2·50	25
O13		2 m. green and brown (1915)	..	5·50	2·75
O14		3 m. mauve and green	..	3·75	70
O15		5 m. scarlet and black	..	1·75	15
O16		1 p. blue and brown	..	2·75	35
O17		2 p. black and blue	..	4·25	65
O18		2 p. purple and orange-yellow (chalk-surfaced paper) (1922)	..	4·00	4·50
O19		5 p. brown and green	..	8·50	1·50
		a. Chalk-surfaced paper	8·50	1·75
O20		10 p. black and mauve (1914)	..	12·00	12·00
		a. Chalk-surfaced paper	12·00	12·00
O12/20			*Set of 9*	40·00	21·00

1922. *Nos. 32/5 punctured "SG" by machine. The "S" has 9 holes and the "G" 10.*

O21	6	3 m. mauve and green	..	11·00	7·00
O22		4 m. green and chocolate	..	11·00	5·50
O23		5 m. olive-brown and black	..	1·00	55
O24		10 m. carmine and black..	..	2·00	60
O21/4 ..			*Set of 4*	23·00	12·00

1927–30. *Nos. 39/42, 44, 45 and 46 punctured "SG" by machine. Nos. O25/8 have 9 holes in the "S" and 10 in the "G"; Nos. O29/31 12 holes in the "S" and 13 in the "G".*

O25	6	3 m. mauve and green (1928)	..	6·00	2·50
O26		4 m. green and chocolate (1930)	..	55·00	35·00
O27		5 m. olive-green and black	..	2·00	10
O28		10 m. carmine and black	..	3·00	35
O29	2	2 p. purple and orange-yellow ..		7·00	85
O30		5 p. chestnut and green	..	13·00	3·50
O31		10 p. black and reddish purple ..		22·00	10·00
O25/31			*Set of 7*	95·00	48·00

The use of Nos. O25/31 on internal official mail ceased in 1932, but they continued to be required for official mail to foreign destinations until replaced by Nos. O32/46 in 1936.

S.G.   S.G.   S.G.

(O 3)   (O 4)   (O 4a)

1936 (19 Sept)–46. *Nos. 37a, 38a, 39/43 optd with Type O 3, and 44, 44ba, 44c, 45, 45ba, 45c, 46 and 46ba with Type O 4. W 7. P 14.*

O32	6	1 m. black and orange (22.11.46)	..	50	6·00
		a. Opt double	..	†	—
O33		2 m. orange and chocolate (4.45)	..	30	2·25
O34		3 m. mauve and green (1.37)	..	1·00	10
O35		4 m. green and chocolate	..	1·50	2·25
O36		5 m. olive-brown and black (3.40)	..	40	10
		a. Ordinary paper	..	7·00	40
O37		10 m. carmine and black (6.46)	..	60	10
O38		15 m. bright blue and chestnut (21.6.37)	2·00	10
		a. Ordinary paper	..	9·00	75
O39	2	2 p. purple and orange-yellow (4.37)	..	4·00	10
		a. Ordinary paper	..	14·00	2·50
O39b		3 p. red-brown and blue (4.46)	..	2·00	70
O39c		4 p. ultramarine and black (4.46)	..	4·50	50
		ca. Ordinary paper	..	20·00	4·00
O40		5 p. chestnut and green (4.46)	..	4·50	10
		a. Ordinary paper	..	20·00	4·25
O40b		6 p. greenish blue and black (4.46)	..	4·50	2·00
O40c		8 p. emerald and black (4.46)	..	4·25	13·00
O41		10 p. black and reddish purple (10.37)	..	12·00	4·00
		a. Ordinary paper. *Black and bright mauve* (1941)	..	20·00	2·25
O42		20 p. pale blue and blue (6.46)	..	13·00	16·00
O32/42			*Set of 15*	50·00	40·00

1948 (1 Jan). *Nos. 96/102 optd with.Type O 3, and 103/111 with Type O 4.*

O43	22	1 m. black and orange	..	10	1·25
O44		2 m. orange and chocolate	..	30	10
O45		3 m. mauve and green	..	50	2·00
O46		4 m. deep green and chocolate	..	50	50
O47		5 m. olive-brown and black	..	30	10
O48		10 m. rose-red and black	..	30	30
O49		15 m. ultramarine and chestnut	..	30	10
O50	23	2 p. purple and orange-yellow	..	45	10
O51		3 p. red-brown and deep blue	..	45	10
O52		4 p. ultramarine and black	..	60	10
		a. Perf 13 (optd Type O 4a)	..	13·00	15·00
O53		5 p. brown-orange and deep green	60	10
O54		6 p. greenish blue and black	..	60	10
O55		8 p. bluish green and black	..	60	40
O56		10 p. black and mauve	..	60	20
O57		20 p. pale blue and deep blue	..	2·50	25
O58		50 p. carmine and ultramarine	..	40·00	20·00
O43/58			*Set of 16*	45·00	23·00

1950 (1 July). *Air. Optd with Type O 4a.*

O59	2 p. black and blue-green (R.)	..	9·00	1·50
O60	2½ p. light blue and red-orange	..	1·25	90
O61	3 p. reddish purple and blue	..	80	70
O62	3½ p. purple-brown and yellow-brown	..	80	4·00
O63	4 p. brown and light blue ..		80	2·75
O64	4½ p. black and ultramarine (R.)	..	2·50	8·50
	a. *Black and steel-blue*	..	3·75	9·00
O65	6 p. black and carmine (R.)	..	1·00	3·50
O66	20 p. black and purple (R.) ..		5·00	10·00
O59/66			*Set of 8*	19·00	29·00

1951 (1 Sept)–62? *Nos. 123/9 optd with Type O 3, and 130/9 with Type O 4a.*

O67	1 m. black and orange (R.)	..	30	2·25
O68	2 m. black and bright blue (R.)	..	30	20
O69	3 m. black and green (R.)	..	1·75	8·50
O70	4 m. black and yellow-green (R.)	..	10	2·25
O71	5 m. black and purple (R.)	..	10	10
O72	10 m. black and pale blue (R.)	..	10	10
O73	15 m. black and chestnut (R.)	..	10	10
O74	2 p. deep blue and pale blue	..	10	10
	a. Opt inverted	..	£375	
	b. *Deep blue and very pale blue* (1962?)	20	10
O75	3 p. brown and pale ultramarine	..	75	10
	a. *Brown and deep blue* (1962?)	2·50	30
O76	3½ p. bright green and red-brown	..	25	10
	a. *Light emerald & red-brown* (1962?)	1·25	30
O77	4 p. ultramarine and black	..	25	10
	a. *Deep blue and black* (1962?)	30	10
O78	5 p. orange-brown and yellow-green	..	25	10
O79	6 p. blue and black	..	30	1·25
	a. *Deep blue and black* (1962?)	2·25	2·50
O80	8 p. blue and brown	..	45	10
	a. *Deep blue and brown* (1962?)	1·25	40
O81	10 p. black and green (R.)	..	50	10
O81a	10 p. black and green (Blk.) (1958)	8·50	30
O82	20 p. blue-green and black	..	1·25	25
	a. Opt inverted	..	—	£550
O83	50 p. carmine and black	..	3·50	1·25
O67/83			*Set of 18*	17·00	15·00

The 5, 10 and 15 m. values were later reissued with a thinner overprint.

ARMY SERVICE STAMPS

ARMY	**OFFICIAL**	**ARMY**	**OFFICIAL**	**Army Service**
(A 1)		(A 2)		(A 3)

1905 (Jan). *T 2 optd at Khartoum as Types A 1 or A 2. Wmk Mult Star and Crescent.* (i) *"ARMY" reading up.*

A1	1 m. brown and carmine (A 1)	..	2·50	2·00
	a. "I" for "T".	..	45·00	24·00
	b. Opt Type A 2	..	32·00	16·00

(ii) *Overprint horizontal*

A2	1 m. brown and carmine (A 1)	..	£325	
	a. "I" for "T".	..	£3500	
	b. Opt Type A 2	..	£2000	

The horizontal overprint exists with either "ARMY" or "OFFICIAL" reading the right way up. It did not fit the stamps, resulting in misplacements where more than one whole overprint appears, or when the two words are transposed.

(iii) "ARMY" reading down
A3 1 m. brown and carmine (A 1) .. .. .. 65·00 55·00
    a. "!" for "I" £700 £700
    b. Opt Type A 2 .. .. £600 £425

1905 (Nov). *As No A 1, but wmk Quatrefoil, W 3.*
A4 1 m. brown and pink (A 1) £110 £120
    a. "!" for "I" £2500 £1600
    b. Opt Type A 2 .. .. £1200 £1200
The 29th stamp in each setting of 30 (Nos. A1–A4) has an exclamation mark for first "I" in "OFFICIAL" while the 6th and 12th stamps are Type A 2.

Two varieties of the 1 millieme
A. 1st Ptg. 14 mm between lines of opt.
B. Later Ptgs. 12 mm between lines.
All other values are Type B.

1906 (Jan)–11. *T 2 optd as Type A 3.*
(i) Wmk Mult Star and Crescent, W 4
A 5 1 m. brown and carmine (Type A) £250 £190
A 6 1 m. brown and carmine (Type B) .. 1·50 20
    a. Opt double, one diagonal .. † £650
    b. Opt inverted £325 £325
    c. Pair, one without opt .. ..
    d. "Service" omitted .. .. † £3250
    e. "Λ" for "A" in "Army" .. £150 £150
A 7 2 m. green and brown .. .. 5·00 1·00
    a. Pair, one without opt .. £1600
    b. "Army" omitted £2500
A 8 3 m. mauve and green .. .. 16·00 40
    a. Opt inverted £1700
A 9 5 m. scarlet and black .. .. 1·50 10
    a. Opt. double £190 £190
    ab. Opt double, one diagonal .. £200
    b. Opt inverted .. .. † £200
    c. "Amry" .. .. † £2250
    d. "Λ" for "A" in "Army" .. — £250
    e. Opt double, one inverted .. £700 £350
A10 1 p. blue and brown.. .. 9·50 15
    a. "Army" omitted .. .. † £2000
A11 2 p. black and blue (1.09) .. 25·00 12·00
    a. Opt double .. .. † £2250
A12 5 p. brown and green (5.08) .. 80·00 45·00
A13 10 p. black and mauve (5.11) .. £450 £550
A6/10 Optd "Specimen" .. *Set of 5* £150
There were a number of printings of these Army Service stamps; the earlier are as Type A 3; the 1908 printing has a narrower "A" in "Army" and the 1910–11 printings have the tail of the "y" in "Army" much shorter.

(ii) Wmk Quatrefoil, W 3
A14 2 p. black and blue .. .. 45·00 9·50
A15 5 p. brown and green .. .. 90·00 £110
A16 10 p. black and mauve .. £120 £160
A14/16 .. .. .. *Set of 3* £225 £250
A14/16 Optd "Specimen" .. *Set of 3* £120

1912 (1 Jan)–**22.** *Nos. 18/20 and 23/8 punctured "AS" by machine. The "A" has 12 holes and the "S" 11.*
A17 2 1 m. brown and carmine .. 14·00 1·75
A18   2 m. green and brown .. .. 3·00 70
A19   3 m. mauve and green .. 20·00 2·25
A20   5 m. scarlet and black .. 2·50 35
    a. On No. 13 .. ..
A21   1 p. blue and brown .. .. 6·50 90
A22   2 p. black and blue .. .. 16·00 2·50
A23   2 p. purple and orange-yellow (*chalk-surfaced paper*) (1922) .. 25·00 16·00
A24   5 p. brown and green .. .. 22·00 11·00
    a. Chalk-surfaced paper .. 22·00 11·00
A25   10 p. black and mauve (1914) .. £400 £225
A17/25 .. .. .. *Set of 9* £450 £225

1922–24. *Nos. 31a and 34/5 punctured "AS" by machine. The "A" has 8 holes and the "S" 9.*
A26 6 2 m. yellow and chocolate (1924) .. 32·00 20·00
A27   5 m. olive-brown and black (4.2.22) .. 4·00 1·00
A28   10 m. carmine and black.. .. 5·50 1·50
A26/8 .. .. .. *Set of 3* 38·00 20·00
The use of Nos. A17/28 on internal Army mail ceased when the Egyptian units were withdrawn at the end of 1924, but existing stocks continued to be used on Army mail to foreign destinations until supplies were exhausted.

Swaziland

TRIPARTITE GOVERNMENT
Following internal unrest and problems caused by the multitude of commercial concessions granted by the Swazi king the British and Transvaal governments intervened during 1889 to establish a tripartite administration under which the country was controlled by their representatives, acting with the agent of the Swazi king.
The Pretoria government had previously purchased the concession to run the postal service and, on the establishment of the tripartite administration, provided overprinted Transvaal stamps for use from the post offices opened at Bremersdorp, Darkton and Embekelweni.

Swazieland
(1)

1889 (18–20 Oct). *Stamps of Transvaal (South African Republic) optd with T 1, in black. (a) P 12½ × 12.*
1 18 1d. carmine .. .. .. 14·00 15·00
    a. Opt inverted.. .. £425 £500
2   2d. olive-bistre .. .. 70·00 15·00
    a. Opt inverted.. .. — £900
    b. "Swazielan" £900 £650
3   1s. green .. .. .. 10·00 13·00
    a. Opt inverted.. .. £475 £450

(b) P 12½
4 18 ½d. grey .. .. .. 8·50 17·00
    a. Opt inverted.. .. £425 £475
    b. "Swazielan" £750 £650
    c. "Swazielan" inverted .. — £2250
5   2d. olive-bistre .. .. 12·00 14·00
    a. Opt inverted.. .. £425 £450
    b. "Swazielan" £425 £450
    c. "Swazielan" inverted .. £1700 £1700
    d. Opt double £1800
6   6d. blue .. .. .. 15·00 30·00
    a. "Swazielan" £120 £160
7   2s. 6d. buff (20 Oct) .. £120 £160
8   5s. slate-blue (20 Oct) .. £120 £160
    a. "Swazielan" £1600 £1700
    b. "Swazielan" £4000
9   10s. fawn (20 Oct) £4500 £2750
The variety without "d" occurs on the left-hand bottom corner stamp in each sheet of certain printings.

1892 (Aug). *Optd in carmine. P 12½.*
10 18 ½d. grey .. .. .. 7·00 13·00
    a. Opt inverted £475
    b. Opt double £400 £400
    c. Pair, one without opt .. £650
A printing of the above with stop after "Swazieland" was made in July 1894 but these were not issued.

After further negotiations in 1894 the British and Transvaal governments agreed that Swaziland would become a protectorate of the Transvaal in February 1895. The overprinted stamps were withdrawn on 7 November 1894 and replaced by ordinary issues of the Transvaal.
Shortly after the outbreak of the Boer War in 1899 the Transvaal administration withdrew from Swaziland and there was no postal service from the area until the country became a British Protectorate in March 1902. From that date, until the introduction of the 1933 definitives, the post offices listed below used Transvaal or South Africa stamps.

The following post offices or postal agencies existed in Swaziland before 1933. Dates given are those on which it is generally accepted that the offices were first opened. Some were subsequently closed before the end of the period.

Bremersdorp (1889)	Mankaiana (1913)
Darkton (1889)	Mbabane (*previously* Embabaan) (1905)
Dwaleni (1918)	
Embabaan (1895)	M'dimba (1898)
Embekelweni (1889)	Mhlotsheni (1910)
Ezulweni (1910)	Mooihoek (1918)
Forbes Reef (1906)	Motshane (1929)
Goedgegun (1925)	Nomahasha (1904)
Hlatikulu (1903)	Nsoko (1927)
Hluti (1912)	Piggs Peak (1899)
Ivy (1912)	Sandhlan (1903)
Kubuta (1926)	Sicunusa (1913)
Mahamba (1899)	Stegi (1910)
Malkerns (1914)	Umkwakweni (1898)
Malomba (1928)	White Umbuluzi (1925)

BRITISH PROTECTORATE

2 King George V

3 King George VI

(Des Rev. C. C. Tugman. Recess D.L.R.)
1933 (2 Jan). *Wmk Mult Script CA. P 14.*
11 2 ½d. green 30 30
12   1d. carmine 30 10
13   2d. brown 30 45
14   3d. blue 45 60
15   4d. orange .. .. .. 1·00 1·40
16   6d. bright purple .. .. 1·00 80
17   1s. olive .. .. .. 1·50 2·75
18   2s. 6d. bright violet .. .. 15·00 28·00
19   5s. grey .. .. .. 35·00 50·00
20   10s. sepia £100 £120
11/20 .. .. .. *Set of 10* £140 £180
11/20 Perf "Specimen" .. *Set of 10* £225
The ½d., 1d., 2d. and 6d. values exist overprinted "OFFICIAL", but authority for their use was withdrawn before any were actually used. However, some stamps had already been issued to the Secretariat staff before instructions were received to invalidate their use (*Price £10000 per set un*).

1935 (4 May). *Silver Jubilee. As Nos. 114/17 of Jamaica. P 11×12.*
21   1d. deep blue and scarlet 40 20
    a. Extra flagstaff £100
    b. Short extra flagstaff .. 60·00
    c. Lightning conductor .. 70·00
    d. Flagstaff on right-hand turret .. 55·00
    e. Double flagstaff .. .. 55·00
22   2d. ultramarine and grey-black .. 40 30
    a. Extra flagstaff .. .. 85·00
    b. Short extra flagstaff .. 60·00
    c. Lightning conductor .. 60·00
23   3d. brown and deep blue .. 55 1·50
    a. Extra flagstaff .. .. 65·00
    b. Short extra flagstaff .. 55·00
    c. Lightning conductor .. 50·00
24   6d. slate and purple .. .. 65 1·00
    a. Extra flagstaff .. .. 75·00
    b. Short extra flagstaff .. 60·00
    c. Lightning conductor .. 60·00
21/4 .. .. .. *Set of 4* 1·75 2·75
21/4 Perf "Specimen" .. *Set of 4* 80·00
For illustrations of plate varieties see Omnibus section following Zimbabwe.

1937 (12 May). *Coronation. As Nos. 118/20 of Jamaica, but ptd by B.W. P 11×11½.*
25   1d. carmine 75 30
26   2d. yellow-brown 75 10
27   3d. blue 75 40
25/7 .. .. .. *Set of 3* 2·00 70
25/7 Perf "Specimen" .. *Set of 3* 60·00

(Recess D.L.R.)
1938 (1 Apr)–**54.** *Wmk Mult Script CA. P 13½ × 13.*
28 3 ½d. green 80 45
    a. Perf 13½ × 14 (1.43) .. 20 1·00
    b. Perf 13½ × 14. *Bronze-green* (2.50) 30 2·00
29   1d. rose-red 65 30
    a. Perf 13½ × 14 (1.43) .. 20 45
30   1½d. light blue .. .. 2·75 50
    a. Perf 14 (1941) 85 95
    b. Perf 13½ × 14 (1.43) .. 20 45
31   2d. yellow-brown .. .. 2·00 65
    a. Perf 13½ × 14 (1.43) .. 20 30
32   3d. ultramarine .. .. 4·25 90
    a. *Deep blue* (10.38) .. 4·25 90
    b. Perf 13½ × 14. *Ultramarine* (1.43) 80 2·00
    c. Perf 13½ × 14. *Light ultram* (10.46) 3·00 3·25
    d. Perf 13½ × 14. *Deep blue* (10.47) 3·00 3·25
33   4d. orange .. .. .. 1·50 85
    a. Perf 13½ × 14 (1.43) .. 45 1·40
34   6d. deep magenta .. .. 3·75 90
    a. Perf 13½ × 14 (1.43) .. 1·75 2·50
    b. Perf 13½ × 14. *Reddish purple* (*shades*) (7.44) .. 2·00 75
    c. Perf 13½ × 14. *Claret* (13.10.54) 2·25 75
35   1s. brown-olive .. .. 5·50 70
    a. Perf 13½ × 14 (1.43) .. 45 40
36   2s. 6d. bright violet .. .. 18·00 4·00
    a. Perf 13½ × 14. *Violet* (1.43) 4·50 2·25
    b. Perf 13½ × 14. *Reddish violet* (10.47) .. .. 3·50 3·75
37   5s. grey .. .. .. 42·00 6·50
    a. Perf 13½ × 14. *Slate* (1.43) 50·00 45·00
    b. Perf 13½ × 14. *Grey* (5.44) 15·00 10·00
38   10s. sepia .. .. .. 42·00 5·00
    a. Perf 13½ × 14 (1.43) .. 6·00 5·50
28/38a .. .. .. *Set of 11* 26·00 16·00
28/38 Perf "Specimen" .. *Set of 11* £190
The above perforations vary slightly from stamp to stamp, but the average measurements are respectively: 13.3 × 13.2 comb (13½ × 13), 14.2 line (14) and 13.3 × 13.8 comb (13½ × 14).

Swaziland
(4)

1945 (3 Dec). *Victory. Nos. 108/10 of South Africa optd with T 4.*
                                    Un Us
                                  pair pair
39   1d. brown and carmine 40 30
40   2d. slate-blue and violet 40 30
41   3d. deep blue and blue .. .. 45 1·25
39/41 .. .. .. *Set of 3 pairs* 1·25 1·75

1947 (17 Feb). *Royal Visit. As Nos. 32/5 of Lesotho.*
                                    Un Us
42   1d. scarlet 10 10
43   2d. green 10 10
44   3d. ultramarine 10 10
45   1s. mauve 10 10
42/5 .. .. .. *Set of 4* 30 30
42/5 Perf "Specimen" .. *Set of 4* 80·00

1948 (1 Dec). *Royal Silver Wedding. As Nos. 143/4 of Jamaica.*
46   1½d. ultramarine 50 10
47   10s. purple-brown .. .. 19·00 13·00

1949 (10 Oct). *75th Anniv of U.P.U. As Nos. 145/8 of Jamaica.*

48	1½d. blue		10	10
49	3d. deep blue		40	50
50	6d. magenta		50	50
51	1s. olive		50	50
48/51		Set of 4	1·40	1·40

1953 (3 June). *Coronation. As No. 153 of Jamaica.*

52	2d. black and yellow-brown		20	20

5 Havelock Asbestos Mine

7 Swazi Married Woman

(Recess B.W.)

1956 (2 July). *T 5, 7 and similar designs. Wmk Mult Script CA. P 13 × 13½ (horiz) or 13½ × 13 (vert).*

53	5	½d. black and orange		10	10
54	–	1d. black and emerald		10	10
55	7	2d. black and brown		30	10
56	–	3d. black and rose-red		20	10
57	–	4½d. black and deep bright blue		60	10
58	–	6d. black and magenta		45	10
59	5	1s. black and deep olive		20	10
60	–	1s. 3d. black and sepia		1·00	75
61	–	2s. 6d. emerald and carmine-red		1·00	1·00
62	–	5s. deep lilac and slate-black		3·75	1·25
63	7	10s. black and deep lilac		9·50	4·00
64	–	£1 black and turquoise-blue		26·00	24·00
53/64		Set of 12	38·00	28·00

Designs: *Horiz*—1d., 2s. 6d. A Highveld view; *Vert*—3d., 1s. 3d. Swazi courting couple; 4½d., 5s. Swazi warrior; 6d., £1. Greater Kudu.

(New Currency. 100 cents = 1 rand)

½c (11)	1c (12)	2c (13)	3½c (14)
2½c (I)	2½c (II)	4c (I)	4c (II)
5c (I)	5c (II)	25c (I)	25c (II)
50c (I)	50c (II)	50c (III)	
R1 (I)	R1 (II)	R1 (III)	R2 (I)	R2 (II)

1961 (14 Feb-May). *Nos. 53/64 surch as T 11 to 14.*

65	½ c. on ½d.		2·50	2·50
	a. Surch inverted		£250	
66	1 c. on 1d.		10	20
	a. Surch double*		£300	
67	2 c. on 2d.		10	20
68	2½ c. on 2d.		10	10
69	2½ c. on 3d. (Type I)		10	10
	a. Type II		10	15
70	3½ c. on 2d. (May)		10	10
71	4 c. on 4½d. (Type I)		10	10
	a. Type II		20	10
72	5 c. on 6d. (Type I)		10	10
	a. Type II		10	10
73	10 c. on 1s.		13·00	3·00
	a. Surch double*		£300	
74	25 c. on 2s. 6d. (Type I)		30	65
	a. Type II (central)		85	60
	b. Type II (bottom left)		£130	£160
75	50 c. on 5s. (Type I)		30	60
	a. Type II		4·00	2·25
	b. Type III		£250	£375
76	1 r. on 10s. (Type I)		1·25	60
	a. Type II		2·75	2·75
	b. Type III		40·00	45·00
77	2 r. on £1 (Type I)		9·00	9·00
	a. Type II (middle left)		4·50	5·50
	b. Type II (bottom)		40·00	75·00
65/77a		Set of 13	20·00	12·00

*On both Nos. 66a and 73a the second surcharge falls across the horizontal perforations.

No. 74b has the thin Type II surcharge at bottom left, in similar position to the thicker Type I, No. 74, with which it should not be confused.

No. 77b has the surcharge centrally placed at bottom. No. 77a has it at middle left, above "KUDU".

No. 66 with surcharge central (instead of bottom left) and No. 75a bottom left (instead of middle left) are believed to be from trial sheets released with the normal stocks. They do not represent separate printings. (No. 66 *price* £35 *un*).

(Recess B.W.)

1961. *As 1956 issue, but with values in cents and rands. Wmk Mult Script CA. P 13 × 13½ (horiz) or 13½ × 13 (vert).*

78	½ c. black and orange (as ½d.) (14.2)		10	20
79	1 c. black and emerald (as 1d.) (14.2)		10	10
80	2 c. black and brown (as 2d.) (10.9)		10	50
81	2½ c. black and rose-red (as 3d.) (14.2)		15	10
82	4 c. black & dp bright bl (as 4½d)(10.9)		15	50
83	5 c. black and magenta (as 6d.)(10.9)		30	15
84	10 c. black and deep olive (as 1s.)(14.2)		15	10
85	12½ c. black and sepia (as 1s 3d.)(14.2)		90	40
86	25 c. emerald and carmine-red (as 2s 6d.) (1.8)		1·25	1·50
87	50 c. deep lilac & slate-blk (as 5s.) (10.9)		2·00	1·40
88	1 r. black and deep lilac (as 10s.) (10.9)		3·00	4·00
89	2 r. black and turquoise-blue (as £1) (1.8)		9·00	11·00
78/89		Set of 12	16·00	18·00

15 Swazi Shields

16 Battle Axe

(Des Mrs. C. Hughes. Photo Enschedé)

1962 (24 Apr)–66. *Various designs as T 15/16. W w 12. P 14×13 (horiz) or 13×14 (vert).*

90	½ c. black, brown and yellow-brown		10	10
91	1 c. yellow-orange and black		10	10
92	2 c. dp bluish green, black & yellow-olive		10	20
93	2½ c. black and vermilion		10	10
	a. Black and dull red (5.66)		10	10
94	3½ c. yellow-green and deep grey		10	20
95	4 c. black and turquoise-green		10	10
	a. Black & deep turquoise-green (5.66)		10	10
96	5 c. black, red and orange-red		30	10
97	7½ c. deep brown and buff		30	15
	a. Blackish brn & yellowish buff (5.66)		40	40
98	10 c. black and light blue		70	10
99	12½ c. carmine and grey-olive		50	80
100	15 c. black and bright purple		1·00	60
101	20 c. black and green		40	80
102	25 c. black and bright blue		40	60
103	50 c. black and rose-red		6·00	2·75
104	1 r. emerald and ochre		2·75	2·25
105	2 r. carmine-red and ultramarine		9·50	6·00
90/105		Set of 16	20·00	13·00

Designs: *Vert*—2 c. Forestry; 2½ c. Ceremonial headdress; 3½ c. Musical instrument; 4 c. Irrigation; 5 c. Long-tailed Whydah; 7½ c. Rock paintings; 10 c. Secretary Bird; 12½ c. Pink Arum; 15 c. Swazi married woman; 20 c. Malaria control; 25 c. Swazi warrior; 1 r. Aloes. *Horiz*—50 c. Southern Ground Hornbill; 2 r. Msinsi in flower.

1963 (4 June). *Freedom from Hunger. As No. 80 of Lesotho.*

106	15 c. reddish violet		40	15

1963 (2 Sept). *Red Cross Centenary. As Nos. 203/4 of Jamaica.*

107	2½ c. red and black		10	10
108	15 c. red and blue		40	20

31 Train and Map

(Des R. A. H. Street. Recess B.W.)

1964 (5 Nov). *Opening of Swaziland Railway. W w 12. P 11½.*

109	31	2½ c. emerald-green and purple	20	10
110		3½ c. turquoise-blue & deep yellow-ol	20	15
111		15 c. red-orange and deep chocolate	30	30
112		25 c. olive-yellow and deep ultram	45	35
109/12		Set of 4	1·00	70

1965 (17 May). *I.T.U. Centenary. As Nos. 98/9 of Lesotho.*

113	2½ c. light blue and bistre		10	10
114	15 c. bright purple and rose		25	20

1965 (25 Oct). *International Co-operation Year. As Nos. 100/1 of Lesotho.*

115	½ c. reddish purple and turquoise-green		10	10
116	15 c. deep bluish green and lavender		40	20

1966 (24 Jan). *Churchill Commemoration. As Nos. 102/5 of Lesotho.*

117	½ c. new blue		10	10
118	2½ c. deep green		20	10
119	15 c. brown		35	15
120	25 c. bluish violet		50	45
117/20		Set of 4	1·00	75

1966 (1 Dec). *20th Anniv of U.N.E.S.C.O. As Nos. 342/4 of Mauritius.*

121	2½ c. slate-violet, red, yellow and orange		10	10
122	7½ c. orange-yellow, violet and deep olive		20	20
123	15 c. black, bright purple and orange		35	30
121/3		Set of 3	60	50

PROTECTED STATE

32 King Sobhuza II and Map

33 King Sobhuza II

(Des and photo Harrison)

1967 (25 Apr). *Protected State. W w 12 (sideways on horiz designs). P 14½.*

124	32	2½ c. multicoloured		10	10
125	33	7½ c. multicoloured		10	10
126	32	15 c. multicoloured		10	10
127	33	25 c. multicoloured		15	10
124/7		Set of 4		35	30

34 Students and University

(Des V. Whiteley. Photo Harrison)

1967 (7 Sept). *First Conferment of University Degrees. P 14 × 14½.*

128	34	2½ c. sepia, ultramarine & lt yellow-orge		10	10
129		7½ c. sepia, ultramarine & lt greenish bl		10	10
130		15 c. sepia, ultramarine and rose		10	10
131		25 c. sepia, ultramarine and light violet		10	10
128/31		Set of 4		30	30

35 Inclawa Ceremony

36 Reed Dance

(Des Mrs. G. Ellison. Photo Harrison)

1968 (5 Jan). *Traditional Customs. P 14.*

132	35	3 c. silver, vermilion and black		10	10
133	36	10 c. silver, light brown, orange and black		10	10
134	35	15 c. gold, vermilion and black		10	10
135	36	25 c. gold, light brown, orange and black		10	10
132/5		Set of 4		30	30

(37) 38 Cattle Ploughing

1968 (1 May). *No. 96 surch with T 37.*

136	3 c. on 5 c. black, red and orange-red		15	10

INDEPENDENT

(Des Mrs. G. Ellison. Photo Enschedé)

1968 (6 Sept). *Independence. T 38 and similar horiz designs. W w 12 (sideways). P 14 × 12½.*

137	3 c. multicoloured		10	10
	a. Imperf (pair)		£120	
138	4½ c. multicoloured		10	10
	a. Imperf (pair)		£120	
139	17½ c. yellow, green, black and gold		15	10
140	25 c. slate, black and gold		45	65
137/40		Set of 4	65	65
MS141	180 × 162 mm. Nos. 137/40 each × 5		14·00	17·00
	a. Error. Imperf		£1300	

Designs:—4½ c. Overhead cable carrying asbestos; 17½ c. Cutting sugar cane; 25 c. Iron ore mining and railway map.

Nos. 137/40 were printed in sheets of 50, but also in miniature sheets of 20 (4 × 5) containing *se-tenant* strips of each value.

INDEPENDENCE 1968
(42) 43 Cape Porcupine

1968 (6 Sept). *Nos. 90/105 optd as T **42**, and No. 93 additionally surch 3 c., by Enschedé.* (a) *Wmk upright.*

142	½ c. black, brown and yellow-brown		10	10
	a. Brown omitted		£170	
	b. Albino opt		40·00	
143	1 c. yellow-orange and black		10	10
144	2 c. dp bluish green, black & yellow-olive		10	10
145	2½ c. black and vermilion		50	30
	a. Black and dull red		40	10
146	3 c. on 2½ c. black and vermilion		10	10
	a. Black and dull red		10	10
147	3½ c. yellow-green and deep grey		15	10
148	4 c. black and turquoise-green		10	10
	a. Black and deep turquoise-green		25	15
	b. Black and pale turquoise-green		20	40
149	5 c. black, red and orange-red		1·50	10
150	7½ c. deep brown and buff		20	10
151	10 c. black and light blue		1·50	10
152	12½ c. carmine and grey-olive		25	30
153	15 c. black and bright purple		25	30
154	20 c. black and green		75	1·00
155	25 c. black and bright blue		35	40
156	50 c. black and rose-red		5·50	2·50
157	1 r. emerald and ochre		2·50	3·00
158	2 r. carmine-red and ultramarine		5·50	7·50

(b) Wmk sideways

159	50 c. black and rose-red		2·75	2·50
160	2 r. carmine-red and ultramarine		5·50	5·00
142/60		*Set of 19*	24·00	21·00

The 2½ c., 3½ c., 5 c., 12½ c., 50 c. (No. 156) and 2 r. (No. 158) exist with gum arabic only, the 1 c., 2 c., 3 c., 4 c., and 15 c. with both gum arabic and PVA gum and the remainder with PVA gum only.

(Des and litho D.L.R.)

1969 (1 Aug)–75. *T **43** and similar designs showing animals. Multicoloured. W w **12** (sideways on 3 c., 3½ c., 1 r., 2 r.). P 13 × 13½ (3 c., 3½ c.), 12½ × 13 (1 r., 2 r.) or 13 × 12½ (others).*

161	½ c. Caracal		10	10
162	1 c. Type **43**		10	10
163	2 c. Crocodile		20	10
	a. Perf 12½ × 12 (29.9.75)		3·50	2·00
164	3 c. Lion		60	10
165	3½ c. African Elephant		60	10
166	5 c. Bush Pig		30	10
167	7½ c. Impala		35	10
168	10 c. Chacma Baboon		45	10
169	12½ c. Ratel		70	1·40
170	15 c. Leopard		1·25	70
171	20 c. Blue Wildebeest		95	60
172	25 c. White Rhinoceros		1·40	1·25
173	50 c. Common Zebra		1·50	2·50
174	1 r. Waterbuck (*vert*)		3·00	4·50
175	2 r. Giraffe (*vert*)		6·00	8·50
161/75		*Set of 15*	15·00	18·00

Nos. 161/73 are horizontal as Type **43** but the 3 c. and 3½ c. are larger, 35 × 24½ mm.
No. 163a was printed by the D.L.R. works in Bogotá, Colombia.
See also Nos. 219/20 and 229.

44 King Sobhuza II and Flags

45 King Sobhuza II, U.N. Building and Emblem

(Des D.L.R. Litho P.B.)

1969 (24 Sept). *Admission of Swaziland to the United Nations. W w **12** (sideways). P 13½.*

176	**44** 3 c. multicoloured		10	10
177	**45** 7½ c. multicoloured		20	20
178	**44** 12½ c. multicoloured		30	10
179	**45** 25 c. multicoloured		45	40
176/9		*Set of 4*	90	55

46 Athlete, Shield and Spears

47 *Bauhinia galpinii*

(Des L. Curtis. Litho Format)

1970 (16 July). *Ninth Commonwealth Games, Edinburgh. T **46** and similar vert designs. Multicoloured. W w **12**. P 14.*

180	3 c. Type **46**		10	10
181	7½ c. Runner		20	10
182	12½ c. Hurdler		30	10
183	25 c. Procession of Swaziland competitors		45	40
180/3		*Set of 4*	90	55

(Des L. Curtis from "Wild Flowers of Natal" by Dr. W. G. Wright. Litho Questa)

1971 (1 Feb). *Flowers. T **47** and similar vert designs. Multicoloured. W w **12**. P 14½.*

184	3 c. Type **47**		20	10
185	10 c. Crocosmia aurea		35	10
186	15 c. Gloriosa superba		50	15
187	25 c. Watsonia densiflora		70	35
184/7		*Set of 4*	1·60	60

48 King Sobhuza II in Ceremonial Dress

49 UNICEF emblem

(Des L. Curtis. Litho Format)

1971 (22 Dec). *Golden Jubilee of Accession of King Sobhuza II. T **48** and similar vert designs. Multicoloured. W w **12**. P 14.*

188	3 c. Type **48**		10	10
189	3½ c. Sobhuza II in medallion		10	10
190	7½ c. Sobhuza II attending Incwala ceremony		10	10
191	25 c. Sobhuza II and aides at opening of Parliament		20	35
188/91		*Set of 4*	30	40

(Des Sylvia Goaman. Litho J.W.)

1972 (17 Apr). *25th Anniv of UNICEF. W w **12** (sideways). P 13½.*

192	**49** 15 c. black and bright lilac		15	10
193	— 25 c. black and yellow-olive		20	20

The 25 c. value is as T **49**, but the inscription is rearranged.

50 Local Dancers

(Des G. Drummond. Litho Questa)

1972 (11 Sept). *Tourism. T **50** and similar horiz designs. Multicoloured. W w **12**. P 13½ × 14.*

194	3½ c. Type **50**		10	10
195	7½ c. Swazi beehive hut		15	10
196	15 c. Ezulwini Valley		30	20
197	25 c. Fishing, Usutu River		95	40
194/7		*Set of 4*	1·40	65

51 Spraying Mosquitoes

(Des PAD Studio. Litho Questa)

1973 (21 May). *25th Anniv of W.H.O. T **51** and similar horiz design. Multicoloured. W w **12**. P 14.*

198	3½ c. Type **51**		20	10
199	7½ c. Anti-malaria vaccination		35	30

52 Mining

(Des G. Drummond. Litho Questa)

1973 (21 June). *Natural Resources. T **52** and similar horiz designs. Multicoloured. W w **12**. P 13½.*

200	3½ c. Type **52**		20	10
201	7½ c. Cattle		25	10
202	15 c. Water		30	15
203	25 c. Rice		35	30
200/3		*Set of 4*	1·00	55

53 Coat of Arms

54 Flags and Mortar-board

(Des J.W. Litho Walsall)

1973 (7 Sept). *Fifth Anniv of Independence. T **53** and similar horiz designs. Multicoloured (except 3 c.). W w **12**. P 14.*

204	3 c. Type **53** (salmon and black)		10	10
205	10 c. King Sobhuza II saluting		20	10
206	15 c. Parliament Buildings		35	35
207	25 c. National Somhlolo Stadium		40	40
204/7		*Set of 4*	95	95

(Des P. Powell. Litho Format)

1974 (29 Mar). *Tenth Anniv of University of Botswana, Lesotho and Swaziland. T **54** and similar vert designs. Multicoloured. W w **12** (sideways). P 14.*

208	7½ c. Type **54**		15	10
209	12½ c. University campus		20	10
210	15 c. Map of Southern Africa		25	20
211	25 c. University badge		35	35
208/11		*Set of 4*	85	60

55 King Sobhuza as College Student

56 New Post Office, Lobamba

(Des Mary Nelson; adapted PAD Studio. Litho Enschedé)

1974 (22 July). *75th Birthday of King Sobhuza II. T **55** and similar vert designs. Multicoloured. W w **12**. P 13 × 10½.*

212	3 c. Type **55**		10	10
213	9 c. King Sobhuza in middle-age		10	10
214	50 c. King Sobhuza at 75 years of age		60	60
212/14		*Set of 3*	70	60

(Des R. Granger Barrett. Litho Questa)

1974 (9 Oct). *Centenary of Universal Postal Union. T **56** and similar horiz designs. Multicoloured. W w **12** (sideways). P 14.*

215	4 c. Type **56**		10	10
216	10 c. Mbabane Temporary Post Office, 1902		25	15
217	15 c. Carrying mail by cableway		45	50
218	25 c. Mule-drawn mail-coach		55	70
215/18		*Set of 4*	1·25	1·25

(New Currency. 100 cents = 1 lilangeni (*plural* emalangeni))

1975 (2 Jan). *New currency. As Nos. 174/5 but inscr in emalangeni. W w **12** (upright). P 12½ × 13.*

219	1 e. Waterbuck		2·00	2·50
220	2 e. Giraffe		4·00	4·50

57 Umcwasho Ceremony

58 Control Tower, Matsapa Airport

(Des PAD Studio. Litho Kynoch Press)

1975 (20 Mar). *Swazi Youth. T **57** and similar multicoloured designs. W w **12** (sideways on 3, 10 and 25 c.). P 14.*

221	3 c. Type **57**		10	10
222	10 c. Butimba (hunting party)		15	10
223	15 c. Lusekwane (sacred shrub) (*horiz*)		30	20
224	25 c. Goina Regiment		40	40
221/4		*Set of 4*	85	65

(Des V. Whiteley Studio. Litho Questa)

1975 (18 Aug). *Tenth Anniv of Internal Air Service. T **58** and similar horiz designs. Multicoloured. W w **14** (sideways). P 14.*

225	4 c. Type **58**		30	10
226	5 c. Fire engine		50	10
227	15 c. Douglas "Dakota"		1·75	80
228	25 c. Hawker Siddeley "748"		2·00	1·25
225/8		*Set of 4*	4·00	2·00

(Litho De La Rue, Bogotá, Colombia)

1975 (29 Sept). *As No. 164 but W w **12** upright.*

229	3 c. Lion		4·00	3·00

NEW INFORMATION

The editor is always interested to correspond with people who have new information that will improve or correct the Catalogue.

75 Defence Force

(Des BG Studio. Litho Questa)

1978 (6 Sept). *10th Anniv of Independence. T* **75** *and similar horiz designs. Multicoloured. W w* **14** *(sideways). P* 14.
300	4 c. Type 75		10	10
301	6 c. The King's Regiment		10	10
302	10 c. Tinkabi tractor (agricultural development)		15	10
303	15 c. Water-pipe laying (self-help scheme)		25	10
304	25 c. Sebenta adult literacy scheme		30	25
305	50 c. Fire emergency service		65	50
300/5		*Set of* 6	1·40	85

76 Archangel Gabriel appearing before Shepherds   77 Prospecting at Phophonyane

(Des V. Whiteley Studio. Litho Harrison)

1978 (12 Dec). *Christmas. T* **76** *and similar horiz designs. Multicoloured. W w* **14**. *P* 14½ × 14.
306	5 c. Type 76		10	10
307	10 c. Three Wise Men paying homage to infant Jesus		10	10
308	15 c. Archangel Gabriel warning Joseph		10	10
309	25 c. Flight into Egypt		20	20
306/9		*Set of* 4	30	35

(Des C. Abbott. Litho Walsall)

1979 (10 Jan). *Handicrafts* (2nd series). *Horiz designs as T* **74**. *Multicoloured. W w* **14** *(sideways). P* 13½.
310	5 c. Sisal bowls		10	10
311	15 c. Pottery		10	10
312	20 c. Basket work		15	15
313	30 c. Hide shield		20	20
310/13		*Set of* 4	45	45

(Des L. Curtis. Litho Questa)

1979 (27 Mar). *Centenary of Discovery of Gold in Swaziland. T* **77** *and similar vert designs. W w* **14**. *P* 14.
314	5 c. gold and deep ultramarine		15	10
315	15 c. gold and deep brown		30	20
316	25 c. gold and deep green		45	30
317	50 c. gold and carmine-red		70	90
314/17		*Set of* 4	1·40	1·25

Designs:—15 c. Early 3-stamp battery mill; 25 c. Cyanide tanks at Piggs Peak; 50 c. Pouring off molten gold.

78 "Girls at the Piano"

(Des BG Studio. Litho Questa)

1979 (8 May). *International Year of the Child. Paintings by Renoir. T* **78** *and similar horiz designs. Multicoloured. W w* **14** *(sideways). P* 13½.
318	5 c. Type 78		10	10
319	15 c. "Madame Charpentier and her Children"		25	10
320	25 c. "Girls picking Flowers"		35	15
321	50 c. "Girl with Watering Can"		70	55
318/21		*Set of* 4	1·25	70
MS322	123 × 135 mm. Nos. 318/21		1·25	1·25

79 1933 1d. Carmine Stamp and Sir Rowland Hill

(Des J.W. Litho Walsall)

1979 (17 July). *Death Centenary of Sir Rowland Hill. T* **79** *and similar horiz designs showing stamps and portrait of Sir Rowland Hill. Multicoloured. W w* **14** *(sideways). P* 14½ × 14.
323	10 c. 1945 3d. Victory commemorative		15	10
324	20 c. Type 79		25	25
325	25 c. 1968 25 c. Independence commemorative		25	30
323/5		*Set of* 3	60	60
MS326	115 × 90 mm. 50 c. 1956 6d. Great Kudu Antelope definitive		65	85

80 Obverse and Reverse of 5 Cents

(Des G. Hutchins. Litho Walsall)

1979 (6 Sept). *Coins. T* **80** *and similar horiz designs. W w* **14** *(sideways). P* 13½.
327	5 c. black and light brown		10	10
328	10 c. black and new blue		15	10
329	20 c. black and yellowish green		25	20
330	50 c. black and yellow-orange		45	45
331	1 e. black and cerise		75	80
327/31		*Set of* 5	1·50	1·50

Designs:—10 c. Obverse and reverse of 10 cents; 20 c. Obverse and reverse of 20 cents; 50 c. Reverse of 50 cents; 1 e. Reverse of 1 lilangeni.

81 Big Bend Post Office

(Des J. Cooter. Litho Questa)

1979 (22 Nov). *Post Office Anniversaries. T* **81** *and similar designs. W w* **14** *(sideways on 5, 20 and 50 c.). P* 13½.
332	5 c. multicoloured		10	10
333	15 c. multicoloured		15	10
334	20 c. black, sage-green and magenta		20	15
335	50 c. multicoloured		40	60
332/5		*Set of* 4	70	80

Designs and commemorations: *Horiz*—5 c. Type 81 (25th anniversary of Posts and Telecommunications Services); 20 c. 1949 75th anniversary of U.P.U. 1s. commemorative stamp (10th anniversary of U.P.U. membership); 50 c. 1974 centenary of U.P.U. 25 c. commemorative stamp (10th anniversary of U.P.U. membership). *Vert*—15 c. Microwave antenna. Mount Ntondozi (25th anniversary of Posts and Telecommunications Services).

82 Map of Swaziland   83 *Brunsvigia radulosa*

(Des BG Studio. Litho Walsall)

1980 (23 Feb). *75th Anniv of Rotary International. T* **82** *and similar vert designs in gold and bright blue. W w* **14**. *P* 13½.
336	5 c. Type 82		10	10
337	15 c. Vitreous cutter and optical illuminator		15	10
338	50 c. Scroll		40	55
339	1 e. Rotary Headquarters, Evanston, U.S.A.		80	1·25
336/9		*Set of* 4	1·40	1·75

(Des BG Studio. Litho Secura, Singapore)

1980 (28 Apr)–**83**. *Flowers. Multicoloured designs as T* **83**.

A. *Without imprint date below design. P* 13½.
340A	1 c. Type 83		15	10
341A	2 c. *Aloe suprafoliata*		15	10
342A	3 c. *Haemanthus magnificus*		15	10
	c. Perf 12		1·50	1·25
343A	4 c. *Aloe marlothii*		20	10
	c. Perf 12		3·00	1·75
344A	5 c. *Dicoma zeyheri*		15	10
	c. Perf 12		2·00	1·50
345A	6 c. *Aloe kniphofioides*		20	20
346A	7 c. *Cyrtanthus bicolor*		15	10
347A	10 c. *Eucomis autumnalis*		25	10
348A	15 c. *Leucospermum gerrardii*		15	10
	c. Perf 12			
349A	20 c. *Haemanthus multiflorus*		40	25
350A	30 c. *Acridocarpus natalitius*		20	20
351A	50 c. *Adenium swazicum*		30	30
352A	1 e. *Protea simplex*		55	60
353A	2 e. *Calodendrum capense*		1·10	1·25
354A	5 e. *Gladiolus ecklonii*		2·75	3·00
340A/54A		*Set of* 15	6·00	5·50

B. *With imprint date. P* 12 (12.83).
340B	1 c. Type 83		60	40
341B	2 c. *Aloe suprafoliata*		60	40
343B	4 c. *Aloe marlothii*		80	40
345B	6 c. *Aloe kniphofioides*		1·00	45
347B	10 c. *Eucomis autumnalis*		1·10	40
349B	20 c. *Haemanthus multiflorus*		1·50	85
340B/9B		*Set of* 6	5·00	2·75

Nos. 347/51 are horizontal, 42 × 25 mm, and Nos. 352/4 vertical, 28 × 38 mm.

84 Mail Runner

(Des A. Theobald. Litho Walsall)

1980 (6 May). *"London 1980" International Stamp Exhibition. T* **84** *and similar horiz designs. Multicoloured. W w* **14** *(sideways). P* 14.
355	10 c. Type 84		15	10
356	20 c. Post Office mail truck		25	15
357	25 c. Mail sorting office		30	20
358	50 c. Ropeway conveying mail at Bulembu		70	70
355/8		*Set of* 4	1·25	1·00

85 Yellow Fish

(Des and litho Walsall)

1980 (25 Aug). *River Fishes. T* **85** *and similar horiz designs. Multicoloured. W w* **14** *(sideways). P* 13½.
359	5 c. Type 85		10	10
360	10 c. Silver Barbel		15	10
361	15 c. Tiger Fish		20	15
362	30 c. Squeaker Fish		40	30
363	1 e. Bream		1·10	1·40
359/63		*Set of* 5	1·75	1·75

86 Oribi

(Des G. Drummond. Litho Harrison)

1980 (1 Oct). *Wildlife Conservation. T* **86** *and similar multicoloured designs. W w* **14** *(sideways on 5 and 50 c.). P* 14.
364	5 c. Type 86		10	10
365	10 c. Nile Crocodile (*vert*)		15	10
366	50 c. Temminck's Ground Pangolin		70	70
367	1 e. Leopard (*vert*)		1·25	1·50
364/7		*Set of* 4	1·90	2·00

87 Public Bus Service

(Des G. Hutchins. Litho Format)

1981 (5 Jan). *Transport. T* **87** *and similar horiz designs. Multicoloured. W w* **14** *(sideways). P* 14½.
368	5 c. Type 87		10	10
369	25 c. Royal Swazi National Airways		25	15
370	30 c. Swaziland United Transport		30	20
371	1 e. Swaziland Railway		1·75	1·75
368/71		*Set of* 4	2·10	2·00

88 Mantenga Falls   89 Prince Charles on Hike

(Des L. Curtis. Litho Format)

1981 (16 Mar). *Tourism. T* **88** *and similar horiz designs. Multicoloured. W w* **14** *(sideways). P* 14.
372	5 c. Type 88		10	10
373	15 c. Mananga Yacht Club		15	10
374	30 c. White Rhinoceros in Mlilwane Game Sanctuary		40	30
375	1 e. Roulette wheel, playing cards and dice ("casinos")		1·40	1·60
372/5		*Set of* 4	1·75	1·90

(Des J.W. Litho Walsall)

1981 (21 July).   *Royal Wedding. T* **89** *and similar vert designs. Multicoloured. W* w **14**. *P* 14.

376	10 c.	Wedding bouquet from Swaziland	..	15	10
377	25 c.	Type **89**		15	10
378	1 e.	Prince Charles and Lady Diana Spencer		60	70
376/8	..		*Set of 3*	80	75

90 Installation of King Sobhuza II, 22 December 1921

91 "Physical Recreation"

(Des J.W. Litho Harrison)

1981 (24 Aug).   *Diamond Jubilee of King Sobhuza II. T* **90** *and similar horiz designs. Multicoloured. P* 14½.

379	5 c.	Type **90**		10	10
380	10 c.	Royal visit, 1947		15	10
381	15 c.	King Sobhuza II and Coronation of Queen Elizabeth II, 1953		20	15
382	25 c.	King Sobhuza taking Royal Salute, Independence, 1968		25	25
383	30 c.	King Sobhuza in youth		30	30
384	1 e.	King Sobhuza and Parliament Buildings		90	1·25
379/84	..		*Set of 6*	1·60	1·90

(Des BG Studio. Litho Questa)

1981 (5 Nov).   *25th Anniv of Duke of Edinburgh Award Scheme. T* **91** *and similar vert designs. Multicoloured. W* w **14**. *P* 14.

385	5 c.	Type **91**		10	10
386	20 c.	"Expeditions"		15	10
387	50 c.	"Skills"		40	25
388	1 e.	Duke of Edinburgh in ceremonial dress		80	80
385/8	..		*Set of 4*	1·25	1·00

92 Disabled Person in Wheelchair

(Des and litho Walsall)

1981 (16 Dec).   *International Year for the Disabled. T* **92** *and similar multicoloured designs. W* w **14** *(sideways on 5 c. and 1 e.). P* 14 × 14½ (5 c., 1 e.) *or* 14½ × 14 *(others).*

389	5 c.	Type **92**	..	25	10
390	15 c.	Teacher with disabled child *(vert)*		40	15
391	25 c.	Disabled craftsman *(vert)*		65	20
392	1 e.	Disabled driver in invalid carriage		2·00	1·75
389/92			*Set of 4*	3·00	2·00

93 *Papilio demodocus*

94 Man holding a Flower, after discarding Cigarettes

(Des I. Loe. Litho Rosenbaum Bros, Vienna)

1982 (6 Jan).   *Butterflies. T* **93** *and similar horiz designs. Multicoloured. W* w **14** *(sideways). P* 14.

393	5 c.	Type **93**	..	40	10
394	10 c.	*Charaxes candiope*		50	10
395	50 c.	*Papilio nireus*		1·50	85
396	1 e.	*Terias desjardinsii*		2·00	2·00
393/6	..		*Set of 4*	4·00	2·75

(Des PAD Studio. Litho Format)

1982 (27 Apr).   *Pan-African Conference on Smoking and Health. T* **94** *and similar vert design. Multicoloured. W* w **14**. *P* 14.

397	5 c.	Type **94**		40	50
398	10 c.	Smoker and non-smoker climbing stairs		60	50

The new-issue supplement to this Catalogue appears each month in

GIBBONS STAMP MONTHLY

—from your newsagent or by postal subscription— sample copy and details on request.

---

95 Male Fishing Owl

96 Swaziland Coat of Arms

(Des G. Drummond. Litho J.W.)

1982 (16 June).   *Wildlife Conservation (1st series). Pel's Fishing Owl. T* **95** *and similar vert designs. Multicoloured. W* w **14**. *P* 13½ × 13.

399	35 c.	Type **95**		1·40	1·60
		a. Horiz strip of 5. Nos. 399/403		6·25	
400	35 c.	Female Fishing Owl at nest		1·40	1·60
401	35 c.	Pair of Fishing Owls		1·40	1·60
402	35 c.	Fishing Owl, nest and egg		1·40	1·60
403	35 c.	Adult Fishing Owl with youngster		1·40	1·60
399/403			*Set of 5*	6·25	7·25

Nos. 399/403 were printed together, *se-tenant*, in horizontal and vertical strips of 5 throughout the sheet.
See also Nos. 425/9 and Nos. 448/52.

97 Irrigation

(Des C. Abbott. Litho W. S. Cowells Ltd)

1982 (1 July).   *21st Birthday of Princess of Wales. T* **96** *and similar vert designs. Multicoloured. W* w **14**. *P* 14½.

404	5 c.	Type **96**		10	10
405	20 c.	Princess leaving Eastleigh Airport, Southampton, August 1981		15	10
406	50 c.	Bride at Buckingham Palace		35	35
407	1 e.	Formal portrait		80	80
404/7	..		*Set of 4*	1·25	1·25

98 Nurse with Child

(Des G. Hutchins. Litho Walsall)

1982 (1 Sept).   *Sugar Industry. T* **97** *and similar horiz designs. Multicoloured. W* w **14** *(sideways). P* 14 × 14½.

408	5 c.	Type **97**	..	10	10
409	20 c.	Harvesting		25	15
410	30 c.	Mhlume mills		35	25
411	1 e.	Sugar transportation by train		1·00	1·40
408/11			*Set of 4*	1·50	1·75

(Des L. Curtis. Litho Questa)

1982 (9 Nov).   *Swaziland Red Cross Society (Baphaladi). T* **98** *and similar horiz designs. Multicoloured. W* w **14** *(sideways). P* 14.

412	5 c.	Type **98**		10	10
413	20 c.	Juniors carrying stretcher		25	15
414	50 c.	Disaster relief		55	60
415	1 e.	Henri Dunant (founder of Red Cross)		1·25	1·40
412/15			*Set of 4*	1·90	2·00

99 Taking the Oath

100 Satellite View of Earth

(Des B. Melton. Litho Format)

1982 (6 Dec).   *75th Anniv of Boy Scout Movement. T* **99** *and similar horiz designs. Multicoloured. W* w **14** *(sideways). P* 14 × 13½.

416	5 c.	Type **99**		10	10
417	10 c.	Hiking and exploration		15	10
418	25 c.	Community development		30	20
419	75 c.	Lord Baden-Powell		1·00	1·00
416/19			*Set of 4*	1·40	1·25
MS420	107 × 109 mm. 1 e. World Scout badge			1·25	1·40

(Des A. Theobald. Litho Harrison)

1983 (14 Mar).   *Commonwealth Day. T* **100** *and similar multicoloured designs. W* w **14** *(sideways on 50 c., 1 e.). P* 14.

421	6 c.	Type **100**	..	10	10
422	10 c.	King Sobhuza II		10	10
423	50 c.	Swazi woman and beehive huts *(horiz)*		35	55
424	1 e.	Spraying sugar crops *(horiz)*		70	1·00
421/4	..		*Set of 4*	1·10	1·50

(Des G. Drummond. Litho J.W.)

1983 (16 May).   *Wildlife Conservation (2nd series). Lammergeier. Vert designs as T* **95**. *Multicoloured. W* w **14**. *P* 13½ × 13.

425	35 c.	Adult male		1·00	1·00
		a. Horiz strip of 5. Nos. 425/9		4·50	
426	35 c.	Pair		1·00	1·00
427	35 c.	Nest and egg		1·00	1·00
428	35 c.	Female at nest		1·00	1·00
429	35 c.	Adult bird with fledgling		1·00	1·00
425/9			*Set of 5*	4·50	4·50

Nos. 425/9 were printed together, *se-tenant*, in horizontal strips of 5 throughout the sheet.

101 Swaziland National Football Team **102** Montgolfier Balloon

(Des G. Vasarhelyi. Litho Format)

1983 (20 Aug).   *Tour of Swaziland by English Football Clubs. Three sheets,* 101 × 72 *mm, each containing one* 75 c. *stamp as T* **101**. *Multicoloured. W* w **14** *(sideways). P* 13½.

MS430	75 c. Type **101**; 75 c. Tottenham Hotspur; 75 c. Manchester United	*Set of 3 sheets*	2·25	3·00

(Des D. Hartley-Marjoram. Litho Format)

1983 (22 Aug).   *Bicentenary of Manned Flight. T* **102** *and similar multicoloured designs. W* w **14** *(sideways on 10 c. to 50 c.). P* 14.

431	5 c.	Type **102**		10	10
432	10 c.	Wright brothers' *Flyer (horiz)*		15	10
433	25 c.	Fokker "Fellowship" *(horiz)*		30	35
434	50 c.	Bell "X-1" *(horiz)*..		60	65
431/4	..		*Set of 4*	95	1·00
MS435	73 × 73 mm. 1 e. Space shuttle *Columbia*		1·25	1·40

103 Dr. Albert Schweitzer (Peace Prize, 1952)

(Des G. Vasarhelyi. Litho Harrison)

1983 (21 Oct).   *150th Birth Anniv of Alfred Nobel. T* **103** *and similar horiz designs. Multicoloured. W* w **14** *(sideways). P* 14.

436	6 c.	Type **103**		30	10
437	10 c.	Dag Hammarskjöld (Peace Prize, 1961)		30	10
438	50 c.	Albert Einstein (Physics Prize, 1921)		1·50	70
439	1 e.	Alfred Nobel		2·00	1·50
436/9	..		*Set of 4*	3·75	2·10

104 Maize

(Des Jennifer Toombs. Litho Harrison)

1983 (29 Nov).   *World Food Day. T* **104** *and similar horiz designs. Multicoloured. W* w **14** *(sideways). P* 14.

440	6 c.	Type **104**	..	10	10
441	10 c.	Rice		10	10
442	50 c.	Cattle herding		55	65
443	1 e.	Ploughing		1·10	1·40
440/3	..		*Set of 4*	1·60	2·00

105 Women's College

106 Male on Ledge

(Des C. Abbott. Litho Format)

1984 (12 Mar). *Education. T* **105** *and similar horiz designs. Multicoloured.* W w **14** (*sideways*). *P* 14. :

444	5 c. Type **105**		10	10
445	15 c. Technical Training School		15	15
446	50 c. University		45	60
447	1 e. Primary school		90	1·10
444/7		*Set of 4*	1·40	1·75

(Des G. Drummond. Litho J.W.)

1984 (18 May). *Wildlife Conservation. (3rd series) Bald Ibis. T* **106** *and similar vert designs. Multicoloured.* W w **14.** *P* 13½ × 13.

448	35 c. Type **106**		1·60	1·75
	a. Horiz strip of 5. Nos. 448/52		7·25	
449	35 c. Male and female		1·60	1·75
450	35 c. Bird and egg		1·60	1·75
451	35 c. Female on nest of eggs		1·60	1·75
452	35 c. Adult and fledgling		1·60	1·75
448/52		*Set of 5*	7·25	8·00

Nos. 448/52 were printed together, *se-tenant,* in horizontal strips of 5 throughout the sheet.

107 Mule-drawn
Passenger Coach

(Des A. Theobald. Litho Walsall)

1984 (15 June). *Universal Postal Union Congress, Hamburg. T* **107** *and similar horiz designs. Multicoloured.* W w **14** (*sideways*). *P* 14½.

453	7 c. Type **107**		20	10
454	15 c. Ox-drawn post wagon		35	15
455	50 c. Mule-drawn mail coach		80	60
456	1 e. Bristol to London mail coach		1·25	1·10
453/6		*Set of 4*	2·40	1·75

108 Running

(Des Harrison. Litho Walsall)

1984 (27 July). *Olympic Games, Los Angeles. T* **108** *and similar horiz designs. Multicoloured.* W w **14** (*sideways*). *P* 14.

457	7 c. Type **108**		10	10
458	10 c. Swimming		10	10
459	50 c. Shooting		45	50
460	1 e. Boxing		90	95
457/60		*Set of 4*	1·40	1·40
MS461	100 × 70 mm. Nos. 457/60		1·50	2·00

109 *Suillus bovinus*

(Des J. Spencer. Litho Format)

1984 (19 Sept). *Fungi. T* **109** *and similar multicoloured designs.* W w **14** (*sideways on* 10 c., 1 e.). *P* 14.

462	10 c. Type **109**		50	10
463	15 c. *Langermannia gigantea* (*vert*)		75	30
464	50 c. *Coriolus versicolor* (*vert*)		1·40	1·10
465	1 e. *Boletus edulis*		1·90	1·75
462/5		*Set of 4*	4·00	2·75

110 King Sobhuza opening
Railway, 1964   (111)

(Des W. Fenton. Litho Walsall)

1984 (5 Nov). *20th Anniv of Swaziland Railways. T* **110** *and similar horiz designs. Multicoloured.* W w **14** (*sideways*). *P* 14.

466	10 c. Type **110**		25	10
467	25 c. Type "15A" locomotive at Siweni Yard		55	30
468	30 c. Container loading, Matsapha Station		55	30
469	1 e. Locomotive No. 268 leaving Alto Tunnel		1·50	1·40
466/9		*Set of 4*	2·50	1·90
MS470	144 × 74 mm. Nos. 466/9		3·75	4·50

1984 (15 Dec). *Nos.* 340B, 341A, 342A, 343A, 345B *and* 346A *surch as T* **111**.

471	10 c. on 4 c. *Aloe marlothii*			
	a. Surch on No. 343Ac		30	10
	b. Surch on No. 343B		2·00	2·00
472	15 c. on 7 c. *Cyrtanthus bicolor*		40	10
473	20 c. on 3 c. *Haemanthus magnificus*		50	15
	a. Surch on No. 342Ac		2·00	2·00
474	25 c. on 6 c. *Aloe kniphofioides*		60	20
	a. Surch triple		†	
	b. Surch double			
475	30 c. on 1 c. Type **83**		70	20
	a. Surch omitted (horiz pair with normal)			
476	30 c. on 2 c. *Aloe suprafoliata*		1·00	1·25
	a. Surch on No. 341B		2·00	2·00
471a/6		*Set of 6*	3·25	1·75

112 Rotary International Logo
and Map of World   113 Male Ground Hornbill

(Des G. Vasarhelyi. Litho Questa)

1985 (23 Feb). *80th Anniv of Rotary International. T* **112** *and similar horiz designs. Multicoloured.* W w **14** (*sideways*). *P* 14.

477	10 c. Type **112**		25	10
478	15 c. Teacher and handicapped children		35	20
479	50 c. Youth exchange		90	55
480	1 e. Nurse and children		1·50	1·10
477/80		*Set of 4*	2·75	1·75

(Des G. Drummond. Litho Harrison)

1985 (15 May). *Birth Bicentenary of John J. Audubon (ornithologist). Southern Ground Hornbills. T* **113** *and similar vert designs. Multicoloured.* W w **14.** *P* 14.

481	25 c. Type **113**		90	1·00
	a. Horiz strip of 5. Nos. 481/5		4·00	
482	25 c. Male and female Ground Hornbills		90	1·00
483	25 c. Female at nest		90	1·00
484	25 c. Ground Hornbill in nest, and egg		90	1·00
485	25 c. Adult and fledgeling		90	1·00
481/5		*Set of 5*	4·00	4·50

Nos. 481/5 were printed together, *se-tenant,* in horizontal strips of 5 throughout the sheet.

114 The Queen Mother in   115 Buick "Tourer"
1975

(Des A. Theobald (2 e.), C. Abbott (others). Litho Questa)

1985 (7 June). *Life and Times of Queen Elizabeth the Queen Mother. T* **114** *and similar vert designs. Multicoloured.* W w **16.** *P* 14½ × 14.

486	10 c. The Queen Mother in South Africa, 1947		10	10
487	15 c. With the Queen and Princess Margaret, 1985 (from photo by Norman Parkinson)		10	10
488	50 c. Type **114**		30	35
489	1 e. With Prince Henry at his christening (from photo by Lord Snowdon)		65	70
486/9		*Set of 4*	1·00	1·10
MS490	91×73 mm. 2 e. Greeting Prince Andrew. Wmk sideways		1·25	1·40

(Des D. Hartley. Litho Walsall)

1985 (16 Sept). *Century of Motoring. T* **115** *and similar horiz designs. Multicoloured.* W w **14** (*sideways*). *P* 14.

491	10 c. Type **115**		30	10
492	15 c. Four cylinder Rover		45	15
493	50 c. De Dion Bouton		1·25	1·00
494	1 e. "Model T" Ford		1·75	2·25
491/4		*Set of 4*	3·25	3·25

116 Youths building Bridge
over Ravine

(Des Vrein Barlocher. Litho Format)

1985 (2 Dec). *International Youth Year* (10, 50 c.), *and 75th Anniv of Girl Guide Movement* (*others*). *T* **116** *and similar horiz designs. Multicoloured.* W w **16** (*sideways*). *P* 14.

495	10 c. Type **116**		15	10
496	20 c. Girl Guides in camp		20	15
497	50 c. Youth making model from sticks		45	60
498	1 e. Guides collecting brushwood		80	1·25
495/8		*Set of 4*	1·40	1·90

117 Halley's Comet   118 King Mswati III
over Swaziland

(Des Jennifer Toombs. Litho B.D.T.)

1986 (27 Feb). *Appearance of Halley's Comet.* W w **14** (*sideways*). *P* 14.

499	**117** 1 e. 50, multicoloured		2·75	2·75

(Des A. Theobald. Litho Format)

1986 (21 Apr). *60th Birthday of Queen Elizabeth II. Vert designs as T* **230a** *of Jamaica. Multicoloured.* W w **16.** *P* 14×14½.

500	10 c. Christening of Princess Anne, 1950		10	10
501	30 c. On Palace balcony after wedding of Prince and Princess of Wales, 1981		20	25
502	45 c. Royal visit to Swaziland, 1947		25	30
503	1 e. At Windsor Polo Ground, 1984		55	60
504	2 e. At Crown Agents Head Office, London, 1983		1·10	1·25
500/4		*Set of 5*	1·90	2·25

(Des L. Curtis. Litho Walsall)

1986 (25 Apr). *Coronation of King Mswati III. T* **118** *and similar designs.* W w **16** (*sideways on* 20 c. *to* 2 e.). *P* 14½×14 (10 c.) *or* 14×14½ (*others*).

505	10 c. black and gold		35	10
506	20 c. multicoloured		60	30
507	25 c. multicoloured		70	35
508	30 c. multicoloured		80	50
509	40 c. multicoloured		85	75
510	2 e. multicoloured		3·00	4·00
505/10		*Set of 6*	5·50	5·50

Designs: *Horiz*—20 c. Prince with King Sobhuza II at Incwala ceremony; 25 c. At primary school; 30 c. At school in England; 40 c. Inspecting guard of honour at Matsapha Airport; 2 e. Dancing the Simemo.

119 Emblems of Round   120 *Precis hierta*
Table and Project Orbis
(eye disease campaign)

(Des M. Kesson, adapted G. Vasarhelyi. Litho Walsall)

1986 (6 Oct). *50th Anniv of Round Table Organization. T* **119** *and similar vert designs showing branch emblems. Multicoloured.* W w **14.** *P* 14.

511	15 c. Type **119**		10	10
512	25 c. Ehlanzeni 51		20	20
513	55 c. Mbabane 30		40	40
514	70 c. Bulembu 54		55	50
515	2 e. Manzini 44		1·40	1·75
511/15		*Set of 5*	2·40	2·75

(Des I. Loe. Litho Questa)

1987 (17 Mar). *Butterflies* (1st series). *T* **120** *and similar horiz designs. Multicoloured.* *P* 14.

516	10 c. Type **120**		10	10
517	15 c. *Hamanumida daedalus*		15	10
518	20 c. *Charaxes boueti*		20	10
519	25 c. *Abantis paradisea*		20	10
520	30 c. *Acraea anemosa*		20	15
521	35 c. *Graphium leonidas*		25	25
522	45 c. *Graphium antheus*		30	30
523	50 c. *Precis orithya*		35	35
524	55 c. *Pinacopteryx eriphia*		35	35
525	70 c. *Precis octavia*		45	45
526	1 e. *Mylothris chloris*		60	60
527	5 e. *Colotis regina*		2·25	2·40
528	10 e. *Spindasis natalensis*		4·50	4·75
516/28		*Set of 13*	9·00	9·00

For these designs, and similar 5 c., with different portrait of King Mswati III see Nos. 606/17.

121 Two White Rhinoceroses   122 Hybrid Tea Rose "Blue Moon"

(Des Doreen McGuinness. Litho Questa)

1987 (1 July). *White Rhinoceros. T 121 and similar horiz designs. Multicoloured. W w 16 (sideways). P 14½.*
529	15 c. Type 121..	..	..	55	15
530	25 c. Female and calf..	..	..	85	55
531	45 c. Rhinoceros charging	..	..	1·50	1·50
532	70 c. Rhinoceros wallowing ..	..	..	2·00	2·50
529/32	..	..	*Set of 4*	4·50	4·25

(Des Josephine Martin. Litho Questa)

1987 (19 Oct). *Garden Flowers. T 122 and similar vert designs. Multicoloured. W w 16. P 14½.*
533	15 c. Type 122..	..	..	55	15
534	35 c. Rambler Rose "Danse du feu"..	..	1·00	60
535	55 c. Pompon Dahlia "Odin"..	..	1·50	1·00
536	2 e. *Lilium davidii var. willmottiae*	..	4·00	4·50
533/6	..	..	*Set of 4*	6·25	5·75

1987 (9 Dec). *Royal Ruby Wedding. Nos. 501/4 optd with T 45a of Kiribati in silver.*
537	30 c. On Palace balcony after wedding of Prince and Princess of Wales, 1981	..	20	20
538	45 c. Royal visit to Swaziland, 1947	..	30	30
539	1 e. At Windsor Polo Ground, 1984	..	80	85
540	2 e. At Crown Agents Head Office, London, 1983	..	1·50	1·75
537/40	..	..	*Set of 4*	2·50	2·75

123 *Zabalius aridus* (grasshopper)

(Des I. Loe. Litho Questa)

1988 (14 Mar). *Insects. T 123 and similar horiz designs. Multicoloured. W w 16 (sideways). P 14.*
541	15 c. Type 123	..	..	45	15
542	55 c. *Callidea bohemani* (shieldbug)	..	1·25	85
543	1 e. *Phymateus viridipes* (grasshopper)	..	2·25	2·25
544	2 e. *Nomadacris septemfasciata* (locust)	..	3·75	4·00
541/4	..	..	*Set of 4*	7·00	6·50

124 Athlete with Swazi Flag and Olympic Stadium

(Des C. Abbott. Litho Format)

1988 (22 Aug). *Olympic Games, Seoul. T 124 and similar horiz designs. Multicoloured. W w 16 (sideways). P 14.*
545	15 c. Type 124	..	..	25	10
546	35 c. Taekwondo	..	..	55	35
547	1 e. Boxing	..	..	1·25	1·25
548	2 e. Tennis	..	..	2·25	2·50
545/8	..	..	*Set of 4*	4·00	3·75

125 Savanna Monkey ("Green Monkey")   126 Dr. David Hynd (founder of Swazi Red Cross)

(Des I. Loe. Litho Questa)

1989 (16 Jan). *Small Mammals. T 125 and similar horiz designs. Multicoloured. W w 16 (sideways). P 14.*
549	35 c. Type 125	..	..	65	25
550	55 c. Large-toothed Rock Hyrax ("Rock Dassie")	..	85	55
551	1 e. Zorilla	..	..	1·75	1·50
552	2 e. African Wild Cat	..	..	3·00	3·25
549/52	..	..	*Set of 4*	5·50	5·00

(Des T. Chance. Litho Security Printers (M), Malaysia)

1989 (21 Sept). *125th Anniv of International Red Cross. T 126 and similar horiz designs. Multicoloured. W w 14 (sideways). P 12.*
553	15 c. Type 126	..	..	20	15
554	60 c. First aid training	..	..	55	40
555	1 e. Sigombeni Clinic	..	..	90	80
556	2 e. Refugee camp	..	..	1·40	1·40
553/6	..	..	*Set of 4*	2·75	2·50

127 King Mswati III with Prince of Wales, 1987   128 Manzini to Mahamba Road

(Des L. Curtis. Litho Harrison)

1989 (15 Nov). *21st Birthday of King Mswati III. T 127 and similar horiz designs. Multicoloured. P 14×14½.*
557	15 c. Type 127	..	..	10	10
558	60 c. King with Pope John Paul II, 1988	..	30	35
559	1 e. Introduction of Crown Prince to people, 1983	..	50	55
560	2 e. King Mswati III and Queen Mother	..	95	1·00
557/60	..	..	*Set of 4*	1·60	1·75

(Des A. Theobald. Litho Questa)

1989 (18 Dec). *25th Anniv of African Development Bank. T 128 and similar horiz designs. Multicoloured. W w 16 (sideways). P 14×14½.*
561	15 c. Type 128	..	..	10	10
562	60 c. Microwave Radio Receiver, Mbabane	..	30	35
563	1 e. Mbabane Government Hospital	..	50	75
564	2 e. Ezulwini Power Station switchyard	..	95	1·50
561/4	..	..	*Set of 4*	1·60	2·40

129 International Priority Mail Van

(Des G. Vasarhelyi. Litho Security Printers (M), Malaysia)

1990 (3 May). *"Stamp World London 90" International Stamp Exhibition. T 129 and similar horiz designs. Multicoloured. W w 14 (sideways). P 12½.*
565	15 c. Type 129	..	..	15	10
566	60 c. Facsimile Service operators	..	40	40
567	1 e. Rural post office	..	..	75	75
568	2 e. Ezulwini Earth Station	..	1·40	1·40
565/8	..	..	*Set of 4*	2·40	2·40
MS569	105×85 mm. 2 e. Mail runner. Wmk upright..	..	1·50	2·00

No. **MS**569 also commemorates the 150th anniversary of the Penny Black.

(Des D. Miller. Litho Questa)

1990 (4 Aug). *90th Birthday of Queen Elizabeth the Queen Mother. Vert designs as T 107 (75 c.) or 108 (4 e.) of Kenya. W w 16. P 14×15 (75 c.) or 14½ (4 e.).*
570	75 c. multicoloured	..	..	50	50
571	4 e. brownish black & dp turquoise-green	2·25	2·25

Designs:—75 c. Queen Mother; 4 e. King George VI and Queen Elizabeth visiting Civil Resettlement Unit, Hatfield House.

130 Pictorial Teaching   131 Rural Water Supply

(Des D. Aryeequaye. Litho Questa)

1990 (21 Sept). *International Literacy Year. T 130 and similar horiz designs. Multicoloured. W w 14 (sideways). P 14.*
572	15 c. Type 130	..	..	10	10
573	75 c. Rural class	..	..	45	45
574	1 e. Modern teaching methods	..	60	60
575	2 e. Presentation of certificates	..	1·10	1·10
572/5	..	..	*Set of 4*	2·00	2·00

(Des D. Aryeequaye. Litho Cartor, France)

1990 (10 Dec). *40th Anniv of United Nations Development Programme. "Helping People to Help Themselves". T 131 and similar vert designs. Multicoloured. W w 14. P 13½×14.*
576	60 c. Type 131	..	..	35	35
577	1 e. Seed multiplication project	..	60	60
578	2 e. Low-cost housing project	..	1·25	1·25
576/8	..	..	*Set of 3*	2·00	2·00

10c

(132)   133 Lobamba Hot Spring

1990 (17 Dec). *Nos. 519/20, 522 and 524 surch as T 132.*
579	10 c. on 25 c. *Abantis paradisea*	..	15	15
580	15 c. on 30 c. *Acraea anemosa*	..	20	20
580a	15 c. on 45 c. *Graphium antheus*	..		
581	20 c. on 45 c. *Graphium antheus*	..	20	20
582	40 c. on 55 c. *Pinacopteryx eriphia*	..	30	30

(Des D. Aryeequaye. Litho Harrison)

1991 (11 Feb). *National Heritage. T 133 and similar horiz designs. Multicoloured. W w 77 of Brunei (sideways). P 14½.*
583	15 c. Type 133	..	..	15	10
584	60 c. Sibebe Rock	..	..	40	40
585	1 e. Jolobela Falls	..	..	70	70
586	2 e. Mantjolo Sacred Pool ..	..	1·25	1·40
583/6	..	..	*Set of 4*	2·25	2·40
MS587	80×60 mm. 2 e. Usushwana River. P 14	1·25	1·50

134 King Mswati III making Speech   135 *Xerophyta retinervis*

(Des D. Aryeequaye. Litho Cartor)

1991 (24 Apr). *5th Anniv of King Mswati III's Coronation. T 134 and similar horiz designs. Multicoloured. W w 14 (sideways). P 14×13½.*
588	15 c. Type 134	..	..	15	10
589	75 c. Butimba Royal Hunt	..	50	50
590	1 e. King and visiting school friends from Sherborne, 1986	..	70	70
591	2 e. King opening Parliament	..	1·25	1·40
588/91	..	..	*Set of 4*	2·40	2·40

(Des D. Miller. Litho Questa)

1991 (17 June). *65th Birthday of Queen Elizabeth II and 70th Birthday of Prince Philip. Vert designs as T 58 of Kiribati. Multicoloured. W w 16 (sideways). P 14½×14.*
592	1 e. Prince Philip	..	..	70	70
	a. Horiz pair. Nos. 592/3 separated by label	..	1·90	2·10
593	2 e. Queen Elizabeth II	..	1·25	1·40

Nos. 592/3 were printed in a similar sheet format to Nos. 366/7 of Kiribati

(Des D. Aryeequaye. Litho Questa)

1991 (30 Sept). *Indigenous Flowers. T 135 and similar vert designs. Multicoloured. W w 14 (sideways). P 14.*
594	15 c. Type 135	..	..	15	10
595	75 c. *Bauhinia galpinii*	..	50	50
596	1 e. *Dombeya rotundifolia*	..	70	70
597	2 e. *Kigelia africana*	..	1·40	1·50
594/7	..	..	*Set of 4*	2·50	2·50

136 Father Christmas arriving with Gifts   137 Lubombo Flat Lizard

(Des D. Aryeequaye. Litho Cartor)

1991 (18 Dec). *Christmas. T 136 and similar vert designs. Multicoloured. W w 14. P 13½.*
598	20 c. Type 136	..	..	15	10
599	70 c. Singing carols	..	..	55	45
600	1 e. Priest reading from Bible	..	70	75
601	2 e. The Nativity	..	..	1·25	1·60
598/601	..	..	*Set of 4*	2·40	2·50

(Des D. Aryeequaye. Litho Cartor)

1992 (25 Feb). *Reptiles. T 137 and similar horiz designs. Multicoloured. W w 14 (sideways). P 13½.*
602	20 c. Type 137	..	..	15	10
603	70 c. Natal Hinged Tortoise	..	55	45
604	1 e. Swazi Thick-toed Gecko	..	70	75
605	2 e. Nile Monitor	..	..	1·25	1·60
602/5	..	..	*Set of 4*	2·40	2·50

138 Precis hierta

139 Missionaries visiting King Sobhuza II and Queen Lomawa

(Des I. Loe. Litho Questa)

1992 (26 Aug). *Butterflies (2nd series). Designs as Nos. 516/26 and new value (5 c.) showing different portrait of King Mswati III as in T 138. Multicoloured. Without imprint date (5 c.) or with imprint date below design (others). P 14.*

606	5 c.	Colotis antevippe	..	10	10
607	10 c.	Type 138	..	10	10
608	15 c.	Hamanumida daedalus	..	10	10
609	20 c.	Charaxes boueti	..	10	10
610	25 c.	Abantis paradisea	..	10	10
611	30 c.	Acraea anemosa	..	15	20
612	35 c.	Graphium leonidas	..	15	20
613	45 c.	Graphium antheus	..	20	25
614	50 c.	Precis orithya	..	20	25
615	55 c.	Pinacopteryx eriphia	..	25	30
616	70 c.	Precis octavia	..	30	35
617	1 e.	Mylothris chloris	..	45	50
606/17			Set of 12	1·75	2·00

(Des D. Aryeequaye. Litho Cartor)

1992 (16 Dec). *Centenary of Evangelical Alliance Missions. T 139 and similar vert design. Multicoloured. P 13½×14.*

620	20 c.	Type 139	..	15	10
621	1 e.	Pioneer missionaries	..	65	75

140 Calabashes

(Des D. Aryeequaye. Litho Cartor)

1993 (18 Mar). *Archaeological and Contemporary Artifacts. T 140 and similar vert designs. Multicoloured. P 13½×14.*

622	20 c.	Type 140	..	10	10
623	70 c.	Contemporary cooking pot	..	30	35
624	1 e.	Wooden bowl and containers	..	45	50
625	2 e.	Quern for grinding seeds	..	85	90
622/5			Set of 4	1·50	1·75

POSTAGE DUE STAMPS

Postage Due 2d

D 1   (D 2)   D 3

(Typo D.L.R.)

1933 (2 Jan)–57. *Wmk Mult Script CA. P 14.*

D1	D 1	1d. carmine	..	20	4·50
		a. Chalk-surfaced paper. Dp carmine (24.10.51)		20	7·00
		ac. Error. St Edward's Crown, W 9b		70·00	
D2		2d. pale violet	..	1·00	13·00
		a. Chalk-surfaced paper (22.2.57)		3·00	19·00
		ab. Large "d"	..	20·00	
D1/2	Perf "Specimen"		Set of 2	40·00	

For illustration of No. D2ab see above No. D1 of Lesotho.

1961 (8 Feb). *No. 55 surch with Type D 2.*

D3	7	2d. on 2d.	..	3·00	5·50

Another 2d. on 2d. Postage Due, with small surcharge as Type D 5, was produced *after the currency change*, to meet the philatelic demand (*Price 15p unused*).

(Typo D.L.R.)

1961 (14 Feb). *Chalk-surfaced paper. Wmk Mult Script CA. P 14.*

D4	D 3	1 c. carmine	..	15	75
D5		2 c. violet	..	15	1·10
D6		5 c. green	..	20	1·10
D4/6			Set of 3	45	2·75

Postage Due 1c (D 4)

Postage Due 1c (D 5)

1961. *No. 55 surcharged. A. As Type D 4. (14 Feb).*

D 7	7	1 c. on 2d.	..	1·25	2·50
D 8		2 c. on 2d.	..	1·25	2·50
D 9		5 c. on 2d.	..	1·50	2·50
D7/9			Set of 3	3·50	6·75

B. As Type D 5. (Date?)

D10	7	1 c. on 2d.	..	80	2·50
D11		2 c. on 2d.	..	55	2·25
D12		5 c. on 2d.	..	1·00	2·50
D10/12			Set of 3	2·10	6·50

D 6

(Des and litho B.W.)

1971 (1 Feb). *Size 18×23 mm. W w 12. P 11½.*

D13	D 6	1 c. bright rose-red	..	65	2·25
D14		2 c. purple	..	85	2·50
D15		5 c. dull green	..	1·25	3·00
D13/15			Set of 3	2·50	7·00

1977 (17 Jan). *Size 18×23 mm. W w 14 (sideways). P 11½.*

D16	D 6	1 c. rose-red	..	55	2·00
D17		2 c. purple	..	75	2·50
D18		5 c. dull green	..	1·25	2·75
D16/18			Set of 3	2·25	6·50

(Litho Harrison)

1978 (20 Apr)–85. *Size 17½×21 mm. W w 14. P 15×14.*

D19	D 6	1 c. carmine	..	30	50
D19a		1 c. brown-red (13.3.85)	..	80	1·60
D20		2 c. purple	..	30	50
D21		5 c. blue-green	..	30	50
D19/21			Set of 4	1·50	2·75

(Litho Harrison)

1991 (17 July). *Size 17½×21 mm. With imprint date. W w 14 (sideways). P 15×14.*

D23	D 6	2 c. purple	..	10	10
D24		5 c. bright blue-green	..	10	10
D25		10 c. pale greenish blue	..	10	10
D26		25 c. red-brown	..	10	15
D23/6			Set of 4	25	30

Tanzania
(*formerly* Tanganyika)

TANGANYIKA

The stamps of GERMANY were used in the colony between October 1890 and July 1893 when issues for GERMAN EAST AFRICA were provided.

PRICES FOR STAMPS ON COVER TO 1945
The Mafia Island provisionals (No. M1/52) are very rare used on cover.

Nos. N1/5	from × 8
Nos. 45/59	from × 6
Nos. 60/2	—
Nos. 63/73	from × 6
Nos. 74/86	from × 8
Nos. 87/8	—
Nos. 89/92	from × 6
Nos. 93/106	from × 3
No. 107	—

MAFIA ISLAND
BRITISH OCCUPATION

Mafia Island was captured by the British from the Germans in January 1915. Letters were first sent out unstamped, then with stamps handstamped with Type M 1. Later the military were supplied with handstamps by the post office in Zanzibar. These were used to produce Nos. M11/52.

G.B.
MAFIA
(M 1)   (M 3)

1915 (Jan). *German East Africa Yacht types, handstamped with Type* M 1. *Wmk Lozenges, or no wmk* (1 r., 2 r.). A. *In black* (2½ h. *in blackish lilac*). B. *In deep purple.* C. *In reddish violet.*

		A	B	C
M 1	2½ h. brown	£350	†	£200
	a. Pair, one without handstamp		†	£1100
M 2	4 h. green	£375	£325	£180
	a. Pair, one without handstamp		†	£1000
M 3	7½ h. carmine	£350	£300	£100
	a. Pair, one without handstamp	£1700	†	£1000
M 4	15 h. ultramarine	£475	£400	£130
	a. Pair, one without handstamp		†	£1000
M 5	20 h. black and red/*yellow* ..	£475	£400	£225
	a. Pair, one without handstamp		†£1700	£1100
M 6	30 h. black and carmine ..	£550	£500	£275
	a. Pair, one without handstamp	£1700	†	£1100
M 7	45 h. black and mauve ..	£600	£500	£325
	a. Pair, one without handstamp	£1700	†	£1200
M 8	1 r. carmine	£3500		†£3000
M 9	2 r. green	£4000		†£3500
M10	3 r. blue-black and red ..	£4500		†£3750

Prices are for unused examples.

A few contemporary Zanzibar stamps (1, 3, 6 and 15 c.) are known with the above handstamp.

1915 (May). *German East Africa Yacht types with handstamped four-line surcharge "G.R.—POST—6 CENTS—MAFIA" in black, green or violet. Wmk Lozenges or no wmk* (1 r., 2 r.).

M11	6 c. on 2½ h. brown	£600 £800
	a. Pair, one without handstamp ..	†
M12	6 c. on 4 h. green	£600 £800
	a. Pair, one without handstamp ..	—
M13	6 c. on 7½ h. carmine	£600 £800
	a. Pair, one without handstamp ..	—
M14	6 c. on 15 h. ultramarine ..	£600 £800
M15	6 c. on 20 h. black and red/*yellow* ..	£600 £800
M16	6 c. on 30 h. black and carmine ..	£800 £900
M17	6 c. on 45 h. black and mauve ..	£800 £900
	a. Pair, one without handstamp ..	—
M18	6 c. on 1 r. carmine ..	£5000
M19	6 c. on 2 r. green ..	£6000
M20	6 c. on 3 r. blue-black and red ..	£7000

The 5, 20 and 40 pesa values of the 1901 Yacht issue are also known with the above surcharge as are the contemporary 1 c. and 6 c. Zanzibar stamps.

1915 (Sept). (*a*) *German East African fiscal stamps.* "Statistik des Waaren-Verkehrs" (*Trade Statistical Charge) handstamped in bluish green or violet,* "O.H.B.M.S. Mafia" *in a circle, as Type* M 3.

M21	24 pesa, vermilion/*buff*	£375 £500
M22	12½ heller, drab	£375 £500
	a. Pair, one without handstamp ..	£1400
M23	25 heller, dull green.. ..	£375 £500
M24	50 heller, slate	£375 £500
	a. Pair, one without handstamp ..	£1400
M25	1 rupee, lilac	£375 £500

(*b*) *German East African "Übersetzungs- Gebühren" (Translation Fee) stamp, overprinted as before*

M26	25 heller, grey	£450 £600

G R
POST
MAFIA
(M 4)

G. R.
Post
MAFIA.
(M 5)

(*c*) *Stamps as above, but with further opt as Type* M 4, *in bluish green or violet*

M27	24 pesa, vermilion/*buff*	£500
M28	12½ heller, drab	£500
M29	25 heller, dull green	£500
M30	50 heller, slate	£500
M31	1 rupee, lilac	£500
M32	25 heller, grey (No. M26) ..	£600
	a. Pair, one without handstamp Type M 4	£2000

Type M 3 is also known handstamped on the 7½ h., 20 h. and 30 h. values of German East Africa 1905 Yacht issue and also on contemporary 1, 3, 6 and 25 c. Zanzibar stamps.

1915 (Sept). *Nos.* E1/2, E4/9, E11 *and* E13 *of Indian Expeditionary Forces (India King George V optd* "I.E.F.") *with a further opt Type* M 4 *handstruck in green, greenish black or dull blue.*

M33	3 p. slate-grey	18·00 38·00
	a. Pair, one stamp without opt ..	— £400
M34	½ a. yellow-green	29·00 40·00
	a. Pair, one stamp without opt ..	— £450
M35	1 a. carmine	32·00 40·00
M36	2 a. mauve	45·00 70·00
M37	2½ a. ultramarine	60·00 85·00
M38	3 a. orange-brown	60·00 85·00
	a. Pair, one stamp without opt ..	— £550
M39	4 a. olive-green	80·00 £110
M40	8 a. purple	£140 £190
	a. Pair, one stamp without opt ..	— £700
M41	12 a. dull claret	£225 £300
M42	1 r. red-brown and blue-green ..	£250 £325
M33/42	.. .. ..	*Set of 10* £850 £1100

All values exist with the overprint inverted, and several are known with overprint double or sideways.

1916 (Oct). *Nos.* E1/2, E4/9, E11 *and* E13 *of Indian Expeditionary Forces (India King George V optd* "I.E.F.") *with further opt Type* M 5 *handstruck in green, greenish black or dull blue.*

M43	3 p. slate-grey	80·00 £100
M44	½ a. yellow-green	80·00 95·00
M45	1 a. carmine	75·00 85·00
M46	2 a. mauve	£100 £120
M47	2½ a. ultramarine	£110 £140
M48	3 a. orange-brown	£110 £140
M49	4 a. olive-green	£140 £160
M50	8 a. purple	£180 £250
M51	12 a. dull claret	£225 £325
M52	1 r. red-brown and blue-green ..	£250 £325
M43/52	.. .. ..	*Set of 10* £1200 £1600

Stamps with handstamp inverted are known.

NYASALAND-RHODESIAN FORCE

This issue was sanctioned for use by the Nyasaland-Rhodesian Force during operations in German East Africa, Mozambique and Nyasaland. Unoverprinted Nyasaland stamps were used by the Force prior to the introduction of Nos. N1/5 and, again, in 1918.

N. F.
(N 1)

1916 (17 Aug—18 Sept*). *Nos.* 83, 86, 90/1 *and* 93 *of Malawi (Nyasaland) optd with Type* N 1 *by Govt Printer, Zomba.*

N1	½d. green	80 4·50
N2	1d. scarlet	70 2·50
N3	3d. purple/*yellow* (15 Sept*) ..	5·00 14·00
	a. Opt double	† £7000
N4	4d. black and red/*yellow* (13 Sept*) ..	20·00 30·00
N5	1s. black/*green* (18 Sept*) ..	23·00 32·00
N1/5		*Set of 5* 45·00 70·00
N1/5	Optd "Specimen"	*Set of 5* £250

* Earliest known dates of use.

Of No. N3a only six copies were printed, these being the bottom row on one pane issued at M'bamba Bay F.P.O., German East Africa in March 1918.

This overprint was applied in a setting of 60 (10 rows of 6) and the following minor varieties occur on all values: small stop after "N" (R. 1/1); broken "F" (R. 4/3); very small stop after "F" (R. 6/5); no serifs at top left and bottom of "N" (R. 10/1).

TANGANYIKA
BRITISH OCCUPATION OF GERMAN EAST AFRICA

Following the invasion of German East Africa by Allied forces civilian mail was accepted by the Indian Army postal service, using Indian stamps overprinted "I.E.F.". Some offices reverted to civilian control on 1 June 1917 and these used stamps of East Africa and Uganda until the "G.E.A." overprints were ready. The last field post offices, in the southern part of the country, did not come under civilian control until 15 March 1919.

G.E.A. **G.E.A.** **G.E.A.**
(1) (2) (3)

1917 (Oct)—21. *Nos.* 44/5, 46a/51, 52b, 53/9 *and* 61 *of Kenya, Uganda and Tanganyika optd with* T 1 *and* 2. *Wmk Mult Crown CA. Ordinary paper* (1 c. *to* 15 c.) *or chalk-surfaced paper* (*others*).

45	1 c. black (R.)	15 70
	a. Vermilion opt	14·00 15·00
47	3 c. green	15 15
48	6 c. scarlet	15 10
	a. Wmk sideways ..	† £1500
49	10 c. yellow-orange ..	15 20
50	12 c. slate-grey	15 1·25
51	15 c. bright blue ..	15 1·75

52	25 c. black and red/*yellow* ..	30 2·25
	a. On pale yellow (1921) (Optd S. £35) ..	1·40 8·50
53	50 c. black and lilac ..	50 2·75
54	75 c. black/*blue-green, olive back* (R.) ..	65 3·00
	a. On emerald back (1921) (Optd S. £42)	2·50 25·00
55	1 r. black/*green* (R.) ..	1·25 5·50
	a. On emerald back (1919) ..	2·75 25·00
56	2 r. red and black/*blue* ..	4·50 23·00
57	3 r. violet and green ..	7·50 38·00
58	4 r. red and green/*yellow* ..	15·00 55·00
59	5 r. blue and dull purple ..	26·00 55·00
60	10 r. red and green/*green* ..	48·00 £120
	a. On emerald back ..	55·00 £160
61	20 r. black and purple/*red* ..	£150 £225
62	50 r. carmine and green (S. £150) ..	£500 £750
45/61		*Set of 16* £225 £475
45/61	Optd "Specimen" ..	*Set of 16* £375

Early printings of the rupee values exist with very large stop after the "E" in "G.E.A." (R.5/3). There are round stops after "E" varieties, which in one position of later printings became a small stop.

The only known example of No. 48a was used at Tanga in August 1918.

1921. *Nos.* 69/74 *of Kenya, Uganda and Tanganyika optd with* T 1 *or* 2. *Wmk Mult Script CA. Chalk-surfaced paper* (50 c. *to* 5 r.).

63	12 c. slate-grey	3·25 40·00
64	15 c. bright blue ..	50 2·75
65	50 c. black and dull purple ..	7·50 45·00
66	2 r. red and black/*blue* ..	32·00 85·00
67	3 r. violet and green ..	48·00 95·00
68	5 r. blue and dull purple ..	60·00 £100
63/8		*Set of 6* £140 £325
63/8	Optd "Specimen" ..	*Set of 6* £200

1922. *Nos.* 65 *and* 68 *of Kenya, Uganda and Tanganyika optd by the Government Printer at Dar-es-Salaam with* T 3. *Wmk Mult Script CA.*

72	1 c. black (R.)	30 9·00
73	10 c. orange.. ..	45 13·00

BRITISH MANDATED TERRITORY

4   Giraffe   5

(Recess B.W.)

1922. *Head in black. Wmk Mult Script CA.* (*a*) *P* 15 × 14.

74	4	5 c. slate-purple	75 20
75		10 c. green	30 20
76		15 c. carmine-red	65 10
77		20 c. orange	45 10
78		25 c. black..	3·00 5·50
79		30 c. blue	3·00 2·75
80		40 c. yellow-brown ..	1·50 3·50
81		50 c. slate-grey	1·25 1·50
82		75 c. yellow-bistre ..	2·75 12·00

(*b*) *P* 14. A. *Wmk sideways.* B. *Wmk upright*

			A	B
83	5	1 s. green	1·75 9·00	1·25 6·50
84		2 s. purple	4·25 10·00	2·50 17·00
85		3 s. black	7·00 22·00	†
86		5 s. scarlet	12·00 55·00	8·00 50·00
87		10 s. deep blue	60·00 £120	38·00 75·00
88		£1 yellow-orange.. ..	£100 £190	£100 £190
74/88		*Set of 15 (incl 85A)*		£150 £350
74/88	Optd "Specimen"	*Set of 15*		£425

In the £1 stamp the words of value are on a curved scroll running across the stamp above the words "POSTAGE AND REVENUE".

1925. *As 1922. Frame colours changed.*

89	4	5 c. green	30 90
90		10 c. orange-yellow ..	1·75 1·25
91		25 c. blue	2·25 13·00
92		30 c. purple	85 7·50
89/92 ..			*Set of 4* 4·75 20·00
89/92	Optd "Specimen"		*Set of 4* 70·00

6   7

(Typo D.L.R.)

1927–31. *Head in black. Wmk Mult Script CA. Chalk-surfaced paper* (5 s., 10 s., £1). *P* 14.

93	6	5 c. green	20 10
94		10 c. yellow	30 10
95		15 c. carmine-red ..	20 10
96		20 c. orange-buff ..	70 10
97		25 c. bright blue ..	90 90
98		30 c. dull purple ..	90 2·50
98a		30 c. bright blue (1931) ..	16·00 30
99		40 c. yellow-brown ..	1·00 2·75
100		50 c. grey	1·00 45
101		75 c. olive-green ..	1·75 8·50
102	7	1 s. green	2·25 1·25
103		2 s. deep purple ..	6·00 2·50
104		3 s. black	8·00 32·00
105		5 s. carmine-red ..	9·00 14·00

106 **7** 10 s. deep blue .. .. .. 42·00 75·00
107 £1 brown-orange .. .. 85·00 £120
93/107 *Set of 16* £150 £225
93/107 Optd/Perf "Specimen" *Set of 16* £250

Tanganyika became part of the joint East African postal administration on 1 January 1933 and subsequently used the stamps of KENYA, UGANDA AND TANGANYIKA.

INDEPENDENT REPUBLIC

8 Teacher and Pupils

9 District Nurse and Child

14 "Maternity"

15 Freedom Torch over Mt Kilimanjaro

(Des V. Whiteley. Photo Harrison)
1961 (9 Dec)-**64**. *Independence. T 8/9, 14/15 and similar designs.* P 14×15 (5 c., 30 c.), 15×14 (10 c., 15 c., 20 c., 50 c.) or 14½ *(others)*.
108 5 c. sepia and light apple-green 10 10
109 10 c. deep bluish green 10 10
110 15 c. sepia and blue 10 10
  a. Blue omitted .. £225
111 20 c. orange-brown 10 10
112 30 c. black, emerald and yellow .. 10 10
  a. Inscr "UHURU 196" .. £375 £140
  b. "1" inserted after "196" .. 10·00
113 50 c. black and yellow 10 10
114 1 s. brown, blue and olive-yellow .. 15 10
115 1 s. 30, red, yellow, black, brown and blue 1·25 10
  a. *Red, yellow, blk, brn & dp bl* (10.3.64) 2·00 10
116 2 s. blue, yellow, green and brown .. 40 10
117 5 s. deep bluish green and orange-red .. 50 40
118 10 s. black, reddish purple and light blue 11·00 3·25
  a. Reddish purple (diamond) omitted £150
119 20 s. red, yellow, black, brown and green 3·00 7·00
108/19 *Set of 12* 15·00 10·00

Designs: *Vert (as T 9)*—15 c. Coffee-picking; 20 c. Harvesting maize; 50 c. Serengeti lions. *Horiz (as T 8)*—30 c. Tanganyika flag. (*As T 14*)—2 s. Dar-es-Salaam waterfront; 5 s. Land tillage; 10 s. Diamond and mine. *Vert*—20 s. Type 15.
No. 112a. The missing "1" in "1961" occurs on emerald Plate 1C, R. 10/10. The "1" was later inserted but it is, however, very slightly shorter and the figure is more solid than normal.

19 Pres. Nyerere inaugurating Self-help Project

20 Hoisting Flag on Mt Kilimanjaro

(Photo Harrison)
1962 (9 Dec). *Inauguration of Republic. Vert designs as T 19/20.* P 14½.
120 30 c. emerald 10 10
121 50 c. yellow, black, green, red and blue .. 10 10
122 1 s. 30, multicoloured 10 10
123 2 s. 50, black, red and blue 15 30
120/3 *Set of 4* 30 35
Designs:—1 s. 30, Presidential emblem; 2 s. 50, Independence Monument.

23 Map of Republic

24 Torch and Spear Emblem

(Des M. Goaman. Photo Harrison)
1964 (7 July). *United Republic of Tanganyika and Zanzibar Commemoration.* P 14 × 14½.
124 **23** 20 c. yellow-green and light blue .. 10 10
125 **24** 30 c. blue and sepia 10 10
126 1 s. 30, orange-brown and ultramarine .. 10 10
127 **23** 2 s. 50, purple and ultramarine .. 50 40
124/7 *Set of 4* 65 50
Despite the inscription on the stamps the above issue was only on sale in Tanganyika and had no validity in Zanzibar.

OFFICIAL STAMPS

OFFICIAL   **OFFICIAL**
(O 1)   (O 2) (3½ mm tall)

1961 (9 Dec). *Nos. 108/14 and 117 optd with Type O 1 (10, 15, 20, 50 c. or larger (17 mm) 5, 30 c.) or with Type O 2 (1 s. or larger (22 mm) 5 s.).*
O1 5 c. sepia and light apple-green .. 10 10
O2 10 c. deep bluish green 10 10
O3 15 c. sepia and blue 10 10
O4 20 c. orange-brown 10 10
O5 30 c. black, emerald and yellow .. 10 10
O6 50 c. black and yellow 10 10
O7 1 s. brown, blue and olive-yellow .. 10 10
O8 5 s. deep bluish green and orange-red .. 65 75
O1/8 .. *Set of 8* 90 90

ZANZIBAR

Stamps of INDIA were used in Zanzibar from 1 October 1875 until 10 November 1895, when the administration of the postal service was transferred from India to British East Africa.
A French post office was opened on the island in January 1889 and this service used the stamps of FRANCE until 1894 when specific stamps for this office were provided. The French postal service on the island closed on 31 July 1904 and it is known that French stamps were again utilised during the final month.
A German postal agency operated in Zanzibar between 27 August 1890 and 31 July 1891, using the stamps of GERMANY.

PRICES FOR STAMPS ON COVER TO 1945

Nos. 1/2	—
Nos. 3/18	*from* ×30
Nos. 19/21	—
Nos. 22/174	*from* ×12
Nos. 175/7	—
Nos. 178/87	*from* ×15
Nos. 188/204	*from* ×10
Nos. 205/9	*from* ×15
Nos. 210/38	*from* ×10
Nos. 239/45	—
Nos. 246/59	*from* ×8
Nos. 260/f	—
Nos. 261/330	*from* ×4
Nos. D1/17	*from* ×12
Nos. D18/30	*from* ×15

PROTECTORATE

Zanzibar
(1)
1895 (10 Nov)-**96**. *Nos. 81, 85, 90/6, 98/101, 103 and 106/9 of India (Queen Victoria) optd with T 1 by Zanzibar Gazette.*
(a) In blue
1 ½ a. blue-green £8000 £2250
2 1 a. plum £1800 £475
  j. "Zanzidar" .. — £9000
(b) In black
3 ½ a. blue-green .. 3·00 2·50
  j. "Zanzidar" .. £700 £500
  k. "Zanzibar" .. £750 £900
  l. Diaeresis over last "a" £550
4 1 a. plum .. 3·25 3·00
  j. "Zanzidar" .. — £1300
  k. "Zanibar" .. £850 £950
  l. Diaeresis over last "a" £650
5 1 a. 6 p. sepia .. 4·00 3·00
  j. "Zanzidar" .. £1900 £750
  k. "Zanibar" .. £850 £950
  l. "Zanzibar" ..
  m. Diaeresis over last "a" £600
6 2 a. pale blue .. 3·75 3·50
7 2 a. blue .. 4·00 3·75
  j. "Zanzidar" .. £1700 £1200
  k. "Zanibar" .. £1800 £1100
  l. Diaeresis over last "a" £600
  m. Opt double £190
8 2½ a. yellow-green .. 4·75 4·25
  j. "Zanzidar" .. £1600 £900
  k. "Zanibar" .. £400 £650
  l. "Zapzibar" ..
  m. "Zanzipar" ..
  n. Diaeresis over last "a" £600 £600
  o. Second "z" italic £160 £250
9 3 a. orange ..
10 3 a. brown-orange .. 7·00 8·50
  j. "Zanzidar" .. £450 £800
  k. "Zanizbar" .. £1800 £1900
11 4 a. olive-green .. 13·00 12·00
  j. "Zanzidar" .. £2500 £1400
12 4 a. slate-green .. 8·00 9·50
  l. Diaeresis over last "a" £800
13 6 a. pale brown .. 9·50 10·00
  j. "Zanzidar" .. £2750 £1500
  k. "Zanibar" .. £600 £900
  l. "Zanzibarr" .. £1800 £1800
  m. Opt double

---

14 8 a. dull mauve .. .. 16·00 16·00
  j. "Zanzidar" .. £3000 £3000
15 8 a. magenta (7.96) .. 9·00 17·00
16 12 a. purple/*red* .. 14·00 10·00
  j. "Zanzidar" .. £3500 £2000
17 1 r. slate .. .. 65·00 65·00
  j. "Zanzidar" .. £3250 £3000
18 1 r. green and aniline carmine (7.96) .. 10·00 15·00
  j. Opt vert downwards £375
19 2 r. carmine and yellow-brown .. 28·00 45·00
  j. "r" omitted £4500
  k. "r" inverted £2750 £2500
20 3 r. brown and green .. 32·00 42·00
  j. "r" omitted £4500
  k. "r" inverted £2500 £2750
21 5 r. ultramarine and violet .. 30·00 48·00
  j. "r" omitted £4500
  k. "r" inverted £2000
  l. Opt double, one inverted £700
3/21 *Set of 15* £200 £250
Many forgeries of this overprint exist and also bogus errors.

MINOR VARIETIES. The following minor varieties of type exist on Nos. 1/21:
A. First "Z" antique (all values)
B. Broken "p" for "n" (all values to 1 r.)
C. Tall second "z" (all values)
D. Small second "z" (all values)
E. Small second "z" and inverted "q" for "b" (all values)
F. Second "z" Gothic (½ a. to 12 a. and 1 r.) (No. 18) (black opts only)
G. No dot over "i" (all values to 1 r.)
H. Inverted "q" for "b" (all values to 1 r.)
I. Arabic "2" for "r" (all values to 1 r.) (black opts only)

The scarcity of these varieties varies from normal catalogue value (D. and E.) to 4 times catalogue value (B.).

$2\tfrac{1}{2}$ $2\tfrac{1}{2}$ $2\tfrac{1}{2}$ $2\tfrac{1}{2}$
(2)   (3)   (4)   (5)

1895-98. *Provisionals. I. Stamps used for postal purposes.*
(a) No. 5 surch in red (12.95)
22 **2** 2½ on 1½ a. sepia .. .. 28·00 28·00
  j. "Zanzidar" .. £1000 £950
  k. "Zanzibar" .. £2250 £1500
  l. Inverted "1" in "½" £900 £800
(b) No. 4 surch in black (11.5.96)
23 **3** 2½ on 1 a. plum .. £120 £100
24 **4** 2½ on 1 a. plum .. £325 £225
  j. Inverted "1" in "½" £1700
25 **5** 2½ on 1 a. plum .. £130 £100

$2\tfrac{1}{2}$ $2\tfrac{1}{2}$ $2\tfrac{1}{2}$
(6)   (7)   (8)

(c) No. 6 surch in red (15.8.96)
26 **6** 2½ on 2 a. pale blue .. .. 32·00 21·00
  j. Inverted "1" in "½" £325 £225
  k. Roman "I" in "½" £200 £150
27 **7** 2½ on 2 a. pale blue .. .. £110 75·00
  j. "2" of "½" omitted £2500
  k. "22" for "2½" £3250
  l. "1" of "½" omitted £2500 £2500
  m. Inverted "1" in "½" £1000
28 **8** 2½ on 2 a. pale blue £2000 £1000
No. 28 only exists with small "z".

(d) No. 5 surch in red (15.11.96)
29 **6** 2½ on 1½ a. sepia .. £110 90·00
  j. Inverted "1" in "½" £950 £850
  k. Roman "I" in "½" £700 £650
30 **7** 2½ on 1½ a. sepia .. £325 £275
31 **8** 2½ on 1½ a. sepia .. £5500 £3750
No. 31 only exists with small "z".

II. *Stamps prepared for official purposes. Nos. 4, 5 and 7 surch as before in red (1.98)*
32 **3** 2½ on 1 a. plum .. £225 £400
33 **4** 2½ on 1 a. plum .. £400 £600
34 **5** 2½ on 1 a. plum .. £250 £425
35 **3** 2½ on 1½ a. sepia .. 65·00 £120
  j. Diaeresis over last "a" £1900
36 **4** 2½ on 1½ a. sepia .. £140 £275
37 **5** 2½ on 1½ a. sepia .. 90·00 £160
38 **3** 2½ on 2 a. dull blue .. 75·00 £140
39 **4** 2½ on 2 a. dull blue .. £140 £275
40 **5** 2½ on 2 a. dull blue .. 90·00 £170
It is doubtful whether Nos. 32/40 were issued to the public.

1896. *Nos. 65/6, 68 and 71/3 of British East Africa (Queen Victoria) optd with T 1.*
41 ½ a. yellow-green (1 June) .. 23·00 16·00
42 1 a. carmine-rose (1 June) .. 22·00 15·00
  j. Opt double £450 £475
43 2½ a. deep blue (R.) (24 May) .. 75·00 40·00
44 4½ a. orange-yellow (12 Aug) .. 32·00 45·00
45 5 a. yellow-bistre (12 Aug) .. 38·00 20·00
  j. "r" omitted — £1500
46 7½ a. mauve (12 Aug) .. 25·00 35·00
41/6 *Set of 6* £200 £150

MINOR VARIETIES. The various minor varieties of type detailed in the note below No. 21 also occur on Nos. 22 to 46 as indicated below:
A. Nos. 23, 25, 27, 30, 35, 38, 41/6
B. Nos. 22, 26, 29/30, 32/3, 36, 39, 44/6
C. Nos. 22, 25/6, 32, 36, 38, 40/6
D. Nos. 22/46
E. Nos. 22/46
F. Nos. 22, 25/6, 29, 41/6
G. Nos. 25/6, 29, 35, 37/8, 40/6
H. Nos. 22, 41/6 (on the British East Africa stamps this variety occurs in the same position as variety C.)
I. Nos. 26, 29, 35, 38, 41/6

The scarcity of these varieties on the surcharges (Nos. 22/40) is similar to those on the basic stamps, but examples on the British East Africa values (Nos. 41/6) are more common.

PRINTERS. All Zanzibar stamps up to Type **37** were printed by De La Rue & Co.

12

13

14 Sultan Seyyid Hamed-bin-Thwain

18

1896 (Dec). *Recess. Flags in red on all values.* W **12**. P **14**.

156	13	½ a. yellow-green		1·75	70
157		1 a. indigo		1·00	1·25
158		1 a. violet-blue		3·00	3·00
159		2 a. red-brown		1·10	65
160		2½ a. bright blue		5·00	70
161		2½ a. pale blue		5·50	70
162		3 a. grey		3·25	3·25
163		3 a. bluish grey		3·75	3·75
164		4 a. myrtle-green		3·25	2·75
165		4½ a. orange		2·50	3·00
166		5 a. bistre		2·25	2·25
		a. Bisected (2½ a.) (on cover)		† £1800	
167		7½ a. mauve		2·25	2·25
168		8 a. grey-olive		5·50	4·75
169	14	1 r. blue		9·00	9·00
170		1 r. deep blue		15·00	12·00
171		2 r. green		13·00	9·50
172		3 r. dull purple		20·00	9·50
173		4 r. lake		14·00	13·00
174		5 r. sepia		19·00	13·00
156/74			Set of 15	90·00	65·00
156/74 Optd "Specimen"			Set of 15	£180	

The ½, 1, 2, 2½, 3 and 8 a. are known without wmk, these being from edges of the sheets.

1897 (5 Jan). *No. 164 surch as before, in red.*

175	3	2½ on 4 a. myrtle-green		48·00	30·00
176	4	2½ on 4 a. myrtle-green		£140	£110
177	5	2½ on 4 a. myrtle-green		60·00	42·00
175/7			Set of 3	£225	£160

1898 (May). *Recess.* W **18**. P **14**.

178	13	½ a. yellow-green		60	35
179		1 a. indigo		60	45
		a. Greenish black		2·50	1·00
180		2 a. red-brown		1·40	75
		a. Deep brown		2·75	1·50
181		2½ a. bright blue		85·	30
182		3 a. grey		2·25	60
183		4 a. myrtle-green		1·50	1·00
184		4½ a. orange		3·00	70
185		5 a. bistre		6·50	1·60
		a. Pale bistre		6·50	2·00
186		7½ a. mauve		2·25	2·75
187		8 a. grey-olive		4·00	2·25
178/87			Set of 10	20·00	9·50

19

20 Sultan Seyyid Hamoud-bin-Mohammed bin Said

1899 (June)–**1901**. *Recess. Flags in red.* W **18** (Nos. 188/99) or W **12** (others). P **14**.

188	19	½ a. yellow-green		55	30
		a. Wmk sideways		4·00	2·50
189		1 a. indigo		1·25	20
		a. Wmk sideways		7·50	80
190		1 a. carmine (1901)		65	10
191		2 a. red-brown		75	40
192		2½ a. bright blue		1·00	50
193		3 a. grey		1·25	1·40
194		4 a. myrtle-green		1·25	1·00
195		4½ a. orange		3·75	2·25
196		4½ a. blue-black (1901)		5·50	5·50
197		5 a. bistre		1·50	1·00
198		7½ a. mauve		2·25	3·25
199		8 a. grey-olive		2·25	4·00
200	20	1 r. blue		15·00	12·00
201		2 r. green		15·00	15·00
202		3 r. dull purple		17·00	24·00
203		4 r. lake		26·00	38·00
204		5 r. sepia		38·00	45·00
188/204			Set of 17	£120	£140
188/204 Optd "Specimen"			Set of 17	£180	

Two & Half (22)

Two & Half (22a) Thin open "w"

Two & Half (22b) Serif to foot of "f"

1904. *Stamps of 1899/1901 surch as T* **21** *and* **22**, *in black or lake* (L.) *by Zanzibar Gazette.*

205	19	1 on 4½ a. orange		1·40	3·25
206		1 on 4½ a. blue-black (L.)		4·25	13·00
207		2 on 4 a. myrtle-green (L.)		13·00	16·00
208		2½ on 7½ a. mauve		12·00	17·00
		a. Opt Type 22a		65·00	85·00
		b. Opt Type 22b		95·00	£130
		c. "Hlaf" for "Half"		£8000	
209		2½ on 8 a. grey-olive		14·00	28·00
		a. Opt Type 22a		85·00	£130
		b. Opt Type 22b		£120	£150
		c. "Hlaf" for "Half"		£7500	£4250
205/9			Set of 5	40·00	70·00

23

24

Monogram of Sultan Seyyid Ali bin Hamoud bin Naherud

1904 (8 June). *Typo. Background of centre in second colour.* W **18**. P **14**.

210	23	½ a. green		75	20
211		1 a. rose-red		75	10
212		2 a. brown		1·25	45
213		2½ a. blue		1·75	35
214		3 a. grey		1·50	1·25
215		4 a. deep green		2·00	1·25
216		4½ a. black		3·00	2·50
217		5 a. yellow-brown		3·25	1·25
218		7½ a. purple		3·50	5·00
219		8 a. olive-green		3·50	2·50
220	24	1 r. blue and red		15·00	8·50
		a. Wmk sideways		48·00	35·00
221		2 r. green and red		12·00	25·00
		a. Wmk sideways		75·00	90·00
222		3 r. violet and red		35·00	60·00
223		4 r. claret and red		40·00	75·00
224		5 r. olive-brown and red		42·00	80·00
210/24			Set of 15	£150	£225
210/24 Optd "Specimen"			Set of 15	£130	

25

26

27 Sultan Ali bin Hamoud

28 View of Port

1908 (May)–**09**. *Recess.* W **18** (sideways on 10 r. to 30 r.). P **14**.

225	25	1 c. pearl-grey (10.09)		25	25
226		3 c. yellow-green		1·40	10
		a. Wmk sideways		1·40	70
227		6 c. rose-carmine		3·50	10
		a. Wmk sideways		3·50	1·00
228		10 c. brown (10.09)		1·50	1·75
229		12 c. violet		4·25	75
		a. Wmk sideways		3·75	50
230	26	15 c. ultramarine		3·50	40
		a. Wmk sideways		4·00	2·50
231		25 c. sepia		2·50	80
232		50 c. blue-green		3·25	3·50
233		75 c. grey-black (10.09)		6·00	8·50
234	27	1 r. yellow-green		14·00	5·50
		a. Wmk sideways		24·00	7·00
235		2 r. violet		12·00	14·00
		a. Wmk sideways		60·00	38·00
236		3 r. orange-bistre		16·00	38·00
237		4 r. vermilion		28·00	65·00
238		5 r. steel-blue		32·00	50·00
239	28	10 r. blue-green and brown (S. £22)		65·00	£120
240		20 r. black and yellow-green (S. £30)		£160	£275
241		30 r. black and sepia (S. £40)		£250	£400
242		40 r. black and orange-brown (S. £50)		£400	
243		50 r. black and mauve (S. £60)		£350	
244		100 r. black and steel-blue (S. £100)		£650	
245		200 r. brown and greenish black (S. £150)		£950	
225/38			Set of 14	£110	£170
225/38 Optd "Specimen"			Set of 14	£140	

Specimen copies of Nos. 239/45 are all overprinted.

29 Sultan Kalif bin Harub

30 Sailing Canoe

31 Dhow

1913. *Recess.* W **18** (sideways on 75 c. and T **31**). P **14**.

246	29	1 c. grey		15	20
247		3 c. yellow-green		35	20
248		6 c. rose-carmine		80	10
249		10 c. brown		80	75
250		12 c. violet		70	15
251		15 c. blue		1·00	30
252		25 c. sepia		80	45
253		50 c. blue-green		2·00	2·75
254		75 c. grey-black		1·75	1·75
255	30	1 r. yellow-green		3·25	4·00
256		2 r. violet		8·00	17·00
257		3 r. orange-bistre		10·00	25·00
258		4 r. scarlet		16·00	45·00
259		5 r. steel-blue		22·00	25·00
260	31	10 r. green and brown		60·00	95·00
260a		20 r. black and green (S. £20)		85·00	£170
260b		30 r. black and brown (S. £30)		£110	£225
260c		40 r. black and vermilion (S. £50)		£225	£375
260d		50 r. black and purple (S. £55)		£225	£375
260e		100 r. black and blue (S. £80)		£300	
260f		200 r. brown and black (S. £110)		£600	
246/60			Set of 15	£110	£190
246/60 Optd "Specimen"			Set of 15	£130	

Specimen copies of Nos. 260a/f are all overprinted.

1914–22. *Wmk Mult Crown CA* (sideways on 10 r.). P **14**.

261	29	1 c. grey		20	25
262		3 c. yellow-green		50	10
		a. Dull green		1·60	15
263		6 c. deep carmine		75	10
		a. Bright rose-carmine		75	10
264		8 c. purple/pale yellow (1922)		60	2·50
265		10 c. myrtle/pale yellow (1922)		60	35
266		15 c. deep ultramarine		90	2·25
268		50 c. blue-green		3·50	4·00
269		75 c. grey-black		2·75	15·00
270	30	1 r. yellow-green		4·00	2·75
271		2 r. violet		4·25	8·00
272		3 r. orange-bistre		11·00	25·00
273		4 r. scarlet		14·00	55·00
274		5 r. steel-blue		16·00	45·00
275	31	10 r. green and brown		55·00	£160
261/75			Set of 14	£100	£275
261/75 Optd "Specimen"			Set of 14	£130	

1921–29. *Wmk Mult Script CA* (sideways on 10 r. to 30 r.). P **14**.

276	29	1 c. slate-grey		10	5·00
277		3 c. yellow-green		30	1·40
278		3 c. yellow (1922)		15	10
279		4 c. green (1922)		50	60
280		6 c. carmine-red		30	50
281		6 c. purple/blue (1922)		35	10
282		10 c. brown		70	4·50
283		12 c. violet		30	30
284		12 c. carmine-red (1922)		40	35
285		15 c. blue		55	4·25
286		20 c. indigo (1922)		1·00	30
287		25 c. sepia		60	5·50
288		50 c. myrtle-green		1·25	2·00
289		75 c. slate		2·50	25·00
290	30	1 r. yellow-green		1·75	1·60
291		2 r. deep violet		2·50	4·75
292		3 r. orange-bistre		4·00	6·50
293		4 r. scarlet		10·00	23·00
294		5 r. Prussian blue		13·00	45·00
295	31	10 r. green and brown		45·00	£110
296		20 r. black and green (Optd S. £55)		£100	£225
297		30 r. black and brown (1929) (Perf S. £65)		£150	£325
276/95			Set of 20	75·00	£200
276/95 Optd "Specimen"			Set of 20	£160	

32

Sultan Kalif bin Harub 33

1926–27. *T* **32** ("CENTS" *in serifed capitals). Recess. Wmk Mult Script CA.* P **14**.

299	32	1 c. brown		15	10
300		3 c. yellow-orange		15	15
301		4 c. deep dull green		20	30
302		6 c. violet		15	10
303		8 c. slate		90	3·00
304		10 c. olive-green		75	40
305		12 c. carmine-red		1·50	10
306		20 c. bright blue		40	30
307		25 c. purple/yellow (1927)		4·00	2·50
308		50 c. claret		90	35
309		75 c. sepia (1927)		3·75	8·50
299/309			Set of 11	11·50	14·00
299/309 Optd "Specimen"			Set of 11	85·00	

(New Currency. 100 cents = 1 shilling)

1936 (1 Jan). *T 33 ("CENTS" in sans-serif capitals), and T 30/1, but values in shillings. Recess. Wmk Mult Script CA. P 14×13½–14.*

310	33	5 c. green		10	10
311		10 c. black		10	10
312		15 c. carmine-red		10	15
313		20 c. orange		10	10
314		25 c. purple/*yellow*		10	10
315		30 c. ultramarine		10	10
316		40 c. sepia		15	10
317		50 c. claret		15	10
318	30	1 s. yellow-green		45	10
319		2 s. slate-violet		55	40
320		5 s. scarlet		2·50	3·50
321		7 s. 50, light blue		8·50	8·50
322	31	10 s. green and brown		5·00	6·00
310/22			Set of 13	16·00	17·00
310/22 Perf "Specimen"			Set of 13	£100	

36 Sultan Kalif bin Harub

1936 (9 Dec). *Silver Jubilee of Sultan. Recess. Wmk Mult Script CA. P 14.*

323	36	10 c. black and olive-green		70	30
324		20 c. black and bright purple		70	30
325		30 c. black and deep ultramarine		2·00	35
326		50 c. black and orange-vermilion		2·50	60
323/6			Set of 4	5·25	1·40
323/6 Perf "Specimen"			Set of 4	60·00	

37 *Sham Alam* (Sultan's dhow)

V I C T O R Y I S S U E

8TH JUNE 1946

(38)

1944 (20 Nov). *Bicentenary of Al Busaid Dynasty. Recess. Wmk Mult Script CA. P 14.*

327	37	10 c. ultramarine		20	40
328		20 c. red		20	75
329		50 c. blue-green		20	30
330		1 s. dull purple		20	45
327/30			Set of 4	70	1·75
327/30 Perf "Specimen"			Set of 4	70·00	

1946 (11 Nov). *Victory. Optd with T 38.*

331	33	10 c. black (R.)		20	20
332		30 c. ultramarine (R.)		20	40
331/2 Perf "Specimen"			Set of 2	45·00	

1949 (10 Jan). *Royal Silver Wedding. As Nos. 143/4 of Jamaica.*

333	20 c. orange		30	60
334	10 s. brown		13·00	18·00

1949 (10 Oct). *75th Anniv of U.P.U. As Nos. 145/8 of Jamaica.*

335	20 c. red-orange		40	60
336	30 c. deep blue		1·40	60
337	50 c. magenta		1·50	75
338	1 s. blue-green		1·50	1·50
335/8		Set of 4	4·25	3·00

39 Sultan Kalif bin Harub

40 Seyyid Khalifa Schools, Beit-el-Ras

1952 (26 Aug)–55. *Wmk Mult Script CA. P 12½ (cent values) or 13 (shilling values).*

339	39	5 c. black		10	10
340		10 c. red-orange		10	10
341		15 c. green		30	40
		a. Yellow-green (12.11.53)		45	40
342		20 c. carmine-red		30	30
343		25 c. reddish purple		45	40
344		30 c. deep bluish green		30	10
		a. Deep green (29.3.55)		2·00	2·25
345		35 c. bright blue		30	80
346		40 c. deep brown		30	50
		a. Sepia (12.11.53)		40	60
347		50 c. violet		30	10
		a. Deep violet (29.3.55)		65	40
348	40	1 s. deep green and deep brown		30	10
349		2 s. bright blue and deep purple		85	40
350		5 s. black and carmine-red		1·50	1·75
351		7 s. 50, grey-black and emerald		15·00	22·00
352		10 s. carmine-red and black		8·00	3·50
339/52			Set of 14	25·00	27·00

41 Sultan Kalif bin Harub

(Photo Harrison)

1954 (26 Aug). *Sultan's 75th Birthday. Wmk Mult Script CA. Chalk-surfaced paper. P 13 × 12.*

353	41	15 c. deep green		10	10
354		20 c. rose-red		10	10
355		30 c. bright blue		10	10
356		50 c. purple		10	10
357		1 s. 25, orange-red		15	40
353/7			Set of 5	30	55

42 Cloves   **43** Dhows

44 Sultan's Barge   **45** Map of East African Coast

46 Minaret Mosque   **47** Dimbani Mosque   **48** Kibweni Palace

(Des W. J. Jennings (T 42), A. Farhan (T 43), Mrs. M. Broadbent (T 44, 46), R. A. Sweet (T 45), A. S. B. New (T 47), B. J. Woolley (T 48). Recess B.W.)

1957 (26 Aug). *W w 12. P 11½ (5 c., 10 c.), 11×11½ (15 c., 30 c., 1 s. 25), 14×13½ (20 c., 25 c., 35 c., 50 c.), 13½×14 (40 c., 1 s., 2 s.) or 13×13½ (5 s., 7 s. 50, 10 s.).*

358	42	5 c. orange and deep green		10	10
359		10 c. emerald and carmine-red		10	10
360	43	15 c. green and sepia		10	40
361	44	20 c. ultramarine		10	10
362	45	25 c. orange-brown and black		10	10
363	43	30 c. carmine-red and black		15	10
364	45	35 c. slate and emerald		15	15
365	46	40 c. brown and black		15	10
366	45	50 c. blue and grey-green		15	10
367	47	1 s. carmine and black		20	10
368	43	1 s. 25, slate and carmine		70	10
369	47	2 s. orange and deep green		60	40
370	48	5 s. deep bright blue		3·50	2·00
371		7 s. 50, green		3·50	4·00
372		10 s. carmine		3·50	3·00
358/72			Set of 15	11·50	9·50

49 Sultan Seyyid Sir Abdulla bin Khalifa   **50** "Protein Foods"

(Recess B.W.)

1961 (17 Oct). *As T 42/8, but with portrait of Sultan Sir Abdulla as in T 49, W w 12. P 13×13½ (20 s.), others as before.*

373	49	5 c. orange and deep green		10	10
374		10 c. emerald and carmine-red		10	10
375	43	15 c. green and sepia		20	60
376	44	20 c. ultramarine		15	10
377	45	25 c. orange-brown and black		15	10
378	43	30 c. carmine-red and black		60	10
379	45	35 c. slate and emerald		30	10
380	46	40 c. brown and black		30	10
381	45	50 c. blue and grey-green		30	10
382	47	1 s. carmine and black		40	10
383	43	1 s. 25, slate and carmine		80	35
384	47	2 s. orange and deep green		40	10
385	48	5 s. deep bright blue		90	1·40
386		7 s. 50, green		2·25	10·00
387		10 s. carmine		2·25	6·50
388		20 s. sepia		15·00	24·00
373/88			Set of 16	22·00	40·00

(Des M. Goaman. Photo Harrison)

1963 (4 June). *Freedom from Hunger. W w 12. P 14 × 14½.*

389	**50**	1 s. 30, sepia		70	30

INDEPENDENT

51 Zanzibar Clove   **53** "Religious Tolerance" (mosques and churches)

(Photo Harrison)

1963 (10 Dec). *Independence. Portrait of Sultan Seyyid Jamshid bin Abdulla. T 51, 53 and similar vert designs. P 12½.*

390		30 c. multicoloured		10	20
391		50 c. multicoloured		10	25
392		1 s. 30, multicoloured		10	1·50
393		2 s. 50, multicoloured		10	2·50
390/3			Set of 4	40	4·00

Designs:—50 c. "To Prosperity" (Zanzibar doorway); 2 s. 50, "Towards the Light" (Mangapwani Cave).

REPUBLIC

When the Post Office opened on 14 January 1964, after the revolution deposing the Sultan, the stamps on sale had the portrait cancelled by a manuscript cross. Stamps thus cancelled on cover or piece used between January 14 and 17 are therefore of interest.

JAMHURI 1964

(55= "Republic")

1964 (17 Jan). *Locally handstamped as T 55 in black.*

(i) Nos. 373/88.

394	49	5 c. orange and deep green		30	10
395		10 c. emerald and carmine-red		30	10
396	43	15 c. green and sepia		30	40
397	44	20 c. ultramarine		30	10
398	45	25 c. orange-brown and black		30	10
399	43	30 c. carmine-red and black		30	10
400	45	35 c. slate and emerald		30	30
401	46	40 c. brown and black		30	40
402	45	50 c. blue and grey-green		30	10
403	47	1 s. carmine and black		30	40
404	43	1 s. 25, slate and carmine		30	55
405	47	2 s. orange and deep green		1·50	55
406	48	5 s. deep bright blue		1·50	55
407		7 s. 50, green		2·00	1·25
408		10 s. carmine		2·00	90
409		20 s. sepia		2·50	3·25

(ii) Nos. 390/3 (Independence)

410		30 c. multicoloured		10	10
411		50 c. multicoloured		15	10
412		1 s. 30, multicoloured		25	10
413		2 s. 50, multicoloured		40	30
		a. Green omitted		£110	
394/413			Set of 20	12·00	8·50

T 55 occurs in various positions—diagonally, horizontally or vertically.

NOTE.—Nos. 394 to 413 are the only stamps officially authorised to receive the handstamp but it has also been seen on Nos. 353/7, 389 and the Postage Dues. There are numerous errors but it is impossible to distinguish between cases of genuine oversight and those made deliberately at the request of purchasers.

JAMHURI

JAMHURI 1964

(56)

1964

(57)

1964 (28 Feb). *Optd by Bradbury, Wilkinson.*

(i) As T 56 on Nos. 373/88.

414	49	5 c. orange and deep green		10	10
415		10 c. emerald and carmine-red		10	10
416	43	15 c. green and sepia		10	10
417	44	20 c. ultramarine		10	10
418	45	25 c. orange-brown and black		10	10
419	43	30 c. carmine-red and black		10	10
420	45	35 c. slate and emerald		10	10
421	46	40 c. brown and black		10	10
422	45	50 c. blue and grey-green		10	10
423	47	1 s. carmine and black		10	10
424	43	1 s. 25, slate and carmine		50	10
425	47	2 s. orange and deep green		30	10
426	48	5 s. deep bright blue		50	35
427		7 s. 50, green		65	1·25
428		10 s. carmine		75	1·25
429		20 s. sepia		1·50	2·00

The opt T 56 is set in two lines on Types 46/8.

(ii) As T 57 on Nos. 390/3 (Independence)

430		30 c. multicoloured		10	10
431		50 c. multicoloured		10	10
432		1 s. 30, multicoloured		10	10
433		2 s. 50, multicoloured		15	10
		a. Green omitted		45·00	
414/33			Set of 20	4·50	5·00

The opt T 57 is set in one line on No. 432.

For the set inscribed "UNITED REPUBLIC OF TANGANYIKA AND ZANZIBAR" see Nos. 124/7 of Tanganyika.

58 Axe, Spear and Dagger

59 Zanzibari with Rifle

(Litho German Bank Note Ptg Co, Leipzig)

1964 (21 June). *T* **58/9** *and similar designs inscr.* "JAMHURI ZANZIBAR 1964". *Multicoloured. P* 13 × 13½ (*vert*) *or* 13½ × 13 (*horiz*).

434	5 c. Type 58			10	10
435	10 c. Bow and arrow breaking chains			10	10
436	15 c. Type 58			10	10
437	20 c. As 10 c.			10	10
438	25 c. Type 59			10	10
439	30 c. Zanzibari breaking manacles			10	10
440	40 c. Type 59			10	10
441	50 c. As 30 c.			10	10
442	1 s. Zanzibari, flag and Sun			10	10
443	1 s. 30, Hands breaking chains (*horiz*)			15	10
444	2 s. Hand waving flag (*horiz*)			20	10
445	5 s. Map of Zanzibar and Pemba on flag (*horiz*)			55	20
446	10 s. Flag on Map			1·75	1·10
447	20 s. National flag (*horiz*)			2·25	8·00
434/47			*Set of 14*	4·75	9·00

68 Soldier and Maps

69 Building Construction

(Litho German Bank Note Ptg Co, Leipzig)

1965 (12 Jan). *First Anniv of Revolution. P* 13 × 13½ (*vert*) *or* 13½ × 13 (*horiz*).

448	68	20 c. apple-green and deep green		10	10
449	69	30 c. chocolate and yellow-orange		10	10
450	68	1 s. 30, light blue and ultramarine		10	10
451	69	2 s. 50, reddish violet and rose		10	15
448/51			*Set of 4*	30	30

70 Planting Rice

(Litho German Bank Note Ptg Co, Leipzig)

1965 (17 Oct). *Agricultural Development. T* **70** *and similar horiz design. P* 13 × 12½.

452	70	20 c. sepia and blue		10	40
453	—	30 c. sepia and magenta		10	40
454	—	1 s. 30, sepia and yellow-orange		30	90
455	70	2 s. 50, sepia and emerald		50	2·50
452/5			*Set of 4*	85	3·75

Design:—30 c., 1 s. 30, Hands holding rice.

72 Freighter, Tractor, Factory, and Open Book and Torch

73 Soldier

(Litho German Bank Note Ptg Co, Leipzig)

1966 (12 Jan). *2nd Anniv of Revolution. P* 12½ × 13.

456	72	20 c. multicoloured		10	10
457	73	50 c. multicoloured		10	10
458	72	1 s. 30, multicoloured		10	10
459	73	2 s. 50, multicoloured		30	30
456/9			*Set of 4*	40	45

For stamps with similar inscription or inscribed "TANZANIA" only, and with commemorative date 26th April 1966, see Nos. Z142/5 of TANZANIA.

74 Tree-felling

75 Zanzibar Street

(Litho German Bank Note Ptg Co, Leipzig)

1966 (5 June). *Horiz designs as T* **74**, *and T* **75**. *P* 12½ × 13 (50 c., 10 s.) *or* 13 × 12½ (*others*).

460	5 c. maroon and yellow-olive			15	30
461	10 c. brown-purple and bright emerald			15	30
462	15 c. brown-purple and light blue			15	30
463	20 c. ultramarine and light orange			15	10
464	25 c. maroon and orange-yellow			15	10
465	30 c. maroon and ochre-yellow			15	10
466	40 c. purple-brown and rose-pink			30	10
467	50 c. green and pale greenish yellow			30	10
468	1 s. maroon and bright blue			30	10
469	1 s. 30, maroon and turquoise			30	50
470	2 s. brown-purple and light blue-green			30	15
471	5 s. rose-red and pale blue			80	3·50
472	10 s. crimson and pale yellow			2·25	11·00
473	20 s. deep purple-brown and magenta			4·25	18·00
460/473			*Set of 14*	8·50	30·00

Designs:—5 c., 20 s. Type 74; 10 c., 1 s. Clove cultivation; 15, 40 c. Chair-making; 20 c., 5 s. Lumumba College; 25 c., 1 s. 30, Agriculture; 30 c., 2 s. Agricultural workers; 50 c., 10 s. Type 75.

81 "Education"

(Litho D.L.R.)

1966 (25 Sept). *Introduction of Free Education. P* 13½ × 13.

474	81	50 c. black, light blue and orange		10	30
475		1 s. 30, black, lt blue and yellow-green		15	45
476		2 s. 50, black, light blue and pink		30	3·50
474/6			*Set of 3*	50	3·75

82 A.S.P. Flag

(Litho D.L.R.)

1967 (5 Feb). *Tenth Anniv of Afro-Shirazi Party (A.S.P.). T* **82** *and similar multicoloured design. P* 14.

477	30 c. Type 82			10	30
478	50 c. Vice-President M. A. Karume of Tanzania, flag and crowd (*vert*)			10	30
479	1 s. 30, As 50 c.			10	65
480	2 s. 50, Type 82			15	1·75
477/80			*Set of 4*	30	2·75

84 Voluntary Workers

(Photo Delrieu)

1967 (20 Aug). *Voluntary Workers Brigade. P* 12½ × 12.

481	84	1 s. 30, multicoloured		15	50
482		2 s. 50, multicoloured		30	3·75

POSTAGE DUE STAMPS

Insufficiently prepaid. Postage due.

1 cent.

D 1

Insufficiently prepaid Postage due.

6 cents.

D 2

(Types D **1** and D **2** typo by the Government Printer)

1929–30. *Rouletted 10, with imperf sheet edges. No gum.*

D 1	D 1	1 c. black/*orange*		10·00	55·00
D 2		2 c. black/*orange*		3·75	24·00
D 3		3 c. black/*orange*		3·75	24·00
		a. "cent.s" for "cents."		80·00	
D 4		6 c. black/*orange*			
		a. "cent.s" for "cents."			
D 5		9 c. black/*orange*		2·25	13·00
		a. "cent.s" for "cents."		13·00	45·00
D 6		12 c. black/*orange*		£5000	£5000
		a. "cent.s" for "cents."			
D 7		12 c. black/*green*		£950	£500
		a. "cent.s" for "cents."		£2500	£1400
D 8		15 c. black/*orange*		2·50	13·00
		a. "cent.s" for "cents."		14·00	45·00
D 9		18 c. black/*salmon*		3·00	22·00
		a. "cent.s" for "cents."		24·00	70·00
D10		18 c. black/*orange*		10·00	30·00
		a. "cent.s" for "cents."		42·00	90·00
D11		20 c. black/*orange*		3·75	22·00
		a. "cent.s" for "cents."		24·00	70·00
D12		21 c. black/*orange*		3·25	16·00
		a. "cent.s" for "cents."		20·00	65·00
D13		25 c. black/*magenta*		£1800	£1100
		a. "cent.s" for "cents."		—	£3250
D14		25 c. black/*orange*		£5000	
D15		31 c. black/*orange*		8·00	38·00
		a. "cent.s" for "cents."		42·00	
D16		50 c. black/*orange*		20·00	80·00
		a. "cent.s" for "cents."		80·00	
D17		75 c. black/*orange*		65·00	£160
		a. "cent.s" for "cents."		£190	

Sheets of the first printings of all values except the 1 c. and 2 c. contained one stamp showing the error "cent.s" for "cents."

1930–33. *Rouletted 5. No gum.*

D18	D 2	2 c. black/*salmon*		5·00	17·00
D19		3 c. black/*rose*		3·00	30·00
D21		6 c. black/*yellow*		3·00	18·00
D22		12 c. black/*blue*		4·00	14·00
D23		25 c. black/*rose*		9·00	35·00
D24		25 c. black/*lilac*		7·00	27·00
D18/24			*Set of 6*	27·00	£130

D 3

(Typo D.L.R.)

1936 (1 Jan)–62. *Wmk Mult Script CA. P* 14.

D25	D 3	5 c. violet		70	3·25
		a. Chalk-surfaced paper (18.7.56)		30	5·50
D26		10 c. scarlet		60	1·25
		a. Chalk-surfaced paper (6.3.62)		30	2·75
D27		20 c. green		65	2·75
		a. Chalk-surfaced paper (6.3.62)		30	5·50
D28		30 c. brown		3·25	7·50
		a. Chalk-surfaced paper (18.7.56)		30	5·00
D29		40 c. ultramarine		3·25	13·00
		a. Chalk-surfaced paper (18.7.56)		40	9·00
D30		1 s. grey		3·25	17·00
		a. Chalk-surfaced paper (18.7.56)		1·00	9·00
D25/30			*Set of 6*	10·50	40·00
D25a/30a			*Set of 6*	2·40	32·00
D25/30 Perf "Specimen"			*Set of 6*	60·00	

See footnote after No. 413.

All Zanzibar issues were withdrawn on 1 January 1968 and replaced by Tanzania issues. Zanzibar stamps remained valid for postage in Zanzibar for a limited period.

TANZANIA

The United Republic of Tanganyika and Zanzibar, formed 26 April 1964, was renamed the United Republic of Tanzania on 29 October 1964.

Issues to No. 176, except Nos. Z142/5, were also valid in Kenya and Uganda.

25 Hale Hydro-Electric Scheme

26 Tanzanian Flag

27 National Servicemen

33 Dar-es-Salaam Harbour

38 Arms of Tanzania

(Des V. Whiteley. Photo Harrison)

1965 (9 Dec). *T 25/7, 33, 38 and similar designs.* P 14 × 14½ (5 c., 10 c., 20 c., 50 c., 65 c.), 14½ × 14 (15 c., 30 c., 40 c.), or 14 (others).

128	5 c. ultramarine and yellow-orange	10	10
129	10 c. black, greenish yellow, green & blue	10	10
130	15 c. multicoloured	10	10
131	20 c. sepia, grey-green and greenish blue	10	10
132	30 c. black and red-brown	10	10
133	40 c. multicoloured	30	20
134	50 c. multicoloured	30	10
135	65 c. green, red-brown and blue	2·00	1·25
136	1 s. multicoloured	50	10
137	1 s. 30, multicoloured	5·00	60
138	2 s. 50, blue and orange-brown	2·75	90
139	5 s. lake-brown, yellow-green and blue	80	20
140	10 s. olive-yellow, olive-green and blue	1·00	1·75
141	20 s. multicoloured	3·75	10·00
128/41	*Set of 14*	15·00	13·50

Designs: *Horiz (as T 25)*—20 c. Road-building; 50 c. Common Zebras, Manyara National Park; 65 c. Mt Kilimanjaro. *Vert (as T 27)*—30 c. Drum, spear, shield and stool; 40 c. Giraffes, Mikumi National Park. *Horiz (As T 33)*—1 s. 30, Skull of *Zinjanthropus* and excavations, Olduvai Gorge, 2 s. 50, Fishing; 5 s. Sisal industry; 10 s. State House, Dar-es-Salaam.

Z 39 Pres. Nyerere and First Vice-Pres. Karume within Bowl of Flame

Z 40 Hands supporting Bowl of Flame

(Des J. Ahmed (Type Z 39), G. Vasarhelyi (Type Z 40). Photo Enschedé)

1966 (26 April). *2nd Anniv of United Republic.* P 14 × 13.

Z142	Z 39	30 c. multicoloured	20	30
Z143	Z 40	50 c. multicoloured	20	30
Z144		1 s. 30, multicoloured	20	30
Z145	Z 39	2 s. 50, multicoloured	30	90
Z142/5		*Set of 4*	80	1·60

Nos. Z142/5 were on sale in Zanzibar only.

39 Cardinal   40 Mud Skipper

41 Scorpion Fish

(Des Rena Fennessy. Photo Harrison)

1967 (9 Dec)–73. *Designs as T 39/41. Chalk-surfaced paper.* P 14 × 15 (5 c. to 70 c.) or 14½ (others).

142	5 c. magenta, yellow-olive and black	10	30
	a. Glazed, ordinary paper (22.1.71)	30	65
143	10 c. brown and bistre	10	10
	a. Glazed, ordinary paper (27.9.72)	30	65
144	15 c. grey, turquoise-blue and black	10	30
	a. Glazed, ordinary paper (22.1.71)	30	90
145	20 c. brown and turquoise-green	10	10
	a. Glazed, ordinary paper (16.7.73)	30	70
146	30 c. sage-green and black	10	10
	a. Glazed, ordinary paper (3.5.71)	2·00	75
147	40 c. yellow, chocolate and bright green	20	10
	a. Glazed, ordinary paper (10.2.71)	35	30
148	50 c. multicoloured	15	10
	a. Glazed, ordinary paper (10.2.71)	30	65
149	65 c. orange-yellow, bronze-green and black	3·50	40
150	70 c. multicoloured (15.9.69)	1·00	2·50
	a. Glazed, ordinary paper (22.1.71)	4·25	6·50
151	1 s. orange-brown, slate-blue and maroon	30	10
	a. Glazed, ordinary paper (3.2.71)	60	10
152	1 s. 30, multicoloured	5·00	
153	1 s. 50, multicoloured (15.9.69)	2·75	50
	a. Glazed, ordinary paper (27.9.72)	2·25	10
154	2 s. 50, multicoloured	3·25	75
	a. Glazed, ordinary paper (27.9.72)	7·50	10
155	5 s. greenish yellow, black & turquoise-grn	5·00	1·25
	a. Glazed, ordinary paper (3.2.71)	3·25	10
156	10 s. multicoloured	2·00	1·40
	a. Glazed, ordinary paper (dull blue-green background) (3.2.71)	2·50	10
	ab. Deep dull green background (12.9.73)	3·00	50
157	20 s. multicoloured	4·00	4·25
	a. Glazed, ordinary paper (3.2.71)	8·00	15
142/57	*Set of 16*	24·00	14·00
142a/57a	*Set of 14*	29·00	10·50

Designs: *Horiz as T 39/40*—15 c. White Spotted Puffer; 20 c. Sea Horses; 30 c. Bat Fish; 40 c. Sweetlips; 50 c. Blue Club-nosed Wrasse; 65 c. Bennett's Butterfly; 70 c. Striped Grouper. *Horiz as T 41*—1 s. 30, Powder Blue Surgeon; 1 s. 50, Fusilier; 2 s. 50, Red Snapper; 5 s. Moorish Idol; 10 s. Picasso Fish; 20 s. Squirrel Fish.

On chalk-surfaced paper all values except the 30 c., exist with PVA gum as well as gum arabic, but the 70 c. and 1 s. 50 exist with PVA gum only. Stamps on glazed, ordinary paper come only with PVA gum.

= 80c

53 *Papilio hornimani*   54 *Euphaedra neophron* (55)

(Des Rena Fennessy. Photo Harrison)

1973 (10 Dec)–78. *Various vert designs as T 53/4.*

(a) *Size as T 53.* P 14½ × 14

158	5 c. light yellow-olive, lt violet-blue & black	30	20
159	10 c. multicoloured	40	15
160	15 c. light violet-blue and black	40	15
161	20 c. reddish cinnamon, orange-yellow & blk	50	15
162	30 c. yellow, orange and black	50	10
	a. Bistre-yellow, orange & black (20.4.78)	75	30
163	40 c. multicoloured	60	15
164	50 c. multicoloured	70	15
165	60 c. lt grey-brown, lemon & reddish brown	1·00	20
166	70 c. turquoise-green, pale orange and black	1·00	20

(b) *Size as T 54.* P 14

167	1 s. multicoloured	1·00	15
168	1 s. 50, multicoloured	2·00	45
169	2 s. 50, multicoloured	2·50	80
170	5 s. multicoloured (brt green background)	2·75	85
	a. Apple-green background (20.4.78)	2·50	60
171	10 s. multicoloured	3·75	3·50
172	20 s. multicoloured	5·50	8·50
158/72	*Set of 15*	21·00	14·00

Butterflies:—10 c. *Colotis ione*; 15 c. *Amauris hyalites* (s sp *makuyuensis*); 20 c. *Libythea labdaca* (s sp *laius*); 30 c. *Danaus chrysippus*; 40 c. *Asterope rosa*; 50 c. *Axiocerses styx*; 60 c. *Terias hecabe*; 70 c. *Acraea insignis*; 1 s. 50, *Precis octavia*; 2 s. 50, *Charaxes eupale*; 5 s. *Charaxes pollux*; 10 s. *Salamis parhassus*; 20 s. *Papilio ophidicephalus*.

Nos. 159 and 164 exist in coils, constructed from normal sheets.

A used example of No. 167 has been seen apparently showing the yellow colour omitted.

1975 (17 Nov). *Nos. 165, 168/9 and 172 surch as T 55.*

173	80 c. on 60 c. *Terias hecabe*	1·75	1·25
174	2 s. on 1 s. 50, *Precis octavia*	3·25	3·75
175	3 s. on 2 s. 50, *Charaxes eupale*	13·00	21·00
176	40 s. on 20 s. *Papilio ophidicephalus*	6·00	8·50
173/6	*Set of 4*	22·00	30·00

1976 (15 Apr). *Telecommunications Development. As Nos. 56/60 of Kenya but inscr "TANZANIA".*

177	50 c. Microwave Tower	10	10
178	1 s. Cordless switchboard	15	10
179	2 s. Telephones	25	30
180	3 s. Message Switching Centre	30	40
177/80	*Set of 4*	70	70
MS181	120 × 120 mm. Nos. 177/80	1·25	1·50

Nos. 177/8 and 180 exist imperforate from stock dispersed by the liquidator of Format International Security Printers Ltd.

1976 (5 July). *Olympic Games, Montreal. As Nos 61/5 of Kenya but inscr "TANZANIA".*

182	50 c. Akii Bua, Ugandan hurdler	15	10
183	1 s. Filbert Bayi, Tanzanian runner	15	10
184	2 s. Steve Muchoki, Kenyan boxer	35	40
185	3 s. Olympic flame and East Africa flags	45	55
182/5	*Set of 4*	1·00	1·00
MS186	129 × 154 mm. Nos. 182/5	5·50	4·00

Nos. 182/4 exist imperforate from stock dispersed by the liquidator of Format International Security Printers Ltd.

1976 (4 Oct). *Railway Transport. As Nos. 66/70 of Kenya but inscr "TANZANIA".*

187	50 c. Tanzania-Zambia Railway	20	10
188	1 s. Nile Bridge, Uganda	30	10
189	2 s. Nakuru Station, Kenya	75	40
190	3 s. Class "A" locomotive, 1896	90	65
187/90	*Set of 4*	1·90	1·00
MS191	154 × 103 mm. Nos. 187/90	5·00	3·50

Nos. 187/8 exist imperforate from stock dispersed by the liquidator of Format International Security Printers Ltd.

1977 (10 Jan). *Game Fish of East Africa. As Nos. 71/5 of Kenya but inscr "TANZANIA".*

192	50 c. Nile Perch	30	10
193	1 s. Tilapia	40	10
194	3 s. Sailfish	1·60	60
195	5 s. Black Marlin	1·75	80
192/5	*Set of 4*	3·50	1·40
MS196	153 × 129 mm. Nos. 192/5	3·75	2·25

1977 (15 Jan). *Second World Black and African Festival of Arts and Culture, Nigeria. As Nos 76/80 of Kenya but inscr "TANZANIA".*

197	50 c. Maasai Manyatta (village), Kenya	15	10
198	1 s. "Heartbeat of Africa" (Ugandan dancers	20	10
199	2 s. Makonde sculpture	45	70
200	3 s. "Early Man and Technology" (skinning hippopotamus)	55	1·00
197/200	*Set of 4*	1·25	1·75
MS201	132 × 190 mm. Nos. 197/200	2·50	3·50

1977 (5 Apr). *25th Anniv of Safari Rally. As Nos 81/5 of Kenya but inscr "TANZANIA".*

202	50 c. Rally-car and villagers	15	10
203	1 s. Pres. Kenyatta starting rally	20	10
204	2 s. Car fording river	50	60
205	5 s. Car and elephants	1·25	1·75
202/5	*Set of 4*	1·90	2·25
MS206	126 × 93 mm. Nos. 202/5	3·50	3·25

1977 (30 June). *Centenary of Ugandan Church. As Nos. 86/90 of Kenya but inscr "TANZANIA".*

207	50 c. Canon Kivebulaya	10	10
208	1 s. Modern Namirembe Cathedral	15	10
209	2 s. The first Cathedral	30	40
210	5 s. Early congregation, Kigezi	60	90
207/10	*Set of 4*	1·00	1·40
MS211	126 × 89 mm. Nos. 207/10	1·50	2·00

1977 (26 Sept). *Endangered Species. As Nos. 96/101 of Kenya but inscr "TANZANIA".*

212	50 c. Pancake Tortoise	20	10
213	1 s. Nile Crocodile	25	10
214	2 s. Hunter's Hartebeest	1·00	55
215	3 s. Red Colobus monkey	1·75	1·00
216	5 s. Dugong	2·00	2·00
212/16	*Set of 5*	4·75	3·25
MS217	127 × 101 mm. Nos. 213/16	5·00	5·50

56 Prince Philip and President Nyerere

(Des G. Vasarhelyi. Litho Questa)

1977 (23 Nov). *Silver Jubilee. T 56 and similar horiz designs. Multicoloured.* P 14 × 13½.

218	50 c. Type 56	15	10
219	5 s. Pres. Nyerere with Queen and Prince Philip	35	35
220	10 s. Jubilee emblem and Commonwealth flags	60	60
221	20 s. The Crowning	1·00	1·00
218/21	*Set of 4*	1·90	1·90
MS222	128 × 102 mm. Nos. 218/21	1·90	2·75

57 Improvements in Rural Living Standards

(Des P. Ndembo. Litho J.W.)

1978 (5 Feb). *First Anniv of Chama Cha Mapinduzi (New Revolutionary Party). T 57 and similar horiz designs.* P 13½ × 14.

223	50 c. multicoloured	10	10
224	1 s. multicoloured	10	10
225	3 s. multicoloured	35	60
226	5 s. black, light green and greenish yellow	55	85
223/6	*Set of 4*	1·00	1·40
MS227	142 × 106 mm. Nos. 223/6	1·00	1·40

Designs:—1 s. Flag raising ceremony, Zanzibar; 3 s. Handing over of TANU headquarters, Dodoma; 5 s. Chairman Julius Nyerere.

1978 (17 Apr). *World Cup Football Championship, Argentina. As Nos. 122/6 of Kenya but inscr "TANZANIA".*

228	50 c. Joe Kadenge and forwards	15	10
229	1 s. Mohamed Chuma and cup presentation	15	10
230	2 s. Omari Kidevu and goalmouth scene	40	60
231	3 s. Polly Ouma and forwards	50	75
228/31	*Set of 4*	1·10	1·25
MS232	136 × 81 mm. Nos. 228/31	2·00	1·75

25th ANNIVERSARY CORONATION	25th ANNIVERSARY CORONATION

2nd JUNE 1953	2nd JUNE 1953
(58)	(59)

1978 (2 June). *25th Anniv of Coronation. Nos. 218/22. A. Optd as T 58.* P 14 × 13½. B. Optd as T 59. P 12 × 11½.

		A		B	
233	50 c. Type 56	10	10	10	10
234	5 s. Pres. Nyerere with Queen and Prince Philip	35	45	35	50
235	10 s. Jubilee emblem and Commonwealth flags	50	65	50	65
236	20 s. The Crowning	80	1·25	80	1·25
233/6	*Set of 4*	1·60	2·25	1·60	2·50
MS237	128 × 102 mm. Nos. 233/6	1·60	2·50	1·60	2·50

NEW INFORMATION

The editor is always interested to correspond with people who have new information that will improve or correct the Catalogue.

60 "Do not Drink and Drive"

61 Lake Manyara Hotel

(Des and litho J.W.)

1978 (1 July). *Road Safety. T* **60** *and similar vert designs.*
P 13½ × 13.
238	50 c. multicoloured			15	10
239	1 s. multicoloured			20	10
240	3 s. orange-red, black and light brown			70	60
241	5 s. multicoloured			1·00	90
238/41			Set of 4	1·90	1·40
MS242	92 × 129 mm. Nos. 238/41. P 14			2·00	2·00

Designs:—1 s. "Show courtesy to young, old and crippled"; 3 s. "Observe the Highway Code"; 5 s. "Do not drive a faulty vehicle".

(Des M. Raza. Litho J.W.)

1978 (11 Sept). *Game Lodges. T* **61** *and similar horiz designs.*
Multicoloured. P 13½ × 13.
243	50 c. Type 61			10	10
244	1 s. Lobo Wildlife Lodge			15	10
245	3 s. Ngorongoro Crater Lodge			30	35
246	5 s. Ngorongoro Wildlife Lodge			45	55
247	10 s. Mafia Island Lodge			80	90
248	20 s. Mikumi Wildlife Lodge			1·75	2·50
243/8			Set of 6	3·00	4·00
MS249	118 × 112 mm. Nos. 243/8			6·00	7·50

62 "Racial Suppression"

63 Fokker "Friendship"

(Des local artist; adapted G. Hutchins. Litho Harrison)

1978 (24 Oct). *International Anti-Apartheid Year. T* **62** *and*
similar vert designs. P 14½ × 14.
250	50 c. multicoloured			10	10
251	1 s. black, yellowish green and yellow			15	10
252	2 s. 50, multicoloured			40	40
253	5 s. multicoloured			70	85
250/3			Set of 4	1·25	1·25
MS254	127 × 132 mm. Nos. 250/3			1·75	2·25

Designs:—1 s. "Racial division"; 2 s. 50, "Racial harmony"; 5 s. "Fall of suppression and rise of freedom".

(Des J. Mzinga; adapted J.W. Litho Walsall)

1978 (28 Dec). *75th Anniv of Powered Flight. T* **63** *and similar*
horiz designs. Multicoloured. P 13½.
255	50 c. Type 63			20	10
256	1 s. "Dragon" on Zanzibar Island, 1930's			25	10
257	2 s. "Concorde"			1·00	45
258	5 s. Wright brothers' *Flyer*, 1903			1·25	85
255/8			Set of 4	2·40	1·25
MS259	133 × 97 mm. Nos. 255/8			2·75	3·25

64 Corporation Emblem

(Des local artists; adapted BG Studio. Litho Harrison)

1979 (3 Feb). *1st Anniv of Tanzania Posts and Telecommuni-*
cations Corporation. T **64** *and similar horiz design. Multi-*
coloured. P 14½ × 14.
260	50 c. Type 64			10	10
261	1 s. Headquarters buildings			50	70
MS262	82 × 97 mm. Nos. 260/1			1·00	1·50

65 Pres. Nyerere (patron of National I.Y.C. Committee) with Children

(66)

30c

(Des J. Mzinga. Litho B.W.)

1979 (25 June). *International Year of the Child. T* **65** *and*
similar horiz designs. Multicoloured. P 14½.
263	50 c. Type 65			10	10
264	1 s. Day care centre			15	10
265	2 s. "Immunisation" (child being vaccinated)			25	45
266	5 s. National I.Y.C. Committee emblem			40	80
263/6			Set of 4	80	1·25
MS267	127 × 91 mm. Nos. 263/6			2·00	1·50

1979 (Aug–Sept*). *Nos. 159 and 166 surch as T* **66** (*No. 269 has*
horiz bar through original value).
268	10 c. + 30 c. multicoloured			75	60
	a. Surch inverted			†	—
269	50 c. on 70 c. turquoise-green, pale orge & bl.			1·50	1·40

* The earliest known postmark date for No. 268 is 15 September and for No. 269 30 August.

The face value of No. 268 was 40 c.; the 30 c. surcharge being added to the original 10 c., which was not obliterated. This method was adopted because of difficulties during the actual surcharging. On No. 269 the 70 c. face value is obliterated by a bar.

Examples of No. 268a were used at Singida in December 1979.

67 Planting Young Trees

68 Mwenge Satellite Earth Station

(Des J. Mzinga. Litho J.W.)

1979 (24 Sept). *Forest Preservation. T* **67** *and similar vert designs.*
Multicoloured. P 14 × 14½.
270	50 c. Type 67			10	10
271	1 s. Replacing dead trees with saplings			20	10
272	2 s. Rainfall cycle			50	50
273	5 s. Forest fire warning			80	1·50
270/3			Set of 4	1·40	2·00

(Des and litho J.W.)

1979 (14 Dec). *Opening of Mwenge Satellite Earth Station. P* 13½.
274	**68** 10 c. multicoloured			10	10
275	40 c. multicoloured			10	10
276	50 c. multicoloured			10	10
277	1 s. multicoloured			20	20
274/7			Set of 4	40	40

69 Tabata Dispensary, Dar-es-Salaam

(Litho J.W.)

1980 (10 Apr). *75th Anniv of Rotary International. T* **69** *and*
similar horiz designs. Multicoloured. P 13.
278	50 c. Type 69			10	10
279	1 s. Ngomvu Village water project			15	10
280	5 s. Flying Doctor service (plane donation)			55	70
281	20 s. Torch and 75th Anniversary emblem			1·75	2·50
278/81			Set of 4	2·25	3·00
MS282	120 × 101 mm. Nos. 278/81. P 14			2·50	3·00

70 Zanzibar 1896 2 r. Stamp and 1964 25 c. Definitive

'LONDON 1980' PHILATELIC EXHIBITION

(71)

(Des J.W. Litho Questa)

1980 (21 Apr). *Death Centenary of Sir Rowland Hill (1979). T* **70**
and similar multicoloured designs. P 14.
283	40 c. Type 70			10	10
284	50 c. Tanganyika 1962 Independence 50 c. commemorative and man attaching stamp to letter (*vert*)			10	10
285	10 s. Tanganyika 1922 25 c. stamp and 1961 1 s. 30, definitive			80	1·25
286	20 s. Penny Black and Sir Rowland Hill (*vert*)			1·25	2·00
283/6			Set of 4	2·00	3·00
MS287	158 × 120 mm. Nos. 283/6			2·00	3·50

1980 (5 May). *"London 1980" International Stamp Exhibition.*
Nos. 283/7 optd with T **71**.
288	40 c. Type 71			10	10
289	50 c. Tanganyika 1962 Independence 50 c. commemorative and man attaching stamp to letter			10	10
290	10 s. Tanganyika 1922 25 c. stamp and 1961 1 s. 30, definitive			75	1·25
291	20 s. Penny Black and Sir Rowland Hill			1·10	1·75
288/91			Set of 4	1·75	2·75
MS292	158 × 120 mm. Nos. 288/91			3·00	3·50

District 920 - 55th Annual Conference, Arusha, Tanzania

(72)

1980 (23 June). *Annual Conference of District 920, Rotary Inter-*
national, Arusha. Nos. 278/82 optd as T **72**.
293	50 c. Type 69			20	10
294	1 s. Ngomvu Village water project			25	10
295	5 s. Flying Doctor service (plane donation)			70	70
296	20 s. Torch and 75th Anniversary of Rotary International Emblem			2·25	2·50
293/6			Set of 4	3·00	3·00
MS297	120 × 101 mm. Nos. 293/6			3·00	3·50

73 Conference, Tanzanian Posts and Telecommunications Corporation and U.P.U. Emblems

(Des and litho J.W.)

1980 (1 July). *P.A.P.U. (Pan-African Postal Union) Plenipoten-*
tiary Conference, Arusha. P 13.
298	**73** 50 c. black and bright violet			10	10
299	1 s. black and ultramarine			15	10
300	5 s. black and orange-red			65	65
301	10 s. black and blue-green			1·25	1·40
298/301			Set of 4	2·00	2·00

74 Gidamis Shahanga (marathon)

(Litho J.W.)

1980 (18 Aug). *Olympic Games, Moscow. T* **74** *and similar horiz*
designs. Multicoloured. P 13.
302	50 c. Type 74			10	15
	a. Horiz strip of 4. Nos. 302/5			2·25	
303	1 s. Nzael Kyomo (sprints)			15	15
304	10 s. Zakayo Malekwa (javelin)			80	1·25
305	20 s. William Lyimo (boxing)			1·50	2·00
302/5			Set of 4	2·25	3·25
MS306	172 × 117 mm. Nos. 302/305. P 14			2·25	3·25

Nos. 302/305 were printed either in separate sheets or together, *se-tenant*, in horizontal strips of 4 throughout the sheet.

75 Spring Hare

76 Impala

(Des Rena Fennessy)

1980 (1 Oct)–85. *Wildlife. Horiz designs as T* **75** (10 c. to 80 c.)
or T **76** (1 s. to 40 s.). *Multicoloured.*

(a) *Litho B.W. P* 14 (10 c. to 80 c.) *or* 14½ (1 s. to 40 s.).
307	10 c. Type 75			10	15
308	20 c. Large-spotted Genet			15	15
309	40 c. Banded Mongoose			20	10
310	50 c. Ratel (light blue panel at foot)			20	10
311	75 c. Large-toothed Rock Hyrax			20	15
312	80 c. Leopard			30	15
313	1 s. Type 76			20	10
314	1 s. 50, Giraffe			30	20
315	2 s. Common Zebra			30	20
316	3 s. Buffalo			30	20
317	5 s. Lion			55	30
318	10 s. Black Rhinoceros			1·10	85
319	20 s. African Elephant			1·75	1·25
320	40 s. Cheetah			2·25	2·75
307/20			Set of 14	7·00	6·00

(b) *Litho J.W. P* 14 (50 c.) *or* 14×14½ (*others*) (1984–85)
320a	50 c. Ratel (turquoise-blue panel at foot)			
320b	1 s. Type 76			
320c	1 s. 50, Giraffe			
320d	2 s. Common Zebra			
320e	3 s. Buffalo			
320f	5 s. Lion			

Both formats of the Waddington printings are slightly smaller than the Bradbury Wilkinson stamps so that No. 320a measures 19½×16 mm, instead of 20×16½ mm, and the larger designs 40×23½ mm, instead of 40½×24 mm. The Swahili inscriptions on the 1 s. and 2 s. appear as one word on the Bradbury Wilkinson printings and as two words on those produced by Waddington.

1980 (2 Dec)–81. *Nos. O41 and O43 with "OFFICIAL" opt Type*
O 1 *obliterated by horizontal line.*
320g	10 c. multicoloured				
320h	40 c. multicoloured (21.2.81)				

Nos. 320g/h exist on commercial mail from Morogoro. The dates given are those of the earliest postmarks reported.

77 Ngorongoro Conservation
Area Authority Emblem

**ROYAL WEDDING
H.R.H. PRINCE CHARLES
29th JULY 1981**
(78)

(Des D. Kyungu. Litho J.W.)

1981 (2 Feb). *60th Anniv of Ngorongoro and Serengeti National
Parks.* T **77** *and similar horiz designs.* P 13.

321	50 c. multicoloured	.. ..	10	10
322	1 s. black, gold and deep blue-green	..	10	10
323	5 s. multicoloured	.. ..	45	60
324	20 s. multicoloured	.. ..	1·75	2·25
321/4		*Set of 4*	2·10	2·75

Designs:—1 s. Tanzania National Parks emblem; 5 s. Friends
of the Serengeti emblem; 20 s. Friends of Ngorongoro emblem.
Nos. 321/4 exist overprinted "75th ANNIVERSARY GIRL
GUIDES 1910 1985" or "CONGRATULATIONS TO THE
DUKE & DUCHESS OF YORK ON THE OCCASION OF
THEIR MARRIAGE", but there is no evidence that these
overprints were available from post offices in Tanzania.

1981 (29 July). *Royal Wedding. Nos. 220/1 optd with* T **78**.

325	10 s. Jubilee emblem and Commonwealth flags	.. .. ..	1·00	75
326	20 s. Crowning	.. ..	1·50	1·00
MS327	88 × 97 mm. Nos. 325/6 ..	..	8·00	5·00

79 Mail Runner

(Des D. Kyungu. Litho State Printing Works, Moscow)

1981 (21 Oct). *Commonwealth Postal Administrations Conference, Arusha.* T **79** *and similar horiz designs. Multicoloured.*
P 12½ × 12.

328	50 c. Type **79**	.. ..	10	10
329	1 s. Letter sorting	..	15	15
330	5 s. Letter Post symbols	..	65	1·00
331	10 s. Flags of Commonwealth nations	..	1·25	2·00
328/31		*Set of 4*	1·90	3·00
MS332	130 × 100 mm. Nos. 328/31		1·90	3·00

80 Morris Nyunyusa (blind drummer)

(Des and litho Harrison)

1981 (30 Nov). *International Year for Disabled Persons.* T **80** *and
similar horiz designs. Multicoloured.* P 14.

333	50 c. Type **80**	.. ..	20	10
334	1 s. Mgulani Rehabilitation Centre, Dar-es-Salaam	..	25	10
335	5 s. Aids for disabled persons	..	1·75	2·00
336	10 s. Disabled children cleaning school compound	..	2·50	3·00
333/6	..	*Set of 4*	4·25	4·75

81 President Mwalimu
Julius K. Nyerere

82 Ostrich

(Litho J.W.)

1982 (13 Jan). *20th Anniv of Independence.* T **81** *and similar
horiz designs. Multicoloured.* P 13 × 13½.

337	50 c. Type **81**	.. ..	10	10
338	1 s. Electricity plant, Mtoni	..	15	10
339	3 s. Sisal industry	..	45	80
340	10 s. "Universal primary education"	..	1·10	2·00
337/40	..	*Set of 4*	1·60	2·75
MS341	120 × 85 mm. Nos. 337/40		2·00	2·75

(Des and litho J.W.)

1982 (25 Jan). *Birds.* T **82** *and similar vert designs. Multicoloured.* P 13½ × 13.

342	50 c. Type **82**	.. ..	40	10
343	1 s. Secretary Bird	..	55	10
344	5 s. Kori Bustard	..	2·00	2·50
345	10 s. Saddle-bill Stork	..	3·00	3·50
342/5	..	*Set of 4*	5·50	5·50

83 Jella Mtaga

(Des P. Ndembo. Litho J.W.)

1982 (2 June). *World Cup Football Championship, Spain.* T **83**
and similar horiz designs. Multicoloured. P 14.

346	50 c. Type **83**	..	30	10
347	1 s. Football stadium	..	35	10
348	10 s. Diego Maradona	..	2·75	3·00
349	20 s. FIFA emblem	..	4·50	5·00
346/9		*Set of 4*	7·00	7·50
MS350	130 × 100 mm. Nos. 346/9		7·50	7·50

Nos. 346/9 exist overprinted "CONGRATULATIONS TO
THE DUKE & DUCHESS OF YORK ON THE OCCASION OF
THEIR MARRIAGE", but there is no evidence that these
overprints were available from post offices in Tanzania.

84 "Jade" of Seronera
(cheetah) with Cubs

(Des and litho Harrison)

1982 (15 July). *Animal Personalities.* T **84** *and similar horiz
designs. Multicoloured.* P 14.

351	50 c. Type **84**	..	20	10
352	1 s. Female Golden Jackal and cubs (incor-rectly inscr "Wild dog")	..	30	10
353	5 s. "Fifi" and two sons of "Gombe" (chimpanzees)	..	1·00	2·00
354	10 s. "Bahati" of Lake Manyara with twins, "Rashidi" and "Ramadhani" (elephants)		1·90	3·00
351/4	..	*Set of 4*	3·00	4·75
MS355	120 × 89 mm. Nos. 351/4. P 14½	..	3·50	5·00

85 Brick-laying   **86** Ploughing Field

(Des P. Ndembo. Litho J.W.)

1982 (25 Aug). *75th Anniv of Boy Scout Movement.* T **85** *and
similar horiz designs. Multicoloured.* P 14.

356	50 c. Type **85** ..	..	15	10
357	1 s. Camping..	..	20	10
358	10 s. Tracing signs	..	1·50	2·25
359	20 s. Lord Baden-Powell	..	2·50	3·75
356/9	..	*Set of 4*	4·00	5·50
MS360	130 × 100 mm. Nos. 356/9	..	5·00	6·00

No. MS360 exists overprinted "75th ANNIVERSARY GIRL
GUIDES 1910–1985", but there is no evidence that this
overprint was available from post offices in Tanzania.

(Des P. Ndembo. Litho J.W.)

1982 (16 Oct). *World Food Day.* T **86** *and similar horiz designs.
Multicoloured.* P 14.

361	50 c. Type **86**	..	10	10
362	1 s. Dairy farming	..	15	10
363	5 s. Maize farming	..	60	75
364	10 s. Grain storage	..	1·00	1·60
361/4	..	*Set of 4*	1·60	2·25
MS365	129 × 99 mm. Nos. 361/4	..	2·00	2·50

87 Immunization

(Des P. Ndembo. Litho State Printing Works, Moscow)

1982 (1 Dec). *Centenary of Robert Koch's Discovery of Tubercle
Bacillus.* T **87** *and similar horiz designs. Multicoloured.*
P 12½ × 12.

366	50 c. Type **87** ..	..	15	10
367	1 s. Dr. Robert Koch..	..	20	10
368	5 s. International Union Against TB emblem	..	65	1·25
369	10 s. World Health Organization emblem	..	1·25	2·25
366/9	..	*Set of 4*	2·00	3·25

88 Letter Post

(Litho State Printing Works, Moscow)

1983 (3 Feb). *5th Anniv of Posts and Telecommunications Corporation.* T **88** *and similar horiz designs. Multicoloured.* P 12.

370	50 c. Type **88**	..	10	10
371	1 s. Training institute	..	10	10
372	5 s. Satellite communications	..	55	90
373	10 s. U.P.U., I.T.U. and T.P.T.C.C. (Tanzania Posts and Telecommunications Corpor-ation) emblems	..	1·10	2·00
370/3	..	*Set of 4*	1·75	2·75
MS374	126 × 96 mm. Nos. 370/3	..	1·75	3·00

89 Pres. Mwalimu Julius Nyerere

(Litho J.W.)

1983 (14 Mar). *Commonwealth Day.* T **89** *and similar horiz
designs. Multicoloured.* P 14.

375	50 c. Type **89**	..	10	10
376	1 s. Athletics and boxing	..	15	10
377	5 s. Flags of Commonwealth countries	..	60	80
378	10 s. Pres. Nyerere and members of British Royal Family	..	1·25	1·75
375/8	..	*Set of 4*	1·90	2·40
MS379	121 × 100 mm. Nos. 375/8	..	1·90	3·00

Nos. 375/8 exist overprinted "CONGRATULATIONS TO
THE DUKE & DUCHESS OF YORK ON THE OCCASION OF
THEIR MARRIAGE", but there is no evidence that these
overprints were available from post offices in Tanzania.

90 Eastern and Southern African Management
Institute, Arusha, Tanzania

(Des P. Ndembo. Litho State Ptg Wks, Moscow)

1983 (12 Sept). *25th Anniv of the Economic Commission
for Africa.* T **90** *and similar horiz designs. Multicoloured.*
P 12½ × 12.

380	50 c. Type **90** ..	..	15	10
381	1 s. 25th Anniversary inscription and U.N. logo	..	20	10
382	5 s. Mineral collections	..	2·50	2·50
383	10 s. E.C.A. Silver Jubilee logo and O.A.U. flag	..	2·50	3·25
380/3	..	*Set of 4*	4·75	5·50
MS384	132 × 102 mm. Nos. 380/3	..	4·75	5·50

91 Telephone Cables

(Des P. Ndembo. Litho J.W.)

1983 (17 Oct). *World Communications Year.* T **91** *and similar
horiz designs. Multicoloured.* P 14.

385	50 c. Type **91**	.. ..	15	10
386	1 s. W.C.Y. logo	..	20	10
387	5 s. Postal service	..	1·25	1·40
388	10 s. Microwave tower	..	1·75	2·25
385/8	..	*Set of 4*	3·00	3·50
MS389	102 × 92 mm. Nos. 385/88	..	3·00	3·50

92 Bagamoyo Boma

(Des J. de Silva and P. Ndembo. Litho State Ptg Wks, Moscow)

1983 (12 Dec). *Historical Buildings. T 92 and similar horiz designs. Multicoloured. P 12½ × 12.*

390	1 s. Type 92		10	10
391	1 s. 50, Beit el Ajaib, Zanzibar		15	25
392	5 s. Anglican Cathedral, Zanzibar		55	1·00
393	10 s. Original German Government House and present State House, Dar-es-Salaam		1·10	2·00
390/3		Set of 4	1·75	3·00
MS394	130×100 mm. Nos. 390/3		1·90	3·00

93 Sheikh Abeid Amani Karume
(founder of Afro-Shirazi Party)

(Des P. Ndembo. Litho J.W.)

1984 (18 June). *20th Anniv of Zanzibar Revolution. T 93 and similar horiz designs. Multicoloured. P 14.*

395	1 s. Type 93		10	10
396	1 s. 50, Clove farming		15	25
397	5 s. Symbol of Industrial Development		55	1·00
398	10 s. New housing schemes		1·10	2·00
395/8		Set of 4	1·75	3·00
MS399	130×100 mm. 15 s. Mapinduzi (ferry) and map		1·50	3·00

94 Boxing

(Des P. Ndembo. Litho State Ptg Wks, Moscow)

1984 (6 Aug). *Olympic Games, Los Angeles. T 94 and similar horiz designs. Multicoloured. P 12½ × 12.*

400	1 s. Type 94		10	10
401	1 s. 50, Running		15	10
402	5 s. Basketball		45	60
403	20 s. Football		1·50	2·75
400/3		Set of 4	2·00	2·75
MS404	130×100 mm. Nos. 400/3		2·00	2·75

95 Icarus in Flight

(Des P. Ndembo. Litho J.W.)

1984 (15 Nov). *40th Anniv of International Civil Aviation Organization. T 95 and similar horiz designs. Multicoloured. P 13 × 12½.*

405	1 s. Type 95		10	10
406	1 s. 50, Aircraft and air traffic controller		15	20
407	5 s. Aircraft undergoing maintenance		55	1·25
408	10 s. I.C.A.O. badge		1·10	2·00
405/8		Set of 4	1·75	3·25
MS409	130×100 mm. Nos. 405/8		1·90	3·00

96 Sochi – Conical House

(Des P. Ndembo. Litho State Ptg Wks, Moscow)

1984 (20 Dec). *Traditional Houses. T 96 and similar horiz designs. Multicoloured. P 12½ × 12.*

410	1 s. Type 96		10	10
411	1 s. 50, Isyenga – circular type		15	20
412	5 s. Tembe – flatroofed type		45	1·25
413	10 s. Banda – coastal type		90	2·00
410/13		Set of 4	1·40	3·25
MS414	129×99 mm. Nos. 410/13		1·50	3·00

97 Production of Cotton Textiles

(Des P. Ndembo. Litho J.W.)

1985 (1 Apr). *5th Anniv of Southern African Development Co-ordination Conference. T 97 and similar horiz designs. Multicoloured. P 14.*

415	1 s. 50, Type 97		30	15
416	4 s. Diamond mining		2·00	1·25
417	5 s. Map of member countries and means of communication		2·00	1·25
418	20 s. Flags and signatures of member countries		2·75	3·00
415/18		Set of 4	6·25	5·00
MS419	110×104 mm. Nos. 415/18		6·25	5·50

98 Tortoise

(Des P. Ndembo (15s., 20s.), J. de Silva (others). Litho J.W.)

1985 (8 May). *Rare Animals of Zanzibar. T 98 and similar multicoloured designs. P 12½×13 (17 s. 50) or 13×12½ (others).*

420	1 s. Type 98		20	10
421	4 s. Leopard		85	80
422	10 s. Civet Cat		1·50	2·50
423	17 s. 50, Red Colobus Monkey (vert).		2·25	3·25
420/3		Set of 4	4·25	6·00
MS424	110×93 mm. 15 s. Black Rhinoceros; 20 s. Giant Ground Pangolin		1·75	2·75

IMPERFORATE STAMPS. Nos. 425/9, 430/4, 456/60, 464/8, 474/8 and 517/21 exist imperforate from restricted printings reported as being unavailable in Tanzania.

99 The Queen Mother

(Litho Holders Press)

1985 (30 Sept). *Life and Times of Queen Elizabeth the Queen Mother. T 99 and similar horiz designs. Multicoloured. P 14.*

425	20 s. Type 99		20	35
426	20 s. Queen Mother waving to crowd		20	35
427	100 s. Oval portrait with flowers		90	1·40
428	100 s. Head and shoulders portrait		90	1·40
425/8		Set of 4	2·00	3·25
MS429	Two sheets, each 125×63 mm. (a) Nos. 425 and 427; (b) Nos. 426 and 428.	Set of 2 sheets	2·00	2·75

100 Locomotive No. 3022   (101)

GOLD MEDAL
HENRY TILLMAN
USA

(Litho Holders Press)

1985 (7 Oct). *Tanzanian Railway Locomotives (1st series). T 100 and similar horiz designs. Multicoloured. P 14.*

430	5 s. Type 100		20	25
431	10 s. Locomotive No. 3107		35	50
432	20 s. Locomotive No. 6004		60	80
433	30 s. Locomotive No. 3129		80	1·10
430/3		Set of 4	1·75	2·40
MS434	125×93 mm. Nos. 430/3		2·00	3·00

See also Nos. 445/50.

1985 (22 Oct). *Olympic Games Gold Medal Winners, Los Angeles. Nos. 400/4 optd as T 101.*

435	1 s. Type 94 (optd with T 101)		10	10
436	1 s. 50, Running (optd "GOLD MEDAL USA")		15	20
437	5 s. Basketball (optd "GOLD MEDAL USA")		45	1·00
438	20 s. Football (optd "GOLD MEDAL FRANCE")		1·75	2·75
435/8		Set of 4	2·25	3·50
MS439	130×100 mm. Nos. 435/8		7·00	8·50

102 Cooking and Water Pots

103 Class "64" Locomotive

(Des J. Mzinga. Litho State Ptg Wks, Moscow)

1985 (4 Nov). *Pottery. T 102 and similar horiz designs. Multicoloured. P 12½×12.*

440	1 s. 50, Type 102		15	10
441	2 s. Large pot and frying pot with cover		20	10
442	5 s. Trader selling pots		50	30
443	40 s. Beer pot		2·00	2·25
440/3		Set of 4	2·50	2·50
MS444	129×98 mm. 30 s. Water pots		2·75	2·75

(Des P. Ndembo. Litho State Ptg Wks, Moscow)

1985 (25 Nov). *Tanzanian Railway Locomotives (2nd series). T 103 and similar horiz designs. P 12½×12.*

445	1 s. 50, multicoloured		30	10
446	2 s. multicoloured		40	20
447	5 s. multicoloured		70	60
448	10 s. multicoloured		1·25	1·40
449	30 s. black, brownish black and red		2·75	3·00
445/9		Set of 5	4·75	4·75
MS450	130×100 mm. 15 s. black, blackish brown and rose-pink; 20 s. black, blackish brown and rose-pink		5·00	5·00

Designs:—2 s. Class "36" locomotive; 5 s. "DFH1013" shunting locomotive; 10 s. "DE 1001" diesel-electric locomotive; 15 s. Class "30" steam locomotive; 20 s. Class "11" steam locomotive; 30 s. Steam locomotive, Zanzibar, 1906.

Nos. 445/6 and 448/9 exist overprinted "CONGRATULATIONS TO THE DUKE & DUCHESS OF YORK ON THE OCCASION OF THEIR MARRIAGE", but there is no evidence that these overprints were available from post offices in Tanzania.

104 Young Pioneers

(Des P. Ndembo. Litho J.W.)

1986 (20 Jan). *International Youth Year. T 104 and similar horiz designs. P 14.*

451	1 s. 50, multicoloured		15	15
452	4 s. reddish brown, pale brown and black		30	45
453	10 s. multicoloured		70	1·10
454	20 s. reddish brown, pale brown and black		1·40	2·00
451/4		Set of 4	2·25	3·25
MS455	130×100 mm. 30 s. reddish brown, pale brown and black		2·25	3·25

Designs:—4 s. Child health care; 10 s. Uhuru Torch Race; 20 s. Young workers and globe; 30 s. Young people farming.

105 Rolls-Royce "20/25" (1936)

(Litho Holders Press)

1986 (10 Mar). *Centenary of Motoring. T 105 and similar horiz designs. Multicoloured. P 14.*

456	1 s. 50, Type 105		15	10
457	5 s. Rolls-Royce "Phantom II" (1933)		20	25
458	10 s. Rolls-Royce "Phantom I" (1926)		35	50
459	30 s. Rolls-Royce "Silver Ghost" (1907)		80	1·10
456/9		Set of 4	1·40	1·75
MS460	125×93 mm. Nos. 456/9		1·40	2·25

106 Rotary Logo and Staunton Queen Chess Piece

(Litho Holders Press)

1986 (17 Mar). *World Chess Championships, Moscow. T 106 and similar horiz design. P 14.*

461	20 s. new blue and magenta		50	50
462	100 s. multicoloured		1·50	2·25
MS463	124×64 mm. Nos. 461/2		2·50	3·25

Design:—100 s. Hand moving Rook.

No. 461 also commemorates Rotary International.

Slightly different versions of Nos. 461/2, incorporating the Chess Championship emblem and with "TANZANIA" and face value at top on the 100 s., were not issued.

107 Mallard

(Litho Holders Press)

1986 (22 May). *Birth Bicentenary of John J. Audubon (ornithologist) (1985). T 107 and similar horiz designs. Multicoloured. P 14.*

464	5 s. Type 107..				30	25
465	10 s. Eider				55	50
466	20 s. Scarlet Ibis				80	1·25
467	30 s. Roseate Spoonbill				1·00	1·50
464/7				Set of 4	2·40	3·25
MS468	122×91 mm. Nos. 464/7 ..				2·40	3·50

108 Pearls

109

(Litho J.W.)

1986 (27 May). *Tanzanian Minerals. T 108 and similar horiz designs. Multicoloured. Phosphorised paper (Nos. 469/72). P 14.*

469	1 s. 50, Type 108				50	15
470	2 s. Sapphire..				65	50
471	5 s. Tanzanite				1·25	85
472	40 s. Diamonds				5·50	6·00
469/72				Set of 4	7·00	6·75
MS473	130×100 mm. 30 s. Rubies. W 109 ..				6·00	6·50

110 Hibiscus calyphyllus   **111** Oryx

(Litho Holders Press)

1986 (25 June). *Flowers of Tanzania. T 110 and similar vert designs. Multicoloured. P 14.*

474	1 s. 50, Type 110				10	10
475	5 s. Aloe graminicola				15	15
476	10 s. Nersium oleander				25	25
477	30 s. Nymphaea caerulea				65	65
474/7				Set of 4	1·00	1·00
MS478	90×119 mm. Nos. 474/7 ..				1·60	1·90

(Litho Holders Press)

1986 (30 June). *Endangered Animals of Tanzania. T 111 and similar vert designs. Multicoloured. P 14.*

479	5 s. Type 111..				30	15
480	10 s. Giraffe				55	45
481	20 s. Rhinoceros				1·00	1·00
482	30 s. Cheetah ..				1·10	1·50
479/82				Set of 4	2·75	2·75
MS483	91×121 mm. Nos. 479/82 ..				2·75	3·50

Four stamps, 10, 20, 60 and 80 s., with accompanying miniature sheets, were prepared in 1986 for the Wedding of the Duke of York, but these were not placed on sale in Tanzania.

112 Immunization   **113** Butterfly Fish

(Des P. Ndembo. Litho State Ptg Wks, Moscow)

1986 (29 July). *U.N.I.C.E.F. Child Survival Campaign. T 112 and similar horiz designs. Multicoloured. P 12½×12.*

484	1 s. 50, Type 112				10	10
485	2 s. Growth monitoring				10	10
486	5 s. Oral rehydration therapy				15	20
487	40 s. Breast feeding				1·00	1·50
484/7				Set of 4	1·25	1·75
MS488	110×101 mm. 30 s. Healthy baby				60	1·25

(Des P. Ndembo. Litho State Ptg Wks, Moscow)

1986 (28 Aug). *Marine Life. T 113 and similar horiz designs. Multicoloured. P 12½×12.*

489	1 s. 50, Type 113				30	10
490	4 s. Parrot Fish				45	30
491	10 s. Turtle				90	90
492	20 s. Octopus				1·50	1·50
489/92				Set of 4	2·75	2·50
MS493	131×101 mm. 30 s. Corals				75	1·25

114 Team Captains shaking Hands   **115** Pres. Nyerere receiving Beyond War Award

(Litho Questa)

1986 (30 Oct). *World Cup Football Championship, Mexico. T 114 and similar horiz designs. Multicoloured. P 14.*

494	1 s. 50, Type 114				15	10
495	2 s. Referee sending player off				15	10
496	10 s. Goalkeeper and ball in net				60	60
497	20 s. Goalkeeper saving ball..				1·00	1·40
494/7				Set of 4	1·75	2·00
MS498	95×72 mm. 30 s. Winning Argentine team				60	70

(Des P. Ndembo. Litho Mardon Printers Ltd, Zimbabwe)

1986 (20 Dec). *International Peace Year. T 115 and similar horiz designs. Multicoloured. P 14½.*

499	1 s. 50, Type 115				30	10
500	2 s. Children of many races				50	20
501	10 s. African cosmonaut and rocket launch				1·25	1·40
502	20 s. United Nations Headquarters, New York				1·75	2·00
499/502				Set of 4	3·50	3·25
MS503	109×86 mm. 30 s. International Peace Year symbols				1·50	1·75

116 Mobile Bank Service

(Des P. Ndembo. Litho Questa)

1987 (7 Feb). *20th Anniv of National Bank of Commerce. T 116 and similar horiz designs. Multicoloured. P 14.*

504	1 s. 50, Type 116				30	10
505	2 s. National Bank of Commerce Head Office				50	20
506	5 s. Pres. Mwinyi laying foundation stone				80	80
507	20 s. Cotton harvesting				2·00	2·50
504/7				Set of 4	3·25	3·25

117 Parade of Young Party Members

(Litho Holders Press)

1987 (10 Mar). *10th Anniv of Chama Cha Mapinduzi Party and 20th Anniv of Arusha Declaration. T 117 and similar horiz designs. Multicoloured. P 14.*

508	2 s. Type 117				15	10
509	3 s. Harvesting coffee				20	10
510	10 s. Pres. Nyerere addressing Second Peace Initiative Reunion				30	20
511	30 s. Presidents Julius Nyerere and Ali Hassan Mwinyi				50	60
508/11				Set of 4	1·10	90

118 Nungu   **119**
Nungu Hair Style

(Litho Leigh-Mardon Ltd, Melbourne)

1987 (16 Mar). *Traditional Hair Styles. T 118 and similar vert designs. Multicoloured. W 119. P 14½.*

512	1 s. 50, Type 118				30	10
513	2 s. Upanga wa jogoo style				45	20
514	10 s. Morani style				80	90
515	20 s. Twende kilioni style				1·50	2·00
512/15				Set of 4	2·75	2·75
MS516	110×99 mm. 30 s. Hair plaiting				2·25	2·50

120 Royal Family on Buckingham Palace Balcony after Trooping the Colour

(Litho Holders Press)

1987 (24 Mar). *60th Birthday of Queen Elizabeth II (1986). T 120 and similar horiz designs. Multicoloured. P 14.*

517	5 s. Type 120				15	10
518	10 s. Queen and Prince Philip at Royal Ascot				25	20
519	40 s. Queen Elizabeth II				80	80
520	60 s. Queen Elizabeth with crowd				1·10	1·25
517/20				Set of 4	2·10	2·10
MS521	125×90 mm. Nos. 517/20 ..				2·25	2·40

121 Apis mellifera (bee)   **122** Crocodile

(Litho State Ptg Wks, Moscow)

1987 (22 Apr). *Insects. T 121 and similar horiz designs. Multicoloured. P 12½×12.*

522	1 s. 50, Type 121 ..				40	10
523	2 s. Prostephanus truncatus (grain borer)				50	20
524	10 s. Glossina palpalis (tsetse fly) ..				1·00	1·60
525	20 s. Polistes sp (wasp)				1·75	2·00
522/5				Set of 4	3·25	3·00
MS526	110×101 mm. 30 s. Anopheles sp (mosquito)				2·25	2·50

(Des J. Mzinga (3 s., 30 s.), P. Ndembo (others). Litho State Ptg Wks, Moscow)

1987 (2 July). *Reptiles. T 122 and similar horiz designs. Multicoloured. P 12½×12.*

527	2 s. Type 122				15	10
528	3 s. Black-striped Grass-snake				20	15
529	10 s. Adder				35	40
530	20 s. Green Mamba				65	70
527/30				Set of 4	1·25	1·10
MS531	101×101 mm. 30 s. Tortoise				85	90

123 Emblems of Posts/Telecommunications and Railways   **124** Basketry

(Des and litho Questa)

1987 (27 July). *10th Anniv of Tanzania Communications and Transport Corporations. T 123 and similar horiz designs. Multicoloured. P 14.*

532	2 s. Type 123				10	10
533	8 s. Emblems of Air Tanzania and Harbours Authority				20	20
MS534	100×66 mm. 20 s. Methods of transport and communication				50	50

(Des P. Ndembo. Litho State Ptg Wks, Moscow)

1987 (15 Dec). *Traditional Handicrafts. T 124 and similar horiz designs. Multicoloured. P 12½×12.*

535	2 s. Type 124				15	10
536	3 s. Decorated gourds				15	15
537	10 s. Stools				25	20
538	20 s. Makonde carvings				40	45
535/8				Set of 4	85	80
MS539	89×89 mm. 40 s. Makonde carver at work				65	75

10th Anniversary of TANZANIA ZAMBIA RAILWAY AUTHORITY 1976-1986

(125)

1987 (30 Dec). *10th Anniv of Tanzania–Zambia Railway (1986). Nos. 445/9 optd with T 125.*

540	103	1 s. 50, multicoloured			10	10
541	—	2 s. multicoloured			15	15
542	—	5 s. multicoloured			20	20
543	—	10 s. multicoloured			30	30
544	—	30 s. black, brownish black and red			50	50
540/4				Set of 5	1·10	1·10

126 Mdako (pebble game)

(Des P. Ndembo. Litho State Ptg Wks, Moscow)

1988 (15 Feb). *Traditional Pastimes. T* **126** *and similar horiz designs. Multicoloured. P* 12½×12.

545	2 s. Type **126**	..	..	10	10
546	3 s. Wrestling	..	..	10	10
547	8 s. Bullfighting, Zanzibar		..	15	15
548	20 s. Bao (board game)		..	35	35
545/8			*Set of 4*	65	65
MS549	100×90 mm. 30 s. Archery		..	50	60

127 Plateosaurus

(Des G. Vasarhelyi. Litho Format)

1988 (22 Apr). *Prehistoric and Modern Animals. T* **127** *and similar trapezium-shaped designs. Multicoloured. P* 12½.

550	2 s. Type **127**	..	..	15	10
	a. *Tête-bêche* (horiz pair)		..	30	20
551	3 s. Pteranodon		..	15	10
	a. *Tête-bêche* (horiz pair)		..	30	20
552	5 s. Apatosaurus ("Brontosaurus")	..	15	10
	a. *Tête-bêche* (horiz pair)		..	30	20
553	7 s. Lion		..	20	15
	a. *Tête-bêche* (horiz pair)		..	40	30
554	8 s. Tiger		..	20	15
	a. *Tête-bêche* (horiz pair)		..	40	30
555	12 s. Orang-utan		..	25	15
	a. *Tête-bêche* (horiz pair)		..	50	30
556	20 s. Elephant		..	50	35
	a. *Tête-bêche* (horiz pair)		..	1·00	70
557	100 s. Stegosaurus		..	1·50	1·25
	a. *Tête-bêche* (horiz pair)		..	3·00	2·50
550/7			*Set of 8*	2·75	2·00

Nos. 550/7 were issued in sheets which had the second and fourth stamps *tête-bêche* in each horizontal row of five.

128 Marchers with Party Flag 129 Population Symbols on Map

(Des P. Ndembo. Litho Questa)

1988 (1 July). *National Solidarity Walk. T* **128** *and similar horiz designs. Multicoloured. P* 14×14½.

558	2 s. + 1 s. Type **128**			15	15
559	3 s. + 1 s. Pres. Mwinyi leading Walk		15	15
MS560	121×121 mm. 50 s. + 1 s. Pres. Ali Hassan Mwinyi (35×25 *mm*). P 14½	..	..	75	85

(Des P. Ndembo. Litho Questa)

1988 (8 Aug). *Third National Population Census. T* **129** *and similar horiz designs. Multicoloured. P* 14.

561	2 s. Type **129**	..	..	10	10
562	3 s. Census official at work		..	10	10
563	10 s. Community health care		..	15	15
564	20 s. Population growth 1967–1988	..	30	30
561/4			*Set of 4*	55	55
MS565	96×91 mm. 40 s. Development of modern Tanzania	..	..	..	55	60

130 Javelin 131 Football

(Litho State Ptg Wks, Moscow)

1988 (5 Sept). *Olympic Games, Seoul (1st issue). T* **130** *and similar horiz designs. Multicoloured. P* 12½×12.

566	2 s. Type **130**	..	..	10	10
567	3 s. Hurdling	..	..	10	10
568	7 s. Long distance running		..	20	15
569	12 s. Relay racing		..	35	25
566/9			*Set of 4*	65	50
MS570	100×70 mm. 40 s. Badminton		..	85	70

(Des D. Miller. Litho Questa)

1988 (5 Sept). *Olympic Games, Seoul (2nd issue). T* **131** *and similar vert designs. Multicoloured. P* 14.

571	10 s. Type **131**	..	..	10	10
572	20 s. Cycling	..	..	20	25
573	50 s. Fencing	..	..	45	50
574	70 s. Volleyball		..	60	65
571/4			*Set of 4*	1·25	1·40
MS575	77×92 mm. 100 s. Gymnastics		90	1·25

(Des D. Miller. Litho Questa)

1988 (5 Sept). *Winter Olympic Games, Calgary. Vert designs as T* **131**. *Multicoloured. P* 14.

576	5 s. Cross-country skiing	..		10	10
577	25 s. Figure skating		..	30	25
578	50 s. Downhill skiing		..	55	50
579	75 s. Bobsleighing		..	75	70
576/9			*Set of 4*	1·50	1·40
MS580	77×92 mm. 100 s. Ice hockey sticks wrapped in Olympic and Canadian colours	..	90	95

132 Goat 133 "Love You, Dad" (Pinocchio)

(Litho Questa)

1988 (9 Sept). *Domestic Animals. T* **132** *and similar multicoloured designs. P* 14.

581	4 s. Type **132**	..	..	15	15
582	5 s. Rabbit (*horiz*)		..	15	15
583	8 s. Cows (*horiz*)		..	20	20
584	10 s. Kitten (*horiz*)		..	25	25
585	12 s. Pony		..	30	30
586	20 s. Puppy		..	55	55
581/6			*Set of 6*	1·40	1·40
MS587	102×73 mm. 100 s. Chicken (*horiz*)		1·50	1·50

(Des Walt Disney Company. Litho Questa)

1988 (9 Sept). *Greetings Stamps. T* **133** *and similar horiz designs showing Walt Disney cartoon characters. Multicoloured. P* 14×13½.

588	4 s. Type **133**			10	10
589	5 s. "Happy Birthday" (Brer Rabbit and Chip n'Dale)	..	..	10	10
590	10 s. "Trick or Treat" (Daisy and Donald Duck)	..	..	15	10
591	12 s. "Be kind to Animals" (Ferdie and Mordie with Pluto)	..	15	10
592	15 s. "Love" (Daisy and Donald Duck)	20	15
593	20 s. "Let's Celebrate" (Mickey Mouse and Goofy)	..	..	30	25
594	30 s. "Keep in Touch" (Daisy and Donald Duck)	..	..	45	35
595	50 s. "Love you, Mom" (Minnie Mouse with Ferdie and Mordie)	..	75	60
588/95			*Set of 8*	2·00	1·50

MS596 Two sheets, each 127×101 mm. (a) 150 s. "Let's work together" (Goofy dressed as a fireman). (b) 150 s. "Have a super Sunday" (Goofy dressed as American footballer)
Set of 2 sheets 3·75 4·00

134 *Charaxes varanes* 135 Independence Torch and Mt Kilimanjaro

(Des Jennifer Toombs. Litho Questa)

1988 (17 Oct). *Butterflies. T* **134** *and similar horiz designs. Multicoloured. P* 14½.

597	8 s. Type **134**	..	..	30	10
598	30 s. *Neptis melicerta*		..	65	30
599	40 s. *Mylothris chloris*		..	75	40
600	50 s. *Charaxes bohemani*		..	90	50
601	60 s. *Myrina silenus* (s sp *ficedula*)	1·00	70
602	75 s. *Papilio phorcas*		..	1·50	90
603	90 s. *Cyrestis camillus*		..	1·75	1·00
604	100 s. *Salamis temora*		..	2·00	1·25
597/604			*Set of 8*	8·00	4·75

MS605 Two sheets, each 80×50 mm. (a) 200 s. *Asterope rosa*. (b) 250 s. *Kallima rumia*
Set of 2 sheets 7·00 6·00

(Des R. Vigurs. Litho Questa)

1988 (1 Nov). *National Monuments. T* **135** *and similar vert designs. Multicoloured. P* 14.

606	5 s. Type **135**	..	..	10	10
607	12 s. Arusha Declaration Monument	..	10	10
608	30 s. Askari Monument	..	..	25	30
609	60 s. Independence Monument	..	55	60
606/9			*Set of 4*	80	90
MS610	100×89 mm. 100 s. Askari Monument statue	..	..	..	1·25	1·40

---

136 Eye Clinic 137 Loading Patient into Ambulance

(Des P. Ndembo. Litho National Printing & Packaging, Zimbabwe)

1988 (19 Dec). *25th Anniv of Dar-es-Salaam Lions Club. T* **136** *and similar horiz designs. Multicoloured. P* 14½.

611	2 s. Type **136**			10	10
612	3 s. Family at shallow water well		10	10
613	7 s. Rhinoceros and map of Tanzania		15	15
614	12 s. Club presenting school desks		15	15
611/14			*Set of 4*	35	35
MS615	100×65 mm. 40 s. Lions International logo	..	..	..	60	65

(Des P. Ndembo. Litho State Ptg Wks, Moscow)

1988 (30 Dec). *125th Anniv of International Red Cross and Red Crescent. T* **137** *and similar horiz designs. Multicoloured. P* 12½×12.

616	2 s. Type **137**	..	..	10	10
617	3 s. Mother and baby health clinic	..	10	10
618	7 s. Red Cross flag		..	10	10
619	12 s. Henri Dunant (founder)		..	15	15
616/19			*Set of 4*	30	30
MS620	90×90 mm. 40 s. Members of Red Cross International Committee, 1863	..	..	50	55

138 Paradise Whydah 139 Bushbaby

(Des S. Barlowe. Litho B.D.T.)

1989 (15 Mar). *Birds. T* **138** *and similar vert designs. Multicoloured. P* 13½.

621	20 s. Type **138**			30	30
	a. Sheetlet. Nos. 621/40		..	5·50	
622	20 s. Black-collared Barbet		..	30	30
623	20 s. Bateleur		..	30	30
624	20 s. Lilac-breasted Roller and African Open-bill Storks in flight	..	30	30
625	20 s. Red-tufted Malachite Sunbird and African Open-bill Stork in flight	30	30
626	20 s. Dark Chanting Goshawk	..	30	30
627	20 s. White-fronted Bee Eater, Carmine Bee Eater and Little Bee Eaters	..	30	30
628	20 s. Narina Trogon and Marabou Stork in flight	..	..	30	30
629	20 s. Grey Parrot	..	..	30	30
630	20 s. Hoopoe	..	..	30	30
631	20 s. Masked Lovebird ("Yellow-collared Lovebird")	..	..	30	30
632	20 s. Yellow-billed Hornbill	..	30	30
633	20 s. Hammerkop	..	..	30	30
634	20 s. Violet-crested Turaco and flamingos in flight	..	..	30	30
635	20 s. Malachite Kingfisher	..	30	30
636	20 s. Greater Flamingos	..	30	30
637	20 s. Yellow-billed Storks	..	30	30
638	20 s. Whale-headed Stork ("Shoebill Stork")	..	..	30	30
639	20 s. Saddle-bill Stork and Blacksmith Plover	..	..	30	30
640	20 s. South African Crowned Crane	..	30	30
621/40			*Set of 20*	5·50	5·50

MS641 Two sheets, each 105×75 mm. (a) 350 s. Helmet Guineafowl (28×42 *mm*). (b) 350 s. Ostrich (28×42 *mm*). P 14 *Set of 2 sheets* 4·25 4·25
Nos. 622/41 were printed together, *se-tenant*, in a sheetlet of 20 forming a composite design of birds at a waterhole.

(Des J. Barbaris (Nos. 642/4, 648, **MS**650a), S. Barlowe (others). Litho Questa)

1989 (20 Mar). *Fauna and Flora. T* **139** *and similar multicoloured designs. P* 14.

642	5 s. Type **139**			10	10
643	10 s. Bushbaby holding insect (*horiz*)	..	15	15
644	20 s. Bushbaby on forked branch	..	20	20
645	30 s. Black Cobra on Umbrella Acacia	..	25	25
646	45 s. Bushbaby at night (*horiz*)	..	35	35
647	70 s. Red-billed Tropic Bird and Tree Ferns	70	70
648	100 s. African Tree Frog on Cocoa Tree	..	90	90
649	150 s. Black-headed Heron and Egyptian Papyrus	..	..	1·40	1·40
642/9			*Set of 8*	3·50	3·50

MS650 Two sheets. (a) 115×85 mm. 350 s. African Palm Civet (*horiz*). (b) 65×65 mm. 350 s. Pink-backed Pelican and Baobab Tree (*horiz*)
Set of 2 sheets 4·25 4·25
Nos. 645, 647/9 and **MS**650 are without the World Wildlife Fund logo.

140 Juma Ikangaa
(marathon runner)

141 Drums

(Des W. Storozuk. Litho Questa)

1989 (10 Apr). *International Sporting Personalities. T 140 and similar vert designs. Multicoloured. P 14.*

651	4 s. Type 140		10	10
652	8 s. 50, Steffi Graf (tennis player)		20	20
653	12 s. Yannick Noah (tennis player)		25	25
654	40 s. Pelé (footballer)		50	50
655	100 s. Erhard Keller (speed skater)		70	70
656	125 s. Sadanoyama (sumo wrestler)		80	80
657	200 s. Taino (sumo wrestler)		1·40	1·40
658	250 s. T. Nakajima (golfer)		1·75	1·75
651/8		*Set of 8*	5·00	5·00

MS659 Two sheets. (a) 100×71 mm. 350 s. Joe Louis (boxer). (b) 100×76 mm. 350 s. I. Aoki (golfer) .. .. *Set of 2 sheets* 4·50 4·50
The captions on Nos. 658 and MS659b are transposed.

(Des P. Ndembo. Litho Harrison)

1989 (29 June). *Musical Instruments. T 141 and similar horiz designs. Multicoloured. P 14.*

660	2 s. Type 141		10	10
661	3 s. Xylophones		10	10
662	10 s. Thumbpiano		15	20
663	20 s. Fiddles		30	40
660/3		*Set of 4*	50	70

MS664 91×80 mm. 40 s. Violins with calabash resonators 55 55

142 Chama Cha
Mapinduzi Party Flag

143 Class "P36" Locomotive,
U.S.S.R.

(Des P. Ndembo. Litho Questa)

1989 (1 July). *National Solidarity Walk. T 142 and similar multicoloured designs. P 14½.*

665	5 s. + 1 s. Type 142		10	10
666	10 s. + 1 s. Marchers with party flag and President Mwinyi		10	10

MS667 122×122 mm. 50 s. + 1 s. President Mwinyi (*vert*) 40 40

(Des W. Wright. Litho B.D.T.)

1989 (22 Aug). *Steam Locomotives. T 143 and similar multicoloured designs. P 14.*

668	10 s. Type 143		10	10
669	25 s. Class "12", Belgium		15	15
670	60 s. Class "C62", Japan		35	35
671	75 s. Pennsylvania Railroad Class "T1", U.S.A.		40	40
672	80 s. Class "WP", India		45	45
673	90 s. East African Railways Class "59"		50	50
674	150 s. Class "People", China		80	80
675	200 s. Southern Pacific "Daylight Express" U.S.A.		1·10	1·10
668/75		*Set of 8*	3·50	3·50

MS676 Two sheets, each 114×85 mm. (a) 350 s. Stephenson's *Planet*, Great Britain (*vert*). (b) 350 s. "Coronation Scot", Great Britain (*vert*)
Set of 2 sheets 4·25 4·50

(Des Design Element. Litho Questa)

1989 (17 Nov). *"World Stamp Expo '89" International Stamp Exhibition, Washington. Landmarks of Washington. Sheet 78×62 mm containing horiz design as T 193a of Lesotho. Multicoloured. P 14.*
MS677 500 s. Union Station .. .. 3·50 3·75

144 "Luna 3" Satellite
orbiting Moon, 1959

Gold-USSR
Silver-Brazil
Bronze-W.Germany

(145)

(Des G. Vasarhelyi. Litho Questa)

1989 (22 Nov). *History of Space Exploration and 20th Anniv of First Manned Landing on Moon. T 144 and similar horiz designs. Multicoloured. P 14.*

678	20 s. Type 144		10	15
679	30 s. "Gemini 6" and "7", 1965		15	20
680	40 s. Astronaut Edward White in space, 1965		20	25

681	60 s. Astronaut Aldrin on Moon, 1969		30	35
682	70 s. Aldrin performing experiment, 1969		35	40
683	100 s. "Apollo 15" astronaut and lunar rover, 1971		50	55
684	150 s. "Apollo 18" and "Soyuz 19" docking in space, 1975		75	80
685	200 s. Spacelab, 1983		1·00	1·10
678/85		*Set of 8*	3·00	3·50

MS686 Two sheets, each 110×90 mm. (a) 250 s. Lunar module *Eagle* and "Apollo 11" emblem. (b) 250 s. Projected U.S. space station *Set of 2 sheets* 2·50 2·75

1989 (11 Dec). *Olympic Medal Winners, Calgary and Seoul. Optd as T 145. (a) On Nos. 571/5.*

687	10 s. Type 131 (optd with T 145)		15	15
688	20 s. Cycling ("Men's Match Sprint, Lutz Hesslich, DDR")		20	20
689	50 s. Fencing (optd "Epee, Schmitt, W. Germany")		50	50
690	70 s. Volleyball (optd "Men's Team, USA")		70	70
687/90		*Set of 4*	1·40	1·40

MS691 77×92 mm. 100 s. Gymnastics ("Women's Team, Gold – USSR") 75 85

(b) On Nos. 576/80

692	5 s. Cross-country skiing (optd "Biathlon, Peter-Roetsch, DDR")		10	10
693	25 s. Figure skating (optd "Pairs, Gordeeva & Grinkov, USSR")		20	20
694	50 s. Downhill skiing (optd "Zurbriggen, Switzerland")		40	40
695	75 s. Bobsleighing (optd "Gold – USSR Silver – DDR Bronze – DDR")		60	60
692/5		*Set of 4*	1·10	1·10

MS696 77×92 mm. 100 s. Ice hockey sticks wrapped in Olympic and Canadian colours (optd "Ice Hockey: Gold – USSR") 75 85

146 Tiger Tilapia

(Des W. Hanson Studio. Litho Questa)

1989 (14 Dec). *Reef and Freshwater Fishes of Tanzania. T 146 and similar multicoloured designs. P 14.*

697	9 s. Type 146		15	15
698	13 s. Picasso Fish		15	15
699	20 s. Powder-blue Surgeonfish		20	20
700	40 s. Butterflyfish		35	35
701	70 s. Guenther's Notho		60	60
702	100 s. Ansorge's Neolebias		80	80
703	150 s. Lyretail Panchax		1·25	1·25
704	200 s. Regal Angelfish		1·50	1·50
697/704		*Set of 8*	4·50	4·50

MS705 Two sheets, each 112×83 mm. (a) 350 s. Jewel Cichlid (50×38 *mm*). P 14×13½. (b) 350 s. Batfish (38×50 *mm*). P 13½×14 *Set of 2 sheets* 4·50 4·75

147 Rural Polling Station

148 Logo

(Des P. Ndembo. Litho State Ptg Wks, Moscow)

1989 (22 Dec). *Centenary of Inter-Parliamentary Union. T 147 and similar horiz designs. P 12½×12.*

706	9 s. multicoloured		10	10
707	13 s. multicoloured		10	10
708	80 s. multicoloured		40	45
709	100 s. black, dull ultramarine and pale blue		50	55
706/9		*Set of 4*	90	1·00

MS710 90×90 mm. 40 s. multicoloured 30 40
Designs:—13 s. Parliament Building, Dar-es-Salaam; 40 s. Sir William Randal Cremer and Frederic Passy (founders); 80 s. Tanzania Parliament in session; 100 s. Logo.

(Des P. Ndembo. Litho Cartor, France)

1990 (10 Jan). *10th Anniv of Pan-African Postal Union. T 148 and similar horiz designs. P 13½.*

711	9 s. greenish yellow, dull green and black		10	10
712	13 s. multicoloured		10	10
713	70 s. multicoloured		25	30
714	100 s. multicoloured		40	40
711/14		*Set of 4*	75	85

MS715 90×90 mm. 40 s. multicoloured. P 12½ 15 20
Designs:—13 s. Collecting mail from post office box; 40 s. Logos of Tanzania Posts and Telecommunications Corporation, P.A.P.U. and U.P.U.; 70 s. Taking mail to post office; 100 s. Mail transport.

149 Admiral's Flag and *Nina*

(Des T. Agans. Litho Questa)

1990 (12 Feb). *500th Anniv of Discovery of America by Columbus* (1992) (50, 60, 75, 200 *s.*) *and Modern Scientific Discoveries* (*others*). T 149 *and similar horiz designs. Multicoloured. P 14.*

716	9 s. Bell X-1 aircraft (first supersonic flight, 1947)		10	10
717	13 s. *Trieste* (bathyscaph) (first dive to depth of 35,000 ft, 1960)		10	10
718	50 s. Type 149		20	25
719	60 s. Fleet flag and *Pinta*		25	30
720	75 s. Standard of Castile and León and *Santa Maria*		30	35
721	150 s. Transistor technology		60	65
722	200 s. Arms of Columbus and map of First Voyage		80	85
723	250 s. DNA molecule		1·00	1·10
716/23		*Set of 8*	3·00	3·25

MS724 Two sheets, each 106×78 mm. (a) 350 s. Caravels in the Caribbean. (b) 350 s. *Voyager II* and Neptune .. .. *Set of 2 sheets* 2·75 3·00

150 Tecopa Pupfish

(Des J. Genzo. Litho Questa)

1990 (20 Feb). *Extinct Species. T 150 and similar multicoloured designs. P 14.*

725	25 s. Type 150		10	15
726	40 s. Thylacine		15	20
727	50 s. Quagga		20	25
728	60 s. Passenger Pigeon		25	30
729	75 s. Rodriguez Saddleback Tortoise		30	35
730	100 s. Toolache Wallaby		40	45
731	150 s. Texas Red Wolf		60	65
732	200 s. Utah Lake Sculpin		80	85
725/32		*Set of 8*	2·50	2·75

MS733 Two sheets. (a) 102×74 mm. 350 s. South Island Whekau. (b) 71×99 mm. 350 s. Hawaii O-o (*vert*) .. .. *Set of 2 sheets* 2·75 3·00

151 Camping

(Des P. Ndembo. Litho State Ptg Wks, Moscow)

1990 (22 Feb). *60th Anniv of Girl Guides Movement in Tanzania. T 151 and similar multicoloured designs. P 12½×12.*

734	9 s. Type 151		15	15
735	13 s. Guides planting sapling		15	15
736	50 s. Guide teaching woman to write		40	40
737	100 s. Guide helping at child-care clinic		65	65
734/7		*Set of 4*	1·25	1·25

MS738 89×89 mm. 40 s. Guide teaching child to read (*vert*). P 12×12½ 40 50

152 Fishing

153 Footballer

(Des P. Ndembo. Litho State Ptg Wks, Moscow)

1990 (25 Apr). *25th Anniv of Union of Tanganyika and Zanzibar. T 152 and similar multicoloured designs. P 12½×12 (horiz) or 12×12½ (vert).*

739	9 s. Type 152		10	10
740	13 s. Vineyard		10	10
741	50 s. Cloves		20	20
742	100 s. Presidents Nyerere and Karume exchanging Union instruments (*vert*)		40	45
739/42		*Set of 4*	70	80

MS743 90×90 mm. 40 s. Arms (*vert*) .. 15 20

(Litho B.D.T.)

1990 (1 June). *World Cup Football Championship, Italy (1st issue). T 153 and similar vert designs. Multicoloured. P 14.*

744	25 s. Type 153		10	15
745	60 s. Player passing ball		25	30
746	75 s. Player turning		30	35
747	200 s. Player kicking ball		80	85
744/7		*Set of 4*	1·25	1·50

MS748 Two sheets, each 105×76 mm. (a) 350 s. Two players fighting for possession. (b) 350 s. Player kicking ball .. .. *Set of 2 sheets* 2·75 3·00
See also Nos. 789/93 and 794/8.

154 Miriam
Makeba

155 Ring of People round
Party Flag

(Des A. Fagbohun. Litho Questa)

1990 (29 June). *Famous Black Entertainers. T* **154** *and similar vert designs. Multicoloured. P* 14.

749	9 s. Type 154	..	..	10	10
750	13 s. Manu Dibango			10	10
751	25 s. Fela	..	..	10	15
752	70 s. Smokey Robinson			25	30
753	100 s. Gladys Knight			40	45
754	150 s. Eddie Murphy			60	65
755	200 s. Sammy Davis Jnr.			80	85
756	250 f. Stevie Wonder			1·00	1·10
749/56			*Set of* 8	3·00	3·25

MS757 Two sheets, each 69×88 mm.(a) 350 s. Bill Cosby (30×39 *mm*). (b) 350 s. Michael Jackson (30×39 *mm*). P 14½ .. *Set of 2 sheets* 2·75 3·00

(Litho Cartor)

1990 (6 July). *Solidarity Walk, 1990. T* **155** *and similar multicoloured designs. P* 13½.

758	9 s. + 1 s. Type 155			10	10
759	13 s. + 1 s. President Mwinyi			10	10

MS760 90×90 mm. 50 s. + 1 s. Handclasp on map (*vert*). P 12½ 20 25

156 Passenger Train

157 Pope John
Paul II

(Des P. Ndembo. Litho Cartor)

1990 (8 Aug). *10th Anniv of Southern African Development Co-ordination Conference. T* **156** *and similar horiz designs. Multicoloured. P* 13½.

761	8 s. Type 156			10	10
762	11 s. 50, Paper-making plant			10	10
763	25 s. Tractor factory and ploughing			10	15
764	100 s. Map and national flags			40	45
761/4			*Set of* 4	65	70

MS765 89×89 mm. 50 s. Map of Southern Africa.
P 12½ 20 25

(Des P. Ndembo. Litho Questa)

1990 (1 Sept). *Papal Visit to Tanzania. T* **157** *and similar multicoloured designs. P* 14.

766	10 s. Type 157			10	10
767	15 s. Pope in ceremonial robes			10	10
768	20 s. Pope giving blessing			10	10
769	100 s. Papal coat of arms			40	45
766/9			*Set of* 4	65	70

MS770 172×143 mm. 50 s. Pope John Paul II (*horiz*); 50 s. St. Joseph's Cathedral, Dar-es-Salaam (*horiz*); 50 s. Christ the King Cathedral, Moshi (*horiz*); 50 s. Saint Theresa's Cathedral, Tabora (*horiz*); 50 s. Cathedral of the Epiphany, Bugando Mwanza (*horiz*); 50 s. St. Mathias Mulumba Kalemba Cathedral, Songea (*horiz*) 1·25 1·40
a. Error. Imperf .. .. .. † —

158 Mickey and Minnie Mouse in Herby the
Love Bug

(Des Walt Disney Co. Litho Questa)

1990 (7 Nov). *Motor Cars from Disney Films. T* **158** *and similar horiz designs. Multicoloured. P* 14×13½.

771	20 s. Type 158			10	10
772	30 s. The Absent-minded Professor's car	..		10	10
773	45 s. Chitty-Chitty Bang-Bang	..		20	25
774	60 s. Mr. Toad's car			25	30
775	75 s. Scrooge's limousine	..		30	35
776	100 s. The Shaggy Dog's car	..		40	45

777	150 s. Donald Duck's nephews cleaning car		60	65
778	200 s. Fire engine from *Dumbo*		80	85
771/8			*Set of* 8	2·50	2·75

MS779 Two sheets, each 127×112, (a) 350 s. The Mickeymobile. (b) 350 s. Cruella De Vil and dog wagon from *101 Dalmations* .. *Set of 2 sheets* 2·75 3·00

159 "St. Mary Magdalen
in Penitence" (detail)

160 Klinsmann of
West Germany

(Litho Questa)

1990 (7 Nov). *Paintings by Titian. T* **159** *and similar vert designs. Multicoloured. P* 13½×14.

780	5 s. Type 159	..		10	10
781	10 s. "Averoldi Polyptych" (detail)			10	10
782	15 s. "Saint Margaret" (detail)			10	10
783	50 s. "Venus and Adonis" (detail)	..		20	25
784	75 s. "Venus and the Lutenist" (detail)	..		30	35
785	100 s. "Tarquin and Lucretia" (detail)			40	45
786	125 s. "Saint Jerome" (detail)			50	60
787	150 s. "Madonna and Child in Glory with Saints" (detail)			60	70
780/7			*Set of* 8	2·10	2·40

MS788 Three sheets. (a) 95×110 mm. 300 s. "Adoration of the Holy Trinity" (detail). (b) 95×110 mm. 300 s. "St. Catherine of Alexandria at Prayer" (detail). (c) 110×95 mm. 300 s. "The Supper at Emmaus" (detail) .. *Set of 3 sheets* 3·50 3·75

(Des Young Phillips Studio. Litho Questa)

1990 (17 Nov). *World Cup Football Championship, Italy (2nd issue). T* **160** *and similar vert designs. Multicoloured. P* 14.

789	10 s. Type 160	..		10	10
790	60 s. Serena of Italy			25	30
791	100 s. Nicol of Scotland			40	45
792	300 s. Susic of Yugoslavia	..		1·10	1·25
789/92			*Set of* 4	1·75	1·90

MS793 Two sheets, each 85×95 mm. (a) 400 s. Montero of Costa Rica. (b) 400 s. Seifo of Belgium
Set of 2 sheets 3·25 3·50

161 Throw-in

(Litho Questa)

1990 (17 Nov). *World Cup Football Championship, Italy (3rd issue). T* **161** *and similar horiz designs. Multicoloured. P* 14.

794	9 s. Type 161			10	10
795	13 s. Penalty kick	..		10	10
796	25 s. Dribbling			15	15
797	100 s. Corner kick	..		70	70
794/7			*Set of* 4	90	90

MS798 82×82 mm. 50 s. World Cup and world map 25 30

162 Canoe

(Des M. Raza. Litho State Ptg Works, Moscow)

1990 (24 Nov). *Marine Transport. T* **162** *and similar horiz designs. Multicoloured. P* 12½×12.

799	9 s. Type 162	..		10	10
800	13 s. Sailing canoe	..		10	10
801	25 s. Dhow	..		10	15
802	100 s. Freighter	..		40	45
799/802			*Set of* 4	65	70

MS803 90×90 mm. 40 s. Mashua dhow .. 15 20

ALTERED CATALOGUE NUMBERS

Any Catalogue numbers altered from the last edition are shown as a list in the introductory pages.

163 Lesser
Masked Weaver

164 Lesser Flamingo

(Litho Questa)

1990 (15 Dec)–**91**. *Birds. Horiz designs as T* **163** (5 *s. to* 30 *s.*) *or* **164** (40 *s. to* 500 *s.*). *Multicoloured. P* 14.

804	5 s. Type 163			10	10
	a. Booklet pane. Nos. 804/9 each × 2 with margins all round	..		80	
805	9 s. African Emerald Cuckoo	..		10	10
806	13 s. Little Bee Eater			10	10
807	15 s. Red Bishop	..		10	10
808	20 s. Bateleur	..		10	15
809	25 s. Scarlet-chested Sunbird	..		10	15
809*a*	30 s. African Wood Pigeon (1.7.91)			10	15
810	40 s. Type 164			15	20
811	70 s. Helmet Guineafowl			25	30
812	100 s. Eastern White Pelican			40	45
813	170 s. Saddle-bill Stork			70	75
814	200 s. South African Crowned Crane			80	85
814*a*	300 s. Pied Crow (1.7.91)	..		1·10	1·25
814*b*	400 s. White-headed Vulture (1.7.91)			1·60	1·90
815	500 s. Ostrich	..		2·00	2·25
804/15			*Set of* 15	6·75	7·50

MS816 100×102 mm. 40 s. Superb Starling; 60 s.
Lilac-breasted Roller 15 20

165 Athletics

(Des P. Ndembo. Litho Questa)

1990 (29 Dec). *14th Commonwealth Games, Auckland, New Zealand. T* **165** *and similar multicoloured designs. P* 14.

817	9 s. Type 165			10	10
818	13 s. Netball (*vert*)	..		10	10
819	25 s. Pole vaulting			15	15
820	100 s. Long jumping (*vert*) ..			70	70
817/20			*Set of* 4	90	90

MS821 100×100 mm. 40 s. Boxing (*vert*) .. 20 25

166 Former German Post
Office, Dar-es-Salaam

(Litho Questa)

1991 (10 Jan). *150th Anniv of the Penny Black and "Stamp World London 90" International Stamp Exhibition. T* **166** *and similar horiz designs. Multicoloured. P* 14.

822	50 s. Type 166	..		20	25
	a. Horiz pair. Nos. 822/3			40	50
823	50 s. *Reichstag* (German mailboat), 1890			20	25
824	75 s. Dhows, Zanzibar			30	35
	a. Horiz pair. Nos. 824/5			60	70
825	75 s. Cobham's *Singapore I* (flying boat), Mwanza, Lake Victoria, 1928			30	35
826	100 s. Air Tanzania Fokker over Livingstone's House, Zanzibar			40	45
	a. Horiz pair. Nos. 826/7			80	90
827	100 s. Mail train at Moshi station	..		40	45
828	100 s. English mail coach, 1840	..		40	45
829	150 s. Stephenson's *Rocket* and mail coach, 1838			60	65
830	200 s. Imperial Airways Handley Page "HP.42" at Croydon ..			80	85
822/30			*Set of* 9	3·25	3·75

MS831 Two sheets, each 85×65 mm. (a) 350 s. Sir Rowland Hill and Penny Black. (b) 350 s. Thurn and Taxis letter of 1860 .. *Set of 2 sheets* 2·75 3·00
Nos. 822/3, 824/5 and 826/7 were each printed together, *se-tenant*, in horizontal pairs throughout the sheets.

167 Petersberg Railway, West
Germany

(Litho Questa)

1991 (10 Jan). *Cog Railways. T **167** and similar horiz designs. Multicoloured.* P 14.

832	8 s. Type **167**		10	10
833	25 s. *Waumbek* (locomotive), Mount Washington Railway, U.S.A.		10	10
834	50 s. Dubrovnik–Sarajevo line, Yugoslavia		20	25
835	100 s. Cog railway, Budapest, Hungary		40	45
836	150 s. Steam locomotive, Vordenberg–Eisenerz line, Austria		60	65
837	200 s. Last train on Rimutaka Incline, New Zealand, 1955		80	85
838	250 s. John Stevens' cog locomotive, U.S.A., 1825		1·00	1·10
839	300 s. Pilatusbahn cog railcar, Switzerland		1·10	1·25
832/9		*Set of 8*	3·75	4·25

MS840 Two sheets, each 117×87 mm. (a) 400 s. Sylvester Marsh and Presidential excursion train, U.S.A., 1869 (51×38 mm). (b) 400 s. Steam locomotive Schneebergbahn, Austria (51×38 mm). P 13½ .. .. *Set of 2 sheets* 3·25 3·50

(Des Walt Disney Co. Litho Questa)

1991 (10 Jan). *International Literacy Year (1st issue). Designs as T **246** of Maldive Islands showing Walt Disney cartoon characters illustrating the Alphabet. Multicoloured.* P 13½×14.

841/67	1, 2, 3, 5, 10, 15, 18, 20, 25, 30, 35, 40, 45, 50, 55, 60, 75, 80, 90, 100, 120, 125, 145, 150, 160, 175, 200 s.	*Set of 27*	6·50	7·25

MS868 Two sheets, each 128×112 mm. (a) 600 s. Tiger Lily and Lost Boys. P 14×13½. (b) 600 s. Mickey Mouse driving miniature railway locomotive (*vert*). P 13½×14 .. *Set of 2 sheets* 4·75 5·00
Nos. 841/67 were issued in three sheetlets, each of nine, the first containing Nos. 841/3, 846, 855, 858, 861, 863, 867, the second Nos. 845, 848, 850, 852, 854, 856, 860, 862, 864 and the third Nos. 844, 847, 849, 851, 853, 857, 859, 865/6.
See also Nos. 905/9.

(Litho Questa)

1991 (10 Jan). *Olympic Games, Barcelona. Vert designs as T **202** of Lesotho. Multicoloured.* P 14.

869	5 s. Archery		10	10
870	10 s. Women's gymnastics		10	10
871	25 s. Boxing		10	10
872	50 s. Canoeing		20	25
873	100 s. Volleyball		40	45
874	150 s. Men's gymnastics		60	65
875	200 s. 4 × 100 metres relay		80	85
876	300 s. Judo		1·10	1·25
869/76		*Set of 8*	3·00	3·50

MS877 Two sheets, each 102×71 mm. (a) 400 s. Cycling. (b) 400 s. 400 metres men's hurdles *Set of 2 sheets* 3·25 3·50

(Litho Questa)

1991 (18 Jan). *"EXPO '90" International Garden and Greenery Exhibition, Osaka. Orchids. Multicoloured designs as T **198** of Lesotho, but vert.* P 14.

878	10 s. *Phalaenopsis* "Lipperose"		10	10
879	25 s. *Lycoste* "Aquila"		10	10
880	30 s. *Vuylstekeara* "Cambria Plush"		10	10
881	50 s. *Vuylstekeara* "Monica Burnham"		20	25
882	90 s. *Odontocidium* "Crowborough Plush"		35	40
883	100 s. *Oncidioda* "Crowborough Chelsea"		40	45
884	250 s. *Sophrolaeliocattleya* "Phena Saturn"		1·00	1·10
885	300 s. *Laeliocattleya* "Lykas"		1·10	1·25
878/85		*Set of 8*	3·00	3·50

MS886 Two sheets, each 100×69 mm. (a) 400 s. *Cymbidium* "Baldoyle Melbury". (b) 400 s. *Cymbidium* "Tapestry Long Beach" *Set of 2 sheets* 3·25 3·50

168 Olympic "Soling" Class Yacht Racing

(Litho Questa)

1991 (18 Jan). *Record-breaking Sports Events. T **168** and similar multicoloured designs.* P 14.

887	5 s. Type **168**		10	10
888	20 s. Olympic downhill skiing		10	10
889	30 s. "Tour de France" cycle race		10	10
890	40 s. Le Mans 24-hour endurance motor race		15	20
891	75 s. Olympic two-man bobsleighing		30	35
892	100 s. Belgian Grand Prix motor cycle race		40	45
893	250 s. Indianapolis 500 motor race		1·00	1·10
894	300 s. Gold Cup power boat championship		1·10	1·25
887/94		*Set of 8*	3·00	3·25

MS895 Two sheets, each 85×64 mm. (a) 400 s. Colorado 500 motor cycle race (*vert*). (b) 400 s. Schneider Trophy air race (*vert*) *Set of 2 sheets* 3·25 3·50

169 Mickey Mouse as Cowboy

(Des Walt Disney Co. Litho Questa)

1991 (20 Feb). *Mickey Mouse in Hollywood. T **169** and similar horiz designs showing Walt Disney cartoon characters as actors. Multicoloured.* P 14×13½.

896	5 s. Type **169**		10	10
897	10 s. Mickey as boxer		10	10
898	15 s. Mickey as astronaut		10	10
899	20 s. Mickey and Minnie as lovers		10	10
900	100 s. Mickey as pirate rescuing Minnie		40	45
901	200 s. Mickey and Donald Duck as policemen arresting Big Pete		80	85
902	350 s. Mickey and Donald with Goofy in historical drama		1·40	1·50
903	450 s. Mickey, Donald and Goofy as sailors		1·75	1·90
896/903		*Set of 8*	4·25	4·50

MS904 Two sheets, each 127×96 mm. (a) 600 s. Mickey, Minnie and Donald in the mummy's tomb. (b) 600 s. Mickey as Canadian Mountie rescuing Minnie from Big Pete .. *Set of 2 sheets* 4·75 5·00

170 Women learning to Read

(Litho Questa)

1991 (15 Mar). *International Literacy Year (2nd issue). T **170** and similar horiz designs. Multicoloured.* P 14.

905	9 s. Type **170**		10	10
906	13 s. Teacher with blackboard		10	10
907	25 s. Literacy aids		10	10
908	100 s. Reading newspaper		40	45
905/8		*Set of 4*	65	70

MS909 104×73 mm. 50 s. Adult education class 20 25

171 Ngorongoro Crater   172 Stegosaurus

(Litho National Printing and Packaging, Zimbabwe)

1991 (28 Mar). *Historical Craters and Caves. T **171** and similar horiz designs. Multicoloured.* P 14×14½.

910	3 s. Type **171**		10	10
911	5 s. Prehistoric rock painting, Kondoa Caves		10	10
912	9 s. Inner crater, Mt Kilimanjaro		10	10
913	12 s. Olduvai Gorge		10	10
910/13		*Set of 4*	35	35

MS914 91×92 mm. 10 s. Discarded bottles, Amboni Caves; 10 s. Rock paintings, Amboni Caves; 10 s. Entrance to Amboni Caves; 10 s. Rock formation, Amboni Caves 15 20

(Litho Questa)

1991 (28 Apr). *350th Death Anniv of Rubens. Cartoons for Decius Mus Tapestries. Multicoloured designs as T **250** of Maldive Islands.* P 14×13½.

915	85 s. "Proclamation of the Vision"		30	35
	a. Sheetlet. Nos. 915/20		1·50	
916	85 s. "Divining of the Entrails"		30	35
917	85 s. "Dispatch of the Lictors"		30	35
918	85 s. "Dedication to Death"		30	35
919	85 s. "Victory and Death of Decius Mus"		30	35
920	85 s. "Funeral Rites"		30	35
915/20		*Set of 6*	1·50	1·90

MS921 70×100 mm. 500 s. "Trophy of War" (detail) (*vert*). P 13½×14 .. .. 2·00 2·10

(Litho State Ptg Wks, Moscow)

1991 (3 June). *Prehistoric Creatures. T **172** and similar vert designs. Multicoloured.* P 12×12½.

922	10 s. Type **172**		10	10
923	15 s. Triceratops		10	10
924	25 s. Edmontosaurus		10	10
925	30 s. Plateosaurus		10	10
926	35 s. Diplodocus		10	10
927	100 s. Iguanodon		40	45
928	200 s. Silviasaurus		80	85
922/8		*Set of 7*	1·40	1·50

MS929 90×90 mm. 150 s. Rhamphorhynchus 60 65

(Litho Questa)

1991 (7 June). *20th Anniv of Tanzania Investment Bank. T **173** and similar horiz designs. Multicoloured.* P 14.

930	10 s. Type **173**		10	10
931	13 s. Industrial development		10	10
932	25 s. Engineering		10	10
933	100 s. Tea picking		40	45
930/3		*Set of 4*	65	70

MS934 93×91 mm. Nos. 930/3 .. 70 75

(Litho Cartor)

1991 (5 July). *National Solidarity Walk. T **174** and similar horiz designs. Multicoloured.* P 13½.

935	4 s. + 1 s. Type **174**		10	10
936	30 s. + 1 s. Pres. Mwinyi planting sapling		10	10

MS937 91×91 mm. 50 s. + 1 s. Pres. Mwinyi sorting cloves. P 12½ 20 25

(Des K. Gromell. Litho Questa)

1991 (15 Aug). *"Phila Nippon '91" International Stamp Exhibition, Tokyo. Japanese Railway Locomotives. Multicoloured designs as T **257** of Maldive Islands, but horiz.* P 14.

938	10 s. First steam locomotive in Japan		10	10
939	25 s. Class "4500" steam locomotive		10	10
940	35 s. Class "C 62" steam locomotive		10	10
941	50 s. Class "Mikado" steam locomotive		20	25
942	75 s. Class "6250" steam locomotive		30	35
943	100 s. Class "C 11" steam locomotive		40	45
944	200 s. Class "E 10" steam locomotive		80	85
945	300 s. Class "8550" steam locomotive		1·10	1·25
938/45		*Set of 8*	2·75	3·00

MS946 Four sheets, each 102×71 mm. (a) 400 s. Class "400" electric train. (b) 400 s. Class "EH 10" electric locomotive. (c) 400 s. Class "DD 51" diesel locomotive. (d) 400 s. Class "EF 58" electric locomotive .. .. *Set of 4 sheets* 6·50 6·75

175 Zebra and Golden-winged Sunbird, Ngorongoro Crater   176 *Eronia cleodora*

(Des Mary Walters. Litho Questa)

1991 (22 Aug). *National Game Parks. T **175** and similar horiz designs. Multicoloured.* P 14.

947	10 s. Type **175**		10	10
948	25 s. Greater Kudu and Elephant, Ruaha Park		10	10
949	30 s. Sable Antelope and Red and Yellow Barbet, Mikumi Park		10	10
950	50 s. Leopard and Wildebeest, Serengeti Park		20	25
951	90 s. Giraffe and Starred Robin, Ngurdoto Park		35	40
952	100 s. Eland and Abbott's Duiker, Kilimanjaro Park		40	45
953	250 s. Lion and Impala, Lake Manyara Park		1·00	1·10
954	300 s. Black Rhinoceros and Ostrich, Tarangire Park		1·10	1·25
947/54		*Set of 8*	3·00	3·50

MS955 Two sheets, each 99×68 mm. (a) 400 s. Blue-breasted Kingfisher and Defassa Waterbuck, Selous Game Reserve. (b) 400 s. Paradise Whydah and Oryx, Mkomazi Game Reserve .. .. *Set of 2 sheets* 3·25 3·50

(Des I. Maclaury. Litho Questa)

1991 (28 Aug). *Butterflies. T **176** and similar vert designs. Multicoloured.* P 14.

956	10 s. Type **176**		10	10
957	15 s. *Precis westermanni*		10	10
958	35 s. *Antanartia delius*		10	10
959	75 s. *Bematistes aganice*		30	35
960	100 s. *Kallima jacksoni*		40	45
961	150 s. *Apaturopsis cleocharis*		60	65
962	200 s. *Colotis aurigineus*		80	85
963	300 s. *Iolaus crawshayi*		1·10	1·25
956/63		*Set of 8*	3·25	3·50

MS964 Four sheets, each 117×76 mm. (a) 400 s. *Charaxes zoolina*. (b) 400 s. *Papilio phorcas*. (c) 400 s. *Charaxes ethalion*. (d) 400 s. *Papilio nobilis* .. .. .. *Set of 4 sheets* 6·50 6·75

173 Dairy Farming   174 Pres. Mwinyi leading Walk

177 Microwave Tower and Dish Aerial   178 Rice Cultivation

(Litho Questa)

1991 (5 Sept). *25th Anniv of Intelsat Satellite System. T* **177** *and similar horiz designs. Multicoloured. P* 14.

965	10 s. Type 177			10	10
966	25 s. Satellite picture of Earth			10	10
967	100 s. Mwenge "B" Earth station			40	45
968	500 s. Mwenge "A" Earth station			2·00	2·10
965/8			*Set of 4*	2·40	2·50
MS969	90×86 mm. 50 s. Satellite links on world map			20	25

(Litho Cartor)

1991 (16 Sept). *40th Anniv of United Nations Development Programme. T* **178** *and similar designs. P* 13½.

970	10 s. multicoloured			10	10
971	15 s. multicoloured			10	10
972	100 s. multicoloured			40	45
973	500 s. multicoloured			2·00	2·10
970/3			*Set of 4*	2·40	2·50
MS974	90×90 mm. 40 s. pale new blue and black. P 12½			15	20

Designs: *Horiz*—15 s. Vocational and Civil Service training; 100 s. Terrace farming. *Vert*—40 s. U.N.D.P. anniversary emblem; 500 s. Renovated Arab door.

179 Netball   180 "TELECOM '91" Logo

(Litho State Ptg Wks, Moscow)

1991 (20 Sept). *All-Africa Games, Cairo. T* **179** *and similar multicoloured designs. P* 12½×12 (*Nos.* 976, 979) *or* 12×12½ (*others*).

975	10 s. Type 179			10	10
976	15 s. Football (*horiz*)			10	10
977	100 s. Tennis			40	45
978	200 s. Athletics			80	85
979	500 s. Baseball (*horiz*)			2·00	2·10
975/9			*Set of 5*	3·00	3·25
MS980	80×60 mm. 500 s. Basketball			2·00	2·10

(Litho Cartor)

1991 (1 Oct). *"TELECOM '91" International Telecommunication Exhibition, Geneva* (10, 15 s.) *and World Telecommunications Day* (*others*). *T* **180** *and similar multicoloured designs. P* 13½×14 (*vert*) *or* 14×13½ (*horiz*).

981	10 s. Type 180			10	10
982	15 s. "TELECOM '91" logo and address on envelope (*horiz*)			10	10
983	35 s. Symbolic telecommunication signals			10	10
984	100 s. Symbolic telecommunication signals (*horiz*)			40	45
981/4			*Set of 4*	65	70

(Litho Questa)

1991 (20 Nov). *Death Centenary of Vincent van Gogh (artist)* (1990). *Multicoloured designs as T* **255** *of Maldive Islands. P* 13½×14.

985	10 s. "Peasant Woman Sewing"			10	10
986	15 s. "Head of Peasant Woman with Greenish Lace Cap"			10	10
987	35 s. "Flowering Orchard"			10	10
988	75 s. "Portrait of a Girl"			30	35
989	100 s. "Portrait of a Woman with Red Ribbon"			40	45
990	150 s. "Vase with Flowers"			60	65
991	200 s. "Houses in Antwerp"			80	85
992	400 s. "Seated Peasant Woman with White Cap"			1·60	1·75
985/92			*Set of 8*	3·50	4·00
MS993	Two sheets, each 127×112 mm. (a) 400 s. "Bulb Fields" (*horiz*). (b) 400 s. "The Parsonage Garden at Nuenen in the Snow" (*horiz*). Imperf.		*Set of 2 sheets*	3·25	3·50

181 Japanese Bobtail Cat

(Des Mary Walters. Litho Questa)

1991 (28 Oct). *Cats. T* **181** *and similar horiz designs. Multicoloured. P* 14.

994	50 s. Type 181			20	25
	a. Sheetlet. Nos. 994/1009			3·00	
995	50 s. Cornish Rex			20	25
996	50 s. Malayan			20	25
997	50 s. Tonkinese			20	25
998	50 s. Abyssinian			20	25
999	50 s. Russian Blue			20	25
1000	50's. Cymric			20	25
1001	50 s. Somali			20	25
1002	50 s. Siamese			20	25
1003	50 s. Himalayan			20	25
1004	50 s. Singapura			20	25
1005	50 s. Manx			20	25
1006	50 s. Oriental Shorthair			20	25
1007	50 s. Maine Coon			20	25
1008	50 s. Persian			20	25
1009	50 s. Birman			20	25
994/1009			*Set of 16*	3·00	3·50

Nos. 994/1009 were printed together, *se-tenant*, as a sheetlet of 16.

182 Shire Horse

(Des Mary Walters. Litho Questa)

1991 (28 Oct). *Horses and Ponies. T* **182** *and similar horiz designs. Multicoloured. P* 14.

1010	50 s. Type 182			20	25
	a. Sheetlet. Nos. 1010/25			3·00	
1011	50 s. Thoroughbred			20	25
1012	50 s. Kladruber			20	25
1013	50 s. Appaloosa			20	25
1014	50 s. Hanoverian			20	25
1015	50 s. Arab			20	25
1016	50 s. Breton			20	25
1017	50 s. Exmoor			20	25
1018	50 s. Connemara			20	25
1019	50 s. Lipizzaner			20	25
1020	50 s. Shetland			20	25
1021	50 s. Percheron			20	25
1022	50 s. Pinto			20	25
1023	50 s. Orlov			20	25
1024	50 s. Palomino			20	25
1025	50 s. Welsh Cob			20	25
1010/25			*Set of 16*	3·00	3·50

Nos. 1010/25 were printed together, *se-tenant*, as a sheetlet of 16, with the backgrounds of each horizontal strip of 4 forming a composite design.

183 Jewel Tetra   184 African Elephant

(Des Mary Walters. Litho Questa)

1991 (28 Oct). *Aquarium Fishes. T* **183** *and similar horiz designs. Multicoloured. P* 14.

1026	75 s. Type 183			30	35
	a. Sheetlet. Nos. 1026/41			4·25	
1027	75 s. Five-banded Barb			30	35
1028	75 s. Simpson Platy			30	35
1029	75 s. Guppy			30	35
1030	75 s. Zebra Danio			30	35
1031	75 s. Neon Tetra			30	35
1032	75 s. Siamese Fighting Fish			30	35
1033	75 s. Tiger Barb			30	35
1034	75 s. Red Lyretail			30	35
1035	75 s. Goldfish			30	35
1036	75 s. Pearl Gourami			30	35
1037	75 s. Angelfish			30	35
1038	75 s. Clown Loach			30	35
1039	75 s. Red Swordtail			30	35
1040	75 s. Brown Discus			30	35
1041	75 s. Rosy Barb			30	35
1026/41			*Set of 16*	4·25	5·00

Nos. 1026/41 were printed together, *se-tenant*, as a sheetlet of 9, with the backgrounds of each stamp forming a composite design.

(Des Mary Walters. Litho Questa)

1991 (28 Oct). *African Elephants. T* **184** *and similar vert designs. Multicoloured. P* 14.

1042	75 s. Type 184			30	35
	a. Sheetlet. Nos. 1042/57			4·25	
1043	75 s. Two elephants fighting			30	35
1044	75 s. Elephant facing forward and tree			30	35
1045	75 s. Elephant facing left and tree			30	35
1046	75 s. Cow elephant and calf facing right standing in water			30	35
1047	75 s. Cow watching over calf in water			30	35
1048	75 s. Two adults and calf in water			30	35
1049	75 s. Cow and calf facing left standing in water			30	35
1050	75 s. Elephant facing right			30	35
1051	75 s. Elephants feeding			30	35
1052	75 s. Elephant feeding			30	35
1053	75 s. Elephant and Zebra			30	35
1054	75 s. Cow and calf drinking			30	35
1055	75 s. Calf suckling			30	35
1056	75 s. Bull elephant			30	35
1057	75 s. Cow with small calf			30	35
1042/57			*Set of 16*	4·25	5·00

Nos. 1042/57 were printed together, *se-tenant*, as a sheetlet of 16, with each horizontal strip of 4 forming a composite design.

185 Budgerigar   186 Indian Elephant

(Des Mary Walters. Litho Questa)

1991 (18 Oct). *Pet Birds. T* **185** *and similar horiz designs. Multicoloured. P* 14.

1058	75 s. Type 185			30	35
	a. Sheetlet. Nos. 1058/73			4·25	
1059	75 s. Rainbow Bunting			30	35
1060	75 s. Golden-fronted Leafbird			30	35
1061	75 s. Black-headed Caique			30	35
1062	75 s. Java Sparrow			30	35
1063	75 s. Diamond Sparrow			30	35
1064	75 s. Peach-faced Lovebird			30	35
1065	75 s. Golden Conure			30	35
1066	75 s. Military Macaw			30	35
1067	75 s. Celestial Parrotlet			30	35
1068	75 s. Sulphur-crested Cockatoo			30	35
1069	75 s. Spectacled Amazon Parrot			30	35
1070	75 s. Paradise Tanager			30	35
1071	75 s. Gouldian Finch			30	35
1072	75 s. Masked Lovebird			30	35
1073	75 s. Hill Mynah			30	35
1058/73			*Set of 16*	4·25	5·00

Nos. 1058/73 were printed together, *se-tenant*, as a sheetlet of 16, forming a composite design.

(Des J. Puvilland. Litho State Ptg Wks, Moscow)

1991 (28 Nov). *Elephants. T* **186** *and similar multicoloured designs. P* 12×12½ (*vert*) *or* 12½×12 (*horiz*).

1074	10 s. Type 186			10	10
1075	15 s. Indian Elephant uprooting tree			10	10
1076	25 s. Indian Elephant with calf			10	10
1077	30 s. African Elephant			10	10
1078	35 s. Head of African Elephants (*horiz*)			10	10
1079	100 s. African Elephant and calf bathing (*horiz*)			40	45
1080	200 s. Two African Elephants (*horiz*)			80	85
1074/80			*Set of 7*	1·40	1·50
MS1081	90×90 mm. 400 s. Mammoth (*horiz*)			1·60	1·75

187 Russian Steam Locomotive, 1930

(Litho State Ptg Wks, Moscow)

1991 (10 Dec). *Locomotives of the World. T* **187** *and similar multicoloured designs. P* 12½×12 (*horiz*) *or* 12×12½ (*vert*).

1082	10 s. Type 187			10	10
1083	15 s. Japanese electric locomotive, 1964			10	10
1084	25 s. Russian steam locomotive, 1834 (*vert*)			10	10
1085	35 s. French electric locomotive, 1979			10	10
1086	60 s. French diesel railcar, 1972			25	30
1087	100 s. U.K. diesel locomotive, 1972			40	45
1088	300 s. Russian steam locomotive, 1837 (*vert*)			1·10	1·25
1082/8			*Set of 7*	1·90	2·00
MS1089	91×91 mm. 100 s. French electric locomotive, 1952 (*vert*)			40	45

(Des Walt Disney Co. Litho Questa)

1991 (24 Dec). *Christmas. Walt Disney Christmas Cards. Multicoloured designs as T* **228** *of St. Vincent. P* 14×13½ (*horiz*) *or* 13½×14 (*horiz*).

1090	10 s. Disney characters in "JOY", 1968 (*horiz*)			10	10
1091	25 s. Mickey, Donald, Pluto and Goofy hanging up stockings, 1981 (*horiz*)			10	10
1092	35 s. Characters from Disney film *Robin Hood*, 1973 (*horiz*)			10	10
1093	75 s. Mickey looking at Christmas tree, 1967 (*horiz*)			30	35
1094	100 s. Goofy, Mickey, Donald and Chip n' Dale on film set, 1969			40	45
1095	150 s. Mickey on giant bauble, 1976			60	65
1096	200 s. Clarabelle Cow with electric cow bell, 1935			80	85
1097	300 s. Mickey's nephews with book, 1935			1·10	1·25
1090/7			*Set of 8*	3·25	3·50
MS1098	Two sheets, each 127×102 mm. (a) 500 s. Mickey handing out presents, 1935. (b) 500 s. Disney cartoon characters, 1968		*Set of 2 sheets*	4·00	4·25

ALTERED CATALOGUE NUMBERS

Any Catalogue numbers altered from the last edition are shown as a list in the introductory pages.

188 Bruce Lee

189 *Malacanthus latovittatus*

(Des J. Iskowitz. Litho Questa)

1992 (14 Feb). *Entertainers. T* **188** *and similar vert designs.*
P 13½.
1099/134	75 s. × 36 multicoloured		*Set of 36*	9·75	11·50

MS1135 Four sheets, each 78×108 mm. 500 s. ×
4 multicoloured (Bruce Lee, Marilyn Monroe,
Elvis Presley, Kouyate & Kouyate, each 28×42
mm). P 14 .. .. .. *Set of 4 sheets* 8·00 8·25
Nos. 1099/134 were issued as four sheetlets, each of nine
different designs, depicting Bruce Lee, Marilyn Monroe, Elvis
Presley and black entertainers (Scott Joplin, Sammy Davis Jnr,
Joan Armatrading, Louis Armstrong, Miriam Makeba, Lionel
Ritchie, Whitney Houston, Bob Marley, Tina Turner).

(Des P. Ndembo. Litho State Ptg Wks, Moscow)

1992 (9 Mar). *Fishes. T* **189** *and similar horiz designs.*
Multicoloured. P 12½×12.
1136	10 s. Type 189	..	..	10	10
1137	15 s. *Lamprologus tretocephalus*			10	10
1138	25 s. *Lamprologus calvus*			10	10
1139	35 s. *Hemichromis bimaculatus*	..		10	10
1140	60 s. *Aphyosemion bivittatum*			25	30
1141	100 s. *Synanceia verrucosa*			40	45
1142	300 s. *Aphyosemion ahli*			1·10	1·25
1136/42			*Set of 7*	1·90	2·10

MS1143 90×90 mm. 100 s. *Regalecus glesue* .. 40 45

190 Chimpanzee in Tree

191 Pope John Paul II in Dominican Republic, 1979

(Des Mary Walters. Litho Questa)

1992 (30 Mar). *Common Chimpanzee. T* **190** *and similar vert designs. Multicoloured.* P 14.
1144	10 s. Type 190	..	..	10	10
1145	15 s. Feeding			10	10
1146	35 s. Two chimpanzees			10	10
1147	75 s. Adult male with arms folded			30	35
1148	100 s. Breaking branch			40	45
1149	150 s. Young chimpanzee in tree			60	65
1150	200 s. Female holding young			80	85
1151	300 s. Chimpanzee sitting in tree			1·10	1·25
1144/51			*Set of 8*	3·25	3·50

MS1152 Two sheets, each 99×68 mm. (a) 400 s.
Eating termites. (b) 400 s. Swinging through
trees .. .. *Set of 2 sheets* 3·25 3·50

(Litho Questa)

1992 (13 Apr). *Papal Visits. T* **191** *and similar vert designs.*
P 14.
1153/272	100 s. × 120 multicoloured	*Set of 120*	42·00	48·00

Nos. 1153/272 were issued in ten sheetlets, each of 12
different designs arranged round a common block of four stamp-
sized labels.

192 Balcony

193 Gogo Costume

(Des J. da Silva. Litho State Ptg Wks, Moscow)

1992 (15 Apr). *Zanzibar Stone Town. T* **192** *and similar multicoloured designs.* P 12½×12 (200 s.) *or* 12×12½ (*others*).
1273	10 s. Type 192	..	..	10	10
1274	20 s. Bahlnara Mosque	..		10	10
1275	30 s. High Court Building			10	10
1276	200 s. National Museum (*horiz*)			80	85
1273/6			*Set of 4*	1·00	1·00

MS1277 91×91 mm. (a) 150 s. Old Fort (*horiz*).
(b) 300 s. Maruhubi ruins (*horiz*). P 12½×12 1·75 1·90

(Des P. Ndembo. Litho National Printing and Packaging,
Zimbabwe)

1992 (30 Apr). *Traditional Costumes. T* **193** *and similar vert designs. Multicoloured.* P 14½.
1278	3 s. Type 193	..	..	10	10
1279	5 s. Swahili			10	10
1280	9 s. Hehe and Makonde	..		10	10
1281	12 s. Maasai			10	10
1278/81			*Set of 4*	20	20

MS1282 91×91 mm. 40 s. Mwarusha .. 15 20

194 Melisa and Mike (chimpanzees)

(Des P. Ndembo. Litho B.D.T.)

1992 (29 May). *Chimpanzees of the Gombe. Multicoloured.*
P 14.

(a) Horiz designs as T **194**
1283	10 s. Type 194	..	..	10	10
1284	15 s. Leakey and David Greybeard			10	10
1285	30 s. Fifi termiting			10	10
1286	35 s. Galahad	..	..	15	20
1283/6			*Set of 4*	40	45

MS1287 90×90 mm. 100 s. Fifi, Flo and Faben 40 45

(b) Vert designs showing individual chimpanzees
1288	10 s. Leakey	..	..	10	10
	a. Sheetlet. Nos. 1288/95			1·75	
1289	15 s. Fifi	..		10	10
1290	20 s. Faben			10	10
1291	30 s. David Greybeard	..		10	10
1292	35 s. Mike			15	20
1293	50 s. Galahad			20	25
1294	100 s. Melisa			40	45
1295	200 s. Flo	..		80	85
1288/95			*Set of 8*	1·75	1·90

Nos. 1288/95 were printed together, *se-tenant*, in sheetlets of
8.

195 Sorghum Farming, Serena

196 *Lambis truncata*

(Des P. Ndembo. Litho Questa)

1992 (22 June). *25th Anniv of National Bank of Commerce.*
T **195** *and similar multicoloured designs.* P 14.
1296	10 s. Type 195	..	..	10	10
1297	15 s. Samora Avenue Branch and computer operator (*vert*)			10	10
1298	35 s. Training centre	..		15	20
1299	40 s. Women dyeing textiles			15	20
1296/9			*Set of 4*	45	55

MS1300 111×117 mm. 30 s. Bank Head Office 10 10

(Litho State Ptg Wks, Moscow)

1991 (30 June). *Shells. T* **196** *and similar vert designs.*
Multicoloured. P 12×12½.
1301	10 s. Type 196	..	..	10	10
1302	15 s. *Cypraecassis rufa*	..		10	10
1303	25 s. *Vexillum rugosum*	..		10	10
1304	30 s. *Conus litteratus*	..		10	10
1305	35 s. *Corculum cardissa*			15	20
1306	50 s. *Murex ramosus*	..		20	25
1307	250 s. *Melo melo*	..	..	1·00	1·10
1301/7			*Set of 7*	1·50	1·75

MS1308 91×91 mm. 300 s. *Tridacha gigas* 1·25 1·40

197 Basketball

198 British-designed Radar, Pearl Harbor

(Des A. Nabola. Litho State Ptg Wks, Moscow)

1992 (23 July). *Olympic Games, Barcelona. T* **197** *and similar vert designs. Multicoloured.* P 12×12½.
1309	40 s. Type 197	..	..	15	20
1310	100 s. Billiards			40	45
1311	200 s. Table Tennis			80	85
1312	400 s. Darts			1·60	1·75
1309/12			*Set of 4*	2·75	2·90

MS1313 91×8 mm. 500 s. Weightlifting .. 2·00 2·10

(Des J. Batchelor. Litho Questa)

1992 (1 Aug). *50th Anniv of Japanese Attack on Pearl Harbor.*
T **198** *and similar horiz designs. Multicoloured.* P 14½.
1314	75 s. Type 198			30	35
	a. Sheetlet. Nos. 1314/23			2·75	
1315	75 s. Winston Churchill			30	35
1316	75 s. Sinking of H.M.S. *Repulse* (battle cruiser)			30	35
1317	75 s. Sinking of H.M.S. *Prince of Wales* (battleship)			30	35
1318	75 s. Surrender of Singapore			30	35
1319	75 s. Sinking of H.M.S. *Hermes* (aircraft carrier)			30	35
1320	75 s. Japanese attack on Malayan airfield		30	35
1321	75 s. Japanese gun crew, Hong Kong		30	35
1322	75 s. Japanese landing craft			30	35
1323	75 s. *Haguro* (Japanese cruiser)			30	35
1314/23			*Set of 10*	2·75	3·25

Nos. 1314/23 were printed together, *se-tenant*, in sheetlets of
10 with the stamps arranged in two horizontal strips of 5
separated by a gutter showing H.M.S. *Exeter* at Battle of Java
Sea.

199 French Resistance Monument and Medal

(Litho Questa)

1992 (1 Aug). *Birth Centenary of Charles de Gaulle (French statesman) (1990). T* **199** *and similar multicoloured designs.*
P 14.
1324	25 s. Type 199	..	..	10	10
1325	30 s. Free French tank on Omaha Beach, D-Day			10	10
1326	150 s. "Concorde" at Charles de Gaulle Airport	..		60	65
1324/6			*Set of 3*	70	75

MS1327 115×92 mm. 500 s. Free French local
Cross of Lorraine opt on Petain 1 f. 50 and De
Gaulle label postmarked 25 August 1944 (39×51
mm) .. .. 2·00 2·10

200 Scout Badge, Giraffe and Elephant

(Litho Questa)

1992 (1 Aug). *50th Death Anniv of Lord Baden-Powell (founder of Boy Scout movement) (1991). T* **200** *and similar multicoloured designs.* P 14.
1328	10 s. Type 200	..	..	10	10
1329	15 s. Scouts in boat			10	10
1330	400 s. John Glenn's space capsule			1·60	1·75
1328/30			*Set of 3*	1·60	1·75

MS1331 90×117 mm. 500 s. Tanzanian Scout
(39×51 mm). P 13½ .. .. 2·00 2·10

201 Marcella Sembrich as Zerlina in *Don Giovanni*

(Litho Questa)

1992 (1 Aug). *Death Bicentenary of Mozart. T* **201** *and similar designs.* P 14.
1332	10 s. black and deep mauve	..	..	10	10
1333	50 s. multicoloured			20	25
1334	300 s. black and deep mauve			1·25	1·40
1332/4			*Set of 3*	1·40	1·60

MS1335 115×87 mm. 500 s. grey-brown, stone
and black .. .. 2·00 2·10
Designs: Horiz—50 s. Planet Jupiter (Symphony No. 41);
300 s. Luciano Pavarotti as Idamente in *Idomeneo*. Vert (35×47
mm)—500 s. Wolfgang Amadeus Mozart.

OFFICIAL STAMPS

(Opt photo Harrison)

1965 (9 Dec). *Nos. 128/32, 134, 136, 139 optd as Types O 1 (15 c., 30 c. or larger (17 mm) 5 c., 10 c., 20 c., 50 c.), or with O 2 of Tanganyika (1 s., 5 s.).*

O 9	5 c. ultramarine and yellow-orange	..		10	20
O10	10 c. black, greenish yellow, green & blue			10	20
O11	15 c. multicoloured	..	..	10	20
O12	20 c. sepia, grey-green and greenish blue		10	20
O13	30 c. black and red-brown	..	..	10	20
O14	50 c. multicoloured	..	..	15	20
O15	1 s. multicoloured	..	..	30	20
O16	5 s. lake-brown, yellow-green and blue	..	1·50	2·50
O9/16			*Set of 8*	2·00	3·50

OFFICIAL
(O 3) (3 mm tall)

(Opt litho Govt Printer, Dar-es-Salaam)

1967 (10–18 Nov). *Nos. 134, 136 and 139 optd as No. O14 (50 c.) or with Type O 3 (others).*

O17	50 c. multicoloured (18.11)..				
O18	1 s. multicoloured (18.11)	..	..	14·00	3·50
O19	5 s. lake-brown, yellow-green and blue ..	9·00	6·50

The issue dates given are for the earliest known postmarked copies.

Nos. O9/16 were overprinted by Harrison in photogravure and Nos. O17/19 have litho overprints by the Government Printer, Dar-es-Salaam. On No. O17 the overprint is the same size (17 mm long) as on No. O14.

1967 (9 Dec)–71. *Nos. 142/6, 148, 151 and 155 optd as Type O 1, but larger (measuring 17 mm) (5 c. to 50 c.) or as Type O 2 of Tanganyika (1 s. and 5 s.). Chalk-surfaced paper.*

O20	5 c. magenta, yellow-olive and black ..		10	55
	a. Glazed, ordinary paper (22.1.71)		1·25	1·50
O21	10 c. brown and bistre	..	..	10	40
O22	15 c. grey, turquoise-blue and black ..		10	40
	a. Glazed, ordinary paper (22.1.71)		1·25	2·00
O23	20 c. brown and turquoise-green ,	..	10	20
O24	30 c. sage-green and black	..	..	10	20
O25	50 c. multicoloured	..	..	15	40
	a. Glazed, ordinary paper (22.1.71)		1·50	1·50
O26	1 s. orange-brown, slate-blue and maroon ..	30	55
	a. Glazed, ordinary paper (3.2.71)	..	2·75	1·50
O27	5 s. greenish yellow, black & turquoise-grn.	2·25	4·00
	a. Glazed, ordinary paper (3.2.71) ..		5·50	7·00
O20/7			*Set of 8*	2·75	6·00
O20a/7a	..	..	*Set of 5*	11·00	12·00

The chalk-surfaced paper exists with both PVA gum and gum arabic, but the glazed, ordinary paper exists PVA gum only.

OFFICIAL   OFFICIAL
(O 4)   (O 5)

1970 (10 Dec)–73. *Nos. 142/8, 151 and 155 optd locally by letterpress as Type O 4 (5 c. to 50 c.) or as Type O 2 of Tanganyika, but measuring 28 mm (1 s. and 5 s.).*

(a) Chalk-surfaced paper

O28	5 c. magenta, yellow-olive and black	..	10	70
	a. "OFFCIAL" (R.7/6)	..	..	10	30
O29	10 c. brown and bistre	..	..	10	30
	a. "OFFCIAL" (R.7/6)	..	..		
O30	20 c. brown and turquoise-green	..	20	50
O31	30 c. sage-green and black	..	..	25	50
O28/31	..	..	*Set of 4*	55	1·75

(b) Glazed, ordinary paper (1973)

O32	5 c. magenta, yellow-olive and black	..	—	1·25
	a. "OFFCIAL" (R.7/6)	..	..	—	22·00
	b. "OFFICIA" (R.10/9)	..	..	—	22·00
O33	10 c. brown and bistre ..	..	..	—	
	a. "OFFCIAL" (R.7/6)	..	..		
O34	15 c. grey, turquoise-blue and black ..			
	a. "OFFCIAL" (R.7/6)	..	..		
O35	20 c. brown and turquoise-green	..		
O36	40 c. yellow, chocolate and bright green	..	—	2·25
	a. Opt double	..	..	—	45·00
	b. "OFFICIA" (R.10/9)	..	..	—	45·00
O37	50 c. multicoloured	..	..	—	1·75
	a. "OFFCIAL" (R.7/6)	..	..	—	35·00
O38	1 s. orange-brown, slate-blue and maroon ..		
	a. Opt double	..	..		
O39	5 s. greenish yellow, black & turquoise-grn		

The letterpress overprint can be distinguished from the photogravure by its absence of screening dots and the overprint showing through to the reverse, apart from the difference in length.

1973 (10 Dec). *Nos. 158/9, 161, 163/4 and 166/70 optd with Type O 1 of Tanganyika (5 to 70 c.) or Type O 5 (others).*

O40	5 c. light yellow-olive, lt violet-blue & black	40	60
O41	10 c. multicoloured	..	..	50	20
O42	20 c. reddish cinnamon, orange-yellow & blk	60	20
O43	40 c. multicoloured	..	..	80	30
O44	50 c. multicoloured	..	..	90	30
O45	70 c. turquoise-green, pale orange and black ..	1·25	65
O46	1 s. multicoloured	..	..	1·25	30
O47	1 s. 50, multicoloured	..	..	2·50	1·75
	a. Pair, one without opt	..	..	†	
O48	2 s. 50, multicoloured	..	..	2·75	2·75
O49	5 s. multicoloured	..	..	3·25	3·75
O40/9	..	..	*Set of 10*	13·00	9·75

No. O47a is due to a paper fold and comes from a sheet used at Kigoma in 1974.

1977 (Feb). *Nos. 159, 161 and 163/4 optd locally by letterpress as Type O 4.*

O50	10 c. multicoloured	..	..	—	1·75
	a. "OFFCIAL" (R. 7/6)	..	..	—	35·00
O51	20 c. multicoloured	..	..	—	1·75
	a. "OFFCIAL" (R. 7/6)	..	..	—	35·00
	b. Opt inverted	..	..		
	c. Opt double	..	..		
O52	40 c. multicoloured	..	..	—	2·25
	a. "OFFCIAL" (R. 7/6)	..	..	—	45·00
O53	50 c. multicoloured	..	..	—	2·25
	a. "OFFCIAL" (R. 7/6)	..	..	—	45·00
	b. Opt inverted	..	..		

OFFICIAL	OFFICIAL	OFFICIAL	OFFICIAL
(O 6)	(O 6a)	(O 7)	(O 7a)

1980 (Nov)–85. *(a) Bradbury Wilkinson printings. Nos. 307/12 optd with Type O 6 (10 mm long) and Nos. 313 and 315/17 optd with Type O 7 (13½ mm long).*

O54	10 c. Type **75**	..	..	15	10
O55	20 c. Large-spotted Genet	..	..	20	15
O56	40 c. Banded Mongoose	..	..	20	15
O57	50 c. Ratel (light blue panel at foot)	..	20	15
O58	75 c. Large-toothed Rock Hyrax	..	30	30
O59	80 c. Leopard	..	..	35	15
O60	1 s. Type **76**	..	..	35	15
O61	2 s. Common Zebra	..	..	55	55
O62	3 s. African Buffalo	..	..	65	70
O63	5 s. Lion	..	..	85	95
O54/63			*Set of 10*	3·50	3·25

(b) John Waddington printings. No. 320a optd with Type O 6a (8½ mm long) and Nos. 320b/f optd with Type O 7a (13 mm long) (1984–85)

O64	50 c. Ratel (turquoise-blue panel at foot) ..		
O65	1 s. Type **76**	..	..		
O66	1 s. 50, Giraffe	..	..	2·50	2·75
O67	2 s. Common Zebra	..	..		
O68	3 s. African Buffalo	..	..		
O69	5 s. Lion	..	..		

On the Bradbury Wilkinson printings the overprint reads downwards on the 10 c., 50 c., 2 s., 5 s. and upwards on the others. All values of the John Waddington printing show the overprint reading upwards.

OFFICIAL   OFFICIAL
(O 8)   (O 9)

1990 (15 Dec)–91. *Nos. 804/12 optd with Type O 8 (5 s. to 30 s.) or Type O 9 (40 s. to 100 s.).*

O70	5 s. Type **163**	..	..	10	10
O71	9 s. African Emerald Cuckoo	..	..	10	10
O72	13 s. Little Bee Eater	..	..	10	10
O73	15 s. Red Bishop	..	..	10	10
O74	20 s. Bateleur	..	..	10	15
O75	25 s. Scarlet-chested Sunbird	..	..	10	15
O76	30 s. African Wood Pigeon (1.7.91)	..	10	15
O77	40 s. Type **164**	..	..	15	20
O78	70 s. Helmet Guineafowl	..	..	25	30
O79	100 s. Eastern White Pelican	..	40	45
O70/9			*Set of 10*	1·10	1·40

Official overprints were reported as being used for normal postal purposes during 1992.

POSTAGE DUE STAMPS

Postage Due stamps of Kenya and Uganda were issued for provisional use as such in Tanganyika on 1 July 1933. The postmark is the only means of identification.

The Postage Due stamps of Kenya, Uganda and Tanganyika were used in Tanganyika until 2 January 1967.

D 1

D 2

(Litho D.L.R.)

1967 (3 Jan). *P 14 × 13½.*

D1	D 1	5 c. scarlet	..	35	4·25
D2		10 c. green	..	45	4·50
D3		20 c. deep blue	..	70	5·50
D4		30 c. red-brown	..	70	6·00
D5		40 c. bright purple	..	70	8·00
D6		1 s. orange	..	1·25	9·50
D1/6	..	..	*Set of 6*	3·75	35·00

1969–71. *As Nos. D1/6, but perf 14 × 15.*
A. *Chalk-surfaced paper* (19.12.69).
B. *Glazed, ordinary paper* (13.7.71).

				A		B	
D 7	D 1	5 c. scarlet	..	25	3·75	3·00	5·00
D 8		10 c. green	..	40	3·75	75	3·25
D 9		20 c. deep blue	..	40	4·50	2·00	6·00
D10		30 c. red-brown	..	50	8·50	85	4·00
D11		40 c. bright purple	..	1·00	8·00	4·75	16·00
D12		1 s. orange	..		†	4·75	17·00
D7A/11A			*Set of 5*	2·25	26·00		
D7B/12B			*Set of 6*			15·00	45·00

The stamps on chalk-surfaced paper exist only with gum arabic, but the stamps on glazed paper exist only with PVA gum.

1973 (12 Dec). *As Nos. D1/6, but glazed ordinary paper. P 15.*

D13	D 1	5 c. scarlet	..	50	4·75
D14		10 c. emerald	..	50	4·75
D15		20 c. deep blue	..	70	6·00
D16		30 c. red-brown	..	75	6·50
D17		40 c. bright mauve	..	75	8·50
D18		1 s. bright orange	..	1·25	11·00
D13/18	..	..	*Set of 6*	4·00	38·00

(Litho Questa)

1978 (31 July). *Chalky paper. P 13½ × 14.*

D19	D 1	5 c. brown-red	..	10	90
D20		10 c. emerald	..	10	90
D21		20 c. steel-blue	..	15	1·25
D22		30 c. red-brown	..	25	1·75
D23		40 c. bright purple	..	25	2·00
D24		1 s. bright orange	..	35	2·50
D19/24	..	..	*Set of 6*	1·00	8·50

(Litho Questa)

1990 (15 Dec). *P 14½×14.*

D25	D 2	50 c. myrtle-green	..	10	10
D26		80 c. ultramarine	..	10	10
D27		1 s. orange-brown	..	10	10
D28		2 s. yellow-olive	..	10	10
D29		3 s. purple	..	10	10
D30		5 s. grey-brown	..	10	10
D31		10 s. reddish brown	..	10	10
D32		20 s. brown-ochre	..	10	15
D25/32	..	..	*Set of 8*	40	45

Appendix

The following stamps have either been issued in excess of postal needs, or have not been made available to the public in reasonable quantities at face value. Miniature sheets, imperforate stamps, etc., are excluded from this section.

1985

Life and Times of Queen Elizabeth the Queen Mother. As Nos. 425/8 but embossed on gold foil. 20 s. × 2, 100 s. × 2.
Tanzanian Railway Locomotives (1st series). As Nos. 430/3, but embossed on gold foil. 5, 10, 20, 30 s.

1986

Caribbean Royal Visit. Optd in silver and gold on previous issues. (a) Nos. 425/8 20 s. × 2, 100 s. × 2. (b) On Nos. 430/3, 5, 10, 20, 30 s.
"Ameripex" International Stamp Exhibition, Chicago. Optd on Nos. 425/8. 20 s. × 2, 100 s. × 2.

1988

Centenary of Statue of Liberty (1986). 1, 2, 3, 4, 5, 6, 7, 8, 10, 12, 15, 18, 20, 25, 30, 35, 40, 45, 50, 60 s.
Royal Ruby Wedding. Optd on No. 378. 10 s.
125th Anniv of Red Cross. Optd on Nos. 486/7. 5, 40 s.
63rd Anniv of Rotary International in Africa. Optd on Nos. 422/3. 10 s., 17 s. 50.

Tasmania
see Australia

Togo

The stamps of GERMANY were used in the colony from March 1888 until June 1897 when issues for TOGO were provided.

ANGLO-FRENCH OCCUPATION

British and French forces invaded Togo on 12 August 1914 and the German administration surrendered on 26 August 1914.

Stamps of German Colonial issue Types A and B 1900 and 1909–14 (5 pf. and 10 pf.)

TOGO
Anglo-French
Occupation   Half penny
(1)   (2)

SETTINGS. Nos. H1/33 were all overprinted or surcharged by the Catholic Mission, Lome.

The initial setting for the 3 pf. to 80 pf. was of 50 (10×5), repeated twice on each sheet of 100. Overprints from this setting, used for Nos. H1/9, had the lines of type 3 mm apart.

Nos. H1/2 were subsequently surcharged, also from a setting of 50, to form Nos. H12/13. The surcharge setting showed a thin dropped "y" with small serifs on R. 1/1–2, 2/1, 3/1, 4/1 and 5/1–2.

The type from the overprint and surcharge was then amalgamated in a new setting of 50 on which the lines of the overprint were only 2 mm apart. On this amalgamated setting, used for Nos. H27/8, the thin "y" varieties were still present and R. 4/7 showed the second "O" of "TOGO" omitted.

The surcharge was subsequently removed from this "2 mm" setting which was then used to produce Nos. H17/19. The missing "O" was spotted and corrected before any of the 30 pf. stamps were overprinted.

The remaining low values of the second issue, Nos. H14/16 and H20/2, were overprinted from settings of 25 (5×5), either taken from the last setting of 50 or from an amended version on which there was no space either side of the hyphen. This slightly narrower overprint was subsequently used for Nos. H29/33. It shows the top of the second "O" broken so that it resembles a "U" on R. 1/5.

The mark values were overprinted from settings of 20 (5×4), showing the same differences in the spacing of the lines as on the low values.

It is believed that odd examples of some German colonial values were overprinted from individual settings in either spacing.

1914 (24 Sept). *Optd with T 1 by Catholic Mission, Lome. Wide setting. Lines 3 mm apart.*
H 1	3 pf. brown	..	£110	95·00
H 2	5 pf. green	..	£100	90·00
H 3	10 pf. carmine (Wmk Lozenges)..	£120	£100
	a. Opt inverted	..	£7500	£4500
	b. Opt tête-bêche in vert pair	†	£6500
	c. No wmk	..	†	£5500
H 4	20 pf. ultramarine	..	28·00	26·00
H 5	25 pf. black and red/yellow	28·00	30·00
H 6	30 pf. black and orange/buff	30·00	35·00
H 7	40 pf. black and carmine	..	£225	£250
H 8	50 pf. black and purple/buff	£9000	£7000
H 9	80 pf. black and carmine/rose ..	£225	£275
H10	1 m. carmine	..	£5000	£2500
H11	2 m. blue..	..	£7500	£8000
	a. "Occupation" double	£12000	£10000
	b. Opt inverted	..	£9500	

The tête-bêche overprint on the 10 pf. is due to the sheet being turned round after the upper 50 stamps had been overprinted so that vertical pairs from the two middle rows have the overprint tête-bêche.

1914 (1 Oct). *Nos. H1 and H2 surch as T 2.*
H12	½d. on 3 pf. brown	..	£200	£200
	a. Thin "y" in "penny"..	£500	£475
H13	1d. on 5 pf. green	..	£200	£200
	a. Thin "y" in "penny"..	£500	£475

TOGO
Anglo-French
Occupation
(3)

TOGO
Anglo-French
Occupation
Half penny
(4)

1914 (Oct). *(a) Optd with T 3. Narrow Setting. Lines 2 mm apart.*
H14	3 pf. brown	..	£4000	£700
H15	5 pf. green	..	£900	£550
H16	10 pf. carmine	..	†	£1800
H17	20 pf. ultramarine	..	14·00	12·00
	a. "TOG"	..	£4000	£4000
	b. Nos. H4 and H17 se-tenant (vert pair)		£6500	
H18	25 pf. black and red/yellow	..	19·00	27·00
	a. "TOG"	..	£12000	
H19	30 pf. black and orange/buff	..	19·00	27·00
H20	40 pf. black and carmine	..	£4000	£1300
H21	50 pf. black and purple/buff	..	†	£6000
H22	80 pf. black and carmine/rose	£1700	£1700
H23	1 m. carmine	..	£7000	£3750
H24	2 m. blue..	..	†	£7500
H25	3 m. violet-black	..	†	£30000
H26	5 m. lake and black	..	†	£30000

(b) Narrow setting, but including value, as T 4.
H27	½d. on 3 pf. brown	..	26·00	26·00
	a. "TOG"	..	£425	£300
	b. Thin "y" in "penny"	..	55·00	55·00
H28	1d. on 5 pf. green	..	4·00	4·25
	a. "TOG"	..	£130	£110
	b. Thin "y" in "penny"	..	12·00	15·00

In the 20 pf. one half of a sheet was overprinted with the wide setting (3 mm), and the other half with the narrow setting (2 mm), so that vertical pairs from the middle of the sheet show the two varieties of the overprint.

TOGO
Anglo-French
Occupation
(6)

TOGO
ANGLO-FRENCH
OCCUPATION
(7)

TOGO
ANGLO-FRENCH
OCCUPATION
(8)

1915 (7 Jan). *Optd as T 6. The words "Anglo-French" measure 15 mm instead of 16 mm as in T 3.*
H29	3 pf. brown	..	£6000	£2500
H30	5 pf. green	..	£200	£130
	a. "Occupation" omitted	..	£6000	
H31	10 pf. carmine	..	£200	£130
	a. No wmk	..	†	£7000
H32	20 pf. ultramarine	..	£1400	£475
H32a	40 pf. black and carmine	..	†	£7500
H33	50 pf. black and purple/buff ..	£9500	£6500

This printing was made on another batch of German Togo stamps, found at Sansane-Mangu.

Stamps of Gold Coast overprinted

1915 (May). *Nos. 70/81, 82a and 83/4 of Gold Coast (King George V) optd locally with T 7 ("OCCUPATION" 14½ mm long).*
H34	½d. green	..	25	60
	g. Opt double	..	£325	£425
H35	1d. red	..	25	30
	g. Opt double	..	£250	£350
	h. Opt inverted	..	£130	£180
	ha. Ditto. "TOGO" omitted			
H36	2d. grey	..	30	40
H37	2½d. bright blue	..	40	70
H38	3d. purple/yellow	..	65	80
	a. White back	..	3·50	7·50
H40	6d. dull and bright purple	65	1·75
H41	1s. black/green	..	1·25	3·25
	g. Opt double	..	£475	
H42	2s. purple and blue/blue	6·00	7·00
H43	2s. 6d. black and red/blue	4·50	10·00
H44	5s. green and red/yellow (white back) ..	8·00	12·00
H45	10s. green and red/green	32·00	48·00
H46	20s. purple and black/red	£120	£120
H34/46		*Set of 12*	£150	£170

Varieties (Nos. indicate positions in pane).
A. *Small "F" in "FRENCH" (25, 58 and 59).*
B. *Thin "G" in "TOGO" (24).*
C. *No hyphen after "ANGLO" (5).*
D. *Two hyphens after "ANGLO" (5).*
E. *"CUPATION" for "OCCUPATION" (33).*
F. *"CCUPATION" for "OCCUPATION" (57).*

Varieties C and E also occur together on position 28 of the ½d. value only.

Prices are for unused. Used are worth more
		A	B	C	D	E	F
H34	½d.	1·50	3·00	†	80·00	42·00
H35	1d.	1·75	4·25	4·25	†	†	£100
	h. Inverted	£650	£1300	£1300	†	†	†
H36	2d.	1·75	5·50	48·00	25·00	†	£100
H37	2½d.	2·50	6·00	24·00	30·00	†	90·00
H38	3d.	2·50	6·00	30·00	†	†	£100
	a. White back	14·00	40·00	†	†	†	†
H40	6d.	4·25	8·00	†	†	†	£150
H41	1s.	4·25	9·00	†	†	†	80·00
H42	2s.	18·00	30·00	85·00	†	†	£200
H43	2s. 6d.	18·00	30·00	90·00	†	†	£375
H44	5s.	25·00	42·00	£120	†	†	£200
H45	10s.	70·00	£120	†	†	†	£200
H46	20s.	£225	£375	†	†	†	£500

1916 (Apr). *Nos. 70/84 of Gold Coast (King George V) optd in London with T 8 ("OCCUPATION" 15 mm long). Heavy type and thicker letters showing through on back.*
H47	½d. green	..	15	75
H48	1d. red	..	15	60
H49	2d. grey	..	35	45
H50	2½d. bright blue	..	45	1·25
H51	3d. purple/yellow	..	55	70
H52	6d. dull and bright purple	55	1·00
H53	1s. black/green	..	1·25	1·50
	a. On blue-green, olive back	3·25	5·00
	b. On emerald back	..	£190	£300
H54	2s. purple and blue/blue	4·50	6·00
H55	2s. 6d. black and red/blue	4·50	6·50
H56	5s. green and red/yellow	8·00	20·00
	a. On orange-buff	..	8·00	24·00
H57	10s. green and red/green	24·00	55·00
	a. On blue-green, olive back	16·00	45·00
H58	20s. purple and black/red	£120	£120
H47/58		*Set of 12*	£140	£160
H47/58	Optd "Specimen"..	*Set of 12*	£300	

Tokelau
see after New Zealand

Tonga

The Tongan Post Office was established in 1885 and FIJI 2d. and 6d. stamps are recorded in use until the arrival of Nos. 1/4.

PROTECTORATE KINGDOM
King George I, 1845–93

1 King George I   2

(Eng Bock and Cousins. Plates made and typo Govt Ptg Office, Wellington)

1886–88. *W 2. P 12½ (line) or 12 × 11½ (comb)*.*
1	1	1d. carmine (p 12½) (27.8.86)	..	£250	6·00
		a. Perf 12½ × 10			
		b. Perf 12 × 11½ (15.7.87)	..	10·00	3·25
		ba. Pale carmine (p 12 × 11½)	..	16·00	8·00
2		2d. pale violet (p 12½) (27.8.86)	..	40·00	10·00
		a. Bright violet	..	60·00	3·50
		b. Perf 12 × 11½ (15.7.87)	..	25·00	2·75
		ba. Bright violet (p 12 × 11½)	..	27·00	3·00
3		6d. blue (p 12½) (9.10.86)	..	42·00	2·25
		a. Perf 12 × 11½ (15.10.88)	..	38·00	2·25
		ab. Dull blue (p 12 × 11½)	..	18·00	2·25
4		1s. pale green (p 12½) (9.10.86)	..	80·00	4·25
		a. Deep green (p 12½)	..	85·00	2·25
		b. Perf 12 × 11½ (15.10.88)	..	42·00	6·00
		ba. Deep green (p 12 × 11½)	..	42·00	3·25

*See note after New Zealand, No. 186.

FOUR   EIGHT
PENCE.   PENCE.
(3)   (4)

(Surch Messrs Wilson & Horton, Auckland, N.Z.)

1891 (10 Nov). *Nos. 1b and 2b surch.*
5	3	4d. on 1d. carmine	..	2·00	11·00
		a. No stop after "PENCE"	..	38·00	80·00
6	4	8d. on 2d. violet	..	35·00	75·00
		a. Short "T" in "EIGHT"	..	£120	£170

No. 5a occurred on R. 6/8 and 9, R. 10/11, all from the righthand pane.

1891 (23 Nov). *Optd with stars in upper right and lower left corners. P 12½.*
7	1	1d. carmine	..	35·00	48·00
		a. Three stars	..	£250	
		b. Four stars	..	£350	
		c. Five stars	..	£500	
		d. Perf 12 × 11½	..	£200	
		da. Three stars	..	£375	
		db. Four stars	..	£450	
		dc. Five stars	..	£700	
8		2d. violet	..	45·00	38·00
		a. Perf 12 × 11½	..	£250	

1892 (15 Aug). *W 2. P 12 × 11½.*
9	1	6d. yellow-orange	..	11·00	23·00

5 Arms of Tonga   6 King George I

(Dies eng A. E. Cousins. Typo at Govt Printing Office, Wellington, N.Z.)

1892 (10 Nov). W 2. P 12 × 11½.
10	5	1d. pale rose	..	12·00	16·00
		a. Bright rose	..	12·00	16·00
		b. Bisected diag (½d.) (1893) (on cover)	..	†	£650
11	6	2d. olive ..	..	12·00	15·00
12	5	4d. chestnut	..	35·00	50·00
13	6	8d. bright mauve	..	50·00	90·00
14		1s. brown ..	..	65·00	90·00
10/14			Set of 5	£160	£225

No. 10b was used from 31 May 1893 to provide a 2½d. rate before the arrival of No. 15, and on subsequent occasions up to 1895.

FIVE
½d. 2½d. PENCE. 7½d.
(7) (8) (9) (10)

1893. Printed in new colours and surch with T 7/10 by Govt Printing Office, Wellington. (a) In carmine. P 12½ (21 Aug).
15	5	½d. on 1d. bright ultramarine	..	23·00	23·00
		a. Surch omitted			
16	6	2½d. on 2d. green.	..	14·00	12·00
17	5	5d. on 4d. orange	..	4·00	6·50
18	6	7½d. on 8d. carmine	..	24·00	65·00

(b) In black. P 12 × 11½ (Nov)
19	5	½d. on 1d. dull blue	..	45·00	48·00
20	6	2½d. on 2d. green.	..	17·00	17·00
		a. Surch double	..	—	£1000

SURCHARGE. HALF-PENNY. SURCHARGE, 2½d.
(11) (12)

(Surch at the Star Office, Auckland, N.Z.)

1894. Surch with T 11 or 12.
21	5	½d. on 4d. chestnut (B.)	..	1·50	7·00
		a. "SURCHARCE"	..	7·50	17·00
		b. "-PENNY" omitted ..			
22	6	½d. on 1s. brown (June)	..	1·50	11·00
		a. "SURCHARCE"	..	10·00	38·00
		b. Surch double	..	£300	
		c. Surch double with "SURCHARCE"	..	£900	
23		2½d. on 8d. bright mauve	..	5·00	8·00
		a. No stop after "SURCHARGE"	..	32·00	50·00
		b. "2½d." omitted	..		
24		2½d. on 1s. green (No. 4a) (June)	..	30·00	20·00
		a. No stop after "SURCHARGE"	..	90·00	
		b. Perf 12×11½	..	15·00	28·00
		ba. No stop after "SURCHARGE"	..	55·00	

Nos. 21/4 were surcharged in panes of 60 (6×10) with No. 21a occurring on R. 2/6, 4/6, 5/6, 8/6 and 10/6, No. 22a on R. 1/6, 3/6, 5/6, 8/6, and 10/6 (after the setting had been rearranged), No. 23a on R. 3/1–3 and Nos. 24a and 24ba on R. 6/3 and R. 7/3 or R. 7/1–2.

(Design resembling No. 11 litho and surch at Star Office, Auckland, N.Z.)

1895 (June). As T 6 surch as T 11 and 12. No wmk. P 12.
25	11	1d. on 2d. pale blue (C.)	..	30·00	22·00
26	12	1½d. on 2d. pale blue (C.)	..	42·00	27·00
		a. Perf 12 × 11	..	35·00	27·00
27		2½d. on 2d. pale blue (C.)*	..	40·00	45·00
		a. No stop after "SURCHARGE"	..	£225	£225
28		7½d. on 2d. pale blue (C.)	..	£250	
		a. Perf 12 × 11	..	55·00	45·00

*The 2½d. on 2d. is the only value which normally has a stop after the word "SURCHARGE".
No. 27a occurs on R. 1/3 of the right-hand pane.

King George II, 1893–1918

Ha l f
Penny
13 King George II (14)

(Litho Star Office, Auckland, N.Z.)

1895 (16 Aug). No wmk. P 12.
29	13	1d. olive-green ..	..	15·00	22·00
		a. Bisected diagonally (½d.) (on cover)	..	†	£650
		b. Imperf between (horiz pair)	..	—	£5500
30		2½d. rose	..	20·00	20·00
		a. Stop (flaw) after "POSTAGE"	..	60·00	60·00
31		5d. blue	..	14·00	38·00
		a. Perf 12×11..	..	16·00	38·00
		b. Perf 11	..	£325	
32		7½d. orange-yellow	..	20·00	38·00
		a. Yellow	..	20·00	38·00

1895 (Sept). T 13 redrawn and surch. No wmk. P 12.
33	11	½d. on 2½d. vermilion ..	..	30·00	32·00
		a. "SURCHARCE"	..	70·00	
		b. Stop after "POSTAGE"	..	75·00	
34		1d. on 2½d. vermilion ..	..	38·00	28·00
		a. Stop after "POSTAGE"	..	80·00	
35	12	7½d. on 2½d. vermilion	..	48·00	48·00
		a. Stop after "POSTAGE"	..	90·00	

In the ½d. surcharge there is a stop after "SURCHARGE" and not after "PENNY". In the 1d. and 7½d. the stop is after the value only.

1896 (May). Nos. 26a and 28a with typewritten surcharge "Half-Penny-", in violet, and Tongan surcharge, in black, as T 14.
A. Tongan surch reading downwards (right panes)
B. Tongan surch reading upwards (left panes)

				A		B	
36	6	½d. on 1½d. on 2d.	..	£275		—	£250
		a. Perf 12	..	£250	£250	£275	£275
		ab. "Haalf" ..		†			£1000
		c. "H" double	..		†		
		d. Tongan surch omitted	..		†		£2500
37		½d. on 7½d. on 2d.	..	55·00	80·00	55·00	80·00
		a. "Hafl" for "Half"	..	£750	£800		†
		b. "Hafl" ("Penny" omitted)	£1100		—		†
		c. "PPenny"	..	£400		—		†
		d. Stops instead of hyphens	£500		—	£550	—
		e. "Halyf"	..	†		—		
		f. "Half-Penny-" inverted	..	£1200		—	£1600	—
		g. No hyphen after "Penny"	—		—		†
		h. "Hwlf"	..	†		—		
		i. No hyphen after "Half" ..		†		£500	
		j. "Penny" double	..	†		—		
		k. "Penny" twice, with "Half" on top of upper "Penny"	..	†		£1200	
		l. Capital "P" over small "p"	—		—		†
		m. Perf 12	..	£425		—	£425	—
		ma. No hyphen after "Half"	..		†		—
		mb. Tongan surch double	..		—		£1300

Nos. 26a and 28a were in sheets of 48 (2 panes 6×4). The panes were separated before the surcharges were applied. There are variations in the relative positions of the words "Half" and "Penny", both vertically and horizontally.

15 Arms

16 Ovava Tree, Kana-Kubolu

17 King George II

18 Prehistoric Trilith at Haamonga

19 Bread Fruit

20 Coral

21 View of Haapai

22 Red Shining Parrot

23 View of Vavau Harbour

I No sword hilt

II Top of hilt showing

---

24 Tortoises (upright)

WATERMARKS. Stamps with W 24 upright show all the tortoise heads pointing upwards, or downwards if inverted. On stamps with sideways watermark the heads point upwards or downwards alternately.

(Recess D.L.R.)

1897 (1 June). W 24. P 14.
38	15	½d. indigo	..	2·00	2·25
		a. Wmk sideways	..	70	90
39	16	1d. black and scarlet	..	80	60
		a. Wmk sideways	..	3·75	2·25
40	17	2d. sepia and bistre (I)	..	8·00	2·75
		a. Wmk sideways	..	60·00	7·00
41		2d. sepia and bistre (II)	..	40·00	6·50
		a. Wmk sideways	..	14·00	2·25
42		2d. grey and bistre (II) ..	..	6·00	85
		a. Wmk sideways	..	4·00	85
43		2½d. black and blue	..	4·00	70
		a. No fraction bar in "½"	..	85·00	85·00
		b. Wmk sideways	..	2·50	1·00
		ba. No fraction bar in "½"	..	60·00	60·00
44	18	3d. black and yellow-green	..	2·75	3·25
		a. Wmk sideways	..	2·50	3·50
45	19	4d. green and purple	..	3·75	4·00
		a. Wmk sideways	..	4·00	4·25
46	17	5d. black and orange	..	22·00	9·50
		a. Wmk sideways			
47	20	6d. red ..	..	8·00	3·50
		a. Wmk sideways	..	7·50	3·25
48	17	7½d. black and green	..	8·00	18·00
		a. Centre inverted	..	£3500	
49		10d. black and lake	..	23·00	28·00
		a. Wmk sideways			
50		1s. black and red-brown	..	11·00	6·50
		a. No hyphen before "TAHA"	..	£140	£140
		b. Wmk sideways			
51	21	2s. black and ultramarine	..	50·00	55·00
		a. Wmk sideways	..	18·00	21·00
52	22	2s. 6d. deep purple	..	45·00	27·00
		a. Wmk sideways	..	60·00	38·00
53	23	5s. black and brown-red	..	42·00	38·00
		a. Wmk sideways	..	25·00	28·00
38/52			Set of 14	£160	£140

The 1d., 3d. and 4d. are known bisected and used for half their value.

T L
1 June. 1899.
(25)

26 Queen Salote

1899 (1 June). Royal Wedding. No. 39a optd with T 25 at "Star" Office, Auckland, N.Z.
54	16	1d. black and scarlet	..	25·00	50·00
		a. "1889" for "1899" (R. 8/1, 8/4)	..	£200	£300
		b. Wmk upright	..	35·00	65·00

The Letters "T L" stand for Taufa'ahau, the King's family name, and Lavinia, the bride.
No. 54 was overprinted from a setting of 30 (3×10) applied twice to the sheets of 60.

Queen Salote, 1918–65

Die I

Die II

(Recess D.L.R.)

1920–37. W 24 (sideways). P 14.
55	15	½d. yellow-green (1934)	..	30	90
		a. Wmk upright	..	6·00	7·50
56	26	1½d. grey-black (1935)	..	20	1·50
57		2d. slate-purple and violet	..	4·00	13·00
		a. Wmk upright	..	8·50	22·00
57b		2d. black and dull purple (Die I) (1924)	4·00	65	
		ba. Wmk upright			
		c. Die II (1937)	..	3·25	2·50

58	26	2½d. black and blue	3·75	22·00
59		2½d. bright ultramarine (1934)	75	40
60		5d. black and orange-vermilion	3·25	3·25
61		7½d. black and yellow-green	1·75	1·75
62		10d. black and lake	1·25	4·50
63		1s. black and red-brown	1·25	1·50
		a. Wmk upright	11·00	12·00
55/63		Set of 10	18·00	45·00

55/63 Optd/Perf "Specimen" .. Set of 9 £170

In Die II the ball of the "2" is larger and the word "PENI-E-UA" is re-engraved and slightly shorter; the "U" has a spur on the left side.

TWO PENCE

TWO PENCE

PENI-E-UA (27)   **PENI-E-UA** (28)

1923 (20 Oct)–24. *Nos. 46, 48/9, 50, 51/2 and 53a surch as T 27 (vert stamps) or 28 (horiz stamps).*

64	17	2d. on 5d. black and orange (B.)	65	85
		a. Wmk sideways	2·00	2·25
65		2d. on 7½d. black and green (B.)	12·00	20·00
		a. Wmk sideways	23·00	32·00
66		2d. on 10d. black and lake (B.)	4·75	26·00
		a. Wmk sideways	13·00	40·00
67		2d. on 1s. black and red-brown (B.)	25·00	22·00
		a. No hyphen before "TAHA"	£275	
		b. Wmk sideways	35·00	35·00
68	21	2d. on 2s. black and ultramarine (R.)	8·00	10·00
		a. Wmk sideways	4·25	4·50
69	22	2d. on 2s. 6d. deep purple (R.)	20·00	6·50
		a. Wmk sideways	60·00	28·00
70	23	2d. on 5s. black and brown-red (R.)	4·00	4·50
		a. Wmk sideways	2·00	2·50
64/70		Set of 7	60·00	75·00

29 Queen Salote

(Recess D.L.R.)

1938 (12 Oct). *20th Anniv of Queen Salote's Accession. Tablet at foot dated "1918–1938". W 24. P 14.*

71	29	1d. black and scarlet	55	2·25
72		2d. black and purple	4·50	1·50
73		2½d. black and ultramarine	4·50	2·25
71/3		Set of 3	8·50	5·50

71/3 Perf "Specimen" .. Set of 3 65·00

For Silver Jubilee issue in a similar design, see Nos. 83/87.

Die III

(Recess D.L.R.)

1942–49. *Wmk Mult Script CA (sideways on 5s.). P 14.*

74	15	½d. yellow-green	15	75
75	16	1d. black and scarlet	30	75
76	26	2d. black and purple (Die II)	40	50
		a. Die III (4.49)	3·50	5·50
77		2½d. bright ultramarine	15	40
78	18	3d. black and yellow-green	15	30
79	20	6d. red	30	60
80	26	1s. black and red-brown	30	1·25
81	22	2s. 6d. deep purple	14·00	17·00
82	23	5s. black and brown-red	15·00	29·00
74/82		Set of 9	28·00	45·00

74/82 Perf "Specimen" .. Set of 9 £170

In Die III the foot of the "2" is longer than in Die II and extends towards the right beyond the curve of the loop; the letters of "PENI-E-UA" are taller and differently shaped.

30

(Recess D.L.R.)

1944 (25 Jan). *Silver Jubilee of Queen Salote's Accession. As T 29, but inscr "1918–1943" at foot, as T 30. Wmk Mult Script CA. P 14.*

83		1d. black and carmine	15	20
84		2d. black and purple	15	20
85		3d. black and green	15	20
86		6d. black and orange	20	55
87		1s. black and brown	20	55
83/7		Set of 5	75	1·50

83/7 Perf "Specimen" .. Set of 5 70·00

1949 (10 Oct). *75th Anniv of U.P.U. As Nos. 145/8 of Jamaica.*

88		2½d. ultramarine	30	15
89		3d. olive	40	1·25
90		6d. carmine-red	40	30
91		1s. red-brown	40	35
88/91		Set of 4	1·40	1·90

31 Queen Salote   33

32 Queen Salote

(Photo Waterlow)

1950 (1 Nov). *Queen Salote's Fiftieth Birthday. Wmk Mult Script CA. P 12½.*

92	31	1d. carmine	30	45
93	32	5d. green	30	45
94	33	1s. violet	30	1·10
92/4		Set of 3	80	1·75

34 Map   35 Palace, Nuku'alofa

(Recess Waterlow)

1951 (2 July). *50th Anniv of Treaty of Friendship between Great Britain and Tonga. T 34/5 and similar designs. Wmk Mult Script CA. P 12½ (3d.), 13 × 13½ (½d.), 13½ × 13 (others).*

95		½d. green	20	70
96		1d. black and carmine	10	40
97		2½d. green and brown	30	70
98		3d. yellow and bright blue	50	70
99		5d. carmine and green	40	40
100		1s. yellow-orange and violet	45	40
95/100		Set of 6	1·75	3·00

Designs: *Horiz*—2½d. Beach scene; 5d. Flag; 1s. Arms of Tonga and G.B. *Vert*—3d. H.M.N.Z.S. *Bellona.*

40 Royal Palace, Nuku'alofa   43 Swallows' Cave, Vava'u

52 Queen Salote   53 Arms of Tonga

(Des J. Berry. Centre litho, frame recess (£1), recess (others) B.W.)

1953 (1 July). *T 40, 43, 52/3 and similar designs. W 24. P 11 × 11½ (vert) or 11½ × 11 (horiz).*

101		1d. black and red-brown	10	10
102		1½d. blue and emerald	10	10
103		2d. deep turquoise-green and black	50	10
104		3d. blue and deep bluish green	20	10
105		3½d. yellow and carmine-red	30	60
106		4d. yellow and deep rose-carmine	45	10
107		5d. blue and red-brown	30	10
108		6d. black and deep blue	30	30
109		8d. emerald and deep reddish violet	50	40
110		1s. blue and black	50	10
111		2s. sage-green and brown	60	60
112		5s. orange-yellow and slate-lilac	14·00	5·50
113		10s. yellow and black	5·50	5·50
114		£1 yellow, scarlet, ultramarine & dp brt bl	8·00	6·50
101/14		Set of 14	28·00	18·00

Designs: *Horiz (as T 40)*—1½d. Shore fishing with throw-net; 2d. *Hifofua and Aoniu;* 4d. Vava'u Harbour; 5d. Post Office, Nuku'alofa; 6d. Aerodrome, Fua'amotu; 8d. Nuku'alofa wharf; 2s. Lifuka, Ha'apai; 5s. Mutiny of the *Bounty. Vert (as T 43)*—1s. Map of Tonga Islands.

54 Stamp of 1886   55 Whaling Ship and Whaleboat

(Des D. M. Bakeley. Photo Harrison)

1961 (1 Dec). *75th Anniv of Tongan Postal Service. T 54/5 and similar horiz designs. W 24. P 14½ × 13½.*

115		1d. carmine and brown-orange	10	10
116		2d. ultramarine	20	10
117		4d. blue-green	10	10
118		5d. violet	25	10
119		1s. red-brown	25	10
115/19		Set of 5	80	30

Designs:—4d. Queen Salote and Post Office, Nuku'alofa; 5d. *Aoniu II* (inter-island freighter); 1s. Mailplane over Tongatapu.

1862
TAU'ATĀINA
EMANCIPATION
1962
(59)   60 "Protein Foods"

1962 (7 Feb). *Centenary of Emancipation. Nos. 101, 104, 107/10, 112, 117 optd with T 59 (No. 126 surch also), in red, by R. S. Wallbank, Govt Printer.*

120		1d. black and red-brown	10	10
121		4d. blue-green	10	15
122		5d. blue and red-brown	15	15
123		6d. black and deep blue	20	20
124		8d. emerald and deep reddish violet	40	30
125		1s. blue and black	20	20
		a. Opt inverted	£350	£190
126		2s. on 3d. blue and deep bluish green	40	65
		a. Missing fraction-bar in surch	10·00	
127		5s. orange-yellow and slate-lilac	1·50	1·10
		a. Opt inverted	£180	£250
120/127		Set of 8	2·75	2·50

(Des M. Goaman. Photo Harrison)

1963 (4 June). *Freedom from Hunger. W 24. P 14 × 14½.*

128	60	11d. ultramarine	30	15

61 Coat of Arms

62 Queen Salote

63 Queen Salote

(Des Ida West. Die-cut Walsall)

1963 (17 June). *First Polynesian Gold Coinage Commemoration. Circular designs. Embossed on gold foil, backed with paper, inscr overall "TONGA THE FRIENDLY ISLANDS". Imperf.*

(a) Postage. ¼ koula coin. Diameter 1⅝ in.

129	61	1d. carmine	..	10	10
130	62	2d. deep blue	..	10	10
131	61	6d. blue-green	..	15	15
132	62	9d. bright purple	..	15	15
133	61	1s. 6d. violet	..	20	25
134	62	2s. light emerald	..	25	30

(b) Air. (i) ½ koula coin. Diam 2⅛ in.

135	63	10d. carmine	..	20	20
136	61	11d. blue-green	..	20	20
137	63	1s. 1d. deep blue	..	20	20

(ii) 1 koula coin. Diam 3⅛ in.

138	63	2s. 1d. bright purple	..	30	30
139	61	2s. 4d. light emerald	..	35	35
140	63	2s. 9d. violet	..	35	40
129/140 *and* O17			*Set of* 13	5·50	7·50

Examples of a 9d. Postage value in the design of the 1s. 6d. exists, but these have been identified as proofs.

64 Red Cross Emblem

(Des V. Whiteley. Litho B.W.)

1963 (7 Oct). *Red Cross Centenary. W 24. P 13½.*

141	64	2d. red and black	..	10	10
142		11d. red and blue	..	20	20

65 Queen Salote

66 Map of Tongatapu

(Des M. Meers. Die-cut Walsall)

1964 (19 Oct). *Pan-Pacific South-East Asia Woman's Association Meeting, Nuku'alofa. Embossed on gold foil, backed with paper inscr overall "TONGA THE FRIENDLY ISLANDS". Imperf.*

(a) Postage

143	65	3d. pink	..	10	10
144		9d. light blue	..	10	10
145		2s. yellow-green	..	15	20
146		5s. lilac	..	35	40

(b) Air

147	66	10d. blue-green	..	10	10
148		1s. 2d. black	..	15	15
149		3s. 6d. cerise	..	20	25
150		6s. 6d. violet	..	40	50
143/150			*Set of* 8	1·40	1·60

(67)

1965 (18 Mar). *"Gold Coin" stamps of 1963 surch as T 67 by Walsall Lithographic Co. New figures of value in gold; obliterating colours shown in brackets. (a) Postage.*

151	61	1s. 3d. on 1s. 6d. violet (R.)		15	15
152	62	1s. 9d. on 9d. bright purple (W.)		15	20
153	61	2s. 6d. on 6d. blue-green (R.)		20	35
154		5s. on 1d. carmine		14·00	17·00
155	62	5s. on 2d. deep blue	..	2·50	3·25
156		5s. on 2s. light emerald		60	75

(b) Air

157	63	2s. 3d. on 10d. carmine	..	15	25
158	61	2s. 9d. on 11d. blue-green (W.)	..	20	35
159	63	4s. 6d. on 2s. 1d. bright purple (R.)	..	10·00	13·00
160	61	4s. 6d. on 2s. 4d. light emerald (R.)		10·00	13·00
161	63	4s. 6d. on 2s. 9d. violet (R.)	..	7·00	8·00
151/161 *and* O18		..	*Set of* 12	42·00	55·00

King Taufa'ahau IV, 16 December 1965

1866-1966
TUPOU COLLEGE
& SECONDARY
EDUCATION

(68)

AIRMAIL
1866 CENTENARY 1966
TUPOU COLLEGE
&
SECONDARY EDUCATION
10d   **XX**

(69)

1966 (18 June). *Centenary of Tupou College and Secondary Education. Nos. 115/16 and 118/19 optd or surch. (a) Postage. As T* **68.**

162		1d. carmine and brown-orange (P.)	..	10	10
163		3d. on 1d. carmine and brown-orange (P.)		10	10
		a. Misplaced "3d" (R. 2/5)	..	2·00	
164		6d. on 2d. ultramarine (R.)	..	10	10
165		1s. 2d. on 2d. ultramarine (R.)	..	10	10
166		2s. on 2d. ultramarine (R.)	..	15	15
167		3s. on 2d. ultramarine (R.)	..	15	15

(b) Air. As T **69**

168		5d. violet	..	10	10
169		10d. on 1d. carmine and brown-orange		10	10
170		1s. red-brown	..	10	10
171		2s. 9d. on 2d. ultramarine	..	15	15
		a. Sideways second "X" (R. 3/4)	..	7·00	
172		3s. 6d. on 5d. violet	..	15	15
		a. Sideways second "X" (R. 3/4)	..	7·00	
173		4s. 6d. on 1s. red-brown	..	20	15
		a. Sideways second "X" (R. 3/4)	..	7·00	
162/173 *and* O19/20			*Set of* 14	2·00	1·75

On No. 163a the "d" is 20 mm from the "X" instead of the normal 22 mm.

(70)

(71)

1966 (16 Dec). *Queen Salote Commemoration. "Women's Association" stamps of 1964 optd as T* **70/1,** *or surch also, by Walsall Lithographic Co. Inscriptions and new figures of value in first colour and obliterating shapes in second colour given.*

(a) Postage. Optd as T **70**

174	65	3d. (silver and ultramarine)	..	10	10
175		5d. on 9d. (silver and black)	..	10	10
176		9d. (silver and black)	..	15	10
177		1s. 7d. on 3d. (silver and ultramarine)	..	20	15
178		3s. 6d. on 9d. (silver and black)	..	35	20
179		6s. 6d. on 3d. (silver and ultramarine)	..	60	30

(b) Air. Optd as T **71**

180	66	10d. (silver and black)	..	10	10
181		1s. 2d. (black and gold)	..	15	10
182		4s. on 10d. (silver and black)	..	40	20
183		5s. 6d. on 1s. 2d. (black and gold)	..	55	30
184		10s. 6d. on 1s. 2d. (gold and black)	..	75	45
174/184			*Set of* 11	3·00	1·75

(New Currency. 100 seniti = 1 pa'anga)

10
Seniti

1 SENITI 1   **10**

(72)   (73)

1967 (25 Mar). *Decimal currency. Various stamps surch as T* **72/3.**

185		1 s. on 1d. (No. 101)		..	10	10
186		2 s. on 4d. (No. 106)		..	10	10
187		3 s. on 5d. (No. 107)		..	10	10
188		4 s. on 5d. (No. 107)		..	30	30
189		5 s. on 3½d. (No. 105)		..	10	10
190		6 s. on 8d. (No. 109)		..	10	10
191		7 s. on 1½d. (No. 102)		..	10	10
192		8 s. on 6d. (No. 108)		..	10	10
193		9 s. on 3d. (No. 104)		..	15	15
194		10 s. on 1s. (No. 110)		..	15	15
195		11 s. on 3d. on 1d. (No. 163)		..	15	20
		a. Misplaced "3d" (R. 2/5)			2·50	
196		21 s. on 3s. on 2d. (No. 167)		..	25	35
197		23 s. on 1d. (No. 101)		..	25	35
198		30 s. on 2s. (No. 111)* (R.)		..	1·25	1·75
199		30 s. on 2s. (No. 111)* (R.)		..	1·50	2·00
200		50 s. on 6d. (No. 108) (R.)		..	85	1·25
201		60 s. on 2d. (No. 103) (R.)		..	1·25	1·75
185/201 *and* O21				*Set of* 18	7·50	10·00

The above surcharges come in a variety of types and sizes. *No. 198 has the surcharged value expressed horizontally; No. 199 has the figures "30" above and below "SENITI".

74 Coat of Arms (reverse)

75 King Taufa'ahau IV (obverse)

(Die-cut Walsall)

1967 (4 July). *Coronation of King Taufa'ahau IV. Circular designs. Embossed on palladium foil, backed with paper inscr overall "The Friendly Islands Tonga", etc. Imperf.*

Sizes

(a) Diameter 1½ *in.*	*(d) Diameter* 2³/₁₀ *in.*
(b) Diameter 1⁷/₁₀ *in.*	*(e) Diameter* 2⁷/₁₀ *in.*
(c) Diameter 2 *in.*	*(f) Diameter* 2⁹/₁₀ *in.*

(a) Postage

202	74	1 s. orange and greenish blue (b)		10	10
203	75	2 s. greenish blue and deep magenta (c)		10	10
204	74	4 s. emerald and bright purple (d)		10	10
205	75	15 s. turquoise and violet (e)	..	25	25
206	74	28 s. black and bright purple (a)	..	50	45
207	75	50 s. carmine-red and ultramarine (c)	..	85	70
208	74	1 p. blue and carmine (f)	..	1·50	1·40

(b) Air

209	75	7 s. carmine-red and black (b)	..	10	10
210	74	9 s. brown-purple and emerald (c)	..	10	10
211	75	11 s. greenish blue and orange (d)	..	15	15
212	74	21 s. black and emerald (e)	..	30	30
213	75	23 s. bright purple and light emerald (a)		40	35
214	74	29 s. ultramarine and emerald (c)	..	50	45
215	75	2 p. bright purple and orange (f)	..	2·00	1·50
202/15			*Set of* 14	6·00	5·50

The commemorative coins depicted in reverse (Type 74) are inscribed in various denominations as follows: 1 s.—"20 SENITI"; 4 s.—"PA'ANGA"; 9 s.—"50 SENITI"; 21 s.—"TWO PA'ANGA"; 28 s.—"QUARTER HAU"; 29 s.—"HALF HAU"; 1 p. "HAU".

The
Friendly Islands
welcome the
United States
Peace Corps

S

(76)

1967 (15 Dec). *Arrival of U.S. Peace Corps in Tonga. As Nos. 101/14, but imperf in different colours and surch as T* **76**.

(a) Postage.

216	1 s. on 1d. black and orange-yellow.		10	10
217	2 s. on 2d. ultramarine and carmine-red		10	10
218	3 s. on 3d. chestnut and yellow		10	10
219	4 s. on 4d. reddish violet and yellow		10	10
220	5 s. on 5d. green and yellow..		10	10
221	10 s. on 1s. carmine-red and yellow		10	10
222	20 s. on 2s. claret and new blue		15	15
223	50 s. on 5s. sepia and orange-yellow..		30	35
224	1 p. on 10s. orange-yellow		50	55

(b) Air

225	11 s. on 3½d. ultramarine (R.)		10	10
226	21 s. on 1½d. emerald		20	20
227	23 s. on 3½d. ultramarine		20	20
216/27 *and* O26/8		*Set of 15*	2·75	3·00

On Nos. 219 and 224 the opt is smaller, and in four lines instead of five. On Nos. 216/20 the surcharge takes the form of an alteration to the currency name as in T **76**.

(77) (78)

1968 (6 Apr). *Various stamps surch as T* **77/8**.

(a) Postage

228	1 s. on 1d. (No. 101) (R.)		10	10
229	2 s. on 4d. (No. 106)..		10	10
230	3 s. on 3d. (No. 104) (B.)		10	10
231	4 s. on 5d. (No. 107) (R.)		10	10
232	5 s. on 2d. (No. 103) (R.)		10	10
233	6 s. on 6d. (No. 108) (R.)		10	10
234	7 s. on 1½d. (No. 102) (R.)		10	10
235	8 s. on 8d. (No. 109) (R.)		10	10
236	9 s. on 3½d. (No. 105)		20	20
237	10 s. on 1s. (No. 110) (R.)		20	20
238	20 s. on 5s. (No. 112) (R.)		40	40
239	2 p. on 2s. (No. 111) (R.)		1·50	1·50

(b) Air. Surch as T **78** *with* "AIRMAIL" *added*

240	11 s. on 10s. (No. 113) (R.)		25	25
241	21 s. on 10s. (No. 113) (R.)		40	40
242	23 s. on 10s. (No. 113) (R.)		40	40
228/42 *and* O22/5		*Set of 19*	6·50	6·50

Friendly Islands
Field & Track Trials
South Pacific Games
Port Moresby
1969

(79) (80)

1968 (4 July). *50th Birthday of King Taufa'ahua IV. Nos. 202/15 optd as T* **79**. *(a) Postage.*

243	**74**	1 s. orange and greenish blue (b) (R.)		10	10
244	**75**	2 s. greenish blue & dp magenta (b) (B.)		10	10
245	**74**	4 s. emerald and bright purple (d) (R.)		10	10
246	**75**	15 s. turquoise and violet (e) (B.)..		25	15
247	**74**	28 s. black and bright purple (a) (R.)		55	30
248	**75**	50 s. carmine-red and ultramarine (c) (B.)		1·00	60
249	**74**	1 p. blue and carmine (f) (R.)		2·25	1·50

(b) Air

250	**75**	7 s. carmine-red and black (b) (B.)		10	10
251	**74**	9 s. brown-purple and emerald (c) (R.)		15	10
252	**75**	11 s. greenish blue and orange (d) (B.)		15	10
253	**74**	21 s. black and emerald (e) (R.)		40	25
		a. Opt (gold only) double		£275	
254	**75**	23 s. bright purple & lt emerald (a) (B.)		40	25
255	**74**	29 s. ultramarine and emerald (c) (R.)		65	35
256	**75**	2 p. bright purple and orange (f) (B.)		4·50	2·75
243/56 *and* O29/32			*Set of 18*	17·00	11·00

The overprints vary in size, but all crescent-shaped as Type **79** and inscribed "H.M'S BIRTHDAY 4 JULY 1968" (Type **79**) or "HIS MAJESTY'S 50th BIRTHDAY" (others).

1968 (19 Dec). *South Pacific Games Field and Track Trials, Port Moresby, New Guinea. Nos. 101/14, but imperf, in different colours and surch as T* **80**. *(a) Postage.*

257	5 s. on 5d. green and yellow (R.)		10	10
258	10 s. on 1s. carmine-red and yellow		10	10
259	15 s. on 2s. claret and new blue		15	15
260	25 s. on 2d. ultramarine and carmine-red		15	15
261	50 s. on 1d. black and orange-yellow..		30	30
262	75 s. on 10s. orange-yellow (G.)		45	45

(b) Air

263	6 s. on 6d. black and yellow*		10	10
264	7 s. on 4d. reddish violet and yellow		10	10
265	8 s. on 8d. black and greenish yellow		10	10
	a. Surch 11½ mm as on 6d.		† 90·00	
266	9 s. on 1½d. ultramarine		10	10
267	11 s. on 3d. chestnut and yellow		10	10
268	21 s. on 3½d. ultramarine		15	15
269	38 s. on 5s. sepia and orange-yellow..		20	20
270	1 p. on 10s. orange-yellow		50	50
257/70 *and* O33/4		*Set of 16*	2·75	2·75

*On No. 263 the surcharge is smaller (11½ mm wide).

(81) (82)

1969. *Emergency Provisionals. Various stamps (Nos. 273/6 are imperf and in different colours) surch as T* **81** *or* **82**. *(a) Postage.*

271	1 s. on 1s. 2d. on 2d. ultramarine (No. 165)		1·25	85
272	1 s. on 2s. on 2d. ultramarine (No. 166)		1·25	85
273	1 s. on 6d. black and yellow (as No. 108)		40	30
274	2 s. on 3½d. ultramarine (as No. 105)		45	30
275	3 s. on 1½d. emerald (as No. 102)		45	30
276	4 s. on 8d. blk & greenish yell (as No. 109)		70	50

(b) Air. Nos. 171/3 surch with T **82**

277	1 s. on 2s. 9d. on 2d. ultramarine		1·25	85
	a. Sideways second "X" (R. 3/4)		7·00	
278	1 s. on 3s. on 5d. violet		1·25	85
	a. Sideways second "X" (R. 3/4)		7·00	
279	1 s. on 4s. 6d. on 1s. red-brown		1·25	85
	a. Sideways second "X" (R. 3/4)		7·00	
271/9		*Set of 9*	7·50	5·00

SELF-ADHESIVE ISSUES. From No. 280 until No. 922 all stamps were manufactured by Walsall Security Printers Ltd and are self-adhesive. The backing paper is separated by roulette or perforations (from No. 780 onwards), and shows on its reverse the words *"TONGA where time begins"*, or, from No. 568 onwards, various texts or illustrations. This also applies to the Official stamps.

83 Banana

1969 (21 Apr). *Coil stamps.*

280	**83**	1 s. scarlet, black and greenish yellow		50	50
281		2 s. brt green, black & greenish yellow		60	60
282		3 s. violet, black and greenish yellow		70	70
283		4 s. ultramarine, black & greenish yell		80	80
284		5 s. bronze-green, black & greenish yell		90	90
280/4			*Set of 5*	3·25	3·25

Nos. 280/4 were produced in rolls of 200, each even stamp having a number applied to the front of the backing paper, with the usual inscription on the reverse.
See also Nos. 325/9, 413/17 and 675/89.

84 Putting the Shot 86 Oil Derrick and Map

1969 (13 Aug). *Third South Pacific Games, Port Moresby. T* **84** *and similar design. (a) Postage.*

285	**84**	1 s. black, red and buff		10	10
286		3 s. bright green, red and buff		10	10
287		6 s. blue, red and buff		10	10
288		10 s. bluish violet, red and buff		10	10
289		30 s. blue, red and buff		15	20

(b) Air

290	—	9 s. black, violet and orange		10	10
291	—	11 s. black, ultramarine and orange		10	10
292	—	20 s. black, bright green and orange		15	15
293	—	60 s. black, cerise and orange		45	55
294	—	1 p. black, blue-green and orange		70	80
285/94 *and* O35/6			*Set of 12*	2·75	3·25

Design:—9, 11, 20, 60 s., 1 p. Boxing.

1969 (23 Dec). *First Oil Search in Tonga. T* **86** *and similar vert design.*

(a) Postage

295	**86**	3 s. multicoloured		10	10
296		7 s. multicoloured		15	15
297		20 s. multicoloured		40	40
298		25 s. multicoloured		45	45
299		35 s. multicoloured		70	70

(b) Air

300	—	9 s. multicoloured		20	20
301	—	10 s. multicoloured		20	20
302	—	24 s. multicoloured		45	45
303	—	29 s. multicoloured		50	50
304	—	38 s. multicoloured		70	70
295/304 *and* O37/8			*Set of 12*	7·50	7·00

Design:—Nos. 300/4, Oil derrick and island of Tongatapu.

87 Members of the British and Tongan Royal Families

1970 (7 Mar). *Royal Visit. T* **87** *and similar design. Multicoloured.*

(a) Postage

305	**87**	3 s. multicoloured		20	10
306		5 s. multicoloured		25	10
307		10 s. multicoloured		40	20
308		25 s. multicoloured		1·00	55
309		50 s. multicoloured		1·75	1·00

(b) Air

310	—	7 s. multicoloured		35	15
311	—	9 s. multicoloured		40	20
312	—	24 s. multicoloured		1·00	55
313	—	29 s. multicoloured		1·25	60
314	—	38 s. multicoloured		1·50	80
305/14 *and* O39/41			*Set of 13*	17·00	10·00

Design:—Nos. 310/14, Queen Elizabeth II and King Taufu'ahau Tupou IV.

89 Book, Tongan Rulers and Flag

1970 (4 June). *Entry into British Commonwealth. T* **89** *and similar design. (a) Postage.*

315	**89**	3 s. multicoloured		10	10
316		7 s. multicoloured		15	15
317		15 s. multicoloured		25	20
318		25 s. multicoloured		35	25
319		50 s. multicoloured		60	50

(b) Air

320	—	9 s. turquoise-blue, gold and scarlet		15	15
321	—	10 s. bright purple, gold and greenish blue		15	15
322	—	24 s. olive-yellow, gold and green		35	35
323	—	29 s. new blue, gold and orange-red		40	30
324	—	38 s. deep orange-yellow, gold & brt emer		50	40
315/24 *and* O42/4			*Set of 13*	5·00	4·50

Design: "Star" shaped (44 × 51 mm)—Nos. 320/4, King Taufa'ahau Tupou IV.

90 Coconut

1970 (9 June). *Coil stamps. (a) As T* **83** *but colours changed.*

325	**83**	1 s. greenish yellow, bright purple & blk		20	20
326		2 s. greenish yellow, ultramarine & black		30	30
327		3 s. greenish yellow, chocolate and black		30	30
328		4 s. greenish yellow, emerald and black		30	30
329		5 s. greenish yellow, orge-red & bl		35	35

(b) T **90**. *Multicoloured; colour of face value given*

330	**90**	6 s. rose-carmine		40	40
331		7 s. bright purple		45	45
332		8 s. bluish violet		55	55
333		9 s. turquoise		65	65
334		10 s. pale orange		65	65
325/34			*Set of 10*	3·75	3·75

Nos. 325/34 and O45/54 were produced in rolls of 200, each even stamp having a number applied to the front of the backing paper, with the usual inscription on the reverse.

MINIMUM PRICE

The minimum price quote is 10p which represents a handling charge rather than a basis for valuing common stamps. For further notes about prices see introductory pages.

91 "Red Cross"

(Litho (postage) or litho and die-stamped (air))

1970 (17 Oct). *Centenary of British Red Cross. T* **91** *and similar "cross" shaped design.* (a) *Postage.*

335	91	3 s. vermilion, black and light green		10	10
336		7 s. vermilion, black and ultramarine	..	15	15
337		15 s. vermilion and bright purple		30	30
338		25 s. vermilion, black and turquoise-blue		50	50
339		75 s. vermilion and deep red-brown	..	3·50	3·50

(b) *Air*

340	–	9 s. vermilion and silver..	..	20	20
341	–	10 s. vermilion and bright purple	..	20	20
342	–	15 s. vermilion and green..	..	35	35
343	–	38 s. vermilion and ultramarine ..	..	1·75	1·75
344	–	1 p. vermilion and turquoise-blue	..	4·50	4·50
335/44 *and* O55/7			*Set of 13*	17·00	17·00

Design: As *T* **91**—Nos. 340/4 as Nos. 335/9 but with inscription rearranged and coat of arms omitted.
On Nos. 335/6 and 338 the black colour is produced as a composite of the other two colours used.

(92)

(93)

1971 (30 Jan). *Fifth Death Anniv of Queen Salote. Nos. 174/84 surch as T* **92**/3. *Obliterating shapes in black; inscriptions and figures of value in colour given.* (a) *Postage. Surch as T* **92**.

345	65	2 s. on 5d. on 9d. (silver)..		10	10
346		3 s. on 9d. (orange-red)	..	10	10
347		5 s. on 3d. (bright green)..	..	15	15
348		15 s. on 3s. 6d. on 9d. (orange-brown)		45	45
		a. Surch double	..	—	30·00
349		25 s. on 6s. 6d. on 3d. (purple)	..	80	65
350		50 s. on 1s. 7d. on 3d. (gold)	..	1·75	1·25

(b) *Air. Surch as T* **93**

351	66	9 s. on 10d. (silver)	..	30	20
352		24 s. on 4s. on 10d. (orange-brown)		80	60
353		29 s. on 5s. 6d. on 1s. 2d. (orange-red)	..	90	80
354		38 s. on 10s. 6d. on 1s. 2d. (bright green)		1·40	1·00
345/54 *and* O58/61			*Set of 14*	15·00	11·50

HONOURING
JAPANESE
POSTAL
CENTENARY
1871-1971

3s ■

PHILATOKYO '71

(94)

15s ■

(95)

1971 (17 Apr). *"Philatokyo 1971" Stamp Exhibition. As Nos. 101/2, 106 and 109/11, but imperf, colours changed and surch as T* **94** *(Nos. 355/6, 358/61 and 363), as T* **95** *(Nos. 357, 362) or with similar surcharge in four lines (No. 364).* (a) *Postage.*

355		3 s. on 8d. blk & greenish yellow (Blk. & R.)	10	10
356		7 s. on 4d. reddish violet & yellow (Blk. & R.)	10	10
357		15 s. on 1s. carmine, red and yellow	..	20	20
358		25 s. on 3s. black & orange-yellow (Blk. & R.)	30	30
359		75 s. on 2s. claret & new blue (Blk. & R.)	85	85

(b) *Air. Additionally surch "AIRMAIL"*

360		9 s. on 1½d. emerald (Blk. and R.)	..	10	10
361		10 s. on 4d. reddish violet & yellow (Blk. & R.)	10	10
362		18 s. on 1s. carmine-red and yellow (V.)	..	20	20
363		38 s. on 1d. black & orange-yellow (Blk. & R.)	40	40
364		1 p. on 2s. claret and new blue		1·00	1·00
355/64 *and* O62/4	..		*Set of 13*	5·50	5·50

AIRMAIL
14s

96 Wristwatch

97 Pole-vaulter

1971 (20 July)–**72**. *Air. Backed with paper bearing advertisements.*

365	96	14 s. multicoloured	..	..	65	65
365a		17 s. multicoloured (20.7.72)	..	..	75	75
366		21 s. multicoloured	..	..	85	85
366a		38 s. multicoloured (20.7.72)	..	1·40	1·40
365/6a *and* O65/6a	..	..		*Set of 8*	6·50	6·50

1971 (20 July). *Fourth South Pacific Games, Tahiti. T* **97** *and similar design.* (a) *Postage.*

367	97	3 s. multicoloured	..	..	10	10
368		7 s. multicoloured	..	..	10	10
369		15 s. multicoloured	..	..	15	15
370		25 s. multicoloured	..	..	25	30
371		50 s. multicoloured	..	..	40	60

(b) *Air*

372	–	9 s. multicoloured	..	..	10	10
373	–	10 s. multicoloured	..	..	10	10
374	–	24 s. multicoloured	..	..	25	30
375	–	29 s. multicoloured	..	..	30	40
376	–	38 s. multicoloured	..	..	35	50
367/76 *and* O67/9	..		*Set of 13*	3·50	5·00

Design: *Horiz*—Nos. 372/6, High-jumper.

98 Medal of Merit
(reverse)

99 Child

1971 (30 Oct). *Investiture of Royal Tongan Medal of Merit. T* **98** *and similar "medal" shaped design. Multicoloured; colour of medal given.*

(a) *Postage*

377	98	3 s. gold	..	..	10	10
378		24 s. silver..	..	..	20	20
379		38 s. brown	..	..	30	30

(b) *Air*

380	–	10 s. gold	..	..	15	15
381	–	75 s. silver..	..	..	65	65
382	98	1 p. brown	..	..	75	75
377/82 *and* O70/2		*Set of 9*	3·75	3·75

Design: As *T* **98**—Nos. 379/81, Obverse of the Medal of Merit.

1971 (31 Dec). *25th Anniv of UNICEF. T* **99** *and similar design.*

(a) *Postage*

383	99	2 s. multicoloured	..	..	10	10
384		4 s. multicoloured	..	..	10	10
385		8 s. multicoloured	..	..	10	10
386		16 s. multicoloured	..	..	20	20
387		30 s. multicoloured	..	..	30	30

(b) *Air*

388	–	10 s. multicoloured	..	..	15	15
389	–	15 s. multicoloured	..	..	20	20
390	–	25 s. multicoloured	..	..	30	30
391	–	50 s. multicoloured	..	..	60	60
392	–	1 p. multicoloured	..	..	1·25	1·25
383/92 *and* O73/5		*Set of 13*	5·50	5·50

Design: *Vert* (21 x 42 *mm*)—Nos. 388/92, Woman.

PRICES OF SETS

Set prices are given for many issues, generally those containing three stamps or more. Definitive sets include one of each value or major colour change, but do not cover different perforations, die types or minor shades. Where a choice is possible the set prices are based on the cheapest versions of the stamps included in the listings.

100 Map of South Pacific, and *Olovaha*

1972 (14 Apr). *Merchant Marine Routes. T* **100** *and similar design.*

(a) *Postage*

393	100	2 s. multicoloured	..	..	15	10
394		10 s. multicoloured	..	..	30	10
395		17 s. multicoloured	..	..	50	20
396		21 s. multicoloured	..	..	60	25
397		60 s. multicoloured	..	..	2·50	1·50

(b) *Air*

398	–	9 s. multicoloured	..	..	30	10
399	–	12 s. multicoloured	..	..	35	10
400	–	14 s. multicoloured	..	..	40	15
401	–	75 s. multicoloured	..	..	2·75	1·75
402	–	90 s. multicoloured	..	..	3·25	2·50
393/402 *and* O76/8	..		*Set of 13*	16·00	10·00

Design:—Nos. 398/402, Map of South Pacific and *Niuvakai*.

101 ¼ Hau Coronation Coin

1972 (15 July). *Fifth Anniv of Coronation. T* **101** *and similar design.*

(a) *Postage*

403	101	5 s. multicoloured	..	..	10	10
404		7 s. multicoloured	..	..	10	10
405		10 s. multicoloured	..	..	15	10
406		17 s. multicoloured	..	..	25	15
407		60 s. multicoloured	..	..	85	40

(b) *Air*

408	–	9 s. multicoloured	..	..	15	10
409	–	12 s. multicoloured	..	..	20	10
410	–	14 s. multicoloured	..	..	25	15
411	–	17 s. multicoloured	..	..	30	15
412	–	75 s. multicoloured	..	..	1·10	45
403/12 *and* O79/81		*Set of 13*	7·00	3·50

Design (47 × 41 *mm*):—Nos. 408/12, as T **101**, but with coins above inscription instead of beneath it.

102 Water Melon

1972 (30 Sept). *Coil stamps.* (a) *As T* **83**, *but inscription altered, omitting "Best in the Pacific", and colours changed.*

413	83	1 s. light yellow, scarlet and black	..	20	10
414		2 s. light yellow, ultramarine and black	25	15
415		3 s. light yellow, yellow-green and black	30	20
416		4 s. light yellow, royal blue and black	..	30	20
417		5 s. light yellow, reddish brn & bl	..	30	20

(b) *As T* **90** *but colours changed. Colour of face value given*

418	90	6 s. dull orange ..	..	..	30	20
419		7 s. ultramarine	..	..	35	25
420		8 s. bright magenta	..	..	35	25
421		9 s. brown-orange	..	..	35	25
422		10 s. bright new blue	..	..	40	30

(c) *T* **102**. *Colour of face value given*

423	102	15 s. new blue	..	..	70	45
424		20 s. reddish orange	..	..	85	60
425		25 s. chocolate	..	..	90	70
426		40 s. yellow-orange	..	..	2·00	1·50
427		50 s. lemon	..	..	2·25	1·75
413/27			*Set of 15*	9·00	6·50

Nos. 413/27 and O82/96 were produced in rolls, each even stamp having a number applied to the front of the backing paper, with the usual inscription on the reverse.

■ **7s**

NOVEMBER 1972
INAUGURAL
Internal Airmail
Nuku'alofa — Vava'u
(103)

1972 (2 Nov). *Inaugural Internal Airmail. No. 398 surch with T* 103.
428   7 s. on 9 s. multicoloured   ..   ..   1·40   2·25

104 Hoisting Tongan Flag

1972 (9 Dec). *Proclamation of Sovereignty over Minerva Reefs. T* 104 *and similar design.* (a) *Postage.*
429   104   5 s. multicoloured   10   10
430   7 s. multicoloured   10   10
431   10 s. multicoloured   15   10
432   15 s. multicoloured   25   15
433   40 s. multicoloured   80   40

(b) *Air*
434   –   9 s. multicoloured   15   10
435   –   12 s. multicoloured   20   10
436   –   14 s. multicoloured   25   15
437   –   38 s. multicoloured   75   35
438   –   1 p. multicoloured   ..   ..   2·00   1·00
429/38 *and* O97/9   ..   *Set of* 13   8·00   4·25
Design: *Spherical* (52 *mm diameter*)—Nos. 434/8, Proclamation in Govt Gazette.

105 Coins around Bank

1973 (30 Mar). *Foundation of Bank of Tonga. T* 105 *and similar design.* (a) *Postage.*
439   105   5 s. multicoloured   10   10
440   7 s. multicoloured   10   10
441   10 s. multicoloured   15   10
442   20 s. multicoloured   25   15
443   30 s. multicoloured   35   25

(b) *Air*
444   –   9 s. multicoloured   20   10
445   –   12 s. multicoloured   20   10
446   –   17 s. multicoloured   25   15
447   –   50 s. multicoloured   80   40
448   –   90 s. multicoloured   ..   ..   1·50   90
439/48 *and* O100/2   ..   *Set of* 13   7·50   4·25
Design: *Horiz* (64 × 52 *mm*)—Nos. 444/8, Bank and banknotes.

106 Handshake and Scout in Outrigger Canoe

1973 (29 June). *Silver Jubilee of Scouting in Tonga. T* 106 *and similar design.* (a) *Postage.*
449   106   5 s. multicoloured   20   10
450   7 s. multicoloured   30   15
451   15 s. multicoloured   95   40
452   21 s. multicoloured   ..   ..   1·25   50
453   50 s. multicoloured   ..   ..   4·50   2·00

(b) *Air*
454   –   9 s. multicoloured   50   25
455   –   12 s. multicoloured   60   30
456   –   14 s. multicoloured   85   50
457   –   17 s. multicoloured   95   60
458   –   1 p. multicoloured   ..   ..   15·00   6·00
449/58 *and* O103/5   ..   *Set of* 13   £110   45·00
Design: *Square* (53 × 53 *mm*)—Nos. 454/8, Scout badge.

107 Excerpt from Cook's Log-book

1973 (2 Oct). *Bicentenary of Capt. Cook's Visit to Tonga. T* 107 *and similar design.* (a) *Postage.*
459   107   6 s. multicoloured   30   20
460   8 s. multicoloured   30   25
461   11 s. multicoloured   50   30
462   35 s. multicoloured   ..   ..   3·50   1·60
463   40 s. multicoloured   ..   ..   3·50   1·60

(b) *Air*
464   –   9 s. multicoloured   60   25
465   –   14 s. multicoloured   ..   ..   1·00   30
466   –   29 s. multicoloured   ..   ..   3·50   1·50
467   –   38 s. multicoloured   ..   ..   4·00   1·75
468   –   75 s. multicoloured   ..   ..   7·50   3·00
459/68 *and* O106/8   ..   *Set of* 13   40·00   17·00
Design: *Vert*—Nos. 464/8, H.M.S. *Resolution.*

(108)   109 Red Shining Parrot

1973 (19 Dec). *Commonwealth Games, Christchurch, New Zealand. Various stamps optd as T* 108 (*No.* 474 *optd* "AIRMAIL" *in addition*). (a) *Postage.*
469   5 s. on 50 s. (No. 371) (Blk. and Gold)   15   10
470   12 s. on 38 s. (No. 379) (R. and Silver) .   30   15
471   14 s. on 75 s. (No. 381) (R. and Gold) . .   30   15
472   20 s. on 1 p. (No. 382) (Blk. and Gold) .   50   25
473   50 s. on 24 s. (No. 378) (Blk. and Silver)   1·25   65

(b) *Air*
474   7 s. on 25 s. (No. 370) (Blk. and Silver)   15   10
475   9 s. on 38 s. (No. 376) (V.)   ..   20   10
476   24 s. (No. 374)   60   25
477   29 s. on 9 s. (No. 454) (B.)   ..   70   35
478   40 s. on 14 s. (No. 456)..   ..   1·00   60
469/78 *and* O109/11   ..   *Set of* 13   9·00   5·50

1974 (20 Mar). *Air.*
479   109   7 s. multicoloured   40   20
480   9 s. multicoloured   45   25
481   12 s. multicoloured   50   30
482   14 s. multicoloured   55   35
483   17 s. multicoloured   65   50
484   29 s. multicoloured   ..   ..   1·10   80
485   38 s. multicoloured   ..   ..   1·50   1·00
486   50 s. multicoloured   ..   ..   2·00   1·50
487   75 s. multicoloured   ..   ..   2·75   2·00
479/87   ..   ..   ..   *Set of* 9   9·00   6·25
Nos. 479/87 and O112/20 were produced in rolls, each stamp having a number applied to the front of the backing paper, with the usual inscription on the reverse.

110 "Stamped Letter"

1974 (20 June). *Centenary of Universal Postal Union. T* 110 *and similar design.* (a) *Postage.*
488   110   5 s. multicoloured   10   10
489   10 s. multicoloured   15   10
490   15 s. multicoloured   25   15
491   20 s. multicoloured   30   25
492   50 s. multicoloured   ..   ..   1·25   75

(b) *Air*
493   –   14 s. multicoloured   25   15
494   –   21 s. multicoloured   35   30
495   –   60 s. multicoloured   ..   ..   1·40   75
496   –   75 s. multicoloured   ..   ..   1·60   85
497   –   1 p. multicoloured   ..   ..   1·90   1·10
488/97 *and* O121/3   ..   *Set of* 13   9·50   5·75
Design: *Horiz*—Nos. 493/7, Carrier pigeon scattering letters over Tonga.

111 Girl Guide Badges

1974 (11 Sept). *Tongan Girl Guides. T* 111 *and similar design.*

(a) *Postage*
498   111   5 s. multicoloured   40   10
499   10 s. multicoloured   60   20
500   20 s. multicoloured   ..   ..   1·50   55
501   40 s. multicoloured   ..   ..   3·25   1·25
502   60 s. multicoloured   ..   ..   4·00   2·00

(b) *Air*
503   –   14 s. multicoloured   ..   ..   1·00   35
504   –   16 s. multicoloured   ..   ..   1·00   35
505   –   29 s. multicoloured   ..   ..   2·00   80
506   –   31 s. multicoloured   ..   ..   2·25   90
507   –   75 s. multicoloured   ..   ..   5·50   2·50
498/507 *and* O124/6 ..   *Set of* 13   32·00   15·00
Design: *Vert*—Nos. 503/7, Girl Guide leaders.

112 H.M.S. *Resolution*

1974 (11 Dec). *Establishment of Royal Marine Institute. T* 112 *and similar design.* (a) *Postage.*
508   112   5 s. multicoloured   55   20
509   10 s. multicoloured   75   25
510   25 s. multicoloured   ..   ..   1·25   55
511   50 s. multicoloured   ..   ..   2·25   1·50
512   75 s. multicoloured   ..   ..   3·25   2·25

(b) *Air*
513   –   9 s. multicoloured   90   25
514   –   14 s. multicoloured   ..   ..   1·25   40
515   –   17 s. multicoloured   ..   ..   1·40   50
516   –   60 s. multicoloured   ..   ..   3·25   2·00
517   –   90 s. multicoloured   ..   ..   4·50   3·25
508/17 *and* O127/9 ..   ..   *Set of* 13   24·00   14·50
Design: *Horiz* (51 × 46 *mm*)—Nos. 513/17, *James Cook* (bulk carrier).

113 Dateline Hotel, Nuku'alofa

1975 (11 Mar). *South Pacific Forum and Tourism. T 113 and similar vert designs.* (a) *Postage.*

518	113	5 s. multicoloured	..	10	10
519		10 s. multicoloured	..	10	10
520		15 s. multicoloured	..	20	20
521		30 s. multicoloured	..	45	45
522		1 p. multicoloured	..	1·60	1·50

(b) *Air*

523	—	9 s. multicoloured	10	10
524	—	12 s. multicoloured	15	15
525	—	14 s. multicoloured	20	20
526	—	17 s. multicoloured	20	20
527	—	38 s. multicoloured	55	55
518/27 *and* O130/2			*Set of* 13	8·00	7·00

Designs (46 × 60 *mm*):—9, 12, 14 s. Beach; 17, 38 s. Surf and sea.

114 Boxing

1975 (11 June). *Fifth South Pacific Games, Guam. T 114 and similar "star"-shaped design.* (a) *Postage.*

528	114	5 s. multicoloured	..	10	10
529		10 s. multicoloured	..	15	10
530		20 s. multicoloured	..	25	20
531		25 s. multicoloured	..	30	25
532		65 s. multicoloured	..	70	55

(b) *Air*

533	—	9 s. multicoloured	15	10
534	—	12 s. multicoloured	20	15
535	—	14 s. multicoloured	20	15
536	—	17 s. multicoloured	25	20
537	—	90 s. multicoloured	90	80
528/37 *and* O133/5			*Set of* 13	5·25	4·00

Design (37 × 43 *mm*):—Nos. 533/7, Throwing the Discus.

115 Commemorative Coin

1975 (3 Sept). *F.A.O. Commemoration. T 115 and similar designs.*

(a) *Postage*

538	5 s. multicoloured	..	10	10
539	20 s. multicoloured	..	30	15
540	50 s. new blue, black and silver		65	35
541	1 p. ultramarine, black and silver		1·25	75
542	2 p. black and silver	..	2·25	1·75

(b) *Air*

543	12 s. multicoloured		25	15
544	14 s. multicoloured		25	15
545	25 s. vermilion, black and silver		35	20
546	50 s. bright magenta, black and silver	..	60	40
547	1 p. black and silver	..	1·25	75
538/47		*Set of* 10	6·50	4·25

Nos. 539/47 are as T 115 but show different coins. Nos. 542 and 544 are horiz, size 75 × 42 mm.

116 Commemorative Coin

1975 (4 Nov). *Centenary of Tongan Constitution. T 116 and similar designs showing coinage. Multicoloured.* (a) *Postage.*

548	5 s. Type 116	..	..	10	10
549	10 s. King George I		..	15	10
550	20 s. King Taufa'ahau IV	..		30	20
551	50 s. King George II		..	60	35
552	75 s. Tongan arms	..		1·00	70

(b) *Air*

553	9 s. King Taufa'ahau IV		..	15	10
554	12 s. Queen Salote		..	20	10
555	14 s. Tongan arms		..	20	10
556	38 s. King Taufa'ahau IV		..	40	25
557	1 p. Four monarchs		..	1·25	70
548/57 *and* O136/8			*Set of* 13	6·00	3·75

Sizes:—60 × 40 mm, Nos. 549 and 551; 76 × 76 mm, Nos. 552 and 557; 57 × 56 mm, others.

117 Montreal Logo

1976 (24 Feb). *First Participation in Olympic Games.* (a) *Postage.*

558	117	5 s. vermilion, black and blue	..	15	10
559		10 s. vermilion, black and emerald	..	25	10
560		25 s. vermilion, black and bistre	..	75	35
561		35 s. vermilion, black and mauve	..	85	40
562		70 s. vermilion, black and olive-yellow	..	2·25	90

(b) *Air. Montreal logo optd on Girl Guide stamps (Nos. 500 etc)*

563	111	12 s. on 20 s. multicoloured		30	15
564	—	14 s. on 16 s. multicoloured	..	30	15
565	—	16 s. multicoloured	..	35	15
566	111	38 s. on 40 s. multicoloured	..	1·25	45
567	—	75 s. multicoloured	..	2·50	95
558/67 *and* O139/41			*Set of* 13	15·00	6·50

118 Signatories of Declaration of Independence

1976 (26 May). *Bicentenary of American Revolution. T 118 and similar horiz designs showing signatories to the Declaration of Independence.* (a) *Postage.*

568	118	9 s. multicoloured	..	40	15
569	—	10 s. multicoloured	..	40	15
570	—	15 s. multicoloured	..	70	35
571	—	25 s. multicoloured	..	1·25	60
572	—	75 s. multicoloured	..	3·75	1·75

(b) *Air*

573	—	12 s. multicoloured	..	50	15
574	—	14 s. multicoloured	..	60	20
575	—	17 s. multicoloured	..	80	35
576	—	38 s. multicoloured	..	1·90	75
577	—	1 p. multicoloured	..	4·50	2·00
568/77 *and* O142/4			*Set of* 13	20·00	9·00

119 Nathaniel Turner and John Thomas
(Methodist missionaries)

1976 (25 Aug). *150th Anniv of Christianity in Tonga. T 119 and similar design.* (a) *Postage.*

578	119	5 s. multicoloured	..	20	15
579		10 s. multicoloured	..	30	25
580		20 s. multicoloured	..	50	40
581		25 s. multicoloured	..	55	45
582		85 s. multicoloured	..	2·25	1·90

(b) *Air. Design showing Missionary Ship "Triton" (45 × 59 mm)*

583	—	9 s. multicoloured	..	30	25
584	—	12 s. multicoloured	..	35	30
585	—	14 s. multicoloured	..	40	35
586	—	17 s. multicoloured	..	50	40
587	—	38 s. multicoloured	..	1·25	1·00
578/87 *and* O145/7			*Set of* 13	12·00	10·00

120 Emperor Wilhelm I and King George Tupou I

1976 (1 Nov). *Centenary of Treaty of Friendship with Germany.*

(a) *Postage*

588	120	9 s. multicoloured	..	20	20
589		15 s. multicoloured	..	30	30
590		22 s. multicoloured	..	40	45
591		50 s. multicoloured	..	90	1·10
592		73 s. multicoloured	..	1·40	1·60

(b) *Air. Circular design (52 mm diameter) showing Treaty Signing*

593	—	11 s. multicoloured	..	25	25
594	—	17 s. multicoloured	..	40	45
595	—	18 s. multicoloured	..	40	45
596	—	31 s. multicoloured	..	60	70
597	—	39 s. multicoloured	..	70	80
588/97 *and* O148/50			*Set of* 13	9·50	10·50

121 Queen Salote and Coronation Procession

1977 (7 Feb). *Silver Jubilee.* (a) *Postage.*

598	121	11 s. multicoloured	..	1·50	30
599		20 s. multicoloured	..	75	30
600		30 s. multicoloured	..	1·00	30
601		50 s. multicoloured	..	1·75	65
602		75 s. multicoloured	..	2·25	85

(b) *Air. Square design (59 × 59 mm) showing Queen Elizabeth and King Taufa'ahau*

603	—	15 s. multicoloured	..	80	25
604	—	17 s. multicoloured	..	90	30
605	—	22 s. multicoloured	..	12·00	1·75
	a. Horiz roul omitted (vert pair)		..		
606	—	31 s. multicoloured	..	90	40
607	—	39 s. multicoloured	..	95	40
598/607 *and* O151/3			*Set of* 13	25·00	6·25

122 Tongan Coins

1977 (4 July). *Tenth Anniv of King's Coronation.* (a) *Postage.*

608	122	10 s. multicoloured	..	20	20
609		15 s. multicoloured	..	25	25
610		25 s. multicoloured	..	35	45
611		50 s. multicoloured	..	75	85
612		75 s. multicoloured	..	1·00	1·25

(b) *Air. Oval design (64 × 46 mm) showing 1967 Coronation Coin*

613	—	11 s. multicoloured	..	25	20
614	—	17 s. multicoloured	..	30	30
615	—	18 s. multicoloured	..	30	30
616	—	39 s. multicoloured	..	45	55
617	—	1 p. multicoloured	..	1·50	1·75
608/17 *and* O154/6			*Set of* 13	7·50	8·50

123 H.M.S. *Resolution*

1977 (28 Sept). *Bicentenary of Capt. Cook's Last Voyage.*

(a) Postage.

618	123	10 s. multicoloured	..	..	1·75	75
619		17 s. multicoloured	..	..	2·25	1·10
620		25 s. multicoloured	..	..	3·75	2·00
621		30 s. multicoloured	..	..	3·75	2·25
622		40 s. multicoloured	..	..	4·50	3·00

(b) Air. Horiz design (52 × 46 mm) showing coin and extract from Cook's journal

623	–	15 s. multicoloured	..	..	1·75	1·25
624	–	22 s. multicoloured	..	..	2·75	2·00
625	–	31 s. multicoloured	..	..	3·25	2·50
626	–	50 s. multicoloured	..	..	4·50	4·00
627	–	1 p. multicoloured	..	..	8·00	7·00
618/27 *and* O157/9			*Set of* 13		48·00	35·00

124 Humpback Whale   **(125)**

1977 (16 Dec). *Whale Conservation. (a) Postage.*

628	124	15 s. black, grey and bright blue	..		1·00	50
629		22 s. black, grey and dull green	..		1·25	70
630		31 s. black, grey and orange	..		1·50	85
631		38 s. black, grey and bright lilac	..		2·00	1·75
632		64 s. black, grey and red-brown	..		3·25	2·00

(b) Air. Hexagonal design (66 × 51 mm) showing Sei and Fin Whales

633	–	11 s. multicoloured	..	..	1·00	35
634	–	17 s. multicoloured	..	..	1·25	50
635	–	18 s. multicoloured	..	..	1·25	60
636	–	39 s. multicoloured	..	..	2·00	1·25
637	–	50 s. multicoloured	..	..	2·75	1·75
628/37 *and* O160/2			*Set of* 13		24·00	14·50

1978 (17 Feb). *Various stamps surch as T* **125.** *(a) Postage.*

638	115	15 s. on 5 s. multicoloured	..		1·00	1·60
639	119	15 s. on 5 s. multicoloured (Br.)	..		1·00	1·60
640	117	15 s. on 10 s. verm, blk & emerald (G.)	..		1·00	1·60
641	119	15 s. on 10 s. multicoloured	..		1·00	1·60
642	121	15 s. on 11 s. multicoloured (Blk. & Sil.)			3·00	3·50
643	114	15 s. on 20 s. multicoloured	..		1·00	1·60
644		15 s. on 38 s. mult (No. O133) (V.)	..		1·00	1·60

(b) Air

645	–	17 s. on 9 s. multicoloured (No. 533)	..		1·00	1·60
646	–	17 s. on 9 s. multicoloured (583) (V.)	..		1·00	1·60
647	–	17 s. on 12 s. multicoloured (534) (V.)	..		1·00	1·60
648	–	17 s. on 12 s. mult (573) (R. & Gold)	..		1·00	1·60
649	–	17 s. on 18 s. mult (595) (Olive & Br.)	..		1·00	1·60
650	–	17 s. on 38 s. multicoloured (527) (G.)	..		1·00	1·60
651	–	17 s. on 38 s. multicoloured (556)	..		1·00	1·60
652	–	1 p. on 35 s. mult (O151) (Silver & B.)	..		24·00	24·00
653	–	1 p. on 38 s. mult (576) (V. & Gold)	..		6·50	8·50
654	–	1 p. on 75 s. mult (572) (G. & Sil.)	..		6·50	8·50
638/54			*Set of* 17		48·00	60·00

The surcharges on Nos. 638/9 are formed by adding a figure "1" to the existing face value.

The surcharge on No. 644 includes the word "POSTAGE".

126 Flags of Canada and Tonga

1978 (5 May). *Commonwealth Games, Edmonton. (a) Postage.*

655	126	10 s. blue, red and black	..		15	15
656		15 s. multicoloured	..		25	25
657		20 s. turquoise-green, black and red			35	35
658		25 s. red, blue and black	..		40	40
659		45 s. black and red	..		90	1·00

(b) Air. Leaf-shaped design (39 × 40 mm) showing Maple Leaf

660	–	17 s. black and red	..		30	30
661	–	35 s. black and blue	..		60	65
662	–	38 s. black, red and turquoise-green			75	85
663	–	40 s. black and green	..		80	90
664	–	65 s. black, red and chestnut	..		1·40	1·60
655/64 *and* O163/5			*Set of* 13		8·00	9·00

127 King Taufa'ahau Tupou IV

1978 (4 July). *60th Birthday of King Taufa'ahau Tupou IV.*

(a) Postage

665	127	2 s. black, deep blue and cobalt	..		10	10
666		5 s. black, deep blue and rose-pink			10	10
667		10 s. black, deep blue and mauve	..		20	20
668		25 s. black, deep blue and brownish grey			45	35
669		75 s. black, deep blue and yellow-ochre			1·10	1·00

(b) Air. Star-shaped design (44 × 51 mm) showing portrait of King

670	–	11 s. black, dp blue & greenish yellow			20	20
671	–	15 s. black, deep blue and cinnamon			30	25
672	–	17 s. black, deep blue and bright lilac			35	25
673	–	39 s. black, dp blue & turquoise-green			60	55
674	–	1 p. black, deep blue and pink	..		1·75	1·40
665/74 *and* O166/8			*Set of* 13		7·00	6·00

128 Banana

1978 (29 Sept)–**82.** *(a) Coil stamps. Designs as T* **128** *showing bananas (the number coinciding with the face value).*

675		1 s. black and greenish yellow	..		10	10
676		2 s. deep blue and greenish yellow	..		15	15
677		3 s. purple-brown, yellow and greenish yellow			20	20
678		4 s. deep blue, yellow and greenish yellow			20	20
679		5 s. vermilion, yellow and greenish yellow	..		20	20

(b) Coil stamps. Coconut-shaped design (18 × 26 mm)

680		6 s. purple, emerald and bistre-brown			30	30
681		7 s. greenish blue, emerald and light brown			30	30
682		8 s. vermilion, emerald and light brown			30	30
683		9 s. deep mauve, emerald and light brown			30	30
684		10 s. emerald and light brown			30	30

(c) Coil stamps. Pineapple-shaped design (17 × 30 mm)

684a		13 s. deep mauve, emerald and cinnamon (17.12.82)	..		3·00	3·00
685		15 s. blue-green, orange-brown and emerald	..		60	60
686		20 s. brown, orange-brown and emerald	..		70	70
687		30 s. magenta, orange-brown and emerald	..		80	80
688		50 s. black, orange-brown and emerald	..		1·25	1·25
689		1 p. purple, orange-brown and emerald	..		1·90	1·90

(d) Mixed fruit oval design (55 × 29 mm)

689a		2 p. multicoloured (17.12.82)	..		7·50	7·50
689b		3 p. multicoloured (17.12.82)	..		9·50	9·50
675/89b			*Set of* 18		25·00	25·00

Nos. 675/89 and O169/83 were produced in rolls, each even stamp having a number applied to the backing paper, with the usual inscription on the reverse.

129 Humpback Whale

1978 (15 Dec). *Endangered Wildlife Conservation. T* **129** *and similarly shaped designs. Multicoloured. (a) Postage.*

690		15 s. Type **129**	..		80	30
691		18 s. Insular Flying Fox	..		80	35
692		25 s. Turtle	..		90	50
693		28 s. Red Shining Parrot	..		1·00	60
694		60 s. Type **129**	..		2·00	1·75

(b) Air

695	17 s. Type **129**	..			80	35
696	22 s. As 18 s.	..			80	45
697	31 s. As 25 s.	..			1·00	65
698	39 s. As 28 s.	..			1·40	90
699	45 s. Type **129**	..			1·75	1·10
690/9 *and* O184/6		*Set of* 13			16·00	10·50

130 Metrication Symbol

1979 (16 Feb). *Decade of Progress. T* **130** *and other multi-angular designs in ultramarine and gold (31 s.) or multicoloured (others).*

(a) Postage

700	5 s. Type **130**	..			10	10
701	11 s. Map of South Pacific Islands	..			15	15
702	18 s. "Building wall of progress" with the assistance of the United States Peace Corps	..			25	20
703	22 s. New churches	..			35	25
704	50 s. Map showing air routes	..			70	50

(b) Air

705	15 s. As 50 s.	..			20	20
706	17 s. As 11 s.	..			25	20
707	31 s. Rotary International emblem	..			40	35
708	39 s. Government offices	..			55	40
709	1 p. "Communications"	..			1·40	1·25
700/9 *and* O187/9		*Set of* 13			6·50	5·00

131 Various Envelopes bearing Self-adhesive Stamps

1979 (1 June). *Death Centenary of Sir Rowland Hill and 10th Anniv of Tongan Self-adhesive Stamps. (a) Postage.*

710	131	5 s. multicoloured	..		10	10
711		10 s. multicoloured	..		20	15
712		25 s. multicoloured	..		55	35
713		50 s. multicoloured	..		1·00	60
714		1 p. multicoloured	..		2·00	1·25
		a. Horiz roul omitted (vert pair)				

(b) Air. Multi-angular design (53 × 53 mm) showing various self-adhesive stamps

715	–	15 s. multicoloured	..		30	20
716	–	17 s. multicoloured	..		35	25
717	–	18 s. multicoloured	..		35	25
718	–	31 s. multicoloured	..		60	40
719	–	39 s. multicoloured	..		75	45
710/19 *and* O190/2			*Set of* 13		9·00	6·00

132

(Des R. Edge and K. Jones)

1979 (17 Aug)–**82.** *Air. Coil stamps.*

720	132	5 s. black and cobalt	..		15	15
721		11 s. black and bright blue	..		25	25
722		14 s. black and violet	..		25	25
723		15 s. black and mauve	..		30	30
724		17 s. black and bright magenta	..		30	30
725		18 s. black and bright rose-red	..		30	30
726		22 s. black and orange-vermilion	..		35	35
726a		29 s. black and rose (17.12.82)	..		4·50	4·50
727		31 s. black and orange-yellow	..		55	55
727a		32 s. black and yellow-ochre (17.12.82)	..		5·00	5·00
728		39 s. black and bright yellow-green	..		70	70
728a		47 s. black and light brown (17.12.82)	..		6·00	6·00
729		75 s. black and bright blue-green	..		1·25	1·50
730		1 p. black and emerald	..		1·75	2·00
720/30			*Set of* 14		19·00	20·00

Nos. 720/30 and O193/203 were produced in rolls, each even stamp having a number applied to the backing paper, with the usual inscription on the reverse.

133 Rain Forest, Island of 'Eua

1979 (23 Nov). *Views as seen through the Lens of a Camera.*

(a) Postage

731	133	10 s. multicoloured	..	..	20	20
732		18 s. multicoloured	..	..	25	25
733		31 s. multicoloured	..	..	35	35
734		50 s. multicoloured	..	..	60	55
735		60 s. multicoloured	..	..	70	70

(b) Air. Design as T 133 but showing Isle of Kao

736	—	5 s. multicoloured	..	..	10	10
737	—	15 s. multicoloured	..	..	25	25
738	—	17 s. multicoloured	..	..	25	25
739	—	39 s. multicoloured	..	..	50	50
740	—	75 s. multicoloured	..	..	80	80
731/40 and O204/6			Set of 13		5·50	5·50

1980 OLYMPIC GAMES

134 King George Tupou I, Admiral Du Bouzet and Map of Tonga

(135)

1980 (9 Jan). *125th Anniv of France–Tonga Treaty of Friendship.*

(a) Postage

741	134	7 s. multicoloured	..	..	10	15
742		10 s. multicoloured	..	..	15	20
743		14 s. multicoloured	..	..	20	25
744		50 s. multicoloured	..	..	70	75
745		75 s. multicoloured	..	..	1·00	1·10

(b) Air. Design as T 134 but showing King George Tupou I, Napoleon III and "L'Aventure" (French warship)

746	—	15 s. multicoloured	..	..	20	25
747	—	17 s. multicoloured	..	..	25	30
748	—	22 s. multicoloured	..	..	35	40
749	—	31 s. multicoloured	..	..	40	45
750	—	39 s. multicoloured	..	..	55	60
741/50 and O207/9			Set of 13		6·50	7·00

1980 (30 Apr). *Olympic Games, Moscow. Nos. 710/19 surch or optd only (No. 755) as T 135 in black on silver background.*

(a) Postage

751	131	13 s. on 5 s. multicoloured	..	..	30	30
752		20 s. on 10 s. multicoloured	..	..	40	40
753		25 s. multicoloured	..	..	45	45
754		33 s. on 50 s. multicoloured	..	..	55	65
755		1 p. multicoloured	..	..	2·00	2·25

(b) Air

756	—	9 s. on 15 s. multicoloured	..	..	25	25
757	—	16 s. on 17 s. multicoloured	..	..	40	40
758	—	29 s. on 18 s. multicoloured	..	..	60	60
759	—	32 s. on 31 s. multicoloured	..	..	65	70
760	—	47 s. on 39 s. multicoloured	..	..	85	95
751/60 and O210/12			Set of 13		9·00	9·75

136 Scout at Camp-fire

1980 (30 Sept). *South Pacific Scout Jamboree, Tonga and 75th Anniv of Rotary International. (a) Postage.*

761	136	9 s. multicoloured	..	..	30	15
762		13 s. multicoloured	..	..	40	20
763		15 s. multicoloured	..	..	40	20
764		30 s. multicoloured	..	..	75	40

(b) Air. Design as T 136 showing Scout activities and Rotary emblem

765	—	29 s. multicoloured	..	..	75	45
766	—	32 s. multicoloured	..	..	80	45
767	—	47 s. multicoloured	..	..	1·10	70
768	—	1 p. multicoloured	..	..	2·00	1·25
761/8 and O214/15			Set of 10		9·50	6·50

(137)

138 Red Cross and Tongan Flags, with Map of Tonga

1980 (3 Dec)–**82.** *Various stamps surch as T 137. (a) Postage.*

769	117	9 s. on 35 s. vermilion, black and mauve	30	30
770	119	13 s. on 20 s. multicoloured	..	..	45	45
771		13 s. on 25 s. multicoloured	..	..	45	45
772	—	19 s. on 25 s. multicoloured (No. 571)	..	65	65
773	114	1 p. on 65 s. multicoloured	..	..	2·75	2·75
773a	—	5 p. on 25 s. multicoloured (No. O214) (B.) (4.1.82)		9·50	9·50
773b	—	5 p. on 2 p. multicoloured (No. O215) (B.) (4.1.82)		9·50	9·50
		ba. Stamp omitted (centre stamp of strip of 3) ..				

(b) Air

774	—	29 s. on 14 s. multicoloured (No. 585)	..	80	80
775	—	29 s. on 39 s. multicoloured (No. 597)	..	80	80
776	—	32 s. on 12 s. multicoloured (No. 554)	..	95	95
777	—	32 s. on 14 s. multicoloured (No. 574)	..	95	95
778	—	47 s. on 12 s. multicoloured (No. 524)	..	1·40	1·40
779	—	47 s. on 12 s. multicoloured (No. 584)	..	1·40	1·40
769/79 and O216			Set of 14		30·00	30·00

On No. 773ba the centre stamp in a vertical strip of 3 became detached so that the surcharge was applied to the white backing paper.

1981 (9 Sept). *International Year for Disabled Persons.*

(a) Postage. P 14½ × 14.

780	138	2 p. multicoloured	..	..	1·50	1·00
781		3 p. multicoloured	..	..	1·75	1·25

(b) Air. Vert design (25 × 33 mm) showing Red Cross flag and map depicting Tongatapu and Eua. P 13½

782	—	29 s. multicoloured	..	..	30	20
783	—	32 s. multicoloured	..	..	35	25
784	—	47 s. multicoloured	..	..	45	30
780/4 ..			Set of 5		4·00	2·75

139 Prince Charles and King Taufa'ahau Tupou IV

1981 (21 Oct). *Royal Wedding and Centenary of Treaty of Friendship between Tonga and Great Britain. T 139 and similar vert designs. Multicoloured. P 13½.*

785	13 s. Type 139	..	..	30	20
786	47 s. Prince Charles and Lady Diana Spencer		45	30
787	1 p. 50, Prince Charles and Lady Diana (different)	..	..	1·10	90
	a. Imperf backing paper (pair)				
788	3 p. Prince and Princess of Wales after wedding ceremony	..	..	2·00	1·40
785/8 ..			Set of 4	3·50	2·50

140 Report of Printing in *Missionary Notices*

141 Landing Scene

1981 (25 Nov). *Christmas. 150th Anniv of first Books Printed in Tonga. T 140 and similar horiz designs. Multicoloured. P 13½.*

789	9 s. Type 140	..	..	..	25	15
790	13 s. Missionary Notices report (different)	..	30	20
791	32 s. Type in chase	..	..	85	40
792	47 s. Bible class	..	..	1·40	70
789/92	..		Set of 4		2·50	1·25

1981 (25 Nov). *Bicentenary of Maurelle's Discovery of Vava'u. T 141 and similar horiz designs. Multicoloured. P 14 × 14½.*

793	9 s. Type 141	..	..	30	20
794	13 s. Map of Vava'u	..	..	50	25
795	47 s. La Princesa	..	..	2·00	1·25
796	1 p. La Princesa (different)	..	..	4·50	3·00
793/6	..		Set of 4		6·50	4·25
MS797	100 × 78 mm. As No. 796. Imperf	..		7·50	7·50

The stamp from No. MS797 is as No. 796 but without inscription at foot of design.

142 Battle Scene

1981 (16 Dec). *175th Anniv of Capture of "Port au Prince" (ship). T 142 and similar horiz designs in black and new blue. P 13½.*

798	29 s. Type 142	..	..	55	25
799	32 s. Battle scene (different)	..	..	65	30
800	47 s. Map of Ha'apai Group	..	..	80	50
801	47 s. Native canoes preparing to attack		80	50
802	1 p. Port au Prince	..	..	1·50	75
798/802			Set of 5		3·75	2·10

The 47 s. values were printed together, *se-tenant*, in horizontal and vertical pairs throughout the sheet.

CYCLONE RELIEF

T$1+50s

POSTAGE & RELIEF

143 Baden-Powell at Brownsea Island, 1907

(144)

1982 (22 Feb). *75th Anniv of Boy Scout Movement and 125th Birth Anniv of Lord Baden-Powell. T 143 and similar vert designs. P 13½.*

803	29 s. Type 143	..	..	55	30
804	32 s. Baden-Powell on his charger "Black Prince"	..	..	65	35
805	47 s. Baden-Powell at Imperial Jamboree, 1924	90	45
806	1 p. 50, Cover of first Scouting for Boys journal	..	..	2·40	1·25
807	2 p. 50, Newsboy, 1900 and Mafeking Siege 3d. stamp	..	..	4·00	2·75
803/7			Set of 5		7·75	4·50

1982 (14 Apr). *Cyclone Relief. No. 788 optd with T 144 in silver.*

808	1 p. + 50 s. on 3 p. Prince and Princess of Wales after wedding ceremony ..	..	2·00	1·60
	a. Imperf backing paper (pair)	..	..	£200	

145 Ball Control   146 M.V. Olovaha II

1982 (7 July). *World Cup Football Championship, Spain. T 145 and similar vert designs. Multicoloured. P 13½.*

809	32 s. Type 145	..		45	45
810	47 s. Goalkeeping	..	..	60	60
811	75 s. Heading	..	..	1·00	95
812	1 p. 50, Shooting	..	..	1·75	1·75
809/12			Set of 4		3·50	3·25

1982 (11 Aug). *Inter-Island Transport.* T **146** *and similar horiz design. Multicoloured.* P 14 × 14½.
813	9 s. Type **146** ..	..	10	10
814	13 s. Type **146** ..	..	15	15
815	47 s. SPIA "Twin Otter"	..	55	60
816	1 p. As 47 s.	..	1·25	1·40
813/16		*Set of 4*	1·90	2·00

147 Mail Canoe

148 Decathlon

1982 (29 Sept). *Tin Can Mail Centenary.* T **147** *and similar vert designs.* P 13½ × 14.
817	13 s. multicoloured	..	15	15
818	32 s. multicoloured	..	25	25
819	47 s. multicoloured	..	35	35
820	2 p. black and pale turquoise-green ..		1·40	1·40
817/20		*Set of 4*	2·00	2·00
MS821	135 × 90 mm. Nos. 817/19. Imperf		1·25	1·50
MS822	135 × 89 mm. As No. 820 but with gold			
	inscriptions. Imperf		2·75	3·25

Designs:—32 s. Mail canoe and ship; 47 s. Collecting Tin Can mail; 2 p. Map of Niuafo'ou.

1982 (25 Oct). *Commonwealth Games, Brisbane.* T **148** *and similar multicoloured design.* P 13½.
823	32 s. Type **148** ..	..	50	30
824	1 p. Tongan Police band at opening ceremony (*horiz*) ..		3·00	1·50

149 Pupils

Christmas
Greetings
1982
(**150**)

1982 (25 Oct). *Tonga College Centenary.* T **149** *and similar multicoloured designs.* P 13½ (*Nos. 825/6*) or 14 × 14½ (*others*).
825	5 s. Type **149** (Tongan inscription)	..	30	15
	a. Pair. Nos. 825/6	..	60	30
826	5 s. Type **149** (English inscription)	..	30	15
827	29 s. School crest and monument (Tongan inscr) (29×22 *mm*)	..	1·25	85
	a. Block of 4. Nos. 827/9	..	5·00	
828	29 s. As No. 827, but inscr in English		1·25	85
829	29 s. King George Tupou I (founder) and school (Tongan inscr) (29×22 *mm*)		1·25	85
830	29 s. As No. 829, but inscr in English		1·25	85
825/30		*Set of 6*	5·00	3·25

Nos. 825/6 were printed together, *se-tenant*, in horizontal and vertical pairs and Nos. 827/30 in different combinations throughout the sheet, giving four blocks of 4 and four single stamps.

1982 (17 Nov). *Christmas. Nos. 817/19 optd as T* **150** *in bright carmine* (13 s.) *or silver* (*others*).
831	13 s. Type **147**.	..	15	15
	a. Bright purple opt			
832	32 s. Mail boat and ship	..	35	35
833	47 s. Collecting Tin Can mail	..	40	50
831/3 ..		*Set of 3*	80	90

151 H.M.S. *Resolution*, and S. S. *Canberra*

1983 (22 Feb). *Sea and Air Transport.* T **151** *and similar horiz designs. Multicoloured.* P 14.
834	29 s. Type **151** (sage-green background)		1·00	80
835	32 s. Type **151** (buff background)	..	1·10	90
836	47 s. Montgolfier's balloon and "Concorde" (pale blue background)		1·75	1·50
837	1 p. 50, As No. 836 (lilac background)		3·00	2·75
834/7 ..		*Set of 4*	6·00	5·50
MS838	120 × 165 mm. 2 p. 50, S.S. *Canberra* and "Concorde" ..		3·50	4·00

152 Globe and Inset of Tonga

153 SPIA DH "Twin Otter"

1983 (14 Mar). *Commonwealth Day.* T **152** *and similar horiz designs. Multicoloured.* P 14.
839	29 s. Type **152** ..	..	35	30
840	32 s. Tongan dancers	..	6·00	2·00
841	47 s. Trawler	..	50	50
842	1 p. 50, King Taufa'ahau Tupou IV and flag		1·75	1·75
839/42		*Set of 4*	7·75	4·00

1983 (11 May). *Inauguration of Niuafo'ou Airport.* T **153** *and similar horiz design. Multicoloured.* P 14 × 14½.
843	32 s. Type **153** ..	..	20	20
844	47 s. Type **153** ..	..	25	25
845	1 p. SPIA Boeing "707"	..	60	70
846	1 p. 50, As 1 p.	..	80	1·25
843/6		*Set of 4*	1·75	2·25

154 "Intelsat IV" Satellite

155 Obverse and Reverse of Pa'anga Banknote

1983 (22 June). *World Communications Year.* T **154** *and similar multicoloured designs.* P 11 (2 p.) *or* 14 × 14½ (*others*).
847	29 s. Type **154** ..	..	20	20
848	32 s. "Intelsat IVA" satellite	..	25	25
849	75 s. "Intelsat V" satellite	..	50	50
850	2 p. Moon post cover (45 × 32 *mm*)		1·10	1·40
847/50		*Set of 4*	1·90	2·10

1983 (3 Aug). *10th Anniv of Bank of Tonga.* P 14.
851	**155**	1 p. multicoloured	..	60	65
852		2 p. multicoloured	..	1·10	1·25

156 Early Printing Press

157 Yacht off Coast

(Des A. Benjamin and R. Edge)

1983 (22 Sept). *Printing in Tonga.* T **156** *and similar vert designs. Multicoloured.* P 14.
853	13 s. Type **156** ..	..	15	15
854	32 s. Arrival of W. Woon	..	25	25
855	1 p. Early Tongan print	..	50	60
856	2 p. *The Tonga Chronicle*	..	90	1·25
853/6		*Set of 4*	1·60	2·00

1983 (17 Nov). *Christmas. Yachting off Vava'u.* T **157** *and similar vert designs. Multicoloured.* P 11.
857	29 s. Type **157** ..	..	25	25
858	32 s. View of yacht from cave ..		25	25
859	1 p. 50, Anchored yacht	..	80	1·00
860	2 p. 50, Yacht off coast (*different*)		1·25	1·50
857/60		*Set of 4*	2·25	2·75

158 Abel Tasman and *Zeehan*

159 *Swainsonia casta*

(Des R. Edge)

1984 (12 Mar). *Navigators and Explorers of the Pacific* (1st series). T **158** *and similar horiz designs.* P 14.
861	32 s. deep dull green and black	..	90	90
862	47 s. reddish violet and black ..		1·40	1·40
863	90 s. light brown and black ..		2·50	2·50
864	1 p. 50, royal blue and black ..		3·75	3·75
861/4 ..		*Set of 4*	7·50	7·50

Designs:—47 s. Samuel Wallis and H.M.S. *Dolphin*; 90 s. William Bligh and H.M.S. *Bounty*; 1 p. 50, James Cook and H.M.S. *Resolution*.
See also Nos. 896/9.

STAMPS DIE-CUT OR PERFORATED. During 1985 developments took place in the production of Tonga and Niuafo'ou self-adhesive stamps. Since 1981 these had been produced in traditional formats on backing paper perforated in the usual way. The individual stamps were, however, separated by the removal of the margins between them by the die-cutting process.

As an experiment some supplies of Tonga Nos. 870, 896, **MS**904, 905/9, 915/18, O225 and Niuafo'ou Nos. 56/60, together with the entire printing of Tonga Nos. 910/14, were produced with the margins intact so that both stamps and backing paper were perforated through.

Such issues are usually inscribed "Bend forward and peel off backing paper" on the reverse.

1984 (10 Apr)–**85**. *Marine Life.* T **159** *and similar multicoloured designs. Stamps die-cut and backing paper perf* 14 (1, 2, 3, 5 p.) *or* 14½ (*others*).
865	1 s. Type **159** ..	..	15	15
866	2 s. *Porites sp* (26.6.84)	..	25	25
867	3 s. *Holocentrus ruber* (18.5.84)		30	30
868	5 s. *Cypraea mappa viridis*	..	30	30
869	6 s. *Dardanus megistos* (crab) (17.9.84)		35	35
870	9 s. *Stegostoma fasciatum* (18.5.84)		35	35
	b. Stamp perforated (28.5.85)	..	35	35
871	10 s. *Conus bullatus*	..	50	45
872	13 s. *Pterois volitans* (18.5.84)..		55	45
873	15 s. *Conus textile*	..	60	50
874	20 s. *Dascyllus aruanus* (18.5.84)		70	60
875	29 s. *Conus aulicus*	..	85	70
876	32 s. *Acanthurus leucosternon* (18.5.84)		1·00	80
877	47 s. *Lambis truncata* ..		1·40	1·40
878	1 p. *Millepora dichotama* (26.6.84)		3·00	3·00
879	2 p. *Birgus latro* (crab) (17.9.84)		4·75	4·75
880	3 p. *Chicoreus palma-rosae* ..		5·50	5·50
881	5 p. *Thunnus albacares* (18.5.84)		8·00	8·00
865/81		*Set of 17*	26·00	25·00

Nos. 878/81 are horizontal, 38 × 23 mm.

For 1, 2, 5, 6, 10, 15, 20, 32 s. and 3 p. with normal gum and perforations see Nos. 976a/b, 999/1017 and 1087/95.

160 Printer checking Newspaper

161 U.S.A. Flag and Running

1984 (26 June). *20th Anniv of Tonga Chronicle* (*newspaper*). *Die-cut.*
882	**160**	3 s. grey-brown and bright blue	..	10	10
		a. Sheetlet of 12	..	50	
883		32 s. grey-brown and vermilion ..		40	45
		a. Sheetlet of 12	..	4·75	

Nos. 882/3 were each printed in sheetlets of 12, the designs being superimposed on a reproduction of the front page from the first edition. This was printed in grey and is in Tongan for the 3 s. and English for the 32 s.

(Des R. Edge)

1984 (23 July). *Olympic Games, Los Angeles.* T **161** *and similar horiz designs, each showing U.S. flag. Each printed in black, scarlet-vermilion and bright new blue.* P 14 × 14½.
884	32 s. Type **161** ..	..	25	25
885	47 s. Javelin-throwing	..	30	30
886	1 p. Shot-putting ..	..	85	85
887	3 p. Olympic torch	..	1·60	1·60
884/7 ..		*Set of 4*	2·75	2·75

162 Sir George Airy and Dateline on World Map

163 Australia 1914 Kookaburra 6d. Stamp

(Des R. Edge)

1984 (20 Aug). *Centenary of International Dateline.* T **162** *and similar horiz design. Multicoloured.* P 14.
888	47 s. Type **162** ..	..	1·00	1·00
889	2 p. Sir Sandford Fleming and Map of Pacific time zones	..	3·25	3·25

1984 (17 Sept). *"Ausipex" International Stamp Exhibition, Melbourne.* T **163** *and similar vert design. Multicoloured.* P 14.
890	32 s. Type **163** ..	..	75	60
891	1 p. 50, Tonga 1897 Parrot 2s. 6d. stamp	..	2·50	2·50
MS892	90 × 100 mm. As Nos. 890/1, but without exhibition logo and with "TONGA" and face values in gold. Die-cut	..	1·90	2·25

Examples of No. **MS**892 without face values are Exhibition Banquet souvenirs without postal validity.

MINIMUM PRICE

The minimum price quote is 10p which represents a handling charge rather than a basis for valuing common stamps. For further notes about prices see introductory pages.

164 Beach at Sunset ("Silent Night") 165 Section of Tonga Trench

(Des R. Edge)

1984 (12 Nov). *Christmas. Carols. T **164** and similar vert designs. Multicoloured. P 14.*

893	32 s. Type **164**			50	45
894	47 s. Hut and palm trees ("Away in a Manger")			75	65
895	1 p. Sailing boats ("I Saw Three Ships")			1·50	1·90
893/5			Set of 3	2·50	2·75

Nos. 893/5 were each issued in sheets of 20 stamps with 5 labels, in the central vertical row, showing progressive stages of the design.

(Des R. Edge)

1985 (27 Feb). *Navigators and Explorers of the Pacific (2nd series). Horiz designs as T **158**. Stamps die-cut and backing paper perf 14.*

896	32 s. black and turquoise-blue			1·40	75
	b. Stamp perforated			30·00	30·00
897	47 s. black and blue-green			1·75	1·00
898	90 s. black and scarlet			2·75	2·50
899	1 p. 50, black and buff			4·00	3·50
896/9			Set of 4	9·00	7·00

Designs:—32 s. Willem Schouten and *Eendracht*; 47 s. Jacob Le Maire and *Hoorn*; 90 s. Fletcher Christian and *Bounty*; 1 p. 50, Francisco Maurelle and *La Princessa*.
No. 896b has no inscription on the reverse.

1985 (10 Apr). *Geological Survey of the Tonga Trench. T **165** and similar multicoloured designs. Stamps die-cut and backing paper perf 14.*

900	29 s. Type **165**			1·25	1·00
901	32 s. Diagram of marine seismic survey			1·25	1·00
902	47 s. Diagram of aerial oil survey (vert)			1·50	1·25
903	1 p. 50, Diagram of sea bed survey (vert)			3·75	4·00
900/3			Set of 4	7·00	6·50
MS904	100×100 mm. 1 p. 50, Angler Fish. Die-cut			2·00	2·00
	b. Stamp perforated			5·00	5·50

166 Port au Prince at Gravesend, 1805 167 Quintal (Byron Russell) and Capt. Bligh (Charles Laughton)

1985 (18 June). *175th Anniv of Will Mariner's Departure for England. T **166** and similar horiz designs. Multicoloured. A. Stamp die-cut and backing paper perf 14. B. Both stamp and backing paper perf 14.*

		A		B	
905	29 s. Type **166**	30	35	30	35
906	32 s. Capture of *Port au Prince*, Tonga, 1806	30	35	30	35
907	47 s. Will Mariner on Tongan canoe, 1807	45	50	45	50
908	1 p. 50, Mariner boarding brig *Favourite*, 1810	1·40	1·50	1·40	1·50
909	2 p. 50, *Cuffnells* in English Channel, 1811	2·40	2·50	2·40	2·50
905/9	Set of 5	4·25	4·50	4·25	4·50

1985 (16 July). *50th Anniv of Film "Mutiny on the Bounty". T **167** and similar horiz designs showing film stills. Multicoloured. Both stamp and backing paper perf 14.*

910	47 s. Type **167**			2·25	2·25
	a. Horiz strip of 5. Nos. 910/14			10·00	
911	47 s. Captain Bligh and prisoners			2·25	2·25
912	47 s. Fletcher Christian (Clark Gable)			2·25	2·25
913	47 s. Mutineers threatening Bligh			2·25	2·25
914	47 s. Bligh and Roger Byam (Franchot Tone) in boat			2·25	2·25
910/14			Set of 5	10·00	10·00

Nos. 910/14 were printed together, *se-tenant*, in horizontal strips of 5 throughout the sheet.

168 Lady Elizabeth Bowes-Lyon, 1910 169 Mary and Joseph arriving at Inn

1985 (20 Aug). *Life and Times of Queen Elizabeth the Queen Mother and 75th Anniv of Girl Guide Movement. T **168** and similar horiz designs. A. Stamp die-cut and backing paper perf 14. B. Both stamp and backing paper perf 14.*

		A		B	
915	32 s. black, salmon-pink and reddish brown	30	35	60	65
916	47 s. black, pale rose-lilac and reddish brown	45	50	90	1·00
917	1 p. 50, black, olive-yellow and reddish brown	1·40	1·50	2·75	3·00
918	2 p. 50, multicoloured	2·40	2·50	4·75	5·00
915/18	Set of 4	4·00	4·25	8·00	8·50

Designs:—47 s. Duchess of York at Hadfield Girl Guides' Rally, 1931; 1 p. 50, Duchess of York in Girl Guide uniform; 2 p. 50, Queen Mother in 1985 (from photo by Norman Parkinson).

1985 (12 Nov). *Christmas. T **169** and similar vert designs. Multicoloured. P 14.*

919	32 s. Type **169**			25	30
920	42 s. The shepherds			35	40
921	1 p. 50, The Three Wise Men			1·25	1·40
922	2 p. 50, The Holy Family			2·10	2·25
919/22			Set of 4	3·50	4·00

NOTE. Unless stated otherwise Tonga issues from No. 922 had the normal form of gum and were not self-adhesive.

170 Comet and Slogan "Maybe Twice in a Lifetime" (171)

(Litho Walsall)

1986 (26 Mar). *Appearance of Halley's Comet. T **170** and similar horiz designs. Multicoloured. P 14.*

923	42 s. Type **170**			1·10	1·10
	a. Horiz strip of 5. Nos. 923/7			5·00	
924	42 s. Edmond Halley			1·10	1·10
925	42 s. Solar System			1·10	1·10
926	42 s. Telescope			1·10	1·10
927	42 s. *Giotto* spacecraft			1·10	1·10
928	57 s. Type **170**			1·25	1·25
	a. Horiz strip of 5. Nos. 928/32			5·50	
929	57 s. As No. 924			1·25	1·25
930	57 s. As No. 925			1·25	1·25
931	57 s. As No. 926			1·25	1·25
932	57 s. As No. 927			1·25	1·25
923/32			Set of 10	10·50	10·50

Nos. 923/7 and 928/32 were each printed together, *se-tenant*, in horizontal strips of five, forming composite designs, throughout the sheets.

1986 (16 Apr). *Nos. 866/7, 869/70, 872, 874, 879 and 881 surch as T **171**.*

933	4 s. on 2 s. *Porites sp.*			15	15
934	4 s. on 13 s. *Pterois volitans*			15	15
935	42 s. on 3 s. *Holocentrus ruber*			45	45
936	42 s. on 9 s. *Stegostoma fasciatum*			45	45
937	57 s. on 6 s. *Dardanus megistos*			65	65
938	57 s. on 20 s. *Dascyllus aruanus*			65	65
939	2 p. 50 on 2 p. *Birgus latro*			3·00	3·25
940	2 p. 50 on 5 p. *Thunnus albacares*			3·00	3·25
933/40			Set of 8	7·75	8·00

172 King Taufa'ahau Tupou IV of Tonga

(Litho Walsall)

1986 (22 May). *Royal Links with Great Britain and 60th Birthday of Queen Elizabeth II. T **172** and similar designs. P 14.*

941	**172** 57 s. multicoloured			65	65
	a. Horiz pair. Nos. 941/2			1·25	1·25
942	— 57 s. multicoloured			65	65
943	— 2 p. 50, reddish brown, blk & pale new bl			2·25	2·50
941/3			Set of 3	3·50	3·75

Designs: *Horiz (as T **172**)*—No. 942, Queen Elizabeth II. *Square (40×40 mm)*—No. 943, Queen Elizabeth II and King Taufa'ahau Tupou IV, Tonga, 1970.

Nos. 941/2 were printed together, *se-tenant*, in horizontal pairs throughout the sheet, and No. 943 in sheetlets of five stamps and one stamp-size label.

173 Peace Corps Nurse giving Injection 174 Hockey (World Hockey Cup for Men, London)

(Litho Walsall)

1986 (22 May). *"Ameripex '86" International Stamp Exhibition, Chicago. 25th Anniv of United States Peace Corps. T **173** and similar horiz design. Multicoloured. P 14.*

944	57 s. Type **173**			45	50
945	1 p. 50, Peace Corps teacher and pupil			1·25	1·40
MS946	90×90 mm. Nos. 944/5, magnifying glass and tweezers. Imperf			2·00	2·50

(Litho Walsall)

1986 (23 July). *Sporting Events. T **174** and similar vert designs. Multicoloured. P 14.*

947	42 s. Type **174**			75	75
948	57 s. Handball (13th Commonwealth Games, Edinburgh)			85	85
949	1 p. Boxing (13th Commonwealth Games, Edinburgh)			1·60	1·60
950	2 p. 50, Football (World Cup Football Championship, Mexico)			4·00	4·00
947/50			Set of 4	6·50	6·50

175 1886 1d. King George I Definitive

(Des A. Benjamin. Litho Walsall)

1986 (27 Aug). *Centenary of First Tonga Stamps. T **175** and similar multicoloured designs. P 14.*

951	32 s. Type **175**			75	75
952	42 s. 1897 7½d. King George II inverted centre error			90	90
953	57 s. 1950 Queen Salote's 50th Birthday 1d.			1·25	1·25
954	2 p. 50, 1986 Royal Links with Great Britain 2 p. 50			3·25	3·25
951/4			Set of 4	5·50	5·50
MS955	132×104 mm. 50 s. × 8 Vert designs forming montage of Tonga stamps			6·50	7·00

Nos. 951/5 were printed with an overall pattern similar to watermark W 24.

176 Girls wearing Shell Jewellery (177)

(Litho Walsall)

1986 (12 Nov). *Christmas. T **176** and similar multicoloured designs. P 14.*

956	32 s. Type **176**			60	45
957	42 s. Boy with wood carvings (vert)			85	60
958	57 s. Children performing traditional dance (vert)			1·10	75
959	2 p. Children in dugout canoe			3·25	3·50
956/9			Set of 4	5·25	4·75

1986 (2 Dec). *Scout Jamboree, Tongatapu. Nos. 957/8 optd with T **177** in silver.*

960	42 s. Boy with wood carvings (vert)			1·75	1·75
961	57 s. Children performing traditional dance (vert)			2·00	2·00

178 Dumont D'Urville and L'Astrolabe 179 Noah's Ark

(Litho Walsall)

1987 (24 Feb). *150th Anniv of Dumont D'Urville's Second Voyage. T **178** and similar horiz designs. Multicoloured. P 14.*

962	32 s. Type **178**			1·40	1·10
963	42 s. Tongan girls (from *Voyage au Pole et dans l'Oceanie*)			1·75	1·40
964	1 p. Contemporary chart			3·25	3·00
965	2 p. 50, Wreck of *L'Astrolabe*			6·00	6·00
962/5			Set of 4	11·00	10·50

(Des and litho Walsall)

1987 (6 May). *World Wildlife Fund. Sheet 115×110 mm containing T **179** and similar vert designs. Multicoloured. P 13½.*

MS966	42 s. Type **179**; 42 s. American Bald Eagles; 42 s. Giraffes and birds; 42 s. Gulls; 42 s. Ostriches and elephants; 42 s. Elephant; 42 s. Lions, zebras, antelopes and giraffes; 42 s. Chimpanzees; 42 s. Frogs and antelopes; 42 s. Lizard and tigers; 42 s. Snake and tiger; 42 s. *Papilio machaon* (butterfly)			10·00	10·00

The stamps within No. **MS966** show a composite design of animals entering Noah's Ark.

180 Two Paddlers in Canoe   181 King Taufa'ahau Tupou IV

(Des C. Abbott. Litho Questa)

1987 (1 July). *"Siv'a'alo" (Tonga-Fiji-Samoa) Canoe Race. T 180 and similar square designs. Multicoloured. P 14.*

967	32 s. Type 180.			25	30
968	42 s. Five paddlers			35	40
969	57 s. Paddlers and canoe bow			45	50
	a. Value omitted (R. 3/2)			£500	
970	1 p. 50, Two paddlers (different)			1·10	1·25
967/70			*Set of 4*	1·90	2·25
MS971	153×59 mm. Nos. 967/70			2·10	2·50

The stamps within No. **MS**971 show a composite design of two canoes racing.

No. 969a occurred on a batch of fifty sheets distributed to local post offices in Tonga. The remainder of the first printing was withdrawn and replaced, later in the month, by sheets showing the error corrected.

(Des and litho Walsall)

1987 (1 July)–88. *20th Anniv of Coronation of King Taufa'ahau Tupou IV. Self-adhesive. Stamps die-cut.*

972	181	1 s. black and olive-green		10	10
		a. Booklet pane. Nos. 972×2, 974×4, 975×2 and 976×4		1·60	
		b. Booklet pane. Nos. 972, 972d×2, 973×2, 974×4 and 975×3 (4.7.88)		95	
		c. Booklet pane. Nos. 972×4, 972d×2 and 976×6 (4.7.88)		1·90	
972d		2 s. black and pale orange (4.7.88)		10	10
973		5 s. black and pale magenta		10	10
		a. Booklet pane. Nos. 973×7, 974×2 and 975×3.		80	
974		10 s. black and reddish lilac		10	10
975		15 s. black and rose-red.		15	20
976		32 s. black and turquoise-blue		30	35
972/6			*Set of 6*	55	70

Nos. 972/6 were only available from stamp booklets. These are self-adhesive stamps and the backing card forms the booklet cover.

(Litho Walsall)

1987 (Sept). *As Nos. 871 and 876 (previously self-adhesive), but printed with normal gum and perforations. Multicoloured. P 14½.*

976a	10 s. *Conus bullatus*		4·00	4·00
976b	32 s. *Acanthurus leucosternon*		11·00	11·00

Nos. 976a/b were printed from the same plates as the self-adhesive issue. They are without imprint date at foot and show a space of 23 mm between the two horizontal lines across each design.

For redrawn versions of these stamps with imprint date see Nos. 1005 and 1008.

182 Arms and Tongan   183 Father Christmas Octopus
Citizens   and Rat with Sack of Presents

(Des and litho Walsall)

1987 (23 Sept). *125th Anniv of First Parliament. P 14½×14.*

977	182	32 s. multicoloured		25	30
978		42 s. multicoloured		35	40
979		75 s. multicoloured		60	65
980		2 p. multicoloured		1·60	1·75
977/80			*Set of 4*	2·50	2·75

(Des and litho Walsall)

1987 (25 Nov). *Christmas. T 183 and similar horiz designs showing cartoons. Multicoloured. P 13½ × 14.*

981	183	42 s. Type 183		40	45
982		57 s. Delivering presents by outrigger canoe		60	65
983		1 p. Delivering presents by motorised tricycle		95	1·00
984		3 p. Drinking cocktails		2·75	3·00
981/4			*Set of 4*	4·00	4·50

PRICES OF SETS

Set prices are given for many issues, generally those containing three stamps or more. Definitive sets include one of each value or major colour change, but do not cover different perforations, die types or minor shades. Where a choice is possible the set prices are based on the cheapest versions of the stamps included in the listings.

---

184 King Taufa'ahau Tupou IV, *Olovaha*
(inter-island ferry), Oil Rig and Pole Vaulting

(Des and litho Walsall)

1988 (4 July). *70th Birthday of King Taufa'ahau Tupou IV. T 184 and similar horiz designs, each showing portrait. Multicoloured. P 11½.*

985	32 s. Type 184		30	35
986	42 s. Banknote, coins, Ha'amonga Trilithon and woodcarver		40	45
987	57 s. Rowing, communications satellite and Red Cross worker		60	65
988	2 p. 50, Scout emblem, 1982 47 s. Scout stamp and Friendly Island Airways aircraft		2·40	2·50
985/8		*Set of 4*	3·25	3·50

For similar designs issued in 1990 for the King's Silver Jubilee see Nos. 1082/5.

185 Capt. Cook and   186 Athletics
Journal

(Des and litho Walsall)

1988 (11 July). *Bicentenary of Australian Settlement. Sheet 115 × 110 mm containing T 185 and similar vert designs. Multicoloured. P 13½.*

MS989 42 s. Type 185; 42 s. Ships in Sydney Harbour and Governor Philip; 42 s. Australia 1952 2s. 6d. aborigine definitive and early settlement; 42 s. Burke and Wills (explorers); 42 s. Emu, opals and gold prospector's licence; 42 s. ANZAC cap badge and soldier; 42 s. Cover from first overland mail by Trans Continental; 42 s. Ross Smith, England–Australia flown cover and G.B. 1969 1s. 9d. commemorative stamp; 42 s. Don Bradman and Harold Larwood (cricketers); 42 s. World War II campaign medals; 42 s. Australia 1978 18 c. Flying Doctor Service stamp and sheep station; 42 s. Sydney Opera House .. .. 7·50 8·00

(Des and litho Walsall)

1988 (11 Aug). *Olympic Games, Seoul. T 186 and similar vert designs. Multicoloured. P 14.*

990	57 s. Type 186			60	65
991	75 s. Yachting			70	75
992	2 p. Cycling			1·90	2·00
993	3 p. Tennis			2·75	3·00
990/3			*Set of 4*	5·25	5·75

187 Traditional Tongan Fale

(Des and litho Walsall)

1988 (9 Sept). *Music in Tonga. T 187 and similar horiz designs. Multicoloured. P 14.*

994	32 s. Type 187		30	35
995	42 s. Church choir		40	45
996	57 s. Tonga Police Band outside Royal Palace		55	60
997	2 p. 50, "The Jets" pop group		2·40	2·50
994/7		*Set of 4*	3·25	3·50

188 Olympic Flame

(Des and litho Walsall)

1988 (9 Sept). *"Sport Aid '88". Sheet 105 × 75 mm, containing T 188 and design as No. 997. Multicoloured. P 14.*

MS998 57 s. Type 188; 57 s. As No. 997 .. 1·10 1·40

Two types of 42 s.:

Type I. Background shading in bright blue extending to the perforation margin. Plumage is light brown.
Type II. Background shading in oval of new blue bleeding off at edges. Plumage is sepia.

(Litho Walsall)

1988 (4 Oct)–92. *Redrawn designs as Nos. 865/6, 868/9, 871/6, 879/81 (previously self-adhesive) and new values (7, 35, 42, 57 s., 1 p., 1 p. 50, 10 p.), all with normal gum, perforations and imprint date at foot. Multicoloured. Chalk-surfaced paper (4, 7, 35, 42, 50, 57 s., 1 p. 50., 2 p., 5 p., 10 p.). P 14 (1 p. to 10 p.) or 14½×14 (others).*

999	1 s. Type 159		10	10
1000	2 s. *Porites sp* (18.10.88)		15	15
	a. Chalk-surfaced paper (4.90)		10	10
1001	4 s. *Pterois volitans* (2.3.89)		10	10
1002	5 s. *Cypraea mappa viridis*		20	20
	a. Chalk-surfaced paper (4.90)		10	10
1003	6 s. *Dardanus megistos* (crab) (18.10.88)		10	10
1004	7 s. Wandering Albatross (2.3.89)		10	10
1005	10 s. *Conus bullatus*		20	20
	a. Chalk-surfaced paper (4.90)		10	10
1006	15 s. *Conus textile* (18.10.88)		15	20
1007	20 s. *Dascyllus aruanus*		15	20
1008	32 s. *Acanthurus leucosternon*		50	40
	a. Chalk-surfaced paper (4.90)		30	35
1009	35 s. Sea Horse (2.3.89)		30	35
1010	42 s. Lesser Frigate Bird (I) (18.10.88)		35	40
	a. Type II		7·00	
1011	50 s. *Conus aulicus* (2.3.89)		45	50
1012	57 s. Brown Booby (18.10.88)		50	55
1013	1 p. *Chelonia mydas* (turtle) (2.3.89)		85	90
1014	1 p. 50, Humpback Whale (2.3.89)		1·25	1·40
1015	2 p. *Birgus latro* (crab) (19.1.89)		1·75	1·90
1016	3 p. *Chicoreus palma-rosae* (18.10.88)		2·50	2·75
1017	5 p. *Thunnus albacares* (19.1.89)		4·25	4·50
1017a	10 p. *Stegostoma fasciatum* (12.5.92)		8·50	8·75
999/1017a		*Set of 20*	19·00	20·00

Nos. 1013/17 are horizontal, 41×26 mm and No. 1017a vertical, 26×41 mm.

On the redrawn designs there is a larger gap between the two horizontal lines on each design. On Nos. 1005 and 1008 this measures 25 mm. For these two values with a gap of 23 mm and no imprint date see Nos. 976a/b.

For 2, 5, 10, 15 and 32 s. values in a smaller format see Nos. 1087/95.

189 Capt. Cook's H.M.S.   190 Girl in Hospital Bed
Resolution

(Des and litho Walsall)

1988 (20 Oct). *Centenary of Tonga–U.S.A. Treaty of Friendship. T 189 and similar horiz designs. Multicoloured. P 14.*

1018	42 s. Type 189			60	50
1019	57 s. *Santa Maria*			75	70
1020	2 p. Cook and Christopher Columbus			2·25	2·50
1018/20			*Set of 3*	3·25	3·25
MS1021	140 × 115 mm. Nos. 1018/20			3·25	3·75

(Des and litho Walsall)

1988 (17 Nov). *Christmas. 125th Anniv of International Red Cross and 25th Anniv of Tongan Red Cross. T 123 and similar horiz designs. Multicoloured. P 14½.*

1022	15 s. Type 190 (A)		15	20
	a. Horiz. pair. Nos. 1022/3		30	40
1023	15 s. Type 190 (B).		15	20
1024	32 s. Red Cross nurse reading to boy (A)		30	35
	a. Horiz. pair. Nos. 1024/5		60	70
1025	32 s. Red Cross nurse reading to boy (B)		30	35
1026	42 s. Red Cross nurse taking pulse (A)		40	45
	a. Horiz. pair. Nos. 1026/7		80	85
1027	42 s. Red Cross nurse taking pulse (B)		40	45
1028	57 s. Red Cross nurse with sleeping child (A)		55	60
	a. Horiz. pair. Nos. 1028/9		1·10	1·25
1029	57 s. Red Cross nurse with sleeping child (B)		55	60
1030	1 p. 50, Boy in wheelchair (A)		1·40	1·50
	a. Horiz. pair. Nos. 1030/1		2·75	3·00
1031	1 p. 50, Boy in wheelchair (B)		1·40	1·50
1022/31		*Set of 10*	5·00	5·50

Nos. 1022/3, 1024/5, 1026/7, 1028/9 and 1030/1 were printed together, se-tenant, in horizontal pairs throughout the sheets with the first stamp in each pair inscribed "INTERNATIONAL RED CROSS 125th ANNIVERSARY" (A) and the second "SILVER JUBILEE OF TONGAN RED CROSS" (B).

191 Map of Tofua Island and   192 *Hypolimnas*
Breadfruit   *bolina*

(Des and litho Walsall)

1989 (28 Apr). *Bicentenary of Mutiny on the* Bounty. *T* **191** *and similar multicoloured designs. P* 13½×14.

1032	32 s. Type **191**	80	70
1033	57 s. H.M.S. Bounty and chronometer	1·00	90
1034	57 s. Captain Bligh and Bounty's launch cast adrift	1·50	1·40
1032/4	*Set of 3*	3·00	2·75

MS1035 106×80 mm. 2 p. Fletcher Christian on H.M.S. Bounty (vert); 3 p. Bligh cast adrift. P 14×13½ (2 p.) or 13½×14×13½×13½ (3 p.) 6·00 7·00

(Litho Walsall)

1989 (18 May). *Butterflies. T* **192** *and similar vert designs. Multicoloured. P* 14½×14.

1036	42 s. Type **192**	70	70
1037	57 s. Jamides bochus	90	90
1038	1 p. 20, Melanitis leda	1·50	1·50
1039	2 p. 50, Danaus plexippus	3·50	3·50
1036/9	*Set of 4*	6·00	6·00

193 Football at Rugby School, 1870

194 Short "S30" Flying Boat, 1939 (50th anniv of first flight)

(Litho Walsall)

1989 (22 Aug). *Inauguration of National Sports Stadium and South Pacific Mini Games, Tonga. T* **193** *and similar horiz designs showing development of rugby, tennis and cricket. Multicoloured. P* 14.

1040	32 s. Type **193**	50	50
	a. Sheetlet. Nos. 1040/4×2	4·50	
1041	32 s. D. Gallaher (All Black's captain, 1905) and Springboks rugby match, 1906	50	50
1042	32 s. King George V with Cambridge team, 1922 and W. Wakefield (England captain, 1926)	50	50
1043	32 s. E. Crawford (Ireland captain, 1926) and players on cigarette cards	50	50
1044	32 s. S. Mafi (Tonga captain, 1970s) and modern rugby match	50	50
1045	42 s. Royal tennis, 1659	70	70
	a. Sheetlet. Nos. 1045/9×2	6·00	
1046	42 s. Major Wingfield and lawn tennis, 1873	70	70
1047	42 s. Oxford and Cambridge tennis teams, 1884	70	70
1048	42 s. Bunny Ryan, 1910, and players on cigarette cards	70	70
1049	42 s. Boris Becker and modern tennis match	70	70
1050	57 s. Cricket match, 1743, and F. Pilch memorial	90	90
	a. Sheetlet. Nos. 1050/4×2	8·00	
1051	57 s. W. G. Grace (19th-century cricketer)	90	90
1052	57 s. Boys Own Paper cricket article, 1909	90	90
1053	57 s. Australian cricket team, 1909, and players on cigarette cards	90	90
1054	57 s. The Ashes urn, and modern cricket match	90	90
1040/54	*Set of 15*	9·50	9·50

Nos. 1040/4, 1045/9 and 1050/4 were each issued in sheetlets of ten containing two horizontal strips of five separated by a central inscribed gutter.

(Litho Walsall)

1989 (23 Oct). *Aviation in Tonga. T* **194** *and similar horiz designs. Multicoloured. P* 14½×14.

1055	42 s. Type **194**	90	80
1056	57 s. Vought "F4U Corsair", 1943	1·40	1·25
1057	90 s. Boeing "737" at Fua'amotu Airport	2·00	1·75
1058	3 p. Montgolfier balloon, Wright biplane, "Concorde" and space shuttle (97×26 mm)	6·50	6·00
1055/8	*Set of 4*	9·75	9·00

195 Aircraft landing

196 Rowland Hill, Mulready Cover and Penny Blacks

(Litho Walsall)

1989 (9 Nov). *Christmas. "Flying Home". T* **195** *and similar vert designs. P* 14×13½.

1059	32 s. blue-green, deep brown & dull orange	50	50
1060	42 s. blue-green, deep brown and emerald	60	60
1061	57 s. blue-green, deep brown and vermilion	80	80
1062	3 p. blue-green, deep brown & deep mauve	3·75	3·75
1059/62	*Set of 4*	5·00	5·00

Designs:—42 s. Villagers waving to aircraft; 57 s. Outrigger canoe and aircraft; 3 p. Aircraft over headland.

(Litho Walsall)

1989 (17 Nov). *20th Universal Postal Union Congress, Washington. Sheet* 115×110 *mm containing T* **196** *and similar vert designs. Multicoloured. P* 13½.

MS1063 57 s. Type **196**; 57 s. Early train and steam ship; 57 s. Stage coach, Pony Express poster and rider; 57 s. French hot-air balloon and flown cover; 57 s. Samuel Morse and telegraph key; 57 s. Early British mail van and pillar box; 57 s. Unloading early mail plane; 57 s. Queen Mary and Graf Zeppelin flown cover; 57 s. Helicopter and mail van; 57 s. Computer and fax machine; 57 s. "Apollo 11" emblem and space cover; 57 s. U.P.U. Monument and space shuttle 8·50 9·00

197 1989 U.P.U. Congress Stamps

198 Boxing

(Litho Walsall)

1989 (17 Nov). *"World Stamp Expo '89" International Stamp Exhibition, Washington. P* 14.

1064	**197** 57 s. multicoloured	1·00	85

(Litho Walsall)

1990 (14 Feb). *14th Commonwealth Games, Auckland. T* **198** *and similar vert designs. Multicoloured. P* 14.

1065	42 s. Type **198**	80	70
1066	57 s. Archery	1·00	85
1067	1 p. Bowls	1·75	1·75
1068	2 p. Swimming	3·00	3·25
1065/8	*Set of 4*	6·00	6·00

199 Wave Power Installation

200 Penny Black

(Litho Walsall)

1990 (11 Apr). *Alternative Sources of Electricity. T* **199** *and similar vert designs. Multicoloured. P* 14.

1069	32 s. Type **199**	60	50
1070	57 s. Wind farm	1·00	85
1071	1 p. 20, Experimental solar cell vehicle	2·25	2·50
1069/71	*Set of 3*	3·50	3·50

MS1072 110×90 mm. 2 p. 50, Planet Earth 5·00 5·50

(Litho Walsall)

1990 (1 May). *150th Anniv of the Penny Black. T* **200** *and similar horiz designs showing stamps. P* 14.

1073	42 s. multicoloured	90	90
	a. Horiz pair. Nos. 1073/4	1·75	1·75
1074	42 s. multicoloured	90	90
1075	57 s. scarlet and black	1·10	90
1076	1 p. 50, multicoloured	2·50	2·50
1077	2 p. 50, multicoloured	4·00	4·00
1073/7	*Set of 5*	8·50	8·50

Designs:—42 s. (No. 1074) Great Britain 1840 Twopence Blue; 57 s. Tonga 1886 1d.; 1 p. 50, 1980 South Pacific Scout Jamboree and Rotary 75th anniv 2 p. official stamp; 2 p. 50, 1990 Alternative Sources of Electricity 57 s.

Nos. 1073/4 were printed together, *se-tenant*, in horizontal pairs throughout the sheet.

Nos. 1073/7 show a faint grey pattern similar to W **24** in the background.

201 Departure of Canoe

202 Iguana searching for Food

(Des G. Bennett. Litho Walsall)

1990 (6 June). *Polynesian Voyages of Discovery. T* **201** *and similar vert designs. P* 14½.

1078	32 s. deep blue-green	65	55
1079	42 s. deep dull blue	90	80
1080	1 p. 20, reddish brown	2·50	2·50
1081	3 p. deep reddish violet	5·50	6·00
1078/81	*Set of 4*	8·50	9·00

Designs:—42 s. Navigating by night; 1 p. 20, Canoe and sea birds; 3 p. Landfall.

(Des and litho Walsal)

1990 (4 July). *Silver Jubilee of King Taufa'ahau Tupou IV. Designs as Nos. 985/8, but inscribed "Silver Jubilee of His Majesty King Taufa'ahau Tupou IV. 1965–1990" and with "TONGA" and values in silver. P* 11½.

1082	32 s. As Type **184**	40	30
1083	42 s. Banknote, coins, Ha'amonga Trilithon and woodcarver	50	40
1084	57 s. Rowing, communications satellite and Red Cross worker	65	55
1085	2 p. 50, Scout emblem, 1982 47 s. Scout stamp and Friendly Island Airways aircraft	3·00	3·25
1082/5	*Set of 4*	4·00	4·00

(Litho Walsall)

1990 (6 July)–**92**. *Designs as Nos.* 1000, 1002, 1003 *(value changed),* 1005 *and* 1008 *redrawn smaller,* 19×22 *mm. Multicoloured. Chalk-surfaced paper. P* 14.

1087	2 s. Porites sp	10	10
	a. Booklet pane. No. 1087×10 (4.9.90)	20	
1089	5 s. Cypraea mappa viridis	10	10
	a. Booklet pane. No. 1089×10 (4.9.90)	45	
1092	10 s. Conus bullatus	10	10
	a. Booklet pane. No. 1092×10 (4.9.90)	90	
1093	15 s. Dardanus megistos (crab) (as No. 1003) (12.5.92)	15	20
1095	32 s. Acanthurus leucosternon	25	30
	a. Booklet pane. No. 1095×10 (4.9.90)	3·00	
1087/95	*Set of 5*	55	65

The outer edges of booklet panes Nos. 1087a, 1089a, 1092a, 1095a are imperforate so that stamps from them have one or two adjacent sides imperforate.

Nos. 1087, 1089 and 1092 exist with different imprint dates below the designs.

(Des G. Drummond. Litho Questa)

1990 (12 Sept). *Endangered Species. Banded Iguana. T* **202** *and similar horiz designs. Multicoloured. P* 14.

1105	32 s. Type **202**	55	45
1106	42 s. Head of male	70	55
1107	57 s. Pair of iguanas during courtship	90	70
1108	1 p. 20, Iguana basking	2·00	2·25
1105/8	*Set of 4*	3·75	3·50

203 Tourism

204 Boy

(Des A. Benjamin and R. Edge. Litho Walsall)

1990 (25 Oct). *40th Anniv of United Nations Development Programme. T* **203** *and similar horiz designs. Multicoloured. P* 13½×14.

1109	57 s. Type **203**	90	90
	a. Pair. Nos. 1109/10	1·75	1·75
1110	57 s. Agriculture and Fisheries	90	90
1111	3 p. Education	4·00	4·00
	a. Pair. Nos. 1111/12	8·00	8·00
1112	3 p. Healthcare	4·00	4·00
1109/12	*Set of 4*	8·75	8·75

The two designs for each value were printed together, *se-tenant*, in horizontal and vertical pairs throughout the sheets.

(Des and litho Walsall)

1990 (28 Nov). *Christmas. Rotary International Interact Project. T* **204** *and similar vert designs. Multicoloured. P* 14.

1113	32 s. Type **204**	50	40
1114	42 s. Young boys	70	55
1115	2 p. Girls in western clothes	2·75	2·75
1116	3 p. Girls in traditional costumes	4·00	4·25
1113/16	*Set of 4*	7·25	7·25

205 Safety at Work

206 Yacht at Dawn

(Des C. Abbott. Litho Walsall)

1991 (10 Apr–11 Aug). *Accident Prevention.* T **205** *and similar vert designs. Multicoloured.* P 14½×14.

1117	32 s. Type 205 (English inscription)	..	50	50
	a. Horiz pair. Nos. 1117/18	..	1·00	1·00
1118	32 s. Safety at home (English inscription)		50	50
1119	32 s. As No. 1118 (Tongan inscription)	..	50	50
	a. Horiz pair. Nos. 1119/20	..	1·00	1·00
	b. Horiz pair. Nos. 1119/20a (11 Aug)		10·00	10·00
1120	32 s. As Type 205 (Tongan inscription)	..	50	50
	a. Tongan inscription corrected to "Ngaue tokanga" (11 Aug)		9·50	9·50
1121	42 s. Safety in cars (English inscription)		70	70
	a. Horiz pair. Nos. 1121/2	..	1·40	1·40
1122	42 s. Safety on bikes (English inscription)		70	70
1123	42 s. As No. 1122 (Tongan inscription)		70	70
	a. Horiz pair. Nos. 1123/4	..	1·40	1·40
1124	42 s. As No. 1121 (Tongan inscription)		70	70
1125	57 s. Safety at sea (English inscription)	..	90	90
	a. Horiz pair. Nos. 1125/6	..	1·75	1·75
1126	57 s. Safety on the beach (English inscription)	..	90	90
1127	57 s. As No. 1126 (Tongan inscription)		90	90
	a. Horiz pair. Nos. 1127/8	..	1·75	1·75
1128	57 s. As No. 1125 (Tongan inscription)		90	90
1117/28		*Set of 12*	7·50	7·50

Nos. 1117/28 were printed in sheets of 20, two panes (2×5) separated by a vertical gutter, for each value with the left-hand panes containing *se-tenant* horizontal pairs of the designs with English inscriptions and the right-hand panes similar pairs inscribed in Tongan.

No. 1120 is incorrectly inscribed in Tongan "Ngauo tokanga".

(Des D. Miller. Litho Walsall)

1991 (2 July). *Around the World Yacht Race. Sheet* 120×103 *mm containing* T **206** *and similar vert designs. Multicoloured.* P 14½×14.

MS1129	1 p. Type 206; 1 p. Yacht in the morning; 1 p. Yacht at midday; 1 p. Yacht at night	..	6·75	7·00

207 Fishes in the Sea

208 Tonga Temple

(Des D. Miller. Litho Walsall)

1991 (2 July). *Heilala Week.* T **207** *and similar vert designs. Multicoloured.* P 14½×14.

1130	42 s. Type 207	..	..	55	45
1131	57 s. Island and yacht	..	..	70	55
1132	2 p. Pile of fruit	..	..	2·40	2·50
1133	3 p. Turtle on beach	..	..	3·00	3·25
1130/3			*Set of 4*	6·00	6·00

(Des R. Edge. Litho Walsall)

1991 (19 Aug). *Centenary of Church of Latter Day Saints in Tonga.* T **208** *and similar vert design. Multicoloured.* P 14½.

1134	42 s. Type 208	..	60	60
1135	57 s. Temple at night	..	65	65

209 Making T.V. Childcare Programme

(Des R. Edge. Litho Walsall)

1991 (15 Oct). *Telecommunications in Tonga.* T **209** *and similar horiz designs. Multicoloured.* P 14½.

1136	15 s. Type 209	..	..	25	25
	a. Horiz strip of 3. Nos. 1136/8	..	65		
1137	15 s. T.V. satellite	..	..	25	25
1138	15 s. Mothers watching programme	..	25	25
1139	32 s. Man on telephone and woman with computer	..	50	50	
	a. Horiz strip of 3. Nos. 1139/41	..	1·40		
1140	32 s. Telecommunications satellite	..	50	50
1141	32 s. Overseas customer on telephone	..	50	50
1142	42 s. Sinking ship	..	..	65	65
	a. Horiz strip of 3. Nos. 1142/4	..	1·75		
1143	42 s. Coastguard controller	..	..	65	65
1144	42 s. Maritime rescue	..	..	65	65
1145	57 s. Weather satellite above Southern Hemisphere	..	..	80	80
	a. Horiz strip of 3. Nos. 1145/7	..	2·25		
1146	57 s. Meteorologists collecting data	..	80	80
1147	57 s. T.V. weather map and storm	..	80	80
1136/47			*Set of 12*	6·00	6·00

The three designs for each value were printed together, *se-tenant*, in horizontal strips of three throughout the sheets.

---

210 Women's Rowing Eight

(Des D. Miller. Litho Walsall)

1991 (29 Oct). *"Siu'a'alo" Rowing Festival.* T **210** *and similar horiz designs. Multicoloured.* P 14.

1148	42 s. Type 210	..	55	45
1149	57 s. Longboat	..	70	55
1150	1 p. Outrigger canoe	..	1·40	1·40
1151	2 p. Stern of fautasi (large canoe)	..	2·50	2·75
	a. Horiz pair. No. 1152/3	..	5·00	5·50
1152	2 p. Bow of fautasi	..	2·50	2·75
1148/52		*Set of 5*	7·00	7·00

Nos. 1151/2 were printed together, *se-tenant*, in horizontal pairs throughout the sheet, forming a composite design

211 Turtles pulling Santa's Sledge · 212 *Pangai* (patrol boat)

(Litho Walsall)

1991 (11 Nov). *Christmas.* T **211** *and similar horiz designs. Multicoloured.* P 14.

1153	32 s. Type 211	..	45	35
1154	42 s. Santa Claus on roof of fala (Tongan house)	..	55	45
1155	57 s. Family opening presents	..	70	55
1156	3 p. 50, Family waving goodbye to Santa	4·00	4·50
1153/6		*Set of 4*	5·00	5·25

(Des R. Edge. Litho Walsall)

1991 (15 Dec). *Royal Tongan Defence Force.* T **212** *and similar multicoloured designs.* P 14.

1157	42 s. Type 212	..	50	50
	a. Horiz pair. Nos. 1157/8	..	1·00	1·00
1158	42 s. Marine in battle dress	..	50	50
1159	57 s. Tonga Royal Guards	..	70	70
	a. Horiz pair. Nos. 1159/60	..	1·40	1·40
1160	57 s. Raising the ensign on *Neiafu*	..	70	70
1161	2 p. *Savea* (patrol boat) (*horiz*)	..	2·25	2·50
	a. Horiz pair. Nos. 1161/2	..	4·50	5·00
1162	2 p. King Taufa'ahau Tupou IV inspecting parade (*horiz*)	..	2·25	2·50
1157/62		*Set of 6*	6·25	6·75

The two designs for each value were printed together, *se-tenant*, in horizontal pairs throughout the sheets.

XXX

1s

(213)

214 Columbus and Signature

1992 (19 Mar). *No.* 1007 *surch with* T **213**.

1163	1 s. on 20 s. *Dascyllus aruanus*	..	20	20

(Des R. Edge. Litho Walsall)

1992 (28 Apr). *500th Anniv of Discovery of America by Columbus. Sheet* 119×109 *mm containing* T **214** *and similar vert designs. Multicoloured.* P 13½.

MS1164 57 s. Type 214; 57 s. Monastery of Santa Maria de la Chevas; 57 s. Obverse and reverse of coin of Ferdinand and Isabella; 57 s. Spain commemorative stamps of 1930; 57 s. Compass and astrolabe; 57 s. Model of *Santa Maria*; 57 s. Sketch map and signature; 57 s. 15th-century woodcut of Columbus arriving in New World; 57 s. Lucayan artefacts and parrot; 57 s. Pineapple, bird pendant and Indian nose ring; 57 s. Columbus reporting to Spanish Court; 57 s. Medal showing Columbus and signature .. 8·00 8·50

---

215 Japanese Attack on Pearl Harbor · 216 Boxing

(Des R. Edge. Litho Walsall)

1992 (26 May). *50th Anniv of Outbreak of Pacific War.* T **215** *and similar horiz designs. Multicoloured.* P 14.

1165	42 s. Type 215	..	50	50
	a. Sheetlet. Nos. 1165/76		5·50	
1166	42 s. Japanese invasion of the Philippines	50	50
1167	42 s. U.S. landings in the Gilbert Islands	50	50
1168	42 s. Landing on Iwo Jima	..	50	50
1169	42 s. Admiral Nimitz and Battle of Midway map	..	50	50
1170	42 s. General MacArthur and liberation of Philippines map	..	50	50
1171	42 s. Lt-Gen. Holland Smith and map of landings on Saipan and Tinian	..	50	50
1172	42 s. Major-Gen. Curtis Lemay and bombing of Japan map	..	50	50
1173	42 s. Japanese Mitsubishi A6M Zero	..	50	50
1174	42 s. Douglas SBD Dauntless	..	50	50
1175	42 s. Grumman FM-2 Wildcat	..	50	50
1176	42 s. Supermarine Seafire Mk.3	..	50	50
1165/76		*Set of 12*	5·50	5·50

Nos. 1165/76 were printed together, *se-tenant*, in sheetlets of 12 (4×3) on which the top row formed a composite design.

(Des J. Smith. Litho Walsall)

1992 (16 June). *Olympic Games, Barcelona.* T **216** *and similar vert designs. Multicoloured.* P 14.

1177	42 s. Type 216	..	..	50	40
1178	57 s. Diving	..	..	65	55
1179	1 p. 50, Tennis	..	..	1·75	1·75
1180	3 p. Cycling	..	..	2·75	3·00
1177/80			*Set of 4*	5·00	5·25

217 King Taufa'ahau Tupou IV and Queen Halaevalu · (218) · 45s 45s

(Des R. Edge. Litho Walsall)

1992 (4 July). *25th Anniv of the Coronation of King Tupou IV.* T **217** *and similar horiz designs.* P 13½×13 (45 s.) or 12 (*others*).

1181	45 s. multicoloured	..	55	45
1182	80 s. multicoloured	..	90	90
	a. Horiz strip of 3. Nos. 1182/4	2·40		
1183	80 s. black and cinnamon	..	90	90
1184	80 s. multicoloured	..	90	90
1185	2 p. multicoloured	..	2·25	2·40
1181/5		*Set of 5*	5·00	5·00

Designs: (48×35 *mm*)—No. 1182, King Tupou IV and Crown; No. 1183, Extract from Investiture ceremony; No. 1184, King Tupou IV and 1967 Coronation 2 p. commemorative; No. 1185, As Type 217, but larger.

Nos. 1182/4 were printed together, *se-tenant*, in horizontal strips of 3 throughout the sheet.

1992 (11 Aug). *No.* 1095 *surch with* T **218**.

1186	45 s. on 32 s. *Acanthurus leucosternon*	..	40	45

(219) · 220 Bats flying Home

1992 (11 Aug). *Nos.* 1121/4 *surch with* T **219** *in black on red.*

1187	60 s. on 42 s. Safety in cars (English inscription)	..	50	55
	a. Horiz pair. Nos. 1187/8	..	1·00	1·10
1188	60 s. on 42 s. Safety on bikes (English inscription)	..	50	55
1189	60 s. on 42 s. As No. 1187 (Tongan inscr)	50	55
	a. Horiz pair. Nos. 1189/90	..	1·00	1·10
1190	60 s. on 42 s. As No. 1188 (Tongan inscr)	50	55
1187/90		*Set of 4*	1·75	2·00

Nos. 1187/90 differ from the unsurcharged printing by showing the order of the stamps in each horizontal pair reversed.

(Des G. Bennett (Nos. 1191/5), D. Miller (No. **MS1196**). Litho Walsall)

1992 (20 Oct). *Sacred Bats of Kolovai. T 220 and similar multicoloured designs. P* 14.

1191	60 s. Type 220 ..	..	50	55
	a. Horiz strip of 5. Nos. 1191/5	..	2·25	
1192	60 s. Tongan Fruit Bat ..	..	50	55
1193	60 s. Bats alighting on branches ..	..	50	55
1194	60 s. Bats hanging from tree	..	50	55
1195	60 s. Tongan Fruit Bat in tree ..	..	50	55
1191/5		*Set of* 5	2·25	2·50

MS1196 96×112 mm. 45 s. Kula leaving Tonga; 45 s. Kula watching Chief's daughter dancing; 2 p. Kula between fires and Hina; 2 p. Kula leaving Samoa with bats (*each* 38×30 *mm*).
P 14×14½ .. .. 4·25 4·50

Nos. 1191/5 were printed together, *se-tenant*, in horizontal strips of five throughout the sheet each strip forming a composite design.

221 Tongan Pearls

222 Tonga Flag and Rotary Emblem (25th anniv of Rotary International in Tonga)

(Litho Walsall)

1992 (10 Nov). *Christmas. T 221 and similar horiz designs. Multicoloured. P* 14.

1197	60 s. Type 221 ..	..	..	..	50	55
1198	80 s. Reef fish ..	..	..	..	70	75
1199	2 p. Pacific orchids	..	..	..	1·75	1·90
1200	3 p. Parrots from Eua ..	..	..	2·50	2·75
1197/1200	..	..	*Set of* 4	5·00	5·25

(Litho Walsall)

1992 (15 Dec). *Anniversaries and Events. T 222 and similar horiz designs. P* 14×14½.

1201	60 s. multicoloured	..	..	50	55
1202	80 s. multicoloured	..	..	70	75
1203	1 p. 50, deep violet, pale lilac and black	1·25	1·40
1204	3 p. 50, multicoloured	..	..	3·00	3·25
1201/4			*Set of* 4	5·00	5·25

Designs:—80 s. Pres. Kennedy and Peace Corps emblem (25th anniv of Peace Corps in Tonga); 1 p. 50, F.A.O. and W.H.O. emblems (International Conference); 3 p. 50, Globe and Rotary Foundation emblem (75th anniv of Rotary Foundation).

223 Mother and Child

(Des G. Bennett. Litho Walsall)

1993 (26 Jan). *Family Planning. T 223 and similar vert designs. P* 14×13½.

1205	15 s. black, new blue & mag (Tongan inscr)		15	20
	a. Horiz pair. Nos. 1205/6 ..	..	30	40
1206	15 s. black, new blue & mag (English inscr)		15	20
1207	45 s. black, greenish yellow and bright yellow-green (Tongan inscr) ..		40	45
	a. Horiz pair. Nos. 1207/8 ..	..	80	90
1208	45 s. black, greenish yellow and bright yellow-green (English inscr)		40	45
1209	60 s. black, dull vermilion and chrome-yellow (Tongan inscr) ..	..	50	55
	a. Horiz pair. Nos. 1209/10 ..	..	1·00	1·10
1210	60 s. black, dull vermilion and chrome-yellow (English inscr) ..	..	50	55
1211	2 p. black, greenish yellow and red-orange (Tongan inscr) ..	..	1·75	1·90
	a. Horiz pair. Nos. 1211/12 ..	..	3·50	3·75
1212	2 p. black, greenish yellow and red-orange (English inscr) ..	..	1·75	1·90
1205/12	..	..	*Set of* 8	5·00	5·50

Designs:—45 s. Child on bike; 60 s. Girl with cats; 2 p. Old man and boy playing chess.

The two designs for each value were printed in horizontal *se-tenant* pairs throughout the sheets with those on the right inscribed in Tongan and those on the left, which have the designs reversed, in English.

224 Anti-smoking and Anti-drugs Symbols with Healthy Food

(Des D. Miller. Litho Walsall)

1993 (16 Mar). *Health and Fitness Campaign. T 224 and similar horiz designs. Multicoloured. P* 14.

1213	60 s. Type **224** ..	..	..	50	55
1214	80 s. Anti-smoking symbol and weight training ..	..		70	75
1215	1 p. 50, Anti-drugs symbol and water sports	..		1·25	1·40
1216	2 p. 50, Healthy food with cyclist and jogger	..		2·10	2·25
1213/16	..	..	..	*Set of* 4	4·00	4·50

EXPRESS STAMP

E 1 Short-eared Owl in Flight

(Litho Walsall)

1990 (21 Feb). *Air. P* 11½.
E1 E 1 10 p. black, vermilion and ultramarine .. 8·50 9·00

OFFICIAL STAMPS

G.F.B. (O 1)   **1D 1/2** (O 2)

(G.F.B. = Gaue Faka Buleaga = On Government Service)

1893 (13 Feb). *Optd with Type O 1 by Govt Printing Office, Wellington, N.Z. W 2. P 12 × 11½.*
O1	5	1d. ultramarine (C.)	..	..	9·00	35·00
		a. Bisected diagonally (½d.) (on cover)				
O2	6	2d. ultramarine (C.)	..	..	22·00	42·00
O3	5	4d. ultramarine (C.)	..	..	38·00	85·00
O4	6	8d. ultramarine (C.)	..	..	80·00	£150
O5		1s. ultramarine (C.)	..	..	90·00	£170
O1/5				Set of 5	£200	£425

Above prices are for stamps in good condition and colour. Faded and stained stamps from the remainders are worth much less.

1893 (Dec). *Nos O1 to O5 variously surch with new value, sideways as Type O 2.*
O 6	5	½d. on 1d. ultramarine	..	..	13·00	40·00
O 7	6	2½d. on 2d. ultramarine	..	..	18·00	35·00
O 8	5	5d. on 4d. ultramarine	..	..	18·00	35·00
O 9	6	7½d. on 8d. ultramarine	..	..	18·00	55·00
		a. "D" of "7½D." omitted				£800
		b. Surch double				£1300
O10		10d. on 1s. ultramarine	..	..	22·00	60·00
O6/10			..	Set of 5	80·00	£200

OFFICIAL AIRMAIL

OFFICIAL AIR MAIL **1862 TAU'ATAINA EMANCIPATION 1962** (O 3)   **40 SENITI** (O 4)

1962 (7 Feb). *Air. Centenary of Emancipation. Nos. 112/14, 116 and 118/19 optd with Type O 3 in red by R. S. Wallbank, Govt Printer.*
O11	—	2d. ultramarine	..	..	11·00	6·00
		a. "OFFICIAI"	..	..	20·00	11·00
		b. "MAII"	..	..	20·00	11·00
O12		5d. violet	..	..	12·00	6·50
		a. "OFFICIAI"	..	..	22·00	12·00
		b. "MAII"	..	..	22·00	12·00
O13	—	1s. red-brown	..	..	7·50	3·75
		a. "OFFICIAI"	..	..	25·00	11·00
		b. "MAII"	..	..	25·00	11·00
		c. Opt double				
		ca. "OFFICIAI"				
		cb. "MAII"				
O14		5s. orange-yellow and slate-lilac	..	..	90·00	55·00
		a. "MAII"	..	..	£200	75·00
O15	52	10s. yellow and black	..	..	42·00	22·00
		a. "MAII"	..	..		£100
O16	53	£1 yellow, scar, ultram & dp brt blue	..	70·00	35·00
		a. "MAII"	..	..		£150
O11/O16				Set of 6	£200	£120

SET PRICES. Official stamps from here onwards are included in the complete commemorative set prices given for any corresponding Postage issues.

1963 (15 July). *Air. First Polynesian Gold Coinage Commemoration. As T 63 but inscr "OFFICIAL AIRMAIL". 1 koula coin (diam 3⅛ in.). Imperf.*
| O17 | 63 | 15s. black | .. | .. | 3·50 | 5·50 |

1965 (18 Mar). *No. O17 surch as T 67.*
| O18 | 63 | 30s. on 15s. black | .. | .. | 3·00 | 3·75 |

1966 (18 June). *Air. Centenary of Tupou College and Secondary Education. No. 117 surch with "OFFICIAL AIRMAIL" and new value, with commemorative inscription as in T 69 but in italic capital letters.*
O19		10s. on 4d. blue-green	..	..	40	35
		a. Surch inverted	..	..	£350	£150
O20		20s. on 4d. blue-green	..	..	60	50

1967 (25 Mar). *Air. Decimal currency. No. 112 surch "OFFICIAL AIRMAIL ONE PA'ANGA" in three lines, in red.*
| O21 | | 1 p. on 5s. | .. | .. | 1·75 | 2·25 |
| | | a. "AIRMAIL" above "OFFICIAL" | .. | .. | | £140 |

No. O21a occurred once in a number of sheets until it was corrected.

1967 (4 July). *Air. No. 114 surch in various denominations as Type O 4.*
O22	53	40 s. on £1	..	..	50	50
O23		60 s. on £1	..	..	70	70
O24		1 p. on £1	..	..	90	90
O25		2 p. on £1	..	..	1·50	1·50

Nos. O22/5 were first used on 4 July 1967, but supplies of unused stamps were not made available until April 1968.

The Friendly Islands welcome the United States Peace Corps *Official Airmail* **30S** (O 5)   **Friendly Islands Trials Field & Track South Pacific Games Port Moresby 1969** *T$ 1·00 OFFICIAL AIRMAIL* (O 6)

1967 (15 Dec). *Air. Arrival of U.S. Peace Corps in Tonga. As No. 114, but imperf, and background colour changed, and surch as Type O 5.*
O26	53	30 s. on £1 yellow, scarlet, ultramarine and emerald-green	..	20	25
O27		70 s. on £1 yellow, scarlet, ultramarine and emerald-green	..	40	45
O28		1 p. 50, on £1 yellow, scarlet, ultramarine and emerald-green..	..	70	85

1968 (4 July). *50th Birthday of King Taufa'ahua IV. No. 207 surch. "HIS MAJESTY'S 50th BIRTHDAY" (as T 79), "OFFICIAL AIRMAIL" and new value.*
O29	75	40 s. on 50 s. (Turq.)	..	..	1·00	60
O30		60 s. on 50 s. (G.)	..	..	1·50	1·10
O31		1 p. on 50 s. (V.)	..	..	2·25	1·75
O32		2 p. on 50 s. (P.)	..	..	4·00	2·50

1968 (19 Dec). *Air. South Pacific Games Field and Track Trials, Port Moresby, New Guinea. As No. 114, but imperf, background colour changed and surch as Type O 6.*
| O33 | 53 | 20 s. on £1 yellow, scarlet, ultramarine and emerald-green | .. | 15 | 15 |
| O34 | | 1 p. on £1 yellow, scarlet, ultramarine and emerald-green.. | .. | 40 | 40 |

1969 (13 Aug). *Air. Third South Pacific Games, Port Moresby. Design as Nos. 290/4.*
| O35 | | 70 s. carmine-red, bright green and turquoise | 45 | 60 |
| O36 | | 80 s. carmine-red, orange and turquoise | 55 | 70 |

OFFICIAL AIRMAIL *Royal Visit* **MARCH 1970**

1969 OIL SEARCH 90s (O 7)   **OFFICIAL AIRMAIL T$1·25** (O 8)

1969 (23 Dec). *Air. First Oil Search in Tonga. As No. 114 but imperf, background colour changed to emerald-green, and surch as Type O 7.*
O37	53	90 s. on £1 multicoloured	..	2·25	2·00
		a. "1966" for "1969"			
O38		1 p. 10 on £1 multicoloured (R.)	..	2·25	2·00
		a. "1966" for "1969"			

No. O38 is surch as Type O 7, but without "OFFICIAL AIRMAIL".

OFFICIAL **Commonwealth Member JUNE 1970 50s** **AIRMAIL** (O 9)

1970 (4 June). *Entry into British Commonwealth. As No. 112 but imperf, background colour changed, and surch as Type O 9.*
O42		50 s. on 5s. orange-yellow and sepia	..	60	50
O43		90 s. on 5s. orange-yellow and sepia (R.)	..	80	70
O44		1 p. 50 on 5s. orange-yellow & sepia (G.)	..	1·50	1·25

1970 (4 June). *As Nos. 325/34, but inscr. "OFFICIAL POST". Colour of "TONGA" given for 6 to 10 s.*
O45	83	1 s. greenish yellow, brt purple & blk	..	15	15
O46		2 s. greenish yellow, ultram & black	..	20	20
O47		3 s. greenish yellow, chocolate & blk	..	25	25
O48		4 s. greenish yellow, emerald and black	..	25	25
O49		5 s. greenish yellow, orange-red & blk	..	30	30
O50	90	6 s. ultramarine	..	..	35	35
O51		7 s. deep mauve	..	..	40	40
O52		8 s. gold	..	..	45	45
O53		9 s. bright carmine	..	..	55	55
O54		10 s. silver	..	..	55	55
O45/54			Set of 10	3·00	3·00

The note after No. 334 also applies here.
See also Nos. O82/91.

Centenary British Red Cross 1870-1970 ✚ **OFFICIAL AIRMAIL 30s** ✚ (O 10)

1970 (17 Oct). *Centenary of British Red Cross. As Nos. 102 and 112 but imperf, colours changed and surch as Type O 10.*
O55		30 s. on 1½d. emerald (Blk. and R.)	..	1·25	1·25
O56		80 s. on 5s. orange-yellow & sepia (B. & R.)	..	3·25	3·25
O57		90 s. on 5s. orange-yellow & sepia (B. & R.)	..	3·25	3·25

★ **OFFICIAL AIRMAIL 20s**

1965 IN MEMORIAM 1970 (O 11)   **PHILATOKYO 71** (O 12)

1971 (30 Jan). *Air. Fifth Death Anniv of Queen Salote. As No. 113, but imperf, colours changed and surch as Type O 11.*
O58	52	20 s. on 10s. orange-yellow	..	70	60
O59		30 s. on 10s. orange-yellow (V.)	..	90	80
O60		50 s. on 10s. orange-yellow (B.)	..	1·75	1·25
O61		2 p. on 10s. orange-yellow (G.)	..	6·50	5·00

1971 (17 Apr). *Air. "Philatokyo 1971" Stamp Exhibition. Unissued Red Cross surcharges on No. 107, but imperf, colours changed and additionally surch as Type O 12.*
O62		30 s. on 5d. green and yellow (B. & R.)	..	40	40
O63		80 s. on 5d. green and yellow (Blk. & R.)	..	1·00	1·00
O64		90 s. on 5d. green and yellow (P. & R.)	..	1·25	1·25

1971 (20 July)–72. *Air. As Nos. 365/6a, but inscr "OFFICIAL AIRMAIL".*
O65	96	14 s. multicoloured	..	..	65	65
O65a		17 s. multicoloured (20.7.72)	..	75	75
O66		21 s. multicoloured	..	..	85	85
O66a		38 s. multicoloured (20.7.72)	..	1·40	1·40

O 13 Football

1971 (20 July). *Air. Fourth South Pacific Games, Tahiti.*
O67	O 13	50 s. multicoloured	..	40	55
O68		90 s. multicoloured	..	60	95
O69		1 p. 50, multicoloured	..	80	1·25

INVESTITURE **1971**

OFFICIAL 60s AIRMAIL (O 14)

(*Illustration reduced. Actual size 61 × 13 mm*)

1971 (30 Oct). *Air. Investiture of Royal Tongan Medal of Merit. Nos. 315, 318 and 316 surch as Type O 14.*
O70	89	60 s. on 3 s. multicoloured	..	50	50
O71		80 s. on 25 s. multicoloured	..	70	70
O72		1 p. 10 on 7 s. multicoloured	..	80	80

O 15 "UNICEF" and Emblem

1971 (31 Dec). *Air. 25th Anniv of UNICEF.*
O73	O 15	70 s. multicoloured	..	90	90
O74		80 s. multicoloured	..	1·00	1·00
O75		90 s. multicoloured	..	1·10	1·10

1972 (14 Apr). *Air. Merchant Marine Routes. Design similar to T 100, but inscr "OFFICIAL AIRMAIL".*
O76		20 s. multicoloured	..	60	40
O77		50 s. multicoloured	..	2·00	1·25
O78		1 p. 20, multicoloured	..	3·75	2·75

Design:—Nos. O76/8, Map of South Pacific, and Aoniu.

1972 (15 July). *Air. Fifth Anniv of Coronation. Design similar to T 101, but inscr "OFFICIAL AIRMAIL".*
O79		50 s. multicoloured	..	80	45
O80		70 s. multicoloured	..	1·10	60
O81		1 p. 50, multicoloured	..	2·40	1·00

Design (47 × 57 mm):—Nos. O79/81, As T 101, but with different background.

1972 (30 Sept). *As Nos. 413/27, but inscr* "OFFICIAL POST".

(a) As Nos. 413/17

O82	83	1 s. light yellow, scarlet and black		15	10
O83		2 s. light yellow, dp blue-green & black		20	15
O84		3 s. light yellow, yellow-green and black		25	20
O85		4 s. light yellow and black	..	25	20
O86		5 s. light yellow and black	..	25	20

(b) As Nos. O50/4, but colours changed. Colour of "TONGA" *given*

O87	90	6 s. light green ..		25	20
O88		7 s. light green ..		30	25
O89		8 s. light green ..		30	25
O90		9 s. light green ..		30	25
O91		10 s. light green ..		35	30

(c) As Nos. 423/7. Colour of face value given

O92	102	15 s. new blue	..	55	45
O93		20 s. reddish orange	..	70	60
O94		25 s. chocolate	..	80	70
O95		40 s. yellow-orange	..	1·75	1·50
O96		50 s. royal blue ..	..	2·00	1·75
O82/96			*Set of 15*	7·50	6·50

The note after No. 427 also applies here.

1972 (9 Dec). *Air. Proclamation of Sovereignty over Minerva Reefs. Design similar to T 104, but inscr* "OFFICIAL AIRMAIL".

O97	25 s. multicoloured	..	40	25
O98	75 s. multicoloured		1·25	70
O99	1 p. 50, multicoloured	..	2·50	1·25

Design: *Horiz (64 × 39 mm)—Nos. O97/9, Flags and map.*

(O 16)

1973 (30 Mar). *Air. Foundation of Bank of Tonga. No. 396 surch as Type O 16.*

O100	100	40 s. on 21 s. mult (Blk. & G.) ..		85	50
O101		85 s. on 21 s. multicoloured (B. & G.)		1·75	90
O102		1 p. 25 on 21 s. multicoloured (Br.)..		2·00	1·10

(O 17)

1973 (29 June). *Silver Jubilee of Scouting in Tonga. Nos. O76, O74 and 319 variously optd or surch as Type O 17 in silver (Nos. O103/4) or silver and blue (No. O105).*

O103	–	30 s. on 20 s. multicoloured ..		15·00	3·50
O104	O 15	80 s. multicoloured	..	32·00	12·00
O105	89	1 p. 40 on 50 s. multicoloured	..	48·00	25·00

1973 (2 Oct). *Air. Bicentenary of Capt. Cook's Visit. Design similar to T 107, but inscr* "OFFICIAL AIRMAIL".

O106	25 s. multicoloured	2·75	1·25
O107	80 s. multicoloured	7·50	3·00
O108	1 p. 30, multicoloured	9·00	4·25

Design: *Horiz (52 × 45 mm)—Nos. O106/8, James Cook (bulk carrier).*

1974

(O 18)

1973 (19 Dec). *Air. Commonwealth Games. Nos. O67/9 optd with Type O 18.*

O109	O 13	50 s. multicoloured (B.)	..	1·00	60
O110		90 s. multicoloured (Blk.)	..	1·75	1·00
O111		1 p. 50, multicoloured (G.)	..	2·50	1·75
		a. Opt double	..	£150	

O 19 Dove of Peace

1974 (20 Mar). *Air.*

O112	O 19	7 s. turq-grn, reddish vio & orge-red		25	20
O113		9 s. turq-grn, reddish vio & red-brn		30	25
O114		12 s. turq-grn, reddish vio & yell-orge		35	30
O115		14 s. turquoise-green, reddish violet			
		and bistre-yellow	..	40	35
O116		17 s. multicoloured	..	50	45
O117		29 s. multicoloured	..	80	70
O118		38 s. multicoloured	..	1·00	90
O119		50 s. multicoloured	..	1·50	1·25
O120		75 s. multicoloured	..	2·00	1·75
O112/120			*Set of 9*	6·50	5·50

1974 (20 June). *Air. Centenary of Universal Postal Union. Design similar to T 110, but inscr* "OFFICIAL AIRMAIL".

O121	25 s. dp red-orange, lt yellow-green & black		60	35
O122	35 s. lemon, magenta and black		75	45
O123	70 s. deep orange, bright blue and black		1·75	1·00

Design: *Square (40 × 40 mm)—Letters "UPU".*

1974 (11 Sept). *Air. Tongan Girl Guides. Design similar to T 111, but inscr* "OFFICIAL AIRMAIL".

O124	45 s. multicoloured	..	4·00	1·75
O125	55 s. multicoloured	..	4·25	2·00
O126	1 p. multicoloured	..	7·50	3·75

Design: *Oval (35 × 52 mm)—Lady Baden-Powell.*

(O 20)

1974 (11 Dec). *Air. Establishment of Royal Marine Institute. Nos. 446 and 451 surch as Type O 20, each obliterating the centre part of the original design.*

O127	30 s. on 15 s. multicoloured (Gold, B. & P.)		2·00	1·00
O128	35 s. on 15 s. multicoloured (Sil., B. & Blk.)		2·25	1·25
	a. Black ("TONGA TONGA") omitted	..	£200	
O129	80 s. on 17 s. multicoloured (Blk. & R.)	..	3·75	2·75

1975 (11 Mar). *Air. South Pacific Forum and Tourism. Designs similar to T 113 but inscr* "OFFICIAL AIRMAIL".

O130	50 s. multicoloured	..	1·10	80
O131	75 s. multicoloured	..	1·75	1·25
O132	1 p. 25, multicoloured	..	2·50	1·75

Designs: *(49 × 43 mm)—50 s. Jungle arch; others, Sunset scene.*

1975 (11 June). *Air. Fifth South Pacific Games. Design similar to T 114 but inscr* "OFFICIAL AIRMAIL".

O133	38 s. multicoloured	..	45	30
O134	75 s. multicoloured	..	80	60
O135	1 p. 20, multicoloured	..	1·40	1·25

Design: *Oval (51 × 27 mm):—Runners on track.*

O 21 Tongan Monarchs

1975 (4 Nov). *Air. Centenary of Tongan Constitution.*

O136	O 21	17 s. multicoloured ..	..	30	25
O137		60 s. multicoloured	..	80	55
O138		90 s. multicoloured	..	1·25	75

1976 (24 Feb). *Air. First Participation in Olympic Games. Design similar to T 117 but inscr* "OFFICIAL AIRMAIL".

O139	45 s. multicoloured	..	2·00	85
O140	55 s. multicoloured	..	2·25	1·00
O141	1 p. multicoloured	..	3·50	1·90

Design: *Oval (36 × 53 mm)—Montreal logo.*

1976 (26 May). *Air. Bicentenary of American Revolution. Designs as T 118 showing signatories to the Declaration of Independence. Inscr* "OFFICIAL AIRMAIL".

O142	20 s. multicoloured	..	1·00	40
O143	50 s. multicoloured	..	2·25	1·00
O144	1 p. 15, multicoloured	..	4·75	2·50

1976 (25 Aug). *Air. 150th Anniv of Christianity in Tonga. Hexagonal design (65 × 52 mm) showing Lifuka Chapel.*

O145	65 s. multicoloured	..	1·75	1·40
O146	85 s. multicoloured	..	2·00	1·75
O147	1 p. 15, multicoloured	..	2·75	2·50

1976 (1 Nov). *Air. Centenary of Treaty of Friendship with Germany. Rectangular design (51 × 47 mm) showing text.*

O148	30 s. multicoloured	..	60	70
O149	60 s. multicoloured	..	1·40	1·60
O150	1 p. 25, multicoloured	..	2·75	3·00

1977 (7 Feb). *Air. Silver Jubilee. Vert design (57 × 66 mm) showing flags of Tonga and the U.K.*

O151	35 s. multicoloured	..	3·00	50
O152	45 s. multicoloured	..	80	30
O153	1 p. 10, multicoloured	..	1·10	50

1977 (4 July). *Air. Tenth Anniv of King's Coronation. Square design (50 × 50 mm) showing 1967 Coronation Coin.*

O154	20 s. multicoloured	..	40	45
O155	40 s. multicoloured	..	80	90
O156	80 s. multicoloured	..	1·75	2·00

1977 (28 Sept). *Air. Bicentenary of Capt. Cook's Last Voyage. Rectangular design (52 × 46 mm) showing text.*

O157	20 s. multicoloured	..	2·75	2·00
O158	55 s. on 20 s. multicoloured	..	6·00	5·00
O159	85 s. on 20 s. multicoloured (V. and Blk.) ..		8·50	7·50

The face values of Nos. O158/9 are surcharged on the stamps, the original face value being incorrect.

1977 (16 Dec). *Air. Whale Conservation. Hexagonal design (66 × 51 mm) showing Blue Whale.*

O160	45 s. multicoloured	..	2·25	1·50
O161	65 s. multicoloured	..	3·25	2·25
O162	85 s. multicoloured	..	3·75	2·75

1978 (5 May). *Air. Commonwealth Games, Edmonton. "Teardrop" design (35 × 52 mm) showing Games Emblem.*

O163	30 s. black, blue and red	..	45	50
O164	60 s. black, red and blue	..	1·00	1·25
O165	1 p. black, red and blue	..	1·60	1·75

1978 (4 July). *Air. 60th Birthday of King Taufa'ahau Tupou IV. Medal-shaped design (21 × 45 mm) showing portrait of King.*

O166	26 s. black, vermilion and yellow	..	35	30
O167	85 s. black, light brown and yellow	..	1·10	1·00
O168	90 s. black, bright violet and yellow..		1·25	1·10

1978 (29 Sept). *Coil stamps. (a) Designs similar to Nos. 675/9 but inscr* "OFFICIAL POST".

O169	1 s. purple and greenish yellow		..	10	10
O170	2 s. brown and greenish yellow		..	10	10
O171	3 s. carmine, yellow and greenish yellow	..		10	10
O172	4 s. brown, yellow and greenish yellow		..	10	10
O173	5 s. blue-green, yellow and greenish yellow		..	10	10

(b) Designs similar to Nos. 680/4 but inscr "OFFICIAL POST"

O174	6 s. yellow-brown, emerald and light brown		15	15
O175	7 s. blue-black, emerald and light brown		20	20
O176	8 s. magenta, emerald and light brown		20	20
O177	9 s. red-brown, emerald and light brown		25	25
O178	10 s. deep green, emerald and light brown		25	25

(c) Designs similar to Nos. 685/9 but inscr "OFFICIAL POST"

O179	15 s. grey-black, orange-brown and emerald		..	45	45
O180	20 s. vermilion, orange-brown and emerald		..	50	50
O181	30 s. emerald and orange-brown		..	60	60
O182	50 s. new blue, orange-brown and emerald	..		1·10	1·10
O183	1 p. reddish violet, orange-brown & emer ..			2·00	2·00
O169/83			*Set of 15*	5·25	5·25

1978 (15 Dec). *Air. Endangered Wildlife Conservation. Designs as Nos. 690/2 but inscr* "OFFICIAL AIRMAIL".

O184	40 s. Type 129	..	1·75	1·00
O185	50 s. Insular Flying Fox	..	1·75	1·10
O186	1 p. 10, Turtle	..	3·00	2·50

1979 (16 Feb). *Air. Decade of Progress. Designs as Nos. 700/9 but inscr* "OFFICIAL AIRMAIL".

O187	38 s. Tonga Red Cross emblem	..	55	40
O188	74 s. As No. 702	..	1·00	75
O189	80 s. As No. 701	..	1·10	80

1979 (1 June). *Air. Death Centenary of Sir Rowland Hill and 10th Anniv of Tongan Self-adhesive Stamps. Hand-shaped design (45 × 53 mm) showing self-adhesive stamps being removed from backing paper.*

O190	45 s. multicoloured	..	90	60
O191	65 s. multicoloured	..	1·25	85
O192	80 s. multicoloured	..	1·60	1·10

O 22 Blue-crowned Lory with foliage   O 23 Blue-crowned Lory without foliage

1979 (17 Aug). *Air. Coil stamps.*

O193	O 22	5 s. mult (face value in black)		20	20
O194		11 s. multicoloured	..	30	30
O195		14 s. multicoloured	..	30	30
O196		15 s. multicoloured	..	40	40
O197		17 s. multicoloured	..	40	40
O198		18 s. multicoloured	..	40	40
O199		22 s. multicoloured	..	45	45
O200		31 s. multicoloured	..	65	65
O201		39 s. multicoloured	..	80	80
O202		75 s. multicoloured	..	1·50	1·75
O203		1 p. multicoloured	..	2·00	2·25
O193/203			*Set of 11*	6·75	7·00

See also No. O213.

1979 (23 Nov). *Air. Views as seen through the Lens of a Camera. Design as T 133 but showing Niuatoputapu and Tafahi.*

O204	35 s. multicoloured	..	45	45
O205	45 s. multicoloured	..	55	55
O206	1 p. multicoloured	..	1·10	1·10

1980 (9 Jan). *Air. 125th Anniv of France-Tonga Treaty of Friendship. Design as T 134 but showing the Establishment of the Principle of Religious Freedom in the Pacific Islands.*

O207	40 s. multicoloured	..	55	60
O208	55 s. multicoloured	..	80	85
O209	1 p. 25, multicoloured	..	1·75	1·90

1980 (30 Apr). *Air. Olympic Games, Moscow. Nos. O190/2 surch as T 135 in black on silver background.*

O210	26 s. on 45 s. multicoloured	..	45	50
O211	40 s. on 65 s. multicoloured	..	75	85
O212	1 p. 10, on 1 p. multicoloured	..	2·25	2·50

1980 (May). *No. O193 redrawn without foliage as Type O 23.*
O213 O 23 5 s. mult (face value in magenta) .. £100

1980 (30 Sept). *Air. South Pacific Scout Jamboree, Tonga and 75th Anniv of Rotary International. Design showing Scout camp and Rotary emblem.*
O214 25 s. multicoloured 70 40
O215 2 p. multicoloured .. .. 3·50 3·00

T$2 OFFICIAL OFFICIAL

(O 24)   (O 25)   (O 26)

1980 (3 Dec). *Air. No. O145 surch with Type O 24.*
O216 2 p. on 65 s. multicoloured .. 4·00 4·50

1983 (22 Feb–Mar). *Nos. 834/6 handstamped with Type O 25 (29 s., 32 s.) or optd with Type O 26 (47 s.).*
O217 29 s. Type 151 .. .. .. 2·75 2·75
O218 32 s. Type 151 .. .. .. 3·50 3·50
O219 47 s. Montgolfier's balloon and "Concorde" (Mar) .. .. .. 5·00 5·00
O217/19 .. .. Set of 3! 10·00 10·00

OFFICIAL OFFICIAL OFFICIAL

(O 27)   (O 28)   (O 29)

1984 (10 Apr)–**85**. *Nos. 865/79 and 881 optd with Type O 27 (1, 5, 10, 15, 29, 47 s.) or with Type O 28 (others).*
O220 1 s. Type 159 .. .. .. 10 10
O221 2 s. *Porites sp* (26.6.84) 10 10
O222 3 s. *Holocentrus ruber* (18.5.84) 10 10
O223 5 s. *Cypraea mappa viridis* 10 10
O224 6 s. *Dardanus megistos* (17.9.84).. .. 10 10
O225 9 s. *Stegostoma fasciatum* (18.5.84) .. 10 10
        b. Optd on No. 870b (28.5.85) .. 30 30
O226 10 s. *Conus bullatus* 10 10
O227 13 s. *Pterois volitans* (18.5.84) .. 15 20
O228 15 s. *Conus textile* 15 20
O229 20 s. *Dascyllus aruanus* (18.5.84) .. 15 20
O230 29 s. *Conus aulicus*.. .. 25 30
O231 32 s. *Acanthurus leucosternon* (18.5.84) .. 25 30
O232 47 s. *Lambis truncata* 40 45
O233 1 p. *Millepora dichotama* (26.6.84) .. 85 90
O234 2 p. *Birgus latro* (17.9.84).. .. 1·75 1·90
O235 5 p. *Thunnus albacares* (28.5.85).. 4·25 4·50
O220/35 .. .. .. Set of 16 8·00 8·75

1986 (16 Apr). *Nos. 933/9 optd with Type O 29.*
O236 4 s. on 2 s. *Porites sp.* 20 20
O237 4 s. on 13 s. *Pterois volitans* 20 20
O238 42 s. on 3 s. *Holocentrus ruber* .. 80 80
O239 42 s. on 9 s. *Stegostoma fasciatum* .. 80 80
O240 57 s. on 6 s. *Dardanus megistos* .. .. 1·00 1·00
O241 57 s. on 20 s. *Dascyllus aruanus* .. 1·00 1·00
O242 2 p. 50 on 2 p. *Birgus latro* .. .. 3·50 3·50
O236/42 .. .. .. Set of 7 6·75 6·75

NIUAFO'OU

The following stamps were provided for the remote island of Niuafo'ou and were not valid for postage in the remainder of Tonga.

SELF-ADHESIVE ISSUES. Nos. 1/63 were manufactured by Walsall Security Printers using the self-adhesive system as described above Tonga No. 280.

T$1

1 Map of Niuafo'ou (2)

NIUAFO'OU
KINGDOM OF TONGA

1983 (11 May). (a) *P* 14.

1	1	1 s. pale stone, black and rosine		10	10
2		2 s. pale stone, black and light emerald		10	10
3		3 s. pale stone, black & dull ultram		10	10
4		3 s. pale stone, black and chestnut		10	10
5		5 s. pale stone, black and deep magenta		10	10
6		6 s. pale stone, black and greenish blue		10	10
7		9 s. pale stone, black & dull yell-grn		15	15
8		10 s. pale stone, black & dull ultram		20	20
9		13 s. pale stone, black and light emerald		40	40
10		15 s. pale stone, black and chestnut		40	40
11		20 s. pale stone, black and greenish blue		45	45
12		29 s. pale stone, black and deep magenta		60	60
13		32 s. pale stone, black & dull yellow-green		70	70
14		47 s. pale stone, black and rosine		90	90

(b) *No. 820 of Tonga surch* (No. 15) *with T* **2** *by lithography or optd only* (No. 16) *by typography. P* 13½

15	1 p. on 2 p. pale turquoise-green & black (V.)		2·00	2·25
	a. Deep mauve surch in typography		11·00	11·00
16	2 p. pale turquoise-green (Gold)		3·00	3·25
1/16		*Set of* 16	8·50	9·50

Most examples of No. 15 have the surcharge printed by lithography. A small quantity did, however, receive a typography surcharge in a different shade to form No. 15a. In addition to the colour the typography printing can be identified by the white rims to the letters and figures. All examples of No. 16 were printed by typography.

1983 (11 May). *Inauguration of Niuafo'ou Airport. As T* 153 *of Tonga. P* 14 × 14½.

17	29 s. multicoloured		80	1·00
18	1 p. multicoloured		2·50	3·25

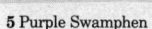

3s

(3)   **4** Eruption of Niuafo'ou

1983 (30 May). *As T* **1**, *but without value, surch with T* **3** *by Tonga Government Printer.*

19	3 s. pale stone, black and royal blue		15	15
20	5 s. pale stone, black and royal blue		15	15
21	32 s. pale stone, black and royal blue		90	90
	a. Surch inverted		£600	
22	2 p. pale stone, black and royal blue		5·50	6·00
	a. Surch inverted		90·00	
	b. Surch double			
19/22		*Set of* 4	6·00	6·50

(Des R. Edge)

1983 (29 Sept). *25th Anniv of Re-settlement. T* **4** *and similar horiz designs. Multicoloured. P* 14.

23	5 s. Type **4**		40	30
24	29 s. Lava flow		1·00	80
25	32 s. Islanders fleeing to safety		1·10	90
26	1 p. 50, Evacuation by canoe		3·50	3·75
23/6		*Set of* 4	5·50	5·25

5 Purple Swamphen   **6** Green Turtle

(Des N. Arlott)

1983 (15 Nov). *Birds of Niuafo'ou. T* **5** *and similar designs. P* 11 (1 p., 2 p.), 14 (20 s. to 47 s.) *or* 14½ (*others*).

27	1 s. black and deep mauve		20	20
28	2 s. black and bright blue		20	20
29	3 s. black and blue-green		20	20

30	5 s. black and yellow				20	20
31	6 s. black and red-orange				20	20
32	9 s. multicoloured				30	30
33	10 s. multicoloured				35	35
34	13 s. multicoloured				45	45
35	15 s. multicoloured				45	45
36	20 s. multicoloured				60	60
37	29 s. multicoloured				1·00	1·00
38	32 s. multicoloured				1·10	1·10
39	47 s. multicoloured				1·75	1·75
40	1 p. multicoloured				3·50	3·50
41	2 p. multicoloured				5·00	5·00
27/41				*Set of* 15	14·00	14·00

Designs: *Vert* (22 × 29 *mm*)—2 s. White-collared Kingfisher; 3 s. Red-headed Parrot Finch; 5 s. Banded Rail; 6 s. Polynesian Scrub Hen ("Niuafo'ou Megapode"); 9 s. Green Honeyeater; 10 s. Purple Swamphen (*different*); (22 × 36 *mm*)—29 s. Red-headed Parrot Finch (*different*); 32 s. White-collared Kingfisher (*different*); (29 × 42 *mm*)—1 p. As 10 s. *Horiz* (29 × 22 *mm*)—13 s. Banded Rail (*different*); 15 s. Polynesian Scrub Hen ("Niuafo'ou Megapode") (*different*); (36 × 22 *mm*)—20 s. As 13 s.; 47 s. As 15 s.; (42 × 29 *mm*)—2 p. As 15 s.

(Des R. Edge)

1984 (7 Mar). *Wildlife and Nature Reserve. T* **6** *and similar multicoloured designs. P* 14.

42	29 s. Type **6**			60	60
43	32 s. Insular Flying Fox (*vert*)			60	60
44	47 s. Humpback Whale			90	90
45	1 p. 50, Polynesian Scrub Hen ("Niuafo'ou Megapode") (*vert*)			3·00	3·00
42/5			*Set of* 4	4·50	4·50

7 Diagram of Time Zones   **8** Australia 1913 £2 Kangaroo Definitive

(Des R. Edge)

1984 (20 Aug). *Centenary of International Dateline. T* **7** *and similar horiz design. Multicoloured. P* 14.

46	47 s. Type **7**			60	50
47	2 p. Location map showing Niuafo'ou		1·90	2·00

1984 (17 Sept). *"Ausipex" International Stamp Exhibition, Melbourne. T* **8** *and similar vert design. Multicoloured. P* 14.

48	32 s. Type **8**			60	50
49	1 p. 50, Niuafo'ou 1983 10 s. map definitive		1·90	2·25
MS50	90 × 100 mm. As Nos. 48/9, but without exhibition logo and with face value at foot. Die cut.		1·75	2·25

Examples of No. MS50 without face values are Exhibition Banquet souvenirs without postal validity.

9 Dutch Brass Band entertaining Tongans   **10** *Ysabel*, 1902

(Des R. Edge)

1985 (20 Feb). *400th Birth Anniv of Jacob Le Maire (discoverer of Niuafo'ou). T* **9** *and similar vert designs. P* 14.

51	13 s. purple-brown, pale cinnamon & brt orge	25	20
52	32 s. purple-brn, pale cinnamon & brt new bl	55	50
53	47 s. purple-brn, pale cinnamon & brt green	75	65
54	1 p. 50, purple-brn, pale cinnamon & lemon	2·25	2·00
51/4		*Set of* 4	3·50	3·00
MS55	90 × 90 mm. 1 p. 50, purple-brown, pale cinnamon and new blue. Imperf		1·50	1·75

Designs:—No. 52, Tongans preparing kava; No. 53, Tongan canoes and outriggers; Nos. 54/5, *Eendracht* at anchor off Tafahi Island.

1985 (22 May). *Mail Ships. T* **10** *and similar horiz designs. Multicoloured.*
A. *Stamp die-cut and backing paper perf* 14.
B. *Both stamp and backing paper perf* 14.

			A		B	
56	9 s. Type **10**		20	20	35	35
57	13 s. *Tofua I*, 1908		25	25	50	50
58	47 s. *Mariposa*, 1934		65	65	1·10	1·10
59	1 p. *Matua*, 1936		1·90	1·90	2·50	2·50
56/9		*Set of* 4	2·75	2·75	4·00	4·00

For description of the two forms of perforation see after Tonga No. 864.

STANLEY GIBBONS
STAMP COLLECTING SERIES

Introductory booklets on *How to Start, How to Identify Stamps* and *Collecting by Theme*. A series of well illustrated guides at a low price.
Write for details.

---

11 Preparing to fire Rocket   **12** Halley's Comet, 684 A.D.

1985 (5 Nov). *Niuafo'ou Rocket Mails. T* **11** *and similar horiz designs. Multicoloured. P* 14.

60	32 s. Type **11**			70	70
61	42 s. Rocket in flight			90	90
62	57 s. Ship's crew watching rocket's descent		1·25	1·25
63	1 p. 50, Islanders reading mail		2·75	2·75
60/3			*Set of* 4	5·00	5·00

(Des and litho Walsall)

1986 (26 Mar). *Appearance of Halley's Comet. T* **12** *and similar vert designs. Multicoloured. P* 14.

64	42 s. Type **12**			1·10	1·10
	a. Horiz strip of 5. Nos. 64/8			5·00	
65	42 s. Halley's Comet, 1066, from Bayeux Tapestry		1·10	1·10
66	42 s. Edmond Halley			1·10	1·10
67	42 s. Halley's Comet, 1910			1·10	1·10
68	42 s. Halley's Comet, 1986			1·10	1·10
69	57 s. Type **12**			1·50	1·50
	a. Horiz strip of 5. Nos. 69/73			6·75	
70	57 s. As No. 65			1·50	1·50
71	57 s. As No. 66			1·50	1·50
72	57 s. As No. 67			1·50	1·50
73	57 s. As No. 68			1·50	1·50
64/73			*Set of* 10	11·50	11·50

Nos. 64/8 and 69/73 were each printed together, *se-tenant*, in horizontal strips of five, forming composite designs, throughout the sheets.

X X

4s

(13)   **14** Swimmers with Mail

1986 (16 Apr). *Nos.* 32/9 *surch as T* **13** *in blue.*

74	4 s. on 9 s. Green Honeyeater		30	30
75	4 s. on 10 s. Purple Swamphen		30	30
76	42 s. on 13 s. Banded Rail		90	90
77	42 s. on 15 s. Polynesian Scrub Hen		90	90
78	57 s. on 29 s. Red-headed Parrot Finch		1·40	1·40
79	57 s. on 32 s. White-collared Kingfisher		1·40	1·40
80	2 p. 50 on 20 s. Banded Rail		4·00	4·00
81	2 p. 50 on 47 s. Polynesian Scrub Hen		4·00	4·00
74/81		*Set of* 8	12·00	12·00

(Des and litho Walsall)

1986 (22 May). *"Ameripex '86" International Stamp Exhibition, Chicago. 25th Anniv of United States Peace Corps. Horiz designs as T* **173** *of Tonga. Multicoloured. P* 14.

82	57 s. Peace Corps surveyor and pipeline		1·25	1·25
83	1 p. 50, Inspecting crops		2·25	2·25
MS84	90 × 90 mm. Nos. 82/3, magnifying glass and tweezers. Imperf		3·75	4·50

(Des Walsall. Litho Questa)

1986 (27 Aug). *Centenary of First Tonga Stamps. T* **14** *and similar horiz designs showing Niuafo'ou mail transport. Multicoloured. P* 14.

85	42 s. Type **14**			90	90
86	57 s. Collecting tin can mail		1·10	1·10
87	1 p. Ship firing mail rocket		2·00	2·00
88	2 p. 50, "Collecting the Mails" (detail) (C. Mayger)		3·50	3·50
85/8		*Set of* 4	6·75	6·75
MS89	135 × 80 mm. No. 88		5·00	6·00

Nos. 85/8 were issued in sheets of twenty stamps and five *se-tenant* labels, in the central vertical column, showing the colour separations of the designs.

PRINTERS AND PROCESS. The following issues were lithographed by Walsall Security Printers, *unless otherwise stated.*

15 Woman with Nourishing Foods ("Eat a balanced diet")   **16** Hammerhead Shark

(Des C. Abbott)

1987 (11 Mar). *Red Cross. Preventive Medicine. T* **15** *and similar horiz designs. Multicoloured.* P 14×14½.

90	15 s. Type **15**			60	60
91	42 s. Nurse with baby ("Give them post-natal care")			1·60	1·60
92	1 p. Man with insecticide ("Insects spread disease")			2·50	2·50
93	2 p. 50, Boxer ("Say no to alcohol, drugs, tobacco")			4·00	4·00
90/3	.. ..		*Set of* 4	8·00	8·00

1987 (29 Apr). *Sharks. T* **16** *and similar horiz designs. Multicoloured.* P 14.

94	29 s. Type **16**			90	90
95	32 s. Tiger Shark			95	95
96	47 s. Grey Nurse Shark			1·40	1·40
97	1 p. Great White Shark			2·50	2·50
94/7			*Set of* 4	5·25	5·25
MS98	90×90 mm. 2 p. Shark and fishes			5·25	6·00

17 Capt. E. C. Musick and Sikorsky "S-42" Flying Boat

1987 (2 Sept). *Air Pioneers of the South Pacific. T* **17** *and similar horiz designs. Multicoloured.* P 14.

99	42 s. Type **17**			95	95
100	57 s. Capt. J. W. Burgess and Shorts "S-30" flying boat			1·40	1·40
101	1 p. 50, Sir Charles Kingsford Smith and Fokker "F.VIIb-3m" *Southern Cross*			2·25	2·25
102	2 p. Amelia Earhart and Lockheed "Electra 10A"			2·75	2·75
99/102	.. ..		*Set of* 4	6·50	6·50

18 Polynesian Scrub Hen and 1983 1 s. Map Definitive

19 Sailing Ship and Ship's Boat

1988 (18 May). *5th Anniversaries of First Niuafo'ou Postage Stamp* (42, 57 s.) *or Niuafo'ou Airport Inauguration* (1, 2 p.). *T* **18** *and similar horiz designs. Multicoloured.* P 14.

103	42 s. Type **18**			75	75
104	57 s. As Type **18**, but with stamp at left			95	95
105	1 p. "Concorde" and 1983 Airport Inauguration 29 s. stamp			2·00	2·00
106	2 p. As 1 p., but with stamp at left			3·00	3·00
103/6	.. ..		*Set of* 4	6·00	6·00

1988 (11 July). *Bicentenary of Australian Settlement. Sheet* 115 × 110 *mm containing T* **19** *and similar vert designs. Multicoloured.* P 13½.

MS107 42 s. Type **19**; 42 s. Aborigines; 42 s. Early settlement; 42 s. Marine and convicts; 42 s. Sheep station; 42 s. Mounted stockman; 42 s. Kangaroos and early Trans Continental locomotive; 42 s. Kangaroos and train carriages; 42 s. Flying Doctor aircraft; 42 s. Cricket match; 42 s. Wicket and Sydney skyline; 42 s. Fielders and Sydney Harbour Bridge .. .. 10·00 10·00
Each horizontal strip of 4 within No. **MS**107 shows a composite design.

20 Audubon's Shearwaters and Blowholes, Houma, Tonga

21 Sextant

1988 (18 Aug). *Islands of Polynesia. T* **20** *and similar vert designs. Multicoloured.* P 14.

108	42 s. Type **20**			95	95
109	57 s. Brown Kiwi at Akaroa Harbour, New Zealand			1·40	1·40
110	90 s. Red-tailed Tropic Birds at Rainmaker Mountain, Samoa			2·00	2·00
111	2 p. 50, Laysan Albatross at Kapoho Volcano, Hawaii			4·50	4·50
108/11	.. ..		*Set of* 4	8·00	8·00

1989 (28 Apr). *Bicentenary of Mutiny on the* Bounty. *Sheet* 115×110 *mm containing T* **21** *and similar vert designs. Multicoloured.* P 13½.

MS112 42 s. Type **21**; 42 s. Capt. Bligh; 42 s. Lieutenant, 1787; 42 s. Midshipman, 1787; 42 s. Tahitian woman and contemporary newspaper; 42 s. Breadfruit plant; 42 s. Pistol and extract from *Mutiny on the Bounty*; 42 s. Book illustration of Bligh cast adrift; 42 s. Profile of Tahitian woman and extract from contemporary newspaper; 42 s. Signatures of *Bounty* officers; 42 s. Fletcher Christian; 42 s. Tombstone of John Adams, Pitcairn Island .. .. 9·50 10·00

22 Hatchet Fish

23 Formation of Earth's Surface

1989 (2 June). *Fishes of the Deep. T* **22** *and similar horiz designs. Multicoloured.* P 14.

113	32 s. Type **22**			65	65
114	42 s. Snipe Eel			80	80
115	57 s. Viper Fish			1·00	1·00
116	1 p. 50, Football Fish			2·25	2·25
113/16			*Set of* 4	4·25	4·25

1989 (6 June–1 Aug). *The Evolution of the Earth. T* **23** *and similar vert designs. Multicoloured.*

(a) *Size* 27×35½ *mm.* P 14½

117	1 s. Type **23**			10	10
118	2 s. Cross-section of Earth's crust			10	10
119	5 s. Volcano			10	10
120	10 s. Cross-section of Earth during cooling			10	10
121	15 s. Sea			15	20
122	20 s. Mountains			15	20
123	32 s. River gorge			25	30
124	42 s. Early plant life, Silurian era			35	40
125	50 s. Fossils and Cambrian lifeforms			45	50
126	57 s. Carboniferous forest and coal seams			50	55

(b) *Size* 25½×40 *mm.* P 14 (1 Aug)

127	1 p. Dragonfly and amphibians, Carboniferous era			85	90
128	1 p. 50, Dinosaurs, Jurassic era			1·25	1·40
129	2 p. Archaeopteryx and mammals, Jurassic era			1·75	1·90
130	5 p. Human family and domesticated dog, Pleistocene era			4·25	4·50
117/30			*Set of* 14	9·25	10·00

24 Astronaut on Moon and Newspaper Headline

25 Lake Vai Lahi

1989 (17 Nov). *"World Stamp Expo '89" International Stamp Exhibition, Washington.* P 14.

131	**24** 57 s. multicoloured			1·00	1·00

1989 (17 Nov). *20th Universal Postal Union Congress, Washington. Miniature sheet, 185 × 150 mm, containing designs as Nos.* 117/31, *but with U.P.U. emblem at top right and some new values.* P 14½×14 *(top two rows) or* 14 *(bottom row).*

MS132 32 s. × 5 (as Nos. 117/21); 42 s. × 5 (as Nos. 122/6); 57 s. × 5 (as Nos. 127/31) .. 9·00 9·00
On No. **MS**132 the row of five 57 s. values are at the foot of the sheet and are perforated in a different gauge from the top two rows.

1990 (4 Apr). *Niuafo'ou Crater Lake. T* **25** *and similar horiz designs. Multicoloured.* P 14.

133	42 s. Type **25**			70	70
	a. Sheetlet. Nos. 133/8			5·50	
134	42 s. Islands in centre of lake			70	70
135	42 s. South-west end of lake and islet			70	70
136	1 p. Type **25**			1·40	1·40
137	1 p. As No. 134			1·40	1·40
138	1 p. As No. 135			1·40	1·40
133/8			*Set of* 6	5·50	5·50

Nos. 133/8 were printed together, *se-tenant*, as a sheetlet of six containing horizontal strips of three of each value forming composite designs and separated by an inscribed horizontal gutter.

COVER PRICES

Cover factors are quoted at the beginning of each country for most issues to 1945. An explanation of the system can be found on page x. The factors quoted do not, however, apply to philatelic covers.

26 Penny Black and Tin Can Mail Service

1990 (1 May). *150th Anniv of the Penny Black. T* **26** *and similar horiz designs, each showing stamp and Tin Can Mail. Multicoloured.* P 14.

139	42 s. Type **26**			80	80
140	57 s. U.S.A. 1847 10 c.			1·10	1·10
141	75 s. Western Australia 1854 1d.			1·25	1·25
142	2 p. 50, Mafeking Siege 1900 1d.			4·00	4·00
139/42			*Set of* 4	6·50	6·50

27 Humpback Whale surfacing

(Des G. Bennett)

1990 (6 June–4 Sept). *Polynesian Whaling. T* **27** *and similar horiz designs. Multicoloured.* P 11½.

143	15 s. Type **27**			55	55
144	42 s. Whale diving under canoe			1·00	1·00
145	57 s. Tail of Blue Whale			1·25	1·25
146	2 p. Old man and pair of whales			3·25	3·25
143/6			*Set of* 4	5·50	5·50
MS147	120×93 mm. 1 p. Pair of whales (38×30 mm). P 14×14½ (4 Sept)			2·25	2·75

No. **MS**147 shows "1990A" as an imprint on the 1p. stamp. Examples of this miniature sheet with "1990" as the imprint were mainly used for the surcharge, No. **MS**156, although a few unsurcharged examples with this imprint were used on Niuafo'ou in 1991.

(Des A. Benjamin and R. Edge)

1990 (25 Oct). *40th Anniv of United Nations Development Programme. Horiz designs as T* **203** *of Tonga. Multicoloured.* P 13½×14.

148	57 s. Agriculture and Fisheries			90	90
	a. Pair. Nos. 148/9			1·75	1·75
149	57 s. Education			90	90
150	2 p. 50, Healthcare			3·25	3·25
	a. Pair. Nos. 150/1			6·50	6·50
151	2 p. 50, Communications			3·25	3·25
148/51			*Set of* 4	7·50	7·50

The two designs for each value were printed together, *se-tenant*, in horizontal and vertical pairs throughout the sheets.

28 H.M.S. *Bounty*

XX

1991 ORNITHOLOGICAL AND SCIENTIFIC EXPEDITION.

T$1

(29)

(Des D. Miller)

1991 (25 July). *Bicentenary of Charting of Niuafo'ou. T* **28** *and similar vert designs. Multicoloured.* P 14½×14.

152	32 s. Type **28**			75	75
	a. Horiz strip of 3. Nos. 152/4			2·50	
153	42 s. Chart of *Pandora's* course			95	95
154	57 s. H.M.S. *Pandora*			1·10	1·10
152/4			*Set of* 3	2·50	2·50
MS155	120×93 mm. 2 p. Capt. Edwards of the *Pandora*; 3 p. Capt. Bligh of the *Bounty*			6·50	7·00

Nos. 152/4 were printed together, *se-tenant*, in horizontal strips of three throughout the sheet.

1991 (31 July). *Ornithological and Scientific Expedition to Niuafo'ou. No.* **MS**147 *surch with T* **29** *in blue by Govt. Printer, Tonga.*

MS156 120×93 mm. 1 p. on 1 p. multicoloured .. 1·50 2·00
No. **MS**156 shows "1990" as the imprint date.

30 Longhorned Beetle Grub

31 Heina meeting the Eel

(Des G. Bennett)

1991 (11 Sept). *Longhorned Beetle. T* **30** *and similar vert designs. Multicoloured. P* 14¹/₂×14.

157	42 s. Type **30**	..	..	..	60	60
158	57 s. Adult beetle	..	..	..	80	80
159	1 p. 50, Grub burrowing		..	..	2·25	2·25
160	2 p. 50, Adult on treetrunk		..	..	3·25	3·25
157/60	..	..	..	*Set of* 4	6·25	6·25

(Des D. Miller)

1991 (12 Nov). *The Legend of the Coconut Tree. T* **31** *and similar horiz designs. Multicoloured. P* 14×14¹/₂.

161	15 s. Type **31**	..	..	..	25	25
162	42 s. Heina crying over the eel's grave		..	60	60
MS163	96×113 mm. 15 s. Type **31**; 42 s. No. 162;					

1 p. 50, Heina's son collecting coconuts; 3 p. Milk
flowing from coconut .. .. 6·00 7·00

(Des R. Edge)

1992 (28 Apr). *500th Anniv of Discovery of America by Columbus. Sheet* 119×109 *mm. containing vert designs as T* **214** *of Tonga. Multicoloured. P* 13¹/₂.

MS164 57 s. Columbus; 57 s. Queen Isabella and
King Ferdinand; 57 s. Columbus being blessed
by Abbot of Palos; 57 s. 15th-century compass;
57 s. Wooden traverse, windrose and the *Nina*;
57 s. Bow of *Santa Maria*; 57 s. Stern of *Santa
Maria*; 57 s. The *Pinta*; 57 s. Crew erecting cross;
57 s. Sailors and Indians; 57 s. Columbus
reporting to King and Queen; 57 s. Coat of Arms 7·50 8·00

(Des R. Edge)

1992 (12 May). *50th Anniv of Outbreak of Pacific War. Horiz designs as T* **215** *of Tonga, each showing contemporary newspaper headline. Multicoloured. P* 14.

165	42 s. American battleship ablaze, Pearl Harbor	..	..	60	60
	a. Sheetlet. Nos. 165/76		..	6·50	
166	42 s. Destroyed American aircraft, Hawaii		60	60
167	42 s. Japanese A6M Zero fighter	..		60	60
168	42 s. Pres. Roosevelt signing Declaration of War	..	..	60	60
169	42 s. Japanese T 95 light tank and Gen. MacArthur	..	..	60	60
170	42 s. Douglas SBD Dauntless dive-bomber and Admiral Nimitz	..	..	60	60
171	42 s. Bren gun and Gen. Sir Thomas Blamey	60	60
172	42 s. Australian mortar crew, Kokoda	..	60	60
173	42 s. U.S.S. *Mississippi* in action and Maj-Gen. Julian C. Smith	..	..	60	60
174	42 s. U.S.S. *Enterprise* (aircraft carrier)	..	60	60
175	42 s. American marine and Maj-Gen. Curtis Lemay	..	..	60	60
176	42 s. B-29 bomber and Japanese surrender, Tokyo Bay	..	..	60	60
165/76	..	..	*Set of* 12	6·50	6·50

Nos. 165/76 were printed together, *se-tenant*, in sheetlets of 12
(4×3) with each horizontal row forming a composite design.

(Des R. Edge)

1992 (4 July). *25th Anniv of the Coronation of King Tupou IV. Horiz designs as T* **217** *of Tonga. P* 13¹/₂×13 (45 s.) *or* 12 (*others*).

177	45 s. multicoloured	..	..	55	55
178	80 s. multicoloured	..	..	1·00	1·00
	a. Horiz strip. Nos. 177/81	..	..	2·75	
179	80 s. black and cinnamon	..	..	1·00	1·00
180	80 s. multicoloured	..	..	1·00	1·00
181	2 p. multicoloured	..	..	2·25	2·25
177/81	..	..	*Set of* 5	5·25	5·25

Designs: (34×23 *mm*)—No. 177, King Taufa'ahau Tupou IV
and Queen Halaevalu during Coronation; (48×35 *mm*)—No.
178, King Tupou IV and Tongan national anthem; No. 179,
Extract from Investiture ceremony; No. 180, Tongan choir; No.
181, As 45 s.

Nos. 177/81 were printed together, *se-tenant*, in horizontal
strips of 3 throughout the sheet.

32 Male and Female Scrub
Hens searching for Food

(Des G. Bennett)

1992 (15 Sept). *Endangered Species. Polynesian Scrub Hen. T* **32** *and similar horiz designs. P* 14.

182	45 s. Type **32**	..	..	60	60
183	60 s. Female guarding egg	..	..	75	75
184	80 s. Chick	..	..	1·00	1·00
185	1 p. 50, Head of male	..	..	1·90	1·90
182/5	..	..	*Set of* 4	3·75	3·75

Transjordan

Transjordan was part of the Turkish Empire from 1516 to 1918. The area was overrun by British and Arab forces, organised by Colonel T. E. Lawrence, in September 1918, and as Occupied Enemy Territory (East), became part of the Syrian state under the Emir Faisal, who was king of Syria from 11 March to 24 July 1920. On 25 April 1920 the Supreme Council of the Allies assigned to the United Kingdom a mandate to administer both Palestine and Transjordan, as the area to the east of the Jordan was called. The mandate came into operation on 29 September 1923. During 1920 the stamps of the Arab Kingdom of Syria were in use.

BRITISH MANDATED TERRITORY

(1000 milliemes = 100 piastres = £1 Egyptian)

"EAST". Where the word "East" appears in the Arabic overprints it is not used in its widest sense but as implying the land or government "East of Jordan".

("East of Jordan") (1)   (1a)

(Optd at Greek Orthodox Convent, Jerusalem)

1920 (Nov). *T* **3** *of Palestine optd with T* **1**. (a) P 15 × 14.

1	1	1 m. sepia		40	80
		a. Opt inverted		£120	
2		2 m. blue-green		5·00	6·50
		a. Silver opt		£180	£200
3		3 m. yellow-brown		50	80
		a. Opt Type 1a		£1100	
4		4 m. scarlet		60	80
5		5 m. yellow-orange		70	1·00
5a		1 p. deep indigo (Silver)		£2000	
6		2 p. olive		2·00	4·50
		a. Opt Type 1a		£1100	
7		5 p. deep purple		18·00	23·00
		a. Opt Type 1a		£1200	
8		9 p. ochre		£1000	£1200
1/7 (ex 5a)			Set of 7	24·00	35·00

(b) P 14

9	1	1 m. sepia		50	60
		a. Opt inverted		£150	
10		2 m. blue-green		40	60
		a. Silver opt		£200	
11		3 m. yellow-brown		8·00	8·50
12		4 m. scarlet		15·00	16·00
13		5 m. orange		1·50	80
14		1 p. deep indigo (Silver)		90	1·75
15		2 p. deep olive		1·75	2·50
16		5 p. purple		2·00	5·00
17		9 p. ochre		3·50	16·00
18		10 p. ultramarine		4·00	16·00
19		20 p. pale grey		8·00	26·00
9/19			Set of 11	40·00	85·00

Emir Abdullah, 1 April 1921–22 May 1946

Abdullah, a son of the King of the Hejaz, was made Emir of Transjordan in 1921. On 26 May 1923 Transjordan was recognised as an autonomous state and on 20 February 1928 it was accorded a degree of independence.

("Tenth of a piastre") (2)   ("Piastre") (3)

1922 (Nov). *Nos. 1/19 additionally handstamped with steel dies at Amman as T* **2** *or* **3**. (a) P 15 × 14.

20	2	1/10 p. on 1 m. sepia		25·00	45·00
		a. Red surch		70·00	70·00
		b. Violet surch		70·00	70·00
21		2/10 p. on 2 m. blue-green		28·00	28·00
		a. Error. Surch "3/10" for "2/10"		£110	£110
		b. Red surch		80·00	80·00
		c. Violet surch		£100	£100
22		3/10 p. on 3 m. yellow-brown		10·00	10·00
		a. Pair, one without surch		£750	
		b. Opt Type 1a		£1500	
		c. Violet surch		£150	£150
23		4/10 p. on 4 m. scarlet		50·00	50·00
24		5/10 p. on 5 m. yellow-orange		£180	£100
		a. Violet surch		£350	£300
25	3	2 p. on 2 p. olive		£250	75·00
		aa. Opt Type 1a		£1500	
		a. Red surch		£275	80·00
		b. Violet surch		£300	90·00
26		5 p. on 5 p. deep purple		50·00	70·00
		a. Opt Type 1a		£1500	
27		9 p. on 9 p. ochre		£300	£350
		a. Red surch		£130	£140

(b) P 14

28	2	1/10 p. on 1 m. sepia		20·00	25·00
		a. Red surch		60·00	60·00
		b. Violet surch		£250	£300
29		2/10 p. on 2 m. blue-green		25·00	25·00
		a. Error. Surch "3/10" for "2/10"		£100	£100
		b. Red surch		80·00	80·00
		c. Violet surch		80·00	80·00

30	2	5/10 p. on 5 m. orange		£250	£100
		a. Violet surch		£275	
31	3	1 p. on 1 p. deep indigo (R.)		£200	60·00
		a. Violet surch		£400	
32		9 p. on 9 p. ochre (R.)		£500	£500
33		10 p. on 10 p. ultramarine		£950	£1000
34		20 p. on 20 p. pale grey		£800	£850
		a. Violet surch		£900	£950

T **3** *of Palestine (perf* 15×14) *similarly surch*

35	3	10 p. on 10 p. ultramarine		£2000	£2500
36		20 p. on 20 p. pale grey		£2500	£3000

T **2** reads "tenths of a piastre". *T* **3** reads "the piastre", both with Arabic figures below. These surcharges were supplied in order to translate the Egyptian face values of the stamps into terms intelligible to the local population, *i.e.* tenths of a piastre (= milliemes) and piastres of the Turkish gold pound; but the actual face value of the stamps remained unchanged.

Being handstamped the surcharge may be found either at the top or bottom of the stamp, and exists double on most values.

("Arab Government of the East, April 1921") (4)

1922 (Dec). *Stamps of 1920, handstamped with a steel die as T* **4** *in red-purple, violet or black.** (a) P 15 × 14.

37	4	1 m. sepia (R.P.)		25·00	25·00
		a. Violet opt		28·00	28·00
		b. Black opt		22·00	22·00
38		2 m. blue-green (R.P.)		22·00	22·00
		a. Violet opt		20·00	20·00
		b. Black opt		18·00	18·00
39		3 m. yellow-brown (R.P.)		25·00	25·00
		a. Opt Type 1a		£1600	
		b. Violet opt		7·00	7·00
		ba. Pair, one without opt		£1000	
		c. Black opt		8·00	8·00
40		4 m. scarlet (R.P.)		45·00	50·00
		a. Violet opt		45·00	50·00
		b. Black opt		45·00	50·00
41		5 m. yellow-orange (R.P.)		35·00	10·00
		a. Violet opt		15·00	10·00
42		2 p. olive (No. 6) (R.P.)		55·00	40·00
		a. Violet opt		20·00	15·00
		b. Black opt		12·00	10·00
		c. On No. 6a (R.P.)		£1500	
		d. On No. 6a (V.)		£1500	£1300
43		5 p. deep purple (R.P.)		80·00	£100
		aa. Pair, one without opt		£1500	
		a. Violet opt		60·00	80·00
44		9 p. ochre (R.P.)		£400	£450
		a. Violet opt		£200	£250
		ab. Opt Type 1a		£2000	
		b. Black opt		65·00	80·00

(b) P 14

45	4	1 m. sepia (R.P.)		12·00	15·00
		a. Pair, one without opt		£1000	
		b. Violet opt		22·00	20·00
		c. Black opt		18·00	18·00
46		2 m. blue-green (R.P.)		25·00	25·00
		a. Violet opt		8·00	8·00
		b. Black opt		10·00	10·00
46c		3 m. yellow-brown (V.)		£750	£350
47		5 m. orange (R.P.)		£300	75·00
		a. Violet opt		25·00	20·00
48		1 p. deep indigo (R.P.)		25·00	15·00
		a. Violet opt		15·00	9·00
49		2 p. olive (V.)		75·00	80·00
50		5 p. purple (R.P.)		90·00	£100
		a. Violet opt		£100	£110
51		9 p. ochre (V.)		£900	£1000
52		10 p. ultramarine (R.P.)		£1800	£1900
		a. Violet opt		£1500	£1600
53		20 p. pale grey (R.P.)		£1900	£2000
		a. Violet opt		£1600	£1700

*The ink of the "black" overprint is not a true black, but is caused by a mixture of inks from different ink-pads. The colour is, however, very distinct from either of the others. Other values may exist with "black" overprint.

Most values are known with inverted and/or double overprints.

("Arab Government of the East, April 1921") (5)

1923 (1 Mar). *Stamps of 1920, with typographed overprint, T* **5**.

(a) P 15 × 14

54	5	1 m. sepia (Gold)		£1800	£2000
55		2 m. blue-green (Gold)		20·00	22·00
56		3 m. yellow-brown (Gold)		12·00	15·00
		a. Opt double		£250	
		b. Opt inverted		£275	
		c. Black opt		75·00	85·00
57		4 m. scarlet		10·00	12·00
58		5 m. yellow-orange		50·00	45·00
59		2 p. olive (No. 6) (Gold)		15·00	15·00
		a. Black opt		£300	
		b. On No. 6a (Gold)		£1200	£1000
60		5 p. deep purple (No. 7) (Gold)		60·00	80·00
		a. Opt inverted		£300	
		b. On No. 7a		£1500	
		ba. Ditto. Gold opt inverted		£2000	

(b) P 14

62	5	1 m. sepia (Gold)		18·00	24·00
		a. Opt inverted		£300	

63	5	2 m. blue-green (Gold)		15·00	18·00
		a. Opt inverted		£350	
		b. Opt double		£275	
64		5 m. orange		12·00	12·00
65		1 p. deep indigo (Gold)		12·00	14·00
		a. Opt double		£450	£475
		b. Black opt		£800	£850
66		9 p. ochre		75·00	£100
67		10 p. ultramarine (Gold)		75·00	£100
68		20 p. pale grey (Gold)		75·00	£100
		a. Opt inverted		£350	
		b. Opt double		£425	
		c. Opt double, one inverted		£425	
		e. Opt double, one gold, one black, latter inverted		£650	
		f. Black opt		£800	
		fa. Black opt inverted		£1200	
		fb. Black opt double, one inverted		£1200	

There are numerous constant minor varieties in this overprint in all values.

The 20 p. exists with top line of overprint only or with the lines transposed, both due to misplacement.

Same overprint on stamp of Palestine, T **3**

69	5	5 m. orange		£1200	£1400

In this variety the overprint, *T* **1** of Jordan, has been applied to the stamp, but is not inked, so that it is hardly perceptible.

(6)   (7)

(8)   (9)

1923 (April–Oct). *Stamps of the preceding issues further surch by means of handstamps.* (a) *Issue of Nov* 1920.

70	—	2½/10ths p. on 5 m. (13) (B.–Blk.)		£160	£160
		a. Black surch		£160	£160
		b. Violet surch		£160	£160

(b) Stamp of Palestine

71	6	5/10 p. on 3 m. (7)		£7500

(c) Issue of Nov 1922

72	6	5/10 p. on 3 m. (22)		£7000	
73		5/10 p. on 5 p. (26) (V.)		70·00	80·00
73b		5/10 p. on 9 p. (27a)		£350	£375
74	7	1/2 p. on 9 p. (26)		70·00	80·00
75		1/2 p. on 9 p. (27)		£7500	
		a. On No. 27a		£350	£400
76		1/2 p. on 9 p. (32)		—	£8000
77	8	1 p. on 5 p. (26)		80·00	£100

(d) Issue of Dec 1922

78	6	5/10 p. on 3 m. (39)		85·00	£100
		a. On No. 39a		£750	
		ab. Pair, one without surch		£1400	
		b. On No. 39b		40·00	50·00
		c. Without numeral of value		£150	
79		5/10 p. on 5 p. (43a)		8·00	14·00
		c. Pair, one without surch		£500	
79d		5/10 p. on 9 p. (44b)		—	£1200
		e. Surch on No. 44a		—	£1300
80	7	1/2 p. on 2 p. (42)		£100	£120
		b. On No. 42a		80·00	£110
		c. On No. 42b		60·00	£110
		e. On No. 42b. Pair, one without surch		£1000	
		f. On No. 42c		£2000	
81		1/2 p. on 5 p. (43a)		£3000	
82		1/2 p. on 5 p. (50)		£1800	
83	8	1 p. on 5 p. (43)		£3750	
		b. On No. 43a		£2000	£2250

(e) Issue of 1 March 1923

84	6	5/10 p. on 3 m. (56)		25·00	30·00
85	7	1/2 p. on 9 p. (p 15×14)		90·00	£150
86		1/2 p. on 9 p. (66)		£150	
87	9	1 p. on 10 p. (67)		£2250	£2500
		a. Violet surch		£2750	
88		2 p. on 20 p. (68)		60·00	80·00
88a		2 p. on 20 p. (68f)		£2000	

The handstamp on No. 88 has an Arabic "2" in place of the "1" shown in the illustration of Type **9**.

Being handstamped many of the above exist inverted or double.

TYPES OF SAUDI ARABIA. The following illustrations are repeated here for convenience from Saudi Arabia.

11   20

21   22

حكومة
الشرق العربية
٩ شعبان ١٣٤١

("Arab Government of the
East, 9 Sha'ban 1341")
(10)

("Arab Government of
the East. Commemoration
of Independence,
25 May 1923")
(11)

It should be noted that as Arabic is read from right to left, the overprint described as reading downwards appears to the English reader as though reading upwards. Our illustration of Type 11 shows the overprint reading downwards.

1923 (April). *Stamps of Saudi Arabia. T 11, with typographed opt, T 10.*

89	10	⅛ p. chestnut			2·00	1·75
		a. Opt double ..	..	..	£200	
		b. Opt inverted			£150	
90		½ p. scarlet	..	..	2·00	1·75
91		1 p. blue ..	..	..	1·25	80
		a. Opt inverted ..	..	£160	£180	
92		1½ p. lilac ..	..	..	1·50	1·75
		a. Opt double ..	..		£225	
		b. Top line omitted ..	..	—	£225	
		c. Pair, one without opt		£300		
93		2 p. orange	..	..	2·00	5·00
94		3 p. brown ..	..	..	3·00	7·00
		a. Opt inverted ..	..		£300	
		b. Opt double ..	..		£300	
		c. Pair, one without opt		£500		
95		5 p. olive ..	..	..	5·00	8·00
89/95				*Set of 7*	15·00	23·00

On same stamps, surcharged with new values (Saudi Arabia, Nos. 47 and 49)

96	10	¼ p. on ⅛ p. chestnut	..	4·00	5·00
		a. Opt and surch inverted	..	£200	
		b. Ditto. but 2nd and 3rd lines of opt omitted		£250	
97		10 p. on 5 p. olive..	..	15·00	20·00

In this setting, the first line of the overprint measures 9 mm, the second 18½–19½ mm, and the third, 19–21 mm. On 35 stamps out of the setting of 36 the Arabic "9" (right-hand character in bottom line) is widely spaced from the rest of the inscription. Minor varieties of this setting exist on all values.
For later setting, varying from the above, see Nos. 121/4.

٩٢٣   ٩٣٣

Normal. "923"   Error. "933"

An error reading "933" instead of "923" occurs as No. 2 in the setting of 24 on all values. As only 24 stamps were overprinted for each of Nos. 103A, 105B, 107B and 108A only one example of the error can exist for each. No such examples have so far been recorded.

1923 (25 May). *T 3 of Palestine optd with T 11, reading up or down, in black or gold. A. Reading downwards. B. Reading upwards.*

				A		B	
98	1 m. (Blk.)	..	..	17·00	17·00	90·00	£100
	a. Opt double, one inverted (Blk.)		£750	£750		†	
	b. Gold opt ..	..	£150	£160	£150	£160
	c. Opt double, one inverted (Gold)		£900		—	†
	d. Opt double (Blk. + Gold)	£900	£900	—	†	
	e. Arabic "933"	..	85·00	—	£250	—
99	2 m. (Blk.)	..	..	28·00	35·00	45·00	50·00
	a. Arabic "933"	..	£140	—	£200	—
100	3 m. (Blk.)	..	..	10·00	12·00	90·00	£100
	a. Arabic "933"	..	70·00	—	£250	—
101	4 m. (Blk.)	..	..	10·00	12·00	25·00	32·00
	a. Arabic "933"	..	70·00	—	£130	—
102	5 m. (Blk.)	..	..	50·00	60·00		†
	a. Arabic "933"	..	£250	—		—
103	1 p. (Gold)	..	..	£750	—	50·00	60·00
	a. Opt double ..		£900	£900	—	†
	b. Black opt	..	†		—	
	c. Arabic "933"	..		—	£250	—
104	2 p. (Blk.)	..	..	50·00	70·00		—
	a. Arabic "933"	..	£250	—		—
105	5 p. (Blk.)	..	..	60·00	70·00	£750	£550
	a. Opt double ..		£650	—		†
	b. Arabic "933"	..	£275	—		—
106	9 p. (Blk.)	..	..	70·00	90·00	50·00	60·00
	a. Arabic "933"	..	£300	—	£250	—
107	10 p. (Blk.)	..	..	60·00	80·00	£600	—
	a. Arabic "933"	..	£275	—		—
108	20 p. (Blk.)	..	..	£700	—	70·00	90·00
	a. Arabic "933"	..		—	£300	—

The 9 and 10 p. are perf 14, all the other values being perf 15×14.

No. 107A surch with T 9

109	1 p. on 10 p. ultramarine	..	..	£6000

نصف قرش
(12)

1923 (Sept). *No. 92 surch with T 12. (a) Handstamped.*

110	12	½ p. on 1½ p. lilac	..	6·00	6·00
		a. Surch and opt inverted		75·00	
		b. Opt double ..	..	75·00	
		c. Opt double, one inverted	90·00	£100	
		d. Pair, one without opt		£180	

This handstamp is known inverted, double and double, one inverted.

(b) Typographed

111	12	½ p. on 1½ p. lilac	..	50·00	50·00
		a. Surch inverted	..	£250	
		b. Surch double	..	£200	
		c. Pair, one without surch		£500	

سكرمة   حكرمة   حكمة

الثرق العربية   الشرق العربية
٩ شبان ١٣٤١   ٩ شمان١٣٤١
(13a)   (13b)
("Arab Government of the East, 9 Sha'ban, 1341")

These two types differ in the spacing of the characters and in the position of the bottom line which is to the left of the middle line in T 13a and centrally placed in T 13b.

1923 (Oct). *T 11 of Saudi Arabia handstamped as T 13a or 13b.*

112	13a	½ p. scarlet	..	..	6·00	7·00
113	13b	½ p. scarlet	..	..	6·00	7·00

د٠ق٠ج

ملك العرب

ا اج٠ث ٣٤٢٠

(15 "Arab Government of the East")   ("Commemorating the coming of His Majesty the King of the Arabs" and date) (16)

1924 (Jan). *T 11 of Saudi Arabia with typographed opt T 15.*

114	15	½ p. scarlet	..	..	6·00	8·00
		a. Opt inverted	..		£250	
115		1 p. blue ..	..	£300	£200	
116		1½ p. lilac..	..	£350		

The ½ p. exists with thick, brown gum, which tints the paper, and with white gum and paper.

1924 (18 Jan). *Visit of King Hussein of Hejaz. T 11 of Saudi Arabia optd T 15 and with further typographed opt T 16.*

A. *In Black.* B. *In Gold.*

			A		B	
117	16	½ p. scarlet	1·00	1·00	2·00	2·00
		a. Type 15 omitted	£150	—	†	
		b. Type 16 inverted	£200	—	†	
		c. Imperf between (pr)	£110		—	
118		1 p. blue	1·25	1·25	2·00	2·00
		a. Type 15 omitted	£150	—	†	
		b. Both opts inverted	£200	—	£300	—
		d. Imperf between (pr)	†		—	
119		1½ p. lilac	2·00	2·00	3·00	3·00
		a. Type 15 inverted	£130	—	£150	—
120		2 p. orange	4·00	6·00	6·00	6·00

The spacing of the lines of the overprint varies considerably, and a variety dated "432" for "342" occurs on the twelfth stamp in each sheet.

1924 (Mar–May). *T 11 of Saudi Arabia optd as T 10 (new setting).*

121		½ p. scarlet ..	..	..	3·00	3·00
		a. Opt inverted	..		£120	
122		½ p. maroon	..	..	10·00	8·00
		a. Opt inverted	..		£120	
123		1 p. blue ..	..	..	5·00	2·00
		a. Opt double	..		£150	
124		1½ p. lilac ..	..	..	7·50	8·50

*This setting is from fresh type, the first line measuring 8¾ mm, the second nearly 20 mm and third 18¼ mm.
On all stamps in this setting (except Nos. 1, 9, 32 and 33) the Arabic "9" is close to the rest of the inscription.
The dots on the character "Y" (the second character from the left in the second line) are on many stamps vertical (:) instead of horizontal (..).
There are many errors. In the third line, No. 24 of the setting reads "Shabál", and No. 27 reads "Shabn" (instead of "Shab'an").
On some sheets of the ½ p. (both colours), the right hand character, "H", in the first line, was omitted from the second stamp in the first row of the sheet.

NEW INFORMATION

The editor is always interested to correspond with people who have new information that will improve or correct the Catalogue.

حكومة الشرق
العربي
١٣٤٢

حكومة
الشرق العربي
سنة ١٣٤٣

("Government of the Arab East, 1342") (17)   ("Government of the Arab East, 1343") (18)

1924 (Sept–Nov). *T 11 of Saudi Arabia with type-set opt as T 17.*

125	17	⅛ p. chestnut	..	..	35	25
		a. Opt inverted	..		£130	
126		¼ p. green	..	..	30	30
		a. Tête-bêche (pair)	..	7·50	10·00	
		b. Opt inverted	..		£100	
127		½ p. scarlet	..	..	30	30
128		½ p. maroon	..	..	1·50	60
129		1 p. blue	..	..	2·50	1·50
		a. Imperf between (horiz pair)		£130		
		b. Opt inverted				
130		1½ p. lilac	..	..	2·50	2·50
131		2 p. orange	..	..	2·00	2·00
132		3 p. brown-red	..	..	1·50	1·50
		a. Opt inverted	..		£100	
		b. Opt double	..		£100	
133		5 p. olive	..	..	2·00	2·50
134		10 p. brown-purple and mauve (R.)	..	4·00	5·00	
		a. Centre inverted	..		£140	
		b. Black opt ..	..			
125/34				*Set of 10*	15·00	15·00

Varieties may be found with dates "1242" or "1343", with "1" or "2" inverted, and other errors exist.

1925 (Aug). *T 20/22 of Saudi Arabia with lithographed opt T 18.*

135	18	⅛ p. chocolate	..	..	30	60
		a. Imperf between (horiz pair)	£110	£130		
136		¼ p. ultramarine	..	..	30	60
137		½ p. carmine	..	..	40	35
138		1 p. green	..	..	40	35
139		1½ p. orange	..	..	75	1·50
140		2 p. blue	..	..	1·00	1·75
		a. Opt treble	..	£150	£200	
141		3 p. sage-green (R.)	..	1·25	2·50	
		a. Imperf between (horiz pair)	£110	£160		
		b. Black opt	..	£120	£150	
142		5 p. chestnut	..	..	2·00	5·00
135/42				*Set of 8*	5·75	11·50

The whole series exists imperforate and (except the 1 and 2 p.) with inverted overprint, both perf and imperf.

شرق
الاردن

("East of the Jordan") (19)   22 Emir Abdullah   23 Emir Abdullah

(Opt typo by Waterlow)

1925 (1 Nov). *Stamps of Palestine, 1922 (without the three-line Palestine opt), optd with T 19. Wmk Mult Script CA. (a) P 14.*

143	19	1 m. deep brown	..	..	10	15
144		2 m. yellow	..	..	10	15
145		3 m. greenish blue	..	..	10	15
146		4 m. carmine-pink	..	..	10	15
147		5 m. orange	..	..	10	15
		a. Yellow-orange	..	35·00	20·00	
148		6 m. blue-green ..	..	..	15	20
149		7 m. yellow-brown	..	..	15	20
150		8 m. scarlet	..	..	20	30
151		13 m. ultramarine	..	..	40	60
152		1 p. grey	..	..	40	40
153		2 p. olive	..	..	60	70
		a. Olive-green	..	£100	25·00	
154		5 p. deep purple	..	..	2·50	3·00
155		9 p. ochre	..	..	4·50	5·00
156		10 p. light blue	..	..	7·50	9·00
		a. Error. "E.F.F." in bottom panel	..	£900	£800	
157		20 p. bright violet	..	..	15·00	17·00
143/57				*Set of 15*	28·00	32·00
143/57		Optd "Specimen"		*Set of 15*	£120	

(b) P 15 × 14

157a	19	9 p. ochre	..	..	£1000	£1100
158		10 p. blue	..	..	75·00	85·00
158a		20 p. bright violet	..	..	£1000	£1000

(New Currency. 1000 milliemes = £1 Palestinian)

(Recess Perkins, Bacon & Co)

1927 (1 Nov)–29. *New Currency. Wmk Mult Script CA. P 14.*

159	22	2 m. greenish blue	..	..	15	15
160		3 m. carmine-pink	..	..	20	20
161		4 m. green	..	..	50	70
162		5 m. orange	..	..	25	20
163		10 m. scarlet	..	..	50	45
164		15 m. ultramarine	..	..	60	25
165		20 m. olive-green	..	..	80	85
166	23	50 m. purple	..	..	2·50	3·00
167		90 m. bistre	..	..	5·00	7·50
168		100 m. blue	..	..	7·00	5·50
169		200 m. violet	..	..	16·00	19·00
170		500 m. brown (1929)	..	..	60·00	75·00
171		1000 m. slate-grey (1929)	..	£100	£130	
159/71				*Set of 13*	£180	£225
159/71		Optd/perf "Specimen"		*Set of 13*	£180	

("Constitution")
(24)

LOCUST CAMPAIGN
(27)

(Optd at Cairo)

1928 (1 Sept). *New Constitution of 20 February 1928. Optd with T 24.*

172	22	2 m. greenish blue	50	1·25
173		3 m. carmine-pink	60	1·75
174		4 m. green	60	2·00
175		5 m. orange	60	1·00
176		10 m. scarlet	1·00	2·50
177		15 m. ultramarine	1·00	1·25
178		20 m. olive-green	3·00	5·50
179	23	50 m. purple	5·00	6·00
180		90 m. bistre	13·00	26·00
181		100 m. blue	22·00	32·00
182		200 m. violet	60·00	85·00
172/82		*Set of 11*	95·00	£150

(Optd at Alexandria by Whitehead, Morris & Co)

1930 (1 Apr). *Locust Campaign. Optd as T 27.*

183	22	2 m. greenish blue	75	2·25
		a. Opt inverted	£250	
184		3 m. carmine-pink	80	2·25
185		4 m. green	60	2·75
186		5 m. orange	9·50	11·00
		a. Opt double	£400	£550
		b. Pair, one without bottom line	£500	
187		10 m. scarlet	55	2·25
188		15 m. ultramarine	80	1·75
		a. Opt inverted	£225	£350
189		20 m. olive-green	1·00	2·75
190	23	50 m. purple	5·00	8·00
191		90 m. bistre	10·00	26·00
192		100 m. blue	12·00	26·00
193		200 m. violet	30·00	65·00
194		500 m. brown	75·00	£110
		a. "C" of "LOCUST" omitted (R. 5/3)	£700	£700
183/94		*Set of 12*	£130	£225

28　　29

(Re-engraved with figures of value at left only. Recess Perkins, Bacon)

1930 (1 June)–**39**. *Wmk Mult Script CA. P 14.*

194b	28	1 m. red-brown (6.2.34)	15	55
		c. Perf 13½ × 13 (1939)	1·75	1·75
195		2 m. greenish blue	20	40
		a. Perf 13½ × 13. *Bluish green* (1939)	4·00	1·75
196		3 m. carmine-pink	30	50
196a		3 m. green (6.2.34)	50	60
		b. Perf 13½ × 13 (1939)	8·00	3·50
197		4 m. green	60	1·00
197a		4 m. carmine-pink (6.2.34)	1·50	80
		b. Perf 13½ × 13 (1939)	40·00	10·00
198		5 m. orange	40	30
		a. Coil stamp. P 13½ × 14 (1936)	14·00	6·00
		b. Perf 13½ × 13 (1939)	35·00	2·50
199		10 m. scarlet	50	15
		a. Perf 13½ × 13 (1939)	60·00	3·75
200		15 m. ultramarine	55	20
		a. Coil stamp. P 13½ × 14 (1936)	14·00	6·50
		b. Perf 13½ × 13 (1939)	22·00	3·50
201		20 m. olive-green	1·25	35
		a. Perf 13½ × 13 (1939)	40·00	10·00
202	29	50 m. purple	1·50	1·00
203		90 m. bistre	2·50	3·75
204		100 m. blue	3·50	3·75
205		200 m. violet	8·50	12·00
206		500 m. brown	20·00	32·00
207		£P1 slate-grey	45·00	75·00
194b/207		*Set of 16*	75·00	£120
194b/207		Perf "Specimen"	*Set of 16*	£130

For stamps perf 12 see Nos. 230/43, and for T 28 lithographed, perf 13½, see Nos. 222/9.

30 Mushetta　　31 Threshing Scene

32 The Khazneh at Petra　　33 Emir Abdullah

(Vignettes from photographs; frames des Yacoub Sukker. Recess Bradbury, Wilkinson)

1933 (1 Feb). *As T 30 (various designs) and T 31/3. Wmk Mult Script CA. P 12.*

208		1 m. black and maroon	40	85
209		2 m. black and claret	40	60
210		3 m. blue-green	50	1·00
211		4 m. black and brown	75	1·75
212		5 m. black and orange	80	1·00
213		10 m. carmine	1·50	2·50
214		15 m. blue	2·50	1·25
215		20 m. black and sage-green	3·25	4·00
216		50 m. black and purple	7·00	9·00
217		90 m. black and yellow	10·00	18·00
218		100 m. black and blue	12·00	18·00
219		200 m. black and violet	40·00	50·00
220		500 m. scarlet and red-brown	£130	£170
221		£P1 black and yellow-green	£425	£650
208/21		*Set of 14*	£600	£800
208/21		Perf "Specimen"	*Set of 14*	£500

Designs: *As T 30*—2 m. Nymphaeum, Jerash; 3 m. Kasr Kharana; 4 m. Kerak Castle; 5 m. Temple of Artemis, Jerash; 10 m. Ajlun Castle; 20 m. Allenby Bridge over the Jordan.

The 90 m., 100 m. and 200 m. are similar to the 3 m., 5 m. and 10m. respectively, but are larger (33½ × 23½ mm). The 500 m. is similar to T 32, but larger (23½ × 33½ mm).

34

(Litho Survey Dept, Cairo)

1942 (18 May). *T 28, but with Arabic characters above portrait and in top left circle modified as in T 34. No wmk. P 13½.*

222	34	1 m. red-brown	50	90
223		2 m. green	80	70
224		3 m. yellow-green	1·00	1·75
225		4 m. carmine-pink	1·10	1·75
226		5 m. yellow-orange	1·75	55
227		10 m. scarlet	1·75	1·75
228		15 m. blue	2·25	1·75
229		20 m. olive-green	5·50	5·50
222/9		*Set of 8*	13·00	13·00

(Recess Bradbury, Wilkinson)

1943 (1 Jan)–**44**. *Wmk Mult Script CA. P 12.*

230	28	1 m. red-brown	10	50
231		2 m. bluish green	20	50
232		3 m. green	50	75
233		4 m. carmine-pink	50	70
234		5 m. orange	40	15
235		10 m. red	1·25	80
236		15 m. blue	1·25	25
237		20 m. olive-green (5.44)	1·25	55
238	29	50 m. purple (5.44)	1·75	85
239		90 m. bistre (5.44)	4·00	2·75
240		100 m. blue (5.44)	4·50	1·25
241		200 m. violet (5.44)	8·00	5·00
242		500 m. brown (5.44)	13·00	11·00
243		£P1 slate-grey (5.44)	24·00	19·00
230/43		*Set of 14*	55·00	40·00

Nos. 237/43 were released in London by the Crown Agents about May 1944 but were not put on sale in Transjordan until 26 August 1946.

Printings of the 3, 4, 10, 12, 15 and 20 m. in changed colours were released on 12 May 1947.

POSTAGE DUE STAMPS

(D 1 "Due")　　(D 2)

1923 (Sept). *Issue of April, 1923, with opt T 10, with further typographed opt Type D 1 (the 3 p. with handstamped surch as T 12 at top).*

D112	½ p. on 3 p. brown		12·00	15·00
	a. "Due" inverted		50·00	55·00
	b. "Due" double		50·00	60·00
	ba. "Due" double, one inverted		£150	
	c. Arabic "t" & "h" transposed		£100	
	ca. As c, inverted		£250	
	d. Surch at foot of stamp		25·00	
	da. Ditto, but with var. c		£120	
	e. Surch omitted		£200	
D113	1 p. blue		8·00	9·00
	a. Type 10 inverted		80·00	
	b. "Due" inverted		45·00	40·00
	c. "Due" double		50·00	
	d. "Due" double, one inverted		£150	
	e. Arabic "t" & "h" transposed		70·00	
	f. "Due" omitted (in vertical pair)		£200	
D114	1½ p. lilac		8·00	9·00
	a. "Due" inverted		45·00	45·00
	b. "Due" double		50·00	
	ba. "Due" double, one diagonal		75·00	
	c. Arabic "t" & "h" transposed		70·00	
	ca. As c, inverted		£200	
	d. "Due" omitted (in pair)		£200	
D115	2 p. orange		9·00	10·00
	a. "Due" inverted		60·00	60·00
	b. "Due" double		70·00	
	ba. "Due" double, one diagonal		£100	
	c. "Due" treble		£150	
	d. Arabic "t" & "h" transposed		70·00	
	e. Arabic "h" omitted		90·00	

The variety, Arabic "t" and "h" transposed, occurred on No. 2 in the first row of all values in the first batch of sheets printed. The variety, Arabic "h" omitted, occurred on every stamp in the first three rows of at least three sheets of the 2 p.

Handstamped in four lines as Type D 2 and surch as on No. D112

D116	½ p. on 3 p. brown		40·00	50·00
	a. Opt and surch inverted	£200	
	b. Opt double	£200	
	c. Surch omitted	£225	
	d. Opt inverted. Surch normal, but at foot of stamp	£150	
	e. Opt omitted and opt inverted (pair)	£300	
	f. "Due" double, one inverted	£160	
	g. "Due" double, one larger	£180	
	h. Surch double	£250	

(D 3)　　("Due. East of the Jordan")
(D 4)

1923 (Oct). *T 11 of Saudi Arabia handstamped with Type D 3.*

D117	½ p. scarlet		1·00	1·75
D118	1 p. blue		1·50	2·00
D119	1½ p. lilac		1·75	2·75
D120	2 p. orange		2·25	3·25
D121	3 p. brown		3·75	6·50
	a. Pair, one without handstamp	£200	
D122	5 p. olive		6·50	9·00
D117/22		*Set of 6*	15·00	22·00

There are three types of this handstamp, differing in some of the Arabic characters. They occur inverted, double etc.

1923 (Nov). *T 11 of Saudi Arabia with opt similar to Type D 3 but first three lines typo and fourth handstruck.*

D123	1 p. blue		50·00
D124	5 p. olive		6·00

(Opt typo by Waterlow)

1925 (Nov). *Stamps of Palestine 1922 (without the three-line Palestine opt), optd with Type D 4. P 14.*

D159	1 m. deep brown		1·40	3·50
D160	2 m. yellow		1·75	2·50
D161	4 m. carmine-pink		2·75	4·00
D162	8 m. scarlet		3·75	6·00
D163	13 m. ultramarine		4·50	6·00
D164	5 p. deep purple		5·00	8·00
	a. Perf 15 × 14		40·00	55·00
D159/64		*Set of 6*	17·00	27·00
D159/64	Optd "Specimen"	*Set of 6*	60·00	

(1 m.)　(2 m.)　(4 m.)
(D 5)

(8 m.)　(13 m.)　(5 p.)

(Surch typo at Jerusalem)

1926. *Postage stamps of 1 November 1925, surch "Due" and new value as Type D 5. Bottom line of surcharge differs for each value as illustrated.*

D165	1 m. on 1 m. deep brown		2·00	3·75
D166	2 m. on 1 m. deep brown		2·25	3·75
D167	4 m. on 3 m. greenish blue		2·50	4·50
D168	8 m. on 3 m. greenish blue		2·50	5·00
D169	13 m. on 13 m. ultramarine		2·50	5·50
D170	5 p. on 13 m. ultramarine		3·50	7·50
D165/70		*Set of 6*	14·00	27·00

(D 6 "Due")　　D 7　　D 8

(Surch at Cairo)

1929 (1 Jan). *Nos. 159 etc. optd only or surch in addition as Type D 6.*

D183	22	1 m. on 3 m. carmine-pink	70	2·00
D184		2 m. greenish blue	80	2·00
		a. Pair, one without surch	£250	
D185		4 m. on 15 m. ultramarine	1·25	2·25
		a. Surch inverted	£100	£150
D186		10 m. scarlet	1·25	2·25
D187	23	20 m. on 100 m. blue	3·75	6·50
		a. Vert pair, one without surch	£250	
D188		50 m. purple	4·75	8·50
		a. Pair, one without surch	£300	
D183/8		*Set of 6*	11·00	21·00

(Recess Perkins, Bacon)

1929 (1 Apr)–**39.** *Wmk Mult Script CA. P 14.*

D189	D 7	1 m. red-brown	30	1·25
		a. Perf 13½ × 13 (1939)	80·00	50·00
D190		2 m. orange-yellow	30	1·50
D191		4 m. green	30	2·00
D192		10 m. scarlet	85	2·25
D193		20 m. olive-green	3·00	6·50
D194		50 m. blue	4·00	8·00
D189/94		.. .. ..Set of 6	8·00	19·00
D189/94 Perf "Specimen"		..Set of 6	50·00	

(Litho Survey Dept, Cairo)

1942 (22 Dec). *Redrawn. Top line of Arabic in taller lettering. No wmk. P 13½.*

D230	D 8	1 m. red-brown	50	3·50
D231		2 m. orange-yellow	2·50	3·50
D232		10 m. scarlet	2·50	2·50
D230/2		.. .. .. Set of 3	5·00	8·50

(Recess Bradbury, Wilkinson)

1944. *Wmk Mult Script CA. P 12.*

D244	D 7	1 m. red-brown	10	90
D245		2 m. orange-yellow	10	1·10
D246		4 m. green	20	1·75
D247		10 m. carmine	50	2·00
D248		20 m. olive-green	9·00	14·00
D244/8		.. .. .. Set of 5	9·00	18·00

OFFICIAL STAMP

("Arab Government of
the East, 1342" = 1924)
(O 1)

1924. *T 11 of Saudi Arabia with typographed opt, Type O 1.*
O117 ½ p. scarlet .. .. 25·00 £100

By treaty of 22 March 1946 with the United Kingdom, Transjordan was proclaimed an independent kingdom on 25 May 1946.
Later issues are listed under JORDAN in Part 19 (*Middle East*) of this catalogue.

Transvaal
see South Africa

Trinidad and Tobago

TRINIDAD

CROWN COLONY

The first post office was established at Port of Spain in 1800 to deal with overseas mail. Before 1851 there was no post office inland service, although a privately-operated one along the coast did exist, for which rates were officially fixed (see No. 1). During 1851 the colonial authorities established an inland postal system which commenced operation on 14 August. Responsibility for the overseas mails passed to the local post authorities in 1858.

No. CC1 is recorded in the G.P.O. Record Book on 21 March 1852 and most examples are found used with the early Britannia 1d. stamps to indicate prepayment of the additional overseas rate in cash or, later, to show that letters were fully franked with adhesive stamps. This is the normal usage of the handstamp and commands little, if any premium over the cover price quoted below for the stamps involved. The use of the handstamp without an adhesive is rare.

PORT OF SPAIN
CROWNED-CIRCLE HANDSTAMPS

CC 1

CC1 CC 1 TRINIDAD (R.) (*without additional adhesive stamp*) (21.3.52) *Price on cover* £500

PRICES FOR STAMPS ON COVER	
No. 1	from × 2
Nos. 2/12	from × 5
No. 8	
Nos. 13/20	from × 2
Nos. 25/9	from × 10
No. 30	
Nos. 31/44	from × 3
No. 45	
Nos. 46/59	from × 3
Nos. 60/3	from × 4
Nos. 64/8	from × 3
Nos. 69/85	from × 12
No. 87	
Nos. 88/90	from × 15
Nos. 91/7	from × 10
Nos. 98/102	from × 5
No. 103	
Nos. 104/5	from × 15
Nos. 106/12	from × 8
No. 113	
Nos. 114/21	from × 4
Nos. 122/4	
No. 125	from × 10
Nos. 126/30	from × 5
No. 131	
Nos. 132/43	from × 3
Nos. 144/5	
Nos. 146/8	from × 3
Nos. D1/17	from × 12

1   2 Britannia

1847 (24 Apr). *Litho. Imperf.*
1 1 (5 c.) blue £13000 £7000
The "LADY McLEOD" stamps were issued in April 1847, by David Bryce, owner of the S.S. *Lady McLeod*, and sold at five cents each for the prepayment of the carriage of letters by his vessel between Port of Spain and San Fernando.
The price quoted for used examples of No. 1 is for pen-cancelled. Stamps cancelled by having a corner skimmed-off are worth less.

(Recess P.B.)

1851 (14 Aug)–**1856.** *No value expressed. Imperf. Blued paper.*

2	2	(1d.) purple-brown (1851) ..	4·75	55·00
3		(1d.) blue to deep blue (1851) ..	4·50	35·00
4		(1d.) deep blue (1853)*	£150	70·00
5		(1d.) grey (1851)	28·00	50·00
6		(1d.) brownish grey (1853) ..	25·00	55·00
7		(1d.) brownish red (1853) ..	£300	45·00
8		(1d.) brick-red (1856) ..	£120	50·00

*No. 4 shows the paper deeply and evenly blued, especially on the back. It has more the appearance of having been printed on blue paper rather than on white paper that has become blued.

1854–57. *Imperf. White paper.*

9	2	(1d.) deep purple (1854)	11·00	55·00
10		(1d.) dark grey (1854)	20·00	65·00
11		(1d.) blue (? date)..		
12		(1d.) rose-red (1857)	£1500	50·00

PRICES. Prices quoted for the unused of most of the above issues and Nos. 25 and 29 are for "remainders" with original gum, found in London. Old colours that have been out to Trinidad are of much greater value.

3 Britannia 4

The following provisional issues were lithographed in the Colony (from die engraved by Charles Petit), and brought into use to meet shortages of the Perkins Bacon stamps during the following periods:
(1) Sept 1852–May 1853; (2) March 1855–June 1855; (3) Dec 1856–Jan 1857; (4) Oct 1858–Jan 1859; (5) March 1860–June 1860.

1852–60. *No value expressed. Imperf.*
A. *First Issue* (Sept 1852). *Fine impression; lines of background clear and distinct.* (i) *Yellowish paper*
13 3 (1d.) blue £8500 £1600
(ii) *Bluish cartridge paper* (Feb 1853)
14 3 (1d.) blue .. .. .. —£1800
B. *Second issue* (March 1855). *Thinner paper. Impression less distinct than before*
15 3 (1d.) pale blue to greenish blue .. — £900
C. *Third issue* (December 1856). *Background often of solid colour, but with clear lines in places*
16 3 (1d.) bright blue to deep blue .. £4500 £1000
D. *Fourth issue* (October 1858). *Impression less distinct, and rarely showing more than traces of background lines*
17 3 (1d.) very deep greenish blue .. — £650
18 3 (1d.) slate-blue £4000 £650
E. *Fifth issue* (March 1860). *Impression shows no (or hardly any) background lines*
19 3 (1d.) grey to bluish grey £4000 £400
20 (1d.) red (*shades*) .. .. 11·00 £450

In the worn impression of the fourth and fifth issues, the impression varies according to the position on the stone. Generally speaking, stamps of the fifth issue have a flatter appearance and cancellations are often less well defined. The paper of both these issues is thin or very thin. In all issues except 1853 (Feb) the gum tends to give the paper a toned appearance.
Stamps in the slate-blue shade (No. 18) also occur in the fifth issue, but are not readily distinguishable.

(Recess P.B.)

1859 (9 May). *Imperf.*

25	4	4d. grey-lilac	55·00	£275
28		4d. deep-green	—	£425
29		1s. indigo	60·00	£275
30		1s. purple-slate	—	£275

No. 30 may be of unissued status.

1859 (Sept). *(a) Pin-perf 12½.*

31	2	(1d.) rose-red	£500	42·00
32		(1d.) carmine-lake	£500	42·00
33	4	4d. dull lilac	—	£700
34		4d. dull purple	—	£700
35		6d. yellow-green	£1800	£150
36		6d. deep green	£1800	£130
37		1s. purple-slate.. ..	£2750	£850

(b) Pin-perf 13½–14

38	2	(1d.) rose-red	65·00	19·00
39		(1d.) carmine-lake	£110	17·00
40	4	4d. dull lilac	£650	65·00
40a		4d. brownish purple	60·00	85·00
41		4d. dull purple	£200	85·00
42		6d. yellow-green	£300	60·00
43		6d. deep green	£250	55·00
43a		6d. bright yellow-green ..	60·00	70·00
		b. Imperf between (vert pair)..	£3500	
44		1s. purple-slate.. ..	—	£550

(c) Compound pin-perf 13½–14 × 12½

45	2	(1d.) carmine-lake		†
45a	4	4d. dull purple	†	—

PRICES. The Pin-perf stamps are very scarce with perforations on all sides and the prices quoted above are for good average specimens.
The note after No. 12 also applies to Nos. 38, 40a, 43a, 46, 47 and 50.

1860 (Aug). *Clean-cut perf 14–16½.*

46	2	(1d.) rose-red	70·00	40·00
		a. Imperf vert (horiz pair) ..	£1100	
47	4	4d. brownish lilac	85·00	65·00
48		4d. lilac	—	£225
49		6d. bright yellow-green ..	£200	75·00
50		6d. deep green	£150	£120

1861 (June). *Rough perf 14–16½.*

52	2	(1d.) rose-red	65·00	20·00
53		(1d.) rose	65·00	17·00
54	4	4d. brownish lilac	£160	45·00
55		4d. lilac	£350	45·00
		a. Imperf		
56		6d. yellow-green	£150	55·00
57		6d. deep green	£350	55·00
58		1s. indigo	£600	£130
59		1s. deep bluish purple ..	£750	£225

(Recess D.L.R.)

1862–63. *Thick paper. (a) P 11½, 12.*

60	2	(1d.) crimson-lake	70·00	10·00
61	4	4d. deep purple	80·00	45·00
62		6d. deep green	£500	50·00
63		1s. bluish slate	£650	65·00

(b) P 11½, 12, compound with 11

63a	2	(1d.) crimson-lake	—	£350
63b	4	6d. deep green	—	£5000

(c) P 13 (1863)

64	2	(1d.) lake	25·00	15·00
65	4	6d. emerald-green	£275	45·00
67		1s. bright mauve	£2750	£225

(d) P 12½ (1863)

68	2	(1d.) lake	23·00	16·00

1863–75. *Wmk Crown CC. P 12½.*

69	2	(1d.) lake	27·00	3·25
		a. Wmk sideways	75·00	7·00
70		(1d.) rose	27·00	1·40
		a. Imperf (pair)		
71		(1d.) scarlet	27·00	90
72		(1d.) carmine	27·00	1·50
73	4	4d. bright violet	70·00	8·00
74		4d. pale mauve	£120	9·00
75		4d. dull lilac	75·00	9·50
77		6d. emerald-green	50·00	10·00
78		6d. deep green	£200	7·50
80		6d. yellow-green	38·00	3·00
81		6d. apple-green	38·00	4·50
82		6d. blue-green	70·00	4·75
83		1s. bright deep mauve ..	90·00	6·00
84		1s. lilac-rose	75·00	5·00
85		1s. mauve (aniline) ..	65·00	4·25

The 1s. in a purple-slate shade is a colour changeling.

5

(Typo D.L.R.)

1869. *Wmk Crown CC. P 12½.*
87 5 5s. rose-lake .. .. .. £120 60·00

1872. *Colours changed. Wmk Crown CC. P 12½.*
88	4	4d. grey		80·00	3·25
89		4d. bluish grey		80·00	4·00
90		1s. chrome-yellow		95·00	1·00

1876. *Wmk Crown CC.* (a) *P* 14.
91	2	(1d.) lake		10·00	50
		a. Bisected (½d.) (on cover)		†	£450
92		(1d.) rose-carmine		10·00	1·00
93		(1d.) scarlet		26·00	75
94	4	4d. bluish grey		70·00	70
95		6d. bright yellow-green		60·00	1·25
96		6d. deep yellow-green		65·00	1·00
97		1s. chrome-yellow		70·00	2·50

(b) *P* 14 × 12½
97a	4	6d. yellow-green		—	£4750

HALFPENNY   ONE PENNY
(6)   (7)

1879–82. *Surch with T* 6 *or* 7. *P* 14.
(a) *Wmk Crown CC* (June 1879)
98	2	½d. lilac		7·00	4·75
99		½d. mauve		7·00	4·75
		a. Wmk sideways		48·00	48·00

(b) *Wmk Crown CA* (1882)
100	2	½d. lilac		£180	60·00
101		1d. rosy carmine		16·00	30
		a. Bisected (½d.) (on cover)		†	£375

1882. *Wmk Crown CA. P* 14.
102	4	4d. bluish grey		£120	5·00

(8)   Various styles

1882 (9 May). *Surch by hand in various styles as T* 8 *in red or black ink and the original value obliterated by a thick or thin bar or bars, of the same colour.*
103	1d. on 6d. (No. 95) (Bk.)		—	£1500
104	1d. on 6d. (No. 95) (R.)		3·25	3·25
105	1d. on 6d. (No. 96) (R.)		3·50	3·25
	a. Bisected (½d.) (on cover)		†	£300

10   11 Britannia   12 Britannia

(Typo D.L.R.)

1883–94. *P* 14. (a) *Wmk Crown CA.*
106	10	½d. dull green		40	30
107		1d. carmine		2·00	10
		a. Bisected (½d.) (on cover)		†	£425
108		2½d. bright blue		5·00	15
110		4d. grey		2·25	20
111		6d. olive-black (1884)		2·00	1·50
112		1s. orange-brown (1884)		2·00	1·50

(b) *Wmk Crown CC*
113	5	5s. maroon (1894)		25·00	48·00
106/13			Set of 7	35·00	48·00
106/12 Optd "Specimen"			Set of 6	£400	

Two types of 1d. value:

ONE PENNY   **ONE PENNY**
(I) (round "o")   (II) (oval "o")

(Typo D.L.R.)

1896 (17 Aug)–**1900.** *P* 14. (a) *Wmk Crown CA.*
114	11	½d. dull purple and green		75	15
115		1d. dull purple and rose (I)		3·00	10
116		1d. dull purple and rose (II) (1900)		80·00	2·50
117		2½d. dull purple and blue		2·25	15
118		4d. dull purple and orange		4·25	7·50
119		5d. dull purple and mauve		5·00	7·00
120		6d. dull purple and black		3·75	4·50
121		1s. green and brown		5·00	5·00

(b) *Wmk CA over Crown. Ordinary paper*
122	12	2s. green and brown		28·00	60·00
123		10s. green and ultramarine		£100	£130
124		£1 green and carmine		85·00	£120
		a. Chalk-surfaced paper			
114/24			Set of 10	£200	£300
114/24 Optd "Specimen"			Set of 10	£150	

No. 119, surcharged "3d." was prepared for use but not issued (*Price* £2750 *unused*). It also exists overprinted "Specimen" (*Price* £75).

Collectors are warned against apparently postally used copies of this issue which bear "REGISTRAR-GENERAL" obliterations and are of very little value.

---

13 Landing of Columbus

(Recess D.L.R.)

1898. *400th Anniv of Discovery of Trinidad. Wmk Crown CC. P* 14.
125	13	2d. brown and dull violet		1·50	60
125 Optd "Specimen"				50·00	

1901–06. *Colours changed. Wmk Crown CA or CA over Crown* (5s.). *Ordinary paper. P* 14.
126	11	½d. grey-green (1902)		35	65
127		1d. black/*red* (II)		80	10
		a. Value omitted		£10000	
128		2½d. purple and blue/*blue* (1902)		5·50	25
129		4d. green and blue/*buff* (1902)		1·50	5·50
		a. Chalk-surfaced paper		1·75	5·50
130		1s. black and blue/*yellow* (1903)		14·00	4·00
131	12	5s. lilac and mauve		27·00	48·00
		a. *Deep purple and mauve* (1906)		42·00	65·00
		ab. Chalk-surfaced paper		50·00	70·00
126/31			Set of 6	45·00	55·00
126/31 Optd "Specimen"			Set of 6	£100	

A pane of sixty of No. 127a was found in a post office in Trinidad but not more than nine copies are believed to have been sold, and the rest withdrawn.

1904–09. *Wmk Mult Crown CA. Ordinary paper* (½d., 1d., 2½d. (No. 137) *or chalk-surfaced paper* (others). *P* 14.
132	11	½d. grey-green		1·25	40
		a. Chalk-surfaced paper		1·50	60
133		½d. blue-green (1906)		4·00	1·25
134		1d. black/*red* (II)		1·40	10
		a. Chalk-surfaced paper		1·40	10
135		1d. rose-red (1907)		80	10
136		2½d. purple and blue/*blue*		12·00	90
137		2½d. blue (1906)		1·50	15
138		4d. grey and red/*yellow* (1906)		1·00	5·00
		a. *Black and red/yellow*		8·00	17·00
139		6d. dull purple and black (1905)		8·50	14·00
140		6d. dull and bright purple (1906)		3·50	5·50
141		1s. black and blue/*yellow*		13·00	7·50
142		1s. purple and blue/*golden yellow*		7·50	9·50
143		1s. black/*green* (1906)		1·25	1·25
144	12	5s. deep purple and mauve (1907)		38·00	65·00
145		£1 green and carmine (1907)		90·00	£120
132/45			Set of 14	£150	£190
135, 137/8, 140, 142/3 Optd "Specimen"			Set of 6	£100	

No. 135 is from a new die, the letters of "ONE PENNY" being short and thick, while the point of Britannia's spear breaks the uppermost horizontal line of shading in the background.

14   15   16

(Typo D.L.R.)

1909. *Wmk Mult Crown CA. P* 14.
146	14	½d. green		1·00	10
147	15	1d. rose-red		1·00	10
148	16	2½d. blue		5·00	1·25
146/8			Set of 3	6·00	1·25
146/8 Optd "Specimen"			Set of 3	50·00	

TOBAGO

Although early postal markings are recorded from 1772 onwards it was not until 1841 that the British G.P.O. established a branch office at Scarborough, the island capital, to handle the overseas mail.

The stamps of Great Britain were in use from May 1858 to the end of March 1860 when the control of the postal service passed to the local authorities.

From 1 April 1860 Nos. CC1/2 were again used on overseas mail, pending the introduction of Tobago stamps in 1879.

SCARBOROUGH
CROWNED-CIRCLE HANDSTAMPS

CC 1   CC 2

CC1	CC 1	TOBAGO (R.) (31.10.1851)	*Price on cover* £600
CC2	CC 2	TOBAGO (R.) (1875)	*Price on cover* £850

Stamps of GREAT BRITAIN *cancelled* "A 14" *as Type Z* 1 *of Jamaica.*

1858 to **1860.**
Z 1	1d. rose-red (1857), *perf* 14		£650
Z 2	4d. rose (1857)		£225
Z 3	6d. lilac (1856)		£200
Z 4	1s. green (1856)		£700

PRICES FOR STAMPS ON COVER
Nos. 1/4	*from* × 25
Nos. 5/7	—
Nos. 8/12	*from* × 10
Nos. 13/19	*from* × 6
Nos. 20/4	*from* × 40
Nos. 26/33	*from* × 25

CANCELLATIONS. Beware of early stamps of Tobago with fiscal endorsements removed and forged wide "A 14" postmarks added.

1   2   2½ PENCE
                   (3)

(T 1 and 2. Typo D.L.R.)

1879 (1 Aug). *Fiscal stamps issued provisionally pending the arrival of stamps inscr* "POSTAGE". *Wmk Crown CC. P* 14.
1	1	1d. rose		65·00	50·00
2		3d. blue		55·00	35·00
3		6d. orange		24·00	38·00
4		1s. green		£350	60·00
		a. Bisected (6d.) (on cover)			£60·00
5		5s. slate		£550	£500
6		£1 mauve		£5000	

The stamps were introduced for fiscal purposes on 1 July 1879. Stamps of T 1, watermark Crown CA, are fiscals which were never admitted to postal use.

1880 (Nov). *No. 3 bisected vertically and surch with pen and ink.*
7	1	1d. on half of 6d. orange		£4500	£750

1880 (20 Dec). *Wmk Crown CC. P* 14.
8	2	½d. purple-brown		20·00	30·00
9		1d. Venetian red		60·00	35·00
		a. Bisected (½d.) (on cover)		†	£1400
10		4d. yellow-green		£180	24·00
		a. Bisected (2d.) (on cover)		†	£1400
		b. Malformed "CE" in "PENCE"		£1100	£400
11		6d. stone		£250	90·00
12		1s. yellow-ochre		45·00	45·00

For illustration of Nos. 10b, 18a, 22b, 30a, 31a and 33b see above No. 4 of Dominica.

1883 (Apr). *No. 11 surch with T* 3.
13	2	2½d. on 6d. stone		23·00	23·00
		a. Surch double		£2500	£1200
		b. Large "2" with long tail		£100	£110

"SLASH" FLAW. Stamps as Type 2 were produced from Key and Duty plates. On the Key plate used for consignments between 2 October 1892 and 16 December 1896, damage in the form of a large cut or "slash" shows after the "E" of "POSTAGE" on R.1/4.

After 1896 an attempt was made to repair the "slash". This resulted in its disappearance, but left an incomplete edge to the circular frame at right.

1882–84. *Wmk Crown CA. P* 14.
14	2	½d. purple-brown (1882)		1·00	11·00
15		1d. Venetian red (1882)		1·00	1·25
		a. Bisected diag (½d.) (on cover)			
16		2½d. dull blue [1883]		8·00	80
		a. *Bright blue*		2·00	75
		b. *Ultramarine*		2·00	75
		c. "Slash" flaw		15·00	22·00
		ca. "Slash" flaw repaired		60·00	
18		4d. yellow-green (1882)		£170	90·00
		a. Malformed "CE" in "PENCE"		£950	£400
19		6d. stone (1884)		£550	£475

1885–96. *Colours changed and new value. Wmk Crown CA. P* 14.
20	2	½d. dull green (1886)		30	35
		a. "Slash" flaw		9·00	20·00
		ab. "Slash" flaw repaired		18·00	
21		1d. carmine (1889)		60	20
		a. "Slash" flaw		8·00	10·00
		ab. "Slash" flaw repaired		25·00	

22	2	4d. grey (1885)	50	55
		a. Imperf (pair) ..	£1700	
		b. Malformed "CE" in "PENCE" ..	50·00	80·00
		c. "Slash" flaw ..	50·00	85·00
		ca. "Slash" flaw repaired ..	75·00	
23		6d. orange-brown (1886) ..	60	2·50
		a. "Slash" flaw ..	50·00	85·00
		ab. "Slash" flaw repaired ..	75·00	
24		1s. olive-yellow (1894) ..	70	7·00
		a. Pale olive-yellow ..	6·50	
		b. "Slash" flaw ..	60·00	£120
		ba. "Slash" flaw repaired ..	85·00	
24c		1s. orange-brown (1896) ..	3·25	
		ca. "Slash" flaw ..	75·00	

20, 21 and 23 Optd "Specimen" .. *Set of 3* £170
No. 24c was printed in the colour of the 6d. by mistake.

½d

½ PENNY   **2½ PENCE**   **POSTAGE**
(4)   (5)   (6)

1886–89. *Nos. 16, 19 and 23 surch as T 4.*

26	½d. on 2½d. dull blue (4.86)	2·25	6·00
	a. Figure further from word ..	14·00	35·00
	b. Surch double ..	£1300	£1100
	c. Surch omitted. Vert pair with No. 26 ..	£8000	
	d. Ditto with No. 26a ..	£15000	
27	½d. on 6d. stone (1.86) ..	1·50	13·00
	a. Figure further from word ..	35·00	85·00
	b. Surch inverted ..	£1300	
	c. Surch double ..	£1500	
28	½d. on 6d. orange-brown (8.87) ..	60·00	80·00
	a. Figure further from word ..	£225	£250
	b. Surch double ..	—	£1000
29	1d. on 2½d. dull blue (7.89) ..	25·00	14·00
	a. Figure further from word ..	70·00	75·00

The surcharge is in a setting of 12 (two rows of 6) repeated five times in the pane. Nos. 7, 9 and 10 in the setting have a raised "P" in "PENNY", and No. 10 also shows the wider spacing between figure and word.

1891–92. *No. 22 surch with T 4 or 5.*

30	½d. on 4d. grey (3.92) ..	8·50	26·00
	a. Malformed "CE" in "PENCE" ..	£275	£400
	b. Surch double ..	£1800	
31	2½d. on 4d. grey (8.91) ..	3·00	6·50
	a. Malformed "CE" in "PENCE" ..	£200	£275
	b. Surch double ..	£1800	£1800

1896. *Fiscal stamp (T 1, value in second colour, wmk Crown CA, P 14), surch with T 6.*

33	½d. on 4d. lilac and carmine ..	25·00	25·00
	a. Space between "½" and "d" ..	55·00	55·00
	b. Malformed "CE" in "PENCE" ..	£375	£400

From 1896 until 1913 Trinidad stamps were used in Tobago.

TRINIDAD AND TOBAGO

PRICES FOR STAMPS ON COVER

Nos. 149/55	from × 3
Nos. 156/7	
Nos. 174/89	from × 10
Nos. 206/56	from × 2
Nos. D18/25	from × 12

17   18

(Typo D.L.R.)

1913–23. *Wmk Mult Crown CA. Ordinary paper (½d. to 4d. and 1s.) or chalk-surfaced paper (others). P 14.*

149	17	½d. green	1·25	10
		a. Yellow-green (1915) ..	1·50	15
		b. Blue-green (thick paper) (1917) ..	2·50	40
		c. Blue-green/bluish (3.18) ..	9·50	9·50
150		1d. bright red ..	60	10
		a. Red (thick paper) (1916) ..	80	10
		b. Pink (1918) ..	6·50	80
		c. Carmine-red (5.18) ..	60	10
151		2½d. ultramarine ..	3·25	30
		a. Bright blue (thick paper) (1916) ..	1·50	30
		b. Bright blue (thin paper) (1918) ..	4·00	40
152		4d. black and red/yellow		
		a. Chalk-surfaced paper ..	70	3·25
		b. White back (12.13) (Optd S. £16) ..	1·75	7·00
		c. On lemon (1917) ..	10·00	
		d. On pale yellow (1923) (Optd S. £20) ..	3·25	7·50
153		6d. dull and reddish purple ..	3·50	3·25
		a. Dull and deep purple (1918) ..	2·00	3·75
		b. Dull purple and mauve (2.18) ..	6·00	6·00
154		1s. black/green ..	75	2·50
		a. White back (Optd S. £16) ..	65	3·25
		b. On blue-green, olive back ..	2·50	4·50
		c. On emerald back (Optd S. £20) ..	1·00	2·50

155	18	5s. dull purple and mauve (1914) ..	30·00	65·00
		a. Deep purple and mauve (1918) ..	32·00	65·00
		b. Lilac and violet ..	60·00	80·00
		c. Dull purple and violet ..	65·00	85·00
		d. Brown-purple and violet ..	27·00	65·00
156		£1 grey-green and carmine (1914) ..	90·00	£110
		a. Deep yellow-green and carmine (1918) ..	90·00	£110

149/56 .. .. *Set of 8* £110 £140
149/56 Optd "Specimen" .. *Set of 8* £140
No. 156a is from a plate showing background lines very worn.

18a

1914 (18 Sept). *Red Cross Label authorised for use as ½d. stamp. Typo. P 11–12.*

157	18a	(½d.) Red ..	9·00	£190

The above was authorised for internal use on one day only, to raise funds for the Red Cross. The used price is for stamp on cover.

(19)   (19a)

1915 (21 Oct). *Optd with T 19. Cross in red with outline and date in black.*

174	17	1d. red	50	50
		a. Cross 2 mm to right ..	12·00	12·00
		b. "1" of "15" forked foot ..	6·00	8·50
		c. Broken "0" in "10" ..	9·00	9·50

The varieties occur in the following positions on the *pane* of 60:
a. No. 11. b. No. 42. c. No. 45. Variety a. is only found on the right-hand pane.

1916 (19 Oct). *Optd with T 19a. Cross in red with outline and date in black.*

175	17	1d. scarlet ..	10	30
		a. No stop after "16" ..	6·50	15·00
		b. "19.10.16" omitted ..		

No. 175a appears on stamp No. 36 on the right-hand pane only.

FORGERIES. Beware of forgeries of the "War Tax" errors listed below. There are also other unlisted errors which are purely fakes.

WAR TAX   WAR TAX   WAR TAX   WAR TAX
(19b)   (20)   (21)   (22)

1917 (2 Apr). *Optd with T 19b.*

176	17	1d. red ..	20	85
		a. Opt inverted ..	£140	
		b. Scarlet ..	20	95

1917 (May). *Optd with T 20.*

177	17	½d. green ..	10	10
		a. Pair, one without opt ..	£180	
178		1d. red ..	15	30
		a. Pair, one without opt ..	£180	
		b. Scarlet ..	45	15
		ba. Opt double ..	80·00	

The varieties without overprint were caused by the type being shifted over towards the left so that one stamp in the lowest row of each pane escaped.

1917 (21 June). *Optd with T 21.*

179	17	½d. yellow-green ..	75	2·25
		a. Pale green ..	10	1·75
		b. Deep green ..	60	2·25
180		1d. red ..	10	10
		a. Pair, one without opt ..		

No. 180a was caused by a shifting of the type to the left-hand side, but only a few stamps on the right-hand vertical row escaped the overprint and such pairs are very rare.

1917 (21 July–Sept). *Optd with T 22.*

181	17	½d. yellow-green ..	2·50	3·75
		a. Deep green ..	10	80
182		1d. red (Sept) ..	45	15

WAR TAX   WAR TAX   WAR TAX
(23)   (24)   (25)

1917 (1 Sept). *Optd with T 23 (closer spacing between lines of opt).*

183	17	½d. deep green ..	10	1·25
		a. Pale yellow-green ..		
184		1d. red ..	11·00	16·00

1917 (31 Oct). *Optd with T 24.*

185	17	1d. scarlet ..	10	75
		a. Opt inverted ..	70·00	

1918 (7 Jan). *Optd with T 25.*

186	17	1d. scarlet ..	10	10
		a. Opt double ..	£130	
		b. Opt inverted ..	80·00	

War   War
Tax   Tax
(26)   (26a)   27

1918 (13 Feb–May). *Optd with T 26.*

187	17	½d. bluish green ..	10	40
		a. Pair, one without opt ..	£400	
		b. "TAX" omitted ..		
188		1d. scarlet ..	10	40
		a. Opt double ..	80·00	
		b. Rose-red (1.5.18) ..	10	30

No. 187b occurs on R. 10/1 and was caused by a paper fold.

1918 (14 Sept). *New printing as T 26, but 19 stamps on each sheet have the letters of the word "Tax" wider spaced, the "x" being to the right of "r" of "War" as T 26a. Thick bluish paper.*

189	17	1d. scarlet ("Tax" spaced) ..	35	2·25
		a. Opt double ..	£140	

1921–22. *Wmk Mult Script CA. Chalk-surfaced paper (6d. to £1). P 14.*

206	17	½d. green ..	35	60
207		1d. scarlet ..	20	20
208		1d. brown (17.2.22) ..	20	30
209		2d. grey (17.2.22) ..	1·00	1·25
210		2½d. bright blue ..	70	6·00
211		3d. bright blue (17.2.22) ..	1·75	1·75
212		6d. dull and bright purple ..	1·50	9·50
213	18	5s. dull purple and purple (1921) ..	32·00	85·00
214		5s. deep purple and purple (1922) ..	32·00	85·00
215		£1 green and carmine ..	75·00	£170

206/15 .. .. *Set of 9* £100 £250
206/15 Optd "Specimen" .. *Set of 9* £200

(Typo D.L.R.)

1922–28. *P 14. Chalk-surfaced paper (4d. to £1).*

(a) Wmk Mult Crown CA

216	27	4d. black and red/pale yellow ..	75	1·25
217		1s. black/emerald ..	1·75	4·50

(b) Wmk Mult Script CA

218	27	½d. green ..	10	10
219		1d. brown ..	15	10
220		1½d. bright rose ..	60	10
		a. Scarlet ..	40	10
222		2d. grey ..	30	40
223		3d. blue ..	40	40
224		4d. black and red/pale yellow (1928) ..	3·00	2·00
225		6d. dull purple and bright magenta ..	2·00	13·00
226		6d. green and red/emerald (1924) ..	80	30
227		1s. black/emerald ..	1·25	90
228		5s. dull purple and mauve ..	14·00	20·00
229		£1 green and bright rose ..	85·00	£170

216/29 .. .. *Set of 13* 95·00 £190
216/29 Optd "Specimen" .. *Set of 13* £225

(New Currency. 100 cents = 1 dollar)

28 First Boca   29 Imperial College of Tropical Agriculture

(Recess B.W.)

1935 (1 Feb)–**37.** *T 28/9 and similar horiz designs. Wmk Mult Script CA (sideways). P 12.*

230		1 c. blue and green ..	30	10
		a. Perf 13 × 12½ (1936) ..	10	10
231		2 c. ultramarine and yellow-brown ..	30	10
		a. Perf 13 × 12½ (1936) ..	35	10
232		3 c. black and scarlet..	20	10
		a. Perf 13 × 12½ (1936) ..	60	10
233		6 c. sepia and blue ..	1·25	50
		a. Perf 13 × 12½ (1937) ..	1·75	90
234		8 c. sage-green and vermilion ..	75	90
235		12 c. black and violet ..	1·25	55
		a. Perf 13 × 12½ (1937) ..	1·75	1·75
236		24 c. black and olive-green ..	45	55
		a. Perf 13 × 12½ (1937) ..	6·00	3·00
237		48 c. deep green ..	4·25	12·00
238		72 c. myrtle-green and carmine ..	19·00	20·00

230/8 .. .. *Set of 9* 25·00 30·00
230/8 Perf "Specimen" .. *Set of 9* 90·00
Designs:—3 c. Mt Irvine Bay, Tobago; 6 c. Discovery of Lake Asphalt; 8 c. Queen's Park, Savannah; 12 c. Town Hall, San Fernando; 24 c. Government House; 48 c. Memorial Park; 72 c. Blue Basin.

1935 (6 May). *Silver Jubilee. As Nos. 114/17 of Jamaica. P 11×12.*

239		2 c. ultramarine and grey-black ..	30	20
		a. Extra flagstaff ..	32·00	
		b. Short extra flagstaff ..	30·00	
		c. Lightning conductor ..	24·00	
		d. Flagstaff on right-hand turret ..	35·00	
240		3 c. deep blue and scarlet ..	30	30
		a. Extra flagstaff ..	50·00	
		c. Lightning conductor ..	35·00	

241	6 c. brown and deep blue	..	..	1·00	1·75
	a. Extra flagstaff	..		85·00	
	b. Short extra flagstaff	..		75·00	
	c. Lightning conductor	..		60·00	
242	24 c. slate and purple	..		4·00	4·75
	a. Extra flagstaff			£110	
	c. Lightning conductor			75·00	
	d. Flagstaff on right-hand turret ..			£100	
239/42			Set of 4	5·00	6·25
239/42	Perf "Specimen"		Set of 4	75·00	

For illustrations of plate varieties see Omnibus section following Zimbabwe.

1937 (12 May). *Coronation. As Nos. 118/20 of Jamaica.*

243	1 c. green	..	..	15	10
244	2 c. yellow-brown	..	..	35	10
245	8 c. orange	..	..	1·10	30
243/5			Set of 3	1·40	45
243/5	Perf "Specimen"		Set of 3	55·00	

37 First Boca   47 King George VI

1938 (2 May)–44. *T 37 and similar horiz designs, and T 47. Wmk Mult Script CA (sideways on 1 c. to 60 c.).*

(a) P 11½ × 11

246	1 c. blue and green	..	..	15	20
247	2 c. blue and yellow-brown	..		20	20
248	3 c. black and scarlet ..	..		10·00	60
248a	3 c. green and purple-brown (1941)			20	20
249	4 c. chocolate ..			26·00	1·00
249a	4 c. scarlet (1941)			40	55
249b	5 c. magenta (1.5.41)			15	15
250	6 c. sepia and blue			30	30
251	8 c. sage-green and vermilion			60	30
252	12 c. black and purple..			9·00	95
	a. Black and slate-purple (1944)			2·25	10
253	24 c. black and olive-green			35	10
254	60 c. myrtle-green and carmine			7·50	55

(b) T 47. P 12

255	$1.20, blue-green (1.40)			5·00	30
256	$4.80, rose-carmine (1.40)	..		18·00	13·00
246/56			Set of 14	65·00	16·00
246/56	exc 249b Perf "Specimen"		Set of 13	£190	

Designs:—2 c. Imperial College of Tropical Agriculture; 3 c. Mt Irvine Bay, Tobago; 4 c. Memorial Park; 5 c. G.P.O. and Treasury; 6 c. Discovery of Lake Asphalt; 8 c. Queen's Park, Savannah; 12 c. Town Hall, San Fernando; 24 c. Government House; 60 c. Blue Basin.

1946 (1 Oct). *Victory. As Nos. 141/2 of Jamaica.*

257	3 c. chocolate ..	..	..	10	10
258	6 c. blue	..	..	10	30
257/8	Perf "Specimen"		Set of 2	45·00	

1948 (22 Nov). *Royal Silver Wedding. As Nos. 143/4 of Jamaica, but $4.80 in recess.*

259	3 c. red-brown	..	..	10	10
260	$4.80, carmine	..	..	15·00	14·00

1949 (10 Oct). *75th Anniv of U.P.U. As Nos. 145/8 of Jamaica.*

261	5 c. bright reddish purple	..		30	20
262	6 c. deep blue ..	..		30	35
263	12 c. violet	..	..	30	40
264	24 c. olive	..	..	30	30
261/4	..		Set of 4	1·10	1·10

1951 (16 Feb). *University College of B.W.I. As Nos. 149/50 of Jamaica.*

265	3 c. green and red-brown	..	..	20	15
266	12 c. black and reddish violet ..	..		20	20

48 First Boca   49 Mt Irvine Bay, Tobago

(Recess B.W.)

1953 (20 Apr)–59. *Designs previously used for King George VI issue, but with portrait of Queen Elizabeth II as in T 48 (1 c., 2 c., 12 c.) or 49 (other values). Wmk Mult Script CA. P 12 (dollar values) or 11½×11 (others).*

267	1 c. blue and green	..	..	20	20
	a. Blue and bluish green (10.6.59)	..		1·75	1·75
268	2 c. indigo and orange-brown	..		20	20
269	3 c. deep emerald and purple-brown	..		20	10
270	4 c. scarlet	..	..	20	20
271	5 c. magenta	..	..	30	20
272	6 c. brown and greenish blue	..		30	20
273	8 c. deep yellow-green and orange-red			70	30
274	12 c. black and purple	..		60	10
275	24 c. black and yellow-olive	..		60	10
	a. Black and olive (16.11.55)	..		1·25	20
	b. Black and greenish olive (12.12.56)			1·75	55
276	60 c. blackish green and carmine	..		9·00	50
277	$1.20, bluish green	..		1·00	15
	a. Perf 11½ (19.1.55)	..		1·00	15
278	$4.80, cerise	..		5·00	13·00
	a. Perf 11½ (16.12.55)	..		5·50	8·50
267/78a			Set of 12	16·00	9·50

Designs: Horiz—2 c. Imperial College of Tropical Agriculture; 4 c. Memorial Park; 5 c. G.P.O. and Treasury; 6 c. Discovery

of Lake Asphalt; 8 c. Queen's Park, Savannah; 12 c. Town Hall, San Fernando; 24 c. Government House; 60 c. Blue Basin. *Vert (18 × 21 mm)*—$1.20, $4.80, Queen Elizabeth II.

1953 (3 June). *Coronation. As No. 153 of Jamaica.*

279	3 c. black and green	..	..	15	10

ONE CENT
(50)

1956 (20 Dec). *No. 268 surch with T 50.*

280	1 c. on 2 c. indigo and orange-brown			30	50

1958 (22 Apr). *Inauguration of British Caribbean Federation. As Nos. 175/7 of Jamaica.*

281	5 c. deep green	..	..	20	10
282	6 c. blue	..	..	25	30
283	12 c. scarlet	..	..	25	10
281/3	..		Set of 3	65	45

PRINTERS. Nos. 284 to 354 were printed in photogravure by Harrison & Sons, *unless otherwise stated.*

51 Cipriani Memorial   52 Queen's Hall

53 Copper-rumped Hummingbird

54 Map of Trinidad and Tobago

(Des V. Whiteley (1, 2, 12, 35, 60 c., $4.80), J. Matthews (5 c.), H. Baxter (6, 8, 10, 15 c.), M. Goaman (25 c., 50 c., $1.20))

1960 (24 Sept)–67. *Designs as T 51/4. W w 12 (upright). P 13½×14½ (1 c., 60 c., $1.20, $4.80) or 14½×13½ (others).*

284	1 c. stone and black	..	..	10	10
285	2 c. bright blue	..	..	10	10
	a. Blue (23.6.64)	..	..	85	10
	b. New blue (18.4.67)	..		85	10
286	5 c. chalky blue	..	..	10	10
287	6 c. red-brown	..	..	10	10
	a. Pale chestnut (13.4.67)	..		85	10
288	8 c. yellow-green	..	..	10	10
289	10 c. deep lilac	..	..	10	10
290	12 c. vermilion	..	..	10	10
291	15 c. orange	..	..	90	45
291a	15 c. orange (15.9.64)	..		1·00	10
292	25 c. rose-carmine and deep blue	..		35	10
293	35 c. emerald and black	..		1·75	10
294	50 c. yellow, grey and blue	..		35	20
295	60 c. vermilion, yellow-green and indigo			45	30
	a. Perf 14½ (1.10.65)*	..		£100	45·00
296	$1.20, multicoloured	..		8·00	1·50
297	$4.80, apple-green and pale blue	..		4·50	5·00
284/97			Set of 15	16·00	7·25

Designs: *Vert as T 51*—60 c. Anthurium Lilies. *Horiz as T 52*—5 c. Whitehall; 6 c. Treasury Building; 8 c. Governor-General's House; 10 c. General Hospital, San Fernando; 12 c. Oil refinery; 15 c. (No. 291), Crest; 15 c. (No. 291a), Coat of arms; 25 c. Scarlet Ibis; 35 c. Pitch Lake; 50 c. Mohammed Jinnah Mosque.

*This is the earliest date reported to us. It comes from an unannounced printing which was despatched to Trinidad on 3 December 1964.

The 2, 5, 6, 12 and 25 c. exist with PVA gum as well as gum arabic.

See also No. 317.

65 Scouts and Gold Wolf Badge

1961 (4 Apr). *Second Caribbean Scout Jamboree. Design multicoloured; background colours below. W w 12. P 13½×14½.*

298	65	8 c. light green	..	15	10
299		25 c. light blue	..	15	10

66 "Buccoo Reef" (painting by Carlisle Chang)   71 "Protein Foods"

1962 (31 Aug). *Independence. T 66 and similar horiz designs. W w 12. P 14½.*

300	5 c. bluish green	..		10	10
301	8 c. grey	..	..	10	10
302	25 c. reddish violet	..		15	10
303	35 c. brown, yellow, green and black ..			1·25	15
304	60 c. red, black and blue	..		1·75	1·10
300/4			Set of 5	3·00	1·25

Designs:—8 c. Piarco Air Terminal; 25 c. Hilton Hotel, Port-of-Spain; 35 c. Greater Bird of Paradise and map; 60 c. Scarlet Ibis and map.

(Des M. Goaman)

1963 (4 June). *Freedom from Hunger. W w 12. P 14 × 13½.*

305	71	5 c. brown-red	..	10	10
306		8 c. yellow-bistre	..	10	10
307		25 c. violet-blue ..	..	20	10
305/7			Set of 3	35	15

72 Jubilee Emblem

1964 (15 Sept). *Golden Jubilee of Trinidad and Tobago Girl Guides' Association. W w 12. P 14½ × 14.*

308	72	6 c. yellow, ultramarine and rose-red ..		10	10
309		25 c. yellow, ultramarine and bright blue		15	15
310		35 c. yellow, ultramarine & emerald-grn		15	15
308/10			Set of 3	30	30

73 I.C.Y. Emblem

(Litho State Ptg Wks, Vienna)

1965 (15 Nov). *International Co-operation Year. P 12.*

311	73	35 c. red-brown, dp green & ochre-yell ..		30	15

74 Eleanor Roosevelt, Flag and U.N. Emblem

1965 (10 Dec). *Eleanor Roosevelt Memorial Foundation. W w 12. P 13½ × 14.*

312	74	25 c. black, red and ultramarine	..	10	10

75 Parliament Building   (79)

1966 (8 Feb). *Royal Visit. T 75 and similar horiz designs. Multicoloured. W w 12 (sideways). P 13½×14½.*

313	5 c. Type 75	..	..	15	10
314	8 c. Map, Royal Yacht Britannia and Arms			1·25	70
315	25 c. Map and flag	..		1·40	55
316	35 c. Flag and panorama	..		1·50	70
313/16			Set of 4	3·75	1·75

1966 (15 Nov). *As No. 284 but W w 12 (sideways).*

317	1 c. stone and black	..	..	10	20

No. 317 exists with PVA gum as well as gum arabic.

1967 (31 Aug). *Fifth Year of Independence. Nos. 288/9, 291a and 295 optd as T 79.*

318	8 c. yellow-green	..	..	10	10
319	10 c. deep lilac	..	..	10	10
320	15 c. orange	..	..	10	10
321	60 c. vermilion, yellow-green and indigo			25	10
318/21			Set of 4	30	30

On No. 321 the overprint is in five lines.

80 Musical Instruments

81 Calypso King

1968 (17 Feb). *Trinidad Carnival. Horiz designs as T* 80 (15 *and* 25 *c.*), *or vert designs as T* 81 (35 *and* 60 *c.*). *Multicoloured. P* 12.

322	5 c. Type 80	..	..	10	10
323	10 c. Type 81	..	..	10	10
324	15 c. Steel band	..	..	10	10
325	25 c. Carnival procession		..	15	10
326	35 c. Carnival King	..	..	15	10
327	60 c. Carnival Queen	..	..	25	30
322/7	..	..	*Set of* 6	50	45

86 Doctor giving Eye-Test

87 Peoples of the World and Emblem

1968 (7 May). *20th Anniv of World Health Organization. W w* 12 (*sideways*). *P* 14.

328	86	5 c. red, blackish brown and gold		10	10
329		25 c. orange, blackish brown and gold	..	20	10
330		35 c. bright blue, black and gold.	.	25	15
328/30			*Set of* 3	50	30

1968 (5 Aug). *Human Rights Year. W w* 12 (*sideways*). *P* 13½ × 14.

331	87	5 c. cerise, black and greenish yellow	..	10	10
332		10 c. new blue, black and greenish yellow		10	10
333		25 c. apple-green, black & greenish yell.	.	20	15
331/3			*Set of* 3	30	30

88 Cycling

(*Des G. Vasarhelyi. Islands additionally die-stamped in gold* (5 *c. to* 35 *c.*))

1968 (14 Oct). *Olympic Games, Mexico. T* 88 *and similar horiz designs. Multicoloured. W w* 12. *P* 14.

334	5 c. Type 88	..	..	10	10
335	15 c. Weightlifting	..	..	10	10
336	25 c. Relay-racing	..	..	10	10
337	35 c. Sprinting	..	..	15	10
338	$1.20, Maps of Mexico and Trinidad	..	55	30
334/8			*Set of* 5	75	50

93 Cocoa Beans

94 Green Hermit

(*Des G. Vasarhelyi. Queen's profile die-stamped in gold* (G.) *or silver* (S.), *also the Islands on* 20, 25 *c.*)

1969–72. *Designs as T* 93/4. *W w* 12 (*sideways on* 1 *to* 8 *c.*, 40 *c.*, 50 *c.*) *P* 14 × 14½ ($2.50, $5) *or* 14 (*others*).

A. *Chalk-surfaced paper* (1.4.69)
B. *Glazed, ordinary paper* (24.3.72*)

				A		B	
339	1 c. multicoloured (S.)	..	10	10	10	10
	a. Queen's head omitted	..	80·00	—	†	
340	3 c. multicoloured (G.)	..	10	10	10	10
341	5 c. multicoloured (G.)	..	60	10	60	10
	a. Queen's head omitted	..	†			
	b. Imperf (pair)	..	†	£200	—	
	ba. Ditto and Queen's head omitted	..	†	£325		
342	6 c. multicoloured (G.)	..	10	10	90	90
	a. Queen's head omitted	..	£110	—	†	
	b. Imperf (pair)	..	£250		†	
343	8 c. multicoloured (S.)	..	40	10		
344	10 c. multicoloured (G.)	..	60	10	60	10
345	12 c. mult (blue-grn leaves) (S.)	..	15	30	30	80
	a. Myrtle-green leaves	..	3·25	2·00	†	

346	15 c. multicoloured (S.)	..	10	10	20	10
	a. Queen's head omitted	..	£350	—	†	
347	20 c. scarlet, black & grey (G.)	15	10	30	30
348	25 c. scarlet, blk & new bl (S.)	15	15	1·50	50
	a. Silver (Queen's head and island) omitted	..	†	£120		
349	30 c. multicoloured (S.)	..	25	10	50	30
350	40 c. multicoloured (G.)	..	2·50	10	4·00	60
351	50 c. multicoloured (S.)	..	25	40	1·50	50
352	$1 multicoloured (G.)	..	60	15	1·50	2·50
	a. Gold (Queen's head) omitted	..	£130	—	†	
353	$2.50, multicoloured (G.)	..	80	2·50		†
	a. Perf 14 (1972)	..	15·00	20·00	†	
354	$5 multicoloured (G.)	..	1·50	3·00		†
	a. Gold (Queen's head) omitted	..	£300	—	†	
	b. Perf 14 (1972)	..	35·00	38·00	†	
339A/54A			*Set of* 16	7·00	6·50	
339B/52B			*Set of* 13		11·00	8·00

Designs: *Horiz as T* 93—3 c. Sugar refinery; 5 c. Rufous-vented Chachalaca; 6 c. Oil refinery; 8 c. Fertilizer plant; 40 c. Scarlet Ibis; 50 c. Maracas Bay; $2.50, Fishing; $5, Red House. *Vert as T* 94—12 c. Citrus fruit; 15 c. Arms of Trinidad and Tobago; 20, 25 c. Flag and outline of Trinidad and Tobago; 30 c. Chaconia plant; $1, Poui tree.

*This was the date of receipt at the G.P.O.; the dates of issue are not known.

The listed missing die-stamped heads have the heads completely omitted and, except for No. 352a which results from a shift, show a blind impression of the die. They should not be confused with stamps from sheets containing a row of partially missing heads progressing down to mere specks of foil. The 20 c. value also exists with the gold omitted from the map only. We have also seen stamps with an additional "blind" profile cutting into the rear of the head but without a second die-stamped impression. Varieties of this nature are outside the scope of this catalogue.

See also Nos. 432/4 and 473.

108 Captain A. A. Cipriani (labour leader) and Entrance to Woodford Square

(*Photo State Ptg Works, Vienna*)

1969 (1 May). *50th Anniv of International Labour Organization. T* 108 *and similar horiz design. P* 12.

355	6 c. black, gold and carmine-red	..	10	10
356	15 c. black, gold and new blue	..	10	10

Design:—15 c. Arms of Industrial Court and entrance to Woodford Square.

110 Cornucopia and Fruit

111 Map showing "CARIFTA" Countries

(*Des and photo State Ptg Works, Vienna*)

1969 (1 Aug). *First Anniv of CARIFTA* (*Caribbean Free Trade Area*). *T* 110/11 *and similar multicoloured designs. P* 13½.

357	6 c. Type 110	..	..	10	10
358	10 c. British and member nations' flags (*horiz*)	10	10
359	30 c. Type 111	..	..	20	10
360	40 c. Boeing "727" in flight (*horiz*)	..	25	15
357/60	..	..	..	*Set of* 4	55	30

114 Space Module landing on Moon

(*Des G. Vasarhelyi. Litho D.L.R.*)

1969 (2 Sept). *First Man on the Moon. T* 114 *and similar multicoloured designs. P* 14.

361	6 c. Type 114	..	..	10	10
362	40 c. Space module and astronauts on Moon (*vert*)	..	15	10
363	$1 Astronauts seen from inside space module	45	20
361/3			*Set of* 3	65	30

The above were released by the Philatelic Agency in the U.S.A. on 1 September, but not sold locally until 2 September.

COVER PRICES

Cover factors are quoted at the beginning of each country for most issues to 1945. An explanation of the system can be found on page x. The factors quoted do not, however, apply to philatelic covers.

---

117 Parliamentary Chamber, Flags and Emblems

(*Photo Harrison*)

1969 (23 Oct*). *15th Commonwealth Parliamentary Association Conference, Port-of-Spain. T* 117 *and similar horiz designs. Multicoloured. W w* 12. *P* 14½ × 13½.

364	10 c. Type 117	..	..	10	10
365	15 c. J.F. Kennedy College	..	..	10	10
366	30 c. Parliamentary maces	..	..	25	15
367	40 c. Cannon and emblem	..	..	25	15
364/7	..	..	..	*Set of* 4	60	30

*This was the local release date; the Philatelic Agency in New York released the stamps ten days earlier.

121 Congress Emblem

122 Emblem and Islands at Daybreak

(*Photo Rosenbaum Bros, Vienna*)

1969 (3 Nov). *International Congress of the Junior Chamber of Commerce. T* 121/2 *and similar vert design. P* 13½.

368	6 c. black, red and gold	..	..	10	10
369	30 c. gold, lake and light blue.	..	..	20	20
370	40 c. black, gold and ultramarine	..	20	20
368/70			*Set of* 3	40	40

Design:—40 c. Emblem, palm-trees and ruin.
The above were released by the Philatelic Agency in the U.S.A. on 2 November, but not sold locally until 3 November.

124 "Man in the Moon"

129 Statue of Gandhi

(*Des V. Whiteley. Litho Questa*)

1970 (6 Feb). *Carnival Winners. T* 124 *and similar multicoloured designs. W w* 12 (*sideways on* 40 *c.*) *P* 14.

371	5 c. Type 124	..	..	10	10
372	6 c. "City beneath the Sea"	..	..	10	10
373	15 c. "Antelope" God Bamibara	..	15	10
374	30 c. "Chanticleer" Pheasant Queen of Malaya	25	10
375	40 c. Steel Band of the Year (*horiz*)	..	25	15
371/5	..	..	..	*Set of* 5	70	30

The above were released by the Philatelic Agency in the U.S.A. on 2 February, but not sold locally until 6 February.

(*Photo State Printing Works, Vienna*)

1970 (2 Mar). *Gandhi Centenary Year* (1969). *T* 129 *and similar multicoloured design. P* 12.

376	10 c. Type 129	..	..	25	10
377	30 c. Head of Gandhi and Indian flag (*horiz*)	..	45	20

131 Symbols of Culture, Science, Arts and Technology

132 New U.P.U. H.Q. Building

(Des G. Lee. Photo State Printing Works, Vienna)

1970 (26 June). *25th Anniv of United Nations. T* **131/2** *and similar designs. Multicoloured. P* 12 (30 c.), 13½ × 14 (10 c.) or 13½ (others).

378	5 c. Type **131**	..	..	10	10
379	10 c. Children of different races, map and flag (34 × 25 mm)			15	10
380	20 c. Noah's Ark, rainbow and dove (35 × 24 mm)			30	15
381	30 c. Type **132** ..			30	15
378/81			Set of 4	75	30

NATIONAL
COMMERCIAL
BANK
ESTABLISHED
1.7.70

(133)   134 "East Indian Immigrants" (J. Cazabon)

1970 (1 July). *Inauguration of National Commercial Bank.* No. 341A *optd with T* **133**.

382	5 c. multicoloured	..	..	..	10	10

(Des from paintings by Cazabon. Litho Questa)

1970 (Oct). *125th Anniv of San Fernando. T* **134** *and similar designs. W w* **12** (*sideways on* 5 c. *and* 40 c.). *P* 13½.

383	3 c. multicoloured	..	..	10	15
384	5 c. black, blue and yellow-ochre	..		10	10
385	40 c. black, blue and yellow-ochre	..		45	15
383/5	..		Set of 3	55	30

Designs: *Horiz*—5 c. "San Fernando Town Hall"; 40 c. "San Fernando Harbour, 1860".

135 "The Adoration of the Shepherds" (detail, School of Seville)

(Des G. Drummond. Litho Format)

1970 (8 Dec). *Christmas. Paintings. T* **135** *and similar vert designs. Multicoloured. P* 13½.

386	3 c. Type **135** ..			10	10
387	5 c. "Madonna and Child with Saints" (detail, Titian)			10	10
388	30 c. "The Adoration of the Shepherds" (detail, Le Nain)			25	15
389	40 c. "The Virgin and Child, St. John and an Angel" (Morando)			25	10
390	$1 "The Adoration of the Kings" (detail, Veronese)			85	85
386/90			Set of 5	1·25	1·00
MS391	114 × 153 mm. Nos. 386/9		..	2·25	2·50

BROCKET-DEER

136 Red Brocket

(Des State Printing Works, Vienna. Litho Questa)

1971 (9 Aug). *Trinidad Wildlife. T* **136** *and similar horiz designs. Multicoloured. W w* **12** (*sideways*).

392	3 c. Type **136**..		..	20	15
393	5 c. Collared Peccary ("Quenk")	..		25	15
394	6 c. Paca ("Lappe")	..	..	30	30
395	30 c. Brazilian Agouti	..	..	1·50	3·00
396	40 c. Ocelot	..	..	1·75	2·75
392/6	..		Set of 5	3·50	5·50

ALTERED CATALOGUE NUMBERS

Any Catalogue numbers altered from the last edition are shown as a list in the introductory pages.

137 A. A. Cipriani   138 "Virgin and Child with St. John" (detail, Bartolommeo)

(Litho D.L.R.)

1971 (30 Aug*). *Ninth Anniv of Independence. T* **137** *and similar vert design. Multicoloured. W w* **12**. *P* 14.

397	5 c. Type **137** ..	..	..	10	10
398	30 c. Chaconia medal	..	..	20	30

*This was the local release date, but the New York agency issued the stamps on 25 August.

(Litho Harrison)

1971 (25 Oct). *Christmas. T* **138** *and similar vert designs. Multicoloured. W w* **12** (*sideways on* 10 *and* 15 c.). *P* 14 × 14½.

399	3 c. Type **138** ..	..	..	10	10
400	5 c. Local crèche	..	..	15	10
401	10 c. "Virgin and Child with Saints Jerome and Dominic" (detail, Lippi)			20	10
402	15 c. "Virgin and Child with St. Anne" (detail, Gerolamo dai Libri)			25	15
399/402			Set of 4	65	30

139 Satellite Earth Station, Matura

(Litho Harrison)

1971 (18 Nov). *Satellite Earth Station. T* **139** *and similar vert designs. Multicoloured. W w* **12** (*sideways on* 10 c.). *P* 14 (10 c.) or 14 × 13½ (others).

403	10 c. Type **139** ..	..	..	10	10
404	30 c. Dish antennae	..	..	20	20
405	40 c. Satellite and the earth	..		30	30
403/5	..		Set of 3	55	55
MS406	140 × 76 mm. Nos. 403/5 (wmk sideways). Imperf			1·25	2·00
	a. Yellow and pale blue omitted				

TRINIDAD & TOBAGO

140 *Morpho peleides × achilleana*

(Des G. Drummond. Photo Harrison)

1972 (18 Feb). *Butterflies. T* **140** *and similar horiz designs. Multicoloured. W w* **12** (*sideways on* 5 c.). *P* 14.

407	3 c. Type **140**	..	..	40	10
408	5 c. *Eryphanis polyxena*	..	..	50	10
409	6 c. *Phoebis philea*	..	..	55	10
410	10 c. *Prepona laertes*	..	..	80	15
411	20 c. *Eurytides telesilaus*	..	..	1·25	1·40
412	30 c. *Eurema proterpia*	..	..	1·75	2·25
407/12			Set of 6	4·75	3·50

141 *Lady McLeod* (paddle-steamer) and McLeod Stamp   142 Trinity Cross

(Des J. Cooter. Litho Harrison)

1972 (24 Apr*). *125th Anniv. of First Trinidad Postage Stamp. T* **141** *and similar horiz designs. W w* **12**. *P* 14.

413	5 c. multicoloured	..	..	15	10
414	10 c. multicoloured	..	..	25	10
415	30 c. greenish blue, reddish chestnut and black			70	45
413/15	..		Set of 3	1·00	55
MS416	83 × 140 mm. Nos. 413/15	..		1·00	1·25
	a. Wmk sideways	..		20·00	25·00

Designs:—10 c. Map and Lady McLeod stamp; 30 c. Lady McLeod stamp and inscription.

*This was the local release date, but the New York Agency issued the stamps on 12 April.

(Des G. Drummond. Photo Enschedé)

1972 (28 Aug). *Tenth Anniv of Independence. T* **142** *and similar vert designs. Multicoloured. W w* **12**. *P* 13½ × 13.

417	5 c. Type **142**	..	..	10	10
418	10 c. Chaconia Medal	..	..	10	10
419	20 c. Hummingbird Medal	..	..	15	15
420	30 c. Medal of Merit	..	..	15	20
417/20			Set of 4	40	40
MS421	93 × 121 mm. Nos. 417/20	..		60	1·00

One example of MS421 has been seen with the blue (background and frame) omitted from the 10 c. Another example has been seen with carmine (background and frame) omitted from the 30 c. See also Nos. 440/4.

143 Bronze Medal, 1964 Relay

(Des G. Drummond. Litho Questa)

1972 (7 Sept). *Olympic Games, Munich. T* **143** *and similar horiz designs. Multicoloured. W w* **12**. *P* 14.

422	10 c. Type **143**	..	..	15	10
423	20 c. Bronze, 1964 200 metres..			35	10
424	30 c. Silver, 1952 weightlifting	..		45	15
425	40 c. Silver, 1964 400 metres ..			45	20
426	50 c. Silver, 1948 weightlifting	..		50	65
422/6			Set of 5	1·75	1·10
MS427	153 × 82 mm. Nos. 422/6 ..			1·75	1·75

144 "Adoration of the Kings" (detail, Dosso)

(Des G. Drummond. Photo J.W.)

1972 (9 Nov). *Christmas. T* **144** *and similar horiz design. Multicoloured. W w* **12**. *P* 14.

428	3 c. Type **144**	..	..	10	10
429	5 c. "The Holy Family and a Shepherd" (Titian)			10	10
430	30 c. As 5 c.	..	..	70	55
428/30			Set of 3	80	60
MS431	73 × 99 mm. Nos. 428/30	..		85	1·50

1973–74. *Nos.* 340/2, *but W w* **12** (*upright*). *Glazed, ordinary paper.*

432	3 c. multicoloured (9.74?)	..	..	4·50	7·50
433	5 c. multicolourex (1973)	..	..	7·50	1·75
	a. Yellow (background) omitted	..		£130	
434	6 c. multicoloured (1974)	..	..	3·50	1·75
432/4	..		Set of 3	14·00	10·00

145 E.C.L.A. Building, Chile

(Des G. Drummond. Litho Questa)

1973 (15 Aug). *Anniversaries. Events described on stamps. T* **145** *and similar horiz designs. Multicoloured. W w* **12**. *P* 14.

435	10 c. Type **145**	..	..	10	10
436	20 c. Interpol emblem ..			45	20
437	30 c. W.M.O. emblem	..	..	45	20
438	40 c. University of the West Indies	..		45	20
435/8	..		Set of 4	1·25	60
MS439	155 × 92 mm. Nos. 435/8 ..			1·25	1·25

(Des J. Cooter. Litho Harrison)

1973 (30 Aug). *Eleventh Anniv of Independence. Vert designs as T* **142**. *Multicoloured. W w* **12**. *P* 14½ × 14.

440	10 c. Trinity Cross	..	..	10	10
441	20 c. Medal of Merit	..	..	20	15
442	30 c. Chaconia Medal ..			20	20
443	40 c. Hummingbird Medal	..		30	30
440/3	..		Set of 4	70	65
MS444	75 × 122 mm. Nos. 440/3. P 14			70	1·25

146 G.P.O., Port-of-Spain   147 "Madonna with Child" (Murillo)

(Des J. Cooter. Photo J.W.)

1973 (8 Oct). *Second Commonwealth Conference of Postal Admin-istrations, Trinidad. T **146** and similar horiz design. Multi-coloured. W w **12** (sideways). P 14.*
445	30 c. Type **146**		20	20
446	40 c. Conference Hall, Chaguaramas*		30	30
MS447	115 × 115 mm. Nos. 445/6		90	90

*Wrongly inscr "CHAGARAMAS" on stamp.

(Des PAD Studio. Photo Harrison)

1973 (22 Oct). *Christmas. W w **12** (sideways on **MS450**). P 14½ × 14.*
448	**147**	5 c. multicoloured	10	10
449		$1 multicoloured	75	60
MS450		94 × 88 mm. Nos. 448/9. P 14	85	1·40

148 Berne H.Q. within U.P.U. Emblem

(Des PAD Studio. Photo Harrison)

1974 (18 Nov). *Centenary of Universal Postal Union. T **148** and similar horiz design. Multicoloured. W w **12** (sideways). P 13 × 14.*
451	40 c. Type **148**		45	25
452	50 c. Map within emblem		45	75
MS453	117 × 104 mm. Nos. 451/2. P 13 × 14½		16·00	18·00

149 *Humming Bird I crossing Atlantic Ocean (1960)*

(Des and photo Harrison)

1974 (2 Dec). *First Anniv of World Voyage by H. and K. La Borde. T **149** and similar horiz design. Multicoloured. W w **12** (side-ways). P 14.*
454	40 c. Type **149**		45	15
455	50 c. *Humming Bird II* crossing globe		55	35
MS456	109 × 84 mm. Nos. 454/5 (wmk upright)		2·00	4·00

150 "Sex Equality"

(Des Hetty J. Mejias de Grannes; adapted V. Whiteley. Litho Harrison)

1975 (23 June). *International Women's Year. W w **14** (sideways). P 14.*
457	**150**	15 c. multicoloured	15	10
458		30 c. multicoloured	35	55

151 Common Vampire Bat, Microscope and Syringe

(Des PAD Studio. Photo Harrison)

1975 (23 Sept). *Isolation of Rabies Virus. T **151** and similar horiz design. Multicoloured. W w **14**. P 14 × 14½.*
459	25 c. Type **151**		40	30
460	30 c. Dr. Pawan, instruments and book		50	35

152 Route-map and Tail of Boeing "707"

(Des C. Abbott. Litho Walsall)

1975 (27 Nov). *35th Anniv of British West Indian Airways. T **152** and similar horiz designs. W w **14** (sideways). P 14.*
461	20 c. Type **152**		25	10
462	30 c. "707" on ground		40	45
463	40 c. "707" in flight		55	65
461/3		*Set of 3*	1·10	1·10
MS464	119 × 110 mm. Nos. 461/3		1·50	1·75

153 "From the Land of the Humming Bird"

(Des and photo Harrison)

1976 (12 Jan). *Carnival. 1974 Prizewinning Costumes. T **153** and similar horiz design. Multicoloured. W w **14** (sideways). P 14.*
465	30 c. Type **153**		10	10
466	$1 "The Little Carib"		40	50
MS467	83 × 108 mm. Nos. 465/6		90	90

154 Angostura Building, Port-of-Spain

(Des Jennifer Toombs. Litho J.W.)

1976 (14 July). *150th Anniv. of Angostura Bitters. T **154** and similar horiz designs. Multicoloured. W w **14** (sideways). P 13.*
468	5 c. Type **154**		10	10
469	35 c. Medal, New Orleans 1885/6		20	25
470	45 c. Medal, Sydney 1879		25	40
471	50 c. Medal, Brussels 1897		25	50
468/71		*Set of 4*	65	1·10
MS472	119 × 112 mm. Nos. 468/71. P 14		90	1·25

REPUBLIC

1976 (2 Aug). *As No. 344B but W w **14**.*
473	10 c. multicoloured	75	75

1976 (4 Oct). *West Indian Victory in World Cricket Cup. As Nos. 419/20 of Jamaica.*
474	35 c. Caribbean map		45	30
475	45 c. Prudential Cup		55	40
MS476	80 × 80 mm. Nos. 474/5		1·75	2·50

155 "Columbus sailing through the Bocas" (Campins)

(Des J.W. Litho Questa)

1976 (1 Nov)–78. *Paintings, Hotels and Orchids. Horiz designs as T **155**. Multicoloured. W w **14**. P 14.*
479	5 c. Type **155**		80	10
480	6 c. Robinson Crusoe Hotel, Tobago (17.1.78)		20	40
482	10 c. "San Fernando Hill" (J. Cazabon)		20	10
483	12 c. *Paphinia cristata* (7.6.78)		1·50	50
484	15 c. Turtle Beach Hotel (17.1.78)		50	55
485	20 c. "East Indians in a Landscape" (J. Cazabon)		50	10
486	25 c. Mt Irvine Hotel (17.1.78)		50	10
487	30 c. *Caularthon bicornutum* (7.6.78)		1·50	45
488	35 c. "Los Gallos Point" (J. Cazabon)		85	10
489	40 c. *Miltassia* (7.6.78).		1·50	10
490	45 c. "Corbeaux Town" (J. Cazabon)		1·00	10
491	50 c. *Oncidium ampliatum* (7.6.78)		1·75	20
492	70 c. Beach facilities, Mt Irvine Hotel (17.1.78)		70	90
494	$2.50, *Oncidium papilio* (7.6.78)		2·25	1·00
495	$5 Trinidad Holiday Inn (17.1.78)		1·75	5·00
479/95		*Set of 15*	14·00	8·50
MS497	171 × 100 mm. Nos. 479, 482, 485, 488 and 490. Wmk sideways		2·00	1·50
MS498	171 × 88 mm. Nos. 480, 484, 486, 492 and 495. Wmk sideways (17.1.78)		3·00	5·00
MS499	170 × 90 mm. Nos. 483, 487, 489, 491 and 494. Wmk sideways (7.6.78)		3·75	4·00

156 Hasely Crawford and Olympic Gold Medal

(Des J.W. Litho D. L. R.)

1977 (4 Jan). *Hasely Crawford Commemoration. W w **14** (side-ways). P 12 × 12½.*
501	**156**	25 c. multicoloured	20	30
MS502		93 × 70 mm. No. 501	30	50

OMNIBUS ISSUES

Details, together with prices for complete sets, of the various Omnibus issues from the 1935 Silver Jubilee series to date are included in a special section following Zimbabwe at the end of Volume 2.

157 Lindbergh's Sikorsky "S–38", 1929   **158** National Flag

(Des and litho J.W.)

1977 (4 Apr). *50th Anniv of Airmail Service. T **157** and similar horiz designs. Multicoloured. W w **14** (sideways). P 13.*
503	20 c. Type **157**		25	20
504	35 c. Arrival of Charles and Anne Lindbergh		35	35
505	45 c. Boeing "707", c. 1960		45	50
506	50 c. Boeing "747", 1969		1·10	2·25
503/6		*Set of 4*	1·90	3·00
MS507	130 × 100 mm. Nos. 503/6. P 14		3·50	3·50

(Des and litho J.W.)

1977 (26 July). *Inauguration of the Republic. T **158** and similar vert designs. Multicoloured. W w **14**. P 13.*
508	20 c. Type **158**		20	10
509	35 c. Coat of Arms		35	35
510	45 c. Government House		45	55
508/10		*Set of 3*	90	90
MS511	125 × 84 mm. Nos. 508/10. P 14		60	1·25

159 White Poinsettia   **160** Miss Janelle (Penny) Commissioning with Trophy

(Des J.W. Litho Walsall)

1977 (11 Oct). *Christmas. T **159** and similar vert design. Multi-coloured. W w **14**. P 14 × 14½.*
512	10 c. Type **159**		15	10
513	35 c. Type **159**		25	10
514	45 c. Red Poinsettia		35	25
515	50 c. As 45 c.		45	60
512/15		*Set of 4*	1·10	90
MS516	112 × 142 mm. Nos. 512/15		1·10	1·50

(Des BG Studio. Litho Questa)

1978 (2 Aug). *Miss Janelle (Penny) Commissiong ("Miss Universe 1977") Commemoration. T **160** and similar vert designs showing Miss Commissiong. Multicoloured. W w **14**. P 14½.*
517	10 c. Type **160**		15	10
518	35 c. Portrait		40	50
519	45 c. In evening dress		55	75
517/19		*Set of 3*	1·00	1·25
MS520	186 × 120 mm. Nos. 517/19		90	1·50
a. 45c. value imperf on three sides			£500	

161 Tayra   **162** "Burst of Beauty"

(Des G. Drummond. Litho Walsall)

1978 (7 Nov). *Wildlife. T **161** and similar horiz designs. Multi-coloured. W w **14** (sideways). P 13½.*
521	15 c. Type **161**		20	10
522	25 c. Ocelot		30	20
523	40 c. Brazilian Tree Porcupine		50	30
524	70 c. Tamandua		65	1·25
521/4		*Set of 4*	1·50	1·75
MS525	128 × 101 mm. Nos. 521/4		1·75	2·50

(Des C. Abbott. Litho Format)

1979 (1 Feb). *Carnival 1978. T **162** and similar vert designs. P 13½.*
526	5 c. multicoloured		10	10
527	10 c. multicoloured		10	10
528	35 c. multicoloured		10	10
529	45 c. multicoloured		10	10
530	50 c. yellow-brown, rosine and deep lilac		10	10
531	$1 multicoloured		20	55
526/31		*Set of 6*	50	75

Designs:—10 c. Rain worshipper; 35 c. "Zodiac"; 45 c. Praying mantis; 50 c. "Eye of the Hurricane"; $1 Steel orchestra.

163 Day Care   164 Geothermal Exploration

(Des BG Studio. Litho J.W.)

1979 (5 June). *International Year of the Child. T 163 and similar vert designs. Multicoloured. P 13.*

532	5 c.	Type 163		10	10
533	10 c.	School feeding programme		10	10
534	35 c.	Dental care		30	15
535	45 c.	Nursery school		30	20
536	50 c.	Free bus transport		30	35
537	$1	Medical care		65	1·00
532/7			Set of 6	1·60	1·60
MS538	114 × 132 mm. Nos. 532/7. P 14 × 13½			1·60	1·75

(Des local artist; adapted L. Curtis. Litho Format)

1979 (3 July). *4th Latin American Geological Congress. T 164 and similar horiz designs. Multicoloured. W w 14 (sideways). P 13½.*

539	10 c.	Type 164		15	10
540	35 c.	Hydrogeology		25	25
541	45 c.	Petroleum exploration		30	30
542	70 c.	Environmental preservation		40	1·00
539/42			Set of 4	1·00	1·50
MS543	185 × 89 mm. Nos. 539/42			1·25	1·60

165 1879 1d. rose and Map of Tobago

(Des J. Cooter. Litho Format)

1979 (1 Aug). *Tobago Stamp Centenary. T 165 and similar horiz designs in black, rose-lilac and dull orange ($1) or multicoloured (others). W w 14 (sideways). P 13½ × 14.*

544	10 c.	Type 165		10	10
545	15 c.	1879 3d. and 1880 ½d. surcharged on half of 6d.		15	10
546	35 c.	1879 6d. and 1886 ½d. surcharged on 6d.		45	30
547	45 c.	1879 1s. and 1886 ½d. surcharged on 2½d.		50	30
548	70 c.	1879 5s. and Great Britain 1856 1s. with "A14" (Scarborough, Tobago) postmark		65	1·25
549	$1	1879 £1 and General Post Office, Scarborough, Tobago		80	1·75
544/9			Set of 6	2·25	3·50
MS550	165 × 155 mm. Nos. 544/9			2·25	3·50

166 1962 60 c. Independence Commemorative and Sir Rowland Hill

(Des and litho J.W.)

1979 (4 Oct). *Death Centenary of Sir Rowland Hill. T 166 and similar horiz designs showing stamps and Sir Rowland Hill. Multicoloured. W w 14 (sideways). P 13.*

551	25 c.	Type 166		30	15
552	45 c.	1977 35 c. Inauguration of Republic commemorative		40	20
553	$1	1879 Trinidad ½d. surcharge and Tobago 1880 4d.		65	1·00
551/3			Set of 3	1·25	1·25
MS554	115 × 125 mm. No. 551/3. P 13½ × 14			1·25	1·50

167 Poui Tree in Churchyard   (168)

1844–1980 POPULATION CENSUS 12th MAY 1980

(Des G. Hutchins. Litho Format)

1980 (21 Jan). *Centenary of Princes Town. T 167 and similar horiz designs. Multicoloured. W w 14 (sideways). P 14½ × 14.*

555	5 c.	Type 167		10	10
556	10 c.	Princes Town Court House		10	10
557	50 c.	Locomotive of the Royal Train, 1880		60	90
558	$1.50	H.M.S. *Bacchante* (corvette)		1·00	1·60
555/8			Set of 4	1·60	2·40
MS559	177 × 102 mm. Nos. 555/8			1·90	2·50

1980 (8 Apr). *Population Census. Nos. 479/80 and 482 optd with T 168.*

560	5 c.	Type 155		15	20
561	6 c.	Robinson Crusoe Hotel, Tobago		15	45
562	10 c.	"Old View" (Cazabon)		15	20
560/2			Set of 3	40	75

169 Scarlet Ibis (male)   170 Silver and Bronze Medals for Weightlifting, 1948 and 1952

(Des G. Drummond. Litho Questa)

1980 (6 May). *Scarlet Ibis. T 169 and similar vert designs. Multicoloured. W w 14. P 14.*

563	50 c.	Type 169		85	85
		a. Strip of 5. Nos. 563/7		3·75	
564	50 c.	Male and female		85	85
565	50 c.	Hen and nest		85	85
566	50 c.	Nest and eggs		85	85
567	50 c.	Chick in nest		85	85
563/7			Set of 5	3·75	3·75

Nos. 563/7 were printed together, *se-tenant*, in horizontal and vertical strips of 5 throughout.

(Des G. Hutchins. Litho Walsall)

1980 (22 July). *Olympic Games, Moscow. T 170 and similar designs. W w 14 (sideways). P 14.*

568	10 c.	multicoloured		10	10
569	15 c.	multicoloured		10	10
570	70 c.	multicoloured		30	45
568/70			Set of 3	30	50
MS571	110 × 149 mm. $2.50, black, silver and orange-vermilion (wmk upright)			1·25	1·75

Designs: *Horiz*—15 c. Hasely Crawford (100 metres sprint winner, 1976) and gold medal; 70 c. Silver medal for 400 metres and bronze medals for 4 × 400 metres relay, 1964. *Vert*—$2.50, Olympic Games emblems for Moscow, 1980, Olympia, 776 B.C. and Athens, 1896.

171 Charcoal Production

(Des J. Cooter. Litho Walsall)

1980 (8 Sept). *11th Commonwealth Forestry Conference. T 171 and similar horiz designs. Multicoloured. W w 14 (sideways). P 14.*

572	10 c.	Type 171		10	10
573	55 c.	Logging		45	25
574	70 c.	Teak plantation		55	40
575	$2.50,	Watershed management		1·40	1·50
572/5			Set of 4	2·25	2·00
MS576	135 × 87 mm. Nos. 572/5			2·50	2·75

172 Beryl McBurnie (dance and culture) and Audrey Jeffers (social worker)

(Des BG Studio. Litho Questa)

1980 (29 Sept). *Decade for Women (1st issue). T 172 and similar horiz designs. Multicoloured. W w 14 (sideways). P 14.*

577	$1	Type 172		55	55
578	$1	Elizabeth Bourne (judiciary) and Isabella Teshier (government)		55	55
579	$1	Dr. Stella Abidh (public health) and Louise Horne (nutrition)		55	55
577/9			Set of 3	1·50	1·50

See also Nos. 680/2.

173 Netball Stadium

(Des BG Studio. Litho Format)

1980 (21 Oct). *World Netball Tournament. W w 14 (sideways). P 13½ × 14.*

580	173	70 c. multicoloured		30	45

---

174 I.Y.D.P. Emblem, Athlete and Disabled Person   175 "Our Land Must Live"

(Des BG Studio. Litho Format)

1981 (23 Mar). *International Year for Disabled Persons. T 174 and similar horiz designs. W w 14. P 14½.*

581	10 c.	black, vermilion and dull yellowish green		15	10
582	70 c.	black, vermilion and buff		50	70
583	$1.50,	black, vermilion and cobalt		90	1·40
584	$2	black, vermilion and flesh		1·25	1·75
581/4			Set of 4	2·50	3·50

Designs:—70 c. I.Y.D.P. emblem and doctor with disabled person; $1.50, Emblem, and blind man and woman; $2 Emblem and inscription.

(Des Debbie Galt; adapted G. Vasarhelyi. Litho J.W.)

1981 (7 July). *Environmental Preservation. T 175 and similar horiz designs. Multicoloured. W w 14 (sideways). P 13 × 13½.*

585	10 c.	Type 175		15	10
586	55 c.	"Our seas must live"		45	30
587	$3	"Our skies must live"		1·60	1·60
585/7			Set of 3	2·00	1·75
MS588	142 × 89 mm. Nos. 585/7			4·50	4·75

176 "Food or Famine"   177 "First Aid Skills"

(Des and litho Harrison)

1981 (16 Oct). *World Food Day. T 176 and similar horiz designs. Multicoloured. W w 14 (sideways). P 14½ × 14.*

589	10 c.	Type 176		10	10
590	15 c.	"Produce more" (threshing and milling rice)		10	10
591	45 c.	"Fish for food" (Bigeye)		30	20
592	55 c.	"Prevent hunger"		35	25
593	$1.50,	"Fight malnutrition"		85	90
594	$2	"Fish for food" (Smallmouth Grunt)		1·10	1·25
589/94			Set of 6	2·40	2·40
MS595	164 × 98 mm. Nos. 589/94			2·75	3·50

(Des L. Curtis. Litho Format)

1981 (17 Nov). *President's Award Scheme. T 177 and similar vert designs. Multicoloured. W w 14. P 14.*

596	10 c.	Type 177		20	10
597	70 c.	"Motor mechanics"		70	45
598	$1	"Expedition"		85	55
599	$2	Presenting an award		1·40	1·40
596/9			Set of 4	2·75	2·25

178 Pharmacist at Work   179 "Production"

(Des C. Abbott. Litho Questa)

1982 (12 Feb). *Commonwealth Pharmaceutical Conference. T 178 and similar vert designs. W w 14. P 14½ × 14.*

600	10 c.	Type 178		15	10
601	$1	Gerritoute (plant)		1·75	1·75
602	$2	Rachette (plant)		2·50	2·75
600/2			Set of 3	4·00	4·25

(Des Debbie Galt; adapted G. Vasarhelyi. Litho Questa)

1982 (28 June). *75th Anniv of Boy Scout Movement. T 179 and similar vert designs. Multicoloured. W w 14. P 14.*

603	15 c.	Type 179		55	10
604	55 c.	"Tolerance"		1·25	25
605	$5	"Discipline"		4·75	4·00
603/5			Set of 3	6·00	4·00

MINIMUM PRICE

The minimum price quote is 10p which represents a handling charge rather than a basis for valuing common stamps. For further notes about prices see introductory pages.

180 Charlotteville   **181** "Pa Pa Bois"

(Des Harrison. Litho Format)

1982 (18 Oct). *25th Anniv of Tourist Board. T* **180** *and similar vert designs. Multicoloured. W* w **14**. *P* 13½ × 14.

606	55 c. Type **180**				35	25
607	$1 Boating				55	55
608	$3 Fort George				1·75	1·90
606/8				Set of 3	2·40	2·40

(Des D. Louison. Litho Harrison)

1982 (8 Nov). *Folklore. Local Spirits and Demons. T* **181** *and similar horiz designs. Multicoloured. W* w **14** (*sideways*).

609	10 c. Type **181**				10	10
610	15 c. "La Diablesse"				10	10
611	65 c. "Lugarhoo", "Phantom" and "Soucouyant"				35	30
612	$5 "Bois de Soleil", "Davens" and "Mamma de l'Eau"				2·50	3·25
609/12				Set of 4	2·75	3·25
MS613	133 × 100 mm. Nos. 609/12				3·50	4·00

182 Cane Harvesting

((Des W. Fenton. Litho Harrison)

1982 (13 Dec). *Canefarmers' Association Centenary. T* **182** *and similar horiz designs. Multicoloured. W* w **14** (*sideways*). *P* 14.

614	30 c. Type **182**				15	15
615	70 c. Farmers loading bullock cart				40	40
616	$1.50, Cane field in bloom				85	95
614/16				Set of 3	1·25	1·40
MS617	72 × 117 mm. Nos. 614/16. P 14½.				1·40	1·50

183 National Stadium

(Des McCombie Skinner. Litho Harrison)

1982 (28 Dec). *20th Anniv of Independence. T* **183** *and similar horiz designs. Multicoloured. W* w **14** (*sideways*). *P* 13 × 14.

618	10 c. Type **183**				10	10
619	35 c. Caroni water treatment plant				20	15
620	50 c. Mount Hope Maternity Hospital				30	25
621	$2 National Insurance Board Mall, Tobago				80	1·25
618/21				Set of 4	1·25	1·50

184 Commonwealth Flags

(Des C. Abbott. Litho Harrison)

1983 (14 Mar). *Commonwealth Day. T* **184** *and similar multicoloured designs. W* w **14** (*sideways on* 10, 55 c.). *P* 14.

622	10 c. Type **184**				10	10
623	55 c. Satellite view of Trinidad and Tobago			25	20
624	$1 "Nodding donkey" oil pump (*vert*)			40	50
625	$2 Map of Trinidad and Tobago (*vert*)			85	1·00
622/5				Set of 4	1·40	1·60

185 BW1A "Tristar"

(Des D. Miller. Litho Format)

1983 (11 July). *10th Anniv of CARICOM. W* w **14** (*sideways*). *P* 14.

626	**185**	35 c. multicoloured			1·00	75

186 V.D.U. Operator

(Des G. Vasarhelyi. Litho Harrison)

1983 (5 Aug). *World Communications Year. T* **186** *and similar horiz designs. Multicoloured. W* w **14** (*sideways*). *P* 14.

627	15 c. Type **186**				20	10
628	55 c. Scarborough Post Office, Tobago			80	20
629	$1 Textel building				1·40	90
630	$3 Morne Blue E.C.M.S. station			2·75	2·50
627/30				Set of 4	4·75	3·25

187 Financial Complex

(Des D. Miller. Litho Format)

1983 (19 Sept). *Conference of Commonwealth Finance Ministers. W* w **14** (*sideways*). *P* 14.

631	**187**	$2 multicoloured			1·50	1·00

188 Kingfish   **189** Bois Pois

(Des N. Weaver. Litho Format)

1983 (17 Oct). *World Food Day. T* **188** *and similar horiz designs. Multicoloured. W* w **14** (*sideways*). *P* 14 × 13½ (10 c., 55 c.) or 13½ (*others*).

632	10 c. Type **188**				20	10
633	55 c. Flying Fish				1·00	40
634	70 c. Queen Conch				1·25	1·00
635	$4 Red Shrimp				4·50	6·00
632/5				Set of 4	6·25	6·75

(Des I. Loe. Litho Questa)

1983 (14 Dec)–84. *Flowers. T* **189** *and similar multicoloured designs. W* w **14** (*sideways on* 5 c. *to* $1.50). *P* 14. A. *Without imprint date. B. With imprint date* (10.84).

					A		B	
636	5 c. Type **189**			30	15	55	40
637	10 c. Maraval Lily			30	15	50	20
638	15 c. Star Grass			35	15	30	30
639	20 c. Bois Caco			10	10		†
640	25 c. Strangling Fig			35	35	60	60
641	30 c. *Cassia moschata*			30	15		†
642	50 c. Chalice Flower			15	15		†
643	65 c. Black Stick			40	25		†
644	80 c. *Columnea scandens*			50	35		†
645	95 c. Cat's Claw			65	40		†
646	$1 Bois L'agli			75	40		†
647	$1.50, *Eustoma exaltatum*			1·00	75		†
648	$2 Chaconia			1·25	1·00		†
649	$2.50, *Chrysothemis pulchella*			75	1·25		†
650	$5 *Centratherum punctatum*			3·00	4·00		†
651	$10 Savanna Flower			4·25	6·00		†
636A/51A			Set of 16	13·00	14·00		†
636B/40B			Set of 4			1·75	1·40

Nos. 648/51 are horizontal, 39 × 29 mm.
No. 637B exists with different imprint dates at foot.
For these designs watermarked w **16** see Nos. 686/701.

190 Rook Chess Pieces in Staunton and 17th-century Styles   **191** Swimming

(Des L. Curtis. Litho Questa)

1984 (14 Sept). *60th Anniv of International Chess Federation. T* **190** *and similar vert designs. Multicoloured. W* w **14**. *P* 14.

652	50 c. Type **190**				1·75	35
653	70 c. Staunton and 12th-century Lewis Bishops			2·00	1·00
654	$1.50, Staunton and 13th-century Swedish Queens			3·00	3·00
655	$2 Staunton and 19th-century Chinese Kings			3·75	4·00
652/5				Set of 4	9·50	7·50

(Des Garden Studio. Litho Harrison)

1984 (21 Sept). *Olympic Games, Los Angeles. T* **191** *and similar vert designs. Multicoloured. W* w **14**. *P* 14 × 14½.

656	15 c. Type **191**				10	10
657	55 c. Track and field events			30	20
658	$1.50, Sailing				70	80
659	$4 Cycling				2·00	2·50
656/9				Set of 4	2·75	3·25
MS660	132 × 85 mm. Nos. 656/9			4·00	6·00

192 Slave Schooner and Shackles   **193** Children's Band

(Des O. Bell. Litho Walsall)

1984 (22 Oct). *150th Anniv of Abolition of Slavery. T* **192** *and similar vert designs. Multicoloured. W* w **14**. *P* 13½ × 13.

661	35 c. Type **192**				75	20
662	55 c. Slave and "Slave Triangle" map			1·00	30
663	$1 *Capitalism and Slavery* (book by Dr. Eric Williams)			1·75	75
664	$2 Toussaint l'Ouverture (Haitian revolutionary)			2·25	1·90
661/4				Set of 4	5·25	2·75
MS665	95 × 100 mm. Nos. 661/4			5·25	5·75

(Des G. Vasarhelyi. Litho J.W.)

1984 (13 Nov). *125th Anniv of St. Mary's Children's Home. T* **193** *and similar horiz designs. Multicoloured. W* w **14** (*sideways*). *P* 13½.

666	10 c. Type **193**				10	10
667	70 c. St. Mary's Children's Home			40	40
668	$3 Group of children				2·00	2·25
666/8				Set of 3	2·25	2·40

194 Parang Band   **195** Capt. A. A. Cipriani and T. U. B. Butler

(Des D. Miller. Litho Questa)

1984 (26 Nov). *Parang Festival. T* **194** *and similar horiz designs. Multicoloured. W* w **14** (*sideways*). *P* 14 × 14½.

669	10 c. Type **194**				15	10
670	30 c. Music and poinsettia			30	15
671	$1 Bandola, bandolin and cuatro (musical instruments)			85	65
672	$3 Double bass, fiddle and guitar (musical instruments)			2·00	2·00
669/72				Set of 4	3·00	2·50

(Des G. Vasarhelyi. Litho Questa)

1985 (17 June). *Labour Day. Labour Leaders. T* **195** *and similar horiz designs. W* w **14**. *P* 14.

673	55 c. black and bright rose			55	55
674	55 c. black and orange-yellow			55	55
675	55 c. black and emerald			55	55
673/5			Set of 3	1·50	1·50

Designs:—No. 674, C. P. Alexander and Q. O'Connor; 675, A. Cola Rienzi and C. T. W. E. Worrell.

196 Lady Nelson (1928)

(Des E. Nisbet. Litho Format)

1985 (20 Aug). *Ships. T* **196** *and similar horiz designs. Multicoloured. W* w **14**. *P* 14½ × 14.

676	30 c. Type **196**				70	15
677	95 c. *Lady Drake* (1928)			1·25	85
678	$1.50, *Federal Palm* (1961)			1·75	2·25
679	$2 *Federal Maple* (1961)			2·25	2·75
676/9				Set of 4	5·50	5·50

197 Marjorie Padmore (music) and Sybil Atteck (art)

(Des Julijana Zappin. Litho Walsall)

1985 (11 Nov). *Decade for Women (2nd issue). T 197 and similar horiz designs. Multicoloured. W w 16 (sideways). P 14.*
680	$1.50, Type **197**		1·10	1·25
681	$1.50, May Cherrie (medical social worker) and Evelyn Tracey (social worker)		1·10	1·25
682	$1.50, Umilta McShine (education) and Jessica Smith-Phillips (public service)		1·10	1·25
680/2	..	Set of 3	3·00	3·25

198 Badge of Trinidad and Tobago Cadet Force (75th Anniv)   **199** Anne-Marie Javouhey (foundress)

(Des D. Slater. Litho Harrison)

1985 (9 Dec). *International Youth Year. T 198 and similar horiz designs. Multicoloured. W w 16 (sideways). P 14 × 14½.*
683	10 c. Type **198**.		20	10
684	65 c. Guide badges (75th anniv of Girl Guide movement)		1·00	1·10
685	95 c. Young people of Trinidad		1·60	1·75
683/5	..	Set of 3	2·50	2·75

1985 (Dec)–**89**. *As Nos. 636/7, 639/41 and 643/51, but W w 16 (sideways on 5, 10, 20, 25, 30, 65, 80, 95 c., $1, $1.50). With imprint date. P 14.*
686	5 c. Type **189**		20	15
687	10 c. Maraval Lily (4.8.86)		20	15
689	20 c. Bois Caco (8.88)		60	40
690	25 c. Strangling Fig (8.88)		60	40
691	30 c. *Cassia moschata* (5.87)		60	40
693	65 c. Black Stick (5.87)		65	65
694	80 c. *Columnea scandens* (5.87)		70	70
695	95 c. Cat's Claw		50	40
696	$1 Bois L'agli		50	30
697	$1.50, *Eustoma exaltatum* (5.87)		1·00	1·25
698	$2 Chaconia (39×29 mm) (5.87)		1·25	1·40
699	$2.50, *Chrysothemis pulchella* (39×29 mm) (5.89)		1·50	1·50
700	$5 *Centratherum punctatum* (39×29 mm)		1·50	1·50
701	$10 Savanna Flower (39×29 mm)		3·00	3·00
686/701	..	Set of 14	11·50	11·00

Nos. 687, 689/91, 693/8 and 700/1 exist with different imprint dates at foot.

(Des Joan Thompson. Litho Format)

1986 (19 Mar). *150th Anniv of Arrival of Sisters of St. Joseph de Cluny. T 199 and similar vert designs. Multicoloured. W w 16 (sideways). P 14 × 14½.*
702	10 c. Type **199**		10	10
703	65 c. St. Joseph's Convent, Port-of-Spain		45	65
704	95 c. Children and statue of Anne-Marie Javouhey		65	90
702/4	..	Set of 3	1·10	1·50

200 Tank Locomotive *Arima*   **201** Scout Camp

(Des J.W. Litho Format)

1986 (26 May). *"Ameripex '86" International Stamp Exhibition, Chicago. Trinidad Railway Locomotives. T 200 and similar horiz designs. W w 16. P 14½×14.*
705	65 c. Type **200**.		25	30
706	95 c. Canadian-built locomotive No. 22		35	40
707	$1.10, Tender engine		40	65
708	$1.50, Saddle tank		60	90
705/8	..	Set of 4	1·40	2·00
MS709	105×80 mm. Nos. 705/8 ..		1·75	2·50

(Des N. Shewring. Litho Questa)

1986 (21 July). *75th Anniv of Trinidad and Tobago Boy Scouts. T 201 and similar horiz design. Multicoloured. W w 16 (sideways). P 14.*
710	$1.70, Type **201**		1·00	1·25
711	$2 Scouts of 1911 and 1986		1·25	1·50

NEW INFORMATION

The editor is always interested to correspond with people who have new information that will improve or correct the Catalogue.

202 Queen and Duke of Edinburgh laying Wreath at War Memorial   **203** Eric Williams at Graduation, 1935

(Des C. Abbott. Litho Walsall)

1986 (16 Sept). *60th Birthday of Queen Elizabeth II. T 202 and similar vert designs. Multicoloured. W w 16. P 14½ × 14.*
712	10 c. Type **202**.		15	10
713	15 c. Queen with Trinidadian dignitaries aboard *Britannia*		30	15
714	30 c. With President Ellis Clarke ..		40	20
715	$5 Receiving bouquet		2·75	3·50
712/15	..	Set of 4	3·25	3·50

(Des D. Miller. Litho Format)

1986 (25 Sept). *75th Birth Anniv of Dr. Eric Williams. T 203 and similar multicoloured designs. W w 14 (sideways on 95 c., $5). P 14.*
716	10 c. Type **203**.		15	10
717	30 c. Premier Eric Williams (wearing red tie)		30	15
718	30 c. As No. 717, but wearing black and orange tie		30	15
719	95 c. Arms of University of West Indies and Dr. Williams as Pro-Chancellor (*horiz*)		60	40
720	$5 Prime Minister Williams and Whitehall (*horiz*)		2·00	2·00
716/20	..	Set of 5	3·00	2·50
MS721	105×100 mm. Nos. 716/17 and 719/20. Wmk sideways ..		5·00	5·00

204 "PEACE" Slogan and Outline Map of Trinidad and Tobago   **205** Miss Giselle La Ronde and BWIA Airliner

(Adapted L. Curtis. Litho Questa)

1986 (3 Nov). *International Peace Year. T 204 and similar horiz design. Multicoloured. W w 16 (sideways). P 14.*
722	95 c. Type **204**.		40	50
723	$3 Peace dove with olive branch ..		1·25	1·75

(Des D. Miller. Litho Walsall)

1987 (27 July). *Miss World 1986. T 205 and similar vert designs. Multicoloured. W w 16. P 14.*
724	10 c. Type **205**.		20	10
725	30 c. In swimsuit on beach		55	15
726	95 c. Miss Giselle La Ronde ..		1·10	75
727	$1.65, Wearing Miss World sash ..		1·75	2·00
724/7	..	Set of 4	3·25	2·75

206 Colonial Bank, Port of Spain   **207** Sergeant in Parade Order and Soldiers in Work Dress and Battle Dress

(Des J.W. Litho Walsall)

1987 (21 Dec). *150th Anniv of Republic Bank. T 206 and similar horiz designs. Multicoloured. W w 14 (sideways). P 14.*
728	10 c. Type **206**.		10	10
729	65 c. Cocoa plantation		50	50
730	95 c. Oil field		1·00	1·00
731	$1.10, Belmont Tramway Company tramcar		1·25	1·50
728/31	..	Set of 4	2·50	2·75

(Des C. Abbott. Litho Questa)

1988 (29 Feb). *25th Anniv of Defence Force. T 207 and similar vert designs. Multicoloured. W w 16 (sideways). P 14.*
732	10 c. Type **207**.		30	10
733	30 c. Women soldiers..		85	20
734	$1.10, Defence Force officers		1·75	1·25
735	$1.50, Naval ratings and patrol boat		2·00	1·50
732/5	..	Set of 4	4·50	2·75

(Des D. Hartley and L. Curtis. Litho Walsall)

1988 (6 June). *West Indian Cricket. Horiz designs as T 243a of Jamaica, each showing portrait, cricket equipment and early belt buckle. Multicoloured. W w 14 (sideways). P 14.*
736	30 c. George John ..		65	20
737	65 c. Learie Constantine		1·25	65
738	95 c. Sonny Ramadhin		1·40	1·10
739	$1.50, Gerry Gomez		2·00	2·00
740	$2.50, Jeffrey Stollmeyer		2·75	3·00
736/40	..	Set of 5	7·25	6·25

208 Uriah Butler (labour leader)   **209** Mary Werges and Santa Rosa Church

(Des G. Vasarhelyi. Litho Walsall)

1988 (11 July). *50th Anniv of Oilfield Workers Trade Union (1987). T 208 and similar vert designs. Multicoloured. W w 16. P 14½ × 14.*
741	10 c. Type **208**		10	10
742	30 c. Adrian Rienzi (O.W.T.U. president, 1937-42)		10	10
743	65 c. John Rojas (O.W.T.U. president, 1943-62)		15	20
744	$5 George Weekes (O.W.T.U. president, 1962-87)		1·25	1·40
741/4	..	Set of 4	1·40	1·60

(Des O. Bell. Litho Walsall)

1988 (22 Aug). *Centenary of Borough of Arima. T 209 and similar horiz designs. Multicoloured. W w 16 (sideways). P 14 × 14½.*
745	20 c. Type **209**		15	10
746	30 c. Governor W. Robinson and Royal Charter		15	10
747	$1.10, Arrival of Governor Robinson		60	75
748	$1.50, Mayor J. F. Wallen and Centenary logo		90	1·10
745/8	..	Set of 4	1·60	1·90

(Des D. Miller (30 c.), S. Noon and D. Miller (others). Litho Questa)

1988 (21 Nov). *300th Anniv of Lloyd's of London. Multicoloured designs as T 167a of Malawi. W w 16 (sideways on $1.10, $1.55). P 14.*
749	30 c. Queen Mother at Topping-out Ceremony of new building, 1984		30	10
750	$1.10, BWIA Tristar "500" airliner (*horiz*)		95	70
751	$1.55, Steel works, Trinidad (*horiz*)		1·25	1·00
752	$2 *Atlantic Empress* on fire off Tobago, 1979		1·75	1·25
749/52	..	Set of 4	3·75	2·75

210 Colonial Arms of Trinidad & Tobago and 1913 1d. Stamp

(Des W. Carr, adapted D. Miller. Litho Questa)

1989 (20 Mar). *Centenary of Union of Trinidad and Tobago. T 210 and similar horiz designs. Multicoloured. W w 16 (sideways). P 14½.*
753	40 c. Type **210**		20	10
754	$1 Pre-1889 Tobago emblem and Tobago 1896 ½d. on 4d. stamp		75	50
755	$1.50, Pre-1889 Trinidad emblem and Trinidad 1883 4d. stamp		1·00	90
756	$2.25, Current Arms of Trinidad and Tobago and 1977 45 c. Republic stamp		1·40	1·40
753/6	..	Set of 4	3·00	2·50

211 Common Piping Guan   **212** Blind Welfare (75th Anniversary)

(Des Doreen McGuinness. Litho Walsall)

1989 (31 July). *Rare Fauna of Trinidad and Tobago. T* **211** *and similar horiz designs. Multicoloured.* W w **14** (*sideways*). *P* 14×14½.

757	$1 Type 211	..	1·40	1·40
	a. Vert strip of 5. Nos. 757/61	..	6·25	
758	$1 *Phyllodytes auratus* (frog)	..	1·40	1·40
759	$1 *Cebus albifrons trinitatis* (monkey)	..	1·40	1·40
760	$1 Tamandua	..	1·40	1·40
761	$1 *Lutra longicaudis* (otter)	..	1·40	1·40
757/61		*Set of 5*	6·25	6·25

Nos. 757/61 were printed together, *se-tenant*, in vertical strips of 5 throughout the sheet, forming a composite background design.

(Des S. Noon. Litho Walsall)

1989 (2 Oct). *Anniversaries. T* **212** *and similar vert designs. Multicoloured.* W w **14**. *P* 14½×14.

762	10 c. Type 212	..	10	10
763	40 c. Port-of-Spain City Hall (75th anniv) ..	25	15
764	$1 Guides and Brownies (75th anniv) ..	85	40
765	$2.25, Red Cross members (50th anniv) ..	1·75	1·40
762/5		*Set of 4*	2·75	1·75

213 Tenor Pan

214 *Xeromphalina tenuipes*

(Des T. Mussio, adapted D. Miller. Litho Questa)

1989 (30 Nov). *Steel Pans (1st series). T* **213** *and similar vert designs. Multicoloured.* W w **16**. *P* 14½×14.

766	10 c. Type 213	..	10	10
767	40 c. Guitar pans ..	..	15	15
768	$1 Cello pans	..	45	45
769	$2.25, Bass pans ..	..	85	85
766/9		*Set of 4*	1·40	1·40

(Des McCombie Skinner. Litho Questa)

1990 (3 May). *"Stamp World London 90" International Stamp Exhibition, London. Fungi. T* **214** *and similar horiz designs. Multicoloured.* W w **16** (*sideways*). *P* 14×13½.

770	10 c. Type 214	..	15	10
771	40 c. *Dictyophora indusiata*	..	35	20
772	$1 *Leucocoprinus birnbaumii*	..	95	75
773	$2.25, *Crinipellis perniciosa*	..	2·00	2·50
770/3		*Set of 4*	3·00	3·25

215 Scarlet Ibis in Immature Plumage

216 Princess Alice and Administration Building

(Litho Questa)

1990 (7 Sept). *Scarlet Ibis. T* **215** *and similar horiz designs. Multicoloured.* W w **16** (*sideways*). *P* 14.

774	40 c. Type 215	..	30	20
775	80 c. Pair in pre-nuptial display	..	55	50
776	$1 Male in breeding plumage	..	70	55
777	$2.25, Adult on nest with chick	..	1·60	1·75
774/7		*Set of 4*	2·75	2·75

(Des L. Curtis. Litho B.D.T.)

1990 (15 Oct). *40th Anniv of University of West Indies. T* **216** *and similar horiz designs. Multicoloured.* W w **14** (*sideways*). *P* 13½×14.

778	40 c. Type 216	..	25	15
779	80 c. Sir Hugh Wooding and Library	..	45	40
780	$1 Sir Allen Lewis and Faculty of Engineering		60	55
781	$2.25, Sir Shridath Ramphal and Faculty of Medical Sciences ..	..	1·40	1·75
778/81		*Set of 4*	2·40	2·50

217 Lockheed Lodestar

218 Yellow Oriole

(Des E. Nisbet. Litho B.D.T)

1990 (27 Nov). *50th Anniv of British West Indies Airways. T* **217** *and similar horiz designs. Multicoloured.* W w **14** (*sideways*). *P* 14.

782	40 c. Type 217	..	30	15
783	80 c. Vickers Viking 1A	..	55	40
784	$1 Vickers Viscount 702	..	60	55
785	$2.25, Boeing 707	..	1·40	1·75
782/5		*Set of 4*	2·50	2·50
MS786	77×52 mm. $5 Lockheed Tristar 500 ..	1·90	2·25

(Des D. Miller. Litho Questa)

1990 (17 Dec). *Birds. T* **218** *and similar vert designs. Multicoloured.* W w **16** (*sideways*). *P* 14.

787	20 c. Type 218	..	10	10
788	25 c. Green-rumped Parrotlet	..	10	10
789	40 c. Fork-tailed Flycatcher	..	10	15
790	50 c. Copper-rumped Hummingbird	..	15	20
791	$1 Bananaquit	..	30	35
792	$2 Violaceous Euphonia ..	..	55	60
793	$2.25, Channel-billed Toucan	..	65	70
794	$2.50, Bay-headed Tanager	..	70	75
795	$5 Green Honeycreeper	..	1·40	1·50
796	$10 Cattle Egret	..	2·75	3·00
797	$20 Golden-olive Woodpecker	..	5·50	5·75
798	$50 Peregrine Falcon	..	14·00	14·50
787/98		*Set of 12*	22·00	23·00

219 *Lygodium volubile*

(Des T. Musio. Litho B.D.T)

1991 (1 July). *Ferns. T* **219** *and similar horiz designs. Multicoloured.* W w **14** (*sideways*). *P* 13½×14.

799	40 c. Type 219	..	25	15
800	80 c. *Blechnum occidentale*	..	45	30
801	$1 *Gleichenia bifida*	..	55	45
802	$2.25, *Polypodium lycopodioides*	..	1·40	1·75
799/802		*Set of 4*	2·40	2·40

220 Trinidad and Tobago Regiment Anti-aircraft Battery

221 H. E. Rapsey (founder)

(Des A. Theobald. Litho Questa)

1991 (7 Dec). *50th Anniv of Second World War. T* **220** *and similar horiz designs. Multicoloured.* W w **16** (*sideways*). *P* 13½×14.

803	40 c. Type 220	..	20	10
804	80 c. Fairey Barracuda attacking U-boat ..	35	35
805	$1 Avro Lancaster	..	45	45
806	$2.25, River class frigate escorting convoy	1·00	1·40
803/06		*Set of 4*	1·75	2·00
MS807	117×85 mm. $2.50, Presentation Spitfire; $2.50, Presentation Wellington bomber	1·75	2·25

(Des G. Vasarhelyi. Litho B.D.T.)

1992 (30 Mar). *Anniversaries. T* **221** *and similar vert designs. Multicoloured.* W w **14**. *P* 14.

808	40 c. Type 221 (centenary of Trinidad Building and Loan Assoc)	15	10
809	80 c. *Inca clathrata quesneli* (beetle) (Trinidad & Tobago Field Naturalists' Club) ..	35	30
810	$1 Holy Name Convent (centenary) ..	50	50
808/10		*Set of 3*	90	80

222 Baptism (Baptist)

223 MD83 Aircraft

(Des Jennifer Toombs. Litho Questa)

1992 (21 Apr). *Religions of Trinidad and Tobago. T* **222** *and similar vert designs. Multicoloured.* W w **14**. *P* 14.

811	40 c. Type 222	..	20	20
812	40 c. Minaret with star and crescent (Islam)	20	20
813	40 c. Logo (Hinduism)	..	20	20
814	40 c. Cross (Christian)	..	20	20
815	40 c. Logo (Baha'i)	..	20	20
811/15		*Set of 5*	90	90

(Des G. Vasarhelyi. Litho B.D.T.)

1992 (6 Aug). *Aircraft. T* **223** *and similar horiz design. Multicoloured.* W w **14** (*sideways*). *P* 14.

816	$2.25, Type 223	..	65	70
817	$2.25, L1011 aircraft	..	65	70

224 *Trinidad Guardian* Title (75th anniv of newspaper)

(Des Jennifer Toombs (No. 819), N. Shewring (others). Litho Questa)

1992 (7–30 Dec). *Anniversaries. T* **224** *and similar multicoloured designs.* W w **16** (*sideways on horiz designs*). *P* 14½.

818	40 c. Type 224	..	10	10
819	40 c. Nativity scene (Christmas) (*vert*) (21 Dec)	10	10
820	$1 National Museum and Art Gallery (centenary) (23 Dec) ..	30	35
821	$2.25, Cover to St. James Internment Camp, 1942 (50th anniv of Trinidad and Tobago Philatelic Society) (30 Dec)	65	70
818/21		*Set of 4*	1·00	1·10

POSTAGE DUE STAMPS

D 1

D 2

(Typo D.L.R.)

1885 (1 Jan). *Wmk Crown CA. P* 14.

D1	D 1	½d. slate-black ..	..	22·00	35·00
D2		1d. slate-black ..	..	1·75	15
D3		2d. slate-black ..	..	13·00	15
D4		3d. slate-black ..	..	30·00	40
D5		4d. slate-black ..	..	20·00	3·75
D6		5d. slate-black ..	..	20·00	60
D7		6d. slate-black ..	..	30·00	5·00
D8		8d. slate-black ..	..	35·00	3·75
D9		1s. slate-black ..	..	40·00	7·00
D1/9			*Set of 9*	£190	48·00

1905–6. *Wmk Mult Crown CA. P* 14.

D10	D 1	1d. slate-black ..	..	1·75	15
D11		2d. slate-black ..	..	6·00	15
D12		3d. slate-black ..	..	3·25	1·00
D13		4d. slate-black ..	..	8·00	7·50
D14		5d. slate-black ..	..	7·50	9·00
D15		6d. slate-black ..	..	6·00	9·50
D16		8d. slate-black ..	..	12·00	14·00
D17		1s. slate-black ..	..	12·00	24·00
D10/17			*Set of 8*	50·00	60·00

1923–45. *Wmk Mult Script CA. P* 14.

D18	D 1	1d. black (1923)	..	30	80
D19		2d. black (1923)	..	30	75
D20		3d. black (1925)	..	30	1·50
D21		4d. black (1929)	..	1·50	8·00
D22		5d. black (1944)	..	24·00	45·00
D23		6d. black (1945)	..	28·00	17·00
D24		8d. black (1945)	..	35·00	75·00
D25		1s. black (1945)	..	55·00	75·00
D18/25			*Set of 8*	£130	£200
D18/25	Optd/Perf "Specimen"		*Set of 8*	£140	

1947 (1 Sept)–61. *Values in cents. Wmk Mult Script CA. Ordinary paper. P* 14.

D26	D 1	2 c. black	..	95	2·25
		a. Chalk-surfaced paper (20.1.53) ..	20	1·75
		ab. Error. Crown missing. W 9a	..	50·00	
		ac. Error. St. Edward's Crown. W 9b	22·00	
D27		4 c. black	..	85	3·00
		a. Chalk-surfaced paper (10.8.55) ..	65	2·75
D28		6 c. black	..	95	6·00
		a. Chalk-surfaced paper (20.1.53) ..	30	4·25
		ab. Error. Crown missing. W 9a	..	£110	
		ac. Error. St. Edward's Crown. W 9b	48·00	
D29		8 c. black	..	90	14·00
		a. Chalk-surfaced paper (10.9.58) ..	35	6·50
D30		10 c. black	..	85	2·75
		a. Chalk-surfaced paper (10.8.55) ..	1·25	4·50
D31		12 c. black	..	90	10·00
		a. Chalk-surfaced paper (20.1.53) ..	40	7·00
		ab. Error. Crown missing. W 9a	..	£150	
		ac. Error. St. Edward's Crown. W 9b	75·00	

D32	D 1	16 c. black	..	..	2·00	20·00
		a. Chalk-surfaced paper (22.8.61)	..		3·75	20·00
D33		24 c. black	..	..	4·00	7·50
		a. Chalk-surfaced paper (10.8.55)	..		2·75	17·00
D26/33	..	..	..	Set of 8	10·50	60·00
D26/33a		..	..	Set of 8	8·75	55·00
D26/33 Perf "Specimen"		..		Set of 8	£140	

(Litho B.W.)

1969 (25 Nov)–**70.** *Size 19 × 24 mm. P 14 × 13½.*

D34	D 2	2 c. pale blue-green	..	..	..	15	1·75
D35		4 c. magenta (1970)	..	..		25	2·50
D36		6 c. brown (1970)	..	..		50	3·50
D37		8 c. slate-lilac (1970)	..	..		65	4·00
D38		10 c. dull red (1970)	..	..		65	4·00
D39		12 c. pale orange (1970)	..	..		70	4·50
D40		16 c. bright apple-green (1970)	..	..		30	2·00
D41		24 c. grey (1970)	..	..		30	2·25
D42		50 c. grey-blue (1970)	..	..		45	2·75
D43		60 c. sage-green (1970)	..	..		55	2·75
D34/43		..	..	Set of 10		4·00	27·00

(Litho Questa)

1976 (3 May)*–**77.** *Redrawn in smaller size (17 × 21 mm).
P 13½ × 14.*

D44	D 2	2 c. pale blue-green (31.3.77)	..		10	75
D45		4 c. light claret	..		15	75
D46		6 c. brown (31.3.77)	..		20	85
D47		8 c. bright lilac (31.3.77)	..		20	85
D48		10 c. dull red (31.3.77)	..		20	85
D49		12 c. pale orange	..		30	1·25
D44/9	..		..	Set of 6	1·00	4·75

*The date for the 4 and 12 c. is the local date; the Crown Agents released the stamps on 19 March.

"TOO LATE" STAMPS

A handstamp with the words "TOO LATE" was used upon letters on which a too-late fee had been paid, and was sometimes used for cancelling the stamps on such letters.

OFFICIAL STAMPS

O S	**OFFICIAL**	**OFFICIAL**
(O 1)	(O 2)	(O 3)

1894. *Optd with Type O 1 (a) Wmk Crown CA. P 14.*

O1	10	½d. dull green	..	..	..	..	28·00	45·00
O2		1d. carmine	..	..	..		32·00	48·00
O3		2½d. ultramarine	..	..			40·00	70·00
O4		4d. grey	..	..			40·00	75·00
O5		6d. olive-black	..	..			40·00	75·00
O6		1s. orange-brown	..	..			50·00	90·00

(b) *Wmk Crown CC. P 12½.*

O7	5	5s. rose-lake	..	..	..	£120	£200

1909. *Optd with Type O 2. Wmk Mult Crown CA. P 14.*

O8	11	½d. green	..	..	..	30	2·75
O9		1d. rose-red	..	..	..	30	2·75
		a. Opt double	..	..		—	£200
		b. Opt vertical	..	..		45·00	
		c. Opt inverted	..	..		—	£150

1910. *Optd with Type O 2. Wmk Mult Crown CA. P 14.*

O10	14	½d. green	..	..	..	1·25	2·25

1913. *Optd with Type O 3.*

O11	17	½d. green	..	..	..	30	1·50
		a. Opt vertical	..	..			

OFFICIAL	**OFFICIAL**	**OFFICIAL**
(O 4)	(O 5)	(O 6)

1914. *Optd with Type O 4.*

O12	17	½d. green	..	..	..	1·10	5·00

1914–17. *Optd with Type O 5 (without stop).*

O13	17	½d. green	..	..	..	90	6·00
		a. Blue-green (thick paper) (1917)	..		40	5·00

1916. *Optd with Type O 5 (with stop).*

O14	17	½d. yellow-green	..	..	..	30	65
		a. Opt double	..	..		20·00	

1917 (22 Aug). *Optd with Type O 6.*

O15	17	½d. green	..	..	..	1·00	6·50
		a. Yellow-green	..	..		1·50	8·50
		b. Blue-green (thick paper)	..	..		30	6·50

Tristan Da Cunha

Although first settled in 1817 no surviving mail is known from Tristan da Cunha until two whaler's letters written in 1836 and 1843, these being carried home in other whaling ships. Then there is a long gap until the late 1800's when other letters are known—surprisingly only some seven in number, up to 1908 when the first of the island cachet handstamps came into use.

The collecting of postal history material from 1908 to 1952, when Tristan's first stamps were issued, revolves around the numerous cachets of origin which were struck on mail from the island during these 44 years. The handstamps producing these cachets were supplied over the years by various people particularly interested in the island and the islanders, and were mostly used by the clergymen who volunteered to go and serve as the community's ministers.

The postal cachets are illustrated below. The use of the different cachets on mail frequently overlapped, at one period in 1930 there were five different types of handstamp in use. As there was no official source for providing them they appeared on the island from various donors; then disappeared without trace once they became worn out. Only one of these early rubber handstamps has apparently survived, Cachet Va.

Covers bearing the cachets are recognised collector's items, but are difficult to value in general terms. As elsewhere the value is discounted by poor condition of the cover, and may be increased by use on a scarce date or with additional postal markings.

Cachet Types V and VII on cover are the commonest, Type Va, used only for three months, and Type IVa are the scarcest, equalling the scarcest use of Type I examples. All cacheted covers, particularly if non-philatelic, are desirable forerunner items. Even a philatelic cover of Type V is, at present, worth in the region of £35.

Dates given are of the first recorded use.

Cachet I   Cachet II

Cat. No.					Value on cover
C1	**1908** (May).	Cachet I	..	..	..*from* £4000
C2	**1919** (31 July).	Cachet II	..	..	..*from* £400

Cachet III

C3	**1921** (8 Feb).	Cachet III	..	..	..*from* £225

Cachet IVa

C4	**1927** (1 Oct).	Cachet IV (*as IVa, but without*		
		centre label)	..	..	..*from* £800
C5	**1928** (28 Oct).	Cachet IVa	..	..	..*from* £5500

Cachet V   Cachet VI

C6	**1929** (24 Feb).	Cachet V	..	..	..*from* 35·00
C7	**1929** (15 May).	Cachet Va (*as V, but without*		
		break in inner ring. Shows "T"		
		"C" and "N" damaged)..	..	..*from* £6500
C8	**1936** (Aug).	Cachet VI	..	..*from* 55·00

Cachet VII

C9	**1936** (1 Feb).	Cachet VII	..	..	..*from* 20·00

During World War II there was little mail from the island as its function as a meteorological station was cloaked by security. Such covers as are known are generally struck with the "tombstone" naval censor mark and postmarked "maritime mail" or have South African postal markings. A few philatelic items from early in the war bearing cachets exist, but this usage was soon stopped by the military commander and the handstamps were put away until peace returned. Covers from the period would be worth from £75 to, at least, £350.

Cachet VIII

C10	**1946** (8 May).	Cachet VIII	..	..	..*from* 70·00

Cachet IX

C11	**1948** (29 Feb).	Cachet IX	..	..	*from* 45·00

Cachet X

C12	**1948** (6 Mar).	Cachet X	..	*from* 35·00

Cachet XI

Cachet XII

RESETTLEMENT SURVEY – 1962

Cachet XIII

Cachets XI to XIII from the 1961/63 "volcano eruption" and "return to the island" period vary in value from £30 to £120, due to philatelic usage on the one hand and scarce mailings from the small survey parties on shore during this period on the other.

TRISTAN DA CUNHA
(1)

1952 (1 Jan). *Stamps of St. Helena, optd with T* 1.

1	**33**	½d. violet	..	..	..	15	85
2		1d. black and green		..	..	30	1·25
3		1½d. black and carmine	..		..	30	1·25
4		2d. black and scarlet	..		..	30	1·50
5		3d. grey ..		..	..	40	1·25
6		4d. ultramarine		..	..	1·50	2·00
7		6d. light blue		..	..	3·00	2·50
8		8d. sage-green	..		..	2·50	3·00
9		1s. sepia		..	..	3·25	2·00
10		2s. 6d. maroon		..	..	19·00	14·00
11		5s. chocolate	..		..	26·00	27·00
12		10s. purple		..	..	48·00	55·00
1/12 ..			..	..	*Set of* 12	95·00	£100

1953 (2 June). *Coronation. As No.* 153 *of Jamaica.*

13	3d. black and grey-green	..	..	..	90	1·50

2 Tristan Crawfish 3 Carting Flax for Thatching

(Recess D.L.R.)

1954 (2 Jan). *T* 2/3 *and similar designs. Wmk Mult Script CA.*
P 12½ × 13 (*horiz*) *or* 13 × 12½ (*vert*).

14	½d. red and deep brown	..		..	10	10
15	1d. sepia and bluish green		..	..	10	20
16	1½d. black and reddish purple		..	..	2·50	40
17	2d. grey-violet and brown-orange		..	..	30	20
18	2½d. black and carmine-red	..		..	2·00	50
19	3d. ultramarine and olive-green		..	..	80	20
20	4d. turquoise-blue and deep blue	..		..	1·25	55
21	5d. emerald and black		..	..	1·25	45
22	6d. deep green and violet	..		..	1·25	55
23	9d. reddish violet and Venetian red		..	..	1·25	45
24	1s. deep yellow-green and sepia	..		..	1·25	45
25	2s. 6d. deep brown and light blue	..		..	26·00	10·00
26	5s. black and red-orange	..		..	48·00	16·00
27	10s. brown-orange and purple	..		..	32·00	20·00
14/27 ..			..		*Set of* 14	£110	45·00

Designs: *Vert*—1½d. Rockhopper Penguin; 3d. Island longboat. *Horiz*.—2d. Big Beach factory; 2½d. Yellow-nosed Albatross; 4d. Tristan from the south-west; 5d. Girls on donkeys; 6d. Inaccessible Island from Tristan; 9d. Nightingale Island; 1s. St. Mary's Church; 2s. 6d. Southern Elephant-Seal at Gough Island; 5s. Inaccessible Island Rail; 10s. Island spinning wheel.

16 Starfish 17 Concha Fish

(Des Mr. and Mrs. G. F. Harris. Recess Waterlow)

1960 (1 Feb). *Marine Life. Vert designs as T* 16/17. *W* w 12. *P* 13.

28	½d. black and orange	..		..	15	30
29	1d. black and bright purple..		..	..	15	15
30	1½d. black and light turquoise-blue	..		..	15	30
31	2d. black and bluish green	..		..	20	30
32	2½d. black and sepia ..		..	..	25	30
33	3d. black and brown-red	..		..	25	20
34	4d. black and yellow-olive	..		..	30	30
35	5d. black and orange-yellow		..	..	45	30
36	6d. black and blue	..		..	50	25
37	9d. black and rose-carmine ..		..	..	55	30
38	1s. black and light brown ..		..	..	75	25
39	2s. 6d. black and ultramarine	..		..	11·00	15·00
40	5s. black and light emerald		..	..	28·00	22·00
41	10s. black and violet ..		..	..	48·00	40·00
28/41			..		*Set of* 14	80·00	70·00

Designs:—1½d. Klip Fish; 2d. Heron Fish; 2½d. Swordfish; 3d. Tristan Crawfish; 4d. Soldier Fish; 5d. "Five Finger" Fish; 6d. Mackerel; 9d. Stumpnose Fish; 1s. Blue Fish; 2s. 6d. Snoek; 5s. Shark; 10s. Black Right Whale.

NEW INFORMATION

The editor is always interested to correspond with people who have new information that will improve or correct the Catalogue.

1961 (15 Apr). *As Nos. 28/30 and 32/41 but values in South African decimal currency.*

42	½ c. black and orange (as ½d.)	..	10	15
43	1 c. black and bright purple (as 1d.)	..	15	15
44	1½ c. black and light turquoise-blue (as 1½d.)		35	20
45	2 c. black and sepia (as 2½d.)	..	40	20
46	2½ c. black and brown-red (as 3d.)	..	50	20
47	3 c. black and yellow-olive (as 4d.)	..	65	20
48	4 c. black and orange-yellow (as 5d.)	..	80	20
49	5 c. black and blue (as 6d)	..	85	20
50	7½ c. black and rose-carmine (as 9d.)		90	20
51	10 c. black and light brown (as 1s.)	..	1·00	20
52	25 c. black and ultramarine (as 2s. 6d.)		6·00	11·00
53	50 c. black and light emerald (as 5s.)		28·00	22·00
54	1 r. black and violet (as 10s.)	..	48·00	42·00
42/54		*Set of 13*	80·00	70·00

Following a volcanic eruption the island was evacuated on 10 October 1961, but resettled in 1963.

TRISTAN DA CUNHA RESETTLEMENT 1963
(30)

1963 (12 Apr). *Tristan Resettlement. As Nos. 176/88 of St. Helena, but Wmk Mult Script CA (sideways on 1d., 2d., 7d., 10d., 2s. 6d., 10s), optd with T 30.*

55	1d. bright blue, dull violet, yellow & carmine		15	20
56	1½d. yellow, green, black and light drab	..	20	20
57	2d. scarlet and grey		25	20
58	3d. light blue, black, pink and deep blue	..	30	30
	a. Black printed double*	..	£350	
59	4½d. yellow-green, green, brown and grey		50	40
60	6d. red, sepia and light yellow-olive ..		75	20
61	7d. red-brown, black and violet ..		50	30
62	10d. brown-purple and light blue		50	20
63	1s. greenish yellow, bluish green & brown ..		50	20
64	1s. grey, black and slate-blue ..		1·50	60
65	2s. 6d. red, pale yellow and turquoise		1·00	45
66	5s. yellow, brown and green..		5·00	1·25
67	10s. orange-red, black and blue		6·50	1·25
55/67		*Set of 13*	15·00	5·00

*No. 58a shows the outline round the Queen's head printed double.

1963 (2 Oct). *Freedom from Hunger. As No. 80 of Lesotho.*

68	1s. 6d. carmine	..	90	30

1964 (1 Feb). *Red Cross Centenary. As Nos. 203/4 of Jamaica.*

69	3d. red and black	..	35	15
70	1s. 6d. red and blue ..		65	20

31 South Atlantic Map   32 Queen Elizabeth II

(Queen's portrait by Anthony Buckley. Des, eng and recess B.W.)

1965 (17 Feb)–**67**. *Designs as T 31/2. W w 12 (sideways on £1). P 11½ × 11 (vert) or 11 × 11½ (horiz).*

71	½d. black and ultramarine	..	15	15
72	1d. black and emerald-green		30	15
73	1½d. black and blue ..		30	15
74	2d. black and purple	..	30	15
75	3d. black and turquoise-blue	..	30	15
75a	4d. black and orange (1.9.67)	..	5·50	4·00
76	4½d. black and brown	..	30	15
77	6d. black and green	..	30	15
78	7d. black and rose-red	..	30	20
79	10d. black and chocolate	..	30	20
80	1s. black and carmine	..	30	20
81	1s. 6d. black and yellow-olive	..	2·50	2·00
82	2s. 6d. black and orange-brown	..	2·75	2·50
83	5s. black and violet	..	4·00	3·50
84	10s. deep blue and carmine..		1·75	1·25
84a	10s. black and deep turquoise-blue (1.9.67)	17·00	11·00
84b	£1 deep blue and orange-brown (1.9.67)	17·00	11·00
71/84b		*Set of 17*	48·00	32·00

Designs: Horiz as T 31—1d. Flagship of Tristão da Cunha; 1½d. Heemstede; 2d. New England whaling ship; 3d. *Shenandoah*; 4d. H.M.S. *Challenger*; 4½d. H.M.S. *Galatea*; 6d. H.M.S. *Cilicia*; 7d. Royal Yacht *Britannia*; 10d. H.M.S. *Leopard*; 1s. M.V. *Tjisadane*; 1s. 6d. M.V. *Tristania*; 2s. 6d. M.V. *Boissevain*; 5s. M.S. *Bornholm*; 10s. (No. 84a), Research Vessel *R.S.A.* Vert—10s. (No. 84), £1, Type 32.

1965 (11 May*). *I.T.U. Centenary. As Nos. 98/9 of Lesotho.*

85	3d. orange-red and grey	..	50	15
86	6d. reddish violet and yellow-orange	..	60	15

*This is the local date of issue; the stamps were not released in London until 17 May.

1965 (25 Oct). *International Co-operation Year. As Nos. 100/1 of Lesotho.*

87	1d. reddish purple and turquoise-green	..	40	15
88	6d. deep bluish green and lavender ..		1·50	25

1966 (24 Jan). *Churchill Commemoration. As Nos. 102/5 of Lesotho.*

89	1d. new blue		50	25
	a. Value omitted		£350	
90	3d. deep green	..	2·50	40
91	6d. brown	..	3·50	45
92	1s. 6d. bluish violet	..	4·00	60
89/92		*Set of 4*	9·50	1·50

No. 89a was caused by misplacement of the gold and also shows the country inscription moved to the right.

45 H.M.S. *Falmouth* at Tristan and Soldier of 1816

(Des V. Whiteley. Litho Harrison)

1966 (15 Aug). *150th Anniv of Tristan Garrison. W w 12 (sideways). P 14½.*

93	45	3d. multicoloured ..	..	20	10
94		6d. multicoloured	..	20	10
95		1s. 6d. multicoloured	..	20	15
96		2s. 6d. multicoloured	..	30	15
93/6			*Set of 4*	80	45

1966 (1 Oct*). *World Cup Football Championships. As Nos. 57/8 of Pitcairn Islands.*

97	3d. violet, yellow-grn, lake & yell-brn		25	10
98	2s. 6d. chocolate, blue-grn, lake & yellow-brn	65	20

*Released in St. Helena on 1 July in error.

1966 (1 Oct). *Inauguration of W.H.O. Headquarters, Geneva. As Nos. 185/6 of Montserrat.*

99	6d. black, yellow-green and light blue	..	1·00	90
100	5s. black, light purple and yellow-brown	..	1·25	70

1966 (1 Dec). *20th Anniv of U.N.E.S.C.O. As Nos. 342/4 of Mauritius.*

101	3d. slate-violet, red, yellow and orange		60	15
102	1s. 6d. orange-yellow, violet and deep olive		65	15
103	2s. 6d. black, bright purple and orange		80	20
101/3	..	..	*Set of 3*	1·90	45

46 Calshot Harbour

(Des V. Whiteley. Litho D.L.R.)

1967 (2 Jan). *Opening of Calshot Harbour. P 14 × 14½.*

104	46	6d. multicoloured	..	10	10
105		10d. multicoloured	..	10	10
106		1s. 6d. multicoloured	..	10	10
107		2s. 6d. multicoloured	..	15	15
104/7	..		*Set of 4*	30	30

4ᵈ
(47)

48 Prince Alfred, First Duke of Edinburgh

1967 (10 May). *No. 76 surch with T 47.*

108	4d. on 4½d. black and brown	..	10	10

(Des M. Goaman. Litho Harrison)

1967 (10 July). *Centenary of First Duke of Edinburgh's Visit to Tristan. W w 12. P 14½.*

109	48	3d. multicoloured	..	10	10
110		6d. multicoloured	..	10	10
111		1s. 6d. multicoloured	..	10	10
112		2s. 6d. multicoloured	..	15	10
109/12			*Set of 4*	30	20

49 Wandering Albatross

(Des V. Whiteley. Photo Harrison)

1968 (15 May). *Birds. T 49 and similar horiz designs. Multicoloured. W w 12. P 14 × 14½.*

113	4d. Type 49		40	10
114	1s. Wilkin's Finch	..	45	10
115	1s. 6d. Tristan Thrush		50	15
116	2s. 6d. Greater Shearwater ..		90	20
113/16	..	*Set of 4*	2·00	45

53 Union Jack and Dependency Flag

(Des Jennifer Toombs. Litho D.L.R.)

1968 (1 Nov). *30th Anniv of Tristan da Cunha as a Dependency of St. Helena. T 53 and similar horiz design. W w 12 (sideways). P 14.*

117	53	6d. multicoloured	..	10	10
118		9d. sepia, blue and turquoise-blue		10	10
119	53	1s. 6d. multicoloured	..	15	10
120		2s. 6d. carmine, blue and turquoise-blue		20	10
117/20			*Set of 4*	50	35

Design:—9d., 2s. 6d. St. Helena and Tristan on chart.

55 Frigate

(Des and recess B.W.)

1969 (1 June). *Clipper Ships. T 55 and similar horiz designs. W w 12. P 11 × 11½.*

121	4d. new blue	..	40	10
122	1s. carmine (full-rigged ship)	..	40	10
123	1s. 6d. blue-green (barque)	..	45	30
124	2s. 6d. chocolate (full-rigged clipper)		50	35
121/4	..	*Set of 4*	1·60	80

59 Sailing Ship off Tristan da Cunha

(Des Jennifer Toombs. Litho Format)

1969 (1 Nov). *United Society for the Propagation of the Gospel. T 59 and similar horiz designs. Multicoloured. W w 12 (sideways). P 14½ × 14.*

125	4d. Type 59	..	10	10
126	9d. Islanders going to first Gospel service ..	10	10
127	1s. 6d. Landing of the first minister	..	10	20
128	2s. 6d. Procession outside St. Mary's Church	15	25
125/8	..	*Set of 4*	40	60

63 Globe and Red Cross Emblem

(Des and litho B.W.)

1970 (1 June). *Centenary of British Red Cross. T 63 and similar designs. W w 12 (sideways on vert designs). P 13.*

129	63	4d. lt emerald, scarlet & dp bluish green	10	10
130		9d. bistre, scarlet and deep bluish green	10	10
131	—	1s. 9d. light drab, scarlet & ultramarine	20	15
132	—	2s. 6d. reddish purple, scarlet & ultram	25	30
129/32			*Set of 4*	60	60

Design: Vert—1s. 9d., 2s. 6d., Union Jack and Red Cross Flag.

64 Crawfish and Longboat   (65)

(Des Harrison. Litho Enschedé)

1970 (1 Nov). *Crawfish Industry. T 64 and similar horiz design. Multicoloured. W w 12. P 12½ × 13.*

133	4d. Type 64	..	20	10
134	10d. Packing and storing Crawfish ..		25	10
135	1s. 6d. Type 64		35	25
136	2s. 6d. As 10d.		40	30
133/6	..	..	*Set of 4*	1·10	70

1971 (14 Feb).* *Decimal Currency. As Nos. 72/4, 75a, 77/83 and 84a surch as T 65, by B.W. in typo. Glazed paper.*

137	½p. on 1d. black and emerald-green		15	15
138	1p. on 2d. black and purple	..	15	15
139	1½p. on 4d. black and orange	..	30	15
140	2½p. on 6d. black and green	..	30	15
141	3p. on 7d. black and rose-red ..		30	15
142	4p. on 10d. black and chocolate ..		30	20
143	5p. on 1s. black and carmine ..		30	20
144	7½p. on 1s. 6d. black and yellow-olive ..		1·75	95
145	12½p. on 2s. 6d. black and orange-brown		2·00	2·50
146	15p. on 1½d. black and blue ..		3·50	3·00
147	25p. on 5s. black and violet ..		3·50	5·00
148	50p. on 10s. black and deep turquoise-blue		8·00	11·00
137/48		*Set of 12*	18·00	21·00

*This was the local release date, but the Crown Agents issued the stamps one day later.

66 Quest

(Des V. Whiteley. Litho J.W.)

1971 (1 June). *50th Anniv of Shackleton–Rowett Expedition. T 66 and similar horiz designs.* W w **12** (sideways). P 13½ × 14.
149	1½p. multicoloured	..	90	30
150	4p. sepia, pale green and apple-green	..	1·00	40
151	7½p. black, bright purple and pale green	..	1·00	40
152	12½p. multicoloured	..	1·40	45
149/52		*Set of 4*	4·00	1·40

Designs:—4p. Presentation of Scout Troop flag; 7½p. Cachet on pair of 6d. G.B. stamps; 12½p. Shackleton, postmarks and longboat taking mail to the *Quest*.

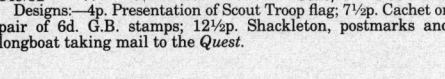

67 H.M.S. *Victory* at Trafalgar and   **68** Cow Pudding
Thomas Swain catching Nelson

(Des R. Granger Barrett. Litho Questa)

1971 (1 Nov). *Island Families. T 67 and similar horiz designs showing ships and the names of families associated with them.* Multicoloured. W w **12** (sideways). P 13½.
153	1½p. Type **67**	..	25	30
154	2½p. *Emily of Stonington* (P. W. Green)	..	35	40
155	4p. *Italia* (Lavarello and Repetto)	..	40	50
156	7½p. H.M.S. *Falmouth* (William Glass)	..	55	65
157	12½p. American whaling ship (Rogers and Hagan)	..	65	80
153/7	..	*Set of 5*	2·00	2·40

(Des M. and Sylvia Goaman. Recess and litho B.W. (50p., £1); Litho A. & M. (others))

1972 (29 Feb). *T 68 and similar multicoloured designs showing flowering plants.* W w **12** (sideways on horiz designs). P 13.
158	½p. Type **68**	..	20	10
159	1p. Peak Berry	..	40	10
160	1½p. Sand Flower (*horiz*)	..	40	15
161	2½p. N.Z. Flax (*horiz*)	..	40	15
162	3p. Island Tree	..	40	15
163	4p. Bog Fern	..	40	15
164	5p. Dog Catcher	..	60	15
165	7½p. Celery	..	2·25	30
166	12½p. Pepper Tree	..	1·75	60
167	25p. Foul Berry (*horiz*)	..	1·75	1·50
168	50p. Tussock	..	6·00	1·75
169	£1 Tussac (*horiz*)	..	5·00	3·00
158/69	..	*Set of 12*	18·00	7·00

69 Launching

(Des R. Svensson. Litho Walsall)

1972 (1 June). *Tristan Longboats. T 69 and similar multicoloured designs.* W w **12** (sideways on 2½p. and 4p.). P 14.
170	2½p. Type **69**	..	15	10
171	4p. Under oars	..	20	10
172	7½p. Coxswain Arthur Repetto (*vert*)	..	25	15
173	12½p. Under sail for Nightingale Island (*vert*)	..	30	20
170/73	..	*Set of 4*	80	50

70 Tristan Thrushes and Wandering Albatrosses

(Des (from photographs by D. Groves) and photo Harrison)

1972 (20 Nov). *Royal Silver Wedding. Multicoloured; background colours given.* W w **12**. P 14 × 14½.
174	**70** 2½p. red-brown	..	35	40
175	7½p. dull ultramarine	..	15	40

71 Church Altar

(Des J. Cooter. Litho Questa)

1973 (8 July). *Golden Jubilee of St. Mary's Church.* W w **12**. P 13½.
176	**71** 25p. multicoloured	..	60	50

72 H.M.S. *Challenger's* Laboratory

(Des V. Whiteley Studio. Litho Questa)

1973 (15 Oct). *Centenary of H.M.S. Challenger's Visit. T 72 and similar horiz designs.* Multicoloured. W w **12**. P 13½.
177	4p. Type **72**	..	30	25
178	5p. H.M.S. *Challenger* off Tristan	..	30	25
179	7½p. *Challenger's* pinnace off Nightingale Is	..	30	30
180	12½p. Survey route	..	40	40
177/80	..	*Set of 4*	1·10	1·10
MS181	145 × 96 mm. Nos. 177/80	..	1·10	3·50

73 Approaching English Port

(Des Jennifer Toombs. Litho Questa)

1973 (10 Nov). *Tenth Anniv of Return to Tristan da Cunha. T 73 and similar horiz designs.* Multicoloured (except 4p.). W w **12**. P 14.
182	4p. Type **73** (reddish brn, lemon & gold)	25	25
183	5p. Survey party	25	25
184	7½p. Embarking on *Bornholm*	35	35
185	12½p. Approaching Tristan	45	45
182/5	..	*Set of 4*	1·10	1·10

1973 (14 Nov). *Royal Wedding. As Nos. 322/3 of Montserrat.*
186	7½p. bright blue	..	15	10
187	12½p. light turquoise-green	..	15	10

74 Rockhopper Penguin and Egg

(Des R. Granger Barrett. Litho Questa)

1974 (1 May). *Rockhopper Penguins. T 74 and similar horiz designs.* W w **12**. P 14.
188	2½p. Type **74**	..	3·00	75
189	5p. Rockhopper Colony, Inaccessible Island	..	3·50	1·00
190	7½p. Penguin fishing	..	4·00	1·25
191	25p. Adult and fledgling	..	4·50	1·50
188/91	..	*Set of 4*	13·50	4·00

75 Map with Rockhopper Penguin and Wandering Albatross

(Des J.W. Litho Questa)

1974 (1 Oct). *"The Lonely Island". Sheet 154 × 104 mm.* W w **12** (sideways). P 13½.
MS192	**75** 35p. multicoloured	..	2·50	2·75

76 Blenheim Palace

(Des Sylvia Goaman. Litho Questa)

1974 (30 Nov). *Birth Centenary of Sir Winston Churchill. T 76 and similar horiz design.* W w **12** (sideways). P 14.
193	7½p. pale yellow and black	..	15	10
194	25p. black, sepia and grey	..	40	25
MS195	93 × 93 mm. Nos. 193/4. W w **12** (sideways)	75	1·60

Design:—25p. Churchill with Queen Elizabeth II.

77 Plocamium fuscorubrum

(Des Sylvia Goaman. Litho Harrison)

1975 (16 Apr). *Sea Plants. T 77 and similar horiz designs.* W w **12** (sideways). P 13 × 13½.
196	4p. rose-carmine, light black and black	..	15	10
197	5p. apple-green, light violet-blue and deep bluish green	..	15	15
198	10p. red-orange, stone and brown-purple	..	20	15
199	20p. multicoloured	..	30	25
196/9	..	*Set of 4*	70	60

Designs:—5p. *Ulva lactua*; 10p. *Epymenia flabellata*; 20p. *Macrocystis pyrifera*.

78 Killer Whale

(Des G. Drummond. Litho Walsall)

1975 (1 Nov). *Whales. T 78 and similar horiz designs.* Multicoloured. W w **12** (sideways). P 13½.
200	2p. Type **78**	..	40	25
201	3p. Rough-toothed Dolphin	..	40	25
202	5p. Black Right Whale	..	45	30
203	20p. Fin Whale	..	1·00	70
200/3	..	*Set of 4*	2·00	1·40

79 ½d. Stamp of 1952   **80** Island Cottage

(Des C. Abbott. Litho J.W.)

1976 (27* May). *Festival of Stamps, London. T 79 and similar designs.* W w **14** (sideways on 5 and 25p). P 13½.
204	5p. black, violet and light lilac	..	15	20
205	9p. black, deep green and turquoise	..	15	25
206	25p. multicoloured	..	40	50
204/6	..	*Set of 3*	65	85

Designs: *Vert*—9p. 1953 Coronation stamp. *Horiz*—25p. Mail carrier *Tristania II*.

*This is the local date of issue. The stamps were released by the Crown Agents on 4 May.

For miniature sheet containing No. 206 see No. **MS218** of Ascension.

(Des C. Abbott. Litho Questa)

1976 (4 Oct). *Paintings by Roland Svensson (1st series). T 80 and similar multicoloured designs.* W w **14** (sideways on 5p., 10p. and **MS211**). P 14.
207	5p. Type **80**	..	15	15
208	5p. the potato patches (*horiz*)	..	15	20
209	10p. Edinburgh from the sea (*horiz*)	..	20	25
210	20p. Huts, Nightingale Island	..	30	35
207/10	..	*Set of 4*	70	85
MS211	125 × 112 mm. Nos. 207/10	..	80	1·75

See also Nos. 234/8 and 272/6.

81 The Royal Standard

(Des and litho J.W.)

1977 (7 Feb). *Silver Jubilee. T* **81** *and similar horiz designs. Multicoloured. W* w **14** *(sideways). P* 13.

212	10p.	Royal Yacht *Britannia*	..	25	30
213	15p.	Type **81**	..	15	20
214	25p.	Royal family	..	25	25
212/14			*Set of 3*	60	65

For Nos. 213/14 surcharged, see Nos. 232/3.

82 H.M.S. *Eskimo*

(Des L. Curtis. Litho Walsall)

1977 (1 Oct). *Ships' Crests. T* **82** *and similar horiz designs. Multicoloured. W* w **14** *(sideways). P* 14.

215	5p.	Type **82**	..	20	15
216	10p.	H.M.S. *Naiad*	..	30	15
217	15p.	H.M.S. *Jaguar*	..	40	25
218	20p.	H.M.S. *London*	..	45	30
215/18			*Set of 4*	1·25	75
MS219	142 × 140 mm. Nos. 215/18			1·75	2·50

83 Great-winged Petrel

(Des BG Studio. Litho Walsall)

1977 (1 Dec). *Multicoloured designs as T* **83** *showing birds. W* w **14** *(sideways on 1 and 2p.). P* 13½.

220	1p.	Type **83**	..	15	10
221	2p.	White-faced Storm Petrel	..	20	15
222	3p.	Hall's Giant Petrel	..	20	15
223	4p.	Soft-plumaged Petrel	..	60	20
224	5p.	Wandering Albatross	..	60	20
225	10p.	Kerguelen Petrel	..	60	30
226	15p.	Swallow-tailed Tern	..	60	50
227	20p.	Greater Shearwater	..	1·00	55
228	25p.	Broad-billed Prion	..	1·25	65
229	50p.	Great Skua	..	1·50	1·00
230	£1	Common Diving Petrel	..	2·00	1·75
231	£2	Yellow-nosed Albatross	..	4·50	3·25
220/31			*Set of 12*	12·00	8·00

The 3p. to £2 are vertical designs.

4ᴾ

(84)	Normal	Straight top to serif in "½" (Pl 1C R. 5/1–5)

1978 (19 Jan*). *Provisional definitives. Nos. 213/14 surch as T* **84**.

232	4p. on 15p. Type **81**	..		1·75	5·50
233	7½p. on 25p. Royal family	..		1·75	5·50
	a. Straight top to serif	..		21·00	

*This is the local date of issue. Covers dated 26 November 1977 are philatelic mail forwarded to the island for cancellation, the stamps having been released in London on 31 October 1977. Supplies for the island population did not arrive until 19 January.

(Des C. Abbott. Litho Questa)

1978 (1 Mar). *Paintings by Roland Svensson (2nd series). Horiz designs as T* **80**. *Multicoloured. W* w **14** *(sideways). P* 14.

234	5p.	St. Mary's Church	..	15	15
235	10p.	Longboats	..	20	25
236	15p.	A Tristan home	..	25	30
237	20p.	The harbour, 1970	..	30	40
234/7			*Set of 4*	80	1·00
MS238	115 × 128 mm. Nos. 234/7			1·60	2·40

ALTERED CATALOGUE NUMBERS

Any Catalogue numbers altered from the last edition are shown as a list in the introductory pages.

85 King's Bull   **86** Sodalite

(Des Jennifer Toombs. Litho Questa)

1978 (21 Apr). *25th Anniv of Coronation. T* **85** *and similar vert designs. W* w **14**. *P* 15.

239	25p.	bistre, bright violet and silver	..	35	35
		a. Sheetlet Nos. 239/41 × 2		1·90	
240	25p.	multicoloured	..	35	35
241	25p.	bistre, bright violet and silver	..	35	35
239/41			*Set of 3*	95	95

Designs:—No. 239, Type **85**; No. 240, Queen Elizabeth II; No. 241, Tristan crawfish.

Nos. 239/41 were printed together in small sheets of 6, containing two *se-tenant* strips of 3, with horizontal gutter margin between.

(Des J.W. Litho Questa)

1978 (9 June). *Local Minerals. T* **86** *and similar horiz designs. Multicoloured. W* w **14** *(sideways). P* 13½.

242	3p.	Type **86**	..	25	10
243	5p.	Aragonite	..	30	15
244	10p.	Sulphur	..	45	25
245	20p.	Lava containing pyroxene crystal	65	35
242/5			*Set of 4*	1·50	75

87 Klipfish

(Des R. Granger Barrett. Litho Harrison)

1978 (29 Sept). *Fish. T* **87** *and similar horiz designs. W* w **14** *(sideways). P* 14.

246	5p.	black, yellow-brown and yellow-green	..	10	10
247	10p.	black, yellow-brown and emerald	..	15	15
248	15p.	multicoloured	..	20	20
249	20p.	multicoloured	..	30	25
246/9			*Set of 4*	65	60

Designs:—10p. Fivefinger; 15p. Concha; 20p. Soldier.

88 R.F.A. *Orangeleaf*   **89** Southern Elephant Seal

(Des R. Granger Barrett. Litho Cartor)

1978 (24 Nov). *Royal Fleet Auxiliary Vessels. T* **88** *and similar horiz designs. Multicoloured. W* w **14** *(sideways). P* 12½ × 12.

250	5p.	Type **88**	..	15	10
251	10p.	R.F.A. *Tarbatness*	..	20	10
252	20p.	R.F.A. *Tidereach*	..	35	25
253	25p.	R.F.A. *Reliant*	..	45	30
250/3			*Set of 4*	1·10	65
MS254	136 × 140 mm. Nos. 250/3 (Wmk inverted)			2·00	3·00

(Des J.W. Litho Questa)

1979 (3 Jan). *Wildlife Conservation. T* **89** *and similar vert designs. Multicoloured. W* w **14**. *P* 14.

255	5p.	Type **89**	..	15	10
256	10p.	Afro-Australian Fur Seal	..	25	15
257	15p.	Tristan Thrush	..	40	20
258	20p.	Nightingale Finch	..	50	25
255/8			*Set of 4*	1·10	60

90 Tristan Longboat

(Des R. Granger Barrett. Litho Questa)

1979 (8 Feb). *Visit of R.M.S. "Queen Elizabeth 2". T* **90** *and similar horiz designs. Multicoloured. W* w **14** *(sideways). P* 14½.

259	5p.	Type **90**	..	20	20
260	10p.	R.M.S. *Queen Mary*	..	25	30
261	15p.	R.M.S. *Queen Elizabeth*	..	30	35
262	20p.	R.M.S. *Queen Elizabeth 2*	..	30	40
259/62			*Set of 4*	95	1·10
MS263	148 × 96 mm. 25p. R.M.S. *Queen Elizabeth 2* (131 × 27 mm)			1·00	2·25

---

91 1952 "TRISTAN DA CUNHA" overprinted St. Helena 10s. Definitive

(Des J.W. Litho Questa)

1979 (27 Aug). *Death Centenary of Sir Rowland Hill. T* **91** *and similar designs showing stamps. W* w **14** *(sideways on 5 and 10p.). P* 14.

264	5p.	black, lilac and bistre-yellow	..	15	15
265	10p.	black, red and apple-green	..	20	20
266	25p.	multicoloured	..	30	30
264/6			*Set of 3*	60	60
MS267	83 × 103 mm. 50p. black and vermilion			60	70

Designs: *Horiz*—10p. 1954 5s. definitive. *Vert*—25p. 1963 3d. Tristan da Cunha Resettlement commemorative; 50p. 1946 1d. 4 Potatoes local label.

92 "The Padre's House"   **93** *Tristania II* (mail ship)

(Des G. Hutchins. Litho Questa)

1979 (26 Nov). *International Year of the Child. Children's Drawings. T* **92** *and similar horiz designs. Multicoloured. W* w **14** *(sideways). P* 14.

268	5p.	Type **92**	..	10	10
269	10p.	"Houses in the Village"	..	15	15
270	15p.	"St. Mary's Church"	..	15	15
271	20p.	"Rockhopper Penguins"	..	25	25
268/71			*Set of 4*	60	60

(Des C. Abbott. Litho Questa)

1980 (29 Feb). *Paintings by Roland Svensson (3rd series). Landscapes. Multicoloured designs as T* **80**. *W* w **14** *(sideways on 5 and 10p.). P* 14.

272	5p.	"Stoltenhoff Island" [*horiz*]	..	10	10
273	10p.	"Nightingale from the East" (*horiz*)	..	15	20
274	15p.	"The Administrator's Abode"	..	20	25
275	20p.	"Ridge where the Goat jump off"	..	25	30
272/5			*Set of 4*	60	75
MS276	126 × 109 mm. Nos. 272/5 (wmk sideways)			70	1·00

(Des C. Abbott. Litho Walsall)

1980 (6 May). *"London 1980" International Stamp Exhibition. T* **93** *and similar vert designs. Multicoloured. W* w **14**. *P* 14.

277	5p.	Type **93**	..	15	15
278	10p.	Unloading mail at Calshot Harbour	..	15	15
279	15p.	Tractor transporting mail to Post Office	25	25
280	20p.	Ringing the "dong" to summons people to Post Office	..	30	30
281	25p.	Distributing mail	..	30	30
277/81			*Set of 5*	1·00	1·00

94 Queen Elizabeth the Queen Mother at Royal Opera House, 1976   **95** *Golden Hind*

(Des Harrison. Litho Questa)

1980 (11 Aug*). *80th Birthday of Queen Elizabeth the Queen Mother. W* w **14** *(sideways). P* 14.

282	**94**	14p. multicoloured	..	25	25

*This is the local date of issue. The Crown Agents released this stamp in London on 4 August.

(Des G. Vasarhelyi. Litho Walsall)

1980 (6 Sept). *400th Anniv of Sir Francis Drake's Circumnavigation of the World. T* **95** *and similar vert designs. Multicoloured. W* w **14**. *P* 14½ × 14.

283	5p.	Type **95**	..	20	10
284	10p.	Drake's route	..	25	15
285	20p.	Sir Francis Drake	..	30	20
286	25p.	Queen Elizabeth I	..	40	25
283/6			*Set of 4*	1·00	65

96 "Humpty Dumpty" **97** South Atlantic Ocean showing Islands on Mid-Atlantic Ridge

108 Formation of Island **109** Tractor pulling Trailer

(Des G. Vasarhelyi. Litho J.W.)

1980 (31 Oct). *Christmas. Scenes from Nursery Rhymes. T* **96** *and similar horiz designs. Multicoloured. W w 14 (sideways).*

287	15p. Type **96**		20	25
	a. Sheetlet Nos. 287/95		1·60	
288	15p. "Mary had a little Lamb"		20	25
289	15p. "Little Jack Horner"		20	25
290	15p. "Hey Diddle Diddle"		20	25
291	15p. "London Bridge"		20	25
292	15p. "Old King Cole"		20	25
293	15p. "Sing a Song of Sixpence"		20	25
294	15p. "Tom, Tom the Piper's Son"		20	25
295	15p. "The Owl and the Pussy Cat"		20	25
287/95		*Set of 9*	1·60	1·75

Nos. 287/95 were printed together, *se-tenant*, within a small sheet of 9 stamps.

(Des A. Crawford, adapted BG Studio. Litho Rosenbaum Bros, Vienna)

1980 (15 Dec). *150th Anniv of Royal Geographical Society. Maps. T* **97** *and similar vert designs. Multicoloured. W w 14. P 13½.*

296	5p. Type **97**		15	20
297	10p. Tristan da Cunha group (Beauforts Survey, 1806)		20	25
298	15p. Tristan Island (Crawford, 1937–38)		30	35
299	20p. Gough Island (1955–56)		35	45
296/9		*Set of 4*	90	1·10

98 Revd. Edwin Dodgson as Young Man **99** Detail from Captain Denham's Plan, 1853

(Des Jennifer Toombs. Litho Questa)

1981 (23 Mar). *Centenary of Revd. Edwin Dodgson's Arrival on Tristan da Cunha. T* **98** *and similar multicoloured designs. W w 14 (sideways on 20p.). P 14.*

300	10p. Type **98**		20	15
301	20p. Dodgson and view of Tristan da Cunha (horiz)		30	30
302	30p. Dodgson with people of Tristan da Cunha		45	45
300/2		*Set of 3*	85	80
MS303	140 × 134 mm. Nos. 300/2 (wmk sideways)		1·00	1·50

(Des L. McCombie. Litho Questa)

1981 (22 May). *Early Maps. T* **99** *and similar horiz designs. Multicoloured. W w 14 (sideways). P 13½ × 14.*

304	5p. Type **99**		15	10
305	14p. Detail from map by A. Dalrymple, 17 March 1781		25	20
306	21p. Detail from Captain Denham's plan, 1853 (different)		35	30
304/6		*Set of 3*	65	55
MS307	110 × 70 mm. 35p. Detail from map by J. van Keulen, circa 1700		50	60

100 Wedding Bouquet from Tristan da Cunha **101** Explorer with Rucksack

(Des J.W. Litho Walsall)

1981 (22 July). *Royal Wedding. T* **100** *and similar vert designs. Multicoloured. W w 14. P 14.*

308	5p. Type **100**		10	10
309	20p. Prince of Wales at Investiture		25	25
310	50p. Prince Charles and Lady Diana Spencer		65	65
308/10		*Set of 3*	90	90

(Des BG Studio. Litho Questa)

1981 (14 Sept). *25th Anniv of Duke of Edinburgh Award Scheme. T* **101** *and similar vert designs. Multicoloured. W w 14. P 14.*

311	5p. Type **101**		10	10
312	10p. Explorer at campsite		15	15
313	20p. Explorer map reading		25	25
314	25p. Duke of Edinburgh		30	30
311/14		*Set of 4*	70	70

102 Inaccessible Island Rail on Nest

(Des R. Granger Barrett. Litho Walsall)

1981 (1 Nov). *Inaccessible Island Rail. T* **102** *and similar horiz designs. Multicoloured. W w 14 (sideways). P 13½ × 14.*

315	10p. Type **102**		30	30
	a. Strip of 4. Nos. 315/18		1·10	
316	10p. Inaccessible Island Rail eggs		30	30
317	10p. Rail chicks		30	30
318	10p. Adult Rail		30	30
315/18		*Set of 4*	1·10	1·10

Nos. 315/18 were printed together, *se-tenant*, in horizontal and vertical strips of 4 throughout the sheet.

103 Six-gilled Shark

(Des I. Loe. Litho Enschedé)

1982 (8 Feb). *Sharks. T* **103** *and similar horiz designs. Multicoloured. W w 14 (sideways). P 13½.*

319	5p. Type **103**		20	10
320	14p. Porbeagle Shark		35	20
321	21p. Blue Shark		50	35
322	35p. Hammerhead Shark		60	50
319/22		*Set of 4*	1·50	1·00

104 *Marcella* **105** Lady Diana Spencer at Windsor, July 1981

(Des J. Cooter. Litho Questa)

1982 (5 Apr). *Sailing Ships (1st series). T* **104** *and similar horiz designs. Multicoloured. W w 14 (sideways). P 13½.*

323	5p. Type **104**		30	35
324	15p. *Eliza Adams*		35	50
325	30p. *Corinthian*		60	80
326	50p. *Samuel and Thomas*		1·00	1·10
323/6		*Set of 4*	2·00	2·50

See also Nos. 341/4.

(Des Jennifer Toombs. Litho Walsall)

1982 (1 July). *21st Birthday of Princess of Wales. T* **105** *and similar vert designs. Multicoloured. W w 14. P 14½ × 14.*

327	5p. Tristan da Cunha coat of arms		15	15
328	15p. Type **105**		25	25
329	30p. Prince and Princess of Wales in wedding portrait		45	45
330	50p. Formal portrait		75	75
327/30		*Set of 4*	1·40	1·40

106 Lord Baden-Powell **(107)**

(Des C. Abbott. Litho J.W.)

1982 (20 Sept). *75th Anniv of Boy Scout Movement. T* **106** *and similar multicoloured designs. W w 14 (sideways on No. 333). P 13 × 13½ (50p.) or 13½ × 13 (others).*

331	5p. Type **106**		20	15
332	20p. First Scout camp, Brownsea, 1907		40	35
333	50p. Local Scouts on parade (horiz)		80	75
331/3		*Set of 3*	1·25	1·10
MS334	88 × 104 mm. 50p. Moral of the Acorn and the Oak. P 14		1·10	1·10

1982 (28 Sept). *Commonwealth Games, Brisbane. Nos. 224 and 228 optd with T* **107**.

335	5p. Wandering Albatross		10	10
336	25p. Broad-billed Prion		35	30

(Des J.W. Litho Questa)

1982 (1 Nov). *Volcanoes. T* **108** *and similar horiz designs. Multicoloured. W w 14 (sideways). P 14 × 14½.*

337	5p. Type **108**		15	15
338	15p. Plan of surface cinder cones and cross-section of volcano showing feeders		30	35
339	25p. Eruption		45	50
340	35p. 1961 Tristan eruption		65	70
337/40		*Set of 4*	1·40	1·50

(Des J. Cooter. Litho Questa)

1983 (1 Feb). *Sailing Ships (2nd series). Multicoloured designs as T* **104**. *W w 14 (sideways on 20p., 35p.). P 13½.*

341	5p. *Islander* (vert)		25	15
342	20p. *Roscoe*		45	35
343	35p. *Columbia*		60	55
344	50p. *Emeline* (vert)		80	80
341/4		*Set of 4*	1·90	1·75

(Des C. Abbott. Litho Format)

1983 (2 May). *Land Transport. T* **109** *and similar horiz designs. Multicoloured. W w 14 (sideways). P 14.*

345	5p. Type **109**		15	15
346	15p. Pack donkeys		25	25
347	30p. Bullock cart		50	50
348	50p. Landrover		75	75
345/8		*Set of 4*	1·50	1·50

110 Early Chart of South Atlantic **111** "Christ's Charge to St. Peter" (detail) (Raphael)

(Des L. Curtis. Litho Questa)

1983 (1 Aug). *Island History. T* **110** *and similar horiz designs. Multicoloured (except 50p. black, bright scarlet and buff). W w 14 (sideways). P 14.*

349	1p. Type **110**		30	30
350	3p. Tristao da Cunha's caravel		40	30
351	4p. Notice left by Dutch on first landing, 1643		40	30
352	5p. 17th-century views of the island		40	30
353	10p. British army landing party, 1815		45	40
354	15p. 19th-century view of the settlement		55	50
355	18p. Governor Glass's house		55	50
356	20p. The Revd. W. F. Taylor and Peter Green		65	65
357	25p. *John and Elizabeth* (American whaling ship)		85	75
358	50p. Letters Patent declaring Tristan da Cunha a dependency of St. Helena		1·40	1·25
359	£1 Commissioning H.M.S. *Atlantic Isle*, 1944		2·50	2·50
360	£2 Evacuation, 1961		3·75	4·00
349/60		*Set of 12*	11·00	10·50

(Des and litho Walsall)

1983 (27 Oct). *500th Birth Anniv of Raphael. T* **111** *and similar designs, showing different details of "Christ's Charge to St. Peter". W w 14. P 14½.*

361	10p. multicoloured		20	20
362	25p. multicoloured		35	35
363	40p. multicoloured		60	60
361/3		*Set of 3*	1·00	1·00
MS364	115 × 90 mm. 50p. multicoloured (horiz). Wmk sideways		70	80

On No. MS364 the Queen's head has been replaced by the Royal Cypher.

ALTERED CATALOGUE NUMBERS

Any Catalogue numbers altered from the last edition are shown as a list in the introductory pages.

112 1952 6d. Stamp   113 *Agrocybe praecox var. cutefracta*

(Des C. Abbott. Litho Questa)

1984 (3 Jan). *150th Anniv of St. Helena as a British Colony. T 112 and similar horiz designs showing 1952 overprints on St. Helena stamps. Multicoloured. W w 14 (sideways). P 14.*

365	10p. Type 112	..	15	15
366	15p. 1952 1s. stamp	..	25	25
367	25p. 1952 2s. stamp	..	35	35
368	60p. 1952 10s. stamp	..	85	85
365/8		*Set of 4*	1·40	1·40

(Des McCombie Skinner Studio. Litho Questa)

1984 (25 Mar). *Fungi. T 113 and similar multicoloured designs. W w 14 (sideways on 30 p., 50 p.). P 14.*

369	10p. Type 113	..	55	55
370	20p. *Laccaria tetraspora*	..	85	85
371	30p. *Agrocybe cylindracea* (horiz)	..	1·00	1·00
372	50p. *Sacoscypha coccinea* (horiz)	..	1·40	1·40
369/72		*Set of 4*	3·50	3·50

114 Constellation of "Orion"   115 Sheep-shearing

(Des Harrison. Litho Questa)

1984 (30 July). *The Night Sky. T 114 and similar vert designs. Multicoloured. W w 14. P 14½ × 14.*

373	10p. Type 114	..	45	45
374	20p. "Scorpius"	..	65	65
375	25p. "Canis Major"	..	75	75
376	50p. "Crux"	..	1·10	1·10
373/6		*Set of 4*	2·75	2·75

(Des G. Wilby. Litho Walsall)

1984 (1 Oct). *Tristan Woollens Industry. T 115 and similar vert designs. Multicoloured. W w 14. P 14½.*

377	9p. Type 115	..	20	25
378	17p. Carding wool	..	30	35
379	29p. Spinning ..	..	50	60
380	45p. Knitting ..	..	75	80
377/80		*Set of 4*	1·60	1·75
MS381	120 × 85 mm. As Nos. 377/80, but without white borders around the designs.	..	1·60	2·50

116 "Christmas Dinner-table"   117 "H.M.S. *Julia* Ashore, 1817" (Midshipman C. W. Browne)

(Des G. Vasarhelyi. Litho Questa)

1984 (3 Dec). *Christmas. Children's Drawings. T 116 and similar horiz designs. Multicoloured. W w 14 (sideways). P 14.*

382	10p. Type 116	..	20	20
383	20p. "Santa Claus in ox cart"	..	30	30
384	30p. "Santa Claus in longboat"	..	50	50
385	50p. "The Nativity"	..	85	85
382/5		*Set of 4*	1·75	1·75

(Des A. Crawford, adapted G. Vasarhelyi. Litho Questa)

1985 (4 Feb). *Shipwrecks (1st series). T 117 and similar designs. W w 14 (sideways on 35p.). P 14 × 13½ (10, 25p.) or 13½ × 14 (35, 60p.).*

386	10p. royal blue and light grey-blue	..	60	70
387	25p. red-brown and emerald ..	..	1·10	1·25
388	35p. yellow-brown and orange-yellow	..	1·40	1·60
386/8		*Set of 3*	2·75	3·25
MS389	142 × 101 mm. 60p. multicoloured. Wmk sideways	..	1·60	1·75

Designs: *Vert*—25p. *Mabel Clark's* Bell, St. Mary's Church. *Horiz*—35p. "Barque *Glenhuntley* foundering, 1898" (John Hagan); 60p. Map of Tristan da Cunha showing sites of shipwrecks.
See also Nos. 411/14 and 426/9.

118 The Queen Mother at Ascot with Princess Margaret   119 Jonathan Lambert and "Isles of Refreshment" Flag, 1811

(Des A. Theobald (80p.), C. Abbott (others). Litho Questa)

1985 (7 June). *Life and Times of Queen Elizabeth the Queen Mother. T 118 and similar vert designs. Multicoloured. W w 16. P 14½ × 14.*

390	10p. The Queen Mother and Prince Charles, 1954	..	20	30
391	20p. Type 118	..	40	60
392	30p. Queen Elizabeth the Queen Mother	..	60	85
393	50p. With Prince Henry at his christening	1·00	1·25
390/3		*Set of 4*	2·00	2·75
MS394	91 × 73 mm. 80p. The Queen Mother and the young Princess Anne at Trooping the Colour. Wmk sideways		2·00	2·00

120 Lifeboat heading for Barque *West Riding*   121 Halley's Comet, 1066, from Bayeux Tapestry

(Des D. Slater. Litho J.W.)

1985 (30 Sept). *Flags. T 119 and similar multicoloured designs. W w 16 (sideways on 10p., inverted on others). P 14.*

395	10p. Type 119	..	60	60
396	15p. 21st Light Dragoons guidon and cannon from Fort Malcolm (1816–17) (vert)	80	80
397	25p. White Ensign and H.M.S. *Falmouth* offshore, 1816 (vert)	1·10	1·25
398	60p. Union Jack and Tristan da Cunha (vert)	2·25	2·50
395/8		*Set of 4*	4·25	4·75

(Des D. Miller. Litho Format)

1985 (28 Nov). *Centenary of Loss of Island Lifeboat. T 120 and similar vert designs. Multicoloured. W w 14. P 14 × 13½.*

399	10p. Type 120 ..	..	35	60
400	30p. Map of Tristan da Cunha	..	80	1·25
401	50p. Memorial plaque to lifeboat crew	1·25	1·75
399/401		*Set of 3*	2·25	3·25

(Des D. Miller. Litho Walsall)

1986 (3 Mar). *Appearance of Halley's Comet. T 121 and similar horiz designs. Multicoloured. W w 16 (sideways). P 14.*

402	10p. Type 121	..	40	55
403	20p. Path of Comet ..	..	65	80
404	30p. Comet over Inaccessible Island	..	85	1·10
405	50p. H.M.S. *Paramour* and map of South Atlantic	..	1·40	1·75
402/5		*Set of 4*	3·00	3·75

(Des A. Theobald. Litho Questa)

1986 (21 Apr). *60th Birthday of Queen Elizabeth II. Vert designs as T 230a of Jamaica. Multicoloured. W w 16. P 14½ × 14.*

406	10p. With Prince Charles, 1950	..	20	25
407	15p. Queen at Trooping the Colour ..	..	30	35
408	25p. In robes of Order of the Bath, Westminster Abbey, 1972	..	50	55
	a. Silver (cypher and logo) omitted		£275	
409	45p. In Canada, 1977..	..	90	95
410	65p. At Crown Agents Head Office, London, 1983	..	1·25	1·40
406/10		*Set of 5*	2·75	3·25

122 "*Allanshaw* wrecked on East Beach, 1893" (drawing by John Hagan)   123 Wandering Albatross

(Des A. Crawford, adapted G. Vasarhelyi. Litho J.W.)

1986 (2 June). *Shipwrecks (2nd series). T 122 and similar designs. W w 16 (sideways on 9p.). P 13½ × 13 (9p.) or 13 × 13½ (others).*

411	9p. dp turquoise-blue, dp grey-blue & black	30	35
412	20p. grey-olive, olive-yellow and black	..	60	60
413	40p. bright blue, bright violet and black	..	1·10	1·40
411/13		*Set of 3*	1·75	2·25
MS414	142 × 80 mm. 65p. orange-brown and black. Wmk sideways. P 13½ × 13	..	1·75	2·50

Designs: *Vert*—20p. Church font from wreck of *Edward Vittery*, 1881; 40p. Ship's figurehead. *Horiz*—65p. Gaetano Lavarello and Andrea Repetto, survivors from *Italia*, 1892.

(Des D. Miller. Litho Questa)

1986 (23 July). *Royal Wedding. Square designs as T 231a of Jamaica. Multicoloured. W w 16. P 14.*

415	10p. Prince Andrew and Miss Sarah Ferguson	..	20	35
416	40p. Prince Andrew piloting helicopter, Digby, Canada, 1985 ..	..	80	1·25

(Des A. Theobald. Litho Questa)

1986 (30 Sept). *Flora and Fauna of Inaccessible Island. T 123 and similar vert designs. Multicoloured. W w 16. P 14.*

417	5p. Type 123	..	20	35
418	10p. *Lagenophora nudicaulis* (daisy)	..	30	45
419	20p. *Cynthia virginiensis* (butterfly)	..	65	85
420	25p. Wilkin's Finch	..	75	95
421	50p. White-chinned Petrel.	..	1·25	1·25
417/21		*Set of 5*	2·75	3·50

124 *Dimorphinoctua cunhaensis* (flightless moth) and Edinburgh   125 Castaways from *Blenden Hall* attacking Sea Elephant, 1821

(Des C. Abbott. Litho Walsall)

1987 (23 Jan). *Island Flightless Insects and Birds. T 124 and similar vert designs. Multicoloured. W w 14. P 14½.*

422	10p. Type 124 ..	..	25	40
423	25p. *Tristanomyia frustilifera* (fly) and Crater Lake ..	..	55	70
424	35p. Inaccessible Island Rail and Inaccessible Island	..	1·00	1·40
425	50p. Gough Island Coot and Gough Island ..	1·50	1·60
422/5		*Set of 4*	3·00	3·75

(Des A. Crawford, adapted G. Vasarhelyi. Litho Walsall)

1987 (2 Apr*). *Shipwrecks (3rd series). T 125 and similar designs. W w 16 (sideways on 17p.). P 13½ × 14 (17p.) or 14 × 13½ (others).*

426	11p. black and olive-brown	..	30	30
427	17p. black and bright lilac ..	..	45	45
428	45p. black and deep blue-green	..	1·00	1·00
426/8		*Set of 3*	1·60	1·60
MS429	131 × 70 mm. 70p. royal blue, bright green and pale blue. Wmk sideways. P 13½ × 14		2·00	2·25

Designs: *Horiz*—17p. Barquentine *Henry A. Paull* stranded at Sandy Point, 1879; 70p. Map of Inaccessible Island showing sites of shipwrecks. *Vert*—45p. Gustav Stoltenhoff, 1871, and Stoltenhoff Island.
*This is the local date of issue. The Crown Agents placed the stamps on sale from 2 February 1987.

126 Rockhopper Penguin swimming   127 Microscope and Published Report

(Des I. Strange. Litho Questa)

1987 (22 June). *Rockhopper Penguins. T 126 and similar horiz designs. Multicoloured. W w 16 (sideways). P 14½.*

430	10p. Type 126	..	35	30
431	20p. Adult with egg ..	..	55	50
432	30p. Adult with juvenile	..	75	70
433	50p. Head of Rockhopper Penguin ..	..	1·25	1·10
430/3		*Set of 4*	2·75	2·40

(Des N. Shewring. Litho Questa)

1987 (7 Dec). *50th Anniv of Norwegian Scientific Expedition. T 127 and similar square designs. Multicoloured. W w 16 (10p., 20p.) or w 14 (30p., 50p.) (all sideways). P 14.*

434	10p. Type 127 ..	..	60	60
435	20p. Scientists ringing Yellow-nosed Albatross	..	1·25	1·25
436	30p. Expedition hut, Little Beach Point	..	1·60	1·60
437	50p. S.S. *Thorshammer* (whale factory ship)	2·25	2·25
434/7		*Set of 4*	5·25	5·25

1988 (9 Mar). *Royal Ruby Wedding. Nos. 406/10 optd with T 45a of Kiribati in silver.*

438	10p.	Princess Elizabeth with Prince Charles, 1950	20	25
439	15p.	Queen Elizabeth II at Trooping the Colour	30	35
440	25p.	In robes of Order of the Bath, West-minster Abbey, 1972	50	55
441	45p.	In Canada, 1977.	90	95
442	65p.	At Crown Agents Head Office, London, 1983	1·25	1·40
438/42		*Set of 5*	2·75	3·25

128 Nightingale Finch ("Tristan Bunting")

129 Painted Penguin Eggs

(Des A. Theobald. Litho Questa)

1988 (21 Mar). *Fauna of Nightingale Island. T 128 and similar vert designs. Multicoloured. W w 16. P 14.*

443	5p.	Type **128**	20	15
444	10p.	Tristan Thrush (immature)	30	25
445	20p.	Yellow-nosed Albatross (chick)	50	45
446	25p.	Greater Shearwater	60	55
447	50p.	Elephant Seal	1·10	1·10
443/7		*Set of 5*	2·40	2·25

(Des O. Bell. Litho Questa)

1988 (30 May). *Tristan da Cunha Handicrafts. T 129 and similar horiz designs. Multicoloured. W w 16 (sideways). P 14 × 14½.*

448	10p.	Type **129**	25	25
449	15p.	Moccasins	35	35
450	35p.	Knitwear	75	75
451	50p.	Model longboat	1·10	1·10
448/51		*Set of 4*	2·25	2·25

130 Processing Blubber

(Des N. Shewring. Litho Questa)

1988 (6 Oct). *19th-century Whaling. T 130 and similar horiz designs. Multicoloured. W w 16 (sideways). P 14 × 14½.*

452	10p.	Type **130**	25	25
453	20p.	Harpoon guns	45	45
454	30p.	Scrimshaw (carved whale bone)	65	65
455	50p.	Whaling ships	1·10	1·10
452/5		*Set of 4*	2·25	2·25
MS456		76 × 56 mm. £1 Right Whale	2·10	2·10

(Des E. Nisbet and D. Miller (25, 35p.), D. Miller (others). Litho Harrison)

1988 (7 Nov). *300th Anniv of Lloyd's of London. Designs as T 167a of Malawi. W w 16 (sideways on 25, 35p.). P 14.*

457	10p.	multicoloured	25	25
458	25p.	multicoloured	55	55
459	35p.	brownish black and emerald	80	80
460	50p.	brownish black and carmine-red	1·25	1·25
457/60		*Set of 4*	2·50	2·50

Designs:—*Vert*—10p. New Lloyd's Building, 1988; 50p. *Kobenhavn* (barque), 1928. *Horiz*—25p. *Tristania II* (crawfish trawler); 35p. *St. Helena* (mail ship).

131 "Government House"

132 Hall's Giant Petrel

(Des N. Harvey. Litho Walsall)

1988 (10 Dec). *Augustus Earle's Paintings, 1824. T 131 and similar horiz designs. Multicoloured. W w 16 (sideways). P 14.*

461	1p.	Type **131**	10	10
462	3p.	"Squall off Tristan"	10	10
463	4p.	"Rafting Blubber"	10	10
464	5p.	"View near Little Beach"	10	15
465	10p.	"Man killing Albatross"	20	25
466	15p.	"View on The Summit"	30	35
467	20p.	"Nightingale Island"	40	45

468	25p.	"Earle on Tristan"	50	55
469	35p.	"Solitude—Watching the Horizon"	70	75
470	50p.	"Northeaster"	1·00	1·10
471	£1	"Tristan Village"	2·00	2·10
472	£2	"Governor Glass at Dinner"	4·00	4·25
461/72		*Set of 12*	8·50	9·25

Examples of Nos. 461/72 showing Earle's dates as "1793–1835" were sold by the U.S.A. agents, and by the authorities on Ascension, in error. Supplies sent to Tristan da Cunha show the correct dates "1793–1838".

(Des A. Theobald. Litho Walsall)

1989 (6 Feb). *Fauna of Gough Island. T 132 and similar vert designs. Multicoloured. W w 16. P 14.*

473	5p.	Type **132**	15	15
474	10p.	Gough Island Moorhen	20	25
475	20p.	Gough Island Finch ("Gough Bunting")	40	45
476	25p.	Sooty Albatross	50	55
477	50p.	Amsterdam Fur Seal	1·00	1·10
473/7		*Set of 5*	2·00	2·25

133 *Eriosorus cheilanthoides*

134 Surgeon's Mortar

(Des Jane Fern. Litho Walsall)

1989 (22 May). *Ferns. T 133 and similar vert designs. Multicoloured. W w 14. P 14×13½.*

478	10p.	Type **133**	35	35
479	25p.	*Asplenium alvarezense*	75	75
480	35p.	*Elaphoglossum hybridum*	85	85
481	50p.	*Ophioglossum opacum*	1·40	1·40
478/81		*Set of 4*	3·00	3·00

(Des Jennifer Toombs. Litho Questa)

1989 (25 Sept). *Nautical Museum Exhibits. T 134 and similar horiz designs. Multicoloured. W w 16 (sideways). P 14.*

482	10p.	Type **134**	35	35
483	20p.	Parts of darting-gun harpoon	60	60
484	30p.	Ship's compass with binnacle-hood	80	80
485	60p.	Rope-twisting device	1·60	1·60
482/5		*Set of 4*	3·00	3·00

135 Cattle Egret

136 *Peridroma saucia*

(Des Josephine Martin and Sally Hynard. Litho Questa)

1989 (20 Nov). *Vagrant Birds. T 135 and similar vert designs. Multicoloured. W w 16. P 14.*

486	10p.	Type **135**	45	35
487	25p.	Spotted Sandpiper	80	70
488	35p.	Purple Gallinule	1·00	90
489	50p.	Barn Swallow	1·40	1·40
486/9		*Set of 4*	3·25	3·00

(Des I. Loe. Litho Questa)

1990 (1 Feb). *Moths. T 136 and similar horiz designs. Multicoloured. W w 14 (sideways). P 14.*

490	10p.	Type **136**	30	35
491	15p.	*Ascalapha odorata*	40	45
492	35p.	*Agrius cingulata*	80	90
493	60p.	*Eumorpha labruscae*	1·50	1·60
490/3		*Set of 4*	2·75	3·00

137 Sea Urchin

138 H.M.S. *Pyramus* (frigate), 1829

(Des Anna Hecht. Litho Questa)

1990 (12 June). *Echinoderms. T 137 and similar vert designs showing starfishes. W w 14. P 13½×14.*

494	10p.	multicoloured	40	30
495	20p.	multicoloured	60	50
496	30p.	multicoloured	85	75
497	60p.	multicoloured	1·50	1·50
494/7		*Set of 4*	3·00	2·75

(Des D. Miller. Litho Questa)

1990 (4 Aug). *90th Birthday of Queen Elizabeth the Queen Mother. Vert designs as T 107 (25p.) or 108 (£1) of Kenya. W w 16. P 14×15 (25p.) or 14½ (£1).*

498	25p.	multicoloured	75	60
499	£1	agate and Prussian blue	2·50	2·40

Designs:—25p. Queen Mother at the London Coliseum; £1 Queen Elizabeth broadcasting to women of the Empire, 1939.

(Des L. Curtis. Litho Walsall)

1990 (13 Sept). *Maiden Voyage of St. Helena II. Horiz designs as T 162 of St. Helena. Multicoloured. W w 14 (sideways). P 14×14½.*

500	10p.	*Dunnottar Castle* (mail ship), 1942	35	35
501	15p.	*St. Helena I* at Tristan	20	50
502	35p.	Launch of *St. Helena II*	1·00	1·00
503	60p.	Duke of York launching *St. Helena II*	1·75	1·75
500/3		*Set of 4*	3·25	3·25
MS504		100×100 mm. £1 *St Helena II* and outline map of Tristan da Cunha	2·50	3·00

No. **MS504** also contains two imperforate designs of similar stamps from Ascension and St. Helena without face values.

(Des E. Nisbet. Litho Questa)

1990 (30 Nov). *Ships of the Royal Navy (1st series). T 138 and similar horiz designs. Multicoloured. W w 14 (sideways). P 14.*

505	10p.	Type **138**	35	35
506	25p.	H.M.S. *Penguin* (sloop), 1815	80	80
507	35p.	H.M.S. *Thalia* (screw corvette), 1886	1·00	1·00
508	50p.	H.M.S. *Sidon* (paddle frigate), 1858	1·60	1·60
505/8		*Set of 4*	3·25	3·25

(Des E. Nisbet. Litho Questa)

1991 (4 Feb). *Ships of the Royal Navy (2nd series). Horiz designs as T 138. Multicoloured. W w 14 (sideways). P 14.*

509	10p.	H.M.S. *Milford* (sloop), 1938	35	35
510	25p.	H.M.S. *Dublin* (cruiser), 1923	80	80
511	35p.	H.M.S. *Yarmouth* (cruiser), 1919	1·00	1·00
512	50p.	H.M.S. *Carlisle* (cruiser), 1937	1·60	1·60
509/12		*Set of 4*	3·25	3·25

No. 512 is inscribed "1938" in error.

Tristan da Cunha £1

139 *Royal Viking Sun* (cruise liner)

(Des L. Curtis. Litho B.D.T.)

1991 (1 Apr). *Visit of Royal Viking Sun. Sheet 62×47 mm. W w 16 (sideways). P 14.*

MS513	**139**	£1 multicoloured	3·00	3·50

140 Prince Alfred and H.M.S. *Galatea*, 1867

(Des D. Miller. Litho Questa)

1991 (10 June). *70th Birthday of Prince Philip, Duke of Edinburgh. T 140 and similar horiz designs. W w 16 (sideways). P 14.*

514	10p.	brownish black, pale blue & dp dull bl	50	50
515	25p.	brownish black, pale blue-green and myrtle-green	90	90
516	30p.	black, deep brown & pale bistre-yellow	1·00	1·00
517	50p.	multicoloured	1·60	1·60
514/17		*Set of 4*	3·50	3·50

Designs:—25p. Prince Philip meeting local inhabitants, 1957; 30p. Prince Philip and Royal Yacht *Britannia*, 1957; 50p. Prince Philip and Edinburgh settlement.

141 Pair of Gough Island Moorhens

142 *Caesioperca coatsii*

(Des G. Vasarhelyi. Litho Questa)

1991 (1 Oct). *Endangered Species. Birds. T 141 and similar horiz designs. Multicoloured. W w 14 (sideways). P 14.*

518	8p.	Type **141**	35	35
519	10p.	Gough Island Finch	40	40
520	12p.	Gough Island Moorhen on nest	45	45
521	15p.	Gough Island Finch feeding chicks	55	55
518/21		*Set of 4*	1·60	1·60

(Des R. Watton. Litho Walsall)

1992 (23 Jan). *500th Anniv of Discovery of America by Columbus and Re-enactment Voyages. Horiz designs as T 168 of St. Helena. Multicoloured. W w 14* (*sideways*). *P* 13½×14.
522	10p. Map of re-enactment voyages and *Eye of the Wind* (cadet ship)				50	50
523	15p. Compass rose and *Soren Larsen* (cadet ship)				75	75
524	35p. Ships of Columbus				1·40	1·40
525	60p. Columbus and *Santa Maria*				1·75	1·75
522/5				Set of 4	4·00	4·00

(Des. D. Miller. Litho Questa (65p.), Walsall (others))

1992 (6 Feb). *40th Anniv of Queen Elizabeth II's Accession. Horiz designs as T 113 of Kenya. Multicoloured. W w 14* (*sideways*). *P* 14.
526	10p. Tristan from the sea				35	35
527	20p. Longboat under sail				60	60
528	25p. Aerial view of Edinburgh				70	70
529	35p. Three portraits of Queen Elizabeth			90	90
530	65p. Queen Elizabeth II				1·75	1·75
526/30				Set of 5	4·00	4·00

(Des Ann Hecht. Litho Questa)

1992 (1 June). *Fishes. T 142 and similar horiz designs. Multicoloured. W w 14* (*sideways*). *P* 14×13½.
531	10p. Type 142				35	35
532	15p. *Mendosoma lineatum*				55	55
533	35p. *Physiculus karrerae*				1·40	1·40
534	60p. *Decapterus longimanus*				1·90	1·90
531/4				Set of 4	3·75	3·75

143 *Italia* leaving Greenock   **144** *Stenoscelis hylastoides*

(Des E. Nisbet. Litho Questa)

1992 (16 Sept). *Centenary of the Wreck of Barque* Italia. *T 143 and similar horiz designs. W w 14* (*sideways*). *P* 13½×14.
535	10p. Type 143				35	35
536	45p. In mid-Atlantic				1·40	1·40
537	65p. Driving ashore on Stony Beach			1·75	1·90
535/7				Set of 3	3·25	3·25
MS538	101×75 mm. £1 *Italia* becalmed			3·00	3·25

Nos. **MS**538 also commemorates "Genova '92" International Thematic Stamp Exhibition.

(Des G. Marx. Litho Questa)

1993 (2 Feb). *Insects. T 144 and similar vert designs. Multicoloured. W w 16. P* 14×13½.
539	15p. Type 144				45	50
540	45p. *Trogloscaptomyza brevilamellata*			1·40	1·50
541	60p. *Senilites tristanicola*				1·75	1·90
539/41				Set of 3	3·25	3·50

POSTAGE DUE STAMPS

D 1   Normal   Lower serif at left of "3" missing (R. 9/1)

(Typo D.L.R.)

1957 (1 Feb). *Chalk-surfaced paper. Wmk Mult Script CA. P* 14.
D1	D 1	1d. scarlet			1·75	6·00
D2		2d. orange-yellow			2·25	4·75
		a. Large "d"			16·00	
D3		3d. green			3·50	5·50
		a. Missing serif			35·00	
D4		4d. ultramarine			6·00	7·00
D5		5d. lake			5·00	18·00
D1/5				Set of 5	17·00	38·00

For illustration of No. D2a see above No. D1 of Lesotho.

D 2   **D 3** Outline Map of Tristan da Cunha

(Des J.W. Litho Questa)

1976 (27 May*). *W w 12* (*sideways*). *P* 13½ × 14.
D 6	D 2	1p. magenta			25	60
D 7		2p. dull emerald			25	70
D 8		4p. bluish violet			25	70
D 9		5p. new blue			25	70
D10		10p. chestnut			40	1·10
D6/10				Set of 5	1·25	3·50

*This is the local date of issue; the Crown Agents released the stamps four days later.

1976 (3 Sept). *W w 14* (*sideways*). *P* 13½ × 14.
D11	D 2	1p. magenta			10	40
D12		2p. dull emerald			15	45
D13		4p. bluish violet			20	55
D14		5p. new blue			20	65
D15		10p. chestnut			20	85
D11/15				Set of 5	75	2·50

(Des L. Curtis. Litho Questa)

1986 (20 Nov). *W w 16. P* 14½ × 14.
D16	D 3	1p. deep brown and cinnamon			10	10
D17		2p. deep brown and bright orange		10	10
D18		5p. deep brown and orange-vermilion		10	15
D19		7p. black and bright reddish violet		15	20
D20		10p. black and violet-blue			20	25
D21		25p. black and pale emerald			50	55
D16/21				Set of 6	95	1·10

POSTAL FISCAL STAMPS

NATIONAL SAVINGS   2½P

(F 1)   (F 2)

1970 (15 May). *No. 77 optd with Type F 1 in red.*
F1	6d. black and green				20	30

No. F1 was originally intended as a National Savings Stamp, but also retained postal validity.

(Handstamped locally by rubber handstamp)

1971 (14 Feb). *Decimal currency. No. F 1 handstamped with Type F 2, in violet.*
F2	2½p. on 6d. black and green			5·00	8·00
	a. Pair, one without handstamp		£375	£375

Beware of forgeries of this handstamp.

Trucial States

The Trucial States consisted of Abu Dhabi, Ajman (with Manama), Dubai, Fujeira, Ras al Khaima, Sharjah and Umm al Qiwain. However the following issue of stamps was only put into use in Dubai, despite the inscription "TRUCIAL STATES".

The first organised postal service in Dubai commenced on 19 August 1909 when an Indian Branch Office, administered from Karachi, was opened, using the unoverprinted stamps of India, principally the ½ a. and 1 a. values.

The initial cancellation was a single-ring type inscribed "DUBAI B.O. PERSIAN GULF", which remained in use until 1933.

1909 Cancellation

Its replacement was of the Indian double-circle type showing a similar inscription.

Dubai was upgraded to Sub-Post Office status on 1 April 1942 and this change was reflected in a new double-ring mark inscribed "DUBAI" only. At the same time the office was provided with a single-ring handstamp which also incorporated a cancelling device of seven wavy lines.

1942 Handstamp

(illustration reduced: actual size 65 × 27 mm)

A further version of the double-ring type appeared in 1946, showing the "PERSIAN GULF" inscription restored to the lower segment of the postmark.

In October 1947 control of the Dubai Post Office passed to Pakistan whose stamps were used there until the end of March 1948.

On 1 April 1948 the post office was transferred, yet again, to British control and Great Britain stamps surcharged for use in the British Postal Agencies in Eastern Arabia were then sold in Dubai until 6 January 1961, being cancelled with British style single and double-ring postmarks.

1 Palms   2 Dhow

(Des M. Goaman. Photo Harrison (T 1). Des M. Farrar-Bell. Recess D.L.R. (T 2))

1961 (7 Jan). *P* 15 × 14 (*T* 1) or 13 × 12½ (*T* 2).

1	1	5 n.p. green	..	..	..	30	10
2		15 n.p. red-brown	..	..	..	30	10
3		20 n.p. bright blue	..	..	..	40	10
4		30 n.p. orange-red	..	..	..	40	10
5		40 n.p. reddish violet	..	..		40	10
6		50 n.p. bistre	..	..	..	40	10
7		75 n.p. grey	..	..	..	60	10
8	2	1 r. green	..	..	..	3·00	50
9		2 r. black	..	..	..	3·00	6·50
10		5 r. carmine-red	..	..	..	4·50	11·00
11		10 r. deep ultramarine	..	..		12·00	20·00
1/11					Set of 11	22·00	35·00

The Dubai Post Department took over the postal services on 14 June 1963. Later issues for Dubai will be found in Part 19 (*Middle East*) of this catalogue.

Turks and Caicos Islands

TURKS ISLANDS

DEPENDENCY OF JAMAICA

A branch of the British Post Office opened at Grand Turk on 11 December 1854 replacing an earlier arrangement under which mail for the islands was sorted by local R.M.S.P. agents.

No. CC1 is known used between 22 October 1857 and 20 April 1862.

GRAND TURK
CROWNED-CIRCLE HANDSTAMPS

CC 1

CC1 CC 1 TURKS-ISLANDS (1857)   *Price on cover £4250*

PRICES FOR STAMPS ON COVER TO 1945	
Nos. 1/5	*from* × 25
No. 6	*from* —
Nos. 7/20	*from* × 25
Nos. 20a/48	
Nos. 49/52	*from* × 4
Nos. 53/7	*from* × 5
Nos. 58/65	*from* × 15
Nos. 66/9	*from* × 5
Nos. 70/2	*from* × 10
Nos. 101/9	*from* × 8
Nos. 110/26	*from* × 6
Nos. 129/39	*from* × 4
Nos. 140/53	*from* × 12
Nos. 154/90	*from* × 3
Nos. 191/3	*from* × 10
Nos. 194/205	*from* × 2

1

(Recess P.B.)

1867 (4 April). *No wmk. P* 11–12.

1	1	1d. dull rose	..	32·00	40·00
2		6d. black	..	70·00	85·00
3		1s. dull blue	..	65·00	55·00

1873–79. *Wmk Small Star. W* w 2 (*sideways on Nos.* 5 *and* 6). *P* 11–12 × 14½–15½.

4	1	1d. dull rose-lake (7.73)	..	40·00	40·00
		a. Wmk sideways	..	75·00	75·00
5		1d. dull red (1.79)	..	48·00	55·00
		a. Imperf between (horiz pair)	..		£9000
		c. Wmk upright	..		60
6		1s. lilac (1.79)	..	£5000	£2000

1881 (1 Jan). *Stamps of the preceding issues surcharged locally, in black.*

There are twelve different settings of the ½d., nine settings of the 2½d., and six settings of the 4d.

(2)   (3)

Setting 1. *T* 2. *Long fraction bar. Two varieties repeated fifteen times in the sheet.*

7	½ on 6d. black	..	60·00	75·00

Setting 2. *T* 3. *Short fraction bar. Three varieties in a vertical strip repeated ten times in sheet.*
Setting 3. *Similar to setting* 2, *but the middle stamp of the three varieties has a longer bar.*

8	½ on 6d. black (*setting* 2 *only*)	..	55·00	
9	½ on 1s. dull blue	..	70·00	£100
	a. Surch double	..		£3750

(4)   (5)   (6)

Three varieties in a vertical strip repeated ten times in sheet.
Section 4.   Types 4, 5, 6.
Setting 5.   Types 4 (*without bar*), 5, 6.
Setting 6.   Types 4, 5, 6 (*without bar*).
Setting 7.   Types 4 (*shorter thick bar*), 6, 6.

10	½ on 1d. dull red (*setting* 7 *only*) (T 6)	..	£1100	
	a. Type 4 (shorter thick bar)		£1800	
11	½ on 1s. dull blue (*setting* 6 *and* 7) (T 4)	..	£550	
	a. Type 4 (shorter thick bar)	..	£550	
	b. Type 5 ..	..	£550	
	c. Type 6	..	£375	
	d. Type 6 (without bar)	..	£550	
	e. Surch double (T 6 without bar)	..		

12	½ on 1s. lilac (T 4)	..	£275	£325
	a. Without bar	..	£450	
	b. With short thick bar	..	£450	
	c. Surch double			
13	½ on 1s. lilac (T 5)	..	£110	£140
	a. Surch double		£1600	
14	½ on 1s. lilac (T 6)	..	£100	
	a. Without bar	..	£475	

(7)   (8)   (9)   (10)

Setting 8. *T* 7. *Three varieties in a vertical strip. All have a very short bar.*

15	½ on 1d. dull red	..	50·00

Setting 9. *T* 8. *Three varieties in a vertical strip. Bars long and thick and* "1" *leaning a little to left.*

16	½ on 1d. dull red	..	£170	£180
	a. Surch double			

Setting 10. *T* 9 *and* 10. *Fifteen varieties repeated twice on a sheet. Ten are of T* 9, *five of T* 10.

17	½ on 1d. dull red (T 9)	..	50·00	60·00
	a. Surch double	..	£2000	
18	½ on 1d. dull red (T 10)	..	75·00	85·00
19	½ on 1s. lilac (T 9)	..	75·00	£100
20	½ on 1s. lilac (T 10)	..	£140	£180
20a	½ on 1s. dull blue (T 9)	..	£6000	

Types 9 *and* 11. The difference is in the position of the "2" in relation to the "1". In setting 10 the "2" is to the left of the "1" except on No. 10 and in setting 11 it is to the right except on No. 2

(11)   (12)   (13)   (14)

Setting 11. *T* 11 *to* 14. *Fifteen varieties repeated twice in a sheet. Ten of T* 11, *three of T* 12, *and one each of T* 13 *and* 14.
Setting 12. *Similar to last, but T* 13 *replaced by another T* 12.

21	½ on 1d. dull red (T 11)	..	70·00
22	½ on 1d. dull red (T 12)	..	£140
23	½ on 1d. dull red (T 13)	..	£1000
24	½ on 1d. dull red (T 14)	..	£325
24a	½ on 1s. dull blue (T 11)	..	£8000

(15)   (16)

Setting 1. *T* 15. *Fraction in very small type.*

25	2½ on 6d. black	..	£6500

Setting 2. *T* 16. *Two varieties repeated fifteen times in a sheet. Large* "2" *on level with top of the* "1", *long thin bar.*

26	2½ on 6d. black	..	£225
	a. Imperf between (pair)	..	£8000
	b. Surch double	..	£4250

(17)   (18)   (19)

Setting 3. *T* 17. *As T* 16, *but large* "2" *not so high up.*

27	2½ on 1s. lilac..	..	£1400

Setting 4. *T* 18. *Three varieties in a vertical strip repeated ten times in sheet. Large* "2" *placed lower and small bar.*

28	2½ on 6d. black	..	£120	£150
	a. Surch double	..		

Setting 5. *T* 19. *Three varieties in a vertical strip repeated ten times in sheet* "2" *further from* "½", *small fraction bar.*

29	2½ on 1s. lilac	..	£550	£650

(20)   (21)

Setting 6. *T* 20 *and* 21. *Fifteen varieties. Ten of T* 20 *and five of T* 21, *repeated twice in a sheet.*

30	2½ on 1s. lilac (T 20)	..	£5500
31	2½ on 1s. lilac (T 21)	..	£8000

(22)   (23)   (24)

Setting 7. T 22. Three varieties in a vertical strip, repeated ten times in a sheet.

32	2½ on 6d. black	..	£7000	
33	2½ on 1s. dull blue ..	..	£7000	

Setting 8. T 23 and 24. Fifteen varieties. Ten of T 23 and five of T 24, repeated twice in a sheet.

34	2½ on 1d. dull red (T 23)	.. ..	..	£550
35	2½ on 1d. dull red (T 24)	.. ..	..	£1000
36	2½ on 1s. lilac (T 23)	..	£500	£550
	a. Surch "½" double	.. ..	..	£2250
37	2½ on 1s. lilac (T 24)	..	£1200	
	a. Surch "½" double	..	£3750	

2 ½ (25)   2 ½ (26)   2 ½ (27)

Setting 9. T 25, 26, and 27. Fifteen varieties. Ten of T 25, three of T 26, one of T 26 without bar, and one of T 27, repeated twice in a sheet.

38	2½ on 1s. dull blue (T 25) ..	..	£550	
39	2½ on 1s. dull blue (T 26)	..	£1600	
40	2½ on 1s. dull blue (T 26) (without bar)	..	£6000	
41	2½ on 1s. dull blue (T 27)	..	£6000	

4 (28)   4 (29)   4 (30)

Setting 1. T 28. "4" 8 mm high, pointed top.

42	4 on 6d. black	..	£250	£300

Settings 2–6. T 29 and 30.

43	4 on 6d. black (T 29)	..	50·00	
44	4 on 6d. black (T 30)	..	£325	£375
45	4 on 1s. lilac (T 29)	..	£375	
	a. Surch double	.. ..		
46	4 on 1s. lilac (T 30)	..	£2000	
	a. Surch double	.. ..		
47	4 on 1d. dull red (T 29)	..	£550	£450
48	4 on 1d. dull red (T 28)	..	£650	£500

The components of these settings can only be distinguished when in blocks. Details are given in the handbook by John J. Challis.

One Penny

31   **(32)**

(Typo D.L.R.)

1881. *Wmk Crown CC (sideways; upright on 4d.). P 14.*

49	1	1d. brown-red (Oct)	..	45·00	55·00
50	31	4d. ultramarine (Die I) (Aug)	..	75·00	60·00
51	1	6d. olive-black (Oct)	..	75·00	£100
52		1s. slate-green (Oct)	..	£100	£100

1882–85. *Wmk Crown CA. P 14.*

53	31	½d. blue-green (Die I) (2.82)	..	6·00	16·00
		a. Pale green (12.85) ..	..	60	3·50
55	1	1d. orange-brown (10.83)	..	42·00	30·00
		a. Bisected (½d.) (on cover)	..	† £1700	
56	31	2½d. red-brown (Die I) (2.82)	..	12·00	13·00
57		4d. grey (Die I) (10.84) ..	..	6·50	2·00
		a. Bisected (2d.) (on cover)	..	† £1500	

1887 (July)**–89.** *Wmk Crown CA. (a) P 12.*

58	1	1d. crimson-lake	..	7·50	2·50
		a. Imperf between (horiz pair) ..		£8000	

(b) P 14

59	1	6d. yellow-brown (2.89) (Optd S. £60)	..	2·00	2·75
60		1s. sepia	..	2·50	2·75

During a shortage of 1d. stamps a supply of JAMAICA No. 27 was sent to the Turks and Caicos Islands in April 1889 and used until replaced by No. 61.

1889 (May). *Surch at Grand Turk with T 32.*

61	31	1d. on 2½d. red-brown	..	4·50	9·50
		a. "ONE" omitted	..		
		b. Bisected (½d.) (on cover)	..	†	

No. 61a was caused by misplacement of the surcharge. Stamps from the same sheet can be found with the surcharge reading "Penny One".

1889–93. *Wmk Crown CA. P 14.*

62	1	1d. crimson-lake (7.89)	..	2·25	3·50
		a. Bisected (½d.) (on cover)	..	†	
63		1d. lake	..	1·25	2·25
		a. Bisected (½d.) (on cover)	..	†	
64		1d. pale rosy lake	..	65	3·75
65	31	2½d. ultram (Die II) (4.93) (Optd S. £55)		1·25	75

NEW INFORMATION

The editor is always interested to correspond with people who have new information that will improve or correct the Catalogue.

(33)   **34**

1893 (July). *No. 57 surch at Grand Turk with T 33.*

Setting 1. Bars between "1d." and "2" separate, instead of continuous across the rows of stamps.

66	½d. on 4d. grey	..	£325	£190

Setting 2. Continuous bars. Thin and thick bar 10¾ mm apart. "2" under the "1".

67	½d. on 4d. grey	..	£120	£120

Setting 3. As last, but bars 11¾ mm apart.

68	½d. on 4d. grey	..	£110	£110

Setting 4. Bars 11 mm apart. Five out of the six varieties in the strip have the "2" below the space between the "1" and "d".

69	½d. on 4d. grey	..	£110	

There is a fifth setting, but the variation is slight.

(Typo D.L.R.)

1894–95. *Wmk Crown CA. P 14.*

70	31	½d. dull green (Die II) (1894) ..		40	85
71		4d. dull purple & ultram (Die II) (5.95)		5·50	11·00
72	34	5d. olive-green and carmine (6.94)		2·25	10·00
		a. Bisected (2½d.) (on cover)		† £2750	
70/2		.. ..	*Set of 3*	7·25	20·00
71/2 Optd "Specimen"		..	*Set of 2*	£100	

TURKS AND CAICOS ISLANDS

35 Badge of the Islands **36**

The dates on the stamps have reference to the political separation from Bahamas.

(Recess D.L.R.)

1900 (10 Nov)**–04.** *Wmk Crown CA (½d. to 1s.) or Wmk Crown CC (2s., 3s.). P 14.*

101	35	½d. green	..	2·50	3·75
102		1d. red ..	..	2·75	75
103		2d. sepia	..	75	1·25
104		2½d. blue	..	4·25	9·50
		a. Greyish blue (1904)	..	90	1·00
105		4d. orange	..	3·50	7·00
106		6d. dull mauve..	..	1·25	5·50
107		1s. purple-brown	..	1·75	11·00
108	36	2s. purple	..	38·00	55·00
109		3s. lake	..	48·00	70·00
101/9 ..		..	*Set of 9*	90·00	£140
101/9 Optd "Specimen"			*Set of 9*	£225	

1905–08. *Wmk Mult Crown CA. P 14.*

110	35	½d. green	..	40	15
111		1d. red ..	..	8·00	50
112		3d. purple/*yellow* (1908) (Optd S. £50)..		90	5·50
110/12			*Set of 3*	8·50	5·50

37 Turk's-head Cactus **38**

(Recess D.L.R.)

1909 (2 Sept)**–11.** *Wmk Mult Crown CA. P 14.*

115	37	¼d. rosy mauve (1910) ..	..	40	1·00
116		¼d. red (1911) ..	..	20	30
117	38	½d. yellow-green	..	30	30
118		1d. red \ ..	..	30	30
119		2d. greyish slate	..	90	1·40
120		2½d. blue ..	..	1·25	3·75
121		3d. purple/*yellow*	..	1·75	2·00
122		4d. red/*yellow*	..	3·00	7·00
123		6d. purple	..	6·00	7·00
124		1s. black/*green*	..	3·00	8·50
125		2s. red/*green*	..	20·00	35·00
126		3s. black/*red*	..	20·00	35·00
115/26			*Set of 12*	50·00	90·00
115/26 Optd "Specimen"			*Set of 12*	£225	

·See also Nos. 154 and 162.

WAR TAX

39   **(40)**

1913 (1 Apr)**–21.** *Wmk Mult Crown CA. P 14.*

129	39	½d. green	..	30	1·00
130		1d. red	..	75	1·10
		a. Bright scarlet	..	1·10	1·75
		b. Rose-carmine (1918)	..	1·25	2·50
131		2d. greyish slate	..	1·10	1·50
132		2½d. ultramarine	..	1·90	2·50
		a. Bright blue (1918)	..	3·00	2·50
133		3d. purple/*yellow*	..	2·25	6·00
		a. On lemon	..	13·00	
		b. On yellow-buff	..	2·50	5·50
		c. On orange-buff	..	70	
		d. On pale yellow	..	1·75	4·00
134		4d. red/*yellow*	..	80	6·50
		a. On orange-buff (Optd S. £48)	..	1·25	6·50
		b. Carmine on pale yellow	..	3·25	10·00
135		5d. pale olive-green (18.5.16)	..	3·50	9·50
136		6d. dull purple	..	2·25	3·25
137		1s. brown-orange	..	1·50	4·00
138		2s. red/*blue-green*	..	6·50	16·00
		a. On greenish white (1919)	..	18·00	55·00
		b. On emerald (3.21) (Optd S. £48)		30·00	55·00
139		3s. black/*red*	..	15·00	25·00
129/39			*Set of 11*	30·00	65·00
129/39 Optd "Specimen"			*Set of 11*	£180	

1917 (3 Jan). *Optd with T 40 at bottom of stamp.*

140	39	1d. red	..	10	60
		a. Overprint double	..	£150	
		b. "TAX" omitted			
		c. "WAR TAX" omitted in vert pair with normal			
		d. Opt inverted at top ..	..	85·00	
		e. Opt double, one inverted*	..	£100	
		f. Opt inverted only, in pair with No. 140e*		£400	
141		3d. purple/*yellow-buff*	..	50	2·25
		a. Opt double	..	42·00	
142		3d. purple/*lemon*	..	1·25	3·50
		a. Opt double ..	..	38·00	
		b. Opt double, one inverted	..	£250	

*In Nos. 140e/f the inverted overprint is at foot and reads "TAX WAR" owing to displacement. No. 140e also exists with "WAR" omitted from the inverted overprint.

In both values of the first printings the stamp in the bottom left-hand corner of the sheet has a long "T" in "TAX", and on the first stamp of the sixth row the "X" is damaged and looks like a reversed "K".

1917 (Oct). *Second printing with overprint at top or in middle of stamp.*

143	39	1d. red	..	10	50
		a. Inverted opt at bottom or centre	..	25·00	
		c. Overprint omitted, in pair with normal	..	£180	
		d. Double overprint, one at top, one at bottom	..	38·00	
		e. As d., but additional overprint in top margin	..	90·00	
		f. Vertical pair, one as d., the other normal	..	£180	
		g. Pair, one overprint inverted, one normal	..	£250	
		h. Double overprint at top (in pair with normal	..	£180	
		i. Overprint double	..	35·00	35·00
144		3d. purple/*yellow*	..	45	1·50
		a. Opt double ..	..	21·00	
		b. Opt double, one inverted	..	£200	
144c		3d. purple/*lemon*	..	80	

1918. *Overprinted with T 40.*

145	39	3d. purple/*yellow* (R.)	..	6·00	16·00
		a. Opt double	..		

WAR   **W A R**   **W A R**

TAX   **T A X**   **TAX**

(41)   **(42)**   **(43)**

1918. *Optd with T 41 in London by D.L.R.*

146	39	1d. rose-carmine	..	20	1·00
		a. Bright rose-scarlet	..	15	90
147		3d. purple/*yellow*	..	20	1·25
146/7 Optd. "Specimen"		..	*Set of 2*	80·00	

1919. *Optd with T 41 in London by D.L.R.*

148	39	3d. purple/*orange-buff* (R.)	..	10	1·25
148 Optd "Specimen"		..	..	40·00	

1919. *Local overprint. T 40, in violet.*

149	39	1d. bright rose-scarlet	..	10	1·25
		a. "WAR" omitted	..	£100	
		b. Opt double	..	17·00	
		c. Opt double in pair with normal	..	£100	
		d. Opt double, one inverted	..		
		e. Rose-carmine ..	..	5·50	8·50
		ea. Opt double			

1919. *Optd with T 42.*

150	39	1d. scarlet	..	10	60
		a. Opt double	..	£100	£100
		b. Opt double, one albino and reversed..			
151		3d. purple/*orange-buff* ..	..	30	1·75

1919 (17 Dec). *Optd with T 43.*

152	39	1d. scarlet	..	10	90
		a. Opt inverted			
153		3d. purple/*orange-buff* ..	..	10	1·00

The two bottom rows of this setting have the words "WAR" and "TAX" about 1 mm further apart.

1921 (23 April). *Wmk Mult Script CA. P* 14.

154	37	¼d. rose-red	..	80	5·50
155	39	½d. green	..	1·10	4·50
156		1d. carmine-red	..	60	3·25
157		2d. slate-grey	..	90	13·00
158		2½d. bright blue	..	1·40	5·50
159		5d. sage-green	..	6·00	26·00
160		6d. purple	..	5·50	28·00
161		1s. brown-orange	..	6·50	20·00
154/161			*Set of* 8	21·00	95·00
154/61 Optd "Specimen"			*Set of* 8	£140	

44   45

(Recess D.L.R.)

1922 (20 Nov)–26. *P* 14. (*a*) *Wmk Mult Script CA.*

162	37	¼d. black (11.10.26)	..	15	50
163	44	½d. yellow-green	..	30	90
		a. Bright green	..	35	85
		b. Apple-green	..	3·00	6·50
164		1d. brown	..	40	3·00
165		1½d. scarlet (24.11.25)	..	2·75	5·50
166		2d. slate	..	40	2·50
167		2½d. purple/*pale yellow*	..	30	60
168		3d. bright blue	..	40	1·50
169		4d. red/*pale yellow*	..	85	5·50
		a. Carmine/*pale yellow*	..	3·25	9·00
170		5d. sage-green	..	65	8·50
171		6d. purple	..	60	2·75
172		1s. brown-orange	..	70	6·00
173		2s. red/*emerald*	..	2·00	4·75

(*b*) *Wmk Mult Crown CA*

174	44	2s. red/*emerald* (24.11.25)	..	16·00	48·00
175		3s. black/*red* (24.11.25)	..	5·00	13·00
162/75			*Set of* 14	27·00	90·00
162/75 Optd "Specimen"			*Set of* 14	£200	

1928 (1 Mar). *Inscr* "POSTAGE & REVENUE". *Wmk Mult Script CA. P* 14.

176	45	½d. green	..	50	40
177		1d. brown	..	50	70
178		1½d. scarlet	..	40	1·25
179		2d. grey	..	35	30
180		2½d. purple/*yellow*	..	35	1·25
181		3d. bright blue	..	45	2·00
182		6d. purple	..	45	3·25
183		1s. brown-orange	..	3·00	3·75
184		2s. red/*emerald*	..	3·50	20·00
185		5s. green/*yellow*	..	11·00	30·00
186		10s. purple/*blue*	..	40·00	80·00
176/86			*Set of* 11	55·00	£130
176/86 Optd "Specimen"			*Set of* 11	£140	

1935 (6 May). *Silver Jubilee. As Nos.* 114/17 *of Jamaica, but ptd by Waterlow. P* 11×12.

187		½d. black and green	..	15	40
		j. Kite and vertical log	..	22·00	
		k. Kite and horizontal log	..	22·00	
188		3d. brown and deep blue	..	1·50	2·00
		j. Kite and vertical log	..	55·00	
189		6d. light blue and olive-green	..	1·50	2·50
		j. Kite and vertical log	..	55·00	
190		1s. slate and purple	..	1·50	3·25
		j. Kite and vertical log	..	55·00	
187/90			*Set of* 4	4·25	7·50
187/90 Perf "Specimen"			*Set of* 4	75·00	

For illustrations of plate varieties see Omnibus section following Zimbabwe.

1937 (12 May). *Coronation. As Nos.* 118/20 *of Jamaica.*

191		½d. myrtle-green	..	10	10
		a. Deep green	..		
192		2d. grey-black	..	60	30
193		3d. bright blue	..	80	30
191/3			*Set of* 3	1·40	60
191/3 Perf "Specimen"			*Set of* 3	55·00	

46 Raking Salt   47 Salt Industry

(Recess Waterlow)

1938 (18 June)–45. *Wmk Mult Script CA. P* 12½.

194	46	¼d. black	..	10	10
195		½d. yellowish green	..	1·75	15
		a. Deep green (6.11.44)	..	20	60
196		1d. red-brown	..	20	10
197		1½d. scarlet	..	30	15
198		2d. grey	..	40	30
199		2½d. yellow-orange	..	2·25	60
		a. Orange (6.11.44)	..	1·20	75
200		3d. bright blue	..	30	30
201		6d. mauve	..	6·50	1·25
201*a*		6d. sepia (9.2.45)	..	15	20
202		1s. yellow-bistre	..	2·50	6·50
202*a*		1s. grey-olive (9.2.45)	..	15	20

203	47	2s. deep rose-carmine	..	29·00	8·00
		a. Bright rose-carmine (6.11.44)	..	15·00	9·00
204		5s. yellowish green	..	40·00	12·00
		a. Deep green (6.11.44)	..	28·00	12·00
205		10s. bright violet	..	5·00	5·00
194/205			*Set of* 14	55·00	30·00
194/205 Perf "Specimen"			*Set of* 14	£200	

1946 (4 Nov). *Victory. As Nos.* 141/2 *of Jamaica.*

206		2d. black	..	10	10
207		3d. blue	..	15	10
206/7 Perf "Specimen"			*Set of* 2	50·00	

1948 (13 Sept). *Royal Silver Wedding. As Nos.* 143/4 *of Jamaica.*

208		1d. red-brown	..	15	10
209		10s. mauve	..	5·00	6·00

50 Badge of the Islands   53 Queen Victoria and King George VI

(Recess Waterlow)

1948 (14 Dec). *Centenary of Separation from Bahamas. T* 50, 53 *and similar designs. Wmk Mult Script CA. P* 12½.

210	50	½d. blue-green	..	15	15
211		2d. carmine	..	30	15
212	—	3d. blue	..	35	15
213	—	6d. violet	..	30	20
214	53	2s. black and bright blue	..	35	35
215		5s. black and green	..	90	60
216		10s. black and brown	..	90	3·00
210/16			*Set of* 7	3·00	4·25

Designs: *Horiz*—3d. Flag of Turks and Caicos Islands; 6d. Map of islands.

1949 (10 Oct). *75th Anniv of U.P.U. As Nos.* 145/8 *of Jamaica.*

217		2½d. red-orange	..	40	55
218		3d. deep blue	..	50	50
219		6d. brown	..	50	50
220		1s. olive	..	50	35
217/20			*Set of* 4	1·75	1·75

65 Bulk Salt Loading

66 Dependency's Badge

(Recess Waterlow)

1950 (1 Aug). *T* 65 *and similar horiz designs, and T* 66. *Wmk Mult Script CA. P* 12½.

221		½d. green	..	15	40
222		1d. red-brown	..	15	75
223		1½d. deep carmine	..	20	55
224		2d. red-orange	..	15	40
225		2½d. grey-olive	..	20	50
226		3d. bright blue	..	20	40
227		4d. black and rose	..	2·00	70
228		6d. black and blue	..	1·25	50
229		1s. black and blue-green	..	55	40
230		1s. 6d. black and scarlet	..	2·25	3·25
231		2s. emerald and ultramarine	..	1·50	3·50
232		5s. blue and black	..	7·00	3·75
233		10s. black and violet	..	14·00	13·00
221/33			*Set of* 13	26·00	25·00

Designs:—1d. Salt Cay; 1½d. Caicos mail; 2d. Grand Turk; 2½d. Sponge diving; 3d. South Creek; 4d. Map; 6d. Grand Turk Light; 1s. Government House; 1s. 6d. Cockburn Harbour; 2s. Government Offices; 5s. Loading salt.

1953 (2 June). *Coronation. As No.* 153 *of Jamaica, but ptd by B.W. & Co.*

234		2d. black and orange-red	..	15	80

67 M.V. *Kirksons*

(Recess Waterlow)

1955 (1 Feb). *T* 67 *and similar horiz design. Wmk Mult Script CA. P* 12½.

235		5d. black and bright green	..	30	30
236		8d. black and brown	..	1·25	20

Design:—8d. Greater Flamingoes in flight.

69 Queen Elizabeth II   70 Bonefish
(after Annigoni)

82 Dependency's Badge

(Recess B.W.)

1957 (25 Nov). *T* 69/70, 82 *and similar horiz designs as T* 70. W w 12. *P* 13½×14 (1d.), 14 (10s.) *or* 13½ (*others*).

237		1d. deep blue and carmine	..	15	20
238		1½d. grey-green and orange	..	15	30
239		2d. red-brown and olive	..	15	15
240		2½d. carmine and green	..	15	15
241		3d. turquoise-blue and purple	..	15	15
242		4d. lake and black	..	20	15
243		5d. slate-green and brown	..	30	40
244		6d. carmine-rose and blue	..	1·00	30
245		8d. vermilion and black	..	2·75	20
246		1s. deep blue and black	..	30	10
247		1s. 6d. sepia and deep ultramarine	..	1·75	50
248		2s. deep ultramarine and brown	..	3·25	2·25
249		5s. black and carmine	..	75	2·00
250		10s. black and purple	..	9·00	8·00
237/250 and 253			*Set of* 15	45·00	27·00

Designs:—2d. Red Grouper; 2½d. Spiny Lobster; 3d. Albacore; 4d. Muttonfish Snapper; 5d. Permit; 6d. Conch; 8d. Greater Flamingoes; 1s. Spanish Mackerel; 1s. 6d. Salt Cay; 2s. *Uakon* (Caicos sloop); 5s. Cable Office.

83 Map of the Turks and Caicos Islands

(Photo D.L.R.)

1959 (4 July). *New Constitution. Wmk Mult Script CA. P* 13½ × 14.

251	83	6d. deep olive and light orange	..	25	15
252		8d. violet and light orange	..	25	15

84 Brown Pelican

(Des Mrs. S. Hurd. Photo Harrison)

1960 (1 Nov). W w 12. *P* 14 × 14½.

253	84	£1 sepia and deep red	..	30·00	16·00

CROWN COLONY

1963 (4 June). *Freedom from Hunger. As No.* 80 *of Lesotho.*

254		8d. carmine	..	30	10

1963 (2 Sept). *Red Cross Centenary. As Nos.* 203/4 *of Jamaica.*

255		2d. red and black	..	15	15
256		8d. red and blue	..	30	25

1964 (23 Apr). *400th Birth Anniv of William Shakespeare. As No.* 156 *of Montserrat.*

257		8d. green	..	10	10

1965 (17 May). *I.T.U. Centenary. As Nos.* 98/9 *of Lesotho.*

258		1d. vermilion and brown	..	10	10
259		2s. light emerald and turquoise-blue	..	20	20

1965 (25 Oct). *International Co-operation Year. As Nos.* 100/1 *of Lesotho.*

260		1s. reddish purple and turquoise-green	..	10	15
261		8d. deep bluish green and lavender	..	20	15

1966 (24 Jan). *Churchill Commemoration. As Nos.* 102/5 *of Lesotho.*

262		1d. new blue	..	10	10
263		2d. deep green	..	15	10
264		8d. brown	..	15	10
		a. Gold ptg double	..	£130	
265		1s. 6d. bluish violet	..	25	35
262/5			*Set of* 4	50	45

1966 (4 Feb). *Royal Visit. As Nos.* 183/4 *of Montserrat.*

266		8d. black and ultramarine	..	25	10
267		8d. black and magenta	..	45	20

85 Andrew Symmer going ashore

(Des V. Whiteley. Photo D.L.R.)

1966 (1 Oct). *Bicentenary of "Ties with Britain"* T **85** *and similar horiz designs. P* 13½.

268	1d. deep blue and orange	..		10	10
269	8d. red, blue and orange-yellow	..		10	10
270	1s. 6d. multicoloured		..	15	15
268/70			*Set of* 3	30	30

Designs:—8d. Andrew Symmer and Royal Warrant; 1s. 6d. Arms and Royal Cypher.

1966 (1 Dec). *20th Anniv of U.N.E.S.C.O. As Nos.* 342/4 *of Mauritius.*

271	1d. slate-violet, red, yellow and orange		10	10
272	8d. orange-yellow, violet and deep olive		15	10
273	1s. 6d. black, bright purple and orange		20	40
271/3	..	*Set of* 3	35	50

88 Turk's-head Cactus   89 Boat-building

90 Arms of Turks and Caicos Islands   91 Queen Elizabeth II

(Des V. Whiteley. Photo Harrison)

1967 (1 Feb). *Designs as* T **88/91**. W w **12**. P 14½ × 14 (*vert*) *or* 14 × 14½ (*horiz*).

274	1d. olive-yellow, vermilion & brt bluish vio		10	10
275	1½d. brown and orange-yellow		10	10
276	2d. deep slate and deep orange-yellow		15	10
277	3d. agate and dull green		20	10
278	4d. bright mauve, black and turquoise		30	10
279	6d. sepia and new blue		30	10
280	8d. yellow, turquoise-blue and deep blue		20	10
281	1s. maroon and turquoise		20	10
282	1s. 6d. orange-yellow, lake-brn & dp turq-bl		50	20
283	2s. multicoloured		60	1·00
284	3s. maroon and turquoise-blue		55	40
285	5s. ochre, blue and new blue		1·25	2·00
286	10s. multicoloured		1·75	2·50
287	£1 Prussian blue, silver and crimson		3·25	5·00
274/287		*Set of* 14	8·25	10·50

Designs: *Vert as* T **88**—2d. Donkey; 3d. Sisal industry; 6d. Salt industry; 8d. Skin-diving; 1s. 6d. Water-skiing. *Horiz as* T **89**—4d. Conch industry; 1s. Fishing; 2s. Crawfish industry; 3s. Maps of Turks and Caicos Islands and West Indies; 5s. Fishing industry.

102 Turks Islands 1d. Stamp of 1867

(Des R. Granger Barrett. Photo Harrison)

1967 (1 May). *Stamp Centenary.* T **102** *and similar horiz designs.* W w **12**. P 14½.

288	1d. black and light magenta	..		10	10
289	8d. black and bluish grey			15	10
290	1s. black and turquoise-blue			15	10
288/90			*Set of* 3	30	20

Designs:—6d. Queen Elizabeth "stamp" and Turks Islands 6d. stamp of 1867; 1s. Turks Islands 1s. stamp of 1867.

104 Human Rights Emblem and Charter

(Des R. Granger Barrett. Photo Harrison)

1968 (1 Apr). *Human Rights Year.* W w **12**. P 14 × 14½.

291	**104**	1d. multicoloured	..	10	10
292		8d. multicoloured		15	10
293		1s. 6d. multicoloured		15	10
291/3		..	*Set of* 3	30	20

105 Dr Martin Luther King and "Freedom March"

(Des V. Whiteley. Photo Harrison)

1968 (1 Oct). *Martin Luther King Commemoration.* W w **12**. P 14 × 14½.

294	**105**	2d. yellow-brown, blackish brn & dp bl	10	10
295		8d. yellow-brown, blackish brn & lake	15	10
296		1s. 6d. yellow-brn, blackish brn & vio	15	10
294/6		..	*Set of* 3	30	20

(New Currency. 100 cents=1 dollar)

(106)   107 "The Nativity with John the Baptist"

1969 (8 Sept)–71. *Decimal currency. Nos.* 274/87 *surch as* T **106** *by Harrison & Sons, and new value* (¼ c.) *as* T **90**.

297	¼ c. pale greenish grey and multicoloured		10	10
	a. Bronze-green & multicoloured (2.2.71)		50	30
298	1 c. on 1d. olive-yell, verm & brt bluish vio		10	10
	a. Wmk sideways		10	10
299	2 c. on 2d. deep slate & deep orange-yellow		10	10
	a. Wmk sideways		10	10
300	3 c. on 3d. agate and dull green		10	10
	a. Wmk sideways		10	10
301	4 c. on 4d. bright mauve, black & turquoise		10	10
302	5 c. on 6d. sepia and new blue		10	10
	a. Wmk sideways		10	10
303	7 c. on 8d. yellow, turquoise-blue & dp blue		10	10
	a. Wmk sideways		10	10
304	8 c. on 1½d. brown and orange-yellow		10	10
305	10 c. on 1s. maroon and turquoise		20	10
306	15 c. on 1s. 6d. orange-yellow, lake-brown			
	and deep turquoise-blue		25	10
	a. Wmk sideways		20	25
307	20 c. on 2s. multicoloured		30	25
308	30 c. on 3s. maroon and turquoise-blue		55	35
309	50 c. on 5s. ochre, blue and new blue		1·00	45
310	$1 on 10s. multicoloured		1·50	1·00
311	$2 on £1 Prussian blue, silver and crimson		4·00	10·00
	a. Wmk sideways		1·50	3·00
297/311		*Set of* 15	7·50	11·50
298a/311a		*Set of* 7	2·50	

The 4, 8, 10, 20, 30, 50 c., and $1 exist with PVA gum as well as gum arabic.

No. 311 was only on sale through the Crown Agents.

(Des adapted by V. Whiteley. Litho D.L.R.)

1969 (20 Oct). *Christmas. Scenes from 16th-cent Book of Hours.* T **107** *and similar vert design. Multicoloured.* W w **12**. P 13 × 12½.

312	1 c. Type **107**	..		10	10
313	3 c. "The Flight into Egypt"	..		10	10
314	15 c. Type **107**	..		15	10
315	30 c. As 3 c.		..	25	10
312/15		..	*Set of* 4	40	30

109 Coat of Arms   110 "Christ bearing the Cross"

(Des L. Curtis. Litho B.W.)

1970 (2 Feb). *New Constitution. Multicoloured; background colours given.* W w **12** (*sideways*). P 13 × 12½.

316	**109**	7 c. brown		20	10
317		35 c. deep violet-blue		35	20

For similar $10 design, but without commemorative inscription, see No. 946.

(Des, recess and litho Enschedé)

1970 (17 Mar). *Easter. Details from the "Small Engraved Passion" by Dürer.* T **110** *and similar vert designs.* W w **12** (*sideways*). P 13 × 13½.

318	5 c. olive-grey and blue	..		10	10
319	7 c. olive-grey and vermilion.	..		10	10
320	50 c. olive-grey and red-brown		..	40	30
318/20			*Set of* 3	50	40

Designs:—7 c. "Christ on the Cross"; 50 c. "The Lamentation of Christ".

113 Dickens and Scene from *Oliver Twist*

(Des Sylvia Goaman. Recess and litho D.L.R.)

1970 (17 June). *Death Centenary of Charles Dickens.* T **113** *and similar horiz designs.* W w **12** (*sideways*). P 13.

321	1 c. black and yellow-brown/*yellow*		10	10
322	3 c. black and Prussian blue/*flesh*		10	10
323	15 c. black and grey-blue/*flesh*		20	10
324	30 c. black and drab/*blue*		40	40
321/4		*Set of* 4	60	60

Designs (each incorporating portrait of Dickens as in T **113**, and a scene from one of his novels):—3 c. *A Christmas Carol*; 15 c. *Pickwick Papers*; 30 c. *The Old Curiosity Shop.*

114 Ambulance—1870

(Des Harrison. Litho B.W.)

1970 (4 Aug). *Centenary of British Red Cross.* T **114** *and similar horiz design. Multicoloured.* W w **12**. P 13½ × 14.

325	1 c. Type **114**	..		10	10
326	5 c. Ambulance—1970			10	10
	a. Wmk sideways			15	10
	ab. Grey omitted			£250	
327	15 c. Type **114**			20	10
	a. Wmk sideways			30	10
328	30 c. As 5 c.			30	10
	a. Wmk sideways			45	40
325/8		..	*Set of* 4	55	30

115 Duke of Albermarle and Coat of Arms

(Des V. Whiteley. Litho Enschedé)

1970 (1 Dec). *Tercentenary of Issue of Letters Patent.* T **115** *and similar horiz design. Multicoloured.* W w **12**. P 12½ × 13½.

329	1 c. Type **115**			20	20
330	8 c. Arms of Charles II and Elizabeth II	..	20	20
331	10 c. Type **115**			20	15
332	35 c. As 8 c.			40	65
329/32			*Set of* 4	75	1·00

116 Boat-building   117 Seahorse

1971 (2 Feb). *Designs as* T **88/91** *etc., but inscr in decimal currency as in* T **116**. W w **12** (*sideways on* 1 c., 2 c., 3 c., 5 c., 7 c., 15 c. *and* $2).

333	1 c. olive-yell, verm & brt bluish vio (as 1d.)		10	10
334	2 c. deep slate & deep orange-yell (as 2d.)		10	10
335	3 c. agate and dull green (as 3d.)		15	10
336	4 c. bright mauve, black & turquoise (as 4d.)		50	10
337	5 c. sepia and new blue (as 6d.)		30	10
338	7 c. yellow, turquoise-blue & dp blue (as 8d.)		30	10
339	8 c. brown and orange-yellow		50	10
340	10 c. maroon and turquoise (as 1s.)		50	10
341	15 c. orange-yellow, lake-brown and deep			
	turquoise-blue (as 1s. 6d.)		1·00	50
342	20 c. multicoloured (as 2s.)		1·25	1·50
343	30 c. maroon and turquoise-blue (as 3s.)		1·75	90

344	50 c. ochre, blue and new blue (as 5s.)	2·50	2·00
345	$1 multicoloured (as 10s.)	2·75	3·00
	a. Green omitted		
346	$2 Prussian blue, silver and crimson (as £1)	4·00	7·50
333/46	Set of 14	14·00	14·00

The ¼ c. value was also re-issued and is listed as No. 297a.

(Des G. Vasarhelyi. Litho J.W.)

1971 (4 May). *Tourist Development. T* **117** *and similar multicoloured designs. W w* **12** (*sideways on Nos.* 348/50). *P* 14 × 14½ (1 c.) *or* 14½ × 14 (*others*).

347	1 c. Type 117	10	10
348	3 c. Queen Conch Shell (*horiz*)	10	10
349	15 c. Oystercatcher (*horiz*)	30	10
350	30 c. Blue Marlin (*horiz*)	30	15
347/50	Set of 4	60	30

118 Pirate Sloop   119 The Wilton Diptych (Left Wing)

(Des and litho J.W.)

1971 (27 July). *Pirates. T* **118** *and similar horiz designs. Multicoloured. W w* **12** (*sideways*). *P* 14.

351	2 c. Type 118	10	10
352	3 c. Pirate treasure	10	10
353	15 c. Marooned sailor	45	15
354	30 c. Buccaneers	70	45
351/4	Set of 4	1·25	70

(Des J.W. Litho Questa)

1971 (12 Oct). *Christmas. T* **119** *and similar vert design. Multicoloured. W w* **12**. *P* 13½.

355	2 c. Type 119	10	10
	a. Horiz pair. Nos. 355/6	10	10
356	2 c. The Wilton Diptych (Right Wing)	10	10
357	8 c. Type 119	20	10
	a. Horiz pair. Nos. 357/8	10	10
358	8 c. As No. 356	20	10
359	15 c. Type 119	40	20
	a. Horiz pair. Nos. 359/60	20	10
360	15 c. As No. 356	20	10
355/60	Set of 6	65	35

The two stamps of each denomination were printed in horizontal se-tenant pairs throughout the sheet.

120 Cape Kennedy Launching Area   121 "Christ before Pilate" (Rembrandt)

(Des V. Whiteley. Litho A. & M.)

1972 (21 Feb). *Tenth Anniv of Colonel Glenn's Splashdown. T* **120** *and similar multicoloured designs. W w* **12** (*sideways on 5, 10 and 15 c.*). *P* 13½.

361	5 c. Type 120	10	10
362	10 c. "Friendship 7" space capsule	10	10
363	15 c. Map of Islands and splashdown	15	10
364	20 c. N.A.S.A. Space Medal (*vert*)	15	10
361/4	Set of 4	40	30

(Des and litho J.W.)

1972 (21 Mar). *Easter. T* **121** *and similar designs. W w* **12** (*sideways on 15 c.*). *P* 13½.

365	2 c. black and lilac	10	10
366	15 c. black and rose-pink	15	10
367	30 c. black and greenish yellow	25	15
365/7	Set of 3	40	30

Designs: *Horiz*—15 c. "The Three Crosses" (Rembrandt). *Vert*—30 c. "The Descent from the Cross" (Rembrandt).

122 Christopher Columbus   123 Turk's-head Cactus and Spiny Lobster

(Des P. Powell. Litho J.W.)

1972 (28 July*). *Discoverers and Explorers. T* **122** *and similar multicoloured designs. W w* **12** (*sideways on 8 and 30 c.*). *P* 13½.

368	¼ c. Type 122		
369	8 c. Sir Richard Grenville (*horiz*)	30	10
370	10 c. Capt. John Smith	35	10
371	30 c. Juan Ponce de Leon (*horiz*)	85	75
368/71	Set of 4	1·40	75

*This was the local date of issue; the Crown Agents released the stamps on 4 July.

(Des (from photograph by D. Groves) and photo Harrison)

1972 (20 Nov). *Royal Silver Wedding. Multicoloured; background colour given. W w* **12**. *P* 14 × 14½.

372	**123** 10 c. dull ultramarine	10	10
373	20 c. myrtle-green	15	10

124 Treasure Hunting, circa 1700   125 Arms of Jamaica and Turks & Caicos Islands

(Des C. Abbott. Litho Questa)

1973 (18 Jan). *Treasure. T* **124** *and similar vert designs. W w* **12** (*sideways*). *P* 14 × 14½.

374	3 c. multicoloured	10	10
375	5 c. reddish purple, silver and black	10	10
376	10 c. magenta, silver and black	20	10
377	30 c. multicoloured	60	30
374/7	Set of 4	85	35
MS378	127 × 108 mm. Nos. 374/7.	1·50	2·00

Designs:—5 c. Silver Bank medallion (obverse); 10 c. Silver Bank medallion (reverse); 30 c. Treasure hunting, 1973.

(Des PAD Studio. Litho Walsall)

1973 (16 Apr). *Centenary of Annexation to Jamaica. W w* **12** (*sideways*). *P* 13½ × 14.

379	**125** 15 c. multicoloured	30	10
380	35 c. multicoloured	60	20

126 Sooty Tern   127 Bermuda Sloop

(Des R. Granger Barrett. Litho Questa)

1973 (1 Aug). *T* **126** *and similar vert designs. W w* **12** (*sideways*). *P* 14.

381	¼ c. Type 126	10	20
382	1 c. Magnificent Frigate Bird	20	40
383	2 c. Common Noddy	30	40
384	3 c. Blue-grey Gnatcatcher	85	40
385	4 c. Little Blue Heron	35	65
386	5 c. Catbird	30	30
387	7 c. Black-whiskered Vireo	3·25	30
388	8 c. Osprey	4·25	85
389	10 c. Greater Flamingo	70	50
390	15 c. Brown Pelican	1·25	50
391	20 c. Parula Warbler	3·50	1·25
392	30 c. Northern Mockingbird	1·75	90
393	50 c. Ruby-throated Hummingbird	3·25	3·00
394	$1 Bananaquit	3·50	4·00
395	$2 Cedar Waxwing	5·50	5·50
381/95	Set of 15	26·00	17·00

See also Nos. 411/14 and 451/64.

(Des R. Granger Barrett. Litho Questa)

1973 (14 Aug). *Vessels. T* **127** *and similar horiz designs. Multicoloured. W w* **12**. *P* 13½.

396	2 c. Type 127	15	10
397	5 c. H.M.S. *Blanche*	25	10

398	8 c. U.S. privateer *Grand Turk* and P.O. packet *Hinchinbrooke*	30	15
399	10 c. H.M.S. *Endymion*	30	15
400	15 c. R.M.S. *Medina*	35	70
401	20 c. H.M.S. *Daring*	45	75
396/401	Set of 6	1·60	1·75
MS402	198 ×101 mm. Nos. 396/401	1·60	2·75

1973 (14 Nov). *Royal Wedding. As Nos. 322/3 of Montserrat.*

403	12 c. light turquoise-blue	10	10
404	18 c. dull indigo	10	10

128 Duho (stool)

(Des Jennifer Toombs. Litho Questa)

1974 (17 July). *Lucayan Remains. T* **128** *and similar horiz designs. Multicoloured. W w* **12** (*sideways*). *P* 14½ × 14.

405	6 c. Type 128	10	10
406	10 c. Broken wood bowl	15	10
407	12 c. Greenstone axe	15	10
408	18 c. Wood bowl	15	10
409	35 c. Fragment of duho	20	20
405/9	Set of 5	65	40
MS410	240 × 90 mm. Nos. 405/9	75	1·25

1974–75. *As Nos. 381 etc, but W w* **12** (*upright*).

411	1 c. Magnificent Frigate Bird (11.6.75)	85	1·25
412	2 c. Common Noddy (27.9.74)	1·50	1·00
413	3 c. Blue-grey Gnatcatcher (19.3.75)	3·25	1·00
414	20 c. Parula Warbler (11.6.75)	2·75	3·50
411/14	Set of 4	7·50	6·00

Nos. 415/25 vacant.

129 G.P.O., Grand Turk

(Des G. Drummond. Litho Questa)

1974 (9 Oct). *Centenary of Universal Postal Union. T* **129** *and similar horiz designs. Multicoloured. W w* **12**. *P* 14.

426	4 c. Type 129	10	10
427	12 c. Sloop and island map	20	10
428	18 c. "U.P.U." and globe	20	10
429	55 c. Posthorn and emblem	35	35
426/9	Set of 4	75	55

130 Churchill and Roosevelt   131 Spanish Captain, circa 1492

(Des V. Whiteley. Litho Questa)

1974 (30 Nov). *Birth Centenary of Sir Winston Churchill. T* **130** *and similar horiz design. Multicoloured. W w* **14** (*sideways*). *P* 14.

430	12 c. Type 130	15	15
431	18 c. Churchill and vapour-trails	15	15
MS432	85 × 85 mm. Nos. 430/1	40	55

(Des J.W. Litho Questa)

1975 (26 Mar). *Military Uniforms. T* **131** *and similar vert designs. Multicoloured. W w* **14**. *P* 14.

433	5 c. Type 131	10	10
434	20 c. Officer, Royal Artillery, 1783	30	15
435	25 c. Officer, 67th Foot, 1798	35	15
436	35 c. Private, 1st West India Regt, 1833	45	25
433/6	Set of 4	1·10	50
MS437	145 × 88 mm. Nos. 433/6	1·25	2·00

132 Ancient Windmill, Salt Cay   133 Star Coral

(Des P. Powell. Litho Questa)

1975 (16 Oct). *Salt-raking Industry. T* **132** *and similar multi-coloured designs.* W w **12** *(sideways on 10 and 20 c.).* P 14.

438	6 c. Type **132**		15	10
439	10 c. Salt pans drying in sun *(horiz)*		15	10
440	20 c. Salt-raking *(horiz)*		25	15
441	25 c. Unprocessed salt heaps		30	20
438/41		*Set of 4*	75	40

(Des C. Abbott. Litho Questa)

1975 (4 Dec). *Island Coral. T* **133** *and similar horiz designs. Multicoloured.* W w **14** *(sideways).* P 14.

442	6 c. Type **133**		15	10
443	10 c. Elkhorn Coral		20	10
444	20 c. Brain Coral		35	15
445	25 c. Staghorn Coral		40	20
442/5		*Set of 4*	1·00	40

134 American Schooner | 135 1s. 6d. Royal Visit Stamp of 1966

(Des J.W. Litho Questa)

1976 (28 May). *Bicentenary of American Revolution. T* **134** *and similar vert designs. Multicoloured.* W w **14.** P 13½.

446	6 c. Type **134**		30	10
447	20 c. British ship of the line		60	15
448	25 c. American privateer *Grand Turk*		60	20
449	55 c. British ketch		1·00	60
446/9		*Set of 4*	2·25	95
MS450	95 × 151 mm. Nos. 446/9		2·25	4·50

Each value depicts, at the top, the engagement between the *Grand Turk* and the P.O. Packet *Hinchinbrooke*, as in T **134**.

1976–77. *As Nos. 381/95, and new value ($5), but* W w **14** *(upright).*

451	¼ c. Type **126** (12.77)		55	1·50
452	1 c. Magnificent Frigate Bird (12.77)		55	75
453	2 c. Common Noddy (12.77)		55	1·50
454	3 c. Blue-grey Gnatcatcher (14.6.76)		90	55
455	4 c. Little Blue Heron (12.77)		1·00	1·00
456	5 c. Catbird (12.77)		1·00	1·25
457	10 c. Greater Flamingo (12.77)		1·25	1·50
458	15 c. Brown Pelican (12.77)		1·25	2·00
459	20 c. Parula Warbler (30.11.76)		1·50	75
460	30 c. Northern Mockingbird (12.77)		1·25	2·25
461	50 c. Ruby-throated Hummingbird (12.77)		1·50	2·25
462	$1 Bananaquit (12.77)		2·25	2·75
463	$2 Cedar Waxwing (12.77)		3·75	4·50
464	$5 Painted Bunting (24.11.76)		3·50	4·00
451/64		*Set of 14*	18·00	24·00

No. 465 vacant.

(Des V. Whiteley Studio. Litho Walsall)

1976 (14 July). *Tenth Anniv of Royal Visit. T* **135** *and similar horiz design. Multicoloured.* W w **14** *(sideways).* P 14½ × 14.

466	20 c. Type **135**		50	30
467	25 c. 8d. Royal Visit stamp		60	30

136 "The Virgin and Child with Flowers" (C. Dolci) | 137 Balcony Scene, Buckingham Palace

(Des G. Drummond. Litho Questa)

1976 (10 Nov). *Christmas. T* **136** *and similar vert designs. Multi-coloured.* W w **14.** P 13½.

468	6 c. Type **136**		10	10
469	10 c. "Virgin and Child with St. John and an Angel" (Studio of Botticelli)		10	10
470	20 c. "Adoration of the Magi" (Master of Paraiso)		30	15
471	25 c. "Adoration of the Magi" (French miniature)		30	20
468/71		*Set of 4*	65	35

(Des J.W. (MS475), C. Abbott (others) Litho Questa)

1977 (7 Feb–6 Dec). *Silver Jubilee. T* **137** *and similar vert designs. Multicoloured.* W w **14.** P 14 × 13½ (MS475) or 13½ (others).

472	6 c. Queen presenting O.B.E. to E. T. Wood		10	10
473	25 c. The Queen with regalia		20	25
474	55 c. Type **137**		40	55
472/4		*Set of 3*	60	75
MS475	120 × 97 mm. $5 Queen Elizabeth II (6.12.77)		1·00	1·40

138 Col. Glenn's "Mercury" Capsule | 139 "Flight of the Holy Family" (Rubens)

(Des and litho J.W.)

1977 (20 June). *25th Anniv of U.S. Tracking Station. T* **138** *and similar multicoloured designs.* W w **14** *(sideways on horiz designs).* P 13½.

476	1 c. Type **138**		10	10
477	3 c. Moon buggy "Rover" *(vert)*		10	10
478	6 c. Tracking Station, Grand Turk		10	10
479	20 c. Moon landing craft *(vert)*		15	15
480	25 c. Col. Glenn's rocket launch *(vert)*		20	20
481	50 c. "Telstar 1" satellite		30	40
476/81		*Set of 6*	70	80

(Des J.W. Litho Questa)

1977 (23 Dec). *Christmas and 400th Birth Anniv of Rubens. T* **139** *and similar vert designs. Multicoloured.* P 14.

482	¼ c. Type **139**		10	10
483	½ c. "Adoration of the Magi" (1634)		10	10
484	1 c. "Adoration of the Magi" (1624)		10	10
485	6 c. "Virgin within Garland"		10	10
486	20 c. "Madonna and Child Adored by Angels"		15	10
487	$2 "Adoration of the Magi" (1618)		1·25	1·25
482/7		*Set of 6*	1·40	1·25
MS488	100 × 81 mm. $1 detail of 20 c.		60	1·00

140 Map of Passage

(Des R. Granger Barrett. Litho J.W.)

1978 (2 Feb). *Turks Islands Passage. T* **140** *and similar horiz designs. Multicoloured.* P 13½. A. *No wmk.* B. W w **14** *(sideways).*

		A		B	
489	6 c. Type **140**	10	10	10	10
490	20 c. Caicos sloop passing Grand Turk Lighthouse	35	55	35	55
491	25 c. Motor cruiser	40	65	40	65
492	55 c. *Jamaica Planter* (freighter)	85	1·60	85	1·60
489/92	*Set of 4*	1·50	2·50	1·50	2·50
MS493	136 × 88 mm. Nos. 489/92. P 14½	1·50	2·25	55·00	—

141 "Queen Victoria" (Sir George Hayter) | 142 Ampulla and Anointing Spoon

(Manufactured by Walsall (Nos. 499/501). Des PAD Studio. Litho Questa (others))

1978 (2 June–July). *25th Anniv of Coronation. Multicoloured.*

(a) *Sheet stamps. Vert designs as T* **141** *showing British monarchs in coronation robes.* P 14

494	6 c. Type **141**		10	10
495	10 c. "King Edward VII" (Sir Samuel Fildes)		10	10
496	25 c. King George V		20	15
497	$2 King George VI		75	1·00
494/7		*Set of 4*	1·00	1·10
MS498	161 × 113 mm. $2.50, Queen Elizabeth II		1·00	1·00

(b) *Booklet stamps. Vert designs as T* **142.** *Imperf × roul 5*. Self-adhesive* (July)

499	15 c. Type **142**		15	30
	a. Booklet pane. Nos. 499/501		1·90	
	b. Booklet pane. Nos. 499/500, each × 3		1·25	
500	25 c. St. Edward's Crown		15	30
501	$2 Queen Elizabeth II in coronation robes		1·75	2·75
499/501		*Set of 3*	1·90	3·00

Nos. 494/7 also exist perf 12 (*Price for set of 4 £1 mint or used*) from additional sheetlets of 3 stamps and 1 label. Stamps perforated 14 are from normal sheets of 50.

Nos. 499/501 are separated by various combinations of rotary-knife (giving a straight edge) and roulette.

143 Wilbur Wright and *Flyer III*

(Des Curtis Design. Litho Format)

1978 (July). *75th Anniv of Powered Flight. T* **143** *and similar horiz designs. Multicoloured.* P 14½.

502	1 c. Type **143**		10	10
503	6 c. Wright brothers and Cessna "337"		10	10
504	10 c. Orville Wright and "Electra"		10	10
505	15 c. Wilbur Wright and "C-47"		15	15
506	35 c. Wilbur Wright and "Islander"		35	35
507	$2 Wilbur Wright and Wright biplane		1·25	1·50
502/7		*Set of 6*	1·75	2·00
MS508	111 × 84 mm. $1 Orville Wright and Wright glider		75	1·40

144 Hurdling

(Des J.W. Litho Format)

1978 (3 Aug). *Commonwealth Games, Edmonton. T* **144** *and similar horiz designs. Multicoloured.* P 14½.

509	6 c. Type **144**		10	10
510	20 c. Weightlifting		15	15
511	55 c. Boxing		30	30
512	$2 Cycling		1·00	1·00
509/12		*Set of 4*	1·25	1·25
MS513	105 × 79 mm. $1 Sprinting		75	1·25

145 Indigo Hamlet | 146 "Madonna of the Siskin"

(Des G. Drummond. Litho Questa)

1978 (17 Nov)–**83.** *Fishes. Horiz designs as T* **145.** *Multicoloured.*

A. *No imprint date.* P 14

514A	1 c. Type **145**		10	25
515A	2 c. Tobacco fish (19.1.79)		40	10
516A	3 c. Passing Jack		15	10
517A	4 c. Porkfish (19.1.79)		40	20
518A	5 c. Spanish Grunt.		20	20
519A	7 c. Yellowtail Snapper (19.1.79)		50	15
520A	8 c. Foureye Butterflyfish (19.1.79)		60	10
521A	10 c. Yellowfin Grouper		30	15
522A	15 c. Beau Gregory		50	30
523A	20 c. Queen Angelfish		30	30
524A	30 c. Hogfish (19.1.79)		1·00	40
525A	50 c. Fairy Basslet (19.1.79)		1·00	65
526A	$1 Clown Wrasse (19.1.79)		1·75	1·60
527A	$2 Stoplight Parrotfish (19.1.79)		3·25	2·50
528A	$5 Queen Triggerfish (19.1.79)		3·25	6·50
514A/28A		*Set of 15*	12·00	11·50

B. *With imprint date at foot of design.* P 14 (15 c.) or 12 (*others*)

514B	1 c. Type **145** (15.12.81)		75	75
518B	5 c. Spanish Grunt (15.12.81)		1·00	1·00
521B	10 c. Yellowfin Grouper (15.12.81)		1·25	1·25
522B	15 c. Beau Gregory (25.1.83)		1·50	1·25
523B	20 c. Queen Angelfish (15.12.81)		1·25	1·00
	a. Perf 14 (25.1.83)		1·25	1·00
525B	50 c. Fairy Basslet (15.12.81)		2·50	2·50
526B	$1 Clown Wrasse (15.12.81)		3·25	3·00
	a. Perf 14 (25.1.83)		2·00	2·75
527B	$2 Stoplight Parrotfish (15.12.81)		5·50	5·00
	a. Perf 14 (25.1.83)		3·00	4·50
528B	$5 Queen Triggerfish (15.12.81)..		9·50	11·00
	a. Perf 14 (25.1.83)		7·50	9·00
514B/28B		*Set of 9*	18·00	22·00

(Des BG Studio. Litho Questa)

1978 (11 Dec). *Christmas. Paintings by Dürer. T* **146** *and similar multicoloured designs.* P 14.

529	6 c. Type **146**		10	10
530	20 c. "The Virgin and Child with St. Anne"		15	10
531	35 c. "Paumgärtner Nativity" *(horiz)*		20	15
532	$2 "Praying Hands"		85	1·00
529/32		*Set of 4*	1·10	1·10
MS533	137 × 124 mm. $1 "Adoration of the Magi" *(horiz)*		60	1·00

MINIMUM PRICE

The minimum price quote is 10p which represents a handling charge rather than a basis for valuing common stamps. For further notes about prices see introductory pages.

147 Osprey

(Des G. Drummond. Litho Questa)

1979 (29 May). *Endangered Wildlife. T **147** and similar horiz designs. Multicoloured. P 14.*

534	6 c.	Type **147**	40	10
535	20 c.	Green Turtle	45	20
536	25 c.	Queen Conch	50	25
537	55 c.	Rough-toothed Dolphin	90	50
538	$1	Humpback Whale	1·50	1·25
534/8		*Set of 5*	3·25	2·10
MS539	117 × 85 mm. $2 Iguana		2·25	3·00

148 "The Beloved" (painting by D. G. Rossetti)

(Des G. Vasarhelyi. Litho Questa)

1979 (2 July). *International Year of the Child. T **148** and similar horiz designs showing paintings and I.Y.C. emblem. Multicoloured. P 14.*

540	6 c.	Type **148**	10	10
541	25 c.	Tahitian Girl (P. Gauguin)	15	10
542	55 c.	"Calmady Children" (Sir Thomas Lawrence)	25	20
543	$1	"Mother and Daughter" (detail, P. Gauguin)	45	45
540/3		*Set of 4*	80	70
MS544	112 × 85 mm. $2 "Marchesa Elena Grimaldi" (A. van Dyck)		55	1·25

149 R.M.S.P. *Medina* and Handstamped Cover

150 Cuneiform Script

(Des J.W. Litho Questa (Nos. 545/51). Des and litho Walsall (Nos. 552/64))

1979 (27 Aug)–80. *Death Centenary of Sir Rowland Hill.*

(a) *Sheet stamps. Horiz designs as T **149**. Multicoloured. P 12 ($2) or 14 (others)*

545	6 c.	Type **149**	10	10
546	20 c.	Sir Rowland Hill and map of Caribbean	15	15
547	45 c.	R.M.S. *Orinoco* and cover bearing Penny Black stamp	25	25
548	75 c.	R.M.S. *Shannon* and letter to Grand Turk	40	40
549	$1	R.M.S.P. *Trent* and map of Caribbean	55	55
550	$2	Turks Islands 1867 and Turks and Caicos Islands 1900 1d. stamps (6.5.80)	90	90
545/50		*Set of 6*	2·10	2·10
MS551	170×113 mm. As No. 550. P 14		1·00	1·75

Nos. 545/9 also exist perf 12 (*Price for set of 5 £1·75 mint or used*) from additional sheetlets of 5 stamps and 1 label. No. 550 only exists in this format and has the inscription "International Stamp Exhibition Earls Court—London 6–14 May 1980. LONDON 1980" overprinted on the sheet margin. The individual stamps are not overprinted. Stamps perforated 14 are from normal sheets of 40.

(b) *Booklet stamps. Designs as T **150**. Imperf × roul 5*. Self-adhesive* (27.9.79)

552	5 c.	black and bright emerald	10	10
	a.	Booklet pane. Nos. 552/7.	80	
553	5 c.	black and bright emerald	10	10
554	5 c.	black and bright emerald	10	10
555	15 c.	black and light blue	20	20
556	15 c.	black and light blue	20	20
557	15 c.	black and light blue	20	20
558	25 c.	black and light blue	30	30
	a.	Booklet pane. Nos. 558/63	2·25	
559	25 c.	black and light blue	60	45
560	25 c.	black and light blue	30	30
561	40 c.	black and bright rosine	45	45
562	40 c.	black and bright rosine	45	45
563	40 c.	black and bright rosine	45	45
564	$1	black and lemon	1·10	1·25
	a.	Booklet pane of 4	4·25	

Designs: *Horiz*—No. 552. Type **150**; No. 553, Egyptian papyrus; No. 554, Chinese paper; No. 555, Greek runner; No. 556, Roman

post horse; No. 557, Roman post ship; No. 558, Pigeon post; No. 559, Railway post; No. 560, Packet paddle-steamer; No. 561, Balloon post; No. 562, First airmail; No. 563, Supersonic airmail. *Vert*—No. 564, Original stamp press.

*Nos. 552/63 are separated by various combinations of rotary knife (giving a straight edge) and roulette. No. 564 exists only with straight edges.

BRASILIANA 79

(151)

1979 (10 Sept). *"Brasiliana 79" International Stamp Exhibition, Rio de Janeiro. No. MS551 optd with T **151**.*
MS565 170 × 113 mm. $2 Turks Islands 1867 and Turks and Caicos Islands 1900 1d. stamps   55   1·25

Stamps from Nos. MS551 and MS565 are identical as the overprint on MS565 appears on the margin of the sheet.

152 "St. Nicholas", Prikra, Ukraine

(Des M. Diamond. Litho Questa)

1979 (19 Oct). *Christmas. Art. T **152** and similar vert designs. Multicoloured. P 13½ × 14.*

566	1 c.	Type **152**	10	10
567	3 c.	"Emperor Otto II with Symbols of Empire" (Master of the Registrum Gregorii)	10	10
568	6 c.	"Portrait of St. John" (Book of Lindisfarne)	10	10
569	15 c.	"Adoration of the Majestas Domini" (Prayer Book of Otto II)	10	10
570	20 c.	"Christ attended by Angels" (Book of Kells)	15	15
571	25 c.	"St. John the Evangelist" (Gospels of St. Medard of Soissons), Charlemagne	20	15
572	65 c.	"Christ Pantocrator", Trocany, Ukraine	30	25
573	$1	"Portrait of St. John" (Canterbury Codex Aureus)	45	45
566/73		*Set of 8*	1·10	1·10
MS574	106 × 133 mm. $2 "Portrait of St. Matthew" (Book of Lindisfarne)		70	1·50

153 Pluto and Starfish

(Litho Format)

1979 (2 Nov). *International Year of the Child. Walt Disney Cartoon Characters. T **153** and similar vert designs showing characters at the seaside. Multicoloured. P 11.*

575	¼ c.	Type **153**	10	10
576	½ c.	Minnie Mouse in summer outfit	10	10
577	1 c.	Mickey Mouse underwater	10	10
578	2 c.	Goofy and turtle	10	10
579	3 c.	Donald Duck and dolphin	10	10
580	4 c.	Mickey Mouse fishing	10	10
581	5 c.	Goofy surfing	10	10
582	25 c.	Pluto and crab	45	20
583	$1	Daisy water-skiing	2·00	1·10
575/83		*Set of 9*	2·50	1·25
MS584	126 × 96 mm. $1.50, Goofy after water-skiing accident. P 13½		1·25	1·40
	a.	Error. Imperf	£180	

154 "Christina's World" (painting by Andrew Wyeth)

(Des J.W. Litho Format)

1979 (19 Dec). *Works of Art. T **154** and similar multicoloured designs. P 13½.*

585	6 c.	Type **154**	10	10
586	10 c.	Ivory Leopards, Benin (19th-cent)	10	10
587	20 c.	"The Kiss" (painting by Gustav Klimt) (*vert*)	15	15
588	25 c.	"Portrait of a Lady" (painting by R. van der Weyden) (*vert*)	15	15

589	80 c.	Bull's head harp, Sumer, *c.* 2600 B.C. (*vert*)	30	30
590	$1	"The Wave" (painting by Hokusai)	45	45
585/90		*Set of 6*	95	95
MS591	110 × 140 mm. $2 "Holy Family" (painting by Rembrandt) (*vert*)		70	1·25

155 Pied-billed Grebe

156 Stamp, Magnifying Glass and Perforation Gauge

(Des G. Drummond. Litho Questa)

1980 (20 Feb). *Birds. T **155** and similar horiz designs. Multicoloured. P 14.*

592	20 c.	Type **155**	60	15
593	25 c.	Ovenbirds at nest	65	20
594	35 c.	Hen Harrier	90	30
595	55 c.	Yellow-bellied Sapsucker	1·10	35
596	$1	Blue-winged Teal	1·40	80
592/6		*Set of 5*	4·25	1·60
MS597	107 × 81 mm. $2 Glossy Ibis		2·75	2·25

(Des BG Studio. Litho Questa)

1980 (6 May). *"London 1980" International Stamp Exhibition. T **156** and similar horiz designs. P 14.*

598	25 c.	black and chrome-yellow	15	15
599	40 c.	black and bright green	25	25
MS600	76 × 97 mm. $2 vermilion, black and blue		70	1·10

Designs:—40 c. Stamp, tweezers and perforation gauge; $2, Earls Court Exhibition Centre.

157 Trumpet Triton

158 Queen Elizabeth the Queen Mother

(Des G. Drummond. Litho Questa)

1980 (26 June). *Shells. T **157** and similar horiz designs. Multicoloured. P 14.*

601	15 c.	Type **157**	20	20
602	20 c.	Measled Cowry	25	25
603	30 c.	True Tulip	35	35
604	45 c.	Lion's Paw	45	45
605	55 c.	Sunrise Tellin	55	55
606	70 c.	Crown Cone	70	70
601/6		*Set of 6*	2·25	2·25

(Des G. Vasarhelyi. Litho Questa)

1980 (4 Aug). *80th Birthday of Queen Elizabeth the Queen Mother. P 14.*

607	**158**	80 c. multicoloured	1·60	1·25
MS608	57 × 80 mm. No. **158** $1.50, multicoloured. P 12.		2·25	2·50

159 Doctor examining Child and Lions International Emblem

(Des Design Images. Litho Questa)

1980 (29 Aug). *"Serving the Community". T **159** and similar horiz designs. Multicoloured. P 14.*

609	10 c.	Type **159**	15	10
610	15 c.	Students receiving scholarships and Kiwanis International emblem	20	10
611	45 c.	Teacher with students and Soroptimist emblem	50	35
612	$1	Lobster trawler and Rotary International emblem	1·00	80
609/12		*Set of 4*	1·75	1·25
MS613	101 × 74 mm. $2 School receiving funds and Rotary International emblem		1·50	2·00

No. MS613 also commemorates the 75th anniversary of Rotary International.

(Litho Walsall)

1980 (30 Sept). *Christmas. Scenes from Walt Disney's Cartoon Film "Pinocchio". Horiz designs as T **153**. Multicoloured. P 11.*

614	¼ c.	Scene from *Pinocchio*	10	10
615	½ c.	As puppet	10	10
616	1 c.	Pinocchio changed into a boy	10	10
617	2 c.	Captured by fox	10	10
618	3 c.	Pinocchio and puppeteer	10	10
619	4 c.	Pinocchio and bird's nest nose	10	10
620	5 c.	Pinocchio eating	10	10
621	75 c.	Pinocchio with ass ears	60	70
622	$1	Pinocchio underwater	80	95
614/22		*Set of 9*	1·50	1·75
MS623	127 × 102 mm. $2 Pinocchio dancing (*vert*)		2·50	2·00

160 Martin Luther King Jr

(Des Design Images. Litho Questa)

1980 (22 Dec). *Human Rights. Personalities. T* **160** *and similar horiz designs. Multicoloured. P* 14 × 13½.

624	20 c. Type **160**		15	10
625	30 c. John F. Kennedy		30	25
626	45 c. Roberto Clemente (baseball player)		45	35
627	70 c. Sir Frank Worrel (cricketer)		90	90
628	$1 Harriet Tubman		1·10	1·25
624/8		*Set of* 5	2·50	2·50
MS629	103 × 80 mm. $2 Marcus Garvey		1·10	1·25

161 Yachts **162** Night Queen Cactus

(Litho Questa)

1981 (29 Jan). *South Caicos Regatta. T* **161** *and similar horiz designs. Multicoloured. P* 14.

630	6 c. Type **161**		10	10
631	15 c. Trophy and yachts		15	15
632	35 c. Spectators watching speedboat race		25	20
633	$1 Caicos sloops		60	50
630/3		*Set of* 4	90	80
MS634	113 × 85 mm. $2 Queen Elizabeth II and map of South Caicos (*vert*)		1·10	1·75

(Des J. Cooter. Litho Questa)

1981 (10 Feb). *Flowering Cacti. T* **162** *and similar vert designs. Multicoloured. P* 13½ × 14.

635	25 c. Type **162**		25	25
636	35 c. Ripsaw Cactus		35	35
637	55 c. Royal Strawberry Cactus		40	50
638	80 c. Caicos Cactus		60	75
635/8		*Set of* 4	1·40	1·75
MS639	72 × 86 mm. $2 Turks Head Cactus. P 14½		1·25	2·00

(Litho Format)

1981 (16 Feb). *50th Anniv of Walt Disney's Cartoon Character, Pluto. Vert designs as T* **153**. *Multicoloured. P* 13½.

640	10 c. Pluto playing on beach with shell		10	10
641	75 c. Pluto on raft, and porpoise		75	75
MS642	127 × 101 mm. $1.50 Pluto in scene from film *Simple Things*		1·60	1·75

(Litho Format)

1981 (20 Mar). *Easter. Walt Disney Cartoon Characters. Vert designs as T* **153**. *Multicoloured. P* 11.

643	10 c. Donald Duck and Louie		20	20
644	25 c. Goofy and Donald Duck		40	40
645	60 c. Chip and Dale		85	85
646	80 c. Scrooge McDuck and Huey		1·25	1·25
643/6		*Set of* 4	2·40	2·40
MS647	126 × 101 mm. $4 Chip (or Dale). P 13½		4·00	3·00

163 "Woman with Fan" **164** Kensington Palace

(Des J.W. Litho Questa)

1981 (28 May). *Birth Centenary of Picasso. T* **163** *and similar vert designs. Multicoloured. P* 13½ × 14.

648	20 c. Type **163**		20	15
649	45 c. "Woman with Pears"		35	30
650	80 c. "The Accordionist"		60	50
651	$1 "The Aficionado"		80	80
648/51		*Set of* 4	1·75	1·60
MS652	102 × 127 mm. $2 "Girl with a Mandolin"		1·10	1·25

(Des J.W. Litho Questa)

1981 (23 June). *Royal Wedding. T* **164** *and similar vert designs. Multicoloured. P* 14.

653	35 c. Prince Charles and Lady Diana Spencer		20	15
654	65 c. Type **164**		35	30
655	90 c. Prince Charles as Colonel of the Welsh Guards		45	45
653/5		*Set of* 3	90	80
MS656	96 × 82 mm. $2 Glass Coach		90	1·00

Nos. 653/5 also exist perforated 12 (*price for set of* 3 £1 *mint or used*) from additional sheetlets of five stamps and one label. These stamps have changed background colours.

165 Lady Diana Spencer **166** Marine Biology Observation

(Manufactured by Walsall)

1981 (7 July). *Royal Wedding. Booklet stamps. T* **165** *and similar vert designs. Multicoloured. Roul* 5 × *imperf*. Self-adhesive.*

657	20 c. Type **165**		25	30
	a. Booklet pane. Nos. 657/8, each × 3		2·25	
658	$1 Prince Charles		50	1·00
659	$2 Prince Charles and Lady Diana Spencer		2·00	2·50
	a. Booklet pane of 1		2·00	
657/9		*Set of* 3	2·50	3·50

*The 20 c. and $1 values were each separated by various combinations of rotary knife (giving a straight edge) and roulette. The $2 value exists only with straight edges.

(Des G. Drummond. Litho Questa)

1981 (21 Aug). *Diving. T* **166** *and similar horiz designs. Multicoloured. P* 14.

660	15 c. Type **166**		20	15
661	40 c. Underwater photography		50	35
662	75 c. Wreck diving		90	70
663	$1 Diving with dolphins		1·25	1·00
660/3		*Set of* 4	2·50	2·00
MS664	91 × 75 mm. $2 Diving flag		1·75	2·25

(Litho Questa)

1981 (2 Nov). *Christmas. Horiz designs as T* **153** *showing scenes from Walt Disney's cartoon film "Uncle Remus". P* 13½.

665	¼ c. multicoloured		10	10
666	½ c. multicoloured		10	10
667	1 c. multicoloured		10	10
668	2 c. multicoloured		10	10
669	3 c. multicoloured		10	10
670	4 c. multicoloured		10	10
671	5 c. multicoloured		10	10
672	75 c. multicoloured		60	60
673	$1 multicoloured		80	80
665/73		*Set of* 9	1·40	1·40
MS674	128 × 103 mm. $2 multicoloured		1·75	1·90

167 Map of Grand Turk, and Lighthouse **168** *Junonia evarete*

(Des J.W. Litho Questa)

1981 (1 Dec). *Tourism. T* **167** *and similar horiz designs. Multicoloured. P* 14.

675	20 c. Type **167**		35	35
	a. Vert strip of 10. Nos. 675/84		3·25	
676	20 c. Map of Salt Cay, and "industrial archaeology"		35	35
677	20 c. Map of South Caicos, and "island flying"		35	35
678	20 c. Map of East Caicos, and "beach combing"		35	35
679	20 c. Map of Grand Caicos (middle), and cave exploring		35	35
680	20 c. Map of North Caicos, and camping and hiking		35	35
681	20 c. Map of North Caicos, Parrot Cay, Dellis Cay, Fort George Cay, Pine Cay and Water Cay, and "environmental studies"		35	35
682	20 c. Map of Providenciales, and scuba diving		35	35
683	20 c. Map of West Caicos, and "cruising and bird sanctuary"		35	35
684	20 c. Turks and Caicos Islands flag		35	35
675/84		*Set of* 10	3·25	3·25

Nos. 675/84 were printed together, *se-tenant*, in vertical strips of 10 throughout the sheet of 40, the two panes (2 × 10), separated by a gutter margin, being *tête-bêche*.

(Des J. Cooter. Litho Questa)

1982 (21 Jan). *Butterflies. T* **168** *and similar vert designs. Multicoloured. P* 14.

685	20 c. Type **168**		30	30
686	35 c. *Strymon maesites*		50	55
687	65 c. *Agraulis vanillae*		90	1·00
688	$1 *Eurema dina*		1·40	2·00
685/8		*Set of* 4	2·75	3·50
MS689	72×56 mm. $2 *Anaea intermedia*		2·75	3·50

OMNIBUS ISSUES

Details, together with prices for complete sets, of the various Omnibus issues from the 1935 Silver Jubilee series to date are included in a special section following Zimbabwe at the end of Volume 2.

169 Flag Salute on Queen's Birthday **170** Footballer

(Litho Questa)

1982 (17 Feb). *75th Anniv of Boy Scout Movement. T* **169** *and similar vert designs. Multicoloured. P* 14.

690	40 c. Type **169**		50	50
691	50 c. Raft building		60	60
692	75 c. Sea scout cricket match		1·10	1·40
693	$1 Nature study		1·50	1·50
690/3		*Set of* 4	3·25	3·75
MS694	100 × 70 mm. $2 Lord Baden-Powell and scout salute		2·50	2·75

(Des G. Vasarhelyi. Litho Questa)

1982 (30 Apr). *World Cup Football Championship, Spain. T* **170** *and similar designs showing footballers. P* 14.

695	10 c. multicoloured		15	15
696	25 c. multicoloured		20	20
697	45 c. multicoloured		25	25
698	$1 multicoloured		80	80
695/8		*Set of* 4	1·25	1·25
MS699	117 × 83 mm. $2 multicoloured (*horiz*)		1·25	2·00

171 Washington crossing the Delaware and Phillis Wheatley (poetess) **172** "Second Thoughts"

(Des Design Images. Litho Questa)

1982 (3 May). *250th Birth Anniv of George Washington* (20, 35 c.) *and Birth Centenary of Franklin D. Roosevelt* (65, 80 c.). *T* **171** *and similar horiz designs. Multicoloured. P* 14.

700	20 c. Type **171**		30	30
701	35 c. George Washington and Benjamin Banneker (surveyor)		45	45
702	65 c. Franklin D. Roosevelt meeting George Washington Carver (agricultural researcher)		80	80
703	80 c. Roosevelt as stamp collector		1·00	1·00
700/3		*Set of* 4	2·25	2·25
MS704	100 × 70 mm. $2 Roosevelt with stamp showing profile of Washington		2·00	2·50

(Litho Questa)

1982 (23 June). *Norman Rockwell* (painter) *Commemoration. T* **172** *and similar vert designs. Multicoloured. P* 14 × 13½.

705	8 c. Type **172**		15	10
706	15 c. "The Proper Gratuity"		20	20
707	20 c. "Before the Shot"		25	25
708	25 c. "The Three Umpires"		25	25
705/8		*Set of* 4	75	70

173 Princess of Wales **174** "Skymaster" over Caicos Cays

(Des PAD Studio. Litho Questa)

1982 (1 July–18 Nov). *21st Birthday of Princess of Wales. T* **173** *and similar vert designs. Multicoloured. P* 14½ × 14.

(a) *Sheet stamps. Pale green frames.*

709	55 c. Sandringham		60	55
710	70 c. Prince and Princess of Wales		70	70
711	$1 Type **173**		95	1·25
709/11		*Set of* 3	2·00	2·25
MS712	102 × 76 mm. $2 Princess Diana (*different*)		1·75	2·25

(b) *Booklet stamps. As Nos.* 709/11 *but printed with new values and blue frame* (18.11.82)

713	8 c. Sandringham		25	35
714	35 c. Prince and Princess of Wales		60	1·00
715	$1.10, Type **173**		1·25	2·00
713/15		*Set of* 3	1·90	3·00

Nos. 713/15 also exist from sheets printed in horizontal *tête-bêche* pairs throughout.

(Des MBI Studios. Litho Questa)

1982 (23 Aug). *Aircraft. T 174 and similar horiz designs. Multicoloured. P 14.*

716	8 c. Type **174**	15	15
717	15 c. "Jetstar" over Grand Turk	20	25
718	65 c. Helicopter over South Caicos	65	80
719	$1.10, Seaplane over Providenciales	1·10	1·25
716/19	*Set of 4*	1·90	2·25
MS720	99 × 69 mm. $2 Boeing "727" over Turks and Caicos Islands	2·00	2·50

(Litho Questa)

1982 (1 Dec). *Christmas. Scenes from Walt Disney's Cartoon Film "Mickey's Christmas Carol". Horiz designs as T 153. Multicoloured. P 13½.*

721	1 c. Donald Duck, Mickey Mouse and Scrooge	10	10
722	1 c. Goofy (Marley's ghost) and Scrooge	10	10
723	2 c. Jiminy Cricket and Scrooge	10	10
724	2 c. Huey, Dewey and Louie	10	10
725	3 c. Daisy Duck and youthful Scrooge	10	10
726	3 c. Giant and Scrooge	10	10
727	4 c. Two bad wolves, a wise pig and a reformed Scrooge	10	10
728	65 c. Donald Duck and Scrooge	1·00	65
729	$1.10, Mortie and Scrooge	1·60	1·10
721/9	*Set of 9*	2·50	1·75
MS730	126 × 101 mm. $2 Mickey and Minnie Mouse with Mortie	2·75	2·00

175 West Caicos Trolley Tram

(Des N. Waldman. Litho Questa)

1983 (18 Jan). *Trams and Locomotives. T 175 and similar horiz designs. Multicoloured. P 14*

731	15 c. Type **175**	20	25
732	55 c. West Caicos steam locomotive	65	70
733	90 c. East Caicos sisal locomotive	90	1·00
734	$1.60, East Caicos steam locomotive	1·75	1·90
731/4	*Set of 4*	3·25	3·50
MS735	99 × 69 mm. $2.50, Steam engine pulling cars of sisal	2·25	2·25

176 Policewoman on Traffic Duty   **177** "St. John and the Virgin Mary" (detail)

(Des N. Waldman. Litho Questa)

1983 (14 Mar). *Commonwealth Day. T 176 and similar horiz designs. Multicoloured. P 14*

736	1 c. Type **176**	15	20
	a. Vert strip of 4. Nos. 736/9	2·40	
737	8 c. Stylised sun and weather vane	15	20
738	65 c. Yacht	85	90
739	$1 Cricket	1·50	1·60
736/9	*Set of 4*	2·40	2·50

Nos. 736/9 were printed together, *se-tenant*, in vertical strips of four throughout the sheet.

(Des Design Images. Litho Questa)

1983 (7 Apr). *Easter. T 177 and similar vert designs showing details from the "Mond Crucifixion" by Raphael. Multicoloured. P 13½ × 14.*

740	35 c. Type **177**	20	25
741	50 c. "Two Women"	30	35
742	95 c. "Angel with two jars"	50	60
743	$1.10, "Angel with one jar"	60	80
740/3	*Set of 4*	1·40	2·00
MS744	100 × 130 mm. $2.50, "Christ on the Cross"	1·60	2·00

178 Minke Whale   **179** First Hydrogen Balloon, 1783

(Des D. Hamilton. Litho Questa)

1983 (16 May–11 July). *Whales. T 178 and similar horiz designs. Multicoloured. P 13½.*

745	50 c. Type **178**	1·25	1·25
746	65 c. Black Right Whale (11.7.83)	1·50	1·50
747	70 c. Killer Whale (13.6.83)	1·75	1·75
748	95 c. Sperm Whale (13.6.83)	2·00	2·00
749	$1.10, Cuvier's Beaked Whale (11.7.83)	2·25	2·25
750	$2 Blue Whale (13.6.83)	4·00	4·00
751	$2.20, Humpback Whale	4·50	4·50
752	$3 Long-finned Pilot Whale	5·50	5·50
745/52	*Set of 8*	20·00	20·00
MS753	112 × 82 mm. $3 Fin Whale (11.7.83)	4·50	5·00

Nos. 745/52 were each issued in sheetlets of four.

(Des BG Studio. Litho Questa)

1983 (30 Aug). *Bicentenary of Manned Flight. T 179 and similar vert designs. Multicoloured. P 14.*

754	25 c. Type **179**	25	25
755	35 c. *Friendship 7*	35	35
756	70 c. First hot air balloon, 1783	70	70
757	95 c. Space shuttle *Columbia*	90	90
754/7	*Set of 4*	2·00	2·00
MS758	112 × 76 mm. $2 Montgolfier balloon and Space shuttle	1·50	2·00

180 Fiddler Pig   **181** Bermuda Sloop

(Litho Format)

1983 (4 Oct). *Christmas. Walt Disney Cartoon Characters. T 180 and similar vert designs. Multicoloured. P 11.*

759	1 c. Type **180**	10	10
760	1 c. Fifer Pig	10	10
761	2 c. Practical Pig	10	10
762	2 c. Pluto	10	10
763	3 c. Goofy	10	10
764	3 c. Mickey Mouse	10	10
765	35 c. Gyro Gearloose	35	35
766	50 c. Ludwig von Drake	50	50
767	$1.10, Huey, Dewey and Louie	1·00	1·00
759/67	*Set of 9*	1·75	1·75
MS768	127 × 102 mm. $2.50, Mickey and Minnie Mouse with Huey, Dewey and Louie. P 13½	3·25	3·00

(Des G. Drummond. Litho Questa)

1983 (5 Oct)–85. *Ships. T 181 and similar horiz designs. Multicoloured. A. P 14. B. P 12½ × 12.*

		A		B	
769	4 c. Arawak dug-out canoe	40	40	60	60
770	5 c. *Santa Maria*	50	40	50	50
771	8 c. British and Spanish ships in battle	2·00	50	75	60
772	10 c. Type **181**	2·00	50	75	60
773	20 c. U.S. privateer *Grand Turk*	70	60	50	50
774	25 c. H.M.S. *Boreas*	3·00	70	50	50
775	30 c. H.M.S. *Endymion* attacking French ship, 1790s	3·00	80	1·25	65
776	35 c. *Caesar* (barque)	1·25	80	60	60
777	50 c. *Grapeshot* (schooner)	3·50	1·10	60	70
778	65 c. H.M.S. *Invincible* (battle cruiser)	4·50	2·00	1·50	1·40
779	95 c. H.M.S. *Magicienne*	4·50	2·00	2·25	1·75
780	$1.10, H.M.S. *Durban*	5·50	3·00	2·75	2·50
781	$2 *Sentinel* (cable ship)	7·00	3·75	2·50	3·00
782	$3 H.M.S. *Minerva*	7·50	5·50	6·50	8·00
783	$5 Caicos sloop	7·50	9·00	9·00	10·00
769/83	*Set of 15*	48·00	27·00	27·00	28·00

Dates of issue:—5.10.83, Nos. 772A, 775A, 778A, 780A/2/2A; 16.12.83, Nos. 771A, 774A, 777A, 779A; 9.1.84, Nos. 769A/70A, 773A, 776A, 783A; 3.85, Nos. 769B, 771B/2B, 775B, 778B, 780B, 783B; 12.8.85, Nos. 770B, 773B/4B, 776B/7B, 779B, 781B; 12.85, No. 782B.

182 President Kennedy and Signing of Civil Rights Legislation

(Des Design Images. Litho Questa)

1983 (22 Dec). *20th Death Anniv of President J. F. Kennedy. P 14.*

784	**182** 20 c. multicoloured	20	15
785	$1 multicoloured	1·10	1·25

---

183 Clarabelle Cow Diving

(Litho Questa)

1984 (21 Feb–Apr). *Olympic Games, Los Angeles. T 183 and similar horiz designs showing Disney cartoon characters in Olympic events. Multicoloured. A. Inscr "1984 LOS ANGELES". P 14 × 13½. B. Inscr "1984 OLYMPICS LOS ANGELES" and Olympic emblem. P 14 × 13½ (MS 795B) or 12 (others) (4.84).*

		A		B	
786	1 c. Type **183**	10	10	10	10
787	1 c. Donald Duck in 500m kayak race	10	10	10	10
788	2 c. Huey, Dewey and Louie in 1000m kayak race	10	10	10	10
789	2 c. Mickey Mouse in single kayak	10	10	10	10
790	3 c. Donald Duck highboard diving	10	10	10	10
791	3 c. Minnie Mouse in kayak slalom	10	10	10	10
792	25 c. Mickey Mouse freestyle swimming	40	45	40	45
793	75 c. Donald Duck playing water-polo	1·25	1·40	1·50	1·40
794	$1 Uncle Scrooge and Donald Duck yachting	1·60	1·75	1·75	1·75
786/94	*Set of 9*	3·25	3·50	3·50	3·50
MS795	117 × 90 mm. $2 Pluto platform diving	2·75	3·00	2·75	3·00

184 "Cadillac V–16", 1933   **185** "Rest during the Flight to Egypt, with St. Francis"

(Des N. Waldman. Litho Questa)

1984 (15 Mar). *Classic Cars and 125th Anniv of first Commercial Oil Well. T 184 and similar horiz designs. Multicoloured. P 14.*

796	4 c. Type **184**	10	10
797	8 c. Rolls-Royce "Phantom III", 1937	15	15
798	10 c. Saab "99", 1969	15	15
799	25 c. Maserati "Bora", 1973	40	40
800	40 c. Datsun "260Z", 1970	65	65
801	55 c. Porsche "917", 1971	80	80
802	80 c. Lincoln "Continental", 1939	90	90
803	$1 Triumph "TR3A", 1957	1·25	1·25
796/803	*Set of 8*	4·00	4·00
MS804	70 × 100 mm. $2 Daimler, 1886	2·00	2·50

(Des S. Karp. Litho Walsall)

1984 (9 Apr). *Easter. 450th Death Anniv of Correggio (painter). T 185 and similar vert designs. Multicoloured. P 14.*

805	15 c. Type **185**	20	15
806	40 c. "St. Luke and St. Ambrose"	45	40
807	60 c. "Diana and her Chariot"	65	65
808	95 c. "The Deposition of Christ"	80	80
805/8	*Set of 4*	1·90	1·75
MS809	100 × 79 mm. $2 "The Nativity with Saints Elizabeth and John the younger" (horiz)	1·50	2·25

19TH UPU CONGRESS, HAMBURG, WEST GERMANY. 1874–1984

(186)

1984 (19 June). *Universal Postal Union Congress, Hamburg. Nos. 748/9 and MS753 optd with T 186.*

810	95 c. Sperm Whale	2·00	1·50
811	$1.10, Cuvier's Beaked Whale	2·00	1·60
MS812	112 × 82 mm. $3 Fin Whale	4·00	4·25

187 "The Adventure of the Second Stain"   **188** Clown-Fish

(Des S. Karp. Litho Walsall)

1984 (16 July). *125th Birth Anniv of Sir Arthur Conan Doyle (author). T* **187** *and similar horiz designs showing scenes from Sherlock Holmes stories. Multicoloured. P* 14.

813	25 c. Type **187**	2·00	1·25
814	45 c. "The Adventure of the Final Problem"	2·75	2·00
815	70 c. "The Adventure of the Empty House"	4·25	3·25
816	85 c. "The Adventure of the Greek Interpreter"	5·00	3·50
813/16	*Set of 4*	12·50	9·00
MS817	100 × 70 mm. $2 Sir Arthur Conan Doyle	8·50	5·00

(Des Susan David. Litho Walsall)

1984 (22 Aug). *"Ausipex" International Stamp Exhibition, Melbourne. 175th Birth Anniv of Charles Darwin. T* **188** *and similar vert designs. Multicoloured. P* 14 × 13½.

818	5 c. Type **188**	40	30
819	35 c. Monitor Lizard	1·75	1·75
820	50 c. Rainbow Lory	2·50	2·50
821	$1.10, Koalas	3·25	3·25
818/21	*Set of 4*	7·00	7·00
MS822	100 × 70 mm. $2 Eastern Grey Kangaroo	3·50	4·25

189 Donald Duck cutting down Christmas Tree

(Litho Questa)

1984 (8 Oct–26 Nov). *Christmas. Walt Disney Cartoon Characters. T* **189** *and similar horiz designs showing scenes from "Toy Tinkers". Multicoloured. P* 12 (75 c.) *or* 14 × 13½ (*others*).

823	20 c. Type **189**	85	45
824	35 c. Donald Duck and Chip n'Dale playing with train set	1·10	65
825	50 c. Donald Duck and Chip n'Dale playing with catapult	1·60	85
826	75 c. Donald Duck, Chip n'Dale and Christmas tree (26.11)	2·25	1·40
827	$1.10, Donald Duck, toy soldier and Chip n'Dale	2·50	1·90
823/7	*Set of 5*	7·50	4·75
MS828	126 × 102 mm. $2 Donald Duck as Father Christmas	3·00	3·25

No. 826 was printed in sheetlets of 8 stamps.

190 Magnolia Warbler | 191 Leonardo da Vinci and Illustration of Glider Wing (15th century)

(Des Susan David. Litho Walsall)

1985 (28 Jan). *Birth Bicentenary of John J. Audubon (ornithologist). T* **190** *and similar vert designs. Multicoloured. P* 14.

829	25 c. Type **190**	1·50	45
830	45 c. Short-eared Owl	2·25	80
831	70 c. Mourning Dove and eggs	2·50	1·50
832	85 c. Caribbean Martin	2·75	1·75
829/32	*Set of 4*	8·00	4·00
MS833	100 × 70 mm. $2 Oystercatcher and chicks	3·75	4·00

(Des K. Gromol. Litho Walsall)

1985 (22 Feb). *40th Anniv of International Civil Aviation Organization. Aviation Pioneers. T* **191** *and similar horiz designs. Multicoloured. P* 14.

834	8 c. Type **191**	40	15
835	25 c. Sir Alliott Verdon Roe and "C.102" jetliner (1949)	85	40
836	65 c. Robert H. Goddard and first liquid fuel rocket (1926)	2·00	95
837	$1 Igor Sikorsky and Sikorsky "VS300" helicopter (1939)	2·50	1·50
834/7	*Set of 4*	5·00	2·75
MS838	100 × 70 mm. $2 Amelia Earhart's Lockheed "10E Electra" (1937)	2·75	3·00

192 Benjamin Franklin and Marquis de Lafayette

(Des Susan David. Litho Walsall)

1985 (28 Mar). *Centenary of the Statue of Liberty's Arrival in New York. T* **192** *and similar horiz designs. Multicoloured. P* 14.

839	20 c. Type **192**	80	50
840	30 c. Frederic Bartholdi (designer) and Gustave Eiffel (engineer)	90	60
841	65 c. Sailing ship *Isere* arriving in New York with statue, 1885	2·25	1·50
842	$1.10, United States fund raisers Louis Agassiz, Charles Sumner, H. W. Longfellow and Joseph Pulitzer	2·50	1·75
839/42	*Set of 4*	5·75	4·00
MS843	99 × 69 mm. $2 Dedication ceremony, 1886	3·00	3·50

193 Sir Edward Hawke and H.M.S. *Royal George*

(Des Susan David. Litho Walsall)

1985 (17 Apr). *Salute to the Royal Navy. T* **193** *and similar multicoloured designs. P* 14.

844	20 c. Type **193**	1·75	1·50
845	30 c. Lord Nelson and H.M.S. *Victory*	2·25	2·00
846	65 c. Admiral Sir George Cockburn and H.M.S. *Albion*	3·00	2·50
847	95 c. Admiral Sir David Beatty and H.M.S. *Indefatigable*	4·00	3·50
844/7	*Set of 4*	10·00	8·50
MS848	99 × 69 mm. $2 18th-century sailor and cannon (*vert*)	3·25	3·50

194 Mark Twain riding on Halley's Comet | 195 The Queen Mother outside Clarence House

(Des J. Iskowitz. Litho Walsall)

1985 (17 May). *International Youth Year. Birth Anniv of Mark Twain (150th) and Jakob Grimm (Bicentenary). T* **194** *and similar multicoloured designs. P* 13½ × 14 (25, 35 c., $2) *or* 14 × 13½ (50, 95 c.).

849	25 c. Type **194**	85	40
850	35 c. *Grand Turk* (Mississippi river steamer)	1·25	55
851	50 c. Hansel and Gretel and gingerbread house (*vert*)	1·50	75
852	95 c. Rumpelstiltskin (*vert*)	2·25	1·50
849/52	*Set of 4*	5·25	3·00
MS853	99 × 68 mm. $2 Mark Twain and the Brothers Grimm	2·75	3·00

(Des J.W. Litho Questa)

1985 (15 July). *Life and Times of Queen Elizabeth the Queen Mother. T* **195** *and similar multicoloured designs. P* 14.

854	30 c. Type **195**	45	45
855	50 c. Visiting Biggin Hill airfield (*horiz*)	75	75
856	$1.10, 80th birthday portrait	1·90	1·90
854/6	*Set of 3*	2·75	2·75
MS857	56 × 85 mm. $2 With Prince Charles at Garter ceremony, Windsor Castle, 1968	2·75	3·00

196 King George II and Score of "Zadok the Priest" (1727) | 197 Harley-Davidson Dual Cylinder (1915) on Middle Caicos

(Des Susan David. Litho Format)

1985 (17 July). *300th Birth Anniv of George Frederick Handel (composer). T* **196** *and similar vert designs. P* 15.

858	4 c. multicoloured	65	40
859	10 c. multicoloured	1·00	50
860	50 c. multicoloured	2·75	1·50
861	$1.10, multicoloured	4·75	3·75
858/61	*Set of 4*	8·25	5·50
MS862	101 × 76 mm. $2 black, deep dull purple and dull violet-blue	6·00	4·50

Designs:—10 c. Queen Caroline and score of "Funeral Anthem" (1737); 50 c. King George I and score of "Water Music" (1714); Queen Anne and score of "Or la Tromba" from *Rinaldo* (1711); $2 George Frederick Handel.

(Des Susan David. Litho Format)

1985 (17 July). *300th Birth Anniv of Johann Sebastian Bach (composer). Vert designs as T* **204a** *of Maldive Islands. Multicoloured. P* 15.

863	15 c. Bassoon	1·00	40
864	40 c. Natural Horn	1·75	85
865	60 c. Viola D'Amore	2·25	1·75
866	95 c. Clavichord	2·75	2·25
863/6	*Set of 4*	7·00	4·25
MS867	102 × 76 mm. $2 Johann Sebastian Bach	4·00	3·50

(Des Mary Walters. Litho Questa)

1985 (4 Sept). *Centenary of the Motor Cycle. T* **197** *and similar multicoloured designs. P* 14.

868	8 c. Type **197**	45	30
869	25 c. Triumph "Thunderbird" (1950) on Grand Turk	1·00	70
870	55 c. BMW "K100RS" (1985) on North Caicos	2·00	1·50
871	$1.20, Honda "1100 Shadow" (1985) on South Caicos	3·25	2·50
868/71	*Set of 4*	6·00	4·50
MS872	106 × 77 mm. $2 Daimler single track (1885) (*vert*)	2·75	3·00

198 Pirates in Prison

(Des Walt Disney Productions. Litho Questa)

1985 (4 Oct). *30th Anniv of Disneyland, U.S.A. T* **198** *and similar horiz designs showing scenes from "Pirates of the Caribbean" exhibition. Multicoloured. P* 14 × 13½.

873	1 c. Type **198**	10	10
874	1 c. The fate of Captain William Kidd	10	10
875	2 c. Bartholomew Roberts	10	10
876	2 c. Two buccaneers	10	10
877	3 c. Privateers looting	10	10
878	3 c. Auction of captives	10	10
879	35 c. Singing pirates	1·50	65
880	75 c. Edward Teach—"Blackbeard"	2·75	1·50
881	$1.10, Sir Henry Morgan	3·25	1·75
873/81	*Set of 9*	7·00	3·50
MS882	123 × 86 mm. $2.50, Mary Read and Anne Bonney	3·50	3·75

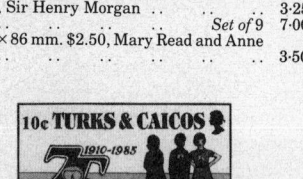

199 Brownies from China, Turks and Caicos and Papua New Guinea

(Des Mary Walters. Litho Questa)

1985 (4 Nov). *75th Anniv of Girl Guide Movement and 35th Anniv of Grand Turk Company. T* **199** *and similar horiz designs. Multicoloured. P* 14.

883	10 c. Type **199**	75	30
884	40 c. Brownies from Surinam, Turks and Caicos and Korea	1·75	1·25
885	70 c. Guides from Australia, Turks and Caicos and Canada	2·50	2·00
886	80 c. Guides from West Germany, Turks and Caicos and Israel	2·75	2·25
883/6	*Set of 4*	7·00	5·25
MS887	107 × 76 mm. $2 75th anniversary emblem	3·00	3·50

200 Iguana and Log | 201 Duke and Duchess of York after Wedding

(Des I. MacLaury. Litho Questa)

1986 (20 Nov). *Turks and Caicos Ground Iguana. T* **200** *and similar horiz designs. Multicoloured. P* 14.

888	8 c. Type **200**	1·25	85
889	10 c. Iguana on beach	1·50	95
890	20 c. Iguana at nest	2·00	2·00
891	35 c. Iguana eating flowers	3·50	3·50
888/91	*Set of 4*	7·50	6·50
MS892	105 × 76 mm. $2 Map showing habitat	8·50	9·00

(Litho Questa)

1986 (19 Dec). *Royal Wedding. T 201 and similar vert designs. Multicoloured. P 14.*

893	35 c.	Type 201	75	55
894	65 c.	Miss Sarah Ferguson in wedding carriage	1·25	1·25
895	$1.10,	Duke and Duchess of York on Palace balcony after wedding	2·00	2·25
893/5		*Set of 3*	3·50	3·50
MS896		85×85 mm. $2 Duke and Duchess of York leaving Westminster Abbey	2·50	3·00

202 "The Prophecy of the Birth of Christ to King Achaz"

203 H.M.S. *Victoria*, 1859, and Victoria Cross

(Litho Questa)

1987 (9 Dec). *Christmas. T 202 and similar vert designs, each showing illuminated illustration by Giorgio Clovio from "Farnese Book of Hours". Multicoloured. P 14.*

897	35 c.	Type 202	1·25	75
898	50 c.	"The Annunciation"	1·75	1·50
899	65 c.	"The Circumcision"	2·25	2·00
900	95 c.	"Adoration of the Kings"	3·25	3·75
897/900		*Set of 4*	7·75	7·25
MS901		76×106 mm. $2 "The Nativity"	4·25	4·75

(Litho Questa)

1987 (24 Dec). *150th Anniv of Accession of Queen Victoria. T 203 and similar horiz designs. Multicoloured. P 14.*

902	8 c.	Type 203	75	45
903	35 c.	*Victoria* (paddle-steamer) and gold sovereign	1·75	1·50
904	55 c.	Royal Yacht *Victoria and Albert I* and 1840 Penny Black stamp	2·00	2·00
905	95 c.	Royal Yacht *Victoria and Albert II* and Victoria Public Library	3·00	3·25
902/5		*Set of 4*	6·75	6·50
MS906		129×76 mm. $2 *Victoria* (barque)	4·50	5·00

(Des and litho Questa)

1987 (31 Dec). *Bicentenary of U.S. Constitution. Multicoloured designs as T 210a of Sierra Leone. P 14.*

907	10 c.	State Seal, New Jersey	20	15
908	35 c.	18th-century family going to church ("Freedom of Worship") (vert)	55	55
909	65 c.	U.S. Supreme Court, Judicial Branch, Washington (vert)	1·00	1·00
910	80 c.	John Adams (statesman) (vert)	1·25	1·40
907/10		*Set of 4*	2·75	2·75
MS911		105×75 mm. $2 George Mason (Virginia delegate) (vert)	2·40	3·00

Nos. 907/10 were each printed in sheetlets of five stamps and one stamp-size label, which appears in the centre of the bottom row.

204 *Santa Maria*

205 Arawak Artifact and Scouts in Cave, Middle Caicos

(Litho Questa)

1988 (20 Jan). *500th Anniv of Discovery of America by Columbus (1992) (1st issue). T 204 and similar horiz designs. Multicoloured. P 14.*

912	4 c.	Type 204	20	15
913	25 c.	Columbus meeting Tainos Indians	85	60
914	70 c.	*Santa Maria* anchored off Indian village	2·25	2·25
915	$1	Columbus in field of grain	2·50	2·50
912/15		*Set of 4*	5·25	5·00
MS916		105×76 mm. $2 *Santa Maria, Pinta* and *Nina*	3·50	4·25

See also Nos. 947/51, 1028/36, 1072/80 and 1166/76.

(Litho Questa)

1988 (12 Feb). *World Scout Jamboree, Australia. T 205 and similar multicoloured designs. P 14.*

917	8 c.	Type 205	20	15
918	35 c.	*Santa Maria*, scouts and Hawks Nest Island (horiz)	55	55
919	65 c.	Scouts diving to wreck of galleon	95	95
920	95 c.	Visiting ruins of 19th-century sisal plantation (horiz)	1·40	1·40
917/20		*Set of 4*	2·75	2·75
MS921		118×82 mm. $2 Splashdown of John Glenn's "Mercury" capsule, 1962	3·75	4·25

No. MS921 is inscribed "Sight" in error.

40TH WEDDING ANNIVERSARY

H.M. QUEEN ELIZABETH II

H.R.H. THE DUKE OF EDINBURGH

(206)

207 Football

1988 (14 Mar). *Royal Ruby Wedding. Nos. 772A, 774A and 781A optd with T 206.*

922	10 c.	Type 181	30	30
923	25 c.	H.M.S. *Boreas*	55	55
924	$2	*Sentinel* (cable ship)	3·25	3·25
922/4		*Set of 3*	3·75	3·75

(Des L. Fried. Litho B.D.T.)

1988 (29 Aug). *Olympic Games, Seoul. T 207 and similar vert designs. Multicoloured. P 14.*

925	8 c.	Type 207	15	15
926	30 c.	Yachting	35	40
927	70 c.	Cycling	85	90
928	$1	Athletics	1·25	1·40
925/8		*Set of 4*	2·25	2·50
MS929		102×71 mm. $2 Swimming	2·40	2·50

208 Game-fishing Launch and Swordfish

209 Princess Alexandra and Government House

(Des L. Birmingham. Litho Questa)

1988 (5 Sept). *Billfish Tournament. T 208 and similar multicoloured designs. P 14.*

930	8 c.	Type 208	30	15
931	10 c.	Competitors with swordfish catch	35	15
932	70 c.	Game-fishing launch	1·75	1·75
933	$1	Blue Marlin	2·40	2·50
930/3		*Set of 4*	4·25	4·00
MS934		119×85 mm. $2 Stylized Sailfish (horiz)	3·00	3·50

(Litho Questa)

1988 (24 Oct). *Christmas. 500th Birth Anniv of Titian (artist). Vert designs as T 186a of Lesotho inscr "CHRISTMAS 1988" and with royal cypher at top right. Multicoloured. P 13½×14.*

935	15 c.	"Madonna and Child with Saint Catherine"	40	30
936	25 c.	"Madonna with a Rabbit"	50	40
937	35 c.	"Virgin and Child with Saints"	60	50
938	40 c.	"The Gypsy Madonna"	70	60
939	50 c.	"The Holy Family and a Shepherd"	80	70
940	65 c.	"Madonna and Child"	95	85
941	$3	"Madonna and Child with Saints"	4·25	4·50
935/41		*Set of 7*	7·50	7·00
MS942		Two sheets, each 110×95 mm. (a) $2 "Adoration of the Magi" (detail). (b) $2 "The Annunciation" (detail) .. *Set of 2 sheets*	6·00	7·00

(Des and litho Questa)

1988 (14 Nov). *Visit of Princess Alexandra. T 209 and similar multicoloured designs. P 14.*

943	70 c.	Type 209	1·50	1·50
944	$1.40,	Princess Alexandra and map of islands	2·50	2·50
MS945		92×72 mm. $2 Princess Alexandra (vert)	4·00	4·50

210 Coat of Arms

210a Andrew Jackson and *De Witt Clinton* Railway Locomotive

(Des and litho Questa)

1988 (15 Dec). *P 14½×15.*

946	210	$10 multicoloured	11·00	13·00

(Des D. Miller. Litho Questa)

1989 (15 May). *500th Anniv of Discovery of America by Columbus (1992) (2nd issue). Pre-Columbian Carib Society. Multicoloured designs as T 69 of St. Vincent Grenadines. P 14.*

947	10 c.	Cutting tree bark for canoe	15	15
948	50 c.	Body painting (horiz)	80	80
949	65 c.	Religious ceremony (horiz)	95	95
950	$1	Canoeing	1·50	1·50
947/50		*Set of 4*	3·00	3·00
MS951		84×70 mm. $2 Cave pictograph (horiz)	3·50	4·00

(Des Design Element. Litho Questa)

1989 (17 Nov). *"World Stamp Expo '89" International Stamp Exhibition, Washington (1st issue). Sheet 77×62 mm containing horiz design as T 193a of Lesotho. Multicoloured. P 14.*

MS952		$1.50, Lincoln Memorial	2·50	2·75

(Des W. Hanson Studio. Litho Questa)

1989 (19 Nov). *"World Stamp Expo '89" International Stamp Exhibition, Washington (2nd issue). Bicentenary of the U.S. Presidency. T 210a and similar horiz designs. Multicoloured. P 14.*

953	50 c.	Type 210a	60	65
		a. Sheetlet. Nos. 953/8	3·50	
954	50 c.	Martin van Buren, Moses Walker and early baseball game	60	65
955	50 c.	William H. Harrison and campaign parade	60	65
956	50 c.	John Tyler, Davy Crockett and the Alamo, Texas	60	65
957	50 c.	James K. Polk, California gold miner and first U.S. postage stamp	60	65
958	50 c.	Zachary Taylor and Battle of Buena Vista, 1846	60	65
959	50 c.	Rutherford B. Hayes and end of Confederate Reconstruction	60	65
		a. Sheetlet. Nos. 959/64	3·50	
960	50 c.	James A. Garfield and Battle of Shiloh	60	65
961	50 c.	Chester A. Arthur and opening of Brooklyn Bridge, 1883	60	65
962	50 c.	Grover Cleveland, Columbian Exposition, Chicago, 1893, and commemorative stamp	60	65
963	50 c.	Benjamin Harrison, Pan-American Union Building and map of Americas	60	65
964	50 c.	William McKinley and Rough Rider Monument	60	65
965	50 c.	Herbert Hoover, Sonya Heine (skater) and Ralph Metcalf (athlete)	60	65
		a. Sheetlet. Nos. 965/70	3·50	
966	50 c.	Franklin D. Roosevelt with dog and in wheelchair	60	65
967	50 c.	Statue of Washington by Frazer and New York World's Fair, 1939	60	65
968	50 c.	Harry S. Truman, Veterans Memorial Building, San Francisco, and U.N. emblem	60	65
969	50 c.	Dwight D. Eisenhower and U.S. troops landing in Normandy, 1944	60	65
970	50 c.	John F. Kennedy and "Apollo 11" astronauts on Moon, 1969	60	65
953/70		*Set of 18*	9·75	10·50

Nos. 953/8, 959/64 and 965/70 were each printed together, se-tenant, in sheetlets of six stamps.

(Litho Questa)

1989 (18 Dec). *Christmas. Paintings by Bellini. Vert designs as T 193b of Lesotho. Multicoloured. P 14.*

971	15 c.	"Madonna and Child"	25	25
972	25 c.	"The Madonna of the Shrubs"	35	35
973	35 c.	"The Virgin and Child"	45	45
974	40 c.	"The Virgin and Child with a Greek Inscription"	55	55
975	50 c.	"The Madonna of the Meadow"	65	65
976	65 c.	"The Madonna of the Pear"	80	80
977	70 c.	"The Virgin and Child" (different)	90	90
978	$1	"Madonna and Child" (different)	1·40	1·40
971/8		*Set of 8*	4·75	4·75
MS979		Two sheets, each 96×72 mm. (a) $2 "The Virgin and Child enthroned". (b) $2 "The Madonna with John the Baptist and another Saint" .. *Set of 2 sheets*	6·50	7·00

211 Lift-off of "Apollo 11"

212 *Zephyranthes rosea*

(Des W. Hanson Studio. Litho Questa)

1990 (8 Jan). *20th Anniv of First Manned Landing on Moon. T 211 and similar vert designs. Multicoloured. P 14.*

980	50 c.	Type 211	60	65
		a. Sheetlet. Nos. 980/4 and 5 labels	2·75	
981	50 c.	Lunar module *Eagle* on Moon	60	65
982	50 c.	Aldrin gathering dust sample	60	65
983	50 c.	Neil Armstrong with camera	60	65
984	50 c.	*Eagle* re-united with command module *Columbia*	60	65
980/4		*Set of 5*	2·75	3·00

Nos. 980/4 were printed together, se-tenant, in sheetlets of five stamps, and five stamp-size labels, with Nos. 981/3 forming a composite design.

(Des C. Abbott. Litho Questa)

1990 (11 Jan–21 May). *Island Flowers. T* **212** *and similar vert designs. Multicoloured. P* 14.

985	8 c. Type **212**	10	10
986	10 c. *Sophora tomentosa*	10	15
987	15 c. *Coccoloba uvifera*	15	20
988	20 c. *Encyclia gracilis*	25	30
989	25 c. *Tillandsia streptophylla*	30	35
990	30 c. *Maurandella antirrhiniflora*	35	40
991	35 c. *Tillandsia balbisiana*	40	45
992	50 c. *Encyclia rufa*	60	65
993	65 c. *Aechmea lingulata*	75	80
994	80 c. *Asclepias curassavica*	95	1·00
995	$1 *Caesalpinia bahamensis*	1·10	1·25
996	$1.10, *Capparis cynophallophora*	1·25	1·40
997	$1.25, *Stachytarpheta jamaicensis*	1·40	1·50
998	$2 *Cassia biflora*	2·25	2·40
999	$5 *Clusia rosea*	5·75	6·00
1000	$10 *Opuntia bahamana* (21 May)	11·50	12·00
985/1000	*Set of* 16	24·00	26·00

213 Queen Parrotfish

(Des J. Barbaris. Litho B.D.T.)

1990 (12 Feb). *Fishes. T* **213** *and similar horiz designs. Multicoloured. P* 14.

1001	8 c. Type **213**	20	15
1002	10 c. Queen Triggerfish	20	20
1003	25 c. Sergeant Major	50	45
1004	40 c. Spotted Goatfish	75	65
1005	50 c. Neon Goby	90	80
1006	75 c. Nassau Grouper	1·25	1·25
1007	80 c. Jawfish	1·40	1·50
1008	$1 Blue Tang	1·50	1·60
1001/8	*Set of* 8	6·00	6·00
MS1009	Two sheets, each 115×80 mm. (a) $2 Butter Hamlet. (b) $2 Queen Angelfish		
	Set of 2 *sheets*	8·00	8·50

214 Yellow-billed Cuckoo

215 *Anartia jatrophae*

(Des W. Wright. Litho B.D.T.)

1990 (19 Feb). *Birds* (1st series). *T* **214** *and similar horiz designs. Multicoloured. P* 14.

1010	10 c. Type **214**	30	20
1011	15 c. White-tailed Tropic Bird	45	30
1012	20 c. Kirtland's Warbler	55	45
1013	30 c. Yellow-crowned Night Heron	65	50
1014	50 c. Black-billed Whistling Duck ("West Indian Tree Duck")	1·00	90
1015	80 c. Yellow-bellied Sapsucker	1·50	1·50
1016	$1 American Kestrel	1·75	1·75
1017	$1.40, Northern Mockingbird	2·50	2·50
1010/17	*Set of* 8	8·00	7·50
MS1018	Two sheets, each 104×78 mm. (a) $2 Yellow Warbler. (b) $2 Osprey *Set of* 2 *sheets*	7·00	8·00
See also Nos. 1050/8.			

(Des Linda Vorovik. Litho Questa)

1990 (19 Mar). *Butterflies* (1st series). *T* **215** *and similar multicoloured designs. P* 14.

1019	15 c. Type **215**	15	20
1020	25 c. *Phoebis sennae* (horiz)	30	35
1021	35 c. *Euptoieta hegesia* (horiz)	40	45
1022	40 c. *Hylephila phylaeus* (horiz)	45	50
1023	50 c. *Eurema chamberlaini* (horiz)	60	65
1024	60 c. *Brephidium exilis* (horiz)	70	75
1025	90 c. *Papilio aristodemus* (horiz)	1·00	1·10
1026	$1 *Marpesia eleuchea*	1·10	1·25
1019/26	*Set of* 8	4·25	4·75
MS1027	Two sheets, each 106×76 mm. (a) $2 *Hemiargus thomasi* (horiz). (b) $2 *Danaus gilippus* (horiz) *Set of* 2 *sheets*	4·75	5·00
See also Nos. 1081/9.			

(Des Mary Walters. Litho Questa)

1990 (2 Apr). *500th Anniv of Discovery of America by Columbus* (1992) *(3rd issue). New World Natural History – Fishes. Horiz designs as T* **60** *of Nevis (St. Kitts-Nevis). Multicoloured. P* 14.

1028	10 c. Rock Beauty	10	15
1029	15 c. Coney	15	20
1030	25 c. Red Hind	30	35
1031	50 c. Banded Butterflyfish	60	65
1032	60 c. French Angelfish	70	75
1033	75 c. Blackbar Soldierfish	85	90
1034	90 c. Stoplight Parrotfish	1·00	1·10
1035	$1 French Grunt	1·10	1·25
1028/35	*Set of* 8	4·25	4·75
MS1036	Two sheets, each 109×75 mm. (a) $2 Blue Chromis. (b) $2 Grey Angelfish		
	Set of 2 *sheets*	4·75	5·00

---

216 Penny "Rainbow Trial" in Blue

217 Pillar Box No. 1, 1855

(Des M. Pollard. Litho B.D.T.)

1990 (3 May). *150th Anniv of the Penny Black. T* **216** *and similar vert designs. P* 14.

1037	25 c. deep violet-blue	30	35
1038	75 c. lake-brown	85	90
1039	$1 blue	1·10	1·25
1037/9	*Set of* 3	2·00	2·25
MS1040	144×111 mm. $2 brownish black	2·25	2·50

Designs:—75 c. 1d. red-brown colour trial of December, 1840; $1 2d. blue of 1840; $2 Penny Black.

(Des M. Pollard. Litho B.D.T.)

1990 (3 May). *"Stamp World London 90" International Stamp Exhibition. British Pillar Boxes. T* **217** *and similar vert designs. P* 14.

1041	35 c. purple-brown and brownish grey	40	45
1042	50 c. deep violet-blue and brownish grey	60	65
1043	$1.25, dull ultramarine & brownish grey	1·40	1·50
1041/3	*Set of* 3	2·10	2·40
MS1044	143×111 mm. $2 brown-lake and black	2·25	2·40

Designs:—50 c. Penfold box, 1866; $1.25, Air mail box, 1935; $2 "K" type box, 1979.

218 Queen Elizabeth the Queen Mother

219 Stripe-headed Tanager

(Des D. Miller. Litho Questa)

1990 (20 Aug). *90th Birthday of Queen Elizabeth the Queen Mother. T* **218** *and similar vert designs showing recent photographs of the Queen Mother. P* 14.

1045	10 c. multicoloured	10	15
1046	25 c. multicoloured	30	35
1047	75 c. multicoloured	85	90
1048	$1.25, multicoloured	1·40	1·50
1045/8	*Set of* 4	2·40	2·50
MS1049	70×73 mm. $2 multicoloured	2·25	2·40

(Des Tracy Pedersen. Litho Questa)

1990 (24 Sept). *Birds* (2nd series). *T* **219** *and similar multicoloured designs. P* 14.

1050	8 c. Type **219**	10	10
1051	10 c. Black-whiskered Vireo (horiz)	10	15
1052	25 c. Blue-grey Gnatcatcher (horiz)	30	35
1053	40 c. Lesser Scaup (horiz)	45	50
1054	50 c. Bahama Pintail (horiz)	60	65
1055	75 c. Black-necked Stilt (horiz)	85	90
1056	80 c. Oystercatcher	95	1·00
1057	$1 Louisiana Heron (horiz)	1·10	1·25
1050/7	*Set of* 8	4·00	4·50
MS1058	Two sheets, each 98×69 mm. (a) $2 American Coot (horiz). (b) $2 Bahama Woodstar (horiz) *Set of* 2 *sheets*	4·75	5·00

220 "Triumph of Christ over Sin and Death" (detail, Rubens)

221 Canoeing

(Litho Questa)

1990 (17 Dec). *Christmas. 350th Death Anniv of Rubens. T* **220** *and similar vert designs. Multicoloured. P* 13½×14.

1059	10 c. Type **220**	10	15
1060	35 c. "St. Theresa Praying" (detail)	40	45
1061	45 c. "St. Theresa Praying" (different detail)	50	55

1062	50 c. "Triumph of Christ over Sin and Death" (different detail)	60	65
1063	65 c. "St. Theresa Praying" (different detail)	75	80
1064	75 c. "Triumph of Christ over Sin and Death" (different detail)	85	90
1065	$1.25, "St. Theresa Praying" (different detail)	1·40	1·50
1059/65	*Set of* 7	4·25	4·50
MS1066	Two sheets, each 70×100 mm. (a) $2 "Triumph of Christ over Sin and Death" (different detail). (b) $2 "St. Theresa Praying" (different detail) *Set of* 2 *sheets*	4·75	5·00

(Des D. Miller. Litho Questa)

1991 (7 Jan). *Olympic Games, Barcelona* (1992). *T* **221** *and similar vert designs. Multicoloured. P* 14.

1067	10 c. Type **221**	10	15
1068	25 c. 100 metre sprint	30	35
1069	75 c. Pole vaulting	85	90
1070	$1.25, Javelin	1·40	1·50
1067/70	*Set of* 4	2·40	2·50
MS1071	109×70 mm. $2 Baseball	2·25	2·40

(Des T. Agans. Litho Questa)

1991 (15 Apr). *500th Anniv of Discovery of America by Columbus* (1992) *(4th issue). History of Exploration. Multicoloured designs as T* **64** *of Nevis (St. Kitts-Nevis). P* 14.

1072	5 c. Henry Hudson in Hudson's Bay, 1611	10	10
1073	10 c. Roald Amundsen's airship *Norge*, 1926	10	15
1074	15 c. Amundsen's *Gjoa* in the Northwest Passage, 1906	15	20
1075	50 c. Submarine U.S.S. *Nautilus* under North Pole, 1958	60	65
1076	75 c. Robert Scott's *Terra Nova*, 1911	85	90
1077	$1 Byrd and Bennett's Fokker aircraft over North Pole, 1926	1·10	1·25
1078	$1.25, Lincoln Ellsworth's *Polar Star* on trans-Antarctic flight, 1935	1·40	1·50
1079	$1.50, Capt. James Cook in the Antarctic, 1772–1775	1·75	1·90
1072/9	*Set of* 8	5·50	6·00
MS1080	Two sheets, each 116×76 mm. (a) $2 The *Santa Maria* (vert). (b) $2 Bow of *Nina* (vert) *Set of* 2 *sheets*	4·75	5·00

222 *Anartia jatrophae*

(Des D. Miller. Litho Questa)

1991 (13 May). *Butterflies* (2nd series). *T* **222** *and similar horiz designs. Multicoloured. P* 14.

1081	5 c. Type **222**	10	10
1082	25 c. *Historis osius*	30	35
1083	35 c. *Agraulis vanillae*	40	45
1084	45 c. *Junonia evarete*	50	55
1085	55 c. *Dryas julia*	65	70
1086	65 c. *Siproeta stelenes*	75	80
1087	70 c. *Appias drusilla*	80	85
1088	$1 *Ascia monuste*	1·10	1·25
1081/8	*Set of* 8	4·25	4·50
MS1089	Two sheets, each 114×72 mm. (a) $2 *Phoebis philea*. (b) $2 *Pseudolycaena marsyas* *Set of* 2 *sheets*	4·75	5·00

223 Protohydrochoerus

(Des R. Frank. Litho Questa)

1991 (3 June). *Extinct Species of Fauna. T* **223** *and similar horiz designs. Multicoloured. P* 14.

1090	5 c. Type **223**	10	10
1091	10 c. Phororhacos	10	10
1092	15 c. Prothylacynus	15	20
1093	50 c. Borhyaena	60	65
1094	75 c. Smilodon	85	90
1095	$1 Thoatherium	1·10	1·25
1096	$1.25, Cuvieronius	1·40	1·50
1097	$1.50, Toxodon	1·75	1·90
1090/7	*Set of* 8	5·50	6·00
MS1098	Two sheets, each 79×59 mm. (a) $2 Astrapotherium. (b) $2 Mesosaurus		
	Set of 2 *sheets*	4·75	5·00

(Des D. Miller. Litho Walsall)

1991 (8 June). *65th Birthday of Queen Elizabeth II. Horiz designs as T* **210** *of Lesotho. Multicoloured. P* 14.

1099	25 c. Queen and Prince Philip at St. Paul's Cathedral, 1988	30	35
1100	35 c. Queen and Prince Philip	40	45
1101	65 c. Queen and Prince Philip at Garter Ceremony, 1988	75	80
1102	80 c. Queen at Windsor, May 1988	95	1·00
1099/1102	*Set of* 4	2·25	2·50
MS1103	68×90 mm. $2 Separate photographs of Queen and Prince Philip	2·25	2·50

224 Pluteus chrysophlebius

(Des Wendy Smith-Griswold. Litho Questa)

1991 (24 June). *Fungi. T* **224** *and similar multicoloured designs.* P 14.

1104	10 c. Type **224**		10	10
1105	15 c. *Leucopaxillus gracillimus*		15	20
1106	20 c. *Marasmius haematocephalus*		25	30
1107	35 c. *Collybia subpruinosa*		40	45
1108	50 c. *Marasmius atrorubens* (vert)		60	65
1109	65 c. *Leucocoprinus birnbaumii* (vert)		75	80
1110	$1.10, *Trogia cantharelloides* (vert)		1·25	1·40
1111	$1.25, *Boletellus cubensis* (vert)		1·40	1·50
1104/11		Set of 8	4·50	4·75

MS1112 Two sheets, each 85×59 mm. (a) $2 *Pyrrhoglossum pyrrhum* (vert). (b) $2 *Gerronema citrinum* .. .. *Set of 2 sheets* 4·75 5·00

(Des D. Miller. Litho Walsall)

1991 (29 July). *10th Wedding Anniv of Prince and Princess of Wales. Horiz designs as T* **210** *of Lesotho. Multicoloured.* P 14.

1113	10 c. Prince and Princess of Wales, 1987		10	10
1114	45 c. Separate photographs of Prince, Princess and sons		50	55
1115	50 c. Prince Henry in fire engine and Prince William applauding		60	65
1116	$1 Princess Diana in Derbyshire, 1990, and Prince Charles		1·10	1·25
1113/16		Set of 4	2·25	2·50

MS1117 68×90 mm. $2 Prince, Princess and family, Majorca, 1990 .. .. 2·25 2·50

(Litho B.D.T.)

1992 (26 Aug). *Death Centenary of Vincent van Gogh (artist) (1990). Multicoloured designs as T* **255** *of Maldive Islands.* P 13.

1118	15 c. "Weaver with Spinning Wheel" (horiz)		15	20
1119	25 c. "Head of a Young Peasant with Pipe"		30	35
1120	35 c. "Old Cemetery Tower at Nuenen" ..		40	45
1121	45 c. "Cottage at Nightfall" (horiz)		50	55
1122	50 c. "Still Life with Open Bible" (horiz) ..		60	65
1123	65 c. "Lane, Jardin du Luxembourg" (horiz)		75	80
1124	80 c. "Pont du Carrousel and Louvre, Paris" (horiz)		95	1·00
1125	$1 "Vase with Poppies, Cornflowers, Peonies and Chrysanthemums"		1·10	1·25
1118/25		Set of 8	4·25	4·75

MS1126 Two sheets, each 117×80 mm. (a) $2 "Ploughed Field" (horiz). (b) $2 "Entrance to the Public Park" (horiz). Imperf .. *Set of 2 sheets* 4·75 5·00

225 Series "8550" Steam Locomotive

(Litho Questa)

1991 (4 Nov). *"Phila Nippon '91" International Stamp Exhibition, Tokyo. Japanese Steam Locomotives. T* **225** *and similar horiz designs. Multicoloured.* P 14.

1127	8 c. Type **225**		10	10
1128	10 c. Class "C 57"		10	10
1129	45 c. Series "4110"		50	55
1130	50 c. Class "C 55"		60	65
1131	65 c. Series "6250"		75	80
1132	80 c. Class "E 10"		95	1·00
1133	$1 Series "4500"		1·10	1·25
1134	$1.25, Class "C 11"		1·40	1·50
1127/34		Set of 8	5·00	5·50

MS1135 Two sheets, each 112×80 mm. (a) $2 Class "C 58". (b) $2 Class "C 62" .. *Set of 2 sheets* 4·75 5·00

(Litho Walsall)

1991 (23 Dec). *Christmas. Religious Paintings by Gerard David. Vert designs as T* **211** *of Lesotho. Multicoloured.* P 12.

1136	8 c. "Adoration of the Shepherds" (detail)		10	10
1137	15 c. "Virgin and Child Enthroned with Two Angels"		15	20
1138	35 c. "The Annunciation" (outer wings) ..		40	45
1139	45 c. "The Rest on the Flight to Egypt"		50	55
1140	50 c. "The Rest on the Flight to Egypt" (different)		60	65
1141	65 c. "Virgin and Child with Angels"		75	80
1142	80 c. "Adoration of the Shepherds"		95	1·00
1143	$1.25, "Perussis Altarpiece" (detail)		1·40	1·50
1136/43		Set of 8	4·25	4·75

MS1144 Two sheets, each 102×127 mm. (a) $2 "The Nativity". (b) $2 "Adoration of the Kings". P 14 .. .. .. *Set of 2 sheets* 4·75 5·00

(Des D. Miller. Litho Questa)

1992 (6 Feb). *40th Anniv of Queen Elizabeth II's Accession. Horiz designs as T* **214** *of Lesotho. Multicoloured.* P 14.

1145	10 c. Garden overlooking sea		10	10
1146	20 c. Jetty		25	30
1147	25 c. Small bay		30	35

1148	35 c. Island road		40	45
1149	50 c. Grand Turk		60	65
1150	65 c. Beach		75	80
1151	80 c. Marina		95	1·00
1152	$1.10, Grand Turk (different)		1·25	1·40
1145/52		Set of 8	4·00	4·50

MS1153 Two sheets, each 75×97 mm. (a) $2 Beach (different). (b) $2 Foreshore, Grand Turk *Set of 2 sheets* 4·75 5·00

(Litho B.D.T.)

1992 (26 May). *"Granada '92" International Stamp Exhibition, Spain. Religious Paintings. Vert designs as T* **250** *of Sierra Leone. Multicoloured.* P 13.

1154	8 c. "St. Monica" (Luis Tristán) ..		10	10
1155	20 c. "The Vision of Ezekiel: The Resurrection of the Flesh" (detail) (Francisco Collantes)		25	30
1156	45 c. "The Vision of Ezekiel: The Resurrection of the Flesh" (different detail) (Collantes)		50	55
1157	50 c. "The Martyrdom of St. Phillip" (José de Ribera)		60	65
1158	65 c. "St. John the Evangelist" (Juan Ribalta)		75	80
1159	80 c. "Archimedes" (De Ribera)		95	1·00
1160	$1 "St. John the Baptist in the Desert" (De Ribera)		1·10	1·25
1161	$1.25, "The Martyrdom of St. Phillip" (detail) (De Ribera)		1·40	1·50
1154/61		Set of 8	5·00	5·50

MS1162 Two sheets, each 95×120 mm. (a) $2 "The Baptism of Christ" (Juan Fernández Navarrete). (b) $2 "Battle at El Sotillo" (Francisco Zurbarán). Imperf .. *Set of 2 sheets* 4·75 5·00

(Des W. Hanson Studio. Litho Questa)

1992 (6 July). *17th World Scout Jamboree, Korea. Multicoloured designs as T* **263** *of Maldive Islands.* P 14.

1163	$1 Boy Scout on duty at New York World's Fair, 1964		1·10	1·25
1164	$1 Lord Baden-Powell (vert)		1·10	1·25

MS1165 117×89 mm. $2 Silver Buffalo award 2·25 2·40

226 Nina and Commemorative Coin

(Litho Questa)

1992 (12 Oct). *500th Anniv of Discovery of America by Columbus (5th issue). T* **226** *and similar horiz designs, each showing a commemorative coin. Multicoloured.* P 14.

1166	10 c. Type **226**		10	10
1167	15 c. Departure from Palos		15	20
1168	20 c. Coat of Arms of Columbus		25	30
1169	25 c. Ships of Columbus		30	35
1170	30 c. *Pinta*		35	40
1171	35 c. Landfall in the New World		40	45
1172	50 c. Christopher Columbus		60	65
1173	65 c. *Santa Maria*		75	80
1174	80 c. Erecting commemorative cross		95	1·00
1175	$1.10, Columbus meeting Amerindian		1·25	1·40
1166/75		Set of 10	4·50	5·00

MS1176 Two sheets, each 70×100 mm. (a) $2 Coins showing ships of Columbus. (b) $2 Coins showing landing in the New World *Set of 2 sheets* 4·75 5·00

(Litho Questa)

1992 (7 Dec). *Christmas. Religious Paintings. Vert designs as T* **218** *of Lesotho. Multicoloured.* P 13½×14.

1177	8 c. "Nativity" (detail) (Simon Bening) ..		10	10
1178	15 c. "Circumcision" (detail) (Bening) ..		15	20
1179	35 c. "Flight to Egypt" (detail) (Bening) ..		40	45
1180	50 c. "Massacre of the Innocents" (detail) (Bening)		60	65
1181	65 c. "The Annunciation" (Dieric Bouts) ..		75	80
1182	80 c. "The Visitation" (Bouts)		95	1·00
1183	$1.10, "Adoration of the Angels" (Bouts)		1·25	1·40
1184	$1.25, "Adoration of the Wise Men" (Bouts)		1·40	1·50
1177/84		Set of 8	5·00	5·50

MS1185 Two sheets, each 77×102 mm. (a) $2 "The Virgin seated with the Child" (detail) (Bouts). (b) $2 "The Virgin and Child" (detail) (Bouts) .. .. .. *Set of 2 sheets* 4·75 5·00

CAICOS ISLANDS

CAICOS ISLANDS
(1)

1981 (24 July). *Nos. 514A, 518A, 520A, 523A and 525A/7A of Turks and Caicos Islands optd with T 1.*

1	1 c. Indigo Hamlet		10	10
2	5 c. Spanish Grunt		10	10
3	8 c. Foureye Butterflyfish		10	10
4	20 c. Queen Angelfish		25	30
5	50 c. Fairy Basslet		65	70
6	$1 Clown Wrasse		1·00	1·25
7	$2 Stoplight Parrotfish		2·50	2·75
1/7		Set of 7	4·25	4·75

(2)   (3)

1981 (24 July). *Royal Wedding. Nos. 653/6 of Turks and Caicos Islands optd. A. With T 2 in London. B. With T 3 in New York.*

		A	B	A	B
8	35 c. Prince Charles and Lady Diana Spencer	25	25	1·25	1·25
	a. Opt inverted	†	£130	—	
9	65 c. Kensington Palace	40	40	2·00	2·00
	a. Opt inverted	†	95·00	—	
10	90 c. Prince Charles as Colonel of the Welsh Guards	50	50	2·25	2·25
	a. Opt inverted	†	£110	—	
	b. Opt double	†	£110	—	
8/10		Set of 3	1·00	1·00	5·00	5·00
MS11	96 × 82 mm. $2 Glass Coach		3·00	3·00	4·50	4·50
	a. Opt inverted	†	—		

Nos. 8B/10 come either in sheets of 40 (2 panes 4 × 5) or in sheetlets of 5 stamps and one label. Examples of Nos. 8Ba, 9Ba and 10Ba are known from both formats, but No. 10Bb only exists from sheetlets.

Nos. 8/10 also exist perforated 12 (*Price for set of 3 with London opt £4 or with New York opt £9, mint or used*) from additional sheetlets of five stamps and one label. These stamps have changed background colours.

1981 (29 Oct). *Royal Wedding. Booklet stamps. As Nos. 657/9 of Turks and Caicos Islands, but each inscr "Caicos Islands". Multi-coloured. Roul 5 × imperf*. Self-adhesive.*

12	20 c. Lady Diana Spencer		30	40
	a. Booklet pane. Nos. 12/13, each × 3	4·25		
13	$1 Prince Charles		1·25	1·50
14	$2 Prince Charles and Lady Diana Spencer	7·50	5·50
	a. Booklet pane of 1	7·50		
12/14		Set of 3	8·00	6·75

*The 20 c. and $1 values were each separated by various combinations of rotary knife (giving a straight edge) and roulette. The $2 value exists only with straight edges.

4 Conch and Lobster Fishing, South Caicos

(Des J. Cooter (8 c. to 21 c.). Litho)

1983 (6 June)–84. *T 4 and similar horiz designs. Multicoloured. P 14.*

15	8 c. Type 4		15	15
16	10 c. Hawksbill Turtle, East Caicos	20	20
17	20 c. Arawak Indians and idol, Middle Caicos	30	40
18	35 c. Boat-building, North Caicos	55	60
19	50 c. Marine biologist at work, Pine Cay	75	75
20	95 c. Boeing "707" airliner at new airport, Providenciales	1·50	1·60
21	$1.10, Columbus' *Pinta*, West Caicos	2·00	1·75
22	$2 Fort George Cay (18.5.84)	3·50	3·00
23	$3 Pirates Anne Bonny and Calico Jack at Parrot Cay (18.5.84)	6·00	4·75
15/23		Set of 9	13·50	12·00

5 Goofy and Patch   6 "Leda and the Swan"

(Litho Walsall)

1983 (7 Nov). *Christmas. T 5 and similar vert designs showing Disney cartoon characters. Multicoloured. P 11.*

30	1 c. Type 5		10	10
31	1 c. Chip and Dale		10	10
32	2 c. Morty		10	10
33	2 c. Morty and Ferdie		10	10
34	3 c. Goofy and Louie		10	10
35	3 c. Donald Duck, Huey, Dewey and Louie	10	10
36	50 c. Uncle Scrooge		1·50	90
37	70 c. Mickey Mouse and Ferdie	2·00	1·25
38	$1.10, Pinocchio, Jiminy Cricket and Figaro	2·50	1·90
30/8		Set of 9	6·00	3·75
MS39	126 × 101 mm. $2 Morty and Ferdie. P 13½ × 14		3·50	3·50

(Des and litho Questa)

1983 (15 Dec). *500th Birth Anniv of Raphael. T 6 and similar vert designs. Multicoloured. P 14.*

40	35 c. Type 6		70	50
41	50 c. "Study of Apollo for Parnassus"	90	70
42	95.c. "Study of two figures for the battle of Ostia"	1·75	1·25
43	$1.10, "Study for the Madonna of the Goldfinch"	2·00	1·50
40/3		Set of 4	4·75	3·50
MS44	71 × 100 mm. $2.50, "The Garvagh Madonna"		3·00	3·25

7 High Jumping

8 Horace Horsecollar and Clarabelle Cow

(Litho Questa)

1984 (1 Mar). *Olympic Games, Los Angeles. T 7 and similar designs. P 14.*

45	4 c. multicoloured		10	10
46	25 c. multicoloured		20	20
47	65 c. black, deep grey-blue and new blue	50	50
48	$1.10, multicoloured		85	85
45/8		Set of 4	1·50	1·50
MS49	105 × 75 mm. $2 multicoloured	2·25	3·00

Designs: *Vert*—25 c. Archery; 65 c. Cycling; $1.10, Football. *Horiz*—$2 Show jumping.

(Des Walt Disney Productions. Litho Questa)

1984 (23 Apr). *Easter. Walt Disney Cartoon Characters. T 8 and similar horiz designs. Multicoloured. P 14 × 13½.*

50	35 c. Type 8		60	60
51	45 c. Mickey and Minnie Mouse, and Chip	75	75
52	75 c. Gyro Gearloose, Chip 'n Dale	1·25	1·25
53	85 c. Mickey Mouse, Chip 'n Dale	1·40	1·40
50/3		Set of 4	3·50	3·50
MS54	127 × 101 mm. $2.20, Donald Duck	3·50	3·75

UNIVERSAL POSTAL UNION 1874-1984

AUSIPEX 1984

(9)   (10)

1984 (19 June). *Universal Postal Union Congress, Hamburg. Nos. 20/1 optd with T 9.*

55	95 c. Boeing "707" airliner at new airport, Providenciales	1·00	1·25
56	$1.10, Columbus' *Pinta*, West Caicos	1·25	1·50

1984 (22 Aug). *"Ausipex" International Stamp Exhibition, Melbourne. No. 22 optd with T 10.*

57	$2 Fort George Cay		2·40	2·50

11 Seamen sighting American Manatees

(Des L. Lightbourne. Litho Walsall)

1984 (12 Sept). *492nd Anniv of Columbus' First Landfall. T 11 and similar horiz designs. Multicoloured. P 14.*

58	10 c. Type 11		30	15
59	70 c. Fleet of Columbus		1·75	1·10
60	$1 First landing in West Indies	2·25	1·60
58/60		Set of 3	4·00	2·50
MS61	99 × 69 mm. $2 Fleet of Columbus (*different*)	2·75	3·00

NEW INFORMATION

The editor is always interested to correspond with people who have new information that will improve or correct the Catalogue.

12 Donald Duck and Mickey Mouse with Father Christmas

(Litho Questa)

1984 (26 Nov). *Christmas. Walt Disney Cartoon Characters. T 12 and similar vert designs. Multicoloured. P 12 ($2) or 13½ × 14 (others).*

62	20 c. Type 12		70	40
63	35 c. Donald Duck opening refrigerator	1·00	65
64	50 c. Mickey Mouse, Donald Duck and toy train	1·25	90
65	75 c. Donald Duck and parcels	1·75	1·25
66	$1.10, Donald Duck and carol singers	2·25	1·75
62/6		Set of 5	6·25	4·50
MS67	127 × 102 mm. $2 Donald Duck as Christmas tree	3·00	3·50

No. 65 was printed in sheetlets of 8 stamps.

13 Thick-billed Vireo

14 Two Children learning to Read and Write (Education)

(Des Susan David. Litho Walsall)

1985 (12 Feb). *Birth Bicentenary of John J. Audubon (ornithologist). T 13 and similar horiz designs. Multicoloured. P 14.*

68	20 c. Type 13		1·00	40
69	35 c. Black-faced Grassquit	1·40	65
70	50 c. Pearly-eyed Thrasher	1·75	90
71	$1 Greater Antillean Bullfinch	2·25	1·75
68/71		Set of 4	5·75	3·25
MS72	100 × 70 mm. $2 Stripe-headed Tanager	3·25	3·50

(Des C. Walters. Litho Walsall)

1985 (8 May). *International Youth Year and 40th Anniv of United Nations. T 14 and similar vert designs. Multicoloured. P 14.*

73	16 c. Type 14		20	25
74	35 c. Two children on playground swings (Health)	50	55
75	70 c. Boy and girl (Love)	1·00	1·10
76	90 c. Three children (Peace)	1·25	1·40
73/6		Set of 4	2·75	3·00
MS77	101 × 71 mm. $2 Child, dove carrying ears of wheat and map of the Americas	2·75	3·00

15 Air Caicos "DC-3" on Ground

16 The Queen Mother visiting Foundation for the Disabled, Leatherhead

(Des K. Gromol. Litho Walsall)

1985 (23 May). *40th Anniv of International Civil Aviation Organization. T 15 and similar horiz designs. Multicoloured. P 14.*

78	35 c. Type 15		85	55
79	75 c. Air Caicos Convair "440"	1·75	1·25
80	90 c. TCNA "Islander"	2·00	1·40
78/80		Set of 3	4·25	3·00
MS81	100 × 70 mm. $2.20, Hang-gliding over the Caicos Islands	3·00	3·25

(Des J.W. Litho Questa)

1985 (8 July). *Life and Times of Queen Elizabeth the Queen Mother. T 16 and similar multicoloured designs. P 14.*

82	35 c. Type 16		50	55
83	65 c. With Princess Anne (*horiz*)	90	95
84	95 c. At Epsom, 1961	1·40	1·60
82/4		Set of 3	2·50	2·75
MS85	56 × 85 mm. $2 visiting Royal Hospital, Chelsea	2·75	3·00

(Des Walt Disney Productions. Litho Questa)

1985 (5 Dec). *150th Birth Anniv of Mark Twain (author). Multicoloured designs as T 160a of Lesotho, but horiz, showing Walt Disney cartoon characters in scenes from "Tom Sawyer, Detective". P 14×13½.*

86	8 c. Huckleberry Finn (Goofy) and Tom Sawyer (Mickey Mouse) reading reward notice		30	10
87	35 c. Huck and Tom meeting Jake Dunlap		1·00	55
88	95 c. Huck and Tom spying on Jubiter Dunlap		2·00	1·40
89	$1.10, Huck and Tom with hound (Pluto)		2·25	1·60
86/9	*Set of 4*		5·00	3·25
MS90	127×101 mm. $2 Tom unmasking Jubiter Dunlap		2·75	3·00

(Des Walt Disney Productions. Litho Questa)

1985 (5 Dec). *Birth Bicentenaries of Grimm Brothers (folklorists). Multicoloured designs as T 160b of Lesotho, but horiz, showing Walt Disney cartoon characters in scenes from "Six Soldiers of Fortune". P 14×13½.*

91	16 c. The Soldier (Donald Duck) with his meagre pay		20	25
92	25 c. The Soldier meeting the Strong Man (Horace Horsecollar)		30	35
93	65 c. The Soldier meeting the Marksman (Mickey Mouse)		85	90
94	$1.35, The Fast Runner (Goofy) winning the race against the Princess (Daisy Duck)		1·75	1·90
91/4	*Set of 4*		2·75	3·00
MS95	126×101 mm. $2 The Soldier and the Strong Man with sack of gold		2·50	2·75

Tuvalu

Formerly known as the Ellice Islands when they shared a joint administration with the Gilbert group. On 1 January 1976 the two island-groups separated and the Ellice Islands were renamed Tuvalu.

CROWN COLONY

1 Gilbertese and Tuvaluan

(Des Iakopo Nivatui; adapted J. Cooter. Litho Questa)

1976 (1 Jan). *Separation of the Islands. T 1 and similar multicoloured designs. W w 14 (sideways on 4 and 35 c.). P 13½.*

1	4 c. Type I		45	80
2	10 c. Map of the islands (*vert*)		55	1·00
3	35 c. Canoes		75	1·50
1/3	*Set of 3*		1·60	3·00

(2)   3 50 c. Coin and Octopus

1976 (1 Jan). *Nos. 173 etc. of Gilbert & Ellice Is optd as T 2 in silver (35 c.) or blue (others). (a) W w 12 (upright).*

4	2 c. Lagoon fishing		£750	£140
5	5 c. Gilbertese canoe		80	60
6	8 c. Weaving pandanus fronds		95	60
7	10 c. Weaving a basket		1·00	80
8	50 c. Local handicrafts		27·00	18·00
9	$1 Weaving coconut screen		55·00	70·00
	(b) W w 12 (sideways)			
10	2 c. Lagoon fishing		£140	30·00
11	3 c. Cleaning pandanus leaves		85	60
12	5 c. Gilbertese canoe		2·25	1·00
13	25 c. Loading copra		4·00	2·50
	(c) W w 14 (inverted)			
14	1 c. Cutting toddy		30	30
15	6 c. De-husking coconuts		90	40
16	15 c. Tiger shark		1·00	50
17	50 c. Local handicrafts		1·50	65
18	$1 Weaving coconut screen		2·00	85
19	$2 Coat of arms		2·50	85
	(d) W w 14 (sideways)			
20	2 c. Lagoon fishing		80	40
21	3 c. Cleaning pandanus leaves		90	30
22	4 c. Casting nets		1·00	45
23	20 c. Beating a rolled pandanus leaf		1·00	75
24	25 c. Loading copra		1·00	75
25	35 c. Fishing at night		1·75	1·00
5/7 and 14/25	*Set of 15*		15·00	8·50

1976 (21 Apr). *New Coinage. Vert designs, each showing coin as in T 3. Multicoloured. W w 14 (inverted). P 13½.*

26	5 c. Type 3		25	15
27	10 c. Red-eyed Crab		35	20
28	15 c. Flying Fish		45	25
29	35 c. Green Turtle		60	45
26/9	*Set of 4*		1·50	95

4 Niulakita and Seven-ridged Leathery Turtle

5 Title page of New Testament

(Des J. Cooter. Litho Questa)

1976 (1 July–1 Sept). *Vert designs showing maps (1 to 25 c.) or horiz designs showing scenes (others). Multicoloured. W w 14 (sideways on 35 c. to $5). P 13½.*

30	1 c. Type 4		85	60
31	2 c. Nukulaelae and sleeping mat		40	35
32	4 c. Nui and talo (vegetable)		40	20
33	5 c. Nanumanga and grass skirt		1·25	20
34	6 c. Nukufetau and Coconut Crab		70	30
35	8 c. Funafuti and Banana tree		75	50
36	10 c. Map of Tuvalu		75	20
37	15 c. Niutao and Flying fish		1·00	20
38	20 c. Vaitupu and Maneapa (house)		70	20
39	25 c. Nanumea and fish-hook		2·50	90
40	35 c. Te Ano (game)		60	20
41	50 c. Canoe pole fishing		75	30
42	$1 Reef fishing by flare		80	40
43	$2 Living house		1·10	60
44	$5 M.V. *Nivanga* (1.9.76)		30·00	10·00
30/44	*Set of 15*		38·00	13·50

See also Nos. 58/69.

(Des G. Drummond. Litho Harrison)

1976 (6 Oct). *Christmas. T 5 and similar horiz designs. Multicoloured. W w 14. P 14 × 14½.*

45	5 c. Type 5		50	40
46	20 c. Lotolelei Church		50	40
47	25 c. Kelupi Church		50	40
48	30 c. Mataloa o Tuvalu Church		60	40
49	35 c. Palatasio o Keliso Church		60	40
45/9	*Set of 5*		2·40	1·75

6 Queen Elizabeth and Prince Philip

(Des G. Vasarhelyi. Litho Format)

1977 (9 Feb). *Silver Jubilee. T 6 and similar horiz designs. Multicoloured. P 13½.*

50	15 c. Type 6		60	30
51	35 c. Prince Philip carried ashore at Vaitupu		70	40
52	50 c. Queen and attendants		80	50
50/2	*Set of 3*		1·90	1·10
MS53	98 × 144 mm. Nos. 50/2. P 15		4·00	4·00

7 "Health"

(Des I. Oliver. Litho Format)

1977 (4 May). *30th Anniv of South Pacific Commission. T 7 and similar horiz designs. Multicoloured. P 13½.*

54	5 c. Type 7		20	20
55	20 c. "Education"		25	20
56	30 c. "Fruit-growing"		25	20
57	35 c. Map of S.P.C. area		30	25
54/7	*Set of 4*		90	75

1977 (13 June)–78. *As Nos. 30/6, 38/9 and 44, but no wmk, or new values and designs. (30, 40 c.).*

58	1 c. Type 4 (9.77)		20	15
59	2 c. Nukulaelae and sleeping mat (3.78)		20	25
60	4 c. Nui and talo (vegetable) (3.78)		20	15
61	5 c. Nanumanga and grass skirt (9.77)		25	15
62	6 c. Nukufetau and Coconut Crab (3.78)		20	35
63	8 c. Funafuti and Banana tree (9.77)		20	25
64	10 c. Map of Tuvalu (9.77)		20	20
65	20 c. Vaitupu and Maneapa (house) (10.78)		90	1·25
66	25 c. Nanumea and fish-hook (9.77)		1·25	20
67	30 c. Fatele (local dancing) (19.4.78)		30	20

68	40 c. Screw Pine (19.4.78)		30	15
69	$5 M.V. *Nivanga*		6·50	4·00
58/69	*Set of 12*		9·50	6·50

Examples of the 15 c. and 35 c. values are known on unwatermarked paper, but there is no evidence that such printings were issued without the Independence overprint of 1 October 1978 (Nos. 94/100).

8 Scout Promise

(Des I. Oliver. Litho Format)

1977 (10 Aug). *50th Anniv of Scouting in the Central Pacific. T 8 and similar horiz designs. Multicoloured. P 13½.*

73	5 c. Type 8		30	25
74	20 c. Canoeing		30	25
75	30 c. Scout shelter		40	30
76	35 c. Lord Baden-Powell		40	30
73/6	*Set of 4*		1·25	1·00

9 Hurricane Beach (Expedition photo)

(Des I. Oliver. Litho Format)

1977 (2 Nov). *Royal Society Expeditions, 1896/7. T 9 and similar designs. P 13½ × 14 (5 and 35 c.) or 14 × 13½ (others).*

77	5 c. multicoloured		25	15
78	20 c. black and light blue		40	20
79	30 c. black and light blue		40	20
80	35 c. multicoloured		40	20
77/80	*Set of 4*		1·25	65

Designs: *Vert*—20 c. Boring apparatus on H.M.S. *Porpoise*; 30 c. Dredging chart. *Horiz*—35 c. Charles Darwin and H.M.S. *Beagle*.

10 Pacific Pigeon   11 *Lawedua* (coaster)

(Des G. Drummond. Litho Format)

1978 (25 Jan). *Wild Birds. T 10 and similar vert designs. Multicoloured. P 14 × 13½.*

81	8 c. Type 10		1·00	35
82	20 c. Eastern Reef Heron		1·25	50
83	30 c. White Tern		1·50	60
84	40 c. Lesser Frigate Bird		1·50	65
81/4	*Set of 4*		4·75	1·90

(Des I. Oliver. Litho Format)

1978 (5 Apr). *Ships. T 11 and similar horiz designs. Multicoloured. P 13½ × 14.*

85	8 c. Type 11		15	15
86	10 c. *Wallacia* (tug)		15	15
87	30 c. *Cenpac Rounder* (freighter)		20	20
88	40 c. *Pacific Explorer* (freighter)		25	20
85/8	*Set of 4*		65	65

(Des G. Drummond. Litho Format)

1978 (2 June). *25th Anniv of Coronation. Horiz designs as Nos. 422/5 of Montserrat. Multicoloured. P 13½ × 14.*

89	8 c. Canterbury Cathedral		10	10
90	30 c. Salisbury Cathedral		10	10
91	40 c. Wells Cathedral		15	10
92	$1 Hereford Cathedral		40	30
89/92	*Set of 4*		60	60
MS93	137 × 108 mm. Nos. 89/92. P 15		80	90

Nos. 89/92 were each printed in sheets containing 2 *se-tenant* stamp-size labels.

INDEPENDENT

INDEPENDENCE
1ST OCTOBER
1978
(12)

13 White Frangipani

1978 (1 Oct). *Independence. Nos. 63/4, 65, 67/8 and as Nos. 37 and 40, but without wmk, optd as T 12 by Format.*

94	8 c. Funafuti and Banana tree		10	10
95	10 c. Map of Tuvalu		10	10
96	15 c. Niutao and Flying fish		10	10
97	20 c. Vaitupu and Maneapa (house)		15	15
98	30 c. Fatele (local dancing)		15	15
99	35 c. Te Ano (game)		20	20
100	40 c. Screw Pine		20	20
94/100		*Set of 7*	75	75

(Des J. Cooter. Litho Format)

1978 (4 Oct). *Wild Flowers. T 13 and similar vert designs. Multicoloured. P 14.*

101	8 c. Type 13		15	10
102	20 c. Susana		15	10
103	30 c. Tiale		20	15
104	40 c. Inato		25	25
101/4		*Set of 4*	65	55

14 Squirrelfish

(Des G. Drummond. Litho Format)

1979 (24 Jan)–**81**. *Fishes. Multicoloured designs as T 14. P 14.*

105	1 c. Type 14		10	10
106	2 c. Yellow-banded Goatfish		10	10
107	4 c. Imperial Angelfish		10	10
108	5 c. Rainbow Butterfly		15	10
109	6 c. Blue Angelfish		15	10
110	8 c. Blue Striped Snapper		15	10
111	10 c. Orange Clownfish		25	10
112	15 c. Chevroned Coralfish		25	10
113	20 c. Fairy Cod		35	15
114	25 c. Clown Triggerfish		35	20
115	30 c. Long-nosed Butterfly		35	10
116	35 c. Yellowfin Tuna		40	20
117	40 c. Spotted Eagle Ray		40	10
117*b*	45 c. Black-tipped Rock Cod (16.6.81)		1·50	2·00
118	50 c. Hammerhead Shark		50	20
119	70 c. Lionfish (*vert*)		65	30
120	$1 White-barred Triggerfish (*vert*). .		70	55
121	$2 Beaked Coralfish (*vert*)		1·50	60
122	$5 Tiger Shark (*vert*)		2·75	80
105/22		*Set of 19*	9·00	5·00

Nos. 105/22 were each printed in sheets containing 2 *se-tenant* stamp-size printed labels.

Both fine (300 lines of dots per linear inch) and coarse (175 lines of dots per linear inch) screens were used to produce plates for this issue. The 1, 5, 8, 10, 30 and 40 c. values can be found with either screen. The 15, 25, 35, 45 and 50 c. only exist with coarse screen and the remainder only with fine screen.

15 "Explorer of the Pacific"

(Des J. Cooter. Litho Format)

1979 (14 Feb). *Death Bicentenary of Captain Cook. T 15 and similar horiz designs. Multicoloured. P 14 × 14½.*

123	8 c. Type 15		30	20
	a. Horiz strip of 4. Nos. 123/6		1·40	
	ab. Imperf. Horiz strip of 4 . .			
124	30 c. "A new island is discovered"		40	25
125	40 c. "Transit of Venus, Tahiti, 3 June, 1769"		40	25
126	$1 Death of Captain Cook, Hawaii, 14 February, 1779		50	35
123/6		*Set of 4*	1·40	95

Nos. 123/6 were printed together, *se-tenant*, in horizontal strips of 4 throughout the sheet.

16 Grumman "Goose G21A" and Nukulaelae Island

(Des J. Cooter. Litho Format)

1979 (16 May). *Internal Air Service. T 16 and similar horiz designs. Multicoloured. P 13½.*

127	8 c. Type 16		15	15
128	20 c. "Goose" and Vaitupu		20	20
129	30 c. "Goose" and Nui		30	30
130	40 c. "Goose" and Funafuti		35	35
127/30		*Set of 4*	90	90

17 Sir Rowland Hill, 1976 4 c. Separation Commemorative and London's First Pillar Box, 1855

18 Child's Face

(Des J. Cooter. Litho Format)

1979 (27 Aug). *Death Centenary of Sir Rowland Hill. T 17 and similar horiz designs. Multicoloured. P 13½ × 14.*

131	30 c. Type 17		25	15
132	40 c. Sir Rowland Hill, 1976 10 c. Separation commemorative and Penny Black		25	15
133	$1 Sir Rowland Hill, 1976 35 c. Separation commemorative and mail coach . .		50	30
131/3		*Set of 3*	90	55
MS134	148 × 140 mm. Nos. 131/3. P 15		1·00	1·25

(Des G. Vasarhelyi. Litho Format)

1979 (20 Oct). *International Year of the Child. T 18 and similar vert designs showing children's faces. P 14 × 13½.*

135	8 c. multicoloured		10	10
136	20 c. multicoloured		15	10
137	30 c. multicoloured		15	15
138	40 c. multicoloured		20	25
135/8		*Set of 4*	55	55

19 Cypraea argus

(Des J. Cooter. Litho Format)

1980 (20 Feb). *Cowrie Shells. T 19 and similar horiz designs. Multicoloured. P 13½ × 14.*

139	8 c. Type 19		15	10
140	20 c. Cypraea scurra		15	10
141	30 c. Cypraea carneola. .		20	15
142	40 c. Cypraea aurantium		30	20
139/42		*Set of 4*	70	45

20 Philatelic Bureau, Funafuti, and 1976 8 c. Definitive

21 Queen Elizabeth the Queen Mother at Royal Variety Performance, 1978

(Des J. Cooter. Litho Questa)

1980 (30 Apr). *"London 1980" International Stamp Exhibition. T 20 and similar horiz designs. Multicoloured. P 13½ × 14.*

143	10 c. Type 20		15	15
144	20 c. Gilbert and Ellice Islands stamp with Nukulaelae postmark of 1946 and 1976 2 c. definitive		25	20
145	30 c. Fleet Post Office, U.S. Navy, airmail letter of 1943		25	25
146	$1 Tuvalu coat of arms and map		50	45
143/6		*Set of 4*	1·00	95
MS147	160 × 136 mm. Nos. 143/6		1·00	1·40

(Des G. Drummond. Litho Format)

1980 (14 Aug). *80th Birthday of Queen Elizabeth the Queen Mother. P 13½.*

148	**21**	50 c. multicoloured	35	25

22 Aethaloessa calidalis

(Des J. Cooter. Litho Format)

1980 (20 Aug). *Moths. T 22 and similar horiz designs. Multicoloured. P 14.*

149	8 c. Type 22		10	10
150	20 c. Parotis suralis		15	10
151	30 c. Dudua aprobola		20	15
152	40 c. Decadarchis simulans		20	15
149/52		*Set of 4*	60	45

23 Air Pacific "Heron" (24)

(Des G. Drummond. Litho Format)

1980 (5 Nov). *Aviation Commemorations. T 23 and similar horiz designs. Multicoloured. P 13½ × 14.*

153	8 c. Type 23		10	10
154	20 c. Hawker Siddeley "748"		15	15
155	30 c. "Sunderland" flying boat		15	15
156	40 c. Orville Wright and *Flyer*		20	15
153/6		*Set of 4*	55	45

Commemorations:—8 c. 1st regular air service to Tuvalu, 1964; 20 c. Air service to Tuvalu; 30 c. War time R.N.Z.A.F. flying boat service to Funafuti, 1945; 40 c. Wright Brothers' 1st flight, 17 December 1903.

TWO TYPES OF SURCHARGE FOR NO. 157

Type I

Type II

Type I. Applied by lithography. Clean lines with an even distribution of the ink.
Type II. Applied by typography. Ragged lines with an uneven distribution of the ink, especially at the edges of the figures and bars. On some stamps the impression of the surcharge is visible on the back.

1981 (19 Jan). *No. 118 surch with T 24.*

157	45 c. on 50 c. Hammerhead Shark (I). .		25	40
	a. Type II (typo) surch		4·00	2·25

25 Hypolimnas bolina (male)   26 Brig Elizabeth, 1809

(Des J. Cooter. Litho Questa)

1981 (3 Feb). *Butterflies. T 25 and similar horiz designs. Multicoloured. P 14 × 14½.*

158	8 c. Type **25**		15	10
159	20 c. *Hypolimnas bolina* (female)		20	15
160	30 c. *Hypolimnas bolina* (female) (*different*)		20	20
161	40 c. *Precis villida* ..		25	20
158/61	..	*Set of 4*	70	60

(Des R. Granger Barrett. Litho Format)

1981 (13 May). *Ships* (1st series). *T 26 and similar horiz designs. Multicoloured.* W w **15** (*sideways*). *P 14.*

162	10 c. Type **26**		20	20
163	25 c. *Brigantine Rebecca, 1819*		25	30
164	35 c. *Whaling ship Independence II, 1821*		30	35
165	40 c. H.M.S. *Basilisk, 1872*		35	40
166	45 c. H.M.S. *Royalist, 1890*		40	50
167	50 c. *Barque Olivebank, 1920*		40	50
162/7	..	*Set of 6*	1·75	2·00

Nos. 162/7 were each produced in sheets of six stamps and two labels, these occurring in the second horizontal row.
See also Nos. 235/40 and 377/80.

(Des D. Shults. Litho Questa)

1981 (10 July–26 Nov). *Royal Wedding. Horiz designs as T 26/27 of Kiribati. Multicoloured.* (a) W w **15**. *P 14.*

168	10 c. *Carolina*		10	15
	a. Sheetlet. No. 168 × 6 and No. 169		90	
169	10 c. *Prince Charles and Lady Diana Spencer*		35	35
170	45 c. *Victoria and Albert III*		15	15
	a. Sheetlet. No. 170 × 6 and No. 171		1·10	
171	45 c. As No. 169		30	30
172	$2 *Britannia* ..		50	50
	a. Sheetlet. No. 172 × 6 and No. 173		3·75	
173	$2 As No. 169		1·25	1·25
168/73	..	*Set of 6*	2·25	2·25
MS174	120 × 109 mm. $1·50, As No. 169. Wmk sideways. P 12 (26 Nov)		1·00	1·00

(b) *Booklet stamps. No wmk. P 12* (26 Nov)

175	10 c. As No. 168		15	15
	a. Booklet pane. No. 175 × 4		55	
176	45 c. As No. 171		75	80
	a. Booklet pane. No. 176 × 2		1·50	

Nos. 168/73 were printed in sheetlets of seven stamps of the same face value, each containing six of the "Royal Yacht" design and one of the larger design showing Prince Charles and Lady Diana.
Nos. 175/6 come from $1.70 stamp booklets.

27 U.P.U. Emblem   **28** Map of Funafuti and Anchor

(Des, eng and recess Harrison)

1981 (19 Nov). *U.P.U. Membership.* W **4** *of Maldive Islands. P 14½ × 14.*

177	**27** 70 c. deep ultramarine		30	30
178	$1 red-brown		50	60
MS179	86 × 71 mm. Nos. 177/8. No wmk		2·25	2·50

(Des J. Cooter. Litho Questa)

1982 (17 Feb). *Amatuku Maritime School. T 28 and similar horiz designs. Multicoloured.* W w **15** (*sideways*). *P 13½ × 14.*

180	10 c. Type **28**		10	10
181	25 c. Motor launch		25	25
182	35 c. School buildings and jetty		35	35
183	45 c. School flag and freighters		40	40
180/3	..	*Set of 4*	1·00	1·00

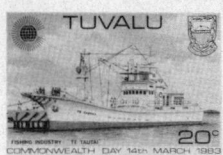

29 Caroline of Brandenburg-Ansbach, Princess of Wales, 1714

TONGA CYCLONE RELIEF 1982 +20c

(30)

(Des D. Shults and J. Cooter. Litho Format)

1982 (19 May). *21st Birthday of Princess of Wales. T 29 and similar vert designs. Multicoloured.* W w **15**. *P 13½ × 14.*

184	10 c. Type **29**		10	10
185	45 c. Coat of arms of Caroline of Brandenburg-Ansbach		20	15
186	$1·50, Diana, Princess of Wales		60	60
184/6	..	*Set of 3*	75	75

1982 (20 May). *Tonga Cyclone Relief. Nos. 170/1 surch as T 30 (words in one line on No. 188).*

187	45 c. + 20 c. *Victoria and Albert III*		30	50
	a. Sheetlet. No. 187 × 6 and No. 188		3·75	
	b. Surch inverted		11·00	
	c. Surch inverted (horiz pair)		20·00	
	d. Surch double		8·00	
188	45 c. + 20 c. Prince Charles and Lady Diana Spencer		50	75
	a. Surch inverted		23·00	
	b. Surch double		22·00	

No. 187c shows the long surcharge, intended for No. 188, inverted and struck across a horizontal pair of No. 187. No. 188a shows two examples of Type **30** inverted on the same stamp.

1982 (14 July). *Birth of Prince William of Wales. Nos. 184/6 optd with T 19 of St. Kitts.*

189	10 c. Type **29**		10	10
190	45 c. Coat of Arms of Caroline of Brandenburg-Ansbach		20	15
	a. Opt inverted		32·00	
191	$1·50, Diana, Princess of Wales		60	60
189/91	..	*Set of 3*	75	75

31 Tuvalu and World Scout Badges   **32** Tuvalu Crest and Duke of Edinburgh's Standard

(Des J. Cooter. Litho Walsall)

1982 (18 Aug). *75th Anniv of Boy Scout Movement. T 31 and similar horiz designs. Multicoloured.* W w **15** (*sideways*). *P 13½ × 14.*

192	10 c. Type **31**		15	15
193	25 c. Camp-fire		40	40
194	35 c. Parade		45	45
195	45 c. Boy Scout		55	55
192/5	..	*Set of 4*	1·40	1·40

(Des J. Cooter. Litho Format)

1982 (26 Oct). *Royal Visit. T 32 and similar vert designs. Multicoloured.* W w **15**. *P 14.*

196	25 c. Type **32**		25	25
197	45 c. Tuvalu flag and Royal Standard		40	40
198	50 c. Portrait of Queen Elizabeth II		40	40
196/8	..	*Set of 3*	95	95
MS199	104 × 85 mm. Nos. 196/8. Wmk inverted		1·00	1·50

33 Fisherman's Hat and Equipment

(Des G. Drummond. Litho Walsall)

1983 (14 Mar)–84. *Handicrafts. T 33 and similar multicoloured designs.* W w **15** (*sideways on 1 c. to 45 c.*). *P 14.*

200	1 c. Type **33**		30	10
201	2 c. Cowrie shell handbags		30	10
202	5 c. Wedding and babyfood baskets		30	10
203	10 c. Model canoe		30	10
203a	15 c. Ladies' sun hats (30.4.84)		1·50	90
204	20 c. Palm climbing rope and platform with toddy pot		30	20
205	25 c. Pandanus baskets		30	20
205a	30 c. Basket tray and coconut stands (18.4.84)		1·75	1·00
206	35 c. Pandanus pillows and shell necklaces		30	30
207	40 c. Round baskets and fans		30	35
208	45 c. Reef sandals and fish trap		35	40
209	50 c. Rat trap (*vert*)		40	45
209a	60 c. Fisherman's waterproof boxes (*vert*) (18.4.84)		2·75	1·25
210	$1 Pump drill and adze (*vert*)		75	70
211	$2 Fisherman's hat and canoe bailers (*vert*)		1·50	1·10
212	$5 Fishing rod, lures and scoop nets (*vert*)		3·50	2·00
200/12	..	*Set of 16*	13·50	8·00

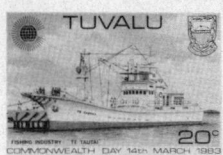

34 *Te Tautai* (trawler)

(Des G. Drummond. Litho Format)

1983 (14 Mar). *Commonwealth Day. T 34 and similar horiz designs. Multicoloured.* W w **15** (*sideways*). *P 14.*

213	20 c. Type **34**		15	15
214	35 c. Traditional dancing, Motufoua School		25	25
215	45 c. Satellite view of Pacific		30	30
216	50 c. *Morning Star* (container ship)		40	40
213/16	..	*Set of 4*	1·00	1·00

No. 214 is incorrectly inscribed "MOTOFOUA SCHOOL".

---

35 *Pantala flavescens*

(Des J. Cooter. Litho Format)

1983 (25 May). *Dragonflies. T 35 and similar horiz designs. Multicoloured.* W w **15** (*sideways*). *P 14.*

217	10 c. Type **35**		20	10
218	35 c. *Anax guttatus*		55	40
219	40 c. *Tholymis tillarga*		60	45
220	50 c. *Diplacodes bipunctata*		75	60
217/20	..	*Set of 4*	1·90	1·40

36 Brigade Members Racing   **(37)**

(Des J. Cooter. Litho Format)

1983 (10 Aug). *Centenary of Boys' Brigade. T 36 and similar multicoloured designs.* W w **15** (*sideways on 10 c., 35 c.*). *P 13½.*

221	10 c. Type **36**		15	15
222	35 c. B. B. members in outrigger canoe		40	45
223	$1 On parade (*vert*)		1·25	1·75
221/3	..	*Set of 3*	1·60	2·10

1983 (26 Aug). *No. 210 surch with T 37.*

224	60 c. on $1 Pump drill and adze		70	70

38 Montgolfier Balloon, 1783   **39** Early Communications

(Des A. Theobald. Litho Format)

1983 (21 Sept). *Bicentenary of Manned Flight. T 38 and similar multicoloured designs.* W w **15** (*sideways on 35 c., 45 c.*). *P 14.*

225	25 c. Type **38**		30	30
226	35 c. McKinnon (Grumman) "Turbo-goose" (*horiz*)		40	40
	a. No wmk			
227	45 c. Beechcraft "Super King Air 200" (*horiz*)		50	50
228	50 c. *Double Eagle II* balloon		60	60
225/8	..	*Set of 4*	1·60	1·60
MS229	114 × 145 mm. Nos. 225/8. Wmk sideways		1·60	1·90

(Des J.W. Litho Questa)

1983 (18 Nov). *World Communications Year. T 39 and similar horiz designs. Multicoloured.* W w **15**. *P 14.*

230	25 c. Type **39**		25	25
231	35 c. Radio operator		30	30
232	45 c. Modern telephone		35	35
233	50 c. Funafuti transmitting station		40	40
230/3	..	*Set of 4*	1·10	1·10

30ᶜ

(40)

1984 (1 Feb). *No. 208 surch with T 40.*

234	30 c. on 45 c. Reef sandals and fish trap		35	40

(Des R. Granger Barrett. Litho Format)

1984 (16 Feb). *Ships* (2nd series). *Horiz designs as T 26. Multicoloured.* W w **15** (*sideways*). *P 14.*

235	10 c. S.S. *Titus, 1897*		15	15
236	20 c. S.S. *Malaita, 1905*		20	20
237	25 c. S.S. *Aymeric, 1906*		20	20
238	35 c. S.S. *Anshun, 1965*		25	25
239	45 c. M.V. *Beaverbank, 1970*		35	35
240	50 c. M.V. *Benjamin Bowring, 1981*		35	35
235/40	..	*Set of 6*	1·40	1·40

Nos. 235/40 were each produced in sheets of six stamps and two labels, these occurring in the second horizontal row.

41 Class "GS-4"

(Des J.W. Litho Format)

1984 (29 Feb). *Leaders of the World. Railway Locomotives (1st series).* T **41** *and similar horiz designs, the first in each pair showing technical drawings and the second the locomotive at work.* P 12½.
241	1 c. multicoloured			10	10
	a. Vert pair. Nos. 241/2			10	10
242	1 c. multicoloured			10	10
243	15 c. multicoloured			20	25
	a. Vert pair. Nos. 243/4			40	50
244	15 c. multicoloured			20	25
245	40 c. multicoloured			25	35
	a. Vert pair. Nos. 245/6			50	70
246	40 c. multicoloured			25	35
247	60 c. multicoloured			35	45
	a. Vert pair. Nos. 247/8			70	90
248	60 c. multicoloured			35	45
241/8			*Set of 8*	1·40	2·00

Designs:—Nos. 241/2, Class "GS-4", U.S.A. (1941); 243/4, Class "AD 60", Australia (1952); 245/6, Class "C 38", Australia (1943); 247/8, *Lord of the Isles*, Great Britain (1892).
See also Nos. 253/68, 273/80, 313/20 and 348/55.

42 *Ipomoea pes-caprae*

(Des Michael and Sylvia Goaman. Litho Questa)

1984 (30 May). *Beach Flowers.* T **42** *and similar horiz designs. Multicoloured.* W w 15. P 14.
249	25 c. Type 42			25	25
250	45 c. *Ipomoea macrantha*			40	40
251	50 c. *Triumfetta procumbens*			45	45
252	60 c. *Portulaca quadrifida*			50	50
249/52			*Set of 4*	1·40	1·40

(Des J.W. Litho Format)

1984 (27 June). *Leaders of the World, Railway Locomotives (2nd series). Designs as* T **41**, *the first in each pair showing technical drawings and the second the locomotive at work.* P 12½.
253	10 c. multicoloured			10	10
	a. Vert pair. Nos. 253/4			15	15
254	10 c. multicoloured			10	10
255	15 c. multicoloured			10	15
	a. Vert pair. Nos. 255/6			20	30
256	15 c. multicoloured			10	15
257	20 c. multicoloured			10	15
	a. Vert pair. Nos. 257/8			20	30
258	20 c. multicoloured			10	15
259	25 c. multicoloured			10	15
	a. Vert pair. Nos. 259/60			20	30
260	25 c. multicoloured			10	15
261	40 c. multicoloured			15	20
	a. Vert pair. Nos. 261/2			30	40
262	40 c. multicoloured			15	20
263	50 c. multicoloured			15	20
	a. Vert pair. Nos. 263/4			30	40
264	50 c. multicoloured			15	20
265	60 c. multicoloured			15	25
	a. Vert pair. Nos. 265/6			30	50
266	60 c. multicoloured			15	25
267	$1 multicoloured			20	30
	a. Vert pair. Nos. 267/8			40	60
268	$1 multicoloured			20	30
253/68			*Set of 16*	1·75	2·75

Designs:—Nos. 253/4, "Casey Jones" type engine, U.S.A. (1896); 255/6, Triplex type, U.S.A. (1914); 257/8, Class "370" Advanced Passenger Train, Great Britain (1981); 259/60, Class "4F", Great Britain (1924); 261/2, Class "Tornado Rover", Great Britain (1888); 263/4, *Broadlands*, Great Britain (1967); 265/6, *Locomotion No.* 1, Great Britain (1825); 267/8, Class "C57", Japan, (1937).
Nos. 253/68 were issued in a similar sheet format to Nos. 241/8.

43 Exhibition Emblem   44 A. Shrewsbury

(Des G. Drummond. Litho Format)

1984 (21 Aug). *"Ausipex" International Stamp Exhibition, Melbourne (Nos. 269/70) and 15th South Pacific Forum (others).* T **43** *and similar horiz designs. Multicoloured,* W w 15 *(sideways).* P 14.
269	60 c. Type 43			30	40
270	60 c. Royal Exhibition Building, Melbourne			30	40
271	60 c. Arms of Tuvalu			30	40
272	60 c. Tuvalu flag			30	40
269/72			*Set of 4*	1·10	1·40

IMPERFORATES AND MISSING COLOURS. Various issues between Nos. 273 and 529 exist either imperforate or with colours omitted. Such items are not listed as there is no evidence that they fulfil the criteria outlined on page xi of this catalogue.

(Des J.W. Litho Format)

1984 (4 Oct). *Leaders of the World. Railway Locomotives (3rd series). Horiz designs as* T **41**, *the first in each pair showing technical drawings and the second the locomotive at work.* P 12½.
273	1 c. multicoloured			10	10
	a. Vert pair. Nos. 273/4			10	10
	b. Error. Wmk w 15			6·00	
	ba. Vert pair. Nos. 273b/4b			12·00	
274	1 c. multicoloured			10	10
	b. Error. Wmk w 15			6·00	
275	15 c. multicoloured			15	20
	a. Vert pair. Nos. 275/6			30	40
276	15 c. multicoloured			15	20
277	30 c. multicoloured			35	40
	a. Vert pair. Nos. 277/8			70	80
	b. Error. Wmk w 15			6·00	
	ba. Vert pair. Nos. 277b/8b			12·00	
278	30 c. multicoloured			35	40
	b. Error. Wmk w 15			6·00	
279	$1 multicoloured			70	1·00
	a. Vert pair. Nos. 279/80			1·40	2·00
	b. Error. Wmk w 15			11·00	
	ba. Vert pair. Nos. 279b/80b			22·00	
280	$1 multicoloured			70	1·00
	b. Error. Wmk w 15			11·00	
273/80			*Set of 8*	2·25	3·00

Designs:—Nos. 273/4, Class "9700", Japan (1897); 275/6, Class "231" C/K, France (1909); 277/8, Class "640", Italy (1907); 279/80, Class "4500", France (1906).
Nos. 273/80 were issued in a similar sheet format to Nos. 241/8.

(Des Court House Studio. Litho Format)

1984 (5 Nov). *Leaders of the World. Cricketers.* T **44** *and similar vert designs, the first listed in each pair showing the cricketer in action and the second a head portrait.* P 12½.
281	5 c. multicoloured			10	10
282	5 c. multicoloured			15	20
	a. Horiz pair. Nos. 281/2			10	10
283	30 c. multicoloured			30	40
	a. Horiz pair. Nos. 283/4			60	80
284	30 c. multicoloured			30	40
285	50 c. multicoloured			40	50
	a. Horiz pair. Nos. 285/6			80	1·00
286	50 c. multicoloured			40	50
287	60 c. multicoloured			50	55
	a. Horiz pair. Nos. 287/8			1·00	1·10
288	60 c. multicoloured			50	55
281/8			*Set of 8*	2·25	2·75

Designs:—Nos. 281/2, A. Shrewsbury; 283/4, H. Verity; 285/6, E. H. Hendren; 287/8, J. Briggs.
Nos. 281/2, 283/4, 285/6 and 287/8 were printed together, se-tenant, in horizontal pairs throughout the sheets.
Similar stamps showing Close (5 c.), (Boycott (15 c.), Bairstow (30 c.), and Evans ($1) were prepared, but not issued. They exist imperforate from stock dispersed by the liquidator of Format International Security Printers Ltd.

45 Trees and Stars

(Des Jennifer Toombs. Litho Format)

1984 (14 Nov). *Christmas. Children's Drawings.* T **45** *and similar horiz designs. Multicoloured.* W w 15 *(sideways).* P 14½ × 14.
289	15 c. Type 45			10	10
290	40 c. Fishing from outrigger canoes			20	20
291	50 c. Three Wise Men bearing gifts			25	25
292	60 c. The Holy Family			35	35
289/92			*Set of 4*	75	75

46 Morris Minor   47 Common Flicker

(Des J.W. ($1), Artists International (others). Litho Format)

1984 (7 Dec). *Leaders of the World. Automobiles (1st series).* T **46** *and similar horiz designs, the first in each pair showing technical drawings and the second the paintings.* P 12½.
293	1 c. black, pale cinnamon and yellow-ochre			10	10
	a. Vert pair. Nos. 293/4			10	10
294	1 c. multicoloured			10	10
295	15 c. black, pale flesh and brown-lilac			10	15
	a. Vert pair. Nos. 295/6			20	30
296	15 c. multicoloured			10	15
297	50 c. black, pale cinnamon and dull mauve			20	20
	a. Vert pair. Nos. 297/8			40	60
298	50 c. multicoloured			20	30

299	$1 black, pale green and cobalt			30	40
	a. Vert pair. Nos. 299/300			60	80
300	$1 multicoloured			30	40
293/300			*Set of 8*	1·10	1·60

Designs:—Nos. 293/4, Morris "Minor"; 295/6, Studebaker "Avanti"; 297/8, Chevrolet "International Six"; 299/300, Allard "J2".
Nos. 293/4, 295/6, 297/8 and 299/300 were printed together, se-tenant, in vertical pairs throughout the sheets.
See also Nos. 321/8, 356/71, 421/32 and 446/70.

(Des R. Vigurs. Litho Format)

1985 (12 Feb). *Leaders of the World. Birth Bicentenary of John J. Audubon (ornithologist).* T **47** *and similar vert designs. Multicoloured.* P 12½.
301	1 c. Type 47			10	10
	a. Horiz pair. Nos. 301/2			10	10
302	1 c. Say's Phoebe			10	10
303	25 c. Townsend's Warbler			30	35
	a. Horiz pair. Nos. 303/4			60	70
304	25 c. Bohemian Waxwing			30	35
305	50 c. Prothonotary Warbler			55	60
	a. Horiz pair. Nos. 305/6			1·10	1·25
306	50 c. Worm-eating Warbler			55	60
307	70 c. Broad-winged Hawk			80	85
	a. Horiz pair. Nos. 307/8			1·60	1·75
308	70 c. Hen Harrier			80	85
301/8			*Set of 8*	3·00	3·25

Nos. 301/2, 303/4, 305/6 and 307/8 were printed together, se-tenant, in horizontal pairs throughout the sheets.

48 Black-naped Tern

(Des G. Drummond. Litho Format)

1985 (27 Feb). *Birds and their Eggs.* T **48** *and similar horiz designs. Multicoloured.* W w 15 *(sideways).* P 14.
309	15 c. Type 48			35	20
310	40 c. White-capped Noddy			75	50
311	50 c. White-tailed Tropicbird			85	60
312	60 c. Sooty Tern			1·00	70
309/12			*Set of 4*	2·75	1·75

(Des J.W. (5 c., $1), T. Hadler (others). Litho Format)

1985 (19 Mar). *Leaders of the World. Railway Locomotives (4th series). Horiz designs as* T **41** *the first in each pair showing technical drawings and the second the locomotive at work.* P 12½.
313	5 c. multicoloured			10	10
	a. Vert pair. Nos. 313/14			10	10
314	5 c. multicoloured			10	10
315	10 c. multicoloured			10	10
	a. Vert pair. Nos. 315/16			20	20
316	10 c. multicoloured			10	10
317	30 c. multicoloured			30	35
	a. Vert pair. Nos. 317/18			60	70
318	30 c. multicoloured			30	35
319	$1 multicoloured			75	1·00
	a. Vert pair. Nos. 319/20			1·50	2·00
320	$1 multicoloured			75	1·00
313/20			*Set of 8*	2·25	2·75

Designs:—Nos. 313/14, "Churchward 28XX", Great Britain (1905); 315/16, Class "KF", China (1935); 317/18, Class "99.77", East Germany (1952); 319/20, Pearson type, Great Britain (1853).
Nos. 313/20 were issued in a similar sheet format to Nos. 241/8.

(Des Artists International. Litho Format)

1985 (3 Apr). *Leaders of the World. Automobiles (2nd series). Horiz designs as* T **46**, *the first in each pair showing technical drawings and the second paintings.* P 12½.
321	1 c. black, apple green and deep dull green			10	10
	a. Vert pair. Nos. 321/2			10	10
322	1 c. multicoloured			10	10
323	20 c. black, pink and rose-red			15	20
	a. Vert pair. Nos. 323/4			30	40
324	20 c. multicoloured			15	20
325	50 c. black, dull violet-blue & brt reddish vio			20	30
	a. Vert pair. Nos. 325/6			40	60
326	50 c. multicoloured			20	30
327	70 c. black, dull pink and grey-brown			20	35
	a. Vert pair. Nos. 327/8			40	70
328	70 c. multicoloured			20	35
321/8			*Set of 8*	1·00	1·50

Designs:—Nos. 321/2, Rickenbacker (1923); 323/4, Detroit-Electric Two Door Brougham (1914); 325/6, Packard "Clipper" (1941; 327/8, Audi "Quattro" (1982).
Nos. 321/8 were issued in a similar sheet format to Nos. 293/300.

49 Curtiss "P-40N"   50 Queen Elizabeth the Queen Mother

70 Rifle-shooting

(Litho Format)

1988 (19 Aug). *Olympic Games, Seoul. T **70** and similar horiz designs. Multicoloured. P 12½.*

534	10 c. Type **70**				10	15
535	20 c. Judo				20	25
536	40 c. Canoeing				40	45
537	60 c. Swimming				55	60
538	80 c. Yachting				75	80
539	$1 Gymnastics				95	1·00
534/9				Set of 6	2·75	3·00

71 Queen Elizabeth II in Ceremonial Canoe   72 Virgin Mary

(Des and litho Questa)

1988 (28 Sept). *10th Anniv of Independence. T **71** and similar designs showing scenes from Royal Visit of 1982. W w **15** (sideways on 60, 90 c., $1.20). P 14.*

540	60 c. multicoloured				60	60
541	90 c. multicoloured				90	90
542	$1 multicoloured (horiz)				1·00	1·00
543	$1.20, multicoloured				1·25	1·25
540/3				Set of 4	3·50	3·50
MS544	Designs as Nos. 540/3 in separate miniature sheets, each 85 × 85 mm					
				Set of 4 sheets	3·50	4·00

(Des M. Pollard. Litho Questa)

1988 (5 Dec). *Christmas. T **72** and similar diamond-shaped designs. Multicoloured. P 14.*

545	15 c. Type **72**				15	20
546	40 c. Christ Child				40	45
547	60 c. Joseph				55	60
545/7				Set of 3	1·00	2·00
MS548	73 × 99 mm. $1.50, Angel				1·40	1·75

73 Dancing Skirt and Dancer

(Des Jennifer Toombs. Litho Questa)

1989 (31 Mar). *Traditional Dancing Skirts. T **73** and similar designs showing skirts and dancer silhouettes. P 14½.*

549	40 c. multicoloured				70	70
550	50 c. multicoloured				80	80
551	60 c. multicoloured				90	90
552	90 c. multicoloured				1·40	1·40
549/52				Set of 4	3·50	3·50
MS553	110×75 mm. $1.50, multicoloured (dancer) (vert)				2·75	3·25

(Litho Questa)

1989 (24 May). *Fungi (2nd series). Vert designs as T **69**. Multicoloured. P 14.*

554	40 c. Trametes muelleri				1·25	1·25
555	50 c. Pestalotiopsis palmarum (grey leaf spot)				1·40	1·40
556	60 c. Trametes cingulata				1·40	1·40
557	90 c. Schizophyllum commune				2·00	2·00
554/7				Set of 4	5·50	5·50

(Des G. Drummond. Litho Questa)

1989 (31 July). *Coral Reef Life (3rd series). Horiz designs as T **60**. Multicoloured. P 14.*

558	40 c. Pennant Coralfish				1·00	1·00
559	50 c. Anemone Fish				1·25	1·25
560	60 c. Batfish				1·40	1·40
561	90 c. Threadfin Coralfish				1·75	1·75
558/61				Set of 4	4·75	4·75
MS562	110×85 mm. Nos. 558/61				5·50	6·50

74 Nivaga II   75 Conch Shell

(Des M. Pollard. Litho Questa)

1989 (9 Oct). *Delivery of Nivaga II (new inter-island ship). Sheet 116×85 mm. P 14.*

MS563	74	$1.50, multicoloured		2·75	3·00

(Des Jennifer Toombs. Litho Questa)

1989 (29 Nov). *Christmas. T **75** and similar vert designs. Multicoloured. P 14.*

564	40 c. Type **75**				65	65
565	50 c. Posy of flowers				80	80
566	60 c. Germinating coconut				85	85
567	90 c. Jewellery				1·50	1·50
564/7				Set of 4	3·50	3·50

76 Cocus nucifera   77 Penny Black with "Stamp World London 90" Emblem

(Des M. Pollard. Litho Questa)

1990 (28 Feb). *Tropical Trees. T **76** and similar vert designs. Multicoloured. P 14½.*

568	15 c. Type **76**				40	40
569	30 c. Rhizophora samoensis				70	70
570	40 c. Messerschmidia argentea				85	85
571	50 c. Pandanus tectorius				95	95
572	60 c. Hernandia nymphaeifolia				1·10	1·10
573	90 c. Pisonia grandis				1·50	1·50
568/73				Set of 6	5·00	5·00

(Des M. Pollard. Litho Questa)

1990 (3 May). *150th Anniv of the Penny Black, and "Stamp World London 90" International Stamp Exhibition. P 14.*

574	77	15 c. multicoloured			45	45
575		40 c. multicoloured			1·10	1·10
576		90 c. multicoloured			2·00	2·00
574/6				Set of 3	3·25	3·25
MS577	115×85 mm. 77	$2 multicoloured			3·50	4·00

78 Japanese Camouflaged Freighter   79 Erythrina fusca

(Litho Questa)

1990 (25 July). *Second World War Ships (1st series). T **78** and similar horiz designs. Multicoloured. P 14.*

578	15 c. Type **78**				45	45
579	30 c. U.S.S Unimack (seaplane tender)				70	70
580	40 c. Amagari (Japanese destroyer)				80	80
581	50 c. U.S.S Platte (transport)				95	95
582	60 c. Japanese Shumushu Class escort				1·10	1·10
583	90 c. U.S.S Independence (aircraft carrier)				1·75	1·75
578/83				Set of 6	5·25	5·25
See also Nos. 613/16.						

(Des Jennifer Toombs. Litho Questa)

1990 (21 Sept). *Flowers. T **79** and similar vert designs. Multicoloured. P 14½×14.*

584	15 c. Type **79**				30	30
585	30 c. Capparis cordifolia				50	50
586	40 c. Portulaca pilosa				60	60
587	50 c. Cordia subcordata				75	75
588	60 c. Scaevola taccada				80	90
589	90 c. Suriana maritima				1·25	1·50
584/9				Set of 6	3·75	4·00

80 Land Resources Survey   81 Mary and Joseph travelling to Bethlehem

(Litho Questa)

1990 (20 Nov). *40th Anniv of United Nations Development Programme. T **80** and similar horiz designs. P 14.*

590	40 c. Type **80**				65	65
591	60 c. Satellite earth station				85	85
592	$1.20, Te Tautai (trawler)				1·90	1·90
590/2				Set of 3	3·00	3·00

(Des M. Pollard. Litho Questa)

1990 (20 Nov). *Christmas. T **81** and similar square designs. Multicoloured. P 14.*

593	15 c. Type **81**				35	35
594	40 c. The Nativity				70	70
595	60 c. Shepherds with flock				1·00	1·00
596	90 c. Wise Men bearing gifts				1·50	1·50
593/6				Set of 4	3·25	3·25

82 Murex ramosus   83 Cylas formicarius (beetle)

(Des D. Miller. Litho Questa)

1991 (18 Jan). *Sea Shells. T **82** and similar vert designs. Multicoloured. P 14.*

597	40 c. Type **82**				60	60
598	50 c. Conus marmoreus				70	70
599	60 c. Trochus niloticus				80	90
600	$1.50, Cypraea mappa				2·00	2·25
597/600				Set of 4	3·75	4·00

(Des D. Miller. Litho Questa)

1991 (22 Mar). *Insects. T **83** and similar horiz designs. Multicoloured. P 14.*

601	40 c. Type **83**				75	75
602	50 c. Heliothis armiger (moth)				85	85
603	60 c. Spodoptera litura (moth)				1·10	1·10
604	$1.50, Agrius convolvuli (moth)				2·75	2·75
601/4				Set of 4	5·00	5·00

84 Green Turtle   85 Football

(Des D. Miller. Litho Questa)

1991 (31 May). *Endangered Marine Life. T **84** and similar vert designs. Multicoloured. P 14.*

605	40 c. Type **84**				60	60
606	50 c. Humpback Whale				70	70
607	60 c. Hawksbill Turtle				80	90
608	$1.50, Sperm Whale				2·25	2·50
605/8				Set of 4	4·00	4·25

(Des D. Miller. Litho Questa)

1991 (31 July). *9th South Pacific Games. T **85** and similar vert designs. Multicoloured. P 14.*

609	40 c. Type **85**				65	65
610	50 c. Volleyball				85	85
611	60 c. Lawn tennis				1·10	1·10
612	$1.50, Cricket				2·75	3·00
609/12				Set of 4	4·75	5·00

The new-issue supplement to this Catalogue appears each month in

GIBBONS STAMP MONTHLY

—from your newsagent or by postal subscription— sample copy and details on request.

86 U.S.S. Tennessee   87 Traditional
(battleship)   Dancers

(Des D. Miller. Litho Questa)

1991 (15 Oct). *Second World War Ships* (2nd series). *T* **86** *and similar horiz designs. Multicoloured.* P 14.

613	40 c. Type 86		75	75
614	50 c. *Haguro* (Japanese cruiser)		90	90
615	60 c. H.M.N.Z.S. *Achilles* (cruiser)		1·10	1·10
616	$1.50, U.S.S. *North Carolina* (battleship)		2·75	3·00
613/16		*Set of 4*	5·00	5·25

(Des D. Miller. Litho Questa)

1991 (13 Dec). *Christmas. T* **87** *and similar vert designs. Multicoloured.* P 14.

617	40 c. Type 87		70	70
618	50 c. Solo dancer		85	85
619	60 c. Dancers in green costumes		1·00	1·00
620	$1.50, Dancers in multicoloured costumes		2·25	2·50
617/20		*Set of 4*	4·25	4·50

88 Southern Fish   89 King George VI and Cargo
Constellation   Liner

(Des D. Miller. Litho Questa)

1992 (29 Jan). *Pacific Star Constellations. T* **88** *and similar vert designs. Multicoloured.* P 14.

621	40 c. Type 88		75	75
622	50 c. Scorpion		90	90
623	60 c. Archer		1·10	1·10
624	$1.50, Southern Cross		2·75	2·75
621/4		*Set of 4*	5·00	5·00

(Des D. Miller. Litho Questa)

1992 (23 Mar). *Centenary of British Occupation of Tuvalu. T* **89** *and similar horiz designs.* P 14.

625	40 c. Type 89		55	55
626	50 c. King George V and freighter with barges at wharf		65	65
627	60 c. King Edward VII and freighter		80	80
628	$1.50, Queen Victoria and warship		2·00	2·25
625/8		*Set of 4*	3·50	3·75

It is probable that the ship shown on No. 628 is intended to be H.M.S. *Royalist* (corvette) launched 1883, but the vessel depicted appears to be H.M.S. *Royalist* (cruiser) launched 1915.

90 Columbus with King
Ferdinand and Queen Isabella
of Spain

(Des D. Miller. Litho Questa)

1992 (22 May). *500th Anniv of Discovery of America by Columbus. T* **90** *and similar horiz designs.* P 14.

629	40 c. deep new blue and black		45	45
630	50 c. brown-purple and black		55	55
631	60 c. myrtle-green and black		70	70
632	$1.50, deep purple and black		1·75	1·90
629/32		*Set of 4*	3·00	3·25

Designs:—50 c. Columbus and Polynesians; 60 c. Columbus and South American Indians; $1.50, Columbus and North American Indians.

OMNIBUS ISSUES

Details, together with prices for complete sets, of the various Omnibus issues from the 1935 Silver Jubilee series to date are included in a special section following Zimbabwe at the end of Volume 2.

---

91 *Chaetodon plebeius*   92 Discus
    Throwing

(Des D. Miller. Litho Questa)

1992 (15 July). *Fishes. T* **91** *and similar multicoloured designs.* P 14.

633	15 c. Type 91		10	10
634	20 c. *Scarus frenatus*		15	20
635	25 c. *Acanthurus lineatus*		25	30
636	30 c. *Thalassoma lunare*		25	30
637	35 c. *Oxymonocanthus longirostis*		30	35
638	40 c. *Gomphosus varius*		35	40
639	45 c. *Bodianus loxozonus*		40	45
640	50 c. *Chromis viridis*		45	50
641	60 c. *Cheilinus undulatus*		50	55
642	70 c. *Chaetodon ornatissimus* (vert)		60	65
643	90 c. *Chaetodon ephippium* (vert)		75	80
644	$1 *Chaetodon vagabundus* (vert)		85	90
645	$2 *Heniochus acuminatus* (vert)		1·75	1·90
646	$3 *Zanclus cornutus* (vert)		3·00	3·25
633/46		*Set of 14*	8·75	9·50

(Des D. Miller. Litho Questa)

1992 (27 July). *Olympic Games, Barcelona. T* **92** *and similar vert designs. Multicoloured.* P 14.

647	40 c. Type 92		40	40
648	50 c. Javelin throwing		50	50
649	60 c. Shotput		55	55
650	$1.50, Competitor's foot		1·50	1·75
647/50		*Set of 4*	2·75	3·00
MS651	100×71 mm. $2 Olympic stadium, Barcelona		2·25	2·40

93 Blue Coral   (94)

(Des G. Drummond. Litho Questa)

1992 (1 Sept). *Endangered Species. Blue Coral. T* **93** *and similar horiz designs showing different coral formations.* P 14.

652	10 c. multicoloured		15	15
653	25 c. multicoloured		35	35
654	30 c. multicoloured		35	35
655	35 c. multicoloured		40	40
652/5		*Set of 4*	1·10	1·10

1992 (1 Sept). *"Kuala Lumpur '92" International Philatelic Exhibition.* Nos. 636, 638 and 640/1 optd with T **94**.

656	30 c. *Thalassoma lunare*		35	35
657	40 c. *Gomphosus varius*		45	45
658	50 c. *Chromis viridis*		55	55
659	60 c. *Cheilinus undulatus*		65	65
656/9		*Set of 4*	1·75	1·75

95 Fishermen and   96 *Calophyllum*
Angel   *inophyllum*

(Des D. Miller. Litho Questa)

1992 (25 Dec). *Christmas. T* **95** *and similar vert designs. Multicoloured.* P 14.

660	40 c. Type 95		35	40
661	50 c. Fishing canoes following star		45	50
662	60 c. Nativity scene		50	55
663	$1.50, Christmas gifts		1·25	1·40
660/3		*Set of 4*	2·25	2·50

(Des D. Miller. Litho Questa)

1993 (2 Feb). *Flowers. T* **96** *and similar vert designs. Multicoloured.* P 14.

664	40 c. Type 96		35	40
665	50 c. *Hibiscus tiliaceus*		45	50
666	60 c. *Lantana camara*		50	55
667	$1.50, *Plumeria rubra*		1·25	1·40
664/7		*Set of 4*	2·25	2·50

POSTAGE DUE STAMPS

D 1 Tuvalu Crest

(Des G. Drummond. Litho Questa)

1981 (3 May). P 13½ × 14.

D1	D 1	1 c. black and bright purple		10	10
D2		2 c. black and greenish blue		10	10
D3		5 c. black and ochre		10	10
D4		10 c. black and blue-green		20	20
D5		20 c. black and purple-brown		35	35
D6		30 c. black and bright orange		40	40
D7		40 c. black and blue		50	50
D8		50 c. black and yellow-green		60	60
D9		$1 black and deep mauve		1·10	1·10
D1/9			*Set of 9*	3·00	3·00

1982 (25 Nov)–**83**. *As Nos.* D1/9 *but* P 14½ × 15 *and with imprint date at foot.*

D10	D 1	1 c. black and bright purple		10	10
D11		2 c. black and greenish blue		10	10
D12		5 c. black and ochre		10	10
D13		10 c. black and blue-green		10	10
D14		20 c. black and purple-brown		15	20
D15		30 c. black and bright orange (25.5.83)		25	30
D16		40 c. black and blue (25.5.83)		35	40
D17		50 c. black and yellow-green (25.5.83)		45	50
D18		$1 black and deep mauve (25.5.83)		85	90
D10/18			*Set of 9*	2·00	2·25

The imprint date on Nos. D10/14 is "1982" and on Nos. D15/18 "1983".

OFFICIAL STAMPS

For the use of the Philatelic Bureau.

OFFICIAL   OFFICIAL

(O 1)   (O 2)

TWO TYPES OF OVERPRINT FOR NOS. O1/19

This issue was overprinted using two different processes.

All values, except for the 35, 45 and 50 c., come with the overprint applied by typography. This process results in ragged lines, uneven distribution of the ink, especially at the edges of the letters, and often has the impression of the letters visible from the reverse.

In addition nine of these values have been found with overprints applied by lithography. These show clean lines and an even distribution of the ink.

The 35, 45 and 50 c. values have only been seen with overprints applied by lithography.

1981 (2 July). Nos. 105/22 optd with Type O 1.

O 1	1 c. Type 14			10	10
	a. Litho opt				
O 2	2 c. Yellow-banded Goatfish			10	10
O 3	4 c. Imperial Angelfish			10	10
O 4	5 c. Rainbow Butterfly			10	10
O 5	6 c. Blue Angelfish			10	10
	a. Litho opt			30	30
O 6	8 c. Blue Striped Snapper			10	10
O 7	10 c. Orange Clownfish			15	15
	a. Litho opt			30	30
O 8	15 c. Chevroned Coralfish			20	20
O 9	20 c. Fairy Cod			25	25
O10	25 c. Clown Triggerfish			25·00	
	a. Litho opt			30	30
O11	30 c. Long-nosed Butterfly			30	30
	a. Litho opt				
O12	35 c. Yellowfin Tuna (litho opt)			35	35
O13	40 c. Spotted Eagle Ray			40	40
O14	45 c. Black-tipped Rock Cod (litho opt)			45	45
O15	50 c. Hammerhead Shark (litho opt)			50	50
O16	70 c. Lionfish			75	75
	a. Litho opt			4·00	3·00
O17	$1 White-barred Triggerfish			1·10	1·10
	a. Litho opt			2·50	2·50
O18	$2 Beaked Coralfish			3·25	3·00
	a. Litho opt			2·25	2·25
O19	$5 Tiger Shark			5·50	6·00
	a. Litho opt			15·00	12·00
O1/19			*Set of 19*	11·00	11·00

1983 (26 Aug)–**85**. Nos. 202/3a, 205/12, 224 and 234 optd as Type O 1, but 20½ × 4 mm. (5 c.), or as Type O 2 (others).

O20	5 c. Wedding and baby food baskets (1.2.84)			10	15
	a. Optd as Type O 2 (5.85)			15	15
O21	10 c. Hand-carved model of canoe (1.2.84)			10	15
O22	15 c. Ladies' sun hats (30.4.84)			15	20
O23	25 c. Pandanus baskets (1.2.84)			25	30
O24	30 c. on 45 c. Reef sandals and fish trap (1.2.84)			50	60
O25	30 c. Basket tray and coconut stand (30.4.84)			30	40
O26	35 c. Pandanus pillows and shell necklaces (1.2.84)			40	45
O27	40 c. Round baskets and fans (1.2.84)			45	50
O28	45 c. Reef sandals and fish trap (1.2.84)			45	50
O29	50 c. Rat trap (1.2.84)			50	60
O30	60 c. on $1 Pump drill and adze (1.2.84)			75	85
O31	60 c. Fisherman's waterproof boxes (30.4.84)			60	80
O32	$1 Pump drill and adze (1.2.84)			1·00	1·00
O33	$2 Fisherman's hat and canoe bailers (1.2.84)			1·75	2·00
O34	$5 Fishing rod, lures and scoop nets (1.2.84)			4·25	4·75
O20/34			*Set of 15*	10·50	12·00

OFFICIAL

(O 3)

1989 (22 Feb). *Nos. 502/17 optd with Type O 3.*

O35	5 c.	Type **66**	10	10
O36	10 c.	White Tern	10	15
O37	15 c.	Common Noddy	15	20
O38	20 c.	Phoenix Petrel	15	20
O39	25 c.	American Golden Plover	25	30
O40	30 c.	Crested Tern	25	30
O41	35 c.	Sooty Tern	30	35
O42	40 c.	Bristle-thighed Curlew	35	40
O43	45 c.	Bar-tailed Godwit	40	45
O44	50 c.	Eastern Reef Heron	45	50
O45	55 c.	Great Frigate Bird	45	50
O46	60 c.	Red-footed Booby	50	55
O47	70 c.	Rufous-necked Sandpiper ("Red-necked Stint")	60	65
O48	$1	Long-tailed Koel ("Long-tailed Cuckoo")	85	90
O49	$2	Red-tailed Tropic Bird	1·75	1·90
O50	$5	Banded Rail	4·25	4·50
O35/50		*Set of* 16	9·75	11·00

Appendix

The following issues for individual islands of Tuvalu fall outside the criteria for full listing as detailed on page xi of this edition.

FUNAFUTI
1984

Leaders of the World. Railway Locomotives (1st series). Two designs for each value, the first showing technical drawings and the second the locomotive at work. 15, 20, 30, 40, 50, 60 c., each × 2

Leaders of the World. Automobiles (1st series). Two designs for each value, the first showing technical drawings and the second the car in action. 1, 10, 40 c., $1, each × 2

Leaders of the World. Railway Locomotives (2nd series). Two designs for each value, the first showing technical drawings and the second the locomotive at work. 5, 15, 25, 35, 40, 55, 60 c., $1, each × 2

1985

Leaders of the World. Automobiles (2nd series). Two designs for each value, the first showing technical drawings and the second the car in action. 1, 30, 55, 60 c., each × 2

Leaders of the World. Railway Locomotives (3rd series). Two designs for each value, the first showing technical drawings and the second the locomotive at work. 5, 15, 35, 40, 50 c., $1, each × 2

Leaders of the World. Life and Times of Queen Elizabeth the Queen Mother. Two designs for each value, showing different portraits. 5, 25, 80 c., $1.05, each × 2

1986

60th Birthday of Queen Elizabeth II. 10, 50 c., $1.50, $3.50

Royal Wedding (1st issue). 60 c., $1, each × 2

Royal Wedding (2nd issue). Previous Royal Wedding stamps optd "Congratulations T.R.H. The Duke & Duchess of York". 60 c., $1, each × 2

Railway Locomotives (4th series). Two designs for each value, the first showing technical drawings and the second the locomotive at work. 20, 40, 60 c., $1.50, each × 2

1987

Automobiles (3rd series). Two designs for each value, the first showing technical drawings and the second the car in action. 10, 20, 40, 60, 75, 80 c., $1, $1.50, each × 2

Royal Ruby Wedding. 20, 50, 75 c., $1.20, $1.75

1988

Olympic Games, Seoul. 10, 20, 40, 50, 80, 90 c.

NANUMAGA
1984

Leaders of the World. Automobiles (1st series). Two designs for each value, the first showing technical drawings and the second the car in action. 5, 10, 25, 30, 40 c., $1, each × 2

Leaders of the World. British Monarchs. Two designs for each value, forming a composite picture. 10, 20, 30, 40, 50 c., $1, each × 2

Leaders of the World. Automobiles (2nd series). Two designs for each value, the first showing technical drawings and the second the car in action. 5, 10, 50 c., each × 2

1985

Leaders of the World. Railway Locomotives. Two designs for each value, the first showing technical drawings and the second the locomotive at work. 10, 25, 50, 60 c., each × 2

Leaders of the World. Flowers. 25, 30, 40, 50 c., each × 2

Leaders of the World. Automobiles (3rd series). Two designs for each value, the first showing technical drawings and the second the car in action. 10, 25, 75 c., $1, each × 2

Leaders of the World. Life and Times of Queen Elizabeth the Queen Mother. Two designs for each value, showing different portraits. 15, 55, 65, 90 c., each × 2

1986

60th Birthday of Queen Elizabeth II. 5 c., $1, $1.75, $2.50

World Cup Football Championship, Mexico. 1, 5, 5, 10, 20, 35, 50, 60, 75 c., $1, $2, $4

Royal Wedding (1st issue). 60 c., $1, each × 2

Royal Wedding (2nd issue). Previous Royal Wedding stamps optd as for Funafuti. 60 c., $1, each × 2

1987

Automobiles (4th series). Two designs for each value, the first showing technical drawings and the second the car in action. 5, 10, 15, 20, 25, 40, 60 c., $1, each × 2

Royal Ruby Wedding. 15, 35, 60 c., $1.50, $1.75

NANUMEA
1984

Leaders of the World. Railway Locomotives (1st series). Two designs for each value, the first showing technical drawings and the second the locomotive at work. 15, 20, 30, 40, 50, 60 c., each × 2

Leaders of the World. Famous Cricketers. Two designs for each value, the first showing a portrait and the second the cricketer in action. 1, 10, 40 c., $1, each × 2

1985

Leaders of the World. Automobiles (1st series). Two designs for each value, the first showing technical drawings and the second the car in action. 5, 40, 50, 60 c., each × 2

Leaders of the World. Railway Locomotives (2nd series). Two designs for each value, the first showing technical drawings and the second the locomotive at work. 1, 35, 50, 60 c., each × 2

Leaders of the World. Automobiles (2nd series). Two designs for each value, the first showing technical drawings and the second the car in action. 15, 20, 50, 60 c., each × 2

Leaders of the World. Cats. 5, 30, 50 c., $1, each × 2

Leaders of the World. Life and Times of Queen Elizabeth the Queen Mother. Two designs for each value, showing different portraits. 5, 30, 75 c., $1.05, each × 2

1986

60th Birthday of Queen Elizabeth II. 10, 80 c., $1.75, $3

World Cup Football Championship, Mexico. 1, 2, 5, 10, 25, 40, 50, 75, 90 c., $1, $2.50, $4

Royal Wedding (1st issue). 60 c., $1, each × 2

Royal Wedding (2nd issue). Previous Royal Wedding stamps optd as for Funafuti. 60 c., $1, each × 2

Automobiles (3rd series). Two designs for each value, the first showing technical drawings and the second the car in action. 10, 20, 35, 50, 75 c., $2, each × 2

1987

Royal Ruby Wedding. 40, 60, 80 c., $1, $2

NIUTAO
1984

Leaders of the World. Automobiles (1st series). Two designs for each value, the first showing technical drawings and the second the car in action. 15, 30, 40, 50 c., each × 2

Leaders of the World. Railway Locomotives (1st series). Two designs for each value, the first showing technical drawings and the second the locomotive at work. 5, 10, 20, 40, 50 c., $1, each × 2

1985

Leaders of the World. Famous Cricketers. Two designs for each value, the first showing a portrait and the second the cricketer in action. 1, 15, 50 c., $1, each × 2

Leaders of the World. Birth Bicent of John J. Audubon (ornithologist). Birds. 5, 15, 25 c., $1, each × 2

Leaders of the World. Automobiles (2nd series). Two designs for each value, the first showing technical drawings and the second the car in action. 20, 25, 40, 60 c., each × 2

Leaders of the World. Railway Locomotives (2nd series). Two designs for each value, the first showing technical drawings and the second the locomotive at work. 10, 30, 45, 60, 75 c., $1.20, each × 2

Leaders of the World. Life and Times of Queen Elizabeth the Queen Mother. Two designs for each value, showing different portraits. 15, 35, 70, 95 c., each × 2

1986

60th Birthday of Queen Elizabeth II. 5, 60 c., $1.50, $3.50

Royal Wedding (1st issue). 60 c., $1, each × 2

Royal Wedding (2nd issue). Previous Royal Wedding stamps optd as for Funafuti. 60 c., $1, each × 2

1987

Royal Ruby Wedding. 60th Birthday of Queen Elizabeth II issue of 1986 optd "40th WEDDING ANNIVERSARY OF H.M. QUEEN ELIZABETH II". 5, 60 c., $1.50, $3.50

NUI
1984

Leaders of the World. Railway Locomotives (1st series). Two designs for each value, the first showing technical drawings and the second the locomotive at work. 15, 25, 30, 50 c., each × 2

Leaders of the World. British Monarchs. Two designs for each value, forming a composite picture. 1, 5, 15, 40, 50 c., $1, each × 2

1985

Leaders of the World. Railway Locomotives (2nd series). Two designs for each value, the first showing technical drawings and the second the locomotive at work. 5, 15, 25 c., $1, each × 2

Leaders of the World. Automobiles (1st series). Two designs for each value, the first showing technical drawings and the second the car in action. 25, 30, 40, 50 c., each × 2

Leaders of the World. Famous Cricketers. Two designs for each value, the first showing a portrait and the second the cricketer in action. 1, 40, 60, 70 c., each × 2

Leaders of the World. Life and Times of Queen Elizabeth the Queen Mother. Two designs for each value, showing different portraits. 5, 50, 75, 85 c., each × 2

Leaders of the World. Automobiles (2nd series). Two designs for each value, the first showing technical drawings and the second the car in action. 5, 15, 40, 60, 90 c., $1.10, each × 2

1986

60th Birthday of Queen Elizabeth II. 10, 80 c., $1.75, $3

Royal Wedding (1st issue). 60 c., $1, each × 2

Royal Wedding (2nd issue). Previous Royal Wedding stamps optd as for Funafuti. 60 c., $1, each × 2

1987

Railway Locomotives (3rd series). Two designs for each value, the first showing technical drawings and the second the locomotive at work. 10, 25, 35, 40, 60, 75 c., $1, $1.25, each × 2

Royal Ruby Wedding. 20, 50, 75 c., $1.20, $1.75

1988

Railway Locomotives (4th series). Two designs for each value, the first showing technical drawings and the second the locomotive at work. 5, 10, 20, 25, 40, 50, 60, 75 c., each × 2

NUKUFETAU
1984

Leaders of the World. Automobiles (1st series). Two designs for each value, the first showing technical drawings and the second the car in action. 10, 25, 30, 50, 60 c., each × 2

Leaders of the World. British Monarchs. Two designs for each value, forming a composite picture. 1, 10, 30, 50, 60 c., $1, each × 2

1985

Leaders of the World. Famous Cricketers. Two designs for each value, the first showing a portrait and the second the cricketer in action. 1, 10, 55 c., $1, each × 2

Leaders of the World. Railway Locomotives (1st series). Two designs for each value, the first showing technical drawings and the second the locomotive at work. 1, 10, 60, 70 c., each × 2

Leaders of the World. Automobiles (2nd series). Two designs for each value, the first showing technical drawings and the second the car in action. 5, 10, 15, 20, 50, 60, 75 c., $1.50, each × 2

Leaders of the World. Life and Times of Queen Elizabeth the Queen Mother. Two designs for each value, showing different portraits. 10, 45, 65 c., $1, each × 2

1986

Leaders of the World. Railway Locomotives (2nd series). Two designs for each value, the first showing technical drawings and the second the locomotive at work. 20, 40, 60 c., $1.50, each × 2

60th Birthday of Queen Elizabeth II. 5, 40 c., $2, $4

Royal Wedding (1st issue). 60 c., $1, each × 2

Royal Wedding (2nd issue). Previous Royal Wedding stamps optd as for Funafuti. 60 c., $1, each × 2

1987

Railway Locomotives (3rd series). Two designs for each value, the first showing technical drawings and the second the locomotive at work. 5, 10, 15, 25, 30, 50, 60 c., $1, each × 2

Royal Ruby Wedding. 60th Birthday of Queen Elizabeth II issue of 1986 optd as for Niutao. 5, 40 c., $2, $4

NUKULAELAE
1984

Leaders of the World. Railway Locomotives (1st series). Two designs for each value, the first showing technical drawings and the second the locomotive at work. 5, 15, 40 c., $1, each × 2

Leaders of the World. Famous Cricketers. Two designs for each value, the first showing a portrait and the second the cricketer in action. 5, 15, 30 c., $1, each × 2

Leaders of the World. Railway Locomotives (2nd series). Two designs for each value, the first showing technical drawings and the second the locomotive at work. 5, 20, 40 c., $1, each × 2

1985

Leaders of the World. Automobiles. Two designs for each value, the first showing technical drawings and the second the car in action. 5, 35, 50, 70 c., each × 2

Leaders of the World. Dogs. 5, 20, 50, 70 c., each × 2

Leaders of the World. Railway Locomotives (3rd series). Two designs for each value, the first showing technical drawings and the second the locomotive at work. 10, 25, 50 c., $1, each × 2

Leaders of the World. Automobiles (2nd series). Two designs for each value, the first showing technical drawings and the second the car in action. 10, 25, 35, 50, 75 c., $1, each × 2

Leaders of the World. Life and Times of Queen Elizabeth the Queen Mother. Two designs for each value, showing different portraits. 5, 25, 85 c., $1, each × 2

1986

60th Birthday of Queen Elizabeth II. 10 c., $1, $1.50, $3

Railway Locomotives (4th series). Two designs for each value, the first showing technical drawings and the second the locomotive at work. 10, 15, 25, 40, 50, 80 c., $1, $1.50, each × 2

Royal Wedding (1st issue). 60 c., $1, each × 2

Royal Wedding (2nd issue). Previous Royal Wedding stamps optd as for Funafuti. 60 c., $1, each × 2

1987

Royal Ruby Wedding. 15, 35, 60 c., $1.50, $1.75

VAITUPU
1984

Leaders of the World. Automobiles (1st series). Two designs for each value, the first showing technical drawings and the second the car in action. 15, 25, 30, 50 c., each × 2

Leaders of the World. British Monarchs. Two designs for each value, forming a composite picture. 1, 5, 15, 40, 50 c., $1, each × 2

Leaders of the World. Automobiles (2nd series). Two designs for each value, the first showing technical drawings and the second the car in action. 5, 15, 25, 30, 40, 50, 60 c., $1, each × 2

1985

Leaders of the World. Railway Locomotives (1st series). Two designs for each value, the first showing technical drawings and the second the locomotive at work. 10, 25, 50, 60 c., each × 2

Leaders of the World, Butterflies. 5, 15, 50, 75 c., each × 2

Leaders of the World. Automobiles (3rd series). Two designs for each value, the first showing technical drawings and the second the car in action. 15, 30, 40, 60 c., each × 2

Leaders of the World. Life and Times of Queen Elizabeth the Queen Mother. Two designs for each value, showing different portraits. 15, 40, 65, 95 c., each × 2

1986

Leaders of the World. Railway Locomotives (2nd series). Two designs for each value, the first showing technical drawings and the second the locomotive at work. 5, 25, 80 c., $1, each × 2

60th Birthday of Queen Elizabeth II. 5, 60 c., $2, $3.50

Royal Wedding (1st issue). 60 c., $1, each × 2

Royal Wedding (2nd issue). Previous Royal Wedding stamps optd as for Funafuti. 60 c., $1, each × 2

1987

Railway Locomotives (3rd series). Two designs for each value, the first showing technical drawings and the second the locomotive at work. 10, 15, 25, 35, 45, 65, 85 c., $1, each × 2

Royal Ruby Wedding. 60th Birthday of Queen Elizabeth II issue of 1986 optd as for Niutao. 5, 60 c., $2, $3.50

Uganda

PROTECTORATE

TYPE-WRITTEN STAMPS. Nos. 2/53 were type-written by the Revd. E. Millar at Mengo. For all "printings" a thin laid paper was used, and all issues were imperforate.

The original typewriter used had wide letters, but in late April, 1895 Millar obtained a new machine on which the type face was in a narrower fount.

Each sheet was made up of whatever values were required at the time, so that different values can be found se-tenant or tête-bêche. These last were caused by the paper being inverted in the machine so that space at the foot could be utilised.

For the first issue the sheets were of 117 (9 × 13), but with the introduction of the narrower width (Nos. 17 onwards) a larger number of stamps per sheet, 143 (11 × 13), was adopted.

The manuscript provisionals, Nos. 9a/16, come from the Mission at Ngogwe, most of the manuscript surcharges including the initials of the Revd. G. R. Blackledge stationed there.

1895 (20 Mar). Wide letters. Wide stamps, 20 to 26 mm wide.

2	1	10 (cowries), black	..	.. £1800 £1000
4		20 (cowries), black	..	.. £2500 £1000
6		30 (cowries), black	..	.. £1100 £1100
7		40 (cowries), black	..	.. £1800 £1100
8		50 (cowries), black	..	.. £1800 £1100
9		60 (cowries), black	..	.. £1300 £1300

It is now believed that the 5, 10 and 25 cowries values in this width, previously Nos. 1, 3 and 5, do not exist.

A strip of three of No. 2 is known on cover of which one copy has the value "10" altered to "5" in manuscript and initialled "E.M.".

1895 (May). Wide stamps with pen-written surcharges, in black.

9a	1	10 on 30 (c.) black	.. ..	† £27000
10		10 on 50 (c.) black	.. ..	† £21000
11		15 on 10 (c.) black	.. ..	† £21000
12		15 on 20 (c.) black	.. ..	† £25000
13		15 on 40 (c.) black	.. ..	† £21000
14		15 on 50 (c.) black	.. ..	† £27000
15		25 on 50 (c.) black	.. ..	† £27000
16		50 on 60 (c.) black	.. ..	† £27000

1895 (April). Wide letters. Narrow stamps, 16 to 18 mm wide.

17	1	5 (c.) black	.. ..	£1100 £850
18		10 (c.) black	.. ..	£1100 £950
19		15 (c.) black	.. ..	£800 £850
20		20 (c.) black	.. ..	£900 £600
21		25 (c.) black	.. ..	£750 £800
22		30 (c.) black	.. ..	£5500 £5500
23		40 (c.) black	.. ..	£5000 £5000
24		50 (c.) black	.. ..	£2500
25		60 (c.) black	.. ..	£3250

1895 (May). Narrow letters. Narrow stamps 16 to 18 mm wide.

26	2	5 (c.) black	.. ..	£500
27		10 (c.) black	.. ..	£475
28		15 (c.) black	.. ..	£475
29		20 (c.) black	.. ..	£400
30		25 (c.) black	.. ..	£475
31		30 (c.) black	.. ..	£500
32		40 (c.) black	.. ..	£600
33		50 (c.) black	.. ..	£475
34		60 (c.) black	.. ..	£1100

1895 (Nov). Narrow letters. Narrow stamps, 16–18 mm wide. Change of colour.

35	2	5 (c.) violet	.. ..	£350 £400
36		10 (c.) violet	.. ..	£325 £350
37		15 (c.) violet	.. ..	£375 £325
38		20 (c.) violet	.. ..	£300 £275
		a. "G U" for "U G"		
39		25 (c.) violet	.. ..	£450 £450
40		30 (c.) violet	.. ..	£550 £450
41		40 (c.) violet	.. ..	£450 £450
42		50 (c.) violet	.. ..	£450 £500
43		100 (c.) violet	.. ..	£2250 £2250

Stamps of 35 (c.) and 45 (c.) have been chronicled in both colours. They were never prepared for postal use, and did not represent a postal rate, but were type-written to oblige a local official.

1896 (June).

44	3	5 (c.) violet	.. .. ..	£300 £375
45		10 (c.) violet	.. .. ..	£300 £300
46		15 (c.) violet	.. .. ..	£300 £350
47		20 (c.) violet	.. .. ..	£250 £190
48		25 (c.) violet	.. .. ..	£325
49		30 (c.) violet	.. .. ..	£350 £475
50		40 (c.) violet	.. .. ..	£350 £475
51		50 (c.) violet	.. .. ..	£425 £475
52		60 (c.) violet	.. .. ..	£1200
53		100 (c.) violet	.. .. ..	£1200 £1200

In the 2 a. and 3 a. the dagger points upwards; the stars in the 2 a. are level with the top of "VR". The 8 a. is as T **6** but with left star at top and right star at foot. The 1 r. has three stars at foot. The 5 r. has central star raised and the others at foot.

(Type-set by the Revd. F. Rowling at Lubwa's, in Usoga)

1896 (7 Nov). (a) Types 4/6.

A. Normal. B. Small "o" in "POSTAGE"

					A		B	
54	4	1 a. black	..	..	60·00	60·00	£225	£225
55	5	1 a. black	..	..	8·00	9·00	32·00	35·00
56	6	2 a. black	..	..	9·50	11·00	35·00	40·00
57		3 a. black	..	..	11·00	13·00	40·00	45·00
58		4 a. black	..	..	11·00	13·00	40·00	45·00
59		8 a. black	..	..	17·00	20·00	55·00	60·00
60		1 r. black	..	..	45·00	50·00	£180	£200
61		5 r. black	..	..	£140	£180	£375	£450

(b) Optd "L", in black as in T **7** for local use, by a postal official, R. R. Racey, at Kampala

					A		B	
70	4	1 a. black	..	..	£100	85·00	£550	—
71	6	2 a. black	..	..	40·00	65·00	£120	£170
72		3 a. black	..	..	95·00	£110	£550	—
73		4 a. black	..	..	55·00	90·00	£180	—
74		8 a. black	..	..	95·00	£120	£500	—
75		1 r. black	..	..	£200	£250	£600	—
76		5 r. black	..	..	£5000	£5000	—	—

Tête-bêche pairs of all values may be found owing to the settings of 16 (4 × 4) being printed side by side or above one another. They are worth a premium. The variety with small "O" occurs on R. 3/1.

UGANDA

(Recess D.L.R.)

1898–1902. P 14. (a) Wmk Crown CA.

84	8	1 a. scarlet	..	..	85	45
		a. Carmine-rose (1902)	..	..	40	45
86		2 a. red-brown	..	..	55	2·50
87		3 a. pale grey	..	..	4·00	8·50
		a. Bluish grey	..	..	4·00	7·00
88		4 a. deep green	..	..	1·75	6·00
89		8 a. pale olive	..	..	3·25	17·00
		a. Grey-green	..	..	4·00	18·00
		(b) Wmk Crown CC				
90	9	1 r. dull blue	..	..	20·00	23·00
		a. Bright blue	..	..	26·00	30·00
91		5 r. brown	..	..	48·00	60·00
84/91			Set of 7		70·00	£100
84/91 Optd "Specimen"			Set of 7		£150	

1902. *T* **11** *of British East Africa (Kenya, Uganda and Tanganyika) optd with T* **10.**

92	½ a. yellow-green	..	..		65	45
	a. Opt omitted (in pair with normal)		..	£1900		
	b. Opt inverted (at foot)	..	..	£900		
	c. Opt double	..	..	£1000		
93	2½ a. deep blue (R.)	..	..		65	1·75
	a. Opt double	..	..	£600		
	b. Inverted "S" (R. 1/1)	..	..	20·00		

For issues between 1903 and 1976 see KENYA, UGANDA AND TANGANYIKA.

SELF-GOVERNMENT

11 Ripon Falls and Speke Memorial

(Des S. Scott. Recess B.W.)

1962 (28 July). *Centenary of Speke's Discovery of Source of the Nile. W* w **12**. *P* 14.

95	**11**	30 c. black and red	..	..	10	10
96		50 c. black and slate-violet	..	..	10	10
97		1 s. 30, black and green	..	..	15	10
98		2 s. 50, black and blue	..		40	55
95/8		.. .. ..		*Set of 4*	55	60

INDEPENDENT

12 Murchison Falls   **13** Tobacco-growing

14 Mulago Hospital

(Des V. Whiteley. Photo Harrison)

1962 (9 Oct)–64. *Independence. Various designs as T* **12/14**. *P* 15×14 (5 c. to 50 c.) or 14½ (others).

99	5 c. deep bluish green	..	..		10	10
100	10 c. reddish brown	..	..		10	10
	a. Brown (coil)				10	10
	b. Deep yellow-brown (17.10.64)				10	10
101	15 c. black, red and green	..			10	10
102	20 c. plum and buff	..			10	10
103	30 c. blue	..	..		10	10
104	50 c. black and turquoise-green		..		10	10
105	1 s. sepia, red and turquoise-green			15	10
106	1 s. 30, yellow-orange and violet	..		20	10
107	2 s. black, carmine and light blue	..		40	30
108	5 s. vermilion and deep green	..		3·00	75
109	10 s. slate and chestnut	..		1·75	1·50
110	20 s. brown and blue	..		4·50	11·00
99/110	.. ..		*Set of 12*	9·50	12·50

Designs: *As T* **12/13**—10 c. Tobacco growing; 15 c. Coffee growing; 20 c. Ankole cattle; 30 c. Cotton; 50 c. Mountains of the Moon. *As T* **14**—1 s. 30, Cathedrals and Mosque; 2 s. Makerere College; 5 s. Copper mining; 10 s. Cement industry; 20 s. Parliament Buildings.

15 South African
Crowned Crane

(Photo Harrison)

1965 (20 Feb). *International Trade Fair, Kampala. P* 14½ × 14.

111	**15**	30 c. multicoloured	..	..	10	10
112		1 s. 30, multicoloured	..	..	20	10

16 Black Bee Eater   **17** African Jacana

---

18 Ruwenzori Turaco

(Des Mrs. R. Fennessy. Photo Harrison)

1965 (9 Oct). *Birds. Various designs as T* **16/18**. *P* 15 × 14 (5 c., 15 c., 20 c., 40 c., 50 c.), 14 × 15 (10 c., 30 c., 65 c.) or 14½ (others).

113	5 c. multicoloured	..			10	10
114	10 c. chestnut, black and light blue			10	10
115	15 c. yellow and sepia	..			20	10
116	20 c. multicoloured	..			20	10
117	30 c. black and brown-red	..		1·50	10
118	40 c. multicoloured	..			90	30
119	50 c. grey-blue and reddish violet			25	10
	a. White bird (grey-blue omitted)	..	£100	
120	65 c. orange-red, black and light grey		2·50	1·25
121	1 s. multicoloured	..			50	10
122	1 s. 30, chestnut, black and yellow	..	4·50	30
123	2 s. 50, multicoloured	..		4·25	65
124	5 s. multicoloured	..		7·00	2·00
125	10 s. multicoloured	..		9·50	6·50
126	20 s. multicoloured	..		21·00	24·00
113/26	..		*Set of 14*	45·00	32·00

Designs: *Vert as T* **16**—15 c. Orange Weaver; 20 c. Narina Trogon; 40 c. Blue-breasted Kingfisher; 50 c. Whale-headed Stork. *Horiz as T* **17**—30 c. Sacred Ibis; 65 c. Red-crowned Bishop. *As T* **18**. *Vert*—1 s. 30, African Fish Eagle; 5 s. Lilac-breasted Roller. *Horiz*—2 s. 50, Great Blue Turaco; 10 s. Black-collared Lovebird; 20 s. South African Crowned Crane.

The 15 c., 40 c., 65 c., and 1 s. exist with PVA gum as well as gum arabic.

19 Carved Screen

(Des Mrs. R. Fennessy. Photo Harrison)

1967 (26 Oct). *13th Commonwealth Parliamentary Association Conference. T* **19** *and similar horiz designs. Multicoloured. P* 14.

127	30 c. Type **19**	..	..		10	10
128	50 c. Arms of Uganda	..	..		10	10
129	1 s. 30, Parliamentary Building	..		10	10
130	2 s. 50, Conference Chamber	..		15	70
127/30	..		*Set of 4*	30	70

20 *Cordia
abyssinica*   **21** *Acacia
drepanolobium*

(Des Mrs. R. Fennessy. Photo Harrison)

1969 (9 Oct)–74. *Flowers. Various designs as T* **20/1**. *Chalk-surfaced paper. P* 14½×14 (5 c. to 70 c.) or 14 (others).

131	5 c. brown, green and light olive-yellow	..	10	50
	a. Glazed, ordinary paper (11.4.73)		40	10
132	10 c. multicoloured	..		10	10
	a. Glazed, ordinary paper (27.9.72)		40	10
133	15 c. multicoloured	..		10	10
134	20 c. bluish violet, yellow-ol & pale sage-grn	15	10
	a. Glazed, ordinary paper (27.9.72)		40	10
135	30 c. multicoloured	..		20	10
136	40 c. reddish violet, yell-grn & pale ol-grey	20	10
137	50 c. multicoloured	..		20	10
138	60 c. multicoloured	..		45	90
	a. Glazed, ordinary paper (9.5.73)		5·50	40
139	70 c. multicoloured	..		35	30
	a. Glazed, ordinary paper (27.9.72)		1·00	45
140	1 s. multicoloured	..		20	10
	a. Glazed, ordinary paper (22.1.71)		80	10
141	1 s. 50, multicoloured (cobalt background)	35	10
	a. Glazed, ordinary paper (3.2.71)		50	10
	b. Azure background (chalk-surfaced paper) (21.1.74)		55	20
142	2 s. 50, multicoloured	..		70	80
	a. Glazed, ordinary paper (3.2.71)		1·25	10
143	5 s. multicoloured	..		1·50	1·10
	a. Glazed, ordinary paper (3.2.71)		1·75	10
144	10 s. multicoloured	..		2·75	3·00
	a. Glazed, ordinary paper (3.2.71)		3·75	10
145	20 s. multicoloured	..		5·00	4·00
	a. Glazed, ordinary paper (22.1.71)		11·00	15
131/45	..		*Set of 15*	11·00	10·00
131a/45a	..		*Set of 11*	24·00	1·40

Designs: *As T* **20**—10 c. *Grewia similis*; 15 c. *Cassia didymobotrya*; 20 c. *Coleus barbatus*; 30 c. *Ockna ovata*; 40 c. *Ipomoea spathulata*; 50 c. *Spathodea nilotica*; 60 c. *Oncoba spinosa*; 70 c. *Carissa edulis. As T* **21**—1 s. 50, *Clerodendrum myricoides*; 2 s. 50, *Acanthus arboreus*; 5 s. *Kigelia aethiopium*; 10 s. *Erythrina abyssinica*; 20 s. *Monodora myristica*.

---

(22)

1975 (29 Sept). *Nos.* 141/2 *and* 145a *surch as T* **22**.

146	2 s. on 1 s. 50, multicoloured	..		2·00	1·50
147	3 s. on 2 s. 50, multicoloured	..	20·00	35·00
148	40 s. on 20 s. multicoloured	..		5·50	3·50
	a. Surch on No. 145	..			6·50	3·50
146/8	..		*Set of 3*	25·00	35·00

23 Millet   **24** Maize

(Des Mrs. R. Fennessy. Photo Harrison)

1975 (9 Oct). *Ugandan Crops. T* **23/4** *and similar horiz designs. P* 14 × 14½ (10 c. to 80 c.) or 14 (others).

149	10 c. black, apple-green and yellow-brown	..	10	10
150	20 c. multicoloured	..	..		10	10
151	30 c. multicoloured	..	..		10	10
152	40 c. multicoloured	..	..		10	10
153	50 c. multicoloured	..	..		10	10
154	70 c. black, apple-green and light blue-green	15	15
155	80 c. multicoloured	..	..		15	15
156	1 s. multicoloured	..	..		15	15
157	2 s. multicoloured	..	..		30	30
158	3 s. multicoloured	..	..		50	45
159	5 s. multicoloured	..	..		75	75
160	10 s. multicoloured	..	..		1·25	1·50
161	20 s. apple-green, black and bright purple	2·00	2·50
162	40 s. apple-green, black and yellow-orange	4·00	4·75
149/62	..		*Set of 14*	8·50	9·50

Designs: *As T* **23**—20 c. Sugar; 30 c. Tobacco; 40 c. Onions; 50 c. Tomatoes; 70 c. Tea; 80 c. Bananas. *As T* **24**—2 s. Pineapples; 3 s. Coffee; 5 s. Oranges; 10 s. Groundnuts; 20 s. Cotton; 40 s. Runner Beans.

Face value colours: 5 s. green; 10 s. brown; 20 s. bright purple; 40 s. yellow-orange. For 5 s. to 40 s. with colours changed see Nos. 220/3.

Nos. 149 and 153 exist in coils constructed from normal sheets.

1976 (15 Apr). *Telecommunications Development. As Nos.* 56/60 *of Kenya, but inscr* "UGANDA".

163	50 c. Microwave tower	..	..		10	10
164	1 s. Cordless switchboard	..		10	10
165	2 s. Telephone	..			20	25
166	3 s. Message Switching Centre	..		30	45
163/6	..		*Set of 4*	60	70
MS167	120 × 120 mm. Nos. 163/6	..		90	1·50

Nos. 164 and 166 exist imperforate from stock dispersed by the liquidator of Format International Security Printers Ltd.

1976 (5 July). *Olympic Games, Montreal. As Nos.* 61/5 *of Kenya, but inscr* "UGANDA".

168	50 c. Akii Bua, hurdler	..	..		15	10
169	1 s. Filbert Bayi, runner	..		20	10
170	2 s. Steve Muchoki, boxer	..		40	30
171	3 s. East African flags	..		55	45
168/71	..		*Set of 4*	1·10	75
MS172	129 × 154 mm. Nos. 168/71	..		4·50	4·50

Nos. 168/70 exist imperforate from stock dispersed by the liquidator of Format International Security Printers Ltd.

1976 (4 Oct). *Railway Transport. As Nos.* 66/70 *of Kenya, but inscr* "UGANDA".

173	50 c. Tanzania–Zambia railway	..		20	10
174	1 s. Nile Bridge, Uganda	..		35	10
175	2 s. Nakuru Station, Kenya	..		75	45
176	3 s. Class A loco, 1896	..		95	55
173/6	..		*Set of 4*	2·00	1·00
MS177	154 × 103 mm. Nos. 173/6	..		3·25	2·50

Nos. 173/4 exist imperforate from stock dispersed by the liquidator of Format International Security Printers Ltd.

1977 (10 Jan). *Game Fish of East Africa. As Nos.* 71/5 *of Kenya, but inscr* "UGANDA".

178	50 c. Nile Perch	..	..		15	10
179	1 s. Tilapia	..	..		20	10
180	3 s. Sailfish	..	..		70	40
181	5 s. Black Marlin	..	..		1·00	60
178/81	..		*Set of 4*	1·90	1·00
MS182	153 × 129 mm. Nos. 178/81	..		4·00	

1977 (15 Jan). *Second World Black and African Festival of Arts and Culture, Nigeria. As Nos.* 76/80 *of Kenya, but inscr* "UGANDA".

183	50 c. Maasai Manyatta (village)	..		15	10
184	1 s. "Heartbeat of Africa" (Ugandan dancers)	20	10
185	2 s. Makonde sculpture	..		45	45
186	3 s. "Early Man and Technology" (skinning hippopotamus)	..		60	80
183/6	..		*Set of 4*	1·25	1·25
MS187	132 × 109 mm. Nos. 183/6	..		2·00	2·25

1977 (5 Apr). *25th Anniv of Safari Rally. As Nos.* 81/5 *of Kenya, but inscr* "UGANDA".

188	50 c. Rally-car and villagers	..		15	10
189	1 s. Starting-line	..		15	10
190	2 s. Car fording river	..		35	35
191	5 s. Car and elephants	..		90	1·00
188/91	..		*Set of 4*	1·40	1·40
MS192	126 × 93 mm. Nos. 188/91	..		1·75	2·50

1977 (30 June). *Centenary of Ugandan Church. As Nos. 86/90 of Kenya, but inscr* "UGANDA".

193	50 c.	Canon Kivebulaya	10	10
194	1 s.	Modern Namirembe Cathedral	15	10
195	2 s.	Old Namirembe Cathedral	30	40
196	5 s.	Early congregation, Kigezi	60	90
193/6		*Set of 4*	1·00	1·25
MS197	126 × 89 mm. Nos. 193/6		1·00	1·75

(25)　　　　　26 Shot Putting

1977 (22 Aug). *Design as No. 155 surch with T 25 in mauve by Harrison.*

198	80 c. on 60 c. multicoloured		30	20
	a. Surch omitted			£180

A 60 c. stamp was to have been added to Nos. 149/62 using the design of the 80 c. (bananas), but it was cancelled and those already printed were surcharged to make No. 198.

1977 (26 Sept). *Endangered Species. As Nos. 96/101 of Kenya, but inscr* "UGANDA".

199	50 c.	Pancake Tortoise	30	10
200	1 s.	Nile Crocodile	45	10
201	2 s.	Hunter's Hartebeest	1·75	40
202	3 s.	Red Colobus monkey	2·00	75
203	5 s.	Dugong	2·25	1·40
199/203		*Set of 5*	6·00	2·50
MS204	127 × 101 mm. Nos. 200/3		6·50	4·00

1978 (10 Apr). *World Cup Football Championship, Argentina (1st issue). As Nos. 122/6 of Kenya but inscr* "UGANDA".

205	50 c.	Joe Kadenge and forwards	15	10
206	1 s.	Mohamed Chuma and cup presentation	15	10
207	2 s.	Omari Kidevu and goalmouth scene	40	35
208	5 s.	Polly Ouma and forwards	70	85
205/8		*Set of 4*	1·25	1·10
MS209	136 × 81 mm. Nos. 205/8		2·50	2·75

(Litho Questa)

1978 (28 Aug). *Commonwealth Games, Edmonton. T 26 and similar horiz designs. Multicoloured. P 14.*

210	50 c.	Type 26	15	10
211	1 s.	Long jumping	15	10
212	2 s.	Running	30	30
213	5 s.	Boxing	55	70
210/13		*Set of 4*	1·00	1·00
MS214	114 × 85 mm. Nos. 210/13. P 12½ × 12		1·75	3·00

1978 (11 Sept). *World Cup Football Championship, Argentina (2nd issue). Designs as Nos. 205/8 but additionally inscr* "WORLD CUP 1978".

215	50 c.	Polly Ouma and forwards	15	10
216	2 s.	Omari Kidevu and goalmouth scene	45	40
217	5 s.	Joe Kadenge and forwards	1·00	90
218	10 s.	Mohamed Chuma and cup presentation	1·75	1·60
215/18		*Set of 4*	3·00	2·75
MS219	140 × 87 mm. Nos. 215/18. P 12 × 11½		3·00	3·25

(Litho Questa)

1978. *As Nos. 159/62 but printing process and colours changed.*

220	5 s.	multicoloured (face value in blue)	70	70
221	10 s.	multicoloured (face value in magenta)	1·00	1·25
222	20 s.	multicoloured (face value in brown)	1·25	1·50
223	40 s.	multicoloured (face value in red)	2·25	2·75
220/3		*Set of 4*	4·75	5·50

27 Measurements of High Blood Pressure

(Litho Questa)

1978 (25 Sept). *"Down with High Blood Pressure". T 27 and similar horiz designs. Multicoloured. P 14 × 13½.*

224	50 c.	Type 27	20	10
225	1 s.	Hypertension and the heart	30	10
226	2 s.	Fundus of the eye in hypertension	70	35
227	5 s.	Kidney and high blood pressure	1·25	80
224/7		*Set of 4*	2·25	1·10
MS228	180 × 115 mm. Nos. 224/7		2·50	2·75

The new-issue supplement to this Catalogue appears each month in

GIBBONS
STAMP MONTHLY

—from your newsagent or by postal subscription—
sample copy and details on request.

---

28 Off Loading Cattle

(Litho Questa)

1978 (16 Dec). *75th Anniv of Powered Flight. T 28 and similar horiz designs. Multicoloured. P 14.*

229	1 s.	Type 28	15	10
230	1 s. 50,	"Domestic services" (passengers boarding "Islander" light aircraft)	20	15
231	2 s. 70,	Export of Uganda coffee	40	35
232	10 s.	"Time machines in the air" (Wright *Flyer* and "Concorde")	1·50	1·25
229/32		*Set of 4*	2·00	1·60
MS233	166 × 110 mm. Nos. 229/32		2·25	2·75

29 Queen Elizabeth II leaving Owen Falls Dam

(Des BG Studio. Litho Ashton-Potter)

1979 (15 Feb). *25th Anniv of Coronation (1978). T 29 and similar horiz designs. Multicoloured. P 12½ × 12.*

234	1 s.	Type 29	15	10
235	1 s. 50,	Regalia	20	10
236	2 s. 70,	Coronation ceremony	45	20
237	10 s.	Royal family on balcony of Buckingham Palace	1·00	60
234/7		*Set of 4*	1·60	80
MS238	150 × 102 mm. Nos. 234/7		1·75	1·75

30 Dr. Joseph Kiwanuka (first Ugandan bishop)

(Des G. Vasarhelyi. Litho Questa)

1979 (15 Feb). *Centenary of Catholic Church in Uganda. T 30 and similar horiz designs. Multicoloured. P 14.*

239	1 s.	Type 30	15	10
240	1 s. 50,	Lubaga Cathedral	15	10
241	2 s. 70,	Ugandan pilgrimage to Rome, Holy Year, 1975	20	25
242	10 s.	Friar Lourdel-Mapeera (early missionary)	60	80
239/42		*Set of 4*	1·00	1·10
MS243	128 × 91 mm. Nos. 239/42		1·40	1·75

31 Immunisation of Children

(Des J.W. Litho Questa)

1979 (28 June). *International Year of the Child. T 31 and similar horiz designs. Multicoloured. P 14.*

244	1 s.	Type 31	15	10
245	1 s. 50,	Handicapped children at play	20	20
246	2 s. 70,	Ugandan I.Y.C. emblem	35	35
247	10 s.	Children in class	80	90
244/7		*Set of 4*	1·40	1·40
MS248	136 × 113 mm. Nos. 244/7		1·40	2·00

UGANDA LIBERATED 1979	UGANDA LIBERATED 1979	UGANDA LIBERATED 1979
(32)	(33)	(34)

1979 (12 July–16 Aug?). *Liberation.*

(a) *Nos. 149/55 optd with T 32 and 156/62 with T 33 (12 July)*

249	10 c.	black, apple-green and yellow-brown	10	10
250	20 c.	multicoloured	10	10
251	30 c.	multicoloured	10	10
252	40 c.	multicoloured	10	10
253	50 c.	multicoloured	10	10
254	70 c.	black, apple-green and light blue-green	10	10
255	80 c.	multicoloured	10	10
	a. Opt double			£110
256	1 s.	multicoloured	15	15
257	2 s.	multicoloured	20	25
258	3 s.	multicoloured	35	40
259	5 s.	multicoloured	55	60
260	10 s.	multicoloured	1·10	1·25
261	20 s.	apple-green, black and bright purple	2·25	2·40
262	40 s.	apple-green, black and yellow-orange	4·50	4·75
	a. Opt double			£130

(b) *Nos. 210/13 (Commonwealth Games) optd with T 34 (1 Aug)*

263	50 c.	Type 26	10	10
264	1 s.	Long jumping	15	20
265	2 s.	Running	25	30
266	5 s.	Boxing	60	65

(c) *Nos. 207, 215 and 217/18 (World Cup Football Championships) optd with T 34 (1 Aug)*

267	50 c.	Polly Ouma and forwards	10	10
268	2 s.	Omari Kidevu and goal-mouth scene	25	30
	a. Optd on No. 216		14·00	23·00
269	5 s.	Joe Kadenge and forwards	60	65
270	10 s.	Mohamed Chuma and cup presentation	1·25	1·40

(d) *Nos. 220/3 optd with T 33 (1979)*

271	5 s.	multicoloured	55	60
272	10 s.	multicoloured	1·10	1·25
273	20 s.	multicoloured	2·25	2·40
274	40 s.	multicoloured	4·50	4·75

(e) *Nos. 229/32 (75th Anniv of Powered Flight) optd with T 34 (1 Aug)*

275	1 s.	Type 28	15	20
276	1 s. 50,	"Domestic services" (passengers boarding "Islander" light aircraft)	20	25
277	2 s. 70,	Export of Uganda coffee	40	45
278	10 s.	"Time machines in the air" (Wright *Flyer* and "Concorde")	1·25	1·40

(f) *Nos. 234/7 (25th Anniv of Coronation) optd as T 33 or surch also and No. MS238 additionally inscr* "Diplomatic Relations Normalised" *with Ugandan and British flags replacing portrait of Amin (12 July)*

279	1 s.	Type 29	15	20
280	1 s. 50,	Regalia	20	25
281	2 s. 70,	Coronation ceremony	40	45
282	15 s. on 10 s.	Royal family on balcony of Buckingham Palace	1·75	1·90
MS283	150 × 102 mm. Nos. 234/6 and 15 s. as No. 237*		2·50	3·00

* The sheet contains unoverprinted stamps; the additional inscriptions and changes in design appear only on the sheet margin.

(g) *Nos. 239/42 (Centenary of Catholic Church in Uganda) optd with T 34 and No. MS243 with additional inscr* "FREEDOM OF WORSHIP DECLARED" *replacing part of the margin decoration (1 Aug)*

284	1 s.	Type 30	15	20
285	1 s. 50,	Lubaga Cathedral	20	25
286	2 s. 70,	Ugandan pilgrimage to Rome, Holy Year, 1975	40	45
287	10 s.	Friar Lourdel-Mapeera (early missionary)	1·25	1·40
MS288	128 × 91 mm. Nos. 239/42*. P 12½ × 12 (1979)		2·25	2·75

* The sheet contains the original overprinted stamps; the additional inscription appears on the sheet margin.

(h) *Nos. 244/8 (International Year of the Child) optd with T 34 (16 Aug)*

289	1 s.	Type 31	15	20
290	1 s. 50,	Handicapped children at play	20	25
291	2 s. 70,	Ugandan I.Y.C. emblem	40	45
292	10 s.	Children in class	1·25	1·40
MS293	136 × 113 mm. Nos. 289/92		2·50	3·00
249/82, 284/7 and 289/92		*Set of 42*	26·00	29·00

35 Radio Wave Symbol

(Des G. Vasarhelyi. Litho Questa)

1979 (11 Sept). *50th Anniv of International Consultative Radio Committee and International Telecommunications Union. P 14.*

294	35	1 s. multicoloured	15	10
295		1 s. 50, multicoloured	20	10
296		2 s. 70, multicoloured	35	35
297		10 s. multicoloured	80	90
294/7		*Set of 4*	1·40	1·25

36 20s. Definitive Stamp of 1965 and Sir Rowland Hill

(Des BG Studio. Litho Questa)

1979 (Oct). *Death Centenary of Sir Rowland Hill. T 36 and similar horiz designs showing stamps and Sir Rowland Hill. Multicoloured. P 14.*

298	1 s.	Type 36	15	10
299	1 s. 50,	1967 13th Commonwealth Parliamentary Association Conference 50 c. commemorative	25	10
300	2 s. 70,	1962 Independence 20 s. commemorative	45	40
301	10 s.	Uganda Protectorate 1898 1 a.	1·00	1·50
298/301		*Set of 4*	1·75	1·75
MS302	154 × 98 mm. Nos. 298/301		1·75	2·00

37 Impala **38 Lions with Cub**

(Des G. Drummond. Litho Questa)

1979 (3 Dec)–**82**. *Wildlife. Horiz designs as T* **37** (10 *to* 80 *c.*) *or* *T* **38** (1 *to* 40 *s.*). *Multicoloured. P* 14 × 13½ (10 *to* 80 *c.*) *or* 14 (1 *to* 40 *s.*). A. *No imprint date.* B. *With imprint date* ("1982") *at foot of design* (1982).

				A		B	
303	10 c.	Type 37	..	10	10	†	
304	20 c.	Large-spotted Genet	..	10	10	†	
305	30 c.	Thomson's Gazelle	..	15	10	†	
306	50 c.	Lesser Bushbaby	..	15	10	†	
307	80 c.	Hunting Dog	..	20	10	†	
308	1 s.	Type 38	..	30	10	15	10
309	1 s. 50,	Gorilla	..	45	10	†	
310	2 s.	Common Zebra	..	45	15	25	20
311	2 s. 70,	Leopard with cub	..	60	15	†	
312	3 s. 50,	Black Rhinoceros	..	70	20	†	
313	5 s.	Waterbuck	..	70	30	40	40
314	10 s.	African Buffalo	..	70	60	†	
315	20 s.	Hippopotamus	..	80	1·25	†	
316	40 s.	African Elephant	..	1·50	2·50	†	
303A/16A			*Set of 14*	6·00	5·00	†	
308B/13B			*Set of 3*	†		70	65

For designs as Nos. 308/12 and 315/16, but with face values in revalued currency, see Nos. 433/9.

(39) **40 Rotary Emblem**

1980 (6 May). "*London 1980*" *International Stamp Exhibition.* Nos. 298/302 *optd as T* **39**.

317	1 s.	Type 36	..	..	..	15	10
318	1 s. 50,	1967 13th Commonwealth Parliamentary Association Conference 50 c. commemorative			..	20	10
319	2 s. 70,	1962 Independence 20s. commemorative			..	35	25
320	10 s.	Uganda Protectorate 1898 1a.			..	80	80
317/20					*Set of 4*	1·40	1·10
MS321	154 × 99 mm. Nos. 317/20			..	..	1·40	1·75

(Des BG Studio. Litho Questa)

1980 (25 Aug). *75th Anniv of Rotary International. T* **40** *and similar multicoloured design. P* 14.

322	1 s.	Type 40	..	..	10	10
323	20 s.	Paul Harris (founder) with wheel-barrow containing "Rotary projects" (*horiz*)		1·50	1·50
MS324	100 × 76 mm. Nos. 322/3. Imperf.	..		2·10	2·50

41 Football (42)

(Des G. Vasarhelyi. Litho Questa)

1980 (29 Dec). *Olympic Games, Moscow. T* **41** *and similar horiz designs. Multicoloured. P* 14.

325	1 s.	Type 41	..	..	..	10	10
326	2 s.	Relay	..	..	..	10	10
327	10 s.	Hurdles	..	..	..	40	60
328	20 s.	Boxing	..	..	..	80	1·25
325/8					*Set of 4*	1·25	1·75
MS329	118 × 90 mm. 2 s. 70, 3 s., 5 s., 25 s. As Nos. 325/8					1·75	2·75

1980 (29 Dec). *Olympic Games, Moscow. Medal Winners. Nos.* 325/9 *optd as T* **42**.

330	1 s.	Type 41	..	..	..	10	10
331	2 s.	Relay	..	..	..	10	15
332	10 s.	Hurdles	..	..	..	40	50
333	20 s.	Boxing	..	..	..	80	1·00
330/3					*Set of 4*	1·25	1·50
MS334	118 × 90 mm. 2 s. 70, 3 s., 5 s., 25 s. As Nos. 330/3					1·50	3·00

Overprints:—2s. "RELAY GOLD MEDALIST U.S.S.R."; 10s. "HURDLES 110 m. GOLD MEDALIST THOMAS MUNKLET, D.D.R."; 20s. "BOXING WELTERWEIGHT SILVER MEDALIST JOHN MUGABI, UGANDA".

NEW INFORMATION

The editor is always interested to correspond with people who have new information that will improve or correct the Catalogue.

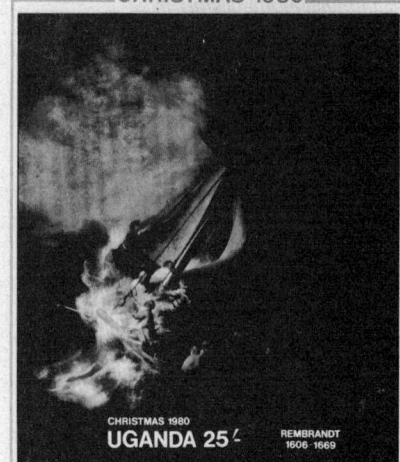

43 "Christ in the Storm on the Sea of Galilee" (*painting, Rembrandt*)

1980 (31 Dec). *Christmas. Sheet* 79 × 101 *mm. Litho. Imperf.*
MS335 **43** 25 s. multicoloured .. .. .. 3·75 4·25

44 Heinrich von Stephan **45 Tower of London**
and U.P.U. Emblem

(Des BG Studio. Litho Questa)

1981 (2 June). *150th Birth Anniv of Heinrich von Stephan* (*founder of U.P.U.*). *T* **44** *and similar horiz designs. Multicoloured. P* 14.

336	1 s.	Type 44	..	..	10	10
337	2 s.	U.P.U. Headquarters	..	..	15	15
338	2 s. 70,	Air mail, 1935	..	..	20	20
339	10 s.	Mail transport by train, 1927	..	80	80
336/9				*Set of 4*	1·10	1·10
MS340	112 × 95 mm. Nos. 336/9		..		2·75	1·90

10/- **10/-** **10/-** **10/-**
(46) (47)

(Des J.W. Litho Questa)

1981 (July). *Royal Wedding. T* **45** *and similar vert designs. Multicoloured. P* 14. (a) *Unissued stamps surcharged* (13 July). A. *As T* **46**. B. *As T* **47**.

			A		B	
341	10 s. on 1 s.	Prince Charles and Lady Diana Spencer	50	65	25	20
	a.	Surch on 5 s. value	40·00	—	†	
	b.	Surch on 20 s. value	35·00	—	†	
	c.	Surch omitted	75·00	—	†	
342	50 s. on 5 s.	Type 45	75	90	40	30
	a.	Surch omitted	70·00	—	†	
343	200 s. on 20 s.	Prince Charles at Balmoral	2·00	2·50	1·00	1·25
	a.	Surch omitted	£110	—	†	
	b.	Surch inverted	40·00	—	†	
	c.	Surch inverted on 1 s. value	40·00	—	†	
	d.	Surch inverted on 5 s. value	40·00	—	†	
341/3		*Set of 3*	3·00	3·50	1·50	1·60
MS344	95 × 80 mm. 250 s. on 25 s. Royal Mews		12·00	12·00	2·25	2·00
	a.	Surch omitted			†	

(*b*) *Redrawn with new face values. Background colours changed* (29 July)

345	10 s.	As No. 341	..	..	15	15
346	50 s.	Type 45	..	..	20	20
347	200 s.	As No. 343	..	..	50	50
345/7			*Set of 3*		75	75
MS348	95 × 80 mm. 250 s. As No. MS344	..	90	1·25

Nos. 345/7 also exist perforated 12 (*price for set of 3 75p mint or used*) from additional sheetlets of 5 stamps and one label. These stamps have changed background colours.

The issue was originally printed with face values of 1, 5 and 20 s. and 25 s. for the miniature sheet. Before it could be placed on sale the Uganda currency was devalued and the stamps were surcharged, and later reprinted with corrected face values.

100th Anniversary of the Birth of Picasso

48 "Sleeping Woman before Green Shutters"

(Des J.W. Litho Questa)

1981 (21 Sept). *Birth Centenary of Picasso. T* **48** *and similar multicoloured designs. P* 14 × 13½.

349	10 s.	Type 48	..	..	10	10
350	20 s.	"Bullfight"	..	..	20	20
351	30 s.	"Detail of a Nude asleep in a Landscape"	25	25
352	200 s.	"Interior with a Girl Drawing"	..	2·25	2·25
349/52			*Set of 4*		2·50	2·50
MS353	120 × 146 mm. 250 s. "Minotaure" (112 × 139 mm). Imperf	..		3·00	3·00

49 Deaf People using Sign Language

(Des Design Images. Litho Format)

1981 (28 Dec). *International Year for Disabled Persons. T* **49** *and similar horiz designs. Multicoloured. P* 15.

354	1 s.	Type 49	..	..	10	10
355	10 s.	Disabled teacher in classroom	..	15	10
356	50 s.	Teacher and disabled children	..	70	50
357	200 s.	Blind person with guide dog	..	2·00	2·00
354/7			*Set of 4*		2·50	2·25
MS358	122 × 93 mm. Nos. 354/7	..	..	5·00	4·00

50 Footballers

(Des G. Vasarhelyi. Litho Questa)

1982 (11 Jan). *World Cup Football Championship, Spain. T* **50** *and similar horiz designs showing World Cup* (250 *s.*) *or footballers* (*others*). *P* 14.

359	1 s.	multicoloured	..	..	10	10
360	10 s.	multicoloured	..	..	15	10
361	50 s.	multicoloured	..	..	70	50
362	200 s.	multicoloured	..	..	2·00	2·00
359/62			*Set of 4*		2·50	2·25
MS363	116 × 77 mm. 250 s. multicoloured	..	2·75	3·00

51 Mpoma Satellite Earth Station

(Des Artists International. Litho Format)

1982 (10 May). "*Peaceful Use of Outer Space*". *T* **51** *and similar horiz designs. Multicoloured. P* 15.

364	5 s.	Type 51	..	..	25	15
365	10 s.	*Pioneer II* (satellite)	..	..	35	25
366	50 s.	Space Shuttle	..	..	1·75	1·75
367	100 s.	*Voyager 2* (satellite)	..	..	2·75	2·75
364/7			*Set of 4*		4·75	4·50
MS368	118 × 89 mm. 150 s. Space Shuttle (*different*)	..	..	3·50	2·00

No. 364 exists imperforate from stock dispersed by the liquidator of Format International Security Printers Ltd.

52 Dr. Robert Koch (53)

(Des R. Vigurs. Litho Questa)

1982 (14 June). *Centenary of Robert Koch's Discovery of Tubercle Bacillus. T 52 and similar multicoloured designs. P 14.*

369	1 s. Type 52	..	..	..	30	10
370	10 s. Microscope	..	..	..	1·25	40
371	50 s. Ugandans receiving vaccinations	..		3·00	2·50
372	100 s. Tubercle virus	..	..	..	4·50	4·25
369/72				*Set of 4*	8·00	6·50
MS373	85×64 mm. 150 s. Medical College classroom scene (*horiz*)..				6·00	3·25

1982 (7 July). *21st Birthday of Princess of Wales. Nos. 345/8 optd with T 53. P 14.*

374	10 s. Prince Charles and Lady Diana Spencer	20	15
375	50 s. Type 45	..	..	..	75	50
376	200 s. Prince Charles at Balmoral	..	2·50	2·00
374/6				*Set of 3*	3·00	2·40
MS377	95×82 mm. 250 s. Royal Mews ..			2·75	2·25

Nos. 374/6 also exist perforated 12 (*price for set of 3 £1·75 mint or used*) from additional sheetlets of 5 stamps and one label. These stamps have changed background colours.

Nos. 374/7, and the sheetlets, also exist with the top line of the overprint shown as "21st Birthday" instead of "21st BIRTHDAY" as in Type 53. (*Price for set of 3 and miniature sheet £8 mint*).

Examples of an unissued 150 s. miniature sheet for the 20th Anniversary of Independence exist from stock dispersed by the liquidator of Format International Security Printers Ltd.

54 Yellow-billed Hornbill

55 Scout Band

(Des Artists International. Litho Questa)

1982 (12 July). *Birds. T 54 and similar vert designs. Multicoloured. P 14.*

378	1 s. Type 54	..	..	..	..	15	10
379	20 s. Superb Starling	..	..	..	60	35
380	50 s. Bateleur	..	..	..	1·25	1·50
381	100 s. Saddle-bill Stork	..	..	2·00	2·50
378/81				*Set of 4*	3·50	4·00
MS382	115×85 mm. 200 s. Laughing Dove		6·50	6·50

(Des G. Vasarhelyi. Litho Questa)

1982 (23 Aug). *75th Anniv of Boy Scout Movement. T 55 and similar horiz designs. Multicoloured. P 14.*

383	5 s. Type 55	..	..	..	40	10
384	20 s. Scout receiving Bata Shoe trophy	1·10	45
385	50 s. Scouts with wheelchair patient..	2·25	1·75
386	100 s. First aid instruction	..	..	3·00	3·00
383/6				*Set of 4*	6·00	4·75
MS387	112×85 mm. 150 s. Lord Baden-Powell				4·00	3·00

56 Swearing-in of Roosevelt

(Des Design Images. Litho Format)

1982 (8 Nov). *250th Birth Anniv of George Washington (Nos. 389/90) and Birth Centenary of Franklin D. Roosevelt (others). T 56 and similar horiz designs. Multicoloured. P 15.*

388	50 s. Type 56	..	..	..	30	30
389	200 s. Swearing-in of Washington	..	1·25	1·25
MS390	100×69 mm. 150 s. Washington at Mt Vernon	..	..	..	..	1·40	1·60
MS391	100×70 mm. 150 s. Roosevelt at Hyde Park Mansion	..	..	..	1·40	1·60

57 Italy v West Germany

(Des D. Miller. Litho)

1982 (30 Dec). *World Cup Football Championship Winners. T 57 and similar horiz designs. Multicoloured. P 14½.*

392	10 s. Type 57	..	..	..	50	25
393	200 s. Victorious Italian team..	..	3·00	3·25
MS394	97×117 mm. 250 s. Espana '82 emblem with Spanish and Italian flags ..		1·90	2·40

58 Dancers

59 "St. George and the Dragon" (Raphael)

(Des and litho Questa)

1983 (14 Mar). *Commonwealth Day. Cultural Art. T 58 and similar horiz designs. Multicoloured. P 14.*

395	5 s. Type 58	..	..	..	10	10
396	20 s. Traditional currency	..	..	20	20
397	50 s. Homestead	..	..	..	45	45
398	100 s. Drums	..	..	..	85	85
395/8				*Set of 4*	1·40	1·40

(Des Design Images. Litho Questa)

1983 (16 Apr). *500th Birth Anniv of Raphael (painter). T 59 and similar vert designs. Multicoloured. P 13½.*

399	5 s. Type 59	..	..	..	10	10
400	20 s. "St. George and the Dragon" (*different*)	30	30
401	50 s. "Crossing the Red Sea" (*detail*)..	70	70
402	200 s. "The Expulsion of Heliodorus" (*detail*) ..	2·25	2·50
399/402				*Set of 4*	3·00	3·25
MS403	126×101 mm. 250 s. "The Meeting of Pope Leo the Great and Attila the Hun" (*detail*)		1·50	1·75

60 Map showing Namibia and U.N. Flag

(Des R. Vigurs. Litho Format)

1983 (15 Aug). *Commemorations. T 60 and similar horiz design. Multicoloured. P 15.*

404	5 s. Type 60	..	..	..	10	10
405	200 s. 7th Non-aligned Summit Conference logo	1·25	1·75

61 Elephants in Grassland

(62)

(Des J. Iskowitz. Litho Format)

1983 (22 Aug). *Endangered Species (1st series). T 61 and similar multicoloured designs. P 15.*

406	5 s. Elephants in "Elephants' Graveyard"	70	20
407	10 s. Type 61	..	..	..	1·00	35
408	30 s. Elephants at waterhole	..	2·25	1·75
409	70 s. Elephants having dust bath	..	3·50	3·00
406/9				*Set of 4*	6·50	4·75
MS410	87×64 mm. 300 s. Grevy's Zebra drinking (*vert*)	..	..	..	2·50	3·00

See also Nos. 642 and 970/4.

1983 (19 Sept). *Centenary of Boys' Brigade. Nos. 383/7 optd with T 62 or surch also.*

411	5 s. Type 55	..	..	..	10	10
412	20 s. Scout receiving Bata Shoe trophy	15	15
413	50 s. Scouts with wheelchair patient	..	25	30
414	400 s. on 100 s. First aid instruction	2·40	2·75
411/14				*Set of 4*	2·50	3·00
MS415	112×85 mm. 150 s. Lord Baden-Powell ..		90	1·25

63 Mpoma Satellite Earth Station

(64)

(Des D. Dorfman. Litho Format)

1983 (3 Oct). *World Communications Year. T 63 and similar horiz designs. Multicoloured. P 15.*

416	20 s. Type 63	..	..	..	25	15
417	50 s. Railroad computer and operator	..	65	65
418	70 s. Cameraman filming lions	..	75	80
419	100 s. Aircraft cockpit	..	..	95	1·25
416/19				*Set of 4*	2·40	2·50
MS420	128×103 mm. 300 s. Communications satellite	..	..	..	..	1·60	2·00

No. 416 has the "o" omitted from "Station".

1983 (7 Oct). *Nos. 303, 305/7, 308A, 309 and 313A surch as T 64.*

421	100 s. on 10 c. Type 37	..	..	55	45
422	135 s. on 1 s. Type 38	..	..	70	60
423	175 s. on 30 c. Thomson's Gazelle	..	85	75
424	200 s. on 50 c. Lesser Bushbaby	..	95	85
425	400 s. on 80 c. Hunting Dog	..	1·75	1·60
426	700 s. on 5 s. Waterbuck	..	..	3·00	3·00
427	1000 s. on 1 s. 50, Gorilla	..	..	4·25	4·00
421/7 ..				*Set of 7*	11·00	10·00

65 The Nativity

(Des PAD Studio. Litho Questa)

1983 (12 Dec). *Christmas. T 65 and similar horiz designs. Multicoloured. P 14.*

428	10 s. Type 65..	..	..	..	10	10
429	50 s. Shepherds and Angels	..	25	30
430	175 s. Flight into Egypt	..	..	80	1·00
431	400 s. Angels blowing trumpets	..	1·90	2·25
428/31				*Set of 4*	2·75	3·25
MS432	85×57 mm. 300 s. The Three Kings ..	1·40	1·50

1983 (19 Dec). *Designs as Nos. 308/12 and 315/16 but with face values in revalued currency.*

433	100 s. Type 38	..	..	..	65	35
434	135 s. Gorilla	..	..	..	75	50
435	175 s. Common Zebra	..	..	95	70
436	200 s. Leopard with cub	..	..	1·25	80
437	400 s. Black Rhinoceros	..	..	2·00	2·00
438	700 s. African Elephant	..	..	3·50	3·75
439	1000 s. Hippopotamus	..	..	4·25	4·75
433/9 ..				*Set of 7*	12·00	11·50

66 Ploughing with Oxen

(Des J.W. Litho Questa)

1984 (16 Jan). *World Food Day. T 66 and similar horiz design. Multicoloured. P 14.*

440	10 s. Type 66..	..	..	..	15	10
441	300 s. Harvesting bananas ..	..	..	3·75	3·75

67 Ruth Kyalisiima, Sportsman of the Year 1983

(Des J. Iskowitz. Litho Format)

1984 (1 Oct). *Olympic Games, Los Angeles. T 67 and similar multicoloured designs. P 15.*

442	5 s. Type 67..	..	..	..	10	10
443	115 s. Javelin-throwing	..	..	40	45
444	155 s. Wrestling..	..	..	50	55
445	175 s. Rowing ..	..	..	..	60	65
442/5 ..				*Set of 4*	1·40	1·50
MS446	108×79 mm. 500 s. Fund-raising walk (*vert*)	..	..	..	..	1·50	1·60

68 Entebbe Airport

(Des BG Studio. Litho Format)

1984 (29 Oct). *40th Anniv of International Civil Aviation Organization. T 68 and similar horiz designs. Multicoloured. P 15.*

447	5 s. Type 68..	..	..	..	15	10
448	115 s. Loading cargo plane ..	..	1·50	1·50
449	155 s. Uganda police helicopter	..	2·50	2·50
450	175 s. East African Civil Flying School, Soroti	2·75	2·75
447/50				*Set of 4*	6·25	6·00
MS451	100×70 mm. 250 s. Balloon race	..	2·50	1·75

69 Charaxes druceanus

(Des J. Johnson. Litho Questa)

1984 (19 Nov). *Butterflies. T 69 and similar horiz designs. Multicoloured. P 14.*

452	5 s. Type **69**			30	10
453	115 s. *Papilio lormieri*			1·90	1·50
454	155 s. *Druryia antimachus*			2·40	1·75
455	175 s. *Salamis temora*			3·25	2·25
452/5			Set of 4	7·00	5·00
MS456	127×90 mm. 250 s. *Colotis protomedia*			1·75	1·75

70 *Nothobranchius taeniopygus*

(Des Associated Creative Designers. Litho Format)

1985 (1 Apr–10 June). *Lake Fishes. T 70 and similar horiz designs. Multicoloured. P 15.*

457	5 s. Type **70**			10	10
458	10 s. *Bagrus dogmac*			15	10
459	50 s. *Polypterus senegalus*			45	15
460	100 s. *Clarias*			60	20
461	135 s. *Mormyrus kannume* (10 June)			60	35
462	175 s. *Synodontis victoriae*			80	80
463	205 s. *Haplochromis brownae*			85	85
464	400 s. *Lates niloticus*			1·25	1·25
465	700 s. *Protopterus aethiopicus*			1·50	1·50
466	1000 s. *Barbus radcliffii*			1·75	1·75
467	2500 s. *Malapterus electricus* (10 June)			1·75	1·75
457/67			Set of 11	8·50	8·00

71 The Last Supper

(Des Associated Creative Designers. Litho Questa)

1985 (13 May). *Easter. T 71 and similar horiz designs. Multicoloured. P 14.*

468	5 s. Type **71**			10	10
469	115 s. Christ showing the nail marks to Thomas			80	50
470	155 s. The raising of the Cross			90	60
471	175 s. Pentecost			1·25	75
468/71			Set of 4	2·75	1·75
MS472	99×70 mm. 250 s. The last prayer in the Garden			80	1·00

72 Breast Feeding   **73** Queen Elizabeth the Queen Mother

(Des Associated Creative Designers. Litho Questa)

1985 (29 July). *U.N.I.C.E.F. Child Survival Campaign. T 72 and similar horiz designs. Multicoloured. P 14.*

473	5 s. Type **72**			10	10
474	115 s. Growth monitoring			1·25	1·25
475	155 s. Immunisation			1·75	1·75
476	175 s. Oral re-hydration therapy			2·00	2·00
473/6			Set of 4	4·50	4·50
MS477	75×55 mm. 500 s. Pregnant woman preparing nourishing food			3·50	3·50

(Des J.W. Litho Questa)

1985 (21 Aug). *Life and Times of Queen Elizabeth the Queen Mother and Decade for Women. T 73 and similar vert design. Multicoloured. P 14.*

478	1000 s. Type **73**			2·00	2·10
MS479	57×81 mm. 1500 s. The Queen Mother inspecting Kings African Rifles, Kampala			3·25	3·50

74 Sedge Warbler   **(75)**

GOLD MEDALIST BENITA BROWN-FITZGERALD USA

(Des S. Heinmann. Litho Questa)

1985 (21 Aug). *Birth Bicentenary of John J. Audubon (ornithologist) (1st issue). T 74 and similar vert designs. Multicoloured. P 14.*

480	115 s. Type **74**			1·25	1·25
481	155 s. Cattle Egret			1·50	1·50
482	175 s. Crested Lark			1·75	1·75
483	500 s. Tufted Duck			2·50	2·50
480/3			Set of 4	6·25	6·25
MS484	99×69 mm. 1000 s. Tawny Owl			7·50	5·50

See also Nos. 494/8.

1985 (21 Aug). *Olympic Gold Medal Winners, Los Angeles. Nos. 442/6 optd or surch as T 75 in gold.*

485	5 s. Type **67** (optd T **75**)			10	10
486	115 s. Javelin-throwing (optd "GOLD MEDALIST ARTO HAERKOENEN FINLAND")			25	30
487	155 s. Wrestling (optd "GOLD MEDALIST ATSUJI MIYAHARA JAPAN")			30	35
488	1000 s. on 175 s. Rowing (surch "GOLD MEDALIST WEST GERMANY")			1·90	2·00
485/8			Set of 4	2·25	2·00
MS489	108×79 mm. 1200 s. on 500 s. Fundraising walk (surch "MEN'S HURDLES EDWIN MOSES USA")			2·25	2·50

On No. MS489 only the new value appears on the stamp, the remainder of the surcharge is on the sheet margin.

76 Women carrying National Women's Day Banner   **77** Man beneath Tree laden with Produce (F.A.O.)

(Des and litho Questa)

1985 (1 Nov). *Decade for Women. T 76 and similar multicoloured designs. P 14.*

490	5 s. Type **76**			10	10
491	115 s. Girl Guides (horiz)			1·50	1·50
492	155 s. Mother Teresa (Nobel Peace Prize winner, 1979)			2·75	2·75
490/2			Set of 3	4·00	4·00
MS493	85×59 mm. 1500 s. As 115 s.			3·75	3·75

Nos. 491 and MS493 also commemorate the 75th anniversary of the Girl Guide movement.

(Litho Questa)

1985 (23 Dec). *Birth Bicentenary of John J. Audubon (ornithologist) (2nd issue). Multicoloured designs as T 201 of Maldive Islands, but horiz, showing original paintings. P 12.*

494	5 s. Rock Ptarmigan			45	10
495	155 s. Sage Grouse			1·50	1·25
496	175 s. Lesser Yellowlegs			1·75	1·75
497	500 s. Brown-headed Cowbird			2·75	2·75
494/7			Set of 4	5·75	5·25
MS498	72×102 mm. 1000 s. Whooping Crane. P 14			7·50	6·50

Nos. 494/7 were each printed in sheetlets of 5 stamps and one stamp-size label which appears in the centre of the bottom row.

(Des BG Studio. Litho Format)

1986 (1 Apr). *40th Anniv of United Nations Organization. T 77 and similar designs. P 15.*

499	10 s. multicoloured			10	10
500	180 s. multicoloured			60	30
501	200 s. new blue, agate and bright green			65	35
502	250 s. new blue, brownish blk & scar-verm			70	40
503	2000 s. multicoloured			3·00	3·00
499/503			Set of 5	4·50	4·25
MS504	69×69 mm. 2500 s. multicoloured			2·50	2·75

Designs: *Horiz*—180 s. Soldier of U.N. Peace-Keeping Force; 250 s. Hands releasing peace dove. *Vert*—200 s. U.N. emblem; 2000 s. Flags of U.N. and Uganda; 2500 s. U.N. Building, New York, and flags of member nations.

78 Goalkeeper catching Ball   **(79)**

NRA LIBERATION 1986

(Des Shelley Haas. Litho Questa)

1986 (17 Apr). *World Cup Football Championship, Mexico. T 78 and similar multicoloured designs. P 14.*

505	10 s. Type **78**			10	10
506	180 s. Player with ball			85	45
507	250 s. Two players competing for ball			1·00	55
508	2500 s. Player running with ball			4·50	4·50
505/8			Set of 4	5·75	5·00
MS509	87×66 mm. 3000 s. Player kicking ball (vert)			4·75	3·50

1986 (30 Apr). *Liberation by National Resistance Army. Nos. 462, 464/7 and MS493 optd with T 79 or larger (22×8 mm) (No. MS493).*

510	175 s. *Synodontis victoriae* (Sil.)			60	60
511	400 s. *Lates niloticus*			1·00	1·00
512	700 s. *Protopteris aethiopicus* (Sil.)			1·75	1·75
513	1000 s. *Barbus radcliffii*			2·00	2·50
514	2500 s. *Malapterus electricus*			3·75	4·25
510/14			Set of 5	8·00	9·00
MS514a	85×59 mm. 1500 s. Girl Guides			3·50	2·50

Nos. 510/14 also exist with the overprint colours transposed.

(Des W. Hanson. Litho Questa)

1986 (30 Apr). *Appearance of Halley's Comet (1st issue). Horiz designs as T 162a of Lesotho. Multicoloured. P 14.*

515	50 s. Tycho Brahe and Arecibo Radio Telescope, Puerto Rico			20	10
516	100 s. Recovery of astronaut John Glenn from sea, 1962			35	15
517	140 s. "The Star in the East" (painting by Giotto)			50	30
518	2500 s. Death of Davy Crockett at the Alamo, 1835			3·50	4·00
515/18			Set of 4	4·00	4·00
MS519	102×70 mm. 3000 s. Halley's Comet over Uganda			5·50	4·00

See also Nos. 544/8.

80 Niagara Falls   **81** *Gloria* (Colombia)

(Des Mary Walters. Litho Format)

1986 (22 May). *"Ameripex'86" International Stamp Exhibition, Chicago. American Landmarks. T 80 and similar horiz designs. Multicoloured. P 15.*

520	50 s. Type **80**			15	10
521	100 s. Jefferson Memorial, Washington D.C.			25	15
522	250 s. Liberty Bell, Philadelphia			50	35
523	1000 s. The Alamo, San Antonio, Texas			1·75	1·60
524	2500 s. George Washington Bridge, New York–New Jersey			3·25	3·25
520/4			Set of 5	5·50	4·75
MS525	87×64 mm. 3000 s. Grand Canyon			3·00	3·25

(Litho Questa)

1986 (24 May). *60th Birthday of Queen Elizabeth II. Vert designs as T 163a of Lesotho. P 14.*

526	100 s. black and yellow			25	15
527	140 s. multicoloured			30	20
528	2500 s. multicoloured			3·00	3·00
526/8			Set of 3	3·25	3·00
MS529	120×85 mm. 3000 s. black & grey-brown			3·25	3·50

Designs:—100 s. Princess Elizabeth at London Zoo; 140 s. Queen Elizabeth at race meeting, 1970; 2500 s. With Prince Philip at Sandringham, 1982; 3000 s. Engagement photograph, 1947.

(Des J. Iskowitz. Litho Questa)

1986 (2 July). *Centenary of Statue of Liberty. T 81 and similar multicoloured designs showing cadet sailing ships. P 14.*

530	50 s. Type **81**			45	15
531	100 s. *Mircea* (Rumania)			75	30
532	140 s. *Sagres II* (Portugal) (horiz)			1·25	90
533	2500 s. *Gazela Primiero* (U.S.A.) (horiz)			6·50	8·00
530/3			Set of 4	8·00	8·50
MS534	113×82 mm. 3000 s. Statue of Liberty			3·25	3·50

(Des and litho Questa)

1986 (23 July). *Royal Wedding. Multicoloured designs as T 170a of Lesotho. P 14.*

535	50 s. Prince Andrew and Miss Sarah Ferguson (horiz)			10	10
536	140 s. Prince Andrew with Princess Anne at shooting match (horiz)			20	20
537	2500 s. Prince Andrew and Miss Sarah Ferguson at Ascot (horiz)			2·75	3·00
535/7			Set of 3	2·75	3·00
MS538	88×88 mm. 3000 s. Prince Andrew and Miss Sarah Ferguson (different)			3·50	3·25

WINNERS

Argentina 3 W.Germany 2

(82)

1986 (15 Sept). *World Cup Football Championship Winners, Mexico. Nos. 505/9 optd as T 82, or surch also, in gold.*

539	50 s. on 10 s. Type **78**			10	10
540	180 s. Player with ball			25	25
541	250 s. Two players competing for ball			35	35
542	2500 s. Player running with ball			2·75	3·25
539/42			Set of 4	3·00	3·50
MS543	87×66 mm. 3000 s. Player kicking ball (vert)			4·00	3·25

1986 (15 Oct). *Appearance of Halley's Comet (2nd issue). Nos. 515/19 optd with T 213b of Maldive Islands (in silver on 3000 s.).*

544	50 s. Brahe and Arecibo Radio Telescope, Puerto Rico	20	15
545	100 s. Recovery of astronaut John Glenn from sea, 1962	35	20
546	140 s. "The Star in the East" (painting by Giotto)	55	40
547	2500 s. Death of Davy Crockett at the Alamo, 1835	4·75	4·75
544/7	*Set of 4*	5·25	5·00
MS548	102 × 70 mm. 3000 s. Halley's Comet over Uganda	3·00	3·50

83 St. Kizito

(Des Associated Creative Designers. Litho Questa)

1986 (15 Oct). *Christian Martyrs of Uganda. T 83 and similar horiz designs. Multicoloured. P 14.*

549	50 s. Type 83	10	10
550	150 s. St. Kizito instructing converts	15	20
551	200 s. Martyrdom of Bishop James Hannington, 1885	20	25
552	1000 s. Burning of Bugandan Christians, 1886	1·00	1·50
549/52	*Set of 4*	1·25	1·75
MS553	89 × 59 mm. 1500 s. King Mwanga of Buganda passing sentence on Christians	1·50	2·00

84 "Madonna of the Cherries" (Titian)

(Litho Questa)

1986 (26 Nov). *Christmas. Religious Paintings. T 84 and similar multicoloured designs. P 14.*

554	50 s. Type 84	20	15
555	150 s. "Madonna and Child" (Dürer) (vert).	50	30
556	200 s. "Assumption of the Virgin" (Titian) (vert)	60	35
557	2500 s. "Praying Hands" (Dürer) (vert)	5·00	5·50
554/7	*Set of 4*	5·75	5·75
MS558	Two sheets, each 102 × 76 mm. (a) 3000 s. "Presentation of the Virgin in the Temple" (Titian). (b) 3000 s. "Adoration of the Magi" (Dürer) *Set of 2 sheets*	6·50	7·00

85 Red-billed Fire Finch and Glory Lily

(Litho Format)

1987 (22 July). *Flora and Fauna. T 85 and similar horiz designs. Multicoloured. P 15.*

559	2 s. Type 85.	15	10
560	5 s. African Pygmy Kingfisher and Nandi Flame	20	15
561	10 s. Scarlet-chested Sunbird and Crown of Thorns	25	25
562	25 s. White Rhinoceros and Yellow-billed Oxpecker	65	60
563	35 s. Lion and Elephant Grass	80	80
564	45 s. Cheetahs and Doum Palm	1·00	1·00
565	50 s. Cordon Bleu and Desert Rose	1·10	1·25
566	100 s. Giant Eland and Acacia	2·00	2·40
559/66	*Set of 8*	5·50	6·00
MS567	Two sheets, each 98 × 67 mm. (a) 150 s. Carmine Bee Eaters and Sausage Tree. (b) 150 s. Cattle Egret and Zebras *Set of 2 sheets*	6·00	7·00

86 Tremml's *Eagle* (longest man-powered flight), 1987

(Des W. Hanson. Litho Format)

1987 (14 Aug). *Milestones of Transportation. T 86 and similar horiz designs. Multicoloured. P 15.*

568	2 s. Type 86.	10	10
569	3 s. Junkers "W-33L" *Bremen* (first east-west transatlantic flight), 1928	10	10
570	5 s. Lockheed *Winnie Mae* (Post's first solo round-the-world flight), 1933.	20	20
571	10 s. *Voyager* (first non-stop round-the-world flight), 1986	40	40
572	15 s. Chanute biplane glider, 1896	60	60
573	25 s. Airship *Norge* and Polar Bear (first transpolar flight), 1926	90	90
574	35 s. Curtis biplane and U.S.S. *Pennsylvania* (first take-off and landing from ship), 1911	1·25	1·25
575	45 s. Shepard and "Freedom 7" spacecraft (first American in space), 1961	1·40	1·40
576	100 s. "Concorde" (first supersonic passenger flight), 1976	3·50	3·50
568/76	*Set of 9*	7·50	7·50

87 Olympic Torch-bearer

(Litho Questa)

1987 (5 Oct). *Olympic Games, Seoul (1988) (1st issue). T 87 and similar horiz designs. Multicoloured. P 14.*

577	5 s. Type 87.	10	10
578	10 s. Swimming	20	25
579	50 s. Cycling	1·00	1·10
580	100 s. Gymnastics	2·00	2·10
577/80	*Set of 4*	3·00	3·25
MS581	100 × 75 mm. 150 s. Boxing	3·00	4·00

See also Nos. 628/32.

88 Child Immunization **89** Golden-backed Weaver

(Des Associated Creative Designers. Litho Questa)

1987 (8 Oct). *25th Anniv of Independence. T 88 and similar horiz designs. P 14.*

582	5 s. multicoloured	15	10
583	10 s. multicoloured	30	25
584	25 s. multicoloured	70	70
585	50 s. multicoloured	1·25	1·50
582/5	*Set of 4*	2·25	3·25
MS586	90 × 70 mm. 100 s. black, bright scarlet and greenish yellow	2·00	2·75

Designs:—10 s. Mulago Hospital, Kampala; 25 s. Independence Monument, Kampala City Park; 50 s. High Court, Kampala; 100 s. Stylized head of Crested Crane, "25" and Ugandan flag.

(Des Jennifer Toombs. Litho Questa)

1987 (19 Oct). *Birds of Uganda. T 89 and similar multicoloured designs. P 14.*

587	5 s. Type 89	30	30
588	10 s. Hoopoe	55	55
589	15 s. Red-throated Bee Eater	75	75
590	25 s. Lilac-breasted Roller	1·10	1·10
591	35 s. African Pygmy Goose	1·40	1·40
592	45 s. Scarlet-chested Sunbird	1·75	1·75
593	50 s. South African Crowned Crane	1·75	1·75
594	100 s. Long-tailed Fiscal	2·75	2·75
587/94	*Set of 8*	9·25	9·25
MS595	Two sheets, each 80 × 60 mm. (a) 150 s. African Fish Eagle. (b) 150 s. Barn Owl *Set of 2 sheets*	6·00	7·00

90 Hippocrates (physician) and Surgeons performing Operation

(Des L. Nelson. Litho Questa)

1987 (2 Nov). *Great Scientific Discoveries. T 90 and similar multicoloured designs. P 14.*

596	5 s. Type 90	40	30
597	25 s. Einstein and Deep Space (Theory of Relativity)	1·50	1·50
598	35 s. Isaac Newton and diagram from *Opticks* (Theory of Colour and Light)	1·75	1·75
599	45 s. Karl Benz, early Benz and modern Mercedes cars	2·25	2·25
596/9	*Set of 4*	5·50	5·25
MS600	97 × 70 mm. 150 s. *Challenger* (space shuttle) (vert)	3·00	3·75

NEW INFORMATION

The editor is always interested to correspond with people who have new information that will improve or correct the Catalogue.

91 Scout with Album and Uganda Stamps

(Des Mary Walters. Litho Questa)

1987 (20 Nov). *World Scout Jamboree, Australia. T 91 and similar horiz designs. Multicoloured. P 14.*

601	5 s. Type 91	10	10
602	25 s. Scouts planting tree	50	55
603	35 s. Canoeing on Lake Victoria	70	75
604	45 s. Hiking	90	95
601/4	*Set of 4*	2·00	2·25
MS605	95 × 65 mm. 150 s. Jamboree and Uganda scout emblems	3·00	3·75

92 "The Annunciation"

(Litho Questa)

1987 (18 Dec). *Christmas. T 92 and similar multicoloured designs showing scenes from French diptych, c. 1250. P 14.*

606	5 s. Type 92.	10	10
607	10 s. "The Nativity".	20	25
608	50 s. "Flight into Egypt"	1·00	1·10
609	100 s. "The Adoration of the Magi"	2·00	2·10
606/9	*Set of 4*	3·00	3·25
MS610	76 × 105 mm. 150 s. "Mystic Wine" (tapestry detail) (vert)	3·00	3·50

93 Class "12" Light Shunter Locomotive **94** Columbite-Tantalite

(Des BG Studio. Litho Questa)

1988 (18 Jan). *Locomotives of East Africa Railways. T 93 and similar horiz designs. Multicoloured. P 14.*

611	5 s. Type 93	30	30
612	10 s. Class "92" diesel-electric	40	40
613	15 s. Locomotive No. 2506	55	55
614	25 s. Tank locomotive No. 126	75	75
615	35 s. Class "31" locomotive	95	95
616	45 s. Class "31" locomotive (different)	1·25	1·25
617	50 s. Class "59" Double Garratt locomotive	1·40	1·40
618	100 s. Class "87" diesel-electric shunter	2·00	2·00
611/18	*Set of 8*	7·00	7·00
MS619	Two sheets, each 100 × 74 mm. (a) 150 s. Class "31". (b) 150 s. Class "59" Double Garratt *Set of 2 sheets*	4·00	4·50

(Des Mary Walters. Litho Questa)

1988 (18 Jan). *Minerals. T 94 and similar vert designs. Multicoloured. P 14.*

620	1 s. Type 94	10	10
621	2 s. Galena	15	15
622	5 s. Malachite	25	25
623	10 s. Cassiterite	40	40
624	35 s. Ferberite	1·25	1·25
625	50 s. Emerald	1·75	1·75
626	100 s. Monazite	2·50	2·50
627	150 s. Microcline	3·50	3·50
620/7	*Set of 8*	9·00	9·00

95 Hurdling

(Des BG Studio. Litho Questa)

1988 (16 May). *Olympic Games, Seoul (2nd issue). T 95 and similar horiz designs. Multicoloured. P 14.*

628	5 s. Type 95	10	10
629	25 s. High jumping	20	25
630	35 s. Javelin throwing	25	30
631	45 s. Long jumping	30	35
628/31	*Set of 4*	70	90
MS632	85 × 114 mm. 150 s. Olympic medals	1·00	1·50

96 *Spathodea campanulata*

(Des L. Nelson. Litho Format)

1988 (29 July). *Flowers. T 96 and similar multicoloured designs. P 15.*

633	5 s. Type **96**	..	10	10
634	10 s. *Gloriosa simplex*	..	10	10
635	20 s. *Thevetica peruviana (vert)*	..	15	15
636	25 s. *Hibiscus schizopetalus*	..	20	25
637	35 s. *Aframomum sceptrum*	..	25	30
638	45 s. *Adenium obesum*	..	30	35
639	50 s. *Kigelia africana (vert)*	..	35	40
640	100 s. *Clappertonia ficifolia*	..	70	75
633/40		*Set of 8*	1·90	2·10

MS641 Two sheets, each 109 × 79 mm. (a) 150 s. *Costus spectabilis.* (b) 150 s. *Canarina abyssinica (vert)* .. .. .. *Set of 2 sheets* 2·00 2·50

97 Elephants in Grassland
(Type **61** redrawn)

(Litho Questa)

1988 (29 July). *Endangered Species (2nd series). P 14.*
642 **97** 10 s. multicoloured .. .. ..

98 Red Cross Worker vaccinating Baby   **99** Giraffes, Kidepo Valley National Park

(Des Associated Creative Art Designers. Litho Questa)

1988 (28 Oct). *125th Anniv of International Red Cross. T 98 and similar designs. P 14.*

643	10 s. bright scarlet, pale yellow and black		20	15
644	40 s. multicoloured	..	60	60
645	70 s. multicoloured	..	1·25	1·25
646	90 s. multicoloured	..	1·75	1·75
643/6		*Set of 4*	3·50	3·25

MS647 110 × 78 mm. 150 s. multicoloured 1·00 1·40
Designs: *Horiz*—10 s. "AIDS" with test tube as "I"; 70 s. Distributing food to refugees; 90 s. Red Cross volunteers with accident victim. *Vert*—150 s. Henri Dunant (founder).

(Litho Questa)

1988 (31 Oct). *500th Birth Anniv of Titian (artist). Vert designs as T 186a of Lesotho. Multicoloured. P 13½×14.*

648	10 s. "Portrait of a Lady"	..	10	10
649	20 s. "Portrait of a Man"	..	15	15
650	40 s. "Isabella d'Este"	..	25	30
651	50 s. "Vincenzo Mosti"	..	35	40
652	70 s. "Pope Paul III Farnese"	..	45	50
653	90 s. "Violante"	..	60	65
654	100 s. "Titian's Daughter Lavinia"	..	70	75
655	250 s. "Dr. Parma"	..	1·75	1·90
648/55		*Set of 8*	3·75	4·25

MS656 Two sheets, each 110 × 95 mm. (a) 350 s. "The Speech of Alfonso D'Avalos" (detail). (b) 350 s. "Cain and Abel" (detail) .. *Set of 2 sheets* 5·00 6·00

(Des Mary Walters. Litho Questa)

1988 (18 Nov). *National Parks of Uganda. T 99 and similar vert designs. Multicoloured. P 14.*

657	10 s. Type **99**		40	20
658	25 s. Zebras, Lake Mburo National Park		65	30
659	100 s. African Buffalo, Murchison Falls National Park		1·75	1·75
660	250 s. Eastern White Pelicans, Queen Elizabeth National Park		4·00	4·25
657/60		*Set of 4*	6·25	6·00

MS661 97×68 mm. 350 s. Roan Antelopes, Lake Mburo National Park .. .. .. 2·50 3·00

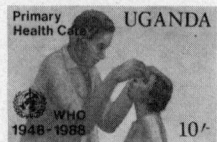

100 Doctor examining Child's Eyes

(Des L. Watkins. Litho Questa)

1988 (1 Dec). *40th Anniv of World Health Organization. T 100 and similar horiz designs. Multicoloured. P 14.*

662	10 s. Type **100**		15	10
663	25 s. Mental health therapist with patient		30	25
664	45 s. Surgeon performing operation	..	45	45
665	100 s. Dentist treating girl	..	90	1·00
666	200 s. Doctor examining child	..	1·75	2·00
662/6		*Set of 5*	3·25	3·50

MS667 107 × 88 mm. 350 s. Delegates approving Declaration of Alma-Ata, 1978 .. .. 2·50 3·00

100a Father Christmas with List   **(101)** 110 M HURDLES R. KINGDOM USA

(Des Walt Disney Co. Litho Questa)

1988 (2 Dec). *Christmas. "Santa's Helpers". T 100a and similar vert designs showing Walt Disney cartoon characters. Multicoloured. P 13½×14.*

668	50 c. Type **100a**	..	50	50
	a. Sheetlet. Nos. 668/75	..	3·50	
669	50 c. Goofy carrying presents	..	50	50
670	50 c. Mickey Mouse on toy train	..	50	50
671	50 c. Reindeer at window	..	50	50
672	50 c. Donald Duck's nephew with building blocks		50	50
673	50 c. Donald Duck holding sack	..	50	50
674	50 c. Chip n'Dale on conveyor belt	..	50	50
675	50 c. Donald Duck's nephew operating conveyor belt		50	50
668/75		*Set of 8*	3·50	3·50

MS676 Two sheets, each 127×102 mm. (a) 350 s. Mickey Mouse loading sack of toys on sleigh (*horiz*). P 14×13½. (b) 350 s. Mickey Mouse and Chip n'Dale grooming reindeer. P 13½×14
.. .. .. *Set of 2 sheets* 5·00 6·00
Nos. 668/75 were printed together, *se-tenant* as a composite design, in sheetlets of eight.

1989 (30 Jan). *Olympic Gold Medal Winners, Seoul. Nos. 628/32 optd as T 101 or surch also.*

677	5 s. Type **95** (optd with T **101**)	..	10	10
678	25 s. High jumping (optd "HIGH JUMP G. AVDEENKO USSR")		20	25
679	35 s. Javelin throwing (optd "JAVELIN T. KORJUS FINLAND")		25	30
680	300 s. on 45 s. Long jumping (optd "LONG JUMP C. LEWIS USA")		2·25	2·40
677/80		*Set of 4*	2·50	2·75

MS681 85×114 mm. 350 s. on 150 s. Olympic medals with medal table optd on sheet margin 3·00 3·50

102 Goalkeeper with Ball   **103** 1895 5 Cowries Stamp

(Des J. Genzo. Litho Questa)

1989 (24 Apr). *World Cup Football Championship, Italy (1990) (1st issue). T 102 and similar multicoloured designs. P 14.*

682	10 s. Type **102**	..	20	15
683	25 s. Player kicking ball (*horiz*)	..	40	25
684	75 s. Heading ball towards net (*horiz*)		70	60
685	200 s. Tackling	..	1·40	1·60
682/5		*Set of 4*	2·40	2·40

MS686 118×87 mm. 300 s. Football and World Cup trophy (*horiz*) .. .. 2·00 2·25
See also Nos. 849/53.

(Litho Questa)

1989 (15 May). *Japanese Art. Paintings by Hokusai. Horiz designs as T 187a of Lesotho. Multicoloured. P 14×13½.*

687	10 s. "Fuji and the Great Wave off Kanagawa"		20	20
688	15 s. "Fuji from Lake Suwa"	..	30	30
689	20 s. "Fuji from Kajikazawa"	..	30	30
690	60 s. "Fuji from Shichirigahama"	..	70	70
691	90 s. "Fuji from Ejiri in Sunshu"	..	90	90
692	120 s. "Fuji above Lightning"	..	1·00	1·00
693	200 s. "Fuji from Lower Meguro in Edo"		1·75	1·75
694	250 s. "Fuji from Edo"	..	1·90	1·90
687/94		*Set of 8*	6·25	6·25

MS695 Two sheets, each 102×76 mm. (a) 500 s. "The Red Fuji from the Foot". (b) 500 s. "Fuji from Umezawa" .. .. *Set of 2 sheets* 4·00 4·50
Nos. 687/94 were each printed in sheetlets of 10 containing two horizontal strips of 5 stamps separated by printed labels commemorating Emperor Hirohito.

(Des U. Purins. Litho B.D.T.)

1989 (7 July). *"Philexfrance 89" International Stamp Exhibition, Paris. T 103 and similar vert designs. P 14.*

696	20 s. black, brt scarlet & pale grey-brown	25	25
697	70 s. black, yellowish green and azure	70	70
698	100 s. black, dull violet and pale brown-rose	90	90
699	250 s. black, orange-yell & pale greenish yell	1·60	1·60
696/9		*Set of 4*	3·00	3·00

MS700 176×131 mm. Nos. 696/9 (*sold at* 500 s.) 3·00 3·25
Designs:—70 s. 1895 10 on 50 cowries stamp; 100 s. 1896 25 cowries stamp; 250 s. 1896 1 rupee stamp.

104 Scout advising on Immunization   **105** *Suillus granulatus*

(Des Associated Creative Designers. Litho Questa)

1989 (3 Aug). *2nd All African Scout Jamboree, Uganda, and 75th Anniv of Ugandan Scout Movement. T 104 and similar multicoloured designs. P 14.*

701	10 s. Type **104**	..	15	15
702	70 s. Poultry keeping	..	60	60
703	90 s. Scout on crutches leading family to immunization centre		80	80
704	100 s. Scouts making bricks	..	90	90
701/4		*Set of 4*	2·25	2·25

MS705 99×67 mm. 500 s. Ugandan Scout logo (*vert*) .. .. .. 3·00 3·25

(Des Mary Walters. Litho B.D.T.)

1989 (14 Aug). *Fungi. T 105 and similar vert designs. Multicoloured. P 14.*

706	10 s. Type **105**	..	20	20
707	15 s. *Omphalotus olearius*	..	30	30
708	45 s. *Oudemansiella radicata*	..	70	70
709	50 s. *Clitocybe nebularis*	..	75	75
710	60 s. *Macrolepiota rhacodes*	..	80	80
711	75 s. *Lepista nuda*	..	85	85
712	150 s. *Suillus luteus*	..	1·50	1·50
713	200 s. *Agaricus campestris*	..	1·75	1·75
706/13		*Set of 8*	6·25	6·25

MS714 Two sheets, each 100×68 mm. (a) 350 s. *Bolbitius vitellinus.* (b) 350 s. *Schizophyllum commune* .. .. .. *Set of 2 sheets* 4·00 4·00

106 Saddle-bill Stork   **107** Rocket on Launch Pad

(Des S. Barlowe. Litho Questa)

1989 (12 Sept). *Wildlife at Waterhole. T 106 and similar vert designs. Multicoloured. P 14½×14.*

715	30 s. Type **106**	..	30	30
	a. Sheetlet. Nos. 715/34	..	5·50	
716	30 s. Eastern White Pelican	..	30	30
717	30 s. Marabou Stork	..	30	30
718	30 s. Egyptian Vulture	..	30	30
719	30 s. Bateleur	..	30	30
720	30 s. African Elephant	..	30	30
721	30 s. Giraffe	..	30	30
722	30 s. Goliath Heron	..	30	30
723	30 s. Black Rhinoceros	..	30	30
724	30 s. Common Zebra and Oribi	..	30	30
725	30 s. African Fish Eagle	..	30	30
726	30 s. Hippopotamus	..	30	30
727	30 s. Black-backed Jackal and Eastern White Pelican		30	30
728	30 s. African Buffalo	..	30	30
729	30 s. Olive Baboon	..	30	30
730	30 s. Bohar Reedbuck	..	30	30
731	30 s. Lesser Flamingo and Serval	..	30	30
732	30 s. Whale-headed Stork ("Shoebill Stork")		30	30
733	30 s. South African Crowned Crane	..	30	30
734	30 s. Impala	..	30	30
715/34		*Set of 20*	5·50	5·50

MS735 Two sheets, each 99×68 mm. (a) 500 s. Lion. (b) 500 s. Long-crested Eagle
.. .. .. *Set of 2 sheets* 5·00 5·00
Nos. 715/34 were printed together, *se-tenant*, in a sheetlet of 20 stamps, forming a composite design showing wildlife at a waterhole.

(Des T. Agans. Litho Questa)

1989 (20 Oct). *20th Anniv of First Manned Landing on Moon. T 107 and similar multicoloured designs. P 14.*

736	10 s. Type **107**	..	15	15
737	20 s. Lunar module *Eagle* on Moon	..	25	25
738	30 s. "Apollo 11" command module	..	30	30
739	50 s. *Eagle* landing on Moon	..	45	45
740	70 s. Astronaut Aldrin on Moon	..	60	60
741	250 s. Neil Armstrong alighting from *Eagle* (*vert*)		1·75	1·75

742	300 s.	*Eagle* over Moon	.. .. ..	1·90	1·90
743	350 s.	Astronaut Aldrin on Moon (*vert*)		2·00	2·00
736/43			*Set of 8*	6·50	6·50

MS744 Two sheets, each 77×104 mm. (a) 500 s. "Saturn" rocket (*vert*). (b) 500 s. "Apollo 11" capsule on parachutes (*vert*) .. *Set of 2 sheets* 5·00 5·50

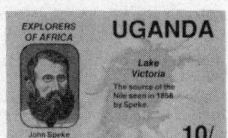

108 *Aphniolaus*   109 John Hanning Speke and
pallene   Map of Lake Victoria

(Des S. Heimann. Litho Questa)

1989 (13 Nov). *Butterflies.* T **108** *and similar vert designs showing "UGANDA" in black. Multicoloured.* P 14.

745	5 s.	Type **108**	.. .. ..	10	10
746	10 s.	*Hewitsonia boisduvali*	..	15	15
747	20 s.	*Euxanthe wakefieldi*	.. ..	20	15
748	30 s.	*Papilio echerioides*	..	25	20
749	40 s.	*Acraea semivitrea*	..	30	25
750	50 s.	*Colotis antevippe*	.. ..	30	25
751	70 s.	*Acraea perenna*	..	35	30
752	90 s.	*Charaxes cynthia*	..	40	30
753	100 s.	*Euphaedra neophron*	..	40	30
754	150 s.	*Cymothoe beckeri*	..	65	55
755	200 s.	*Vanessula milca*	..	75	65
756	400 s.	*Mimacraea marshalli*	..	1·10	1·25
757	500 s.	*Axiocerses amanga*	..	1·25	1·50
758	1000 s.	*Precis hierta*	..	1·00	1·25
745/58			*Set of 14*	6·50	6·50

For these, and similar, designs showing "UGANDA" in blue, see Nos. 864/80.

(Des A. Granberg. Litho Questa)

1989 (15 Nov). *Exploration of Africa.* T **109** *and similar horiz designs. Multicoloured.* P 14.

760	10 s.	Type **109**	.. .. ..	15	15
761	25 s.	Sir Richard Burton and map of Lake Tanganyika		25	25
762	40 s.	Richard Lander and Bakota bronze ..		35	35
763	90 s.	René Caillié and mosque, Timbuktu		55	55
764	125 s.	Sir Samuel Baker and Dorcas Gazelle		70	70
765	150 s.	Pharaoh Necho and ancient Phoenician merchant ship		85	85
766	250 s.	Vasco da Gama and 15th-century caravel		1·00	1·00
767	300 s.	Sir Henry Morton Stanley and *Lady Alice* (sectional boat)		1·25	1·25
760/7			*Set of 8*	4·75	4·75

MS768 Two sheets, each 73×103 mm. (a) 500 s. Dr. David Livingstone and steam launch *Ma Robert;* (b) 500 s. Mary Kingsley and map of Ogooué River .. .. .. *Set of 2 sheets* 5·00 5·50

110 Logo (25th anniv of   111 *Aerangis*
African Development Bank)   *kotschyana*

(Des D. Miller. Litho Questa)

1989 (12 Dec). *Anniversaries.* T **110** *and similar horiz designs. Multicoloured.* P 14.

769	10 s.	Type **110**	.. .. ..	15	15
770	20 s.	Arrows and dish aerials (World Telecommunication Day)		20	20
771	75 s.	Nehru and Gandhi (birth centenary of Nehru)		60	60
772	90 s.	Pan Am *Dixie Clipper* flying boat (50th anniv of first scheduled trans-Atlantic airmail flight)		70	70
773	100 s.	George Stephenson and *Locomotion*, 1825 (175th anniv of first practical steam locomotive)		75	75
774	150 s.	"Concorde" cockpit (20th anniv of first test flight)		1·25	1·25
775	250 s.	*Wapen von Hamburg* and *Leopoldus Primus* (galleons) (800th anniv of Port of Hamburg)		1·50	1·50
776	300 s.	"Concorde" and cockpit interior (20th anniv of first test flight)		1·60	1·60
769/76			*Set of 8*	6·00	6·00

MS777 Two sheets (a) 91×87 mm. 500 s. Revolutionary with musket and Bastille, Paris (bicentenary of French Revolution). (b) 110×82 mm. 500 s. Emperor Frederick I Barbarossa and Hamburg charter (800th anniv of Port of Hamburg) .. .. *Set of 2 sheets* 3·25 3·50

(Des W. Wright. Litho Questa)

1989 (18 Dec). *Orchids.* T **111** *and similar vert designs. Multicoloured.* P 14.

778	10 s.	Type **111**	..	15	15
779	15 s.	*Angraecum infundibulare*	..	20	20
780	45 s.	*Cyrtorchis chailluana*	..	45	45
781	50 s.	*Aerangis rhodosticta*	..	50	50
782	100 s.	*Eulophia speciosa*	..	80	80
783	200 s.	*Calanthe sylvatica*	..	1·40	1·40
784	250 s.	*Vanilla imperialis*	..	1·50	1·50
785	350 s.	*Polystachya vulcanica*		1·75	1·75
778/85			*Set of 8*	6·00	6·00

MS786 Two sheets, each 110×82 mm. (a) 500 s. *Ansellia africana.* (b) 500 s. *Ancistrochilus rothschildianus* .. .. *Set of 2 sheets* 5·00 5·50

(Litho Questa)

1989 (21 Dec). *Christmas. Paintings by Fra Angelico Vert designs as T* **193***b of Lesotho. Multicoloured.* P 14.

787	10 s.	"Madonna and Child"	..	10	10
788	20 s.	"Adoration of the Magi"	..	15	15
789	40 s.	"Virgin and Child enthroned with Saints"		25	25
790	75 s.	"The Annunciation"	..	45	45
791	100 s.	"Virgin and Child" (detail, "St. Peter Martyr" triptych)		55	55
792	150 s.	"Virgin and Child enthroned with Saints" (*different*)		70	70
793	250 s.	"Virgin and Child enthroned"	..	1·00	1·00
794	350 s.	"Virgin and Child" (from Annalena altarpiece)		1·25	1·25
787/94			*Set of 8*	4·00	4·00

MS795 Two sheets, each 72×96 mm. (a) 500 s. "Virgin and Child" (from Bosco ai Frati altarpiece). (b) 500 s. "Madonna and Child with Twelve Angels" .. .. *Set of 2 sheets* 4·00 4·50

112 *Thevetia*   (113)
peruviana

(Des Jennifer Toombs. Litho B.D.T.)

1990 (17 Apr). *"EXPO '90" International Garden and Greenery Exhibition, Osaka* (1st issue). *Flowering Trees. T* **112** *and similar vert designs. Multicoloured.* P 14.

796	10 s.	Type **112**	..	10	10
797	20 s.	*Acanthus eminens*	..	10	10
798	90 s.	*Gnidia glauca*	..	10	15
799	150 s.	*Oncoba spinosa*	..	15	20
800	175 s.	*Hibiscus rosa-sinensis*	..	20	25
801	400 s.	*Jacaranda mimosifolia*	..	40	45
802	500 s.	*Erythrina abyssinica*	..	50	60
803	700 s.	*Bauhinia purpurea*	..	75	80
796/803			*Set of 8*	2·10	2·40

MS804 Two sheets, each 93×85 mm. (a) 1000 s. *Delonix regia.* (b) 1000 s. *Cassia didymobotrya*   *Set of 2 sheets* 2·10 2·25

See also Nos. 820/8.

(Des W. Wright. Litho Questa)

1990 (8 June). *50th Anniv of Second World War. Multicoloured designs as T* **242** *of Maldive Islands.* P 14.

805	5 s.	Allied penetration of German West Wall, 1944		10	10
806	10 s.	Flags of the Allies, VE Day, 1945 ..		10	10
807	20 s.	Capture of Okinawa, 1945 ..		10	10
808	75 s.	Appointment of Gen. De Gaulle to command all Free French forces, 1944		10	15
809	100 s.	Invasion of Saipan, 1944		10	15
810	150 s.	Airborne landing, Operation Market Garden, 1944		15	20
811	200 s.	MacArthur's return to Philippines, 1944		20	25
812	300 s.	Japanese attack on U.S. carrier, Coral Sea, 1942		30	35
813	350 s.	First Battle of El Alamein, 1942		35	40
814	500 s.	Naval Battle of Guadalcanal, 1942 ..		50	55
805/14			*Set of 10*	1·75	2·10

MS815 112×83 mm. 1000 s. Battle of Britain, 1940 (*vert*) .. .. 1·00 1·10

(Des Young Phillips Studio. Litho Questa)

1990 (5 July). *90th Birthday of Queen Elizabeth the Queen Mother. Vert designs as T* **198***a of Lesotho, showing portraits, 1940–49.* P 14.

816	250 s.	black, deep magenta and new blue ..		25	30
		a. Strip of 3. Nos. 816/18		70	
817	250 s.	black, deep magenta and new blue ..		25	30
818	250 s.	black, deep magenta and new blue ..		25	30
816/18			*Set of 3*	80	95

MS819 90×75 mm. 1000 s. multicoloured .. 1·00 1·10
Designs:—No. 816, Queen Elizabeth with corgi; No. 817, **MS**819, Queen Elizabeth wearing feathered hat; No. 818, Queen Elizabeth at wartime inspection.
Nos. 816/18 were printed together, horizontally and vertically se-tenant, in sheetlets of 9 (3×3).

1990 (30 July). *"EXPO 90" International Garden and Greenery Exhibition, Osaka* (2nd issue). *Nos.* 778/86 *optd as T* **113** *in silver.*

820	10 s.	Type **111**		10	10
821	15 s.	*Angraecum infundibulare*	..	10	10
822	45 s.	*Cyrtorchis chailluana*	..	10	10
823	50 s.	*Aerangis rhodosticta*	..	10	10
824	100 s.	*Eulophia speciosa*	..	10	15
825	200 s.	*Calanthe sylvatica*	..	20	25

826	250 s.	*Vanilla imperialis*	..	25	30
827	350 s.	*Polystachya vulcanica*	..	35	40
820/7			*Set of 8*	1·00	1·10

MS828 Two sheets, each 110×82 mm. (a) 500 s. *Ansellia africana.* (b) 500 s. *Ancistrochilus rothschildianus* .. .. *Set of 2 sheets* 1·00 1·10
The overprint on No. **MS**828 occurs on the sheet margin and includes an additional inscription.

114 P.A.P.U. Emblem   115 Unissued
                  G. B. "V R" Penny
                  Black

(Des L. Fried. Litho B.D.T.)

1990 (3 Aug). *Tenth Anniv of Pan-African Postal Union* (80 s.) *and Second United Nations Conference on Least Developed Countries, Paris* (750 s.). *T* **114** *and similar horiz design.* P 14.

829	80 s.	multicoloured		10	15

MS830 97×67 mm. 750 s. black and new blue 80 85
Design:—750 s. Clasped hands.

(Des and litho B.D.T.)

1990 (6 Aug). *150th Anniv of the Penny Black. T* **115** *and similar designs.* P 14.

831	25 s.	multicoloured	.. ..	10	10
832	50 s.	brown-lake, blk & pale turquoise-grn		10	10
833	100 s.	multicoloured	.. ..	10	15
834	150 s.	multicoloured	.. ..	15	20
835	200 s.	multicoloured	.. ..	20	25
836	300 s.	multicoloured	.. ..	30	35
837	500 s.	multicoloured	.. ..	50	55
838	600 s.	multicoloured	.. ..	65	70
831/8			*Set of 8*	1·90	2·10

MS839 Two sheets (a) 107×77 mm. 1000 s. multicoloured. (b) 119×85 mm. 1000 s. black and rosine .. .. .. *Set of 2 sheets* 2·10 2·25
Designs:—50 s. Canada 1858-59 3d. Beaver; 100 s. Baden 1851 9 k. on green error; 150 s. Basel 1845 2½ r. Dove; 200 s. U.S.A. 1918 24 c. Inverted "Jenny" error; 300 s. Western Australia 1854 1d. Black Swan; 500 s. Uganda 1895 20 c. "narrow" typewritten stamp; 600 s. Great Britain Twopenny blue; 1000 s. (No. **MS**839a), Uganda 1895 20 c. "wide" typewritten stamp; 1000 s. (No. **MS**839b), Sir Rowland Hill.
No. **MS**839 also commemorates "Stamp World London 90" International Stamp Exhibition.

116 African Jacana

(Des P. Gonzalez. Litho Questa)

1990 (3 Sept). *Wild Birds of Uganda. T* **116** *and similar multicoloured designs.* P 14.

840	10 s.	Type **116**	.. ..	10	10
841	15 s.	Southern Ground Hornbill	..	10	10
842	45 s.	Kori Bustard (*vert*) ..		10	10
843	50 s.	Secretary Bird	.. ..	10	10
844	100 s.	Egyptian Geese	.. ..	10	15
845	300 s.	Goliath Heron (*vert*)	..	30	35
846	500 s.	Ostrich with chicks (*vert*)	..	50	55
847	650 s.	Saddle-bill Stork (*vert*)	..	75	80
840/7			*Set of 8*	1·75	1·90

MS848 Two sheets, each 98×69 mm. (a) 1000 s. Lesser Flamingo (*vert*). (b) 1000 s. Vulturine Guineafowl (*vert*) .. *Set of 2 sheets* 2·10 2·25

117 Roger Milla of Cameroun

(Des Young Phillips Studio. Litho Questa)

1990 (21 Sept). *World Cup Football Championship, Italy* (2nd issue). *T* **117** *and similar horiz designs. Multicoloured.* P 14.

849	50 s.	Type **117**	.. ..	10	10
850	100 s.	Ramzy of Egypt	.. ..	10	15
851	250 s.	David O'Leary of Ireland	..	25	30
852	600 s.	Littbarsky of West Germany	..	65	70
849/52			*Set of 4*	1·00	1·10

MS853 Two sheets, each 75×90 mm. (a) 1000 s. Ali McCoist of Scotland. (b) 1000 s. Ekstrom of Sweden .. .. *Set of 2 sheets* 2·10 2·25

118 Mickey and Minnie Mouse at Breakfast

(Des Walt Disney Co. Litho B.D.T.)

1990 (19 Oct). *Health and Safety Campaign. T **118** and similar multicoloured designs showing Walt Disney cartoon characters. P* 13.

854	10 s.	Type 118		10	10
855	20 s.	Donald Duck's nephews doing kerb drill		10	10
856	50 s.	Donald and Mickey stopping Big Pete smoking		10	10
857	90 s.	Mickey stopping Donald choking		10	15
858	100 s.	Mickey and Goofy using seat belts		10	15
859	250 s.	Mickey and Minnie dancing		25	30
860	500 s.	Donald Duck's fitness class		50	55
861	600 s.	Mickey's nephews showing lights at night		65	70
854/61			*Set of* 8	1·60	1·90

MS862 Two sheets, each 135×115 mm. (a) 1000 s. Mickey weighing nephew (*vert*). (b) 1000 s. Mickey and Pluto walking (*vert*)

Set of 2 *sheets*   2·10   2·25

(Litho Questa)

1990 (1 Nov)–*92. As Nos.* 746/55 *and new values, showing butterflies, as T **108** with "UGANDA" in blue. Multicoloured. P* 14. A. *Without imprint date.* B. *With imprint date.*

			A		B	
864	10 s.	Hewitsonia boisduvali	10	10		†
865	20 s.	Euxanthe wakefieldi	10	10	10	†
866	30 s.	Papilio echerioides	10	10		†
867	40 s.	Acraea semivitrea	10	10		†
868	50 s.	Colotis antevippe	†		10	10
869	70 s.	Acraea perenna	10	10		†
870	90 s.	Charaxes cynthia	10	10		†
871	100 s.	Euphaedra neophron	10	10	10	†
872	150 s.	Cymothoe beckeri	15	20		†
873	200 s.	Vanessula milca	20	25	20	25
874	400 s.	Mimacraea marshalli		†	40	45
875	500 s.	Axiocerses amanga		†	50	55
876	1000 s.	Precis hierta		†	1·00	1·10
877	2000 s.	Precis hierta	2·10	2·25	2·10	2·25
878	3000 s.	Euphaedra eusemoides	3·00	3·25		†
879	4000 s.	Acraea natalica	4·25	4·50		†
880	5000 s.	Euphaedra themis	5·25	5·50		†
864A/80A			*Set of* 13	14·00	15·00	†
865B/77B			*Set of* 8			4·00	4·50

Dates of issue:—1.11.90, Nos. 864A/77A; 4.11.91, Nos. 865B, 868B, 871B, 873B/7B; 9.10.92, 878A/80A.

(Litho Questa)

1990 (17 Dec). *Christmas.* 350*th Death Anniv of Rubens. Multicoloured designs as T **250** of Maldive Islands, but inscr* "CHRISTMAS 1990". P 13½×14.

881	10 s.	"Baptism of Christ" (detail) (*vert*)		10	10
882	20 s.	"St. Gregory the Great and other Saints" (detail) (*vert*)		10	10
883	100 s.	"Saints Nereus, Domitilla and Achilleus" (detail) (*vert*)		10	15
884	150 s.	"St. Gregory the Great and other Saints" (different detail) (*vert*)		15	20
885	300 s.	"Saint Augustine" (detail) (*vert*)		30	35
886	400 s.	"St. Gregory the Great and other Saints" (different detail) (*vert*)		40	45
887	500 s.	"Baptism of Christ" (different detail) (*vert*)		50	55
888	600 s.	"St. Gregory the Great and other Saints" (different detail) (*vert*)		65	70
881/8			*Set of* 8	2·10	2·40

MS889 Two sheets, each 110×71 mm. (a) 1000 s. "The Triumph of Faith" (detail). (b) 1000 s. "The Victory of Eucharistic Truth over Heresy" (detail). P 14×13½   *Set of* 2 *sheets*   2·10   2·25

119 Census Emblem   120 Damselfly

(Litho Questa)

1990 (28 Dec). *National Population and Housing Census. T **119** and similar horiz design. Multicoloured. P* 14.

890	20 s.	Type 119		10	10

MS891 105×73 mm. 1000 s. Symbolic people and dwellings   1·00   1·10

(Des I. Maclaury. Litho B.D.T.)

1991 (8 Jan). *Fauna of Uganda's Wetlands. T **120** and similar multicoloured designs. P* 14.

892	70 s.	Type 120		10	10
		a. Sheetlet of 16. Nos. 892/907		1·25	
893	70 s.	Purple Swamphen ("Gallinule")		10	10
894	70 s.	Sitatunga		10	10
895	70 s.	Western Reef Heron ("Purple Heron")		10	10
896	70 s.	Bushpig		10	10
897	70 s.	Vervet Monkey		10	10
898	70 s.	Long Reed Frog		10	10
899	70 s.	Malachite Kingfisher		10	10
900	70 s.	Marsh Mongoose		10	10
901	70 s.	Painted Reed Frog		10	10
902	70 s.	African Jacana		10	10
903	70 s.	Charaxes butterfly		10	10
904	70 s.	Nile Crocodile		10	10
905	70 s.	Herald Snake		10	10
906	70 s.	Dragonfly		10	10
907	70 s.	Lungfish		10	10
892/907			*Set of* 16	1·25	1·40

MS908 118×78 mm. 1000 s. Nile Monitor (*horiz*)   1·00   1·10

Nos. 892/907 were printed together, *se-tenant*, in sheetlets of 16 forming a composite design.

121 *Haplochromis limax*

(Des Susan Fuller. Litho B.D.T.)

1991 (18 Jan). *Fishes of Uganda. T **121** and similar horiz designs. Multicoloured. P* 14.

909	10 s.	Type 121		10	10
910	20 s.	Nothobranchius palmqvisti		10	10
911	40 s.	Distichodus affinis		10	10
912	90 s.	Haplochromis sauvagei		10	15
913	100 s.	Aphyosemion calliurum		10	15
914	350 s.	Haplochromis johnstoni		35	40
915	600 s.	Haplochromis dichrourus		65	70
916	800 s.	Hemichromis bimaculatus		85	90
909/16			*Set of* 8	2·00	2·25

MS917 Two sheets, each 100×74 mm. (a) 1000 s. *Haplochromis* sp. (b) 1000 s. *Aphyosemion striatum*   *Set of* 2 *sheets*   2·10   2·25

(Des B. Grout. Litho Questa)

1991 (25 Feb). *Olympic Games, Barcelona (1992). Multicoloured designs as T **202** of Lesotho. P* 14.

918	20 s.	Women's 100 metres hurdles		10	10
919	40 s.	Long jump		10	10
920	125 s.	Table tennis		15	20
921	250 s.	Football		25	30
922	500 s.	Men's 800 metres		50	55
918/22			*Set of* 5	1·00	1·10

MS923 Two sheets, each 110×71 mm. (a) 1200 s. Opening Ceremony at Seoul Games (*horiz*). (b) 1200 s. Women's 4 × 100 metres relay (*horiz*)

Set of 2 *sheets*   2·50   2·75

122 Class "10" Steam Locomotive, Zimbabwe

(Des O. Fernandez. Litho Walsall)

1991 (2 Apr). *African Railway Locomotives. T **122** and similar horiz designs. Multicoloured. P* 14.

924	10 s.	Type 122		10	10
925	20 s.	Class "12" steam locomotive, Zimbabwe		10	10
926	80 s.	Class "Tribal" steam locomotive, Tazara Railway		10	10
927	200 s.	4-6-0 type steam locomotive, Egypt		20	25
928	300 s.	Mikado type steam locomotive, Sudan		30	35
929	400 s.	Class "Mountain" Garrat steam locomotive, Uganda		40	45
930	500 s.	Mallet type steam locomotive, Uganda		50	55
931	1000 s.	5 F 1 electric locomotive, South Africa		1·00	1·10
924/31			*Set of* 8	2·40	2·75

MS932 Four sheets, each 100×70 mm. (a) 1200 s. Atlantic type steam locomotive, Egypt. (b) 1200 s. 4-8-2 type steam locomotive, Zimbabwe. (c) 1200 s. 4-8-2 type steam locomotive, Angola. (d) 1200 s. Mallet compound type steam locomotive, Natal   *Set of* 4 *sheets*   4·75   5·00

STANLEY GIBBONS
STAMP COLLECTING SERIES

Introductory booklets on *How to Start, How to Identify Stamps* and *Collecting by Theme*. A series of well illustrated guides at a low price.
Write for details.

---

123 Lord Baden-Powell and   124 General
Scout Emblem   Charles de
                                Gaulle

(Des W. Hanson Studio. Litho Questa)

1991 (27 May). *World Scout Jamboree Mount Sorak, Korea. T **123** and similar horiz designs. P* 14.

933	20 s.	multicoloured		10	10
934	80 s.	multicoloured		10	15
935	100 s.	multicoloured		10	15
936	150 s.	black and pale yellow-olive		15	20
937	300 s.	multicoloured		30	35
938	400 s.	multicoloured		40	45
939	500 s.	multicoloured		50	55
940	1000 s.	multicoloured		1·00	1·25
933/40			*Set of* 8	2·40	2·75

MS941 Two sheets. (a) 76×115 mm. 1200 s. black and stone. (b) 115×76mm. 1200 s. black and dull violet-blue   *Set of* 2 *sheets*   2·50   2·75
Designs:—80 s. Scouts and Uganda 1982 100 s. anniversary stamp; 100 s. Scout encampment, New York World's Fair, 1939; 150 s. Cover and illustration from *Scouting for Boys*; 300 s. Cooking on campfire; 400 s. Aldrin and Armstrong on Moon; 500 s. Scout salutes; 1000 s. Statue to the Unknown Scout, Gillwell Park; 1200 s. (MS941a) Jamboree emblem; 1200 s. (MS941b) Lord Baden-Powell, W. Boyce and Revd. L. Hadley.

(Des Walt Disney Co. Litho Questa)

1991 (29 May). *"Phila Nippon '91" International Stamp Exhibition, Tokyo. Multicoloured designs as T **204** of Lesotho showing Walt Disney cartoon characters and Japanese traditions. P* 14×13½.

942	10 s.	Uncle Scrooge celebrating Ga-No-Iwai		10	10
943	20 s.	Mickey Mouse removing shoes		10	10
944	70 s.	Goofy leading cart-horse		10	10
945	80 s.	Daisy Duck and Minnie Mouse exchanging gifts		10	15
946	300 s.	Minnie kneeling at doorway		30	35
947	400 s.	Donald Duck and Mickey taking a hot volcanic sand bath		40	45
948	500 s.	Clarabelle Cow burning incense		50	55
949	1000 s.	Mickey and Minnie writing New Year cards		1·00	1·10
942/9			*Set of* 8	2·25	2·50

MS950 Two sheets, each 127×112 mm. (a) 1200 s. Mickey conducting (*vert*). (b) 1200 s. Mickey in public bath (*vert*). P 13½×14

Set of 2 *sheets*   2·50   2·75

(Litho Walsall)

1991 (26 June). *Death Centenary of Vincent van Gogh (artist)* (1990). *Multicoloured designs as T **255** of Maldive Islands. P* 13½.

951	10 s.	"Snowy Landscape with Arles" (*horiz*)		10	10
952	20 s.	"Peasant Woman binding Sheaves" (*horiz*)		10	10
953	60 s.	"The Drinkers" (*horiz*)		10	10
954	80 s.	"View of Auvers" (*horiz*)		10	10
955	200 s.	"Mourning Man"		20	25
956	400 s.	"Still Life: Vase with Roses" (*horiz*)		40	45
957	800 s.	"The Raising of Lazarus" (*horiz*)		85	90
958	1000 s.	"The Good Samaritan"		1·00	1·25
951/8			*Set of* 8	2·50	2·75

MS959 Two sheets, each 102×76 mm. (a) 1200 s. "First Steps" (95×71 *mm*). (b) 1200 s. "Village Street and Steps in Auvers" (95×71 *mm*). Imperf

Set of 2 *sheets*   2·50   2·75

(Des D. Miller. Litho Walsall)

1991 (5 July). *65th Birthday of Queen Elizabeth II. Horiz designs as T **210** of Lesotho. Multicoloured. P* 14.

960	70 s.	Queen and Prince Charles after polo match		10	10
961	90 s.	Queen at Balmoral, 1976		10	10
962	500 s.	Queen with Princess Margaret, August 1980		50	55
963	600 s.	Queen and Queen Mother leaving St. George's Chapel, Windsor		65	70
960/3			*Set of* 4	1·25	1·25

MS964 68×90 mm. 1200 s. Separate photographs of Queen and Prince Philip   1·25   1·40

(Des D. Miller. Litho Walsall)

1991 (5 July). *10th Wedding Anniv of Prince and Princess of Wales. Horiz designs as T **210** of Lesotho. Multicoloured. P* 14.

965	20 s.	Prince and Princess of Wales in July 1986		10	10
966	100 s.	Separate photographs of Prince, Princess and sons		10	10
967	200 s.	Prince Henry and Prince William		20	25
968	1000 s.	Separate photographs of Prince and Princess in 1988		1·00	1·10
965/8			*Set of* 4	1·25	1·40

MS969 68×90 mm. 1200 s. Princes William and Henry on Majorca and Prince and Princess of Wales in Cameroun   1·25   1·40

(Litho Questa)

1991 (15 July). *Birth Centenary of Charles de Gaulle (French statesman)* (1990). *T* **124** *and similar multicoloured designs.* *P* 14.

970	20 s. Type **124**		10	10
971	70 s. Liberation of Paris, 1944		10	10
972	90 s. De Gaulle with King George VI, 1940		10	10
973	100 s. Reviewing Free French troops, 1940 (*horiz*)		10	10
974	200 s. Broadcasting to France, 1940 (*horiz*)		20	25
975	500 s. De Gaulle in Normandy, 1944 (*horiz*)		50	55
976	600 s. De Gaulle at Albert Hall, 1940 (*horiz*)		65	70
977	1000 s. Inauguration as President, 1959		1·00	1·10
970/7		*Set of 8*	2·25	2·50

MS978 Two sheets. (a) 104×76 mm. 1200 s. De Gaulle entering Paris, 1944. (b) 107×76 mm. 1200 s. De Gaulle with Eisenhower, 1942 (*horiz*) .. .. *Set of 2 sheets* 2·50 2·75

125 *Volvariella bingensis*

126 *Anigozanthos manglesii*

(Des K. Botis. Litho Questa)

1991 (19 July). *Fungi. T* **125** *and similar multicoloured designs.* *P* 14.

979	20 s. Type **125**		10	10
980	70 s. *Agrocybe broadwayi*		10	10
981	90 s. *Camarophyllus olidus*		10	10
982	140 s. *Marasmius arborescens*		15	20
983	180 s. *Marasmiellus subcinereus*		20	25
984	200 s. *Agaricus campestris*		20	25
985	500 s. *Chlorophyllum molybdites*		50	55
986	1000 s. *Agaricus bingensis*		1·00	1·10
979/86		*Set of 8*	2·10	2·40

MS987 Two sheets, each 96×65 mm. (a) 1200 s. *Leucocoprinus cepaestipes* (*horiz*). (b) 1200 s. *Laccaria lateritia* (*horiz*) .. *Set of 2 sheets* 2·50 2·75

(Des J. Iskowitz (Nos. 988/91), O. Fernandez (No. **MS992**). Litho Questa (Nos. 988/91) or Cartor (No. **MS992**))

1991 (1 Aug). *Endangered Species (3rd series). As Nos. 406/9, but with changed face values, and additional horiz designs as T* **61**. *Multicoloured. P* 14.

988	100 s. Elephants in "Elephants' Graveyard"		10	10
989	140 s. Type **61**		15	20
990	200 s. Elephants at waterhole		20	25
991	600 s. Elephants having dust bath		65	70
988/91		*Set of 4*	1·00	1·10

MS992 Two sheets, each 102×74 mm. (a) 1200 s. Giraffe. (b) 1200 s. Rhinoceros and Red-billed Oxpecker. P 13×12 .. .. *Set of 2 sheets* 2·50 2·75

(Des Jennifer Toombs. Litho Questa)

1991 (25 Nov). *Botanical Gardens of the World. T* **126** *and similar vert designs. Multicoloured. P* 14½.

993/1032	90 s. × 20, 100 s. × 20	*Set of 40*	3·50	3·50

MS1033 Two sheets, each 110×75 mm. (a) 1400 s. The Pagoda, Kew. (b) 1400 s. Temple of the Winds, Melbourne .. *Set of 2 sheets* 2·50 2·75

Nos. 993/1032 were issued together, *se-tenant*, as two sheetlets of 20. The 90 s. values show *Anigozanthos manglesii, Banksia grandis, Clianthus formosus, Gossypium sturtianum, Callistemon lanceolatus, Saintpaulia ionantha, Calodendrum capense, Aloe ferox × arborescens, Bolusanthus speciousus, Lithops schwantesii, Protea repens, Plumbago capensis, Clerodendrum thomsoniae, Thunbergia alata, Schotia latifolia, Epacris impressa, Acacia pycnantha, Telopea speciosissima, Wahlenbergia gloriosa, Eucalyptus globulus* from Melbourne, and the 100 s. *Cypripedium calceolus, Rhododendron thomsonii, Ginkgo biloba, Magnolia campbellii, Wisteria sinensis, Clerodendrum ugandense, Eulophia horsfallii, Aerangis rhodosticta, Abelmoschus moschatus, Gloriosa superba, Carissa edulis, Ochna kirkii, Canarina abyssinica, Nymphaea caerulea, Ceropegia succulenta, Strelitzia reginae, Strongylodon macrobotrys, Victoria amazonica, Orchis militaris* and *Sophora microphylla* from Kew.

▬▬ **20/-**

(127)

1991 (4 Dec). *No. 573 surch with T* **127**.

1034 20 s. on 25 s. Airship *Norge* and Polar Bear (first transpolar flight), 1926 ..

(Litho Walsall)

1991 (18 Dec). *Christmas. Paintings by Piero della Francesca. Vert designs as T* **211** *of Lesotho. Multicoloured. P* 12.

1035	20 s. "Madonna with Child and Angels"		10	10
1036	50 s. "The Baptism of Christ"		10	10
1037	80 s. "Polyptych of Mercy"		10	10
1038	100 s. "Polyptych of Mercy" (detail)		10	10
1039	200 s. "The Annunciation" from "The Legend of the True Cross"		20	25
1040	500 s. "Pregnant Madonna"		50	55

1041	1000 s. "The Annunciation" from "Polyptych of St. Anthony"		1·00	1·10
1042	1500 s. "The Nativity"		1·50	1·60
1035/42		*Set of 8*	3·00	3·25

MS1043 Two sheets, each 102×127 mm. (a) 1800 s. "The Brera Altarpiece". (b) 1800 s. "Madonna and Child" from "Polyptych of St. Anthony". P 14 .. .. *Set of 2 sheets* 3·75 4·00

(Des W. Hanson Studio. Litho Questa)

1992 (6 Jan). *50th Death Anniv of Lord Baden-Powell and World Scout Jamboree, Korea. Multicoloured designs as T* **263** *of Maldive Islands. P* 14.

1044	20 s. Boy Scout Monument, New York, and Ernest Thompson (first chief scout of U.S.A.)		10	10
1045	50 s. Treehouse design and Daniel Beard (*vert*)		10	10

MS1046 117×89 mm. 1500 s. Ugandan Boy Scout badge .. .. .. 1·50 1·60

(Litho Questa)

1992 (6 Jan). *Bicentenary of Brandenburg Gate, Berlin. Horiz design as T* **264** *of Maldive Islands. Multicoloured. P* 14.

1047 500 s. Demonstrator demolishing Berlin Wall 50 55

(Litho Questa)

1992 (6 Jan). *Death Bicentenary of Mozart. Horiz design as T* **265** *of Maldive Islands. Multicoloured. P* 14.

1048 700 s. *The Magic Flute* 70 75

(Des W. Wright. Litho Questa)

1992 (6 Jan). *Centenary of Trans-Siberian Railway. Sheet* 114×85 *mm, containing multicoloured design as T* **266** *of Maldive Islands. P* 14.

MS1049 1200 s. Electric train leaving tunnel (*horiz*) .. .. 1·25 1·40

(Des W. Wright. Litho Questa)

1992 (6 Jan). *Centenary of Otto Lilienthal's First Gliding Experiments. Horiz design as T* **267** *of Maldive Islands. P* 14.

1050 400 s. Lilienthal's signature and *Flugzeug Nr. 8* 40 45

128 U.S.S. *Vestal* (transport) under Attack

(Des W. Hanson Studio. Litho Questa)

1992 (6 Jan). *50th Anniv of Japanese Attack on Pearl Harbor. T* **128** *and similar horiz designs. Multicoloured. P* 14½.

1051	200 s. Type **128**		20	25
	a. Sheetlet. Nos. 1051/60		1·75	
1052	200 s. Japanese Zero		20	25
1053	200 s. U.S.S. *Arizona* (battleship) on fire		20	25
1054	200 s. U.S.S. *Nevada* (battleship) passing burning ships		20	25
1055	200 s. "Val" bomber attacking		20	25
1056	200 s. Dauntless bombers attacking *Hiryu* (carrier) at Midway		20	25
1057	200 s. Japanese aircraft attacking Midway Island		20	25
1058	200 s. U.S. Marine Buffalo (fighter) defending Midway		20	25
1059	200 s. American Wildcat aircraft and carrier		20	25
1060	200 s. U.S.S. *Yorktown* (carrier) torpedoed		20	25
1051/60		*Set of 10*	1·75	2·25

Nos. 1051/60 were printed together, *se-tenant*, in sheetlets of 10 with the stamps arranged in two horizontal strips of 5 forming composite designs separated by a gutter showing photograph of Pearl Harbor model and text.

129 Three Modern Hot Air Balloons

(Litho Questa)

1992 (6 Jan). *120th Anniv of Paris Balloon Post* (1990). *T* **129** *and similar horiz designs. Multicoloured. P* 14.

1061	200 s. Type **129**		20	25
	a. Sheetlet. Nos. 1061/9		1·60	
1062	200 s. Sport balloons and top of *Double Eagle II*		20	25
1063	200 s. Pro Juventute balloon and top of Branson's *Virgin*		20	25
1064	200 s. Blanchard's balloon		20	25
1065	200 s. Nadar's *Le Geant* and centre of *Double Eagle II*		20	25
1066	200 s. Branson's *Virgin*		20	25
1067	200 s. Montgolfier balloon		20	25
1068	200 s. *Double Eagle II* basket and Paris balloon of 1870		20	25
1069	200 s. Early captive balloon		20	25
1061/9		*Set of 9*	1·60	2·00

Nos. 1061/9 were printed together, *se-tenant*, as a sheetlet of 9 forming a composite design.

(Des Walt Disney Co. Litho B.D.T.)

1992 (20 Feb). *Mickey's World Tour. Multicoloured designs as T* **270** *of Maldive Islands showing Walt Disney cartoon characters in different countries. P* 13.

1070	20 s. Mickey Mouse and Goofy on African safari (*horiz*)		10	10
1071	50 s. Mickey charming Pluto's tail, India (*horiz*)		10	10
1072	80 s. Minnie Mouse, Donald and Daisy Duck as Caribbean calypso band (*horiz*)		10	10
1073	200 s. Goofy pulling Donald and Daisy in rickshaw, China (*horiz*)		20	25
1074	500 s. Mickey and Minnie on camel, Egypt (*horiz*)		50	55
1075	800 s. Donald and Pete sumo wrestling, Japan (*horiz*)		85	90
1076	1000 s. Goofy bullfighting, Spain (*horiz*)		1·00	1·10
1077	1500 s. Mickey playing football, Italy (*horiz*)		1·50	1·60
1070/7		*Set of 8*	4·00	4·25

MS1078 Two sheets, each 83×104 mm. (a) 2000 s. Mickey as Cossack dancer, Russia. (b) 2000 s. Daisy as Wagnerian diva, Germany .. .. .. *Set of 2 sheets* 4·25 4·50

(Des D. Miller. Litho Questa)

1992 (26 Feb). *40th Anniv of Queen Elizabeth II's Accession. Horiz designs as T* **214** *of Lesotho. Multicoloured. P* 14.

1079	100 s. Lake Victoria		10	10
1080	200 s. Lake and mountains		20	25
1081	500 s. Lakeside fields		50	55
1082	1000 s. River Nile		1·00	1·10
1079/82		*Set of 4*	1·60	1·75

MS1083 Two sheets, each 74×97 mm. (a) 1800 s. Waterfalls. (b) 1800 s. Owen Falls Dam .. .. .. *Set of 2 sheets* 3·75 4·00

130 Kentrosaurus

131 "The Entry into Jerusalem" (detail) (Giotto)

(Des D. Burkhart. Litho Walsall)

1992 (8 Apr). *Prehistoric Animals. T* **130** *and similar horiz designs. Multicoloured. P* 14.

1084	50 s. Type **130**		10	10
1085	200 s. Iguanodon		20	25
1086	250 s. Hypsilophodon		25	30
1087	300 s. Brachiosaurus		30	35
1088	400 s. Peloneustes		40	45
1089	500 s. Pteranodon		50	55
1090	800 s. Tetralophodon		85	90
1091	1000 s. Megalosaurus		1·00	1·10
1084/91		*Set of 8*	3·25	3·50

MS1092 Two sheets, each 100×70 mm. (a) 2000 s. As 250 s. (b) 2000 s. As 1000 s. .. .. .. *Set of 2 sheets* 4·25 4·50

(Litho Questa)

1992 (7 May). *Easter. Religious Paintings. T* **131** *and similar vert designs. Multicoloured. P* 13½×14.

1093	50 s. Type **131**		10	10
1094	100 s. "Pilate and the Watch" (Psalter of Robert de Lisle)		10	10
1095	200 s. "The Kiss of Judas" (detail) (Giotto)		20	25
1096	250 s. "Christ washing the Feet of the Disciples" (Vita Christi manuscript)		25	30
1097	300 s. "Christ seized in the Garden" (Melissende Psalter)		30	35
1098	500 s. "Doubting Thomas" (Vita Christi manuscript)		50	55
1099	1000 s. "The Marys at the Tomb" (detail) (anon)		1·00	1·10
1100	2000 s. "The Ascension" (Florentine manuscript)		2·10	2·25
1093/100		*Set of 8*	4·00	4·50

MS1101 Two sheets, each 72×102 mm. (a) 2500 s. "The Piercing of Christ's Side" (detail) (Limoges enamel). (b) 2500 s. "Agony at Gethsemane" (detail) (Limoges enamel) .. .. *Set of 2 sheets* 5·25 5·50

132 Adungu

133 Map of Known World, 1486

(Des R. Sauber. Litho Questa)

1992 (20 July). *Traditional Musical Instruments. T **132** and similar vert designs. Multicoloured. P 14.*

1102	50 s. Type 132	10	10
1103	100 s. Endingidi	10	10
1104	200 s. Akogo	20	25
1105	250 s. Nanga	25	30
1106	300 s. Engoma	30	35
1107	400 s. Amakondere	40	45
1108	500 s. Akakyenkye	50	55
1109	1000 s. Ennanga	1·00	1·10
1102/9	Set of 8	2·50	2·75

(Des A. Granberg. Litho Questa)

1992 (27 July). *500th Anniv of Discovery of America by Columbus and "World Columbian Stamp Expo '92" Exhibition, Chicago. T **133** and similar multicoloured designs. P 14.*

1110	50 s. Type 133	10	10
1111	100 s. Map of Africa, 1508	10	10
1112	150 s. Map of West Indies, 1500	15	20
1113	200 s. *Nina* and astrolabe	20	25
1114	600 s. *Pinta* and quadrant	65	70
1115	800 s. Sand glass	85	90
1116	900 s. 15th-century compass	90	95
1117	1000 s. Map of World, 1492	1·00	1·10
1110/17	Set of 8	3·50	3·75
MS1118	Two sheets, each 95×75 mm. (a) 2500 s. Sections of globe, 1492. (b). 2500 s. Europe and Africa from map by Henricus Martellus, 1490 (*vert*) ... Set of 2 sheets	5·25	5·50

(Litho Questa)

1992 (28 Aug). *Hummel Figurines. Vert designs as T **256** of Maldive Islands. Multicoloured. P 14.*

1119	50 s. Girl with washing	10	10
1120	200 s. Girl scrubbing floor	20	25
1121	250 s. Girl sweeping floor	25	30
1122	300 s. Girl with baby	30	35
1123	600 s. Boy mountaineer	65	70
1124	900 s. Girl knitting	90	95
1125	1000 s. Boy on stool	1·00	1·10
1126	1500 s. Boy with telescope	1·50	1·60
1119/26	Set of 8	4·50	4·75
MS1127	Two sheets, each 97×122 mm. (a) 500 s. As No. 1119; 500 s. As No. 1120; 500 s. As No. 1121; 500 s. As No. 1122. (b) 500 s. As No. 1124; 500 s. As No. 1123; 500 s. As No. 1125; 500 s. As No. 1126 ... Set of 2 sheets	4·25	4·50

134 Spotted Hyena

135 Red-headed Falcon

(Litho Questa)

1992 (25 Sept). *Wildlife. T **134** and similar horiz designs. Multicoloured. P 14.*

1128	50 s. Type 134	10	10
1129	100 s. Impala	10	10
1130	200 s. Giant Forest Hog	20	25
1131	250 s. Pangolin	25	30
1132	300 s. Golden Monkey	30	35
1133	800 s. Serval	85	90
1134	1000 s. Small-spotted Genet ("Bush Genet")	1·00	1·10
1135	3000 s. Waterbuck	3·25	3·50
1128/35	Set of 8	5·50	6·00
MS1136	Two sheets, each 100×70 mm. (a) 2500 s. Gorilla. (b) 2500 s. Hippopotamus ... Set of 2 sheets	5·25	5·50

(Litho Questa)

1992 (2 Oct). *Olympic Games, Barcelona. Multicoloured designs as T **216** of Lesotho. P 14.*

1137	50 s. Men's javelin	10	10
1138	100 s. Men's highjump (*horiz*)	10	10
1139	200 s. Fencing (Pentathlon)	20	25
1140	250 s. Men's volleyball	25	30
1141	300 s. Women's platform diving	30	35
1142	500 s. Men's team cycling	50	55
1143	1000 s. Women's tennis	1·00	1·10
1144	2000 s. Boxing (*horiz*)	2·10	2·25
1137/44	Set of 8	4·00	4·50
MS1145	Two sheets, each 100×70 mm. (a) 2500 s. Men's basketball. (b) 2500 s. Baseball ... Set of 2 sheets	5·50	6·00

(Litho Questa)

1992 (9 Oct). *Birds. T **135** and similar vert designs. Multicoloured. P 15×14.*

1146	20 s. Type 135	10	10
1147	30 s. Yellow-billed Hornbill	10	10
1148	50 s. Purple Heron	10	10
1149	100 s. Regal Sunbird	10	10
1150	150 s. White-browed Robin Chat	15	20
1151	200 s. Shining-blue Kingfisher	20	25
1152	250 s. Great Blue Turaco	25	30
1153	300 s. African Emerald Cuckoo	30	35
1154	500 s. Abyssinian Roller	50	55
1155	800 s. South African Crowned Crane	85	90
1156	1000 s. Doherty's Bush Shrike	1·00	1·10
1157	2000 s. Splendid Glossy Starling	2·10	2·25
1158	3000 s. Little Bee Eater	3·25	3·50
1159	4000 s. Red-faced Lovebird ("Red-headed Lovebird")	4·25	4·50
1146/59	Set of 14	12·00	13·00

136 United Nations Headquarters

137 Goofy in Hawaiian Holiday, 1937

(Des Kerri Schiff. Litho Questa)

1992 (28 Oct). *Postage Stamp Mega Event, New York. Sheet 100×70 mm. P 14.*

MS1160	**136** 2500 s. multicoloured	2·50	2·75

(Des Walt Disney Co. Litho Questa)

1992 (2 Nov). *60th Anniv of Goofy. T **137** and similar multicoloured designs. P 13½.*

1161	50 s. Type 137	10	10
1162	100 s. Riding pennyfarthing cycle, 1941	10	10
1163	200 s. Goofy and Mickey Mouse as firemen, 1935	20	25
1164	250 s. Skiing, 1941 (*horiz*)	25	30
1165	300 s. One man band, 1937 (*horiz*)	30	35
1166	1000 s. Asleep against boat, 1938 (*horiz*)	1·00	1·10
1167	1500 s. Ancient Olympic champion, 1942	1·50	1·60
1168	2000 s. Pole vaulting, 1942	2·10	2·25
1161/8	Set of 8	5·00	5·50
MS1169	Two sheets. (a) 105×115 mm. 3000 s. Goofy and Wilbur the grasshopper, 1939 (*horiz*). (b) 92×116 mm. 3000 s. Wyatt Goofy and Goofy today ... Set of 2 sheets	6·25	6·50

138 "The Annunciation" (Zurbaran)

(Litho Questa)

1992 (16 Nov). *Christmas. Religious Paintings by Francisco Zurbaran. T **138** and similar vert designs. Multicoloured. P 13½×14.*

1170	50 s. Type 138	10	10
1171	200 s. "The Annunciation" (*different*)	20	25
1172	250 s. "The Virgin of the Immaculate Conception"	25	30
1173	300 s. "The Virgin of the Immaculate Conception" (detail)	30	35
1174	800 s. "Holy Family with Saints Anne, Joachim and John the Baptist"	85	90
1175	900 s. "Holy Family with Saints Anne, Joachim and John the Baptist" (detail)	90	95
1176	1000 s. "Adoration of the Magi"	1·00	1·10
1177	2000 s. "Adoration of the Magi" (detail)	2·10	2·25
1170/7	Set of 8	5·25	5·50
MS1178	Two sheets, each 76×102 mm. (a) 2500 s. "The Virgin of the Immaculate Conception" (*different*). (b) 2500 s. "The Virgin of the Immaculate Conception" (*different*) ... Set of 2 sheets	5·50	6·00

139 Man cleaning Granary

(Litho Questa)

1992 (7 Dec). *United Nations World Health Organization Projects. T **139** and similar horiz designs. Multicoloured. P 14.*

1179	50 s. Type 139	10	10
1180	200 s. Mother breast-feeding	20	25
1181	250 s. Mother feeding baby	25	30
1182	300 s. Boy collecting water from pump	30	35
1183	800 s. Mother and baby	85	90
1179/83	Set of 5	1·50	1·75

NEW INFORMATION

The editor is always interested to correspond with people who have new information that will improve or correct the Catalogue.

140 Count Ferdinand von Zeppelin and Airship

(Litho Questa)

1992 (7 Dec). *75th Death Anniv of Count Ferdinand von Zeppelin (airship pioneer). T **140** and similar horiz designs showing portrait and early airships. P 14.*

1184	1000 s. multicoloured	1·00	1·10
1185	3000 s. multicoloured	3·00	3·25
MS1186	116×85 mm. 2500 s. multicoloured	2·50	2·75

141 "Voyager 2" passing Jupiter

(Des W. Wright and L. Fried. Litho Questa)

1992 (7 Dec). *International Space Year. T **141** and similar horiz designs. Multicoloured. P 14.*

1187	300 s. Type 141	30	35
1188	2000 s. "Voyager 2" passing Neptune	2·10	2·25
MS1189	115×86 mm. 2500 s. "Voyager 2" and Jupiter	2·50	2·75

142 Impala

(Litho Questa)

1992 (7 Dec). *United Nations Earth Summit '92, Rio de Janeiro. T **142** and similar horiz designs. Multicoloured. P 14.*

1190	800 s. Type 142	85	90
1191	1000 s. Mountain Zebra	1·00	1·10
MS1192	116×85 mm. 2500 s. Warthog	2·50	2·75

143 Doctor inoculating Boy

(Litho Questa)

1992 (7 Dec). *75th Anniv of International Association of Lions Clubs. Sheet 115×85 mm. P 14.*

MS1193	**143** 2500 s. multicoloured	2·50	2·75

POSTAGE DUE STAMPS

The Postage Due stamps of Kenya, Uganda and Tanganyika were used in Uganda until 2 January 1967.

D 1

(D 2)   **D 3** Lion

(Litho D.L.R.)

1967 (3 Jan). *Chalk-surfaced paper. P 14 × 13½.*

D1	D 1 5 c. scarlet	20	3·25
D2	10 c. green	20	3·25
D3	20 c. deep blue	35	3·50
D4	30 c. red-brown	40	4·50
D5	40 c. bright purple	60	7·00
D6	1 s. orange	1·50	10·00
D1/6	Set of 6	3·00	28·00

1970 (31 Mar). *As Nos. D1/6, but on glazed ordinary paper.*
P 14 × 15.

D 7	D 1	5 c. scarlet	..	..	..	15	1·75
D 8		10 c. green	..		..	15	1·75
D 9		20 c. deep blue	..	..	..	25	2·25
D10		30 c. red-brown	..	..	..	35	2·75
D11		40 c. bright purple	..	..	..	55	3·50
D7/11		..	..	..	Set of 5	1·25	11·00

1973 (12 Dec). *Glazed, ordinary paper. P* 15.

D12	D 1	5 c. scarlet	..	..	..	70	3·75
D13		10 c. emerald	..	..	..	70	3·75
D14		20 c. deep blue	..	..	..	1·00	4·25
D15		30 c. red-brown	..	..	..	1·25	5·00
D16		40 c. bright mauve	..	..	..	1·75	7·50
D17		1 s. bright orange	..	..	..	2·50	8·50
D12/17		..	..	..	Set of 6	7·25	30·00

"UGANDA LIBERATED" OVERPRINTS. Nos. D1/17 were overprinted "UGANDA LIBERATED 1979", in very limited quantities, using a style of overprint similar to Type **32** (*Prices: Nos.* D1/6 *set of 6* £275; D7/11 *set of 5* £125; D12, 14/17 *set of 5* £100; D13 £90, *all mint*).

(Litho Questa)

1979 (Dec). *Liberation. As Nos.* D1/6 *optd with Type D* **2.** *Chalk-surfaced paper. P* 13½ × 14.

D18	D 1	5 c. scarlet	..	..	..	20	35
D19		10 c. green	..	..	..	20	35
D20		20 c. dull ultramarine	..	..	..	25	35
D21		30 c. red-brown	..	..	..	25	50
D22		40 c. bright purple	..	..	..	30	50
D23		1 s. orange	..	..	..	30	50
D18/23		..	..	..	Set of 6	1·40	2·25

(Litho Questa)

1985 (11 Mar). *Animals. Type D* **3** *and similar vert designs.*
P 14½ × 14.

D24	5 s. black and bright turquoise-green	..		10	10
D25	10 s. black and dull rose-lilac	..	..	15	15
D26	20 s. black and dull orange	..	..	25	25
D27	40 s. black and bright lilac	..	..	40	45
D28	50 s. black and pale greenish blue	..	..	45	50
D29	100 s. black and mauve		..	85	1·00
D24/9	..		Set of 6	2·00	2·25

Designs:—10 s. African Buffalo; 20 s. Kob; 40 s. African Elephant; 50 s. Common Zebra; 100 s. Black Rhinoceros.

Vanuatu
(*formerly* New Hebrides)

NEW HEBRIDES

Stamps of NEW SOUTH WALES were used by various Postal Agencies in the New Hebrides from 1891 onwards. Similar Postal Agencies supplying the stamps of NEW CALEDONIA were opened from 1903 onwards.

PRICES FOR STAMPS ON COVER TO 1945

Nos. 1/8 (F1/5)	*from* × 10
No. 9	*from* × 2
Nos. 10/16 (F6/10)	*from* × 8
Nos. 18/28 (F11/32)	*from* × 6
Nos. 30/4 (F33/7)	*from* × 4
No. 35 (F32*a*)	
Nos. 36/9	*from* × 3
Nos. 40/2 (F38/41)	*from* × 4
Nos. 43/51 (F42/52)	*from* × 5
Nos. 52/63 (F53/64)	*from* × 3
Nos. D1/10 (FD53/69)	*from* × 8

ANGLO-FRENCH CONDOMINIUM

The New Hebrides, an island group in the south-west Pacific, were recognised as an area of joint Anglo-French influence in 1878. The position was regularised by the Convention of 20 October 1906 which created a Condominium, the two nations having equal rights and shares in the administration of the islands.

Stamps inscribed in English or French were issued concurrently and had equal validity throughout the islands. A common currency was reflected in the face values from 1938.

Where common designs were used the main differences between stamps inscribed in English and those in French are as follows:
(a) Inscriptions in English or French.
(b) Position of cyphers. French issues normally have "RF" to the right or above the British royal cypher.
(c) French issues are without watermark, *unless otherwise stated.*

Inscriptions in English

Inscriptions in French

I. STAMPS INSCRIBED IN ENGLISH

New Hebrides.   NEWHEBRIDES

Condominium.   CONDOMINIUM
(1)   (2)

1908 (29 Oct). *T 23 and 24 of Fiji optd with T 1 by Govt Printing Establishment, Suva. On the bicoloured stamps the word "FIJI" obliterated by a bar in the colour of the word. P 14.*

(a) Wmk Multiple Crown CA. Ordinary paper (½d., 1d.) or chalk-surfaced paper (1s.)

1	½d. green and pale green (No. 115)		1·75	10·00
1*a*	½d. green (No. 118)		40	7·00
2	1d. red		45	40
	a. Opt omitted (in vert pair with normal) £5000			
3	1s. green and carmine		16·00	8·00

(b) Wmk Crown CA

4	½d. green and grey-green		50·00	80·00
5	2d. dull purple and orange		60	70
6	2½d. dull purple and blue/*blue*		60	70
7	5d. dull purple and green		80	2·00
8	6d. dull purple and carmine		70	1·25
9	1s. green and carmine		£150	£200
1/9		*Set of 9*	£180	£250

1910 (15 Dec). *Types as last optd with T 2 by D.L.R. Wmk Multiple Crown CA. Ordinary paper (½d. to 2½d.) or chalk-surfaced paper (5d., 6d., 1s.). P 14.*

10	½d. green		3·50	24·00
11	1d. red		10·00	8·50
12	2d. grey		60	3·00
13	2½d. bright blue		65	3·75
14	5d. dull purple and olive-green		65	5·50
15	6d. dull and deep purple		85	5·00
16	1s. black/*green* (R.)		85	7·50
10/16		*Set of 7*	15·00	50·00
10/16 Optd "Specimen"		*Set of 7*	£250	

3 Weapons and Idols   (4)
1d.

(Des J. Giraud. Recess D.L.R.)

1911 (25 July). *Wmk Mult Crown CA. P 14.*

18	3	½d. green		85	1·60
19		1d. red		2·75	2·00
20		2d. grey		3·50	3·75
21		2½d. ultramarine		1·60	4·25
24		5d. sage-green		2·25	4·25
25		6d. purple		1·75	4·75
26		1s. black/*green*		1·50	8·00
27		2s. purple/*blue*		14·00	19·00
28		5s. green/*yellow*		27·00	48·00
18/28			*Set of 9*	50·00	85·00
18/28 Optd "Specimen"			*Set of 9*	£160	

1920 (June)**–21.** *Surch with T 4 at Govt Printing Establishment, Suva.*

(a) On Nos. 24 and 26/8

30	3	1d. on 5d. sage-green (10.3.21)		7·00	60·00
		a. Surch inverted		£1200	
31		1d. on 1s. black/*green*		1·00	11·00
32		1d. on 2s. purple/*blue*		1·00	10·00
33		1d. on 5s. green/*yellow*		1·00	10·00

(b) On No. F16

34	3	2d. on 40 c. red/*yellow*		1·00	13·00

(c) On No. F27

35	3	2d. on 40 c. red/*yellow*		£120	£300

1921 (Sept–Oct). *Wmk Mult Script CA. P 14.*

36	3	1d. scarlet		2·00	13·00
37		2d. slate-grey		3·25	22·00
39		6d. purple		12·50	55·00
36/9			*Set of 3*	16·00	80·00
36/9 Optd "Specimen"			*Set of 3*	65·00	

1924 (1 May). *Surch as T 4, at Suva.*

40	3	1d. on ½d. green (No. 18)		2·75	18·00
41		3d. on 1d. scarlet (No. 36)		2·50	11·00
42		5d. on 2½d. ultramarine. (No. 21)		4·75	18·00
		a. Surch inverted		£1000	
40/2			*Set of 3*	9·00	42·00

5

(Recess D.L.R.)

1925 (June). *Wmk Mult Script CA. P 14.*

43	5	½d. (5 c.) black		75	5·50
44		1d. (10 c.) green		1·00	5·50
45		2d. (20 c.) slate-grey		1·75	2·25
46		2½d. (25 c.) brown		1·00	5·50
47		5d. (50 c.) ultramarine		1·75	2·50
48		6d. (60 c.) purple		3·00	8·00
49		1s. (1.25 fr.) black/*emerald*		3·00	13·00
50		2s. (2.50 fr.) purple/*blue*		6·00	19·00
51		5s. (6.25 fr.) green/*yellow*		6·00	22·00
43/51			*Set of 9*	22·00	75·00
43/51 Optd "Specimen"			*Set of 9*	£180	

CURRENCY. The currency used for the face values of issues to 1977 was an artificial, rather than an actual, monetary unit. The actual currencies in use being Australian dollars and the local franc.

6 Lopevi Is and Copra Canoe

(Des J. Kerhor. Recess B.W.)

1938 (1 June). *Gold Currency. Wmk Mult Script CA. P 12.*

52	6	5 c. blue-green		2·50	2·25
53		10 c. orange		1·25	50
54		15 c. bright violet		2·50	2·00
55		20 c. scarlet		1·60	80
56		25 c. reddish brown		1·60	1·00
57		30 c. blue		1·60	1·25
58		40 c. grey-olive		4·50	2·50
59		50 c. purple		1·60	50
60		1 f. red/*green*		4·00	6·50
61		2 f. blue/*green*		28·00	16·00
62		5 f. red/*yellow*		70·00	48·00
63		10 f. violet/*blue*		£180	70·00
52/63			*Set of 12*	£275	£130
52/63 Perf "Specimen"			*Set of 12*	£225	

(Recess Waterlow)

1949 (10 Oct). *75th Anniv of U.P.U. As Nos. 145/8 of Jamaica. Wmk Mult Script CA. P 13½ × 14.*

64		10 c. red-orange		30	15
65		15 c. violet		30	15
66		30 c. ultramarine		30	15
67		50 c. purple		40	20
64/7			*Set of 4*	1·10	60

MINIMUM PRICE

The minimum price quote is 10p which represents a handling charge rather than a basis for valuing common stamps. For further notes about prices see introductory pages.

---

7 Outrigger Sailing Canoes

(Des C. Hertenberger (1 f. to 5 f.), R. Serres (others). Recess Waterlow)

1953 (30 Apr). *T 7 and similar horiz designs. Wmk Mult Script CA. P 12½.*

68	7	5 c. green		50	10
69		10 c. scarlet		50	10
70		15 c. yellow-ochre		50	10
71		20 c. ultramarine		50	10
72		25 c. olive		50	10
73		30 c. brown		50	10
74		40 c. blackish brown		50	10
75		50 c. violet		1·00	10
76		1 f. orange		6·50	70
77		2 f. reddish purple		7·50	9·00
78		5 f. scarlet		12·00	32·00
68/78			*Set of 11*	27·00	38·00

Designs:—5 to 20 c. Type **7**; 25 to 50 c. Native carving; 1 to 5 f. Two natives outside hut.

1953 (2 June). *Coronation. As No. 153 of Jamaica.*

79		10 c. black and carmine		30	30

10 Quirós Galleon and Map

(Photo Harrison)

1956 (20 Oct). *50th Anniv of Condominium. T 10 and similar horiz design. Wmk Mult Script CA. P 14½ × 14.*

80		5 c. emerald		10	10
81		10 c. scarlet		10	10
82		20 c. deep bright blue		10	10
83		50 c. deep lilac		15	15
80/3			*Set of 4*	35	30

Designs:—5, 10 c. Type **10**; 20, 50 c. "Marianne", "Talking Drum" and "Britannia".

12 Port Vila: Iririki Islet   13 River Scene and Spear Fisherman

(Des H. Cheffer (T **12**), P Gandon (others). Recess Waterlow)

1957 (3 Sept). *Wmk Mult Script CA. T 12/13 and similar horiz design. P 13½.*

84	12	5 c. green		40	10
85		10 c. scarlet		30	10
86		15 c. yellow-ochre		50	20
87		20 c. ultramarine		40	10
88	13	25 c. olive		45	10
89		30 c. brown		45	10
90		40 c. sepia		45	10
91		50 c. violet		45	10
92		1 f. orange		1·00	80
93	—	2 f. mauve		6·00	4·00
94	—	5 f. black		15·00	6·00
84/94			*Set of 11*	23·00	10·00

Design:—1 to 5 f. Woman drinking from coconut.

1963 (2 Sept). *Freedom from Hunger. As No. 80 of Lesotho.*

95		60 c. green		50	15

INTERNATIONAL **RED CROSS CENTENARY** ℞ 1863 1963 **15** GOLD CENTIMES NEW HEBRIDES CONDOMINIUM

15 Red Cross Emblem

(Des V. Whiteley. Litho B.W.)

1963 (2 Sept). *Red Cross Centenary. W w 12. P 13½.*

96	15	15 c. red and black		35	10
97		45 c. red and blue		45	20

16 Exporting Manganese, Forari   17 Cocoa Beans

(Des V. Whiteley, from drawings by J. White (10 c., 20 c.), K. Penny (40 c.), C. Robin (3 f.). Photo Harrison. Des C. Robin (5 c., 1 f.), J. White (15 c.), G. Vasarhelyi (25 c., 5 f.), A. Larkins, Turrell and Thomas (30 c., 50 c., 2 f.). Recess Govt Printing Works, Paris)

1963 (25 Nov)–72. *T* **16/17** *and similar horiz designs. W* w **12**
(10 c., 20 c., 40 c., 3 f.) *or no wmk* (*others*). *P* 14 (3 f.), 12½
(10 c., 20 c., 40 c.) *or* 13 (*others*).

98	5 c. lake, purple-brown and greenish blue (15.8.66)	..	35	30
	a. *Lake and greenish blue** (29.2.72)	..	35·00	35·00
99	10 c. light brown, buff & emerald (16.8.65)	..	15	10
100	15 c. yellow-bistre, red-brown & deep violet	..	15	10
101	20 c. black, olive-grn & greenish bl (16.8.65)	..	45	10
102	25 c. reddish violet, orange-brown and crimson (15.8.66)	..	50	70
103	30 c. chestnut, bistre and violet	..	75	10
104	40 c. vermilion and deep blue (16.8.65)	..	80	1·40
105	50 c. green, yellow and greenish blue..	..	60	10
106	1 f. red, black & deep bluish green (15.8.66)..	2·50	3·00
107	2 f. black, brown-purple & yellow-olive	..	2·50	1·75
108	3 f. deep violet, orange-brown, emerald and black (16.8.65)	..	13·00	8·00
109	5 f. blue, deep blue and black (24.1.67)	..	18·00	16·00
98/109		*Set of 12*	35·00	28·00

Designs:—15 c. Copra; 20 c. Fishing from Palikulo Point; 25 c. Picasso Fish; 30 c. Nautilus shell; 40 c. Stingfish; 50 c. Blue-lined Surgeon (fish); 1 f. Cardinal Honeyeater; 2 f. Buff-bellied Flycatcher; 3 f. Thicket Warbler; 5 f. White-collared Kingfisher.
*In No. 98a the globe is printed in the same colour as the centre, instead of in purple-brown.
See also No. 129.

28 I.T.U. Emblem

(Des M. Goaman. Litho Enschedé)

1965 (17 May). *I.T.U. Centenary. W* w **12**. *P* 11 × 11½.

110	**28**	15 c. scarlet and drab	..	20	10
111		60 c. blue and light red	..	35	20

29 I.C.Y. Emblem

(Des V. Whiteley. Litho Harrison)

1965 (24 Oct). *International Co-operation Year. W* w **12**. *P* 14½.

112	**29**	5 c. reddish purple and turquoise-green	15	10
113		55 c. deep bluish green and lavender	..	20	20

30 Sir Winston Churchill and St. Paul's Cathedral in Wartime

(Des Jennifer Toombs. Photo Harrison)

1966 (24 Jan). *Churchill Commemoration. W* w **12**. *P* 14.

114	**30**	5 c. black, cerise, gold and new blue	..	20	10
115		15 c. black, cerise, gold and deep green	..	40	10
116		25 c. black, cerise, gold and brown	..	50	10
117		30 c. black, cerise, gold and bluish violet	50	10
114/17		..	*Set of 4*	1·40	35

31 Footballer's Legs, Ball and Jules Rimet Cup

(Des V. Whiteley. Litho Harrison)

1966 (1 July). *World Cup Football Championships. W* w **12** (*sideways*). *P* 14.

118	**31**	20 c. violet, yellow-green, lake & yell-brn	20	15
119		40 c. chocolate, blue-grn, lake & yell-brn	30	15

32 W.H.O. Building

(Des M. Goaman. Litho Harrison)

1966 (20 Sept). *Inauguration of W.H.O. Headquarters, Geneva. W* w **12** (*sideways*). *P* 14.

120	**32**	25 c. black, yellow-green and light blue	..	20	10
121		60 c. black, light purple and yellow-brown	55	20

33 "Education"

(Des Jennifer Toombs. Litho Harrison)

1966 (1 Dec). *20th Anniv of U.N.E.S.C.O. W* w **12** (*sideways*). *T* **33** *and similar horiz designs. P* 14.

122	15 c. slate-violet, red, yellow and orange	..	20	10
123	30 c. orange-yellow, violet and deep olive	..	65	10
124	45 c. black, bright purple and orange..	..	70	15
122/4		*Set of 3*	1·40	30

Designs:—30 c. "Science"; 45 c. "Culture".

36 The Coast Watchers

(Des R. Granger Barrett. Photo Enschedé)

1967 (26 Sept). *25th Anniv of the Pacific War. T* **36** *and similar horiz designs. Multicoloured. W* w **12**. *P* 14 × 13.

125	15 c. Type **36**	..	10	10
126	25 c. Map of war zone, U.S. marine and Australian soldier	..	15	15
127	60 c. H.M.A.S. *Canberra*	..	20	15
128	1 f. "Flying Fortress"	..	25	15
125/8 ..		*Set of 4*	65	40

1967 (5 Dec). *New value with W* w **12** *sideways.*

129	60 c. vermilion and deep blue (as No. 104)	..	40	15

40 Globe and Hemispheres

(Des and eng J. Combet. Recess Govt Printing Works, Paris)

1968 (23 May). *Bicentenary of Bougainville's World Voyage. T* **40** *and similar horiz designs. P* 13.

130	15 c. emerald, slate-violet and red	..	10	10
131	25 c. deep olive, maroon and ultramarine	..	15	10
132	60 c. bistre-brown, brown-pur & myrtle-grn	..	15	15
130/2 ..		*Set of 3*	35	30

Designs:—25 c. Ships *La Boudeuse* and *L'Etoile*, and map; 60 c. Bougainville, ship's figure-head and bougainvillea flowers.

43 "Concorde" and Vapour Trails   45 Kauri Pine

(Des S. W. Moss (25 c.), R. Granger Barrett (60 c.). Litho D.L.R.)

1968 (9 Oct). *Anglo-French "Concorde" Project. T* **43** *and similar horiz design. W* w **12** (*sideways*). *P* 14.

133	25 c. lt blue, orange-red & deep violet-blue	..	50	20
134	60 c. red, black and bright blue	..	60	25

Design:—60 c. "Concorde" in flight.

(Des V. Whiteley. Litho Format)

1969 (30 June). *Timber Industry. W* w **12**. *P* 14½.

135	**45**	20 c. multicoloured (*shades*)	..	10	10

No. 135 was issued in small sheets of 9 (3 × 3) printed on a simulated wood-grain background and with a decorative border showing various stages of the local timber industry. There is a wide range of shades on the printing.

ALTERED CATALOGUE NUMBERS

Any Catalogue numbers altered from the last edition are shown as a list in the introductory pages.

46 Cyphers, Flags and Relay Runner receiving Baton   48 Diver on Platform

(Des C. Haley. Photo Delrieu)

1969 (13 Aug). *Third South Pacific Games, Port Moresby. T* **46** *and similar horiz design. Multicoloured. P* 12½.

136	25 c. Type **46**	..	10	10
137	1 f. Cyphers, flags and relay runner passing baton	..	20	20

(Des V. Whiteley. Litho P.B.)

1969 (15 Oct). *Pentecost Island Land Divers. T* **48** *and similar vert designs. Multicoloured. W* w **12** (*sideways*). *P* 12½.

138	15 c. Type **48**	..	10	10
139	25 c. Diver jumping	..	10	10
140	1 f. Diver at end of fall	..	20	20
138/40		*Set of 3*	30	30

51 U.P.U. Emblem and New Headquarters Building   52 General Charles de Gaulle

(Des and eng J. Gauthier. Recess Govt Ptg Wks, Paris)

1970 (20 May). *Inauguration of New U.P.U. Headquarters Building. P* 13.

141	**51**	1 f. 05, slate, red-orange & bright purple	15	15

(Des V. Whiteley. Photo Govt Ptg Wks, Paris)

1970 (20 July). *30th Anniv of New Hebrides' Declaration for the Free French Government. P* 13.

142	**52**	65 c. multicoloured	..	35	20
143		1 f. 10, multicoloured	..	45	20

(53)   54 "The Virgin and Child" (Bellini)

1970 (15 Oct). *As No. 101, but W* w **12** (*sideways*) *and surch with T* **53**.

144	35 c. on 20 c. black, ol-grn & greenish black	..	30	30

(Des V. Whiteley. Litho Harrison)

1970 (30 Nov). *Christmas. T* **54** *and similar vert design. Multicoloured. W* w **12** (*sideways*). *P* 14½ × 14.

145	15 c. Type **54**	..	10	10
146	50 c. "The Virgin and Child" (Cima)	..	20	20

(55)

1971 (19 Jan). *Death of General Charles de Gaulle. Nos. 142/3 optd with T* **55**, *vertical bars in black, inscriptions in gold.*
147	**52**	65 c. multicoloured	..	15	10
148		1 f. 10, multicoloured	.. ..	15	20

56 Football

(Des G. Bétemps. Photo Delrieu)

1971 (13 July). *Fourth South Pacific Games, Papeete, French Polynesia. T* **56** *and similar multicoloured design. P* 12½.
149	20 c. Type **56**	.. ..	10	10
150	65 c. Basketball (*vert*) ..	.. ..	30	20

57 Kauri Pine, Cone and Arms of Royal Society

58 "The Adoration of the Shepherds" (detail, Louis le Nain)

(Des P. Powell. Litho Harrison)

1971 (7 Sept). *Royal Society Expedition to New Hebrides, 1971. W w* **12** (*sideways*). *P* 14½ × 14.
151	**57**	65 c. multicoloured	20	10

(Des G. Drummond. Litho Questa)

1971 (23 Nov). *Christmas. T* **58** *and similar vert design. Multicoloured. W w* **12**. *P* 14 × 13½.
152	25 c. Type **58**	.. ..	10	10
153	50 c. "The Adoration of the Shepherds" (detail, Tintoretto)		20	20

59 "Drover" Mk III

60 Ceremonial Headdress, South Malekula

(Des M. Goaman. Photo Delrieu)

1972 (29 Feb). *Aircraft. T* **59** *and similar horiz designs. Multicoloured. P* 13.
154	20 c. Type **59**	..	35	15
155	25 c. "Sandringham" flying-boat	..	45	15
156	30 c. D.H. "Dragon Rapide"	..	45	15
157	65 c. "Caravelle"	..	1·25	1·25
154/7 ..	.. .. ..	*Set of* 4	2·25	1·50

(Des Odette Baillais (bird designs), Pierrette Lambert (others). Photo Govt Printing Works, Paris)

1972 (24 July). *T* **60** *and similar vert designs. Multicoloured. P* 12½ × 13.
158	5 c. Type **60**	..	10	10
159	10 c. Baker's Pigeon	..	25	10
160	15 c. Gong and carving, North Ambrym	..	15	15
161	20 c. Red-headed Parrot Finch	..	40	25
162	25 c. *Cribraria fischeri* (shell) ..	..	40	25
163	30 c. *Oliva rubrolabiata* (shell)	..	50	30
164	35 c. Chestnut-bellied Kingfisher	..	65	40
165	65 c. *Strombus plicatus* (shell)	..	75	60
166	1 f. Gong (North Malekula) and carving (North Ambrym)..	..	1·25	1·00
167	2 f. Palm Lorikeet	..	4·00	4·50
168	3 f. Ceremonial headdress, South Malekula (*different*)..		3·75	6·00
169	5 f. Green snail shell..	..	7·50	14·00
158/69 *and* 199	..	*Set of* 13	27·00	42·00

PRICES OF SETS

Set prices are given for many issues, generally those containing three stamps or more. Definitive sets include one of each value or major colour change, but do not cover different perforations, die types or minor shades. Where a choice is possible the set prices are based on the cheapest versions of the stamps included in the listings.

61 "Adoration of the Kings" (Spranger)

62 Royal and French Cyphers

(Des G. Drummond. Litho J.W.)

1972 (25 Sept). *Christmas. T* **61** *and similar vert design. Multicoloured. W w* **12**. *P* 14.
170	25 c. Type **61**	.. ..	10	10
171	70 c. "The Virgin and Child in a Landscape" (Provoost)	.. ..	20	20

(Des (from photographs by D. Groves) and photo Harrison)

1972 (20 Nov). *Royal Silver Wedding. Multicoloured; background colour given. W w* **12**. *P* 14 × 14½.
172	**62**	35 c. violet-black ..	15	10
173		65 c. yellow-olive ..	20	10

63 *Dendrobium teretifolium*

64 New Wharf at Vila

(Des Jennifer Toombs. Litho Questa)

1973 (26 Feb). *Orchids. T* **63** *and similar vert designs. Multicoloured. W w* **12** (*sideways*). *P* 14 × 14½.
174	25 c. Type **63**	..	25	10
175	30 c. *Ephemerantha comata*	..	30	10
176	35 c. *Spathoglottis petri*	..	35	10
177	65 c. *Dendrobium mohlianum*	..	60	55
174/7 ..	.. ..	*Set of* 4	1·40	70

(Des PAD Studio. Litho Questa)

1973 (14 May). *Opening of New Wharf at Vila. P* 14 × 14½ (25 c.) *or* 14½ × 14 (70 c.).
178	**64**	25 c. multicoloured	20	10
179		70 c. multicoloured	40	30
The 70 c. is as T **64**, but in a horizontal format.

65 Wild Horses

66 Mother and Child

(Des Pierrette Lambert. Photo Govt Printing Works, Paris)

1973 (13 Aug). *Tanna Island. T* **65** *and similar horiz design. Multicoloured. P* 13 × 12½.
180	35 c. Type **65**	..	30	15
181	70 c. Yasur Volcano	..	55	50

(Des Moutouh (35 c.), Tatin d'Avesnières (70 c.); adapted PAD Studio. Litho Questa)

1973 (19 Nov). *Christmas. T* **66** *and similar vert design. Multicoloured. W w* **12** (*sideways*). *P* 13½.
182	35 c. Type **66**	..	10	10
183	70 c. Lagoon scene	..	20	20

67 Pacific Pigeon

(**68**)

ROYAL VISIT 1974

(Des J. and H. Bregulla. Photo Govt Printing Works, Paris)

1974 (11 Feb). *Wild Life. T* **67** *and similar horiz designs. Multicoloured. P* 13 × 12½.
184	25 c. Type **67**	..	95	35
185	35 c. *Lyssa curvata* (moth) ..	..	1·25	60
186	70 c. Green Sea Turtle	..	1·25	70
187	1 f. 15, Grey-headed Flying Fox	..	1·50	1·50
184/7	..	*Set of* 4	4·50	2·75

1974 (11 Feb). *Royal Visit of Queen Elizabeth II. Nos.* 164 *and* 167 *optd with T* **68**.
188	35 c. Chestnut-bellied Kingfisher (R.)	..	15	10
189	2 f. Palm Lorikeet	..	30	40

69 Old Post Office

(Des Odette Baillais. Photo Govt Printing Works, Paris)

1974 (6 May). *Inauguration of New Post Office, Vila. T* **69** *and similar triangular design. Multicoloured. P* 12.
190	35 c. Type **69**	..	15	50
	a. *Tête-bêche* (pair). Nos. 190/1	..	30	1·10
191	70 c. New Post Office	..	15	60
Nos. 190/1 were printed together, in *tête-bêche* pairs throughout the sheet.

70 Capt. Cook and Map

(Des J. Cooter. Litho J.W.)

1974 (1 Aug). *Bicentenary of Discovery. T* **70** *and similar horiz designs. Multicoloured. W w* **12** (*sideways on* 1 f. 15). *P* 11 (1 f. 15) *or* 13 (*others*).
192	35 c. Type **70**	..	1·75	2·00
	a. Horiz strip of 3. Nos. 192/4	..	5·00	
193	35 c. William Wales and beach landing	..	1·75	2·00
194	35 c. William Hodges and island scene	..	1·75	2·00
195	1 f. 15, Capt Cook, map and H.M.S. *Resolution* (59 × 34 *mm*)	..	4·00	4·50
192/5 ..	..	*Set of* 4	8·00	9·50
Nos. 192/4 were printed together, *se-tenant*, in horizontal strips of 3 throughout the sheet forming a composite design.

71 U.P.U. Emblem and Letters

72 "Adoration of the Magi" (Velazquez)

(Des Pierrette Lambert. Photo Govt Printing Works, Paris)

1974 (9 Oct). *Centenary of Universal Postal Union. P* 13 × 12½.
196	**71**	70 c. multicoloured	..	30	60

(Des J. Cooter. Litho Questa)

1974 (14 Nov). *Christmas. T* **72** *and similar multicoloured design. W w* **12** (*sideways on* 70 c.). *P* 14 × 13½ (35 c.) *or* 13½ × 14 (70 c.).
197	35 c. Type **72**	..	10	10
198	70 c. "The Nativity" (Gerard van Honthorst) (*horiz*)	..	20	20

73 Charolais Bull

74 Canoeing

(Des and eng J. Pheulpin. Recess Govt Printing Works, Paris)

1975 (29 Apr). *P* 13 × 12½.
199	**73**	10 f. bistre-brown, green & dull ultram	11·00	20·00

(Des J. Cooter. Litho Questa)

1975 (5 Aug). *World Scout Jamboree, Norway. T 74 and similar vert designs. Multicoloured. P 13½.*

200	25 c. Type **74** ..	30	10
201	35 c. Preparing meal ..	30	10
202	1 f. Map-reading ..	70	15
203	5 f. Fishing ..	2·50	2·50
200/3	.. Set of 4	3·50	2·50

75 "Pitti Madonna" (Michelangelo)

(Des PAD Studio. Litho Harrison)

1975 (11 Nov). *Christmas. Michelangelo's Sculptures. T 75 and similar vert designs. Multicoloured. W w 12 (sideways). P 14½ × 14.*

204	35 c. Type **75** ..	10	10
205	70 c. "Bruges Madonna" ..	15	10
206	2 f. 50, "Taddei Madonna" ..	70	50
204/6	.. Set of 3	85	55

76 "Concorde"

(Des J. B. F. Chesnot. Typo Edila)

1976 (30 Jan). *First Commercial Flight of "Concorde". P 13.*

207	**76** 5 f. multicoloured ..	12·00	6·00

77 Telephones of 1876 and 1976 **78** Map of the Islands

(Des J. Gauthier. Photo Delrieu)

1976 (31 Mar). *Telephone Centenary. T 77 and similar vert designs. Multicoloured. P 13½.*

208	25 c. Type **77** ..	15	10
209	70 c. Alexander Graham Bell ..	30	10
210	1 f. 15, Satellite and Nouméa Earth Station	50	50
208/10	.. Set of 3	85	60

(Des Odette Baillais. Photo Govt Printing Works, Paris)

1976 (29 June). *Constitutional Changes. T 78 and similar multicoloured designs. P 13 (25 c.) or 13 × 12½ (others).*

211	25 c. Type **78** ..	20	15
212	1 f. View of Santo (36 × 27 mm)	45	60
213	2 f. View of Vila (36 × 27 mm)	65	1·25
211/13	.. Set of 3	1·10	1·75

No. 211 shows the incorrect longitude, 116°E instead of 166°E.

79 "The Flight into Egypt" **80** Royal Visit, 1974
(Lusitano)

(Des J. Cooter. Litho Walsall)

1976 (8 Nov). *Christmas. T 79 and similar vert designs. Multicoloured. W w 14. P 13½.*

214	35 c. Type **79** ..	10	10
215	70 c. "Adoration of the Shepherds"	15	10
216	2 f. 50, "Adoration of the Magi"	45	50
214/16	.. Set of 3	60	55

Nos. 215/16 show retables by the Master of Santos-o-Novo.

(Des BG Studio. Litho Walsall)

1977 (7 Feb). *Silver Jubilee. T 80 and similar vert designs. Multicoloured. W w 14. P 13½.*

217	35 c. Type **80** ..	15	10
218	70 c. Imperial State Crown ..	20	10
219	2 f. The Blessing ..	40	65
217/19	.. Set of 3	65	70

(New Currency: 100 centimes=1 New Hebrides franc)

FNH	**FNH**	**FNH**	**25 FNH**
(81) (5 f.)	**(82)** (10 f., 20 f.)	**(83)** (15 f.)	**(84)**

1977 (1 July). *Currency change. Surch by Govt. Ptg Works, Paris. Nos. 220/3 as T 81/3, others as T 84.*

220	5 f. on 5 c. Type **60** ..	40	30
221	10 f. on 10 c. Baker's Pigeon ..	80	35
222	15 f. on 15 c. Gong and carving ..	60	60
223	20 f. on 20 c. Red-headed Parrot Finch	1·25	55
224	25 f. on 25 c. *Cribraria fischeri* (shell)	1·00	1·00
225	30 f. on 30 c. *Oliva rubrolabiata* (shell)	1·25	50
226	35 f. on 35 c. Chestnut-bellied Kingfisher	1·50	1·25
227	40 f. on 65 c. *Strombus plicatus* (shell)	1·25	1·50
228	50 f. on 1 f. Gong and carving ..	1·50	1·50
229	70 f. on 2 f. Palm Lorikeet ..	3·00	1·00
230	100 f. on 5 f. Ceremonial headdress ..	3·00	4·25
231	200 f. on 5 f. Green snail shell. ..	7·00	14·00
232	500 f. on 10 f. Type **73** ..	17·00	24·00
220/32	.. Set of 13	35·00	45·00

FNH	**FNH**	**FNH**
(85) (5 f.)	**(86)** (10 f.)	**(87)** (15 f.)

Two settings of 35 f. and 200 f. surcharges:
Setting I. Space of 1.4 mm between figures and "FNH".
Setting II. Space of 2.1 mm between figures and "FNH".

1977 (18 July)–**78**. *Nos. 158/60, 162/5 and 169 surch by I.P.V., Port Vila, in typography with T 85/7 or similar surcharges.*

233	5 f. on 5 c. Type **60** (10.8.77)	50	15
	a. Surch double		
234	10 f. on 10 c. Baker's Pigeon (10.7.77)	50	10
235	15 f. on 15 c. Gong and carving (18.7.77)	2·50	1·25
	b. Short bar in surcharge (5.8.77)	1·50	90
	ba. Surch inverted		
236	25 f. on 25 c. *Cribraria fischeri* (shell) (10.9.77)	50·00	20·00
	a. "FHN" for "FNH" (R. 5/1)	£400	
237	30 f. on 30 c. *Oliva rubrolabiata* (shell) (Setting I) (10.9.77)	£225	65·00
	a. "FHN" for "FNH" (R. 5/1)	£1200	
	b. Setting II (6.1.78)		
238	35 f. on 35 c. Chestnut-bellied Kingfisher (10.9.77)	2·00	55
239	40 f. on 65 c. *Strombus plicatus* (shell) (12.9.77)	1·50	55
240	200 f. on 5 f. Green snail shell (Setting I) (22.8.77)	17·00	17·00
	a. Setting II (13.1.78)		
241	500 f. on 10 f. Type **73** (14.9.77)	19·00	17·00
233/41	.. Set of 9	£275	£110

50 f. and 100 f. local surcharges were also prepared but these were not put on general sale, being available from the Philatelic Bureau only (*Price for set of 2 £40 mint, £40 used*).
Dates are those on which the various values were surcharged.
Surcharges on Nos. 236/41 are similar to Type **84**, but with new currency inscription as Type **86**.

89 Island of Erromango **90** "Tempi Madonna"
and Kauri Pine (Raphael)

(Des L. Curtis. Litho J.W. (15, 30, 40 f.), Walsall (10, 35, 70, 500 f.), Questa (others))

1977 (6 Sept)–**78**. *Maps of the Islands. T 89 and similar vert designs. Multicoloured. W w 14. P 13½ × 13 (15, 30, 40 f.) or 14 (others).*

242	5 f. Type **89** ..	30	10
243	10 f. Territory map and copra-making (9.5.78) ..	40	30
244	15 f. Espiritu Santo and cattle (23.11.77) ..	30	30
245	20 f. Efate and Vila P.O. ..	30	25
246	25 f. Malekula and headdresses (23.11.77)	40	40
247	30 f. Aoba, Maewo and pigs' tusks (23.11.77)	45	50
248	35 f. Pentecost and land diver (9.5.78) ..	50	65
249	40 f. Tanna and John Frum cross (23.11.77)	70	60
250	50 f. Shepherd Island and canoe ..	70	40
251	70 f. Banks Island and dancers (9.5.78) ..	1·75	1·75
252	100 f. Ambrym and idols ..	1·75	90
253	200 f. Aneityum and baskets ..	2·75	2·50
254	500 f. Torres Islands and archer fisherman (9.5.78) ..	6·00	7·50
242/54	.. Set of 13	14·00	14·50

(Des J.W. Litho Cartor S.A., France)

1977 (8 Dec). *Christmas. T 90 and similar vert designs. Multicoloured. W w 14. P 12.*

255	10 f. Type **90** ..	10	10
256	15 f. "The Flight into Egypt" (Gerard David)	15	15
257	30 f. "Virgin and Child" (Batoni) ..	20	40
255/7	.. Set of 3	40	60

91 "Concorde" over New York **92** White Horse of
Hanover

(Des BG Studio. Litho Rosenbaum Bros, Vienna)

1978 (9 May). *"Concorde" Commemoration. T 91 and similar horiz designs. Multicoloured. W w 14 (sideways). P 13½.*

258	10 f. Type **91** ..	65	65
259	20 f. "Concorde" over London ..	85	85
260	30 f. "Concorde" over Washington ..	1·10	1·10
261	40 f. "Concorde" over Paris ..	1·40	1·40
258/61	.. Set of 4	3·50	3·50

(Des Jennifer Toombs. Litho Questa)

1978 (2 June). *25th Anniv of Coronation. T 92 and similar vert designs. P 15.*

262	40 f. sepia, turquoise-blue and silver ..	35	55
	a. Sheetlet. Nos. 262/4, each × 2 ..	1·90	
263	40 f. multicoloured ..	35	55
264	40 f. sepia, turquoise-blue and silver ..	35	55
262/4	.. Set of 3	95	1·50

Designs:—No. 262, Type **92**. No. 263, Queen Elizabeth II; No. 264, Gallic Cock.
Nos. 262/4 were printed together in small sheets of 6, containing two *se-tenant* strips of 3 with horizontal gutter margin between.

93 "Madonna and Child" **(94)**

(Des C. Abbott. Litho Questa)

1978 (1 Dec). *Christmas. Paintings by Dürer. T 93 and similar vert designs. Multicoloured. W w 14. P 14 × 13½.*

265	10 f. Type **93** ..	10	10
266	15 f. "The Virgin and Child with St. Anne" ..	10	10
267	30 f. "Madonna of the Siskin" ..	10	10
268	40 f. "The Madonna of the Pear" ..	15	15
265/8	.. Set of 4	40	30

1979 (11 Jan). *1st Anniv of Internal Self-Government. As No. 211 surch as T 94.*

269	**78** 10 f. on 25 c. multicoloured (blue background) ..	10	10
270	40 f. on 25 c. multicoloured (pale blue-green background) ..	20	20

95 1938 5 c. Stamp and
Sir Rowland Hill

96 Chubwan Mask

(Des J.W. Litho Questa)

1979 (10 Sept). *Death Centenary of Sir Rowland Hill. T **95** and
similar horiz designs showing stamps and Sir Rowland Hill.
Multicoloured. W w **14** (sideways). P 14.*

271	10 f. Type **95**	10	10
272	20 f. 1969 25 c. Pentecost Island Land Divers commemorative	15	10
273	40 f. 1925 2d. (20 c.)	20	20
271/3	Set of 3	35	30
MS274	143 × 94 mm. No. 272 and as No. F286, but W w **14** (sideways)	75	90

(Des BG Studio. Litho Format)

1979 (16 Nov). *Festival of Arts. T **96** and similar vert designs.
Multicoloured. W w **14**. P 14.*

275	5 f. Type **96**	10	10
276	10 f. Nal-Nal clubs and spears	10	10
277	20 f. Ritual puppet	15	10
278	40 f. Neqatmalow headdress	25	15
275/8	Set of 4	55	30

97 "Native Church" (Metas Masongo)

(Litho Delrieu)

1979 (4 Dec). *Christmas and International Year of the Child. Children's Drawings. T **97** and similar multicoloured designs. No
wmk. P 13 × 13½ (horiz) or 13½ × 13 (vert).*

279	5 f. Type **97**	10	10
280	10 f. "Priest and Candles" (Herve Rutu)	10	10
281	20 f. "Cross and Bible" (Mark Deards) (vert)	10	10
282	40 f. "Green Candle and Santa Claus" (Dev Raj) (vert)	15	15
279/82	Set of 4	30	30

98 White-bellied Honeyeater

(Des G. Drummond. Litho Walsall)

1980 (27 Feb). *Birds. T **98** and similar horiz designs. Multicoloured. W w **14** (sideways). P 14.*

283	10 f. Type **98**	50	10
284	20 f. Scarlet Robin	70	10
285	30 f. Yellow-fronted White Eye	90	45
286	40 f. Fan-tailed Cuckoo	1·00	70
283/6	Set of 4	2·75	1·25

POSTAGE DUE STAMPS

POSTAGE DUE (D 1)   POSTAGE DUE (D 2)   **POSTAGE DUE** (D 3)

1925 (June). *Optd with Type D **1**, by D.L.R.*

D1	**5** 1d. (10 c.) green	38·00	1·00
D2	2d. (20 c.) slate-grey	45·00	1·00
D3	3d. (30 c.) red	50·00	2·50
D4	5d. (50 c.) ultramarine	55·00	4·50
D5	10d. (1 f.) carmine/blue	60·00	5·50
D1/5	Set of 5	225	13·00
D1/5 Optd "Specimen"	Set of 5	225	

1938 (1 June). *Optd with Type D **2**, by B.W.*

D 6	**6** 5 c. blue-green	15·00	23·00
D 7	10 c. orange	15·00	23·00
D 8	20 c. scarlet	22·00	30·00
D 9	40 c. grey-olive	32·00	45·00
D10	1 f. red/green	45·00	55·00
D6/10	Set of 5	120	160
D6/10 Perf "Specimen"	Set of 5	120	

1953 (30 Apr). *Nos. 68/9, 71, 74 and 76 optd with Type D **3**, by
Waterlow.*

D11	5 c. green	5·00	7·50
D12	10 c. scarlet	1·75	5·00
D13	20 c. ultramarine	5·50	12·00
D14	40 c. blackish brown	8·50	22·00
D15	1 f. orange	6·00	22·00
D11/15	Set of 5	24·00	60·00

1957 (3 Sept). *Nos. 84/5, 87, 90 and 92 optd with Type D **3**, by
Waterlow.*

D16	**12** 5 c. green	30	1·25
D17	10 c. scarlet	30	1·25
D18	20 c. ultramarine	1·25	1·75
D19	**13** 40 c. sepia	2·50	3·50
D20	– 1 f. orange	4·00	6·50
D16/20	Set of 5	7·50	12·50

II. STAMPS INSCRIBED IN FRENCH

NOUVELLES

HEBRIDES   **NOUVELLES-HEBRIDES**

(F 1)   (F 2)

1908 (21 Nov). *T **15/17** of New Caledonia optd with Types F **1** or
F **2** (1 f.), by Govt Ptg Wks, Paris.*

F1	5 c. green	1·25	1·75
F2	10 c. carmine	80	90
F3	25 c. blue/greenish (R.)	3·50	2·75
F4	50 c. red/orange	6·50	6·00
F5	1 f. blue/green (R.)	9·00	6·50
F1/5	Set of 5	19·00	16·00

CONDOMINIUM   **10c.**

(F 3)   (F 4)

1910 (Aug)–**11**. *Nos. F**1/5** further optd with Type F **3**, or larger
(1 f.), by Govt Ptg Wks, Paris.*

F 6	5 c. green	1·50	1·75
F 7	10 c. carmine	1·50	70
F 8	25 c. blue/greenish (R.) (1911)	2·00	3·50
F 9	50 c. red/orange (1911)	5·50	5·50
F10	1 f. blue/green (R.)	13·00	15·00
F6/10	Set of 5	21·00	24·00

All the above were released in Paris on 16 March 1910. The 5 c.,
10 c. and 1 f. were issued in New Hebrides in August but the
25 c. and 50 c. were not received until 1911 after the issue of the
definitive stamps and they were placed in reserve, although some
may have been issued on request.

1911 (12 July). *Wmk Mult Crown CA. P 14.*

F11	**3** 5 c. green	1·00	2·00
F12	10 c. carmine	55	60
F13	20 c. greyish slate	1·00	1·50
F14	25 c. ultramarine	3·25	4·50
F15	30 c. brown/yellow	6·50	3·25
F16	40 c. red/yellow	1·40	2·75
F17	50 c. sage-green	2·00	2·75
F18	75 c. orange	7·00	13·00
F19	1 f. red/blue	2·50	2·50
F20	2 f. violet	8·00	14·00
F21	5 f. red/green	11·00	19·00
F11/21	Set of 11	38·00	60·00

1913. *As last but wmk "R F" in sheet or without wmk.*

F22	**3** 5 c. green	75	2·75
F23	10 c. carmine	75	1·75
F24	20 c. greyish slate	80	2·50
F25	25 c. ultramarine	75	3·00
F26	30 c. brown/yellow	1·50	5·50
F27	40 c. red/yellow	24·00	42·00
F28	50 c. sage-green	13·00	16·00
F29	75 c. orange	13·00	24·00
F30	1 f. red/blue	5·00	6·00
F31	2 f. violet	8·50	19·00
F32	5 f. red/green	12·00	25·00
F22/32	Set of 11	70·00	130

The above were placed on sale in Paris on 29 April 1912.

1920–21. *Surch as Type F **4**, at Govt Printing Establishment,
Suva, Fiji. (a) On stamps of 1908–11 (June 1920).*

F32a	5 c. on 50 c. red/orange (F4)	£375	£375
F33	5 c. on 50 c. red/orange (F9)	2·25	4·00
F33a	10 c. on 25 c. blue/greenish (F8)	30	1·25

(b) On stamps of 1911–13 (10.3.21).

F34	**3** 5 c. on 40 c. red/yellow (F27)	24·00	55·00
F35	20 c. on 30 c. brown/yellow (F15)	8·00	35·00
F36	20 c. on 30 c. brown/yellow (F26)	14·00	38·00

(c) On Inscr in English (10.3.21)

F37	**3** 10 c. on 5d. sage-green (24)	14·00	25·00

1924 (1 May). *Stamps of 1911–13 surch as Type F **4**, at Suva.*

F38	**3** 10 c. on 5 c. green (F22)	1·50	2·25
F39	30 c. on 10 c. carmine (F23)	1·25	1·50
F40	50 c. on 25 c. ultramarine (F14)	28·00	50·00
F41	50 c. on 25 c. ultramarine (F25)	2·50	15·00
F38/41	Set of 4	30·00	60·00

France Libre

F 5   (F 6)

(Recess D.L.R.)

1925 (June). *Wmk "R F" in sheet or without wmk. P 14.*

F42	**5** 5 c. (½d.) black	60	6·00
F43	10 c. (1d.) green	50	5·00
F44	20 c. (2d.) greyish slate	50	1·75
F45	25 c. (2½d.) brown	50	3·50
F46	30 c. (3d.) red	50	3·25
F47	40 c. (4d.) red/yellow	80	3·25
F48	50 c. (5d.) ultramarine	90	2·50

F49	**5** 75 c. (7½d.) yellow-brown	2·00	6·00
F50	1 f. (10d.) carmine/blue	2·00	3·00
F51	2 f. (1/8) violet	4·50	16·00
F52	5 f. (4s.) carmine/green	6·00	20·00
F42/52	Set of 11	17·00	65·00
F42/52 Optd "Specimen"	Set of 11	£250	

In July 1929 a batch of mail was carried by aircraft from Port
Vila to the French cruiser *Tourville* for sorting and forwarding at
Nouméa, New Caledonia. Stamps of the above issue (including
those with English inscriptions) were affixed to covers and handstamped "PAR AVION" before cancellation.

1938 (1 June). *Gold Currency. Wmk "R F" in sheet or without
wmk. P 12.*

F53	**6** 5 c. blue-green	1·50	1·50
F54	10 c. orange	1·50	1·00
F55	15 c. bright violet	1·25	1·25
F56	20 c. scarlet	1·25	1·00
F57	25 c. reddish brown	3·00	1·40
F58	30 c. blue	3·00	1·40
F59	40 c. grey-olive	1·25	3·00
F60	50 c. purple	1·25	1·00
F61	1 f. lake/pale green (shades)	1·50	2·50
F62	2 f. blue/pale green (shades)	20·00	18·00
F63	5 f. red/yellow	32·00	17·00
F64	10 f. violet/blue	90·00	60·00
F53/64	Set of 12	£140	£110
F53/64 Optd "Specimen"	Set of 12	£275	

1941 (15 Apr). *Adherence to General de Gaulle. Optd with Type
F **6**, at Nouméa, New Caledonia.*

F65	**6** 5 c. blue-green	2·75	14·00
F66	10 c. orange	3·25	12·00
F67	15 c. bright violet	4·75	17·00
F68	20 c. scarlet	12·00	17·00
F69	25 c. reddish brown	12·00	18·00
F70	30 c. blue	12·00	17·00
F71	40 c. grey-olive	12·00	18·00
F72	50 c. purple	12·00	16·00
F73	1 f. lake/pale green	12·00	16·00
F74	2 f. blue/pale green	12·00	17·00
F75	5 f. red/yellow	12·00	17·00
F76	10 f. violet/blue	13·00	18·00
F65/76	Set of 12	£110	£180

1949 (10 Oct). *75th Anniv of U.P.U. As Nos. 64/7. Wmk "R F" in
sheet or without wmk. P 13½.*

F77	10 c. red-orange	2·25	3·00
F78	15 c. violet	4·25	4·75
F79	30 c. ultramarine	5·50	7·50
F80	50 c. purple	6·50	8·00
F77/80	Set of 4	17·00	21·00

1953 (30 Apr). *As Nos. 68/78. Wmk "R F" in sheet or without wmk.
P 12½.*

F81	**7** 5 c. green	30	50
F82	10 c. scarlet	70	50
F83	15 c. yellow-ochre	70	60
F84	20 c. ultramarine	70	50
F85	– 25 c. olive	50	50
F86	– 30 c. brown	50	50
F87	– 40 c. blackish brown	50	70
F88	– 50 c. violet	50	50
F89	– 1 f. orange	13·00	4·00
F90	– 2 f. reddish purple	16·00	16·00
F91	– 5 f. scarlet	26·00	55·00
F81/91	Set of 11	55·00	80·00

1956 (20 Oct). *Fiftieth Anniv of Condominium. As Nos. 80/3. Wmk
"R F" in sheet or without wmk. P 14½ × 14.*

F92	**10** 5 c. emerald	1·25	1·00
F93	10 c. scarlet	1·25	1·00
F94	20 c. deep bright blue	1·25	1·10
F95	50 c. deep lilac	1·50	1·75
F92/5	Set of 4	4·75	4·25

1957 (3 Sept). *As Nos. 84/94. Wmk "R F" in sheet or without wmk.
P 13½.*

F 96	**12** 5 c. green	75	60
F 97	10 c. scarlet	75	40
F 98	15 c. orange-yellow	1·25	60
F 99	20 c. ultramarine	1·25	60
F100	**13** 25 c. yellow-olive	1·25	50
F101	30 c. brown	1·25	60
F102	40 c. sepia	1·25	60
F103	50 c. reddish violet	1·25	50
F104	– 1 f. red-orange	8·00	2·75
F105	– 2 f. mauve	20·00	24·00
F106	– 5 f. black	30·00	35·00
F96/106	Set of 11	60·00	60·00

F 7 Emblem and Globe   F 8 Centenary Emblem

(Des and eng J. Derrey. Recess Govt Ptg Wks, Paris)

1963 (2 Sept). *Freedom from Hunger. P 13.*

F107	**F 7** 60 c. deep bluish green and chestnut	15·00	11·00

(Des and eng J. Combet. Recess Govt Ptg Wks, Paris)

1963 (2 Sept). *Red Cross Centenary. P 13.*

F108	**F 8** 15 c. red, grey and orange	8·50	6·00
F109	45 c. red, grey and yellow-bistre	16·00	18·00

1963 (25 Nov)–**72**. *As Nos. 98/109 and 129. No wmk.*
P 12½ (10, 20, 40, 60 c.), 14 (3 f.) or 13 (others).
F110	5 c. lake, purple-brown and greenish blue (15.8.66)		40	30
	a. Lake and greenish blue (29.2.72)		50·00	50·00
F111	10 c. lt brown, buff & emerald* (16.8.65)		80	80
F112	10 c. lt brown, buff and emerald (5.8.68)		30	15
F113	15 c. yellow-bistre, red-brown & dp violet		5·50	40
F114	20 c. black, ol-green & grnsh bl* (16.8.65)		2·25	3·00
F115	20 c. black, ol-green & grnsh bl (5.8.68)		60	25
F116	25 c. reddish violet, orange-brown and crimson (15.8.66)		60	60
F117	30 c. chestnut, bistre and violet		6·50	60
F118	40 c. vermilion and deep blue* (16.8.65)		3·50	6·00
F119	50 c. green, yellow and greenish blue		6·50	60
F120	60 c. vermilion and deep blue (5.12.67)		1·50	80
F121	1 f. red, black & dp bluish grn (15.8.66)		2·00	3·00
F122	2 f. black, brown-purple & yellow-olive		20·00	8·00
F123	3 f. multicoloured* (16.8.65)		11·00	20·00
F124	3 f. multicoloured (5.8.68)		5·50	8·50
F125	5 f. blue, deep blue and black (24.1.67)		20·00	24·00
F110/25		Set of 16	75·00	65·00

*Normally all French New Hebrides issues have the "RF" inscription on the right to distinguish them from the British New Hebrides stamps which have it on the left. The stamps indicated by an asterisk have "RF" wrongly placed on the left.

F 9 "Syncom" Communications Satellite, Telegraph Poles and Morse Key

(Des and eng J. Combet. Recess Govt Ptg Wks, Paris)

1965 (17 May). *Air. I.T.U. Centenary. P 13.*
F126	**F 9** 15 c. blue, emerald and red-brown		7·00	6·00
F127	60 c. cerise, slate and deep bluish green		18·00	20·00

1965 (24 Oct). *International Co-operation Year. As Nos. 112/13. P 14½.*
F128	**29** 5 c. dp reddish purple & turquoise-grn		3·50	3·00
F129	55 c. deep bluish green and lavender		9·50	9·00

1966 (24 Jan). *Churchill Commemoration. As Nos. 114/17. P 14.*
F130	**30** 5 c. black, cerise, gold and new blue		1·00	75
F131	15 c. black, cerise, gold and deep green		3·25	1·00
F132	25 c. black, cerise, gold and brown		3·75	3·50
F133	30 c. black, cerise, gold and bluish violet		4·50	4·50
F130/3		Set of 4	11·00	8·75

1966 (1 July). *World Cup Football Championships. As Nos. 118/19. P 14.*
F134	**31** 20 c. violet, yellow-grn, lake & yell-brn		3·00	2·75
F135	40 c. chocolate, bl-grn, lake & yell-brn		4·50	4·25

1966 (20 Sept). *Inauguration of W.H.O. Headquarters, Geneva. As Nos. 120/1. P 14.*
F136	**32** 25 c. black, yellow-green and light blue		3·50	2·00
F137	60 c. black, mauve and yellow-ochre		5·50	5·00

1966 (1 Dec). *20th Anniv of U.N.E.S.C.O. As Nos. 122/4. P 14.*
F138	**33** 15 c. slate-violet, red, yellow and orange		1·50	1·00
F139	– 30 c. orange-yellow, violet & dp olive		2·50	2·25
F140	– 45 c. black, bright purple and orange		2·50	2·75
F138/40		Set of 3	6·00	5·50

1967 (26 Sept). *25th Anniv of the Pacific War. As Nos. 125/8. P 14 × 13.*
F141	15 c. Type **36**		50	40
F142	25 c. War Zone map, U.S. marine and Australian soldier		75	50
F143	60 c. H.M.A.S. Canberra		1·10	1·25
F144	1 f. "Flying Fortress"		1·75	2·00
F141/4		Set of 4	3·75	3·75

1968 (23 May). *Bicentenary of Bougainville's World Voyage. As Nos. 130/2. P 13.*
F145	**40** 15 c. emerald, slate-violet and red		20	20
F146	– 25 c. dp olive, maroon & ultramarine		40	40
F147	– 60 c. bistre-brn, brn-pur & myrtle-grn		90	90
F145/7		Set of 3	1·40	1·40

1968 (9 Oct). *Anglo–French "Concorde" Project. As Nos. 133/4. P 14.*
F148	**43** 25 c. lt blue, orange-red & dp violet-bl		2·00	1·50
F149	– 60 c. red, black and bright blue		3·50	3·00

1969 (30 June). *Timber Industry. As No. 135. P 14½.*
F150	**45** 20 c. multicoloured (shades)		20	30

1969 (13 Aug). *3rd South Pacific Games, Port Moresby, Papua New Guinea. As Nos. 136/7. Multicoloured. P 12½.*
F151	25 c. Type **46**		30	30
F152	1 f. Runner passing baton, and flags		1·50	1·75

1969 (15 Oct). *Pentecost Island Land Divers. As Nos. 138/40. Multicoloured. P 12½.*
F153	15 c. Type **48**		30	30
F154	25 c. Diver jumping		40	40
F155	1 f. Diver at end of fall		1·40	1·40
F153/5		Set of 3	1·90	1·90

1970 (20 May). *Inauguration of New U.P.U. Headquarters Building, Berne. As No. 141. P 13.*
F156	**51** 1 f. 05, slate, red-orange & brt purple		50	70

1970 (20 July). *30th Anniv of New Hebrides' Declaration for the Free French Government. As Nos. 142/3. P 13.*
F157	**52** 65 c. multicoloured		55	55
F158	1 f. 10, multicoloured		1·10	1·10

1970 (15 Oct). *No. F115 surch with T **53**.*
F159	35 c. on 20 c. black, ol-green & greenish blue		60	50

1970 (30 Nov). *Christmas. As Nos. 145/6. Multicoloured. P 14½ × 14.*
F160	15 c. Type **54**		15	15
F161	50 c. "The Virgin and Child" (G. Cima)		25	40

1971 (19 Jan). *Death of General Charles de Gaulle. Nos. F157/8 optd with T **55**, the vertical bars in black and inscriptions in gold.*
F162	**52** 65 c. multicoloured		75	55
	a. Gold opt omitted			
F163	1 f. 10, multicoloured		1·50	1·50

On No. F162a the vertical black bars are still present.

1971 (13 July). *4th South Pacific Games, Papeete, French Polynesia. As Nos. 149/50. Multicoloured. P 12½.*
F164	20 c. Type **56**		35	20
F165	65 c. Basketball (vert)		95	80

1971 (7 Sept). *Royal Society's Expedition to New Hebrides. As No. 151. P 14½ × 14.*
F166	**57** 65 c. multicoloured		50	50

1971 (23 Nov). *Christmas. As Nos. 152/3. Multicoloured. P 14 × 13½.*
F167	25 c. Type **58**		15	20
F168	50 c. "Adoration of the Shepherds" (J. Tintoretto)		30	35

1972 (29 Feb). *Aircraft. As Nos. 154/7. Multicoloured. P 13.*
F169	20 c. Type **59**		1·00	60
F170	25 c. "Sandringham" flying-boat		1·00	70
F171	30 c. DH "Dragon Rapide"		1·10	75
F172	65 c. "Caravelle"		3·00	4·00
F169/72		Set of 4	5·50	5·50

1972 (24 July). *As Nos. 158/69. Multicoloured. P 12½ × 13.*
F173	5 c. Type **60**		40	10
F174	10 c. Baker's Pigeon		1·75	50
F175	15 c. Gong and carving, North Ambrym		50	15
F176	20 c. Red-headed Parrot Finch		2·25	30
F177	25 c. Cribraria fischeri (shell)		1·75	30
F178	30 c. Oliva rubrolabiata (shell)		1·75	30
F179	35 c. Chestnut-bellied Kingfisher		3·00	40
F180	65 c. Strombus plicatus (shell)		2·50	60
F181	1 f. Gong, North Malekula and carving, North Ambrym		2·50	1·75
F182	2 f. Palm Lorikeet		15·00	10·00
F183	3 f. Ceremonial headdress, South Malekula (different)		9·50	13·00
F184	5 f. Green snail shell		17·00	22·00
F173/84 and F213		Set of 13	75·00	75·00

1972 (25 Sept). *Christmas. As Nos. 170/1. Multicoloured. P 14.*
F185	25 c. Type **61**		25	20
F186	70 c. "Virgin and Child" (Provoost)		50	45

1972 (20 Nov). *Royal Silver Wedding. As Nos. 172/3. W w 12. P 14 × 14½.*
F187	**62** 35 c. multicoloured		75	50
F188	65 c. multicoloured		1·25	1·50

1973 (26 Feb). *Orchids. As Nos. 174/7. Multicoloured. P 14 × 14½.*
F189	25 c. Type **63**		1·00	40
F190	30 c. Ephemerantha comata		1·10	60
F191	35 c. Spathoglottis petri		1·25	75
F192	65 c. Dendrobium mohlianum		3·00	4·00
F189/92		Set of 4	5·50	5·25

1973 (14 May). *Opening of New Wharf, Vila. As Nos. 178/9. Multicoloured. P 14 × 14½ (25 c.) or 14½ × 14 (70 c.).*
F193	25 c. Type **64**		75	50
F194	70 c. View of wharf (horiz)		1·50	2·00

1973 (13 Aug). *Tanna Island. As Nos. 180/1. Multicoloured. P 13 × 12½.*
F195	35 c. Type **65**		2·25	1·25
F196	70 c. Yasur Volcano		3·25	3·25

1973 (19 Nov). *Christmas. As Nos. 182/3. Multicoloured. P 14 × 13½.*
F197	35 c. Type **66**		45	35
F198	70 c. Lagoon scene		1·00	75

1974 (11 Feb). *Wild Life. As Nos. 184/7. Multicoloured. P 13 × 12½.*
F199	25 c. Type **67**		3·75	1·50
F200	35 c. Lyssa curvata		5·50	1·75
F201	70 c. Green Sea Turtle		5·50	3·75
F202	1 f. 15, Grey-headed Flying Fox		6·00	8·50
F199/202		Set of 4	19·00	14·00

VISITE ROYALE
1974

(F 10)

1974 (11 Feb). *Royal Visit of Queen Elizabeth II. Nos. F179 and F182 optd with Type F 10.*
F203	35 c. Chestnut-bellied Kingfisher (R.)		2·00	50
F204	2 f. Palm Lorikeet		5·00	6·00

1974 (6 May). *Inauguration of New Post Office, Vila. As Nos. 190/1. Multicoloured. P 12.*
F205	35 c. Type **69**		50	65
	a. Tête-bêche (pair). Nos. F205/6		1·10	1·50
F206	70 c. New Post Office		60	85

1974 (1 Aug). *Bicentenary of Discovery. As Nos. 192/5. Multicoloured. P 11 (1 f. 15) or 13 × 13½ (others).*
F207	35 c. Type **70**		4·50	4·00
	a. Horiz strip of 3. Nos. F207/9		12·00	

F208	35 c. William Wales and beach landing		4·50	4·00
F209	35 c. William Hodges and island scene		4·50	4·00
F210	1 f. 15, Capt. Cook, *Resolution* and map of islands (64 × 39 mm)		10·00	8·50
F207/10		Set of 4	21·00	18·00

1974 (9 Oct). *Centenary of Universal Postal Union. As No. 196. P 13 × 12½.*
F210a	**71** 70 c. dp turquoise-blue, rosine & black		1·25	1·50

1974 (4 Nov). *Christmas. As Nos. 197/8. Multicoloured. P 14 × 13½ (35 c.) or 13½ × 14 (70 c.).*
F211	35 c. Type **72**		25	20
F212	70 c. "The Nativity" (G. van Honthorst) (horiz)		55	45

1975 (29 Apr). *As No. 199. P 13 × 12½.*
F213	**73** 10 f. bistre-brown, yellow-green & blue		28·00	35·00

1975 (5 Aug). *World Scout Jamboree, Norway. As Nos. 200/3. Multicoloured. P 14 × 13½.*
F214	25 c. Type **74**		55	20
F215	35 c. Preparing meal		75	30
F216	1 f. Map-reading		1·90	1·10
F217	5 f. Fishing		10·00	9·00
F214/17		Set of 4	12·00	9·50

1975 (11 Nov). *Christmas. As Nos. 204/6. Multicoloured. P 14½ × 14.*
F218	35 c. Type **75**		25	15
F219	70 c. "Bruges Madonna"		40	25
F220	2 f. 50, "Taddei Madonna"		2·25	2·75
F218/20		Set of 3	2·75	2·75

1976 (30 Jan). *First Commercial Flight of "Concorde". As No. 207. P 13.*
F221	**76** 5 f. multicoloured		18·00	13·00

1976 (31 Mar). *Telephone Centenary. As Nos. 208/10. Multicoloured. P 13½.*
F222	35 c. Type **77**		55	40
F223	70 c. Alexander Graham Bell		1·40	1·50
F224	1 f. 15, Satellite and Earth Station, Nouméa		1·75	2·25
F222/4		Set of 3	3·50	3·75

1976 (29 June). *Constitutional Changes. As Nos. 211/13. Multicoloured. P 13 (25 c.) or 13 × 12½ (others).*
F225	25 c. Type **78**		50	30
F226	1 f. Luganville (36 × 27 mm)		1·50	1·00
F227	2 f. Vila (36 × 27 mm)		2·50	1·90
F225/7		Set of 3	4·00	2·75

No. F225 shows the incorrect longitude, 116°E, instead of 166°E.
Nos. F226/7 exist with the inscription "PREMIERE ASSEMBLEE REPRESENTATIVE 1975" and the name of the city. These stamps were not available in the New Hebrides.

1976 (8 Nov). *Christmas. As Nos. 214/16. Multicoloured. P 13½.*
F228	35 c. Type **79**		25	15
F229	70 c. "Adoration of the Shepherds"		40	25
F230	2 f. 50, "Adoration of the Magi"		2·25	2·75
F228/30		Set of 3	2·75	2·75

1977 (7 Feb). *Silver Jubilee. As Nos. 217/19. Multicoloured. P 13½.*
F231	35 c. Type **80**		50	20
F232	70 c. Imperial State Crown		75	50
F233	2 f. The Blessing		1·00	1·25
F231/3		Set of 3	2·00	1·75

1977 (1 July). *Currency Change. Nos. F173/84 and F214 surch as T 81/3 (Nos. F234/7) or as T 84 (others) by Govt Ptg Wks, Paris.*
F234	5 f. on 5 c. Type **60**		40	40
F235	10 f. on 10 c. Baker's Pigeon		85	40
F236	15 f. on 15 c. Gong and carving, North Ambrym		70	60
F237	20 f. on 20 c. Red-headed Parrot Finch		1·50	85
F238	25 f. on 25 c. Cribraria fischeri (shell)		1·50	1·00
F239	30 f. on 30 c. Oliva rubrolablata		1·75	1·50
F240	35 f. on 35 c. Chestnut-bellied Kingfisher		2·50	1·50
F241	40 f. on 65 c. Strombus plicatus (shell)		2·50	2·00
F242	50 f. on 1 f. Gong, North Malekula, and carving, North Ambrym		2·50	2·00
F243	70 f. on 2 f. Palm Lorikeet		4·25	4·50
	a. Surch double			
F244	100 f. on 3 f. Ceremonial headdress, South Malekula		4·50	4·50
F245	350 f. on 5 f. Green snail shell		14·00	19·00
F246	500 f. on 10 f. Type **73**		26·00	25·00
F234/46		Set of 13	55·00	65·00

1977 (18 July)–**78**. *Nos. F173/5, F177/180, F184 and F213 surch by I.P.V., Port Vila, in typography with T 85/7 or similar surcharges.*
F247	5 f. on 5 c. Type **60** (10.8.77)		1·00	1·00
F248	10 f. on 10 c. Baker's Pigeon (20.7.77)		1·75	55
F249	15 f. on 15 c. Gong and carving (18.7.77)		2·75	1·50
	a. Short bar in surcharge (5.8.77)		2·50	2·25
F250	25 f. on 25 c. Cribraria fischeri (shell)		£120	60·00
	a. "FHN" for "FNH" (R. 5/1)		£750	
F251	30 f. on 30 c. Oliva rubrolabiata (shell) (10.9.77)		£250	60·00
	a. "FHN" for "FNH" (R. 5/1)		£1400	
F252	35 f. on 35 c. Chestnut-bellied Kingfisher (Setting I) (10.9.77)		4·00	4·25
	a. "NH" for "FNH" (R. 4/2)			
	b. Setting II (6.1.78)		23·00	14·00
F253	40 f. on 65 c. Strombus plicatus (shell) (12.9.77)		4·50	4·50
F254	200 f. on 5 f. Green snail shell (Setting I) (22.8.77)		35·00	45·00
	a. Setting II (13.1.78)		40·00	45·00
F255	500 f. on 10 f. Type **73** (14.9.77)		40·00	48·00
F247/55		Set of 9	£400	£200

Dates are those on which the various values were surcharged.
50 f., 70 f. and 100 f. local surcharges were also prepared, but were not put on general sale, being available from the Philatelic Bureau only.

1977 (7 Sept)–**78.** *Maps of the Islands. As Nos. 242/54. Multi-coloured. P* 13½ × 13 (15, 30, 40 *f.*) *or* 14 (*others*).

F256	5 f. Type **89**	40	20
F257	10 f. Territory map and copra-making (9.5.78)	60	20
F258	15 f. Espiritu Santo and cattle (23.11.77)	60	20
F259	20 f. Efate and Vila Post Office	65	30
F260	25 f. Malekula and headdresses (23.11.77)	70	40
F261	30 f. Aoba, Maewo and pigs' tusks (23.11.77)	70	45
F262	35 f. Pentecost and land diver (9.5.78)	1·25	60
F263	40 f. Tanna and John Frum cross (23.11.77)	1·25	75
F264	50 f. Shepherd Island and canoe	2·00	75
F265	70 f. Banks Island and dancers (9.5.78)	3·25	2·25
F266	100 f. Ambrym and idols	3·00	2·50
F267	200 f. Aneityum and baskets	4·75	8·00
F268	500 f. Torres Islands and archer fisherman (9.5.78)	10·00	13·00
F256/68	*Set of* 13	26·00	26·00

1977 (8 Dec). *Christmas. As Nos. 255/7. Multicoloured. P* 12.

F269	10 f. Type **90**	20	20
F270	15 f. "The Flight into Egypt" (G. David)	35	35
F271	30 f. "Virgin and Child" (Pompeo Batoni)	85	85
F269/71	*Set of* 3	1·25	1·25

1978 (9 May). *"Concorde". As Nos. 258/61. Multicoloured. P* 13½.

F272	10 f. Type **91**	2·00	1·00
F273	20 f. "Concorde" over London	2·25	1·50
F274	30 f. "Concorde" over Washington	2·75	2·00
F275	40 f. "Concorde" over Paris	3·50	3·25
F272/5	*Set of* 4	9·50	7·00

1978 (2 June). *25th Anniv of Coronation. As Nos. 262/4. P* 15.

F276	**92** 40 f. sepia, turquoise-blue and silver	50	85
	a. Sheetlet. Nos. F276/8 × 2	2·75	
F277	– 40 f. multicoloured	50	85
F278	– 40 f. sepia, turquoise-blue and silver	50	85
F276/8	*Set of* 3	1·40	2·25

Nos. F276/278 were printed together in small sheets of 6, containing two *se-tenant* strips of 3, with horizontal gutter margin between.

1978 (1 Dec). *Christmas. As Nos. 265/8. Multicoloured. P* 14 × 13½.

F279	10 f. Type **93**	20	20
F280	15 f. "The Virgin and Child with St. Anne"	25	30
F281	30 f. "The Madonna with the Goldfinch"	40	60
F282	40 f. "The Madonna with the Child"	50	70
F279/82	*Set of* 4	1·25	1·60

(F 11)

1979 (11 Jan). *1st Anniv of Internal Self-Government. As No. F225 surch as Type F* 11.

F283	**78** 10 f. on 25 c. multicoloured (blue background)	45	30
F284	40 f. on 25 c. multicoloured (pale blue-green background)	1·10	1·25

1979 (10 Sept). *Death Centenary of Sir Rowland Hill. As Nos. 271/3. Multicoloured. P* 14.

F285	10 f. Type **95**	30	35
F286	20 f. 1969 Land Divers 25 c. commemorative	45	55
F287	40 f. 1925 20 c. (2d.)	65	75
F285/7	*Set of* 3	1·25	1·50

For miniature sheet containing No. F286, see No. **MS274**.

1979 (16 Nov). *Festival of Arts. As Nos. 275/8. Multicoloured. P* 14.

F288	5 f. Type **96**	20	10
F289	10 f. Nal-Nal clubs and spears	25	15
F290	20 f. Ritual puppet	45	40
F291	40 f. Neqatmalow headdress	75	1·00
F288/91	*Set of* 4	1·50	1·50

1979 (4 Dec). *Christmas and International Year of the Child. As Nos. 279/82. Multicoloured. P* 13 × 13½ (*horiz*) *or* 13½ × 13 (*vert*).

F292	5 f. Type **97**	55	35
F293	10 f. "Priest and Candles" (Herve Rutu)	75	35
F294	20 f. "Cross and Bible" (Mark Deards) (*vert*)	1·00	1·00
F295	40 f. "Green Candle and Santa Claus" (Dev Raj) (*vert*)	1·90	2·00
F292/5	*Set of* 4	3·75	3·25

1980 (27 Feb). *Birds. As Nos. 283/6. Multicoloured. P* 14.

F296	10 f. Type **98**	1·00	45
F297	20 f. Scarlet Robin	1·25	1·00
F298	30 f. Yellow-fronted White Eye	1·75	1·75
F299	40 f. Fan-tailed Cuckoo	2·00	2·25
F296/9	*Set of* 4	5·50	5·00

POSTAGE DUE STAMPS

CHIFFRE TAXE   CHIFFRE TAXE   **TIMBRE-TAXE**

(FD 1)   (FD 2)   (FD 3)

1925 (June). *Optd with Type FD* 1, *by D.L.R.*

FD53	F **5** 10 c. (1d.) green		40·00	2·25
FD54	20 c. (2d.) greyish slate		40·00	2·25
FD55	30 c. (3d.) red		40·00	2·25
FD56	50 c. (5d.) ultramarine		40·00	2·25
FD57	1 f. (10d.) carmine/*blue*		40·00	2·25
FD53/7		*Set of* 5	£180	10·00
FD53/7 Optd "Specimen"		*Set of* 5	£200	

Although on sale in Paris, the Postmaster would not issue any in unused condition for about a year and most copies are cancelled-to-order.

1938 (1 June). *Optd with Type FD* 2, *by Bradbury, Wilkinson.*

FD65	**6** 5 c. blue-green		12·00	24·00
FD66	10 c. orange		15·00	24·00
FD67	20 c. scarlet		20·00	32·00
FD68	40 c. grey-olive		40·00	50·00
FD69	1 f. lake/*pale green*		45·00	60·00
FD65/9		*Set of* 5	£120	£170
FD65/9 Optd "Specimen"		*Set of* 5	£200	

1941 (15 Apr). *Nos. FD65/9 optd with Type F* 6 *at Nouméa, New Caledonia.*

FD77	**6** 5 c. blue-green		8·00	22·00
FD78	10 c. orange		8·00	22·00
FD79	20 c. scarlet		8·00	22·00
FD80	40 c. grey-olive		8·00	22·00
FD81	1 f. lake/*pale green*		12·00	22·00
FD77/81		*Set of* 5	40·00	£100

1953 (30 Apr). *Optd with Type FD* 3, *by Waterlow.*

FD92	**7** 5 c. green		3·50	9·00
FD93	10 c. scarlet		3·50	8·50
FD94	20 c. ultramarine		10·00	16·00
FD95	– 40 c. blackish brown		14·00	30·00
FD96	– 1 f. orange		24·00	35·00
FD92/6		*Set of* 5	50·00	90·00

1957 (3 Sept). *Optd with Type FD* 3, *by Waterlow.*

FD107	**12** 5 c. green		2·00	5·00
FD108	10 c. scarlet		2·00	5·00
FD109	20 c. ultramarine		4·50	7·00
FD110	**13** 40 c. sepia		9·50	13·00
FD111	– 1 f. red-orange		12·00	17·00
FD107/11		*Set of* 5	27·00	42·00

VANUATU

The former Condominium of the New Hebrides became the Republic of Vanuatu on 30 July 1980 and was admitted as a member of the Commonwealth.

99 Island of Erromango and Kauri Pine

100 Rotary International

(Des L. Curtis. Litho J.W. (15, 30, 40 f.), Walsall (10, 35, 70, 500 f.), Questa (others))

1980 (30 July). *As Nos. 242/54 of New Hebrides but inscr "VANUATU" and without cyphers as in T* 99. *P* 13 (15, 30, 40 *f.*) *or* 14 (*others*).
E. *Inscr in English.* W w 14.   F. *Inscr in French. No wmk.*

			E		F	
287	5 f. Type **99**		15	15	35	15
288	10 f. Territory map and copra making		15	15	40	15
289	15 f. Espiritu Santo and cattle		25	25	45	25
290	20 f. Efate and Vila P.O.		30	30	50	30
291	25 f. Malakula and headdresses		35	35	55	35
292	30 f. Aoba, Maewo and pigs' tusks		45	45	55	45
293	35 f. Pentecost and land diver		50	50	60	50
294	40 f. Tanna and John Frum cross		60	60	90	60
295	50 f. Shepherd Island and outrigger canoe		65	70	1·00	70
296	70 f. Banks Island and custom dancers		1·00	1·00	1·40	1·00
297	100 f. Ambrym and idols		1·25	80	1·50	1·10
298	200 f. Aneityum and baskets		1·40	1·40	1·75	1·75
299	500 f. Torres Island and archer fisherman		2·50	3·00	4·00	3·50
287/99		*Set of* 13	8·50	8·50	12·50	9·50

(Des L. Curtis. Litho Walsall)

1980 (16 Sept). *75th Anniv of Rotary International. T* 100 *and similar multicoloured design. P* 14. E. *Inscr in English.* W w 14 (*sideways on* 10 *f.*). F. *Inscr in French. No wmk.*

			E		F	
300	10 f. Type **100**		10	10	10	10
301	40 f. Rotary emblem (*vert*)		30	20	30	20

MINIMUM PRICE

The minimum price quote is 10p which represents a handling charge rather than a basis for valuing common stamps. For further notes about prices see introductory pages.

Christmas 1980–Noël 1980

101 Kiwanis Emblem and Globe

102 "The Virgin and Child enthroned with Saints and Angels" (Umkreis Michael Pacher)

(Des L. Curtis. Litho Walsall)

1980 (16 Sept). *Kiwanis International (service club), New Zealand District Convention, Port Vila. T* 101 *and similar design. P* 14. E. *Inscr in English.* W w 14 (*sideways on* 40 *f.*). F. *Inscr in French. No wmk.*

			E		F	
302	10 f. gold, ultram & chestnut		10	10	20	10
303	40 f. gold, blue-grn & brt bl		30	20	50	25

Design: *Horiz*—40 f. Kiwanis and Convention emblems.

(Des BG Studio. Litho Questa)

1980 (12 Nov). *Christmas. Details from Paintings. T* 102 *and similar vert designs. Multicoloured.* W w 14. *P* 14 × 13½.

304	10 f. Type **102**		10	10
305	15 f. "The Virgin and Child with Saints, Angels and Donors" (Hans Memling)		10	10
306	30 f. "The Rest on the Flight to Egypt" (Adriaen van der Werff)		20	20
304/6		*Set of* 3	35	35

103 Blue-faced Parrot Finch

104 Tribesman with Portrait of Prince Philip

(Des G. Drummond. Litho Questa)

1981 (18 Feb). *Birds (1st series). T* 103 *and similar vert designs. Multicoloured.* W w 14. *P* 14.

307	10 f. Type **103**		40	20
308	20 f. Emerald Dove		60	40
309	30 f. Golden Whistler		80	60
310	40 f. Silver-shouldered Fruit Dove		90	75
307/10		*Set of* 4	2·50	1·75

See also Nos. 327/30.

(New Currency. Vatus)

(Des A. Theobald. Litho Format)

1981 (10 June). *60th Birthday of Prince Philip, Duke of Edinburgh. T* 104 *and similar vert designs. Multicoloured.* W w 14. *P* 14 × 14½.

311	15 v. Type **104**		20	15
312	25 v. Prince Philip in casual dress		30	20
313	35 v. Queen and Prince Philip with Princess Anne and Master Peter Phillips		40	25
314	45 v. Prince Philip in ceremonial dress		50	35
311/14		*Set of* 4	1·25	85

105 Prince Charles with his Dog, Harvey

106 National Flag and Map of Vanuatu

(Des J.W. Litho Walsall)

1981 (22 July). *Royal Wedding. T* 105 *and similar vert designs. Multicoloured.* W w 14. *P* 14.

315	15 v. Wedding bouquet from Vanuatu		15	15
316	45 v. Type **105**		25	25
317	75 v. Prince Charles and Lady Diana Spencer		45	45
315/17		*Set of* 3	75	75

(Des C. Abbott. Litho Format)

1981 (30 July). *First Anniv of Independence. T* **106** *and similar designs. W* w **14** (*sideways on 25 and 45 v.*). *P* 14.

318	15 v. multicoloured	20	15
319	25 v. multicoloured	25	20
320	45 v. greenish yellow and brown-lake	35	30
321	75 v. multicoloured	60	70
318/21	.. .. .. *Set of* 4	1·25	1·25

Designs: *Horiz*—25 v. Vanuatu emblem; 45 v. Vanuatu national anthem. *Vert*—75 v. Vanuatu coat of arms.

107 Three Shepherds

108 New Caledonian Myiagra Flycatcher

(Adapted G. Vasarhelyi. Litho Questa)

1981 (11 Nov). *Christmas. Children's Paintings. T* **107** *and similar multicoloured designs. W* w **14** (*sideways on 25 and 45 v.*). *P* 14.

322	15 v. Type **107**	10	10
323	25 v. Vanuatu girl with lamb (*vert*) ..	15	15
324	35 v. Angel as butterfly	15	20
325	45 v. Boy carrying torch and gifts (*vert*)	25	30
322/5	.. .. *Set of* 4	60	65
MS326	133 × 94 mm. Nos. 322/5 (wmk sideways)	80	1·25

(Des G. Drummond. Litho Questa)

1982 (8 Feb). *Birds* (2nd series). *T* **108** *and similar vert designs. Multicoloured. W* w **14**. *P* 14½ × 14.

327	15 v. Type **108**	45	20
328	20 v. Rainbow Lorys	50	30
329	25 v. Buff-bellied Flycatchers ..	55	35
330	45 v. Collared Grey Fantails ..	80	65
327/30	.. .. .. *Set of* 4	2·10	1·40

109 Flickingeria comata

110 Scouts round Camp-fire

(Des Jennifer Toombs. Litho Enschedé)

1982 (15 June). *Orchids. Multicoloured designs as T* **109**. *W* w **14** (*sideways on 35, 45, 50 and 75 v.*). *P* 13½.

331	1 v. Type **109**	10	30
332	2 v. *Calanthe triplicata*	10	30
333	10 v. *Dendrobium sladei*	15	20
334	15 v. *Dendrobium mohlianum* ..	20	20
335	20 v. *Dendrobium macrophyllum* ..	25	30
336	25 v. *Dendrobium purpureum* ..	30	35
337	30 v. *Robiquetia mimus*	35	40
338	35 v. *Dendrobium mooreanum* (*horiz*)	40	50
339	45 v. *Spathoglottis plicata* (*horiz*) ..	55	70
340	50 v. *Dendrobium seemannii* (*horiz*)	60	80
341	75 v. *Dendrobium conanthum* (*horiz*)	95	1·50
342	100 v. *Dendrobium macranthum* ..	1·25	1·50
343	200 v. *Coelogyne lamellata*	2·25	2·50
344	500 v. *Bulbophyllum longioscapum* ..	5·00	6·00
331/44	.. .. *Set of* 14	11·00	14·00

(Des L. Curtis. Litho Questa)

1982 (1 Sept). *75th Anniv of Boy Scout Movement. T* **110** *and similar horiz designs. Multicoloured. W* w **14** (*sideways*). *P* 14.

345	15 v. Type **110**	45	20
346	20 v. First aid	50	25
347	25 v. Constructing tower	55	40
348	45 v. Constructing raft	80	70
349	75 v. Scout saluting	1·25	1·25
345/9	.. .. *Set of* 5	3·25	2·50

111 Baby Jesus

112 Euploea sylvester

(Des G. Vasarhelyi. Litho Questa)

1982 (1 Nov). *Christmas. Nativity Scenes. T* **111** *and similar multicoloured designs. W* w **14** (*sideways on 15, 25 v.*). *P* 14.

350	15 v. Type **111**	30	15
351	25 v. Mary and Joseph	45	35
352	35 v. Shepherds (*vert*)	55	70
353	45 v. Kings bearing gifts (*vert*) ..	70	1·00
350/3	.. .. *Set of* 4	1·75	2·00
MS354	132 × 92 mm. As Nos. 350/3 but without yellow borders	2·00	2·75

(Des J. Cooter. Litho Questa)

1983 (17 Jan). *Butterflies. T* **112** *and similar horiz designs. Multicoloured. W* w **14** (*sideways*). *P* 14 × 14½.

355	15 v. Type **112**	30	25
	a. Pair. Nos. 355/6 ..	60	50
356	15 v. *Hypolimnas octocula* ..	30	25
357	20 v. *Papilio canopus*	45	35
	a. Pair. Nos. 357/8 ..	90	70
358	20 v. *Polyura sacco*	45	35
359	25 v. *Luthrodes cleotas*	50	40
	a. Pair. Nos. 359/60 ..	1·00	80
360	25 v. *Danaus pumila*	50	40
355/60	.. .. *Set of* 6	2·25	1·75

Nos. 355/6, 357/8 and 359/60 were each printed in *se-tenant* pairs, horizontally and vertically throughout the sheets.

113 President Afi George Sokomanu

114 Map of Northern Vanuatu

(Des L. Curtis. Litho Enschedé)

1983 (14 Mar). *Commonwealth Day. T* **113** *and similar horiz designs. Multicoloured. W* w **14** (*sideways*). *P* 13½ × 14.

361	15 v. Type **113**	15	10
362	20 v. Fisherman and liner *Oriana* ..	20	15
363	25 v. Herdsman and cattle ..	25	15
364	75 v. World map showing position of Vanuatu with Commonwealth and Vanuatu flags	50	70
361/4	.. .. *Set of* 4	1·00	1·00

(Des A. Theobald. Litho Harrison)

1983 (23 May). *Economic Zone. Sheet* 120 × 120 *mm containing T* **114** *and similar vert designs. Multicoloured. W* w **14**. *P* 13½ × 13.

MS365	25 v. × 6 Yellowfin Tuna; Type **114**; Map of Matthew Island; Map of Hunter Island; Grouper; Oceanic Bonito	1·75	1·90

115 Montgolfier Balloon of De Rozier and D'Arlandes, 1783

116 Mail at Bauerfield Airport

(Des A. Theobald. Litho Questa)

1983 (4 Aug). *Bicentenary of Manned Flight. T* **115** *and similar multicoloured designs, each with manned flight logo. W* w **14** (*sideways on 35, 40 and 45 v.*). *P* 13½.

366	15 v. Type **115**	15	15
367	20 v. J. A. C. Charles balloon (first use of hydrogen), 1783 ..	25	25
368	25 v. Blanchard and Jeffries crossing English Channel, 1785 ..	30	30
369	35 v. Giffard's airship, 1852 (*horiz*)	40	40
370	40 v. *La France* (airship of Renard and Krebs), 1884 (*horiz*) ..	45	45
371	45 v. *Graf Zeppelin* (first aerial circumnavigation), 1929 (*horiz*) ..	55	55
366/71	.. .. *Set of* 6	1·90	1·90

(Des L. McCombie. Litho Questa)

1983 (10 Oct). *World Communications Year. T* **116** *and similar horiz designs. Multicoloured. W* w **14** (*sideways*). *P* 14.

372	15 v. Type **116**	20	25
373	20 v. Switchboard operator ..	30	35
374	25 v. Telex operator	35	40
375	45 v. Satellite Earth station ..	65	70
372/5	.. .. *Set of* 4	1·40	1·50
MS376	138 × 95 mm. Nos. 372/5 ..	1·50	1·75

117 Cymatoderma elegans var. lamellatum

118 Port Vila

(Des P. Cox. Litho Questa)

1984 (9 Jan). *Fungi. T* **117** *and similar multicoloured designs. W* w **14** (*sideways on 35 v., inverted on 45 v.*). *P* 14.

377	15 v. Type **117**	50	30
378	25 v. *Lignosus rhinoceros* ..	70	50
379	35 v. *Stereum ostrea* (*horiz*)	85	75
380	45 v. *Ganoderma boninense* ..	1·25	1·00
377/80	.. .. *Set of* 4	3·00	2·25

(Des D. Miller. Litho Questa)

1984 (30 Apr). *250th Anniv of "Lloyd's List"* (newspaper). *T* **118** *and similar designs. Multicoloured. W* w **14**. *P* 14½ × 14.

381	15 v. Type **118**	20	25
382	20 v. *Induna* (container ship) ..	30	35
383	35 v. Air Vanuatu aircraft ..	35	40
384	45 v. *Brahman Express* (container ship)	65	70
381/4	.. .. *Set of* 4	1·40	1·50

(Des A. Theobald. Litho Questa)

1984 (11 June). *Universal Postal Union Congress, Hamburg. As No.* **371** *but inscribed "UPU CONGRESS HAMBURG" and with U.P.U. logo. W* w **14** (*sideways*). *P* 13½ × 14.

385	45 v. multicoloured	80	70

119 Charolais

(Des Doreen McGuinness. Litho J.W.)

1984 (24 July). *Cattle. T* **119** *and similar horiz designs. Multicoloured. W* w **14** (*sideways*). *P* 14.

386	15 v. Type **119**	20	25
387	25 v. Charolais-afrikander ..	35	40
388	45 v. Friesian	65	70
389	75 v. Charolais-brahman ..	1·10	1·25
386/9	.. .. *Set of* 4	2·10	2·40

120 Makambo

(Des L. Dunn. Litho Walsall)

1984 (7 Sept). *"Ausipex" International Stamp Exhibition, Melbourne. T* **120** *and similar horiz designs showing ships. Multicoloured. W* w **14** (*sideways*). *P* 14.

390	25 v. Type **120**	70	50
391	45 v. *Rockton*	1·10	90
392	100 v. *Waroonga*	2·00	2·75
390/2	.. .. *Set of* 3	3·50	3·75
MS393	140 × 70 mm. Nos. 390/2 ..	3·50	3·75

5

121 Father Christmas in Children's Ward

(122)

(Des D. Slater. Litho Questa)

1984 (19 Nov). *Christmas. T* **121** *and similar horiz designs. Multicoloured. W* w **14** (*sideways*). *P* 14.

394	25 v. Type **121**	40	40
395	45 v. Nativity play	70	70
396	75 v. Father Christmas distributing presents	1·25	1·25
394/6	.. .. *Set of* 3	2·10	2·10

1985 (16 Jan). *No.* **331** *surch with T* **122**.

397	5 v. on 1 v. Type **109**	40	40

PRICES OF SETS

Set prices are given for many issues, generally those containing three stamps or more. Definitive sets include one of each value or major colour change, but do not cover different perforations, die types or minor shades. Where a choice is possible the set prices are based on the cheapest versions of the stamps included in the listings.

123 Ambrym Island Ceremonial Dance

124 Peregrine Falcon diving

(Des D. Slater. Litho Questa)

1985 (22 Jan). *Traditional Costumes. T* **123** *and similar vert designs. Multicoloured.* W w **14**. *P* 14.

398	20 v. Type **123**	..	..	30	35
399	25 v. Pentecost Island marriage ceremony	..	..	35	40
400	45 v. Women's grade ceremony, South West Malakula			65	70
401	75 v. Ceremonial dance, South West Malakula			1·10	1·25
398/401	..	..	*Set of* 4	2·10	2·40

(Des N. Arlott. Litho Questa)

1985 (26 Mar). *Birth Bicentenary of John J. Audubon (ornithologist). Peregrine Falcon. T* **124** *and similar vert designs. Multicoloured.* W w **14**. *P* 14.

402	20 v. Type **124**	..	..	60	35
403	35 v. Peregrine Falcon in flight	..	..	75	50
404	45 v. Peregrine Falcon perched on branch	..		90	80
405	100 v. "Peregrine Falcon" (John J. Audubon)	..	..	1·60	1·75
402/5	..	..	*Set of* 4	3·50	3·00

125 The Queen Mother on her 80th Birthday

126 *Mala* (patrol boat)

(Des A. Theobald (100 v.), C. Abbott (others). Litho Questa)

1985 (7 June). *Life and Times of Queen Elizabeth the Queen Mother. T* **125** *and similar vert designs. Multicoloured.* W w **16**. *P* 14½×14.

406	5 v. Duke and Duchess of York on wedding day, 1923	..	..	10	10
407	20 v. Type **125**	..	..	35	35
408	35 v. At Ancona, Italy	..	..	55	50
409	55 v. With Prince Henry at his christening (from photo by Lord Snowdon)	..		85	80
406/9	..	..	*Set of* 4	1·60	1·50
MS410	91×73 mm. 100 v. At Royal Opera House, Covent Garden. Wmk sideways	..		1·40	1·50

(Des A. Theobald. Litho Format)

1985 (26 July). *5th Anniv of Independence and "Expo '85" World Fair, Japan. T* **126** *and similar horiz designs. Multicoloured.* W w **16** *(sideways). P* 14.

411	35 v. Type **126**	..	..	45	50
412	45 v. Japanese fishing fleet	..	..	65	70
413	55 v. Vanuatu Mobile Force Band	..	..	75	80
414	100 v. Prime Minister Fr. Walter H. Lini	..		1·40	1·50
411/14	..	..	*Set of* 4	3·00	3·25
MS415	116×102 mm. Nos. 411/14	..	..	3·25	3·75

127 "Youth Activities" (Alain Lagaliu)

(Des D. Miller. Litho Questa)

1985 (16 Sept). *International Youth Year. Children's Paintings. T* **127** *and similar horiz designs. Multicoloured.* W w **14** *(sideways). P* 14.

416	20 v. Type **127**	..	..	40	35
417	30 v. "Village" (Peter Obed)	..	..	50	45
418	50 v. "Beach and "PEACE" Slogan" (Mary Estelle)	..		85	75
419	100 v. "Youth Activities" (*different*) (Abel Merani)	..		1·50	1·50
416/19	..	..	*Set of* 4	3·00	2·75

NEW INFORMATION

The editor is always interested to correspond with people who have new information that will improve or correct the Catalogue.

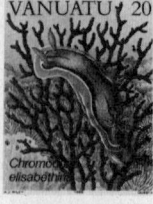

128 Map of Vanuatu with National and U.N. Flags

129 *Chromodoris elisabethina*

(Des D. Hartley. Litho Questa)

1985 (24 Oct). *4th Anniv of United Nations Membership.* W w **14** *(sideways). P* 14.

420	**128** 45 v. multicoloured	..	..	70	70

(Des A. Riley. Litho Questa)

1985 (11 Nov). *Marine Life (1st series). Sea Slugs. T* **129** *and similar multicoloured designs.* W w **14** *(sideways on* 35, 55 *v.). P* 14½×14 (20, 100 *v.) or* 14×14½ *(others).*

421	20 v. Type **129**	..	..	30	35
422	35 v. *Halgerda aurantiomaculata* (*horiz*)	..	45	50
423	55 v. *Chromodoris kuniei* (*horiz*)	..	75	80
424	100 v. *Notodoris minor*	..	..	1·40	1·50
421/4	..	..	*Set of* 4	2·50	2·75

See also Nos. 442/5 and 519/22.

130 Scuba Diving

131 Liner S.S. *President Coolidge* leaving San Francisco

(Des O. Bell. Litho Walsall)

1986 (22 Jan). *Tourism. T* **130** *and similar vert designs. Multicoloured.* W w **16**. *P* 14.

425	30 v. Type **130**	..	..	70	40
426	35 v. Yasur volcano, Tanna	..	1·00	45
427	55 v. Land diving, Pentecost Island	..	1·00	70
428	100 v. Windsurfing	..	..	1·40	1·25
425/8	..	..	*Set of* 4	3·75	2·50

For miniature sheet containing Nos. 427/8 with additional Australian Bicentenary symbol see No. **MS**501.

(Des A. Theobald. Litho Format)

1986 (21 Apr). *60th Birthday of Queen Elizabeth II. Vert designs as T* **230***a of Jamaica. Multicoloured.* W w **16**. *P* 14×14½.

429	20 v. With Prince Charles and Princess Anne, 1951	..		25	30
430	35 v. Prince William's Christening, 1982	..	40	45
431	45 v. In New Hebrides, 1974	..	..	55	60
432	55 v. On board Royal Yacht *Britannia*, Mexico, 1974	..		65	70
433	100 v. At Crown Agents Head Office, London, 1983	..		1·10	1·25
429/33	..	..	*Set of* 5	2·75	3·00

(Des L. Curtis. Litho Walsall)

1986 (19 May). *"Ameripex '86" International Stamp Exhibition, Chicago. Sinking of S.S. President Coolidge. T* **131** *and similar horiz designs. Multicoloured.* W w **16** *(sideways). P* 14.

434	45 v. Type **131**	..	..	65	60
435	55 v. S.S. *President Coolidge* as troopship, 1942	..		75	70
436	135 v. Map of Espiritu Santo showing site of sinking, 1942	..		1·60	1·60
434/6	..	..	*Set of* 3	2·75	2·50
MS437	80×105 mm. Nos. 434/6	..	..	4·00	3·00

132 Halley's Comet and Vanuatu Statue

(Des Jennifer Toombs. Litho Questa)

1986 (23 June). *Appearance of Halley's Comet. T* **132** *and similar horiz designs. Multicoloured.* W w **16** *(sideways). P* 14½.

438	30 v. Type **132**	..	..	90	50
439	45 v. Family watching Comet	..	1·25	1·00
440	55 v. Comet passing Earth	..	1·40	1·25
441	100 v. Edmond Halley	..	..	2·00	2·50
438/41	..	..	*Set of* 4	5·00	4·75

---

133 Daisy Coral

(Des I. Loe. Litho Walsall)

1986 (27 Oct). *Marine Life (2nd series). Corals. T* **133** *and similar horiz designs. Multicoloured.* W w **16** *(sideways). P* 14.

442	20 v. Type **133**	..	..	50	30
443	45 v. Organ Pipe Coral	..	..	80	70
444	55 v. Sea Fan	..	..	90	90
445	135 v. Soft Coral	..	..	2·00	2·50
442/5	..	..	*Set of* 4	3·75	4·00

134 Children of Different Races

135 Datsun "240Z" (1969)

(Des C. Austin. Litho Harrison)

1986 (3 Nov). *Christmas. International Peace Year. T* **134** *and similar horiz designs. Multicoloured.* W w **14** *(sideways). P* 14.

446	30 v. Type **134**	..	..	80	50
447	45 v. Church and boy praying	..	1·10	85
448	55 v. U.N. discussion and Headquarters Building, New York	..		1·25	1·25
449	135 v. People of different races at work	..	2·50	3·50
446/9	..	..	*Set of* 4	5·00	5·50

(Des J.W. Litho Questa)

1987 (22 Jan). *Motor Vehicles. T* **135** *and similar horiz designs. Multicoloured.* W w **14** *(sideways). P* 14.

450	20 v. Type **135**	..	..	30	30
451	45 v. Ford "Model A" (1927)	..	..	60	60
452	55 v. Unic lorry (1924–5)	..	..	70	70
453	135 v. Citroen "DS19" (1975)	..	..	1·60	1·90
450/3	..	..	*Set of* 4	3·00	3·25

Hurricane Relief Fund

+10

(136)

137 Young Coconut Plants

1987 (12 May). *Hurricane Relief Fund. No. 332, already surch as T* **122**, *and Nos. 429/33, all surch as T* **136**.

454	20 v. + 10 v. on 2 v. *Calanthe triplicata*	..	35	40
455	20 v. + 10 v. Princess Elizabeth with Prince Charles and Princess Anne, 1951	..	35	40
456	35 v. + 15 v. Prince William's Christening, 1982	..		60	70
457	45 v. + 20 v. Queen in New Hebrides, 1974	..	75	90
458	55 v. + 25 v. Queen on board Royal Yacht *Britannia*, Mexico, 1974	..	95	1·10
459	100 v. + 50 v. Queen at Crown Agents Head Office, London, 1983	..	1·75	2·00
454/9	..	..	*Set of* 6	4·25	5·00

The surcharge as T **136** on No. 454 includes the word "Surcharge" in addition to the inscription illustrated.

(Des R. Corringe. Litho Format)

1987 (13 May). *25th Anniv of I.R.H.O. Coconut Research Station. T* **137** *and similar horiz designs. Multicoloured.* W w **16** *(sideways). P* 14.

460	35 v. Type **137**	..	..	40	45
461	45 v. Coconut flower and fronds	..	55	60
462	100 v. Coconuts	..	..	1·10	1·25
463	135 v. Research Station	..	..	1·60	1·75
460/3	..	..	*Set of* 4	3·25	3·75

The inscriptions on Nos. 462/3 are in French.

138 Spotted Hawkfish

139 *Xylotrupes gideon* (beetle)

(Des N. Harvey. Litho Questa)

1987 (15 July). *Fishes. T* **138** *and similar horiz designs. Multicoloured.* W w **16** *(sideways). P* 14×14½.

464	1 v. Type **138**	..	..	10	10
465	5 v. Moorish Idol	..	..	10	10
466	10 v. Black-saddled Puffer	..	..	10	15
467	15 v. Anemone Fish	..	..	15	20
468	20 v. Striped Surgeon	..	..	20	25
469	30 v. Six-barred Wrasse	..	..	30	35
470	35 v. Purple Queenfish	..	..	35	40
471	40 v. Long-jawed Squirrelfish	..	..	40	45

472	45 v. Clown Triggerfish	..	..	45	50
473	50 v. Scribed Wrasse	..	..	50	55
474	55 v. Regal Angelfish	..	..	55	60
475	65 v. Lionfish	..	..	65	70
476	100 v. Fosters Hawkfish	..	..	1·00	1·10
477	300 v. Vermiculated Triggerfish	..	..	3·00	3·25
478	500 v. Saddled Butterfly Fish	..	..	5·00	5·25
464/78	.. ..		*Set of 15*	11·50	12·50

(Des I. Loe. Litho Questa)

1987 (22 Sept). *Insects. T* **139** *and similar horiz designs. Multicoloured. W w* **16** *(sideways). P* 14.

479	45 v. Type **139**			55	60
480	55 v. *Phyllodes imperialis* (moth)	..		65	70
481	75 v. *Cyphogastra* sp (beetle)	..		75	80
482	100 v. *Othreis fullonia* (moth)	..		1·10	1·25
479/82	.. ..		*Set of 4*	2·75	3·00

140 Away in a Manger"   **141** Dugong Cow and Calf

(Des Josephine Martin. Litho Security Printers (M), Malaysia)

1987 (10 Nov). *Christmas. Christmas Carols. T* **140** *and similar vert designs. Multicoloured. W w* **14**. *P* 13½ × 14.

483	20 v. Type **140**..			25	30
484	45 v. "Once in Royal David's City"			55	60
485	55 v. "While Shepherds watched their Flocks"			65	70
486	65 v. "We Three Kings of Orient Are"	..		75	80
483/6	.. ..,		*Set of 4*	2·00	2·10

1987 (9 Dec). *Royal Ruby Wedding. Nos. 429/33 optd with T* **45***a of Kiribati in silver.*

487	20 v. Princess Elizabeth with Prince Charles and Princess Anne, 1951			25	30
488	35 v. Prince William's Christening, 1982..			40	45
489	45 v. Queen in New Hebrides, 1974			55	60
490	55 v. Queen on board Royal Yacht *Britannia*, Mexico, 1974			65	70
491	100 v. Queen at Crown Agents Head Office, London, 1983	..		1·10	1·25
487/91	.. .. ..		*Set of 5*	2·75	3·00

(Des Doreen McGuinness. Litho Walsall)

1988 (29 Feb). *Dugong. T* **141** *and similar horiz designs. Multicoloured. W w* **16** *(sideways). P* 13 × 13½.

492	5 v. Type **141**..			40	20
493	10 v. Dugong underwater			60	20
494	20 v. Two dugons surfacing to breathe	..		90	65
495	45 v. Four dugongs swimming	..		1·50	1·75
492/5	.. .. ..		*Set of 4*	3·00	2·50

142 S.S. *Tambo*   **143** Captain James Cook

(Des E. Nisbet. Litho Security Printers (M), Malaysia)

1988 (18 May). *Bicentenary of Australian Settlement. Ships. T* **142** *and similar horiz designs. Multicoloured. W w* **14** *(sideways). P* 12.

496	20 v. Type **142**			20	25
497	45 v. S.S. *Induna* ..			50	55
498	55 v. S.S. *Morinda*			60	65
499	65 v. S.S. *Marsina*			70	75
496/9	.. ..		*Set of 4*	1·75	2·00

(Des A. Theobald. Litho Format)

1988 (29 July). *"Sydpex '88" National Stamp Exhibition, Sydney. W w* **16**. *P* 14.

500 **143** 45 v. black and rosine   ..   75   75
No. 500 was printed in small sheets of 10 (5 × 2), the two strips separated by a horizontal gutter of five illustrated stamp-size labels. The outer edges of the sheet are imperforate so that the stamps have one or two adjacent sides imperforate.

(Des O. Bell, adapted D. Miller. Litho Walsall)

1988 (24 Aug). *"Expo '88" World Fair, Brisbane. Sheet* 100 × 80 *mm. containing designs as Nos.* 427/8, *but with addition of Australian Bicentenary symbol and imprint date. Multicoloured. W w* **14**. *P* 14.

MS501   55 v. Land diving, Pentecost Island; 100 v. Windsurfing   ..   ..   ..   2·25   1·90

ALTERED CATALOGUE NUMBERS

Any Catalogue numbers altered from the last edition are shown as a list in the introductory pages.

144 Boxer in training   **145** Agricultural Crops

(Des S. Noon. Litho Security Printers (M), Malaysia)

1988 (19 Sept). *Olympic Games, Seoul. T* **144** *and similar vert designs. Multicoloured. W w* **14**. *P* 13½ × 14.

502	20 v. Type **144**	..		20	25
503	45 v. Athletics			50	55
504	55 v. Signing Olympic agreement			60	65
505	65 v. Soccer			70	75
502/5			*Set of 4*	1·75	2·00
MS506	54 × 66 mm. 150 v. Tennis. P 13½			1·75	1·90

(Des O. Bell and D. Miller (55, 65 v.), D. Miller (20, 145 v.). Litho Questa)

1988 (25 Oct). *300th Anniv of Lloyd's of London. Multicoloured designs as T* **167***a of Malawi. W w* **16** *(sideways on* 55, 65 *v.). P* 14.

507	20 v. Interior of new Lloyd's Building, 1988		30	25
508	55 v. *Shirrabank* (freighter) *(horiz)*		75	65
509	65 v. *Adela* (ferry) *(horiz)* ..		85	75
510	145 v. *General Slocum* (excursion steamer) on fire, New York, 1904		2·00	1·75
507/10	.. ..	*Set of 4*	3·50	3·00

(Des A. Edmonston. Litho Format)

1988 (14 Nov). *Food and Agriculture Organization. T* **145** *and similar multicoloured designs. W w* **16** *(sideways on* 45, 120 *v.). P* 14½ × 14 *(horiz) or* 14 × 14½ *(vert).*

511	45 v. Type **145**			50	55
512	55 v. Fisherman with catch *(vert)* ..		60	65
513	65 v. Livestock on smallholding *(vert)*		70	75
514	120 v. Market women with produce		1·25	1·40
511/14	.. .. ..	*Set of 4*	2·75	3·00

146 Virgin and Child ("Silent Night")   **147** *Periclimenes brevicarpalis*

(Des Josephine Martin. Litho Format)

1988 (1 Dec). *Christmas. Carols. T* **146** *and similar horiz designs. Multicoloured. W w* **16** *(sideways). P* 14½ × 14.

515	20 v. Type **146**			20	25
516	45 v. Angels ("Angels from the Realms of Glory")			50	55
517	65 v. Shepherd boy with lamb ("O Come all ye Faithful")			70	75
518	155 v. Baby ("In that Poor Stable how Charming Jesus Lies")			1·75	1·90
515/18	.. .. ..		*Set of 4*	2·75	3·00

(Des A. Riley. Litho Questa)

1989 (1 Feb). *Marine Life (3rd series). Shrimps. T* **147** *and similar horiz designs. Multicoloured. W w* **16** *(sideways). P* 14.

519	20 v. Type **147**	..		20	25
520	45 v. *Lysmata grabhami*			50	55
521	65 v. *Rhynchocinetes* sp			70	75
522	150 v. *Stenopus hispidus*			1·75	1·90
519/22	.. ..		*Set of 4*	2·75	3·00

148 Consolidated "Catalina" Flying Boat   **149** Porte de Versailles Hall No. 1

(Des A. Theobald. Litho Security Printers (M), Malaysia)

1989 (5 Apr). *Economic and Social Commission for Asia and the Pacific. Aircraft. T* **148** *and similar horiz designs. W w* **14** *(sideways). P* 12.

523	20 v. black and cobalt	..		30	30
524	45 v. black and turquoise-green	..		65	65
525	55 v. black and orange-yellow			80	80
526	200 v. black and orange-red			2·75	3·00
523/6	..		*Set of 4*	4·00	4·25

Designs:—45 v. Douglas "DC-3"; 55 v. Embraer "EMB110 Bandeirante"; 200 v. Boeing "737-300".

(Des O. Bell (Nos. 527/8), D. Miller (No. **MS529**). Litho Security Printers, Malaysia (Nos. 527/8), B.D.T. (No. **MS529**))

1989 (5 July). *"Philexfrance '89" International Stamp Exhibition, Paris. T* **149** *and similar horiz designs. W w* **14**. *P* 12.

527	**149**	100 v. multicoloured		1·75	1·40
		a. Horiz pair. Nos. 527/8		3·50	2·75
528	–	100 v. multicoloured (Eiffel Tower)		1·75	1·40
MS529		115×101 mm. 100 v. black, grey and scarlet (Revolt of French troops, Nancy, 1790 (42×28 *mm*)). W w **16** (sideways). P 14		1·40	1·50

Nos. 527/8 were printed together, *se-tenant*, in horizontal pairs throughout the sheet, each pair forming a composite design.

(Des A. Theobald (100 v.), D. Miller (others). Litho Questa)

1989 (20 July). *20th Anniv of First Manned Landing on Moon. Multicoloured designs as T* **51***a of Kiribati. W w* **16** *(sideways on* 55, 65 *v.). P* 14×13½ (45, 120 *v.) or* 14 *(others).*

530	45 v. Command module seen from lunar module			70	70
531	55 v. Crew of "Apollo 17" (30×30 *mm*)			80	80
532	65 v. "Apollo 17" emblem (30×30 *mm*)			90	90
533	120 v. Launch of "Apollo 17"			1·60	1·60
530/3			*Set of 4*	3·50	3·50
MS534	99×82 mm. 100 v. Recovery of "Apollo 11". Wmk inverted. P 14×13½			1·40	1·50

(150)   **151** New Hebrides 1978 "Concorde" 30 f. (French inscr) Stamp

1989 (18 Oct). *"Melbourne Stampshow '89". No. 332 surch with T* **150**.

535   100 v. on 2 v. *Calanthe triplicata*   ..   .. 2·00   2·00

(Des A. Theobald. Litho Leigh-Mardon Ltd, Melbourne)

1989 (6 Nov). *"World Stamp Expo '89", International Stamp Exhibition, Washington. T* **151** *and similar horiz designs. Multicoloured. W w* **16** *(inverted). P* 13½.

536	65 v. Type **151**			90	90
MS537	105×100 mm. 65 v. New Hebrides 1978 "Concorde" 10 f. (English inscr) stamp; 100 v. White House, Washington			4·50	4·75

152 *Alocasia macrorrhiza*   **153** Kava (National plant)

(Des Jennifer Toombs. Litho Security Printers (M), Malaysia)

1990 (5 Jan). *Flora. T* **152** *and similar vert designs. Multicoloured. W w* **14**. *P* 12.

538	45 v. Type **152**			65	65
539	55 v. *Acacia spirorbis*			75	75
540	65 v. *Metrosideros collina*			85	85
541	145 v. *Hoya australis*			2·00	2·25
538/41			*Set of 4*	3·75	4·00

(Des O. Bell. Litho Security Printers (M), Malaysia)

1990 (30 Apr). *"Stamp World London 90" International Stamp Exhibition. T* **153** *and similar vert designs. Multicoloured. W w* **14** *(sideways). P* 13½.

542	45 v. Type **153**			85	75
543	65 v. Luganville Post Office			1·25	1·00
544	100 v. Mail plane and sailing packet			2·00	2·00
545	200 v. Penny Black and Vanuatu 1980 10 f. definitive			3·25	3·50
542/5			*Set of 4*	6·50	6·50
MS546	110×70 mm. 150 v. New Hebrides 1974 New Post Office *tête-bêche* pair with first day postmark. Wmk upright			4·50	5·00

1990   VANUATU   25

154 National Council of Women Logo

(Des D. Ashby. Litho Security Printers (M), Malaysia)

1990 (30 July). *10th Anniv of Independence. T* **154** *and similar horiz designs. W w* **14** *(sideways). P* 14×13½.
547	25 v. black and pale blue	.. ..	40	40
548	50 v. multicoloured	.. ..	75	75
549	55 v. bright purple, black and buff		75	75
550	65 v. multicoloured	.. ..	90	90
551	80 v. multicoloured	.. ..	1·40	1·40
547/51		*Set of 5*	3·75	3·75

MS552 109×82 mm. 150 v. multicoloured. Wmk upright.. .. .. .. 4·25 4·50
Designs:—50 v. President Frederick Kalomuana Timakata; 55 v. Preamble to the Constitution; 65 v. Vanuaaku Pati party flag; 80 v. Reserve Bank of Vanuatu; 150 v. Prime Minister Fr. Walter Lini taking oath.
No. **MS**552 also commemorates the South Pacific Forum, Port Vila, 1990.

155 General De Gaulle at Bayeux, 1944 **156** Angel facing Right

(Des G. Vasarhelyi. Litho B.D.T)

1990 (22 Nov). *Birth Centenary of General Charles de Gaulle (French statesman). T* **155** *and similar horiz designs. Multicoloured. W w* **14** *(sideways). P* 14.
553	20 v. Type **155**	.. ..	80	80
	a. Sheetlet. Nos. 553/4, and 555/8 each × 2		8·50	
554	25 v. Generals De Lattre de Tassigny, De Gaulle, Devers and Patch in Alsace, 1945		80	80
555	30 v. De Gaulle as President of the French Republic		75	75
556	45 v. De Gaulle at Biggin Hill, 1942		90	90
557	55 v. Roosevelt, De Gaulle and Churchill, Casablanca, 1943		1·00	1·00
558	65 v. General De Gaulle and Liberation of Paris, 1944		1·00	1·00
553/8		*Set of 6*	4·75	4·75

Nos. 553/8 were printed together, *se-tenant,* in sheetlets of 12 (4×3) containing one each of the 20 c. and 25 c. values and two each of the others plus two labels, showing the Cross of Lorraine, at each end of the centre row.

(Des Jennifer Toombs. Litho Cartor, France)

1990 (5 Dec). *Christmas. T* **156** *and similar vert designs. Multicoloured. W w* **14** *(sideways). P* 13.
559	25 v. Type **156**	.. ..	45	55
	a. Horiz strip of 5. Nos. 559/63		3·50	
560	50 v. Shepherds	.. ..	75	85
561	65 v. Nativity	.. ..	85	95
562	70 v. Three Kings	.. ..	90	1·00
563	80 v. Angel facing left	.. ..	1·00	1·00
559/63		*Set of 5*	3·50	4·00

Nos. 559/63 were printed together, *se-tenant,* in horizontal strips of 5 throughout the sheet, forming a composite design.

157 *Parthenos sylvia* **158** Dance Troupe from South-west Malakula

(Des I. Loe. Litho Questa)

1991 (9 Jan). *Butterflies. T* **157** *and similar horiz designs. Multicoloured. W w* **16**. *P* 14×14½.
564	25 v. Type **157**	.. ..	40	30
565	55 v. *Euploea leucostictus*	.. ..	80	60
566	80 v. *Lampides boeticus*	.. ..	1·10	1·25
567	150 v. *Danaus plexippus*	.. ..	2·40	2·75
564/7		*Set of 4*	4·25	4·50

Nos. 564/7 were each printed in sheets of 10 with the two horizontal rows of five being separated by a row of labels illustrating the butterfly's life cycle.

(Des Sue Wickison. Litho Cartor)

1991 (2 May). *Second National Art Festival, Luganville. T* **158** *and similar vert designs. Multicoloured. W w* **14.** *P* 13½×14.
568	25 v. Type **158**	.. ..	55	35
569	65 v. Women weavers and baskets		1·25	1·00
570	80 v. Woodcarver and carved animals, masks, dish and ceremonial figures		1·60	1·75
571	150 v. Musicians playing bamboo flute, youtatau and pan pipes		3·00	3·50
568/71		*Set of 4*	5·75	6·00

160 White-collared Kingfisher

20 (159) **20** (159a)

Type **159**. Surch by Mercury-Walch Pty, Hobart. 2½ mm between "20" and bars. Bars 5½ mm long.
Type **159a**. Surch by Southern Colour Print, Dunedin. 2 mm between "20" and bars. Bars 6½ mm long.

1991 (12 June–3 Dec). *Nos. 332/4 and 337 surch as T* **159** *by Mercury-Walch Pty, Hobart.*
572	20 v. on 2 v. *Calanthe triplicata*		20	25
	a. Surch with Type **159a** (3 Dec)		50	25
573	60 v. on 10 v. *Dendrobium sladei*		60	65
574	70 v. on 15 v. *Dendrobium mohlianum*		70	75
575	80 v. on 30 v. *Robiquetia mimus*		80	85
572/5		*Set of 4*	2·10	2·25

(Des D. Miller. Litho Questa)

1991 (17 June). *65th Birthday of Queen Elizabeth II and 70th Birthday of Prince Philip. Vert designs as T* **58** *of Kiribati. Multicoloured. W w* **16** *(sideways). P* 14½×14.
576	65 v. Queen Elizabeth II		1·00	1·00
	a. Horiz pair. Nos. 576/7 separated by label		2·00	2·00
577	70 v. Prince Philip	.. ..	1·00	1·00

Nos. 576/7 were printed in a similar sheet format as Nos. 366/7 of Kiribati.

(Des N. Arlott. Litho Questa)

1991 (15 Nov). *"Phila Nippon '91" International Stamp Exhibition, Tokyo. Birds. T* **160** *and similar vert designs. Multicoloured. W w* **14.** *P* 14½×14.
578	50 v. Type **160**	.. ..	75	75
579	55 v. Palm Lorikeet	.. ..	80	80
580	80 v. Scarlet Robin	.. ..	1·25	1·25
581	100 v. Pacific Swallow	.. ..	1·40	1·40
578/81		*Set of 4*	3·75	3·75

MS582 75×56 mm. 150 v. Eastern Reef Heron 2·25 2·50

161 Group of Islanders

(Des C. Bulewal and Sue Wickison (80 v.), Sue Wickison (others). Litho Questa)

1991 (29 Nov). *World AIDS Day. T* **161** *and similar horiz designs. Multicoloured. W w* **16** *(sideways). P* 14.
583	25 v. Type **161**	.. ..	40	30
584	65 v. Caring for AIDS victim		85	85
585	80 v. AIDS Shark	.. ..	1·25	1·25
586	150 v. Children's playground		2·50	2·75
583/6		*Set of 4*	4·50	4·75

(Des D. Miller. Litho Questa (70 v.), Leigh-Mardon Ltd, Melbourne (others))

1992 (6 Feb). *40th Anniv of Queen Elizabeth II's Accession. Horiz designs as T* **113** *of Kenya. Multicoloured. W w* **14** *(sideways) (70 v.) or w* **16** *(sideways) (others). P* 14.
587	20 v. Reserve Bank of Vanuatu building, Port Vila		35	30
588	25 v. Port Vila	.. ..	40	40
589	60 v. Mural, Parliament House		85	85
590	65 v. Three portraits of Queen Elizabeth		90	90
591	70 v. Queen Elizabeth II	.. ..	1·25	1·40
587/91		*Set of 5*	3·25	3·50

162 Grumman F4F-4 Wildcat **163** Meteorological Station, Port Vila

(Des E. Nisbet. Litho Enschedé)

1992 (22 May). *50th Anniv of Outbreak of the Pacific War. T* **162** *and similar horiz designs. Multicoloured. W w* **14** *(sideways). P* 13½×14.
592	50 v. Type **162**	.. ..	90	90
593	60 v. Douglas SBD-3 Dauntless		1·00	1·00
594	65 v. Consolidated PBY-5A Catalina		1·25	1·25
595	80 v. U.S.S. *Hornet* (aircraft carrier)		1·40	1·40
592/5		*Set of 4*	4·00	4·00

MS596 94×62 mm. 200 v. Vought-Sikorsky OS2U-3 Kingfisher over Port Vila .. 3·25 3·50

(Des Sue Wickison. Litho Leigh-Mardon Ltd, Melbourne)

1992 (20 June). *10th Anniv of Vanuatu's Membership of World Meteorological Organization. T* **163** *and similar horiz designs. Multicoloured. W w* **14.** *P* 14.
597	25 v. Type **163**	.. ..	45	35
598	60 v. Satellite picture of tropical cyclone		95	85
599	80 v. Weather chart of Pacific showing cyclone		1·25	1·25
600	105 v. Radio Vanuatu broadcasting cyclone warning		1·60	1·75
597/600		*Set of 4*	3·75	3·75

164 Vanuatu National Football Team **165** Breast-feeding

(Des S. Noon. Litho Questa)

1992 (20 July). *Vanuatu's Participation in Melanesian Football Cup and Olympic Games, Barcelona. T* **164** *and similar horiz designs. Multicoloured. W w* **14** *(sideways). P* 13½×14.
601	20 v. Type **164**	.. ..	35	25
602	65 v. Melanesian Cup Final, 1990		95	85
603	70 v. Baptiste Firiam (800 metres)		1·10	1·10
604	80 v. Mary Estelle Kapalu (400, 400 hurdles and 800 metres)		1·25	1·50
601/4		*Set of 4*	3·25	3·25

(Des Sue Wickison. Litho B.D.T.)

1992 (16 Oct). *World Food Day. T* **165** *and similar vert designs. Each reddish brown and bronze-green. W w* **16.** *P* 14×13½.
605	20 v. Type **165**	.. ..	30	25
606	70 v. Central Hospital, Port Vila		90	90
607	80 v. Children eating	.. ..	1·10	1·10
608	150 v. Nutritious food	.. ..	2·25	2·50
605/8		*Set of 4*	4·00	4·25

166 Leatherback Turtle **167** *Hibiscus rosa-sinensis* "Agnes Goult"

(Des Sue Wickison. Litho Questa)

1992 (15 Dec). *Turtles. T* **166** *and similar horiz designs. Multicoloured. W w* **16** *(sideways). P* 14×14½.
609	55 v. Type **166**	.. ..	80	80
610	65 v. Loggerhead Turtle laying eggs		90	90
611	70 v. Hawksbill Turtle swimming		1·00	1·00
612	80 v. Green Turtle under water		1·25	1·25
609/12		*Set of 4*	3·50	3·50

MS613 81×96 mm. 200 v. Green Turtle hatchlings on beach. Wmk upright .. 3·50 3·75

(Des Jennifer Toombs. Litho Questa)

1993 (3 Mar). *Hibiscus Flowers. T* **167** *and similar vert designs. Multicoloured. W w* **16.** *P* 14.
614	25 v. Type **167**	.. ..	25	30
615	55 v. *Hibiscus tiliaceus*	.. ..	55	60
616	80 v. *Hibiscus rosa-sinensis linnaeus*		80	85
617	150 v. *Hibiscus rosa-sinensis* "Rose of China"		1·50	1·60
614/17		*Set of 4*	2·75	3·00

Victoria
see Australia

Virgin Islands
see British Virgin Islands

Western Australia
see Australia

Western Samoa
see Samoa

Zambia
(*formerly* Northern Rhodesia)

NORTHERN RHODESIA

The north-eastern and north-western provinces of Rhodesia, previously administered by the British South Africa Company, were annexed by the British Government on 12 September 1923.

PRICES FOR STAMPS ON COVER TO 1945	
Nos. 1/21	*from* × 2
Nos. 22/4	*from* × 5
Nos. 25/45	*from* × 2
Nos. D1/4	*from* × 15

1   2

(Eng W. G. Fairweather. Recess Waterlow)

1925 (1 April)–**29**. *Wmk Mult Script CA. P* 12½.
1	1	½d. green		50	20
2		1d. brown		50	10
3		1½d. carmine-red		50	30
4		2d. yellow-brown		65	10
5		3d. ultramarine		75	40
6		4d. violet		1·25	40
7		6d. slate-grey		1·00	40
8		8d. rose-purple		3·75	17·00
9		10d. olive-green		3·75	15·00
10	2	1s. yellow-brown and black		1·00	75
11		2s. brown and ultramarine		5·50	12·00
12		2s. 6d. black and green		6·50	4·75
13		3s. violet and blue (1929)		16·00	9·50
14		5s. slate-grey and violet		13·00	10·00
15		7s. 6d. rose-purple and black		85·00	£120
16		10s. green and black		42·00	50·00
17		20s. carmine-red and rose-purple		£150	£160
1/17			*Set of* 17	£300	£350
1/17 Optd/Perf "Specimen"			*Set of* 17	£750	

A used example of the 4d. exists imperforate between the stamp and a fragment of another below it.

1935 (6 May). *Silver Jubilee. As Nos.* 114/17 *of Jamaica, but ptd by D.L.R. P* 13½×14.
18		1d. light blue and olive-green		50	20
		f. Diagonal line by turret		32·00	
		h. Dot by flagstaff		35·00	
		i. Dash by turret		35·00	
19		2d. green and indigo		50	50
		f. Diagonal line by turret		42·00	
		g. Dot to left of chapel		42·00	
20		3d. brown and deep blue		2·50	3·00
		g. Dot to left of chapel		75·00	
21		6d. slate and purple		2·00	1·00
		a. Frame printed double, one albino		£1500	
		h. Dot by flagstaff		75·00	
18/21			*Set of* 4	5·00	4·25
18/21 Perf "Specimen"			*Set of* 4	80·00	

For illustrations of plate varieties see Omnibus section following Zimbabwe.

THERN_RHODE

Hyphen between
"NORTHERN" AND "RHODESIA"
(R. 9/6)

1937 (12 May). *Coronation. As Nos.* 118/20 *of Jamaica, but ptd by B.W. P* 11×11½.
22		1½d. carmine		40	35
23		2d. buff		70	35
24		3d. blue		1·25	1·75
		a. Hyphen flaw		65·00	
22/4			*Set of* 3	2·10	2·25
22/4 Perf "Specimen"			*Set of* 3	60·00	

3   4

"Tick bird" flaw
(R. 7/1)

(Recess Waterlow)

1938 (1 Mar)–**52**. *Wmk Mult Script CA. P* 12½.
25	3	½d. green		10	10
26		½d. chocolate (15.11.51)		10	70
		a. Perf 12½ × 14 (22.10.52)		1·25	3·50
27		1d. brown		10	10
		a. Chocolate (1948)		75	60
28		1d. green (15.11.51)		60	60
29		1½d. carmine-red		30·00	25
		a. Imperf between (horiz pair)		£9500	
		b. "Tick bird" flaw		£800	35·00
30		1½d. yellow-brown (10.1.41)		10	10
		b. "Tick bird" flaw		27·00	12·00
31		2d. yellow-brown		65·00	85
32		2d. carmine-red (10.1.41)		30	20
33		2d. purple (1.12.51)		45	30
34		3d. ultramarine		30	10
35		3d. scarlet (1.12.51)		50	50
36		4d. dull violet		30	20
37		4½d. blue (5.5.52)		40	2·75
38		6d. grey		30	10
39		9d. violet (5.5.52)		40	2·00
40	4	1s. yellow-brown and black		1·00	20
41		2s. 6d. black and green		5·50	1·50
42		3s. violet and blue		10·00	4·00
43		5s. grey and dull violet		7·00	3·25
44		10s. green and black		6·00	10·00
45		20s. carmine-red and rose-purple		26·00	40·00
25/45			*Set of* 21	£140	60·00
25/45 Perf "Specimen"			*Set of* 15	£275	

Nos. 26a and 28 exist in coils, constructed from normal sheets.

1946 (26 Nov). *Victory. As Nos.* 141/2 *of Jamaica. P* 13½×14.
46		1½d. red-orange		10	10
		a. Perf 14 × 13½		2·00	2·25
47		2d. carmine		10	10
46/7 Perf "Specimen"			*Set of* 2	48·00	

1948 (1 Dec). *Royal Silver Wedding. As Nos.* 143/4 *of Jamaica, but* 20s. *ptd in recess.*
48		1½d. orange		30	10
49		20s. brown-lake		38·00	40·00

1949 (10 Oct). *75th Anniv of U.P.U. As Nos.* 145/8 *of Jamaica.*
50		2d. carmine		30	30
51		3d. deep blue		85	1·25
52		6d. grey		85	1·25
53		1s. red-orange		85	1·00
50/3			*Set of* 4	2·50	3·50

5 Cecil Rhodes and Victoria Falls

(Recess D.L.R.)

1953 (30 May). *Birth Centenary of Cecil Rhodes. Wmk Mult Script CA. P* 12 × 11½.
54	5	½d. brown		40	40
55		1d. green		40	40
56		2d. mauve		40	15
57		4½d. blue		40	3·25
58		1s. orange and black		65	2·50
54/8			*Set of* 5	2·00	6·00

6 Arms of the Rhodesias and Nyasaland

(Recess Waterlow)

1953 (30 May). *Rhodes Centenary Exhibition. Wmk Mult Script CA. P* 14 × 13½.
59	6	6d. violet		30	40

1953 (2 June). *Coronation. As No.* 153 *of Jamaica.*
60		1½d. black and yellow-orange		30	10

7   8

(Recess Waterlow)

1953 (15 Sept). *Wmk Mult Script CA. P* 12½ × 14 (*pence values*) *or* 12½ × 13½ (*shilling values*).
61	7	½d. deep brown		65	10
62		1d. bluish green		65	10
63		1½d. orange-brown		60	10
64		2d. reddish purple		75	10
65		3d. scarlet		60	10
66		4d. slate-lilac		1·25	50
67		4½d. deep blue		60	1·00
68		6d. grey-black		1·25	10
69		9d. violet		60	90
70	8	1s. orange-brown and black		60	10
71		2s. 6d. black and green		6·00	2·75
72		5s. grey and dull purple		6·50	12·00
73		10s. green and black		6·00	17·00
74		20s. rose-red and rose-purple		18·00	25·00
61/74			*Set of* 14	38·00	55·00

For issues from 1954 to 1963, see RHODESIA AND NYASALAND.

9   Arms   10

(Photo Harrison)

1963 (10 Dec). *Arms black, orange and blue; portrait and inscriptions black; background colours below. P* 14½ (*T* 9) *or* 13½×13 (*T* 10).
75	9	½d. bright violet		30	35
		a. Value omitted		£425	
76		1d. light blue		40	10
		a. Value omitted		7·00	
77		2d. brown		30	10
78		3d. yellow		20	10
		a. Value omitted		65·00	
		b. Value and orange (eagle) omitted		90·00	
		c. Eagle printed double		£375	
79		4d. green		30	10
		a. Value omitted		80·00	
80		6d. light olive-green		30	10
		a. Value omitted		£250	
81		9d. yellow-brown		30	40
		a. Value omitted		£160	
		b. Value and orange (eagle) omitted		£250	
82		1s. slate-purple		30	10
83		1s. 3d. bright purple		80	10
84	10	2s. orange		70	90
85		2s. 6d. lake-brown		80	80
86		5s. magenta		3·00	3·50
		a. Value omitted		£900	
87		10s. mauve		3·00	4·50
88		20s. blue		5·00	14·00
		a. Value omitted		£600	
75/88			*Set of* 14	14·00	22·00

Nos. 75/6 exist in coils, constructed from normal sheets.
A used example of the 3d. has been seen on which only the orange (eagle) has been omitted.

The stamps of Northern Rhodesia were withdrawn on 23 October 1964 when the territory attained independence as the Republic of Zambia.

ZAMBIA

INDEPENDENT

11 Pres. Kaunda   12 College of Further
and Victoria Falls   Education, Lusaka

(Des M. Goaman (3d., 6d.), Mrs. G. Ellison (1s. 3d.). Photo Harrison)

1964 (24 Oct). *Independence. T 11/12 and similar vert design.*
P 13½ × 14½ (6d.) or 14½ × 13½ (others).

91	3d. sepia, yellow-green and blue	10	10
92	6d. deep violet and yellow	15	10
93	1s. 3d. red, black, sepia and orange	20	15
91/3	*Set of 3*	40	30

Design:—1s. 3d. Barotse dancer.

14 Maize-Farmer and Silo 15 Health—Radiographer

21 Fishing at Mpulungu 22 Tobacco Worker

(Des Mrs. G. Ellison. Photo Harrison)

1964 (24 Oct). *T 14/15, 21/2 and similar designs. P 14½ (½d. to 4d.), 14½ × 13½ (1s. 3d., 2s. and £1) or 13½ × 14½ (others).*

94	½d. red, black and yellow-green	10	20
95	1d. brown, black and bright blue	10	10
96	2d. red, deep brown and orange	10	10
97	3d. black and red	10	10
98	4d. black, brown and orange	15	10
99	6d. orange, deep brown & deep bluish green	15	10
100	9d. carmine, black and bright blue	15	10
101	1s. black, yellow-bistre and blue	15	10
102	1s. 3d. light red, yellow, black and blue	20	10
103	2s. bright blue, black, deep brown & orange	25	10
104	2s. 6d. black and orange-yellow	60	35
105	5s. black, yellow and green	1·25	45
106	10s. black and orange	3·25	3·25
107	£1 black, brown, yellow and red	3·25	4·25
94/107	*Set of 14*	8·50	8·00

Designs: *Vert (as T 15)*—2d. Chinyau dancer; 3d. Cotton-picking. *(As T 22)*—2s. Tonga basket-making; £1 Makishi dancer. *Horiz (as T 14)*—4d. Angoni bull. *(As T 21)*—6d. Communications, old and new; 9d. Zambezi sawmills and Redwood flower; 2s. 6d. Luangwa Game Reserve; 5s. Education—student; 10s. Copper mining.
Nos. 94/5 and 97 exist in coils, constructed from normal sheets.

28 I.T.U. Emblem and Symbols 29 I.C.Y. Emblem

(Photo Harrison)

1965 (26 July). *I.T.U. Centenary. P 14 × 14½.*

108	28	6d. light reddish violet and gold	15	10
109		2s. 6d. brownish grey and gold	70	1·25

(Photo Harrison)

1965 (26 July). *International Co-operation Year. P 14½.*

110	29	3d. turquoise and gold	10	10
111		1s. 3d. ultramarine and gold	35	45

30 State House, Lusaka 34 W.H.O. Building and U.N. Flag

(Des Mrs. G. Ellison. Photo Harrison)

1965 (18 Oct). *First Anniv of Independence. T 30 and similar multicoloured designs. No wmk. P 13½ × 14½ (3d.), 14 × 13½ (6d.) or 13½ × 14 (others).*

112	3d. Type 30	10	10
113	6d. Fireworks, Independence Stadium	10	10
	a. Bright purple (fireworks) omitted	50·00	
114	1s. 3d. Clematopsis (*vert*)	10	10
115	2s. 6d. *Tithonia diversifolia* (*vert*)	25	60
112/15	*Set of 4*	40	70

(Des M. Goaman. Photo Harrison)

1966 (18 May). *Inauguration of W.H.O. Headquarters, Geneva. P 14½.*

116	34	3d. lake-brown, gold and new blue	15	10
		a. Gold omitted	70·00	
117		1s. 3d. gold, new blue & deep bluish vio	30	30

35 University Building 36 National Assembly Building

(Des Mrs. G. Ellison. Photo Harrison)

1966 (12 July). *Opening of Zambia University. P 14½.*

118	35	3d. blue-green and copper-bronze	10	10
119		1s. 3d. reddish violet and copper-bronze	10	10

(Des Mrs. G. Ellison. Photo Harrison)

1967 (2 May). *Inauguration of National Assembly Building. P 14½.*

120	36	3d. black and copper-bronze	10	10
121		6d. olive-green and copper-bronze	10	10

37 Airport Scene

(Des Mrs. G. Ellison. Photo Harrison)

1967 (2 Oct). *Opening of Lusaka International Airport. P 13½ × 14½.*

122	37	6d. violet-blue and copper-bronze	10	10
123		2s. 6d. brown and copper-bronze	40	60

38 Youth Service Badge 39 "Co-operative Farming"

(Des Mrs. G. Ellison. Photo Harrison)

1967 (23 Oct). *National Development. T 38/9 and similar designs. P 13½ × 14½ (6d., 1s. 6d.) or 14½ × 13½ (others).*

124	4d. black, red and gold	10	10
125	6d. black, gold and violet-blue	10	10
126	9d. black, grey-blue and silver	15	25
127	1s. multicoloured	40	10
128	1s. 6d. multicoloured	60	1·25
124/8	*Set of 5*	1·25	1·60

Designs: *Vert*—9d "Communications"; 1s. Coalfields. *Horiz*—1s. 6d. Road link with Tanzania.

(New Currency. 100 ngwee=1 kwacha)

43 Lusaka Cathedral 44 Baobab Tree

52 Chokwe Dancer 53 Kafue Railway Bridge

(Des Mrs. G. Ellison. Photo Harrison)

1968 (16 Jan). *Decimal Currency. T 43/4, 52/3 and similar designs. P 13½ × 14½ (1, 3, 15, 50 n.) or 14½ × 13½ (others).*

129	1 n. multicoloured	10	10
	a. Copper-bronze (including value) omitted	65·00	
	b. Ultramarine (windows) omitted	65·00	
130	2 n. multicoloured	10	10
131	3 n. multicoloured	10	10
132	5 n. bistre-brown and copper-bronze	10	10
133	8 n. multicoloured	15	10
	a. Copper-bronze (background) omitted		
	b. Blue (of costumes) omitted	50·00	
134	10 n. multicoloured	25	10
135	15 n. multicoloured	2·75	10
136	20 n. multicoloured	2·50	10
137	25 n. multicoloured	25	10
138	50 n. chocolate, red-orange & copper-bronze	30	15
139	1 k. royal blue and copper-bronze	3·25	20
140	2 k. black and copper-bronze	2·25	1·25
129/40	*Set of 12*	11·00	1·75

Designs: *Horiz (as T 43)*—3 n. Zambia Airways jetliner. (*As T 53*)—15 n. *Imbrasia zambesina* (moth); 2 k. Eland. *Vert (as T 44)*—5 n. National Museum, Livingstone; 8 n. Vimbuza dancer; 10 n. Tobacco picking. (*As T 52*)—20 n. South African Crowned Cranes; 25 n. Angoni warrior.
All values exist with PVA gum as well as gum arabic.
Nos. 129/30 and 132 exist in coils, constructed from normal sheets.

55 Ndola on Outline of Zambia 56 Human Rights Emblem and Heads

(Des Mrs G. Ellison. Photo Harrison)

1968 (29 June). *Trade Fair, Ndola. P 14.*

141	55	15 n. green and gold	10	10

(Des Mrs. G. Ellison. Photo and die-stamped (gold emblem) Harrison)

1968 (23 Oct). *Human Rights Year. P 14.*

142	56	3 n. deep blue, pale violet and gold	10	10

57 W.H.O. Emblem 58 Group of Children

(Des Mrs. G. Ellison. Photo and die-stamped (gold staff and "20") Harrison)

1968 (23 Oct). *20th Anniv of World Health Organization. P 14.*

143	57	10 n. gold and bluish violet	10	10

(Des Mrs. G. Ellison. Photo and die-stamped (gold children) Harrison)

1968 (23 Oct). *22nd Anniv. of U.N.I.C.E.F. P 14.*

144	58	25 n. black, gold and ultramarine	15	70

59 Copper Miner 61 Zambia outlined on Map of Africa

(Des Mrs. G. Ellison. Photo Harrison)

1969 (18 June). *50th Anniv of International Labour Organization. T 59 and similar design. P 14½ × 13½ (3 n.) or 13½ × 14½ (25 n.).*

145	3 n. copper-bronze and deep violet	15	10
146	25 n. pale yell, copper-bronze & blackish brn	85	80

Design:—25 n. Poling a furnace.
A used example of No. 145 exists with the copper-bronze omitted.

(Des Mrs. G. Ellison. Photo Harrison)

1969 (23 Oct). *International African Tourist Year. T 61 and similar multicoloured designs. P 14 × 14½ (5 n., 25 n.) or 14½ × 14 (others).*

147	5 n. Type 61	10	10
148	10 n. Waterbuck (*horiz*)	15	10
149	15 n. Golden Perch (*horiz*)	35	40
150	25 n. Carmine Bee Eater	1·00	1·00
147/50	*Set of 4*	1·40	1·40

PREVENTIVE MEDICINE

65 Satellite "Nimbus 3" orbiting the Earth   **66** Woman collecting Water from Well

(Des Mrs. G. Ellison. Litho Enschedé)

1970 (23 Mar). *World Meteorological Day.* P 13 × 10½.
151	**65**	15 n. multicoloured	..	20	50

(Des V. Whiteley (from local designs). Litho B.W.)

1970 (4 July). *Preventive Medicine. T* **66** *and similar vert designs.* P 13½ × 12.
152	3 n. multicoloured	..	10	10
153	15 n. multicoloured	..	20	15
154	25 n. greenish blue, rosine and sepia	..	40	30
152/4		*Set of 3*	60	45

Designs:—15 n. Child on scales; 25 n. Child being immunized.

67 "Masks" (mural by Gabriel Ellison)   **68** Ceremonial Axe

(Des Mrs. G. Ellison. Litho Harrison)

1970 (8 Sept). *Conference of Non-Aligned Nations.* P 14 × 14½.
155	**67**	15 n. multicoloured	..	45	30

(Des Mrs. G. Ellison. Litho D.L.R.)

1970 (30 Nov). *Traditional Crafts. T* **68** *and similar multicoloured designs.* P 13½ (15 n.), 12½ (25 n.) or 14 (others).
156	3 n. Type **68**	..	10	10
157	5 n. Clay Smoking-Pipe Bowl	..	15	10
158	15 n. Makishi Mask (30 × 47 mm)	..	35	40
159	25 n. Kuomboka Ceremony (72 × 19 mm)	..	70	1·00
156/9		*Set of 4*	1·10	1·60
MS160	133 × 83 mm. Nos. 156/9. Imperf. ..		10·00	13·00

69 Dag Hammarskjöld and U.N. General Assembly

(Des J.W. Litho Questa)

1971 (18 Sept). *Tenth Death Anniv of Dag Hammarskjöld. T* **69** *and similar horiz designs, each with portrait of Hammarskjöld. Multicoloured.* P 13½.
161	4 n. Type **69** ..	..	10	10
162	10 n. Tail of aircraft	..	10	10
163	15 n. Dove of Peace	..	15	25
164	25 n. Memorial tablet ..	..	35	1·50
161/4		*Set of 4*	55	1·75

70 Red-breasted Bream   **71** North African Crested Porcupine

(Des G. Drummond. Litho J.W.)

1971 (10 Dec). *Fish. T* **70** *and similar horiz designs. Multicoloured.* P 13½.
165	4 n. Type **70**	..	25	10
166	10 n. Green-headed Bream	..	45	30
167	15 n. Tiger fish ..	..	85	1·75
165/7		*Set of 3*	1·40	2·00

(Des and litho J.W.)

1972 (15 Mar). *Conservation Year (1st issue). T* **71** *and similar multicoloured designs.* P 13½.
168	4 n. Cheetah (58 × 21 mm)	..	20	25
169	10 n. Lechwe (58 × 21 mm)	..	50	60
170	15 n. Type **71**	..	80	85
171	25 n. African Elephant	..	2·00	2·25
168/71		*Set of 4*	3·25	3·50

(Des and litho J.W.)

1972 (30 June). *Conservation Year (2nd issue). Designs similar to T* **71**. *Multicoloured.* P 13½.
172	4 n. Soil conservation..	..	..	20	20
173	10 n. Forestry	..	..	40	45
174	15 n. Water (58 × 21 mm)	..	60	70
175	25 n. Maize (58 × 21 mm)	..	1·25	1·40
172/5			*Set of 4*	2·25	2·50

72 Giraffe and Common Zebra

(Des and litho J.W.)

1972 (30 June). *National Parks. Sheet* 114 × 140 *mm containing T* **72** *and similar vert designs. Multicoloured.* P 13½.
MS176 10 n. (× 4). Type **72**; Black Rhinoceros; Hippopotamus and Common Panther; Lion   .. 8·00 14·00
Each design includes part of a map showing Zambian National Parks, the four forming a composite design.

73 Zambian Flowers

(Des and litho J.W.)

1972 (22 Sept). *Conservation Year (3rd issue). T* **73** *and similar horiz designs. Multicoloured.* P 13½.
177	4 n. Type **73**	..	30	30
178	10 n. *Papilio demodocus* (butterfly)	70	70
179	15 n. *Apis mellifera* (bees)	..	1·25	1·25
180	25 n. *Nomadacris septemfasciata* (locusts)	2·00	2·00
177/80		*Set of 4*	3·75	3·75

74 Mary and Joseph   **75** Oudenodon and Rubidgea

(Des V. Whiteley. Litho Questa)

1972 (1 Dec). *Christmas. T* **74** *and similar horiz designs. Multicoloured.* P 14.
181	4 n. Type **74**	..	10	10
182	9 n. Mary, Joseph and Jesus ..	10	10
183	15 n. Mary, Jesus and the shepherds ..	10	10
184	25 n. The Three Wise Men	..	20	40
181/4		*Set of 4*	35	50

(Des Mrs. G. Ellison; adapted J.W. Litho Questa)

1973 (1 Feb). *Zambian Prehistoric Animals. T* **75** *and similar horiz designs. Multicoloured.* P 14 × 13½ (4 n.) or 13½ × 14 (others).
185	4 n. Type **75**	..	85	85
186	9 n. Broken Hill Man	..	90	90
187	10 n. Zambiasaurus	..	1·00	1·50
188	15 n. *Luangwa drysdalli*	..	1·10	2·00
189	25 n. Glossopteris	..	1·25	3·00
185/9		*Set of 5*	4·50	7·50

76 "Dr. Livingstone, I Presume"

(Des J.W. Litho Format)

1973 (1 May). *Death Centenary of Dr. Livingstone. T* **76** *and similar horiz designs. Multicoloured.* P 13½.
190	3 n. Type **76**	..	35	15
191	4 n. Scripture Lesson ..	..	35	15
192	9 n. Victoria Falls	..	80	40
193	10 n. Scattering slavers	..	80	45
194	15 n. Healing the sick	..	1·00	1·50
195	25 n. Burial place of Livingstone's heart	1·40	2·25
190/5		*Set of 6*	4·25	4·50

77 Parliamentary Mace

(Des Mrs. G. Ellison. Litho Questa)

1973 (24 Sept). *Third Commonwealth Conference of Speakers and Presiding Officers, Lusaka.* P 13½.
196	**77**	9 n. multicoloured	80	65
197	15 n. multicoloured	1·00	1·75
198	25 n. multicoloured	1·50	2·50
196/8	..	*Set of 3*	3·00	4·50

78 Inoculation   **79** U.N.I.P. Flag

(Des Mrs. G. Ellison. Litho Questa)

1973 (16 Oct). *25th Anniv of W.H.O. T* **78** *and similar multicoloured designs.* P 14.
199	4 n. Mother washing baby (vert)	..	48·00	23·00
200	9 n. Nurse weighing baby (vert)	..	45	1·75
201	10 n. Type **78** ..	..	50	2·25
202	15 n. Child eating meal	..	90	4·00
199/202		*Set of 4*	48·00	28·00

Only a small quantity of No. 199 was produced, and most examples were issued to post offices for local use.

(Des Mrs. G. Ellison. Litho Questa)

1973 (13 Dec). *1st Anniv of Second Republic. T* **79** *and similar vert designs. Multicoloured.* P 14 × 13½.
203	4 n. Type **79** ..	..	10·00	8·00
204	9 n. Freedom House	..	40	1·75
205	10 n. Army band	..	40	2·25
206	15 n. "Celebrations" (dancers)..	..	70	3·75
207	25 n. Presidential chair	..	1·40	6·00
203/7 ..		*Set of 5*	11·50	20·00

80 President Kaunda at Mulungushi   **81** Nakambala Sugar Estate

(Des Mrs. G. Ellison. Litho Harrison)

1974 (28 Apr). *President Kaunda's 50th Birthday. T* **80** *and similar horiz designs. Multicoloured.* P 14½ × 14 (4 n.) or 14 × 14½ (others).
208	4 n. Type **80**	..	1·00	1·00
209	9 n. President's former residence	50	50
210	15 n. President holding Independence flame	1·40	2·50
208/10	..	*Set of 3*	2·50	3·50

(Des G. Vasarhelyi. Litho Questa)

1974 (23 Oct). *Tenth Anniv of Independence. T* **81** *and similar horiz designs. Multicoloured.* P 13½.
211	3 n. Type **81**	..	20	15
212	4 n. Local market	..	20	15
213	9 n. Kapiri glass factory	..	35	45
214	10 n. Kafue hydro-electric scheme	..	40	50
215	15 n. Kafue Railway Bridge ..	70	1·50
216	25 n. Non-aligned Conférence, Lusaka, 1970	1·10	1·75
211/16		*Set of 6*	2·75	4·00
MS217	141 × 105 mm. 15 n. (× 4) Academic Education; Teacher Training College; Technical Education; Zambia University	..	8·00	9·00

82 Mobile Post-van

(Des Mrs. G. Ellison. Litho Format)

1974 (15 Nov). *Centenary of Universal Postal Union. T 82 and similar horiz designs. Multicoloured. P 13½.*

218	4 n. Type 82			20	15
219	9 n. Aeroplane on tarmac			40	30
220	10 n. Chipata Post Office			40	40
221	15 n. Modern training centre			65	1·75
218/21			*Set of 4*	1·50	2·40

83 Dish Aerial

(Des Mrs. G. Ellison. Litho Questa)

1974 (16 Dec). *Opening of Mwembeshi Earth Station (21 October). T 83 and similar horiz designs. Multicoloured. P 13½.*

222	4 n. Type 83			30	20
223	9 n. View at dawn			65	50
224	15 n. View at dusk			1·00	1·25
225	25 n. Aerial view			1·50	2·25
222/5			*Set of 4*	3·00	3·75

84 Black Rhinoceros
and Calf

85 Independence Monument

(Des Mrs. G. Ellison. Litho J.W.)

1975 (3 Jan). *T 84/5 and similar horiz designs. Multicoloured.*

(a) Size as T 84. P 13½ × 14

226	1 n. Type 84			30	20
227	2 n. Helmet Guineafowl			30	20
228	3 n. National Dancing Troupe			15	20
229	4 n. African Fish Eagle			40	10
230	5 n. Knife-edge Bridge			55	20
231	8 n. Sitatunga (antelope)			55	20
232	9 n. African Elephant, Kasaba Bay			85	20
233	10 n. Temminck's Ground Pangolin			20	10

(b) Size as T 85. P 13

234	15 n. Type 85			30	10
	a. Magenta omitted				
235	20 n. Harvesting groundnuts			75	75
236	25 n. Tobacco-growing			85	30
237	50 n. Flying-Doctor service			90	1·60
238	1 k. Lady Ross's Turaco			2·50	1·75
239	2 k. Village scene			2·75	4·25
226/39			*Set of 14*	10·00	9·00

No. 234a shows much of the design in yellow-green due to the omission of the magenta which was used as an overlay on other colours.

Nos. 226/7 exist in coils, constructed from normal sheets.

86 Map of Namibia

87 Erection of Sprinkler Irrigation

(Des PAD Studio. Litho Questa)

1975 (26 Aug). *Namibia Day. P 13½.*

240	**86**	4 n. green and light yellow-green			20	20
241		9 n. steel-blue and light turquoise-green			30	30
242		15 n. orange-yellow and greenish yellow			65	75
243		25 n. orange and light orange			85	1·25
240/3				*Set of 4*	1·75	2·25

(Des and litho J.W.)

1975 (16 Dec). *Silver Jubilee of the International Commission on Irrigation and Drainage. T 87 and similar horiz designs. Multicoloured. P 13.*

244	4 n. Type 87			15	15
245	9 n. Sprinkler irrigation (*different*)			30	40
246	15 n. Furrow irrigation			65	1·25
244/6			*Set of 3*	1·00	1·60

88 Mutondo

(Des A. Chimfwembe. Litho J.W.)

1976 (22 Mar). *World Forestry Day. T 88 and similar horiz designs showing trees. Multicoloured. P 13.*

247	3 n. Type 88			25	10
248	4 n. Mukunyu			25	10
249	9 n. Mukusi			45	25
250	10 n. Mopane			45	25
251	15 n. Musuku			70	1·40
252	25 n. Mukwa			85	1·75
247/52			*Set of 6*	2·75	3·50

89 Passenger Train

(Des A. Chimfwembe. Litho J.W.)

1976 (10 Dec). *Opening of Tanzania-Zambia Railway. T 89 and similar horiz designs. Multicoloured. P 13½ (MS257) or 13 (others).*

253	4 n. Type 89			30	30
254	9 n. Copper exports			55	55
255	15 n. Machinery imports			90	95
256	25 n. Goods train			1·40	1·75
253/6			*Set of 4*	2·75	3·25
MS257	140 × 106 mm. 10 n. Clearing bush; 15 n. Laying track; 20 n. Railway workers; 25 n. Completed track			3·50	4·00

90 Kayowe Dance

91 Grimwood's Longclaw

(Des BG Studio. Litho Questa)

1977 (18 Jan). *Second World Black and African Festival of Arts and Culture, Nigeria. T 90 and similar horiz designs. Multicoloured. P 13½.*

258	4 n. Type 90			15	10
259	9 n. Lilombola dance			25	25
260	15 n. Initiation ceremony			45	50
261	25 n. Munkhwele dance			75	1·25
258/61			*Set of 4*	1·40	1·90

(Des Mrs. G. Ellison. Litho Questa)

1977 (1 July). *Birds of Zambia. T 91 and similar vert designs. Multicoloured. P 14½.*

262	4 n. Type 91			40	10
263	9 n. Shelley's Sunbird			70	60
264	10 n. Black-cheeked Lovebird			70	60
265	15 n. Locust Finch			1·40	2·00
266	20 n. Black-chinned Tinkerbird			1·60	2·25
267	25 n. Chaplin's Barbet			2·00	2·75
262/7			*Set of 6*	6·00	7·50

92 Girls with Building Blocks

(Des Mrs. G. Ellison. Litho Questa)

1977 (20 Oct). *Decade for Action to Combat Racism and Racial Discrimination. T 92 and similar horiz designs. Multicoloured. P 14 × 14½.*

268	4 n. Type 92			10	10
269	9 n. Women dancing			15	20
270	15 n. Girls with dove			25	60
268/70			*Set of 3*	45	80

93 Angels and Shepherds

(Des Mrs. G. Ellison. Litho J.W.)

1977 (20 Dec). *Christmas. T 93 and similar horiz designs. Multicoloured. P 14.*

271	4 n. Type 93			10	10
272	9 n. The Holy Family			10	10
273	10 n. The Magi			10	15
274	15 n. Jesus presented to Simeon			20	60
271/4			*Set of 4*	40	85

94 African Elephant and
Road Check

(95)

(Des Mrs. G. Ellison. Litho Questa)

1978 (1 Aug). *Anti-Poaching Campaign. T 94 and similar horiz designs. Multicoloured. P 14 × 14½.*

275	8 n. Type 94			25	10
276	18 n. Lechwe and canoe patrol			40	55
277	28 n. Warthog and helicopter			60	85
278	32 n. Cheetah and game guard patrol			75	1·10
275/8			*Set of 4*	1·75	2·40

1979 (15 Mar). *Nos. 228, 232, 234 and 236 surch as T 95.*

279	8 n. on 9 n. African Elephant, Kasaba Bay			40	10
	a. Surch inverted				
280	10 n. on 3 n. National Dancing Troupe			10	10
	a. Surch inverted				
	b. Surch omitted (in pair with normal)				
281	18 n. on 25 n. Tobacco-growing			15	15
	a. Surch inverted				
282	28 n. on 15 n. Type 85			20	25
	a. Surch inverted			8·00	
	b. Albino surch				
279/82			*Set of 4*	75	55

No. 280b was caused by a corner paper fold.

96 Kayowe Dance

97 "Kalulu and the
Tug of War"

(Des Mrs. G. Ellison. Litho Questa)

1979 (1 Aug). *Commonwealth Summit Conference, Lusaka. T 96 and similar horiz designs. Multicoloured. P 14.*

283	18 n. Type 96			15	25
284	32 n. Kutambala dance			25	40
285	42 n. Chitwansombo drummers			35	60
286	58 n. Lilombola dance			50	80
283/6			*Set of 4*	1·10	1·90

(Des Mrs. G. Ellison. Litho Questa)

1979 (21 Sept). *International Year of the Child. Illustrations from Children's Books. T 97 and similar vert designs. Multicoloured. P 14.*

287	18 n. Type 97			40	30
288	32 n. "Why the Zebra has no Horns"			55	55
289	42 n. "How the Tortoise got his Shell"			60	85
290	58 n. "Kalulu and the Lion"			80	1·10
287/90			*Set of 4*	2·10	2·50
MS291	90 × 120 mm. Nos. 287/90			2·25	2·75

98 Children of Different Races holding
Anti-Apartheid Emblem

(Des Mrs. G. Ellison. Litho Questa)

1979 (13 Nov). *International Anti-Apartheid Year. T 98 and similar horiz designs showing children of different races together. Multicoloured. P 14½.*

292	18 n. Type 98			15	25
293	32 n. Children with toy car			25	40
294	42 n. Young children with butterfly			35	60
295	58 n. Children with microscope			50	80
292/5			*Set of 4*	1·10	1·90

LONDON 1980

99 Sir Rowland Hill and 2s. Definitive (100)
Stamp of 1964

(Des Mrs. G. Ellison. Litho Format)

1979 (20 Dec). *Death Centenary of Sir Rowland Hill. T* **99** *and similar horiz designs. Multicoloured. P* 14½.

296	18 n. Type 99			20	25
297	32 n. Sir Rowland Hill and mailman			40	55
298	42 n. Sir Rowland Hill and Northern Rhodesia 1963 ½d. definitive stamp			50	70
299	58 n. Sir Rowland Hill and mail-carrying oxwaggon			65	1·10
296/9			*Set of* 4	1·60	2·40
MS300	112 × 89 mm. Nos. 296/9			2·00	2·75

1980 (16 May). *"London 1980" International Stamp Exhibition. Nos.* 296/300 *optd with T* **100**.

301	18 n. Type 99			35	40
302	32 n. Sir Rowland Hill and mailman			55	70
303	42 n. Sir Rowland Hill and Northern Rhodesia 1963 ½d. definitive stamp			70	90
304	58 n. Sir Rowland Hill and mail-carrying oxwaggon			90	1·10
301/4			*Set of* 4	2·25	2·75
MS305	112 × 89 mm. Nos. 301/4			3·00	3·75

101 Rotary Anniversary Emblem

(Des J.W. Litho Questa)

1980 (18 June). *75th Anniv of Rotary International. P* 14.

306	101	8 n. multicoloured		10	10
307		32 n. multicoloured		40	55
308		42 n. multicoloured		45	80
309		58 n. multicoloured		70	1·00
306/9			*Set of* 4	1·50	2·25
MS310		115 × 89 mm. Nos. 306/9		2·00	2·50

102 Running

(Des Mrs. G. Ellison. Litho J.W.)

1980 (19 July). *Olympic Games, Moscow. T* **102** *and similar horiz designs. Multicoloured. P* 13.

311	18 n. Type 102			25	25
312	32 n. Boxing			35	45
313	42 n. Football			40	80
314	58 n. Swimming			70	1·25
311/14			*Set of* 4	1·50	2·50
MS315	142 × 144 mm. Nos. 311/14. P 14.			1·50	2·50

103 *Euphaedra zaddachi*   **104** Zambia Coat of Arms

(Des Mrs. G. Ellison. Litho Questa)

1980 (27 Aug). *Butterflies. T* **103** *and similar horiz designs. Multicoloured. P* 14.

316	18 n. Type 103			15	15
317	32 n. Aphnaeus questiauxi			25	40
318	42 n. Abantis zambesiaca			40	80
319	58 n. Spindasis modesta			60	1·10
316/19			*Set of* 4	1·25	2·25
MS320	114 × 86 mm. Nos. 316/19			3·25	3·00

(Des Mrs. G. Ellison. Litho Format)

1980 (27 Sept). *26th Commonwealth Parliamentary Association Conference, Lusaka. P* 14.

321	104	18 n. multicoloured		15	25
322		32 n. multicoloured		25	45
323		42 n. multicoloured		30	65
324		58 n. multicoloured		40	90
321/4			*Set of* 4	1·00	2·00

105 Nativity and St. Francis   **106** Musikili
of Assisi (stained glass window,
Ndola Church)

(Des Mrs. G. Ellison. Litho Questa)

1980 (3 Nov). *50th Anniv of Catholic Church on the Copperbelt. P* 13½.

325	105	8 n. multicoloured		10	10
326		28 n. multicoloured		35	60
327		32 n. multicoloured		35	60
328		42 n. multicoloured		40	75
325/8			*Set of* 4	1·10	1·90

(Des Mrs. G. Ellison. Litho Questa)

1981 (21 Mar). *World Forestry Day. Seedpods. T* **106** *and similar horiz designs. Multicoloured. P* 14.

329	8 n. Type 106			10	10
330	18 n. Mupapa			30	45
331	28 n. Mulunguti			40	80
332	32 n. Mulama			45	1·25
329/32			*Set of* 4	1·10	2·25

107 I.T.U. Emblem   **108** Mask Maker

(Des J.W. Litho Format)

1981 (15 May). *World Telecommunications and Health Day. T* **107** *and similar vert design. Multicoloured. P* 14½.

333	8 n. Type 107			20	10
334	18 n. W.H.O. emblems			45	35
335	28 n. Type 107			80	60
336	32 n. As 18 n.			95	75
333/6			*Set of* 4	2·25	1·60

(Des Mrs. G. Ellison. Litho Harrison)

1981 (2 June)–**83**. *Multicoloured designs as T* **108**. *P* 14 × 13½ (50 n., 75 n., 1 k., 2 k.) *or* 14½ *(others)*.

337	1 n. Type 108			10	10
338	2 n. Blacksmith			10	10
339	5 n. Pottery making			10	10
340	8 n. Straw-basket fishing			10	10
341	10 n. Thatching			10	10
342	12 n. Mushroom picking (17.2.83)			1·75	85
343	18 n. Millet grinding on stone			20	10
344	28 n. Royal Barge paddler (11.11.81)			40	10
345	30 n. Makishi tightrope dancer (11.11.81)			40	10
346	35 n. Tonga Ila granary and house (11.11.81)			45	10
347	42 n. Cattle herding (11.11.81)			45	50
348	50 n. Traditional healer (38 × 26 *mm*) (11.11.81)			45	10
349	75 n. Women carrying water (38 × 26 *mm*) (17.2.83)			45	50
350	1 k. Pounding maize (38 × 26 *mm*) (17.2.83)			45	50
351	2 k. Pipe-smoking, Gwembe Valley Belle (38 × 26 *mm*)			45	50
337/48			*Set of* 15	5·00	3·00

Nos. 338/9 and 341 exist in coils, constructed from normal sheets.

109 Kankobele   **110** Banded Ironstone

(Des Mrs. G. Ellison. Litho Format)

1981 (30 Sept*). *Traditional Musical Instruments. T* **109** *and similar vert designs. Multicoloured. P* 15.

356	8 n. Type 109			30	10
357	18 n. Inshingili			65	40
358	28 n. Ilimba			90	1·00
359	32 n. Bango			1·00	1·40
356/9			*Set of* 4	2·50	2·50

*It has been reported that the Ndola Philatelic Bureau inadvertently sold some of these stamps some days earlier, and that cancelled-to-order examples exist postmarked 14 or 15 September.

(Des Mrs. G. Ellison. Litho Questa)

1982 (5 Jan). *Minerals (1st series). T* **110** *and similar vert designs. Multicoloured. P* 14.

360	8 n. Type 110			40	10
361	18 n. Cobaltocalcite			1·00	70
362	28 n. Amazonite			1·25	1·00
363	32 n. Tourmaline			1·40	1·60
364	42 n. Uranium ore			1·75	2·00
360/4			*Set of* 5	5·25	4·75

See also Nos. 370/4.

111 Zambian Scouts

(Des Mrs. G. Ellison. Litho Questa)

1982 (30 Mar). *75th Anniv of Boy Scout Movement. T* **111** *and similar horiz designs. Multicoloured. P* 14.

365	8 n. Type 111			30	10
366	18 n. Lord Baden-Powell and Victoria Falls			70	40
367	28 n. African Buffalo and Zambian Scout patrol pennant			70	50
368	1 k. African Fish Eagle and Zambian Conservation badge			2·00	3·00
365/8			*Set of* 4	3·25	3·50
MS369	105 × 78 mm. Nos. 365/8			3·25	4·00

(Des Mrs. G. Ellison. Litho Questa)

1982 (1 July). *Minerals (2nd series). Vert designs as T* **110**. *Multicoloured. P* 14.

370	8 n. Bornite			70	10
371	18 n. Chalcopyrite			1·75	75
372	28 n. Malachite			2·25	2·25
373	32 n. Azurite			2·25	2·25
374	42 n. Vanadinite			2·75	3·50
370/4			*Set of* 5	8·75	8·00

112 Drilling Rig, 1926

(Des Mrs G. Ellison. Litho Harrison)

1983 (26 Jan). *Early Steam Engines. T* **112** *and similar horiz designs. Multicoloured. P* 14 × 14½.

375	8 n. Type 112			50	10
376	18 n. Fowler road locomotive, 1900			70	60
377	28 n. Borsig ploughing engine, 1925			1·10	1·75
378	32 n. Class "7" railway locomotive, 1900			1·40	2·00
375/8			*Set of* 4	3·25	4·00

113 Cotton Picking   **114** *Eulophia cucullata*

(Des Mrs G. Ellison. Litho Harrison)

1983 (10 Mar). *Commonwealth Day. T* **113** *and similar horiz designs. Multicoloured. P* 14 × 13½.

379	12 n. Type 113			20	10
380	18 n. Mining			30	30
381	28 n. Ritual pot and traditional dances			30	50
382	1 k. Violet-crested Turaco and Victoria Falls			2·50	3·75
379/82			*Set of* 4	3·00	4·25

(Des Mrs G. Ellison. Litho Questa)

1983 (26 May). *Wild Flowers. T* **114** *and similar vert designs. Multicoloured. P* 14.

383	12 n. Type 114			20	10
384	28 n. Kigelia africana			35	40
385	35 n. Protea gaguedi			45	70
386	50 n. Leonotis nepetifolia			65	1·40
383/6			*Set of* 4	1·50	2·40
MS387	141 × 71 mm. Nos. 383/6. P 12			1·50	2·75

115 Giraffe

(Des Mrs. G. Ellison. Litho Harrison)

1983 (21 July). *Zambia Wildlife. T* **115** *and similar horiz designs. Multicoloured. P* 14 × 13½.
388	12 n. Type 115	..	70	10
	a. Orange-brown and brown (inscr and face value) omitted	..		
389	28 n. Blue Wildebeest	.. ..	90	70
390	35 n. Lechwe ..	.. ..	1·25	90
391	1 k. Yellow-backed Duiker ..		2·50	3·50
388/91	.. ..	*Set of* 4	4·75	4·75

116 Tiger Fish

117 The Annunciation

(Des Mrs. G. Ellison. Litho J.W.)

1983 (29 Sept). *Zambia Fishes. T* **116** *and similar horiz d signs. Multicoloured. P* 14.
392	12 n. Type 116 ..		20	15
393	28 n. Silver Barbel	.. ..	40	60
394	35 n. Spotted Squeaker	..	45	1·00
395	38 n. Red-breasted Bream	..	50	1·00
392/5	.. ..	*Set of* 4	1·40	2·50

(Des Mrs. G. Ellison. Litho J.W.)

1983 (12 Dec). *Christmas. T* **117** *and similar vert designs. Multicoloured. P* 14.
396	12 n. Type 117 ..		10	10
397	28 n. The Shepherds	..	25	40
398	35 n. Three Kings	..	30	90
399	38 n. Flight into Egypt	..	35	1·25
396/9	.. .. ..	*Set of* 4	90	2·40

118 Boeing "737"

(Des Mrs. G. Ellison. Litho Harrison)

1984 (26 Jan). *Air Transport. T* **118** *and similar horiz designs. Multicoloured. P* 14 × 13½.
400	12 n. Type 118 ..		15	10
401	28 n. "Beaver" ..	.. ..	30	40
402	35 n. Short "Solent" flying boat	..	35	70
403	1 k. "D.H.66 Hercules"	..	85	2·25
400/3	.. ..	*Set of* 4	1·50	3·00

119 Receiving Flowers

120 Football

(Des and litho J.W.)

1984 (28 Apr). *60th Birthday of President Kaunda. T* **119** *and similar multicoloured designs. P* 14½ × 14 (12 *n.*, 60 *n.*) *or* 14 × 14½ (*others*).
404	12 n. Type 119 ..	..	40	10
405	28 n. Swearing-in ceremony (*vert*)	..	65	40
406	60 n. Planting cherry tree	..	1·50	1·75
407	1 k. Opening of 5th National Assembly (*vert*)		2·00	2·50
404/7	.. .. ..	*Set of* 4	4·00	4·25

(Des Mrs. G. Ellison. Litho Format)

1984 (18 July). *Olympic Games, Los Angeles. T* **120** *and similar vert designs. Multicoloured. P* 14½ × 14.
408	12 n. Type 120	..	25	10
409	28 n. Running ..	.. ..	35	50
410	35 n. Hurdling ..	.. ..	50	75
411	50 n. Boxing ..	.. ..	60	1·10
408/11	.. ..	*Set of* 4	1·50	2·25

121 Gaboon Viper

(Des Mrs. G. Ellison. Litho Harrison)

1984 (5 Sept). *Reptiles. T* **121** *and similar horiz designs. Multicoloured. P* 14.
412	12 n. Type 121 ..	..	15	10
413	28 n. Chameleon	..	30	40
414	35 n. Nile Crocodile	..	40	60
415	1 k. Blue-headed Agama	..	85	2·25
412/15		*Set of* 4	1·50	3·00
MS416	120 × 101 mm. Nos. 412/15	..	2·00	3·50

122 Pres. Kaunda and Mulungushi Rock

123 *Amanita flammeola*

(Des Mrs. G. Ellison. Litho Harrison)

1984 (22 Oct). *26th Anniv of United National Independence Party* (12 *n.*) *and 20th Anniv of Independence* (*others*) (1st issue). *T* **122** *and similar horiz designs. Multicoloured. P* 14.
417	12 n. Type 122 ..	..	40	10
418	28 n. Freedom Statue	..	60	50
419	1 k. Pres. Kaunda and agricultural produce ("Lima Programme") ..	..	1·50	2·50
417/19		*Set of* 3	2·25	2·75

See also Nos. 438/40.

(Des Mrs. G. Ellison. Litho J.W.)

1984 (12 Dec). *Fungi. T* **123** *and similar vert designs. Multicoloured. P* 14 × 14½.
420	12 n. Type 123 ..	..	65	15
421	28 n. *Amanita zambiana*	..	85	60
422	32 n. *Termitomyces letestui*	..	1·25	95
423	75 n. *Cantharellus miniatescens*	..	2·25	2·50
420/3	..	*Set of* 4	4·50	3·75

K5

(124)

125 Chacma Baboon

1985 (5 Mar). *No.* 237 *surch with T* **124**.
424	5 k. on 50 n. Flying-doctor service	..	1·25	1·75

(Des Mrs. G. Ellison. Litho Harrison)

1985 (25 Apr). *Zambian Primates. T* **125** *and similar horiz designs. Multicoloured. P* 14.
425	12 n. Type 125	..	35	10
426	20 n. Diademed Monkey	..	55	30
427	45 n. Diademed Monkey (*different*) ..		1·00	1·00
428	1 k. Savanna Monkey	..	1·75	2·00
425/8	..	*Set of* 4	3·25	3·00

126 Map showing S.A.D.C.C. Member States

127 The Queen Mother in 1980

(Des Mrs. G. Ellison. Litho Harrison)

1985 (9 July). *5th Anniv of Southern African Development Co-ordination Conference. T* **126** *and similar horiz designs. P* 14.
429	20 n. multicoloured	..	50	15
430	45 n. black, new blue and pale blue ..		1·25	85
431	1 k. multicoloured	..	1·75	2·50
429/31		*Set of* 3	3·25	3·25

Designs:—45 n. Mining; 1 k. Flags of member states and Mulungushi Hall.

(Des and litho Harrison)

1985 (2 Aug). *Life and Times of Queen Elizabeth the Queen Mother. T* **127** *and similar designs. P* 14.
432	25 n. multicoloured	..	10	10
433	45 n. deep violet-blue and gold	..	10	15
434	50 n. deep violet-blue and gold	..	15	20
435	5 k. multicoloured	..	1·25	2·00
432/5		*Set of* 4	1·40	2·25

Designs: *Vert*—45 n. The Queen Mother at Clarence House, 1963. *Horiz*—55 n. With the Queen and Princess Margaret, 1980; 5 k. At Prince Henry's christening, 1984.

20n

(128)

129 Postman and Lusaka Post Office, 1958

1985 (12 Sept–25 Nov). *Nos.* 340 *and* 342 *surch as T* **128** *in chestnut* (20 *n.*) *or greenish blue* (25 *n.*).
436	20 n. on 12 n. Mushroom picking	..	1·75	30
437	25 n. on 8 n. Straw-basket fishing (25.11) ..		75	50

1985 (23 Oct). *26th Anniv of United National Independence Party* (*No.* 438) *and 20th Anniv of Independence* (*others*) (2nd issue). *Designs as Nos.* 417/19 *but larger,* 55 × 34 *mm, embossed on gold foil. P* 10.
438	5 k. Type 122	..	1·75	2·75
439	5 k. Freedom Statue ..	..	1·75	2·75
440	5 k. Pres. Kaunda and agricultural produce ("Lima Programme")		1·75	2·75
438/40		*Set of* 3	4·75	7·50

(Des Mrs. G. Ellison. Litho J.W.)

1985 (12 Dec). *10th Anniv of Posts and Telecommunication Corporation. T* **129** *and similar horiz designs. Multicoloured. P* 13 × 12½.
441	20 n. Type 129	..	35	10
442	45 n. Postman and Livingstone Post Office, 1950 ..	..	65	20
443	55 n. Postman and Kalomo Post Office, 1902	..	75	50
444	5 k. Africa Trans-Continental Telegraph Line under construction, 1900		2·50	4·00
441/4	..	*Set of* 4	3·75	4·25

130 Boy in Maize Field

131 *Mylabris tricolor*

(Des Mrs. G. Ellison. Litho Harrison)

1985 (19 Dec). *40th Anniv of United Nations Organization. T* **130** *and similar vert designs. P* 14.
445	20 n. multicoloured	..	40	10
446	45 n. black, new blue and brownish black ..		65	20
447	1 k. multicoloured	..	1·25	1·50
448	2 k. multicoloured	..	2·00	2·50
445/8	..	*Set of* 4	3·75	3·75

Designs:—45 n. Logo and "40"; 1 k. President Kaunda addressing U.N. General Assembly, 1970; 2 k. Signing of U.N. Charter, San Francisco, 1945.

(Des Mrs. G. Ellison. Litho Harrison)

1986 (20 Mar). *Beetles. T* **131** *and similar horiz designs. Multicoloured. P* 14.
449	35 n. Type 131	..	15	10
450	1 k. *Phasgonocnema melanianthe* ..		20	20
451	1 k. 70, *Amaurodes passerinii*	..	30	50
452	5 k. *Ranzania petersiana*	..	85	2·00
449/52	..	*Set of* 4	1·40	2·50

(Des A. Theobald. Litho Format)

1986 (21 Apr). *60th Birthday of Queen Elizabeth II. Vert designs as T* **230a** *of Jamaica. Multicoloured. W w* **16**. *P* 14×14½ (1 *k.* 95) *or* 14×13½ (*others*).
453	35 n. Princess Elizabeth at Flower Ball, Savoy Hotel, 1951	..	10	10
	a. Perf 14 × 14½	..	1·00	
454	1 k. 25, With Prince Andrew, Lusaka Airport, 1979	..	15	20
	a. Perf 14 × 14½	..	15·00	
455	1 k. 70, With President Kaunda	..	20	25
	a. Perf 14 × 14½	..	12·00	
456	1 k. 95, In Luxembourg, 1976	..	25	30
457	5 k. At Crown Agents Head Office, London, 1983	..	60	85
453/7	..	*Set of* 5	1·10	2·50

(Des D. Miller. Litho Questa)

1986 (23 July). *Royal Wedding. Square designs as T* **231a** *of Jamaica. Multicoloured. W w* **16**. *P* 14.
458	1 k. 70, Prince Andrew and Miss Sarah Ferguson	..	30	30
459	5 k. Prince Andrew in Zambia, 1979	..	80	1·25

ALTERED CATALOGUE NUMBERS

Any Catalogue numbers altered from the last edition are shown as a list in the introductory pages.

132 Goalkeeper
saving Goal

133 Sculpture of Edmond
Halley by Henry Pegram

(Des Mrs. G. Ellison. Litho Mardon Printers Ltd, Zimbabwe)

1986 (30 July). *World Cup Football Championship, Mexico.*
T 132 and similar vert designs. Multicoloured. P 14½.

460	35 n. Type 132		..	..	60	15
461	1 k. 25, Player kicking ball..		..		1·50	1·25
462	1 k. 70, Two players competing for ball				1·75	1·75
463	5 k. Player scoring goal			..	3·50	4·00
460/3	..	..	..	.. *Set of 4*	6·50	6·50

(Des Jennifer Toombs. Litho Mardon Printers Ltd, Zimbabwe)

1986 (6 Aug). *Appearance of Halley's Comet. T 133 and similar*
horiz designs. P 14½.

464	1 k. 25, multicoloured		..	..	65	45
465	1 k. 70, multicoloured		..	..	85	65
466	2 k. multicoloured		..	..	1·25	1·25
467	5 k. light blue and blue-black		..		3·00	3·50
464/7	..	..	..	*Set of 4*	5·25	5·25

Designs:—1 k. 70, *Giotto* spacecraft approaching nucleus of
Comet; 2 k. Studying Halley's Comet in 1682 and 1986; 5 k. Part
of Halley's chart of southern sky.

134 The Nativity

(Des and litho Harrison)

1986 (15 Dec). *Christmas. Children's Paintings. T 134 and*
similar horiz designs. Multicoloured. P 14.

468	35 n. Type 134		..	..	30	10
469	1 k. 25, The Visit of the Three Kings		..		1·00	65
470	1 k. 60, The Holy Family with Shepherd and King				1·25	90
471	5 k. Angel and Christmas Tree		..		3·00	4·00
468/71	..	..	..	*Set of 4*	5·00	5·00

135 Train in Kasama Cutting

(Des G. Vasarhelyi. Litho Questa)

1986 (22 Dec). *10th Anniv of Tanzania-Zambia Railway. T 135*
and similar horiz designs. Multicoloured. P 14.

472	35 n. Type 135		..	..	25	10
473	1 k. 25, Train leaving Tunnel No. 21		..		45	50
474	1 k. 70, Train between Tunnels No. 6 and 7				50	70
475	5 k. Trains at Mpika Station		..		1·00	2·00
472/5	..	..	..	*Set of 4*	2·00	3·00

136 President Kaunda and
Graduate

137 Arms of Kitwe

(Litho Harrison)

1987 (27 Jan). *20th Anniv of University of Zambia. T 136 and*
similar multicoloured designs. P 14.

476	35 n. Type 136		..	..	25	10
477	1 k. 25, University Badge (*vert*)		..		75	55
478	1 k. 60, University Statue		..		85	75
479	5 k. President Kaunda laying foundation stone (*vert*)				2·50	3·50
476/9	..	..	..	*Set of 4*	4·00	4·50

(Litho Harrison)

1987 (26 Mar). *Arms of Zambian Towns. T 137 and similar vert*
designs. Multicoloured. P 14.

480	35 n. Type 137		..	..	10	10
481	1 k. 25, Ndola		..	..	15	20
482	1 k. 70, Lusaka		..	..	20	25
483	20 k. Livingstone		..	..	2·40	3·75
480/3	..	..	..	*Set of 4*	2·50	3·75

138 Chestnut-headed Crake

139 Look-out
Tree, Livingstone

Two types of surcharge for 20 n., 75 n.:

20n **20n** **75n** **75n**
= = = =
I II I II

I Surch by Format in Great Britain
II Surch in Zambia

(Des Mrs. G. Ellison. Litho Questa)

1987 (16 Apr)–**88**. *Birds* (1st *series*). *T 138 and similar vert*
designs, some additionally surch as T 128. Multicoloured.
P 11×13. (5 n. to 40 n., 75 n., 1 k. 65) *or* 14 (*others*).

484	5 n. Cloud-scraping Cisticola (8.10.87)		10	10
485	10 n. White-winged Starling (8.10.87)		10	10
486	20 n. on 1 n. Yellow Swamp Warbler (I) (10.3.88)		30	10
	a. Surch Type II		20	10
487	25 n. Type 138		40	30
488	30 n. Red-fronted Barbet ("Miombo Pied Barbet") (8.10.87)		10	10
489	35 n. Black and Rufous Swallow		50	30
490	40 n. Wattled Crane (8.10.87)		10	10
491	50 n. Red-throated Heron ("Slaty Egret") (8.10.87)		10	10
492	75 n. on 2 n. Olive-flanked Robin Chat (I) (10.3.88)		30	40
	a. Surch Type II		30	40
493	1 k. Bradfield's Hornbill		60	15
494	1 k. 25, Boulton's Puff-back Flycatcher ("Margaret's Batis")		60	60
495	1 k. 60, Anchieta's Sunbird		60	60
496	1 k. 65 on 30 n. Red-fronted Barbet (10.3.88)		30	50
497	1 k. 70, Boehm's Bee Eater		75	75
498	1 k. 95, Perrin's Bush Shrike		75	75
499	2 k. Whale-headed Stork ("Shoebill") (8.10.87)		35	35
500	5 k. Taita Falcon ..		1·00	55
501	10 k. on 50 n. Red-throated Heron (10.3.88)		1·10	1·60
502	20 k. on 2 k. Whale-headed Stork (10.3.88)		2·10	2·75
484/502	..	*Set of 19*	9·00	9·00

Nos. 491, 493/5 and 497/502 are larger, size 24×39 mm.
The 1 n. and 2 n. values were not officialy issued without
surcharge, but examples with c-t-o cancellations of 10 March
1988 are known.
No. 502 is surcharged "K 20" only. For "K 20·00" surcharge
see No. 594.
For further surcharges see Nos. 587/95, and for different
designs see Nos. 625/8.

(Litho Questa)

1987 (30 June). *Tourism. T 139 and similar horiz designs.*
Multicoloured. P 14.

503	35 n. Type 139		30	15
504	1 k. 25, Rafting on Zambezi		65	40
505	1 k. 70, Tourists photographing lions, Luangwa Valley		1·00	70
506	10 k. Eastern White Pelicans		4·50	4·50
503/6	..	*Set of 4*	5·75	5·25

= K3

(140)

141 De Havilland "Beaver"

1987 (14 Sept). *Various stamps surch as T 140.*

(*a*) *On Nos. 432/5 in gold*

507	**127**	3 k. on 25 n. multicoloured	..	55	55
508	–	6 k. on 45 n. deep violet-blue and gold		1·00	1·00
509	–	10 k. on 55 n. deep violet-blue and gold		1·60	1·60
510	–	20 k. on 5 k. multicoloured		3·25	3·75

(*b*) *On Nos. 453/7*

511	3 k. on 35 n. Princess Elizabeth at Flower Ball, Savoy Hotel, 1951		55	55
512	4 k. on 1 k. 25, With Prince Andrew, Lusaka Airport, 1979		65	65
513	6 k. on 1 k. 70, With President Kaunda		1·00	1·00
514	10 k. on 1 k. 95, In Luxembourg, 1976		1·60	1·60
515	20 k. on 5 k. At Crown Agents Head Office, London, 1983		3·25	3·75

(*c*) *On Nos. 460/3*

516	3 k. on 35 n. Type 132		55	55
517	6 k. on 1 k. 25, Player kicking ball		1·00	1·00
518	10 k. on 1 k. 70, Two players competing for ball		1·60	1·60
519	20 k. on 5 k. Player scoring goal		3·25	3·75

(*d*) *On Nos. 464/7 in gold*

520	**133**	3 k. on 1 k. 25, multicoloured		55	55
		a. Surch omitted (in horiz pair with normal)		80·00	
521	–	6 k. on 1 k. 70, multicoloured		1·00	1·00
522	–	10 k. on 2 k. multicoloured		1·60	1·60
523	–	20 k. on 15 k. light blue and blue-black		3·25	3·75
507/23		..	*Set of 17*	23·00	25·00

(Des and litho Questa)

1987 (21 Sept). *20th Anniv of Zambia Airways. T 141 and*
similar horiz designs showing aircraft. Multicoloured. P 14.

524	35 n. Type 141		35	10
525	1 k. 70, Douglas "DC-10"	..	1·00	45
526	5 k. Douglas "DC-3 Dakota"		2·25	2·00
527	10 k. Boeing "707"	..	4·00	4·25
524/7	..	*Set of 4*	7·00	6·00

142 Friesian/Holstein Cow

143 Mpoloto Ne Mikobango

(Des Mrs. G. Ellison. Litho Format)

1987 (1 Oct). *40th Anniv of Food and Agriculture Organiza-*
tion. T 142 and similar horiz designs. Multicoloured.
P 14½×15.

528	35 n. Type 142		10	10
529	1 k. 25, Simmental bull		20	25
530	1 k. 70, Sussex bull ..		25	30
531	20 k. Brahman bull		2·75	3·00
528/31	..	*Set of 4*	3·00	3·25

(Litho Format)

1987 (3 Nov). *People of Zambia. T 143 and similar vert designs.*
Multicoloured. P 12½.

532	35 n. Type 143		10	10
533	1 k. 25, Zintaka		20	25
534	1 k. 70, Mufuluhi		25	30
535	10 k. Ntebwe ..		1·40	1·50
536	20 k. Kubangwa Aa Mbulunga		2·75	3·00
532/6	..	*Set of 5*	4·25	4·50

144 Black Lechwe
at Waterhole

145 Cassava Roots

(Des Mrs. G. Ellison. Litho Questa)

1987 (21 Dec). *Black Lechwe. T 144 and similar multicoloured*
designs. P 14.

537	50 n. Type 144	..	40	10
538	2 k. Black Lechwe resting by pool (*horiz*)		1·25	40
539	2 k. 50, Running through water (*horiz*)		1·40	60
540	10 k. Watching for danger		2·75	2·75
537/40	..	*Set of 4*	5·25	3·50
MS541 Two sheets, each 105×74 mm. (a) 20 k. Caracal (predator). (b) 20 k. Cheetah (predator)				
		Set of 2 sheets	5·50	6·00

(Des Mrs. G. Ellison. Litho Questa)

1988 (20 May). *International Fund for Agricultural Develop-*
ment. T 145 and similar horiz designs. Multicoloured. P 14.

542	50 n. Type 145		10	10
543	2 k. 50, Fishing		30	35
544	2 k. 85, Farmer and cattle		35	40
545	10 k. Picking coffee beans ..		1·25	1·40
542/5	..	*Set of 4*	1·75	2·00

146 Breast feeding

147 Asbestos
Cement

(Des Mrs. G. Ellison. Litho Format)

1988 (12 Sept). *U.N.I.C.E.F. Child Survival Campaign. T 146*
and similar vert designs. Multicoloured. P 12½.

546	50 n. Type 146		15	10
547	2 k. Growth monitoring		35	30
548	2 k. 85, Immunization		45	50
549	10 k. Oral rehydration		1·25	2·25
546/9	..	*Set of 4*	2·00	2·75

(Des Mrs. G. Ellison. Litho Format)

1988 (10 Oct). *Preferential Trade Area Fair. T 147 and similar*
vert designs. Multicoloured. P 12½.

550	50 n. Type 147		10	10
551	2 k. 35, Textiles		25	30
552	2 k. 50, Tea		30	40
553	10 k. Poultry		1·25	2·25
550/3	..	*Set of 4*	1·60	2·75

148 Emergency Food
Distribution

(Des Mrs. G. Ellison. Litho Questa)

1988 (20 Oct). *125th Anniv of International Red Cross. T* **148** *and similar horiz designs. Multicoloured. P* 14.

554	50 n. Type 148		15	10
555	2 k. 50, Giving first aid		40	50
556	2 k. 85, Practising bandaging		45	60
557	10 k. Henri Dunant (founder)		1·50	2·25
554/7		Set of 4	2·25	3·00

149 Aardvark

(Des Mrs. G. Ellison. Litho Questa)

1988 (5 Dec). *Endangered Species of Zambia. T* **149** *and similar horiz designs. Multicoloured. P* 14.

558	50 n. Type 149		15	10
559	2 k. Temminck's Ground Pangolin		40	35
560	2 k. 85, Hunting Dog		50	60
561	20 k. Black Rhinoceros and calf		3·25	5·00
558/61		Set of 4	3·75	5·50

150 Boxing   151 Red Toad

(Des Mrs. G. Ellison. Litho Questa)

1988 (30 Dec). *Olympic Games, Seoul. T* **150** *and similar horiz designs. Multicoloured. P* 14.

562	50 n. Type 150		15	10
563	2 k. Athletics		30	40
564	2 k. 50, Hurdling		35	50
565	20 k. Football		2·75	4·50
562/5		Set of 4	3·25	5·00
MS566	Two sheets, each 97×72 mm. (a) 30 k.			
	Tennis. (b) 30 k. Karate	Set of 2 sheets	8·00	9·50

(Des Mrs. G. Ellison. Litho Format)

1989 (25 Jan). *Frogs and Toads. T* **151** *and similar horiz designs. Multicoloured. P* 12½.

567	50 n. Type 151		15	10
568	2 k. 50, Puddle Frog		50	50
569	2 k. 85, Marbled Reed Frog		55	65
570	10 k. Young Reed Frogs		1·60	2·50
567/70		Set of 4	2·50	3·25

152 Common Slit-faced
Bat

153 Pope John
Paul II and Map of
Zambia

(Des Mrs. G. Ellison. Litho Format)

1989 (22 Mar). *Bats. T* **152** *and similar horiz designs. Multicoloured. P* 12½.

571	50 n. Type 152		15	10
572	2 k. 50, Little Free-tailed Bat		45	55
573	2 k. 85, Hildebrandt's Horseshoe Bat		55	65
574	10 k. Peters' Epauletted Fruit Bat		1·50	2·50
571/4		Set of 4	2·40	3·50

(Des and litho Harrison)

1989 (2 May). *Visit of Pope John Paul II. T* **153** *and similar vert designs each with inset portrait. Multicoloured. P* 12½.

575	50 n. Type 153		40	15
576	6 k. 85, Peace dove with olive branch		2·00	2·25
577	7 k. 85, Papal arms		2·25	2·50
578	10 k. Victoria Falls		3·00	3·50
575/8		Set of 4	7·00	7·50

K19.50 =

(154)

K20.00 =

(155)

1989 (1 July–1 Nov). *Various stamps surch.*

(a) *Nos.* 339, 341/3, 345/6, 349 *and* 351 *surch as T* **154**
(1 *k.* 20, 19 *k.* 50, 20 *k.* 50) *or as T* **155** (*others*)

579	1 k. 20 on 35 n. Tonga Ila granary and house (Br.) (1 Nov)	15	15
580	3 k. 75 on 5 n. Pottery making	20	20
581	8 k. 11 on 10 n. Thatching	40	40
582	9 k. on 30 n. Makishi tightrope dancer	40	40
583	10 k. on 75 n. Women carrying water (38×26 mm)	40	40
584	18 k. 50 on 2 k. Pipe-smoking, Gwembe Valley Belle (38×26 mm)	90	90
585	19 k. 50 on 12 n. Mushroom picking (Br.) (1 Nov)	90	90
586	20 k. 50 on 18 n. Millet grinding on stone (V.) (1 Nov)	90	90

(b) *Nos.* 484, 489, 493/5 *and* 497/500 *surch as T* **158**.

587	10 k. on 35 n. Black and Rufous Swallow	10	10
588	3 k. on 5 n. Cloud-scraping Cisticola	20	20
589	8 k. on 1 k. 25, Boulton's Puff-back Flycatcher	40	40
590	9 k. 90 on 1 k. 70, Boehm's Bee Eater	50	50
591	10 k. 40 on 1 k. 60, Anchieta's Sunbird	50	50
592	12 k. 50 on 1 k. Bradfield's Hornbill	60	60
593	15 k. on 1 k. 95, Perrin's Bush Shrike	70	70
594	20 k. on 2 k. Whale-headed Stork	90	90
595	20 k. 35 on 5 k. Taita Falcon	90	90
579/95	Set of 17	8·00	8·00

No. 594 shows the surcharge as "K20·00". The previously listed 20 k. on 2 k., No. 502, is surcharged "K20" only.

156 *Parinari
curatellifolia*

157 *Lamarckiana* sp

1989 (26 July). *Edible Fruits. T* **156** *and similar vert designs. Multicoloured. P* 14½.

596	50 n. Type 156		15	10
597	6 k. 50, *Uapaca kirkiana*		1·25	1·50
598	6 k. 85, Wild Fig		1·25	1·75
599	10 k. Bottle Palm		2·25	2·50
596/9		Set of 4	4·50	5·25

(Des Mrs. G. Ellison. Litho Cartor, France)

1989 (8 Nov). *Grasshoppers. T* **157** *and similar horiz designs. Multicoloured. P* 14×13½.

600	70 n. Type 157		15	10
601	10 k. 40, *Dictyophorus* sp		1·25	1·25
602	12 k. 50, *Cymatomera* sp		1·50	1·50
603	15 k. *Phymateus iris*		2·00	2·00
600/3		Set of 4	4·50	4·25

158 Fireball

159 Postvan, Postman on
Bicycle and Main Post Office,
Lusaka

(Des Mrs. G. Ellison. Litho National Printing & Packing, Zimbabwe)

1989 (6 Dec). *Christmas. Flowers. T* **158** *and similar vert designs. Multicoloured. P* 14½.

604	70 n. Type 158		15	10
605	10 k. 40, Flame Lily		1·00	1·00
606	12 k. 50, Foxglove Lily		1·40	1·40
607	20 k. Vlei Lily		2·40	2·40
604/7		Set of 4	4·50	4·50

(Des D. Miller. Litho Questa)

1990 (2 May). *"Stamp World London 90" International Stamp Exhibition. T* **159** *and similar horiz designs. Multicoloured. P* 14.

608	1 k. 20, Type 159	10	10
609	19 k. 50, Zambia 1980 18 n. butterflies stamp	1·50	1·50
610	20 k. 50, Rhodesia and Nyasaland 1962 9d. and Northern Rhodesia 1925 ½d. stamps	1·50	1·50
611	50 k. 1840 Penny Black and Maltese Cross cancellation	3·50	3·75
608/11	Set of 4	6·00	6·00

COVER PRICES

Cover factors are quoted at the beginning of each country for most issues to 1945. An explanation of the system can be found on page x. The factors quoted do not, however, apply to philatelic covers.

---

160 Footballer and
Ball

161 Road Tanker

(Des R. Vigurs. Litho Questa)

1990 (7 July). *World Cup Football Championship, Italy. T* **160** *and similar vert designs showing football scenes. P* 14.

612	1 k. 20, multicoloured		10	10
613	18 k. 50, multicoloured		1·25	1·25
614	19 k. 50, multicoloured		1·25	1·25
615	20 k. 50, multicoloured		1·25	1·25
612/15		Set of 4	3·50	3·50
MS616	100×73 mm. 50 k. multicoloured		4·00	4·50

No. **MS**616 also exists imperforate.

(Litho Harrison)

1990 (23 July). *10th Anniv of Southern African Development Co-ordination Conference. T* **161** *and similar horiz designs, each showing map of Southern Africa. Multicoloured. P* 12½.

617	1 k. 20, Type 161		10	10
618	19 k. 50, Telecommunications		1·25	1·25
619	20 k. 50, "Regional Co-operation"		1·25	1·25
620	50 k. Transporting coal by cable		3·50	3·50
617/20		Set of 4	5·50	5·50

162 Irrigation

163 The Bird and
the Snake

(Des Mrs. G. Ellison. Litho Questa)

1990 (23 Oct). *26th Anniv of Independence. T* **162** *and similar horiz designs. Multicoloured. P* 14.

621	1 k. 20, Type 162		10	10
622	19 k. 50, Shoe factory		70	70
623	20 k. 50, Mwembeshi II satellite earth station		70	70
624	50 k. "Mother and Child" (statue)		1·75	2·00
621/4		Set of 4	2·75	3·25

(Des Mrs. G. Ellison. Litho Questa)

1990 (30 Oct)–**91**. *Birds* (2nd series). *Vert designs as T* **138**. *Multicoloured. P* 11×13 (10, 15, 30, 50 n., 1 k., 1 k. 20, 2 k., 3 k., 5 k.) *or* 14 (*others*).

625	10 n. Livingstone's Flycatcher		10	10
626	15 n. Bar-winged Weaver		10	10
627	30 n. Purple-throated Cuckoo Shrike		10	10
628	50 n. Retz's Red-billed Helmet Shrike		10	10
629	50 n. As 10 n. (7.5.91)		10	10
630	1 k. As 15 n. (7.5.91)		10	10
631	1 k. 20, Bronze-naped Pigeon		10	10
632	2 k. As 30 n. (7.5.91)		10	10
633	3 k. As 50 n. (No. 628) (7.5.91)		10	10
634	5 k. As 1 k. 20 (7.5.91)		10	10
635	15 k. Corncrake		10	10
636	20 k. Dickinson's Kestrel (7.5.91)		10	10
637	20 k. 50, As 20 k.		10	10
638	50 k. Barrow's Bustard ("Denham's Bustard")		20	25
625/38		Set of 14	80	85

Nos. 635/8 are larger, size 23×39 mm.

(Des Mrs. G. Ellison. Litho Questa)

1991 (11 Jan). *International Literacy Year. Folklore. T* **163** *and similar vert designs. Multicoloured. P* 14.

639	1 k. 20, Type 163		15	10
640	18 k. 50, Kalulu and the Leopard		1·25	1·25
641	19 k. 50, The Mouse and the Lion		1·25	1·25
642	20 k. 50, Kalulu and the Hippopotamus		1·25	1·25
639/42		Set of 4	3·50	3·50

K2

164 Genet

(165)

(Des Mrs. G. Ellison. Litho Questa)

1991 (25 Jan). *Small Carnivores. T* **164** *and similar horiz designs. Multicoloured. P* 14.

643	1 k. 20, Type 164		15	10
644	18 k. 50, Civet		1·25	1·25
645	19 k. 50, Serval		1·25	1·25
646	20 k. 50, African Wild Cat		1·25	1·25
643/6		Set of 4	3·50	3·50

1991 (4 Mar). *Nos. 441/4 surch with T 165.*
647	2 k. on 20 n. Type **129**			65	40
648	2 k. on 45 n. Postman and Livingstone Post Office, 1950			65	40
649	2 k. on 55 n. Postman and Kalomo Post Office, 1902			65	40
650	2 k. on 5 k. African Trans-Continental Telegraph Line under construction, 1900			65	40
647/50			*Set of 4*	2·40	1·40

166 Woman Cooking **167** Chilubula Church near Kasama

(Des A. Mwansa and Daniela Schepp. Litho Cartor)

1991 (28 June). *Soya Promotion Campaign. T 166 and similar vert designs. Multicoloured. P 13½.*
651	1 k. Type **166**			10	10
652	2 k. Soya bean and field			10	10
653	5 k. Mother feeding child			15	15
654	20 k. Healthy and malnourished children			1·00	1·00
655	50 k. President Kaunda holding child			2·00	2·00
651/5			*Set of 5*	3·00	3·00

1991 (5 July). *Various stamps surch as T 165.*
656	**130**	2 k. on 20 n. multicoloured		
657	**127**	2 k. on 25 n. multicoloured (Gold)		
658	–	2 k. on 28 n. multicoloured (No. 344)		
659	–	2 k. on 28 n. multicoloured (No. 393)		
660	–	2 k. on 28 n. multicoloured (No. 401)		
661	–	2 k. on 28 n. multicoloured (No. 418)		
662	–	2 k. on 32 n. multicoloured (No. 422)		
663	–	2 k. on 35 n. multicoloured (No. 453)		
664	**134**	2 k. on 35 n. multicoloured		
665	**137**	2 k. on 35 n. multicoloured		
666	–	2 k. on 45 n. multicoloured (No. 427)		
667	–	2 k. on 45 n. black, new blue and pale blue (No. 430)		
668	–	2 k. on 45 n. deep violet-blue and gold (No. 433)		
669	–	2 k. on 45 n. black, new blue & brownish black (No. 446) (Gold + Blk.)		
670	–	2 k. on 1 k. 60, multicoloured (No. 470)		
671	–	2 k. on 1 k. 70, multicoloured (No. 451)		
672	–	2 k. on 1 k. 70, multicoloured (No. 482)		
673	–	2 k. on 5 k. multicoloured (No. 435)		
674	–	2 k. on 5 k. multicoloured (No. 452)		
675	–	2 k. on 6 k. 50, multicoloured (No. 597)		
676	–	2 k. on 6 k. 85, multicoloured (No. 576)		
677	–	2 k. on 6 k. 85, multicoloured (No. 598)		
678	–	2 k. on 7 k. 85, multicoloured (No. 577)		

The surcharge for No. 669 shows "K2" in gold and the bars in black over gold.

(Des Mrs. G. Ellison. Litho Cartor)

1991 (18 July). *500th Birth Anniv of St. Ignatius Loyola. T 167 and similar vert designs. Multicoloured. P 13½.*
679	1 k. Type **167**			10	10
680	2 k. Chikuni Church near Monze			10	10
681	20 k. Bishop Joseph du Pont			1·00	1·00
682	50 k. Saint Ignatius Loyola			2·00	2·00
679/82			*Set of 4*	3·00	3·00

168 *Adansonia digitata* **169** *Disa hamatopetala*

(Des Mrs G. Ellison. Litho Cartor)

1991 (28 Nov). *Flowering Trees. T 168 and similar horiz designs. Multicoloured. P 13½.*
683	1 k. Type **168**			10	10
684	2 k. *Dichrostachys cinerea*			10	10
685	10 k. *Sterospermum kunthianum*			50	50
686	30 k. *Azana garckeana*			1·40	1·40
683/6			*Set of 4*	1·90	1·90

(Des D. Miller. Litho Cartor)

1992 (6 Feb). *40th Anniv of Queen Elizabeth II's Accession. Horiz designs as T 113 of Kenya. Multicoloured. W w 14 (sideways). P 13½.*
687	4 k. Queen's House			10	10
688	32 k. Traditional village			60	55
689	35 k. Fishermen hauling nets			65	65
690	38 k. Three portraits of Queen Elizabeth			75	75
691	50 k. Queen Elizabeth II			90	1·25
687/91			*Set of 5*	2·75	3·00

(Des Mrs G. Ellison. Litho Cartor)

1992 (28 Feb). *Orchids. T 169 and similar vert designs. Multicoloured. P 13½.*
692	1 k. Type **169**			10	10
693	2 k. *Eulophia paivaeana*			15	15
694	5 k. *Eulophia quartiniana*			30	30
695	20 k. *Aerangis verdickii*			1·50	1·50
692/5			*Set of 4*	1·75	1·75

170 Kasinja Mask **171** Bushbuck

(Des Mrs. G. Ellison. Litho Cartor)

1992 (10 Mar). *Tribal Masks. T 170 and similar vert designs. Multicoloured. P 13½.*
696	1 k. Type **170**				10	10
697	2 k. Chizaluke				10	10
698	10 k. Mwanapweu				25	25
699	30 k. Maliya				90	90
696/9				*Set of 4*	1·25	1·25

(Des Mrs. G. Ellison. Litho Questa)

1992 (14 Sept). *Antelopes. T 171 and similar horiz designs. Multicoloured. P 14.*
700	4 k. Type **171**				10	10
701	40 k. Eland				40	40
702	45 k. Roan Antelope				45	45
703	100 k. Sable Antelope				1·10	1·10
700/3				*Set of 4*	1·75	1·75

172 DH66 Hercules

(Des Mrs G. Ellison. Litho Questa)

1992 (24 Nov). *60th Anniv of Airmail Service. T 172 and similar horiz designs. Multicoloured. P 14.*
704	4 k. Type **172**				10	10
705	40 k. VC10				40	40
706	45 k. "C" Class flying boat				45	45
707	100 k. DC10				1·10	1·10
704/7				*Set of 4*	1·75	1·75

173 Wise Men with Gifts **174** Hurdling

(Litho Questa)

1992 (23 Dec). *Christmas. T 173 and similar horiz designs. Multicoloured. P 14.*
708	10 k. Type **173**				10	10
709	80 k. Nativity				80	80
710	90 k. Angelic choir				90	90
711	100 k. Angel and shepherds				1·00	1·00
708/11				*Set of 4*	2·50	2·50
MS712	209×57 mm. Nos. 708/11				2·75	3·00

(Des R. Vigurs. Litho Questa)

1992 (28 Dec). *Olympic Games, Barcelona. T 174 and similar vert designs. Multicoloured. P 14.*
713	10 k. Type **174**				10	10
714	40 k. Boxing				40	40
715	80 k. Judo				80	80
716	100 k. Cycling				1·00	1·00
713/16				*Set of 4*	2·00	2·00

POSTAGE DUE STAMPS

D 1 D 2

(Typo D.L.R.)

1929–52. *Wmk Mult Script CA. Ordinary paper. P 14.*
D1	D 1	1d. grey-black			2·50	2·50
		a. Chalk-surfaced paper. *Blk* (22.1.52)			6·00	12·00
		ab. Error. St. Edward's Crown, W9*b*			£500	
D2		2d. grey-black			3·00	3·00
D3		3d. grey-black			3·00	21·00
		a. Chalk-surfaced paper. *Blk* (22.1.52)			8·50	35·00
		ab. Error. Crown missing, W9*a*			£160	
		ac. Error. St. Edward's Crown, W9*b*			£130	
D4		4d. grey-black			6·00	26·00
D1/4				*Set of 4*	13·00	48·00
D1/4	Perf "Specimen"			*Set of 4*	80·00	

The 2d. is known bisected and used as a 1d. at Nkana on various dates between 1937 and 1951 and on understamped letters from South Africa at Chingola in May 1950 (*Price on cover from* £250).

Following the increase in the internal letter rate from 1½d. to 2d. on 1 July 1953 stocks of postage due stamps at Mkushi became exhausted. As an emergency measure the sub-post-master was authorised to surcharge examples of Nos. 28 and 55 "POSTAGE DUE 1d." in red by typewriter. Examples properly used on cover between 6 July and 15 September 1953 are of considerable scarcity (*Price on cover* £1200). No unused examples exist.

(Des D. Smith. Litho Govt Ptr, Lusaka)

1963 (10 Dec). *P 12½.*
D 5	D 2	1d. orange			40	2·00
D 6		2d. deep blue			40	2·25
D 7		3d. lake			45	2·75
D 8		4d. ultramarine			60	4·00
D 9		6d. purple			1·40	4·50
D10		1s. light emerald			4·00	11·00
		a. Imperf (vert pair)			£170	
		b. Block of four imperf horiz and imp between vert			£500	
D5/10				*Set of 6*	6·50	24·00

In all values the stamps in the right-hand vertical row of the sheet are imperforate on the right.

D 3

(Des D. Smith. Litho Govt Printer, Lusaka)

1964 (24 Oct). *P 12½.*
D11	D 3	1d. orange			30	1·00
D12		2d. deep blue			35	1·40
D13		3d. lake			45	1·60
D14		4d. ultramarine			45	2·00
D15		6d. purple			45	2·25
D16		1s. light emerald			55	4·25
D11/16				*Set of 6*	2·25	11·50

In all values the left-hand vertical row of the sheet is imperf at left and the bottom horizontal row is imperf at bottom. The above were crudely perforated, resulting in variations in the sizes of the stamps.

The above were withdrawn on 15 January 1968 and thereafter decimal currency postage stamps were used for postage due purposes with appropriate cancellations.

Appendix

The following stamps have either been issued in excess of postal needs, or have not been made available to the public in reasonable quantities at face value. Miniature sheets, imperforate stamps etc., are excluded from this section.

1984

Olympic Games, Los Angeles. 90 n. × 5, each embossed on gold foil.

1986

Classic Cars. 1 k. 50 × 25, each embossed on gold foil.

Zanzibar
see Tanzania

Zimbabwe
(formerly Rhodesia)

SOUTHERN RHODESIA

PRICES FOR STAMPS ON COVER TO 1945
Nos. 1/61 *from* × 2

SELF-GOVERNMENT

The southern part of Rhodesia, previously administered by the British South Africa Company, was annexed by the British Government on 12 September 1923 and granted the status of a self-governing colony.

1   **2** King George V   **3** Victoria Falls

(Recess Waterlow)

1924 (1 Apr)–29. *P* 14.

1	1	½d. blue-green		80	10
		a. Imperf between (horiz pair)		£500	£500
		b. Imperf between (vert pair)		£600	£600
		c. Imperf vert (horiz pair)		£650	
2		1d. bright rose		1·10	10
		a. Imperf between (horiz pair)		£600	£550
		b. Imperf between (vert pair)		£750	
		c. Perf 12½ (coil) (1929)		2·75	60·00
3		1½d. bistre-brown		80	45
		a. Imperf between (horiz pair)		£7000	
		b. Imperf between (vert pair)		£3750	
		c. Printed double, once albino		£100	
4		2d. black and purple-grey		55	30
		a. Imperf between (horiz pair)		£6000	
5		3d. blue		1·50	2·00
6		4d. black and orange-red		1·10	2·75
7		6d. black and mauve		1·10	2·25
		a. Imperf between (horiz pair)		£9000	
8		8d. purple and pale green		10·00	12·00
9		10d. blue and rose		11·00	35·00
10		1s. black and light blue		3·50	3·25
11		1s. 6d. black and yellow		18·00	27·00
12		2s. black and brown		17·00	17·00
13		2s. 6d. blue and sepia		35·00	50·00
14		5s. blue and blue-green		55·00	85·00
1/14			*Set of* 14	£140	£225

Prices for "imperf between" varieties are for adjacent stamps from the same pane and not for those separated by wide gutter margins between vertical or horizontal pairs, which come from the junction of two panes.

(T **2** recess by B.W.; T **3** typo by Waterlow)

1931 (1 April)–**37**. *T* **2** *(line perf 12 unless otherwise stated) and* **3** *(comb perf 15 × 14). (The 11½ perf is comb.)*.

15	2	½d. green		30	20
		a. Perf 11½ (1933)		30	10
		b. Perf 14 (1935)		75	10
16		1d. scarlet		40	10
		a. Perf 11½ (1933)		60	10
		b. Perf 14 (1935)		50	10

16c	2	1½d. chocolate (1933)		55·00	30·00
		d. Perf 11½ (1.4.32)		1·25	55
17	3	2d. black and sepia		3·25	70
18		3d. deep ultramarine		8·50	11·00
19	2	4d. black and vermilion		1·10	70
		a. Perf 11½ (1935)		15·00	5·00
		b. Perf 14 (10.37)		32·00	40·00
20		6d. black and magenta		2·00	85
		a. Perf 11½ (1933)		12·00	55
		b. Perf 14 (1936)		16·00	60
21		8d. violet and olive-green		1·75	3·25
21b		9d. vermilion and olive-green (1.9.34)		6·00	7·50
22		10d. blue and scarlet		6·00	3·00
		a. Perf 11½ (1933)		6·00	13·00
23		1s. black and greenish blue		1·75	2·25
		a. Perf 11½ (1935)		70·00	45·00
		b. Perf 14 (10.37)		£180	£130
24		1s. 6d. black and orange-yellow		10·00	16·00
		a. Perf 11½ (1936)		48·00	60·00
25		2s. black and brown		14·00	4·50
		a. Perf 11½ (1933)		35·00	30·00
26		2s. 6d. blue and drab		30·00	35·00
		a. Perf 11½ (1933)		28·00	30·00
27		5s. blue and blue-green		48·00	48·00
		a. Printed on gummed side		£3250	
15/27			*Set of* 15	£120	£110

No. 16c was issued in booklets only.

PRINTERS. All stamps from Types **4** to **29** were recess-printed by Waterlow and Sons, Ltd, London, except where otherwise stated.

4

1932 (1 May). *P* 12½.

29	4	2d. green and chocolate		2·50	40
30		3d. deep ultramarine		3·25	1·75
		a. Imperf horiz (vert pair)		£6000	£6500
		b. Imperf between (vert pair)		£8500	

5 Victoria Falls

1935 (6 May). *Silver Jubilee. P* 11 × 12.

31	5	1d. olive and rose-carmine		2·00	75
32		2d. emerald and sepia		3·50	3·00
33		3d. violet and deep blue		5·00	10·00
34		6d. black and purple		7·00	9·50
31/4			*Set of* 4	16·00	21·00

1935–41. *Inscr* "POSTAGE AND REVENUE".

35	4	2d. green and chocolate (p 12½)		1·40	4·00
		a. Perf 14 (1941)		30	10
35b		3d. deep blue (p 14) (1938)		1·25	10

6 Victoria Falls and Railway Bridge   **7** King George VI

1937 (12 May). *Coronation. P* 12½.

36	6	1d. olive and rose-carmine		80	30
37		2d. emerald and sepia		80	75
38		3d. violet and blue		3·75	5·00
39		6d. black and purple		2·25	2·25
36/9			*Set of* 4	7·00	7·50

1937 (25 Nov). *P* 14.

40	7	½d. green		40	10
41		1d. scarlet		30	10
42		1½d. red-brown		65	10
43		4d. red-orange		1·25	10
44		6d. grey-black		1·25	10
45		8d. emerald-green		1·75	90
46		9d. pale blue		1·25	20
47		10d. purple		1·40	1·75
48		1s. black and blue-green		1·00	10
		a. Double print of frame		£700	
49		1s. 6d. black and orange-yellow		6·50	1·25
50		2s. black and brown		9·50	55
51		2s. 6d. ultramarine and purple		6·50	2·50
52		5s. blue and blue-green		26·00	2·00
40/52			*Set of* 13	50·00	8·50

Nos. 40/1 exist in coils, constructed from normal sheets.

8 British South Africa Co's Arms   **9** Fort Salisbury, 1890

10 Cecil John Rhodes (after S. P. Kendrick)   **15** Lobengula's Kraal and Govt House, Salisbury

Recut shirt collar (R. 6/1)

(Des Mrs. L. E. Curtis (½d., 1d., 1½d., 3d.), Mrs I. Mount (others))

1940 (3 June). *British South Africa Company's Golden Jubilee. T* **8/10, 15** *and similar designs. P* 14.

53		½d. slate-violet and green		10	15
54		1d. violet-blue and scarlet		10	10
55		1½d. black and red-brown		10	20
		a. Recut shirt collar		8·00	
56		2d. green and bright violet		30	30
57		3d. black and blue		30	40
58		4d. green and brown		1·40	1·10
59		6d. chocolate and green		30	85
60		1s. blue and green		45	1·50
53/60			*Set of* 8	2·75	4·00

Designs: *Horiz* (*as T* **8**)—2d. Fort Victoria; 3d. Rhodes makes peace. *Vert* (*as T* **10**)—4d. Victoria Falls Bridge; 6d. Statue of Sir Charles Coghlan.

16 Mounted Pioneer   Hat brim retouch (P1 1B R. 1/8)

(Roto South African Govt Printer, Pretoria)

1943 (1 Nov). *50th Anniv of Occupation of Matabeleland. W 9 of South Africa (Mult Springbok) sideways. P* 14.

61	**16**	2d. brown and green	10	30
		a. Hat brim retouch	10·00	

17 Queen Elizabeth II when Princess and Princess Margaret

1947 (1 Apr). *Royal Visit. T* **17** *and similar horiz design. P* 14.

62	½d. black and green	10	30
63	1d. black and scarlet	10	30

Design:—1d. King George VI and Queen Elizabeth.

19 Queen Elizabeth   **20** King George VI   **21** Queen Elizabeth II when Princess

22 Princess Margaret   Damage to right-hand frame (R.1/10)

1947 (8 May). *Victory. P* 14.

64	**19**	1d. carmine	10	10
65	**20**	2d. slate	10	10
		a. Double print	£850	
		b. Damaged frame	5·00	
66	**21**	3d. blue	20	30
67	**22**	6d. orange	20	30
64/7		*Set of* 4	50	70

(Recess B.W.)

1949 (10 Oct). *75th Anniv of U.P.U. As Nos. 145/8 of Jamaica.*

68	2d. slate-green	65	20
69	3d. blue	1·10	2·50

23 Queen Victoria, Arms and King George VI

1950 (12 Sept). *Diamond Jubilee of Southern Rhodesia. P* 14.

70	**23**	2d. green and brown	20	30

24 "Medical Services"

(Des A. R. Winter (2d.), Mrs. J. M. Enalim (others))

1953 (15 Apr). *Birth Centenary of Cecil Rhodes. T* **24** *and similar horiz designs. P* 14.

71	½d. pale blue and sepia	15	70
72	1d. chestnut and blue-green	15	10
73	2d. grey-green and violet	15	10
74	4½d. deep blue-green & deep ultramarine	75	1·75
75	1s. black and red-brown	3·00	70
71/5	*Set of* 5	3·75	3·00

Designs:—1d. "Agriculture"; 2d. "Building"; 4½d. "Water Supplies"; 1s. "Transport".

No. 74 also commemorates the Diamond Jubilee of Matabeleland.

1953 (30 May). *Rhodes Centenary Exhibition, Bulawayo. As No. 59 of Zambia, but without watermark.*

76	6d. violet	20	30

30 Queen Elizabeth II

(Recess D.L.R.)

1953 (1 June). *Coronation. P* 12 × 12½.

77	**30**	2s. 6d. carmine	5·50	5·00

31 Sable Antelope   **33** Rhodes's Grave

34 Farm Worker   **42** Basket Maker

43 Balancing Rocks   **44** Coat of Arms

(Recess, centre typo (4d.), B.W.)

1953 (31 Aug). *T* **31**, **33/4**, **42/4** *and similar designs. P* 13½ × 14 (2d., 6d., 5s.), 14 (10s., £1) *or* 13½ × 13½ (*others*).

78	½d. grey-green and claret	15	30
79	1d. green and brown	15	10
80	2d. deep chestnut and reddish violet	15	10
81	3d. chocolate and rose-red	55	60
82	4d. red, green and indigo	1·75	10
83	4½d. black and deep bright blue	1·75	1·75
84	6d. brown-olive & deep turquoise-green	2·25	30
85	9d. deep blue and reddish brown	3·50	1·75
86	1s. reddish violet and light blue	75	10
87	2s. purple and scarlet	7·50	3·25
88	2s. 6d. yellow-olive and orange-brown	6·00	3·75
89	5s. yellow-brown and deep green	14·00	7·50
90	10s. red-brown and olive	16·00	35·00
91	£1 rose-red and black	25·00	35·00
78/91	*Set of* 14	70·00	80·00

Designs: *Vert* (as *T* **31**)—1d. Tobacco planter. (As *T* **33**)—6d. Baobab tree. *Horiz* (as *T* **34**)—4d. Flame Lily; 4½d. Victoria Falls; 9d. Lion; 1s. Zimbabwe Ruins; 2s. Birchenough Bridge; 2s. 6d. Kariba Gorge.

For issues from 1954 to 1963 see under RHODESIA AND NYASALAND.

ALTERED CATALOGUE NUMBERS

Any Catalogue numbers altered from the last edition are shown as a list in the introductory pages.

---

45 Maize   **50** Flame Lily

56 Cattle   **58** Coat of Arms

(Des V. Whiteley. Photo Harrison)

1964 (19 Feb). *T* **45**, **50**, **56**, **58** *and similar horiz designs. P* 14½ (½d. to 4d.), 13½ × 13 (6d. to 2s. 6d.) *or* 14½ × 14 (*others*).

92	½d. yellow, yellow-green and light blue	15	50
93	1d. reddish violet and yellow-ochre	15	10
	a. Reddish violet omitted	£850	
94	2d. yellow and deep violet	15	10
95	3d. chocolate and pale blue	15	10
96	4d. yellow-orange and deep green	30	10
97	6d. carmine-red, yellow & deep dull green	40	10
98	9d. red-brown, yellow and olive-green	2·00	80
99	1s. blue-green and ochre	2·50	10
	a. Blue-green (Queen and emeralds) omitted	£1100	
100	1s. 3d. red, violet and yellow-green	3·25	10
101	2s. blue and ochre	2·50	85
102	2s. 6d. ultramarine and vermilion	3·75	70
	a. Vermilion omitted	£1000	
	b. Ultramarine omitted	£1600	
103	5s. light brown, bistre-yellow & light blue	4·50	2·00
104	10s. black, yell-ochre, lt blue & carmine-red	11·00	6·50
105	£1 brown, yellow-grn, buff & salmon-pink	7·00	13·00
92/105	*Set of* 14	35·00	21·00

Designs: (As *T* **45**)—1d. African Buffalo; 2d. Tobacco; 3d. Greater Kudu; 4d. Citrus. (As *T* **50**)—9d. Ansellia Orchid; 1s. Emeralds; 1s. 3d. Aloe; 2s. Lake Kyle; 2s. 6d. Tiger Fish. (As *T* **56**)—10s. Helmet Guineafowl.

Nos. 92 and 93 exist in coils constructed from normal sheets. Nos. 102a and 102b each occurred on one vertical row of stamps from separate sheets. They were caused by the printing press being stopped and then restarted.

See also Nos. 359/72 of Rhodesia.

In October 1964 Southern Rhodesia was renamed Rhodesia.

RHODESIA

59 "Telecommunications"   **60** Bangala Dam

(Des V. Whiteley. Photo Harrison)

1965 (17 May). *I.T.U. Centenary. P* 14½.

351	**59**	6d. violet and light yellow-olive	1·00	25
352		1s. 3d. violet and lilac	1·00	35
353		2s. 6d. violet and light brown	2·00	3·00
351/3		*Set of* 3	3·50	3·25

(Des V. Whiteley. Photo Harrison)

1965 (19 July). *Water Conservation. T* **60** *and similar vert designs. Multicoloured. P* 14.

354	3d. Type **60**	20	10
355	4d. Irrigation canal	85	75
356	2s. 6d. Cutting sugar cane	1·75	2·25
354/6	*Set of* 3	2·50	2·75

63 Sir Winston Churchill, Quill, Sword and Houses of Parliament

(Des H. Baxter. Photo Harrison)

1965 (16 Aug). *Churchill Commemoration. P* 14½.

357	**63**	1s. 3d. black and bright blue	50	35

UNILATERAL DECLARATION OF INDEPENDENCE

Independence was declared by Rhodesia on 11 November 1965 but this was not recognised by the British Government. Following a conference in London during 1979 it was agreed that the British Government should resume control, pending elections to be held in February 1980.

After the elections Rhodesia became an independent republic within the Commonwealth on 18 April 1980, as ZIMBABWE.

64 Coat of Arms

(Des Col. C. R. Dickenson. Litho Mardon Printers, Salisbury)

1965 (8 Dec). *"Independence"*. P 11.
358	64	2s. 6d. multicoloured	..	15	15
		a. Imperf (pair)	..	£600	

INDEPENDENCE
11th November
1965

INDEPENDENCE = 5/-
11th November 1965

(65)   (66)

1966 (17 Jan). (a) Nos. 92/105 optd with **T 65** or larger (5s. to £1).
359		½d. yellow, yellow-green and light blue	..	10	10
		a. Pair, one stamp without opt.	..	£1800	
360		1d. reddish violet and yellow-ochre	..	10	10
361		2d. yellow and deep violet ..	..	10	10
362		3d. chocolate and pale blue ..	..	10	10
363		4d. yellow-orange and deep green	..	15	10
364		6d. carmine-red, yellow & dp dull green	..	15	10
365		9d. red-brown, yellow and olive-green	..	20	10
		a. Opt double	..	£190	
366		1s. blue-green and ochre	..	25	10
		a. Opt double	..	£190	
367		1s. 3d. red, violet and yellow-green	..	80	10
368		2s. blue and ochre ..	..	90	2·50
369		2s. 6d. ultramarine and vermilion	..	60	25
370		5s. light brown, bistre-yellow & lt blue	..	6·00	4·00
		a. Opt double	..	£275	
371		10s. black, yellow-ochre, lt bl & carm-red	..	3·00	1·25
372		£1 brown, yell-green, buff & salmon-pink	..	1·50	1·50

(b) No. 357 surch with **T 66**
373		5s. on 1s. 3d. black and bright blue (R.)	..	16·00	30·00
		a. "5/-" omitted	..	..	
359/73			Set of 15	27·00	35·00

Owing to the existence of forgeries, No. 370a should only be purchased when accompanied by a certificate of genuineness.

67 Emeralds   **68 Zeederberg Coach, circa 1895**

(Des V. Whiteley. Photo Harrison)

1966 (9 Feb). *As Nos. 92/105, but inscr "RHODESIA" as T 67.* Some designs and colours changed. P 14½ (1d. to 4d.), 13½×13 (6d. to 2s. 6d) or 14½×14 (5s. to £1).
374	–	1d. reddish violet and yellow-ochre	..	10	10
375	–	2d. yellow-orange and dp grn (as No. 96)	..	10	10
		a. Yellow-orange omitted	..	£700	
376	–	3d. chocolate and pale blue	..	10	10
		a. Chocolate omitted ..	..	£1000	
		b. Pale blue omitted ..	..	£800	
377	67	4d. emerald and sepia ..	..	30	10
378	50	6d. carmine-red, yellow & dp dull green	..	15	10
379	–	9d. yellow and deep violet (as No. 94)	..	15	20
380	45	1s. yellow, yellow-green and light blue	..	15	10
381	–	1s. 3d. blue and ochre (as No. 101)	..	25	15
		a. Ochre omitted	..		
382	–	1s. 6d. red-brn, yell & ol-grn (as No. 98)	..	75	25
383	–	2s. red, violet and yell-grn (as No. 100)	..	40	80
384	–	2s. 6d. blue, vermilion & turquoise-blue	..	40	20
385	56	5s. light brown, bistre-yellow & lt blue	..	40	90
386	–	10s. black, yell-ochre, lt blue & carm-red	..	2·50	4·00
387	58	£1 brown, yell-grn, buff & salmon-pink	..	14·00	8·00
374/87			Set of 14	17·00	13·00

Nos. 379/80 are in larger format, as T 50.

No. 374 exists in coils constructed from normal sheets. Coil-vending machines were withdrawn from service in 1967.

No. 376a occurred in the bottom row of a sheet, No. 376b in the top two rows of a sheet and No. 381a in the third vertical row on two sheets.

For stamps printed by lithography, see Nos. 397/407.

PRINTERS. All the following stamps were printed by lithography by Mardon Printers, Salisbury.

(Des V. Whiteley (Nos. 388/90))

1966 (2 May). *28th Congress of Southern Africa Philatelic Federation ("Rhopex"). T 68 and similar horiz designs. P 14½.*
388		3d. multicoloured	..	30	10
389		9d. grey-buff, sepia and grey-green ..	..	40	35
390		1s. 6d. pale blue and black	..	60	50
391		2s. 6d. salmon-pink, pale dull grn & blk	..	70	80
388/91			Set of 4	1·75	1·50
MS392		126×84 mm. Nos. 388/91 (toned paper)		17·00	25·00
		a. White paper ..	..	25·00	28·00

Designs:—9d. Sir Rowland Hill; 1s. 6d. The Penny Black; 2s. 6d. Rhodesian stamp of 1892 (No. 12).

69 De Havilland "Rapide" (1946)   **70 Kudu**

1966 (1 June). *20th Anniv of Central African Airways. T 69 and similar horiz designs. P 14½ × 14.*
393	6d. black, blue, yellow and green	..	1·00	35
394	1s. 3d. blue, yellow-orange, black and green		1·25	55
395	2s. 6d. black, blue, yellow and green	..	3·50	1·75
396	5s. black and blue	..	6·00	3·50
393/6		Set of 4	10·50	5·50

Aircraft:—1s. 3d. Douglas "DC3." (1953); 2s. 6d. Vickers "Viscount" (1956); 5s. Modern jet.

1966–69. *As Nos. 374/87 but litho. P 14½ (1d. to 2s.) or 14½ × 14 (others).*
397	1d. reddish violet and yellow-ochre (shades) (2.6.66)	..	15	10
398	2d. orange and green (1.11.67)	..	85	40
399	3d. chocolate-brn & pale grnsh bl (29.1.68)	..	75	10
400	4d. emerald, bistre-brown & drab (21.9.66)		65	10
401	6d. carmine-red, yell & ol-grey (1.11.66)	..	60	40
402	9d. yellow and violet (20.11.67)	..	30	10
403	1s. 3d. blue and ochre (1.11.66)	..	4·50	30
404	2s. dull red, violet & sage-green (18.7.66)	..	3·75	5·00
405	5s. yellow-brown, deep bistre-yellow and light blue (25.6.66)	..	8·00	4·50
406	10s. black, buff, lt bl & carm-red (10.8.66)	..	35·00	38·00
407	£1 pale brown, yellow-green, brown-ochre and salmon (10.8.66)	..	40·00	42·00
397/407		Set of 11	85·00	80·00

In addition to the change in printing process from photogravure to lithography and the difference in perforation in the 6d. to 2s. values (14½ instead of 13½ × 13) and shade variations, the oval portrait frame is larger (and in some values thicker) in the 1d. to 2s., and in the 1s. 3d. the Queen's head is also larger.

Trial printings, made in June 1966, exist of the 5s., 10s., and £1 values on a slightly thinner paper. These are rare.

1967–68. *Dual Currency Issue. As Nos. 376, 380 and 382/4 but value in decimal currency in addition as in T 70. P 14½. White gum (No. 408) or cream gum (others).*
408	3d./2½ c. chocolate-brown and pale greenish blue (15.3.67)	..	60	20
409	1s./10 c. yell, grn & greenish bl (1.11.67)	..	70	45
410	1s. 6d./15 c. red-brown, yellow and yellow-green (11.3.68)	..	4·75	90
411	2s./20 c. dull red, viol and sage-grn (11.3.68)		10·00	9·00
412	2s. 6d./25 c. ultramarine-blue, vermilion and bright turquoise-blue (9.12.68)		45·00	60·00
408/12		Set of 5	55·00	65·00

71 Dr. Jameson (administrator)

(Des from painting by F. M. Bennett)

1967 (17 May). *Famous Rhodesians (1st issue) and 50th Death Anniv of Dr. Jameson. P 14½.*
413	71	1s. 6d. multicoloured	30	35

See also Nos. 426, 430, 457, 458, 469, 480, 488 and 513.

72 Soapstone Sculpture (Joram Mariga)

1967 (12 July). *Tenth Anniv of Opening of Rhodes National Gallery. T 72 and similar vert designs. P 14½ × 14 (3d., 9d.) or 14 (others).*
414	3d. reddish chestnut, yellow-olive and black	10	10
415	9d. lt greenish blue, dp olive-brown & black	20	20
	a. Perf 13½ ..	..	7·50	18·00
416	1s. 3d. multicoloured	..	20	25
417	2s. 6d. multicoloured	..	25	35
414/17		Set of 4	65	75

Designs:—9d. "The Burgher of Calais" (detail, Rodin); 1s. 3d. "The Knight" (stamp design wrongly inscr) (Roberto Crippa); 2s. 6d. "John the Baptist" (M. Tossini).

73 Baobab Tree

1967 (6 Sept). *Nature Conservation. T 73 and similar designs. P 14½.*
418	4d. light brown and black	..	20	25
419	4d. yellow-olive and black	..	20	25
420	4d. deep grey and black	..	20	25
421	4d. yellow-orange and black..	..	20	25
418/21		Set of 4	70	90

Designs: *Horiz*—No. 418, Type 73; No. 419, White Rhinoceros; No. 420, African Elephants. *Vert*—No. 421, Wild Gladiolus.

74 Wooden Hand Plough

(Des Rose Martin)

1968 (26 Apr). *15th World Ploughing Contest, Norton, Rhodesia. T 74 and similar horiz designs. P 14½.*
422	3d. pale orange, orange-verm & lake-brown	10	10
423	9d. multicoloured	..	20	20
424	1s. 6d. multicoloured	..	30	45
425	2s. 6d. multicoloured	..	35	70
422/5		Set of 4	85	1·40

Designs:—9d. Early wheel plough; 1s. 6d. Steam powered tractor, and ploughs; 2s. 6d. Modern tractor, and plough.

75 Alfred Beit (national benefactor)   **76 Raising the Flag, Bulawayo, 1893**

(Des from painting by A. Haywood)

1968 (15 July). *Famous Rhodesians (2nd issue). P 14½.*
426	75	1s. 6d. pale orange, black and brown	30	30

(Des Rose Martin)

1968 (4 Nov). *75th Anniv of Matabeleland. T 76 and similar vert designs. P 14½.*
427	3d. pale orange, red-orange and black	..	10	10
428	9d. multicoloured	..	15	20
429	1s. 6d. pale turquoise-green, deep emerald and blackish green	..	20	35
427/9		Set of 3	40	55

Designs:—9d. View and coat of arms of Bulawayo; 1s. 6d. Allan Wilson (combatant in the Matabele War).

77 Sir William Henry Milton (administrator)

(Des from painting by S. Kendrick)

1969 (15 Jan). *Famous Rhodesians (3rd issue). P 14½.*
430	77	1s. 6d. multicoloured ..	20	45

78 2 ft Gauge Steam Locomotive, Beira-Salisbury Line, 1899

(Des Rose Martin)

1969 (22 May). *70th Anniv of Opening of Beira-Salisbury Railway. T 78 and similar horiz designs showing locomotives. Multicoloured. P 14½.*
431	3d. Type 78	..	1·00	10
432	9d. Steam locomotive, 1904	..	1·50	75
433	1s. 6d. Articulated steam locomotive, 1950	..	5·50	3·25
434	2s. 6d. Diesel locomotive, 1955	..	7·50	6·50
431/4		Set of 4	14·00	9·50

79 Low Level Bridge

(Des Rose Martin)

1969 (18 Sept). *Bridges of Rhodesia. T* **79** *and similar horiz designs. Multicoloured. P* 14½.

435	3d. Type **79**	..	75	10
436	9d. Mpudzi bridge	..	1·00	30
437	1s. 6d. Umniati bridge	..	2·50	1·25
438	2s. 6d. Birchenough bridge	..	3·50	1·75
435/8		*Set of 4*	7·00	3·00

(New Currency. 100 cents = 1 dollar)

80 Harvesting Wheat   81 Devil's Cataract, Victoria Falls

(Des from colour-transparencies (3, 6 c.), Rose Martin (others))

1970 (17 Feb)–**73**. *Decimal Currency. T* **80/1** *and similar horiz designs. P* 14½.

439	1 c. multicoloured	..	10	10
	a. Booklet pane of 4	..	20	
440	2 c. multicoloured	..	10	10
441	2½ c. multicoloured	..	10	10
	a. Booklet pane of 4	..	20	
441c	3 c. multicoloured (1.1.73)	..	1·25	10
	ca. Booklet pane of 4	..	4·50	
442	3½ c. multicoloured	..	10	10
	a. Booklet pane of 4	..	40	
442b	4 c. multicoloured (1.1.73)	..	1·50	30
	ba. Booklet pane of 4	..	5·50	
443	5 c. multicoloured	..	15	10
443b	6 c. multicoloured (1.1.73)	..	4·00	3·00
443c	7½ c. multicoloured (1.1.73)	..	7·50	80
444	8 c. multicoloured	..	1·25	20
445	10 c. multicoloured	..	60	10
446	12½ c. multicoloured	..	1·00	10
446a	14 c. multicoloured (1.1.73)	..	15·00	90
447	15 c. multicoloured	..	2·50	15
448	20 c. multicoloured	..	1·75	15
449	25 c. multicoloured	..	3·00	65
450	50 c. turquoise and ultramarine	..	2·25	70
451	$1 multicoloured	..	3·00	3·00
452	$2 multicoloured	..	11·00	22·00
439/52		*Set of 19*	48·00	26·00

Designs: *Size as T* **80**—2 c. Pouring molten metal; 2½ c. Zimbabwe Ruins; 3 c. Articulated lorry; 3½ c. and 4 c. Statue of Cecil Rhodes; 5 c. Mine headgear. *Size as T* **81**—6 c. Hydrofoil *Seaflight*; 7½ c. As 8 c.; 10 c. Yachting on Lake McIlwaine; 12½ c. Hippopotamus in river; 14 c. and 15 c. Kariba Dam; 20 c. Irrigation canal. *As T* **80/1** *but larger* (31 × 26 *mm*)—25 c. Bateleur Eagles; 50 c. Radar antenna and Vickers "Viscount"; $1 "Air Rescue"; $2 Rhodesian flag.

82 Despatch Rider, *circa* 1890

(Des Rose Martin)

1970 (1 July). *Inauguration of Posts and Telecommunications Corporation. T* **82** *and similar horiz designs. Multicoloured. P* 14½.

453	2½ c. Type **82**	..	25	10
454	3½ c. Loading mail at Salisbury airport	..	40	25
455	15 c. Constructing telegraph line, *circa* 1890	..	1·25	2·00
456	25 c. Telephone and modern telecommunications equipment	..	2·00	3·50
453/6		*Set of 4*	3·50	5·25

83 Mother Patrick (Dominican nurse and teacher)

(Des Rose Martin from photograph)

1970 (16 Nov). *Famous Rhodesians (4th issue). P* 14½.

457	**83** 15 c. multicoloured	..	40	40

84 Frederick Courteney Selous (big-game hunter, explorer and pioneer)

(Des from painting by L. C. Dickinson)

1971 (1 Mar). *Famous Rhodesians (5th issue). P* 14½.

458	**84** 15 c. multicoloured	..	40	40

85 Hoopoe   86 Porphyritic Granite

(Des from photographs by Peter Ginn)

1971 (1 June). *Birds of Rhodesia (1st series). T* **85** *and similar multicoloured designs. P* 14½.

459	2 c. Type **85**	..	1·25	20
460	2½ c. Half-collared Kingfisher (*horiz*)	..	1·25	20
461	5 c. Golden-breasted Bunting	..	3·50	60
462	7½ c. Carmine Bee Eater	..	4·00	1·00
463	8 c. Red-eyed Bulbul	..	4·00	1·25
464	25 c. Senegal Wattled Plover (*horiz*)	..	8·50	2·75
459/64		*Set of 6*	20·00	5·50

See also Nos. 537/42.

(Des from photographs by University of Rhodesia and Dept of Geological Survey)

1971 (30 Aug). *"Granite 71" Geological Symposium. T* **86** *and similar vert designs. Multicoloured. P* 14.

465	2½ c. Type **86**	..	75	10
466	7½ c. Muscovite mica seen through microscope	..	1·75	80
467	15 c. Granite seen through microscope	..	2·50	3·25
468	25 c. Geological map of Rhodesia	..	3·25	4·75
465/8		*Set of 4*	7·50	8·00

87 Dr. Robert Moffat (missionary)

1972 (14 Feb). *Famous Rhodesians (6th issue). P* 14½.

469	**87** 13 c. multicoloured	..	1·00	90

88 Bird ("Be Airwise")   89 "The Three Kings"

(Des C. Lawton)

1972 (17 July). *"Prevent Pollution". T* **88** *and similar horiz designs. Multicoloured. P* 14½.

470	2½ c. Type **88**	..	20	10
471	3½ c. Antelope ("Be Countrywise")	..	20	10
472	7 c. Fish ("Be Waterwise")	..	30	45
473	13 c. City ("Be Citywise")	..	45	70
470/3		*Set of 4*	1·00	1·25

1972 (28 Aug). *"Rhophil '72". As Nos.* 439a, 441a *and* 442a *with commemorative inscr in margins. Each* 66 × 78 *mm.*

MS474	1 c. multicoloured	..	2·50	3·50
MS475	2½ c. multicoloured	..	2·50	3·50
MS476	3½ c. multicoloured	..	2·50	3·50
MS474/6		*Set of 3 sheets*	6·75	9·50

(Des Rose Martin)

1972 (18 Oct). *Christmas. P* 14.

477	**89** 2 c. multicoloured	..	10	10
478	5 c. multicoloured	..	20	15
479	13 c. multicoloured	..	50	55
477/9		*Set of 3*	70	70

90 Dr. David Livingstone   91 W.M.O. Emblem

1973 (2 Apr). *Famous Rhodesians (7th issue). P* 14.

480	**90** 14 c. multicoloured	..	70	75

(Des S. J. Ivey)

1973 (2 July). *I.M.O./W.M.O. Centenary. P* 14.

481	**91** 3 c. multicoloured	..	15	10
482	14 c. multicoloured	..	50	60
483	25 c. multicoloured	..	1·00	1·50
481/3		*Set of 3*	1·50	2·00

92 Arms of Rhodesia

1973 (10 Oct). *50th Anniv of Responsible Government. P* 14.

484	**92** 2½ c. multicoloured	..	15	10
485	4 c. multicoloured	..	20	20
486	7½ c. multicoloured	..	35	70
487	14 c. multicoloured	..	60	1·75
484/7		*Set of 4*	1·10	2·40

93 George Pauling (construction engineer)

(Des P. Birch)

1974 (15 May). *Famous Rhodesians (8th issue). P* 14.

488	**93** 14 c. multicoloured	..	1·00	1·50

94 Greater Kudu   95 Thunbergia   96 *Charaxes varanes*

(Des J. Huntly)

1974 (14 Aug)–**76**. *Various vert designs as T* **94/6**. *Multicoloured. P* 14½ (1 *to* 14 c.) *or* 14 (*others*). (*a*) *Antelopes. Size as T* **94**.

489	1 c. Type **94**	..	10	10
490	2½ c. Eland	..	75	10
	a. Booklet pane of 4	..	2·75	
491	3 c. Roan Antelope	..	10	10
	a. Booklet pane of 4	..	70	
492	4 c. Reedbuck	..	20	10
	a. Booklet pane of 4	..	75	
493	5 c. Bushbuck	..	40	10

(*b*) *Wild Flowers. Size as T* **95**

494	6 c. Type **95**	..	40	10
495	7½ c. Flame Lily	..	3·00	35
496	8 c. As 7½ c. (1.7.76)	..	40	10
497	10 c. Devil Thorn	..	30	10
498	12 c. Hibiscus (1.7.76)	..	70	70
499	12½ c. Pink Sabi Star	..	4·50	50
500	14 c. Wild Pimpernel	..	7·50	70
501	15 c. As 12½ c. (1.7.76)	..	70	60
502	16 c. As 14 c. (1.7.76)	..	70	45

(*c*) *Butterflies. Size as T* **96**

503	20 c. Type **96**	..	1·75	35
504	24 c. *Precis hierta* (s sp *cebrene*) (1.7.76)	..	1·50	40
505	25 c. As 24 c.	..	8·50	3·00
506	50 c. *Colotis regina*	..	70	90
507	$1 *Graphium antheus*	..	70	1·25
508	$2 *Hamanumida daedalus*	..	80	1·50
489/508		*Set of 20*	28·00	11·00

97 Collecting Mail   98 Thomas Baines (artist)

(Des M. Chase)

1974 (20 Nov). *Centenary of Universal Postal Union. T* **97** *and similar horiz designs. Multicoloured. P* 14.

509	3 c. Type **97**	..	15	10
510	4 c. Sorting mail	..	20	10
511	7½ c. Mail delivery	..	50	65
512	14 c. Weighing parcel	..	1·00	1·75
509/12		*Set of 4*	1·75	2·25

(Des from self-portrait)

1975 (12 Feb). *Famous Rhodesians (9th issue). P* 14.

513	**98** 14 c. multicoloured	..	80	1·25

99 *Euphorbia confinalis*

100 Prevention of Head Injuries

(Des Nancy Abrey)

1975 (16 July). *International Succulent Congress, Salisbury ("Aloe '75"). T 99 and similar vert designs. Multicoloured. P 14½.*

514	2½ c. Type **99**		..	20	10
515	3 c. *Aloe excelsa*		..	20	10
516	4 c. *Hoodia lugardii*		..	30	15
517	7½ c. *Aloe ortholopha*		..	45	55
518	14 c. *Aloe musapana*		..	1·25	1·25
519	25 c. *Aloe saponaria* ..		..	1·75	2·00
514/19	..		*Set of 6*	3·75	3·50

(Des Val Bond)

1975 (15 Oct). *Occupational Safety. T 100 and similar horiz designs. Multicoloured. P 14.*

520	2½ c. Type **100**		..	15	10
521	4 c. Bandaged hand and gloved hand		..	20	10
522	7½ c. Broken glass and eye		..	35	20
523	14 c. Blind man and welder with protective mask		..	50	60
520/3	..		*Set of 4*	1·10	80

101 Telephones, 1876 and 1976   **(102)**   **8c**

(Des M. Chase)

1976 (10 Mar). *Telephone Centenary. T 101 and similar vert design. P 14.*

524	3 c. grey-black and pale blue..		..	10	10
525	14 c. brownish black and light stone ..		..	20	45

Design:—14 c. Alexander Graham Bell.

1976 (1 July). *Nos. 495, 500 and 505 surch as T 102.*

526	8 c. on 7½ c. Flame Lily ..		..	15	15
	a. Surch double, one albino		..		
527	16 c. on 14 c. Wild Pimpernel		..	20	25
528	24 c. on 25 c. *Precis hierta* (s sp *cebrene*)		..	30	60
526/8	..		*Set of 3*	60	90

103 Roan Antelope

104 Msasa

(Des N. Pedersen)

1976 (21 July). *Vulnerable Wildlife. T 103 and similar horiz designs. Multicoloured. P 14.*

529	4 c. Type **103**		..	20	10
530	6 c. Brown Hyena		..	25	10
531	8 c. Hunting Dog		..	35	45
532	16 c. Cheetah		..	45	45
529/32	..		*Set of 4*	1·10	75

(Des Nancy Abrey)

1976 (17 Nov). *Trees of Rhodesia. T 104 and similar vert designs. Multicoloured. P 14.*

533	4 c. Type **104**		..	15	10
534	6 c. Red Mahogany		..	15	10
535	8 c. Mukwa		..	20	30
536	16 c. Rhodesian Teak		..	25	50
533/6	..		*Set of 4*	65	75

105 Common Bulbul

106 "Lake Kyle" (Joan Evans)

638

(Des B. Finch)

1977 (16 Mar). *Birds of Rhodesia (2nd series). T 105 and similar vert designs. Multicoloured. P 14.*

537	3 c. Type **105**		..	20	10
538	4 c. Yellow-mantled Whydah		..	20	10
539	6 c. Cape Longclaw		..	25	35
540	8 c. Eastern Long-tailed Shrike		..	45	50
541	16 c. Lesser Blue-eared Glossy Starling		..	75	1·00
542	24 c. Green Wood Hoopoe		..	95	1·25
537/42			*Set of 6*	2·50	3·00

1977 (20 July). *Landscape Paintings. T 106 and similar horiz designs. Multicoloured. P 14.*

543	3 c. Type **106**		..	15	10
544	4 c. "Chimanimani Mountains" (Joan Evans)		..	15	10
545	6 c. "Rocks near Bonsor Reef", (Alice Balfour)		..	15	10
546	8 c. "A Dwala near Devil's Pass" (Alice Balfour)		..	25	10
547	16 c. "Zimbabwe" (Alice Balfour)		..	35	50
548	24 c. "Victoria Falls" (Thomas Baines)		..	40	60
543/8	..		*Set of 6*	1·25	1·25

107 Virgin and Child

108 Fair Spire

(Des Dianne Deudney)

1977 (16 Nov). *Christmas. P 14.*

549	**107**	3 c. multicoloured	..	10	10
550		6 c. multicoloured	..	10	10
551		8 c. multicoloured	..	15	10
552		16 c. multicoloured	..	30	50
549/52		..	*Set of 4*	75	65

1978 (15 Mar). *Trade Fair Rhodesia, Bulawayo. T 108 and similar vert design. Multicoloured. P 14.*

553	4 c. Type **108**		..	15	10
554	8 c. Fair Spire (*different*)		..	20	25

109 Morganite

110 White Rhinoceros

111 Odzani Falls

(Des N. Pedersen (1 to 17 c.), D. Myles (21 c. to $2))

1978 (16 Aug). *Multicoloured.*

(a) Horiz designs as T 109 showing gemstones. P 14½

555	1 c. Type **109**		..	20	10
556	3 c. Amethyst		..	30	10
557	4 c. Garnet		..	30	10
558	5 c. Citrine		..	30	10
559	7 c. Blue Topaz		..	30	10

(b) Horiz designs as T 110 showing wild animals. P 14½

560	9 c. Type **110**		..	20	10
561	11 c. Lion		..	20	15
562	13 c. Warthog		..	20	15
563	15 c. Giraffe		..	20	15
564	17 c. Common Zebra		..	20	10

(c) Horiz designs as T 111 showing waterfalls. P 14

565	21 c. Type **111**		..	20	30
566	25 c. Goba Falls		..	20	40
567	30 c. Inyangombi Falls		..	25	30
568	$1 Bridal Veil Falls..		..	50	80
569	$2 Victoria Falls		..	75	1·00
555/69	..		*Set of 15*	3·50	3·00

112 Wright *Flyer*

(Des C. Herbert)

1978 (18 Oct). *75th Anniv of Powered Flight. T 112 and similar horiz designs. Multicoloured. P 14.*

570	4 c. Type **112**		..	10	10
571	5 c. Blériot "XI"		..	10	10
572	7 c. Vickers "Vimy" *Silver Queen* II ..		..	10	10
573	14 c. "A.W. 15 Atalanta"		..	10	10
574	17 c. Vickers "Viking 1B"		..	15	15
575	25 c. Boeing "720B"		..	20	30
570/5	..		*Set of 6*	65	65

ZIMBABWE

REPUBLIC

Rhodesia became independent under majority rule on 18 April 1980 and was renamed Zimbabwe.

PRINTERS. All stamps of Zimbabwe were printed in lithography by Mardon Printers (Pvt) Ltd, subsequently (from Nos. 724/7) National Printing and Packaging, Harare, *unless otherwise stated.*

113 Morganite

114 Rotary Anniversary Emblem

1980 (18 Apr)–**83.** *As Nos. 555/69 and new value (40 c.), all inscr "ZIMBABWE" as in T 113.*

576	1 c. Type **113**		..	20	20
577	3 c. Amethyst ..		..	30	20
578	4 c. Garnet		..	30	10
579	5 c. Citrine		..	35	10
580	7 c. Blue Topaz		..	35	10
581	9 c. White Rhinoceros		..	15	10
582	11 c. Lion		..	15	10
583	13 c. Warthog		..	15	15
584	15 c. Giraffe		..	15	15
585	17 c. Common Zebra		..	15	20
586	21 c. Odzani Falls		..	20	25
587	25 c. Goba Falls		..	25	30
588	30 c. Inyangombi Falls		..	30	50
588a	40 c. Bundi Falls (14.3.83)		..	5·00	4·50
589	$1 Bridal Veil Falls		..	1·10	2·00
590	$2 Victoria Falls		..	2·00	3·75
576/90			*Set of 16*	10·00	11·50

1980 (18 June). *75th Anniv of Rotary International. P 14½.*

591	**114**	4 c. multicoloured	..	10	10
592		13 c. multicoloured	..	20	30
593		21 c. multicoloured	..	35	55
594		25 c. multicoloured	..	45	80
591/4			*Set of 4*	95	1·60
MS595	140 × 84 mm. Nos. 591/4.		..	1·25	1·60

115 Olympic Rings

(Des Nancy Abrey)

1980 (19 July). *Olympic Games, Moscow. P 14½.*

596	**115**	17 c. multicoloured	..	30	40

116 Gatooma Post Office, 1912

117 Stylised Blind Person

(Des Mortimer Tiley and Partners Ltd)

1980 (17 Oct). *75th Anniv of Post Office Savings Bank. T 116 and similar horiz designs. P 14.*

597	5 c. black and yellow-brown		..	10	10
598	7 c. black and red-orange		..	10	10
599	9 c. black and olive-yellow		..	10	10
600	17 c. black and light blue		..	25	25
597/600			*Set of 4*	40	40
MS601	125 × 84 mm. Nos. 597/600		..	1·00	1·25

Designs:—7 c. Salisbury Post Office, 1912; 9 c. Umtali Post Office, 1901; 17 c. Bulawayo Post Office, 1895.

(Des Rose Martin)

1981 (23 Sept). *International Year for Disabled Persons. T 117 and similar vert designs showing stylised figures. Multicoloured. P 14.*

602	5 c. Type **117** ..		..	15	10
603	7 c. Deaf person		..	20	10
604	11 c. Person with one leg		..	25	15
605	17 c. Person with one arm		..	35	35
602/5	..		*Set of 4*	85	60

118 Msasa

119 Painting from Gwamgwadza Cave, Mtoko Area

(Des Nancy Abrey)

1981 (4 Dec). *National Tree Day. T* **118** *and similar vert designs. Multicoloured. P* 14½.

606	5 c. Type **118**	20	10
607	7 c. Mopane	25	15
608	21 c. Flat-crowned Acacia	80	70
609	30 c. Pod Mahogany	1·10	1·10
606/9	.. .. *Set of 4*	2·10	1·90

1982 (17 Mar). *Rock Paintings. T* **119** *and similar horiz designs showing paintings from various locations. Multicoloured. P* 14½.

610	9 c. Type **119**	75	20
611	11 c. Epworth Mission, near Harare ..	1·00	20
612	17 c. Diana's Vow, near Harare ..	1·00	65
613	21 c. Gwamgwadza Cave, Mtoko Area (*different*) ..	1·40	1·25
614	25 c. Mucheka Cave, Msana Communal Land	1·75	2·00
615	30 c. Chinzwini Shelter, Chiredzi Area	2·00	2·25
610/15	.. .. *Set of 6*	7·00	6·00

120 Scout Emblem

121 Dr. Robert Koch

(Des Rose Martin)

1982 (21 July). *75th Anniv of Boy Scout Movement. T* **120** *and similar vert designs. Multicoloured. P* 14½ × 14.

616	9 c. Type **120**	45	15
617	11 c. Scouts around campfire	45	15
618	21 c. Scouts map-reading	70	85
619	30 c. Lord Baden-Powell	90	1·60
616/19	.. .. .. *Set of 4*	2·25	2·50

(Des Rose Martin)

1982 (17 Nov). *Centenary of Dr. Robert Koch's Discovery of Tubercle Bacillus. T* **121** *and similar horiz design. P* 14.

620	11 c. salmon, black and greenish grey	1·00	25
621	30 c. multicoloured	2·25	2·75

Design:—30 c. Man looking through microscope.

122 "Wing Woman" (Henry Mudzengerere)

123 Traditional Ploughing Team (moving right)

1983 (14 Mar). *Commonwealth Day. Sculptures. T* **122** *and similar multicoloured designs. P* 14.

622	9 c. Type **122**	10	10
623	11 c. "Telling Secrets" (Joseph Ndandarika) (*horiz*) ..	15	10
624	30 c. "Hornbill Man" (John Takawira) (*horiz*)	35	45
625	$1 "The Chief" (Nicholas Mukomberanwa)	1·00	2·00
622/5	.. .. *Set of 4*	1·40	2·40

(Des Rose Martin)

1983 (13 May). *30th World Ploughing Contest, Zimbabwe. T* **123** *and similar horiz designs. Multicoloured. P* 14.

626	21 c. Type **123**	25	35
	a. Horiz pair. Nos. 626/7 ..	50	70
627	21 c. Traditional ploughing team (moving left)	25	35
628	30 c. Tractor ploughing	40	45
	a. Horiz pair. Nos. 628/9 ..	80	1·25
629	30 c. Modern plough	40	45
626/9	.. .. .. *Set of 4*	1·25	1·75

The two designs of each value were issued in horizontal *se-tenant* pairs, forming composite designs, throughout the sheets.

NEW INFORMATION

The editor is always interested to correspond with people who have new information that will improve or correct the Catalogue.

---

124 Postman on Cycle

125 Map of Africa showing Zimbabwe

(Des R. Phillips)

1983 (12 Oct). *World Communications Year. T* **124** *and similar multicoloured designs. P* 14.

630	9 c. Type **124**	20	10
631	11 c. Aircraft controller directing aircraft	25	10
632	15 c. Switchboard operator	30	30
633	17 c. Printing works	35	30
634	21 c. Road transport (*horiz*) ..	50	60
635	30 c. Rail transport (*horiz*) ..	75	1·25
630/5	.. .. .. *Set of 6*	2·10	2·40

(Des Bunty Woods and Nancy Abrey)

1984 (11 Apr). *Zimbabwe International Trade Fair. T* **125** *and similar vert designs. Multicoloured. P* 14½.

636	9 c. Type **125**	10	10
637	11 c. Globe	15	10
638	30 c. Zimbabwe flag and Trade Fair logo	45	35
636/8	.. .. .. *Set of 3*	65	50

126 Cycling

(Des Vivienne Fick (11 c.), Joanna Hogg (21 c.), Blessing Chikoore (30 c.), Wayne Gubb (40 c.))

1984 (18 July). *Olympic Games, Los Angeles. Children's Pictures. T* **126** *and similar horiz designs. Multicoloured. P* 14½.

639	11 c. Type **126**	30	15
640	21 c. Swimming	40	40
641	30 c. Running	55	65
642	40 c. Hurdling	70	80
639/42	.. .. .. *Set of 4*	1·75	1·75

127 Liberation Heroes

128 African Fish Eagle

(Des N. Pearce (11 c.), J. Akester (others))

1984 (8 Aug). *Heroes' Days. T* **127** *and similar multicoloured designs showing various aspects of Heroes' Acre. P* 14½.

643	9 c. Type **127**	30	10
644	11 c. Symbolic tower and flame (*vert*)..	30	10
645	17 c. Bronze sculpture (*vert*) ..	50	20
646	30 c. Section of bronze mural ..	70	35
643/6	.. .. .. *Set of 4*	1·60	65

(Des B. Finch)

1984 (10 Oct). *Birds of Prey. T* **128** *and similar vert designs. Multicoloured. P* 14½.

647	9 c. Type **128**	50	20
648	11 c. Long-crested Eagle ..	50	20
649	13 c. Bateleur	65	45
650	17 c. Verreaux's Eagle ..	80	45
651	21 c. Martial Eagle	90	1·25
652	30 c. Bonelli's Eagle	1·25	2·00
647/52	.. .. *Set of 6*	4·25	4·00

129 Class "9" Locomotive No. 86

130 "Intelsat V" Telecommunications Satellite

(Des G. Cameron)

1985 (15 May). *"Zimbabwe Steam Safaris". Railway Locomotives. T* **129** *and similar horiz designs. Multicoloured. P* 14½.

653	9 c. Type **129**	85	20
654	11 c. Class "12" No. 190 ..	85	20
655	17 c. Class "Garratt 15A" *Isilwane* ..	1·50	85
656	30 c. Class "Garratt 20A" *Gwaai* ..	2·50	2·75
653/6	.. .. *Set of 4*	5·25	3·50

1985 (8 July). *Earth Satellite Station, Mazowe. T* **130** *and similar multicoloured design. P* 14½ × 14 (26 c.) *or* 14½ (57 c.).

657	26 c. Type **130**	1·75	50
658	57 c. Earth Satellite Station, Mazowe (65 × 25 *mm*)	3·25	4·00

131 Tobacco

132 Chief Mutapa Gatsi Rusere and 17th-century Seal

(Des Rose Rigden)

1985 (21 Aug)–88. *National Infrastructure. T* **131** *and similar horiz designs. Multicoloured. P* 14½.

659	1 c. Type **131**	10	10
660	3 c. Maize	10	10
	a. Perf 14	—	10
661	4 c. Cotton	10	10
	a. Perf 14	—	10
662	5 c. Tea	10	10
	a. Perf 14	—	10
663	10 c. Cattle	15	10
	a. Perf 14	—	10
664	11 c. Birchenough Bridge	30	10
665	12 c. Ore stamp mill	60	10
666	13 c. Gold pouring	70	15
	a. Perf 14	—	15
667	15 c. Dragline coal mining	70	15
	a. Perf 14	—	15
668	17 c. Uncut amethyst	70	15
669	18 c. Electric locomotive	70	30
670	20 c. Kariba Dam	70	15
	a. Perf 14	—	15
671	23 c. Elephants at water hole	70	15
672	25 c. Sunset over Zambezi	55	20
	a. Perf 14	—	20
673	26 c. Baobab tree	55	20
674	30 c. Ruins of Great Zimbabwe ..	60	20
675	35 c. Traditional dancing	60	30
676	45 c. Village women crushing maize	65	40
677	57 c. Woodcarving	75	55
678	$1 Playing Mbira (musical instrument)	1·25	75
679	$2 Mule-drawn Scotch cart	2·00	2·50
680	$5 Zimbabwe coat-of-arms	3·75	5·00
659/80	.. .. .. *Set of 22*	14·50	10·50

The stamps perforated 14 date from the introduction of a new perforating head in 1988.

(Des C. Herbert)

1985 (18 Sept). *50th Anniv of National Archives. T* **132** *and similar horiz designs. Multicoloured. P* 14½.

681	12 c. Type **132**	20	15
682	18 c. Chief Lobengula, seal and 1888 Treaty	25	40
683	26 c. Exhibition gallery	35	45
684	35 c. National Archives building ..	45	75
681/4	.. .. .. *Set of 4*	1·10	1·60

MACHINE LABELS. From 24 October 1985 gummed labels in the above design varying in value from 1 c. to $99.99, were available from four automatic machines located at the Philatelic Bureau and at the main post offices in Bulawayo, Gwelo and Harare.

133 Computer Operator

(Des C. Herbert)

1985 (13 Nov). *United Nations Decade for Women. T* **133** *and similar horiz designs. Multicoloured. P* 14½.

685	10 c. Type **133**	55	10
686	17 c. Nurse giving injection	85	60
687	26 c. Woman student	1·60	2·00
685/7	.. .. .. *Set of 3*	2·75	2·40

134 Harare Conference Centre

(Des C. Herbert)

1986 (29 Jan). *Harare International Conference Centre. T 134 and similar horiz design. Multicoloured. P 14½.*
688	26 c. Type 134.	..	75	30
689	35 c. Interior of conference hall	..	1·25	1·40

135 Grain Storage Silo   **136** *Bunaeopsis jacksoni*

(Des C. Herbert)

1986 (1 Apr). *6th Anniv of Southern African Development Co-ordination Conference. T 135 and similar horiz designs. Multicoloured. P 14½.*
690	12 c. Type 135.	..	55	20
691	18 c. Rhinoceros and hawk at sunset	..	1·75	1·25
692	26 c. Map showing S.A.D.C.C. member states, and Boeing "737"		2·00	1·75
693	35 c. Map and national flags of S.A.D.C.C. members..		2·25	2·00
690/3	.. ..	*Set of 4*	6·00	4·75

1986 (18 June). *Moths of Zimbabwe. T 136 and similar horiz designs. Multicoloured. P 14½×14.*
694	12 c. Type 136.	..	1·10	20
695	18 c. *Deilephila nerii*	..	1·60	80
696	26 c. *Bunaeopsis zaddachi*	..	2·00	1·25
697	35 c. *Heniocha apollonia*	..	2·40	2·75
694/7	.. ..	*Set of 4*	6·50	4·50

137 Victoria Falls   **138** Sopwith Motorcycle (1921)

(Des C. Herbert)

1986 (26 Aug). *8th Non-Aligned Summit Conference. T 137 and similar horiz design. Multicoloured. P 14½×14 (26 c.) or 14½ ($1).*
698	26 c. Type 137.	..	1·25	30
699	$1 Ruins of Great Zimbabwe (62×24 mm)	..	3·75	4·25

(Des G. Cameron)

1986 (8 Oct). *Centenary of Motoring. T 138 and similar horiz designs. Multicoloured. P 14½.*
700	10 c. Type 138.	..	65	10
701	12 c. Gladiator motor car (1902)	..	65	30
702	17 c. Douglas motorcycle (1920)	..	1·00	40
703	26 c. Ford "Model A" (1930)	..	1·40	70
704	35 c. Schacht motor car (1909)	..	1·60	2·00
705	40 c. Benz three-wheeled car (1886)	..	1·60	2·00
700/5	.. ..	*Set of 6*	6·25	5·00

139 Growth Monitoring   **140** Barred Owlet

(Des Barbara Chalk)

1987 (11 Feb). *Child Survival Campaign. T 139 and similar vert designs. Multicoloured. P 14×14½.*
706	12 c. Type 139.	..	1·40	1·40
	a. Block of 4. Nos. 706/9	..	5·00	
707	12 c. Breast-feeding	..	1·40	1·40
708	12 c. Oral rehydration therapy	..	1·40	1·40
709	12 c. Immunization	..	1·40	1·40
706/9	.. ..	*Set of 4*	5·00	5·00
Nos. 706/9 were printed together, *se-tenant*, in blocks of four throughout the sheet.

141 Brownie, Guide and Ranger saluting ("Commitment")   **142** Common Grey Duiker

(Des B. Finch)

1987 (15 Apr). *Owls. T 140 and similar vert designs. Multicoloured. P 14½.*
710	12 c. Type 140	..	1·25	20
711	18 c. Pearl-spotted Owlet	..	1·75	80
712	26 c. White-faced Scops Owl..	..	2·25	1·25
713	35 c. African Scops Owl	..	3·00	3·50
710/13	..	*Set of 4*	7·50	5·25

(Des Barbara Connelly)

1987 (24 June). *75th Anniv of Girl Guides' Association of Zimbabwe. T 141 and similar horiz designs. Multicoloured. P 14½.*
714	15 c. Type 141.	..	40	15
715	23 c. Guides preparing meal over campfire ("Adventure")		55	30
716	35 c. Guide teaching villagers to read ("Service")		65	35
717	$1 Handshake and globe ("International Friendship")		1·50	1·25
714/17		*Set of 4*	2·75	1·90

(Des Patricia Wilson)

1987 (7 Oct). *Duikers of Africa Survey. T 142 and similar horiz designs, each showing duiker and distribution map. Multicoloured. P 14½×14.*
718	15 c. Type 142.	..	35	15
719	23 c. Zebra Duiker	..	40	20
720	25 c. Yellow-backed Duiker	..	40	35
721	30 c. Blue Duiker	..	55	40
722	35 c. Jentink's Duiker	..	55	40
723	38 c. Red Duiker	..	65	60
718/23		*Set of 6*	2·75	1·90

143 *Pseudocreobotra wahlberghi* (mantid)   **144** "Cockerel" (Arthur Azevedo)

(Des Janet Duff)

1988 (12 Jan). *Insects. T 143 and similar horiz designs. Multicoloured. P 14½.*
724	15 c. Type 143	..	40	15
725	23 c. *Dicranorrhina derbyana* (beetle)		55	25
726	35 c. *Dictyophorus spumans* (grasshopper)		75	40
727	45 c. *Chalcocoris rutilus* (bug)		90	65
724/7		*Set of 4*	2·40	1·25

1988 (14 Apr). *30th Anniv of National Gallery of Zimbabwe. T 144 and similar multicoloured designs showing painting (38 c.) or sculptures (others). P 14×14½ (vert) or 14½×14 (horiz).*
728	15 c. Type 144	..	15	10
729	23 c. "Man into Hippo" (Bernard Matemera)		25	20
730	30 c. "Spirit Python" (Henry Munyaradzi)		30	25
731	35 c. "Spirit Bird carrying People" (Thomas Mukarobgwa) (*horiz*)		30	25
732	38 c. "The Song of the Herd Boy" (George Nene) (*horiz*)		30	30
733	45 c. "War Victim" (Joseph Muzondo) (*horiz*)		35	40
728/33		*Set of 6*	1·50	1·40

145 *Aloe cameronii var. bondana*   **146** White-faced Whistling Duck

(Des Nancy Abrey)

1988 (14 July). *Aloes. T 145 and similar vert designs. Multicoloured. P 14½.*
734	15 c. Type 145	..	20	10
735	23 c. *Orbeopsis caudata*	..	35	20
736	25 c. *Euphorbia wildii*	..	35	20
737	30 c. *Euphorbia fortissima*	..	40	30
738	35 c. *Aloe aculeata*	..	40	35
739	38 c. *Huernia zebrina*	..	45	35
734/9		*Set of 6*	2·00	1·40

(Des B. Finch and C. Herbert)

1988 (6 Oct). *Wild Ducks and Geese of Zimbabwe. T 146 and similar horiz designs. Multicoloured. P 14½ × 14.*
740	15 c. Type 146	..	20	10
741	23 c. African Pygmy Goose	..	30	20
742	30 c. Hottentot Teal	..	40	25
743	35 c. Comb Duck ("Knob-billed Duck")		45	30
744	38 c. White-backed Duck	..	45	35
745	45 c. Maccoa Duck	..	65	45
740/5		*Set of 6*	2·25	1·50

147 O'Shaughnessy's Banded Gecko   **148** Spotted Leaved Arum-Lily

1989 (10 Jan). *Geckos. T 147 and similar horiz designs. Multicoloured. P 14½.*
746	15 c. Type 147	..	30	10
747	23 c. Tiger Rock Gecko	..	45	20
748	35 c. Tasman's Gecko	..	65	45
749	45 c. Bibron's Gecko	..	75	55
746/9		*Set of 4*	1·90	1·10

1989 (12 Apr). *Wild Flowers. T 148 and similar vert designs. Multicoloured. P 14½.*
750	15 c. Type 148	..	25	10
751	23 c. Grassland Vlei-lily	..	30	20
752	30 c. Manica Protea	..	35	30
753	35 c. Flame Lily	..	40	30
754	38 c. Poppy Hibiscus	..	45	35
755	45 c. Blue Sesbania	..	50	40
750/5		*Set of 6*	2·00	1·50

149 Red-breasted Bream   **150** Black Rhinoceros

(Des C. Herbert)

1989 (12 July). *Fishes. T 149 and similar horiz designs. Multicoloured. P 14½.*
756	15 c. Type 149	..	25	10
757	23 c. Chessa	..	35	20
758	30 c. Eastern Bottle-nose	..	45	30
759	35 c. Vundu	..	45	35
760	38 c. Largemouth Black Bass	..	50	50
761	45 c. Tiger Fish	..	70	70
756/61		*Set of 6*	2·40	1·90

1989 (10 Oct). *Endangered Species. T 150 and similar horiz designs. Multicoloured. P 14½×14.*
762	15 c. Type 150	..	45	20
763	23 c. Cheetah	..	60	35
764	30 c. Wild Dog	..	75	55
765	35 c. Pangolin	..	75	60
766	38 c. Brown Hyena	..	80	80
767	45 c. Roan Antelope	..	90	1·10
762/7		*Set of 6*	3·75	3·25

151 Tiger Fish   **152** Headrest

153 Bicycles

(Des Janet Duff (1 to 9 c.), Rose Rigden (15 to 30 c.), Nancy Abrey (33 c. to $2))

1990 (2 Jan). *Multicoloured.*

(a) Horiz designs as T 151 showing wildlife. P 14
768	1 c. Type 151	..	10	10
769	2 c. Helmet Guineafowl	..	10	10
	a. Perf 14½	..	10	10
770	3 c. Scrub Hare	..	10	10
	a. Perf 14½	..	10	10
771	4 c. Temminck's Ground Pangolin		10	10
	a. Perf 14½	..	10	10

772	5 c. Greater Kudu	..	..	..	10	10
	a. Perf 14½				10	10
773	9 c. Black Rhinoceros				10	10
	a. Perf 14½				10	10

(b) Horiz designs as T 152 showing cultural artifacts.
P 14½×14

774	15 c. Type 152				10	10
775	20 c. Hand axe and adze				10	10
776	23 c. Gourd and water pot				10	10
777	25 c. Snuff container				10	10
778	26 c. Winnowing tray and basket				10	10
779	30 c. Grinding stone				10	10

(c) Horiz designs as T 153 showing transport. P 14½

780	33 c. Type 153				10	10
781	35 c. Buses	..			10	10
782	38 c. Passenger train				10	15
783	45 c. Mail motorcycle and trailer	..			10	15
784	$1 Air Zimbabwe Boeing airliner				25	30
785	$2 Lorry	..	..		50	55
768/85	..	..		*Set of 18*	1·60	1·75

154 Pres. Mugabe and Joshua Nkomo at Signing of Unity Accord, 1987

155 Runhare House, 1986

(Adapted Nancy Abrey)

1990 (17 Apr). *10th Anniv of Independence. T 154 and similar horiz designs. Multicoloured. P 14½×14.*

786	15 c. Type 154				15	10
787	23 c. Conference Centre, Harare	..			20	15
788	30 c. Children in class				25	20
789	35 c. Intelsat aerial, Mazowe Earth Satellite Station				30	30
790	38 c. National Sports Stadium	..			30	40
791	45 c. Maize field	..			50	55
786/91	..	..		*Set of 6*	1·50	1·50

1990 (11 July). *Centenary of the City of Harare. T 155 and similar horiz designs. Multicoloured. P 14½.*

792	15 c. Type 155				20	10
793	23 c. Market Hall, 1894	..			30	20
794	30 c. Charter House, 1959				35	25
795	35 c. Supreme Court, 1927				40	30
796	38 c. Standard Chartered Bank, 1911	..			40	40
797	45 c. The Town House, 1933				55	65
792/7	..	..		*Set of 6*	2·00	1·75

156 Speaker's Mace

157 Small-spotted Genet

1990 (17 Sept). *36th Commonwealth Parliamentary Conference, Harare. T 156 and similar vert design. Multicoloured. P 14½.*

798	35 c. Type 156	..	..		30	25
799	$1 Speaker's chair	..			70	75

(Des Barbara Chalk)

1991 (15 Jan). *Small Mammals. T 157 and similar horiz designs. Multicoloured. P 14½×14.*

800	15 c. Type 157				30	10
801	23 c. Red Squirrel	..			35	15
802	35 c. Night-ape				55	45
803	45 c. Bat-eared Fox				65	75
800/3	..	..		*Set of 4*	1·75	1·25

158 Hosho (rattles)

159 Snot-apple

(Des R. Pletts)

1991 (16 Apr). *Traditional Musical Instruments. T 158 and similar vert designs. Multicoloured. P 14½.*

804	15 c. Type 158	..			15	10
805	23 c. Mbira (thumb piano)	..			20	10
806	30 c. Ngororombe (pan pipes)				25	20

807	35 c. Chipendani (mouth bow)	..			25	25
808	38 c. Marimba (xylophone)				25	30
809	45 c. Ngoma (drum)				35	45
804/9	..	..		*Set of 6*	1·25	1·25

(Des Barbara Chalk)

1991 (17 July). *Wild Fruits. T 159 and similar vert designs. Multicoloured. P 14×14½.*

810	20 c. Type 159				20	10
811	39 c. Marula	..			20	20
812	51 c. Mobola Plum	..			30	30
813	60 c. Water Berry				35	35
814	65 c. Northern Dwaba Berry				35	35
815	77 c. Mahobohobo	..			45	55
810/15	..	..		*Set of 6*	1·75	1·75

160 Bridal Veil Falls

161 Lion

(Des R. Jeffrey)

1991 (16 Oct). *Commonwealth Heads of Government Meeting, Harare. T 160 and similar vert designs. Multicoloured. P 14½.*

816	20 c. Type 160				20	10
817	39 c. Meeting logo	..			20	15
818	51 c. Chinhoyi Caves				30	30
819	60 c. Kariba Dam	..			40	40
820	65 c. Victoria Falls				40	45
821	77 c. Balancing rocks				50	55
816/21	..	..		*Set of 6*	1·75	1·75

(Des R. Pletts)

1992 (8 Jan). *Wildlife Conservation. Big Cats. T 161 and similar horiz designs. Multicoloured. P 14½×14.*

822	20 c. Type 161				15	10
823	39 c. Leopard	..			20	15
824	60 c. Cheetah				40	40
825	77 c. Serval	..			50	60
822/5	..	..		*Set of 4*	1·10	1·10

162 *Amanita zambiana*

163 Common Bulbul

(Des R. Pletts)

1992 (8 Apr). *Edible Mushrooms. T 162 and similar vert designs. Multicoloured. P 14×14½.*

826	20 c. Type 162				15	10
827	39 c. *Boletus edulis*				20	15
828	51 c. *Termitomyces*				25	25
829	60 c. *Cantharellus densifolius*				30	30
830	65 c. *Cantharellus longisporus*				35	35
831	77 c. *Cantharellus cibarius*				45	55
826/31	..	..		*Set of 6*	1·50	1·50

(Des R. Pletts)

1992 (7 July). *Birds. T 163 and similar vert designs. Multicoloured. P 14½.*

832	25 c. Type 163				15	10
833	59 c. Fiscal Shrike	..			30	30
834	77 c. Forktailed Drongo	..			40	40
835	90 c. Cardinal Woodpecker				50	50
836	98 c. Yellow-billed Hornbill				50	50
837	$1.16, Crested Francolin				65	65
832/7	..	..		*Set of 6*	2·25	2·25

164 *Charaxes jasius*

165 Uranium

(Des R. Pletts)

1992 (15 Oct). *Butterflies. T 164 and similar horiz designs. Multicoloured. P 14½×14.*

838	25 c. Type 164				15	10
839	59 c. *Eronia leda*				30	30
840	77 c. *Princeps ophidicephalus*				40	40
841	90 c. *Junonia oenone*				50	50
842	98 c. *Danaus chrysippus*	..			50	50
843	$1.16, *Junonia octavia*				55	55
838/43	..			*Set of 6*	2·25	2·25

(Des R. Jeffrey)

1993 (12 Jan). *Minerals. T 165 and similar horiz designs. Multicoloured. P 14½×14.*

844	25 c. Type 165				10	10
845	59 c. Chrome				15	20
846	77 c. Copper				15	20
847	90 c. Coal				20	25
848	98 c. Gold				25	30
849	$1.16, Emerald	..			25	30
844/9	..	..		*Set of 6*	1·00	1·25

POSTAGE DUE STAMPS

SOUTHERN

RHODESIA

(D 1)

D 2

1951 (1 Oct). *Postage Due stamps of Great Britain optd with Type D 1.*

D1	D 1	½d. emerald (No. D27)	..		3·25	9·00
D2		1d. violet-blue (No. D36)			2·00	65
D3		2d. agate (No. D29)	..		4·00	1·75
D4		3d. violet (No. D30)	..		2·75	1·25
D5		4d. blue (No. D38)	..		1·50	2·25
D6		4d. dull grey-green (No. D31)	..		£130	£325
D7		1s. deep blue (No. D33)	..		3·00	1·75
D1/5, 7				*Set of 6*	15·00	15·00

No. D6 is reported to have been issued to Fort Victoria and Gwelo main post offices only.

(Typo Printing and Stationery Dept, Salisbury)

1965 (17 June). *Roul 9.*

D 8	D 2	1d. orange-red (*roul 5*) ..			70	10·00
		a. Roul 9			1·75	4·00
D 9		2d. deep blue			50	8·00
D10		4d. green			60	8·00
D11		6d. plum			60	6·00
D8a/11				*Set of 4*	2·25	23·00

The 2d. has a stop below the "D".

D 3 Zimbabwe Bird (soapstone sculpture)

D 4 Zimbabwe Bird (soapstone sculpture)

(Litho Mardon Printers, Salisbury)

1966 (15 Dec). *P 14½.*

D12	D 3	1d. red	..		1·00	2·50
D13		2d. bluish violet			1·50	2·75
D14		4d. pale green			1·50	4·50
D15		6d. reddish violet			1·50	2·75
D16		1s. red-brown			1·50	3·00
D17		2s. black			2·00	6·50
D12/17				*Set of 6*	8·00	20·00

1970 (17 Feb)–73. *Decimal Currency. As Type D 3, but larger (26 × 22½ mm). P 14½.*

D18	D 3	1 c. bright green			1·00	1·40
D19		2 c. ultramarine			1·00	80
D20		5 c. bright reddish violet			2·50	2·00
D21		6 c. pale lemon (7.5.73) ..			4·25	3·25
D22		10 c. cerise			2·50	3·50
D18/22				*Set of 5*	10·00	10·00

1980. *P 14½.*

D23	D 4	1 c. bright green			30	80
D24		2 c. ultramarine			40	90
D25		5 c. bright reddish violet			50	90
		a. Imperf (pair)	..		90·00	
D26		6 c. pale lemon			70	1·60
D27		10 c. cerise			90	2·00
D23/7				*Set of 5*	2·50	5·75

D 5

(D 6)

1985 (21 Aug). *P 14½.*

D28	D 5	1 c. yellow-orange	..		10	10
D29		2 c. magenta	..		10	10
D30		6 c. blue-green			10	10
D31		10 c. orange-brown			10	10
D32		13 c. new blue	..		10	10
D28/32				*Set of 5*	25	30

1990 (2 Jan). *No. D27 surch with Type D 6.*

D33	D 4	25 c. on 10 c. cerise	..		6·00	6·00

No. D33 is reported to have been issued to the main post offices at Bulawayo, Gweru, Harare and Mutare.

Zululand
see South Africa

Set Prices for British Commonwealth Omnibus Issues

The composition of these sets is in accordance with the tables on the following pages. Only such items considered basic stamps are included; varieties such as shades, perforation changes and watermark changes are excluded. Great Britain issues which come on both ordinary paper and on paper with phosphor bands are however covered.

Stamps issued in connection with any of the events by countries which are no longer in the British Commonwealth and which are not listed in the Part 1 Catalogue are omitted.

	Price	
	Un	Used
1935. Silver Jubilee. *Complete set of 250 stamps*	£800	£900

The concept initiated by the 1935 Silver Jubilee omnibus issue has provided a pattern for a series of Royal commemoratives over the past 50 years which have introduced countless collectors to the hobby.

The Crown Colony Windsor Castle design by Harold Fleury is, surely, one of the most impressive produced in the 20th-century and its reproduction in the recess process by three of the leading stamp-printing firms of the era has provided a subject for philatelic research which has yet to be exhausted.

Each of the three, Bradbury, Wilkinson & Co. and Waterlow and Sons, who both produced fifteen issues, together with De La Rue & Co. who printed fourteen, used a series of vignette (centre) plates coupled with individual frame plates for each value. All were taken from dies made by Waterlow. Several worthwhile varieties exist on the frame plates, but most interest has been concentrated on the centre plates, each of which was used to print a considerable number of different stamps.

Sheets printed by Bradbury, Wilkinson were without printed plate numbers, but research has now identified eleven centre plates which were probably used in permanent pairings. A twelfth plate awaits confirmation. Stamps from some of these centre plates have revealed a number of prominent plate flaws, the most famous of which, the extra flagstaff, has been eagerly sought by collectors for many years.

Extra flagstaff
(Plate "1" R.9/1)

Short extra flagstaff
(Plate "2" R.2/1)

Lightning conductor
(Plate "3" R.2/5)

Flagstaff on right-hand
turret (Plate "5" R.7/1)

Double flagstaff
(Plate "6" R.5/2)

De La Rue sheets were initially printed with plate numbers, but in many instances these were subsequently trimmed off. Surviving examples do, however, enable a positive identification of six centre plates, 2A, 2B, (2A), (2B), 4 and 4/ to be made. The evidence of sheet markings and plate flaws clearly demonstrates that there were two different pairs of plates numbered 2A 2B. The second pair is designated (2A) (2B) by specialist collectors to avoid further confusion. The number of major plate flaws is not so great as on the Bradbury, Wilkinson sheets, but four examples are included in the catalogue.

Diagonal line by turret
(Plate 2A R. 10/2)

Dot to left of chapel
(Plate 2B R.8/3)

Dot by flagstaff
(Plate 4 R.8/4)

Dash by turret
(Plate 4/ R.3/6)

Much less is known concerning the Waterlow centre plate system as the sheets did not show plate numbers. Ten individual plates have, so far, been identified and it is believed that these were used in pairs. The two versions of the kite and log flaw from plate "2" show that this plate exists in two states.

Kite and vertical log
(Plate "2A" R.10/6)

Kite and horizontal log
(Plate "2B" R.10/6)

| **1937.** Coronation. *Complete set of 202 stamps* | £110 | 80·00 |

| **1945–46.** Victory. *Complete set of 164 stamps* | 27·00 | 27·00 |

1948–49. Royal Silver Wedding.
Complete set of 138 stamps £1400 £1400

| **1949.** U.P.U. 75th Anniversary | | |
| *Complete set of 310 stamps* | £275 | £250 |

| **1951.** B.W.I. University College | | |
| *Complete set of 28 stamps* | 8·50 | 5·25 |

| **1953.** Coronation. *Complete set of 106 stamps* | 90·00 | 55·00 |

| **1953–54.** Royal Visit. *Complete set of 13 stamps* | 2·50 | 2·50 |

| **1958.** Caribbean Federation. | | |
| *Complete set of 30 stamps* | 13·50 | 8·75 |

| **1963.** Freedom from Hunger. | | |
| *Complete set of 77 stamps* | £150 | 75·00 |

1963. Red Cross Centenary.
Complete set of 108 stamps and 2 miniature sheets £225 £160

1964. Shakespeare. 400th Birth Anniversary.
Complete set of 25 stamps   20·00   17·00

1965. I.T.U. Centenary.
Complete set of 112 stamps and 1 miniature sheet   £140   80·00

1965. I.C.Y.
Complete set of 107 stamps and 2 miniature sheets   £120   65·00

1965–67. Churchill.   *Complete set of 182 stamps*   £200   £100

1966. Royal Visit to the Caribbean.
Complete set of 34 stamps   28·00   11·50

1966. World Cup Football Championship.
Complete set of 68 stamps and 1 miniature sheet   90·00   60·00

1966. W.H.O. New Headquarters.
Complete set of 58 stamps and 1 miniature sheet   75·00   45·00

1966–67. U.N.E.S.C.O. 20th Anniversary.
Complete set of 110 stamps and 1 miniature sheet   £120   80·00

1972. Royal Silver Wedding.
Complete set of 78 stamps   35·00   30·00

1973. Royal Wedding.
Complete set of 72 stamps and 6 miniature sheets   35·00   20·00

1977. Silver Jubilee.   *Set of 220 basic stamps*   £100   80·00
   Set of 24 miniature sheets   42·00   50·00

1977. Royal Visit.   *Set of 46 basic stamps*   10·50   9·00
   Set of 8 miniature sheets   7·00   10·00

1978. Coronation. 25th Anniversary.
   Set of 195 basic stamps   65·00   65·00
   Set of 21 sheetlets   42·00
   Set of 27 miniature sheets   50·00   38·00

1980. Queen Mother's Birthday.
   Set of 41 stamps   32·00   26·00
   Set of 12 miniature sheets   29·00   27·00

1981. Royal Wedding.   *Set of 244 basic stamps*   £130   £120
   Set of 35 miniature sheets   70·00   65·00

1982. Princess Diana's 21st Birthday.
   Set of 162 basic stamps   90·00   90·00
   Set of 19 miniature sheets   45·00   48·00

1982. Birth of Prince William.

Set of 124 basic stamps	£130	£100
Set of 22 miniature sheets	70·00	65·00

The Life and Times of
Her Majesty Queen Elizabeth The Queen Mother

(Illustration reduced)

1985. Life and Times of Queen Elizabeth the Queen Mother.

Set of 226 stamps	£110	£120
Set of 47 miniature sheets	£100	£110

1986. 60th Birthday of Queen Elizabeth II.

Set of 233 stamps	£150	£160
Set of 28 miniature sheets	95·00	£110

1986. Royal Wedding.

Set of 142 stamps	£110	£110
Set of 24 miniature sheets	80·00	90·00

1987. Royal Ruby Wedding.

Set of 117 stamps	£100	£100
Set of 14 miniature sheets	38·00	42·00

1990. 90th Birthday of Queen Elizabeth the Queen Mother.

Set of 119 stamps	£110	£110
Set of 19 miniature sheets	70·00	75·00

1991. 65th Birthday of Queen Elizabeth II and 70th Birthday of Prince Philip.

Set of 85 stamps	80·00	85·00
Set of 11 miniature sheets	25·00	27·00

1992. 40th Anniversary of Queen Elizabeth II's Accession.

Set of 171 stamps	£110	£120
Set of 23 miniature sheets	55·00	60·00

1935 SILVER JUBILEE TO 1973 ROYAL WEDDING

Issuing Countries	1935 Silver Jubilee	1937 Coronation	1945–46 Victory	1948 Silver Wedding	1949 U.P.U.	1951 B.W.I. Univ	1953 Coronation	1953–54 Royal Visit	1958 Caribbean Fed.	1963 F.F.H.	1963 Red Cross	1964 Shakespeare	1965 I.T.U.	1965 I.C.Y.	1965–66 Churchill	1966 Royal Visit	1966 Football Cup	1966 W.H.O.	1966–67 UNESCO	1972 Silver Wedding	1973 Royal Wedding
Great Britain	4	1	2	2	4	—	4	—	—	2+2	3+3	5+4	2+2	2+2	2+2	—	3+3	—	—	2	2
Guernsey	—	—	—	—	—	—	—	—	—	—	—	—	—	—	—	—	—	—	—	4	1
Isle of Man	—	—	—	—	—	—	—	—	—	—	—	—	—	—	—	—	—	—	—	—	1
Jersey	—	—	—	—	—	—	—	—	—	—	—	—	—	—	—	—	—	—	—	4	2
Anguilla	—	—	—	—	—	—	—	—	—	—	—	—	—	—	—	—	—	—	—	2	2
Antigua	4	3	2	2	4	2	1	—	3	1	2	1	2	2	4	2	2	2	3	2	2+MS
Barbuda	—	—	—	—	—	—	—	—	—	—	—	—	—	—	—	—	—	—	—	2	2
Ascension	4	3	2	2	4	—	1	—	—	1	2	—	2	2	4	—	2	2	3	2	2
Australia	3	—	3	—	1	—	3	3	—	—	1	—	1	1	1	—	—	—	—	—	—
Bahamas	4	3	2	2	4	—	1	—	—	1	2	1	2	2	4	2	2	2	3	2	—
Bahrain	—	—	—	2	4	—	4	—	—	—	—	—	—	—	—	—	—	—	—	—	—
Barbados	4	3	2	2	4	2	1	—	3	—	—	—	2	—	2	—	—	—	3	—	—
Belize/British Honduras	4	3	2	2	4	2	1	—	—	1	2	—	2	2	4	—	2	—	—	2	2
Bermuda	4	3	2	2	4	—	1	1	—	1	2	—	2	2	4	—	2	—	3	2	2
Botswana/Bechuanaland	4	3	3×2	2	4	—	1	—	—	1	2	1	2	2	4	—	—	—	—	2	2
British Antarctic Territory	—	—	—	—	—	—	—	—	—	—	—	—	—	—	4	—	—	—	—	2	2
British Indian Ocean Terr.	—	—	—	—	—	—	—	—	—	—	—	—	—	—	—	—	—	—	—	2	—
British P.A.'s in Eastern Arabia	—	—	—	2	4	—	4	—	—	—	—	—	—	—	—	—	—	—	—	—	—
British Virgin Islands	4	3	2	2	4	2	1	—	—	1	2	1	2	2	4	2	—	—	3	2	2
Brunei	—	—	—	—	4	—	1	—	—	1	—	—	2	2	4	—	2	2	3	2	2
Burma	—	—	4	—	—	—	—	—	—	—	—	—	—	—	—	—	—	—	—	—	—
Canada	6	1	—	—	—	—	1	—	—	—	—	—	—	—	—	—	—	—	—	—	—
Newfoundland	4	14	—	—	—	—	—	—	—	—	—	—	—	—	—	—	—	—	—	—	—
Cayman Islands	4	3	2	2	4	—	1	—	—	1	2	1	2	2	4	2	2	2	3	2	2+MS
Cook Islands	3	3	4	—	—	—	2	—	—	—	—	—	—	—	6	—	—	—	—	4	3+MS
Aitutaki	—	—	—	—	—	—	—	—	—	—	—	—	—	—	—	—	—	—	—	2	2+MS
Penrhyn	—	—	—	—	—	—	—	—	—	—	—	—	—	—	—	—	—	—	—	—	3
Cyprus	4	3	2	2	4	—	1	—	—	2	2	4	3	2	—	—	—	—	1	—	—
Dominica	4	3	2	2	4	2	1	—	3	1	2	1	2	2	4	2	2	2	3	2	2+MS
Egypt/British Forces in Egypt	1	—	—	—	—	—	—	—	—	—	—	—	—	—	—	—	—	—	—	—	—
Falkland Islands	4	3	2	2	4	—	1	—	—	1	2	1	2	2	4	—	—	—	—	2	2
Falkland Islands Dependencies	—	—	2	2	4	—	1	—	—	—	—	—	—	—	—	—	—	—	—	—	—
South Georgia	—	—	—	—	—	—	—	—	—	—	—	—	—	—	—	—	—	—	—	2	2
Fiji	4	3	2	2	4	—	1	1	—	1	2	—	2	2	4	—	2	2	—	2	—
Gambia	4	3	2	2	4	—	1	—	—	1	2	1	2	—	3	—	—	—	—	—	—
Ghana/Gold Coast	4	3	2	2	4	—	1	—	—	3	4+MS	—	4+MS	4+MS	—	—	5+MS	4+MS	5+MS	—	—
Gibraltar	4	3	2	2	4	—	1	1	—	1	2	1	2	2	4	—	2	2	3	2	2
Gilbert and Ellice Islands	4	3	2	2	4	—	1	—	—	1	2	—	2	2	4	—	2	2	3	2	2
Grenada	4	3	2	2	4	2	1	—	3	1	2	—	2	2	4	2	2	2	3	2	2+MS
Grenadines	—	—	—	—	—	—	—	—	—	—	—	—	—	—	—	—	—	—	—	—	2+MS
Guyana/British Guiana	4	3	2	2	4	2	1	—	—	1	2	—	2	2	2	2	—	—	—	—	—
Hong Kong	4	3	2	2	4	—	1	—	—	1	2	—	2	2	4	—	2	2	3	2	2
India	7	—	4	—	4	—	—	—	—	1	1	—	1	1	—	—	—	—	—	—	—
Hyderabad	—	—	1	—	—	—	—	—	—	—	—	—	—	—	—	—	—	—	—	—	—
Ireland	—	—	—	—	—	—	—	—	—	2	2	—	2	2	—	—	—	—	—	—	—
Jamaica	4	3	2	2	4	2	1	1	3	2	1	—	1	—	2	4	—	—	—	—	—
K.U.T./East Africa	4	3	2	2	4	—	1	1	—	4	2	—	4	4	—	—	—	—	4	—	—
Kuwait	—	—	—	2	4	—	4	—	—	—	—	—	—	—	—	—	—	—	—	—	—
Leeward Islands	4	3	2	2	4	2	1	—	—	—	—	—	—	—	—	—	—	—	—	—	—
Lesotho/Basutoland	4	3	3×2	2	4	—	1	—	—	1	2	—	2	2	4	—	—	—	4	—	—
Malawi/Nyasaland	4	3	2	2	4	—	1	—	—	—	—	—	—	—	—	—	—	—	—	—	—
Malayan States, etc.	4	3	—	22	44	—	11	—	—	3	—	—	3	—	—	—	—	—	—	—	—
North Borneo	—	—	—	2	4	—	1	—	—	1	—	—	—	—	—	—	—	—	—	—	—
Sarawak	—	—	—	2	4	—	1	—	—	—	—	—	—	—	—	—	—	—	—	—	—
Maldive Islands	—	—	—	—	—	—	—	—	—	7	5	—	—	5+MS	6	—	—	—	6	—	—
Malta	4	3	2	2	4	—	1	1	—	1	2	—	—	—	4	—	—	—	—	—	—
Mauritius	4	3	2	2	4	—	1	—	—	—	—	—	2	2	4	—	—	—	3	—	—
Montserrat	4	3	2	2	4	2	1	—	3	1	2	1	2	2	4	2	—	2	3	2	2
Morocco Agencies/Tangier	15	3	2	4	4	—	4	—	—	—	—	—	—	—	—	—	—	—	—	—	—
Namibia/South West Africa	4	8×2	3×2	1×2	3×2	—	5	—	—	—	2	—	—	—	—	—	—	—	—	—	—
Nauru	4	4	—	—	—	—	—	—	—	—	—	—	—	—	—	—	—	—	—	—	—
New Zealand	3	3	11	—	—	—	5	2	—	—	—	—	1	1	1	—	—	—	—	—	—
Tokelau Islands	—	—	—	—	—	—	1	—	—	—	—	—	—	—	—	—	—	—	—	—	—
Nigeria	4	3	2	2	4	—	1	—	—	2	3+MS	—	3	3	—	—	—	—	3	—	—
Niue	3	3	4	—	—	—	2	—	—	—	—	—	—	—	—	—	—	—	—	—	—
Pakistan	—	—	—	—	—	—	—	—	—	2	1	—	1	2	—	—	—	—	1	—	—
Bahawalpur Postage and Officials	—	—	1	—	4+4	—	—	—	—	—	—	—	—	—	—	—	—	—	—	—	—
P.N.G./Papua	4	4	—	—	—	—	—	—	—	—	—	1	—	—	—	—	—	—	—	—	—
New Guinea	2	4	—	—	—	—	—	—	—	—	—	—	—	—	—	—	—	—	—	—	—
Pitcairn Islands	—	—	2	2	4	—	1	—	—	1	2	—	2	2	4	—	2	2	3	2	2
Rhodesia and Nyasaland	—	—	—	—	—	—	—	—	—	1	1	—	—	—	—	—	—	—	—	—	—
St. Helena	4	3	2	2	4	—	1	—	—	1	2	—	2	2	4	—	2	2	3	2	2
St. Kitts-Nevis	4	3	2	2	4	2	1	—	3	1	2	1	2	2	4	2	2	2	3	2	2
St. Lucia	4	3	2	2	4	2	1	—	3	1	2	1	2	2	4	2	2	2	3	2	2
St. Vincent	4	3	2	2	4	2	1	—	3	1	2	—	2	—	4	2	2	2	3	2	2
Grenadines	—	—	—	—	—	—	—	—	—	—	—	—	—	—	—	—	—	—	—	—	2
Samoa	3	—	4	—	—	—	2	—	—	—	—	—	—	—	—	—	—	4	—	—	—
Seychelles	4	3	2	2	4	—	1	—	—	1	2	—	2	2	4	—	2	2	3	2	2
Sierra Leone	4	3	2	2	4	—	1	—	—	2	3	—	—	—	11	—	—	—	—	—	—
Singapore	—	—	—	2	4	—	1	—	—	—	—	—	—	—	—	—	—	—	—	—	—
Solomon Islands	4	3	2	2	4	—	1	—	—	1	2	—	2	2	4	—	2	2	3	2	2
Somaliland Protectorate	4	3	2	—	—	—	—	—	—	—	—	—	—	—	—	—	—	—	—	—	—
South Africa	4×2	5×2	3×2	1×2	3×2	—	1	—	—	1	2	—	2	2	—	—	—	—	—	—	—
South Arabian Fed./Aden	4	3	2	2	4	—	1	1	—	1	—	—	2	—	4	—	2	2	3	—	—
Seiyun	—	—	2	2	4	—	1	—	—	—	—	—	7	—	1	—	7	—	—	—	—
Shihr and Mukalla	—	—	2	2	4	—	1	—	—	—	—	—	8	3	—	—	8	—	—	—	—
Sri Lanka/Ceylon	4	3	2	—	3	—	1	1	—	2	—	—	2	2	—	—	—	2	—	2	—
Swaziland	4	3	3×2	2	4	—	1	—	—	1	2	—	2	2	4	—	—	—	3	—	—
Tanzania/Zanzibar	—	—	—	2	4	—	1	—	—	—	—	—	—	—	—	—	—	—	—	—	—
Tonga	—	—	—	—	4	—	—	—	—	1	2	—	—	—	—	—	—	—	—	—	—
Trinidad and Tobago	4	3	2	2	4	2	1	—	3	3	—	—	2	—	4	4	—	—	—	—	—
Tristan da Cunha	—	—	—	—	—	—	1	—	—	1	2	—	2	2	4	—	2	2	3	2	2
Turks and Caicos Islands	4	3	2	2	4	—	1	—	—	1	2	1	2	2	4	2	—	—	3	2	2
Vanuatu/New Hebrides (English & French inscr)	—	—	—	—	4+4	—	1	—	—	1+1	2+2	—	2+2	2+2	4+4	—	2+2	2+2	3+3	2+2	—
Zambia/Northern Rhodesia	4	3	2	2	4	—	1	—	—	—	—	—	2	2	—	—	2	—	—	—	—
Zimbabwe/Southern Rhodesia	4	4	4	—	2	—	1	—	—	—	—	—	3	—	1	—	—	—	—	—	—
Total number of stamps	250	202	164	138	310	28	106	13	30	77	108 +2 MS	25	112 +MS	107 +2 MS	182	34	68 +MS	58 +MS	110 +MS	78	72 +6 MS

NOTE Countries marked with an asterisk are those which comprise the Crown Agents Omnibus issue.

1977 SILVER JUBILEE

Country	Catalogue Nos.	Stamps	MS
Great Britain	1033/7	5	—
Guernsey	149/50	2	—
Isle of Man	94/6	3	—
Jersey	168/70	3	—
Anguilla	269/73	4	1
Antigua	526/31	5	1
Barbuda	298/304, 323/28	11	2
Ascension*	222/4	3	—
Australia	645/6	2	—
Bahamas	488/92	4	1
Bangladesh	93/6	3	1
Barbados*	574/6	3	—
Belize*	449/51	3	—
Bermuda*	371/3	3	—
Botswana*	391/3	3	—
British Antarctic Territory*	83/5	3	—
British Virgin Islands*	364/6	3	—
Brunei	264/6	3	—
Canada	855	1	—
Cayman Islands*	427/9	3	—
Christmas Island	83	1	—
Cook Islands	564/70	6	1
Aitutaki	225/9	4	1
Penrhyn	100/3	3	1
Cyprus	485	1	—
Dominica	562/7	5	1
Falkland Islands*	325/7	3	—
South Georgia*	50/2	3	—
Fiji*	536/8	3	—
Gambia*	365/7	3	—
Gibraltar	371/3	2	1
Grenada	857/62	5	1
Grenadines of Grenada	215/18	3	1
Hong Kong*	361/3	3	—
Kenya	91/5	4	2
Kiribati / Gilbert Islands*	48/50	3	—
Maldive Islands	673/9	6	1
Mauritius*	516/18	3	—
Montserrat	396/8	3	—
New Zealand	MS1137	—	1
Niue	213/15	2	1
Norfolk Island	196	1	—
Papua New Guinea	330/2	3	—
Pitcairn Islands*	171/3	3	—
St. Helena*	332/4	3	—
St. Kitts-Nevis*	367/9	3	—
St. Lucia	443/7	4	1
St. Vincent	502/14	12	1
Grenadines of St. Vincent	93/5	3	—
Samoa	479/82	4	—
Seychelles	393/401	8	1
Sierra Leone	597/8	2	—
Solomon Islands*	334/6	3	—
Swaziland*	268/70	3	—
Tanzania	218/22	4	1
Tonga	598/607, O151/3	13	—
Tristan da Cunha*	212/14	3	—
Turks and Caicos Islands*	472/5	3	1
Tuvalu	50/3	3	1
Vanuatu/New Hebrides* (English & French inscr)	217/19 F231/3	3+3	—
Total number of items		**220**	**24**

The Turks and Caicos Islands miniature sheet, **MS**475, did not form part of the Crown Agents Omnibus issue.

1977 ROYAL VISIT

Country	Catalogue Nos.	Stamps	MS
Anguilla	298/302	4	1
Antigua	548/53	5	1
Barbuda	345/54	8	2
Bahamas	500/4	4	1
Barbados	590/2	3	—
British Virgin Islands	371/3	3	—
Dominica	591/6	5	1
Grenada	894/9	5	1
Grenadines of Grenada	239/42	3	—
Montserrat	409/11	3	—
St. Vincent	540	1	—
Grenadines of St. Vincent	104/5	2	—
Total number of items		**46**	**8**

1978 CORONATION ANNIVERSARY

Country	Catalogue Nos.	Stamps	Sheetlets	MS
Great Britain	1059/62	4	—	—
Guernsey	167	1	—	—
Isle of Man	132	1	—	—
Jersey	195/6	2	—	—
Anguilla	320/4	4	—	1
Antigua	581/6	5	—	—
Barbuda	408/20, 445/6	12	—	3
Ascension*	233/5	3	1	—
Bahamas	515/17	3	—	1
Bangladesh	116/20	4	—	1
Barbados*	597/9	3	1	—
Belize*	464/6, 495/503	11	1	2
Bermuda	384/6	3	—	—
British Antarctic Territory*	86/8	3	1	—
British Virgin Islands*	384/6	3	1	—
Brunei	267/9	3	—	—
Cayman Islands*	468/70	3	1	—
Christmas Island*	96/8	3	1	—
Cook Islands	593/601	8	—	1
Aitutaki	257/60	3	—	1
Penrhyn	121/4	3	—	1

Country	Catalogue Nos.	Stamps	Sheetlets	MS
Dominica	612/15	3	—	1
Falkland Islands*	348/50	3	1	—
South Georgia*	67/9	3	1	—
Fiji*	549/51	3	1	—
Gambia*	397/9	3	1	—
Gibraltar	400/3	4	—	—
Grenada	946/9	3	—	1
Grenadines of Grenada	272/5	3	—	1
Hong Kong	373/4	2	—	—
Kiribati/Gilbert Islands*	68/70	3	1	—
Maldive Islands	755/61	6	—	1
Mauritius*	549/51	3	1	—
Montserrat	422/6	4	—	1
New Zealand Dependency of Tokelau	61/4	4	—	—
Niue	245/8	3	—	1
Norfolk Island	207/8	2	—	—
Pitcairn Islands	MS189	—	—	1
St. Helena	338/40	3	1	—
St. Kitts-Nevis*	389/91	3	1	—
St. Lucia	468/72	4	—	1
St. Vincent	556/60	4	—	1
Grenadines of St. Vincent	130/4	4	—	1
Samoa*	508/10	3	1	—
Seychelles	428/32	4	—	1
Sierra Leone	601/3	3	—	—
Solomon Islands*	357/9	3	1	—
Swaziland	293/5	3	1	—
Tanzania	233/7	4	—	1
Tristan da Cunha*	239/41	3	1	—
Turks and Caicos Islands	494/8	4	—	1
Tuvalu	89/93	4	—	1
Uganda	234/8	4	—	1
Vanuatu/New Hebrides* (English & French inscr)	262/4, F276/8	3+3	1+1	—
Total number of items		**195**	**21**	**27**

The Crown Agents Omnibus issue was printed in matching sheetlets, each containing two *se-tenant* strips of the three designs.
Barbuda Nos. 445/6 form part of a general anniversaries issue.
Belize Nos. 495/503 were not part of the Crown Agents Omnibus issue.

1980 QUEEN MOTHER's 80th BIRTHDAY

Country	Catalogue Nos.	Stamps	MS
Great Britain	1129	1	—
Anguilla	411/15	4	1
Antigua	663/5	2	1
Barbuda	533/5	2	1
Ascension*	269	1	—
Bangladesh	172/4	2	1
Belize	592/3	1	1
Bermuda*	425	1	—
Cayman Islands*	506	1	—
Cook Islands	701/2	1	1
Penrhyn	150/1	1	1
Dominica	732/4	2	1
Falkland Islands*	383	1	—
Gambia*	440	1	—
Gibraltar*	436	1	—
Hong Kong*	390	1	—
Lesotho	423/5	3	—
Maldive Islands	886/7	1	1
Niue	364/5	1	1
Norfolk Island	252/3	2	—
Pitcairn Islands*	206	1	—
St. Helena*	366	1	—
St. Kitts-Nevis			
St. Kitts	48	1	—
Nevis	50	1	—
St. Lucia	534/6	2	1
Samoa*	572	1	—
Solomon Islands*	421	1	—
Tristan da Cunha*	282	1	—
Turks and Caicos Islands	607/8	1	1
Tuvalu	148	1	—
Total number of items		**41**	**12**

1981 ROYAL WEDDING

Country	Catalogue Nos.	Stamps	MS
Great Britain	1160/1	2	—
Guernsey	232/9	7	1
Isle of Man	202/4	2	1
Jersey	284/5	2	—
Anguilla	464/7	3	1
Antigua	702/5	3	1
Barbuda	565/75	9	2
Ascension*	302/4	3	—
Australia	821/2	2	—
Bahamas	586/8	2	1
Barbados*	674/6	3	—
Belize	614/20	6	1
Bermuda*	436/8	3	—
British Virgin Islands*	463/5	3	—
Brunei*	304/6	3	—
Cayman Islands*	534/6	3	—
Cocos (Keeling) Islands	70/1	2	—
Cook Islands	812/14	2	1
Aitutaki	391/3	3	—
Penrhyn	223/8	5	1
Cyprus	580	1	—
Turkish Cypriot Posts	121	1	—
Dominica	747/50	3	1
Falkland Islands*	402/4	3	—
Dependencies*	95/7	3	—
Fiji*	612/14	3	—
Gambia*	454/6	3	—
Ghana	948/54	6	1
Gibraltar	450	1	—
Grenada	1130/5	5	1
Grenadines of Grenada	444/9	5	1
Guyana	769/70, 841/3, 930/6	12	—
Hong Kong*	399/401	3	—

Country	Catalogue Nos.	Stamps	MS
Jamaica	516/20	4	1
Kenya	207/11	4	1
Kiribati	149/55	6	1
Lesotho*	451/4	3	1
Maldive Islands	918/21	3	1
Mauritius*	615/17	3	—
Montserrat	510/15	6	1
New Zealand	1247/8	2	—
Niue	430/3	3	1
Norfolk Island*	262/4	3	—
Pitcairn Islands*	219/21	3	—
St. Helena*	378/80	3	—
St. Kitts-Nevis			
St. Kitts	75/81	6	1
Nevis	72/8	6	1
St. Lucia	576/9	3	1
St. Vincent	668/74	6	1
Grenadines of St. Vincent	195/201	6	1
Samoa*	599/601	3	—
Seychelles	505/11	6	1
Zil Elwagne Sesel	23/9	6	1
Sierra Leone*	668/74	6	1
Solomon Islands*	445/7	3	—
Swaziland*	376/8	3	—
Tanzania	325/7	2	1
Tonga	785/8	4	—
Tristan da Cunha*	308/10	3	—
Turks and Caicos Islands	653/6	3	1
Caicos Islands	8/11	3	1
Tuvalu	168/74	6	1
Uganda	341/8	6	2
Vanuatu*	315/17	3	—
Total number of items		**244**	**35**

The Lesotho miniature sheet, No. **MS**454, and Sierra Leone Nos. 671/3 do not form part of the Crown Agents Omnibus issue.

1982 PRINCESS DIANA'S 21st BIRTHDAY

Country	Catalogue Nos.	Stamps	MS
Anguilla	507/14	6	2
Antigua	748/51	3	1
Barbuda	624/30	6	2
Ascension*	322/5	4	—
Bahamas*	622/5	4	—
Barbados*	705/8	4	—
Belize	680/6	6	1
British Antarctic Territory*	109/12	4	—
British Virgin Islands*	488/91	4	—
Cayman Islands*	549/52	4	—
Cook Islands	833/7	4	1
Aitutaki	411/14	3	1
Penrhyn	250/5	5	1
Dominica	821/4	3	1
Falkland Islands*	426/9	4	—
Dependencies*	108/11	4	—
Fiji*	640/3	4	—
Gambia*	476/9	4	—
Grenada	1188/94	6	1
Grenadines of Grenada	493/9	6	1
Guyana	979/81	3	—
Jamaica	551/7	6	1
Kiribati	183/5	3	—
Lesotho*	514/17	4	—
Maldive Islands	964/7	3	1
Mauritius*	643/6	4	—
Montserrat	542/4	3	—
Niue	454/7	3	1
Pitcairn Islands*	226/9	4	—
St. Helena*	397/400	4	—
St. Kitts-Nevis			
St. Kitts	95/7	3	—
Nevis	85/7	3	—
St. Lucia	625/8	3	1
St. Vincent	694/6	3	—
Grenadines of St. Vincent	229/31	3	—
Sierra Leone	707/10	3	1
Solomon Islands*	467/70	4	—
Swaziland*	404/7	4	—
Tristan da Cunha*	327/30	4	—
Turks and Caicos Islands	709/12	3	1
Tuvalu	184/6	3	—
Uganda	374/7	1	1
Total number of items		**162**	**19**

1982 BIRTH OF PRINCE WILLIAM

Country	Catalogue Nos.	Stamps	MS
Great Britain			
Isle of Man	MS227	—	1
Antigua	757/60	3	1
Barbuda	613/16, 632/5	6	2
Belize	707/20	12	2
Cook Islands	838/47, 856/61	13	3
Aitutaki	415/24	9	1
Penrhyn	256/72	15	2
Dominica	830/3	3	1
Grenada	1200/6	6	1
Grenadines of Grenada	505/11	6	1
Guyana	982/7	6	—
Jamaica	558/64	6	1
Kiribati	186/8	3	—
Lesotho	521/2	2	—
Maldive Islands	968/72	4	1
Mauritius	647	1	—
Niue	458/74	13	4
St. Kitts-Nevis			
St. Kitts	98/100	3	—
Nevis	88/90	3	—
St. Vincent	699/701	3	—
Grenadines of St. Vincent	234/6	3	—
Sierra Leone	711/14	3	1
Tuvalu	189/91	3	—
Total number of items		**124**	**22**

1985 LIFE AND TIMES OF QUEEN ELIZABETH THE QUEEN MOTHER

Country	Catalogue Nos.	Stamps	MS
Anguilla	655/8	3	1
Antigua	946/9	3	1
Barbuda	776/82, 809/15 826/9	17	1
Ascension*	376/80	4	1
Bahamas*	712/16	4	1
Barbados*	779/83	4	1
Belize	827/31	4	1
Bermuda*	494/8	4	1
British Virgin Islands	579/87	8	1
Cook Islands	1035/9	4	1
Aitutaki	523/7	4	1
Penrhyn	378/82	4	1
Dominica	949/52	3	1
Falkland Islands*	505/9	4	1
Dependencies*	129/33	4	1
Fiji*	701/5	4	1
Gambia	586/9	3	1
Ghana	1140/3	3	1
Grenada	1426/9	3	1
Grenadines of Grenada	689/92	3	1
Guyana	1536/9	3	1
Hong Kong*	493/6	4	—
Jamaica*	625/9	4	1
Lesotho	635/9	4	1
Maldive Islands	1099/102	4	1
Mauritius*	699/703	4	1
Montserrat	636/44	8	1
Niue	587/90	3	1
Norfolk Island*	364/8	4	1
Pitcairn Islands*	268/72	4	1
St. Helena*	454/8	4	1
St. Kitts-Nevis Nevis	309/17	8	1
St. Lucia	832/40	8	1
St. Vincent	910/18	8	1
Grenadines of St. Vincent	403/11	8	1
Samoa*	700/4	4	1
Seychelles*	614/18	4	1
Zil Elwannyen Sesel*	115/19	4	1
Sierra Leone	872/5	3	1
Solomon Islands*	538/42	4	1
Swaziland*	486/90	4	1
Tanzania	425/9	4	1
Tonga	915/18	4	—
Tristan da Cunha*	390/4	4	1
Turks and Caicos Islands	854/7	3	1
Caicos Islands	82/5	3	1
Tuvalu	334/42	8	1
Uganda	478/9	1	1
Vanuatu*	406/10	4	1
Zambia	432/5	3	1
Total number of items		226	47

1986 QUEEN ELIZABETH II's 60TH BIRTHDAY

Country	Catalogue Nos.	Stamps	MS
Great Britain	1316/19	4	—
Guernsey	365	1	—
Isle of Man	328/30	3	—
Jersey	389	1	—
Anguilla	711/14	3	1
Antigua	1005/8	3	1
Barbuda	861/4, 872/5	6	2
Ascension*	397/401	5	—
Australia	1009	1	—
Bahamas*	741/5	5	—
Barbados*	810/14	5	—
Belize	905/9	4	1
Bermuda*	524/8	5	1
British Virgin Islands	600/4	4	1
Cayman Islands*	621/5	5	—
Cook Islands	1065/8	3	1
Aitutaki	542/3	1	1
Penrhyn	394/6	3	—
Cyprus—Turkish Cypriot Posts	201	1	—
Dominica	998/1001	3	1
Falkland Islands*	522/6	5	—
Fiji*	714/18	5	—
Gambia	641/4	3	1
Gibraltar	540	1	—
Grenada	1499/502	3	1
Grenadines of Grenada	753/6	3	1
Guyana	1684/5	1	1
Hong Kong*	512/16	5	—
Jamaica*	646/50	5	—
Kiribati*	251/5	5	—
Lesotho	701/4	3	1
Maldive Islands	1170/3	3	1
Mauritius*	724/8	5	—
Montserrat	677/81	4	1
Niue	615/19	3	2
Norfolk Island	389/92	4	—
Papua New Guinea*	520/4	5	—
Pitcairn Islands*	285/9	5	—
St. Helena*	477/81	5	—
St. Kitts—Nevis St. Kitts	185/8	4	—
Nevis	384/8	4	1
St. Lucia	876/85	8	2
St. Vincent	978/82, 996/1000	8	2
Grenadines of St. Vincent	459/63	4	1
Samoa*	726/30	5	—
Seychelles*	639/43	5	—
Zil Elwannyen Sesel*	128/32	5	—
Sierra Leone	937/40	3	1
Solomon Islands*	562/6	5	—
South Georgia and Sandwich Islands*	153/7	5	—
Swaziland*	500/4	5	—
Tanzania	517/21	4	1
Tonga	941/3	3	—
Trinidad and Tobago	712/15	4	—
Tristan da Cunha*	406/10	5	—

Country	Catalogue Nos.	Stamps	MS
Tuvalu	381/5	4	1
Uganda	526/9	3	1
Vanuatu*	429/33	5	—
Zambia*	453/7	5	—
Total number of items		233	28

1986 ROYAL WEDDING

Country	Catalogue Nos.	Stamps	MS
Great Britain	1333/4	2	—
Guernsey	369/70	2	—
Isle of Man	326/7	2	—
Jersey	395/6	2	—
Anguilla	720/4	4	1
Antigua	1019/22	3	1
Barbuda	891/4	3	1
Ascension*	407/8	2	—
Bahamas*	756/7	2	—
Barbados*	822/3	2	—
Belize	941/4	3	1
British Virgin Islands	605/9	4	1
Cayman Islands*	633/4	2	—
Christmas Island*	220/1	2	—
Cook Islands	1075/7	3	—
Aitutaki	547/8	1	1
Penrhyn	400/1	2	—
Cyprus—Turkish Cypriot Posts	200	1	—
Dominica	1018/21	3	1
Falkland Islands	536/8	3	1
Gambia	664/7	3	1
Gibraltar	MS545	—	1
Grenada	1512/15	3	1
Grenadines of Grenada	762/5	3	1
Jamaica*	656/7	2	—
Lesotho	736/9	3	1
Maldive Islands	1179/82	3	1
Montserrat	691/5, 705/8	8	1
Niue	625/6	1	1
Pitcairn Islands*	290/1	2	—
St. Helena*	486/7	2	—
St. Kitts—Nevis St. Kitts*	189/90	2	—
Nevis	406/10, 454/7	8	1
St. Lucia	890/3, 897/901	8	1
St. Vincent	1009/13, 1022/5	8	1
Grenadines of St. Vincent	481/5, 486/9	8	1
Seychelles*	651/2	2	—
Zil Elwannyen Sesel*	133/4	2	—
Sierra Leone	946/9	3	1
Solomon Islands*	568/9	2	—
South Georgia and Sandwich Islands	158/60	3	—
Tristan da Cunha*	415/16	2	—
Turks and Caicos Islands	893/6	3	1
Tuvalu	397/401, 433/6	8	1
Uganda	535/8	3	1
Zambia*	458/9	2	—
Total number of items		142	24

1987 ROYAL RUBY WEDDING

Country	Catalogue Nos.	Stamps	MS
Anguilla	788/91	4	—
Antigua	1149/53	4	1
Barbuda	1029/33	4	1
Ascension*	447/51	5	—
Belize	980/4	4	1
Cook Islands	1193/4	2	—
Aitutaki	572/4	3	—
Penrhyn	413/14	2	—
Dominica	1109/13	4	1
Gambia	765/9	4	1
Grenada	1737/41	4	1
Grenadines of Grenada	928/32	4	1
Guyana	2233/4	1	1
Kiribati*	279/83	5	—
Lesotho	806/9	3	1
Maldive Islands	1282/5	3	1
Montserrat	739/42	8	—
Niue	657/8	2	—
St. Helena*	514/18	5	—
St. Vincent	1079/84	5	1
Grenadines of St. Vincent	536/41	5	1
Seychelles*	674/8	5	—
Zil Elwannyen Sesel*	157/61	5	—
Sierra Leone	1116/20	4	1
Swaziland*	537/40	4	—
Tristan da Cunha*	438/42	5	—
Turks and Caicos Islands	922/4	3	—
Tuvalu	484/9	5	1
Vanuatu*	487/91	5	—
Total number of items		117	14

1990 QUEEN MOTHER'S 90TH BIRTHDAY

Country	Catalogue Nos.	Stamps	MS
Great Britain	1507/10	4	–
Isle of Man	448	1	–
Anguilla	859	1	–
Antigua	1415/19	4	1
Barbuda	1206/10	4	1
Ascension*	525/6	2	–
Bahamas*	880/1	2	–
Barbados*	919/20	2	–

Country	Catalogue Nos.	Stamps	MS
British Antarctic Territory*	186/7	2	–
British Indian Ocean Territory*	106/7	2	–
British Virgin Islands	746/50	4	1
Cayman Islands*	711/12	2	–
Cook Islands	1246/7	1	1
Aitutaki	MS614	–	1
Penrhyn	445/6	1	1
Dominica	1373/7	4	1
Falkland Islands*	606/7	2	–
Gambia	1060/3	3	1
Grenada	2131/4	3	1
Grenadines of Grenada	1262/5	3	1
Kenya*	545/6	2	–
Kiribati*	341/2	2	–
Lesotho	967/70	3	1
Maldive Islands	1396/9	3	1
Niue	689/90	1	1
Pitcairn Islands*	378/9	2	–
St. Helena*	570/1	2	–
St. Kitts-Nevis Nevis	555/8	3	1
St. Lucia*	1053/4	2	–
St. Vincent	1536/9	3	1
Grenadines of St. Vincent	705/32	27	1
Seychelles*	782/3	2	–
Zil Elwannyen Sesel*	212/13	2	–
Sierra Leone	1493/6	3	1
Solomon Islands*	675/6	2	–
South Georgia and South Sandwich Islands*	195/6	2	–
Swaziland*	570/1	2	–
Tristan da Cunha*	498/9	2	–
Turks and Caicos Islands	1045/9	4	1
Uganda	816/19	3	1
Total number of items		119	19

65TH BIRTHDAY OF QUEEN ELIZABETH II AND 70TH BIRTHDAY OF PRINCE PHILIP

Country	Catalogue Nos.	Stamps	MS
Ascension*	539/40	2	—
Australia	1286	1	—
Bahamas*	913/14	2	—
Belize*	1104/5	2	—
Bermuda*	634/5	2	—
Cook Islands	1255	1	—
Aitutaki	622	1	—
Penrhyn	456	1	—
Dominica	1433/7	4	1
Gambia	1165/9	4	1
Grenada	2299/303	4	1
Grenada Grenadines	1393/7	4	1
Kiribati*	366/7	2	—
Maldive Islands	1506/10	4	1
Mauritius*	849/50	2	—
Niue	706	1	—
Pitcairn Islands*	399/400	2	—
St. Helena*	591/2	2	—
St. Kitts-Nevis St. Kitts*	336/7	2	—
Nevis	622/6	4	1
St. Vincent	1686/90	4	1
Grenadines of St. Vincent	750/4	4	1
Samoa*	861/2	2	—
Seychelles*	799/800	2	—
Zil Elwannyen Sesel*	234/5	2	—
Sierra Leone	1639/43	4	1
Solomon Islands*	692/5	2	—
South Georgia and South Sandwich Islands*	201/2	2	—
Swaziland*	592/3	2	—
Tristan da Cunha	514/17	4	—
Turks and Caicos Islands	1099/1103	4	1
Uganda	960/4	4	1
Vanuatu*	576/7	2	—
Total number of items		85	11

40TH ANNIV OF QUEEN ELIZABETH II'S ACCESSION

Country	Catalogue Nos.	Stamps	MS
Great Britain	1602/6	5	—
Guernsey	552/5	4	—
Isle of Man	508/12	5	—
Ascension*	569/73	5	—
Bahamas*	928/32	5	—
Bermuda*	640/4	5	—
British Indian Ocean Territory*	119/23	5	—
Cayman Islands*	737/41	5	—
Dominica	1515/19	4	2
Falkland Islands*	647/51	5	—
Gambia	1284/8	4	2
Gibraltar*	673/7	5	—
Grenada	2375/9	4	2
Grenada Grenadines	1469/73	4	2
Hong Kong*	691/5	5	—
Kenya*	565/9	5	—
Kiribati*	377/81	5	—
Lesotho	1084/8	4	1
Maldive Islands	1626/30	4	2
Pitcairn Islands*	409/13	5	—
St. Helena*	607/11	5	—
St. Kitts-Nevis St. Kitts*	350/4	5	—
Nevis	655/9	4	2
St. Vincent	1861/5	4	2
St. Vincent Grenadines	809/13	4	2
Samoa*	876/80	5	—
Seychelles*	810/14	5	—
Zil Elwannyen Sesel*	240/4	5	—
Sierra Leone	1774/8	4	2
Solomon Islands*	713/17	5	—

BRITISH COMMONWEALTH OMNIBUS ISSUES

Country	Catalogue Nos.	Stamps	MS
South Georgia and South Sandwich Islands*	209/13	5	—
Tristan da Cunha*	526/30	5	—
Turks and Caicos Islands	1145/53	8	2
Uganda	1079/83	4	2
Vanuatu*	587/91	5	—
Zambia*	687/91	5	—
Total number of items		171	23

Addenda

NEW ZEALAND

Add to Nos. 1459a/68:
1467a   80 c. New Zealand Falcon (31.3.93)   ..   55   60
          ab. Booklet pane. No. 1467a×10   ..   5·50
          No. 1467a was only issued in $8 stamp booklets.

491 Women
signing Petition

(Des Lindy Fisher. Litho Southern Colour Print, Dunedin)

1993 (31 Mar). *Centenary of Women's Suffrage.* T **491** *and similar vert designs. Multicoloured.* P 13½.
1725   45 c. Type **491**   30   35
1726   80 c. Aircraft propeller and woman on
          tractor   55   60
1727 $1 Housewife with children   65   70
1728 $1.50, Modern women   ..   ..   1·00   1·10
1725/8   ..   ..   *Set of* 4   2·25   2·50

NIGERIA

275 Map of World and   **276** Gathering
Stamp on Globe   Plantain Fruit

(Des Mrs. A. Adeyeye)

1992 (3 July). *"Olymphilex '92" Olympic Stamp Exhibition, Barcelona.* T **275** *and similar horiz design. Multicoloured.* W **189**. P 14.
630   50 k. Type **275**   10   10
631   1 n. 50, Examining stamps   10   10
MS632   120×109 mm. Nos. 630/1. No wmk   ..   20   20

(Des S. Eluare (50 k., 1 n.), N. Lasisi (1 n. 50), G. Osuji 2 n.).

1992 (17 July). *25th Anniv of International Institute of Tropical Agriculture.* T **276** *and similar designs. No wmk.* P 14.
633   50 k. multicoloured   10   10
634   1 n. multicoloured   10   10
635   1 n. 50, black, reddish brown and emerald   10   10
636   2 n. multicoloured   10   10
633/6   ..   ..   *Set of* 4   35   35
MS637   121×118 mm. Nos. 633/6   40   40
   Designs: *Vert*—1 n. 50, Harvesting cassava tubers; 2 n.
Stacking yams. *Horiz*—1 n. Tropical foods

277 Centre   **278** Healthy Food and
Emblem   Emblem

(Des Mrs. A. Adeyeye (50 k., 2 n.), G. Osuji (others))

1992 (16 Oct). *Commissioning of Maryam Babangida National Centre for Women's Development.* T **277** *and similar designs. No wmk.* P 14.
638   50 k. gold, emerald and blue-green   ..   10   10
639   1 n. multicoloured   10   10
640   1 n. 50, multicoloured   10   10
641   2 n. multicoloured   10   10
638/41   ..   ..   *Set of* 4   35   35
   Designs: *Vert*—1 n. Women working in fields; 2 n. Woman at
loom. *Horiz*—1 n. 50, Maryam Babangida National Centre.
   All examples of No. 641 are without a "NIGERIA" inscription.

1992 (1 Dec). *International Conference on Nutrition, Rome.* T **278** *and similar multicoloured designs. No wmk.* P 14.
642   50 k. Type **278**   10   10
643   1 n. Child eating   10   10
644   1 n. 50, Fruit (*vert*)   10   10
645   2 n. Vegetables   10   10
642/5   ..   ..   *Set of* 4   35   35

279 Sabada
Dance

(Des S. Eluare (50 k.), Mrs A. Adeyeye (1 n.), G. Osuji
(1 n. 50), G. Akinola (2 n.))

1992 (15 Dec). *Traditional Dances.* T **279** *and similar vert designs. Multicoloured. No wmk.* P 14.
646   50 k. Type **279**   10   10
647   1 n. Sato   10   10
648   1 n. 50, Asian Ubo Ikpa   10   10
649   2 n. Dundun   10   10
646/9   ..   ..   *Set of* 4   35   35

Note. The first supplement recording new stamps not in this Catalogue or the Addenda appeared in the August 1993 number of *Gibbons Stamp Monthly*.

650

Index

The
Philatelic
Register

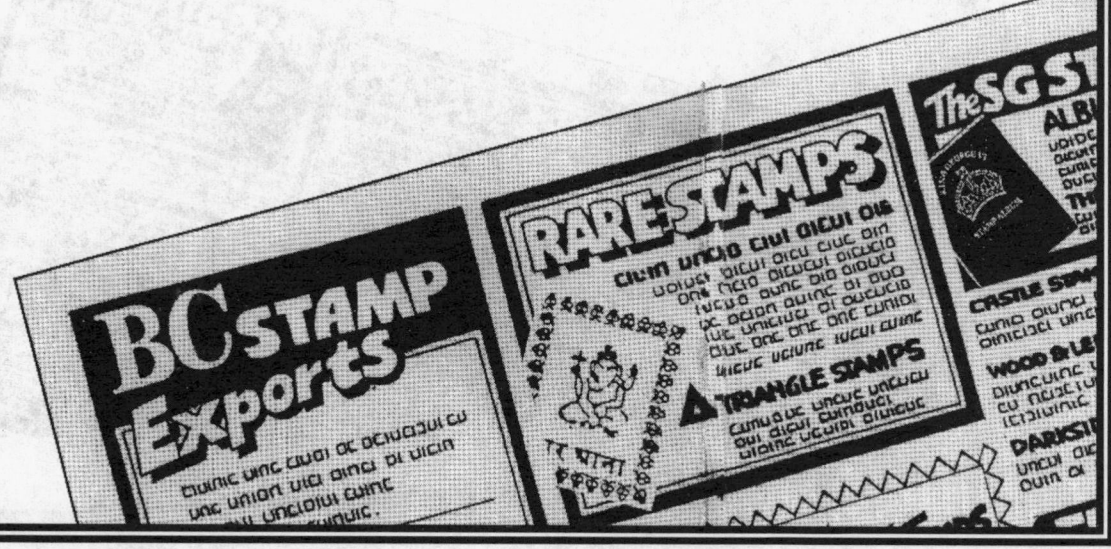

PUBLISHERS NOTES

The Philatelic Register

The Philatelic Register is your comprehensive, at-a-glance guide to the philatelic industry. Broken down by classification, the Philatelic Register is an invaluable information source covering many dealers, manufacturers and trade.

Whatever you require, simply turn to the Directory for a complete selection of names, addresses and telephone numbers covering your specialist area.

Free Lineage Entry

All future editions of the British Commonwealth Part One will include the Philatelic Register in the back as a comprehensive directory to the philatelic world.

If you feel that your business would benefit from inclusion in the next Philatelic Register, simply contact Carol Flynn who'll be able to organise your free lineage entry.

Every business is entitled to a free entry, however there is no limit to the number of additional entries you can have in the Philatelic Register to ensure all aspects of your current and future business activity is given the best possible advantage.

However, to ensure your business stands out from the others and to compliment your free lineage entry, an advertisement can be placed in an alternative part of the Register. For further details simply contact Carol Flynn on (0425) 472363.

Compliation

The Philatelic Register is compiled and published by Stanley Gibbons Publications Limited. Every effort has been made to ensure the accuracy of all the entries in the directory, however, Stanley Gibbons Publications Ltd cannot in any circumstances be responsible for or accept any liability for any loss or damage of any kind which may arise or result from any errors or omissions in any entry, whether relating to wording, space, position, artwork or telephone number.

This disclaimer applies both to the contractual entries and to the free entries for business subscribers which are included solely at the discretion of Stanley Gibbons Publications Limited.

Copyright

Stanley Gibbons Publications Limited copyright reserved. No reproduction of this directory, in whole or in part is allowed without the express permission of Stanley Gibbons Publications Ltd.

This directory must not be stored in a retrieval system of any type without the written consent of Stanley Gibbons Publications Ltd.

Why you should advertise in the Philatelic Register

The Philatelic Register will quickly become established as the information source for the stamp world providing a vital link between collectors and dealers.

With a wealth of classifications to choose from, the Philatelic Register will be used by everyone in the industry looking for a variety of services and you'll want to ensure that your company stands out from the rest.

Advertising in the Philatelic Register is so easy. Our sales representatives can offer professional advice on the advertising programme that suits your business, in addition to helping with the style and content of your advertisement.

For more information on how to advertise in the Philatelic Register, simply contact us at the address shown below.

Alternatively, contact the telephone number below for further information on your eligibility for a free entry in the Philatelic Register or have an amendment to a current entry.

The Philatelic Register
Stanley Gibbons Publications Ltd
5/7 Parkside, Christchurch Road
Ringwood, Hampshire. BH24 3SH
Tel: (0425) 472363

WORLD TIME & DISTANCE
INTERNATIONAL DIALLING
CODES & PROCEDURES

Procedure when dialling out of the UK

1. Dial International Direct Dialling (DD) access code 010
2. Then dial country and city code listed below followed by the customers number.
   NB. In most countries the 0 or 9 is usually omitted from the area or city code.

Procedure when dialling the UK from abroad

Dial relevant country's IDD access code followed by the UK country code (always 44).
This is followed by the area or city code and then the customers number. Again the 0 should be dropped from the area or city code. Await for a Second Tone at this stage.

	TIME	DIST. MILES FROM LONDON	DIAL OUT CODE (prefix with 0)	Dial in Code (+44 to UK)		TIME	DIST. MILES FROM LONDON	DIAL OUT CODE (prefix with 0)	Dial in Code (+44 to UK)
Algiers	13.00	856	213	00*	Kuala Lumpur	19.00	6,557	60 3	00
Amsterdam	13.00	231	31 20	09*	Kuwait	15.00	2,898	965	00
Ankara	14.00	1,765	90 41	99*	Lagos	13.00	3,107	234 1	009
Auckland	24.00	11,404	64 9	00	Lisbon	12.00	972	3511	00
Athens	14.00	1,500	30 1	00	Los Angeles	04.00	5,360	1 213	011
Bagdad	15.00	2,970	964 1	00	Madrid	13.00	774	34 1	07*
Bahrain	15.00	3,180	973	0	Malta	13.00	1,305	356	00
Bangkok	19.00	6,132	66 2	001	Mauritius	16.00	6,075	230	NA
Barbados	08.00	4,198	1 809	011	Milan	13.00	609	39 2	00
Barcelona	13.00	712	34 3	07*	Montreal	07.00	3,241	1 514	011
Beirut	14.00	2,162	9611	00	Moscow	15.00	1,557	7 095	810
Belgrade	13.00	1,055	38 11	99	Munich	13.00	590	49 89	00
Berlin (East)	13.00	594	37 2	Varies	Nairobi	15.00	4,247	254 2	000
Berlin (West)	13.00	594	49 30	00	Naples	13.00	1,011	39 81	00
Bermuda	08.00	3,437	1 809 29	1	Nassau	07.00	4,361	1 809 32	011
Bombay	17.30	4,478	91 22	00	New York	07.00	3,440	1 212	011
Boston	07.00	3,250	1 617	011	Nice	13.00	647	33 93	19*
Brisbane	21.00	11,229	617	0011	Oslo	13.00	749	47 2	095
Brussels	13.00	217	32 2	00* or 00	Palma	13.00	833	34 71	07*
Budapest	13.00	924	36 1	00	Paris	13.00	215	33 1	19*
Buenos Aires	09.00	6,915	54 1	00	Peking	20.00	5,073	861	00
Cairo	14.00	2,188	20 2	00	Perth	20.00	9,008	619	0011
Calcutta	17.30	4,958	91 33	00	Prague	13.00	650	42 2	00
Chicago	06.00	3,953	1 312	011	Rangoon	18.30	5,581	95 1	0
Copenhagen	13.00	605	45 1	009	Rio de Janeiro	09.00	5,746	55 21	00
Dakar	12.00	2,706	22 1	00*	Rome	13.00	907	39 6	00
Darwin	20.30	9,457	61 89	0011	Salzburg	13.00	652	43 662	00
Delhi	17.30	4,180	91 11	00	San Francisco	04.00	5,351	1 415	011
Detroit	07.00	3,901	1 313	011	Singapore	20.00	6,754	65	005
Dubai	16.00	3,460	9714	010	Stockholm	13.00	898	46 8	009
Dublin	12.00	279	0001	031	Sydney	22.00	10,568	61 2	0011
Dusseldorf	13.00	311	49 211	00	Teheran	15.30	2,741	89 21	00
Frankfurt	13.00	406	49 611	00	Tel Aviv	14.00	2,222	972 3	00
Geneva	13.00	468	41 22	00	Tokyo	21.00	5,955	81 3	001
Gibraltar	13.00	1,085	350	00	Toronto	07.00	3,545	1 416	011
Gothenburg	13.00	651	46 31	009	Tripoli	14.00	1,457	218 21	00
Helsinki	14.00	1,147	358 0	990	Turin	13.00	570	39 11	00
Hong Kong	20.00	5,989	852 5	001	Vancouver	04.00	4,707	1 604	011
Honolulu	02.00	8,470	1 808	011	Venice	13.00	715	39 41	00
Istanbul	14.00	1,561	90 1	99*	Vienna	13.00	790	43 222	00
Jamaica	07.00	4,687	1 809	NA	Warsaw	13.00	913	48 22	0*0
Johannesburg	14.00	5,634	27 11	09	Washington	07.00	3,665	1 202	011
Karachi	17.00	3,935	92 21	00	Zurich	13.00	490	41 1	00

 Don't forget The Philatelic Register is only a telephone call away!   Tel: 0425 472363

Classification Headings

GREAT BRITAIN

- Channel Islands
- Errors and Varieties
- Falklands/Antarctica
- Isle of Man
- Four Kings: King Edward VII to King George VI
- Postal History
- Queen Elizabeth II Issues
- Queen Victoria Issues

FOREIGN

- Far East
- France
- Germany
- Italy
- Latin America
- Middle East
- Other European Countries
- Postal History
- Rest of the World
- Scandinavia
- Spain
- Switzerland
- U.S.A

BRITISH COMMONWEALTH

- Africa
- Australia
- Canada
- Cyprus, Gibraltar & Malta
- Errors & Varieties
- Four Kings: King Edward VII to King George VI
- Falkland Islands & Antarctica
- India
- Ireland
- Malaysia
- New Zealand
- Pacific Islands
- Postal History
- Queen Elizabeth II Issues
- Queen Victoria Issues
- Southern Africa
- Stamp Booklets
- West Indies

GENERAL

- Aerophilately
- Albums & Accessories
- Approvals
- Auctions
- Fair Organisers
- First Day Covers
- Hinges & Mounts
- Kiloware
- Philatelic Accessories
- Philatelic Literature
- Philatelic Mail Order
- Postal Auctions
- Postcards & Postcard Albums
- Publications
- Shops
- Societies & Clubs
- Stamp Album Manufacturers & Suppliers
- Stamp Booklets
- Thematics

GREAT BRITAIN

◆ Great Britain

Cleveland, G.
39 Station Road, North Harrow, Middlesex HA2 7SU,
England. .... Tel : Middlesex 081 8630155
Fax : Middlesex 081 8631227
Galleon Philatelists,
P.O. Box 1517, Gloucester, Virginia 23061, U.S.A.
Stevens, Denis
12 Compton Court, Benhill Wood Road, Sutton,
Surrey SM1 4HP. .... Tel : Surrey 081 6610367

◆ Great Britain – Channel Islands

Green, Tom, Associates,
Fairfield, Low Ham, Langport, Somerset TA10 9DR.
England. .... Tel : Langport 0458 250832
Fax : Langport 0458 253226
Ringdale Philatelics,
242 Stroud Road, Gloucester GL4 0AU, England.
Tel : Gloucester 0452 411942
Robbe Ltd., G.
York Chambers, York Street, St. Helier, Jersey JE4 8XZ,
Channel Islands. .... Tel : Jersey 0534 23084
Fax : Jersey 0534 67680
Russell, D.J.
2 Brunswick Square, Herne Bay, Kent CT6 5QF, England.
Tel : Herne Bay 0227 361135
Windsor Stamps,
3 Brock House, Brock Road, St Peter Port, Guernsey,
Channel Islands. .... Tel : Guernsey 0481 710208

◆ Great Britain – Errors & Varieties

Worboys, Derek
Philatelic Faultfinders, 36 Bedford Grove, London,
SW20 9LB, England........ Tel : London 081 542 4868
Fax : London 081 542 5588

◆ Great Britain – Isle of Man

Corlett, H.
4 Glencree, Billericay, Essex CM11 1EB England.
Tel : Billericay 0277 656577
Isle Of Man Sales Ltd.,
19B Arlington Drive, Mapperley Park, Nottingham
NG3 5EN, England...... Tel : Nottingham 0602 856736
Parkinson, W A.
Sea Front, Promenade, Isle of Man.
Tel: Isle of Man 0624 83 3303

◆ Great Britain – King Edward VII to King George VI (Four Kings)

Candlish McCleery Ltd.,
P.O. Box 11, Worcester WR8 9BQ, England.
Tel : Worcester 0386 750063
Fax : Worcester 0386 750170
Hill, Rowland Stamps
27A Comberton Hill, Kidderminster, Worcs. Dy10 1QN
Tel: Kidderminster 0562 824060
Fax: Kidderminster 0562 743767
Larkswood Stamps,
Shop 3, The Georgian Village, 100 Wood Street,
Walthamstow, London E17 3HX, England.
Tel : London 081 520 3451

Page, S.
14 Hilary Grove, Anlaby Park Road South, Hull HU4 7DS,
England. .... Tel : Hull 0482 643025

◆ Great Britain – Postal History

Goodman, Michael
111 Green Lane, Edgware, Middlesex HA8 8EL, England.
Tel Edgware 081 958 6973

Bay Stamps,
Freepost, Colwyn Bay, Clwyd LL29 9YZ, England.
Tel : Colwyn Bay 0492 516644
Border Stamps,
23 Abbotsford Road, Galashiels, Selkirkshire TD1 3QR,
Scotland................... Tel : Galashiels 0896 56822
Fax : Galashiels 0896 56822
Danzig, R
P O Box 7, Newport, Isle of Wight PO30 2PY, England.
Tel : Isle of Wight 0983 527215
Fax : Isle of Wight 0983 527425
Forces Postal History Society,
71 Victory Road,Wimbledon, London SW19 1HP England.
Harris, Stewart,
Christopher Cottage, Margaret Street, Thaxted, Essex
CM6 2QN, England. .... Tel : Thaxted 0371 830293
Jackson, Michael
P.O. Box 77, Huntingdon, Cambridgeshire PE18 6TZ,
England. .... Tel : Huntingdon 0480 456254
Fax : Huntingdon 0480 456255
Jubilee Stamps (Leeds),
12 Malvern Grove, Chellow Dene, Bradford,
West Yorkshire BD9 6BU, England.
Tel : Bradford 0274 546887
Fax : Bradford 0274 546887
Postal History Display,
146 Chapel Road, Oldham OL8 4QJ, England.
Tel : Manchester 061 682 9652
Postings,
P.O. Box 1, Oxted, Surrey RH8 0FD, England.
Tel : Oxted 0883 722646
Fax : Oxted 0883 722646
Shaw, Alastair G.
Shiel House, 31 Gayton Road, Heswall, Wirral Merseyside
L60 8QF, England......... Tel : Liverpool 051 342 1281
Steinhart, Allan L.
35 Church Street, Suite 305, Toronto, Ontario, Canada.
Tel: Toronto 0101 416 362 8257
Townsend, Martin
P.O. Box 10, Hitchin, Hertfordshire SG4 9PE, England.
Tel : Hitchin 0462 420678
Vale Stamps,
21 Tranquil Vale, Blackheath, London SE3 0BU, England.
Tel : London 081 852 9817
Whitworth, Andrew A.
1 Prizet House, Kendal, Cumbria LA8 8AB, England
Tel: 05395 60848
Yorkshire Cover Auctions,
10 Lombard Street, Halton, Leeds LS15 0LT, England.
Tel : Leeds 0532 641 845
Fax : Leeds 0532 641 845

◆ Great Britain – QE II Issues

Bond, A.G.
6 Rollestone Crescent, Pennsylvania, Exeter, Devon
EX4 5EB, England............. Tel : Exeter 0392 50283
Fax : Exeter 0392 50283
Dauwalders,
92-94 Fisherton Street, Salisbury, Wiltshire SP2 7QY,
England.................. Tel : Salisbury 0722 412100
Fax : Salisbury 0722 412100
Talent Pastimes Ltd.,
85 Kettering Road, Northampton, Northamptonshire
NN1 4AW, England. .... Tel : Northampton 0604 36396

Daniels, P.
70 Moor Park Close, Rainham, Gillingham, Kent ME8
8QT,
England.................. Tel : Gillingham 0634 376268

Davey, Peter.
West View, Low Road,Evesham,Worcestershire England.
Tel: Evesham 0386 870171
Edge, J. & K.
3 Newborough Avenue, Llanishen, Cardiff,
South Glamorgan CF4 5BY, Wales.
Tel : Cardiff 0222 758309
Holt, Mike
P O Box 177, Stourbridge, West Midlands DY8 3DE,
England................ Tel : Stourbridge 0384 443317
Fax : Stourbridge 0384 440877

Jakab, A J.
27 Larkhall Rise, London SW4 6HU England.
Tel: London 081 622 8432
Not Just Stamps
17/19 Crendon Street, High Wycombem,
Buckinghamshire, HP13 6LJ.
Tel : High Wycombe 0494 441717
Numismery, The
68a Pillar Avenue, Brixham, South Devon TQ5 8LB,
England..................... Tel : Brixham 0803 854717

Waldie, David A.
6 Shielswood Court, Galashiels, Selkirkshire
Scotland TD1 3RH .... Tel: 0896 58308
Fax: 0896 58308

◆ GB – Queen Victoria Issues

Avalon Stamp & Postcard Shop,
1 Citywalls, Rufus Court, Northgate Street, Chester
CH1 2JG,................... Tel : Chester 0244 318406
Downsway Stamp Co.,
12 Downs Way, Epsom, Surrey KT18 5LU, England.
Tel : Surrey 0372 723743
London International Stamp Centre,
110 St. Martin's Lane, Trafalgar Square, London
WC2N 4AZ England. .... Tel: London 071 240 1963

Portsmouth Stamp Shop,
184 Chichester Road, North End, Portsmouth, Hampshire
PO2 0AX, England.......Tel : Portsmouth 0705 663450
Fax : Portsmouth 0705 664884
Rushstamps (Retail) Limited
P.O. Box One, Lyndhurst, Hampshire, SO43 7PP England
Tel: 0703 282044
Fax: 0703 282981
Sayer, Stephen J.
49 Mount Road, Southdown, Bath, Avon BA2 1LG,
England......................... Tel : Bath 0225 446766

Bolton Stamp Centre,
27 Mawdsley Street, Bolton, Lancashire BL1 1LN,
England........................ Tel : Bolton 0204 29271

King, Stephen
258 High Street, Erdington, Birmingham B23 6SN,
England................ Tel : Birmingham 021 382 8222

Lea & Co., J.E.
22 Chartfield Square, London SW15 6DR, England.
Tel : London 081 785 9882
Fax : London 081 788 4404
Mann, Grahame W.
14 Lakeside Court, Brierley Hill, West Midlands DY5 3RQ,
England.................. Tel : Brierley Hill 0384 423233
Fax : Brierley Hill 0384 898588

BRITISH COMMONWEALTH

◆ British Commonwealth

British Commonwealth Stamp Co.
B C

LARGEST PRICE LIST OF QUALITY MINT/USED STAMPS

1840 - 1952

- Australia & States
- India & States
- New Zealand
- Oceania
- British Africa
- British Europe
- British Asia
- BR. WI & NA

100 PAGE PRICE LIST

check one: SG# ☐ or SCOTT# ☐

Name _____

Address _____

_____

Country _____

British Commonwealth Stamp Co.,
Box 248G1, Gedney Station
White Plains, New York 10605 USA
Fax=: 914-686-1413

British Commonwealth Stamp Co.
Box 248G1, Gedney Station, White Plains, New York
10605 USA.................... Fax: 0101 914 686 1413

B & S Stamps
Byron House, 21/23 Rectory Road, West Bridgford,
Nottingham. NG2 6BE .... Tel: 0602 816214
Fax: 0602 455499

Doreen Royan & Associates (Pty) Ltd,
P.O. Box 310, Sunninghill, Johannesburg, Transvaal,
2157 South Africa.
Tel: Johannesburg 010 2711 803 3237
Fax: Johannesburg 010 2711 803 4899

M. & N. Haworth

WORLDWIDE — BY COUNTRY OR BY THEME
1840 to date
WANTS LISTS WELCOME — N.I.S.
COLLECTIONS BOUGHT & SOLD
EXTENSIVE STOCKS
30 YEARS EXPERIENCE
PERSONAL PROFESSIONAL SERVICE

061-834 2929
FAX 061-839 4714
PO BOX 20, CLITHEROE, LANCS BB7 2JQ

Haworth, M & N
P.O. Box 20, Clitheroe, Lancs BB7 2JQ
Tel: 061 834 2929
Fax: 061 839 4714

Rcs Stamps.
37 Surrey Road, Nelson, Lancashire. BB9 7TZ.
Tel : Nelson 0443 690997

Whyte, Macdonnell, Ltd.,
(David MacDonnell), 102 Leinster Road, Dublin 6,
Ireland................................ Tel : 353 1 977449
Fax : 353 1 977 440

◆ British Commonwealth – Africa

Ellis, Steve
The Laurels, Bristol Road, Churchill, Bristol, Avon BS19
5NL, England. .... Tel : Churchill 0934 852199
Fax : Churchill 0934 852199
Morely Stamps.
PO Box 28, Wokingham, Berkshire RG11 2LS, England.
Tel : Wokingham 0734 781477
Ormskirk Stamps,
c/o Roos Post Office, Roos, Hull HU12 0HN England
Tel : Hull 0964 670239
Fax : Hull 0964 671204
Pollard, Derrick
PO Box 148,Market Wavington,Devizes, Wilts.SN104AJ
Tel: Devizes 0380 813652
Fax: Devizes 0380 812902

◆ British Commonwealth – Australia

A-One Stamps,
PO Box 35, Woollahra, New South Wales, 2025 Australia.
Tel: Sydney 010 612 362 3636
Fax: Sydney 010 612 363 2303
A.T. Philatelics
Mantra House, South Street, Keighley, West Yorkshire
BD21 1SX England.
Tel: 0535 603372
Bexley Stamps,
415 Forest Rd, Bexley NSW 2207, Australia.
Tel : Sydney 010 612 567 5242
Fax : Sydney 010 612 597 4307
Cockerill, Nick
17 Home Farm Gardens, Walton-on-Thames, Surrey
KT12
3DN England.
Tel: Walton-on-Thames 0932 228345
Dunkerley Pty Ltd, Simon
P.O. Box 461, Blackburn, Victoria 3130, Australia.
Tel : Victoria 010 61 3 8781142
Fax : Victoria 010 61 3 8781154
Falcon Stamps Pty Ltd,
PO BOX 571, Milsons Point, New South Wales 2061
Australia................. Tel: Sydney 010 612 922 1770
Fax: Sydney 010 612 922 1770

Gabriele's Philatelic Service
Ground Floor, Mirvac Building, 160 Castlereagh St.,
Sydney NSW2000 .... Tel: (02) 283 1311
Fax: (02) 283 1311
Glen Stephens Stamps,
Lothlorien, 4 The Tor Walk Castlecrag, Sydney,
New South Wales 2068, Australia.
Tel : Sydney 2958 1333
Fax : Sydney 2958 1444
Gregson Ltd., J.M.A.
P.O. Box 11, Patchway, Bristol, BS12 4BH, England.
Tel : Bristol 0454 617600
Fax : Bristol 0454 617600
Hill, Rowland Stamps
27A Comberton Hill, Kidderminster, Worcs. DY10 1QN
Tel: Kidderminster 0562 824060
Fax: Kidderminster 0562 743767
Kelland, V.
39 Parc-y-Coed, Creigiau, Cardiff CF4 8LY, Wales.
Tel : Cardiff 0222 890130
Linke, Robin
181 Jersey Street, Wembley, Western Australia, 6014
Australia.................... Tel: Perth 010 619 387 5327
Fax: Perth 010 619 387 1646

J.M.A. GREGSON LTD

*See our main catalogue advert
under Australia*

P.O. Box 11
Patchway   Tel: 0454 617600
Bristol BS12 4BH   Fax: 0454 617600

Luis, FA. Philatelic Sales,
PO Box 15, Nobby Beach, Gold Coast, 4218 Australia.
Tel: Australia 010 61 75 920265
Fax: Australia 010 61 75 701548

Mowbray J.R. (Philatelist) Ltd.,
P.O. Box 63, Otaki Railway, Gisborne New Zealand.
Tel : Gisborne 010 646 3648270
Fax : Gisborne 010 646 3648252

Perry, Ian. Stamps,
29 Chetwynd Grove, Newport, Shropshire TF10 7JW,
England................... Tel : Newport 0952 825941
Fax : Newport 0952 820042

Piccadilly Stamps.
Shop 27 , Hyde Park Square, Cnr Park & Castlereagh
Streets, Sydney, NSW 2000 Australia.
Tel : Sydney 010 612 264 7034

Skinner, D.J.
53 Armytage Road, Hounslow, Middlesex TW5 9JL,
England. .... Tel : London 081 570 1726

MAX STERN

*See our main catalogue advert
under Australia*

234 Flinders Street
(Port Philip Arcade), Box 997H, GPO
Melbourne, 3001   Tel: (03) 654 6751
Australia   Fax: (03) 650 7192

Stern, Max
234 Flinders Street, (Port Philip Arcade), Box 997H,
GPO Melbourne, 3001 Australia.
Tel: (03) 654 6751
Fax: (03) 650 7192
Strich Peter, Stamps & Coins
GPO Box 216D, Melbourne, Victoria 3001, Australia.
Tel : Melbourne 010 613 661 2945
Fax : Melbourne 010 613 661 3770
Strich, Peter. Stamps & Coins,
GPO Box 216D, Melbourne, 3001 Australia.
Tel: Melbourne 010 613 661 2945
Fax: Melbourne 010 613 661 3770
Sydney Philatelic Pty Ltd
P.O. Box 382, Strawberry Hills, N.S.W. 2012, Australia.
Tel. 010 61 2 319 1533
Fax. 010 61 2 319 1531
Taunton Stamp Shop,
66 Bridge Street, Taunton, Somerset. TA1 1UD, England.
Tel : Taunton 0823 283327
Fax : Taunton 0823 325882
Victoria Stamp Traders,
65 Station Street, Malvern, Victoria 3144, Australia.
Tel : Melbourne 010 613 509 8255
Fax : Melbourne 010 613 509 4230
Whitehead & Associates, Colin.
P.O. Box 316, Purley, Surrey CR2 3YW, England.
Tel : Purley 081 660 9063
Fax : Purley 081 660 9063

◆ British Commonwealth – Canada

Colonial Stamp Co.
5410 Wilshire Blvd., Suite 202, Los Angeles, CA90036
USA .... Tel: (213) 933 9435
Fax: (213) 939 9930
Eastern Auctions
P.O. Box 250G, Bathurst, N.B., Canada E2A 3ZA
Tel: (506) 548 8986
Fax: (506) 546 6627

Harris, Peter
11 North Parade, Lowestoft, Suffolk NR32 4PA, England.
Tel : Lowestoft 0502 564705

COLONIAL STAMP CO.

*See our main catalogue advert
under Bermuda*

5410 Wilshire Blvd.
Suite 202
Los Angeles, CA90036   Tel: (213) 933 9435
United States of America   Fax: (213) 939 9930

EASTERN AUCTIONS LIMITED

*See our main catalogue advert
under Canada*

P.O. Box 250G
Bathurst, N.B.   Tel: (506) 548 8986
Canada E2A 3ZA   Fax: (506) 546 6627

Need The Number?

FIND IT FAST IN
THE **ALPHA** LISTING

◆ British Commonwealth – Cyprus, Gibraltar & Malta

Faure, Peter
  151 St Mary Street, Tarxien PLA 11, Malta.
                     Tel : Malta 010 356 882160
Gills Stamps,
  5 Tenter Ground, London E1 7NH, England.
                 Tel : London 071 377 8565
                Fax : London 071 377 8565

GOING TO AUCTION?

TRY AUCTIONS ON PAGE 19

Hillman, H.
  124 Walm Lane, London NW2 4RT, England.
                    Tel: 081 452 9937
Ricky Richardson International Ltd
  P.O. Box 552, Gibraltar.......... Tel : 010 3452 375900

◆ British Commonwealth – Errors & Varieties

Muscott's.
  Meadrow, Godalming, Surrey GU7 3HL, England.
               Tel : Surrey 0483 417884
              Fax : Surrey 0483 860572
Warboys, Derek
  36 Beaford Grove, London SW20 9LB
              Tel: London 081 542 4868
            Fax: London 081 542 5588

◆ British Commonwealth – Edward VII to George VI (Four Kings)

Archer, D.L.
  2 Litchfield Way, Broxbourne, Hertfordshire EN10 6PT,
  England. .... Tel : Broxbourne 0992 462548
Field, Tony Stamps,
  8 Wildcroft Gardens, Edgware, Middlesex. HA8 6TL
                Tel: Edgware 081 952 4573
             Fax: Edgware 081 951 4630
Baresch, Leo, Ltd
  PO Box 791, Hassocks, West Sussex, BN6 8PZ,England.
              Tel: Hassocks 0273 845501
            Fax: Hassocks 0273 845501

Goldcast (Philatelics),
  43 London Street, Southport, Merseyside PR9 0TH,
  England. .... Tel : Southport 0704 543985
Gravesend Stamp Centre, The
  7 Queen Street, Gravesend, Kent DA12 2EQ, England.
              Tel : Gravesend 0474 534166
Hanley Stamp Centre Ltd.,
  36 Broad Street, Hanley, Stoke-on-Trent, Staffordshire
  ST5 0LB, England.... Tel : Stoke-on-Trent 0782 280524
Hill, Rowland Stamps,
  27A Comberton Hill, Kidderminster, Worcs. DY10 1QN
             Tel: Kidderminster 0562 824060
            Fax: Kidderminster 0562 743767
Irons, G.
  37 Tiverton Road, Potters Bar, Herts. EN6 5HX
             Tel : Potters Bar 0707 659434
Jones, A.C.
  47 Marylands Avenue, Hockley, Essex SS5 5AH, England.
             Tel : Hockley 0702 206526

Murray Payne Ltd,
  P.O. Box 1135, Axbridge, Somerset BS26 2EW, England.
            Tel : Axbridge 0934 732511
           Fax : Axbridge 0934 733498
McMorris, P.
  7 Swiss Close, Watford, Hertfordshire WD1 7LW,England.
            Tel : Watford 0923 223826

◆ British Commonwealth – Falklands and Antarctica

Colonial Stamp Co.
  5410 Wilshire Blvd., Suite 202, Los Angeles,
  CA90036, USA .... Tel: (213) 933 9435
              Fax: (213) 939 9930

Victoria Stamp Company
  P.O. Box 745, Ridgewood, NJ 07541, USA
              Tel: (201) 652 7283
             Fax: (201) 612 0024

◆ British Commonwealth – Far East

Colonial Stamp Co.
  5410 Wilshire Blvd., Suite 202, Los Angeles,
  CA90036, USA ....Tel: (213) 933 9435
              Fax: (213) 939 9930

◆ British Commonwealth – India

Singh, M.M.
  19 Union Park, Chembur, Bombay, India 400071
               Tel: 91 22 5515957
      Fax: (Pre-fix M.M. Singh) 91 22 511 3850

◆ British Commonwealth – Ireland

Ballard, A.R.
  P.O. Box 780, London SE13 5QA, England.
              Tel : London 081 852 7031
Rodgau Philatelic Service Pts & Aphy,
  Eisenbahnstr, 8, Postfach 1124, D-63083 Rodgau,
  Germany.   Tel: Germany 010 49 6106 3023
             Fax: Germany 010 49 6106 3024
Whyte, Ian
  27 Mount Street, Upper, Dublin 2, Ireland.
           Tel : Dublin 010 353 1676 7228
          Fax : Dublin 010 353 1676 7229
Whyte, MacDonnell, Ltd
  102 Leinster Road, Dublin 6, Ireland.
             Tel : Dublin 010 3531 977449
           Fax : Dublin 010 3531 977440

◆ Great Britain – Falklands / Antartica

Grove Philatelics
  PO Box 326, Kenley, Surrey, CR8 5YW, England.
             Tel: Kenley 081 668 7001
            Fax: Kenley 081 985 5389

◆ British Commonwealth – Malaysia

Flowerdew, J & M
  31 North Street, Sheringham, Norfolk NR26 8LW,England.
             Tel : Sheringham 0263 822379
International Stamp & Coin Co. Ltd.,
  2.4-2.5 Pertama Complex, Jalan Tuanku, Abdul Rahman,
  Kuala Lumpur 50100, Malaysia.
           Tel: Malaysia 010 603 292 6117
          Fax: Malaysia 010 603 292 8380

◆ British Commonwealth – New Zealand

Campbell Paterson Ltd.
  (Warwick Paterson) PO Box 5555, Auckland 1
  New Zealand. .... Tel : Auckland 010 649 3793086
           Fax : Auckland 010 649 3793087
Campbell Paterson Ltd.,
  PO Box 17, Woking, Surrey GU22 7BL, ENGLAND.
            Tel : Woking 0483 715887
          Fax : Woking 0483 747149
Craig, Alan s.
  Arcadia Building, Worley Place, P.O. Box 1313, Hamilton
  New Zealand. .... Tel : Hamilton 010 6471 8340630

Tel: Kidderminster 0562 824060
Fax: Kidderminster 0562 743767

Olorenshaw, Peter
Box 700, Manly, NSW 2095, Australia.
Tel : Sydney 010 612 971 8839

Palmerston North Stamp Centre Ltd
PO Box 1781, 121 Broadway Avenue, Palmerston North,
New Zealand. .... Tel: New Zealand 010 646 357 2751
Fax: New Zealand 010 646 357 2751

PNG Philatelic Bureau
UK & Europe Mailing Point - 45A Main Street, Gorebridge,
Midlothian EH23 4BX, Scotland. UK.

PHG Philatelic
P.O. Box 1, Boroko Papua New Guinea
Tel: (675) 274 170
Fax: (675) 252-502
Telex: NE 23090

PNG Philatelic Bureau
USA Mailing Point - P.O. Box 321 West Hempstead,
New York 11552 USA

Visini, A G
319 Motutara Road, Muriwai Beach, Auckland,
New Zealand. .... Tel : Auckland 010 9411 8199

World Wide Stamps,
(S R Bennett) PO Box 354, Timaru New Zealand.
Tel : Timaru 03 688 6637
Fax : Timaru 03 688 6637

◆ British Commonwealth – Pacific Islands

Carson. William,
P.O. Box 1836, 109 Canterbury Arcade, Queen Street,

Auckland New Zealand.
Tel : Auckland 010 649 3794527
Fax : Auckland 010 649 3794527

Ovpt Philatelics
P.O. Box 36217, Los Angeles, CA90036, USA
Tel: (818) 893 4603

◆ British Commonwealth – Postal History

Allman, William S.
828 Arrow Lane, Ridgewood, NJ 07450 USA

Tel: 0101 201 652 4858

Auld, John
1 Hill View Villas, Hastingwood, Nr. Harlow, Essex
CM17 9JK, England. .... Tel : Harlow 0279 433910
Fax : Harlow 0279 433910

Crown Colony Stamps
P.O. Box 1198, Bellaire, Texas 77401, USA.
Tel: (from UK) 0101 713 781 6563
Fax: 0101 713 789 9998

Empire Stamp Auctions,
Thornton Lodge, Stanshalls Lane, Felton, Bristol
BS18 7UQ, England. .... Tel : Bristol 0275 474766

ERCOLE GLORIA SRL.,
Topical Specialist & Postal History.
(G. Zuskis), Piazza Pio XI, 1, Milano, 20123, Italy.

Interstamp
1015 Chestnut Avenue, Suite H3, Carsbad,
California 92008 USA......... Fax: 0101 619 729 6408

Philaclassica,
Gerbergasse 24, Postfach 563, Basel CH-4001,
Switzerland........ Tel : Switzerland 010 4161 2617379
Fax : Switzerland 010 4161 2617377

Proud-Bailey Co. Ltd.,
P.O. Box 74, Heathfield, East Sussex TN21 8PZ, England.
Tel : Heathfield 0435 862540
Fax : Heathfield 0435 865200

Ronald Lee,
PO Box 1567, Geelong, Victoria 3220 Australia.
Tel: Victoria 010 61 052 295099
Fax: Victoria 010 61 052 789090

Werner Wetzel,
Alte Postgasse 21, Weinheim/Bergstr., D-6940, Germany.
Tel: Germany 010 6201 65794

◆ British Commonwealth – QE II

Anglia Stamp Bureau
P.O.Box 88, Norwich, England NR1 4PQ

B & S Stamps,
Byron House, 21/23 Rectory Road, West Bridgford,
Nottinghamshire NG2 6BE, England.
Tel : Nottingham 0602 816214
Fax : Nottingham 0602 455499

Cambridge Stamp Centre,
9 Sussex Street, Cambridge CB1 1PA, England.
Tel : Cambridge 0223 63980

Deering, John
The Machins, PO Box 2, South Molton, Devon, EX36 4YZ
Tel: South Molton 03984 564
Fax: South Molton03984 564

Grampian Stamp Shop,
38 Union Terrace, Aberdeen AB1 1NP, Scotland.
Tel : Aberdeen 0224 639704

Hill, Rowland Stamps,
27A Comberton Hill, Kidderminster, Worcs. DY10 1QN
Tel: Kidderminster 0562 824060
Fax: Kidderminster 0562 743767

Lister, John Ltd.,
49 Shelton Street, London WC2H 9SP, England.
Tel : London 071 240 6693
Fax : London 071 379 8007

Mewse, R.A & D.M,
3 Butterwick Road, Freiston, Boston, Lincolnshire
PE22 0LF, England. .... Tel : Boston 0205 760875

Somerset Stamp Service,
South Petherton, Somerset TA13 5EN, England.
Tel : South Petherton 0460 41172
Fax : South Petherton 0460 41172

◆ British Commonwealth – Queen Victoria

Aylward, K
The Outlook 2 Roedean Path Brighton BN2 5RP
Tel : Brighton 0273 696189

Baresch, Leo, Ltd
PO Box 791, Hassocks, W.Sussex, BN6 8PZ, England
Tel / Fax: 0273 845501

Castle Stamps,
2a Warwick Lane, Warwick Street, Worthing, West Sussex
BN11 2DP, England. ...... Tel : Worthing 0903 230064

Classic Collector
P.O. Box 6277, Station 'J', Ottawa, Canada. K2A 1TA
Tel: (613) 722 1621
Fax: (613) 728 7305

Harvey, Mark R.
P.O. Box 50, Chiddingfold, Surrey GU8 4XQ, England.
Tel : Chiddingfold 0428 685207

Penrith Coin & Stamp Centre
37 King Street, Penrith, Cumbria.
Tel: 0768 64185

Rushstamps (Retail) Limited
P.O. Box 1, Lyndhurst, hants. SO43 7PP
Tel: 0703 282044
Fax: 0703 282981

The Stamp Shop,
Unit 10 Granby Arcade, Water Street, Bakewell,
Derbyshire DE45 1EG England.
Tel: Derbyshire 0629 812191

◆ British Commonwealth – Southern Africa

Filatelic Phriends CC.
P.O. Box 26456, Hout Bay, Cape Town 7872 South Africa.
Tel : Cape Town 010 2721 790 5943/4
Fax : Cape Town 010 2721 790 5745

Macgregor, Alan Philatelist,
P.O. Box 3130, Cape Town 8000, South Africa.
Tel: Cape Town 010 2721 697 3030
Fax: Cape Town 010 2721 696 4797

Ormskirk Stamps,
c/o Roos Post Office, Roos, Hull HU12 0HN England.
Tel : Hull 0964 670239
Fax : Hull 0964 671204

SANDTON STAMPS (PTY) LTD
Specialists in British Southern Africa & Thematics
Shop L 40, Sandton City, P.O. Box 782564, Sandton,
South Africa. 2146................... Tel. 011 783 8309
Fax: 011 783 2706

Stephan Welz & Co.
  P.O. Box 52431, Saxonwold, 2132, South Africa.
                                    Tel: 2711 8803125/9
                                    Fax: 2711 8802656

WHITWORTH ANDREW. A.
  South Africa & SWA cyl blks from 1948
  49p SAE 9"x6.5" for lists
  1 Prizat House, Kendal, Cumbria,England LA8 8AB
                                    Tel: 0539 560848

SOUTH AFRICAN - SWA - RHODESIAS

- In fact, all issues of SOUTHERN AFRICA are special features in our AUCTIONS every 3 months.
- We offer the UNUSUAL (Cinderellas, Fiscals etc.) as well as the standard issues.
- We also attend to WANT LISTS of this area at competitive prices.
- Settlement by draft or banknotes in all major currencies without hassles.

Durban
Stamp Auctions

PO BOX 461
PINETOWN 3600
SOUTH AFRICA
Phone 031-783 722 all hours

◆ **British Commonwealth – Stamp Booklets**

STAMP BOOKLETS
(of the World)

Worlds oldest established booklet specialist/dealer urgently requires older better grade complete stamp booklets. Please send details or booklets by registered mail (refundable) for quote.

I can also supply hard to find items as well as modern issues, if you advise wants.

Dr. W.L. MAYO
P.O. Box 256
Avalon, NSW, 2107
Australia
Tel: + 612 918 6825
Fax: + 612 918 8619

ST. HELENA
Stamp Booklet
4/6

Dr. W.L. Mayo
  P.O. Box 256, Avalon, NSW 2107 Australia.
                                    Tel: 612 918 6825
                                    Fax: 612 918 8619

◆ **British Commonwealth – West Indies**

COLONIAL STAMP CO.

See our main catalogue advert under Falklands

5410 Wilshire Blvd.
Suite 202
Los Angeles, CA90036   Tel: (213) 933 9435
United States of America   Fax: (213) 939 9930

Colonial Stamp Co.
  5410 Wilshire Blvd., Suite 202, Los Angeles, CA90036
  USA .... Tel: (213) 933 9435
                                    Fax: (213) 939 9930

GOLDCAST (Philatelics)

See our main catalogue advert under Bermuda

43 London Street
Southport
Merseyside PR9 0TH   Tel: 0704 543985

Goldcast (Philatelics)
  43 London Street, Southport, Merseyside, PR9 0TH
                                    Tel: 0704 543985
Hamilton, M.
  5 Winbrook Fold, Winfrith, Newburgh, Dorset, DT2 8LR.
  England. .... Tel : Newburgh 0305 854398
                             Fax : Newburgh 0305 854246

MURRAY PAYNE LIMITED

See our main catalogue advert under Bermuda

P.O. Box 1135
Axbridge
Somerset BS26 2EW   Tel: 0934 732511
                            Fax: 0934 733498

Murray-Payne Limited
  P.O. Box 1135, Axbridge, Somerset. BS26 2EW
                                    Tel: 0934 732511
                                    Fax: 0934 733498

MUSCOTT'S

See our main catalogue advert under Bermuda

6 Meadrow
Goldaming
Surrey GU7 3HL   Tel: 0483 471884
                         Fax: 0483 860572

Muscott's
  6 Meadrow, Goldaming, Surrey. GU7 3HL
                                    Tel: 0483 471884
                                    Fax: 0483 860572

Pennymead Auctions,
  1 Brewerton Street Knaresborough, North Yorkshire
  HG5 8AZ, England... Tel : Knaresborough 0423 865962
                                    Fax: 0423 865962

VICTORIA STAMP COMPANY

See our main catalogue advert under Bermuda

P.O. BOX 745
Ridgewood
NJ 07541   Tel: (201) 652 7283
United States of America Fax: (201) 612 0024

Victoria Stamp Company
  P.O. Box 745, Ridgewood, NJ 07541, USA
                                    Tel: (201) 652 7283
                                    Fax: (201) 612 0024

Know The Name?

Need The Number?
FIND IT FAST IN THE
ALPHA LISTING

S.A.P.D.A
S.A.F.A

STEPHAN WELZ & CO.
JOHANNESBURG
In Association With
SOTHEBY'S
FOUNDED 1744

Regular all world sales of postage stamps and postal history featuring strong sections of Southern Africa including pre-Union, the Rhodesias and South West Africa.

Complimentary catalogue available on request. Annual subscriptions R230 overseas.

ENQUIRIES: DANNY SWART OR HENK DE LANGE. Tel. +2711-8803125/9 Fax: +2711-8802656
P.O. Box 52431, Saxonwold, 2132, South Africa

To Advertise in The Philatelic Register Tel: 0425 472363

Name	Address	Number

FOREIGN

◆ Foreign

Filatco
P.O. Box 1461, Dept A, Appleton, Wisconsin 54913 USA
Tel: 414 735 0701
Fax: 414 735 9453
Meyer, Stephen
5 Waveney Road, Leeds, LS12 4EY, England.
Tel : Leeds 0532 638633
Williams, A.L.
Woodspring House, 17 Hill Road. Clevedon, Avon
BS21 7NE, England.
Tel : Clevedon 0275 343424

◆ Foreign – Far East

A.S.M. Stamps,
PO Box 143, Alderley, Queensland, 4051 Australia
Tel: Brisbane 010 617 356 0824
Fax: Brisbane 010 617 856 4731
C.K.V. Stamps,
16 Northumberland Avenue, Market Bosworth, Nuneaton,
Warwickshire CV13 0RJ, England.
Tel : 01455 292314

◆ Foreign – France

Coleman, Robert
11 The Chase, Chatham, Kent ME4 6UP, England.
Philatelie Fauquex,
19, rue du Rhone, 1204 Geneva, Switzerland.
Tel: Geneva 010 41 22 311 6795
Stadler And George,
2 Park House Green Cottages, Cranleigh, Surrey
GU6 7DN, England........ Tel : Cranleigh 0483 275464

◆ Foreign – Germany

Lorien Stamps,
P.O. Box 47, Chesterfield S40 1JH, England.
South Yara Stamps,
PO Box 536, South Yara, Victoria, Australia.
Tel: Victoria 010 613 827 7593
Fax: Victoria 010 613 826 0861

◆ Foreign – Italy

Baresch, Leo. Ltd.
P.O. Box 791, Hassocks, W. Sussex BN6 8PZ
Tel: 0273 845501
0273 845501

◆ Foreign – Latin America

Coles Philatelic Gems,
476 Kedleston Road, Allestree, Derby DE22 2NE,
England. ....Tel : Derby 0332 556312
Fax : Derby 0332 557919
Earle, Patrick & Barbara
P.O. Box 2, Nairn, IV12 4DZ, Scotland.
Tel : Nairn 0667 52310
Fax : Nairn 0667 52109
Paper Heritage,
PO Box 438, Brighton BN1 6LX, England.
Tel : Brighton 0273 558066
Shelron,
Yealm House, 9 Brackley Road, Towcester,
Northamptonshire NN12 7DH England.
Tel : Towcester 0327 50242
South American Stamp Supplies,
P.O. Box 105, Peterborough, Cambridgeshire PE3 9TQ,
England. .... Tel : Peterborough 0733 268708
Fax : Peterborough 0733 262838

◆ Foreign – Middle East

Feltus, Peter R.
PO Box 5339, Berkeley, California 94705 USA.
Tel: USA 0101 510 658 9627
Filatco
P.O. Box 1461, Dept A, Appleton, Wisconsin 54913 USA
Tel: 414 735 0701
Fax: 414 735 9453
Galibov, Ze'ev
48 Portland Place, London W1N 3DG, England.
Tel : London 071 636 4193
Fax : London 071 323 0392
Middle East Stamps,
P O Box 707, N.W.D.O, Edinburgh EH4 6JS, Scotland.

◆ Foreign – Other European Countries

Barefoot Ltd., J.
P.O. Box 8, Catterick, North Yorkshire YO3 7GL, England.
Tel : York 0904 654241
Fax : York 0904 654241
Cosmos Stamps,
P.O. Box 7, Heswall, Wirral, Merseyside L61 3YA,
England. .... Tel : Liverpool 051 648 5777
Fax : Liverpool 051 648 5777
D Meulemans,
PO Box 1370, 1000 Brussels Belgium
Tel: Brussels 010 322 2230341
Fax: Brussels 010 322 2230341
Filasta Sre,
Via Fontana 6B, Rovereto 38068, Italy
Tel : 010 39 464 421 267
Fax : 010 39 464 422 2272
Torres, A.M.
Mayor, 22-5 28013, Madrid, SPAIN.
Tel : 010 341 3655510
Fax : 010 341 3640689

◆ Foreign – Postal History

Campbell, Richard
P.O. Box 734, Arundel, Sussex BN18 0QS, England.
Tel : Arundel 0243 542167
Carmichael & Todd,
P.O. Box 494, London SW19 8DN England.
Tel : London 081 946 0760
Fax : London 081 879 1438
Robstine Stamps,
The Stamp Centre, 77 The Strand, London WC2R 0DE,
England. .... Tel : Amersham 0494 729345
Fax: Amersham 0494 721881
Steinhart, Allan L.
35 Church Street, Suite 305, Toronto, Ontario
M5E 1T3, Canada.... Tel : Toronto 0101 416 362 8257
The Stamp Pad,
186 Southbourne Grove, Westcliff, Essex SS0 0AA,
England. ....Tel : Westcliff 0702 335 802
Wegg, George S. Limited,
53 Adelaide Street East, Toronto, Ontario M5C 1K6
Canada. .... Tel: Toronto 0101 416 363 1596

◆ Foreign – Rest of the World

COLONIAL STAMP CO.

*See our main catalogue advert
under Falklands*

5410 Wilshire Blvd.
Suite 202
Los Angeles, CA90036
United States of America

Tel: (213) 933 9435
Fax: (213) 939 9930

Colonial Stamp Co.
5410 Wilshire Blvd., Suite 202, Los Angeles,
CA90036, USA .... Tel: (213) 933 9435
Fax: (213) 939 9930

B. KLEINBERG

*See our main catalogue advert
under Ascension*

40 Waxwell Lane
Pinner
Middlesex HA5 3EN   Tel: 081 866 0993

Kleinberg, B.
40 Waxwell Lane, Pinner, Middlesex. HA5 3EN
Tel: 081 866 0993

◆ Foreign – Scandinavia

Jahr, Capt. K.
2 Priory Avenue, Lincluden, Dumfries DG2 0PA, Scotland.
Tel : Dumfries 0387 55929
Nilfrim,
Moseager 4, P.O. Box 92, Hedehusene, DK-2640,
Denmark.............. Tel : Denmark 010 4542 163857
Fax : Denmark 010 4542 163980

◆ Foreign – Spain

Filatelia Llach, S.L.,
Diagonal 489, Barcelona E-08029, Spain.
Tel : Barcelona 010 343 410 5000
Fax : Barcelona 010 343 419 4728
Tlx : 9329 RTX E

◆ Foreign – Switzerland

Behar, H.
Place Pepinet 4, Lausanne 1003, Switzerland.
Tel : Lausanne 010 4121 234207
Fax : Lausanne 010 4121 234207
Baresh, Leo, Ltd
PO Box 791, Hassocks, W.Sussex, BN6 8PZ, England.
Tel: Hassocks 0273 845501
Fax: Hassocks 0273 845501
De Rosa International S.A.
Av. du Tribunal Fédéral 34 CH-1005 Lausanne
Switzerland......................... Tel: 41-21-202431
Fax: 41-21-202433
I.G. Stamps,
P.O. Box 15, Harrogate, North Yorkshire HG1 1SL,
England.................. Tel : Harrogate 0423 523152
Fax : Harrogate 0423 564210
Katcher, H L.
PO Box 242, London N2 0YE England.
Tel: London 081 348 0296
Fax: London 081 347 8397
Rolli-Schor R & B AG,
Seidenhofstr. 10, CH 6003, Lucerne, Switzerland.
Tel: Lucerne 010 4141 234545
Fax: Lucerne 010 4141 234541
Summit Stamps,
Oldfield House, Fryern Road, Storrington, West Sussex
RH20 4BJ, England...... Tel : Storrington 0903 743654

◆ Foreign – U.S.A.

Bick International,
P.O. Box 854, Van Nuys, California 91408, U.S.A.
Tel : California 010 1818 9976496
Fax : California 010 1818 9884337
Brookman/Barrett & Worthen,
10 Chestnut Drive, Bedford, 03110 USA.
Tel: Bedford 0101 603 472 5575
Fax: Bedford 0101 603 472 8795
Edelman's,
301 Old York Road, Jenkintown, PA 19046, U.S.A.
Tel : Philadelphia 215 572 6480

GENERAL

◆ Aerophilately

Rickenback, Peter C.
14 Rosslyn Hill, Hampstead, London NW3 1PF England.
Tel : London 071 435 0231

◆ Albums & Accessories

Antiques & Collectors Centre,
35 St Nicholas Cliff, Scarborough, North Yorkshire,
YO11 2ES England... . Tel: Scarborough 0723 365 221

Barrington-Smith, G.
Cross Street, Oadby, Leicestershire LE2 4DD, England.
Tel : Leicester 0533 719181
Fax : Leicester 0533 712114

Boscombe Collectors Centre,
726A Christchurch Road, Boscombe, Bournemouth,
BH7 6BE . . . . Tel: Bournemouth 0202 393199

Frank Godden Ltd.
Finest Quality Albums, Leaves & Exhibition Protectors
The Barn, Heaton Royds, Shay Lane, Bradford BD9 6SH
Tel: 0274 544 446
Fax: 0274 545 634

Safe Albums (Uk) Ltd,
16 Falcon Business Park, Hogwood Lane,
Finchampstead, Berkshire RG11 4QW England.
Tel : Reading 0734 328976
Fax : Reading 0734 328612

Seven Seas Stamps Pty. Ltd
26 Waterloo Street, Surry Hills, GPO Box 3273, Sydney,
Australia . . . . Tel: Sydney 010 612 690 6317
Fax: Sydney 010 612 8165

Vera Trinder Ltd,
38 Bedford Street, London WC2E 9EV England.
Tel : London 071 836 8332
Fax : London 071 836 9873

Uitgeverij Davo B.V.
7411 AP Deventer, Holland Netherlands
Tel : Holland 010 5700 30304
Fax : Holland 010 5700 37368

West Cornwall Stamp Centre,
Lelant Garden Centre, Hayle, Cornwall, TR26 2PT,
England. . . . . Tel : Hayle 0736 754604
Fax : Hayle 0736 756555

◆ Approvals

Aldworth, S.
Cwmbedw, Rhydlewis, Llandysul, Dyfed SA44 5PR,
Wales. . . . . Tel : Rhydlewis 0239 851335

Archer, D.L.
2 Litchfield Way, Broxbourne, Herts. EN10 6PT, England.
Tel : Broxbourne 0992 462548

Avon Approvals
P.O. Box 29, Stroud, Gloucs GL6 6RW, England.

Brookvale Stamps,
196 Ivyfield Road, Birmingham, B23 7HS, England.
Tel : Birmingham 021 382 5937

Card, Mary
14 Mulberry Close, Brighton, East Sussex BN1 6QE,
England. . . . . Tel : Brighton 0273 557729

Creeting Stamps,
5 Church Close, Creeting St. Mary, Ipswich IP6 8NL,
England. . . . . Tel : Ipswich 0449 72113

Cussans, Martin
22 Joiners Road, Linton, Cambridgeshire CB1 6NX
England. . . . . Tel: Cambridgeshire 0223 893 264

Emsworth Philatelic,
8 Christopher Way, Emsworth, Hampshire PO10 7QZ
England. . . . . Tel : Emsworth 0243 374349

Hoye, K. & N.
94 Gawsworth Road, Macclesfield, Cheshire SK11 8UF,
England. . . . . Tel : Macclesfield 0625 420316
Fax : Macclesfield 0625 420316

Jones, Derek L.
14 Bentley Road, Castle Bromwich, Birmingham. B36 0ES
England . . . . Tel: Birmingham 021 748 6478

Keef, G.P.
Willingdon, Eastbourne, Sussex BN20 9HR, England.
Tel : Eastbourne 0323 502067

Maxwell, T
28 Cedar Grove, Dunfermline, Fife KY11 5BH, Scotland.
Tel : Dunfermline 0383 727010

Milburn, K.E.
77 Endlebury Road, Chingford, London E4 6QB,
England. . . . . Tel : Chingford 081 529 2948

Milton, P.J.
17 Joy Street, Barnstable, N.Devon. EX33 1JZ
Tel : Barnstable 0271 44300
Fax : Barnstable 0271 42810

Newtown Stamps,
PO Box 14, Livingston, West Lothian EH54 8HA,
Scotland.

Ominiphil
P.O. Box 29, Stroud, Gloucs GL6 6RW, England.

Strads R.O., M.A.,
7 Brookside, Halton, Aylesbury, Buckinghamshire HP22
5PB, England. . . . . Tel : Aylesbury 0296 625070

Thompson G.W.W.
13 Pelstream Avenue, St Ninians, Sterling FK7 0BE
England . . . . Tel : Sterling 0786 475524

Walker, Graham
6 Fintry Crescent, Bishopbriggs, Glasgow G64 1SH
Tel: 041 762 2759

WHAT'S THE NEWS?

See Publications

Warren Ltd., R.
Oaklands, Crowhurst, Lingfield, Surrey RH7 6LS,
England. . . . . Tel : 0342 833413
Fax : 0342 833892

◆ Auctions

Abbey Philatelic Co. Ltd.,
83 London Fruit Exchange, Brushfield Street, London E1
6EP, England. . . . . Tel : London 071 247 4601

ABC Stamp auctions
29 Chetwynd Grove, Newport, Shropshire TF10 7JW

Acorn Philatelic Auctions,
27 Pine Road, Didsbury, Manchester M20 0UZ, England.
Tel : Manchester 061 434 2580

Cavendish Philatelic Auctions Ltd.,
Sitwell Street, Derby, Derbyshire DE1 2JP, England.
Tel : Derby 0332 46753
Fax : Derby 0332 294440

Chiani Auctions,
Hochschorenstr.31, Postfach, CH-9202, Gossau
Switzerland. . . . . . . Tel: Switzerland 010 41 071 85 85 66
Fax: Switzerland 010 41 071 85 97 36

Christie's Robson Lowe Auctioneers
Stamp Department, 8 King Street, St James's, London
SW1Y 6QT, England. . . . . . . Tel : London 071 839 9060
Fax : London 071 389 2688

Dalkeith Auctions,
Dalkeith Hall, Dalkeith Steps, Rear 81 Old Christchurch
Road, Bournemouth BH1 1VL England.
Tel: Bournemouth 0202 292 905
Fax: Bournemouth 0202 292 905

Dean, W.H.B.
6 Pen-Y-Bryn, Sychdyn, Mold Clwyd, CH7 6EN England.
Tel : Mold 0352 754782

Eriksson, L.T. Stamp Auctions,
P O Box 250 S-39123 Kalmar Sweden
Tel : Sweden 01046 480 15090
Fax : Sweden 01046 480 15006

Eriksson, Lars-Tore,
FRIMARKEN, P.O. Box 250, Kalmar, S-39123, Sweden.
Tel : Sweden 010 46 480 15090
Fax : Sweden 010 46 480 15006

Europhil Frimarksauktioner HB.,
Box 95, Forsvik, S-546 03 Sweden.
Tel : Forsvik 010 46 50520260
Fax : Forsvik 010 46 50520260

Express Stamp Auctions Ltd.,
35 Eaton Rise, London W5 2HE, England.
Tel : London 081 997 1312

Field, David. Limited,
1 Hobart Place, London SW1 0HU England.
Tel: London 071 235 7340
Fax: London 071 245 6276

Firby, Charles G.
6695 Highland Road, Waterford, Mi 48327 USA
Tel : USA 0101 313 666 3946
Fax : USA 0101 313 887 3091

Glasgow Philatelic Auctions
2 Broomley Drive, Giffnock, Glasgow G46 6PD
Tel: 041 638 1824

Guido Craveri Harmers Auctions SA.
via Pocobelli 16, 6815 - Melide, Switzerland
Tel: Lugano 010 4191684285
Fax: 010 4191684294

Interstamps
4 Woods View Road, Bournemouth, Dorset BH9 2LN
Tel: 0202 515756

Lancaster, Bobbie,
(Mrs E.J. Lancaster), 13 Mimosa Street, London SW6
4DS, England. . . . . Tel : London 071 736 4672
Fax : London 071 371 0139

Lester, Tony
29 Momus Boulevard, Binley Road, Stoke, Coventry, CV2
5NA, England. . . . . Tel : Stoke 0203 454908
Fax : Stoke 0203 454908

Linke, Robin
181 Jersey Street, Wembley, Western Australia 6014,
Australia. . . . . Tel : Perth (WA) 010 619 387 5327
Fax : Perth (WA) 010 619 387 1646

MP Stamps.
PO Box 61, Chatham, Kent ME4 5RL, England.
Tel : Ramsgate 0843 582938

North Western Philatelic Auctions (1990) Ltd,
North West House, Grange Road, West Kirby, Wirral,
Merseyside England. . . . . Tel: Wirral 051 625 5589
Fax: Wirral 051 625 2032

Palmerston Philatelic Auctions,
Loreburn Chambers, 11 Great King Street, Dumfries DG1
1BA, Scotland. . . . . Tel : Dumfries 0387 55508

PH Stamp Auctions,
Harbour Lights, 19 Station Road, Bishopstone, Seaford
BN25 2RB East Sussex . . . . Tel: Seaford 0323 899 565

Phillips Son & Neale,
101 New Bond Street, London W1Y 0AS, England.
Tel : London 071 629 1877
Fax : London 071 409 3466

Postiljonen AB,
Box 4118, Malmo, S-203 12, Sweden.
Tel : Malmo 010 040 72290
Fax: Malmo 010 040 72299

R J Auctions,
P.O. Box 271, Bedford, Bedfordshire MK40 3YQ,
England. . . . . Tel : Bedford 0234 358642

Rickmansworth Philatelic Auctions.
14 Langham Place, Egham, Surrey. TW20 9EB, England.
Tel : Egham 0784 436383
Fax : Egahm 0784 471705

Robson Lowe
Hinton Road, Bournemouth BH1 2EF Dorset, England.
Tel: 0202 299277
Fax: 0202 298203

Schiff, Jacques C Jr. Inc.,
195 Main Street, Ridgefield Park, New Jersey 07660
USA. . . . . Tel: New Jersey 0101 201 641 5566
Fax: New Jersey 0101 201 641 5705

Skilling, Jim
PO Box 626, New Plymouth, New Zealand
Tel: New Zealand 010 646 758 6453
Fax: New Zealand 010 646 758 6453

South Eastern Auctions,
182 Turners Hill, Cheshunt, Hertfordshire EN8 9DE,
England. . . . . Tel: Cheshunt 0992 36978

Stamp Enterprises
4 Chandri Chowk Street, Calcutta, India 700072
Tel: Calcutta 010 9133 278475
Fax: Calcutta 010 9133 2481602

Stanley Gibbons Auctions Limited
399 Strand, London. WC2R 0LX . . . . . Tel: 071 836 8444
Fax: 071 836 7342

Thames Stamp Auctions,
35 Wheathill Road, London, SE20 7XQ, England.
Tel: London 081 778 7001

Warwick & Warwick Ltd.,
Pageant House, Jury Street, Warwick, Warwickshire
CV34 4EW, England. . . . . . . Tel: Warwick 0926 499031
Fax: Warwick 0926 491906

Western Auctions Ltd.,
Bank House, 225 City Road, Cardiff, CF2 3JD, Wales.
Tel: Cardiff 0222 484934
Fax: Cardiff 0222 450522

Whyte, Macdonnell, Ltd.
102 Leinster Road, Dublin 6, Ireland.
Tel: Dublin 010 3531 977449
Fax: Dublin 010 3531 977440

Windsor Stamps
3 Brock House, Brock Road, St. Peter Port, Guernsey,
Channel Islands . . . . Tel: Guernsey 0481 710208

◆ Fair Organisers

Clent Stamps,
38 Bromsgrove Road, Romsley, Halesowen,
West Midlands B62 0LF, England.
Tel: Romsley 0562 710424

Fairsaxon Stamp Fairs,
41 Bingley Close, Snodland, Kent ME6 5TS, England.
Tel: Snodland 0634 244247
Mobile: 0850 482789

H.M.S. Stamp Fairs,
29 Basing Road, Rickmansworth, Hertforshire WD3 2QH,
England. . . . . Tel: Rickmansworth 0923 777872
Fax: Rickmansworth 0923 896063

Newton Philatelics,
53 Middle Row, Stargate, Ryton, Tyne & Wear NE40 3EE,
England. . . . . Tel: Tyneside 091 413 6316

Trio Fairs,
5 Glebe Close, Blythe Bridge, Stoke-on-Trent ST11 9JN,
England. . . . . Tel: Stoke-on-Trent 0782 394147

Watts, Ray. Stamp Fairs.
Martins Weft, Duke Street, Bildeston, Suffolk. IP7 7EW
Tel: Bildeston 0449 740821

◆ First Day Covers

Dawn Cover Productions
Official Football and Tramway Cover Producers
27 Ashfield Road, Davenport, Stockport SK3 8UD
Tel: 061 483 1297
Fax: 061 483 1297

Fourpenny Post,
30 Dinsdale Avenue, Kings Estate, Wallsend, Tyneside,
Tel: Wallsend 091 262 8844

Hull Schools Covers,
68 Davenport Avenue, Hessle, North Humberside
HU13 0RW England.
Tel: North Humberside 0482 646392

London Road Stamps,
54a London Road, Leicester, Leicestershire LE2 OQD
England. . . . . Tel: Leicester 0533 551544

Markton Stamps Ltd.
Ridlington, North Walsham, Norfolk NR28 9NS.
Tel: Norfolk 0692 651350

Newbiggen Stamps,
58 Newbiggen Street, Thaxted, Dunmow, Essex
CM6 2QT, England . . . . Tel: Thaxted 0371 830693

◆ Hinges & Mounts

Prinz Publications (Uk) Ltd.,
Lelant Garden Centre, Hayle, Cornwall, TR27 6JA,
England. . . . . Tel: Hayle 0736 756742
Fax: Hayle 0736 756555

◆ Kilo Ware

Australian Bulk,
PO Box 146, North Melbourne 3051, Victoria, Australia.
Tel: Melbourne 010 613 328 2340
Fax: Melbourne 010 613 326 6697

Davies, Richard
170 Wells Road, Bristol, BS4 2AJ, England.

Gibson, W.J.
55 Town Lane, Southport, Lancashire. PR8 6NJ England.
Tel: Southport 0704 540816

Klondyke Philatelic co.,
119 Penny Lane, Liverpool, Merseyside L18 1DF,
England. . . . . Tel: Liverpool 051 733 5826
Fax: Liverpool 051 734 0293

Leslie Sandor,
2 Wallis PDE, North Bondi, 2026 New South Wales
Australia . . . . Tel: Australia 010 613 01705

Rodgers, J.A.
3 Sea View, St. Bees, Cumbria CA27 0BB, England.
Tel: 0946 822690

◆ Philatelic Accessories

D & L Philatelic Services Australia,
No 38 Hillhouse Road, Templestowe, Victoria 3106,
Australia . . . . Tel: Victoria 010 613 846 1831/1509
Fax: Victoria 010 613 846 6286

Morley-Bright Ltd,
Coombe Head Farm, Okehampton, Devon EX20 1QL
England. . . . . Tel: Okehampton 0837 840 108
Fax: Okehampton 0837 840 108

Prinz Publications (UK) Ltd.,
Lelant Garden Centre, Hayle, Cornwall, TR27 6JA,
England. . . . . Tel: Hayle 0736 756742
Fax: Hayle 0736 756555

◆ Philatelic Literature

AFA Forlaget
Bruunsgade 42, DK-8000, Aarhus C, Denmark
Tel: Denmark 010 4586 125288
Fax: Denmark 010 4586 199281

General Image, Inc.,
PO Box 335, Maplewood, NJ 07040 U.S.A.

H H Sales Limited
Philatelic Literature Auctions, Publications, Lists.
The Barn, Heaton Royds, Shay Lane, Bradford. BD9 6SH
Tel: 0274 544 446
Fax: 0274 545 634

House Of Antiquity,
St Mary Street, Nether-Stowey, Nr. Bridgwater, Somerset
TA5 1LJ, England. . . . . Tel: Somerset 0278 732426

Pennymead Auctions,
1 Brewerton Street Knaresborough, North Yorkshire
HG5 8AZ, England. . . Tel: Knaresborough 0423 865962
Fax: 0423 865962

◆ Philatelic Mail Order

Allen, Harry
P.O. Box 5, Watford, Hertfordshire WD2 5SW, England.
Tel: Watford 0923 211522
Fax: Watford 0923 249950

B.P. Stamps Ltd.,
P.O. Box 1062, Thornbury, Bristol, Avon BS12 2BZ,
England. . . . . Tel: Thornbury 0454 419010

Ball, Gerald
34 Larchdene Avenue, Wollaton, Nottingham NG8 2PF
England. . . . . Tel: Nottingham 0602 284140

Bird, W.P.
Warfield Dale Cottage, Nuptown, Nr Warfield, Berkshire
RG12 6HR, England. . . . . . . Tel: Bracknell 0344 885552

Boyd, Tony
200 Latrobe Terrace, Paddington, Queensland 4064,
Australia. . . . . Tel: Brisbane 010 617 369 0488

Bradberry, L.R.
86 Hartwell Road, Hanslope, Milton Keynes,
Buckinghamshire MK19 7BZ, England.
Tel: Milton Keynes 0908 510679

Bradford Stamp Centre,
389 Thornton Road, Girlington, Bradford, West Yorkshire
BD8 9BJ, England. . . . . Tel: Bradford 0274 487352
Fax: Bradford 0274 481043

Bridgnorth Stamp Co. Ltd.,
Bridgnorth, Shropshire WV16 5AG, England.
Tel: Bridgnorth 0746 763259

Brownlee Stamps Ltd.,
P.O. Box 116, Macclesfield, Cheshire SK10 4XZ, England.
Tel: Macclesfield 0625 828060

Church, W & B.
Hillside Headcorn, Ashford, Kent TN27 9JE, England.
Tel: Ashford 0622 890779

Garcia's African Index,
80 Willingdon Road, Eastbourne, East Sussex BN21 1TW,
England. . . . . Tel: Eastbourne 0323 721444

Kishor Patel,
98 The Mall, Kenton, Harrow, Middlesex HA3 9TG,
England.

Lowe, David
2 Vicarage Close, Westonzoyland, Bridgewater, Somerset
TA7 0LG, England. . . . . . Tel: Bridgewater 0278 691755

Milton, David
P O Box 139, Ruislip, Middlesex HA4 8UX, England.
Tel: Ruislip 0895 637283

Moody, Keith L.
341 Burringham Road, Scunthorpe, South Humberside
DN17 2BJ, England. . . . . . Tel: Scunthorpe 0724 851132

Negev Holyland Stamps Ltd.,
P.O. Box 1, Ilfracombe, Devon EX34 9BR, England.
Tel: Ilfracombe 0271 862857
Fax: Ilfracombe 0271 867161

Rosen G. & Son Ltd.,
50 Byron Road, Walthamstow London E17 4SW England
Tel: London 081 520 4133
Fax: London 081 520 4141

Rowland Hill Stamps,
27a Comberton Hill, Kidderminster, Worcestershire,
DY10 1QN, England.. Tel : Kidderminster 0562 824060
Fax : Kidderminster 0562 743767

Rushstamps (Retail) Ltd,
P.O. Box 1, Lyndhurst, Hampshire SO43 7PP, England.
Tel : Lyndhurst 0703 282044
Fax: Lyndhurst 0703 282981

Ryan, Arthur
2 The Square, The Quadrant, Richmond, Surrey,
TW9 1DY England. .... Tel : London 081 940 7777
Fax : London 081 940 7777

Schley, John
P.O. Box 189, Barnet, Hertfordshire EN5 5PL, England.
Tel : Barnet 081 440 8835

Sedgwick, David
Station House, Wylam, Northumberland NE41 8HR,
England. .... Tel : Wylam 0661 853951

Stanley Gibbons Limited
399 Strand, London. WC2R 0LX ..... Tel: 071 836 8444
Fax: 071 836 7342

Stanley Gibbons Publications Limited
5/7 Parkside, Christchurch Road, Ringwood,
Hampshire. BH24 3SH .... Tel: 0425 472363
Fax: 0425 470247

 ⬤ **Collecting GB - Channel Islands?** *- see page 8*

Thomson, J.D.,
17 Clydeshore Road, Dumbarton, Strathclyde G82 4AF,
Scotland.

Westminster Collection
PO Box 100, Watford, Herts. WD2 5JY
Tel: Watford 0923 254022

◆ **Postal Auctions**

Allan, Richard
Longden, Shrewsbury, Shropshire SY5 8EX, England.
Tel : Shrewsbury 0743 860960

China Philately,
14 Langham Place, Egham, Surrey. TW20 9EB
Tel : Egham 0784 436383
Fax : Egham 0784 471705

County Philatelic Auctions,
Clarence Road, Fleet, Hampshire GU13 9RS, England.
Tel : Fleet 0252 624162

Folemoor Philatelics,
Little Bull Lane, Waltham Chase, Southampton SO3 2LT,
England................ Tel : Southampton 0489 892110

Fraise, Sydney,
27 Kingswood Gardens Leeds Yorkshire LS8 2BT
England...................... Tel : Leeds 0532 667386

Mountford, Trevor M.
P O Box 38, Lymington, Hampshire SO41 0WY, England
Tel : Lymington 0590 645837
Fax : Lymington 0590 645837

Penhey, P. & Associates
23 Manor Way, Woodmansterne, Surrey SM7 3PN,
England.................... Tel : Surrey 0737 357 869

Select Stamps,
PO Box 20, Northampton NN1 1EH, England.
Fax : Northampton 0604 791187

Stanley Gibbons Holdings Plc Addresses

STANLEY GIBBONS LIMITED, STANLEY GIBBONS AUCTIONS LIMITED

399 Strand, London WC2R 0LX

Auction Room and Specialist Departments. Open Monday-Friday 9.30a.m. to 5p.m.
Shop. Open Monday-Friday 8.30a.m. to 7p.m. and Saturday 10a.m. to 4p.m.
Telephone 071 836 8444 and Fax 071 836 7342 for all departments

STANLEY GIBBONS PUBLICATIONS LIMITED

5 Parkside, Christchurch Road, Ringwood, Hants BH24 3SH.
Telephone 0425 472363 (24 hour answer phone service) and Fax 0425 470247
Publications Shop (at above address). Open Monday-Friday 9a.m. to 3p.m.
Publications Mail Order: FREEPHONE: 0800 611622
Monday-Friday 8.30a.m. to 5p.m.

STANLEY GIBBONS PUBLICATIONS LTD OVERSEAS REPRESENTATION

Stanley Gibbons Publications Ltd are represented overseas by the following sole distributors (*), distributors (**), or licensees(***).

Australia
Lighthouse Philatelic (Aust.) Pty Ltd*
PO Box 763
Strawberry Hills
New South Wales 2012
Australia

Stanley Gibbons (Australia) Pty Ltd***
PO Box 863J
Melbourne 3001
Australia

Belgium and Luxembourg**
Davo c/o Philac
Rue du Midi 48
Bruxelles 1000
Belgium

Canada*
Lighthouse Publications (Canada) Ltd
255 Duke Street
Montreal
Quebec
Canada H3C 2M2

Denmark**
Davo
c/o Lindner Falzlos
GI Randersvej 28
8450 Hammel
Denmark

Finland**
Davo
c/o Suomen Postimerkkeily
Ludvingkatu 5
SF-00130 Helsinki
Finland

France*
Davo France
25 Rue Monge
75005 Paris
France

Germany and Austria*
Leuchtturm Albenverlag
Paul Koch KG
Am Spakenberg 45
Postfach 1340
D-2054 Geesthacht
Germany

Hong Kong**
Po-On Stamp Service
GPO Box 2498, Hong Kong

Israel**
Capital Stamps
PO Box 3769
Jerusalem 91036
Israel

Italy*
Secrian Sri
Via Pantelleria 2, 1-20156 Milano
Italy

Japan**
Japan Philatelic Co Ltd
PO Box 2
Suginami-Minami
Tokyo
Japan

Netherlands*
Davo Publications
PO Box 411
7400 AK Deventer
Netherlands

New Zealand*
Philatelic Distributors Ltd
PO Box 863
New Plymouth
New Zealand

Norway**
Davo Norge A/S
PO Box 738 Sentrum
N-01 05 Oslo
Norway

Singapore***
Stanley Gibbons (Singapore) Plc Ltd
Raffles City
PO Box 1689
Singapore 9117

South Africa
Philatelic Holdings (Pty) Ltd ***
PO Box 930, Parklands
RSA 2121

Republic Coin and Stamp Accessories (Pty) Ltd**
PO Box 260325
Excom 2023
Johannesburg
RSA

Sweden*
Chr Winther Sorensen AB
Box 43
S-310 Knaered
Sweden

Switzerland**
Phila Service
Burgstrasse 160
CH 4125 Richen
Switzerland

USA*
Lighthouse Publications Inc
PO Box 705
274 Washington Avenue
Hackensack
New Jersey 07602-0705
USA

West Indies/Caribbean**
Hugh Dunphy
PO Box 413
Kingston 10
Jamaica

Stamp House,
404 Yorktown Road, College Town, Camberley,
Surrey GU15 4PR, England.
Tel : Camberley 0276 32587
Fax : Camberley 0276 32505

◆ Postcards & Postcard Albums

Taylor, Walter
Stirling Close, Seaford, East Sussex BN25 3UT, England.
Tel : Seaford 0323 890617

◆ Publications

AFA Forlaget,
Bruunsgade 42, DK-8000, Aarhus C, Denmark.
Tel: Denmark 010 4586 125288
Fax: Denmark 010 4586 199281

Gibbons Stamp Monthly,
Stanley Gibbons Publications Ltd, 5/7 Parkside,
Christchurch Road, Ringwood BH24 3SH England.
Tel : Ringwood 0425 472363
Fax : Ringwood 0425 470247

Gretton, J.R.
5 Quebec Road, Dereham, Norfolk NR19 2DP, England.
Tel : Dereham 0362 692707

H H SALES LIMITED
Philatelic Literature Auctions, Publications, Lists.
The Barn, Heaton Royds, Shay Lane, Bradford. BD9 6SH
Tel: 0274 544 446
Fax: 0274 545 634

THE PHILATELIC EXPORTER,
World's Greatest Stamp Trade Journal
– request a free sample copy.
PO Box 137, Hatfield, Hertfordshire AL10 9DB, England.
Tel : Hatfield 0707 266331
Fax : Hatfield 0707 274782

Stamp & Coin Mart,
Maze Media, Castle House, 97 High Street, Colchester,
Essex England. .... Tel : Colchester 0206 579 660
Fax : Colchester 0206 571 607

The Stamp Collector
G.P.O. Box 3780, Sydney, N.S.W. 2001, Australia
Tel: 010 612 957 2882
Fax: 010 61 2 959 5159

Stamp Magazine,
Link House Magazines Ltd, Link House, Dingwall Avenue,
Croydon, Surrey England. . . Tel : London 081 686 2599
Fax : London 081 781 6046

The Stamp Wholesalers,
Van Dahl Publications, Stamp Collector Newspaper,
520 E. 1st Street, Albany USA.
Tel: USA 0101 503 928 4484
Fax: USA 0101 503 967 9272

Stanley Gibbons Publications Limited
5/7 Parkside, Christchurch Road, Ringwood,
Hampshire. BH24 3SH. . . . . Tel: 0425 472363
Fax: 0425 470247

◆ Shops

Antiques & Collectors Centre,
35 St. Nicholas Cliff, Scarborough, N.Yorks. YO11 2ES,
England. . . . . Tel: Scarborough 0723 365221

Bath Stamp & Coin Shop, The
12/13 Pulteney Bridge, Bath, Avon BA2 4AY, England.
Tel : Bath 0225 463073

BARESCH, LEO. LTD
Foreign & Brit. Comm.Open Mo-Fri.10.30-6.00, Sat.10-3
London Int. Stamp Centre,110 St. Martin's Lane,Trafalgar
Square, London, WC2N 4AZ
Tel: 071 240 1963
Fax: 0273 845501

Baxters Coin & Stamp Exchange,
20-22 Hepworths Arcade, Silver Street, Hull,
Humberside HU1 1JU, England.
Tel : Hull 0482 223875

Buchanan Street Stamps,
205 Buchanan Street, Glasgow G1 2JZ, Scotland.
Tel : Glasgow 041 333 9724

Collectors Gallery,
6/7 Castle Gates, Shrewsbury, SY1 2AE, England.
Tel: Shrewsbury 0743 272140
Fax: Shrewsbury 0743 366041

LIBRITZ STAMPS
Stamps— Coins — Banknotes— Cigarette Cards—
Accessories
Open Monday to Saturday, 10am - 6pm

70 London Road,Apsley,Hemel Hempstead,Herts. HP3 9SD
Tel: (0442) 242691

Dumfries Stamp Shop,
11 Great King Street, Dumfries DG1 1BA, England.
Tel : Dumfries 0387 55508
Epsom Stamp Co.
23 Waterloo Road, Epsom, Surrey KT19 8EX, England.
Tel : Epsom 0372 720051
Fenwick Philatelics,
52 Fenwick Street, Liverpool L2 7ND, England.
Tel : Liverpool 051 236 5997
Fax : Liverpool 051 255 0509
Green D.L.
2A Leanne Business Centre, Sandford Lane, Wareham,
Dorset BH20 4DY, England.
Tel : Wareham 0929 550750
Harrogate Stamp Shop,
125 Cold Bath Road, Harrogate, North Yorkshire
HG2 0NU, England. . . . . . . Tel : Harrogate 0423 568428
Harrow Stamp Shop,
Unit 1 15 Springfield Road, Greenhall Way, Harrow,
Middlesex HA1 1QF England.
Tel: London 081 424 0990
Haworth, M & N. (Manchester) Ltd,
Royal Exchange Antique Gallery, St Ann's Square,
Manchester M2 7DB, England.
Tel: Manchester 061 834 2929
Fax: Manchester 061 839 4714
Heckmondwike Stamp Centre,
3 Walkley Lane, Heckmondwike, West Yorkshire,
WF16 0LU England. . . Tel: Heckmondwike 0924 408 848
Kemp, I & B
St. Stephen's House, Catherine Street, Exeter, Devon
EX1 1EU, England. . . . . Tel : Exeter 0392 434282
Masons Hill Stamp Shop.
127 Masons Hill, Bromley, Kent. BR2 9HT
Tel : Bromley 081 464 7862
Newcastle Stamp,
c/o Starbeck Ave.Post Office,Sandyford,Newcastle-upon
-Tyne, NE2 1RJ. . . . . .Tel: 091 232 0017
Stamp Shop, The
Unit 10,Granby Arcade,Water Street,Bakewell,Derbyshire
Tel: Bakewell 0629 812191

To Advertise in
The Philatelic Register

Tel: 0425 472363
Fax: 0425 470247

Miles & Miles,
96 Marmion Road, Southsea, Hampshire, PO5 2BB,
England. .... Tel : Portsmouth 0705 826864
　　　　　　　　Fax : Portsmouth 0705 862466
Murray. Robert, Stamp Shop
5 & 6 Inverleith Gardens, Ferry Road, Edinburgh,
EH3 5PU, Scotland...... Tel : Edinburgh 031 552 1220
Oliver, Barry
404 Yorktown Road, College Town, Camberley, Surrey
GU15 4PR, England....... Tel : Camberley 0276 32587
　　　　　　　　Fax : Camberley 0276 32505
Penrith Coin & Stamp Centre
37 King Street, Penrith, Cumbria.
　　　　　　　　　Tel: 0768 64185
Portsmouth Stamp Shop
184 Chichester Road, North End, Portsmouth
Hants PO2 0AX .... Tel: 0705 663450
　　　　　　　　　Fax: 0705 664884
Ross-Shiells Ltd.
4/5 Eldon Street, London EC2M 7LS, England.
　　　　　　　Tel : London 071 247 8011
Saywell A.J. Ltd.,
(The Oxford Stamp Shop) 15 Hollybush Row Oxfordshire
OX1 1JH, England. .... Tel : Oxford 0865 248889

Stamp Centre, The
7 Queen Street, Gravesend, Kent DA12 2EQ, England.
　　　　　　　Tel : Gravesend 0474 534166
Surrey Philatelics,
21 Victoria Street, Englefield Green, Egham, Surrey
TW20 0QY England......... Tel: Egham 0784 436 383
　　　　　　　　Fax: Egham 0784 471 705
The Stamp Shop,
PO Box 18, High Street, Alderney, Channel Islands.
　　　　　　　Tel: Alderney 0481 82 2514

Everything For The Philatelist

Visit Stanley Gibbons at the Strand, London for a choice of philatelic material that is second to none! The extensive range of stamps and philatelic products available includes the complete Stanley Gibbons range, products from Davo, Lighthouse and Kabe to name a few.

Open at your convenience from 8.30am until 7pm Monday–Friday and from 10am until 4pm Saturday.

Stanley Gibbons Limited
399 Strand, London. WC2R 0LX
Tel: 071 836 8444 Fax: 071 836 7342

Stanley Gibbons Limited
399 Strand. London. WC2R 0LX.....Tel: 071 836 8444
　　　　　　　　Fax: 071 836 7342
Wyon Classics,
Corridor Stamp Shop, 7a The Corridor, Bath, Avon
BA1 5AP. .... Tel : Bath 0225 463368

Collecting
BR COMMONWEALTH
- Falklands
& Antarctica
see page 11

see page 11

◆ Societies & Clubs

Philatelic Traders Society
107 Charterhouse Street, London EC1M 6PT England.
　　　　　　　Tel : London 071 490 1005

◆ Stamp Album Manfs & Supps

FRANK GODDEN LTD.
Finest Quality Albums,
Leaves & Exhibition Protectors
The Barn, Heaton Royds, Shay Lane, Bradford BD9 6SH
　　　　　　　Tel: 0274 544 446
　　　　　　　Fax: 0274 545 634

A Complete Range of Albums Available

A wide range of albums available for all purposes, first day covers, postcards, stock systems and stamps.

Versatile and long lasting, the complete Collecta range of albums is well known for their combination of quality and value for money.

All albums manufactured to a high specification.

Collecta
Stanley Gibbons Publications Ltd,
5/7 Parkside, Christchurch Road,
Ringwood, Hampshire. BH24 3SH.
Tel: 0425 472363 Fax: 0425 470247

Stanley Gibbons Limited
Collecta Limited, 5/7 Parkside, Christchurch Road,
Ringwood, Hampshire. BH24 3SH
　　　　　　　Tel: 0425 472363
　　　　　　　Fax: 0425 470247

◆ Stamp Booklets

Booklets International.
Postbus 1051, Waalwyk, HOLLAND Netherlands.
　　　　　　　Tel: Holland 010 31 4160 31451
　　　　　　　Fax: Holland 010 31 4160 42856

◆ Thematics

Anglia Stamp Bureau
P.O. Box 88, Norwich, England NR1 4PQ
Arlington, J & M.
45 Lakenheath, London N14 4RL, England.
　　　　　　　Tel : London 081 886 6744
　　　　　　　Fax : London 081 886 6744
Avion Stamps,
61 Monument Lane, Codnor Park, Nottingham NG16 5PJ,
England. .... Tel : Nottingham 0773 608899
　　　　　　　Fax : Nottingham 0773 609821
Chatwin, R.J.
5 Flats Lane, Barwick-in-Elmet, Leeds, West Yorkshire
LS15 4LJ, England............ Tel : Leeds 0532 812562

Cliffe, Thomas, Ltd.,
84 March Road, Rhyl Clwyd LL18 2AF, Wales.
　　　　　　　Tel : Rhyl 0745 353524
　　　　　　　Fax : Rhyl 0745 353524
DAWN COVER PRODUCTIONS
Official Football and Tramway Cover Producers
27 Ashfield Road, Davenport, Stockport SK3 8UD
　　　　　　　Tel: 061 483 1297
　　　　　　　Fax: 061 483 1297
Grainger, A.
42 Lee Lane East, Horsforth, Leeds, West Yorkshire
LS18 5RE, England.......... Tel : Leeds 0532 583790

Gustamps,
12 Prince Albert Street, Brighton, East Sussex BN1 1HE,
England..................... Tel : Brighton 0273 326994
Healey & Wise,
P.O. Box 7, Tadworth, Surrey KT20 7QA, England.
　　　　　　　Tel : Tadworth 0737 812455
　　　　　　　Fax : Tadworth 0737 814407
Jenkinson, D.
5 Orde Avenue, Gorleston-on-Sea, Great Yarmouth,
Norfolk NR31 6SZ, England.
　　　　　　　Tel : Great Yarmouth 0493 668512
Monsoon Philatelics,
Serangoon Garden, P.O. Box 413, Singapore 1955,
Singapore.............. Tel : Singapore 010 65 3388944
　　　　　　　Fax : Singapore 010 65 2782327
Philatelic Supplies,
42 Willian Way, Letchworth, Hertfordshire SG6 2HH,
England.................. Tel : Letchworth 0462 684191
Philcard International,
PO Box 1000, London N3 3TD, England.
　　　　　　　Tel : 081 349 1610
　　　　　　　Fax : 081 349 1610
Phoenix International,
Ashleigh, Monument Lane, Codnor Park,
Nottingham NG16 5PJ, London.
　　　　　　　Tel : Nottingham 0773 608899
　　　　　　　Fax : Nottingham 0773 609821
Rosen. G & Son Ltd
50 Byron Road, Walthamstow, London E17 4SW
　　　　　　　Tel: London 081 520 4133
　　　　　　　Fax: London 081 520 4141
Sandton Stamps (Pty) Ltd
Specialists in British Southern Africa & Thematics
Shop L 40, Sandton City, P.O. Box 782564, Sandton,
South Africa. 2146.................. Tel. 011 783 8309
　　　　　　　Fax: 011 783 2706
Sellinger. Martin,
P.O. Box 47, 4 Woodland Place, White Plains, New York
10602 U.S.A....... Tel : New York 010 1 914 948 4246
Shield Stamp Company,
PO Box 2977, Grand Central Station, New York, NY 10163
USA. .... Tel: New York 0101 212 629 7979
　　　　　　Fax: New York 0101 212 629 3350
　　　　　　　　　　236440 IGPC UR
Stamp Publicity (Worthing) Ltd.,
28 Windlesham Road, Shoreham-by-Sea, West Sussex
BN43 5AE, England.

Collect Thematics?

Then make sure you contact Stanley Gibbons for their current list of thematic stamps and catalogues.

Whatever your thematic collecting interest there promises to be something of interest to you — from birds to butterflies, fungi to chess — contact us now!

Stanley Gibbons Limited
399 Strand, London. WC2R 0LX
Tel: 071 836 8444 Fax: 071 836 7342

Stanley Gibbons Limited
399 Strand. London. WC2R 0LX .... Tel: 071 836 8444
　　　　　　　　Fax: 071 836 7342

ALPHA LISTING

Allen, Harry
P.O.Box5, Watford, Hertfordshire WD2 5SW, England.
Tel: Watford 0923 211522
Fax: Watford 0923 249950

A-One Stamps,
PO Box 35, Woollahra, New South Wales, 2025 Australia.
Tel: Sydney 010 612 362 3636
Fax: Sydney 010 612 363 2303

A.S.M. Stamps,
PO Box 143, Alderley, Queensland, 4051 Australia
Tel: Brisbane 010 617 356 0824
Fax: Brisbane 010 617 856 4731

A.T. Philatelics
Mantra House, South Street, Keighley, West Yorkshire BD21 1SX England.
Tel : Keighley 0535 603372

Abbey Philatelic Co. Ltd.,
83 London Fruit Exchange, Brushfield Street, London E1 6EP, England.
Tel : London 071 247 4601

ABSP, Inc
PO Box 155, Warminister, PA 18974, U.S.A.
Tel : Philadelphia 215 672 6040
Fax : Philadelphia 215 672 8295

Acorn Philatelic Auctions,
27 Pine Road, Didsbury, Manchester M20 0UZ, England.
Tel : Manchester 061 434 2580

AFA Forlaget,
Bruunsgade 42, DK-8000, Aarhus C, Denmark.
Tel: Denmark 010 4586 125288
Fax: Denmark 010 4586 199281

Aldworth, S.
Cwmbedw, Rhydlewis, Llandysul, Dyfed SA44 5PR, Wales.
Tel : Rhydlewis 0239 851335

Allan, Richard
Longden, Shrewsbury, Shropshire SY5 8EX, England.
Tel : Shrewsbury 0743 860960

Allen, Harry
P.O. Box 5, Watford, Hertfordshire WD2 5SW, England.
Tel : Watford 0923 211522
Fax : Watford 0923 249950

Anglia Stamp Bureau
P.O.Box 88, Norwich, England NR1 4PQ

Antiques & Collectors Centre,
35 St Nicholas Cliff, Scarborough, North Yorkshire, YO11 2ES England.
Tel: Scarborough 0723 365 221

Ararat Commodity Agency,
P.O. Box 416, Ararat, Victoria 3377, Australia.
Tel: Ballarat 010 61 353 524410

Archer, D.L.
2 Litchfield Way, Broxbourne, Hertfordshire EN10 6PT, England.
Tel : Broxbourne 0992 462548

Argyll Etkin Ltd.,
48 Conduit Street, New Bond Street, London W1R 9FB, England.
Tel : London 071 437 7800
Fax : London 071 434 1060

Arlington, J & M.
45 Lakenheath, London N14 4RL, England.
Tel : London 081 886 6744
Fax : London 081 886 6744

Auld, John
1 Hill View Villas, Hastingwood, Nr. Harlow, Essex CM17 9JK, England.
Tel : Harlow 0279 433910
Fax : Harlow 0279 433910

Australian Bulk,
PO Box 146, North Melbourne 3051, Victoria, Australia.
Tel: Melbourne 010 613 328 2340
Fax: Melbourne 010 613 326 6697

Avalon Stamp & Postcard Shop,
1 Citywalls, Rufus Court, Northgate Street, Chester CH1 2JG,
Tel : Chester 0244 318406

Avion Stamps,
61 Monument Lane, Codnor Park, Nottingham NG16 5PJ, England.
Tel : Nottingham 0773 608899
Fax : Nottingham 0773 609821

Axtner,
Frauenstrasse 11, Muenchen 5, D-8000, West Germany.
Tel: Germany 010 49 89 227 7571
Fax: Germany 010 49 89 228 5385

Aylward, k
The Outlook 2 Roedean Path Brighton BN2 5RP
Tel : Brighton 0273 696189

B & S Stamps,
Byron House, 21/23 Rectory Road,
West Bridgford, Nottinghamshire NG2 6BE, England.
Tel : Nottingham 0602 816214
Fax : Nottingham 0602 455499

B.P. Stamps Ltd.,
P.O. Box 1062, Thornbury, Bristol, Avon BS12 2BZ, England.
Tel : Thornbury 0454 419010

Balasse, Willy.
45a Rue du Midi, Brussels, B-1000 Belgium.
Tel : Brussels 010 322 513 5061
Fax : Brussels 010 322 513 5061

Ball, G.
34 Larchdene Avenue, Wollaton, Nottingham NG8 2PF, England.
Tel : Wollaton 0602 284140

Ball, Gerald
34 Larchdene Avenue, Wollaton, Nottingham NG8 2PF England.
Tel: Wollaton 0602 284140

Ballard, A.R.
P.O. Box 780, London SE13 5QA, England.
Tel : London 081 852 7031

Barefoot Ltd., J.
P.O. Box 8, Catterick, North Yorkshire YO3 7GL, England.
Tel : York 0904 654241
Fax : York 0904 654241

Barrington-Smith,
G. Cross Street, Oadby, Leicestershire LE2 4DD, England.
Tel : Leicester 0533 719181
Fax : Leicester 0533 712114

Bath Stamp & Coin Shop, The
12/13 Pulteney Bridge, Bath, Avon BA2 4AY, England.
Tel : Bath 0225 463073

Baxters Coin & Stamp Exchange,
20-22 Hepworths Arcade, Silver Street, Hull, Humberside HU1 1JU, England.
Tel : Hull 0482 223875

Bay Stamps,
Freepost, Colwyn Bay, Clwyd LL29 9YZ, England.
Tel : Colwyn Bay 0492 516644

Behar, H.
Place Pepinet 4, Lausanne 1003, Switzerland.
Tel : Lausanne 010 4121 234207
Fax : Lausanne 010 4121 234207

Bexley Stamps,
415 Forest Rd, Bexley NSW 2207, Australia.
Tel : Sydney 010 612 567 5242
Fax : Sydney 010 612 597 4307

Bick International,
P.O. Box 854, Van Nuys, California 91408, U.S.A.
Tel : California 010 1818 9976496
Fax : California 010 1818 9884337

Bird, W.P.
Warfield Dale Cottage, Nuptown, Nr Warfield, Berkshire RG12 6HR, England.
Tel : Bracknell 0344 885552

Bolton Stamp Centre,
27 Mawdsley Street, Bolton, Lancashire BL1 1LN, England.
Tel : Bolton 0204 29271

Bond, A.G.
6 Rollestone Crescent, Pennsylvania, Exeter, Devon EX4 5EB, England.
Tel : Exeter 0392 50283
Fax : Exeter 0392 50283

Booklets International.
Postbus 1051, Waalwyk, HOLLAND Netherlands.
Tel: Holland 010 31 4160 31451
Fax: Holland 010 31 4160 42856

Border Stamp Centre,
23 Abbotsford Road, Galashiels, Selkirkshire TD1 3QR, Scotland.
Tel : Galasheils 0896 56822
Fax : Galasheils 0896 56822

Boscombe Collectors Centre,
726A Christchurch Road, Boscombe, Bournemouth,
BH7 6BE ....Tel:Bournemouth 0202 393199

Boyd, Tony
200 Latrobe Terrace, Paddington, Queensland 4064,
Australia.
Tel : Brisbane 010 617 369 0488

Bradberry, L.R.
86 Hartwell Road, Hanslope, Milton Keynes, Buckinghamshire MK19 7BZ, England.
Tel : Milton Keynes 0908 510679

Bradford Stamp Centre,
389 Thornton Road, Girlington, Bradford, West Yorkshire
BD8 9BJ, England.
Tel : Bradford 0274 487352
Fax : Bradford 0274 481043

Bridgnorth Stamp Co. Ltd.,
Bridgnorth, Shropshire WV16 5AG, England.

OOKMAN, Barrett & Worthen,
10 Chestnut Drive, Bedford, New Hampshire 03110,
U.S.A.
Tel : Bedford (NH) 0101 603 472 5575
Fax : Bedford (NH) 0101 603 472 8795

Brookman/Barrett & Worthen,
10 Chestnut Drive, Bedford, 03110 USA.
Tel: Bedford 0101 603 472 5575
Fax: Bedford 0101 603 472 8795

Brookvale Stamps,
196 Ivyfield Road, Birmingham, B23 7HS, England.
Tel : Birmingham 021 382 5937

Brownlee Stamps Ltd.,
P.O. Box 116, Macclesfield, Cheshire SK10 4XZ, England.
Tel : Macclesfield 0625 828060

Buchanan Street Stamps,
205 Buchanan Street, Glasgow G1 2JZ, Scotland.
Tel : Glasgow 041 333 9724

Budget Stamp Sales,
8th Floor, 94 Elizabeth Street, Melbourne, Vic. 3000
Australia.
Tel: Australia 010 613 650 7748

C.K.V. Stamps,
16 Northumberland Avenue, Market Bosworth, Nuneaton,
Warwickshire CV13 0RJ, England.
Tel : 01455 292314

Cambridge stamp centre,
9 Sussex Street, Cambridge CB1 1PA, England.
Tel : Cambridge 0223 63980

Campbell Paterson Ltd. (Warwick Paterson)
PO Box 5555, Auckland 1 New Zealand.
Tel : Auckland 010 649 3793086
Fax : Auckland 010 649 3793087

Campbell Paterson Ltd.,
PO Box 17, Woking, Surrey GU22 7BL, ENGLAND.
Tel : Woking 0483 715887
Fax : Woking 0483 747149

Campbell, Richard
P.O. Box 734, Arundel, Sussex BN18 0QS, England.
Tel : Arundel 0243 542167

Candlish McCleery ltd.,
P.O. Box 11, Worcester WR8 9BQ, England.
Tel : Worcester 0386 750063
Fax : Worcester 0386 750170

Card, Mary
14 Mulberry Close, Brighton, East Sussex BN1 6QE,
England.
Tel : Brighton 0273 557729

Carmichael & Todd,
P.O. Box 494, London SW19 8DN England.
Tel : London 081 946 0760
Fax : London 081 879 1438

Carson. William,
P.O. Box 1836, 109 Canterbury Arcade, Queen Street,
Auckland New Zealand.
Tel : Auckland 010 649 3794527
Fax : Auckland 010 649 3794527

Castle Stamps,
2a Warwick Lane, Warwick Street, Worthing, West Sussex
BN11 2DP, England.
Tel : Worthing 0903 230064

Cavendish Philatelic Auctions Ltd.,
Sitwell Street, Derby, Derbyshire DE1 2JP, England.
Tel : Derby 0332 46753
Fax : Derby 0332 294440

Central Stamps & Supplies,
CNR Melbourne 2, Merivale Street, South Brisbane,
Queensland, Australia.
Tel: Brisbane 010617 846 2412
Fax: Brisbane 010617 846 2412

Centre 22 Stamps,
22 Centre Place, Melbourne, Victoria 3000 Australia.
Tel: Melbourne 010 613 650 3687

Chalon Stamps & Coins
Gloucester Arcade, 129 Gloucester Street, Christchurch,
New Zealand.
Tel : Christchurch 010 643 3657 880

Chatwin, R.J.
5 Flats Lane, Barwick-in-Elmet, Leeds, West Yorkshire
LS15 4LJ, England.
Tel : Leeds 0532 812562

Cherrystone Stamp Center Inc.,
119 West 57th Street, Third Floor, New York, NY-10019,
U.S.A.
Tel: NewYork 0101 212 977 7334
Fax: NewYork 0101 212 977 8653

Chiani Auctions,
Hochschorenstr.31, Postfach, CH-9202, Gossau Switzer-
land.
Tel : Switzerland 010 41 071 85 85 66
Fax : Switzerland 010 41 071 85 97 36

China Philately,
14 Langham Place, Egham, Surrey. TW20 9EB
Tel : Egham 0784 436383
Fax : Egham 0784 471705

Christchurch City Stamps Ltd
53 Cathedral Square, PO Box 2323, Christchurch New
Zealand.
Tel: Christchurch 010 643 366 1173

Christie's Robson Lowe Auctioneers
Stamp Department, 8 King Street, St James's, London
SW1Y 6QT, England.
Tel : London 071 839 9060
Fax : London 071 389 2688

Church, W & B.
Hillside Headcorn, Ashford, Kent TN27 9JE, England.
Tel : Ashford 0622 890779

Clent Stamps,
38 Bromsgrove Road, Romsley, Halesowen, West Midlands B62 0LF, England.
Tel : Romsley 0562 710424

Cleveland, G.
39 Station Road, North Harrow, Middlesex HA2 7SU,
England.
Tel : Middlesex 081 8630155
Fax : Middlesex 081 8631227

Cliffe, Thomas, Ltd.,
84 March Road, Rhyl Clwyd LL18 2AF, Wales.
Tel : Rhyl 0745 353524
Fax : Rhyl 0745 353524

Cockerill, Nick
17 Home Farm Gardens, Walton-on-Thames, Surrey
KT12 3DN England.
Tel: Walton-on-Thames 0932 228345

Coleman, Robert
11 The Chase, Chatham, Kent ME4 6UP, England.

Coles Philatelic Gems,
476 Kedleston Road, Allestree, Derby DE22 2NE,
England.
Tel : Derby 0332 556312
Fax : Derby 0332 557919

Collectors Gallery,
6 and 7 Castle Gates, Shrewsbury SY1 2AE England.
Tel: Shrewsbury 0743 272140
Fax: Shrewsbury 0743 366041

Corlett, H.
4 Glencree, Billericay, Essex CM11 1EB England.
Tel : Billericay 0277 656577

Cosmos Stamps,
P.O. Box 7, Heswall, Wirral, Merseyside L61 3YA,
England.
Tel : Liverpool 051 648 5777
Fax : Liverpool 051 648 5777

County Philatelic Auctions,
Clarence Road, Fleet, Hampshire GU13 9RS, England.
Tel : Fleet 0252 624162

Craig, Alan S.
Arcadia Building, Worley Place, P.O. Box 1313, Hamilton
New Zealand.
Tel : Hamilton 010 6471 8340630

Creeting Stamps,
5 Church Close, Creeting St. Mary, Ipswich IP6 8NL,
England.
Tel : Ipswich 0449 721133

Crown Agents Stamp Bureau,
Old Inn House, 2 Carshalton Road, Sutton, Surrey SM1
4RN, England.
Tel : London 081 770 0707
Fax : London 081 642 0769 Tlx : 948116

Curtin, John. Ltd,
P.O. Box 31, Sunbury-on-Thames, Middlesex TW16 6HS,
England.
Tel : Sunbury on Thames 0932 785635
Fax : Sunbury on Thames 0932 770523

Cussans, Martin
22 Joiners Road, Linton, Cambridgeshire CB1 6NX
England.
Tel : Cambridgeshire 0223 893 264

D & L Philatelic Services Australia,
No 38 Hillhouse Road, Templestowe, Victoria 3106,
Australia.
Tel : Victoria 010 613 846 1831/1509
Fax : Victoria 010 613 846 6286

D Meulemans,
PO Box 1370, 1000 Brussels Belgium
Tel: Brussels 010 322 2230341
Fax: Brussels 010 322 2230341

Dalkeith Auctions,
Dalkeith Hall, Dalkeith Steps, Rear 81 Old Christchurch
Road, Bournemouth BH1 1VL, England.
Tel: Bournemouth 0202 292 905
Fax: Bournemouth 0202 292 905

Daniels, P.
70 Moor Park Close, Rainham, Gillingham, Kent ME8
8QT, England.
Tel : Gillingham 0634 376268

Danzig, R
P O Box 7, Newport, Isle of Wight PO30 2PY, England.
Tel : Isle of Wight 0983 527215
Fax : Isle of Wight 0983 527425

Dauwalders,
92-94 Fisherton Street, Salisbury, Wiltshire SP2 7QY,
England.
Tel : Salisbury 0722 412100
Fax : Salisbury 0722 412100

Davey, Peter.
West View, Low Road, Evesham, Worcestershire Eng-
land.
Tel: Evesham 0386 870171

Davidson, A&M. (Philatelists),
No 8 Aerodrome Road, St. Helens, Tasmania 7216
Australia.
Tel: Tasmania 0103 763 089

De Rosa International S.A.
Av. du Tribunal-Federal 34, Lausanne CH-1005, Switzer-
land.
Tel: 41 21 202431
Fax: 41 21 202433

Dean, W.H.B.
The Poplars, New Brighton, Mold, Clwyd CH7 6QQ Wales.
Tel: Clwyd 0352 754 782

Doreen Royan & Associates (Pty) Ltd,
P.O. Box 310, Sunninghill, Johannesburg, Transvaal,
2157 South Africa.
Tel: Johannesburg 010 2711 803 3237
Fax: Johannesburg 010 2711 803 4899

Downsway Stamp Co.,
12 Downs Way, Epsom, Surrey KT18 5LU, England.
Tel : Surrey 0372 723743

Dumfries Stamp Shop,
11 Great King Street, Dumfries DG1 1BA, Scotland.
Tel : Dumfries 0387 55508

Dunkerley Pty Ltd, Simon
P.O. Box 461, Blackburn, Victoria 3130, Australia.
Tel : Victoria 010 61 3 8781142
Fax : Victoria 010 61 3 8781154

Durban Stamp Auctions
P.O.Box 461, Pinetown 3600,South Africa
Tel:031 783 722

Earle, Patrick & Barbara
P.O. Box 2, Nairn, IV12 4DZ, Scotland.
Tel : Nairn 0667 52310
Fax : Nairn 0667 52109

East Riding Philatelics,
46 Carrs Meadow, Withernsea, North Humberside HU19
2ER, England.

Edelman's,
301 Old York Road, Jenkintown, PA 19046, U.S.A.
Tel : Philadelphia 215 572 6480

Edge, J. & K.
3 Newborough Avenue, Llanishen, Cardiff, South Glamorgan CF4 5BY, Wales.
Tel : Cardiff 0222 758309

Ellis, Steve
The Laurels, Bristol Road, Churchill, Bristol, Avon BS19
5NL, England.
Tel : Churchill 0934 852199
Fax : Churchill 0934 852199

Empire Stamp Auctions,
Thornton Lodge, Stanshalls Lane, Felton, Bristol BS18
7UQ, England.
Tel : Bristol 0275 474766

Emsworth Philatelic,
8 Christopher Way, Emsworth, Hampshire PO10 7QZ,
England.
Tel : Emsworth 0243 374349

Epsom Stamp Co.
23 Waterloo Road, Epsom, Surrey KT19 8EX, England.
Tel : Epsom 0372 720051

Ercole Gloria SRL.,
(G. Zuskis), Piazza Pio XI, 1, Milano, 20123, Italy.

Eriksson, Lars-Tore, Frimarken,
P.O. Box 250, Kalmar, S-39123, Sweden.
Tel : Sweden 010 46 480 15090
Fax : Sweden 010 46 480 15006

Ets Willy Balasse S.A.
45-45a Rue du Midi, Bruxelles, B-1000, Belgium.
Tel: Bruxelles 010 322 513 5061
Fax: Bruxelles 010 322 513 5061

Europhil Frimarksauktioner HB.,
Box 95, Forsvik, S-546 03 Sweden.
Tel : Forsvik 010 46 50520260
Fax : Forsvik 010 46 50520260

Express Stamp Auctions Ltd.,
35 Eaton Rise, London W5 2HE, England.
Tel : London 081 997 1312

Fairsaxon Stamp Fairs,
41 Bingley Close, Snodland, Kent ME6 5TS, England.
Tel : Snodland 0634 244247
Mobile : 0850 482789

Falcon Stamps Pty Ltd,
PO BOX 571, Milsons Point, New South Wales 2061
Australia.
Tel: Sydney 010 612 922 1770
Fax: Sydney 010 612 922 1770

Faure, Peter
151 St Mary Street, Tarxien PLA 11, Malta.
Tel : Malta 010 356 882160

Feltus, Peter R.
PO Box 5339, Berkeley, California 94705 USA.
Tel: USA 0101 510 658 9627

Fenwick Philatelics,
52 Fenwick Street, Liverpool L2 7ND, England.
Tel : Liverpool 051 236 5997
Fax : Liverpool 051 255 0509

Field. David, Ltd
1 Hobart Place, London SW1W 0HU, England.
Tel : London 071 235 7340
Fax : London 071 245 6276

Filastrs SRE
Via Fontana 6B, Rovereto 38068, Italy
Tel: 010 39 464 421 267
Fax: 010 39 464 422 2272

Filatelia Llach, S.L.,
Diagonal 489, Barcelona E-08029, Spain.
Tel : Barcelona 010 343 410 5000
Fax : Barcelona 010 343 419 4728
Tlx : 9329 RTX E

Filatelic Phriends CC.
P.O. Box 26456, Hout Bay, Cape Town 7872 South Africa.
Tel : Cape Town 010 2721 790 5943/4
Fax : Cape Town 010 2721 790 5745

Firby, Charles G.
6695 Highland Road, Waterford, MI48372, U.S.A.
Tel: Miami 0101 313 666 3946
Fax: Miami 010 313 887 3091

Fisher, E.A.
Flat 2 22 Victoria Grove Bridport Dorset DT6 2AA

Fleming, R.
1A Parr Street, Warrington, Cheshire WA1 2JP, England.

Flowerdew, J & M
31 North Street, Sheringham, Norfolk NR26 8LW,
England.
Tel : Sheringham 0263 822379

Folemoor Philatelics,
Little Bull Lane, Waltham Chase, Southampton SO3 2LT,
England.
Tel : Southampton 0489 892110

Forces Postal History Society,
71 Victory Road, Wimbledon, London SW19 1HP
England.

Fourpenny Post Stamps & Postcards.
30 Dinsdale Avenue, King's Estate, Wallsend Tyneside
NE28 9JD, England.
Tel : Wallsend 091 262 8844

Fraise, Sydney,
27 Kingswood Gardens Leeds Yorkshire LS8 2BT
England.
Tel : Leeds 0532 667386

Galibov, Ze'ev
48 Portland Place, London W1N 3DG, England.
Tel : London 071 636 4193
Fax : London 071 323 0392

Galleon Philatelists,
P.O. Box 1517, Gloucester, Virginia 23061, U.S.A.

Garcia's African Index,
80 Willingdon Road, Eastbourne, East Sussex BN21 1TW,
England.
Tel : Eastbourne 0323 721444

General Image, Inc.,
PO Box 335, Maplewood, NJ 07040 U.S.A.

Gibson, W.J.
55 Town Lane, Southport, Lancashire. PR8 6NJ England.
Tel : Southport 0704 540816

Gills Stamps,
5 Tenter Ground, London E1 7NH, England.
Tel : London 071 377 8565
Fax : London 071 377 8565

Glasgow Philatelic Auctions
2 Broomley Drive, Giffnock, Glasgow G46 6PD
Tel: 041 638 1824

Glen Stephens Stamps,
Lothlorien, 4 The Tor Walk Castlecrag, Sydney, New
South Wales 2068, Australia.
Tel : Sydney 2958 1333
Fax : Sydney 2958 1444

Goldcast (Philatelics),
43 London Street, Southport, Merseyside PR9 0TH,
England.
Tel : Southport 0704 543985

Goldfield Collectables,
Shop 9, Carlton Courts, Papanui Road, Christchurch, New
Zealand.
Tel : Christchurch 010 643 355 2251

Goodman, Michael
111 Green Lane, Edgware, Middlesex HA8 8EL, England.
Tel Edgware 081 958 6973

Grainger, A.
42 Lee Lane East, Horsforth, Leeds, West Yorkshire LS18
5RE, England.
Tel : Leeds 0532 583790

Grampian Stamp Shop,
38 Union Terrace, Aberdeen AB1 1NP, Scotland.
Tel : Aberdeen 0224 639704

Gravesend Stamp Centre, The
7 Queen Street, Gravesend, Kent DA12 2EQ, England.
Tel : Gravesend 0474 534166

Green D.L.
2A Leanne Business Centre, Sandford Lane, Wareham,
Dorset BH20 4DY, England.
Tel : Wareham 0929 550750

Green, Tom, Associates,
Fairfield, Low Ham, Langport, Somerset TA10 9DR.
England.
Tel : Langport 0458 250832
Fax : Langport 0458 253226

Gregson Ltd., J.M.A.
P.O. Box 11, Patchway, Bristol, BS12 4BH, England.
Tel : Bristol 0454 617600
Fax : Bristol 0454 617600

Gretton, J.R.
5 Quebec Road, Dereham, Norfolk NR19 2DP, England.
Tel : Dereham 0362 692707

Grove Philatelics,
P.O. Box 326, Kenley, Surrey CR8 5YW, England.
Tel : Kenley 081 668 7001
Fax : Kenley 081 985 5389

Guido Craveri Harmers Auctions SA.
Via Pocobelli 16, 6815 Melide, Switzerland.
Tel:Lugano 010 4191684285
Fax: 010 4191684294

Gustamps,
12 Prince Albert Street, Brighton, East Sussex BN1 1HE,
England.
Tel : Brighton 0273 326994

H.M.S. Stamp Fairs,
29 Basing Road, Rickmansworth, Hertforshire WD3 2QH,
England.
Tel : Rickmansworth 0923 777872
Fax : Rickmansworth 0923 896063

Hache, C.
Edif Somiades, Camillo, Andorra.
Tel: Andorra 010 33628 51636

Hails, D.R.
6 Dalcairn, Pen Y Maes, Ruthin, Clwyd North Wales LL15
1DD

Hallmark Stamps.
1st Floo, 2/14 James Place, Adelaide, SA 5000 Australia.
Tel : Adelaide 010 618 2316358
Fax : Adelaide 010 618 2316358

Hamilton, M.
5 Winbrook Fold, Winfrith, Newburgh, Dorset, DT2 8LR.
England.
Tel : Newburgh 0305 854398
Fax : Newburgh 0305 854246

Hanley Stamp Centre Ltd.,
36 Broad Street, Hanley, Stoke-on-Trent, Staffordshire
ST5 0LB, England.
Tel : Stoke-on-Trent 0782 280524

Harris, Peter
11 North Parade, Lowestoft, Suffolk NR32 4PA, England.
Tel : Lowestoft 0502 564705

Harris, Stewart,
Christopher Cottage, Margaret Street, Thaxted, Essex
CM6 2QN, England.
Tel : Thaxted 0371 830293

Harrogate Stamp Shop,
125 Cold Bath Road, Harrogate, North Yorkshire HG2
ONU, England.
Tel : Harrogate 0423 568428

Harrow Stamp Shop,
Unit 1 15 Springfield Road, Greenhall Way, Harrow,
Middlesex HA1 1QF England.
Tel: London 081 424 0990

Harvey, Mark R.
P.O. Box 50, Chiddingfold, Surrey GU8 4XQ, England.
Tel : Chiddingfold 0428 685207

Haworth, M & N. (Manchester) Ltd,
Royal Exchange Antique Gallery, St Ann's Square,
Manchester M2 7DB, England.
Tel: Manchester 061 834 2929
Fax: Manchester 061 839 4714

Healey & Wise,
P.O. Box 7, Tadworth, Surrey KT20 7QA, England.
Tel : Tadworth 0737 812455
Fax : Tadworth 0737 814407

Heckmondwike Stamp Centre,
3 Walkley Lane, Heckmondwike, West Yorkshire, WF16
0LU England.
Tel: Heckmondwike 0924 408 848

Herman Herst JR,
PO Box 1583 Boca Raton, Fla 33429 0494 USA.
Tel: USA 0101 407 391 3223
Fax: USA 0101 407 381 8859 800-321-6180

Holt, Mike
P O Box 177, Stourbridge, West Midlands DY8 3DE,
England.
Tel : Stourbridge 0384 443317
Fax : Stourbridge 0384 440877

House Of Antiquity,
St Mary Street, Nether-Stowey, Nr. Bridgwater, Somerset
TA5 1LJ, England.
Tel: Somerset 0278 732426

Hoye, K. & N.
94 Gawsworth Road, Macclesfield, Cheshire SK11 8UF,
England.
Tel : Macclesfield 0625 420316
Fax : Macclesfield 0625 420316

Hull Schools Covers,
68 Davenport Avenue, Hessle, North Humberside HU13
0RW England.
Tel: North Humberside 0482 646392

I.G. Stamps,
P.O. Box 15, Harrogate, North Yorkshire HG1 1SL,
England.
Tel : Harrogate 0423 523152
Fax : Harrogate 0423 564210

International Stamp & Coin Co. Ltd.,
2.4-2.5 Pertama Complex, Jalan Tuanku, Abdul Rahman,
Kuala Lumpur 50100, Malaysia.
Tel: Malaysia 010 603 292 6117
Fax: Malaysia 010 603 292 8380

Interstamps
4 Woods View Road, Bournemouth, Dorset BH9 2LN
Tel: 0202 515756

Irons, G.
37 Tiverton Road, Potters Bar, Herts. EN6 5HX
Tel : Potters Bar 0707 659434

Isle Of Man Sales Ltd.,
19B Arlington Drive, Mapperley Park, Nottingham NG3
5EN, England.
Tel : Nottingham 0602 856736

Jackson, Michael
P.O. Box 77, Huntingdon, Cambridgeshire PE18 6TZ,
England.
Tel : Huntingdon 0480 456254
Fax : Huntingdon 0480 456255

Jacques C Schiff Jr. Inc.,
195 Main Street, Ridgefield Park, New Jersey 07660 USA.
Tel: New Jersey 0101 201 641 5566
Fax: New Jersey 0101 201 641 5705

Jahr, Capt. K.
2 Priory Avenue, Lincluden, Dumfries DG2 0PA, Scotland.
Tel : Dumfries 0387 55929

Jakab, A J.
27 Larkhall Rise, London SW4 6HU England.
Tel: London 081 622 8432

Jenkinson, D.
5 Orde Avenue, Gorleston-on-Sea, Great Yarmouth,
Norfolk NR31 6SZ, England.
Tel : Great Yarmouth 0493 668512

Jones, A.C.
47 Marylands Avenue, Hockley, Essex SS5 5AH, England.
Tel : Hockley 0702 206526

Jubilee Stamps (Leeds),
12 Malvern Grove, Chellow Dene, Bradford, West Yorkshire BD9 6BU, England.
Tel : Bradford 0274 546887
Fax : Bradford 0274 546887

Jury Len, Ltd.
PO Box 4400, Auckland New Zealand
Tel : 010 649 3770275
Fax : 010 649 6387768

Karl Peinelt Jr.,
Eibenkamp 18, Muelheim-Ruhr 13, D-4330 Germany.
Tel: Muelheim 01049 0203 23148
Fax: Muelheim 01049 0203 299711

Katcher, H L.
PO Box 242, London N2 0YE England.
Tel: London 081 348 0296
Fax: London 081 347 8397

Keef, G.P.
Willingdon, Eastbourne, Sussex BN20 9HR, England.
Tel : Eastbourne 0323 502067

Kelland, V.
39 Parc-y-Coed, Creigiau, Cardiff CF4 8LY, Wales.
Tel : Cardiff 0222 890130

Kemp, I & B
St. Stephen's House, Catherine Street, Exeter, Devon EX1 1EU, England.
Tel : Exeter 0392 434282

King, Stephen
258 High Street, Erdington, Birmingham B23 6SN England.
Tel: Birmingham 021 382 8222

Kishor Patel,
98 The Mall, Kenton, Harrow, Middlesex HA3 9TG, England.

Klondyke Philatelic Co.,
119 Penny Lane, Liverpool, Merseyside L18 1DF, England.
Tel : Liverpool 051 733 5826
Fax : Liverpool 051 734 0293

Lancaster, Bobbie, (Mrs E.J. Lancaster),
13 Mimosa Street, London SW6 4DS, England.
Tel : London 071 736 4672
Fax : London 071 371 0139

Larch Stamps
79 Norbiton Avenue Norbiton Kingston-Upon-Thames Surrey KT1 3QY
Tel : Kingston Upon Thames 081 547 1123

Larkswood Stamps,
Shop 3, The Georgian Village, 100 Wood Street, Walthamstow, London E17 3HX, England.
Tel : London 081 520 3451

Lea & Co., J.E.
22 Chartfield Square, London SW15 6DR, England.
Tel : London 081 785 9882
Fax : London 081 788 4404

Leslie Sandor,
2 Wallis PDE, North Bondi, 2026 New South Wales Australia
Tel: Australia 010 613 01705

Lester, Tony
29 Momus Boulevard, Binley Road, Stoke, Coventry, CV2 5NA, England.
Tel : Stoke 0203 454908
Fax : Stoke 0203 454908

Leuchtturm Albenverlag GMBH & Co.,
Post Box 1340, AM Spakenburg 45, Geesthacht, D-2054, Germany.
Tel: Germany 010 49 4152 8010
Fax: Germany 010 49 4152 801 222
Telex: Germany 218 722

Linke, Robin
181 Jersey Street, Wembley, Western Australia, 6014 Australia.
Tel: Perth 010 619 387 5327
Fax: Perth 010 619 387 1646

Lister, John Ltd.,
49 Shelton Street, London WC2H 9SP, England.
Tel : London 071 240 6693
Fax : London 071 379 8007

London International Stamp Centre,
110 St. Martin's Lane, Trafalgar Square, London WC2N 4AZ England.
Tel: London 071 240 1963

London Road Stamps,
54a London Road, Leicester, Leicestershire LE2 0QD England.
Tel : Leicester 0533 551544

Lorien Stamps,
P.O. Box 47, Chesterfield S40 1JH, England.

Lowe, David
2 Vicarage Close, Westonzoyland, Bridgewater, Somerset TA7 0LG, England.
Tel : Bridgewater 0278 691755

Luis, FA. Philatelic Sales,
PO Box 15, Nobby Beach, Gold Coast, 4218 Australia.
Tel: Australia 010 61 75 920265
Fax: Australia 010 61 75 701548

Macgregor, Alan Philatelist,
P.O. Box 3130, Cape Town 8000, South Africa.
Tel: Cape Town 010 2721 697 3030
Fax: Cape Town 010 2721 696 4797

Mann, Grahame W.
14 Lakeside Court, Brierley Hill, West Midlands DY5 3RQ, England.
Tel : Brierley Hill 0384 423233
Fax : Brierley Hill 0384 898588

Marks, P.
1 Maxted Road, London, SE15 4LL, England.

Markton Stamps Ltd.
Ridlington, North Walsham, Norfolk NR28 9NS.
Tel : Norfolk 0692 651350

Masons Hill Stamp Shop.
127 Masons Hill, Bromley, Kent. BR2 9HT
Tel : Bromley 081 464 7862

Maxwell, T
28 Cedar Grove, Dunfermline, Fife KY11 5BH, Scotland.
Tel : Dunfermline 0383 727010

McMorris, P.
7 Swiss Close, Watford, Hertfordshire WD1 7LW, England.
Tel : Watford 0923 223826

Mewse, R.A & D.M,
3 Butterwick Road, Freiston, Boston, Lincolnshire PE22 0LF, England.
Tel : Boston 0205 760875

Meyer, Stephen
5 Waveney Road, Leeds, LS12 4EY, England.
Tel : Leeds 0532 638633

Middle East Stamps,
P O Box 707, N.W.D.O, Edinburgh EH4 6JS, Scotland.

Milburn, K.E.
77 Endlebury Road, Chingford, London E4 6QB, England.
Tel : Chingford 081 529 2948

Miles & Miles,
96 Marmion Road, Southsea, Hampshire, PO5 2BB, England.
Tel : Portsmouth 0705 826864
Fax : Portsmouth 0705 862466

Milton, David
P O Box 139, Ruislip, Middlesex HA4 8UX, England.
Tel: Ruislip 0895 637283

MIlton. P,J.
17 Joy Street, Barnstable, N.Devon. EX33 1JZ
Tel : Barnstable 0271 44300
Fax : Barnstable 0271 42810

Monsoon Philatelics,
Serangoon Garden, P.O. Box 413, Singapore 1955, Singapore.
Tel : Singapore 010 65 3388944
Fax : Singapore 010 65 2782327

Moody, Keith I.
341 Burringham Road, Scunthorpe, South Humberside DN17 2BJ, England.
Tel : Scunthorpe 0724 851132

Morely Stamps.
PO Box 28, Wokingham, Berkshire RG11 2LS, England.
Tel : Wokingham 0734 781477

Morley-Bright Ltd,
Coombe Head Farm, Okehampton, Devon EX20 1QL England.
Tel: Okehampton 0837 840 108
Fax: Okehampton 0837 840 108

Mountford, Trevor M.
P O Box 38, Lymington, Hampshire SO41 0WY, England
Tel : Lymington 0590 645837
Fax : Lymington 0590 645837

Mowbray J.R. (Philatelist) Ltd.,
P.O. Box 63, Otaki Railway, Gisborne New Zealand.
Tel : Gisborne 010 646 3648270
Fax : Gisborne 010 646 3648252

MP Stamps.
PO Box 61, Chatham, Kent ME4 5RL, England.
Tel : Ramsgate 0843 582938

Murray Payne Ltd,
P.O. Box 1135, Axbridge, Somerset BS26 2EW, England.
Tel : Axbridge 0934 732511
Fax : Axbridge 0934 733498

Murray. Robert, Stamp Shop
5 & 6 Inverleith Gardens, Ferry Road, Edinburgh, EH3 5PU, Scotland.
Tel : Edinburgh 031 552 1220

Muscott's.
Meadrow, Godalming, Surrey GU7 3HL, England.
Tel : Surrey 0483 417884
Fax : Surrey 0483 860572

Negev Holyland Stamps Ltd.,
P.O. Box 1, Ilfracombe, Devon EX34 9BR, England.
Tel : Ilfracombe 0271 862857
Fax : Ilfracombe 0271 867161

Newbiggen Stamps,
58 Newbiggen Street, Thaxted, Dunmow, Essex CM6 2QT, England
Tel : Thaxted 0371 830693

Newton Philatelics,
53 Middle Row, Stargate, Ryton, Tyne & Wear NE40 3EE, England.
Tel : Tyneside 091 413 6316

Newtown Stamps,
PO Box 14, Livingston, West Lothian EH54 8HA, Scotland.

Nilfrim,
Moseager 4, P.O. Box 92, Hedehusene, DK-2640, Denmark.
Tel : Denmark 010 4542 163857
Fax : Denmark 010 4542 163980

North Of England Philatelic Counter,
c/o Starbeck Avenue Post Office, Off Sandyford Road, Newcastle-upon-Tyne, NE2 1RH England.
Tel: Newcastle 091 232 0017

North Western Philatelic Auctions (1990) Ltd,
North West House, Grange Road, West Kirby, Wirral, Merseyside England.
Tel: Wirral 051 625 5589
Fax: Wirral 051 625 2032

Not Just Stamps
17/19 Crendon Street, High Wycombem, Buckinghamshire, HP13 6LJ.
Tel : High Wycombe 0494 441717

Numismery, The
68a Pillar Avenue, Brixham, South Devon TQ5 8LB, England.
Tel : Brixham 0803 854765

Oliver, Barry
404 Yorktown Road, College Town, Camberley, Surrey GU15 4PR, England.
Tel : Camberley 0276 32587
Fax : Camberley 0276 32505

Olorenshaw, Peter
Box 700, Manly, NSW 2095, Australia.
Tel : Sydney 010 612 971 8839

Paaskesen,Erik
Brusselse Steenweg 78, 3080 Tervuren, B-1980, Belgium.
Tel: Belgium 010 323 767 6497
Fax: Belgium 010 323 767 1983

Page, S.
14 Hilary Grove, Anlaby Park Road South, Hull HU4 7DS, England.
Tel : Hull 0482 643025

Palmerston North Stamp Centre Ltd
PO Box 1781, 121 Broadway Avenue, Palmerston North, New Zealand.
Tel: New Zealand 010 646 357 2751
Fax: New Zealand 010 646 357 2751

Palmerston Philatelic Auctions,
Loreburn Chambers, 11 Great King Street, Dumfries DG1 1BA, Scotland.
Tel : Dumfries 0387 55508

Paper Heritage,
PO Box 438, Brighton BN1 6LX, England.
Tel : Brighton 0273 558066

Parkinson, W A.
Sea Front, Promenade, Isle of Man.
Tel: Isle of Man 0624 83 3303

Peinelt Jr., Karl
Eibenkamp 18, Muelheim-Ruhr 13, D-4330, Germany.
Tel : Muelheim-Ruhr 203 23148
Fax : Muelheim-Ruhr 203 299711

Penhey, P. & Associates
23 Manor Way, Woodmansterne, Surrey SM7 3PN, Englanfd.
Tel : Surrey 0737 357 869

Pennymead Auctions,
1 Brewerton Street Knaresborough, North Yorkshire HG5 8AZ, England.
Tel : Knaresborough 0423 865962

Perry, Ian. Stamps,
29 Chetwynd Grove, Newport, Shropshire TF10 7JW, England.
Tel : Newport 0952 825941
Fax : Newport 0952 820042

PH Stamp Auctions,
Harbour Lights, 19 Station Road, Bishopstone, Seaford BN25 2RB East Sussex
Tel: Seaford 0323 899 565

Philaclassica,
Gerbergasse 24, Postfach 563, Basel CH-4001, Switzerland.
Tel : Switzerland 010 4161 2617379
Fax : Switzerland 010 4161 2617377

Philatelic Bureau.
Department of Posts, Auberge d'Italie, Valetta, MALTA.
CMR 02
Tel : 010 356 224421

Philatelic Exporter,
PO Box 137, Hatfield, Hertfordshire AL10 9DB, England.
Tel : Hatfield 0707 266331
Fax : Hatfield 0707 274782

Philatelic Supplies,
42 Willian Way, Letchworth, Hertfordshire SG6 2HH,
England.
Tel : Letchworth 0462 684191

Philatelie Fauquex,
19, rue du Rhone, 1204 Geneva, Switzerland.
Tel: Geneva 010 41 22 311 6795

Philcard International,
PO Box 1000, London N3 3TD, England.
Tel : 081 349 1610
Fax : 081 349 1610

Phillips Son & Neale,
101 New Bond Street, London W1Y 0AS, England.
Tel : London 071 629 1877
Fax : London 071 409 3466

Phoenix International,
Ashleigh, Monument Lane, Codnor Park, Nottingham
NG16 5PJ, London.
Tel : Nottingham 0773 608899
Fax : Nottingham 0773 609821

Piccadilly Stamps.
Shop 27 , Hyde Park Square, Cnr Park & Castlereagh
Streets, Sydney, NSW 2000 Australia.
Tel : Sydney 010 612 264 7034

Pollard, Derrick
POBox 148, Market Wavington,Devizes, Wilts. SN10 4AJ
Tel : Devizes 0380 813652
Fax: Devizes 0380 812902

Portsmouth Stamp Shop,
184 Chichester Road, North End, Portsmouth, Hampshire
PO2 0AX, England.
Tel : Portsmouth 0705 663450
Fax : Portsmouth 0705 664884

Postal History Display,
146 Chapel Road, Oldham OL8 4QJ, England.
Tel : Manchester 061 682 9652

Postiljonen AB,
Box 4118, Malmo, S-203 12, Sweden.
Tel : Malmo 010 040 72290
Fax: Malmo 010 040 72299

Postings,
P.O. Box 1, Oxted, Surrey RH8 0FD, England.
Tel : Oxted 0883 722646
Fax : Oxted 0883 722646

Price & Co,
Mount Merrion, PO Box 3, Dublin Republic of Ireland
Tel: Ireland 010 353 2889 269
Fax: Ireland 010 353 0492 650 422

Prinz Publications (UK) Ltd.,
Lelant Garden Centre, Hayle, Cornwall, TR27 6JA,
England.
Tel : Hayle 0736 756742
Fax : Hayle 0736 756555

Proud-Bailey Co. Ltd.,
P.O. Box 74, Heathfield, East Sussex TN21 8PZ, England.
Tel : Heathfield 0435 862540
Fax : Heathfield 0435 865200

R J Auctions,
P.O. Box 271, Bedford, Bedfordshire MK40 3YQ, England.
Tel : Bedford 0234 358642

Raikes, A.
37 Julian Road, Ludlow, Shropshire SY8 1HA, England.

RCS Stamps.
37 Surrey Road, Nelson, Lancashire. BB9 7TZ.
Tel : Nelson 0443 690997

Rickenback, Peter C.
14 Rosslyn Hill, Hampstead, London NW3 1PF England.
Tel : London 071 435 0231

Rickmansworth Philatelic Auctions.
14 Langham Place, Egham, Surrey. TW20 9EB, England.
Tel : Egham 0784 436383
Fax : Egahm 0784 471705

Ricky Richardson International Ltd
P.O. Box 552, Gibraltar.
Tel : 010 3452 375900

Ringdale Philatelics,
242 Stroud Road, Gloucester GL4 0AU, England.
Tel : Gloucester 0452 411942

Robbe Ltd., G.
York Chambers, York Street, St. Helier, Jersey JE4 8XZ,
Channel Islands.
Tel : Jersey 0534 23084
Fax : Jersey 0534 67680

Robstine Stamps,
The Stamp Centre, 77 The Strand, London WC2R 0DE,
England.
Tel: Amersham 0494 729345
Fax: Amersham 0494 721881

Rodgau Philatelic Service Pts & Aphy,
Eisenbahnstr, 8, Postfach 1124, D-63083 Rodgau,
Germany.
Tel: Germany 010 49 6106 3023
Fax: Germany 010 49 6106 3024

Rodgers, J.A.
3 Sea View, St. Bees, Cumbria CA27 0BB, England.
Tel : 0946 822690

Rolli-Schor R & B AG,
Seidenhofstr. 10, CH 6003, Lucerne, Switzerland.
Tel: Lucerne 010 4141 234545
Fax: Lucerne 010 4141 234541

Ronald Lee,
PO Box 1567, Geelong, Victoria 3220 Australia.
Tel: Victoria 010 61 052 295099
Fax: Victoria 010 61 052 789090

Rosen G. & Son Ltd.,
50 Byron Road, Walthamstow London E17 4SW England
Tel : London 081 520 4133
Fax : London 081 520 4141

Ross-Shiells Ltd.
4/5 Eldon Street, London EC2M 7LS, England.
Tel : London 071 247 8011

Rowland Hill Stamps,
27a Comberton Hill, Kidderminster, Worcestershire, DY10
1QN, England.
Tel : Kidderminster 0562 824060
Fax : Kidderminster 0562 743767

Roxburys Auction House,
PO Box 12149, Elizabeth Street, Brisbane 4002 Australia.
Tel: Brisbane 010 617 229 9466
Fax: Brisbane 010 617 229 3852

Rushstamps (Retail) Ltd,
P.O. Box 1, Lyndhurst, Hampshire SO43 7PP, England.
Tel : Lyndhurst 0703 282044
Fax: 0703 282981

Russell, D.J.
2 Brunswick Square, Herne Bay, Kent CT6 5QF, England.
Tel : Herne Bay 0227 361135

Ryan, Arthur
2 The Square, The Quadrant, Richmond, Surrey, TW9
1DY England.
Tel : London 081 940 7777
Fax : London 081 940 7777

Safe Albums (UK) Ltd,
16 Falcon Business Park, Hogwood Lane, Finchampstead, Berkshire RG11 4QW England.
Tel : Reading 0734 328976
Fax : Reading 0734 328612

Sayer, Stephen J.
49 Mount Road, Southdown, Bath, Avon BA2 1LG,
England.
Tel : Bath 0225 446766

Saywell A.J. Ltd., (The Oxford Stamp Shop)
15 Hollybush Row Oxfordshire OX1 1JH, England.
Tel : Oxford 0865 248889

Schley, John
P.O. Box 189, Barnet, Hertfordshire EN5 5PL, England.
Tel : Barnet 081 440 8835

Schwarzenbach, R.
Oberdorfstrasse 8, Postfach 174, CH-8024 Zurich Switzer-
land.
Tel: Zurich 0101 251 4612
Fax: Zurich 0101 261 3060

Sedgwick, David
Station House, Wylam, Northumberland NE41 8HR,
England.
Tel : Wylam 0661 853951

Select Stamps,
PO Box 20, Northampton NN1 1EH, England.
Fax: Northampton 0604 791187

Sellinger. Martin,
P.O. Box 47, 4 Woodland Place, White Plains, New York
10602 U.S.A.
Tel : New York 010 1 914 948 4246

Seven Seas Stamps Pty. Ltd
26 Waterloo Street, Surry Hills, GPO Box 3273, Sydney,
Australia.
Tel: Sydney 010 612 690 6317
Fax: Sydney 010 612 8165

Shades Stamp Shop Ltd.
Shop 54, Shades Arcase, Cashel Street, Christchurch
New Zealand.
Tel : Christchurch 010 643 3666390
Fax : Christchurch 010 643 3772377

Shaw, Alastair G.
Shiel House, 31 Gayton Road, Heswall, Wirral, Mersey-
side L60 8QF, England.
Tel : Liverpool 051 342 1281

Shelron,
Yealm House, 9 Brackley Road, Towcester, Northampton-
shire NN12 7DH England.
Tel : Towcester 0327 50242

Shield Stamp Company,
PO Box 2977, Grand Central Station, New York, NY 10163
USA.
Tel: New York 0101 212 629 7979
Fax: New York 0101 212 629 3350 236440 IGPC UR

Skilling, Jim
PO Box 626, New Plymouth, New Zealand
Tel: New Zealand 010 646 758 6453
Fax: New Zealand 010 646 758 6453

Skinner, D.J.
53 Armytage Road, Hounslow, Middlesex TW5 9JL,
England.
Tel : London 081 570 1726

Somerset Stamp Service,
South Petherton, Somerset TA13 5EN, England.
Tel : South Petherton 0460 41172
Fax : South Petherton 0460 41172

South American Stamp Supplies,
P.O. Box 105, Peterborough, Cambridgeshire PE3 9TQ,
England.
Tel : Peterborough 0733 268708
Fax : Peterborough 0733 262838

South Eastern Auctions,
182 Turners Hill, Cheshunt, Hertfordshire EN8 9DE,
England.
Tel : Cheshunt 0992 36978

South Yarra Stamps,
PO BOX 536, South Yarra Victoria 3141 Australia.
Tel: 010 613 827 7593
Fax: 010 613 826 0861

Stadler And George,
2 Park House Green Cottages, Cranleigh, Surrey GU6
7DN, England.
Tel : Cranleigh 0483 275464

Stamp Center, (Finnur Kolbeinsson),
P.O. Box 78, Reykjavik IS-121 Iceland.
Tel : Reykjavik 176 844
Fax : Reykjavik 128 518

Stamp Centre, The
7 Queen Street, Gravesend, Kent DA12 2EQ, England.
Tel : Gravesend 0474 534166

Stamp Collector, The
G.P.O. Box 3780, Sydney, N.S.W. 2001, Australia.
Tel: 010 612 957 2882
Fax: 010 612 959 5159

Stamp Garden Co Ltd,
NO25 Sec.2 Shanmin Road, Taichung, Taiwan 40099
Republic of China
Tel: Taiwan 010 8864 223 5888
Fax: Taiwan 010 8864 223 4931

Stamp House,
404 Yorktown Road, College Town, Camberley, Surrey
GU15 4PR, England.
Tel : Camberley 0276 32587
Fax : Camberley 0276 32505

Stamp Publicity (Worthing) Ltd.,
28 Windlesham Road, Shoreham-by-Sea, West Sussex
BN43 5AE, England.

Stampman, The
PO Box 2122, Brick, NJ 08723 U.S.A.
Tel : New Jersey 0101 908 364 5322

Steinhart, Allan L.
35 Church Street, Suite 305, Toronto, Ontario M5E 1T3,
Canada.
Tel : Toronto 0101 416 362 8257

Stevens, Denis
12 Compton Court, Benhill Wood Road, Sutton, Surrey
SM1 4HP.
Tel : Surrey 081 6610367

Strads R.O., M.A.,
7 Brookside, Halton, Aylesbury, Buckinghamshire HP22
5PB, England.
Tel : Aylesbury 0296 625070

Strand Stamp Centre,
Shop 7 Sanville Court, 40 Playne Street, Frankston,
Victoria 3930, Australia.
Tel: Melbourne 010 613 781 5207

Strich Peter, Stamps & Coins
GPO Box 216D, Melbourne, Victoria 3001, Australia.
Tel : Melbourne 010 613 661 2945
Fax : Melbourne 010 613 661 3770

Summit Stamps,
Oldfield House, Fryern Road, Storrington, West Sussex
RH20 4BJ, England.
Tel : Storrington 0903 743654

Surrey Philatelics,
21 Victoria Street, Englefield Green, Egham, Surrey TW20
0QY England.
Tel: Egham 0784 436 383
Fax: Egham 0784 471 705

Sydney Philatelics Pty Ltd.
P.O. Box 382, Strawberry Hills, N.S.W. 2012, Australia.
Tel: 010 61 2 319 1533
Fax: 010 61 2 319 1531

Talent Pastimes Ltd.,
85 Kettering Road, Northampton, Northamptonshire NN1 4AW, England.
Tel : Northampton 0604 36396

Taunton Stamp Shop,
66 Bridge Street, Taunton, Somerset. TA1 1UD, England.
Tel : Taunton 0823 283327
Fax : Taunton 0823 325882

Taylor, Walter
Stirling Close, Seaford, East Sussex BN25 3UT, England.
Tel : Seaford 0323 890617

Thames Stamp Auctions,
35 Wheathill Road, London, SE20 7XQ, England.
Tel : London 081 778 7001

The Stamp Pad,
186 Southbourne Grove, Westcliff, Essex SS0 0AA, England.
Tel : Westcliff 0702 335 802

The Stamp Place,
Shop 14, Cat & Fiddle Arcade, Collins Street, Hobart, Tasmania, Australia.
Tel: Hobart 010 002 342 085

The Stamp Shop,
Unit 10 Granby Arcade, Water Street, Bakewell, Derbyshire DE45 1EG England.
Tel: Derbyshire 0629 812191

The Stamp Shop,
PO Box 18, High Street, Alderney, Channel Islands.
Tel: Alderney 0481 82 2514

The Stamp Wholesalers,
Van Dahl Publications, Stamp Collector Newspaper, 520 E. 1st Street, Albany USA.
Tel: USA 0101 503 928 4484
Fax: USA 0101 503 967 9272

Thompson G.W.W.
13 Pelstream Avenue, St Ninians, Sterling FK7 0BE
Tel : Sterling 0786 475524

Thomson J.D.,
17 Clydeshore Road, Dumbarton, Strathclyde G82 4AF.

Tony Field Stamps.
8 Wildcroft Gardens, Edgeware, Middlesex. HA8 6TJ
Tel : Edgeware 081 952 4573
Fax : Edgeware 081 951 4630

Torres, A.M. Mayor,
22-5 28013, Madrid, Spain.
Tel : 010 341 3655510
Fax : 010 341 3640689

Townsend, Martin
P.O. Box 10, Hitchin, Hertfordshire SG4 9PE, England.
Tel : Hitchin 0462 420678

Trinder, Vera Ltd
38 Bedford Street, London WC2E 9EV
Tel: London 071 836 8332
Fax: London 071 836 9873

Trio Fairs,
5 Glebe Close, Blythe Bridge, Stoke-on-Trent ST11 9JN,.
Tel : Stoke-on-Trent 0782 394147

Vale Stamps,
21 Tranquil Vale, Blackheath, London SE3 0BU, England.
Tel : London 081 852 9817

Victoria Stamp Traders,
65 Station Street, Malvern, Victoria 3144, Australia.
Tel : Melbourne 010 613 509 8255
Fax : Melbourne 010 613 509 4230

Visini, A G
319 Motutara Road, Muriwai Beach, Auckland, New Zealand.
Tel : Auckland 010 9411 8199

Waldie, David A.
6 Shielswood Court, Galashiels, Selkirkshire, Scotland
TD1 3RH...Tel: 0866 58308
Fax: 0896 58308

Walker, Graham
6 Fintry Crescent, Bishopbriggs, Glasgow G64 1SH
Tel: 041 762 2759

Warren Ltd., R.
Oaklands, Crowhurst, Lingfield, Surrey RH7 6LS, England.
Tel : 0342 833413
Fax : 0342 833892

Warwick & Warwick Ltd.,
Pageant House, Jury Street, Warwick, Warwickshire CV34 4EW, England.
Tel : Warwick 0926 499031
Fax : Warwick 0926 491906

Watts, Ray. Stamp Fairs.
Martins Weft, Duke Street, Bildeston, Suffolk. IP7 7EW
Tel : Bildeston 0449 740821

Wegg, George S. Limited.
53 Adelaide Street East, Toronto, Ontario M5C 1K6 Canada.
Tel: Toronto 0101 416 363 1596

Werner Wetzel,
Alte Postgasse 21, Weinheim/Bergstr., D-6940, Germany.
Tel: Germany 010 6201 65794

West Cornwall Stamp Centre,
Lelant Garden Centre, Hayle, Cornwall, TR26 2PT, England.
Tel : Hayle 0736 754604
Fax : Hayle 0736 756555

Western Auctions Ltd.,
Bank House, 225 City Road, Cardiff, CF2 3JD, Wales.
Tel : Cardiff 0222 484934
Fax : Cardiff 0222 450522

Whitehead & Associates, Colin.
P.O. Box 316, Purley, Surrey CR2 3YW, England.
Tel : Purley 081 660 9063
Fax : Purley 081 660 9063

Whitworth, Andrew, A.
1 Prizat House, Kendal, Cumbria, England LA8 8AB

Whyte, Ian
27 Mount Street, Upper, Dublin 2, Ireland.
Tel : Dublin 010 353 1676 7228
Fax : Dublin 010 353 1676 7229

Whyte, Macdonnell, Ltd., (David Macdonnell),
102 Leinster Road, Dublin 6, Ireland.
Tel : 353 1 977449
Fax : 353 1 977 440

Williams, A.L.
Woodspring House, 17 Hill Road. Clevedon, Avon BS21 7NE, England.

Windsor Stamps,
3 Brock House, Brock Road, St Peter Port, Guernsey, Channel Islands.
Tel : Guernsey 0481 710208

Wittmann, Dr., (Dr H.W. Lantelme),
Postfach 202604, Bayerstrasse 15, Muenchen 2, D-8000, West Germany.
Tel : Muenchen 010 4989 596101
Fax : Muenchen 010 4989 598528

Worboys, Derek Philatelic Faultfinders,
36 Bedford Grove, London, SW20 9LB, England.
Tel : London 081 542 4868
Fax : London 081 542 5588

World Wide Stamps, (S R Bennett)
PO Box 354, Timaru New Zealand.
Tel : Timaru 03 688 6637
Fax : Timaru 03 688 6637

Wyon Classics,
Corridor Stamp Shop, 7a The Corridor, Bath, Avon BA1 5AP.
Tel : Bath 0225 463368

Yorkshire Cover Auctions,
10 Lombard Street, Halton, Leeds LS15 0LT, England.
Tel : Leeds 0532 641 845
Fax : Leeds 0532 641 845